THE
ENCYCLOPEDIA
OF PHYSICS

THE ENCYCLOPEDIA OF PHYSICS

SECOND EDITION

EDITED BY

Robert M. Besançon
Physical Sciences Administrator
Air Force Materials Laboratory
Wright-Patterson Air Force Base, Ohio

VAN NOSTRAND REINHOLD COMPANY
New York Cincinnati Toronto London Melbourne

Van Nostrand Reinhold Company Regional Offices:
New York Cincinnati Chicago Millbrae Dallas

Van Nostrand Reinhold Company International Offices:
London Toronto Melbourne

Manufactured in the United States of America

Published by Van Nostrand Reinhold Company
450 West 33rd Street, New York, N.Y. 10001

Published simultaneously in Canada by Van Nostrand Reinhold Ltd.

15 14 13 12 11 10 9 8 7 6 5 4 3 2

Library of Congress Cataloging in Publication Data

Besançon, Robert Martin, ed.
    The encyclopedia of physics.

    Includes bibliographical references.
    1. Physics—Dictionaries.   I. Title
QC5.B44 1974   530′.03   73-17022
ISBN 0-442-20691-7

CONTRIBUTORS

KÊITSIRO AIZU, Hitachi Central Research Laboratory, Tokyo, Japan. *Ferroelectricity.*

DOUGLAS L. ALLEN, U.S. Industrial Chemicals Company, Tuscola, Illinois. *Vapor Pressure and Evaporation.*

CHARLES L. ALLEY, Department of Electrical Engineering, University of Utah, Salt Lake City, Utah. *Modulation.*

ROBERT C. AMME, Department of Physics, University of Denver, Denver, Colorado. *Ionization.*

DAVID L. ANDERSON, Department of Physics, Oberlin College, Oberlin, Ohio. *Electron.*

ERNEST R. ANDERSON, U.S. Naval Undersea Center, San Diego, California. *Sonar.*

C. L. ANDREWS, Department of Physics, State University of New York at Albany, New York. *Doppler Effect.*

H. L. ARMSTRONG, Department of Physics, Queen's University, Kingston, Ontario, Canada. *States of Matter.*

G. E. BACON, University of Sheffield, Sheffield, England. *Neutron Diffraction.*

RADU C. BALESCU, Université Libre De Bruxelles, Brussels, Belgium. *Statistical Mechanics.*

WILLIAM BAND, Department of Physics, Washington State University, Pullman, Washington. *Mathematical Physics.*

MYRON BANDER, Department of Physics, University of California, Irvine, California. *Regge Poles and Regge Theory.*

L. E. BARBROW, National Bureau of Standards, Washington, D.C. *Photometry.*

WILLIAM L. BAUN, U.S. Air Force Materials Laboratory, Wright-Patterson Air Force Base, Ohio. *X-Rays.*

JESSE W. BEAMS, Department of Physics, University of Virginia, Charlottesville, Virginia. *Centrifuge.*

CLIFFORD K. BECK, Office of Government Liaison−Regulation, U.S. Atomic Energy Commission. *Nuclear Reactors.*

JOSEPH J. BECKER, General Electric Research and Development Center, Schenectady, New York. *Magnetism.*

ALBERT C. BEER, Battelle-Columbus Laboratories, Columbus, Ohio. *Hall Effect and Related Phenomena.*

DAVID A. BELL, Department of Electronic Engineering, University of Hull, Hull, England. *Cybernetics.*

H. E. BENNETT, Michelson Laboratory, Naval Weapons Center, China Lake, California. *Reflection.*

REUBEN BENUMOF, Staten Island Community College of the City University of New York. *Alternating Currents.*

MARK J. BERAN, Towne School of Civil and Mechanical Engineering, University of Pennsylvania, Philadelphia, Pennsylvania. *Coherence.*

LEO L. BERANEK, Bolt Beranek and Newman Inc. and Massachusetts Institute of Technology, Cambridge, Massachusetts. *Architectural Acoustics.*

ERIK BERGSTRAND, Korsudden, 610 42 Gryt, Sweden, *Velocity of Light.*

ARTHUR I. BERMAN, Institute for Studies in Higher Education, University of Copenhagen and the National Research Council, Copenhagen, Denmark. *Astronautics, Physics of.*

ROBERT M. BESANÇON, U.S. Air Force Materials Laboratory, Wright-Patterson Air Force Base, Ohio. *Physics. Temperature and Thermometry.*

GEORGE L. BEYER, Eastman Kodak Company, Rochester, New York. *Molecular Weight.*

P. J. BILLING (Formerly) Radyne, Ltd., Wokingham, England. *Induction Heating.*

RAYMOND C. BINDER, Department of Mechanical Engineering, University Park, University of Southern California, Los Angeles, California. *Fluid Statics.*

JOHN P. BLEWETT, Brookhaven National Laboratory, Upton, New York. *Accelerators, Linear.*

M. HILDRED BLEWETT, ISR Department, CERN, Geneva, Switzerland. *Accelerators, Particle.*

N. BLOEMBERGEN, Harvard University, Cambridge, Massachusetts. *Light.*

WARREN B. BOAST, Department of Electrical Engineering, Iowa State University, Ames, Iowa. *Potential.*

HENRY V. BOHM, Department of Physics, Wayne State University, Detroit, Michigan. *Fermi Surface* (with N. Tepley).

ROBERT M. BOYNTON, Center for Visual Science, University of Rochester, Rochester, New York. *Vision and the Eye.*

H. J. J. BRADDICK. *Measurements, Principles of.*

J. N. BRADLEY, Department of Chemistry, University of Essex, Colchester, England. *Shock Waves.*

JULIUS J. BRANDSTATTER, Tel-Aviv University, Ramat Aviv, Israel, *Propagation of Electromagnetic Waves.*

JOHN W. BRENEMAN (deceased). *Simple Machines.*

G. E. BRIGGS, Emeritus, University of Cambridge, England. *Osmosis.*

STANLEY J. BRODSKY, Stanford Linear Accelerator Center, Stanford University, Stanford, California. *Quantum Electrodynamics.*

STEPHEN G. BRUSH, Department of History and Institute for Fluid Dynamics and Applied Mathematics, University of Maryland, College Park, Maryland. *Irreversibility. Kinetic Theory.*

H. A. BUCHDAHL, Department of Theoretical Physics, Australian National University, Canberra, A.C.T., Australia. *Thermodynamics.*

DONALD A. BURGH. *Microscope.*

DONALD G. BURKHARD, Department of Physics and Astronomy, University of Georgia, Athens, Georgia. *Microwave Spectroscopy.*

LEONARD M. BUTSCH, JR. *Bionics* (with Cecil W. Gwinn).

ROBERT L. BYER, W. W. Hansen Laboratories of Physics, Stanford University, Stanford, California. *Kerr Effects.*

E. R. CAIANIELLO, University of Salerno and Laboratorio di Cibernetica del Consiglio Nationale delle Ricerche, Naples, Italy. *Field Theory.*

EARL CALLEN, Department of Physics, American University, Washington, D.C. *Magnetostriction.*

THOMAS R. CARVER, Department of Physics, Princeton University, Princeton, New Jersey. *Optical Pumping.*

E. J. CASEY. *Biophysics.*

NICHOLAS CHAKO, Department of Mathematics, Queens College of the City University of New York, Flushing, New York. *Aberrations.*

B. S. CHANDRASEKHAR, Case Western Reserve University, Cleveland, Ohio. *Superconductivity.*

FRANK CHORLTON, Department of Mathematics, University of Aston in Birmingham, England. *Differential Equations in Physics.*

DAN E. CHRISTIE, Department of Mathematics, Bowdoin College, Brunswick, Maine. *Vector Physics.*

KENNETH J. CLOSE, Department of Physics, The Polytechnic of Central London, London, W. I., England. *Vacuum Techniques* (with J. Yarwood).

IRA COCHIN, Department of Mechanical Engineering, Newark College of Engineering, Newark, New Jersey. *Gyroscope.*

E. RICHARD COHEN, Science Center, Rockwell International, Thousand Oaks, California. *Constants Fundamental.*

E. A. B. COLE, School of Mathematics, University of Leeds, Leeds, England. *Semiconductors, Inhomogeneous.*

B. THOMPSON COLEBERD, Farmville, Virginia. *Planetary Atmospheres* (with Paul Harteck).

W. DALE COMPTON, Scientific Research Staff, Ford Motor Company, Dearborn, Michigan. *Color Centers.*

C. SHARP COOK, Department of Physics, University of Texas at El Paso, Texas. *Fallout.*

JOHN C. CORBIN, JR., U.S. Air Force Aerospace Research Laboratories, Wright-Patterson Air Force Base, Ohio. *Skin Effect.*

H. COTTON, University of Nottingham, Nottingham, England. *Optics, Geometrical.*

HERMAN V. COTTONY, Electromagnetics Division, National Bureau of Standards, Boulder, Colorado. *Antennas.*

F. H. CRAWFORD, Emeritus, Department of Physics, Williams College, Williamstown, Massachusetts. *Heat.*

W. CULSHAW, Palo Alto Research Laboratory, Lockheed Missiles and Space Company, Palo Alto, California. *Zeeman and Stark Effects.*

ROBERT G. CUNNINGHAM, Research Laboratories, Eastman Kodak Co., Rochester, New York. *Static Electricity* (with D. J. Montgomery).

L. F. CURTISS, Englewood, Florida. *Neutron.*

ERNST R. CZERLINSKY, Pötterhoek, West Germany. *Magnetometry.*

R. H. DAVIS. *Proton.*

JACK E. DAY, Electros, Inc., Tigard, Oregon. *Oscilloscopes.*

L. WALLACE DEAN III, Pratt & Whitney Aircraft Division of United Aircraft Corp., East Hartford, Connecticut. *Physical Acoustics.*

PETER G. DEBRUNNER, Department of Physics, University of Illinois, Urbana, Illinois. *Mössbauer Effect* (with Robert L. Ingalls).

JOHN P. DELVAILLE, Center for Space Research, Massachusetts Institute of Technology, Cambridge, Massachusetts. *Cosmic Rays.*

N. G. DESHPANDE, Physics Department, University of Texas at Austin, Texas. *Current Algebra.*

R. E. DE WAMES, North American Rockwell Science Center, Thousand Oaks, California. *Spin Waves* (with T. Wolfram).

DAVID L. DEXTER, Department of Physics and Astronomy, University of Rochester, Rochchester, New York. *Solid State Theory.*

EDWARD J. DIEBOLD. *Rectifiers.*

G. J. DIENES, Brookhaven National Laboratory, Upton, New York. *Irradiation, Displaced Atoms.*

A. DINSDALE, British Ceramic Research Association, Stoke-on-Trent, England. *Viscosity.*

ROBERT H. DOREMUS, School of Engineering, Rensselaer Polytechnic Institute, Troy, New York. *Crystallization.*

GLENN L. DOWNEY, Department of Mechanical Engineering and Engineering Mechanics, University of Nebraska, Lincoln, Nebraska. *Dynamics.*

G. DRESSELHAUS, Lincoln Laboratory, Massachusetts Institute of Technology, Lexington, Massachusetts. *Cyclotron Resonance (Diamagnetic Resonance).*

MILDRED S. DRESSELHAUS, Department of Electrical Engineering and Center for Materials Science and Engineering, Massachusetts Institute of Technology, Cambridge, Massachusetts. *Semiconductors.*

H. G. DRICKAMER, School of Chemical Sciences, University of Illinois, Urbana, Illinois. *Pressure, Very High.*

C. HARRISON DWIGHT, Emeritus, Department of Physics, University of Cincinnati, Cincin-

nati, Ohio. *Absorption Spectra. Optics, Physical.*

ERNST R. G. ECKERT, Emeritus, Heat Transfer Laboratory, University of Minnesota, Minneapolis, Minnesota. *Heat Transfer.*

D. EDELSON, Bell Telephone Laboratories, Murray Hill, New Jersey. *Polar Molecules.*

JOHN A. EISELE, Space Systems Division, Naval Research Laboratory, Washington, D.C. *Tensors and Tensor Analysis* (with Robert M. Mason).

LEONARD EISNER, Stamford, Conneticut. *Radiation, Thermal.*

RAYMOND J. EMRICH, Department of Physics, Lehigh University, Bethlehem, Pennsylvania. *Fluid Dynamics.*

DUANE D. ERWAY, Xerox Corporation, Rochester, New York. *Solar Energy Utilization* (with A. M. Zarem).

HOWARD T. EVANS, JR., U.S. Geological Survey, Washington, D.C. *Crystal Structure Analysis. Crystallography.*

HENRY EYRING, Department of Chemistry, University of Utah, Salt Lake City, Utah. *Physical Chemistry.*

N. FEATHER, Department of Physics, University of Edinburgh, Edinburgh, Scotland. *Vibration.*

A. G. FISCHER, Department of Electrical Engineering, University of Dortmund, 46 Dortmund, West Germany. *Electroluminescence.*

P. J. FOLEY, Faculty of Applied Science, University of Toronto, Toronto, Canada. *Luminance.*

GRANT R. FOWLES, Physics Department, University of Utah, Salt Lake City, Utah, *Schrödinger Equation.*

MARTIN M. FREUNDLICH, Department of Electrical Technology, Queensborough Community College of the City University of New York, Bayside, New York. *Electron Microscope.*

HAROLD P. FURTH, Plasma Physics Laboratory, Princeton University, Princeton, New Jersey. *Magnetic Field.*

T. H. GEBALLE, Department of Applied Physics, Stanford University, Stanford, California. *Calorimetry* (with J. E. Kunzler).

BARRY GEORGE, Applied Electronics Laboratories, Marconi Space and Defense Systems, Ltd., Portsmouth, England. *Electron Optics.*

ANTHONY B. GIORDANO, School of Graduate Studies, Polytechnic Institute of Brooklyn, Brooklyn, New York. *Microwave Transmission.*

JOSHUA N. GOLDBERG, Physics Department, Syracuse University, Syracuse, New York. *Gravitation.*

PAUL GOLDHAMMER, Department of Physics, University of Kansas, Lawrence, Kansas. *Nuclear Structure.*

R. H. GOOD, JR., Department of Physics, Pennsylvania State University, University Park, Pennsylvania. *Photon.*

JOHN B. GOODENOUGH, Lincoln Laboratory, Massachusetts Institute of Technology, Lexington, Massachusetts. *Diamagnetism.*

CHARLES D. GOODMAN, Oak Ridge National Laboratory, Oak Ridge, Tennessee. *Critical Mass. Isospin.*

CLARK GOODMAN, Department of Physics, University of Houston, Houston, Texas. *Cross Section and Stopping Power.*

JOSEPH W. GOODMAN, Department of Electrical Engineering, Stanford University, Stanford, California. *Fourier Analysis.*

DONALD C. GREGG, Department of Chemistry, University of Vermont, Burlington, Vermont. *Chemistry.*

S. J. GREGG, Brunel University, Uxbridge, Middlesex, England. *Adsorption and Absorption.*

B. CLARK GROSECLOSE, Lawrence Livermore Laboratory, Livermore, California. *Positron* (with William W. Walker).

E. A. GUGGENHEIM (deceased). *Boltzmann's Distribution Law.*

VINCENT P. GUINN, Department of Chemistry, University of California, Irvine, California. *Neutron Activation Analysis.*

CECIL W. GWINN, U.S. Air Force Avionics Laboratory, Wright-Patterson Air Force Base, Ohio. *Bionics* (with L. M. Butsch).

WALTER J. HAMER, Washington, D.C. *Electrochemistry.*

A. O. HANSON, Department of Physics, University of Illinois, Urbana, Illinois. *Compton Effect.*

AKIRA HARASIMA, Tokyo Woman's Christian College, Tokyo, Japan. *Surface Tension.*

FOREST K. HARRIS, Electricity Division, National Bureau of Standards, Washington, D.C. *Electrical Measurements.*

ROLAND H. HARRISON, U.S. Bureau of Mines, Bartlesville Energy Research Center, Bartlesville, Oklahoma. *Gases: Thermodynamic Properties.*

R. W. HART, Applied Physics Laboratory, Johns Hopkins University, Silver Spring, Maryland. *Light Scattering.*

PAUL HARTECK, Department of Chemistry, Rensselaer Polytechnic Institute, Troy, New York. *Planetary Atmospheres* (with B. Thompson Coleberd).

HARRY P. HARTKEMEIER, Los Altos, California. *Ballistics.*

RYUKITI R. HASIGUTI, Department of Metallurgy and Materials Science, University of Tokyo, Tokyo, Japan. *Lattice Defects.*

SHERWOOD K. HAYNES, Physics Department, Michigan State University, East Lansing, Michigan. *Auger Effect.*

RAYMOND W. HAYWARD, Center for Radiation Research, National Bureau of Standards, Washington, D.C. *Parity.*

JOHN HEADING, Department of Applied Mathematics, University College of Wales, Aberystwyth, Wales, U.K. *Matrices.*

LAWRENCE J. HEIDT, Emmanuel College, Boston, and Massachusetts Institute of Technology, Cambridge, Massachusetts. *Photochemistry.*

WILMOT N. HESS, Environmental Research Laboratories, National Oceanic and Atmo-

spheric Administration, Boulder, Colorado. *Radiation Belts.*

M. HETÉNYI. *Photoelasticity.*

ANTONY HEWISH, Cavendish Laboratory, University of Cambridge, Cambridge, England. *Pulsars.*

JOHN F. HOGERTON, S. M. Stoller Corporation, New York. *Atomic Energy.*

M. G. HOLLAND, Raytheon Research Division, Waltham, Massachusetts. *Phonons.*

CHARLES A. HOLT, Department of Electrical Engineering, Virginia Polytechnic Institute, Blacksburg, Virginia. *Induced Electromotive Force.*

ROBERT E. HOPKINS, Tropel, Inc., Fairport, New York. *Lens.*

ROLF HOSEMANN, Fritz-Haber-Institut der Max-Planck-Gesellschaft, West Berlin, Germany. *Diffraction by Matter and Diffraction Gratings. Paracrystal* (translation by Walter J. Trapp).

W. V. HOUSTON (deceased). *Atomic Physics.*

KAREL HUJER, Department of Physics and Astronomy, University of Tennessee at Chattanooga, Tennessee. *History of Physics.*

MCALLISTER H. HULL, JR., The Graduate School, State University of New York at Buffalo, New York. *Calculus of Physics.*

CURTIS J. HUMPHREYS, Department of Physics, Purdue University, West Lafayette, Indiana. *Molecular Spectroscopy.*

FREDERICK V. HUNT (deceased). *Cavitation.*

T. S. HUTCHISON. *Ultrasonics.*

ROBERT L. INGALLS, Department of Physics, University of Washington, Seattle, Washington. *Mössbauer Effect* (with Peter Debrunner).

WILLIAM W. JACOBI. *Batteries.*

MAX JAMMER, Department of Physics, Bar-Ilan University, Ramat-Gan, Israel. *Statics.*

J. V. JELLEY, Nuclear Physics Division, Atomic Energy Research Establishment, Harwell, England. *Čerenkov Radiation.*

R. J. JOENK, I. B. M. Journal of Research and Development, Armonk, New York. *Ferromagnetism.*

RUSSELL H. JOHNSEN, Department of Chemistry, Florida State University, Tallahassee, Florida. *Elements, Chemical.*

FRANCIS S. JOHNSON, Center for Advanced Studies, University of Texas at Dallas, Texas. *Space Physics.*

J. B. JOHNSON (deceased). *Thermionics.*

JESS J. JOSEPHS, Department of Physics, Smith College, Northampton, Massachusetts. *Musical Sound.*

DEANE B. JUDD (deceased). *Color.*

P. K. KABIR, Department of Physics, University of Virginia, Charlottesville, Virginia. *Weak Interactions.*

WILLIAM M. KAULA, Institute of Geophysics and Planetary Physics, University of California, Los Angeles, California. *Geodesy.*

ROBERT W. KENNEY, Lawrence Berkeley Laboratory, University of California, Berkeley, California. *Bremsstrahlung and Photon Beams.*

DONALD W. KERST, Physics Department, University of Wisconsin, Madison, Wisconsin. *Betatron.*

WILLIAM F. KIEFFER, College of Wooster, Wooster, Ohio. *Mole Concept.*

ALLEN L. KING, Department of Physics and Astronomy, Dartmouth College, Hanover, New Hampshire. *Refrigeration.*

GERALD W. KING, Department of Chemistry, McMaster University, Hamilton, Ontario, Canada. *Molecules and Molecular Structure.*

RUDOLPH KINGSLAKE, Institute of Optics, University of Rochester, Rochester, New York. *Refraction.*

R. H. KINGSTON, Lincoln Laboratory, Massachusetts Institute of Technology, Lexington, Massachusetts. *Laser.*

HENRY J. KOSTKOWSKI, Optical Radiation Section, Heat Division, National Bureau of Standards, Washington, D.C. *Pyrometry.*

HOWARD E. KREMERS, Kerr-McGee Chemical Corporation, Oklahoma City, Oklahoma. *Rare Earths.*

REINOUT P. KROON, Towne School of Civil and Mechanical Engineering, University of Pennsylvania, Philadelphia, Pennsylvania. *Dimensions.*

H. G. KUHN, Department of Astrophysics, Oxford University, Oxford, England. *Atomic Spectra.*

KAILASH KUMAR, Research School of Physical Sciences, Australian National University, Canberra, A. C. T., Australia. *Many-Body Problem.*

J. E. KUNZLER, Bell Telephone Laboratories, Murray Hill, New Jersey, *Calorimetry* (with T. H. Geballe).

C. G. KUPER, Department of Physics, Technion—Israel Institute of Technology, Haifa, Israel. *Polaron.*

BEHRAM KURŞUNOĞLU, Center for Theoretical Studies, University of Miami, Coral Gables, Florida. *Quantum Theory.*

ROBERT T. LAGEMANN, Department of Physics and Astronomy, Vanderbilt University, Nashville, Tennessee. *Wave Motion.*

RONALD A. LAING, Boston University School of Medicine, Boston, Massachusetts, *Paramagnetism.*

H. E. LANDSBERG, Institute of Fluid Dynamics and Applied Mathematics, University of Maryland. *Geophysics.*

C. T. LANE, Department of Physics, Yale University, New Haven, Connecticut. *Superfluidity.*

D. F. LAWDEN, University of Aston in Birmingham, England. *Mathematical Principles of Quantum Mechanics.*

REUBEN LEE, Baltimore, Maryland. *Transformer.*

R. J. W. LEFÈVRE, Emeritus, School of Chemistry, Macquarie University, North Ryde, N. S. W., Australia. *Dipole Moments.*

JOSEPH LEVINE, Experimental Meteorology Laboratory, National Oceanic and Atmo-

spheric Administration, Miami, Florida. *Cloud Physics.*

BERNARD R. LINDEN (deceased). *Photomultiplier.*

ROBERT LINDSAY, Department of Physics, Trinity College, Hartford, Connecticut. *Resonance.*

ELLIS R. LIPPINCOTT. *Spectroscopy* (with Linda S. Whatley).

RAPHAEL M. LITTAUER, Laboratory of Nuclear Studies, Cornell University, Ithaca, New York. *Pulse Generation.*

F. B. LLEWELLYN (deceased). *Circuitry.*

A. L. LOEB, Department of Visual and Environmental Studies, Harvard University, Cambridge, Massachusetts. *Heisenberg Uncertainty Principle.*

JOSEPH J. LOFERSKI, Division of Engineering, Brown University, Providence, Rhode Island. *Photovoltaic Effect.*

EDWARD J. LOFGREN, Lawrence Berkeley Laboratory, University of California, Berkeley, California. *Cyclotron.*

ROBERT A. LUFBURROW, Department of Physics, St. Lawrence University, Canton, New York. *Carnot Cycles and Carnot Engines.*

H. R. LUKENS, Intercom Radiation Technology, San Diego, California. *Radioactive Tracers.*

PAUL S. LYKOUDIS, Department of Nuclear Engineering, Purdue University, West Lafayette, Indiana. *Magneto-Fluid-Mechanics.*

DAVID N. LYON, Department of Chemical Engineering, University of California, Berkeley, California. *Liquefaction of Gases.*

JOSEPH E. MACHUREK, United States Atomic Energy Commission, Washington, D.C. *Nucleonics.*

J. D. MACKENZIE, School of Engineering and Applied Science, University of California, Los Angeles, California. *Vitreous State.*

ALFRED U. MAC RAE, Bell Telephone Laboratories, Murray Hill, New Jersey. *Electron Diffraction.*

FRED C. MAIENSCHEIN, Neutron Physics Division, Oak Ridge National Laboratory, Oak Ridge, Tennessee. *Nuclear Radiation Shielding.*

STEPHEN P. MARAN, Laboratory of Solar Physics, NASA-Goddard Space Flight Center, Greenbelt, Maryland. *Radio Astronomy.*

JOHN W. MARTIN, Department of Metallurgy, University of Oxford, Oxford, England. *Metallurgy.*

L. L. MARTON, Smithsonian Institution, Washington, D.C. *Photoelectricity.*

ROBERT M. MASON, Naval Research Laboratory, Washington, D.C. *Tensors and Tensor Analysis* (with John A. Eisele).

P. T. MATTHEWS, Department of Physics, Imperial College, London, England. *Strong Interactions.*

R. D. MATTUCK, Physics Laboratory I, H. C. Ørsted Institute, University of Copenhagen, Denmark. *Feynman Diagrams.*

JOSEPH E. MAYER, University of California, San Diego, La Jolla, California. *Liquid State.*

C. B. A. MCCUSKER, Falkimer Nuclear Department, University of Sydney, Sydney, Australia. *Quarks.*

RAYMOND H. MCFEE, McDonnell Douglas Astronautics Co., Huntington Beach, California. *Infrared Radiation.*

J. W. MCGRATH, Graduate School and Research, Kent State University, Kent, Ohio. *Chemical Physics.*

DONALD P. MCINTYRE, Dames & Moore, Consultants in Applied Earth Sciences, Toronto, Canada. *Meteorology.*

A. E. E. MCKENZIE (deceased). *Optical Instruments* (with Nigel C. McKenzie).

NIGEL C. MCKENZIE, Research Institute for Fundamental Physics, Kyoto University, Kyoto, Japan. *Optical Instruments* (with A. E. E. McKenzie).

GEORGE TERRENCE MEADEN, Artech International, Trowbridge, England. *Conductivity, Electrical.*

HOWARD C. MEL, *Radiation, Ionizing, Basic Interactions* (with Paul W. Todd).

CARL H. MELTZER, RCA Corporation, Electronic Components and Devices, Harrison, New Jersey. *Electron Tubes.*

MAEL A. MELVIN, Department of Physics, Temple University, Philadelphia, Pennsylvania. *Antiparticles.*

DIETRICH MEYERHOFER, R C A Laboratories, Princeton, New Jersey. *Tunneling.*

JOHN L. MILES, Arthur D. Little, Inc., Cambridge, Massachusetts. *Cryogenics.*

WOLFGANG E. MOECKEL, Physical Science Division, NASA-Lewis Research Center, Cleveland, Ohio. *Electric Propulsion.*

ORREN C. MOHLER, Department of Astronomy, University of Michigan, Ann Arbor, Michigan. *Solar Physics.*

DONALD J. MONTGOMERY, College of Engineering, Michigan State University, East Lansing, Michigan. *Static Electricity* (with R. G. Cunningham).

KARL Z. MORGAN, School of Nuclear Engineering, Georgia Institute of Technology, Atlanta, Georgia. *Health Physics.*

E. W. MÜLLER, Department of Physics, Pennsylvania State University, University Park, Pennsylvania. *Field Emission.*

ALBERT A. MULLIN, *Feedback.*

RAYMOND R. MYERS, Department of Chemistry, Kent State University, Kent, Ohio. *Rheology.*

NORMAN H. NACHTRIEB, Department of Chemistry, University of Chicago, Chicago, Illinois. *Diffusion in Liquids.*

GÉRARD NADEAU, Départment de Physique, Université Laval, Québec, Canada. *Elasticity.*

JACOB NEUBERGER, Department of Physics, Queens College of the City University of New York, Flushing, New York. *Expansion, Thermal.*

LAWRENCE E. NIELSEN, Monsanto Company, St. Louis, Missouri. *Polymer Physics.*

CARL OBERMAN, Princeton University, Princeton, New Jersey. *Plasmas.*

JACK OLIVER, Department of Geological Sciences, Cornell University, Ithaca, New York. *Seismology.*

HARRY F. OLSON, RCA Laboratories, Princeton, New Jersey. *Noise, Acoustical.*

JOHN M. OLSON, Biology Department, Brookhaven National Laboratory, Upton, New York. *Photosynthesis.*

STEPHEN J. O'NEIL, Naval Weapons Engineering Support Activity, Washington Navy Yard, Washington, D.C. *Servomechanisms.*

RALPH T. OVERMAN. *Radioactivity.*

THORNTON PAGE, Naval Research Laboratory, Washington, D.C. *Astrophysics.*

WILLIAM E. PARKINS, Research and Technology, Atomics International Division, Rockwell International, Canoga Park, California. *Energy Levels. Work, Power, and Energy.*

RICHARD H. PARVIN, Astrodynamics. *Inertial Guidance.*

MARTIN PETER, Department of Solid State Physics, University of Geneva, Geneva, Switzerland. *Atomic Clocks.*

ROBERT W. PETERS, Institute of Speech and Hearing Sciences, University of North Carolina at Chapel Hill, North Carolina. *Hearing.*

NORMAN E. PHILLIPS, Department of Chemistry and Inorganic Materials Research Division of the Lawrence Berkeley Laboratory, University of California, Berkeley, California. *Heat Capacity.*

JULIAN M. PIKE, National Center for Atmospheric Research, Boulder, Colorado. *Coriolis Effect.*

J. J. PINAJIAN, Isotopes Development Center, Oak Ridge National Laboratory, Oak Ridge, Tennessee. *Isotopes* (with A. F. Rupp).

MARTIN A. POMERANTZ, Bartol Research Foundation of the Franklin Institute, Swarthmore, Pennsylvania. *International Geophysical Year and International Years of the Quiet Sun.*

ALAN Y. POPE, Sandia Laboratories, Albuquerque, New Mexico. *Aerodynamics.*

ALAN M. PORTIS, Department of Physics, University of California, Berkeley, California. *Faraday Effect.*

G. M. POUND, Materials Science Department, Stanford University, Stanford, California. *Condensation.*

R. D. PRESENT, Department of Physics and Astronomy, University of Tennessee, Knoxville, Tennessee. *Gas Laws. Intermolecular Forces.*

WILLIAM J. PRICE, Air Force Office of Scientific Research, Washington, D.C. *Nuclear Instruments.*

A. F. PUCHSTEIN (Retired), Jeffrey Mining Machinery Company, Columbus, Ohio. *Motors, Electric.*

ERNEST RABINOWICZ, Department of Mechanical Engineering, Massachusetts Institute of Technology, Cambridge, Massachusetts. *Friction.*

STANLEY RAIMES, Department of Mathematics, Imperial College, University of London, London, England. *Wave Mechanics.*

R. RAJARAMAN, University of Delhi, Delhi, India. *Mass and Inertia.*

N. RASHEVSKY (deceased). *Mathematical Biophysics.*

LAWRENCE L. RAUCH, Computer, Information and Control Engineering, University of Michigan, Ann Arbor, Michigan. *Telemetry.*

HUBERT REEVES. *Solar Energy Sources.*

F. REINES, School of Physical Sciences, University of California, Irvine, California. *Neutrino.*

J. A. REYNOLDS, Culham Laboratory, United Kingdom Atomic Energy Authority, Culham, England. *Fusion.*

JAMES A. RICHARDS, JR., Agricultural and Technical College, State University of New York, Delhi, New York. *Brownian Motion. Fermi-Dirac Statistics and Fermions.*

WOLFGANG RINDLER, Department of Physics and Mathematics, University of Texas at Dallas, Texas. *Relativity.*

B. L. ROBERTSON, Emeritus, Department of Electrical Engineering and Computer Sciences, University of California, Berkeley, California. *Electric Power Generation.*

JACQUES E. ROMAIN, Centre de Recherches Routières, Sterrebeek, Belgium. *Time.*

MILTON A. ROTHMAN, Department of Physics, Trenton State College, Trenton, New Jersey. *Conservation Laws and Symmetry.*

ARTHUR G. ROUSE (deceased). *Rotation— Circular Motion.*

A. F. RUPP, Oak Ridge National Laboratory, Oak Ridge, Tennessee. *Isotopes* (with J. J. Pinajian).

ROGERS D. RUSK, Emeritus, Physics Department, Mount Holyoke College, South Hadley, Massachusetts. *Nuclear Radiation.*

GEORGE E. RYSCHKEWITSCH, Department of Chemistry, University of Florida, Gainesville, Florida. *Bond Chemical.*

R. T. SANDERSON, Department of Chemistry, Arizona State University, Tempe, Arizona. *Periodic Law and Periodic Table.*

W. L. W. SARGENT, California Institute of Technology, Pasadena, California. *Cosmology.*

LEONARD I. SCHIFF (deceased). *Matrix Mechanics.*

H. M. SCHLICKE, Allen-Bradley Company, Milwaukee, Wisconsin. *Capacitance.*

GLENN T. SEABORG, University of California, Berkeley, California. *Transuranium Elements.*

ARTHUR H. SEIDMAN, Pratt Institute School of Engineering, Brooklyn, New York. *Diode (Semiconductor).*

J. M. H. LEVELT SENGERS, Institute for Basic Standards, National Bureau of Standards, Washington, D.C. *Compressibility, Gas.*

R. S. SHANKLAND, Department of Physics, Case

Western Reserve University, Cleveland, Ohio. *Michelson-Morley Experiment.*

A. G. SHARKEY, JR., Pittsburgh Energy Research Center, U.S. Bureau of Mines, Pittsburgh, Pennsylvania. *Mass Spectroscopy.*

EDGAR A. G. SHAW, Division of Physics, National Research Council of Canada, Ottawa, Ontario, Canada. *Electroacoustics.*

WILLIAM F. SHEEHAN, Department of Chemistry, University of Santa Clara, Santa Clara, California. *Chemical Kinetics.*

E. S. SHIRE, University of Cambridge and King's College, Cambridge, England. *Electricity.*

HOWARD A. SHUGART, Department of Physics, University of California, Berkeley, California. *Atomic and Molecular Beams.*

WILLIAM A. SHURCLIFF, Cambridge Electron Accelerator, Harvard University, Cambridge, Massachusetts. *Polarized Light.*

R. P. SHUTT, Brookhaven National Laboratory, Upton, New York. *Spark and Bubble Chambers.*

MIRIAM SIDRAN, Department of Physics, Baruch College, City University of New York, New York. *Photography.*

LESTER S. SKAGGS, Department of Radiology, University of Chicago, Chicago, Illinois. *Medical Physics.*

MERRILL I. SKOLNIK, Naval Research Laboratory, Washington, D.C. *Radar.*

LAWRENCE SLIFKIN, Department of Physics, University of North Carolina, Chapel Hill, North Carolina. *Diffusion in Solids.*

J. SMIDT, Laboratorium voor Technische Natuurkunde, Technische Hogeschool Delft, Delft, the Netherlands. *Relaxation.*

HOWARD M. SMITH, Eastman Kodak Company, Rochester, New York. *Holography.*

JAMES T. SMITH, International Business Machines Corp., Boulder, Colorado. *Magnetic Resonance.*

M. G. SMITH, Department of Mathematics and Statistics, Sir John Cass School of Science and Technology, City of London Polytechnic, London, England. *Laplace Transforms.*

CHARLES P. SMYTH, Princeton University, Princeton, New Jersey. *Dielectric Theory.*

S. L. SOO, Department of Mechanical and Industrial Engineering, University of Illinois, Urbana, Illinois, *Equilibrium.*

WALTER W. SOROKA, Emeritus, Department of Mechanical Engineering, University of California, Berkeley, California. *Acoustics.*

J. W. T. SPINKS, University of Saskatchewan, Saskatoon, Canada. *Radiation Chemistry* (with R. J. Woods).

M. T. SPRACKLING, Department of Physics, Queen Elizabeth College (University of London, England. *Mechanical Properties of Solids.*

H. EUGENE STANLEY, Department of Physics, Massachusetts Institute of Technology, Cambridge, Massachusetts. *Critical Phenomena.*

ROBERT L. STEARNS, Department of Physics and Astronomy, Vassar College, Poughkeepsie,

New York. *Bose-Einstein Statistics and Bosons.*

WILLIAM E. STEPHENS, Department of Physics, University of Pennsylvania, Philadelphia, Pennsylvania. *Electron Spin.*

REGINALD J. STEPHENSON (deceased). *Mechanics.*

ERNEST J. STERNGLASS, Department of Radiology, School of Medicine, University of Pittsburgh, Pittsburgh, Pennsylvania. *Secondary Emission.*

K. AA. STRAND, U.S. Naval Observatory, Washington, D.C., *Astrometry.*

E. C. G. SUDARSHAN, Center for Particle Theory and Department of Physics, University of Texas, Austin, Texas. *Elementary Particles.*

ANDRIS SUNA, Central Research Department, Experimental Station, E. I. du Pont de Nemours and Company, Wilmington, Delaware. *Excitons.*

CHARLES SÜSSKIND, College of Engineering, University of California, Berkeley, California. *Electronics.*

G. P. SUTTON, Envirotech Corporation, c/o Sumitomo Jukikai Envirotech, Inc., Tokyo, Japan. *Flight Propulsion Fundamentals.*

RICHARD M. SUTTON (deceased). *Kepler's Laws of Planetary Motion.*

J. D. SWIFT, School of Physics, University of Bath, Claverton Down, Bath, England. *Electrical Discharges in Gases.*

S. M. SZE, Bell Telephone Laboratories, Murray Hill, New Jersey. *Semiconductor Devices.*

DALE T. TEANEY, Thomas J. Watson Research Center, International Business Machines, Corp., Yorktown Heights, New York. *Antiferromagnetism.*

NORMAN TEPLEY, Department of Physics, Oakland University, Rochester, Michigan. *Fermi Surface* (with H. V. Bohm).

JAMES TERRELL, University of California Los Alamos Scientific Laboratory, Los Alamos, New Mexico. *Fission.*

MATTHEW P. THEKAEKARA, NASA-Goddard Space Flight Center, Greenbelt, Maryland. *Interference and Interferometry. Solar Constant and Solar Spectrum.*

A. C. THORSEN, Rockwell International Science Center, Thousand Oaks, California. *De Haas-van Alphen Effect.*

RUDOLF E. THUN, Raytheon Company, Bedford, Massachusetts. *Thin Films.*

PAUL W. TODD. *Radiation, Ionizing, Basic Interactions* (with H. C. Mel).

RICHARD TOUSEY, Space Science Division, Naval Research Laboratory, Washington, D.C. *Ultraviolet Radiation.*

WALTER J. TRAPP, U.S. Air Force Materials Laboratory, Wright-Patterson Air Force Base, Ohio. Translator of article, *Paracrystal.*

MYRON TRIBUS, Information Technology Group, Xerox Corporation, Rochester, New York. *Entropy.*

G. J. F. TROUP, Physics Department, Monash University, Clayton 3168, Victoria, Australia. *Maser*.

JOHN G. TRUMP, Department of Engineering, Massachusetts Institute of Technology, Cambridge, Massachusetts. *Accelerator, Van de Graaff. High Voltage Research*.

N. W. TSCHOEGL, California Institute of Technology, Pasadena, California. *Viscoelasticity*.

R. S. UNWIN, Geophysical Observatory, Physics and Engineering Laboratory, D. S. I. R., Christchurch, New Zealand. *Aurora and Airglow*.

ROLAND W. URE, JR., Electrical Engineering Department and Division of Materials Science and Engineering, University of Utah, Salt Lake City, Utah. *Thermoelectricity*.

LEOPOLD B. VALDES, T R W Systems Group, Redondo Beach, California, *Transistor*.

THOMAS E. VANZANDT, Aeronomy Laboratory, National Oceanic and Atmospheric Administration, Boulder, Colorado. *Ionosphere*.

EDGAR VILLCHUR, Foundation for Hearing Aid Research, Woodstock, New York. *Reproduction of Sound*.

WILHELM H. VON AULOCK, Bell Telephone Laboratories, Whippany, New Jersey. *Ferrimagnetism*.

WILLIAM W. WALKER, Department of Physics, University of Alabama at Tuscaloosa, Alabama. *Positron* (with B. Clark Groseclose).

ROALD K. WANGSNESS, Department of Physics, University of Arizona, Tucson, Arizona. *Theoretical Physics*.

KENNETH M. WATSON, Department of Physics, University of California, Berkeley, California. *Collisions of Particles*.

ELBERT C. WEAVER, Sterling Laboratory, Yale University, New Haven, Connecticut. *Density and Specific Gravity*.

M. B. WEBB. *Surface Physics*.

WALTER L. WEEKS, School of Electrical Engineering, Purdue University, West Lafayette, Indiana. *Electromagnetic Theory*.

VERNON G. WELSBY, Department of Electronic and Electrical Engineering, University of Birmingham, Birmingham, England. *Inductance*.

H. L. WELSH, University of Toronto, Toronto, Canada. *Raman Effect and Raman Spectroscopy*.

CHARLES WERT, Department of Metallurgy and Mining Engineering, University of Illinois, Urbana, Illinois. *Solid State Physics*.

LINDA S. WHATLEY. *Spectroscopy* (with E. R. Lippincott).

GERSHON J. WHEELER, Los Altos, California. *Waveguides*.

MILTON G. WHITE, Department of Physics, Princeton University, Princeton, New Jersey. *Synchrotrons*.

FERD WILLIAMS, Physics Department, University of Delaware, Newark, Delaware. *Luminescence*.

JOHN H. WILLS, Cheyney, Pennsylvania. *Phase Rule*.

A. J. C. WILSON, Department of Physics, University of Birmingham, Birmingham, England. *X-ray Diffraction*.

G. MILTON WING, Los Alamos, New Mexico. *Transport Theory*.

DENNIS E. WISNOSKY, U.S. Air Force Materials Laboratory, Wright-Patterson Air Force Base, Ohio. *Computers*.

FRANK L. WOLF, Department of Mathematics, Carleton College, Northfield, Minnesota. *Statistics*.

HUGH C. WOLFE, American Institute of Physics, New York. *Symbols, Units and Nomenclature*.

T. WOLFRAM, North American Rockwell Science Center, Thousand Oaks, California. *Spin Waves* (with R. E. De Wames).

JOSEPH F. WOODS (deceased). *Photoconductivity*.

R. J. WOODS, Department of Chemistry, University of Saskatchewan, Saskatoon, Saskatchewan, Canada. *Radiation Chemistry* (with J. W. T. Spinks).

JOHN YARWOOD, Department of Physics, The Polytechnic of Central London, London, England. *Vacuum Techniques* (with K. J. Close).

HSUAN YEH, Towne School of Civil and Mechanical Engineering, University of Pennsylvania, Philadelphia, Pennsylvania. *Impulse and Momentum*.

A. M. ZAREM, Beverly Hills, California. *Solar Energy Utilization* (with Duane D. Erway).

ALEXANDER ZUCKER, Oak Ridge National Laboratory, Oak Ridge, Tennessee. *Nuclear Reactions*.

PREFACE TO SECOND EDITION

This second edition of the *Encyclopedia of Physics* follows the same general plan as was used for the first edition; that is, each article is written so as to be of primary value to the type of reader who is most apt to look for the particular topic. There are articles on major areas of physics which are at a low technical level, so as to be of maximum value to the reader with little prior knowledge of physics. There are also articles on major divisions and subdivisions of these areas. In general, these latter start with an introduction intended to define the topic and describe the concepts involved. This is followed by more detailed and advanced treatment for the reader with a stronger background in physics.

To cover more of physics, the book has been considerably expanded, both by adding new articles and by including new material on topics in the first edition. Many of the articles have been completely rewritten, others received major changes, while others, particularly those on major areas of physics, required little or no change.

As in the first edition, the major credit for any success the book may achieve belongs to the authors, many of whom not only contributed a tremendous amount of time and effort in preparing articles, but made valuable suggestions for other parts of the book.

The editors at the Van Nostrand Reinhold Company contributed a great deal to the readability and accuracy of the book, and to my wife, Leigh, goes credit for much careful proofreading, for the preparation of the extensive index, and for the typing and detailed record-keeping required in assembling a book of this magnitude.

To all of these workers my heartfelt thanks are due.

ROBERT M. BESANÇON

Dayton, Ohio
April 10, 1974

PREFACE TO FIRST EDITION

THE AIM of this book is to provide in one volume concise and accurate information about physics. It should be of use to physicists who need information outside of their own special areas of interest, to teachers and librarians who must answer inquiries, to students who wish to add to their funds of knowledge, and to engineers and scientists who encounter physical concepts in pursuit of their professions. The book has been made possible by the thoughtful and generous cooperation of more than 300 authors, both in this country and abroad, who have unstintingly contributed their time, skill and knowledge. Their names and affiliations are shown immediately before this preface.

The most challenging problem for the editor was deciding which topics to include and which to leave out, since the space available was very limited compared with the vast amount of knowledge that could have been included. The approach used was to provide short introductory articles on physics, on the history of physics, on measurements, and on symbols, units and nomenclature, plus general articles on the major areas of physics: heat, light, mechanics, acoustics, etc. To these were added entries on divisions and subdivisions of the major areas; these are more detailed and pitched at somewhat higher technical levels than the broader, more general articles. Other topics lie on the interfaces between major areas of physics or are on subjects that include both physics and other disciplines. These include, among others, astrophysics, geophysics, biophysics, and mathematical biophysics. Finally, a few articles cover sciences that are so closely related to physics that the differences are frequently merely matters of emphasis.

Each article attempts to provide not just a definition of a term but an explanation of an area of physics. No attempt was made to hold all articles at the same technical level; on the contrary, the level for each entry was aimed at those readers who would be most apt to look for information on that specific topic. The contents of each article was left to the discretion of the author as the one most capable of making the proper selection. Some of the authors found it necessary to use mathematics, as is done in many books on physics. However, the reader with a limited mathematical background will find many articles with no mathematics at all, and others with very little, while the reader who is so inclined can sink his teeth into the more mathematical paragraphs.

Most of the authors have provided references to summary articles and books, and in addition, cross-references to other articles in this book have been added wherever it was felt that they might be of particular help to the reader. A few cross-references are shown by the use of small capitals in the body of the text (thus, MECHANICS); others are listed at the end of the article. The index should serve to locate particular topics that might not be subjects of complete articles.

I should like to extend by heartfelt thanks to the authors who contributed so much and to Mr. G. G. Hawley and Mr. H. Simonds of the Reinhold Publishing Corporation who invited me to compile and edit this book as one of the series of scientific and technical encyclopedias published by that company. I also owe a very great deal to Mrs. Alberta Gordon and her staff, who did much of the editing and proofreading, and to my wife, Leigh, who contributed the bulk of the tremendous amount of clerical work involved as well as adding a great deal of enthusiasm and inspiration.

ROBERT M. BESANÇON

Dayton, Ohio
November 1, 1965

A

ABERRATIONS

The two sections of this article give a theoretical treatment. For an introductory discussion, see the article entitled LENS.

Geometrical Theory When a light wave passes through an instrument, the wave front suffers deformation due to the imperfection of the instrument. The optical distance between the emerging wave front (actual) and the converging wave front (ideal) when the mapping of object points is perfect is a measure of the aberration of the instrument. For an ideal instrument, the mathematical relation of such a mapping is given by the equations

$$\bar{x}_i = Mx_i \quad (1a), \qquad \bar{\xi}_i = m\xi_i \quad (i = 1, 2, 3), \quad (1b)$$

where M, m are constants characterizing the optical instrument and $(x_i, \bar{x}_i)$, $(\xi_i, \bar{\xi}_i)$ are the coordinates and optical direction cosines of a ray in the object and image space respectively. If the z-coordinates are fixed, $x_3 = z_0$, $\bar{x}_3 = z_1$, the ray enters the object plane z_0 and exits from the image plane z_1.

In general, the above relationship between the object and image points is not realized in actual practice and instead of (1a), (1b) we have

$$\bar{x} = Mx_i + f(x_i, \xi_i) \tag{2a}$$

$$\bar{\xi}_i = m\xi_i + g(x_i, \xi_i) \tag{2b}$$

where $f(x_i, \xi_i)$, $g(x_i, \xi_i)$ are complicated functions of the arguments. The functional dependence of these functions on x_i and ξ_i characterizes the optical instrument. These are called the aberrations of the optical instrument or system.

For a given optical system, such as a lens or a number of lenses as in a microscope or telescope objective, the aberrations can be calculated by tracing rays from the object plane to the image plane—object and stop positions—using the law of refraction. This method of computing the aberrations numerically is very laborious and does not yield a clear picture of the various types of aberrations even in simple optical systems. On the other hand, when the Hamilton characteristic functions are introduced, representing the actual emerging wave fronts, one obtains an analytical expression for the aberration function of an instrument and furthermore is able to classify various types of aberrations

caused by an optical system. The so-called point characteristic expressing the distance from a point on the object plane to the corresponding point of the same ray on the stop plane is hardly used in actual practice. However, the mixed characteristic W, which is a function of the object position of a ray and its emerging direction on the image or stop plane, forms the basis of the Hamilton, Seidel, and Schwarzschild theory of aberrations, and the fourth characteristic of Hamilton, the angular characteristic, is taken as the basis of the Smith theory.[11] However, the derivation of an explicit form of the mixed or angular characteristic is a very difficult mathematical problem and only in a few simple optical systems has the characteristic function been calculated in a closed form. For rotational systems, the characteristic functions (the point, the two mixed, and the angular characteristic) depend on three variables or invariants, and when the aberration is small they are expanded in power series of the invariants. In the following section on diffraction theory we give the expansion of the mixed characteristic $W(x_i, \xi_i)$ in two different forms, known as the standard and the Zernike-Nijboer expansions, and explain briefly the various classifications of the terms of the series arranged according to the powers of the invariants. For an extended analysis of the geometrical aberrations and their classifications we refer the reader to the general references listed, in particular, to recent studies[11,12,13,14] and to the following comprehensive treatises on the subject: M. Herzberger, "Modern Geometrical Optics," New York, Interscience Publishers, 1958, and H. Buchdahl, "Optical Aberration Coefficients," Oxford, Oxford University Press, 1954, where references to their researches and to more recent developments are to be found.

Diffraction Theory The starting point of the modern theory of diffraction of optical instruments may be traced to the famous paper on diffraction theory of the phase contrast method by Zernike.[1] The extension to the diffraction theory of aberrations was carried out by him in collaboration with his pupils, especially, Nijboer.[2] Since then, many advances have taken place, both in theory and experimental observation leading to important applications in the improvement of optical instruments. However, prior to Zernike's pioneering work, some significant contributions to the theory were made by

1

a number of authorities, notably Ignatowski, Fischer, Steward,[3] and Picht.[4]

The basis of the diffraction theory of optical instruments is founded on Kirchhoff's integral or a modified form of it, namely

$$U(P) = -\frac{ikn}{2\pi} \iint_S \sqrt{K} U_0(Q)$$

$$\cdot \exp ik \left[W + (\mathbf{r} \cdot \mathbf{s})\right] dS \quad (1)$$

where $U_0(Q)$ is the value of the field on the wave surface (front) S, K and $\mathbf{s}$ are respectively the Gaussian curvature and optical normal vector of S, n is the refractive index of the medium in the image space, and W is the Hamiltonian mixed characteristic of the optical system. The image field $U(P)$ at an image point $P(x, y, z)$ is the geometrical optics wave solution of the scalar wave equation, or Maxwell equations.

A more convenient form of Eq. (1) used frequently in actual problems is

$$U(P) = -\frac{ik}{2\pi} \iint_{p^2+q^2 \leqslant n^2} g(p,q) \exp ik\phi(P;p,q)$$

$$dp \, dq,$$

$$\phi(P;p,q) = W + (\mathbf{r} \cdot \mathbf{s}) \quad (2)$$

where a point Q on the wave surface $S(Q)$ is represented parametrically in terms of (p, q), $x = -W_p + \lambda p$, $y = -W_q + \lambda q$, $z = \lambda\sqrt{n^2 - p^2 - q^2}$, $\lambda = \lambda(p,q)$. Here p, q and $(n^2 - p^2 - q^2)^{1/2}$ are the optical direction cosines (components) of the normal vector $\mathbf{s}$. The amplitude function $g(p,q) = |n| \|\Delta|^{1/2} \cdot U_0(p,q)$ remains constant along a ray $(p \cdot q)$ in image space, and Δ is the discriminant of the second differential form of S. Equations (1) or (2) are known as the Picht-Luneburg integrals.[4,5]

The above formulas give all the information about the image produced by an optical instrument for a monochromatic source. Thus the problem is reduced to the evaluation of such integrals over the arbitrary wave front S. In general, W is not known explicitly (closed form) on S, so instead of the wave surface S one takes a reference surface S_0, usually a spherical wave front with center at the Gaussian image point of the optical system, and expands W in a Taylor series in the parameters. In practice S_0 is the aperture (entrance or exit-pupil) of the instrument. For rotational symmetric systems, most frequently employed in practice, W depends on three invariants, $u_1 = x_0^2 + y_0^2$, $u_2 = p^2 + q^2$, $u_3 = x_0 p + y_0 q$, and an additional invariant $u_4 = x_0 q - y_0 p$ for electron optical systems. Therefore, the expansion of W is of the form

$$W = W_0 + \Sigma a_i u_i + \Sigma a_{ij} u_i u_j + \Sigma a_{ijk} u_i u_j u_k + \cdots,$$

$$(i, j, k = 1, 2, 3),$$

$$= W_0 + \sum_{\rho=1}^{\infty} \sum_{n=1}^{\infty} \sum_{m=1}^{n} b_{lnm} \sigma^{2l+m} \rho^n \cos^m \phi =$$

$$W_0 + \sum_{n=1}^{\infty} \sum_{m=0}^{n} f_{nm}(\sigma) \rho^n \cos^m \phi \quad (3)$$

l, n, m are positive integers, $n - m$ even > 0 and $u_1 = \sigma^2$, $u_2 = \rho^2$, $u_3 = \sigma\rho \cos \phi$. The individual constants b_{lnm} are the aberration coefficients. This standard development has been used by Steward and others in their treatment of diffraction of aberrations. However, even for individual aberrations of lower order, the evaluation of the diffraction integral leads to complicated expressions for the image field or intensity distribution, since the various orders of a single type aberration are not separated; consequently, it is difficult to separate the contributions of each order to the total intensity in the image plane. For these reasons, both Steward and Picht and later Born obtained incomplete figures of the intensity distributions of the image. On the other hand, Nijboer, following Zernike's ideas, was able to calculate to a great degree of accuracy (unknown before) the intensity distribution for several types of aberrations and high orders. The experimental observations made at Zernike's laboratory, as well as those made at McGill University on microwaves[2a] are in agreement with Nijboer's figures or with those calculated by Nijboer's method.[2a]

The Zernike-Nijboer diffraction theory of aberration is based on the development of the aberration function, or W, in terms of orthogonal polynomials (functions) over the region of integration (wave front) which, in their case, was a circle. Instead of Eq. (3), W is expanded in the form

$$W = W_0 + \sum_{n=1}^{\infty} \sum_{m=0}^{\infty} f_{mn}(\sigma) Z_n^m(\rho) \cos m\phi,$$

$$(m = 0, 1, \cdots, n; n = 1, 2, \cdots) \quad (4)$$

where $Z_n^m(\rho)$ are called the Zernike polynomials, which are orthogonal over a unit circle. In this development, a typical aberration term is of the form $b_{lnm} \sigma^{2l+m} Z_n^m(\rho) \cos m\phi$. On account of the orthogonality of Z_n^m, the various orders of a single aberration enter individually (are not mixed) in the expression representing the intensity distribution function; i.e., different aberrations cannot counterbalance each other's contribution for all σ. In general, the amplitude function can also be expanded in Zernike polynomials, or other functions such as Fourier-Bessel, or Dini functions,[10] if the field over the aperture is not constant (coating of lenses). In general, the idea of expanding both the amplitude and the phase function in orthogonal functions over the domain of integration has many advantages over previous methods, since the double integral cannot be reduced into a single

integral, except for the simplest type of apertures. However, when only spherical aberration of all orders is considered, the method of integration by parts of the diffraction integral leads to rather simple expression for the image field. This case has been treated exhaustively for both circular and annular apertures by Boivin.[8] The calculation of the diffracted field in the presence of higher order aberrations including the more general problem of nonsymmetric optical systems is given in reference 14.

All the methods discussed above are valid only for small aberrations. For large or moderately large aberrations, one must resort to asymptotic methods, which at present are sufficiently developed to include most of the interesting cases occurring in the theory of diffraction of optical systems. When these analytical methods are combined with the present progress in computational methods, the intensity distribution produced by an optical system can be calculated to any desired degree of accuracy.

NICHOLAS CHAKO

References

1. Zernike, F., *Physica*, **1**, 689 (1934).
2. Nijboer, B. R. A., "The Diffraction Theory of Aberrations," Groningen thesis, 1942. For the experimental part, see the thesis by Nienhuis, K., Groningen, 1948. For microwave experiments see: Bachynski, M. P. and Bekefi, G., *IRE Trans.*, **AP-4**, No. 3, 412 (1955). "Studies in Microwave Optics," *McGill Univ. Tech. Rept.*, 38 (1957).
3. Steward, G. C., "The Symmetrical Optical System," Cambridge, Cambridge Univ. Press, 1928.
4. Picht, Johannes, "Optische Abbildung," Braunschweig, 1931.
5. Luneburg, R. K., "Mathematical Theory of Optics," Providence, R.I., Brown University, 1944. Reproduced by the University of California Press, Berkeley and Los Angeles, 1964.
6. Linfoot, E. H., "Recent Advances in Optics," London, Oxford Univ. Press, 1955.
7. Born, M., and Wolf, E., "Principles of Optics," New York, Pergamon Press, 1959.
8. Boivin, A., "Théorie et Calcul des Figures de Diffraction de Révolution," Paris, Les Presses de l'Université Laval, Québec and Gauthier-Villars, 1964.
9. Maréchal, A., and Françon, M., Diffraction Structure des Images, Paris, Masson et Cie, Editeurs, 1970.
10. Françon, M., in "Handbuch der Physik," Vol. 24, Berlin, Springer, 1956.
11. Pegis, R. J., "The Modern Development of Hamiltonian Optics," *Progress in Optics*, **I**, Ed. E. Wolf, Amsterdam, North Holland Publ. Co. (1961). Focke, J., "High Order Aberration Theory," *Progress in Optics*, **IV** (1965).
12. "Handbuch der Physik," Vol. XXIX, Ed. S. Flügge, Berlin, Springer Verlag, 1967. Articles by Welford, Walter T., "Optical Calculations and Optical Instruments, An Introduction"; Marechal, Andre, "Methode de Calcul des Systèmes Optiques"; Helmut, Max, "Theorie der Geometrisch-Optischen Bildfehler."
13. Hawkes, P. W., "Quadrupole Optics, Electron Optical Properties of Orthogonal Systems," Springer Series, "Tracts in Modern Physics," Vol. 42, Berlin, 1966.
14. Chako, Nicholas, "Contribution à la Théorie de la Diffraction," Centre d'Etudes Nucléaires de Saclay, CEA-R-3151, Saclay, France, 1969. "Etudes sur les Développements Asymptotiques des Intégrales Multiples de la Physique Mathématique" (large aberration diffraction), CEA-R-3263, Saclay, France, 1968.

Cross-references: DIFFRACTION BY MATTER AND DIFFRACTION GRATINGS; LENS; OPTICAL INSTRUMENTS; OPTICS, GEOMETRICAL; OPTICS, PHYSICAL.

ABSORPTION SPECTRA

The first experiment in which the light from the sun was dispersed into its spectrum was performed by Sir Isaac Newton in 1666. The chief effect was, obviously, the transformation of the round pinhole image of the sun in white light into a sausage-shaped array of colors, starting with red and ending, further up the wall, with violet. There was only a gradual transition from one color to the next, and apparently no colors were missing between violet and red.

The next step in the new optical topic of spectroscopy was the observation by W. H. Wollaston (1766–1828) in 1802 that the solar spectrum is not complete, but is crossed by a large number of dark lines—apparently missing wavelengths. A dozen years later Joseph von Fraunhofer (1787–1826) again observed these dark lines in the solar spectrum. In 1859 they were explained by Kirchhoff as due to the fact that the elements which, when in the laboratory, give characteristic bright lines in their spectrum, would in the solar atmosphere absorb those very lines—hence relative darkness is apparent at these places in the spectra when viewed from the earth.

Distinctions should be made at this point between several terms used in the discussion of absorption spectroscopy.

The *absorption coefficient* of a material (α) is expressed in the equation, known as the law of absorption and enunciated by Bouguer and Lambert,*

$$I_x = I_0 e^{-\alpha x}$$

*Pierre Bouguer (1698–1758) and Johann Lambert (1728–1777). It was later shown by Beer that the absorption coefficient for a solution is directly proportional to the concentration of the absorbing species. The relationship, known today as Beer's law, is

$$I = I_0 10^{-abc}$$

where a is the *absorptivity*, b is the thickness through which the initial intensity I_0 drops to I, and c is the concentration of the absorbing material.

in which the intensity of an incident plane wave I_0 is shown to decrease as the reciprocal of an exponential function to a value I_x after the energy has penetrated to a distance x in the sample of the material. In other words, the fraction dI/I_0 of the initial intensity is "lost" in traversing the distance dx, since $dI/I_0 = -\alpha dx$.

Absorption is the general phenomenon taking place within the body of the material as measured by the absorption coefficient.

Absorbance is the common logarithm of the ratio of the incident to the transmitted intensities.

Absorptance is the measure of the amount of light that disappears at a single reflection.

No substance has been found to exist that does not strongly absorb some wavelengths if the range be sufficiently extended. Dielectrics usually exhibit three extensive regions of large transmission, one in each of the three distinctive portions of the electromagnetic spectrum—very short wavelengths, intermediate wavelengths, and very long wavelengths.

A *blackbody* absorbs all of the radiant energy incident upon it—is a perfect absorber—and likewise acts as a perfect radiator. Kirchhoff's law of radiation states that the ratio of the *emissive power* to the *absorptive power* is the same for all bodies at a specified absolute temperature, or $E/A =$ a constant $= E_B$. E is the total energy radiated per square centimeter of surface per second and A, the *absorptive power*, is the fraction of the incident energy that is not reflected or transmitted by the surface. Obviously, A is unity for a blackbody, and hence the constant in the above equation is E_B, the emissive power of a blackbody at the specified temperature. Absorption lines in a spectrum can be explained on the assumption of RESONANCE of the atoms of the absorbing material to that portion of the incident energy spectrum which presents the same oscillation frequency. The atoms reradiate all of the absorbed energy *but in all directions*, so that the portion in the line of sight of the observer is relatively less than what would have been in that position without the intervening vapor.

A material that reduces the intensity of incident light almost entirely without regard to wavelength is said to exhibit *general absorption*. White light becomes gray. In the instances cited in this article, there is *selective absorption*. Flowers, paints, skin, etc., have color by selective absorption since some of the light penetrates ever so slightly into the body of the material.

The absorption bands in the spectra of solids and liquids are usually continuous, gradually fading out along the wavelength axis, but gases show narrow lines in their absorption spectra as a general rule.

We know from elementary optics that the *index of refraction* (n) of a nonconducting material (dielectric) at a definite wavelength is its essential property, for by its use in Snell's law, we can obtain the sequence of deviations of a ray as it passes through or from an interface bound-

ing two media (see REFRACTION). The case is very different for metals (conductors) due to the presence of free electrons in among the atoms. Strong absorption at once occurs so that metals are opaque, certainly to visible light. When the optical properties of metals are being considered, it is more efficacious to use the quantity known as the *absorption index*, defined for a given wavelength λ by

$$\kappa = \frac{\alpha\lambda}{4\pi n}$$

where n is best determined by the measurement of Brewster's angle. (see POLARIZED LIGHT). For silver at $\lambda = 589.3$ nm, $n = 0.177$ and $\kappa = 20.554$.

The theory of dispersion shows that generally, in the visible region, transparent materials exhibit a decrease in refractive index with wavelength (section AB of Fig. 1). This part of the

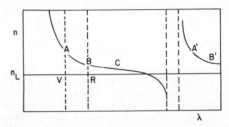

FIG. 1. Index of refraction vs. wavelength for a typical material. Adapted from Fig. 23D of *Fundamentals of Physical Optics*, by Francis A. Jenkins and Harvey E. White, courtesy of McGraw-Hill Book Co., New York, 3rd Edition, 1957.

graph (AB) is known as the *normal dispersion curve* for the material and can readily be plotted from data taken with a prism spectrometer. The earliest attempt to relate n to λ was made by Cauchy in 1836, namely,

$$n = A + \frac{B}{\lambda^2} + \frac{C}{\lambda^4}$$

where A, B and C are constants. Although based, as we now know it, on false assumptions, this relationship has proved valuable as a practical working equation, as long as one keeps far from an absorption band. Considering the effect of the frequency of the incident light (ν) upon the particles of the medium, having a natural frequency ν_0, Sellmeier (1971) derived the more acceptable relation

$$n^2 = 1 + \frac{A\lambda^2}{\lambda^2 - \lambda_0{}^2}$$

where A is a constant proportional to the number of oscillators affected and λ_0 is the wavelength corresponding to ν_0 in a vacuum. We see from this equation that at resonance (when $\nu = \nu_0$), the index of refraction becomes very large. In

the event that there are many possible natural frequencies, the Sellmeier equation can be generalized to

$$n^2 = 1 + \sum_i \frac{A_i\lambda^2}{\lambda^2 - \lambda_0{}^2}$$

A very familiar illustration of absorption is the traffic signal. Even the layman realizes that the practically white light of the high wattage incandescent lamp inside the bowl is *modified* by the presence of the colored material through which the light reaches his eyes. What colors he does *not* see, he assumes are "absorbed." The following experiment may serve to clarify this point.

Let a beam of white light fall upon a flat slab of some dyed material and assume that we are able to measure wavelength by wavelength the percentage of the reflected energy (reflectance *R*), the percentage of the absorbed energy (absorptance *A*) and the percentage of the transmitted energy (transmittance *T*). Because of the law of conservation of energy, it is evident that

REFLECTANCE + ABSORPTANCE

+ TRANSMITTANCE = 100(%)

(See Fig. 2.)

If the particular values of these characteristic factors are read off at, say, 600 nm, it is seen that about 4 per cent is reflected, 31 per cent is absorbed (turned into heat), and the remainder, 65 per cent, is transmitted. The material is said to exhibit *selective* reflectance, absorptance and transmittance, since not all wavelengths are equally affected. In fact, it is observed from the curves that the slab is probably somewhat reddish by reflected light and amber by transmitted light. No light at all is passed below about 520 nm.*

The situation would be somewhat different if the sample of material were a thin film of a normally colorless material, such as glass, gelatin, cellophane or acetate, which has been colored by means of a dye—as in the case of a filter. The first surface of the vehicle will not exhibit any selective reflection and the energy distribution will be that of the light source. (It should be observed, however, that the *amount of energy reflected* will depend upon the *angle of incidence*, in accord with Fresnel's reflection formulas.) The dyed material will show selective absorption and transmission. The transmittance curve for a certain blue filter, obtained with a spectrophotometer, is given in Fig. 3. Note should be made of the broad absorption band between about 550 and 630 nm. Still more striking is the spectrophotometric curve for didymium (Fig. 4), a material shown originally by von Welsbach to be a mixture of two rare earth elements, praseo-

*The hue ranges in the visible spectrum are (nm): violet, 400–450; blue, 450–500; green, 500–570; yellow, 570–590; orange, 590–610, and red, 610–700.

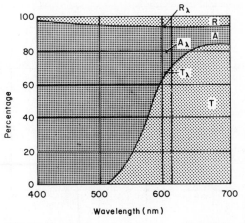

FIG. 2. Distribution of energy vs. wavelength for a slab of dyed material.

dymium and neodymium, each of which in solution exhibits intense absorption spectra. To the eye, a didymium filter appears to be pale pink. The range of absorption becomes sharper as the temperature approaches that of liquid air.

Absorption in the visible region (400 to 700 nm) has been illustrated by the transmittance curve of the blue filter (Fig. 3) and may be quite graphically understood by the behavior of many dyes in the solid state. As an example, fuchsin exhibits strong absorption in the green region of the spectrum and at the same time reflects a brilliant green. As an absorption band is approached during the determination of dispersion data (Fig. 1), the index of refraction is found to change rapidly as the band is entered—in fact, measurements become very difficult if not impossible. Reflection is greater in this region than elsewhere. The matter is summed up in the first diagram (Fig. 1) indicating that the *normal dispersion* curve for the material extends from A to B, where the Cauchy equation holds

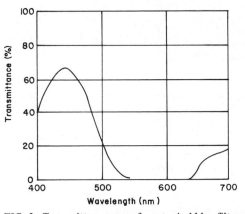

FIG. 3. Transmittance curve for a typical blue filter.

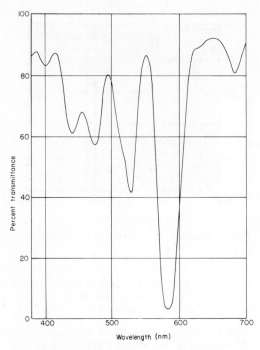

FIG. 4. Transmittance of a didymium filter.

and possible fluorescence, then we must write

$$\mu = \sigma + \tau$$

where μ is now the total fraction of the incident energy lost by the beam per unit volume of material, σ is the fraction of the incident energy *scattered* per unit volume and τ is the fraction transformed into *fluorescent radiation*. If ρ is the density of the material, then the mass absorption coefficient* of the material is

$$\frac{\mu}{\rho} = \frac{\sigma}{\rho} + \frac{\tau}{\rho}$$

and represents the fraction of the energy removed from the incident beam of unit cross section per unit mass. If M is the atomic mass of the isotope of the element being investigated and N_0 is Avogadro's number, then the *atomic absorption coefficient* is defined by

$$\mu_a = \frac{\mu}{\rho} \frac{M}{N_0}$$

As an example, for copper, with x-rays of wavelength 7 nm, the value of μ_a for copper is 50 X 10^{-22} cm^2/atom. From a study of the variation of μ/ρ with λ, knowledge of the energy levels within an atom has been gained.

Included among the practical uses of absorption spectroscopy as an experimental tool are: (a) to learn which wavelengths of electromagnetic radiation are absorbed, (b) to discover how much of this energy is absorbed under given conditions and then, (c) as a final goal, to find out *why* absorption takes place—and *where*. If we wish to obtain information as to the location and brightness of the absorption lines or bands, a spectroscope or spectrograph is used; if we wish to learn how the energy is distributed throughout the spectral region under investigation, we use a spectrophotometer. Reflectance and transmittance curves are obtained with the latter instrument and a specification of the "color" of the sample in either case can be determined using the C.I.E. methods.

Absorption spectrophotometry is the technique whereby one establishes the relationship between wavelength and radiant energy as the latter proceeds into a given material.

C. HARRISON DWIGHT

quite well, but behaving in a peculiar manner at some point C where the Cauchy equation will not give the observed effects. Once the absorption band is passed, as indicated by the two vertical dashed lines, in this case in the infrared, Cauchy's equation, with new constants, begins again to apply, A'B' corresponding to AB. Absorption bands can be observed for hydrogen chloride in the infrared and for ammonia in the microwave region.

X-ray absorption spectra form a very important part of the subject of absorption. Essentially the procedure is to direct a narrow beam of x-rays upon a sample of the material (of thickness x), and then allow the modified beam to impinge upon the atom planes of a crystal of known spacing (d). The diffracted x-rays come out of the crystal at such angles θ as to satisfy Bragg's law

$$n\lambda = 2d \sin \theta$$

and are received by a detector. The latter may be an ionization chamber or a photographic plate. Each setting of the x-ray spectrometer corresponds to a definite wavelength. The values of the intensities measured by the detector with the sample in place (I) and without the sample (I_0) are found from

$$I = I_0 e^{-\mu x}$$

where μ is the absorption coefficient of the material. If we are to take account of scattering

References

Bauman, Robert P., "Absorption Spectroscopy," New York, John Wiley & Sons, 1962.

Harrick, N. J., "Internal Reflection Spectroscopy," New York, Interscience, 1961.

Harrison, George R., Lord, Richard C. and Loofbourow, John R., "Practical Spectroscopy," Englewood Cliffs, N.J., Prentice-Hall, 1948.

*Considerable research on mass absorption coefficients has been done by Professor S. J. M. Allen at the University of Cincinnati.

Evans, Ralph M., "An Introduction to Color," New York, John Wiley & Sons, 1948.

Jenkins, Francis A., and White, Harvey E., "Fundamentals of Physical Optics," Third edition, New York, McGraw-Hill Book Co. 1957.

Cross-references: COLOR; OPTICS, PHYSICAL; POLARIZED LIGHT; RADIATION, THERMAL; REFRACTION; SPECTROSCOPY; X-RAYS

ACCELERATORS, LINEAR

Linear accelerators (often abbreviated to "linacs") are used for acceleration of electrons, protons, and heavy ions. Electron linear accelerators have yielded electrons at energies above 20 GeV; proton linear accelerators have not yet reached energies above 800 MeV.

Although the term "linear accelerator" is occasionally used to describe systems in which particles are accelerated by electrostatic fields (Cockcroft-Walton or electrostatic accelerators), the term is generally used to apply to systems in which particles are accelerated along a linear path by application of rf fields. Only accelerators of this type will be discussed in this article.

The linear accelerator has the advantage that the accelerated beam is easily extracted for experimental use. In principle it is capable of producing well-focused beams of higher intensity than are available from circular machines of the synchrotron or synchrocyclotron type. It does, however, require very high power levels at frequencies where conversion equipment is relatively expensive. For a given final energy, a linear accelerator will usually be materially more expensive than a synchrotron. (For a general discussion of accelerators see ACCELERATORS, PARTICLE.)

Field Patterns Used in Linear Accelerators The rf fields used for acceleration are set up in a long cylindrical cavity whose axis is to be the axis of the accelerated beam. Hence for acceleration the field pattern must have a major electric field component parallel to the axis. This requirement is satisfied by the TM_{010} waveguide mode in which a paraxial electric field has its maximum strength at the axis and falls to zero at the cavity wall. Azimuthal magnetic fields lie in planes normal to the axis, have small values near the axis and increase to maximum values at the cavity walls. Usually the field pattern is maintained by coupling to these magnetic fields by loops or apertures excited by external power sources. Corresponding to the high rf magnetic field at the wall, paraxial currents flow in the walls and are responsible for a major fraction of the power loss in the system. When high electric fields are required on the axis to accelerate to high energy in reasonable distances, the wall currents are correspondingly high. For acceleration rates of 2 MeV/m, power losses in copper walls will be of the order of 50 kW/m.

Both standing wave and traveling wave patterns are used in linear accelerators. If traveling waves are used, as is the case in most *electron* machines, the phase velocity of the waves must be made equal to the velocity of the particles accelerated; as the particle velocity increases, the phase velocity also must increase. But phase velocities in simple waveguides always are greater than the velocity of light, and loading must be introduced to reduce the phase velocity to the desired value. This is accomplished by introduction at intervals of washer-shaped irises, as shown in Fig. 1.

Standing wave patterns are used in *proton* linear accelerators. Cavities many meters in length are excited in the TM_{010} mode in which the axial field is uniform from one end of the cavity to the other. Protons which enter the cavity at a low injection velocity may arrive at a phase of the rf field at which they are immediately accelerated, but before they have traveled more than a few centimeters, the field will reverse and become decelerating. To protect the particles from the field in its decelerating phase, "drift tubes" are introduced, as shown in Fig. 2. These are pipes coaxial with the cavity and of such length that the particle is protected from the field during its reverse phase and emerges only after a complete rf cycle when the field again is accelerating. As the particles gain energy, the drift tubes are increased in length.

It would appear that the rather complicated drift-tube structure is conceptually and mechanically inferior to the rather simple iris-loaded traveling-wave system. It is adopted at the relatively low phase velocities required for protons

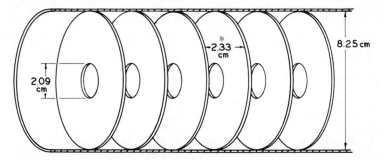

FIG. 1. Cutaway of iris-loaded waveguide for electron linear accelerator.

in the range below about 200 MeV because the extreme loading required to reduce the phase velocity of the iris-loaded system to velocities below one-half of the velocity of light results in very high losses. From the point of view of rf power consumption, the drift-tube structure is much superior at low phase velocities.

Electron Linear Accelerators Electrons very rapidly approach the velocity of light (c) as they are accelerated. At 1 MeV an electron already has reached 94 per cent of its ultimate velocity. At energies higher than this satisfactory acceleration will be achieved if all sections of the accelerator are made to have phase velocities equal to c. This makes much easier the tasks of construction and of operation. For example, rf excitation of a section of the accelerator may fail and the whole machine will still be operative, although at a slightly lower final energy.

Losses per unit length in waveguides generally decrease as the square root of the rf wavelength for equal axial fields. Hence, where possible, it is desirable to operate at as high a frequency as possible. But, as wavelength is decreased the diameter of the structure and of the beam aperture decrease correspondingly. The highest frequency that gives convenient beam apertures and at which adequate power sources are available is in the 3000-MHz range. For reasons that are primarily historic, most electron linear accelerators in the United States are operated at a frequency of 2856 MHz.

Both the phase velocity and the group velocity in the guide are determined by the dimensions of the guide and the loading irises. The group velocity is fixed also by the capabilities of the rf power sources. Klystrons with outputs of the order of 20 MW have become standard; each klystron can excite a section of waveguide 3 m long to axial fields of 10 MV/m. The group velocity suitable for this operation is 1 per cent of the velocity of light. The dimensions indicated in Fig. 1 result in a phase velocity of c and a group velocity of $0.01c$ when the guide is excited at 2856 MHz.

Injection is from a conventional electron gun. In some cases a short "bunching section" pregroups the electrons around the peak of the accelerating wave. In this section, the phase velocity is matched to the electron velocity by suitable choices of dimensions.

The power levels required are so high as to preclude continuous operation. Typical operation is with two-microsecond (2-μsec) pulses repeated several hundred times per second. Of the 2-μsec pulse, the first half is required to build up the accelerating field.

Electron linear accelerators in the energy range below 100 MeV are widely used for x-ray production and are commercially available. Most of the pioneer work on electron linear accelerators was done at Stanford where a machine two miles long is in operation at 20 GeV. At Orsay, France, a 1.3-GeV electron machine is in operation, and in Kharkov in the USSR a 2-GeV accelerator is also in operation.

Proton Linear Accelerators Because of the lower velocities of protons at million-electron-volt energies, proton linear accelerators suffer from several limitations from which the electron machines are free. Injectors for protons usually are Cockcroft-Walton voltage multiplier sets giving energies of 500 to 750 keV. At 750 keV the velocity of a proton is only $0.04c$. The accelerating field component at such low phase velocities varies strongly with radius at a rate that is approximately proportional to the square of the frequency. This effect sets an upper limit of about 200 MHz for the frequency of the accelerating field, and most proton linear accelerators are operated in the neighborhood of 200 MHz. A cavity resonant in the TM_{010} mode at that frequency will be about 90 cm in diameter.

Figure 2 is a schematic cross section through a 50-MeV proton linac formerly used at the Brookhaven National Laboratory as the injector for the 33-GeV synchrotron. Sections are shown at the injector end, at the region where the protons have an energy of about 10 MeV, and at the high-energy end. The over-all length of the machine is about 33 m. The drift tube shapes indicated have the purpose of keeping each section of the machine resonant to give a uniform accelerating field pattern and, at the same time, of holding the resistive losses in the walls of drift tubes to levels as low as possible.

The principle of phase stability is operative in proton linacs whereas, at the extreme relativistic velocities of multi-MeV electrons, electron linacs do not enjoy phase stability and require extreme precision in axial dimensions. In the proton linac, the drift tube lengths increase at a rate corresponding to acceleration at a phase displaced $20°$ or $30°$ from the peak of the wave. The phenomenon of phase stability (see ACCELERATORS, PARTICLE) results in continual restoration to the correct phase of protons which enter the machine at phases in the neighborhood of the correct phase. Often prebunchers are used to collect a large fraction of the injected beam around the accelerating phase. These prebunchers have the same design as the modulating gap in a klystron and function in the same fashion.

At the stable phase the field across an accelerating gap is rising as the proton crosses the gap. As the proton enters the gap, the accelerating field has a focusing component, but as it enters the next drift tube it feels a larger defocusing field and the net effect is a strong defocusing. In early proton linacs this effect was overcome by the introduction of rudimentary grids at the downstream end of each gap. These grids give unsatisfactory performance because they intercept a large fraction of the beam and because their poor optical quality results in loss of many protons. With the advent of alternating gradient focusing, grids in linacs were largely abandoned and focusing is now accomplished by quadrupole magnets imbedded in the drift tubes. This has resulted in an increase in output current by

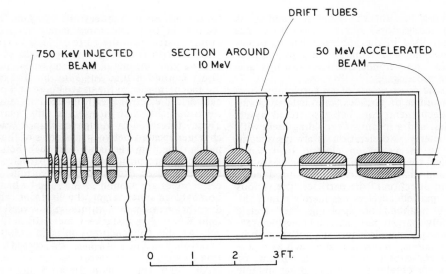

FIG. 2. Cross section through proton linac.

two orders of magnitude to levels of the order of 100 mA.

As in electron machines, the high rf power level required forces operation at a relatively low duty cycle. Since, at this frequency, the time required to build up the field in the linac cavity is about 200 μsec, pulse lengths for research use are chosen to be several hundred microseconds. Duty cycles are rarely larger than 1 per cent.

The first proton linac was the 40-ft machine at the Lawrence Radiation Laboratory in which protons were accelerated to 32 MeV. Fifty-MeV linacs are used as injectors for the synchrotrons at Argonne and CERN. The 50-MeV machine formerly used as injector for the AGS at Brookhaven was replaced in 1971 by a 200-MeV linac. A similar 200-MeV machine is the first stage of the injection system for the 200- to 500-GeV synchrotron at the National Accelerator Laboratory near Chicago.

The highest energy reached (early in 1972) in a proton linear accelerator was achieved at Los Alamos in preliminary operation of a linear accelerator "meson factory" designed for final operation at 800 MeV. This interesting machine combines a 100-MeV drift-tube linac with an iris-loaded section that will carry the protons from 100 to 800 MeV. At 100 MeV the proton velocity is approaching about half of the velocity of light and the iris-loaded system becomes comparable in efficiency to the drift-tube structure.

Heavy-ion Linear Accelerators Heavy ions such as C, N, O, Ne, and even higher masses can be accelerated in a structure similar to a proton linac but operated at a lower frequency, typically 70 MHz. Multiply charged ions are injected at a few hundred kiloelectron volts and are accelerated to about 1 MeV/nucleon. They then pass through a "stripper," a gas jet in which their charge-to-mass ratio is doubled. The accelerating field now can be twice as effective,

and the ions enter a second cavity in which they are accelerated to about 10 MeV/nucleon.

Heavy ion linacs are used in research in nuclear physics and nuclear chemistry and have been particularly useful in the production of transuranium elements.

JOHN P. BLEWETT

References

Smith, Lloyd, "Linear Accelerators," in "Handbuch der Physik," Vol. 44, pp. 341–389, Berlin, Springer-Verlag.

Livingston, M. S., and Blewett, J. P., "Particle Accelerators," Ch. 10, New York, McGraw-Hill Book Co., 1962.

Livingood, J. J., "Principles of Cyclic Particle Accelerators," Ch. 14, New York, Van Nostrand Reinhold, 1961.

"Linear Accelerators," edited by P. M. Lapostolle and A. L. Septier, Amsterdam, North-Holland Publishing Co., 1970, 1204 pp.

"The Stanford Two-Mile Accelerator," edited by R. B. Neal, New York, W. A. Benjamin, 1968, 1169 pp.

Cross-references: ACCELERATORS, PARTICLE; ACCELERATORS, VAN DE GRAAFF; BETATRON; CYCLOTRON; SYNCHROTRONS.

ACCELERATORS, PARTICLE

Particle accelerators have been developed primarily to serve as artificial sources of well-defined beams of radiation for studies in nuclear science. Not only are the intensities much greater than those provided by cosmic rays, but the energies and directions of motion of the particles are known to high precision. The development has emphasized ever-increasing energy with parallel effort to increase intensity

where possible. But the greatest number of existing accelerators, albeit at the lower energies, are used in the applied sciences, in nuclear medicine and radiation therapy, and industrially for nondestructive testing and radiation processing.

The basic components of an accelerator consist of a source of particles, an evacuated chamber to keep them from being scattered by air molecules, and a means of providing them with kinetic energy. Acceleration is always accomplished by means of an electric field, since mechanical forces or gravitational fields are too weak, and magnetic fields only produce a change in direction of the particles. The various types of particle accelerators merely reflect the different methods of applying the electric fields. Only charged particles can be accelerated, but these may include electrons, positrons, protons, deuterons, or heavier ions such as multiply ionized carbon, nitrogen, etc. Beams of neutrons are obtained by bombarding suitable targets (D, Li, Be, etc.) usually with deuterons.

The simplest type of electric field is provided by applying the required amount of voltage between two terminals. A large number of existing accelerators are of this direct-potential-drop type but their energies are limited to a few million electron volts.* The methods by which this direct voltage may be obtained are of two basic types: (1) by means of electric circuitry, and (2) by charging up a terminal through actual transportation of charge.

There are many varieties of the former type, including resonant transformers, cascade-rectifiers, and Marx generators. With a source of particles and a suitably designed discharge tube, they can accelerate positive or negative particles to a few MeV. Conventional cascade-rectifiers are sometimes known as *Cockcroft-Walton* generators; the *Dynamitron* is a high-frequency (100 to 300 kHz) cascade-rectifier system.

The second method is used in the *electrostatic*, or *Van de Graaff*, generator, where a moving belt carries charge, sprayed on it from corona points, to a field-free region inside a spherical metal terminal. The whole is enclosed in a pressure tank and operated at about 10 atmospheres. In this form, typical energies for both electrons and positive ions are from 1 to 6 MeV; breakdown between the terminal and its surroundings sets a maximum close to 10 MeV. However, double the energy can be attained by accelerating negative ions to a positively charged terminal; then, through electron-stripping, positive ions are created which can be accelerated again as they pass from the terminal

*The energy acquired by the particles in an accelerator is expressed in electron volts (eV), the amount of energy gained by a particle, bearing a charge equal to that of an electron, when it falls through a potential difference of one volt. 10^3 eV = 1 keV; 10^6 eV = 1 MeV; 10^9 eV = 1 GeV (preferred) or 1 BeV (U.S. usage).

to ground. Such "tandem" Van de Graaff generators, in two- and three-stage versions, can provide particles in the 10 to 30 MeV range.

An electric field may also be produced by a time-varying magnetic field and such a semidirect method is used in a *betatron*. The changing magnetic flux in the central core of a pulsed cylindrical electromagnet induces a transverse electric field that accelerates the particles. These travel in a doughnut-shaped vacuum chamber located between the poles of the magnet surrounding the core. Although betatrons can accelerate positively charged particles, they have been used exclusively for electrons. Typical energies are around 25 MeV, and when they bombard an inner target, the electrons can produce beams of x-rays as intense as several thousand R/min at a distance 1 meter from the target. At the University of Illinois, a 300-MeV betatron was built but has now ceased operation.

All other types of accelerators use various forms of rf electric fields, at relatively low voltage, which are applied many times in a given direction to the particles and are prevented from influencing them when the rf field is reversed.

One way of applying this principle is used in *linear accelerators* ("linacs") where the particles travel in a straight line down the center of a cylindrical pipe that acts as a waveguide. The waveguide has an rf electromagnetic field pattern whose axial electric-field component provides the accelerating force. To keep the length to a reasonable size, quite high fields (several MV/meter) are needed with associated high power requirements. This means that linacs are relatively more costly for a given energy than other accelerators, but they have the advantage that a well-focused beam, with small energy spread, can emerge and be readily available for experiments. Recent developments in superconducting cavities (usually niobium) give promise of reducing operating costs and increasing the duty cycle.

The structures of electron linacs differ quite markedly from those for protons and heavy ions due to the fact that electrons reach very nearly the speed of light at energies of a few MeV, whereas protons do not reach this velocity until they are accelerated to the GeV range. In a *proton linear accelerator*, the waveguide is a resonant cavity where the particles are shielded from a standing rf wave, during the part of the cycle not suitable for acceleration, by a series of "drift tubes" and then are accelerated when traveling across the gaps between the drift tubes. As the protons' velocity increases, the drift-tube length increases so that the particles which arrive at a gap at an accelerating phase continue to be accelerated at succeeding gaps. The protons are injected into the linac at energies from 500 to 1000 keV, usually from a Cockcroft-Walton generator. In principle, there is no limit to the energy, but to date (1972) 800 MeV is the highest achieved. Most proton linacs are used

as injectors for synchrotrons but the Los Alamos proton linac. LAMPF, began operation for research at 800 MeV in June, 1972. Currents of more than 100 mA are obtained for pulses of 150 μsec to 1 msec with a duty cycle of 1 percent or less. Heavy-ion linacs, similar in design to proton machines, have been built to give energies, of about 10 MeV/nucleon.

The waveguide in an *electron linac* is a relatively simple pipe, consisting of many small cavities, and the electrons travel in step with the electromagnetic wave. The cavities are coupled by a series of irises (hollow disks) that are constructed to give the proper phase velocity. The whole structure requires extremely close tolerances and strict temperature control. It is usual to use a traveling-wave mode of operation but this is not essential. Electron linacs can also accelerate positrons which are created by the electrons at lower energy through the insertion of a metal-foil converter. Many electron linacs are in operation from 50 to 400 MeV, at currents of several hundred mA. The highest energy achieved is the 22-GeV, 2-mile long linac at the Stanford Linear Accelerator Center (SLAC) with electron currents of about 80 mA. Pulse lengths in electron linacs range from 0.01 to 5 μsec at rates of 50 to 1000 pulses/sec. A superconducting 2-GeV electron linac for 100 μA, at 100 per cent duty cycle, is under construction at Stanford University.

Another method of applying relatively small voltages many times to raise the energy of particles is used in the cyclic accelerators. A magnetic field is applied in a direction perpendicular to the particles' plane of motion resulting in a spiraling or circular orbit. Single or multiple rf sources, located on such an orbit, provide increments in energy on each revolution, and the particles continue to circulate until the design energy is reached. In such motion, the magnetic force must balance the centrifugal force, i.e.,

$$\frac{mv^2}{r} = evB \qquad (1)$$

where e is the charge, m the mass, and v the velocity of the particle, r is the radius of the path, and B is the magnetic flux density.

In a *cyclotron*, the magnetic field is almost uniform over the region between two cylindrical poles, and it is constant in time. Positive ions, from a source located near the center, are accelerated across the gaps between two hollow D-shaped electrodes which each cover almost half the area between the magnet poles. Between the "dees" a constant frequency rf field is applied. From Eq. (1), it can be seen that the angular velocity, v/r, of the particle is given by eB/m, i.e., it is independent of radius. Thus, the particles, as they travel on an orbit of half-circles of ever-increasing radius, arrive at each gap always at the proper phase to continue to be accelerated. Protons and deuterons are accelerated in cyclotrons to energies between 5

and 20 MeV, and heavy ions such as multiply ionized carbon and nitrogen, to about 100 MeV. Continuous currents of about 1 mA can be obtained for use with internal targets, or about one-tenth this can be extracted for external use by means of a deflecting field situated at the outer radius. An upper limit in energy, about 30 MeV for protons and 40 MeV for deuterons, is set by the relativistic increase in mass of the particles which causes them to reach the accelerating gap progressively later and to fall out of resonance with the accelerating field.

In the *synchrocyclotron*, this limitation is overcome by varying the frequency of the accelerating field to keep it in step with the decreasing frequency of revolution of the circulating particles. Thus, it has been possible to raise the energy, and synchrocyclotrons have been built to accelerate positive ions (chiefly protons) from 100 to 700 MeV, the latter being about the practical maximum due to the size of the magnet. This is similar in design to the cyclotron, the almost constant magnetic field being produced between cylindrical poles. For a 700-MeV design, such a magnet weighs about 7000 tons and the frequency must drop to less than 60 per cent of its initial value. With such a frequency modulation over the accelerating period, it is no longer possible to have continuous acceleration, the output is pulsed, and time-average currents are only a few μA. Cycling rates vary from 30 to 100 Hz.

Another way of going beyond the classical cyclotron's energy is used in the isochronous, *AVF* (azimuthally-varying-field), or *sector-focused cyclotrons*. A radial increase in magnetic field can keep the particles in resonance but results in axial defocusing. This is provided by varying the magnetic field in azimuth through adding on the poles several raised spiraling sectors which give alternately positive and negative gradients (cf. AG focusing, below). The rf accelerating fields can again be constant in frequency (but usually variable for different modes of operation) so the intensity in AVF cyclotrons is higher than in synchrocyclotrons, i.e., it can be from 0.1 to 1 mA. These machines can provide variable energy for a wide variety of positive ions, and recent interest is in using them for very heavy ions. Many AVF cyclotrons exist that give proton energies of 25 to 100 MeV and two large ones are being built in Canada and Switzerland for energies to 500 MeV.

The *microtron* is a variant of the cyclotron that accelerates electrons. Its magnetic field is constant and the accelerating rf field has a constant frequency. The accelerating gap is located at one edge of the magnet and the circular orbits of the electrons are tangent at this point. The amount of energy given to them is adjusted so that the time of revolution in each orbit is one or more rf periods longer than in the previous orbit. Thus, the electrons return to the accelerating gap at the same phase on each turn. Several microtrons exist for energies from 10 to

30 MeV, with currents of 30 to 100 mA; two serve as injectors for electron synchrotrons. A 600-MeV microtron, with a 30-MeV superconducting linac as an accelerating unit, is being built at the University of Illinois.

The highest energies for protons, and until recently for electrons, have been reached in the *synchrotron*. In this type of accelerator, the particles are kept moving on an orbit that is almost circular, and of a fixed radius, between the poles of a magnet that is annular in shape. From Eq. (1) it can be seen that to keep the particles' orbit of constant radius, the magnetic field must be increased during the period of acceleration from a low value corresponding to the injection energy to a final value corresponding to the maximum energy. The radius of the accelerator is determined by the value of this maximum energy and the maximum value obtainable for the magnetic field (usually 10 to 15 kilogauss). With this time-varying field, operation must be pulsed. Accelerating fields are provided by one or more rf stations located at points on the magnet ring, and the frequency must increase exactly in step with the increasing velocity of the particles.

Focusing forces to keep the particles within the limits of the vacuum chamber are provided by shaping the magnet poles to give a field that varies with radius. Synchrotrons fall into two general classes: (1) weak-focusing, constant-gradient (CG) synchrotrons where a small negative gradient has a constant value in azimuth and (2) strong-focusing, alternating-gradient (AG) synchrotrons where large radial gradients alternate in sign with azimuth. From the equations of motion of particles in an azimuthally uniform field, the radial field index n [$n = - (dB/dr) (r/B)$] must have values between 0 and 1 for stability in both radial and vertical directions. Stronger gradients provide strong focusing in one plane but result in defocusing in the other plane. Alternating-gradient systems depend upon the principle that a focusing combination can result from an alternation of focusing and defocusing sections (as in optical lenses). AG systems may also separate the bending and focusing functions by interleaving quadrupoles at proper locations between uniform-field bending magnets. Synchrotron magnets are usually made up of several (or many) sections separated by field-free regions that are used for injection, for ejection, for rf accelerating stations, beam observation, and control mechanisms, and for targeting.

Electron synchrotrons have been built for about 100 MeV to somewhat over 1 GeV with CG magnets and from 1.2 GeV to 10 GeV with AG magnets, the largest (10 GeV) being at Cornell University. There is a practical limit to the energy arising from the fact that electrons, when traveling on circular orbits at relativistic velocities, radiate electromagnetic energy. To prevent disturbance to the particles' orbits, compensation must be provided for these radiation losses which amount to as much as 10 MeV per revolution at 10 GeV. Since, above a few MeV, the velocity of electrons is so close to that of light, the accelerating frequency can be constant. To reach this energy, small electron synchrotrons have included some flux bars inside the orbit to provide betatron-type acceleration, but the larger ones use another accelerator as an injector, such as a microtron or electron linac. Intensities are around 10^{11} electrons per pulse and repetition rates vary from 10 to 60 per second. The electron beams can be extracted or hit an internal target to produce emergent photon beams.

Proton synchrotrons have been built only for energies of 1 GeV and higher since synchrocyclotrons can produce positive particles up to several hundred MeV. The constant-gradient type requires large magnetic apertures, vacuum chambers several feet wide, and massive magnets with cross sections of many square feet. The highest energy of this type is the 12.5-GeV machine at the Argonne National Laboratory, where its octant magnets have uniform field except at the ends where shaping gives focusing fields. In the alternating-gradient type, the stronger forces keep the protons within a cross-sectional area of a few square inches, resulting in a simple vacuum pipe and magnets about 3 ft by 3 ft, or less, in cross section. However, the stronger forces necessitate extreme precision in location and stability, and stricter controls.

Since protons must reach GeV energies before velocities are close to that of light, the accelerating systems have a wide frequency range, increasing from the injection value to the final one, yet very precisely controlled to correspond to the particles' instantaneous energy. In the early CG proton synchrotrons, the rf frequency was that of the frequency of revolution of the particles but in newer machines, both CG and AG, a higher harmonic is used. The location and behavior of the beam is observed by placing, adjacent to the beam, "pickup electrodes" upon which charge is induced. Signals fed back from these electrodes can be used to provide corrections to the accelerating rf program. Such control is essential in AG accelerators.

To overcome difficulties at injection (magnetic fields, rf systems, space-charge effects, etc.), other accelerators are used to raise the protons' energy before entering the main synchrotron. These are usually proton linacs with energies from 10 to 200 MeV. The time taken to complete acceleration to full energy in a proton synchrotron is of the order of 1 sec, repetition rates vary from 10 to 20 pulses/min, and typical intensities are around 10^{12} protons/pulse. The highest energy achieved up to 1971 was by the 76-GeV AG machine at Serpukhov, USSR, but the NAL proton synchrotron began operation at 200 GeV in March, 1972, reached 300 GeV in July, and 400 GeV in December, 1972. This is a cascade of accelerators where a 200-MeV linac sends protons to an 8-GeV booster synchrotron

that feeds the 2-km diameter main accelerator. Construction has started on a 300-GeV AG proton synchrotron at CERN, Switzerland, using the present 28-GeV synchrotron as injector; operation is scheduled to begin in 1976. There seems to be no basic limitation to the energy achievable in AG proton synchrotrons, except cost. Developments in superconducting magnets to give much higher maximum fields may lead to reductions in price and operating costs for even higher energies.

When relativistic particles hit a fixed target, only a small fraction of the energy is available in the center-of-mass system for producing new particles and interesting reactions, e.g., in a 300-GeV proton accelerator, only about 24 GeV is useful, available, reaction energy. But in *colliding-beam*, or *storage-ring* devices, beams travel in opposite directions to collide head-on and provide their total kinetic energy in the center-of-mass system. For acquiring data at rates comparable to those at accelerators, colliding beams require high intensities and must circulate for a long time. Thus, only relatively stable particles can be used and the vacuum system must operate at extremely low pressures (10^{-9} to 10^{-10} torr). Colliding beams cannot provide the copious supply of particles now available in secondary beams at accelerators but they do provide means of studying certain very high energy interactions. Storage rings are usually similar in structure to synchrotrons and the particles may be injected at the desired energy from another accelerator or they may be accelerated after injection in some designs. Oppositely charged particles need only one ring but similarly charged particles require two rings which intersect at one or more locations.

Several electron-positron storage rings have been built, or are under construction for energies up to about 3 GeV. In 1971, the proton-proton Intersecting Storage Rings (ISR) at CERN, Switzerland, began operation where collisions between two 26-GeV beams correspond to a 1500-GeV beam hitting a fixed target. Many hundred pulses from the synchrotron injector are stored to give beams of several amperes; an rf system carries out the "stacking" process. A 25-GeV proton-antiproton colliding-beam machine is under construction at Novosibirsk, USSR, but will probably be used first for 6-GeV electron-positron colliding beams.

An entirely new method of accelerating positive particles has been studied in recent years, namely, *electron-ring*, or *collective-ion*, acceleration. The principle is to embed a small number of ions in a dense cloud of electrons. Then, if the whole can be accelerated to high velocity, the heavier mass of the ions would allow them to attain much higher kinetic energy than the electrons. At Dubna, USSR, it was proposed to make such a system stable by rapidly compressing a highly intense toroidal ring of electrons whose deep potential well could hold the ions. Stable rings have been made of about 10^{13} electrons loaded with about 1 per cent of positive ions. The loaded ring must then be transferred to another region for acceleration. To reach energies of 1 GeV or so, a solenoidal magnetic field which decreases slowly with distance from the compressor can be used. Higher energies require accelerating systems like those of a linac together with a solenoidal magnetic field to keep the rings intact. There are many theoretical and practical problems, connected with both ring formation and subsequent acceleration, that are not yet (in 1971) solved but are being studied at laboratories in the United States, Western Europe, as well as at Dubna, USSR.

M. HILDRED BLEWETT

References

Proceedings of national and international conferences on accelerators; the most recently published are:

Proceedings of the 1971 Particle Accelerator Conference, Accelerator Engineering and Technology, *IEEE Trans. Nucl. Sci.*, NS-18, No. 3 (June 1971).

Proceedings of the 8th International Conference on High-Energy Accelerators, 1971, published by the CERN Scientific Information Service, Geneva, Switzerland (December 1971).

Proceedings (in Russian) of the Second Soviet-Union Conference on Accelerators (held 11–18 November 1970), published by the Academy of Science, Moscow (1972).

Proceedings of the 1973 Particle Accelerator Conference, Accelerator Engineering and Technology, *IEEE Trans. Nucl. Sci.*, 1973.

Cross-references: ACCELERATORS, LINEAR; BETATRON; CYCLOTRON; SYNCHROTRON; ACCELERATORS, VAN DE GRAAFF.

ACCELERATORS, VAN DE GRAAFF

The electrostatic particle accelerator originated by American physicist Robert Jemison Van de Graaff is widely used for nuclear structure research. These constant-potential accelerators make use of the electrostatic belt generator invented by Van de Graaff about 1930. They belong to the *direct* accelerator family in which the high voltage power is applied directly across the terminals of a highly evacuated multi-electrode tube. Electrified atoms or electrons from a source within the high-voltage terminal gain velocity and energy as they move along the tube axis to ground under the action of the applied electric field. As each particle emerges from the accelerator, it is moving with a kinetic energy equal to qV where q is the particle charge and V the generator voltage.

While a Rhodes Scholar at Oxford during 1927 and 1928, Van de Graaff selected the electrostatic approach to fulfill the need, much emphasized by Rutherford, for more copious sources of atomic particles comparable in energy

to those spontaneously emitted from naturally radioactive materials (see ELECTROSTATICS). Subsequently, at Princeton University, Van de Graaff produced over one million volts between the spherical terminals of two small electrostatic belt generators of a new and surprisingly simple design; in 1931, he described the electrostatic belt generator principles, and their suitability for the bombardment of atomic nuclei, before the American Physical Society. The method was first applied to nuclear investigations at the Carnegie Institution of Washington in 1932. The early machines, insulated in atmospheric air, produced streams of light positive ions such as protons and deuterons homogeneous in energy and with smooth control over the voltage range of the machine. General acceptance of the Van de Graaff accelerator as the precision instrument for experimental nuclear research followed rapidly, and its further development for this purpose has been continuous since that time. Greater compactness and higher voltage were attained by insulating the belt generator and tube with compressed gas; greater beam intensity came through improved ion source and acceleration tube technology. About 300 such accelerators were in use by 1960, producing particles and radiation with energies from 400 keV to 10 MeV. At that time, Van de Graaff accelerators for nuclear science incorporated the "tandem acceleration" principle described below. It opened the way to far higher particle energies by applying the tandem principles to multiply charged heavy atoms.

Van de Graaff accelerators can accelerate any electrified particle, including any of the 92 elements, electrons, and clumps of matter simulating micrometeorites. In addition to use in experimental nuclear physics with high-energy positive ions, Van de Graaff electron accelerators designed for voltages in the 1 to 5 MeV range are used to produce megavolt x-rays for the treatment of malignant disease and for the radiographic inspection of heavy opaque structures such as metal forgings, weldments, and rocket engines. Streams of electrons from such accelerators are also used for radiobiological and radiochemical research and for the treatment of skin malignancies. Radiation processing studies for such purposes as the sterilization of surgical materials, the cross-linking of polyethylene and other plastics, the deinfestation of grains, and increased shelf life of foods have often made use of Van de Graaff accelerators.

Van de Graaff Generator Operating Principles
Although a variety of electrostatic machines had been developed since the first frictionally excited generator of Otto von Guericke in the middle of the seventeenth century, all have been superseded by the Van de Graaff generator because of its greater voltage capability and comparative simplicity. The essential components of the generator, outlined in Fig. 1, include a well-rounded metal terminal supported by an insulating column and an endless insulating belt

system which physically conveys electric charge from ground to the high voltage terminal.

Electric charge of the desired polarity is deposited on the moving belt surface by corona from a row of metal points at a controllable voltage with respect to the lower pulley toward which they are directed. In addition to overcoming friction and windage, the motor-driven belt does work in carrying this charge from ground to the terminal potential. Transfer of the charge from belt to terminal is accomplished by again presenting a row of points toward the electrified belt. This time the electric field of the surface-bound charge produces the gaseous ionization needed for conduction across the point-to-belt gap. Van de Graaff pointed out that these ionized charge-transfer processes remain independent of the terminal voltage if they are located in the field-free space within the hollow terminal or below the ground plane. The current of such an electrostatic generator is limited by the maximum charge density which can be insulated in the gaseous medium surrounding the belt and by the total area per second of charge-laden surface entering or leaving the terminal. To increase the current capability of the system, the return run of belt may be charged within the terminal in a similar manner but with the opposite polarity.

The potential, V, of the high voltage terminal of a Van de Graaff generator is determined by the amount and polarity of the accumulated charge on its insulated terminal. At any instant $V = Q/C$ where Q is the net positive or negative charge on the terminal and C is the capacitance of the terminal system to ground. Although the Van de Graaff generator is inherently a constant-current machine, it can be maintained steadily at the desired voltage by balancing the current arriving at the terminal against the total current delivered to the load. The load usually includes the particle current through the accelerating tube, the current through resistors which divide the terminal voltage uniformly along the supporting column, and any corona from the terminal itself arising from the high electric field at its surface. By adjusting either the belt current or the load current, the terminal voltage may be maintained at any desired value up to the maximum which can be insulated. This maximum voltage depends only on the physical size and geometry of the terminal and on the electrical strength of dielectric medium surrounding it. An isolated metallic sphere would be the ideal terminal, but modifications are necessitated by the supporting column, belt, and tube.

The pair of generators built by Van de Graaff at Princeton in 1930 each had an aluminum spherical terminal 2 ft in diameter supported in air by a slender glass rod 7 ft long. A silk ribbon was employed as the insulating charge conveyor. The voltage insulated in atmospheric air between these two generators, one accumulating positive and the other negative charge, was

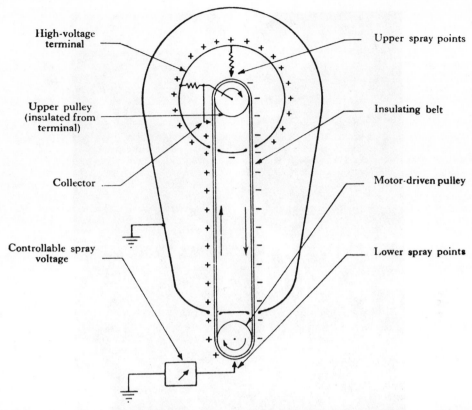

FIG. 1. Diagram of Van de Graaff electrostatic belt generator. Reproduced by permission of The Institute of Physics and The Physical Society from the article by R. J. Van de Graaff, J. G. Trump, and W. A. Buechner, *Reports on Progress in Physics*, **11**, 1 (1948).

more than twice any previously attained constant voltage.

About 5.5 million volts were insulated in air between two larger generators constructed by Van de Graaff in the early 1930s for nuclear research. This voltage required spherical terminals 15 ft in diameter supported on insulating tubular columns 25 ft high. This historic equipment, shown in an early sparking demonstration in Fig. 2, was used in a modified form for precision nuclear research at Massachuesetts Institute of Technology for nearly 20 years. It is now installed at the Boston Museum of Science for demonstrations of the principles and phenomena of electrical science.

The need for still higher constant voltages for nuclear investigations, and the desire for more compact apparatus, led to the use of high-pressure gases for the insulation of electrostatic accelerators. Today nearly all Van de Graaff accelerators operating at potentials in excess of one-half million volts are within a steel pressure tank and insulated in gases compressed to 10 to 25 atmospheres. Electronegative gases such as sulfur hexafluoride (SF_6) and "Freon" (CCI_2-F_2) are now increasingly used instead of mix-

tures of nitrogen and CO_2, since they insulate approximately the same voltages at one-third gas pressure.

Acceleration System The evacuated acceleration tube, the source of positive ions or electrons, and the target to which the energized particles are directed, constitute the particle accelerating system of the Van de Graaff accelerator. The insulating length of the evacuated acceleration tube is divided into many sections by metal disk-like electrodes, each with an axial opening for the passage of the particle beam. Each disk is mounted between annular rings of glass or porcelain to form a slender vacuum-tight accelerating column. The tube electrodes take their potential from the metallic members in the generator column along which the terminal voltage is divided by resistors. The charged particles, acted upon by the electric field between these electrodes, are progressively accelerated and focused as they move through the electric fields between the electrodes. At the remote end, the beam emerges as a collimated and directed stream of energetic particles.

Tandem Acceleration and Multiply Charged Ions Van de Graaff accelerators for nuclear

FIG. 2. 5.5-million volt Van de Graaff generator in sparking demonstration.

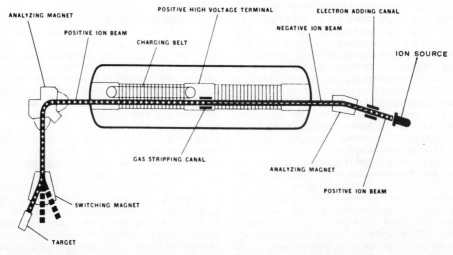

FIG. 3. Diagram of two-stage tandem Van de Graaff accelerator. Reproduced from the article by R. J. Van de Graaff in *Nuclear Instruments and Methods*, **8**, 195–202 (1960), by permission of the North-Holland Publishing Co.

science now reach higher particle energies with a given terminal voltage by switching the polarity of the accelerated particles. In the two-stage tandem diagramed in Fig. 3, negatively charged ions are produced at ground and then accelerated toward a high-voltage positive terminal. Within this terminal, the swiftly moving negative ions are stripped of electrons by passing through a thin gaseous region. The resultant positive ions continue through the tube under the second accelerating action of the positive terminal. A singly charged particle, such as a proton, thus arrives at the ground end of the system with an energy of $2qV$.

At sufficiently high energy, atoms of higher atomic number may be stripped of several or even of all their satellite electrons. An ion which lacks N electric charges during the second acceleration stage gains a total energy of $(N + 1)V$ in a two-stage tandem accelerator. Three-stage acceleration is secured by adding an additional in-line two-stage accelerator with a central negative terminal and using it to produce one stage of negative ion acceleration for injection into the second tandem. In 1967 the first three-stage tandem Van de Graaff, developed by the High Voltage Engineering Corporation and using terminals at 6 MV, was brought into use for nuclear research at the University of Pittsburgh. This was shortly followed by a three-stage tandem 7.5-MV terminal at the University of Washington in Seattle and in 1970 by two in-line 10-MV "Emperor" tandem Van de Graaffs at the Brookhaven National Laboratory.

Although the light elements, hydrogen and helium, were almost exclusively used as atomic projectiles in nuclear structure physics until 1960, interest in heavier nuclei developed rapidly as higher energies became possible. It is estimated that, by applying tandem acceleration principles, a two-stage Van de Graaff accelerator with a 15-MV positive terminal can produce a beam of uranium ions with energies up to 400 MeV. In large part because of the more complete electron stripping attained at higher energies, three-stage acceleration could produce uranium ions with energies over 1000 MeV.

Medical Applications of Van de Graaff Accelerators Since x-rays are the form of electromagnetic energy, similar to light, produced by the sudden stopping of high-energy electrons, Van de Graaff accelerators are often used as x-ray sources for the treatment of malignant disease and for radiography. In this application, the high-voltage terminal is operated at negative polarity, the electrons are emitted from a tungsten source at the terminal end of the acceleration tube, and they are suddenly stopped after traversing the length of the tube by striking a water-cooled metal target, usually of tungsten or gold.

A 2 million volt x-ray generator of this type, in which a gold target is bombarded with 300 μA of electrons, yields an x-ray intensity of 100 r/min measured 1 meter from the target in the electron direction. The quality of this radiation is closely similar in its physical properties to that of the gamma rays from radium or from the radioactive isotope cobalt 60. To equal this x-ray intensity would require over 4000 curies of cobalt 60 or 6000 grams of radium. This Van de Graaff accelerator for therapy is housed in a steel tank 3 ft in diameter and 6 ft long and is insulated by a mixture of nitrogen and CO_2 at 300 psi.

JOHN G. TRUMP

References

Van de Graaff, R. J., Trump, J. G., and Buechner, W. W., "Electrostatic Generators for the Acceleration of Charged Particles," *Rept. Progr. Phys.*, **11**, 1 (1948).

Van de Graaff, R. J., "Tandem Electrostatic Accelerators." *Nuclear Instr. and Methods*, **8**, 195–202 (1960).

Wittkower, A. B., Rose, P. H., Bastide, R. P., and Brooks, N. B., "Injection of Intense Neutral Beams into a Tandem Accelerator," *Rev. Sci. Instr.* **35**, 1–11 (January 1964).

Wright, K. A., Proimos, B. S., and Trump, John G., "Physical Aspects of Two Million Volt X-ray Therapy," *Surg. Clin. North Am.*, **39**, 1–12 (June 1959).

Livingston, M. Stanley, and Blewett, J. P., "Particle Accelerators," Ch. 3, New York, McGraw-Hill Book Co., 1962.

Trump, J. G., "New Developments in High Voltage Technology," *IEEE Trans. Nuclear Sci.*, **NS-14**, No. 3, 113–119 (1967).

Cross-references: ACCELERATORS, LINEAR; ACCELERATORS, PARTICLE; CYCLOTRON; STATIC ELECTRICITY; SYNCHROTRON.

ACOUSTICS

Physical acoustics deals with the properties and behavior of longitudinal waves of "infinitesimal" amplitude in solid, liquid, or gaseous media. These waves are propagated at the velocity of sound, or phase velocity, which is independent of frequency in a nondissipating free medium. In such a case, the shape of a complex wave remains unchanged during its propagation, although its amplitude may change. When the velocity of sound, or phase velocity, becomes dependent on frequency, the shape of a complex wave changes during propagation and dispersion is said to occur. In such cases groups of waves comprising a limited range of frequencies travel at a velocity called the group velocity, different from the phase velocity. It is the group velocity which carries the energy of such complex waves.

Acoustic waves are dispersive (1) in a *free* medium in which viscosity, heat conduction, and molecular, thermal, or chemical relaxation cause an increase in phase velocity with frequency, (2) in a *confined* medium in a capillary tube in which viscosity causes a decrease in phase velocity with frequency, (3) in a *confined*

medium in *non-dissipative* tubes of increasing cross section, where the rate of change of cross-sectional area differs from the conical (i.e., different from proportionality to the square of the distance along the tube)—examples of such tubes being the exponential and catenoidal horns, in which the phase velocity increases with decreasing frequency, (4) in nondissipative cylindrical tubes with *flexible* walls, and (5) in waves of *finite* amplitude, where the higher-frequency components have a higher phase velocity than the lower-frequency components, a transfer of energy occurring from the lower-frequency components to the higher-frequency components.

In physical acoustics, waves are reflected, refracted, diffracted, and absorbed. They exhibit all the properties of wave motion, such as reinforcement and destructive interference. They are accompanied by pressure and particle-velocity fluctuations detectable by the ear or by in-instruments capable of measuring the frequency, instantaneous values, and mean intensity of these fluctuations.

Geometrical acoustics is a special case of physical acoustics in which diffraction and interference are disregarded. Energies of direct and reflected waves are considered to add irrespective of relative phase, a condition applicable to incoherent (i.e., uncorrelated) waves.

Electroacoustics deals with the manner and means of energy transfer between electromechanical devices and the medium propagating sound waves. It is concerned with microphones of various types (dynamic, electrostatic, piezoelectric, magnetostrictive), loudspeakers of equivalent types (to which Maxwell's reciprocity theorem applies), and amplifiers for the faithful transfer of signals received by a microphone to those reproduced by a loudspeaker, tape recorder, or oscilloscope.

Architectural acoustics deals with the problems of distribution of beneficial sounds within buildings and with the exclusion or reduction of undesirable sounds. Here it is shown that mass and limpness of barriers such as partitions are most significant in providing high sound transmission loss. However, new developments using dual-ply gypsum board on each side of thin-gauge sheet-metal studs, with mineral-wool batts in the cavity, have resulted in lightweight partitions of high sound transmission loss (STL). Laboratory measurements of STL in partition development are based on the ASTM (American Society for Testing and Materials) standard recommended practice E90-70. Specimens having approximate dimensions 2.75 m by 4.25 m are in current use, since earlier smaller specimens produced unreliable test results. A single-number rating system, the Sound Transmission Class (STC) has been developed for rank-ordering the sound-insulation effectiveness of partitions and floors (see ASTM RM 14-2). An *in situ* testing procedure on existing partitions has been introduced in ASTM standard recommended practice E336-71. Also under development is a floor-

ceiling rating for heel noise, called the Impact Insulation Class (IIC). For details on both STC and IIC, reference should be made to "A Guide to Airborne, Impact, and Structure Borne Noise-Control in Multifamily Dwellings," September 1967, Superintendent of Public Documents, U.S. Government Printing Office, Washington, D.C.

In auditoriums, reflective ceilings and reflective walls, combined with convex irregularities of random design, provide for reinforcement and diffuseness of sound found so beneficial for speech and music. Reflecting surfaces, giving short time-delay reflections (about 20 msec or less), are particularly desirable in concert halls. Delays of 65 msec or more may result in echoes and speech unintelligibility.

Psychological acoustics deals with the emotional and mental reactions of persons and animals to various sounds. Here questions arise as to which sounds are acceptable to most people under various living conditions and which are not. For this purpose, various noise criteria have been developed, related to the so-called preferred speech interference level (PSIL). By definition, PSIL is the average of the sound pressure levels in decibels (L_p, see below) in the three octave frequency bands centered on 500 Hz, 1000 Hz, and 2000 Hz. The loudness level in phons (L_N, see below) of a broad-band noise (no outstanding pure tones) should be not over 22 phons (at the most, not over 30 phons) greater than the PSIL, in decibels, of the background noise. Two noise control criteria, so-called NC and NCA, are designed to fulfill these conditions for various sound fields ranging from radio broadcasting studios, through bedrooms, offices, restaurants, sports arenas, and factories.

Physiological acoustics deals with hearing and its impairment, the voice mechanism, and the physical effects in general of sounds on living bodies.

The frequency range of sound is divided into three somewhat overlapping regions, namely, an audio-frequency band ranging from approximately 20 to 20000 Hz flanked by an *infrasonic* region below 30 Hz and an *ultrasonic* region above 15000 Hz. Human ears do not respond in general to frequencies outside the audio band, although small animals such as cats and bats do hear in the lower ultrasonic region. At one time called supersonics, the term ultrasonics is now accepted to distinguish this area of high-frequency sound propagation from the cases of supersonic aircraft, supersonic fluid flow, and shock waves in fluids, which have to do with speeds higher than the speeds of sound.

The *strength* of a sound field is measured by its mean square pressure expressed as sound pressure level (L_p) in decibels. Decibels are logarithmic units defining the range of sound pressure levels (L_p) between the minimum audible value at 1000 Hz (4dB*—the threshold of hear-

---

*0 dB at 1000 Hz is defined in older work as the threshold of hearing.

ing) for the average pair of good young (high school age) ears and the maximum audible value of L_p at which effects other than hearing (such as tickling in the ears—the threshold of *feeling*) begin to appear. This upper limit shows up at about 120 dB at 1000 Hz.

Higher values of L_p (e.g., 130 dB) begin to cause pain in the average ear, and values of 160 dB may well cause instantaneous physical damage (perforation) to the tympanic membrane. The minimum audible sound pressure, p_0, at 1000 Hz is internationally accepted as 2×10^{-5} N/m² rms, and the sound pressure level at any other rms value of sound pressure, p, irrespective of frequency, is given by $L_p = 20 \log_{10} \cdot (p/p_0)$ dB. The bel (seldom used) is simply equal to 10 decibels. The bel appears first used in connection with power loss in telephone lines and and is named in honor of Alexander Graham Bell.

Other reference pressures, p_0, may be used in special applications, instead of 2×10^{-5} N/m², so it is essential to specify the reference pressure when quoting values of L_p.

The *loudness* of a sound field is judged by the ear in the audio frequency range. Loudness judgments by groups of observers have established a *loudness level* scale. The loudness level (L_N) in phons in arbitrarily taken equal to the sound pressure level L_p in dB at the reference frequency of 1000 Hz over the range from the threshold of hearing to the threshold of feeling. Jury judgment of equality in loudness between test tones at different frequencies (f) and 1000-Hz reference tones of known sound pressure level (L_p) have established *equal loudness contours* (contours of constant L_N) in the L_p-f plane.

These contours show in general a marked decrease in ear sensitivity to sounds at frequencies below about 200 Hz and this decrease is much more pronounced in the lower loudness levels. For example, at 50 Hz the 4-phon contour has an L_p of about 43 dB, the 80-phon contour about 93 dB. At higher frequencies, the ear shows some 8-dB increase in sensitivity in the region around 3500 Hz, then a loss in sensitivity beyond about 6000 Hz. These characteristics of hearing are significant in the design of lecture and music halls, noise-control devices, and high-fidelity audio equipment.

Also based on jury judgments, a scale of *loudness*, N (in sones), has been established for sound (for pure tones and for broad band noise). On this scale, a given percentage change in sone value denotes an equal percentage change in the subjective loudness of the sound. The scale provides single numbers for judging the relative loudnesses of different acoustical environments, for evaluating the percentage reduction in noise due to various noise control measures, and for setting limits on permissible noise in factories, from motor vehicles, etc.

Loudness N is related to loudness level L_N in the range 40 to 100 phons by the equation $\log_{10} N = 0.03 L_N - 1.2$. A loudness of 1 sone

corresponds to a loudness level of 40 phons and is typical of the low-level background noise in a quiet home.

Various methods are available for estimating loudness of complex sounds from their sound pressure levels in octave, half-octave, or third-octave bands. For traffic noises, readings on a standard sound level meter using the A-scale (which incorporates a frequency-weighting network approximating the variation of ear sensitivity with frequency to tones of 40-dB sound pressure level) appear to correlate reasonably well with jury judgments of vehicle loudness.

The *noisiness* of a broadband noise is more related to the annoyance it causes than to its loudness. Thus, corresponding to the scale of sones created to measure loudness, a scale of *noys* has been developed as a measure of the noisiness of jet aircraft noise in particular. Noys give more importance to the high-frequency bands than do sones. Also, corresponding to the scale of loudness levels in phons, there has been established a scale of *perceived noise levels* in PN dB. Rules have been established for converting sound pressure level measured in octave bands, half-octave bands and third-octave bands into noys and then into PN dB. This scale was developed as a means for the assessment of the "noisiness" of jet aircraft flying over inhabited communities.

W. W. SOROKA

References

Books

Beranek, Leo L., "Acoustics," New York, McGraw-Hill Book Co., 1954.

Harris, Cyril M., "Handbook of Noise Control," New York, McGraw-Hill Book Co., 1957.

Beranek, Leo L., "Noise Reduction," New York, McGraw-Hill Book Co., 1960.

Officer, C. B., "Introduction to the Theory of Sound Transmission," New York, McGraw-Hill Book Co., 1958.

Ewing, W. Maurice, Jardetzky, Wenceslas S., and Press, Frank, "Elastic Waves in Layered Media," New York, McGraw-Hill Book Co., 1957.

Morse, Philip M., "Vibration and Sound," Second edition, New York, McGraw-Hill Book Co., 1948.

Kinsler, Lawrence E., and Frey, Austin R., "Fundamentals of Acoustics," Second edition, New York, John Wiley & Sons, 1962.

Beranek, Leo L., "Noise and Vibration Control," New York, McGraw-Hill Book Co., 1971.

Morse, Philip M., and Ingard, K. Uno, "Theoretical Acoustics," New York, McGraw-Hill Book Co., 1968

Periodicals

Journal of the Acoustical Society of America (1929-).

Acustica (1951-).

Proceedings of the International Congresses on Acoustics.

Journal of the Audio Engineering Society (1953-).

Journal of Sound and Vibration (1964-).

Applied Acoustics (1968-).

Cross-references: ARCHITECTURAL ACOUSTICS; ELECTROACOUSTICS; HEARING; MUSICAL SOUND; NOISE, ACOUSTICAL; PHONONS; PHYSICAL ACOUSTICS; REPRODUCTION OF SOUND; RESONANCE; SONAR; ULTRASONICS; VIBRATION; WAVE MOTION.

ADSORPTION AND ABSORPTION

When a porous solid such as charcoal is exposed, in a closed space, to a gas such as ammonia, the pressure of the gas diminishes and the weight of the solid increases; this is an example of the adsorption of a gas by a solid. It is termed physical adsorption because the forces bringing it about are the "van der Waals" forces of attraction which act between the molecules of the gas and the atoms or ions comprising the solid. It is now known that all solids, whether porous or nonporous, will adsorb all gases physically, whereas the phenomenon of *chemisorption* is specific in nature. Thus hydrogen is chemisorbed by transition metals such as nickel or iron but not by oxides such as alumina.

In physical adsorption the amount, say w grams, of gas or vapor taken up per gram of solid depends greatly on the nature of the gas and of the solid, as well as on the pressure p and the temperature T. In mathematical form, $w = f(p, T, \text{gas}, \text{solid})$. For a given gas and solid at a fixed temperature, w depends only on pressure, and the relationship between w and p (i.e., $w = f(p)_{T, \text{gas}, \text{solid}}$) is called the *adsorption isotherm*. Data of adsorption are usually quoted in the form of the adsorption isotherm of the gas or vapor under consideration (the "adsorbate") on the given solid (the "adsorbent"). For vapors it is more appropriate to express the isotherm in terms of relative pressure so that $w = f_0(p/p_0)_{T, \text{vapor}, \text{solid}}$, where p_0 is the saturated vapor pressure of the adsorbate at the temperature of the experiment.

With the great majority of solids, the isotherm at the low-pressure end is concave towards the pressure axis. Its further course depends on the nature of the solid: if the solid is nonporous (e.g., a powder) the isotherm reaches a point of inflection at a relative pressure in the region 0.1 to 0.3 and thereafter turns upwards (Type II isotherm); if it is porous, with pores having radii between tens and hundreds of angstroms, the form of the isotherm is similar, except that at pressures near saturation it bends over and becomes almost horizontal; it also shows a *hysteresis loop* in the middle range of pressures, the desorption branch lying above the adsorption branch (Type IV isotherm). If the solid contains an extensive series of pores of molecular width (< 20 Å), the isotherm shows no point of inflection but continuously diminishes in slope and finally becomes nearly horizontal (Type I isotherm).

Measurements on solids having a known surface area have shown that at low pressures the adsorbed layer is only one molecule thick and

as pressure increases the molecules in this "monolayer" become more and more crowded, till at or near the point of inflection in the isotherm the monolayer is completely full up. Further increase in pressure then leads to the formation of a multimolecular layer—a "multilayer"—of gradually increasing thickness.

Adsorption is an exothermic process so that by elementary thermodynamic principles the amount adsorbed by a given solid at a given pressure must diminish as temperature increases. The differential heat of adsorption $\bar{q}$ [i.e., the limit of the ratio $\delta q/(\delta w/M)$ where δq is the heat evolved when the adsorption increases by $\delta w/M$, M being the molecular weight of adsorbate] is rather larger than the latent heat of condensation L of the adsorbate. The value of $\bar{q}$ depends somewhat on the amount adsorbed; it is relatively high for small adsorptions—perhaps about $2L$—then diminishes as w increases, till in the multilayer region it scarcely exceeds the latent heat. There is usually a low maximum ($\sim 1.3L$ or so) in the region where the monolayer is just complete. The values quoted are only by way of example, and minor, generally unpredictable, differences are found between one system and another. The falling branch of the $\bar{q}$ vs w curve is usually ascribed to heterogeneity of the surface (adsorption occurring first on the more "active" parts of the surface), and the branch rising to the maximum is probably produced by mutual attraction of the molecules within the monolayer.

Since physical adsorption results from van der Waals forces, the greater the condensability of the gas or vapor as measured by its boiling point or its critical temperature, the greater is the amount of gas or vapor adsorbed at a given pressure. Thus at room temperature and atmospheric pressure, the "permanent gases" such as hydrogen or nitrogen are only slightly adsorbed even on a good adsorbent such as charcoal, while carbon dioxide is more adsorbed, and benzene and carbon tetrachloride are strongly adsorbed. At very low temperatures the adsorption is correspondingly greater, so that nitrogen at its boiling point of $-195°$C has an adsorption, on a given solid, comparable with that of benzene at $25°$C. For the adsorption to be readily measurable, however, the solid needs to have a relatively large area—a completed monolayer of nitrogen, 1 square meter in extent, weighs only 0.3 mg, for example—so that adsorption phenomena may escape notice unless the solid is "highly disperse," i.e., has an area exceeding several square meters per gram.

Numerous attempts have been made to interpret the detailed course of the different types of isotherm theoretically; but only limited success has been achieved because the models used are necessarily oversimplified and can rarely correspond in detail to the complex systems encountered in practice. However, it is generally agreed that at or near the point of inflection, the monolayer is complete; thus by assuming a

value for the cross-sectional area of an adsorbed molecule, it is possible to estimate from a Type II or a Type IV isotherm the surface area of the solid (the "Brunauer-Emmett-Teller" method). Further, from the course of the desorption loop of a Type IV isotherm, by assuming the adsorbate to be condensed as a liquid in pores which are regarded as cylinders, and by applying the Kelvin equation, one can calculate the pore size distribution of the solid; because of the assumptions made, the accuracy of the method is severely limited, but it is useful for comparative purposes and is virtually the only method applicable in the pore size range of tens to hundreds of angstroms.

Chemisorption results from valency forces— from the sharing of electrons between the adsorbate molecule and the adsorbent—so that, in effect, a surface chemical compound is formed. Chemisorption is characterized by a high heat of adsorption (of the order of tens of kilocalories per mole, in contrast to the few kilocalories of physical adsorption) and by difficulty of reversal: to desorb a chemisorbed gas in a reasonable time requires a temperature much higher than that at which the chemisorption occurred. Even so the adsorbate may be released in a chemically changed form; thus carbon monoxide chemisorbed on zinc oxide at room temperature is desorbed as carbon *dioxide* at at 300°C.

Chemisorption is an essential primary step in heterogeneous catalysis. At least one of the reactants must be chemisorbed on the surface of the catalyst, and each of its molecules then forms, on the surface, a "transition complex" with a chemisorbed molecule of the second reactant B, or with a molecule of B which hits it directly from the gas phase.

Physical adsorption is an extremely widespread phenomenon, frequently unwanted. The adsorption of water vapor by chemicals, by textiles, by building materials and by glass is frequently troublesome and can only be avoided by taking extreme precautions; sometimes, however, the adsorption of water may be beneficial, and it plays an important role, for instance, in the hygiene of clothing.

Adsorption, whether physical or chemical, also reduces the adhesion, and therefore the friction, between solids; gases can accordingly act as lubricants. In addition, adsorption diminishes the tensile strength of brittle solids; the breaking stress of glass when exposed to nearly saturated water vapor is four times less than when exposed to a vacuum. The mechanism is a matter of controversy, but it is probably connected with the fact that adsorption reduces the free surface energy (in the thermodynamic sense) of the solid. Adsorption also causes a small (a fraction of 1 per cent) expansion of the solid, but the swelling pressure set up—i.e., the pressure which would have to be exerted on the solid to prevent expansion—is very high and may reach many atmospheres. Stresses set up in structures made up of porous solids, such as cement and mortar, when they take up or lose vapors, particularly water, may be so great as to cause cracking.

Absorption is said to occur when the molecules of the gas or vapor actually penetrate into the solid phase itself, so that a solid solution is formed; hydrogen is absorbed by iron at elevated temperature in this way, and many synthetic polymers absorb water vapor; benzene vapor is extensively taken up by rubber and water vapor by gelatin. Extensive swelling occurs and if the solid is mechanically weak, the absorption may continue until the system becomes a liquid. An absorption isotherm (analogous to the *adsorption* isotherm discussed earlier) can be determined, but is generally complicated and is best handled theoretically as a branch of solution thermodynamics.

In *adsorption from solution*, when a solid having appreciable surface area (say $\sim$1 square meter per gram) is shaken up with a solution of substance A in solvent B, both A *and* B are adsorbed, but to different relative extents. This manifests itself in a change in the composition, e.g., a change Δx_A in the mole fraction of A in the solution. The problem is thus more complicated than in the adsorption of gases, and the measured isotherm—the curve of Δx_A against x_A—is not susceptible to any simple theoretical treatment. In a *dilute* solution of A, however, A is always relatively more adsorbed than the solvent B; and if A is colored, the resulting diminution in the concentration of A in the solution will be readily detected by eye or colorimetrically.

S. J. GREGG

References

Gregg, S. J., and Sing, K. S. W., "Adsorption, Surface Area and Porosity," London, Academic Press, 1967.

Flood, E. A., Editor, "The Gas-Solid Interface," 2 Vols., London, Arnold, 1967.

Young, D. M., and Crowell, A. D., "Physical Adsorption of Gases," London, Butterworths, 1962.

Hayward, D. O., and Trapnell, B. M. W., "Chemisorption," London, Butterworth's, 1964.

Kipling, J. J., "Adsorption from Solution of Non-Electrolytes," London, Academic Press, 1965.

Cross-references: INTERMOLECULAR FORCES, VAPOR PRESSURE AND EVAPORATION.

AERODYNAMICS

Aerodynamics is the science of the flow of air and/or of the motion of bodies through air. It is usually directed at achieving flow or flight with the maximum efficiency. Aerodynamics is a branch of aeromechanics; the other main branch is *aerostatics* (lift of balloons, etc.). In popular usage aerodynamics differs from *Gas-*

dynamics in that the latter considers other gases and products of combustion (and combustion); from *aerophysics*, which implies substantial molecular changes in the gas; and from *hydrodynamics*, which implies employing a medium of density approximating that of useful bodies in it, and not infrequently a sharp limit to its extent (i.e., a water surface).

Aerodynamics is conveniently divided into low and high speed regimes. (The latter is in the articles on COMPRESSIBILITY, FLUID DYNAMICS, and SHOCK WAVES; here low-speed aerodynamics is discussed.)

The many facets of aerodynamics include: (1) aerodynamic performance, (2) aerodynamic design, (3) aerodynamic loads, (4) aerodynamic structures, (5) aero-elasticity, (6) aerodynamic heating, (7) aerodynamic compressibility, and (8) aerodynamic research for all of the above.

The computation of aerodynamic effects is based on four laws (given as adapted for fluids):

(1) *Newton's Second Law*: "A force applied to a fluid results in an equal but opposite reaction which in turn causes a rate of change of momentum in the fluid."

(2) *The Equation of State*: (also called the Gas Law): "The product of pressure and volume of a gas, divided by its absolute temperature, is a constant."

(3) *The Continuity Equation*: "The mass that passes a station in a duct, or in a natural tube bounded by streamlines in a given time, must equal that passing a second station in the same time."

(4) *The Energy Equation*: "The total energy in a mass of air remains constant unless heat or work is added or subtracted."

The above relations, written algebraically and limited or combined, yield a vast array of equations used to calculate the practical problems of aerodynamics. One of the *equations* thus derived is due to Bernoulli and is widely used in low speed aerodynamics. It states that in free flow the sum of the static and dynamic pressures is a constant. Static pressure is that pressure which is equal in all directions; dynamic pressure is the pressure rise realized by bringing the fluid to rest. Bernoulli's equation states that as air speeds up, its pressure falls, thus explaining the "lifting suction" as the airstream traverses the curved upper surface of a wing.

The overwhelmingly important *law* of low speed aerodynamics is that due to Newton (1, above). Thus a helicopter gets a lifting force by giving air a downward momentum. The wing of a flying airplane is always at an angle such that it deflects air downward. Birds fly by pushing air downward. Propellers and jet engines make a forward force ("thrust") by giving air a rearward momentum. In the above statements, it is much more accurate to use the expression "downward (or rearward) momentum," rather than "downward (or rearward) velocity," since less dense air at high altitudes produces smaller forces for comparable velocity changes. Forcing the air downward does not occur instanta-

neously; it takes place over the lifting surface. Indeed, the motion reaches ahead of the airplane so that some downward velocity occurs before the airplane arrives. Thus, airplanes (helicopters, birds, etc.) are always "flying uphill" which is another way of saying it takes a force to fly even when the air is considered frictionless. This force is used to push air *forward*, and is called "drag due to lift." It *increases* as an airplane *slows down* or *flies higher*, and it may be reduced (for low-speed aircraft) by *increasing* the wing span. Supersonic aircraft, operating under the same laws, but in a different manner, still have a drag due to lift which increases as above, but is reduced designwise by *reducing* the span; hence the new airplanes whose wings crank back for high-speed flight. (The "uphill" concept has an analogy in the rolling resistance of a wheel. The weight a wheel carries deflects the surface on which it rests so that it sits in a "gully." Either way it rolls, the path is uphill).

A second important phenomenon (but not a "law" in the sense that it cannot be circumvented) is the manner in which air flows over say, an airplane surface. Away from the surface some free-stream velocity exists. As the surface is approached the local velocity becomes less than freestream and finally becomes zero at the surface. The zone in which the air is appreciably slower is called the *boundary layer*. Slowing the air reduces its momentum, and by Newton's law (above), a force is produced which acts in a direction to slow the airplane. Like forward force needed to produce lift, this *frictional drag* force must have a forward force supplied from somewhere to balance it. For high-speed aircraft a heating occurs in the boundary layer which requires additional force. Skin friction drag is *decreased* by reducing the amount of surface the air scrapes against (i.e., making the aircraft smaller) and by *flying slower* or *higher*—essentially the opposite of the actions which reduce the drag due to lift. Thus the science of aerodynamics seeks the most efficacious melding of the two types of losses. Factors which must be added include providing space for fuel and people, and enough wing to yield a reasonable landing speed. The drag due to lift and the drag due to friction are balanced by the forward thrust provided by the propeller or jet engine (which also operates by Newton's law). However, this is not enough. The distribution of lift on wing and tail must be so located that the aircraft is aerodynamically balanced. Like a child's swing, upon being disturbed it should tend to return to its original ("trimmed") condition.

In the above paragraphs the concern has been for aerodynamic efficiency through optimum design for optimum performance. After these have been achieved (by studies of previous designs and tests in *wind tunnels*) the aerodynamicist provides aerodynamic loads to which an aero-structural engineer must design. Aerostructural design is one of the most challenging of all design problems as the loads must be carried by minimum weight. Aeroplanes carry no

"factor of safety" (sometimes called "factor of ignorance"). The aerodynamic-loads engineer furnishes the maximum air loads the aircraft is ever expected to see; the structure is designed to withstand these loads without being permanently bent. If it ever sees a greater load it will be bent or destroyed; there is about a 50 per cent difference between maximum no-permanent set load and catastrophic destruction, depending on the material of which the aircraft is constructed.

In an effort to keep aerodynamic structures light, they often become flexible, and, in turn, become susceptible to flutter, a motion similar to that of a flag in a wind. The motion gets worse with speed. It is the job of the aero-elasticity engineer to assure that flutter will not occur, usually through a redistribution of internal weights (fuel, etc.) and, rarely, through strengthening the structure.

At the higher speeds, the performance, loads, structures and elasticity problems are greatly worsened by the aerodynamic heating which occurs. This is discussed in the article on COMPRESSIBILITY.

Aerodynamics is not only concerned with aircraft. The wind loads on signs, buildings, trees; the aerodynamics drag of autos, boats, trains; the air pollution from smoke stacks of factories and ships; the evaporation of open water; the blowing of sand and snow; and the internal losses of air-conditioning ducts—all deserve and are getting scrutiny by aerodynamicists. The forces on all are proportional to the rate of change of momentum they give, or is given by the air; and all have friction drag in their boundary layers. Aerodynamic research scientists seek to further understand and improve the air flow involved in each.

Aerostatics Aerostatics is the science of making things (balloons, zeppelins, etc.) statically buoyant in the air.

The basic principle of aerostatics is due to Archimedes. "A body immersed in a fluid [or gas] is buoyed up by a force equal to the weight of the fluid [or gas] displaced." Thus for buoyancy the weight of structure plus the weight of the contained gas must equal the weight of the air displaced.

Wind Tunnels Wind tunnels are devices which provide an airstream of known and steady conditions in which models requiring aerodynamic study are tested. The essential elements of a tunnel are:

(1) A drive system consisting of either a compressor for continuous operation or a tank of compressed air for intermittent operation;

(2) a test section in which models are held and their orientation is charged;

(3) instrumentation capable of reading force, pressure, temperature, and optical effects produced by the model;

(4) an air efflux system consisting of free exit to the atmosphere or to a vacuum tank, or a tunnel returning the air to the compressor.

There are approximately 500 wind tunnels in the country, ranging in test section size from 1 in. × 1 in. to 30 ft × 60 ft, with speeds from 50 to 7000 mph.

ALAN POPE

References

Perkins, Courtland, D., and Hage, Robert E., "Airplane Performance, Stability, and Control," New York, John Wiley & Sons, Inc., 1949.

Kuethe, A. M., and Shetzer, J. D., "Foundations of Aerodynamics," New York, John Wiley & Sons, Inc., 1959.

Pope, Alan, and Harper, John J., "Low-Speed Wind Tunnel Testing," New York, John Wiley & Sons, 1960.

Pope, Alan, and Goin, Kenneth, "High-Speed Wind Tunnel Testing," New York, John Wiley & Sons, 1966.

Cross-references: ASTRONAUTICS, DYNAMICS, MECHANICS.

ALTERNATING CURRENTS

Definition of Alternating Current An alternating current is a periodic function of the time, the function being such that the average value is zero. A special case of an alternating current is shown in Fig. 1. The square wave is clearly periodic, and in any one cycle, the area under the curve above the horizontal axis is equal to the area below the horizontal axis. If the two areas are not equal, the current may be described as an alternating current superposed on a direct current, provided the resultant current varies in a cyclic manner.

In general, any alternating current may be considered to be the sum of a Fourier series of sinusoidal waves. For example, the square wave shown in Fig. 1 may be written as

$$\frac{4A}{\pi} \left(\sin 2\pi ft + \frac{1}{3} \sin 6\pi ft + \frac{1}{5} \sin 10\pi ft + \cdots \right)$$

where A is the amplitude of the square wave, f is the frequency in hertz (cycles per second), and t is the time in seconds. Since any alternating current may be expressed as the sum of a series of sinusoidal terms, the remainder of this

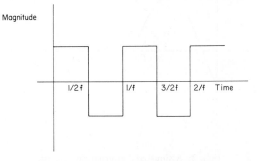

FIG. 1. A square wave alternating current.

article will be devoted to a discussion of sinusoidal voltages and currents.

Root-mean-square Value   The equation for an alternating current i may be written as

$$i = I_m \sin (\omega t - \delta) \qquad (1)$$

where I_m is the maximum or peak value of the current, ω is 2π times the frequency f in hertz (Hz), and δ is a phase angle. A graph of the current i is shown in Fig. 2. Since the positive and negative loops are mirror images, the average value of the current over a complete cycle is zero. The latter statement is valid for all alternating currents and, hence, gives no information about a particular alternating current.

A useful way of stating the magnitude of an alternating current is to give its effective or root-mean-square value. The term root-mean-square is derived from the idea of taking the square root of an average square of the current. Thus, by definition, the effective value I_e of the current i given by Eq. (1) is

$$I_e = \sqrt{\frac{\omega}{2\pi} \int_0^{2\pi/\omega} I_m{}^2 \sin^2 (\omega t - \delta) \, dt} \qquad (2)$$

where $2\pi/\omega$ is the time for one cycle. In effect, the quantity under the square root sign is the sum of the squares of the currents during one cycle divided by the time for one cycle. The value of I_e may be found by performing the integration. The result is

$$I_e = \frac{I_m}{\sqrt{2}} = 0.707 \, I_m \qquad (3)$$

Clearly, the effective value of a sinusoidal alternating current is 70.7 per cent of the maximum or peak value. Similarly the effective value of a sinusoidal voltage is 70.7 per cent of the maximum or peak value.

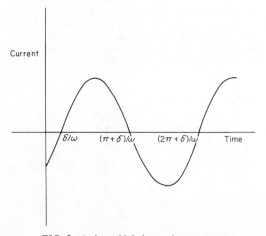

FIG. 2. A sinusoidal alternating current.

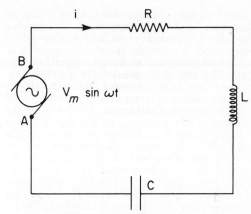

FIG. 3. An ac series circuit.

Alternating-current Series Circuit   A simple alternating-current series circuit is shown in Fig. 3. At the instant considered in the diagram, the current is in the direction shown. The circuit consists of a generator connected in series to a pure resistance R, a pure inductance L, and a capacitance C. It is important to understand the relationship of the current to the potential difference across each element. In each case, the best starting point is a basic definition. According to Ohm's law for a pure resistance,

$$R = \frac{V_R}{i} \qquad (4)$$

where V_R is the voltage drop across the resistance. The inductance L of a coil is given by

$$L = \frac{N\phi}{i} \qquad (5)$$

where N is the number of turns and ϕ is the magnetic flux passing through one of the turns of the coil as a result of the current i. Writing Eq. (5) as

$$Li = N\phi$$

and then differentiating both sides, we obtain

$$L \frac{di}{dt} = N \frac{d\phi}{dt} \qquad (6)$$

According to Faraday's law, the right-hand side of Eq. (6) is the magnitude of the induced emf. The left-hand side, $L \, di/dt$, therefore, is the voltage drop V_L across the inductance L. Finally, the capacitance C is by definition

$$C = \frac{q}{V_C} \qquad (7)$$

where q is the instantaneous charge on the positive plate and V_C is the drop in potential in going from the positive plate to the negative plate.

The relation between the impressed voltage $V_m \sin \omega t$ and the instantaneous current i follows from Kirchhoff's law that the sum of the differences in potential in going around a complete circuit must be zero. At the instant shown in Fig. 3, there is a potential rise $V_m \sin \omega t$ in going from A to B and there are potential drops, V_R, V_L, and V_C in traversing the rest of the circuit. According to Kirchhoff's law

$$V_m \sin \omega t - V_R - V_L - V_C = 0$$

$$V_m \sin \omega t - Ri - L\frac{di}{dt} - \frac{q}{C} = 0$$

Since the current is the rate of flow of charge

$$i = \frac{dq}{dt} \qquad (8)$$

It is now possible to express the current i as a function of t. The result neglecting initial transient effects is

$$i = \frac{V_m \sin (\omega t - \delta)}{\sqrt{R^2 + (\omega L - 1/\omega C)^2}} \qquad (9)$$

where $\tan \delta = (\omega L - 1/\omega C)/R$. The phase angle δ is the angle by which the current i lags behind the impressed voltage.

The maximum or peak value of i is

$$I_m = \frac{V_m}{\sqrt{R^2 + (\omega L - 1/\omega C)^2}}$$

If both sides of this equation are divided by $\sqrt{2}$, we obtain

$$\frac{I_m}{\sqrt{2}} = \frac{V_m/\sqrt{2}}{\sqrt{R^2 + (\omega L - 1/\omega C)^2}}$$

$$I_e = \frac{V_e}{\sqrt{R^2 + (\omega L - 1/\omega C)^2}} \qquad (10)$$

Equation (10) states the relation between the effective value of the current and the effective value of the impressed voltage.

Impedance and Reactance The denominator of Eq. (10) may be defined as the impedance Z of the circuit. We may therefore write

$$I_e = \frac{V_e}{Z} \qquad (11)$$

Equation (11) is similar in form to Ohm's law, Eq. (4). The impedance Z is the square root of the sum of the squares of two terms. The first is the resistance R, and the second is $\omega L - 1/\omega C$. The latter is called the reactance. The quantity ωL is the inductive reactance whereas $1/\omega C$ is capacitative reactance. If the inductive reactance is greater than the capacitative reactance, the phase angle δ is positive and the current lags behind the voltage. If the inductive reactance is less than the capacitative reactance, the current leads the voltage.

Vector Diagram The current and the various voltages may be related in a meaningful way by means of a vector diagram. Equation (10) may be rewritten as follows:

$$V_e = \sqrt{R^2 I_e^2 + (\omega L I_e - I_e/\omega C)^2} \qquad (12)$$

Equation (12) implies that V_e is the resultant of a vector RI_e at right angles to a vector $\omega L I_e - I_e/\omega C$. This is shown in Fig. 4. The cur-

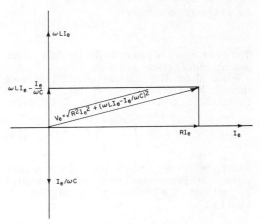

FIG. 4. A vector diagram for an ac series circuit.

rent I_e is drawn along the horizontal axis, and the effective voltage drop across the resistance, RI_e, is also drawn along this axis. The effective voltage drop across the coil is $\omega L I_e$, and this potential difference is drawn along the positive vertical axis. Finally, the effective potential drop across the capacitor is $I_e/\omega C$, and this vector is drawn along the negative vertical axis. The resultant of the three vectors is V_e, in agreement with Eq. (12).

Resonance If the capacitance C can be varied, the current I_e will be a function of C in accordance with Eq. (10). When

$$\omega L = \frac{1}{\omega C} \qquad (13)$$

the effective current will be a maximum. The circuit is then said to be in resonance. Actually, the inductance L or the angular frequency ω may be varied instead of the capacitance C. The circuit will be in resonance whenever Eq. (13) holds. At resonance, the impedance Z is equal to R, and the circuit, under such circumstances, acts as though it contains resistance only. The process of obtaining resonance is called tuning the circuit.

Average Power The potential difference V across an ac generator at any instant is the work required to transfer a unit charge from the negative to the positive terminal. The work done in transferring a charge dq is consequently

$V \, dq$, and the work done per unit time is

$$P = \frac{V \, dq}{dt} \qquad (14)$$

where P is, by definition, the instantaneous power and dt is the time interval to transfer the charge dq. Since

$$i = \frac{dq}{dt}$$

Eq. (14) may be written

$$P = Vi$$

The instantaneous power is the product of the instantaneous voltage and current.

When alternating current circuits are considered, the average power $\overline{P}$ rather than the instantaneous power is of interest. By definition

$$\overline{P} = \frac{\omega}{2\pi} \int_0^{2\pi/\omega} Vi \, dt \qquad (15)$$

where, as before, $2\pi/\omega$ is the time for a complete cycle. The average power may be evaluated by making the following substitutions in Eq. (15):

$$V = V_m \sin \omega t$$

$$i = I_m \sin (\omega t - \delta)$$

The result is

$$\overline{P} = \tfrac{1}{2} V_m I_m \cos \delta \qquad (16)$$

Equation (16) may be rewritten

$$\overline{P} = \frac{V_m}{\sqrt{2}} \frac{I}{\sqrt{2}} \cos \delta$$

$$\overline{P} = V_e I_e \cos \delta \qquad (17)$$

Evidently, the average power is the effective voltage times the effective current multiplied by the cosine of the phase angle. In this connection, $\cos \delta$ is called the power factor. Equation (17) may be interpreted to mean that only the component of V_e in phase with I_e contributes to the average power. The other component may be said to be wattless. Since

$$V_e = I_e Z$$

and

$$\cos \delta = \frac{R}{Z}$$

Eq. (17) may be written as follows:

$$\overline{P} = I_e^2 R \qquad (18)$$

From the latter form, it may be concluded that the average power is the average rate at which heat is developed in the circuit. Equation (18)

also shows that a direct current having a value I_e would produce the same heating effect as an alternating current having an effective value I_e.

The Complex-number Method In the foregoing, an alternating-current series circuit was discussed by representing voltages as vectors in the real plane. For more complicated circuits, this method is too clumsy. It is much more convenient to deal with vectors analytically by utilizing the j-operator. By definition,

$$j = \sqrt{-1}$$

When a real number is multiplied by j, it becomes an imaginary number. In other words, a point on the real axis is rotated through $90°$ so that it becomes a point on the imaginary axis. The "complex" impedance of a series circuit may thus be written

$$Z = R + j\left(\omega L - \frac{1}{\omega C}\right) \qquad (19)$$

since the reactance may be considered to be at right angles to the resistance. When several impedances are connected in series, the total complex impedance is

$$Z = Z_1 + Z_2 + Z_3 + \cdots \qquad (20)$$

and, when several impedances are connected in parallel, the total impedance is given by

$$\frac{1}{Z} = \frac{1}{Z_1} + \frac{1}{Z_2} + \frac{1}{Z_3} + \cdots \qquad (21)$$

The effective voltage V across the generator may be considered to be a vector along the real axis. The effective current I furnished by the generator is therefore

$$I = \frac{V}{Z} \qquad (22)$$

By solving Eq. (22), the magnitude of I and the phase relation between I and V may be found. Although new mathematical techniques are needed, the saving of time usually justifies the use of the complex number method of handling complicated ac circuits.

REUBEN BENUMOF

References

Benumof, Reuben, "Concepts in Electricity and Magnetism," Ch. 14, New York, Holt, Rinehart, and Winston, 1961.

Benumof, Reuben, "Concepts in Physics," Second Edition, Ch. 14, Englewood Cliffs, N.J., Prentice-Hall, Inc., 1972.

Scott, W. T., "The Physics of Electricity and Magnetism," Second Edition, Ch. 9, New York, John Wiley & Sons, 1966.

Sears, F. W., and Zemansky, M. W., "University Physics," Fourth Edition, Ch. 35, Reading, Mass., Addison-Wesley Publishing Co., 1970.

Kurrelmeyer, B., and Mais, W. H., "Electricity and

Magnetism," Ch. 14, New York, Van Nostrand Reinhold, 1970.

Pugh, E. M., and Pugh, E. W., "Principles of Electricity and Magnetism," Second Edition, Reading, Mass., Addison-Wesley Publishing Co., 1970.

Cross-references: CIRCUITRY, ELECTRICITY, POTENTIAL, RESONANCE.

ANTENNAS

Communication systems, characteristically, consist of cascaded networks, each network designed to carry out some operation on the energy conveying the information. In radio communication systems, antennas are the networks serving to transfer the signal energy from circuits to space and, conversely, from space to circuits. In circuits, the flow of energy is restricted to one of two directions. The effectiveness of transfer of energy between the antenna and the adjacent circuit element is, therefore, determined solely by the terminal impedance of the antenna and that of the adjacent circuit. The knowledge of the antenna terminal impedance over the desired frequency range, therefore, fully describes the joint performance of the antenna and the circuit element.

The relationship between the antenna and space, however, is much more complex. The distribution of the radiated energy varies with the direction in space and with the distance from the antenna. This gives rise to the directive properties of the antenna. Further, the energy is radiated in the form of electric and magnetic fields. These are vector quantities which, at a distance from the source, are at right angles to each other and to the direction of propagation. The planes in which these vectors are located, and whether they are stationary or rotate with time, determine the polarization of the radiated field. The performance of an antenna can, therefore, be fully described only by specifying several parameters, such as radiation pattern, power gain[1,2] and directive gain, and polarization. In discussing antenna properties, it is convenient to consider the antenna as a radiating rather than a receiving network. The antennas are, however, linear networks and are subject to the law of reciprocity.[3] The performance of an antenna, therefore, in terms of radiation pattern, gain, or polarization is the same, irrespective of whether the antenna radiates or absorbs radiation.

Except for the immediate neighborhood of the antenna, referred to as the "near-field region" of the antenna, radiated energy propagates radially away from the antenna, and the radiation intensity* varies inversely as the square of the distance from the antenna. This is

*In this discussion, radiation intensity has the dimensions of power flow per unit area, normally, watts per square meter. Electric field strength, on the other hand, is in volts per meter. Definitions of these and other terms can be found in ref. 1.

a propagation effect. In discussing the antenna performance, it is customary to disregard this and to represent the distribution of the radiated power as a function of the two direction angles only. Such a distribution is commonly represented graphically and is then known as the radiation pattern of the antenna. The radiation patterns can take a variety of forms. Sometimes they are in the form of a polar diagram, with the radial distance proportional to either field strength* or intensity. The intensity may be represented linearly, as power, or logarithmically, in decibels.[4] For representing the directive properties of an antenna in all directions, contours of equal radiation intensity may be plotted, with the two direction angles as abscissas and ordinates, respectively.

The directive properties of an antenna also lead to the concept of antenna "gain." The directive gain of an antenna in a specified direction is the radiation intensity in that direction compared to what it would be if the total radiated power were distributed equally in all directions. Besides "directive gain" there is also the concept of "power gain." The latter differs in that the total input power rather than the radiated power is used as the reference. The power gain for an antenna is always smaller than the directive gain by the factor of "radiation efficiency." IEEE Standards Publications 145 and 149 (references 1 and 2) should be consulted for exact terminology. For some applications, such as point-to-point communication, high values of antenna gain are desired because such antennas concentrate the available power, thus effectively increasing it. Conversely, in receiving applications, such antennas are more responsive to radiation arriving from one direction. For other applications such as broadcasting, broadly directional antennas with low directivity may be desired.

The gain of an antenna is dependent principally upon the size of the antenna, expressed in wavelengths. The larger the antenna, the greater is likely to be its gain. The values of gain for different antennas range from 1.5 for an electrically small dipole to hundreds and even thousands of times that. In practice, antenna gains are usually expressed logarithmically, in decibels. For the low-frequency end of the radio spectrum (15 kHz to 3 MHz), antennas, although large physically, are relatively small in terms of wavelengths. Therefore, the directive gains of these antennas seldom exceed 3 (4.8 dB). The radiation efficiency of the low-frequency antennas is usually very low. As a result the power gains are much lower than directive gains and are negative when expressed in decibels. In the high-frequency band (3 to 30 MHz), which is used principally for long-distance communication, antenna gains of 10 to 100 (10 to 20 dB) are frequently encountered. At microwave frequencies, where the wavelengths are a fraction of a meter, gains of several hundred, and even thousand times (20 to over 30 dB), are common.

When an antenna has one or more of its dimensions significantly larger than a wavelength, its radiation pattern is likely to have more than one maximum. The radiation pattern, in such cases, is said to have a lobe structure. That part of the radiation pattern which encompasses the direction of the largest maximum and the radiation immediately to each side of it, is referred to as the main lobe. The radiation about the minor maxima is referred to as the secondary or side lobes. One of the frequent goals in antenna design is reduction in the levels of secondary lobes. These may, at times, be a source of interference to other transmissions.

In common with light, radio waves consist of electric and magnetic fields at right angles to each other and to the direction of propagation. The orientation of these fields relative to the observer determines the polarization of the wave. In radio terminology, the orientation of the electric vector of a radio wave is taken as the direction of polarization. Thus, if the electric field vector is parallel to the ground, the radio wave is termed "horizontally polarized." Although the polarization of the energy radiated by an antenna, in general, varies with the direction, an antenna is usually designated as being horizontally (or vertically, or circularly, etc.) polarized, depending on the polarization of its radiation in the direction of the main lobe maximum.

The importance of polarization in radio engineering lies principally in the different reflective properties of the ground for waves with electric field parallel to the ground and those normal to the ground. Different radio services are served best by different polarizations. Antennas for use in the low-frequency end of the radio spectrum, 15 kHz through about 3 MHz, are almost invariably vertically polarized. This includes the AM broadcast band. In the high-frequency band, 3 to 30 MHz, both horizontal and vertical polarizations are used. For television broadcast service in the United States and many other countries (but not in the United Kingdom), horizontal polarization is employed. In the United States horizontal polarization is standard for FM broadcasting service. However, to accommodate reception in private automobiles, the FM stations are now permitted to add vertically polarized transmission, not to exceed the horizontally polarized component.

The types and variations of antennas encountered in practice are extremely numerous. Each type has some advantage over the others for some specific requirement. Among some of the more important and frequently encountered requirements are those for operating bandwidth, high radiation efficiency, specified degree of directivity, whether high or low, and polarization. A few of the representative types of antennas frequently encountered in practice are illustrated in Figs. 1, 2, and 3. Figure 1 shows two of the elementary types of radiators, a

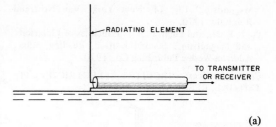

(a)

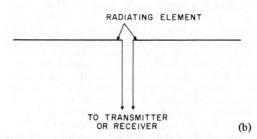

(b)

FIG. 1. Two types of elementary radiators: (a) Monopole over ground. (b) A dipole.

monopole and a dipole. A monopole, shown in Fig. 1(a), in one form or another, is employed almost exclusively throughout the low-frequency end of the radio spectrum. The dipole, shown in Fig. 1(b), is somewhat more versatile, since it can be oriented to give either horizontal or vertical polarization. It is frequently used as an elementary radiator in large array-type antennas.

Figure 2 presents two, highly directive, but otherwise radically different, types of antenna. The rhombic antenna shown in (a) has broadband properties and is used widely in point-to-point communication service. The Yagi antenna displayed in (b) illustrates a relatively compact antenna with high gain for its size. Its operating frequency band is quite narrow.

Figure 3 shows two antenna types frequently used at microwave frequencies. The horn antenna is used generally where moderate directivity suffices. The parabolic antenna, on the other hand, is used for high-gain applications and is a quasi-optical device.

Gain, whether power or directive, is not always the most important consideration in the selection of an antenna. For some applications a capability for operating over a very wide frequency band is more important. One example of this is a long-distance HF communications circuit using ionospheric propagation. Over a 24-hour period the ionospheric conditions change radically and it is necessary to change the operating frequency repeatedly over several octaves in order to maintain communications. Most antennas operate efficiently only over a limited frequency band; this may make it necessary to switch between different antennas. There is a class of frequency-independent an-

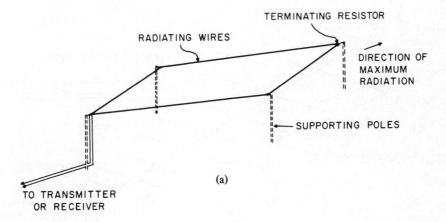

(a)

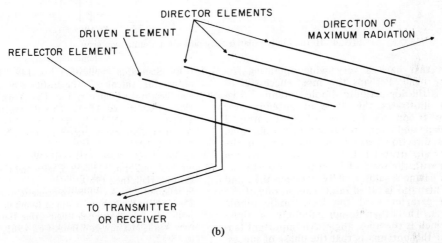

(b)

FIG. 2. Examples of directive antennas: (a) Rhombic antenna. (b) Yagi antenna.

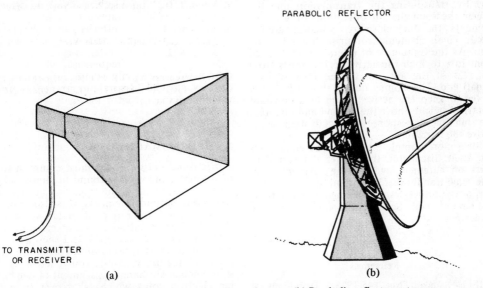

(a)   (b)

FIG. 3. Microwave-type antennas: (a) Horn antenna. (b) Parabolic-reflector antenna.

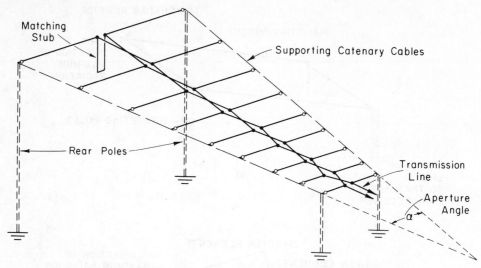

FIG. 4. Horizontally polarized log-periodic antenna over ground.

tennas that have a very wide operating frequency band. Perhaps the most successful of these is the log-periodic dipole antenna.[5] Figure 4 illustrates this type of antenna over ground. It consists of a series of dipoles arrayed in a plane and connected to a transmission line. In the direction away from the terminals the dipoles are arranged in the order of increasing length with the ratio of lengths of adjacent elements having a value usually between 0.75 and 0.9. This ratio is called tau (τ) and is one of the design parameters of the log-periodic dipole antenna. The other design parameter is alpha (α), which is the apex angle. An important feature of this antenna is that the phase of successive dipole elements is reversed. Figure 4 shows this by transposing the transmission line between the elements. In operation, only a few elements, the ones close to resonance, are excited. These elements comprise the active region. As the frequency of operation is changed from low to high the active region shifts from the rear of the antenna to the forward (terminal) end. The sloping design shown in Fig. 4 serves to keep the active region at a constant electrical height above the ground and maintain the maximum response at a constant angle above the horizon.

For a more complete listing of antenna types and their discussion, the reader is referred to texts on antennas such as the "Antenna Engineering Handbook."[6] For additional discussion of the principles underlying antennas, texts by Kraus[7] and Schelkunoff and Friis[8] are suggested.

H. V. COTTONY

References

1. IEEE Standard No. 145-1973, "Definitions of Terms for Antennas," The Institute of Electrical Engineers, Inc., New York.

2. IEEE Standards Publication No. 149 "Test Procedure for Antennas," The Institute of Electrical and Electronics Engineers, Inc., New York, January 1965. (Reaffirmed 1971). This document is also available as ANSI Standard No. C16.11-1971 American National Standard Institute, New York, March 1, 1971.

3. Jordan, E. C., "Electromagnetic Waves and Radiating Systems," pp. 327–328, Englewood Cliffs, N.J., Prentice Hall, Inc., 1950.

4. Schelkunoff, S. A., "Electromagnetic Waves," pp. 25–26, New York, Van Nostrand Reinhold, 1943.

5. Jasik, H., Ed., "Antenna Engineering Handbook," New York, McGraw-Hill Book Co., 1961, pp. 18-1 to 18-32.

6. Jasik, H., op. cit.

7. Kraus, J. D., "Antennas," New York, McGraw-Hill Book Co., 1950.

8. Schelkunoff, S. A., and Friis, H. T., "Antennas, Theory and Practice," New York, John Wiley & Sons, 1952.

Cross-References: ALTERNATING CURRENTS, CIRCUITRY, PROPAGATION OF ELECTROMAGNETIC WAVES, WAVEGUIDES.

ANTIFERROMAGNETISM

Antiferromagnetism is the most common form of magnetic order. It is found in almost all inorganic compounds of the transition metals, rare earths and actinide elements; it is also found in Cr, Mn, Pt, Pd, and rare earth metals and alloys, although the situation is rather more complicated in the case of metals, and the discussion here will be most appropriate to insulators. The principal feature of antiferromagnetism is the spontaneous antiparallel alignment of neighboring electron spins which takes over from the paramagnetic state. The critical temperature of this second-order phase transition is called the

Néel temperature (T_N). The strength of the ordering interaction is characterized by the magnitude of T_N which ranges from below 1 K to above room temperature. A few antiferromagnets whose properties have been studied in detail are listed along with their Néel temperatures: NiO, 520 K; Cr_2O_3, 310 K; MnF_2, 67.4 K; $CuCl_2 \cdot 2H_2O$, 4.3 K.

The ordering interaction between neighboring metal spins in an insulator is called superexchange since it takes place via an intervening anion, O, F, S, etc. (cf. direct exchange between adjacent ions as encountered in FERROMAGNETISM). Superexchange results from charge transfer (see BOND, CHEMICAL), and it is best illustrated by a typical example, say MnO.

Ground and Excited States of $(MnOMn)^{++}$

$$Mn^{++}O^{--}Mn^{++} \qquad Mn^{+(+-)}O^-Mn^{++}$$

ground state   *excited state*

In the ground state, the purely ionic configuration, there is no interaction between metal ions. If, however, one of the two bonding electrons of O^{--} is transferred to the Mn^{++} at left, there will be strong Hund's rule coupling within that ion, and also, the unpaired electron on O^- can couple with the Mn^{++} at right. Since the two bonding electrons on O^{--} have opposite spins, the overall interaction will appear as antiparallel exchange coupling between the two Mn ions.

As with ferromagnetism, the magnetic properties of the exchange interaction can be described by assuming an energy in the form

$$\mathcal{H} = \sum J_{ij} S_i \cdot S_j$$

where S_i and S_j are the spin angular momentum vectors of a pair of ions. The dominant exchange constant is between near-neighbor pairs and is negative in sign, so that antiparallel arrangement results. The magnetic structure of an antiferromagnet can be decomposed into two interpenetrating sublattices having oppositely directed magnetizations, M^+ and M^-. The exchange interaction can then be simply represented in terms of the sublattice magnetizations by defining an exchange field proportional to the sublattice magnetization and acting on one sublattice in a direction opposite that of the other:

$$H_E^{\pm} = -\lambda M^{\mp}$$

The exchange parameter λ is nearly temperature independent, and the sublattice magnetization grows from zero at T_N to 100 percent aligned at low temperatures in exactly the same way that the saturation magnetization of a ferromagnet behaves below T_c. Also like ferromagnetism, spin wave theory describes low-lying fluctuations from alignment.

While the exchange interaction produces antiparallel alignment of the spins, their direction with respect to the crystalline axes is a consequence of the magnetic anisotropy, the energetic

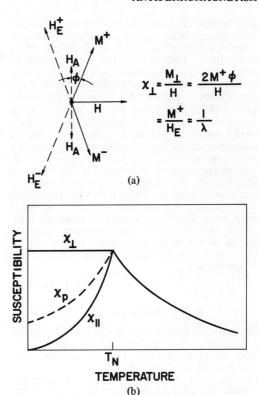

$$\chi_\perp = \frac{M_\perp}{H} = \frac{2M^+\phi}{H}$$
$$= \frac{M^+}{H_E} = \frac{1}{\lambda}$$

(a)

(b)

FIG. 1. (a) The vector model of a simple antiferromagnet is used to calculate the susceptibility to an applied field perpendicular to the easy axis. (b) The susceptibility of a typical antiferromagnet. χ_p is the spherical average of the parallel and perpendicular susceptibilities that is observed in a powder specimen.

inequivalence of direction. There are three origins of anisotropy: (1) dipole-dipole interaction among the array of atomic moments which gives anisotropy in all but cubic symmetry; (2) Stark-effect interaction of each single ion with the local crystalline electric fields; and (3) anisotropic exchange, a result of spin-orbit coupling and isotropic superexchange between excited orbital states. The latter two mechanisms are important for non-S-state ions, especially in crystals of low symmetry. The anisotropy energy, $K(\alpha, \beta, \gamma)$, is expressed as a function of the direction cosines of the sublattice magnetizations. When the sublattice is close to the equilibrium direction, called the easy axis, an effective field along the easy axis called the anisotropy field, $H_A^\pm$, is defined in such a way as to produce the appropriate restoring torque on $M^\pm$ for small deviations from the easy axis.

The vector model, which uses exchange and anisotropy fields, is very useful in explaining the major experimental features of antiferromagnetism. It is used in Fig. 1(a) to calculate the perpendicular static susceptibility of a typical antiferromagnet, which is shown in Fig. 1(b). At absolute zero, the susceptibility parallel to the easy axis is zero, since no spin is able to turn

over against the exchange field; thermal fluctuations permit an increasing susceptibility with increasing temperature. The dynamic susceptibility may also be derived from the vector model by writing the Bloch equations for both sublattices, including the approximate effective fields. Antiferromagnetic resonance occurs at a frequency $\omega \cong \gamma\sqrt{2H_E H_A}$ where γ is the electron gyromagnetic ratio, 2.8 Mc/oersted. Antiferromagnetic resonance has been observed in several materials, often being found at submillimeter wavelengths. In addition to static susceptibility and antiferromagnetic resonance, the principal experiments in antiferromagnetism have been neutron diffraction, which yields the spin structure and sublattice magnetization and sometimes even more details, and nuclear magnetic resonance, which yields high-precision measurements of the sublattice magnetization and insight into the details of charge distributions around ions.

DALE T. TEANEY

References

Nagamiya, T., Yosida, K., and Kubo, R., "Antiferromagnetism," in *Advan. Phys.*, **4**, 1 (1955).

Rado, G. T., and Suhl, H., Eds., "Magnetism," New York, Academic Press, 1963.

Gray, D. E., Ed., "American Institute of Physics Handbook," Third Edition, New York, McGraw-Hill, 1972.

Cross-references: BOND, CHEMICAL; FERRIMAGNETISM; FERROMAGNETISM; MAGNETISM; MAGNETOMETRY; PARAMAGNETISM.

ANTIPARTICLES

One of the great discoveries of modern physics is that for every type of elementary entity of matter and radiation—"particle"—there exists a corresponding conjugate type of entity—"antiparticle." In the antiparticle certain of the particle-defining properties are identical—"conjugation-invariant"—and others—"conjugation-reversing"—are reversed in sign. The reversed sign in a conjugation-reversing property allows one to maintain a conservation law for that property in the dramatic processes of *pair creation* and *pair annihilation* in which an antiparticle is observed to appear and disappear together with the particle to which it is conjugate. In those cases where all the conjugation-reversing properties occur with zero values, the antiparticle is identical with the particle. The progressive recognition of the existence of antiparticles was initiated by Dirac's relativistic anti-electron theory in 1931, and by Anderson's independent experimental discovery of the anti-electron (positron) in 1932.

A simple descriptive and inductive introduction to the fact of existence of antiparticles, and conceptualizations of it, is given in the article entitled ANTIPARTICLES in the first edition of this encyclopedia, and in the articles in the present edition on FIELD THEORY and ELEMENTARY PARTICLES. An enumeration of known particles and antiparticles up to 1972 will be found in the latter. Here we attempt to convey the most general theoretical setting in which the existence of antiparticles, and symmetry of conjugation between particles and antiparticles, may be established. At first a brief overview will be given and then a more detailed systematic discussion. Some of the technical terms used are defined in the sequel.

A major classification of all particle types is according to their statistics or "social behavior." This is based on symmetry or antisymmetry of the mathematical function describing an identical multiparticle state (i.e., a state with two or more particles of the same kind) under interchange in any pair. Those particle types for which there is symmetry under intrapair exchange are *bosons;* those for which there is antisymmetry are *fermions.*

Cutting across the boson-fermion classification of particle types according to their statistical behavior are other classifications based on the four fundamental physical interactions found in nature. These four—hadronic, electromagnetic, weak, and gravitational—are distinguished by markedly different intrinsic strengths (coupling constants), roughly in the ratio $1:10^{-2}:10^{-14}:10^{-39}$, as well as different symmetries; of the four fundamental interactions, only the first three have hitherto played an important role in quantum particle physics. Particles subject to hadronic interactions are called *hadrons* (the photon is a borderline case); all others are called *leptons*. Fermionic hadrons are called *baryons;* all other hadrons are *mesons*. It is found that baryons all carry a nonvanishing integral *baric charge B* which—like electric charge Q, from which it is quite distinct—is *absolutely conserved*, that is, *in all reactions the total baric charge of the component entities before a reaction equals the total baric charge of the products of the reaction*. At both ends of the reaction the total baric charge is computed by simple addition. The baric charge of all mesons (bosonic hadrons) is zero; likewise for all leptons. The leptons in turn display what seems to be (not quite as certainly as in the case of baric charge) conserved charges. There appear to be two types, mu-leptic charge (for muon and its neutrino) and e-leptic charge (for electron and its neutrino). Table 1 diagrams these classifications.

As we have already indicated, it is one of the great theoretical and empirical discoveries of modern physics that there is a general *duality* in nature in that to every particle type there exists a mutually annihilating "antiparticle" type with certain *exactly* identical and certain other *exactly* reversed defining properties. The exact duality of particle and antiparticle serves to classify the two sets, that of exactly identical and that of exactly reversing properties. Among

TABLE 1

Classification of Particle Types According to Symmetry
Under Permutation of Identical Particles (Statistics)

		BOSONS	FERMIONS
Classification of Particle Types According to Participation or Nonparticipation in Hadronic Interactions	**HADRONS** — Baric Charge 0	Mesons	
	HADRONS — Baric Charge ≠ 0		Baryons (nucleons, hyperons, baryon resonances, ...)
		Photon	
	LEPTONS — Leptic Charge 0	Weak-Interaction Boson (?)	
	LEPTONS — Leptic Charge ≠ 0		Mu-Leptons (muons and mu-neutrinos) e-Leptons (electrons and e-neutrinos)
		Graviton (?)	

the exactly identical properties are the mass and spin, and among the exactly reversing properties are all the fundamental charges. The members of both sets will be called *type-observables* and much of the following discussion will be concerned with specifying them.

Both sets of type-observables are associated with exact symmetries of the particle types and their interactions. What a "symmetry," or "symmetry operator," is will be defined more precisely later; here we shall designate the aspects of nature to which it applies, and indicate the meaning of the symmetry concept, by the following statement: Nature lends itself to a classification into two kinds of aspects, that of *systems* and that of *natural processes*. A natural process (e.g., motion in an electromagnetic field) is generally considered to be a more fundamental feature than a particular system (e.g., the earth) since the process is taken to correspond with a *law of nature* whereas a particular system corresponds to the more special features which we label *side conditions*. (There is a blurring of the distinction in microphysics where the properties—to a certain extent unexplained—of isolated microphysical systems appear to be instances of laws of nature rather than of side conditions; this goes, of course, with the fact that these isolated microphysical systems are found in vast numbers of identical replicas: "elementary particles.") Symmetry operators are applicable to either side conditions or laws of nature or, alternatively, to either systems or natural processes: A symmetry operator of a system or process is a possible change which leaves certain overall relevant characteristics of the system or process unaltered (a possible change is one that can be actually, or in imagination, carried out on the system or process). If we are looking at nature as a whole, and are concerned principally about processes, the relevant characteristics to be preserved are the *dynamics* of transitions between arbitrary initial conditions and the possible final conditions in all *spontaneous natural processes*. In classical physics this dynamics is given by *differential equations* and it is the form of these and certain parameters appearing in the equations which are to be preserved; in the truer-to-nature quantum physics the dynamics may be expressed even more directly by an array (S-matrix) of *transition probabilities* each of which is to be preserved individually. The additional invariant parameters here are such quantities as the mass and spin of the system (see next paragraph).

The symmetry operators which preserve the dynamics are, first of all, those which correspond to the *homogeneity* (invariance under translations) and *isotropy* (invariance under space-space and space-time rotations) of space-time in regions small enough so that the effects of gravitation may be neglected, i.e., over regions small compared with the reciprocal of the local value of the acceleration of gravity—in units in which the speed of light is 1 and all speeds are dimensionless ratios to this speed. (For all moderate gravitational fields these are

very large regions, e.g., for an acceleration equal to the earth's surface gravity the linear dimension of the limiting region is $\approx 10^{18}$ cm ≈ 1 light year.) This set of homogeneity and isotropy operators characterizes the special relativity theory of spacetime and is called the *Poincaré group*. Thus, besides the fundamental conjugation-reversing interaction charges, the principal symmetry-related observables which define particles and antiparticles are those which result from the continuous spacetime symmetries which express homogeneity and isotropy: The invariance of natural evolution processes under an arbitrary spacetime translation (homogeneity) implies existence of conserved four-component energy-momentum $\underset{\sim}{P}$; the invariance under an arbitrary spacetime rotation (isotropy) implies existence of conserved six-component angular momentum $J \sim (\overline{M}, \overline{\pi})$. The conjugation-invariant type-observables here *are mass m* (with which may be associated phenomenologically, as an imaginary part, lifetime τ) and magnitude of *spin*—intrinsic angular momentum—*s*. Both mass *m* and spin-magnitude *s* are spacetime scalars or "invariants," which are algebraic functions of $\underset{\sim}{P}$ and $\underset{\sim}{J}$; by saying that they are invariants, we mean that they are left unchanged by any spacetime translation or rotation. (Actually, as we shall see, it is natural to require that they be invariants—but not necessarily functions—of *every symmetry operation*.) Because two translations *commute* (give the same result if performed in alternate order) there is no theoretical restriction on the spectrum—possible values—of the mass, though empirically such restrictions exist. Because rotations are noncommuting in characteristic manner, the theoretically allowed values of spin are integral or half-integral multiples of an elementary unit, as observed. In short, the theory of (linear operator) representations of the relativity symmetry group (Poincaré group) prescribes clearly the *existence* of the particle-characterizing properties of spin and mass but only partially explains their *values:* (1) The specific *range* of observed spin values (all half-integral or integral multiples of a fundamental unit) is fully explained; the *allocations* to specific types of particles are partly explained by the general spin-statistics theorem (see following). (2) The specific range of observed masses is not fundamentally interpreted; however, a partial interpretation for the *mass differences* among the strongly interacting particles in a multiplet and supermultiplet in terms of an *approximate algebraic internal symmetry group*, SU_3, does exist.

The occurrence of the multiplicity or degeneracy of particle types with the same conjugation-invariant properties (like mass and spin) but opposite conjugation-reversing properties (like electric and baric charge) has been much discussed. In general each member of the double is called the "antiparticle" of the other, and the basic fact that all particle types may be ranged in doubles (allowing for cases of identity between particle and antiparticle types) may be called the *"antiparticle existence principle."* Later we shall discuss the derivation of this principle as a theorem in the context of other more general principles. We shall review the general basis that has been proposed for it in quantum field theory—which adds the principle of *locality* to general algebraic quantum theory—and in *S*-matrix theory—which is a stripped-down and occasionally extrapolated version of quantum field theory.

The validity of the antiparticle principle or theorem means that there exists an operator $\hat{\Theta}$ which divides all particle type-observables into two sets and thereby ranges existing particle and antiparticle types in one-to-one correspondence. We call this operator *particle conjugation* and we may restate the antiparticle existence principle: *There exists a particle conjugation operator* $\hat{\Theta}$, *and a division of symmetry-related observables ("type-observables") in two sets, such that* $\hat{\Theta}$ *acting on the type-observables of any existing elementary entity of matter and radiation—"particle"—gives the type-observables for an existing conjugate entity—"antiparticle" —with the first set of observables identical— "conjugation-invariant"—and second set reversed—"conjugation-reversing"—in sign. Further,* $\hat{\Theta}$ *is an "involution": acting on the type-observables of antiparticles it restores the values for the corresponding particles. Thus the operator* $\hat{\Theta}$ *and the identity, together, make up a two-member "particle-conjugation group," with the conjugation-invariant and conjugation-reversing type-observables belonging respectively to the even and odd irreducible representations of the group.*

What "acting on" an observable means formally will be defined later.

It is to be emphasized that the *exact doubling*, and no more than doubling, as between particle and antiparticle types, is in contrast to the approximate higher multiplicities found in nature. Such are the pion triplet and N* quadruplet of electric charge values, which themselves fit into the larger multiplicities of the meson charge-hypercharge octet and the baryon charge-hypercharge decuplet; these are ascribed to representations of higher algebraic *groups of approximate symmetry*, which will be discussed at a later point.

The conjugation exists not only for free particles and antiparticles but also for *interacting* systems of particles and antiparticles. This larger content of the antiparticle existence principle may be stated as follows: *The conjugation* $\hat{\Theta}$ *acting on any type-observable of any possible system of particles and antiparticles gives the observable of a corresponding possible system of antiparticles and particles.*

Again, in the following we shall discuss the derivation of this extended principle as a theorem—in the usual interpretation of $\hat{\Theta}$ known

as the "C$\mathscr{P}$T theorem"—in quantum field theory and S-matrix theory.

Besides the antiparticle *existence* principle there appears to be another principle relating to the *uniqueness* of particle-antiparticle conjugates which, as far as we know, has not been emphasized in the literature. This may be called *the principle of unique superselective conjugation*. We now describe it.

Among the type-observables—the basic observable properties used to define particle types—it is an empirical fact that there are some which are *simultaneously sharply measurable with all other observables*, and yet are not trivial "constant observables"—they are not trivial in that they exhibit different values for different systems. These "superselection observables" which we discuss in detail later are principally the "*superselection charges*" baric B, electric Q, mu-leptic L and electron-leptic ℓ (the latter two are included with some reservations in that their empirical basis is not as firm as that for B and Q), B, Q, and (L, ℓ) are related respectively to the hadronic, electromagnetic, and weak interactions. Besides these, by virtue of the Poincaré-group spacetime symmetry, there exists another superselection observable; this is the *valence* index $(-1)^{2s_3}$ [for massless particles $(-1)^{2\lambda}$] defined by the *observable component* s_3 of spin [or, for massless particles, the *helicity* λ] defined in the following. The empirical *evidence* for the superselection nature of all these quantities is the total absence of interference terms between systems with different values of any of the charges or of the valence index. (The superselection of the valence index can be correlated theoretically with the fact that the continuous mathematical function describing half-integral spin [helicity] particles requires *two* whole rotations to repeat, in contrast with the continuous function describing integral spin [helicity] particles, which is periodic with respect to a single whole rotation about a point; thus *no coherent linear combination* of the two mathematical functions—i.e., with a definite complex-number phase of one function with respect to the other—is consistent, and physically this means: *no interference phenomena*.)

Besides spin and mass, the numerical values of all the "*superselectables*" (superselection observables) are the principal quantities needed to specify a particle type and to distinguish antiparticle from particle. Under conjugation the valence index remains unaltered: The antiparticle of an integral (half-integral) spin particle also has integral (half-integral) spin. That this must be so is a clear consequence of the fact that s_3 or λ remains integral or half-integral under conjugation; even with s_3 or λ reversed in sign, $(-1)^{2s_3}$ or $(-1)^{2\lambda}$ remains unchanged. By contrast, under conjugation the superselective charges are all reversed. Except in those "totally neutral" cases where these charge values are all zero, the particle type can be distinguished uniquely, under all circumstances,

from its antiparticle type by a reversal of sign in all charge values. How is it that when more than one charge occurs with a nonzero value, they all reverse *together* for the antiparticle type? Thus, for example, there is a unique antiproton, negative electrically ($Q = -1$) and with negative baric number ($B = -1$); there does not exist a negative baryon ($Q = -1$, $B = +1$) or a positive antibaryon with protonic mass and spin. The striking general fact that there is exact doubling—with whatever occurring nonzero B, Q, L or ℓ, and λ reversing simultaneously—seems to be of special significance.

In our discussion we asserted that the spin [helicity], and therefore the valence, remains unchanged under conjugation while the superselective charges undergo the required reversal. A priori there were two possibilities, of which this was one. The other would have been that there exist mutually annihilating particle–antiparticle conjugates which have the spin (helicity) integral for one and half-integral for the other; the two members of such a doublet would exhibit the same, or equal opposite, baric, electric, or leptic charge but opposite valence. Because of conservation of angular momentum, upon annihilation an odd number of half-integral spin particles would appear. Such a situation seems to be in marked contrast to what we observe in nature where, for example, any antimeson and its meson (both hadrons with zero baric charge) have the same integral spin, whereas an antibaryon and its baryon have the same half-integral spin.

The principle involved may be stated as follows: *For reasons as yet unknown, there exist the three fundamental quantum-relevant interactions: hadronic, electromagnetic, weak, with associated superselective charges: baric B, electric Q, mu-leptic L, and e-leptic ℓ. The principle of unique superselective conjugation—an empirically verifiable (or, in principle refutable) assertion—states: The multiplication of particle types by reversals of sign of superselective charges is an exact doubling; i.e., there is a simultaneous reversal of sign of all superselective charges, whereas the type-observables associated with the Poincaré group—mass, spin, and valence—remain unchanged. This allows us to speak of a "unique" antiparticle to every particle. Alternatively described: The particle conjugation operator $\hat{\Theta}$ is unique and, together with the identity operator, defines a unique particle conjugation group such that all superselective charges belong to its odd representation.* Only the situation we have described under the heading of the "principle of unique superselective conjugation" appears to occur in nature. The behavior of the valence can be accounted for from the fact that the conjugation is a symmetry operation, and all symmetry operations leave Poincaré-group type-observables unchanged.

The uniqueness of conjugation—the simultaneous reversal of sign of all the superselective charges—requires a more subtle explanation. It is customary to interpret the rigorous conjugation

operator to be what is commonly called $C\mathcal{P}T$; here C is the electric charge-conjugation operator found to be an exact symmetry in quantum electrodynamics, as are also $\mathcal{P}$ the parity or space reflection operator, and T "time-inversion" (actually "motion reversal") which unlike the first two is an *antilinear* operator (defined formally in the following). By taking the product only of the first two, one defines a linear operator Θ' commonly known as $C\mathcal{P}$ (it has also been called "coparity" by the writer). To our present knowledge Θ' is an exact symmetry for all processes with the sole exception of the weak decays of a single particle—the kaon; in these decays invariance under Θ' appears to be broken at the level $\sim 10^{-3}$ [the number 10^{-3} refers to the ratio: Rate $(K^0{}_L \rightarrow 2\pi)/$Rate $(K^0{}_L \rightarrow 3\pi)$].

Following the survey here, and an introductory theoretical orientation, we propose a reason why the principle of unique superselective coniugation must hold: If the universal conjugation operator can be identified with Θ — a symmetry which though nonobservable is linear—and we also assume the von Neumann property of the algebra of all observables, then the principle follows. In connection with this we also suggest a possible (radical) explanation for the apparent violation of Θ' which has been such a riddle for the last eight years. If this explanation should prove tenable, it may then be possible to regard Θ' as the true universally invariant "physical parity" operator, interpreting it as the additional operator to be adjoined to the proper Poincaré group to get it extended by discrete reflections. In the standard interpretation of the conjugation,

$$\hat{\Theta} = C\mathcal{P}T \equiv \Theta$$

all the homogeneity operators, energy-momentum $\underset{\sim}{P}$, are conjugation-invariant and all the isotropy operators, space-space and space-time angular momentum $\underset{\sim}{J}$, are conjugation-reversing and so likewise is the (related) observable component s_3 of the spin. These quantities are not type-observables but rather "state-observables" and we shall discuss them in the following. Their behavior under conjugation is not so clearly indicated empirically as that of the type-observables. For example, with Θ' as a conjugation operator, the $\vec{P}$ components, rather than the $\underset{\sim}{M}$ components, are conjugation-reversing.

Following the discussion of Θ' we give an account of some of the conventional formalism which has been successful in deriving the antiparticle existence principle and the conjugation principle (Θ interpreted as $C\mathcal{P}T$) as theorems in a general context of relativistic quantum theory. There then follows a brief discussion of the special and more stringent form which the general conjugation operator takes for the basic interactions: By combining Θ with parity $\mathcal{P}$ and time-inversion T, or Θ' with $\mathcal{P}$, one defines the operator $\Theta\mathcal{P}T \equiv \Theta'\mathcal{P} \equiv C$, known traditionally as "charge conjugation," which is a kind of

"purely internal and unitary conjugation operator." Except for weak-interaction systems and processes, it is again a symmetry.

To understand all this in detail it is necessary first to clarify what we mean by "particles." The fundamental entities of matter and radiation constituting the physical world are associated with observables which are: (I) *quantum-mechanical*; (II) *symmetry-governed*; (III) *invariant* or *covariant* under the governing symmetry. (I) By the quantum-mechanical aspect we mean that a key role is played by probabilistic—more explicitly: *statistically deterministic*—concepts rather than detailed deterministic concepts as in classical physics. This is because of the fundamental fact of nature that any two observables A and B are *not necessarily compatible*, i.e., starting in a given situation and *measuring* the two observables *in alternation*, they do not each repeat their original measure values; instead, the measurements give for each a distribution of *measure-value probabilities* characteristic for that observable when preceded by a measurement of the other. (II) By the symmetry-governing aspect we mean that it is of central importance to classify observables according to their behavior under physically relevant *groups of symmetries*; each individual symmetry is by definition a transformation ("change") which (a) leaves measure-value *probabilities unchanged*, (b) is evolution-independent, and (c) leaves the spacetime type-observables, mass, spin, and valence, unchanged. (III) By the invariance-covariance aspect we mean that among all possible observables—and *relative to a given degree of generality of observation procedures*—there is a division into two classes—the type-observables which are *invariant* with respect to the groups of symmetries, i.e., go into themselves when transformed by any symmetry, and the state-observables which are *covariant*, i.e., mix nontrivially with other members of a set of observables when transformed.

A more explicit discussion follows:

(I) The modern algebraic version of the quantum-mechanical concepts is streamlined in comparison with the earlier formulations in that the concept of a given state space has receded to the background; with the greater economy and generality of algebraic quantum theory, many results may be demonstrated more elegantly.

(Ia) We consider all directly or indirectly measurable properties which we call *observables* A. The observables constitute an algebra with a certain formal structure. We first remark that observables in quantum mechanics are not all mutually sharp or compatible: In any given situation, keeping all other conditions constant, if we measure an observable A repeatedly we get consistently the same measure value. The same is not necessarily the case if any two observables A and B are measured in alternation repeatedly, keeping all other conditions constant; we find a distribution of values for each rather than a single value. We then say: "A and B are not compatible." Two observables are compatible if in a

given system, prepared appropriately and repeatedly in the same way, each observable always exhibits one characteristic definite measure number ("quantum number," "eigenvalue") upon consecutive repeated measurements appropriate to each observable in either order. Constant observables, i.e., those which exhibit only one measure value under *all* circumstances with *all* systems (multiples of the "identity"), are of course compatible with all others. If there is also a nonconstant observable–i.e., in experiments with various systems it yields differing measure numbers–which is compatible with all other observables, we call it a *superselection observable*. We shall discuss some examples later, among them electric charge Q.

In the following, let the complex conjugate of a scalar number, e.g., λ, be represented by a superior bar, $\bar{\lambda}$. Consider an infinite-dimensional linear complex vector space $\mathcal{H}$ with an inner product (ϕ, ψ), i.e.,

$$(\phi, \psi + \theta) = (\phi, \psi) + (\phi, \theta)$$

$$(\phi, \lambda\psi) = \lambda(\phi, \psi) \quad (\lambda\phi, \psi) = \bar{\lambda}(\phi, \psi)$$

$$(\phi, \psi) = (\overline{\psi, \phi})$$

for all vectors ϕ and ψ; $\mathcal{H}$ is assumed complete in the norm $\| \phi \|$ defined by $| \phi, \phi |^{1/2} \equiv \| \phi \|$, and has a countable basis (every Cauchy sequence of vectors has a limit vector in the space and a complete orthonormal basis can be introduced), i.e., $\mathcal{H}$ is a Hilbert space. The unit vectors of physical interest are only those lying in certain subspaces of $\mathcal{H}$ defined by certain values of the superselectables. These unit vectors, up to an arbitrary phase factor, represent states. Each observable is represented formally by a linear *self-adjoint operator* or "matrix" A acting on the vectors of $\mathcal{H}$. The eigenvalue λ of A for an eigenstate ϕ, i.e., such that $A\phi = \lambda\phi$, is the measure value found for the observable corresponding to A when measured in the state ϕ. The role of self-adjointness is to ensure that all such eigenvalues are bounded and real. What "self-adjoint" means formally and what further properties are to be expected of A is clear from the following discussion.

Besides their action on the vectors of $\mathcal{H}$, one also has the effect of one operator in $\mathcal{H}$ acting on another to give a resultant operator, and in the case of the operators representing two observables, this product of operators represents the successive measurement of the two observables. Two compatible observables are then represented by two commuting operators corresponding to the fact that the two successive measurements give the same result in either order. For brevity the operator representing an observable will also be called an observable. A general operator A is said to be *bounded* or to have a *norm* if there exists a positive number b such that

$$\| A\phi \| \leq b \| \phi \|. \quad \text{all } \phi \text{ in } \mathcal{H}$$

The smallest number b with this property is the *norm of A* and is denoted $\| A \|$. It follows that

$$\| A + B \| \leq \| A \| + \| B \| \quad \| AB \| \leq \| A \| \| B \|$$

$$\| \lambda A \| = | \lambda | \| A \|$$

We now turn to the characterization of the algebra of observables in $\mathcal{H}$. What the algebra formalizes are (1) the property that the numerical values obtained as the result of any measurement are (a) real and (b) bounded; (2) the property that not only is every observable or algebraic function of observables compatible with all superselectables, but that every operator compatible with all superselectables is an observable or algebraic function of observables; in short compatibility with superselectables characterizes the algebra of observables.

The formal structure which satisfies the requirements of these two sets of properties is that of a *von Neumann algebra*, a type of subalgebra $\mathfrak{C} \equiv \{A\}$ of the algebra of all linear bounded (or, equivalently, continuous) operators in $\mathcal{H}$, which subalgebra satisfies two conditions:

1. $\mathfrak{C}$ *IS A C* ALGEBRA.* A C^* algebra involves (a) an *involution* applied to (b) *normed operators.*

a. *Involutive application:* There is a * or adjoint application of $\mathfrak{C}$ into itself such that, for any A in $\mathfrak{C}$, A^*–the adjoint of A–has the properties

$$(A+B)^* = A^* + B^*, \quad (\lambda A)^* = \bar{\lambda}A^*,$$

$$(AB)^* = B^*A^*, \quad A^{**} = A.$$

An operator for which $A^* = A$ is said to be *self-adjoint.*

b. *Normed operators:* In a C^* algebra we have that all operators are normed and that their norms satisfy

$$\|A^*\| = \|A\|, \quad \|A^*A\| = \|A\|^2, \quad \text{(all A)}.$$

An operator H which satisfies the equation between inner products

$$(\psi, H\phi) = (H\psi, \phi)$$

is called hermitian. It is easy to verify that every eigenvalue of a hermitian operator is real:

$$(\phi, H\phi) = (\phi, \lambda\phi) = \lambda(\phi, \phi) = (H\phi, \phi) = \bar{\lambda}(\phi, \phi).$$

Likewise for every operator which is self-adjoint. Every self-adjoint operator is hermitian, but unbounded hermitian operators are not self-adjoint. (It can be proved conversely that a hermitian operator which is everywhere self-adjoint is necessarily bounded.)

2. $\mathfrak{C}$ *IS EQUAL TO ITS DOUBLE-COMMUTANT $\mathfrak{C}''$.* The latter is the set of all linear operators in $\mathcal{H}$ which commute with the first commutant which, in turn, is the set of all linear operators in $\mathcal{H}$ which commute with $\mathfrak{C}$.

The algebra of observables is a von Neumann algebra based on self-adjoint operators where

simultaneous observability of observables means that the representative self-adjoint operators commute. Since $\mathfrak{A}$ contains all observables and algebraic functions of them, condition (2) means here that a linear operator which is a non-member of the observable algebra cannot commute with all members of the commutant $\mathfrak{A}'$ of $\mathfrak{A}$. Since $\mathfrak{A}'$ contains, besides the constant operators, only the set of all superselectables and functions of these, the assumption that $\mathfrak{A}$ is a von Neumann algebra requires such a linear nonmember of the observable algebra not to commute with one or more of these superselectables. We shall see in the sequel that this is one of the key points in rationalizing the occurrence of *unique* superselective conjugation as described above.

The possible measure numbers of the observables are represented by the *spectrum of eigenvalues* a_i of A. For simplicity suppose these spectra are discrete. By the *spectral theorem* of Hilbert space theory, A is a linear combination with real coefficients of bounded self-adjoint operators called *projections* (or "projectors") P^A, having the idempotent property $(P^A)^2 = P^A$, with P^A corresponding to the eigenvalue λ. In particular, for describing various specific conditions in which a given system is prepared, one is interested in the subset $\mathfrak{S}$ of self-adjoint operators with all eigenvalues a_i nonnegative and such that the sum of all a_i—the "trace"—is equal to unity. We call these unit-trace nonnegative self-adjoint operators "density matrices." These are in one-to-one correspondence with the "states," both pure and mixed, of the earlier less-streamlined formulation of quantum mechanics. (It should be noted, however, that the modern C^*-algebraic quantum theory recognizes much more general "states" than can be represented by density matrices.) Even this subset, consisting of nonnegative self-adjoint operators of trace 1, however, is too large for physics when superselection observables are present. $\mathcal{H}$ is then divided up into mutual totally incoherent subspaces corresponding to the different eigenvalues of the superselection observables; the operators representing *physical observables* act only within each subspace but not between them.

(Ib) *Probabilities.* The concept of probability gives physical meaning to the projection $P\chi^A$ corresponding to an eigenvalue λ. Suppose a system is prepared repeatedly in the same manner, so that a given density matrix M describes the state of the system, and we measure the observable A each time. On the one hand, the occurrence frequency or *probability measure* for the eigenvalue λ of A in the state M is $|\dim P\chi^A| a_\lambda$ where a_λ is the coefficient of $P\chi^A$ in the spectral-theoretic direct sum expansion of M—and this probability measure is given by Trace $(MP\chi^A)$. On the other hand, the eigenvalue λ itself occurs as the coefficient of $P\chi^A$ in the expansion of A. Thus if—having prepared the system each time in the same way—we repeatedly measure the observable A, the expectation value of A over a large number of similar trials is Trace (MA).

(II) *Symmetries.* A symmetry is a mapping of the set $\mathfrak{S}$ of all density matrices onto $\mathfrak{S}$ which
  (a) preserves probabilities,
  (b) is evolution-independent,
  (c) leaves mass, spin, and valence index invariant.
A symmetry may or may not also be an observable.

(IIa) Just as in the case of complex numbers in the complex plane, each of the operators in state space may be viewed in an active role as operating on other objects or in a passive role as one of the objects being operated on. A particular kind of operation on an operator A by another operator G is called "transformation of A by G" or a similarity mapping of A by G: GAG^{-1}. (This gives the operator in the G-transformed state space which corresponds to A in the original space, i.e., it accomplishes the corresponding operation upon corresponding states.) If under transformation by G, A goes into itself: $GAG^{-1} = A$, then A is said to be *invariant under* G; more generally, if for each member of a set $\{A_i\}$, GA_iG^{-1} gives a member $A_i' = A_i$ of the set, A_i and all its partners in $\{A_i\}$ are said to be *covariant under* G. If the entire set $\mathfrak{A}$ of all observables is transformed onto itself by G, then we say G performs a similarity mapping of $\mathfrak{A}$.

Condition (IIa) says that a symmetry is a probability-conserving similarity mapping of $\mathfrak{S}$. Probabilities are given by the coefficients in the "convex" (i.e., with real positive coefficients) linear combinations into which density matrices can be decomposed according to the spectral theorem. Thus the preservation of probabilities is equivalent to the preservation of convex linear combinations or projectors. There are two kinds of operators which, acting as transforming operators, preserve convex linear combinations of projectors.

1. A *unitary* operator U is *linear*

$$U(\alpha\phi + \beta\psi) = \alpha U\phi + \beta U\psi$$

and *isometric*, meaning there is equality in absolute value of both sides of

$$(U\phi, U\psi) = (\phi, \psi).$$

2. An *antiunitary* operator Θ differs only in that it is *antilinear isometric*, i.e.,

$$\Theta(\alpha\phi + \beta\psi) = \bar{\alpha}\Theta\phi + \bar{\beta}\Theta\psi; (\Theta\phi, \Theta\psi) = (\overline{\phi, \psi}).$$

The second condition implies that the antiunitary transform of an operator A is given by

$$A' = (\Theta^{-1} A\Theta)^*, \text{ and therefore } (AB)' = B'A',$$

or there is a reversal of order of operator products if Θ is antiunitary.

It is clear that the transformation $\hat{\Theta}A\hat{\Theta}^{-1}$, where $\hat{\Theta}$ is a unitary or antiunitary operator, preserves convex linear combinations of observables. When we limit A to the subalgebra $\mathfrak{S}$ of all density matrices in $\mathfrak{A}$, the converse is also true. By the general Wigner-Kadison theo-

rem (Wigner, 1931–1959; Bargmann, 1964; Kadison, 1951) every convex combination-preserving one-to-one map of $\mathcal{S}$ on $\mathcal{S}$ is either unitary or antiunitary. Moreover this mapping operator is unique up to a phase factor. (Wigner's formulation of the theorem was in terms of preservation of absolute scalar products of states rather than of convex linear combinations of density matrices).

We should qualify that, in the presence of superselectables, the symmetry mapping may be from a subalgebra $\mathcal{S}_1$ of density matrices onto some other coherent subalgebra $\mathcal{S}_2$ isomorphic with $\mathcal{S}_1$, but labeled by different values for the superselective observables. This is the case when the symmetry operator Θ' is not a member of the observable algebra. If, in addition, Θ' is linear, we can draw an important conclusion. As we have already emphasized, in this case—because the algebra of observables is a von Neumann algebra—the linear nonobservable symmetry operator Θ' cannot commute with all superselective charges. As the notation has already indicated $CP \equiv \Theta'$ is such an operator; unlike $\Theta \equiv C\mathcal{P}T$, Θ' is linear—$\mathcal{P}$ is linear and C (see end of article), as dictated for instance by quantum electrodynamics, is linear. Also, unlike $\mathcal{P}$ or C separately, Θ' is a symmetry operator in all cases, with the apparent exception of the neutral kaon decays. Further, except in the small subspace of totally neutral particle states, Θ' is not a member of the observable algebra: There is no preparation or measurement procedure, or combination of such procedures, corresponding to turning particles into antiparticles. Thus, overlooking for the moment the difficulty with the neutral kaon decays, Θ' is the natural candidate for a nonobservable linear symmetry operator representing particle conjugation, which cannot commute with all the superselective charges. That Θ' must actually anticommute with the superselective charges, e.g., letting Q be the relevant charge:

$$\Theta'Q = -Q\Theta'$$

follows from the fact that all probabilities, including the square of the expected value of the charge, must be preserved. That this happens simultaneously with all superselective charges (principle of "unique superselective conjugation") becomes evident when we recognize the empirical fact that there exist particle types for each case of only one charge differing from zero—all other charges having zero values:

	B	Q	L	ℓ
baryon, otherwise neutral: Λ^0	1	0	0	0
electrically charged hadron, otherwise neutral: π^+	0	1	0	0
mu-lepton, otherwise neutral: ν_μ	0	0	1	0
e-lepton, otherwise neutral: ν_e	0	0	0	1

Considering each of these systems in turn, we draw the conclusion that each of the superselective charges, when occurring singly, anticom-

mutes with the symmetry operator Θ', so that, for consistency, when several occur together with nonzero values, they must all reverse together. An example is the proton p ($B = 1, Q = 1$) which, under conjugation of the decay $\Lambda^0 \to p^+ + \pi^-$ has to give the unique antiparticle $\bar{p}$ ($B = -1, Q = -1$).

We note that to be able to draw the conclusion that a superselective charge is reversed by a non-observable symmetry—"conjugation"—it was necessary for that superselective charge to occur with an eigenvalue unequal to zero, while all others have zero eigenvalues (this is what we mean by "otherwise neutral"). The argument will, however, not go through if we have not established the conjugation invariance of that one remaining superselective observable, which is not a charge, i.e., the valence $(-1)^{2s_3}$ [or $(-1)^{2\lambda}$ for the massless case]. This conjugation invariance is assured, however, because the valence must always be +1 or −1 depending upon the integer or half-odd integer value of the spin; but, by condition (c), a symmetry leaves the spin and therefore the valence index invariant.

It is striking that the only violations of Θ' which prevent it from being taken as a universal conjugation under which interactions are invariant are in the neutral kaon decays. The neutral kaon case is precisely the one in which there exists no superselective charge which by its reversal defines the difference between particle and antiparticle. Only the approximately conserved "strangeness" or "hypercharge" (see following) is available as a possible charge to discriminate between K and $\bar{K}$. It has been assumed universally that the hypercharge is opposite in K and $\bar{K}$, but from our analysis we see that there is another possibility: The only conjugation operator under which the kaon decays can be invariant, and which distinguishes K from $\bar{K}$, is $C\mathcal{P}T \equiv \Theta$, and this being nonlinear does not imply that the hypercharge of $\bar{K}$ is opposite to that of K. An analysis of the K^0 decay phenomena from this point of view is given by the writer elsewhere.

(IIb) We note with emphasis the importance of condition (IIb). Though every unitary or antiunitary operator preserves probabilities, it is not necessarily a symmetry. The requirement of evolution independence is what brings the enormous number of unitary and antiunitary operators in $\mathcal{H}$ down to the physically significant subset of symmetry operators. Evolution independence may be described as a "generalized time independence." The evolution matrix—known as the "S-operator" or "S-matrix"—is an operator which takes any one of a set of initial asymptotic states to any one of a set of final asymptotic states, where the states are characterized by the values of certain observables and where "initial" and "final" refer to appropriate boundary conditions. The initial and final set can be the same and be a complete set spanning the entire state space. (In the case of the "collision states" appropriate to scattering problems, this condition is known as asymptotic completeness,

and it goes with unitarity, $S^* = S^{-1}$, of the S-matrix). The evolution matrix is a replacement of a "moment-to-moment" time-displacement operator by an overall or global "before-and-after" operator. The need for such a replacement is evident when we reflect on the fact that the passage of "time" is relative to the observer, according to the special relativity principle which governs nature—at least locally. In fundamental processes, only the before-and-after relations described by the S-matrix have an observer-invariant significance, and *the formal expression of the property of evolution independence, which every symmetry G must satisfy may be stated: When the symmetry is performed first and followed by evolution, it gives the same result as when evolution is performed first and then the symmetry.*

For a unitary symmetry U this condition takes the form

$$SU = US$$

which may be read either way as: $SUS^{-1} = U$, "the evolution matrix leaves every unitary symmetry invariant"; or $USU^{-1} = S$, "every unitary symmetry leaves the evolution matrix invariant."

For an antiunitary symmetry Θ, because initial and final states are interchanged under the action of Θ, the evolution-independence condition has to be stated as

$$S\Theta = \Theta S^*$$

where S^*, the adjoint of S, takes final to initial states; this equation is easily checked by letting the right and left hand sides operate respectively on a final state f. The results of the sequence of operations on the right and left can be symbolized as follows (primes indicate Θ-transformed states and f indicates the result of S operating on i):

$$(f' \leftarrow i', i' \leftarrow f) = (f' \leftarrow i, i \leftarrow f).$$

The relation for S and Θ may then be rewritten

$$S^* = \Theta^{-1} S \Theta$$

and, referring back to the expression given earlier for the antiunitary transform of an operator, we see that, even though it is not a simple similarity invariance, this relation can be expressed by a statement parallel to that for the unitary case: "every antiunitary symmetry leaves the evolution matrix invariant." It is clear that for finding the S-matrix, which is central in elucidating fundamental processes, the knowledge of its symmetries is invaluable.

The symmetries of any system form one or more groups. In general there are discrete groups of symmetries (e.g., the permutations of identical particles in a multiparticle system), and continuous groups of symmetries. In the latter case the *generators* are of particular importance. Let G be any symmetry operator differing infinitesimally from the identity operator I. Then the "business end" of this operator defines a generator $\mathcal{G}$: $G = I + \epsilon \mathcal{G}$. In this case the transformation by G of any operator A goes—to the first order in ϵ—into A plus the commutator $[\mathcal{G}, A]$ of $\mathcal{G}$ with A:

$$GAG^{-1} \simeq A + \epsilon[\mathcal{G}, A] \qquad [\mathcal{G}, A] \equiv \mathcal{G}A - A\mathcal{G}.$$

The invariance of A under all members of a group $\{G\}$ requires then that the commutator of A with all generators of $\{G\}$ be zero. In particular the S-operator must commute with the generators of any symmetry group.

The S-operator governing the evolution of fundamental processes, is a particular though important case. Its structure, as well as the definition of particle types which undergo the fundamental processes, is elucidated by considering the invariant and covariant bedfellows of the S operator. Quite generally, in its passive role as an operand, any operator will be found to have certain transformation or covariance properties under all the generators of a given group of state space transformations. This characteristic transformation behavior, as well as the relation structure of operators with each other, plays a key role in deciding whether an operator may be interpreted as representing a physical quantity having that transformation behavior. The generators themselves are usually merely covariants of the group, but certain polynomials or functions of them may be invariant; a function of generators which is invariant—i.e., commutes with all generators—is called a "Casimir operator" or "Casimir invariant" of the group.

(IIc) This condition is roughly equivalent to the one otherwise expressed by the statement that a symmetry operation should leave the subspace of one-particle states invariant. We have already seen its usefulness in our argument concerning the invariance of the valence index under conjugation.

(III) As we have already indicated, by the "invariance-covariance" aspect of the fundamental physical entities we mean that among all possible observables there is a (heuristic) division in two classes:

I. A subset which we call "invariant" or "particle type-defining";

II. all other observables which we call "covariant" or "state-defining."

In our formulation both subsets will be characterized by labels associated with symmetry groups. The first set of observables—used to define fundamental *particles*—are certain *external and internal Casimir invariants*, so called because they are associated with external and internal symmetry groups governing the fundamental systems. In contrast the second set of observables—used to characterize the *states* in which fundamental particles are found—are *covariants* of these same external and internal symmetry groups. We shall see how this very valuable distinction is nevertheless relative to

the degree of generality of the phenomena being considered.

The external symmetry group is the *proper spacetime symmetry group*, i.e., the group of all rigid translations and rotations in spacetime (Poincaré group). The covariants here are physical representatives of the four translation generators—the components of the energy-momentum P—and of the six rotation generators— the space-space and space-time components of the angular momentum $J \sim (\vec{M}, \vec{\mathfrak{M}})$. The two principal Casimir invariants here define the principal external properties of elementary particles: Their magnitudes give the numerical values of the first two of these properties, mass m and spin s. These numerical values label the possible "symmetry types" or *irreducible representations* ("reps") of the proper spacetime symmetry group. Later we discuss the external and internal symmetries in detail.

We have discussed the general doubling in Nature of particle types for which the conjugation-invariant observables are identical, whereas the values of all other type-defining observables are exactly opposite for the two members of the double; and we have introduced the mapping operator $\hat{\Theta}$ which acts on observables. Formally, $\hat{\Theta}$ "acting on" an observable means transforming according to $\hat{\Theta}(\ )\hat{\Theta}^{-1}$. The super-selective charges: B, Q, L and ℓ, and λ are included among the type-defining conjugation-reversing observables, and give $-B$, $-Q$, $-L$, $-\ell$, $-\lambda$ under this transformation.

What about the behavior of state-characterizing observables under $\hat{\Theta}$? These also may be sorted out once and for all into two sets, conjugation-invariant and conjugation-reversing. From now on we use the generic symbol Σ to represent all conjugation-invariant observables, and the symbol R to represent all conjugation-reversing observables, whether type or state. Thus, $\hat{\Theta}$ is an operator which maps the subalgebra of symmetry-related observables onto itself according to

$$\hat{\Theta} \Sigma \hat{\Theta}^{-1} = \Sigma \qquad \hat{\Theta} R \hat{\Theta}^{-1} = -R.$$

Closely related to the existence of antiparticles—almost but not quite as firmly established empirically—is the further fundamental fact that not only may all *types* be arranged in matched particle-antiparticle pairs by $\hat{\Theta}$, but also that $\hat{\Theta}$ is *represented in $\mathcal{H}$ by an antiunitary symmetry* Θ. We call this *the conjugation principle*. That $\hat{\Theta}$ should be represented ("implemented") by an *operator* Θ, unitary or antiunitary, in $\mathcal{H}$ is a purely mathematical consequence of $\hat{\Theta}$ mapping onto itself the subalgebra of density matrices (Wigner-Kadison). The nontrivial physical point of the conjugation principle—a key point, commonly referred to as "the $C\mathcal{P}T$ Theorem"—is that Θ is not just an operator but is a *symmetry* operator.

In other words the evolution operator S, and the Poincaré invariants, mass spin, and valance (and therefore the dynamics of all fundamental processes), are invariant under $\hat{\Theta}$, i.e., $\hat{\Theta}$, *which we have defined as a mapping of symmetries on symmetries, itself gives rise to an antiunitary symmetry*. More explicitly, the conjugation principle may be stated: *The conjugation operator $\hat{\Theta}$ is represented in state space $\mathcal{H}$ by* (1) *an evolution-independent mapping Θ of states in $\mathcal{H}$ onto other states in $\mathcal{H}$, such that:* (2) *transition probabilities are preserved, with initial states being mapped on final and final on initial;* and (3) *mass, spin, and valence are preserved.*

$$S\Theta - \Theta S = 0 \qquad\qquad (1)$$

$$(\psi_{\Sigma', R'}, \psi_{\Sigma, R}) \longrightarrow (\Theta\psi_{\Sigma', R'}, \Theta\psi_{\Sigma, R})$$

$$= (\psi_{\Sigma, -R}, \psi_{\Sigma', -R'}) \quad (2)$$

$$\Theta m^2 - m^2\Theta = 0 \qquad \Theta s(s+1) - s(s+1)\Theta = 0 \quad (3)$$

We emphasize that the conjugate of the original initial (final) state plays the role of the final (initial) state in the conjugate process, of which the rate is identical to that of the original process. Again we shall discuss later how the conjugation principle may be derived as a theorem in the context of general theory.

Conjugation-Invariant and Conjugation-Reversing Observables The mass squared is the squared magnitude of the energy-momentum four-vector (Table 2). The spin comes in as follows: In general there is defined a four-component polarization operator W_α made up by the outer product of the linear momentum operators and the angular momentum operators. (The time component $W_0 = \vec{P} \cdot \vec{M}$ is the *longitudinal polarization*.) There are two cases generally recognized to be of physical interest, $m^2 > 0$ and $m^2 = 0$. In the massive case, W_α yields as the measure of its invariant magnitude the spin s according to the formula $W^2 = m^2 s(s+1)$.

By a general spin-statistics theorem of relativistic quantum theory, the spin of a one-boson system is integral and of a one-fermion system half-integral.

In the case of zero-mass particles, W splits into two parts, each consisting of a pair of components. The pair of components perpendicular to the momentum define, by the sum of their squares, the "continuous spin" invariant r^2 where r is a real nonnegative number. The remaining components, longitudinal and time-like, are equal in this case, and they yield another invariant, the projective index $\sigma = 0$ or $\frac{1}{2}$ or valence index $+1$ or -1, which specifies the integral or half-integral character of the forward angular momentum (i.e., the projection along the direction of motion). For $r > 0$ this forward angular momentum takes on an infinite discrete ladder of values, while for $r = 0$ the ladder breaks up into its individual segments (the representation matrix reduces to the di-

TABLE 2. GENEALOGY OF THE EXTERNAL-PROPERTY INVARIANTS
MASS m AND SPIN s OR HELICITY λ

	Energy-Momentum	Total Angular Momentum	Polarization Vector
	Four Components of a Spacetime Four-vector $$P_0, P_1, P_2, P_3$$	Three Space-space Components of a Spacetime Six-vector $J_{23} \equiv M_1\ J_{31} \equiv M_2\ J_{12} \equiv M_3$; and Three Spacetime Components $J_{10} \equiv \mathfrak{M}_1\ J_{20} \equiv \mathfrak{M}_2\ J_{30} \equiv \mathfrak{M}_3$	Four Components of a Spacetime Four-vector (Axial) $W_0 \equiv P_1 J_{23} + P_2 J_{31} + P_3 J_{12}$ $W_1 \equiv P_0 J_{23} + P_2 J_{30} + P_3 J_{02}$ $W_2 \equiv P_0 J_{31} + P_3 J_{10} + P_1 J_{03}$ $W_3 \equiv P_0 J_{12} + P_1 J_{20} + P_2 J_{01}$
Timelike Energy Momentum. Standard form taken when state is limited to the subspace of states in which the center of mass is at rest.	$P_0^2 - \sum_{k=1}^{3} P_k^2 \equiv m^2$ $P_0 = m$ $P_1 = 0$ $P_2 = 0$ $P_3 = 0$	$M_1 = S_1$ $M_2 = S_2$ $M_3 = S_3$	$\sum_{k=1}^{3} W_k^2 - W_0^2 = m^2\, s(s+1)$ $W_0 = 0$ $W_1 = mS_1$ $W_2 = mS_2$ $W_3 = mS_3$
Lightlike Energy Momentum. Standard form taken when state space is limited to the subspace of states in which the momentum is in the x_3 direction.	$m = 0$ $P_0 = p$ $P_1 = 0$ $P_2 = 0$ $P_3 = p$	$M_1 - \mathfrak{M}_2 = T_1$ $M_2 + \mathfrak{M}_1 = T_2$ $M_3 \qquad\ = \mathcal{H}_3$	$\sum_{k=1} W_k^2 - W_0^2 = r^2$ $W_0 = W_3 = \mathrm{p}H_3$ $W_1 = pT_1$ $W_2 = pT_2$ In case $r = 0$ $W_a \equiv \lambda\, P_a$ $\lambda = \underset{\sim}{M} \cdot \underset{\sim}{P}/|\underset{\sim}{P}|$

rect sum of its diagonal entries). In these $r = 0$ cases the forward angular momentum—now an invariant—takes on a unique integral or half-integral value, the helicity, λ, and the valence index ceases to be an independent invariant—just as it happens in the massive case. All these relations and cases are summarized in Table 2.

In nature only cases where the continuous invariant r is equal to zero seem to occur. As we have indicated, the two sets—particle-defining observables and state-defining observables—are associated respectively with two sets of labels of mathematical groups—groups which describe the symmetries of natural systems. We have discussed one of these sets: Each fundamental entity belongs (in its mathematical description) to an irreducible representation—"rep"—of the symmetry groups governing all physical systems, and the type-characterizing observables are associated with the Casimir operators whose eigenvalues are the labels specifying the rep. What are the other labels with which the state-characterizing properties are associated? They are the labels for the *rows* of the reps and do not have the same invariant significance as the rep labels since various basis systems of states may be chosen to span the vector space constituted by each rep. The type-observables have relatively stable values, defining the identity of the particle, so that it may be recognized as the

same at the end as at the beginning of a process; whereas the state observables are more labile, having values which can vary between the beginning and end of the many processes in which the identity—e.g., m and s—of the particle is unaltered. For example, a rep of the Poincaré group comprises a vector space of states, the vector space consisting, e.g., of states of all momenta and longitudinal polarizations associated with a particle of given mass and spin. Alternatively, a basis of angular momentum might be chosen. The state-characterizing observables include then energy-momentum $\underset{\sim}{P}$, and angular momentum $\underset{\sim}{J}$, or $\underset{\sim}{W}$, depending on the basis chosen.

We have in the Poincaré group an example of how the very valuable distinction between particle-defining labels and state-defining labels is relative to the degree of generality of the observations. Suppose that we limit the allowed changes of observation systems (or "frames of reference") to space rotations, so that the external symmetry group reduces to the rotation subgroup of the Poincaré group. Then the fourth component—the energy P_0—of $\underset{\sim}{P}$, which in the full group is merely a covariant, becomes an invariant, $P_0 = (\vec{P}^2 + m^2)^{1/2}$, corresponding to the Casimir operator $\vec{P}^2$ of the space rotation group. This example illustrates the general

proposition that as the scope of observation is increased, it becomes more and more natural to view different particles merely as different states associated with one supersystem.

We turn now to the internal properties of particles. As already remarked, Fermionic hadrons are called *baryons*, bosonic hadrons are called *mesons*; nature permits us to define *baric* charge B equal to ± 1 for the former and 0 for the latter in such a way that the total baric charge is conserved in all processes. For some unknown reason baric charge is related to spin or statistics.

So far only fermionic leptons of two types— electron or e-type and muon or mu-type—are known, but the existence of bosonic leptons involved in weak interactions has been conjectured. Again, in accord with exact conservation in all processes, nature permits us to define: (1) *electron leptic charge* ℓ, equal to ± 1 for electrons and e-neutrinos, and 0 for muons and mu-neutrinos; (2) *mu leptic charge* L, equal to ± 1 for muons and mu-neutrinos, and 0 for electrons and e-neutrinos. (The universality of the muon- and electron-leptic charge labeling— based on the phenomena observed in weak interactions—is not quite certain.)

Intermediate between hadronic and weak interactions in strength is the electromagnetic interaction. Here nature permits the definition of a conserved *electric charge* Q equal to ± 1 and 0 for various particles, hadronic and leptonic, as the case may be.

Another way to regard the existence of these internal charges, in which the aspect of conservation is derivative rather than primary, is in terms of symmetries. In this way too we are led to four independent universally observable internal properties; baric, electric, muon- and electron-leptic charge B, Q, L, and ℓ, defined by symmetries associated with the behavior of particles under the three fundamental quantum-relevant interactions: strong, electromagnetic, weak. Each of the types of charge may be associated with an SU_1 ("special"—i.e., unimodular—"unitary" group on one object), i.e., groups of *evolution-independent* transformations having the form $e^{iB\phi}$, $e^{iQ\phi}$, $e^{iL\phi}$, $e^{i\ell\phi}$, respectively (ϕ is an arbitrary parameter ranging over all elements of each group). In these cases B, Q, L, and ℓ are the sole generators—indeed Casimir operators of their respective SU_1 groups.

With the specification that they are generators of symmetries—i.e., evolution-independent—it comes about that, as in the case of energy-momentum and angular momentum, the sum total value of each of the internal charges is conserved in any process. In the case of mass and spin of a composite system, the addition is vectorial rather than simply algebraic, and in the case of mass, there may also be a contribution due to internal energy changes. In contrast, the charges have values which are simply additive in a composite system. As already mentioned, the sign reversal of the values of the charges for antiparticles is essential to maintaining the conservation laws in the processes of *pair creation* and *pair annihilation* in which antiparticles are observed appearing and disappearing with their conjugate particles. Only those particles for which the values of all charges are zero, e.g., the photon γ, the neutral pion π^0, and the η, ρ, ω, and ϕ mesons are identical with their antiparticles; these are called "self-conjugate particles." Any number of these may occur together with pair creation or annihilation. Examples are

$$e^- + e^+ \to 2\gamma \qquad e^- + e^+ \to 3\gamma$$

depending upon whether the spins of the electrons are antiparallel or parallel.

As indicated earlier there is an external property or type observable, the *parity operator* $\mathcal{P}$ associated with invariance of non-weak evolution processes with respect to the discrete operation of space inversion (reflection). When one extends the proper Poincaré group to include space inversion, the symmetry types and the corresponding states double. Naively one says that $\mathcal{P}^2 = 1$, and that the parity of a one-particle state or one-antiparticle state is +1 or −1 according as the state function is preserved or reversed in sign when the space coordinates upon which the state function depends are all reversed. (Properly speaking the term "parity" as used here means "the eigenvalue of the parity operator when applied to the state," and the state must therefore be an eigenstate of $\mathcal{P}$.) Actually the result of a double inversion can be asserted to equal the identity only up to a phase factor—a complex number of modulus 1, namely $\mathcal{P}^2 = \exp(i2\alpha_R)$, where α_R is some arbitrary phase angle which may be different for the states associated with each superselective family—i.e., for each set of particle types with given values of the charges, electric, baric, muleptic, electron-leptic, and hypercharge Y (see later discussion): $\{Q\ B, L, \ell; Y\} \equiv \{R\}$. Examples of such families are (1) the self-conjugate or totally neutral ($Q = B = L = \ell = 0$) "non-strange" ($Y = 0$) mesons; (2) all the nonstrange mesons of positive electric charge; etc. With $\mathcal{P}^2 = \exp(i2\alpha_R)$ the two possibilities for the effect of $\mathcal{P}$ are multiplication by $\exp(i\alpha_R)$ and $-\exp(i\alpha_R)$. Within any given family, by renormalizing, $\mathcal{P} \to \exp(i\alpha_R)\mathcal{P}$, one can reduce to the two alternatives +1 and −1. See PARITY.

More explicitly, we describe the situation as follows. Within any *superselective sector*, i.e., a superselectively separated subspace of state space, we assume the "principle of maximum coherence" to hold: *any two physical states ϕ and ψ can cohere into a single physical state, with the relative phase angle of ψ with respect to ϕ in the coherent superposition $\phi + \psi$ unambiguously determined.* Observationally the phase angle β appears in the interference term $2 \mid \phi, \psi) \mid \cos \beta$ in the scalar product

$$(\phi + \psi, \phi + \psi) = (\phi, \phi) + (\psi, \psi)$$

$$+ 2 \mid (\phi, \psi) \mid \cos \beta.$$

If, under reflection, ϕ and ψ behave the same ($\phi + \psi \to \phi + \psi$) the interference term remains unchanged, and we say the *relative parity* of ϕ and ψ is $+1$; if they behave oppositely ($\phi + \psi \to \phi - \psi \equiv \beta \to \beta + \pi$) the interference term changes sign, and ϕ and ψ are said to be of relative parity -1. Relative parity, being a special case of relative phase factor, has the transitivity property, i.e.,

$$\mathscr{P}(A \text{ with respect to } B) \times \mathscr{P}(B \text{ with respect to } C)$$

$$= \mathscr{P}(A \text{ with respect to } C).$$

In the coherent superposition case where ψ has relative parity -1 with respect to ϕ, $\phi + \psi$ is not a parity eigenstate though it is a physical state. For simplicity and brevity we shall refer to all physical states with definite charges and Poincaré group indices, which are also parity eigenstates, simply as particles, even though from some points of view they are composite: n-particle states, particle-antiparticle states, etc.

The vacuum state (i.e., with no particles present) has the same values, $\{R\} = 0$, for the superselective charges as the totally neutral particles. Thus the relative parity of any totally neutral particle with respect to the conventionally chosen parity of the vacuum, $\mathscr{P} = +1$, is empirically determined. This is called the *intrinsic parity* of the particle. Because of the extraordinary empirical fact that the set of all fermions is coextensive with that of all leptons or baryons, as exhibited by the equivalence: half integral spin $\rightleftharpoons$ either B or L or $\ell \neq 0$, the totally neutral particles occur only among the bosons and only for these is the intrinsic parity unambiguously determined. Another way of obtaining the same result follows from the fermion side of the above empirical equivalence. The reason why a boson can have an unambiguous parity (relative to the conventionally chosen parity of the vacuum, $\mathscr{P} = +1$) is that the continuous function describing it obeys the "Columbus principle," i.e., that a 360^{δ} movement of the observing apparatus around an axis restores the original description. Because the description of a one-fermion system does not obey this principle, the intrinsic parity of a one-fermion system is not uniquely defined.

A fermion intrinsic parity is, however, often assigned conventionally, as for the nucleon family where it is taken to be $+1$. More generally, as a consequence of the isospin and SU_3 groupings of particle types with respect to hadronic interactions (see later discussion), it is natural to assign those in the SU_3 multiplet the same intrinsic parity. It is important to emphasize however that the choice of relative parity between two superselectively separated particle types (e.g., neutron and proton) is only conventional. This is because any two physical states ϕ and ψ lying in different superselective sectors can not cohere into a physical state, and the behavior of the relative sign of ϕ with respect to ψ under a space inversion cannot be deduced since there is no interference to be observed. It is true however that within each superselective sector a choice, albeit conventional, of the intrinsic parity of one particle, A, determines that of any other particle, B, according to the rule derivable from the transitivity property

(Intrinsic Parity)$_B$

$= $ (Relative Parity)$_{B/A}$ (Intrinsic Parity)$_A$

By its nature as a phase factor—the eigenvalue of a discrete symmetry operation rather than of a generator of a continuous symmetry operation—the parity of a composite system (product state) is the product of the parities of the parts. Thus given the parities of the parts the parity of the composite is determined, but there are cases where the converse is not true: other than in totally neutral cases, particle states are prevented from combining into states (coherent superpositions) with the antiparticle states by the different values—of one or more superselective charges. This has the consequence that the intrinsic parity of the antiparticle with respect to that of the particle is not defined. In the case of a system made up of a particle and its own antiparticle (which is therefore always equivalent to a totally neutral boson and consequently in the same superselective sector as the vacuum) the intrinsic parity of the *pair* is however defined. In the case where the pair consists of a boson and its antiboson the intrinsic parity of the system is $+1$. (If the boson itself is totally neutral then of course it and the antiboson must have the same parity, either $+1$ or -1; but if it is not totally neutral it can be assigned $\mathscr{P} = e^{i\alpha}$, and then the antiboson must be assigned $\mathscr{P} = e^{-i\alpha}$; α can be arbitrary, e.g., $\alpha = \pi/2$ so that boson and antiboson could be assigned opposite parity.) The intrinsic parity of a given fermion-antifermion pair (constituting, therefore, a one-boson system) is, however, always -1. (If the conventional assignment of $\mathscr{P} = +1$ is made for the nucleon, then $\mathscr{P} = -1$ for the antinucleon; but if $\mathscr{P} = e^{i\phi}$ for the nucleon, then $\mathscr{P} = e^{i(\pi-\phi)}$ for the antinucleon—and ϕ can be arbitrary, e.g., $\phi = \pi/2$ so that both nucleon and antinucleon have the same parity, i.)

The general result that $\mathscr{P} = +1$ for a boson particle-antiparticle pair and $\mathscr{P} = -1$ for a fermion particle-antiparticle pair is derivable theoretically by applying the assumption of analyticity, in the sense of complex function theory, to the description of scattering processes. This is done in the manner indicated later, in connection with the derivation of the antiparticle existence theorem, by analytic continuation of the scattering amplitude for the process

$$a + b \to a + c$$

to a region where it corresponds to the process

$$b \to \bar{a} + a + c.$$

It is confirmed observationally by selection rules which hold in various pair annihilation processes.

We also have some observables associated with approximate internal symmetries in processes in which only the strong interactions are important: The hypercharge Y, isospin I, and isoparity G are observables characterizing certain isomultiplets of nearly coincident mass but differing electric charge into which the mesons or baryons group. These isomultiplets are of the internal symmetry group SU_2. The members of each isomultiplet have the same baric charge and differ by consecutive values of the electric charge Q. The hypercharge Y is the sum of the lowest and the highest electric charges in the isomultiplet. The isospin magnitude I is a number which measures the multiplicity of the isomultiplet as $2I + 1$. The full significance of Y comes in a further grouping of these SU_2 isomultiplets into hypermultiplets belonging to the higher symmetry group SU_3 which has been found very successful. The isomultiplets within each hypermultiplet still have the same baric charge B but differ by consecutive values of the hypercharge Y. Further suggested higher infernal symmetries have been found partially successful.

In the hadronically relevant isomultiplets (associated with an SU_2 group) the generator I_3 is an observable which is conjugation-reversing. The hypercharge Y which, under purely hadronic interactions, is a generator of an SU_1 symmetry group, is again a conjugation-reversing observable, i.e., behaves like a "charge." Both of these results are confirmed as follows. There are three generators I_1, I_2, I_3 for the isospin group SU_2. This group has identically the same Lie algebra—and therefore the same theory—as spatial angular momentum. By convention the observable component—represented by a diagonal matrix—is taken to be I_3. The ladder of diagonal elements has of course the three properties found with angular momentum: (1) It is equal-runged; (2) it is symmetrical about zero—thereby specifying integral or half-integral units of isospin as eigenvalues; (3) it is finite, i.e., begins with $(I_3)_{min} = -I$ and ends with $(I_3)_{max} = I$. The operational significance of the observability of I_3, i.e.,

$$I_3 = Q + \text{const}$$

plus the definition of Y as $Q_{max} + Q_{min}$, then leads to the Gell-Mann-Nishijima relation

$$Q = I_3 + Y/2.$$

Clearly, along with Q, I_3 and Y are conjugation-reversing.

The invariant isospin I of an isomultiplet is, like spin s to which it is analogous, conjugation-invariant. Under appropriate conditions there is also an *isoparity* G which, like space parity $\mathcal{P}$, is conjugation-invariant. G is defined unambiguously only for hadronically interacting systems for which $B = Y = 0$ (and of course $L =$

$\ell = 0$), i.e., for hadronic systems which, "neutral" in every other respect, need not be electrically neutral. All such systems can be connected directly or through a sequence of intermediate systems to a basic number of pions; the latter are stable against hadronic decays. The isoparity G equals $+1$ or -1 according to whether the basic number of pions is even or odd. Individual pions then have odd isoparity and, as its name and the rule indicate, isoparity is multiplicative for a composite system. Among mesons, G can be defined only for the $Y = 0$ "nonstrange" isomultiplets for which I is integer because $Q_{max} = -Q_{min} = I$ cannot be half-integral insofar as has been established for any actual particle. (In practice such isomultiplets are either isosinglets or isotriplets since in none of the well established meson systems does I exceed 1.) There are 17 such hadronically unstable mesons for which G is very well known; in every case it is found to be conserved in the purely hadronic decays of these particles. (*Review of Particle Properties*, April 1973). G is violated in other interactions as, for instance, in the decay of the hadronically stable lightest η meson (550 Mev) into three pions by virtual electromagnetic interactions.

In the generalization to SU_3, with the grouping of isomultiplets to hypermultiplets, B remains an invariant while Y which was (a non-Casimir operator) invariant for SU_2 becomes a (covariant) generator. The electric charge Q which was originally the unique generator—and therefore, trivially, the Casimir invariant—of an SU_1 group, and became a displaced generator of the isospin SU_2 group through the Gell-Mann-Nishijima relation, becomes a regular generator in the SU_3 group.

To sum up then, the set of type-defining observables includes (in the massive case) mass m, spin s, parity $\mathcal{P}$ (with certain qualifications in fermion systems), and also electric, baric, muon- and electron-leptic charges (Q, B, L, ℓ) and (with certain qualifications) hypercharge Y, isospin I, isoparity G, and SU_3 rep labels p and q. In the massless cases occurring in nature the type-characterizing observables comprise besides helicity λ, parity $\mathcal{P}$, isoparity G, and muon- and electron-leptic charges L and ℓ (the latter three with qualifications). The values taken by these observables classify all existing entities into particle types.

We turn now to a discussion of proposed theoretical derivations of the antiparticle principle and the conjugation principle from very general theory with a minimum of supplementary features.

Successful theories in physics are often built in stages: (1) a *general theory* with room for further structure (thermodynamics, Maxwell's *E-M* theory without constitutive relations, etc.); (2) more particular theories filling out the structure. The primary general theory of elementary particles and antiparticles is *relativistic general quantum theory*, and the two more particular theories which fill out, in alternative ways, what

is to a large extent the same structure are: (1) *general quantum field theory* and (2) its somewhat stripped-down version known as *S-matrix theory*. (In taking these theories to be adequate we are trusting that the problems of making them applicable universally, i.e., also to infinite range interactions—zero mass quanta—as in electrodynamics, can be resolved by appropriate procedures or reformulations, e.g., algebraic quantum theory. It is to be noted that difficulties associated with the possible occurrence of zero mass particles are common to both the *S*-matrix theory and the field theory.)

The formal ingredients of relativistic general quantum theory, which is the common basis of the two more particular theories, are:

(I) Relativistic elements expressing: (A) continuous *spacetime symmetry or invariance* of natural processes under the Poincaré (inhomogeneous Lorentz) group of translations, rotations, and uniform velocity shifts; (B) operational *possibility of distinguishing before and after* in natural processes (distinction between forward and backward light cones). (C) More specific than any of the preceding postulated elements is the assumption that no zero mass particles occur.

(II) Quantum mechanical elements expressing: (A) the merely *statistical determination* in nature; (B) *the disturbance by the act of observation of physical systems*—which is related to mere statistical determination; (C) within the context of mere statistical determination, the *causal independence* of well separated experiments; (D) *analyticity of the collision or S-matrix elements* in its arguments.

(III) A somewhat more specific quantum mechanical assumption than the above refers to the operational *impossibility of counting, as distinct, particles of the same kind.*

(I) We have already discussed in some detail the manner in which the existence of spacetime symmetry allows us to define particle types and states.

(IIA) This general quantum mechanical principle takes the form of assuming the existence of a Hilbert space of *asymptotically free 1-particle momentum eigenstates*. A scalar product of these states with themselves and with each other is defined. The one-particle states may be added. When added they obey the *superposition principle*: Any linear combination (except for certain superselection restrictions) is itself a state. Conversely any given first state may be considered as a linear combination of a complete set of states built up beginning with any other second state. The probability of finding the second state immediately after establishing the first state is given by the square of the *probability amplitude* which is itself given by the scalar product of the second state with the first.

(IIB) Takes the form of recognizing that arbitrarily chosen observables are not necessarily compatible with each other. A *complete set of compatible observables* (C.S.C.O.) is any set needed to define the states uniquely, and the individual state is labeled by the set of values which the C.S.C.O. takes on for it. The states are represented as rays in a Hilbert space, the observables as linear operators. Compatibility (noncompatibility) of two observables is represented by commutativity (noncommutativity) of the corresponding two operators. In many instances two such operators anticommute, and this is how quantum theory describes the reversals of sign of certain properties under Θ as indicated above. Thus we have

$$\Theta Q + Q \Theta = 0 \quad \text{or} \quad \Theta Q \Theta^{-1} = -Q$$

$$\Theta B + B \Theta = 0 \quad \text{or} \quad \Theta B \Theta^{-1} = -B, \text{ etc.}$$

where the similarity transformation on the left of the second equation on each line represents the effect of conjugation on the corresponding charge operator.

(IIC) Besides the scalar product and the addition of one-particle states, one may also consider taking ordered outer products of one-particle states with the objective of representing multiparticle states. This is straightforward in the quantum field theory. In a somewhat old-fashioned but picturesque manner the quantum field may be described as a linear superposition of creation and annihilation operators. The field with its constituent operators and associated excitation states may be described as somewhat analogous to an idealized piano constructed with an infinitude of key-hammers (creation operators) and individual pedals (destruction operators) associated with each possible tone (excitation state); this tone can be excited to various degrees (corresponding to the number of particles in that state). All nonempty states are produced by the creation operators, acting on the *vacuum state*; the latter corresponds to the totally quiescent piano. In this formalism, in the simple case of noninteraction the basic states are *n-particle states*, n having all possible values. A specific *n*-particle state $|n_1, n_2, \cdots> \equiv |\underline{n}>$ is characterized by the set of *occupation numbers* $n_1, n_2, \cdots (n_1 + n_2 + \cdots = n)$ specifying the numbers of particles having quantum numbers $q_1, q_2, \cdots$. The state $|0, 0, \cdots> = |vac>$ is called the *vacuum state*, and assumption (IC) excluding zero mass particles implies that there is a *mass-gap above the vacuum state*.

In the quantum field theory the assumption that corresponds to causal independence of well separated regions is that of locality, i.e., that field operators at spacelike-separated points commute. This, together with the assumption (IC) that zero mass particles do not occur, suffices to derive the existence and uniqueness of the set of *stationary collision states* in which arbitrary numbers of beams of stable particles collide and produce final stable particles as interaction products. These collision states define

a unique *evolution-governing collision matrix* (*S*-matrix) whose matrix elements are the probability amplitudes for transitions between the asymptotic initial and final states at $t = -\infty$ and $t = +\infty$ (assumption (IB) tells us that we can distinguish between these "in" and "out" states). The collision matrix has the "*cluster decomposition*" or "*connectedness*" *property*; i.e., when particles interact the interaction (amplitude) is a sum of subinteractions (subamplitudes) by clusters, of particles two at a time, three at a time, etc., each cluster accompanied by a remaining set of noninteracting particles. The contribution to the *S*-matrix subamplitude for each noninteracting particle involves a Dirac δ-function expressing the constancy of momentum and energy of that particle, whereas the interacting clusters contribute combinations of amplitudes which are non-δ-functions with momentum-energy variables as arguments.

In the *S*-matrix approach, which seeks to circumvent the assumption of a local field, the existence of the *S*-matrix is postulated directly, with the cluster decomposition property as that one of its properties which expresses the causal independence of well separated experiments. This leads (Froissart and Taylor, 1967) to the representation of multiparticle or collision states by ordered outer products of one-particle states, such that these are given by the standard creation operator formalism of the field theory.

If in addition one more assumption is made: *asymptotic completeness*—that there are no additional states besides those that are superpositions of collision states—the quantum field theory also derives the *unitarity*, $SS^+ = S^+S = 1$, and certain *analyticity properties of the collision matrix*. The unitarity expresses the fact that the total probability summed over all processes is unity—the conservation of probability. Unitarity and analyticity have to be assumed ad hoc in the *S*-matrix approach, as the price of avoiding the locality assumption of the field theory.

The dependent variables of which the *S*-matrix elements are functions are prescribed by the "relativity" or "Lorentz-Poincaré invariance" of the theory (IA). This requires that the laws of nature be invariant under spacetime-interval preserving transformations. Here it means that any *S*-matrix element is a scalar under these transformations, or that the amplitude combinations corresponding to interacting clusters are functions of spacetime-invariant variables only, i.e., scalar products of the four-momenta of the interacting particles (or their sums and differences).

(IID) This assumption is that of *analyticity of the probability amplitudes* as functions of the invariant variables. As we have remarked, it is derivable—in a complicated way—from locality in the field theory, but it has to be introduced ad hoc in the sparser short-circuiting *S*-matrix

approach. The assumption is sometimes called "causality," but it is probably more restrictive mathematically than what is implied by the causality concept.

(III) leads to a condition on the *statistics* associated with a given particle type. *Identical multiparticle states*, i.e., states containing two or more particles of the same kind, occur in nature only with *symmetry or antisymmetry* (of the mathematical function describing the multiparticle state) under interchange in any pair. This symmetry difference gives a major classification of all particle types; this is usually described as a classification according to "statistics" or "social behavior," since those with interchange symmetry—called *bosons*—tend to aggregate in the same momentum state, whereas those with antisymmetry—called *fermions*—tend to exclude each other from the same state.

From these general ingredients, either in the field theory version (Streater and Wightman, 1964; Jost, 1965), or in the stripped-down *S*-matrix version subject to a subtle proviso concerning analytic continuations (Olive, 1964; Lu and Olive, 1966; Froissart and Taylor, 1967), one can derive a number of remarkable general results:

1. *Hermitian analyticity*. Hermitian conjugate amplitudes are associated with the same analytic functions.

2. *Existence of antiparticles*. The argument by traditional field theory is detailed later. The argument as presented by the *S*-matrix protagonists is interesting and worth sketching. It depends on matching singularity structures of different subamplitudes when the cluster-structure is inserted in the unitarity relation $SS^* = 1$. This leads, e.g., to a relation between the amplitude A_{44} for the complete cluster interaction

$$A + B + C + D \rightarrow E + F + G + H$$

and the amplitudes A_{23}, A_{32} for the sequential interactions

$$A + B \rightarrow E + F + J \qquad C + D + J \rightarrow G + H.$$

The bubble diagrams and the equation below express this relation

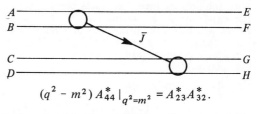

$$(q^2 - m^2)\, A_{44}^* \big|_{q^2 = m^2} = A_{23}^*\, A_{32}^*.$$

Left and right sides of this equation are analytic functions of their variables and one can continue the equation analytically to a different part of the physical region for A_{44}. In the new part of the physical region the continued pole represents the two successive interactions

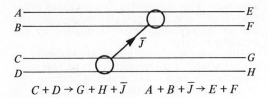

$$C + D \to G + H + \bar{J} \qquad A + B + \bar{J} \to E + F$$

The new particle $\bar{J}$ has the same mass as J but opposite internal charges (since they obey a rule of additivity). Thus the antiparticle principle is proved and becomes the *antiparticle theorem* (provided the analytic continuation brings us back to the "right side" of the physical region singularity of $A_{44}{}^*$).

3. *Crossing.* Since, under analytic continuation, residues also continue (provided there exists a path of analytic continuation in the complete amplitude joining the two points and lying within the mass shell section—sufficient condition) the argument also demonstrates the property known as "crossing," i.e., that the amplitude for a process in which a given initial particle disappears without issue is the same function as for a process, otherwise identical, except that the corresponding antiparticle appears without antecedent:

$$\text{Ampl}\,(A + \cdots + N + J \to A' + \cdots + N')$$

$$\sim \text{Ampl}\,(A + \cdots + N \to \bar{J} + A' + \cdots N').$$

4. *C𝒫T or Conjugation Theorem.* In the S-matrix approach to the $C\mathcal{P}T$ theorem, similar considerations of residues of single particle poles are used as in discussing the crossing theorem. The proviso, made in all the S-matrix arguments, concerning existence of "right paths" joining particle and antiparticle poles are related to the two basic facts used in the field theory proofs of the conjugation theorem:

a) vacuum expectation values of products of field operators are boundary values of analytic functions;

b) the spacetime inversion $x \to -x$ can be connected with the identity transformation through complex Lorentz transformations.

With the help of these two facts one can prove the existence of an antiunitary Θ, acting on fields, which has the properties of a symmetry. For example, for a scalar field $\Phi(x)$ the two basic facts a) and b) lead to the identities (ψ_0 is the vacuum state):

$$[\psi_0, \Phi(x_1) \cdots \Phi(x_n)\,\psi_0]$$

$$= [\psi_0, \Phi(-x_n) \cdots \Phi(-x_1)\psi_0]$$

for the vacuum expectation values of the products of field operators at any number of spacetime points $x_1, \cdots x_n$. Because of the reversal of order of operators, these identities are equivalent to the existence of an antiunitary Θ

satisfying

$$\Theta\Phi(x)\Theta^{-1} = \bar{\Phi}(-x).$$

But then it follows that Θ maps stationary collision in-states onto stationary out-states of the corresponding antiparticles with the same momenta and opposite spin projection.

$$\Theta\psi_{\text{in}}(p_1 \cdots p_k) = \psi_{\text{out}}(p_1' \cdots p_k').$$

The symbol p_j represents the momentum p_j and spin of the jth particle of the colliding beams, and p_j' stands for the same momentum but opposite spin projection for the antiparticle. As an immediate consequence, we have the equation between the S-matrix element for the particle reaction $p_1 \cdots p_k \to \underline{p}_1 \cdots \underline{p}_m$ and the S-matrix element for the antiparticle reaction $\underline{p}_1' \cdots \underline{p}_m' \to p_1' \cdots p_k'$:

$$[\psi_{\text{out}}(\underline{p}_1, \cdots \underline{p}_m), \psi_{\text{in}}(p_1 \cdots p_k)]$$

$$= [\Theta\psi_{\text{out}}(\underline{p}_1 \cdots \underline{p}_m), \Theta\psi_{\text{in}}(p_1 \cdots p_k)]$$

$$= \overline{[\psi_{\text{in}}(\underline{p}_1' \cdots \underline{p}_m'), \psi_{\text{out}}(p_1' \cdots p_k')]}$$

$$= [\psi_{\text{out}}(p_1' \cdots p_k'), \psi_{\text{in}}(\underline{p}_1' \cdots \underline{p}_m')]$$

5. *Spin-statistics theorem.* It is found in nature, so far without any demonstrated exception, that bosons have integral spin and fermions half-integral spin. This is the spin-statistics relation. It has been derived in field theory with various degrees of generality. (See Streater and Wightman, 1964, for a very general proof.) In the S-matrix approach (Lu and Olive, 1966), again provided certain plausible features are contained in the singularity structure, the relation between spin and statistics is established. It is found that connectedness—together with Lorentz invariance, unitarity, and analyticity—implies that the connected parts for processes involving particles with the wrong relation between spin and statistics vanish, so that such particles are unobservable.

Besides the behavior under Θ of the S-matrix and the type- and state-characterizing observables, we may be interested in the behavior under Θ of fields, and interactions between fields, which are also operators in quantum field theory. For all but the weak interactions, an additional symmetry over and above the universal Θ symmetry holds. This is what is traditionally known as "charge conjugation" and denoted by the symbol C. As we have already remarked, it corresponds to $\Theta\mathcal{P}T$ where $\mathcal{P}$ is the (unitary) space reflection operator, and T is the (antiunitary) time-inversion (more properly "motion-reversal") operator. Besides interchanging initial with final states, T reverses the signs of the three space-space components of $\underline{J}$ (the angular momentum $\vec{M}$) and of the three space components of linear momentum $\vec{P}$; $\mathcal{P}$ reverses the

signs of the latter and of the three spacetime components of J, the centroidal moments $\vec{\mathfrak{M}}$, The net result of combining T with Θ then is to undo the antiunitarity, restoring the original order of before and after, and also to undo the conjugations of all external state observables. Thus $\Theta \mathcal{P} T \equiv C$ is a kind of "internal conjugation operator."

C-conjugation ("charge conjugation") plays an important role in the history and elementary discussions of fundamental particles. We here review its traditional treatment in the Lagrangian form of quantum field theory—a theory which was originally inspired by the analysis of oscillations and waves in classical physics where fields are simply numerical functions of space and time. The quantum version of the theory requires that the fields be operators. Also, the theory, necessarily a many-particle theory, is best described at first for the noninteracting case when we can take the basic states to be n-particle states, characterized by the set of *occupation numbers* $n_1, n_2, \cdots (n_1 + n_2 + \cdots = n)$ specifying the numbers of particles having quantum numbers $q_1, q_2, q_3, \cdots$ corresponding to a complete set of commuting observables (C.S.C.O.): $Q_1, Q_2, Q_3, \cdots$. The state $|0,0,0,0, \cdots >$ with all $n_i = 0$ is the *vacuum state*. As in any vector space, there is also the *zero vector* 0. The single-step destruction operator a_α for particles, and creation operator b_α^* for antiparticles associated with the αth quantum number are introduced in the usual way (see FIELD THEORY) such that they satisfy the standard commutation (anticommutation) rules if the particles satisfy Einstein-Bose (Fermi-Dirac) statistics. One then introduces the *field operator*, which is a linear expansion in the a_α and b_α^* (all α), and which formally satisfies certain field equations, the latter usually being chosen on the basis of a classical analogy or on the basis of relativistic covariance and general agreement with experiment. All of the consequences of interest then follow from the definition of the field operator and from that of the C-conjugation operator:

$$Ca_\alpha C^{-1} = \eta_c b_\alpha \qquad Ca_\alpha^* C^{-1} = \overline{\eta}_c \, b_\alpha^*$$
$$Cb_\alpha^* C^{-1} = \eta_c a_\alpha^* \qquad Cb_\alpha C^{-1} = \overline{\eta}_c \, a_\alpha.$$

Here η_c is a phase constant ($|\eta_c| = 1$) which is nonmeasurable and can be chosen +1 by convention. If particle and antiparticle are identical then $b_\alpha = a_\alpha$, and η_c becomes measurable and equal to ± 1, two physically distinct cases.

For a specific theory, particularly if it is given in Lagrangian form in which case each of the symmetry observables is defined by a symmetry operation on the Lagrangian, these observables can be written as bilinear functionals in the field operators.

As an example, we consider the case of a scalar (spin zero) charged field $\Phi(x)$ associated with a mass m, and satisfying the Klein-Gordon equation

$$(\Box + m^2)\,\Phi(x) = 0$$

For the C.S.C.O. we choose the linear momentum and the (not-independent) energy. Denoting the destruction operator for the particle of momentum k and energy $k_0 = \sqrt{\underset{\sim}{k}^2 + m^2}$ by a_k, and the creation operator for the corresponding antiparticle by b_k^*, the field operator is given by

$$\Phi(x) = \frac{1}{\sqrt{2(2\pi)^3}} \int \frac{d^3 k}{k_0} \, (a_k e^{-ikx} + b_k^* e^{ikx})$$

An explicit representation for C is

$$C = \exp\left[\frac{\pi i}{2} \sum_k (a_k^* - \overline{\eta}_c \, b_k^*)(a_k - \eta_c b_k) \right]$$

and for the total energy-momentum operator, obtained for instance from the Lagrangian for the Klein-Gordon equation above, we have

$$P_\mu = \int \frac{d^3 k}{k_0} \, k_\mu (a_k^* a_k + b_k^* b_k)$$

It is now possible by direct calculation to establish whether P_μ (or any other observable) commutes or anticommutes with C. In this way we can derive for all the free physical fields which have been considered applicable to nature, the results stated earlier in this article concerning preservation and reversal of signs of the fundamental quantum numbers.

It is possible in a similar way to examine the validity of invariance under C-conjugation of the *interactions* between fields. For instance, the electromagnetic interaction between the electron-field current j_μ and the photon-field potential A_μ is $j_\mu A_\mu$. The two results found for the separate fields by the methods described in the foregoing.

$$Cj_\mu C^{-1} = -j_\mu \qquad CA_\mu C^{-1} = -A_\mu$$

then guarantee that

$$Cj_\mu A_\mu C^{-1} = j_\mu A_\mu$$

Similarly, C-invariance holds for the accepted forms of strong interactions.

C-invariance *does not hold* for the V-A (polar vector minus axial vector), four-fermion type of weak interaction occurring, e.g., in β-radioactivity. As we have seen, however, for quite general interactions with *proper orthochronous* spacetime symmetry, provided they are *local*, there is automatically invariance under the combined operation $C \mathcal{P} T \equiv \Theta$ ($C \mathcal{P} T$ theorem). "Proper orthochronous" spacetime symmetry of the interactions means that they are invariant under rotations, translations in space and time, and shifts

to uniformly moving frames: "locality," in practice, means that the interactions consist of a linear combination of products of the fields and finite-order derivatives of the fields. Equality of mass and lifetime, antiequality of charge and magnetic moment, and (with certain restrictions) conjugacy of decay schemes for a particle and its antiparticle all follow from $C\mathcal{P}T$ invariance alone. And this rests only on proper spacetime symmetry, general principles of quantum theory, and the locality requirement (or, in the S-matrix rendition, the requirements of connectedness and analyticity).

M. A. MELVIN

References

Dirac, P. A. M., "Quantized Singularities in the Electromagnetic Field," *Proc. Roy. Soc. London, Ser. A*, **133**, 60 (1931).

Wigner, E. P., "Gruppentheorie" (Germany, Frederick Vieweg und Sohn, Braunschweig, 1931, pp. 251–254; "Group Theory," (New York, Academic Press, 1959, pp. 233–236.

Kadison, R., "Isometries of Operator Algebras," *Ann. Math.*, **54**, 325 (1951).

Wick, G. C., Wightman, A. S., and Wigner, E. P., "The Intrinsic Parity of Elementary Particles," Phys. Rev., **88**, 101 (1952).

Bargmann, V., *J. Math. Phys.*, **5**, 862 (1964).

Wolfenstein, L., and Ravenhall, D. G., "Some Consequences of Invariance under Charge Conjugation," *Phys. Rev.*, **88**, 279 (1952).

Lee, T. D., and Yang, C. N., "Elementary Particles and Weak Interactions," Office of Technical Services, Department of Commerce, Washington, D.C., 1957.

Melvin, M. A., "Elementary Particles and Symmetry Principles," *Rev. Mod. Phys.*, **32**, 477 (1960).

Melvin, M. A., "Remarks on the Infinite Spin Case for Zero Mass Particles," *Particles and Nuclei*, **1**, 34 (1970).

Jost, R., "TCP-Invarianz der Streumatrix und interpolierende Felder," *Helv. Phys. Acta*, **36**, 77 (1963).

Jost, R., "General Theory of Quantized Fields," Amer. Math. Soc. Publications, 1963.

Olive, D., "Exploration of S-Matrix Theory," *Phys. Rev.*, **135**, B 745 (1964).

Streater, R. F. and Wightman, A. S., "PCT Spin and Statistics and All That," New York, Benjamin, 1964.

Ekstein, H., "Rigorous Symmetries of Elementary Particles," *Ergebnisse der exakten Naturwissenschaften*, 37 (Berlin, Springer, 1965).

Lu, E. Y. C., and Olive, D. I., "Spin and Statistics in S-Matrix Theory," *Nuovo Cimento*, **45**, 205 (1966).

Froissart, M., and Taylor, J. R., "Cluster Decomposition and the Spin-Statistics Theorem in S-Matrix Theory," *Phys. Rev.*, **153**, 1636 (1967).

Wightman, A. S., "What is the Point of So-Called 'Axiomatic Field Theory?' " *Physics Today*, p. 53 (September 1969).

Armenteros, R., and French, B., "Antinucleon-Nucleon Interactions," in "High Energy Physics," Vol. IV, New York, Academic Press, 1969.

Lasinski, Thomas A. et al., "Review of Particle Properties," Rev. Med. Phys., **45**, Supplement, 51 (Apr 1973).

Cross-references: BOSE-EINSTEIN STATISTICS AND BOSONS, CONSERVATION LAWS AND SYMMETRY, ELEMENTARY PARTICLES, FIELD THEORY, QUANTUM THEORY, RELATIVITY.

ARCHITECTURAL ACOUSTICS

Although the practice of architectural acoustics involves a wide variety of special problems and techniques, the basic reasons for acoustical design are simply:

(a) to provide a satisfactory acoustical environment, not too noisy and often not too quiet, for people at work and relaxation;

(b) to provide good hearing conditions for speech; and

(c) to provide a pleasant acoustical environment for listening to music.

Designing for Satisfactory Acoustical Environment Each acoustical situation must be treated as a system comprised of three parts: source, transmission path, and listener. When the properties of the source are known, the transmission path can be modified to attenuate the sound to suit the listener's needs.

Sources. Noise sources are specified in terms of the total acoustical power radiated in each of a number (generally between 8 and 25) of contiguous frequency bands.[1,2] A standard set of ten bands is listed in Table 1.

TABLE 1   STANDARD OCTAVE FREQUENCY BANDS

Lower and Upper Frequency Limits of Each Band (Hz)		Geometric Mean Frequency of Each Band (Hz)
22.1–	44.2	31.5
44.2–	88.5	63
88.5–	177	125
177 –	354	250
354 –	707	500
707 –	1,414	1,000
1,414 –	2,828	2,000
2,828 –	5,655	4,000
5,655 –	11,310	8,000
11,310 –	22,620	16,000

Because of the wide range of sound powers encountered in practice, it is customary to express them in a logarithmic form. Thus we speak of the strength of a sound source in terms of *sound power level, W*, in decibels, defined by item 1 in Table 2.

We note that sound power W is expressed in watts.

A listener does not experience the total sound power from a source, since it radiates in all directions, but rather the proportion that arrives at his ear. Thus we speak of *sound intensity, I*, as the sound power passing through a small area at the point of observation. The units are watts per square centimeter or per square meter. *Sound*

TABLE 2

Decibel Scale	Abbreviation	Reference Quantity	Definition
Sound power level	Lw	$W_{ref} = 10^{-12}$ watt	$10 \log_{10} \dfrac{W}{W_{ref}}$ dB
Sound intensity level	L_I	$I_{ref} = 10^{-12}$ watt/m^2 $= 10^{-16}$ watt/cm^2	$10 \log_{10} \dfrac{I}{I_{ref}}$ dB
Sound pressure level	L_p	$p_{ref} = 0.00002$ newton/m^2 $= 0.0002$ microbar	$10 \log_{10} \dfrac{p^2}{p^2_{ref}}$ $= 20 \log_{10} \dfrac{p}{p_{ref}}$ dB

intensity level, L_I, in decibels, is defined by item 2 in Table 2.

There is no commercially available instrument for measuring sound intensity, so it must be determined indirectly from the mean-square sound pressure, p^2, i.e., the time average of the square of the instantaneous sound pressure in the acoustic wave. This quantity can be determined readily with a pressure microphone. The relation is given by:

$$I = p^2/\rho c \text{ watts/m}^2 \qquad (1)$$

where, ρ is the density of air (or other gas) in kilograms per cubic meter and c is the speed of sound in air in meters per second. *Sound pressure level*, L_p, in decibels, is defined by item 3 in Table 2.

Instruments and techniques for the measurement of sound pressure levels are widely available.[2] Typical measured values of sound power levels for many sources are given in references 1 to 3.

Paths. Sound may travel from a source to a receiver by many paths, some in the air (outdoors or in a room), some through walls, and some along solid structures. In the latter two cases, the sound is radiated into the air from the vibrations of the surfaces.

Outdoors, the relation between the sound pressure level measured at distance r from a source and the sound power level of the source is given by,

$$L_{p_\theta} \doteq Lw + DI_\theta - 20 \log_{10} r - 11 \text{ dB} \qquad (2)$$

where it is assumed that the source is near a hard-ground plane at a distance r in meters from the receiver (also near the plane) and that the source produces different sound intensities in different directions, θ, as described by a *directivity index*, DI_θ (see reference 2). If the source radiates sound equally in all directions, then $DI = 0$. In practice, sources generally have directivity indexes in the range of 0 to 12 dB in the direction of maximum radiation. At large distances, r, there will be losses in the air itself at frequencies above 1500 Hz. Also, wind, temperature gradients, and air turbulence may reduce or augment the L_{p_θ} determined from Eq. (2).

In a room, the sound pressure level produced by a nondirective source is given by,

$$L_p \doteq Lw + 10 \log_{10}\left(\frac{1}{4\pi r^2} + \frac{4}{R}\right) \text{dB} \qquad (3)$$

where r is the distance between the receiver and the microphone and R is the *room constant* in square meters (see reference 2). Typical values of R are found in Fig. 1.

In practical cases, we are often interested in the sound pressure level produced in a room separated by a partition (wall) from a room in which the source is located. We assign a *transmission loss, TL*, in decibels to the intervening wall. Curves of transmission loss versus frequency for several different building structures are given in Fig. 2 and reference 4. The equation relating L_p to the Lw of the source is,

$$L_{p_2} = Lw_1 - TL + 10 \log_{10}\left(\frac{S_w}{R_1}\right)$$
$$+ 10 \log_{10}\left(\frac{1}{S_w} + \frac{4}{R_2}\right) \text{dB} \qquad (4)$$

where L_{p_2} is the sound pressure level in the second room produced by a source in the first room; TL is the transmission loss; S_w is the area of the wall in square meters, and R_1 and R_2 are the room constants for the first and second rooms, respectively, in square meters. It is assumed that the sound pressure level is measured near the common wall; in the center of the room it may be 3 to 5 dB lower.

Technique. It is apparent from Eq. (4) that the techniques for noise reduction indoors are threefold. First, make every effort to reduce the sound power radiated by the source, i.e., use quiet ventilating fans, quiet typewriters, quiet factory machinery, and so forth. Enclose noisy machinery in separate rooms or in enclosures. Mount vibrating machinery on resilient pads or springs. Second, provide walls with suitably high transmission losses between rooms. For example,

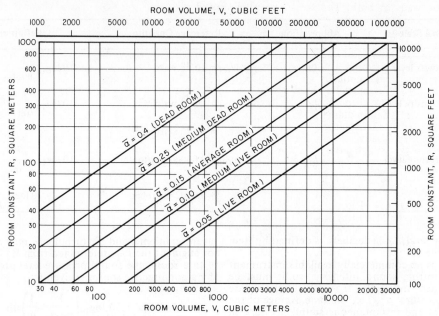

FIG. 1. Approximate value of room constant R for five categories of rooms ranging from "live" to "dead." Metric units referenced at bottom and left, English units top and right. The Greek letter $\bar{\alpha}$ indicates the percentage of the energy that is removed from a sound wave when it reflects from an "average" surface of the room. It is called the average sound absorption coefficient.

between adjoining apartments, walls 4 to 6 of Fig. 2 are usually satisfactory, while walls 1 to 3 are not. On the other hand, walls 2 and 3 would be satisfactory between rooms of the same

apartment, while wall 1 would not. Finally, increase the room constants by adding sound-absorbing materials to either or both rooms, e.g., carpets and draperies, or acoustical materials on

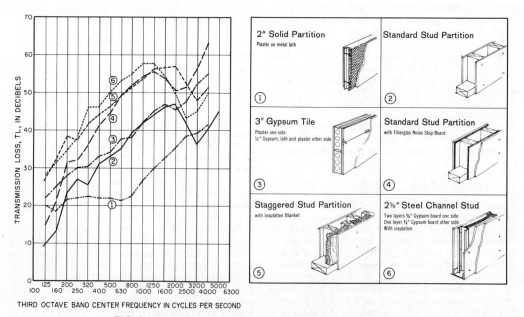

FIG. 2. Transmission loss, TL, of six typical building structures.

ceiling or walls or both. The sound-absorbing efficiencies of various materials are given in references 2, 3, and 5.

It is of great importance to observe that when a wall is placed between two rooms or when an enclosure is built around a noisy machine, the structure must be hermetically sealed, or, if air-flow is necessary, it must be conducted in and out of the enclosure through suitable silencers. A hole even as small in diameter as a pencil can render an otherwise satisfactory wall or enclosure inadequate acoustically.

In cases of very high noise levels where it is impractical acoustically to quiet or isolate the machine, then ear plugs, ear cushions, or both, must be worn by personnel exposed to the noise.

Criteria for Design. Acceptable noise levels in rooms of various types in each of eight octave frequency bands are shown by Fig. 3 and Table 3.

Auditoriums for Speech Three goals must be met in the design of auditoriums for speech. First, the ambient noise levels must be sufficiently low (see Table 3). Second, speech must be loud enough in all parts of the room so that faint syllables can be heard in the presence of normal audience noise. This second goal is achieved in small auditoriums (under about 500

TABLE 3   RECOMMENDED CATEGORY CLASSIFICATION AND SUGGESTED
NOISE CRITERIA RANGE FOR STEADY BACKGROUND NOISE AS HEARD IN
VARIOUS INDOOR FUNCTIONAL ACTIVITY AREAS.

Type of Space (and acoustical requirements)	PNC Curve	Approximate L_A, dBA
Concert halls, opera houses, and recital halls (for listening to faint musical sounds)	10 to 20	21 to 30
Broadcast and recording studios (distant micro-phone pickup used)	10 to 20	21 to 30
Large auditoriums, large drama theaters, and churches (for excellent listening conditions)	Not to exceed 20	Not to exceed 30
Broadcast, television, and recording studios (close microphone pickup only)	Not to exceed 25	Not to exceed 34
Small auditoriums, small theaters, small churches, music rehearsal rooms, large meeting and conference rooms (for good listening), or executive offices and conference rooms for 50 people (no amplification)	Not to exceed 35	Not to exceed 42
Bedrooms, sleeping quarters, hospitals, residences, apartments, hotels, motels, etc. (for sleeping, resting, relaxing)	25 to 40	34 to 47
Private or semiprivate offices, small conference rooms, classrooms, libraries, etc. (for good listening conditions)	30 to 40	38 to 47
Living rooms and similar spaces in dwellings (for conversing or listening to radio and TV)	30 to 40	38 to 47
Large offices, reception areas, retail shops and stores, cafeterias, restaurants, etc. (for moderately good listening conditions)	35 to 45	42 to 52
Lobbies, laboratory work spaces, drafting and engineering rooms, general secretarial areas (for fair listening conditions)	40 to 50	47 to 56
Light maintenance shops, office and computer equipment rooms, kitchens, and laundries (for moderately fair listening conditions)	45 to 55	52 to 61
Shops, garages, power-plant control rooms, etc. (for just acceptable speech and telephone communication). Levels above PNC-60 are not recommended for any office or communication situation	50 to 60	56 to 66
For work spaces where speech or telephone communication is not required, but where there must be no risk of hearing damage	60 to 75	66 to 80

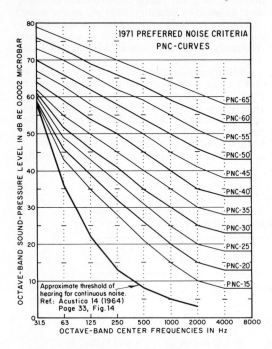

FIG. 3. Preferred Noise Criteria (PNC) curves for various types of building spaces given in Table 3. Measurements are made with an octave band filter and the readings in each band should not exceed that shown on the appropriate PNC curve.

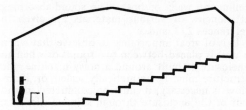

FIG. 4. Satisfactory ceiling shape for a speech auditorium with less than 500 seats.

Music of the Baroque period (Bach and earlier), except for organ music, was composed for small halls with relatively short reverberation times. (That is to say, a loud sound should take about 1.5 seconds to die down to inaudibility after its source is cut off abruptly. This quantity, *called mid-frequency reverberation time*, is measured with full audience present at 500 to 1000 Hz and averaged.) Music of the Classical period (early Beethoven, Mozart and Haydn) was composed for larger halls with medium reverberation times (about 1.8 sec). On the other hand, music of the Romantic period (after 1850), was in general, composed for fairly large halls with long reverberation times (about 2.2 sec). Today, halls must not only accomodate a musical repertoire extending over centuries, but often they must seat so large an audience that they become an entirely new type of space in which to perform music.

In the development of the design of a hall, the acoustics dictate the cubic volume and strongly influence the orientation of every sound-reflecting surface, the interior materials, and even the seating.

Concert hall and opera house design is complex,[6,7] but some guiding principles stand out. The seating capacity should be low, below 2200 if possible. The ceiling should have an average height of 45 ft, if there are no balconies, or 55 ft with balconies, measured above the floor be-

seats) by proper shaping of the front part of the hall so that the speaker's voice is directed uniformly to all parts of the hall. In large halls (over 500 seats), electronic amplification of speech is usually necessary. Third, the reverberation in the auditorium should be sufficiently low that speech is distinct. In auditoriums where there is no sound system, this requirement means that either the ceiling should have an average height of less than 30 ft above the main floor, assuming that the seats are upholstered and that there are no large floor areas without seats. If the ceiling height is over 30 ft, sound-absorbing materials will have to be added to the walls, and perhaps, the rear ceiling to control the reverberation. A satisfactory shape of a 500-seat auditorium for unamplified speech is shown in Fig. 4.

Auditoriums for Music There appears to be no single, ideal architectural solution for the acoustical design of a hall for music. Successful acoustics have been achieved with rectangular, fan or wedge, horseshoe, and even asymmetrical, plans. But though this is true, the many attributes of musical-architectural acoustics are so closely interrelated that if a hall is to be successful, the architect must solve all requirements simultaneously.

The music of each era of the past was composed for a different acoustical environment.

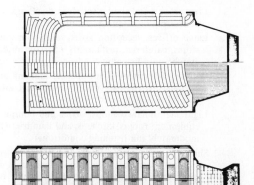

FIG. 5. Drawings of Symphony Hall, Boston, Mass.

neath the main floor seats. The hall should be narrow, or other means such as suspended panels should be provided for producing early sound reflections at listener's positions. Finishes for the interior should primarily be plaster. Not over 20 percent should be wooden if the strength of the bass tone is to be preserved. Irregularities on all the surfaces should be provided to produce diffusion and blending of the sound. Above all, avoid echo, noise and tonal distortion. Finally, the orchestra enclosure should provide sectional balance in the orchestra and permit the musicians to hear each other.

Boston Symphony Hall, one of the world's best-liked concert halls, is rectangular, as shown in Fig. 5, and meets the general requirements listed above. Its mid-frequency reverberation time, with full audience, is 1.8 sec.

LEO L. BERANEK

References

1. Peterson, A. P. G., and Gross, E. E., Jr., "Handbook of Noise Measurement," General Radio Co., West Concord, Mass. (Seventh Ed.) 1972.
2. Beranek, L. L., Ed., "Noise and Vibration Control," New York, McGraw-Hill Book Co., 1971.
3. Harris, C. M., Ed., "Handbook of Noise Control," New York, McGraw-Hill Book Co., 1957.
4. "Performance Data—Architectural Acoustical Materials," Acoustical Materials Association, New York, N.Y., published annually (A.I.A. No. 39–B).
5. "Solutions to Noise Control Problems in the Construction of Houses, Apartments, Motels, and Hotels," Owens-Corning Fiberglas Corp., Toledo, Ohio, 1963 (A.I.A. No. 39–E).
6. Beranek, L. L., "Music, Acoustics, and Architecture," New York, John Wiley & Sons, Inc., 1962.
7. Furrer, W., "Room and Building Acoustics" (translated by E. R. Robinson and P. Lord), London, Butterworths, 1964. W. Furrer and A. Lauber, "Raum- und Bauakustik-Laermabwehr" (3rd Ed.) Birhauser Verlag, Basel, Switzerland, 1972.
8. Kinsler, L. E., and Frey, A. R., "Fundamentals of Acoustics," New York, John Wiley & Sons, Inc., 1950.
9. Beranek, L. L., "Acoustics," New York, McGraw-Hill Book Co., 1949.

Cross-references: ACOUSTICS; HEARING; MUSICAL SOUND; NOISE, ACOUSTICAL; PHYSICAL ACOUSTICS; RESONANCE; VIBRATION.

ASTRODYNAMICS*

Astrodynamics is the study of how bodies move in space, particularly under "free fall," or the influence of gravitational forces alone, but also as influenced by nongravitational forces such as drag, thrust, electromagnetic forces, and corpuscular radiation. The science of astrodynamics is

*Editor was unable to locate author. Article is reprinted from first edition.

a modern application of classical celestial mechanics to space flight. Behavior of the body in a single central gravitational force field (Keplerian flight) will be treated first, and asphericity, n-bodies, and nongravitational forces will be considered as perturbations. Atmospheric aerodynamics is not included (see AERODYNAMICS).

Ballistic Trajectories When a projectile is fired in a vacuum from the flat earth, its trajectory after leaving the gun barrel is determined by the momentum due to the initial velocity vector and the acceleration due to the gravity vector. As shown in Fig. 1, the horizontal component of

FIG. 1. Ballistic trajectory over a flat earth.

velocity remains constant until impact, while the vertical component of velocity is summed algebraically with the time integral of the acceleration due to gravity. If the vertical component of velocity is high enough, the projectile will travel so far that the flat earth assumption is not valid because the gravity vector rotates as the horizontal distance increases. In this case, the trajectory is seen to become an ellipse (Fig. 2) with the center of mass of the earth at one focus.

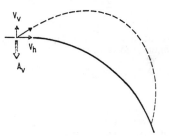

FIG. 2. Ballistic trajectory over a spherical earth.

The range of a ballistic missile is a function of initial or burnout velocity and the elevation angle. As the burnout velocity is increased, the missile will travel farther before impact. At one critical velocity vector (25900 ft/sec at zero-degree elevation angle), the projectile will not fall fast enough to hit the earth, but (neglecting atmospheric braking) would circle it. At this velocity, the centrifugal force exactly equals the mass attraction of the earth.

Orbital Energy. The kinetic energy of a moving mass (m) with velocity (V) is

$$E_k = \tfrac{1}{2} m V^2$$

The potential energy, referenced to zero energy at an infinite distance from the attracting mass (and becoming more negative as it ap-

proaches the attracting mass), is

$$E_p = \frac{-mMG}{r}$$

where $MG = K = g_0 r_0^2$ is the gravitational constant for the attracting mass and r is the distance between the masses.

For the earth (used in satellite calculations):

$$K \approx 1.407(10^{16}) \text{ft}^3 / \text{sec}^3$$

For the sun (used in planet and solar system travel calculations):

$$K \approx 4.679(10^{21}) \text{ft}^3 / \text{sec}^2$$

For the moon (used in lunar orbit calculations);

$$K \approx 1.727(10^{14}) \text{ft}^3 / \text{sec}^2$$

The total energy per unit mass, then, is

$$\frac{E}{m} = \frac{1}{2} V^2 - \frac{K}{r}$$

In a ballistic flight after power cutoff and before reentry, the total energy of a vehicle remains constant.

It was observed by early astronomers, and can be verified by integrating the equations of motion of a particle in space, that the total energy per unit mass is related to the semimajor axis a of the conic Keplerian trajectory

$$\frac{E}{m} = \frac{-2K}{a}$$

This is reduced to the famous and very useful *vis viva* energy equation:

$$V^2 - \frac{2K}{r} = \frac{-K}{a} \qquad (1)$$

which is constant for any given trajectory.

This discloses the interesting fact that the semimajor axis of the orbital ellipse (a) is determined by the velocity and radius at the injection point, or for that matter, at any instant during orbital flight. It is

$$a = \frac{-K}{V^2 - 2K/r}$$

The energy constant ($-K/a$) is also called C_3 energy in the literature. It is a very important parameter:

(1) It is a measure of the total energy of an orbit (and therefore is useful in comparing orbits).

(2) It defines the size of an orbit.

(3) Given the periapsis distance (the distance at closest approach), it defines the shape of an orbit.

From the *vis viva* equation, the velocity required for circular orbit (where $a = r = r_0 + h$) at an altitude h above the earth is found to be

$$V_c = \sqrt{\frac{K}{r_0 + h}}$$

and the period is

$$P = \frac{2\pi(r_0 + h)}{V_c}$$

$$= 2\pi \sqrt{\frac{(r_0 + h)^3}{K}}$$

The theoretical minimum orbit period of an earth satellite (at treetop height, neglecting air drag) is when $h = 0$ and the period is

$$P = 2\pi \sqrt{\frac{r_0}{g_0}} \approx 84.5 \text{ minutes}$$

Notice that the velocity and the period are both dependent on the gravitational attraction and the altitude. The mass of the vehicle is not a factor as long as it is negligible compared with the attracting mass.

Also, as will be shown shortly, the *vis viva* integral is a measure of the hyperbolic excess velocity—the residual velocity of a vehicle after it has left the field of the attracting mass. Notice that so far, both the orbital characteristics and the orbital energy are referenced to a particular attracting mass, and the center of mass attraction always lies on the plane of the trajectory and at the focus. Notice also that in central force field theory, the radius of the earth has no significance except in establishing the launch point and the point of impact. In addition, the fact that the launch point is rotating in space merely establishes an initial velocity vector before launching the vehicle. For this reason, it requires less energy to reach circular orbit velocity to the east than to the west. Of course, some orbital information may be given in terms of altitude which is simply the instantaneous radius minus the earth's radius.

Cotangential Orbits If the injection velocity is greater or less than the circular velocity for that injection altitude, or if the injection angle is not zero, the orbit will not be circular. It can be shown that the most efficient injection angle for satellite or space flight orbits is near zero.

For injection angles of zero degrees, if the velocity is less than the circular velocity, the orbit will be a subcircular ellipse with the injection point the farthest point from the center of mass attraction (focus) or apoapsis. If the injection velocity exceeds the circular velocity but is less than $V_c\sqrt{2}$, the orbit will be a hypercircular ellipse, with the injection point the nearest or periapsis point. These cotangential orbits are shown in Fig. 3. If the injection angle is not zero degrees, the orbit is not a circle and the injection point is neither the apoapsis nor the periapsis.

Criterion for Escape The kinetic energy exactly equals the potential energy when

$$V^2 = \frac{2K}{r}$$

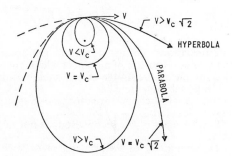

FIG. 3. Cotangential orbits.

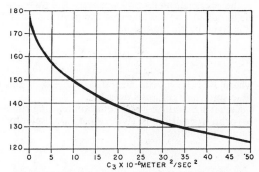

FIG. 4. Angle between outward radial (asymptote) and perigee as a function of energy.

or

$$V = \sqrt{2K/r} = V_c\sqrt{2}$$

Therefore, if the injection velocity V_0 equals $\sqrt{2}$ times the circular velocity, the vehicle has just enough kinetic energy to overcome the potential energy of mass attraction, and it escapes from the earth or other attracting mass, theoretically reaching zero velocity at infinite distance from the center of mass attraction (assuming the vehicle is influenced by the gravity of only one body).

For $V_0 = V_c\sqrt{2}$, the trajectory is parabolic. For $V_0 > V_c\sqrt{2}$, the trajectory is hyperbolic. These trajectories are all in the family of curves called "conics"—the circle, ellipse, parabola, and hyperbola (and the trivial cases of the line and the point).

Notice that each of the closed orbits passes through its own injection point in space. The point will not generally be the same point over the earth due to the earth's rotation. Notice also that since the velocity vector and the position vector at any point on the orbit determine the entire trajectory, the orbits are dynamically reversible. Therefore, a vehicle approaching a planet with hyperbolic velocity will, if it does not impact, pass the periapsis and continue outbound on the symmetrical continuation of the approach hyperbola.

The Velocity Asymptote The residual velocity (at an infinite distance from the attracting mass or hyperbolic excess velocity) is described by the velocity asymptote vector $\mathbf{V}_\infty$ which defines the injection requirements and is, therefore, a very useful parameter in describing mission guidance and energy requirements.

The square of the hyperbolic excess velocity is the C_3 energy of the orbit.

$$V_\infty{}^2 = C_3 = -\frac{K}{a}$$

where the semimajor axis (a) goes negative for hyperbolic flight.

For parabolic trajectories, the direction of the velocity asymptote is 180° from the perigee radius and the C_3 energy is zero. For hyperbolic trajectories, the angle between the velocity asymptote and the perigee radius is less than 180° and is a function of the C_3 energy (Fig. 4).*

Guidance Requirements for Space Flight Since the laws of astrodynamics describe the flight path under gravitational forces, the function of the guidance system is to guide the vehicle during the thrust period to the required injection altitude and position and velocity vectors, and to cut off the thrust promptly.

The dynamic position of the vehicle in orbit is given by its instantaneous radius vector (r) from the attracting mass and by the true anomaly (η), which is the angle from the periapsis radius to the instantaneous position radius measured at the focus. Two other angles are very useful in relating the position of the vehicle in orbit to time: the eccentric anomaly and the mean anomaly. The eccentric anomaly (E) is the angle measured at the center of the orbit (rather than at the focus (from the periapsis radius to a point on an auxiliary circle which just contains the ellipse, the location of the point being the extension of a line perpendicular to the major axis and passing through the vehicle position. The true anomaly and the eccentric anomaly are shown in Fig. 5.

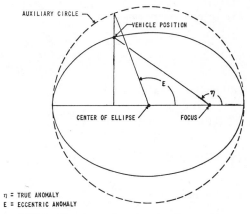

η = TRUE ANOMALY
E = ECCENTRIC ANOMALY

FIG. 5. True anomaly and eccentric anomaly.

*Taken from reference 6 by permission.

The mean anomaly (M) is merely the time angle in radians, or the phase of the orbital period. It is given by the equation

$$M = \frac{2\pi}{P}(t - t_0)$$

where P is the orbital period, and $t - t_0$ is the time since last periapsis passage.

Kepler's Equation. The equation relating time to orbital position is given most concisely by Kepler's equation

$$M = E - e \sin E$$

Useful Orbit Relationships A number of useful equations can be derived based on the relationship of velocity to altitude at any instant for a given attracting mass (K) and orbit size (a). It should be emphasized here that the trajectory curves are loci of the center of mass of the orbiting vehicle and are independent of vehicle attitude. The flight path direction does not describe the pointing direction of the vehicle in free flight.

Some useful orbit equations for the circle, ellipse, parabola, and hyperbola are shown below:

(1) Eccentricity $e = \sqrt{\dfrac{a^2 - b^2}{a^2}}$
$$\begin{aligned} &= 0 \text{ (C)}\\ &< 1 \text{(E)}\\ &= 1 \text{ (P)}\\ &> 1 \text{ (H)} \end{aligned}$$

(2) Apoapsis radius $r_a = a(1 + e)$

(3) Periapsis radius $r_p = a(1 - e)$

(4) Semimajor axis $a = \dfrac{-K}{V^2 - 2K/r}$
$$\begin{aligned} &= r \text{ (C)}\\ &< \infty \text{ (E)}\\ &= \infty \text{ (P)}\\ &= -\frac{K}{V_\infty{}^2} \text{ (H)} \end{aligned}$$

(5) Orbital energy constant

$$C_3 = -\frac{K}{a} = V^2 - \frac{2K}{r}$$
$$\begin{aligned} &< 0 \text{ (C, E)}\\ &= 0 \text{ (P)}\\ &= V_\infty{}^2 \text{(H)} \end{aligned}$$

(6) Radius $r = a(1 - e \cos E)$

(7) True anomaly $\eta = \cos^{-1}\left(\dfrac{\cos E - e}{1 - e \cos E}\right)$(E)

(8) Flight path angle $\theta = \tan^{-1}\left(\dfrac{e \sin \eta}{1 + e \cos \eta}\right)$

(9) Velocity $V = \sqrt{\dfrac{2K}{r} - \dfrac{K}{a}}$

(10) Periapsis velocity $V_p = \sqrt{\dfrac{K}{r_p}(1 + e)}$

(11) Apoapsis velocity $V_a = \sqrt{\dfrac{K}{r_a}(1 - e)}$

Perturbations Perturbations are the components of acceleration of an object which are not accountable by the simple inverse-square central gravitational force field.

Examples of such perturbations to Keplerian trajectories are:

(1) The mass of the second body is not negligible.

(2) Asphericity of the principal mass (such as the equatorial bulge),

(3) Nongravitational forces—thrust, drag, electromagnetic forces, and those due to radiation.

The Keplerian conics are useful not only for approximations and feasibility studies but as reference orbits from which perturbations may be calculated.

The Twenty-four Hour Orbit The circular orbit with 19000-nautical-mile altitude is of interest because its period is 24 hours and so the satellite can be made to hover over one place on the earth.

Hohmann Transfer Since impulsive velocity increments are more efficient than long continuous thrust to injection, the ascent to the 19000-mile altitude is made by a low-altitude injection into an elliptical orbit with the desired apogee. At apogee, about $5\frac{1}{2}$ hours flight from injection, a second injection into the circular orbit is made. This transfer is the classical Hohmann ellipse (Fig. 6).

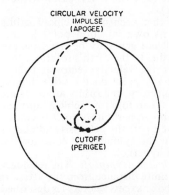

FIG. 6. The Hohmann transfer ellipse.

Change of Orbital Plane The inclination of an orbit to the equator varies with launch azimuth, but the minimum angle of inclination is the latitude of the launch site unless a change of plane is made in flight. A change of plane can be made most efficiently by a thrust applied normal to the orbital plane as the vehicle crosses the equator. If more than one orbit is involved—such as the low altitude parking orbit, the Hohmann transfer, and the high-altitude circular orbit—it can be shown that the ΔV required for change of plane is less at the highest orbit.

Station Keeping To maintain a desired orbit, 24-hour or otherwise, an occasional small incre-

ment of velocity may be required. The velocity increment to maintain a low-altitude orbit (100 to 200 miles) against the tenuous atmospheric drag is in the order of a few feet per second each week, depending on the ballistic coefficient of the vehicle.

Lunar Flight The minimum energy flight to the moon would again be a Hohmann transfer, injecting at the perigee and reaching the moon at apogee. However, the minimum energy flight would require a 90-hour flight time. The time can be considerably reduced with relatively little increase in injection velocity. The minimum energy ellipse is very nearly parabolic ($e = 0.97$), requiring a velocity (35 860 ft/sec) very close to escape velocity, so a relatively small increase in velocity will greatly increase the semimajor axis of the ellipse beyond the moon and reduce the flight time to the moon. A flight with an injection velocity of 36 093 ft/sec would reduce the flight time to 66 hours. Instead of being at apogee, the moon would be along one side of the ellipse.

Interplanetary Flight If planetary orbits were circular and coplanar, the minimum energy flight would be that required to provide the additional velocity to put the spacecraft into a sun-centered Hohmann transfer to Mars, or the retrograde velocity necessary for the spacecraft to fall into the smaller ellipse for a Hohmann transfer to Venus. The minimum energy flight opportunity would be when the earth at launch and the target planet at arrival have a 180° heliocentric central angle.

Synodic Periods These opportunities occur at synodic periods due to the different orbital periods of the planets. For Mars, the synodic period is 25.6 months; Venus is 19.2 months; and Mercury is 3.8 months.

However, the planetary orbits are not circular, and they are not coplanar (Table 1); therefore, the minimum energy flights are not Hohmann

TABLE 1. PLANET ORBIT ECCENTRICITY AND INCLINATION TO ECLIPTIC [a]

Planet	Orbit Eccentricity	Inclination to Ecliptic (degrees)
Earth	0.017	0
Venus	0.007	3.39
Mars	0.093	1.85

[a]Taken from reference 6 by permission.

transfers. The best launch dates are still very close to the synodic period (except for Mercury), but the minimum energy required is not the same at each period. Table 2 shows the minimum energy (geocentric), flight time, and planetary distance from the sun at arrival for various launch dates at the synodic period.

The energy required at each synodic period varies with the planet-to-sun distance and the distance from the ecliptic at encounter. These periodic best-launch opportunities usually last from two to five days before serious energy penalties begin.

Summary of Astrodynamic Rules For Keplerian flight (only one force: a point gravitational attraction):

(1) The minimum velocity required for circular orbit decreases as injection latitude increases.

(2) The period of a closed orbit increases with the mean altitude of the orbit.

(3) The mean velocity of a closed orbit decreases as the mean altitude of the orbit increases.

(4) The escape velocity equals $\sqrt{2}$ times the circular orbit velocity.

(5) Orbits with injection velocity greater than circular velocity but less than escape velocity are ellipses.

(6) Orbits with injection velocity greater than escape velocity are hyperbolas.

TABLE 2. CHARACTERISTICS OF MINIMUM ENERGY TRANSFERS[5]

Launch Date	Flight Time (days)	Geocentric Injection Energy (m²/sec² × 10⁸)	Heliocentric Central Angle (degrees)	Sun-planet Distance at Arrival (10⁶ km)	Celestial Latitude of Planet on Arrival (degrees)
			Mars		
19 Nov 64	244	0.090	174.1	231.2	−0.047
5 Jan 67	202	0.091	152.2	221.9	−0.833
2 Mar 69	178	0.088	139.3	209.7	−1.75
24 May 71	210	0.079	156.0	216.6	−0.352
30 July 73	192	0.146	141.4	234.2	1.16
			Venus		
30 Mar 64	112	0.123	126.8	108.9	−2.93
12 Nov 65	108	0.132	129.5	107.6	3.31
11 Jun 67	142	0.065	175.6	107.7	−0.082
13 Jan 69	126	0.077	150.5	108.6	−0.393
19 Aug 70	116	0.085	134.5	107.5	1.36

(7) The orbital energy (hence semimajor axis, mean velocity, mean altitude, and period) remains constant in Keplerian trajectories. The energy is positive for hyperbolas, zero for parabolic escape, and becomes more negative as the semimajor axis decreases.

(8) The center of mass attraction is at the focus of the conic trajectory.

(9) Multibody trajectories can be approximated by "patched conics"—a series of Keplerian trajectories (earth-centered, sun-centered, planet-centered).

(10) Conic trajectories define the locus of the center of mass under gravitational forces. Vehicle attitude is not defined by the trajectory.

(11) The trajectory is defined by position and velocity vectors at any instant. Hence, guidance is needed only during the thrust periods.

RICHARD H. PARVIN

References

1. Baker, Robert, and Makemsen, Maude, "An Introduction to Astrodynamics," New York, Academic Press, 1960.
2. Seifert, Howard, Ed., "Space Technology," New York, John Wiley & Sons, 1959.
3. Ehricke, Krafft, "Space Flight," Vols. I and II, New York, Van Nostrand Reinhold, 1960, 1962.
4. Nelson, Walter and Loft, Ernest, "Space Mechanics," Englewood Cliffs, N.J., Prentice-Hall, 1962.
5. Clarke, Victor C., Jr., "A Summary of the Characteristics of Ballistic Interplanetary Trajectories, 1962–1977," Jet Propulsion Laboratory Tech. Report 32-209, Pasadena, 15 January 1962.
6. Clarke, Victor C., Jr., "Design of Lunar and Interplanetary Ascent Trajectories," Jet Propulsion Laboratory Tech. Report 32-20, Pasadena, 15 March 1962.
7. Clarke, Victor C., Jr., "Constants and Related Data Used in Trajectory Calculations at the Jet Propulsion Laboratory," Jet Propulsion Laboratory Tech. Report 32-273, Pasadena, 1 May 1962.
8. Seddon, J., "Space Dynamics," *Spaceflight* (November 1963).

Cross-references: AERODYNAMICS; ASTRONAUTICS, PHYSICS OF; DYNAMICS; FLIGHT PROPULSION FUNDAMENTALS; KEPLER'S LAWS OF PLANETARY MOTION; MECHANICS; ROTATION—CIRCULAR MOTION; WORK, POWER, AND ENERGY.

ASTROMETRY

Astrometry deals with the space-time behavior of celestial bodies and therefore belongs to the classical field of astronomical studies. It is often referred to as fundamental, positional or observational astronomy.

Early astrometric investigations were directed mainly toward establishing a suitable frame of reference for the determination of the complex motions of the planets, while the studies of the positions and motions of the individual stars as well as the various stellar systems gradually developed as improved precision of observations made it possible to discover and observe these motions.

The fundamental, and perhaps most difficult, problem of astrometry is the establishment of a reference system against which the motions of the celestial bodies can be measured.

The principal planes involved in the spherical coordinate systems usually used in astrometry are the equator, defined by the rotation of the earth on its axis, and the ecliptic, defined by the revolution of the earth around the sun. The positions of both these planes vary continuously in a most complicated manner due to gravitational forces and couples between earth and the moon, the sun, and the principal planets. Such motions of the reference planes are reflected in the positions of the stars referred to them.

The motions of these planes cannot be derived entirely from theory alone, but must be deduced from observed changes in the positions of the stars which, in turn, are also in motion. This complication has forced the construction of the astronomical coordinate system to proceed by a series of successive approximations which are still in progress. Initially, the sun, and planets were observed against the "fixed stars." From these observations came the first approximations of the motions of the solar system by the laws of dynamics and of the effect of the changing orientation of the earth's axis of rotation (precession) upon the positions of the stars. Successive repetitions of the observational process have gradually improved our knowledge of these and other motions affecting the fundamental planes of the coordinate system, each improvement resulting in an increase in our knowledge of the positions and motions of the stars.

Observational programs for the improvement of the celestial coordinate system are long and tedious and must be conducted with meticulous care. They make use of highly developed instruments and observing techniques which, in combination with adopted theories of the rotation of the earth and its motion around the sun, enable the positions of the equator and equinox to be derived anew and the positions of the stars to be related to them. Each such program is an independent effort to reconstruct the celestial coordinate system. Meridian circles have generally been used for this kind of work. The results of such programs are said to be fundamental and are usually published in the form of star catalogs.

From time to time, when sufficient fundamentally observed catalogues have accumulated, they are combined with similar earlier material to form a *Fundamental Star Catalog*. This catalog is usually regarded as the best representation that may be had of the celestial coordinate system at the time of its publication; the right ascensions and declinations of the stars in the

catalog define the system for the equinox and epoch chosen for the catalog. The proper motions in combination with the adopted values of the constant precession permit the system to be referred to equinoxes and equators at other epochs.

The latest and most precise of the fundamental catalogs is designated the *FK4* and was published by the Astronomischen Rechen-Instituts, Heidelberg, Germany in 1963. The catalog contains the positions (right ascension and declination) and the changes with time (precession and proper motion) of 1535 stars. These data were compiled from nearly 200 star catalogs containing observations over a span of 110 years. Two other fundamental catalogs that have been extensively used are the *GC, Albany General Catalogue of 33342 Stars* and the *N30, Catalog of 5268 Stars.*

The coordinate system provided by the positions and motions of the stars in a fundamental catalog serves as a reference system for the measurement of other star positions and proper motions which must be carried out for a variety of problems originating in the study of stellar motions, in geodesy, in the determination of time, in space research and others.

With the exception of the *GC*, which contains all the stars brighter than the 7th magnitude, fundamental catalogs do not contain a complete list of all stars down to a certain magnitude as, for example, the survey catalogs do. The prototype of the survey catalogs for star positions is the *Bonner Durchmusterung* which contains the positions of 320000 stars to a limiting magnitude of 9.5 and north of declination $-2°$. Although the observations for the catalog were made in the middle of the past century, the catalog and the charts made from it have been an extremely useful tool for astronomers for identification of star fields. The survey was later extended to the south celestial pole by the Bonn, Cape and Cordoba Observatories.

Positions of the fainter stars on a fundamental system are obtained by a close coordination between visual and photographic programs. The positions of a selected number of moderately bright stars (7th to 9th magnitude) are related to the fundamental system by meridian circle observations. These stars are then used as a position reference for the photographic observations of the fainter stars, thus tying them to the fundamental system.

An example of this procedure is the large astrometric project initiated toward the end of the nineteenth century and carried out by international cooperation.

The fundamental system adopted for this undertaking was embodied in the *FC (Fundamental-Catalog für die Zonen-Beobachtungen am Nördlichen Himmel)* developed by Auwers. The visual program, designated the *AGK (Astronomische Gesellschaft Katalog)*, was carried out through the collaboration of 12 northern hemisphere observatories and resulted in the determination of the positions with respect to the *FC* of 144128 stars to the limiting magnitude of 9 and north of $-2°$ declination. The extension of the visual work into the southern skies was gradually carried out by other observatories. The adjunct photographic program known as the *Carte du Ciel* or the *Astrographic Catalogue* called for observations down to approximately the 11th magnitude covering the entire sky by $2° \times 2°$ fields. Originating in 1887, the program has only recently been completed and involved the participation of 18 different observatories. The positions in the catalogs are given in the form of rectangular coordinates as measured on the plates, but by means of auxiliary tables, these coordinates can be translated into right ascension and declination. Each field was photographed a second time with a longer exposure with a limiting magnitude of 14 to be used for the purpose of star charts.

Several other catalogs of photographically derived positions have been published. Among the catalogs of this nature may be mentioned the *AGK2 (Zweiter Katalog der Astronomischen Gesellschaft)* and the Yale and Cape photographic catalogs.

The *AGK2* was rigorously related to the fundamental system represented by the *FK3 (Dritter Fundamentalkatalog des Berliner Astronomischen Jahrbuchs)* through the use of simultaneous visual observations of about 13000 moderately bright stars in making the plate reductions. The *AGK2* plates were taken at the Bonn and Bergedorf Observatories and covered the sky in $5° \times 5°$ overlapping fields from $-2°$ to the north pole. The resulting catalog contains the positions of over 180000 stars for the mean epoch of 1930. A second photographic series of observations of these stars was carried out at the Bergedorf Observatory. The measured positions on the plates were reduced to the system of the *FK4* by use of the positions of some 21000 reference stars observed simultaneously through an international cooperative program involving 12 meridian circles in the northern hemisphere. A comparison of the plate results at the two epochs gives rather accurate proper motions with respect to the fundamental system for the entire 180000 stars. The majority of these stars are brighter than the 9th magnitude. A good many, however, are as faint as the 11.5 photographic magnitude. The catalog is named *AGK3*. Except for gaps between $+85°$ to $+60°$, and $+50°$ to $+30°$ declination, the Yale photographic catalogs cover the sky from $+90°$ to $-50°$ declination, while the Cape catalogs provide a complete coverage from $-30°$ declination to the south pole. Both series of catalogs were taken by zones of declination by use of wide-angle cameras (from $5° \times 5°$ to $10° \times 14°$) and were reduced to a fundamental system (not always the same one) by use of contemporary meridian circle observations. The mean epochs of the positions in these catalogs range from the early 1930's to the late 1940's. The stars in these catalogs are similar in magni-

tude range to those in the *AGK2* and *AGK3*. A program of observing 20000 stars in the Southern Hemisphere with meridian circles is now nearing completion. Known as the *SRS* (*Southern Reference Star*) *Program,* it is carried out through international cooperation with northern observatories (U. S. Naval Observatory, Pulkovo Observatory, and Hamburg-Bergedorf) participating with stations in Argentina, Chile, and Australia, respectively. The positions and proper motions of these stars in the fundamental system are intended for use in obtaining new positions and proper motions of some 200000 stars in the Southern Hemisphere observed photographically.

An important source for obtaining proper motions of the fainter stars is a combination of early photographic plates with recent ones taken with the same telescope. The proper motions derived in this way are relative proper motions and require further reductions for transformation into absolute proper motions in a fundamental system. This procedure has been followed in several extensive programs aimed at solving such problems as determining the solar motion, and deriving secular parallaxes and galactic rotation.

Proper motions for tens of thousands of stars have been obtained by this method while radial velocities for a lesser number of stars have been determined from the spectroscopic application of the Doppler principle. Besides the proper motion and radial velocity, the distance of a star is needed to determine its motion in space. For stars beyond 30 parsecs from the solar system it becomes increasingly difficult to obtain all three factors involved, and often knowledge of stellar motion is either based on proper motions or radial velocities alone. However, by various statistical devices substantial information about stellar motions has been obtained.

On the basis of these studies, the sun's velocity has been determined to be about 20 km/sec towards a point in space not far from Vega, although the amount and direction of the motion varies depending upon the chosen group of stars.

As a result of the sun's motion through space, the stars show a parallactic or secular shift which can be used to determine their distances. Because of the individual motions of the stars, this method is applicable only to groups of stars with the assumption that their individual motions are random. By means of the secular parallax method, general ideas of the distances of stars up to 1000 parsecs have been obtained.

From statistical studies of proper motions and radial velocities, it was found in 1927 that the stars in our galaxy are moving in orbits not greatly inclined to the galactic equator. The observations are consistent with the assumption that the principal force governing the motions is gravitational with the center of mass near the galactic center. The period of rotation at the sun's distance from the center is 2×10^8 years.

There are, at the present time, two programs in progress which will attempt to establish absolute stellar proper motions using the distant galaxies as a reference frame, the assumption being made that those objects do not show any systematic rotation with respect to the local inertial frame of rest.

A large number of proper motion studies of galactic clusters has been carried out in order to establish membership of the individual stars in the field. Because of the high internal precision required for this work, these studies have been confined primarily to long-focus telescopes, with plates taken over time intervals of 50 or more years.

Several surveys of the sky for stars with high proper motion, largely with the aim of finding absolutely faint stars, have been carried out over the past several decades. Two surveys are still in progress, one with the 48-inch Schmidt telescope at Mt. Palomar and the other with the 13-inch telescope at Lowell Observatory, the latter being by far the most extensive survey to date. It will cover 80 per cent of the sky to a limiting magnitude of 17, and in the course of its completion, upwards of 240 million star images will have been examined. In surveys of this magnitude, it is essential that telescopes of not too large focal length be used to limit the number of plates needed to cover the sky and that the "moving" stars be found by rapid scanning of the plates. These surveys have drastically increased the known number of white-dwarf, sub-dwarf, and faint red-dwarf stars, which, at the present time attract much interest among astronomers.

An important area within astrometry is the determination of the distances of individual stars. Because of the extremely small quantities to be measured, the ultimate in precision is required. The geometric method of measuring distances is based upon the surveyor's principle: the object is observed from both ends of a base line. In determining the trigonometric parallax of a star, the semimajor axis of the earth's orbit is used as the base line. Reliable individual distances have been measured in this way for several thousands of stars within 30 parsecs of the solar system. Beyond this limit, the annual parallactic effect measured against a background of more distant stars becomes so small that it cannot be measured accurately. On the plates taken with telescopes having the largest scale, the parallactic shifts of stars near the limit of 30 parsecs amounts to no more than 3μ. Shifts of this order require series of photographic plates taken over several years for their measurement. This necessitates the use of telescopes with high stability in their optical systems and the application of the most refined techniques of photography and measurement. It is only since the turn of the century that sufficiently precise instrumentation and techniques for this task have been available. The importance of stellar distance determination is realized from the fact that the distance of a

star must be known before its intrinsic luminosity and its rate of energy generation can be determined.

Studies of the stars in the solar neighborhood have revealed that the majority of them are components of double and multiple systems. Since the motions of the stars within a system are governed by their mutual gravitational attraction, it is possible to determine their masses by use of Kepler's third law (see KEPLER'S LAWS OF PLANETARY MOTION), whenever their orbital motions and the parallax of the system become known. This is the only direct way masses of the stars can be determined.

Routine observations of the motions in binary systems began about 135 years ago. Originally all observations were carried out visually. Although this method continues to be used for close pairs, it has been largely replaced by a more accurate photographic method for wider pairs.

Various searches for double stars have produced some 65000 visual binary systems, but for only a small fraction (approximately 50) of these systems are data available for determining the individual masses with an accuracy of 30 per cent or better. These masses range from about 0.08 solar mass for a star 3000 times less luminous than the sun to 6 times the sun's mass for a star 100 times more luminous than the sun. Larger masses, as high as 50 to 100 times the solar mass, are found among the very close binaries such as eclipsing and spectroscopic binaries. Although these objects cannot be resolved into individual components, their orbital motions can be determined from the periodic variation in light and radial velocity (observed Doppler shift).

Stellar masses smaller than the value of 0.08 quoted above have been discovered in recent years by intensive photographic studies of nearby single stars and components in double stars. These studies, representing the ultimate in accuracy in photographic astrometry, have revealed unseen companions of such small masses that, according to theoretical estimates, they are either stars so small that they will never burn nuclear fuel or planets of the size of Jupiter.

Aside from demands for such utilitarian purposes as navigation, geodesy and space research, astronomers themselves are making heavy demands for substantial gains in quality and quantity in astrometric observations, extended to fainter and fainter stars.

The discovery of the intrinsically faint stars in the solar neighborhood has demanded an extensive parallax program with an entirely new telescope of special design.

Positions and space velocities on a large scale of the individual stars and of stellar systems within our galaxy are essential to understand its dynamics and evolution as well as the physical properties and evolution of the individual stars which populate it.

To accomplish this, new instrumental and analytical techniques are currently being introduced which take advantage of the latest technological developments in automation.

K. AA. STRAND

References

Hiltner, W. A., "Astronomical Techniques," Chicago, University of Chicago Press, 1962.

Smart, W. M., "Spherical Astronomy," Cambridge, The University Press, 1931.

Smart, W. M., "Stellar Dynamics," Cambridge, The University Press, 1938.

Strand, K. Aa., "Basic Astronomical Data," Chicago, University of Chicago Press, 1963.

Trumpler, R. J., and Weaver, H. F., "Statistical Astronomy," University of California Press, 1953.

Cross-references: ASTROPHYSICS, COSMOLOGY, DOPPLER EFFECT, KEPLER'S LAWS OF PLANETARY MOTION.

ASTRONAUTICS, PHYSICS OF

Future historians may record that the age of space flight marked a turning point in modern times. Its physical principles—the laws of motion of celestial bodies—marked the turning point of medieval times. From Copernicus to Kepler to Galileo to Newton, the Aristotelian myth of a man-oriented universe succumbed to the conception of a detached mechanically oriented universe, operating through laws which were a synthesis of the new knowledge gained in the formerly separate domains of terrestrial and celestial mechanics. Mankind never quite recovered from that detachment.

Weight and Weightlessness In Newtonian mechanics, weight is understood to mean the force that an object exerts upon its support. This would depend on two factors: the strength of gravity at the object's location (things weigh less on the moon) and, as Newton called it, the quantity of matter in a body (its "mass"). At any given location, where gravity is fixed, mass can be measured relative to a standard by noting the extension of a spring to which it and the standard are successively attached. Alternatively, the unknown and standard may be hung at opposite ends of a rod and the balance point noted. However, by an entirely separate experiment, mass can also be measured by noting the resistance of the object to a fixed force applied horizontally on a frictionless table. The measured acceleration provides the required basis of comparison with the standard. Needless to say, all objects measure identical accelerations when freely falling in the vertical force of gravity. This merely means that, unlike the arbitrary force we apply horizontally in the experiment above, gravity has the property of adjusting itself in just the right amount, raising or lowering its applied force, to maintain the acceleration constant.

It was well known that objects appear to increase or decrease their weight (alter the extension of the spring) if the reference frame in which the measurement takes place accelerates up or down. As gravity did not really change, however, most people were inclined to draw a distinction between *weight* defined as $m\mathbf{g}$, where m is the mass and $\mathbf{g}$ is the local gravity field, and the *appearance of weight*, the force of an object on its support as measured by the spring's extension. One way to avoid the difficulty has been to speak of an *effective* $\mathbf{g}$, which takes into consideration the frame's acceleration. For example, at the equator of the earth, we measure, say by timing the oscillation of a pendulum, the effective $\mathbf{g}$, some 0.34 per cent less than the $\mathbf{g}$ produced by the mass of earth beneath our feet. If the earth were rotating with a period of an hour and a half instead of 24 hours, our centripetal acceleration at the equator would cause the effective $\mathbf{g}$ to vanish completely, our scales would not register, objects would be unsupported, and for all practical purposes we would be weightless.

Formally, we could state that any accelerating frame produces a local gravitational field $\mathbf{g}_{acc}$ that is equal and opposite to the acceleration. Thus, a rotating frame generates a centrifugal $\mathbf{g}_{acc}$ opposing the centripetal acceleration. We have at any point

$$\mathbf{g}_{eff} = \mathbf{g} + \mathbf{g}_{acc} \qquad (1)$$

where $\mathbf{g}$ is the field produced by matter alone (e.g., the earth). By identical reasoning, an object in orbit, whether falling freely in a curved or in a straight path, will carry a reference frame in which $\mathbf{g}_{eff}$ is zero, for its acceleration will always exactly equal the local $\mathbf{g}$ by the definition of the phrase, "freely falling."

This concept was placed on a firm footing by Einstein who maintained that Eq. (1) is reasonable not only in mechanics but in all areas of physics including electromagnetic phenomena. We arrive at the inevitable conclusion that we cannot distinguish by any physical experiment between an apparent $\mathbf{g}$ accountable to an accelerating frame and a "real" $\mathbf{g}$ derived from a local accumulation of mass. This central postulate of the General Theory of Relativity also unified the two separate conceptions of mass. An object resting on a platform that is accelerating toward it will resist the acceleration in an amount depending on its inertia. It presses against the platform with a force equal to that it would have if placed at rest on the surface of a planet with local field equal and opposite to the acceleration of the frame.

General Principles of Central Force Motion
The gravitational force between point masses is inverse square, written

$$m\mathbf{g} = - \frac{\gamma m' m}{r^2} \hat{\mathbf{r}} \qquad (2)$$

where the center of coordinates from which the unit vector $\hat{\mathbf{r}}$ is described lies in m', one of the masses. Thus, the force on m is directed $-\hat{\mathbf{r}}$, toward m' and is proportional to $1/r^2$ with γ the constant of proportionality. The quantity $\mathbf{g}$ is the force on m *divided by* m (or normalized force) for which the name "gravitational field of m'" is reserved. Of course, if m were in the field of a collection of mass points, or even in a continuous distribution of mass, the summated or integrated $\mathbf{g}$ at the location of m would no longer be an inverse square function with respect to any coordinate center. However, in one special case, the inverse square functional form would be preserved: if the source mass were symmetrically distributed about the coordinate center. This would be the case if the source were a spherical shell or solid sphere, of density constant or a function only of r. The sun and earth can be regarded, at least to a first approximation, as sources of inverse square gravitational fields.

There are some important general statements we can make about the motion of an object placed with arbitrary position and velocity in a centrally directed force field, i.e., a field such as the one described, which depends only on distance from a central point (regardless of whether or not the dependence is inverse square). As the force has only a radial and no angular components, it cannot exert a torque about an axis through the center. This means that the initial angular momentum is conserved. Now angular momentum is a vector quantity and therefore is conserved both in direction and magnitude. It is defined by $\mathbf{r} \times \mathbf{p}$, where $\mathbf{r}$ is the position vector to the mass of momentum $\mathbf{p}$. The direction of the angular momentum vector is thus perpendicular to the plane containing $\mathbf{r}$ and $\mathbf{p}$. As this direction is permanent, so also must be the plane. The planar motion of the object can be expressed in polar coordinates, so that by writing $\mathbf{r} = r\hat{\mathbf{r}}$ and $\mathbf{p} = m(\dot{r}\hat{\mathbf{r}} + r\dot{\phi}\hat{\boldsymbol{\phi}})$, we find the specific angular momentum (angular momentum per unit mass) called h, to be

$$h = r^2 \dot{\phi} \qquad (3)$$

This too then must be a constant of the motion.

Consider now the rate at which area is swept out by the radius vector, dS/dt. We recall from analytic geometry that $dS = \frac{1}{2}r^2 \phi$. Thus

$$\frac{dS}{dt} = \frac{h}{2} \qquad (4)$$

so that this is a constant of the motion as well. On integration, we conclude that the size of a sector that is swept out is proportional to the time required to sweep it out. In the case of a closed orbit, the total area S would then be related to the specific angular momentum as

$$S = \frac{hT}{2} \qquad (5)$$

This sector area-time relationship is Kepler's

second law of planetary motion which was induced from Tycho Brahe's observation of Mars without prior knowledge of gravity and its central character.

The Laws of Kepler Kepler stated two other laws of planetary motion: The orbits of all the planets about the sun are ellipses (a radical departure from the circles of Copernicus), and the squares of their periods are proportional to the cubes of their mean distance from the sun, this mean being the semimajor axis of their ellipses. The third law pertained to the one characteristic common to all the planets: the sun. Taken together, the three laws led Newton to the concept of gravitational force and its inverse-square form.

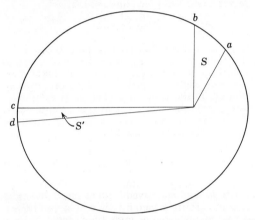

FIG. 1. Kepler's second law. The sector area S swept out is proportional to the time required for the planet to move from a to b. Thus, if $t_{cd} = t_{ab}$, then $S' = S$ (from Berman A. I., "The Physical Principles of Astronautics," New York, John Wiley & Sons, 1961).

By applying Newton's law of motion $\mathbf{F} = m\mathbf{a}$, a relationship between $\mathbf{a}$, the second derivative of the position vector, expressed in polar form, and $\mathbf{F}/m$ or $\mathbf{g}$, as given by Eq. (2), leads to the familiar conic solution for the trajectory of an object in an inverse square field.

$$\frac{1}{r} = \frac{\gamma m'}{h^2} + A \cos(\phi - \phi_0) \qquad (6)$$

where A and ϕ_0 are constants. A rotation of axis will eliminate ϕ_0, thereby aligning the coordinate axis with the conic's major axis. Also, by expressing the general conic, an ellipse or hyperbola, in terms of the usual parameters of semimajor axis a and eccentricity ϵ, we can relate the geometric parameters to the gravitational-dynamical constants, viz:

$$h = [\gamma m' a (1 - \epsilon^2)]^{1/2} \qquad (7)$$

and

$$\frac{1}{r} = \frac{\gamma m'}{h^2}(1 + \epsilon \cos\phi) \qquad (8)$$

Note that by substituting Eq. (7) into Eq. (5) and expressing the area of an ellipse as $S = \pi a^2 (1 - \epsilon^2)^{1/2}$ we arrive at Kepler's third law,

$$T = \frac{2\pi}{(\gamma m')^{1/2}} a^{3/2} \qquad (9)$$

The *energy* of the orbiting object can be calculated with ease by evaluating it at an extremal point, say the nearest point to the gravitational source, called pericenter or perifocus. As the energy is constant, it is immaterial where the calculation is made. Here the velocity has only an angular component so that the kinetic energy for a unit orbiting mass is $\frac{1}{2}v^2 = \frac{1}{2}r^2\dot\phi^2$. The potential energy at pericenter is $-(\gamma m'/r_{pe})$ where r_{pe} is the distance of the unit mass from m', the focal point. Here $\phi = 0$ so that by Eq. (8),

$$\frac{1}{r_{pe}} = \frac{\gamma m'}{h^2}(1 + \epsilon) \qquad (10)$$

On substituting Eq. (7), we find the total kinetic and potential energy to be

$$E = -\frac{\gamma m'}{2a} \qquad (11)$$

Our conclusion: All objects in orbit with the same major axes have identical periods and identical energies per unit mass. Knowledge of E is invaluable in determining an object's speed when its distance from the source is known, and vice versa.

In the event that the orbiting object's mass is not negligibly small compared with that of the gravitational source, one must take note that the combined center of mass, from which the acceleration is described, no longer may be assumed to lie in the center of the gravitational source. This complicates our equations somewhat, for the accelerating force still is expressed relative to the center of the source (if spherical). The adjustment that results, when center of mass coordinates are transformed to relative coordinates in the expression for acceleration, requires our equations to take the form $\gamma(m' + m)$ wherever formerly $\gamma m'$ appeared.

Disturbances in the Central Field The earth, of course, is spherical only to a first approximation. More accurately, it is an ellipsoid of revolution about a minor axis—an oblate spheroid. Still more accurately, it appears to be slightly pear-shaped and, in addition, its figure is distorted by continuous local variations. The spheroidal figure, nevertheless, accounts for nearly all the anomalous effects of satellite orbits. For one thing, the gravitational force on the satellite is no longer centrally directed; the excessive mass in the equatorial plane produces a force on the satellite directed out of its orbital plane. The resultant torque causes the direction of the angular momentum vector to change; i.e., the plane containing the satellite's ellipse turns. The plane turns continuously about the polar axis maintaining its angle with the axis and with the

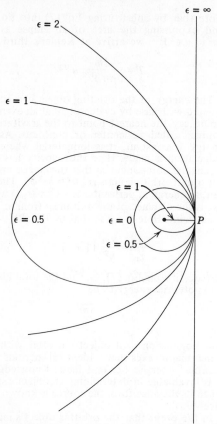

$\epsilon = \infty$

$\epsilon = 2$

$\epsilon = 1$

$\epsilon = 1$

$\epsilon = 0.5$

$\epsilon = 0$

P

$\epsilon = 0.5$

FIG. 2. Orbits of differing eccentricities and major axes which pass through a common point. Higher speeds correspond to higher energies and longer major axes (from Berman, A. I., "The Physical Principles of Astronautics," New York, John Wiley & Sons, 1961).

equatorial plane constant. The turning rate is greatest for low orbits and small angles of inclination with the equator. For polar satellites, the plane remains fixed. A separate effect of this equatorial bulge perturbative force is the slow turning of the ellipse's major axis *within* the orbital plane. This effect vanishes at an inclination of 63.4°; the major axis turns backward at inclinations above this angle and forward below.

Rocket Propulsion A rocket operates by the simple principle that if a small part of its total mass is ejected at high speed, the remaining mass will receive an impulse driving it in the opposite direction at a moderate speed. As δm_e, the propellant, leaves at speed v_e with respect to the rocket, the remaining rocket mass m receives a boost in speed δv such that

$$\delta m_e v_e = m \, \delta v \qquad (12)$$

If additional equal propellant mass is ejected at the same speed, the boost in rocket speed is slightly greater than before as the rocket mass has been slightly depleted by the prior ejection. Indeed, if the residual rocket mass eventually were minuscule, its boost in speed could reach an enormous value. The integrated effect of these nonlinear boosts is found as

$$v_t - v_0 = v_e \log_e \frac{m_0}{m_t} \qquad (13)$$

where v_0 and m_0 are the rocket speed and mass at some arbitrary initial time and v_t and m_t are the same quantities at some time t later.

From these simple considerations, it is apparent that the highest rocket velocities are attained if we could increase the propellant speed as well as the mass ratio m_0/m_t. The mass ratio can be maximized by obvious methods such as

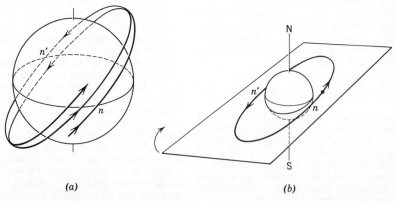

(a)

(b)

FIG. 3. The orbit of an earth satellite. The earth's equatorial bulge causes retrograde motion of the points of intersection n and n' of the orbit and equatorial plane. This can alternatively be interpreted as a retrograde motion, about the north-south axis, of the plane containing the closed orbit. The plane moves in the direction shown by the arrow in (b), maintaining a constant angle with the axis (from Berman, A. I., "The Physical Principles of Astronautics," New York, John Wiley & Sons, 1961).

choosing a high-density propellant which cuts
the tankage requirement or avoiding unneces-
sarily complicated apparatus for ejecting propellant at high speed. A nuclear rocket, for example, may perform well in its ability to eject
propellant an order of magnitude higher in
velocity than conventional chemical rockets;
nevertheless, the penalty required in reactor
weight and shielding severely limits its
effectiveness.

Specific impulse is one performance characteristic which applies to the propellant's ability
to be ejected at high speed regardless of the
weight penalty required to do this. It is the impulse produced per mass of propellant ejected,
or $m\delta v/\delta m_e$, or, by Eq. (12), simply v_e. In engineering usage, it is impulse per *weight* of propellant ejected, or v_e/g_e where g_e is the acceleration of gravity at the earth's surface. Its units
are seconds, and it can be interpreted as the
thrust produced by a rocket per weight of propellant ejected per second. By itself, thrust is of
little importance unless it is sustained for a significant time by a large backup of propellant
tankage. It is here that the mass-ratio term in
Eq. (13) would play an important role in any
evaluation of a rocket's true performance.

Transfer Orbits If one wishes to leave one
orbit and enter another by rocket, an optimum
path is generally chosen to minimize the total
propellant required. Nevertheless, this should
not be done at the expense of unduly long
flight times, complicated guidance equipment,
or high acceleration stresses. These would require unprofitable weight expenditures which
would offset the frugality in propellant
tankage.

Let us examine a simple but recurring example of a transfer problem, that of leaving a space
platform in one circular orbit and entering another larger one concentric with the first. If the
transfer path were radial or near radial (a so-
called ballistic orbit) then one would have to
launch at a large angle to the direction of motion of the platform, accomplished only by a
velocity component opposed to the platform's
motion. On reaching the outer platform, a soft
landing can be made only by a substantial
rocket velocity boost tangent to the orbit.
Clearly, the total propellant expenditure would
be far greater than one alternative of launching
the rocket in the direction of motion of the
first platform with just sufficient speed to
reach the outer circle, timed so that the outer
platform will meet the spacecraft. The transfer
orbit will be an ellipse contangent with both
circles. The outer platform will be moving
much faster of course at the contact point as
the major axis of its orbit is much greater [see
Eq. (11)], but the difference in speed is not
nearly as pronounced as for the ballistic transfer case. A differential speed increment at contact completes the maneuver.

The return trip, from an outer to inner circle,
is made by following the second half of this co-

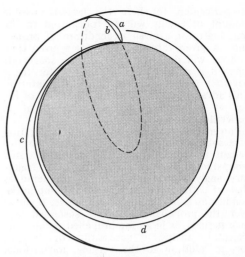

FIG. 4. Four launch trajectories into a satellite
orbit about a planet. (a) If that planet has an atmosphere, the rocket may ascend in a "synergic" trajectory from the planetary surface to the final orbit,
i.e., it cuts through the denser portions in an initially
vertical path and gradually bends over into a horizontal path during burnout. (b) If there is no atmosphere it may ascend from the ground in a ballistic
ellipse. This same ascent path may be chosen if the
departure is from a parking orbit or "space platform"
close to ground level. A far better choice would be
(c) the Hohmann ellipse, with pericenter at the
planet's surface and apocenter at the satellite orbit.
Burnout time is assumed short in both this and the
ballistic case. (d) A vehicle such as an ion rocket,
which can sustain a microthrust for a very long time,
cannot be launched from the ground but only from a
parking orbit. It will spiral out to the desired altitude
with few or many turns about the planet, depending
on the magnitude of the thrust relative to that of the
gravitational force (from Berman, A. I., "The Physical
Principles of Astronautics," New York, John Wiley
& Sons, 1961.

tangent ellipse, named the Hohmann transfer
orbit after the German engineer who discovered
its optimal property with regard to propellant
expenditure. In the return case, the spacecraft
is launched in opposition to the outer platform's motion. This removes kinetic energy and
forces the spacecraft to fall in closer to the attractive center in order to make cotangent
contact with the inner circle. The total propellant expenditure from the outer to the inner
platform is the same as for the original journey.

An interesting question arises if one wishes to
leave a platform for an outer orbit when it
initially is in an elliptical orbit rather than a
circle. Should we depart from apocenter where
we are furthest from the gravitational source
and closest to our destination? Or should we
depart instead from some other point in the
ellipse? Paradoxically, our best launch point is

at pericenter, for here the largest possible amount of energy will be transferred to the spacecraft for a given expenditure of propellant. A given thrust applied for a given time interval will do more work on the spacecraft when it is moving fast, as at pericenter, for it covers a greater distance during the interval. This advantage offsets the undesirability of being at a lower potential energy point at pericenter.

Powered Trajectories In the usual operation of a solid- or liquid-propelled rocket, the propellant is depleted in a time negligibly small compared with the total flight time. The trajectory analysis may generally be considered as that of a free orbit subject to burnout initial conditions as in the discussion above. If, however, the propellant ejection is sustained over long periods, as in an ion-propelled rocket, the trajectory analysis is necessarily complicated, for, in addition to the varying gravitational force, the vehicle, of slowly diminishing mass, is subject to a thrust which may be changing both in direction and magnitude. Even one of the simplest thrust programs, a constant thrust in the direction of motion, requires an electronic computer analysis in order to obtain the position and velocity at future times (see ELECTRIC PROPULSION).

The continuous-thrust trajectory is a spiral with many advantages over the orbital ellipses. First, the lower sustained thrust precludes the high-acceleration stresses associated with rapid-burning chemical rockets. Much of the structural weight usually needed to withstand these stresses can be replaced by propellant. Also, flights to the extremities of a gravitational region may take a shorter time in a spiral trajectory. In a long Hohmann ellipse, for example, most of the journey is made at very low speed. In a powered spiral, on the other hand, the spacecraft could be made to move fast, for the thrust, though small, is integrated over many months.

The spiral concept is ideal for rockets where very high ejection velocities are feasible by using electromagnetic or electrostatic particle accelerators, but only at the expense of a low propellant flow rate and relatively heavy power-generating equipment. However, the propellant reserve, and thrust, could then last the required long time. Such an ion rocket with its very low thrust-to-weight ratio could hardly be expected to take off from the ground, and could only take off from an orbital platform. In the vacuum of space, the ion beam meets its ideal environment.

ARTHUR I. BERMAN

References

Berman, Arthur I., "The Physical Principles of Astronautics," New York, John Wiley & Sons, 1961.

Moulton, Forest Ray, "An Introduction to Celestial Mechanics," New York, The Macmillan Co., 1914.

Danby, J. M. A., "Fundamentals of Celestial Mechanics," New York, The Macmillan Co., 1962.

Sterne, Theodore E., "An Introduction to Celestial Mechanics," New York, Interscience Publishers, 1960.

Berman, Arthur I., "Notes from a Lonely Planet: The Physics of Space Flight," New York, Doubleday Book Co., 1972.

Cross-references: AERODYNAMICS; ASTRODYNAMICS; DYNAMICS; ELECTRIC PROPULSION; FLIGHT PROPULSION FUNDAMENTALS; GRAVITATION; INERTIAL GUIDANCE; KEPLER'S LAWS OF PLANETARY MOTION; MASS AND INERTIA; ROTATION–CIRCULAR MOTION; WORK, POWER, AND ENERGY.

ASTROPHYSICS (See also ASTROMETRY, COSMOLOGY, SOLAR PHYSICS)

Starting with the advent of photography and the study of stellar spectra in the second half of the nineteenth century, astrophysics now includes optical and radio observations of stars, clusters, interstellar material, galaxies and clusters of galaxies, and their interpretation. Radiation from these external sources provides information on the direction of the source, its velocity, composition, temperature and other physical conditions, including magnetic fields, density, degree of ionization, and turbulence. The term "astrophysics" is generally understood to include all these aspects except the measurement of direction (positions of stars in the sky and changes due to parallax and proper motion), and the orbits of planets, asteroids and comets (celestial mechanics). Because of its proximity, the sun can be studied in more detail than other stars; its structure and its influence on the nearby planets and comets are the concern of SOLAR PHYSICS and are closely related to geophysics and stellar astrophysics. Study of the motions of stars in pairs, groups, clusters, associations, and galaxies is the overlap of celestial mechanics with astrophysics, and the study of the distribution and patterns of motion of the distant galaxies is the overlap with "COSMOLOGY."

Early studies of stellar spectra revealed differences due primarily to surface temperature and described by the sequence of spectral types ranging from "O" (30 000 K or more) through "B," "A," "F," "G," and "K" to "M" (2000 to 3000 K). The type of a spectrum is set by relative intensities of lines and bands due to ions, atoms, and molecules. The earth's atmosphere limits the wavelength region observable from terrestrial observatories since ozone and other constituents are opaque at wavelengths $\lambda < 3000\text{Å}$, and water vapor bands block much of the region $1.2\mu < \lambda < 8\mu$. The ionized layers block radio waves longer than 20 meters. Nevertheless, thousands of spectrum lines, mostly in absorption, have been identified in the range $3000 < \lambda < 12000\text{Å}$, and the pattern of lines within one spectral type has been found to vary

with a second parameter, the "luminosity class" designated by roman numerals "I" (highly luminous "super giants") through "II", "III", "IV" to "V" ("dwarfs" of relatively low luminosity).

The continuum between spectral lines has an intensity distribution with wavelength that roughly matches Planck's theoretical distribution for a blackbody, $B(\lambda)\,d\lambda = 2hc^2\lambda^{-5}(e^{hc/\lambda kT} - 1)^{-1}$ where T is the temperature that accounts approximately for the ionization and excitation of atoms producing the star's line spectrum, or the dissociation of molecules producing bands—that is, for the spectral type. In so far as the lines can be ignored, the color of a star is approximately that of a blackbody of temperature T and the total ("bolometric") luminosity is given by $L_b = 4\pi R^2 \sigma T^4$, where R is the radius of the star and σ is Stefan's constant. The "apparent brightness" of a star (observed optical flux) depends upon its distance, D, and its luminosity in the wavelength region observed—approximately $4000 < \lambda < 6500$Å for visual observations and $3700 < \lambda < 5000$Å for photographic observations through glass optics. Recently the introduction of photoelectric equipment has allowed more accurate measurements in smaller wavelength regions. Standard measures are designated U (ultraviolet), B (blue), V (visual), I (infrared), etc., and are usually expressed in magnitudes, an inverse, logarithmic scale. By successive approximations in such measurements of many stars, it has been possible to correct for the effects of interstellar absorption and limited wavelength range, as well as for the inverse-square law $(1/D^2)$, to obtain total luminosities and colors. The luminosities are often expressed in "suns", that is, multiples of the sun's luminosity (about 4×10^{33} ergs/sec). Analogous measurements at radio frequencies are expressed as the flux in watts/square meter/cycle/second. Spectrophotometric measurements from rockets and artificial satellites above the earth's atmosphere have been made in the far ultraviolet, and it is to be expected that the intensity distribution, $I(\lambda)$, will soon be observed for all wavelengths.

X-ray observations started in 1962, using ionization chambers and Geiger counters mounted on rockets and sent up for a few minutes above the earth's atmosphere. As the rocket rotated, the x-ray detectors scanned part of the sky, but the angular resolution was at first poor (about 3°). Still, these early observations showed several discrete sources (Sco X-1, Sco X-2, Tau X-1, Cyg X-1, etc.) named for the constellation in which each is located. The nature of these x-ray sources is uncertain; they are many light-years distant, and their energy output is very high. Some are star-like in size, and thought to be the remnants of old supernovae—possibly neutron stars; others are whole galaxies, and our Milky Way has a faint x-ray background. The measured flux is given in counts/cm^2-sec, each count representing a quantum of about 1 Å wavelength, or about 10^4 eV, or 1.6×10^{-8} erg.

Gamma rays of wavelength about 10^{-3} Å (energy 10 MeV) can also be detected above the atmosphere using scintillation counters—crystals that emit a flash of light when penetrated by a gamma ray. There are very few discrete gamma-ray sources strong enough to be detected; the spectrum of x-ray sources decreases rapidly with decreasing wavelength. However, strong solar flares emit gamma rays, and there is a faint background over the whole sky associated with COSMIC RAYS.

The major gap in observed spectra, $I(\lambda)$, is from $\lambda = 0.08$ to 2.5 mm, between the far infrared and short radio waves. In the far infrared, measurements from high-flying aircraft and spacecraft show many star-like objects and a few galaxies that are strong emitters between $\lambda = 0.02$ and 0.08 mm.

The *masses* of stars are determined from motions of double stars, ranging from widely separated visual binaries whose relative motions can be photographed, to close spectroscopic and eclipsing binaries with orbits calculated from variations in radial velocity or observed Doppler shift. Among some 50 pairs, masses of individual stars are found from 0.08 to 20 solar masses, and there is less definite evidence of others as low as 0.03 and as high as 50 or 100. (One solar mass is 2×10^{33} gm.) Over most of this range the luminosity L is proportional to M^3.

Astrophysical theory has achieved considerable success in explaining the spectra of stars by theoretical models of the atmospheres, involving the surface temperature, surface gravity, abundances of chemical elements, turbulence, rotation, and magnetic fields. The strengths of absorption lines are found to fit a "curve of growth," the relation between measured line strengths and the strengths predicted by quantum theory for unit abundance of the one ion, atom, or molecule involved. The theory of stellar interiors further relates mass M, luminosity L, and radius R with chemical abundances, the opacity of the material, and the generation of energy by nuclear reactions. More spectacularly, it has explained stellar evolution in terms of changes due to nuclear reactions.

The theoretical models of *stellar interiors* are based on stability and two modes of transferring energy outward to the surface: radiative transfer and convective transfer. Radiative transfer, by repeated emission, absorption, and emission of light, implies a temperature gradient dependent on the opacity and on the flow of radiative energy, or L. After calculating the opacity of gaseous stellar material (about 60 per cent hydrogen, 35 per cent helium, and 5 per cent heavier elements, by weight) at various temperatures and densities, the astrophysicist can compute the temperature, density and pressure in shells at various depths inside a star, starting with a definite radius and surface temperature, and adding up the shell masses to get the total

mass. At some level, the temperature and density are sufficiently high for nuclear reactions to take place, the simplest being conversion of hydrogen to helium generating 7×10^{18} ergs of energy per gram. The rate of energy generation over the whole inner core must match L. Calculations for convective transfer follow a similar pattern but depend upon matching the adiabatic gas law for over-all stability. A combined model may have a convective core surrounded by a radiative shell and that surrounded by an outer convective shell.

The successful fitting of nuclear energy generation into such gas-sphere models of stars by 1940 led to the idea of *stellar evolution*, the conversion of hydrogen to helium in its core causing a star to age. Direct evidence of this aging was first obtained from clusters of stars. The stars in one cluster, relatively close together in space, are assumed to have been formed at the same time, and the pattern of stellar characteristics differs from one cluster to another in a systematic way. The pattern is easily recognized on a Hertzsprung-Russell ("H-R") diagram of log L vs spectral type (or color) on which the vast majority of stars appear near a diagonal line, the "main sequence."

Several other classes of stars can be distinguished by location on the H-R diagram ("red giants," "white dwarfs," etc.) and theories of stellar evolution account for a change in location along an "evolutionary track" for any one star. The rate of such change will vary in general; for instance, the large-mass, high-L blue stars are expected to exhaust their hydrogen in a few million years, whereas yellow and red dwarfs remain for billions of years on the main sequence. H-R diagrams for clusters confirm the aging (also the theoretical star models and the assumption of cluster origin) and provide evidence of the age of each cluster.

A large part of astrophysical research is devoted to filling in the details of stellar evolution and the variety of nuclear reactions involved. For example, after its hydrogen is exhausted, the core of a giant star contracts and heats up to a billion degrees; then helium combines to form carbon, providing a new intense source of energy, and gas is probably blown off the star. Later, a small white dwarf remains. The explosion driving off a large fraction of a star's mass probably accounts for *supernovae*, which are seen every 100 years or so in our Milky Way and in other galaxies. One that was seen to blow up in A.D. 1054 now has a large expanding cloud of ionized gas around it—the Crab Nebula in Taurus. Near the center is a peculiar small star thought to be the core of the supernova, possibly a *neutron star* with density (of pure neutrons) about 10^{15} gm/cm^3 .

In 1968 this was confirmed when astronomers in England discovered a rapidly pulsating radio source, the first of about 50 *pulsars* now known, one of which is near the center of the Crab Nebula. By 1970 it was fairly well agreed that pulsars are rapidly rotating neutron stars with strong magnetic fields that interact with surrounding gas to emit a radio pulse on each rotation. This pulse timing is accurately periodic—1.33730 sec for the first pulsar discovered —but the pulses measured in different radio frequencies (wavelengths) are out of step, an effect due to the ionized gas along the line of sight. In several cases, the period of the pulses (star rotation period) has been found to be increasing by 10^{-6} sec or so each year, showing the "braking" action of the surrounding gas. (see PULSARS).

The *formation of a star* starts with gravitational contraction of a large cloud ("nebula") of interstellar gas and dust, including matter ejected from previous generations of giant stars. The recycling of material back and forth from nebulae to stars involves changes in composition—the abundances of helium and heavy elements increasing with time. Since 1954, astrophysicists have therefore been concerned with *nucleogenesis*, the creation of the chemical elements in stars (or in an early stage of the evolving universe). Differences in composition of stars in various locations are now interpreted as evidence of past star making.

The *formation of the solar system* (sun, planets, asteroids, meteors, and comets) is one case of star formation studied in great detail by astrophysicists, geologists and chemists. Radioactive dating of minerals in the earth, moon, and meteorites places this event about five billion years ago when a slowly rotating nebula contracted, forming earth and planets, but losing a good deal of its mass in the process. Fractionation of chemical elements and compounds during the condensation is linked with astrophysical interpretation of chemical analyses of meteorites, and lunar and terrestrial minerals.

Interstellar material in the form of bright nebulae has been known since telescopes were first used. During the first two decades of this century, evidence was collected showing less obvious clouds of dust and interstellar gas in the plane of the Milky Way, based on the obscuring and color effects of dust and the spectral absorption lines of gas (primarily sodium and ionized calcium). In 1945 the polarization of starlight caused by the interstellar dust was discovered, and in 1950 the radio telescope added the emission by interstellar atomic hydrogen at 21-cm wavelength. This interstellar medium is now known to extend in a thin, flat slab centered in the Milky Way. When highly luminous blue stars are in or near it, the gas is ionized by ultraviolet radiation, and the resulting electrons produce emission lines of hydrogen, oxygen, helium and other elements by recombination or by electron excitation. In addition to such "H II regions," the dimensions of which depend on the temperature and luminosity of the exciting star and the density of the medium, astrophysicists have studied more complex nebulae in which the material density varies from one place to another. The interstellar medium is often denser near young clusters or individual

blue stars, as expected from the theory of star formation

Since 1963, radio astronomers have detected 20 different kinds of molecules in the intersteller medium, mostly in dark clouds of dust where light from stars cannot penetrate. These molecules consist of the most common atoms, H, C, N, and O; two include sulfur (S), and one silicon (Si). Absorption lines of CH and CN were discovered in optical spectra of stars about 1940, and H_2 in far-ultraviolet spectra was taken from a rocket above the atmosphere in 1969. The study of these molecules is the new subject of *astrochemistry*, and involves such questions as how the interstellar molecules are formed, what other ones should be there, and the conditions (density, temperature, turbulent motions) of the gas. Preliminary estimates are that most of the simple diatomic molecules (8 of the 20) may be formed by collisions in space; the more complex ones, such as H_2CO_2, CH_3CN, and NH_3CO, are probably formed on grains of interstellar dust in clouds where the concentration of hydrogen molecules (H_2) is $10^6/cm^3$ or higher.

The molecular absorption lines are at slightly different wavelengths when heavy *isotopes* ^{13}C or ^{18}O are involved instead of ^{12}C or ^{16}O, and the line strengths show the relative abundances, or "isotope ratios," which are related to the source of the interstellar gas. Relative strengths of different spectral lines from the same molecule show that the excitation temperature in instellar clouds is very low—about 3 K, and the absolute strengths of the spectral lines show that the density of, for instance, CO is 20 molecules/cm³. Two molecules, OH and H_2O, show maser interaction; i.e., these molecules are excited so as to "pump" energy into a few selected radio wavelengths, which may come out of the gas cloud in a preferred direction.

The whole *Milky Way system* of stars, nebulae and interstellar gas and dust is assumed to be in dynamic equilibrium; that is, the mass distribution can be calculated from individual motions under the gravitational attraction of the whole galaxy, another important part of modern astrophysics. Since 1920 the dimensions of the galaxy have been determined from distances of the large bright globular clusters and from the distances of nearer stars. The resulting model, a flat disk with a high-density nucleus (total mass about 10^{11} suns) also fits the average motions of stars within a few thousand light years' distance from the sun, and the radial motions of cold atomic hydrogen out to 50 000 light-years determined by Doppler shifts in the 21-cm radio emission line. The stellar motions are derived from statistics of Doppler shifts and changes in direction, allowing for random individual motions differing from the general circulation.

Most of the stars in the Milky Way share in a circular velocity, v_c, around the center of the galaxy, and the mass distribution is inferred from the observed decrease of v_c with distance from the center. The globular clusters and many other stars appear to move in orbits at high inclination to the Milky Way plane, forming a "halo" around the center having little or no angular momentum. It thus appears that there are two populations in the galaxy: "Population I" stars, nebulae, gas and dust in the outer parts of a thin rotating disk, and "Population II" stars in the nonrotating halo, probably formed at an earlier time. A large fraction of Population I in the disk is in the form of nonluminous interstellar dust and gas, although this interstellar material is only 10 to 15 percent of the total mass of the system.

There is a weak *magnetic field* between the disk stars which probably lines up the interstellar dust particles like small magnetic needles, and this pattern accounts for the polarization of starlight passing through. The field also deflects moving ions and electrons, and may account for the energy of very high-speed *cosmic rays*. Lower-speed cosmic rays are ejected by solar flares, and other stars probably do the same. It is possible that these ejected ions are accelerated to enormous speeds by the uneven magnetic field in the Milky Way system. Cosmic rays are studied above the atmosphere to determine the relative abundance of different ions, their energy spectrum, and source. Their energy flux is about the same as starlight, and they probably affect the temperature of the interstellar gas. They certainly produce x-rays and gamma rays by collisions with atoms and molecules.

The many *other galaxies* well outside our own are found to include some (classed as "spirals") very similar to our Milky Way galaxy in structure and internal motions. Others are strikingly different (classed as "ellipticals"), probably due to different conditions of formation. All the techniques of astrophysics are being applied to the study of these objects: measurement of their sizes, luminosities, colors and masses, their proportion of interstellar material, the formation and evolution of their stars, etc. These physical characteristics are fairly well correlated with morphological type; the spirals are similar to our Milky Way, but the ellipticals have almost no interstellar material, and are much more massive for their size and luminosity than the spirals. The mass of a single galaxy can be measured from the rotational velocity, v_c, near the rim and the radius, R. Then $M = v_c^2 R/G$, where G is the gravitational constant, and $v_c = v/\sin i$, where v is measured from the relative Doppler shift (rim to center), and i is the inclination of the disk to the line of sight. However, R is poorly determined because galaxies do not have sharp rims. Many galaxies are in pairs, one orbiting around the other, for which $M_1 + M_2 = (v_1 - v_2)^2 S/G$, where S is the separation. However, the inclination of the orbit cannot be measured, and an average value of M must be obtained from statistics of many pairs. These two methods show that the average spiral has $M_S = 4 \times 10^{10}$ suns = 8×10^{43} gm, while the average elliptical has 30 times this mass. The

luminosity of either type is 10^{10} suns, on the average, so a spiral has about four times as much mass per watt of light output as the sun does, while an elliptical has over 100 times as much.

Most of the mass is concentrated in the nucleus of a galaxy, and several nuclei look as if they are exploding, possibly due to the *gravitational collapse* of about 10^{43} gm compressing itself into a very high-density object. Such explosions may explain the highly luminous quasars, and the high-density objects may become "black holes" that can explain the mass discrepancy in clusters.

Galaxies are observed in increasing numbers at larger and larger distances, roughly in uniform distribution, but with marked clustering. There is some evidence that compact clusters contain a preponderance of ellipticals; the total number of galaxies in the Coma Cluster is about 500, of which only a dozen are spirals. The total mass of such clusters can be measured by the relative velocities of galaxies near the edge, and when this was done (first in 1932), astrophysicists were surprised to find that the cluster mass is 5 to 10 times larger than the sum of all galaxy masses in it. This *mass discrepancy* means that we see only 10 to 20 percent of the material in a large region of space—possibly in the rest of the observed universe, as well. The "missing mass" may be a thin intergalactic gas or discrete, nonluminous objects.

The spectra of distant galaxies all show large red shifts which, if interpreted as Doppler shifts, indicate a recessional velocity proportional to distance (Hubble's Law). In fact, the red shift is used to measure all distances (D) larger than about 40 million light-years by $D = v_R / H$, where H = 17 km/sec/million light years. Starting in 1958, radio astronomers began to survey the whole sky for faint radio sources, and found that many galaxies are strong radio emitters. The most puzzling were faint, starlike (quasistellar) objects, soon named *quasars*. In 1963 these were found to have very large red shifts, therefore very far away (up to 5 billion light-years) and about 100 times more luminous than the average galaxy. This large energy output is probably an enormous explosion, lasting but a brief fraction of a galaxy's life. At these large distances, we see now the quasars as they were 5 billion years ago, and it seems likely that many galaxies exploded at that time (see QUASARS).

Here astrophysics leads into COSMOLOGY, based on general RELATIVITY. Observations of the short-wave (3-mm) radio emission coming from all over the sky (isotropic) seems to confirm the "big-bang" cosmological model of the universe, and to disprove the steady-state theory which assumes continuous creation of matter. The *isotropic background radiation* with $I(\lambda)$ matching a black body at 3 K, is the remnant of the very hot explosion about 20 billion years ago that sent the galaxies moving outward to the great distances where we see them today.

Astrophysical evidence for the missing mass in clusters of galaxies shows that the average density of matter in the universe is probably higher than 10^{-28} gm/cm^3 so that the space curvature predicted by general relativity fits the numbers of galaxies we count at different distances. For higher density of matter, the predicted curvature is larger, and at the extreme, space "wraps itself around" a large collapsed mass so that no light or radio waves can get in or out. This leaves a *"black hole"* which exerts gravitational attraction on distant masses, but cannot be seen—a possible explanation of the missing mass in clusters of galaxies.

THORNTON PAGE

References

Abel, G. O., "Exploring the Universe," 2nd Ed., New York, Holt, Rinehart and Winston, 1969.

Struve, Otto, and Zeebergs, "Astronomy of the 20th Century," New York, Macmillan, 1962.

Page, T., and Page, L. W., "The Evolution of Stars," New York, Macmillan, 1968.

Page, T., and Page, L. W., "Stars and Clouds of the Milky Way," New York, Macmillan, 1968.

Page, T., and Page, L. W., "Beyond the Milky Way," New York, Macmillan, 1969.

Aller, L. H., "Astrophysics," Vols. I and II, Ronald, 1953, 1963.

Allen, C. W., "Astrophysical Quantities," Athlone Press, 1963.

Burbidge, Burbidge, Fowler, and Hoyle, "Synthesis of the Elements in Stars," *Rev. Mod. Phys.*, **29**, 547 (1957).

Menzel, D. H., Whipple, F., and deVaucouleurs, G., "Survey of the Universe," Englewood Cliffs, N.J., Prentice-Hall, 1971.

Cross-references: ASTROMETRY, COSMOLOGY, DOPPLER EFFECT, PULSARS, QUASARS, RELATIVITY, SOLAR ENERGY SOURCES, SOLAR PHYSICS.

ATOMIC AND MOLECULAR BEAMS

This field of research utilizes a collision-free stream of neutral atoms or molecules as they traverse a vacuum chamber. With 10^{-6} mm Hg pressure in a vacuum chamber, air molecules at room temperature travel on the average about 300 meters between collisions and move with an average speed of about 500 m/sec. Between collisions these molecules are essentially "free" and unperturbed by molecules of the residual gas or by atoms in the walls of the apparatus. The mathematical description of such isolated systems is much less complicated than for denser gases, liquids, or solids containing interacting particles.

Since 1911, when Dunoyer proved that a stream of neutral atoms would remain collimated

in a vacuum, atomic- and molecular-beam research has become one of the most versatile, precise, and sensitive techniques for studying the properties of isolated atomic systems and interactions between such systems. Numerous fundamental discoveries in beam research have contributed to the present understanding of physical laws. The earliest experiments (1920) sought the molecular velocity distribution, which is important in the kinetic theory of gases. Atomic diameters (cross sections), van der Waals' interaction potentials, and polymer vapor composition were obtained after later refinements of technique. The Stern-Gerlach experiment (1924) demonstrated the validity of space quantization of angular momentum and established the electron spin as 1/2. This historic work placed quantum mechanics on a firmer foundation and initiated beam investigations of atomic and nuclear electromagnetic properties. Although many low-precision results appeared in subsequent years, high-precision spectroscopy began in 1937 with the introduction of the magnetic-resonance method by Rabi. In this method, transitions between quantum states separated by an energy $h\nu$ are induced by a radio-frequency field of frequency ν (h is Planck's constant). From the Heisenberg uncertainty principle, the width of the rf resonance is small, owing to the long lifetimes of the beam quantum states and to the ability to irradiate the beam with radio frequency for as long as a few milliseconds along its path.

Precision atomic-beam measurements have contributed to many theoretical and practical developments. The deuteron quadrupole moment (1939) pointed to the necessity of a tensor interaction in nuclear forces. The anomalous electron moment (1949) and the Lamb shift (1950) in the atomic-hydrogen fine structure were resolved by quantum electrodynamics. Nuclear spins (I) as well as magnetic-dipole (μ) and electric-quadrupole (Q) moments have been important in providing test information for the shell model (1949) and collective model (1953) of the nucleus. Atomic hyperfine-structure constants (dipole, a; quadrupole, b; and octupole, c), which describe the interaction between the electrons and the nucleus, as well as the numerous constants required to describe a molecule and its internal interactions, have contributed to the theory of atomic and molecular structure. The cesium "clock" or frequency standard (1952) represents a widespread practical application of beam technology by using the hyperfine-structure transition at 9192.631770 Hz (Ephemeris time) to regulate a quartz-crystal oscillator. Other frequency standards such as the thallium clock, ammonia maser (1954), and hydrogen maser (1960) also employ beam techniques for quantum-state selection. Very recent, high-energy nuclear accelerators have been equipped with atomic-beam sources to produce polarized protons.

Among nonresonant experiments, beams impinging on solid surfaces produce information on the wave nature of particles, work functions, and accomodation coefficients. Charge-exchange cross sections and interaction potentials are obtained from experiments with crossed beams, one neutral and one charged. Chemical reaction kinetics in isolated systems are studied in crossed beams of two reactants.

Four individuals have received Nobel Prizes for beam research: Otto Stern (1943) "for his contribution to the development of the molecular-ray method and for his discovery of the magnetic moment of the proton"; I. I. Rabi (1944) "for his application of the resonance method to the measurement of the magnetic properties of atomic nuclei"; P. Kusch (1955) "for his precision determination of the magnetic moment of the electron"; and W. E. Lamb (1955) "for his discoveries concerning the fine structure of the hydrogen spectrum."

A discussion of the energy levels of a simple atom and of one particular apparatus will illustrate the magnetic-resonance technique. An isolated atom in an external field, H, has energy states which are calculable from the Hamiltonian

$$\mathcal{H}/h \text{ (Hz)} = a\mathbf{I} \cdot \mathbf{J} + b \text{ (quadrupole operator)}$$

$$- g_J(\mu_0/h)\mathbf{J} \cdot \mathbf{H} - g_I(\mu_0/h)\mathbf{I} \cdot \mathbf{H}.$$

where some symbols have been defined previously, $g_J = \mu_J/(J\mu_0)$, $g_I = \mu_I/(I\mu_0)$, and μ_0 is the magnitude of the Bohr magneton. The first two terms represent the dipole and quadrupole hyperfine-structure interactions between the electrons and nucleus; the last two terms express the interaction of the electron and nuclear magnetic moments with the external magnetic field. For the simple case of $I = 1/2$, $J = 1/2$, $b = 0$, as in the ground electronic state of atomic hydrogen, the energy levels that arise from different "relative orientations" of the nuclear (I) and electronic (J) spins are shown in Fig. 1 as a function of the magnetic-field parameter $X = [(-g_J + g_I)\mu_0 H]/\Delta W$. Here ΔW is the hyperfine-structure separation at $H = 0$. The levels are labeled by either the low-field quantum numbers (F, m_F) or by the high-field numbers (m_J, m_I), where $F = |I \pm J|$, and the m's are the projections of F, I, or J along the field direction.

Of the many magnetic or electric resonance apparatuses, one specialized type has proved valuable for measuring atomic properties of both stable and radioactive isotopes. In Fig. 2, the "oven" or source, O, may take one of many forms—a microwave discharge to dissociate gaseous diatomic molecules, a closed tantalum crucible (with an exit slit) heated by electron bombardment, or one of many other devices for evaporating atoms. The atoms pass between the poles of three separate electromagnets (denoted A, C, and B, successively, from oven to detector). The inhomogeneous A and B magnets have eccentric cylindrical pole tips which produce a field gradient, $\partial H/\partial Z$. In this field, an atom experiences a force $\mathbf{F} = \mu_{\text{eff}}(\partial \mathbf{H}/\partial Z)$, where

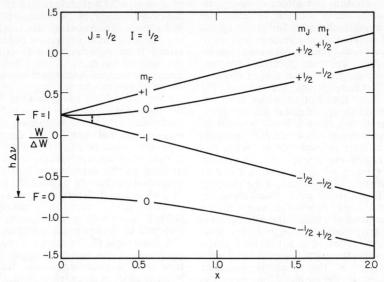

FIG. 1. Hyperfine-structure energies (ordinate) of an atom with $J = 1/2$ and $I = 1/2$ in an external magnetic field (abscissa).

$\mu_{\text{eff}}(= -\partial W/\partial H)$ is the negative slope of an energy level in Fig. 1. Within the homogeneous C field, a superimposed rf field induces state changes. Thus an atom which remains in a single state [(1, 0) for example] is deflected similarly by the strong A and B magnets and follows trajectory 1 in Fig. 2. The stopwire, S, shields the detector from fast atoms and atoms with small deflections. If, in the C-field region, a transition occurs that causes the high-field slope ($-\mu_{\text{eff}}$) to change sign [e.g., $(1, 0) \rightarrow (1, -1)$], the A and B deflections are opposite, and the atom follows trajectory 2 to the detector D. A resonance is observed as an increase in beam intensity at the

detector. Values of the constants in the Hamiltonian are deduced from the observed resonant frequencies of the atoms in known magnetic fields. Some detection methods in frequent use are:

(a) Deposition on a surface with subsequent assay by radioactive counting, neutron activation, or optical means (earliest detector).

(b) Ionization of alkali atoms on a hot tungsten wire, and measurement of the resulting ion current.

(c) Electron-bombardment ionization with subsequent mass analysis to discriminate against background gas ions. The beam ions are fre-

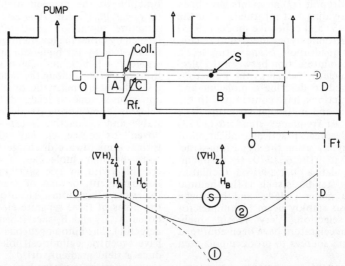

FIG. 2. Schematic of an atomic-beam, magnetic resonance apparatus.

quently counted by using electron multiplier tubes.

(d) Other detectors employing the principles of radiometers, pressure manometers, thermopiles, bolometers, and changes in space charge.

HOWARD A. SHUGART

References

English, T. C., and Zorn, J. C., "Molecular Beam Spectroscopy" in "Methods of Experimental Physics," vol. 3, 2nd edition, Academic Press Inc., New York, 1973.

Estermann, I., Ed., "Recent Research in Molecular Beams," a collection of papers dedicated to Otto Stern, on the occasion of his seventieth birthday, New York, Academic Press, 1959.

Kopfermann, H., "Nuclear Moments," English translation by E. E. Schneider, New York, Academic Press, 1958.

Kusch, P., and Hughes, V. W., in Flügge, S., Ed., "Handbuch der Physik," Vol. 37/1, Berlin, Springer Verlag, 1959.

Nierenberg, W. A., in *Ann. Rev. Nucl. Sci.*, 7, 349 (1957)

Ramsey, N. F., "Molecular Beams," London Oxford University Press, 1956.

Smith, K. F., "Molecular Beams," London, Methuen and Company, 1955.

Cross-references: ATOMIC CLOCKS, CROSS SECTION AND STOPPING POWER, MAGNETIC RESONANCE, CHEMICAL KINETICS.

ATOMIC CLOCKS

Atomic clocks make use of a property that is generally found only in systems of atomic dimensions: such systems cannot contain arbitrary amounts of energy, but are restricted to an array of allowed energy values $E_0, E_1, \cdots, E_n$. If an atomic system wants to change its energy between two allowed values, it must emit (or absorb) the energy difference, for instance by emission (or absorption) of a quantum of electromagnetic radiation. The frequency f_{ij} of this radiation is determined by the famous relation

$$| E_i - E_j | = \Delta E = h f_{ij}$$

(h is Planck's constant). The rate of an atomic clock is controlled by the frequency f_{ij} association with the transition from the state of energy E_i to the state of energy E_j of a specified atomic system (such as a cesium atom or an ammonia molecule). A high-frequency electromagnetic signal is stabilized in the atomic frequency f_{ij} and a frequency converter relates the frequency f_{ij} to a set of lower frequencies which then may be used to run a conventional electric clock.

The atomic frequency f_{ij} is, according to present knowledge, free of inherent errors; it is in particular not subject to "aging" since any transition which the system makes puts it in a state of completely different energy, where it cannot falsify the measurement. Herein lies the principal advantage over other methods of time measurement. Two atomic clocks have exactly the same calibration as long as they are calibrated against the same atomic transition. Atomic readings made in Boulder, Colorado and Neuchâtel, Switzerland between 1960 and 1963 differed on the average by less than 3 msec, whereas the deviation of the astronomically measured time TU_2 from atomic time is of the order of 50 msec[1]. For this reason, the atomic second was adopted as the new time unit, by the Twelfth General Conference on Weights and Measures, in October, 1964, and temporarily defined as the time interval spanned by 9 192 631 770 cycles of the transition frequency between two hyperfine levels of the atom of cesium-133 undisturbed by external fields.

The accuracy with which f_{ij} can be measured depends mainly on the degree to which the atomic resonator can be isolated from outside influences such as chemical and electromagnetic forces, and the extent to which Doppler shift can be avoided. Atomic transitions are chosen which have a minimum dependence on electromagnetic fields, and such fields as the magnetic field of the earth are carefully shielded out. Residual fields are nevertheless at present a major source of error in the most accurate clock. In many of the currently available clocks, the atomic systems are moving through vacuum with velocities of the order of 10^4 cm/sec. This motion introduces longitudinal Doppler shifts of the order $\sim 10^{-6} f_{ij}$. The transversal velocity causes only second-order shifts of the order $10^{-12} f_{ij}$. The transitions have to be observed mostly in the transverse direction, and residual longitudinal components must occur with either sign with equal probability, so as to produce, instead of shift, only a broadening that is symmetrical about f_{ij}. Whenever the systems collide with each other or are in contact with surrounding material, such as a buffer gas, they are perturbed by chemical forces and f_{ij} undergoes further shifts. Another source of error is the fact that most systems are observed only during a finite time τ. This circumstance gives rise to observation-time broadening of the order $1/\tau$ (typically, 10^2 Hz). The error introduced hereby is not given by the broadening δf, but only by $\delta f/r$, where r is the signal-to-noise ratio with which f_{ij} is observed. However, if the phase shift of the observing system varies appreciably over the line width δf, additional errors known as "pulling" are introduced.

Two main problems have to be solved in atomic clocks: the atomic system has to be suspended without perturbation from chemical forces, and the frequency f_{ij} has to be measured. The most radical solution of the first problem is found in molecular-beam devices. The atomic systems are observed in free flight, and only during the relatively short transit time, so that

observation-time broadening and Doppler shifts are large. Such devices have nevertheless provided the clocks with the highest accuracy so far, of the order of a few parts in 10^{11}. The problems associated with Doppler shift and observation-time broadening can be alleviated by enclosing the atomic system in a box that is small compared to the wavelength $\lambda = c/f_{ij}$. The problem is to find atomic systems and wall materials such that the radiative process is not interrupted, and the frequency f_{ij} not appreciably influenced, during collision of the atomic systems with the walls. Instead of walls, a buffer gas can also serve as a "container" for the atomic systems. Very long observation times, giving rise to resonances of very high Q, have been produced by this technique. The accuracy of such clocks depends on the degree to which the influence of chemical forces can be neutralized. An indication of the accuracy of which such devices may ultimately be capable can be found in the fact that the measurement of resonance radiation due to Fe^{57} nuclei built into a crystal lattice has made possible frequency determinations with a relative accuracy of some parts in 10^{14}, and effects on time due to general relativity have been measured by this method. However, very high frequencies ($\sim 10^{20}$ Hz) were involved, and no clock has been built for lack of a suitable frequency converter.[2]

The main methods of measuring f_{ij} are the following: in thermal equilibrium, the atomic systems in the lower-energy state outnumber the ones in the higher-energy state, and radiation of frequency f_{ij} induces more absorption than emission, giving rise to a net absorption signal. Several methods are known by which the population of either energy state is enhanced, giving rise to stronger absorption or emission signals. Particularly elegant is the maser principle. The higher-energy state population is sufficiently enhanced so that the emitted radiation itself can sustain the emission process. Often it is preferable to observe the absorption or emission of radiation of frequency f_{ij} indirectly. It is possible to observe microwave absorption via the change in the interaction of the absorbing atomic systems with optical radiation. Another example of indirect absorption is given by the atomic-beam method, where the microwave absorption is monitored by the deflection of the atoms from their trajectory. Indirect observation can be more economical since each microwave transition can be counted, whereas it takes several transitions to make a count by direct observation as long as the quanta to be counted carry less energy than the quanta of thermal radiation.

Several articles describing modern atomic clocks can be found in the Proceedings of the Third International Congress on Quantum Electronics, particularly in the third chapter of the first volume.[3]

MARTIN PETER

References

1. Bonanomi, J., Kartaschoff, P., Newman, J., Barnes, J. A., and Atkinson, W. R., "A Comparison of the TA-1, and NBS-A Atomic Time Scales," *Proc. I.E.E.E.*, **52**, 439 (1964).
2. Wertheim, G. K., "The Mössbauer Effect," *Nucleonics* (January, 1961).
3. Grivet, P., and Bloembergen, N., "Quantum Electronics," Vol. 1, Paris, New York, Columbia University Press, 1964.

Cross-references: ATOMIC AND MOLECULAR BEAMS, ATOMIC PHYSICS, ATOMIC SPECTRA, DOPPLER EFFECT, LASERS, MASER, QUANTUM THEORY, RELATIVITY.

ATOMIC ENERGY

The terms "atomic energy" and "nuclear energy" are used interchangeably in the contemporary literature to mean energy that originates within the atomic nucleus. Events that release atomic energy involve basic changes in nuclear structure and result in the formation of one or more different nuclides, which may be isotopes of the original atom or altogether different elements. The release of atomic energy is thus a more fundamental process than the release of chemical energy, which merely involves a regrouping of intact atoms into different molecular forms.

To date, three basic atomic energy mechanisms have been exploited in practical applications: (1) the fission of certain heavy nuclides; (2) the fusion of certain light nuclides; and (3) the process of radioactive decay. These will be discussed in the order listed.

Fission In fission, a heavy nuclide splits into two lighter and predominantly unstable nuclides, commonly referred to as fission products, with the accompanying emission of several neutrons and the release of approximately 200 MeV of energy. Nuclides that readily undergo fission on interaction with low-energy or "slow" neutrons (< 0.5 eV) are referred to as fissile materials. There are three primary fissile materials:

(1) Uranium 235, which is a natural constituent of the uranium element and accounts for 0.71 per cent by weight of that element as found in nature.

(2) Plutonium 239, formed by neutron irradiation of uranium 238.

(3) Uranium 233, formed by neutron irradiation of thorium 232.

Uranium 238, which does not undergo fission on interaction with slow neutrons, does so on interaction with high-energy or "fast" neutrons (> 0.1 MeV). Table 1 lists representative fission energy distributions for the four nuclides cited.

A useful rule of thumb is that an energy release of 200 MeV per fissioning atom corresponds to an output of approximately one

TABLE 1. ENERGY DISTRIBUTION IN FISSION

| Type of Energy | Quantity of Energy (MeV) | | | |
| | Slow Fission | | | Fast Fission |
	^{235}U	^{239}Pu	^{233}U	^{238}U
Kinetic energy of fission products	165	172	163	163
Kinetic energy of neutrons emitted	5	6	5	5
Instantaneous emission of gamma rays	8	7	7	7
Beta emission during fission product decay	9	9	9	9
Gamma emission during fission product decay	7	7	7	7
Total[a]:	194	201	191	191

[a]Exclusive of nonrecoverable energy associated with neutrino emission during fission product decay. All numbers are rounded to the nearest integer. It should be mentioned that 8 or 9 MeV of additional energy become available in a nuclear reactor as the result of neutron capture and subsequent gamma-decay phenomena.

megawatt-day of thermal energy per gram of fissioned matter.

Practical applications of fission are based on the principle of a self-sustaining fission chain reaction, i.e., a reaction in which a neutron emitted by atom A triggers the fission of atom B, and one from atom B triggers the fission of atom C, and so on. For this to be achieved requires the assembly of a "critical mass" of fissile material, i.e., an amount sufficient to reduce the probability of neutron losses to a threshold value. The amount required depends on a number of factors, notably the concentration of the fissile material used and the composition and geometry of the reaction system.

There are two basic application concepts. One is the essentially instantaneous fission of a mass of highly concentrated fissile material in such a way as to generate an explosive force. This, of course, is what occurs in atomic weapons. Atomic explosives are also of interest in connection with peaceful uses such as large-scale excavation projects, a field of application that is currently being studied by the U.S. Atomic Energy Commission.

The other application concept is that of the controlled and gradual fission of an atomic fuel in a nuclear reactor, which may be designed for one or more of the following principal purposes:

(1) To provide fluxes or beams of neutrons for experimental purposes. This category of use includes research and materials-testing reactors.

(2) To produce materials by neutron irradiation. Examples are reactors used primarily to produce plutonium for atomic weapon stockpiles or for the production of various radioisotopes for use in science and industry.

(3) To supply energy in the form of heat for such applications as the generation of electric power, the propulsion of ships or space vehicles, or the production of process steam.

The first demonstration of a fission chain reaction was achieved by E. Fermi and coworkers on December 2, 1942 when the world's first nuclear reactor (Chicago Pile No. 1) was successfully operated in a converted squash court beneath Stagg Field at the University of Chicago.

The most important application of fission promises to be in the electric power field. The basis for this expectation is that, if exploited efficiently, known and inferred deposits of atomic fuels represent a potential energy reserve many times larger than that of the fossil fuels (coal, oil and natural gas) on which the world's electric energy economy largely depends at present.

At this writing (1973), approximately 150,000 electrical megawatts of atomic power capacity are in operation, under construction, or planned for construction in the United States. In the neighborhood of 130,000 megawatts are expected to be in commercial service by 1980, which means that atomic power would then account for nearly 25 percent of the nation's total electric power capacity at that point in time and for a somewhat larger share of the total national electricity output. By the end of this century atomic power is expected to account for half the total electrical output and for substantially all major generating plant additions.

Fusion Fusion is a general term for reactions in which the nuclei of light elements combine to form heavier and more tightly bound nuclei with the simultaneous release of large amounts of energy. In order for this to occur the interacting nuclei must be brought sufficiently close together to permit short-range nuclear forces to become operative. This means that one or both nuclei must be accelerated ("heated") to velocities sufficient to overcome the strong electrostatic repulsion that exists between particles having the same electrical charge. The velocities required correspond to particle "temperatures" of the order of tens or hundreds of millions of degrees, which in turn correspond to particle energies of thousands or tens of thousands of electron volts. The term "thermonuclear" re-

actions is reserved for fusion reactions in which both nuclei are traveling at high velocity (as distinct from reactions between an accelerated projectile particle and a static target nucleus, as in particle accelerator experiments).

The only practical application of thermonuclear reactions developed to date is in thermonuclear weapons (so-called "hydrogen bombs") in which the energy released by a charge of fissile material serves to create the conditions required to bring about the reaction of "fusionable" materials. The first test of a thermonuclear weapon, which was the first demonstration of a man-made thermonuclear reaction, took place on October 31, 1952 at a U.S. testing site in the Marshall Islands. Peaceful uses of thermonuclear explosives are being studied and have the advantage, relative to straight fission-based explosives, that problems of radioactive contamination are greatly reduced. This reflects the fact that the nuclides formed by fusion are stable and hence, apart from neutron activation effects, the formation of radioactive substances is limited to the fission component of the explosive.

Research has been in progress for more than a decade on techniques for controlling the fusion process as a means of supplying energy for electric power generation. The thermonuclear reactions of primary interest in this context are the deuterium-tritium reaction:

$$D + T \rightarrow {}^4He + n + 17.6 \text{ MeV}$$

and the deuterium-deuterium reactions:

$$D + D \nearrow {}^3He + n + 3.2 \text{ MeV}$$
$$\searrow T + p + 4.0 \text{ MeV}$$

Deuterium is a stable isotope of hydrogen with a natural abundance of 0.0015 per cent. Tritium is an unstable hydrogen isotope with a radioactive half-life of 12.3 years and is produced from lithium 6 by the neutron-alpha reaction. The latter thus represents a relatively expensive "fuel" for thermonuclear reactions; however, the ignition temperature of the deuterium-tritium reaction is roughly an order of magnitude lower than that of the deuterium-deuterium reactions and the energy release is greater.

In most controlled fusion systems as presently conceived, the fuel is in the form of an ionized gas, or "plasma," confined by magnetic pressure within a high-vacuum apparatus. In effect, the plasma is held in a "magnetic bottle," thereby preventing fuel particles from dissipating heat in collisions with the physical walls of the apparatus. The objective is to achieve a situation in which an adequately hot plasma of adequate density can be magnetically confined for a long enough interval of time for the desired reaction to take place. One approach is to constrict and confine a high-current discharge of fuel ions and hold the resulting dense plasma in confinement while its temperature is raised by adiabatic compression or other methods. Another approach is to accelerate fuel ions to high energies and then trap them in a magnetic field, maintaining confinement long enough for a dense plasma to accumulate.

In experiments in various experimental devices, the time-temperature-density multiple has steadily been increased; however, there is as yet no conclusive evidence that true thermonuclear conditions have been achieved in any laboratory. Beyond laboratory demonstration of controlled fusion per se lies the problem of demonstrating that devices can be designed to produce more power than they consume and beyond that lies the problem of demonstrating the economic feasibility of practical thermonuclear power plants. Thus, at present (1973), controlled fusion is still at the stage of basic research.

The chief incentive for thermonuclear power development is the promise of a virtually inexhaustible energy source, assuming the ultimate use of deuterium as the primary fuel.

Radioactive Decay As radioactive atoms undergo decay by alpha, beta or gamma emission, heat is generated by the interaction of the radiation with surrounding matter. Devices that utilize this heat to produce electricity are known as isotopic power generators. A family of such devices is being developed by the U.S. Atomic Energy Commission for specialized applications requiring from fractions of a watt to tens of watts of electricity. Thermoelectric or thermionic techniques are used to convert the heat to electricity. Costs are presently about $10 000 per watt of electrical capacity. With further development and with volume production of isotopic "fuels," costs are expected to be reduced to the order of $100 per watt. At present, isotopic power generators are being used on an experimental basis in a number of applications such as navigational satellites, automatic weather stations and coastal light buoys, all of which require a compact power source that can operate unattended for sustained periods (months or years). In the case of space applications, alpha-emitting radionuclides such as plutonium 238 or curium 244 are mainly used as the fuel. In terrestrial applications, the principal fuel used to date is strontium 90, a beta emitter.

JOHN F. HOGERTON

References

Hogerton, John F., "The Atomic Energy Deskbook," New York, Van Nostrand Reinhold, 1963.
Glasstone, Samuel, "Sourcebook on Atomic Energy," New York, Van Nostrand Reinhold, 1958.

Cross-references: FISSION, FUSION, NUCLEAR REACTIONS, NUCLEAR REACTORS, NUCLEONICS, RADIOACTIVITY.

ATOMIC PHYSICS*

It is generally accepted by those who inquire into the properties of matter that these properties can be understood in terms of small constituents called atoms. The nature and structure of atoms was a principal subject of study by physicists and chemists during the first half of the twentieth century. As a consequence of the success of such studies, research into the structure of matter has become divided into two moderately well-separated fields. One of these concerns the further details of the structure of the atomic nucleus which is described under the terms "nuclear physics," and "high-energy physics." The other is a study of the behavior of large groups of atoms, and is generally described under the heading "solid-state physics." This article is devoted to the structure of atoms themselves, a field which, in a sense, lies between the fields of nuclear physics and solid-state physics.

The idea of atoms is very old and was known to the Greeks during the classical period. It appeared from time to time in medieval works, although the concepts expressed now seem to us very vague. They seemed to have been based on the idea that there could be a limit to the divisibility of matter and, consequently, the idea of a final indivisible particle out of which large pieces of matter could be built.

At the beginning of the nineteenth century, it became clear that chemical reactions could be most simply explained if each chemical element is thought of as composed of very small identical atoms characteristic of the element. There thus arose a rather well-defined idea of a chemical element composed of identical atoms, as distinguished from a compound composed of groups of different atoms combined into molecules. During the latter part of the nineteenth century, the kinetic theory of gases made use of the idea of atoms, and molecules, in explaining the behavior of gases. By the end of the century only a few physicists and chemists still doubted the actual material existence and "reality" of atoms.

It is perhaps rather curious that the idea of atoms became really well-established only after it became clear that the atoms were not in any true sense indivisible, but that instead they had a complex structure which could be extensively investigated. Since this investigation required equipment and methods which had been developed by physicists rather then chemists, physicists took the lead and the work has taken the name of atomic physics or the physics of atomic structure. It was inaugurated in the 1890's when J. J. Thomson first isolated and established the existence of electrons. He showed these to have only about 1/2000 the mass of the lightest

*Author deceased. Article is reprinted from first edition.

known atom, hydrogen. He showed also that these electrons, as indicated by their name, carried negative electrical charges. It was later proved by R. A. Millikan that all the electronic charges are the same. Thus the identification of electrons, as small electrically charged pieces of matter, and as constituents of all matter, became firmly established.

Since it was clear that normal matter is electrically neutral, it had to be assumed that each atom contained a positive electrical charge, as well as negative electrons. J. J. Thomson developed the picture of a somewhat spherical jelly-like mass of positive electricity, in which electrons were located at various positions, and bound to them by quasi-elastic forces.

A principal means of investigating the structure of atoms has been the examination of the light emitted by the material in the gaseous state. This LIGHT is found to consist of a number of discrete wavelengths, or colors. Each of these wavelengths was associated, in the early days of this century, with a mode of vibration of the electrons in the positive jelly. In particular, H. A. Lorentz of the University of Leiden was able to show that such electrons, when placed in a magnetic field, would have their modes of vibration changed in a way that explained findings of P. Zeeman, who had made early observations of the wavelengths of the light emitted by a radiating gas in a magnetic field.

Nevertheless, the picture was unsatisfactory. The number of different frequencies emitted by each atom was very much larger than the number of electrons which could be attributed to the atom. Furthermore, these frequencies did not show the harmonic relationship to be expected on the simple picture.

During 1910 and 1911, Sir Ernest Rutherford suggested an experiment, carried out by Geiger and Marsden, in which alpha particles from a radioactive source were scattered from thin foils. The angles at which the alpha particles were scattered were found to be such as could be best described by the close approach of a heavy positively charged particle, the alpha particle, to another heavier and more highly positively charged particle, representing the scattering atom. From the results of these experiments, Rutherford concluded that the mass in the positive charge of an atom, instead of being distributed throughout the volume of a sphere of the order of 10^{-8} cm in radius, was concentrated in a very small volume of the order of 10^{-12} cm in radius. He thus developed the idea of a nuclear atom. The atom was pictured as a small solar system with the very heavy and highly charged nucleus occupying the position of a sun, and with electrons moving around it, as planets in their respective orbits.

Although this picture of nuclear atoms served to describe the alpha-particle scattering experiments, it still left many questions unsolved. One

of these questions referred to the apparent stability of the atoms. An ELECTRON moving around the nucleus would tend to emit radiation, to lose its energy, and thereby to spiral into the nucleus. Why did it not do so? Why did the atoms all seem to be quite stable, and all to be of approximately the same size, even though some contain 90 or more electrons, while hydrogen contains only one?

The first approach to a treatment of these problems was made by Niels Bohr in 1913 when he formulated and applied rules for "quantization" of electron motion around the nucleus. He postulated states of motion of the electron, satisfying these quantum rules, as peculiarly stable. In fact, one of them would be really permanently stable and would represent the ground state of the atom. The others would be only approximately stable. Occasionally an atom would leave one such state for another and, in the process, would radiate light of a frequency proportional to the difference in energy between the two states. By this means he was able to account for the spectrum of atomic hydrogen in a spectacular way. Bohr's paper in 1913 may well be said to have set the course of atomic plysics on its latest path.

Out of the experimental work on the scattering of alpha particles and the theoretical work of Niels Bohr, there grew a fairly definite picture of an atom which could be correlated with its chemical properties. The chemical properties were determined in the first place by the nuclear charge. The nucleus contained most of the atomic mass and carried an electric charge equal to an integral number of positive charges, each of the same magnitude as an electronic charge. This positive nucleus then accumulated around itself a number of electrons just sufficient to neutralize its positive charge and form a neutral atom.

The number of positive charges, or the number of negative electrons around the nucleus was designated as the atomic number of the atom. These showed a close parallelism with atomic weights, and an even closer parallelism with the arrangement of atoms in the periodic system. Through the formulation of a number of rules based on Bohr's picture of quantized orbits, the periodic system of the elements could be understood. Hydrogen was given one electron, and helium two. The two electrons in helium constituted a "closed shell" which exhibited almost perfect spherical symmetry and chemical inactivity. Since the first two electrons constituted a closed shell the third electron in the case of lithium gave the atom properties very similar to those of hydrogen. Outside of the first closed shell could be placed eight more electrons to form a second closed shell in neon. The four outer electrons necessary for the atom of carbon provided a description of the chemical properties of that ubiquitous element, and the one electron short of a closed shell in the case of fluorine gave some understanding of fluorine's vigorous chemical activity.

Thus, during the years after 1913, the feeling grew that the chemical properties of atoms could be pretty well understood. The idea that there were undiscovered elements, as indicated by gaps in the periodic system, was reinforced. Systematic search has now discovered them.

However, it was not until 1925 that Bohr's ideas were developed into a mathematical form, complete enough and precise enough to permit their general application, under the name of quantum mechanics. This development associated with the names of Dirac, Heisenberg, Schrödinger, provided the basic laws which permit, in principle, the complete and quantitative description of an atom consisting of a heavy positively charged nucleus, and surrounded by enough electrons to make the whole system electrically neutral.

The principal feature of quantum mechanics is that it ascribes to electrons something of the nature of waves. It requires that calculations of the motion of an electron in the neighborhood of a nucleus be made in terms of wave motion rather than the motion of particles. One has immediately the explanation of the stability of atoms. The waves representing the electrons cannot collapse to points, or to the small size of the nucleus, without involving extremely large amounts of "kinetic" energy. The ground state of an atom is determined as the balance between the attraction of the nucleus for the electron wave and what might be called the elastic resistance to compression of the wave itself.

Other states of the atom may be pictured as states of vibration of the electronic waves around the nucleus. The state with a minimum number of nodes is the ground state, and states with more complicated vibration forms represent higher energies and are called excited states. The excited states are in general unstable in the presence of an electromagnetic field. Most excited states decay into states of lower energy with a lifetime of about 10^{-8} second. In the process, the atom radiates an electromagnetic wave of a rather sharply defined frequency, equal to the energy difference between the two states divided by Planck's constant h.

The details of these states and of their rates of decay can all be calculated in principle, although the calculation involves as much mathematical difficulty as any calculation of the behavior of a large number of particles interacting with each other.

One of the properties of electrons that became evident during the study of the optical spectra of atoms was that of ELECTRON SPIN. The suggestion was made by Uhlenbeck and Goudsmit in 1925 that one of the features of such spectra could be understood if each electron had associated with it a quantity called spin, which is similar in many ways to angular momentum. Each electron also has a certain magnetic moment which affects the energy in the presence of a magnetic field. This property also has been incorporated into the wave ideas

of quantum mechanics, and may be thought of as leading to two similar waves existing at the same time but each corresponding to a different "spin."

It is widely believed that the subject of atomic physics is closed in principle except for detailed and complicated calculations which can be made with computing machines. On the one hand, physicists have gone on to investigating the detailed properties of the atomic nucleus. Most of these properties have little effect on the atoms themselves. On the other hand, the properties of atoms in combination, and the way in which they form large pieces of solid matter, has led to an extensive and comprehensive field known as solid-state physics. These two directions lead to the exciting frontiers of physics in the second half of the twentieth century.

W. V. HOUSTON

References

Fano, U., and Fano, L., "Basic Physics of Atoms and Molecules," New York, John Wiley & Sons, 1959.
Blackwood, Osgood, and Ruark, "An Outline of Atomic Physics," New York, John Wiley & Sons, 1955.

Cross-references: ELECTRON; ELECTRON SPIN; ELEMENTS, CHEMICAL; MOLECULES AND MOLECULAR STRUCTURE; NUCLEAR STRUCTURE; PERIODIC LAW AND PERIODIC TABLE; QUANTUM THEORY; SPECTROSCOPY; ZEEMAN AND STARK EFFECTS.

ATOMIC SPECTRA

Fundamental Facts Light from electric discharges in gases shows *line spectra* due to free atoms excited by electron collisions. Noble gases and metal vapors produce almost pure atomic spectra, while discharges in molecular gases show both molecular *band spectra* and atomic line spectra. Some spectral lines can also be observed in absorption when white light is made to pass through the gas into a spectroscope. Under high spectroscopic resolution, all lines are found to have nonzero width. This is due to random motion (DOPPLER EFFECT) and disturbing influences of neighboring atoms, molecules, ions or electrons (pressure broadening); but even after allowance for these effects, a spectral line has a definite, generally very small, width due to radiation damping (natural width). Precision measurement of wavelengths or resolution of very fine structures requires light sources giving narrow lines—discharges at low gas- and current-density and low temperature—or even atomic beams at right angles to the line of sight. *Continuous* atomic spectra are generally weak under laboratory conditions; in emission, they are due to recombination of an electron with a positive ion; in absorption, to the reverse process of *photoionization*.

The term atomic spectra includes positive ions, with the following terminology: spectrum of Na, *arc spectrum*, NaI; of Na^+, Na^{++}, $\cdots$: first, second, $\cdots$ *spark spectrum*, or NaII, NaIII, $\cdots$. Spectra of highly ionized or *stripped* atoms are important in astrophysics and occur in high-temperature plasmas. Systems with the same number of electrons, such as Na, Mg^+, Al^{++} show marked similarities and are called *iso-electronic* sequences.

In the ultraviolet, visible or infrared, the spectroscope, in the form of a grating or interferometer, measures primarily the wavelength (λ) of the spectral lines. It is generally expressed in angstrom units (Å) defined as 10^{-8} cm or, by recent international convention, the fraction 1/6056.12525 of the wavelength of a line of the isotope 86 of krypton, in air under standard conditions. The wave number ($\tilde{\nu}$ or σ), the reciprocal of the wavelength in vacuo, is measured in cm^{-1} or kayser (K), or in millikayser (mK). The frequency ν is derived by multiplying by c, the velocity of light in vacuo; in the range of microwaves and radio frequencies, ν is measured directly (1 mK = 29.9793 MHz).

In contrast to frequencies, intensities of lines are strongly dependent on experimental conditions, and special experiments are required for deriving quantities expressing the strength of a line as a characteristic constant of the atom. This can be defined in various forms; the f-value is a number giving the ratio of the absorptive or dispersive power of the line to that of the classical, harmonic electron oscillator of the same frequency; the transition probability or Einstein A-value is the probability, per second, of an excited atom emitting a light quantum.

Hydrogen-like Spectra The spectra of atoms containing one electron only (H, He^+, Be^{++} $\cdots$) are very simple if the fine structure is disregarded; they form the basis of the classification and theory of atomic spectra. Balmer's empirical discovery of a numerical relationship between the wavelengths of the visible hydrogen lines led to a formula expressing the wave numbers of all hydrogen-like spectra by one constant R, the charge number Z (=1 for H; =2 for He^+, $\cdots$) and two integral numbers, $n, n' > n$:

$$\tilde{\nu} = Z^2 R(1/n^2 - 1/n'^2) = T_n - T_{n'} \qquad (1)$$

A *series* arising from a sequence of values n' is characterized by regularly decreasing spacings and intensities of the lines towards increasing wave numbers. Substitution of $n = 1, 2$ and 3 in Eq. (1) with $Z = 1$ gives the Lyman, Balmer and Paschen series, in the ultraviolet, visible and near infrared respectively. The wavelengths of the Balmer lines, H_α, H_β and H_γ ($n' = 3, 4, 5$) are 6562.8, 4861.3 and 4340.5 Å. The Lyman α line, the *resonance line* of hydrogen, has the wavelength 1215.7Å.

The relation of Eq. (1) can be derived theoretically by applying nonrelativistic quantum theory to a model consisting of a point electron of mass m and charge $-e$ and a fixed point nu-

cleus of charge Ze. In the *Bohr-Sommerfeld* theory, this is done by imposing quantum conditions on the classical orbit of the electron; in the more rigorous Schrödinger theory, by solving the wave equation with the assumption of constant energy E. Provided $E < 0$ (bound state), it assumes discrete values, those of the stationary states of motion or the *eigenvalues* of the wave equation. Emission and absorption arise from transitions between two energy levels E_n, $E_{n'}$, with the frequency of the light given by

$$\nu_{n,n'} = (E_{n'} - E_n)/h \tag{2}$$

where h is Planck's constant. Equation (1) is a special case of Eq. (2), with $E_n = -hZ^2 Rc/n^2$. Allowance for the motion of the nucleus of finite mass M causes R to differ slightly for different M; it is given by $R_\infty/(1 + m/M)$ where $R_\infty = 109737.3$ cm^{-1}.

The solution of the SCHRÖDINGER EQUATION for a mass point in space leads to 3 quantum numbers. In polar coordinates, with a force derived from a central potential $V(r)$, the quantum numbers n_r, μ and m give the numbers of nodes of the wave function in the range of the coordinates r, ϑ and φ. Introducing the *azimuthal quantum number* $l = |m| + \mu$ and the *principal quantum number* $n = n_r + l + 1$, we find the set n, l, m to have the following meaning: the z-component of the angular momentum is $L_z = m\hbar$, where $\hbar = h/2\pi$, the square of its absolute value is $|\mathbf{L}|^2 = l(l + 1)\hbar^2$, and the energy E depends on n and l only. For the special case of the Coulomb field $V \sim 1/r$, E depends on n alone: $E_n = \text{constant}/n^2$. An energy level E_n has to be considered as consisting of a number g of *states* of different l and m. This situation is described as *degeneracy*, and g is the *statistical weight* of the level. The degeneracy in m is due to the central symmetry of the force field and occurs in all atoms in the absence of external fields. The degeneracy in l is peculiar to the Coulomb field in nonrelativistic treatment.

Alkali-like Spectra The spectra of the alkali atoms and their isoelectronic ions (Li, Na, $\cdots$, Be$^+$, Mg$^+$, $\cdots$) show lines arranged in series similar to those of hydrogen. Their wave numbers can be represented by empirical relations which are generalizations of Eq. (1). Series of term values T_n can be defined in such a way that $T_n \to 0$ for $n \to \infty$, and the observed wave numbers are equal to term differences $T_n - T_{n'}$ (Ritz combination principle). In contrast to Eq. (1), however, there are several series of terms, so that apart from n, a second index number l has to be introduced. The term values $T_{n,l}$ can then be identified with quantized values of $-E/ch$ and the index numbers n and l with quantum numbers, as implied by the letters chosen, if we assume that in these atoms one electron moves in a central force field different from a Coulomb field. This *valency* or *optical* electron has to be imagined as more loosely bound than the others and moving in the field of electrostatic attraction by the *core* consisting of the nucleus of charge Ze and the remaining

$Z - 1$ electrons. At large distances from the core, the field is like that caused by a single charge e as in hydrogen. At smaller distances, the optical electron penetrates into the electron cloud of the core and experiences an increased attraction. This picture leads to a qualitative understanding of the term diagrams and spectra of alkali atoms as exemplified for Na in Fig. 1, where terms

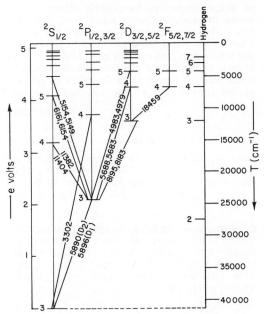

FIG. 1. Term diagram of Na. Approximate wavelengths in angstroms. The doublet splitting of the terms is not shown.

with $l = 0, 1, 2, 3, 4, \cdots$ are conventionally described as $S, P, D, F, G, \cdots$ terms. For any given n, an energy level is the further below that of hydrogen (the term value the larger) the smaller l becomes, because a smaller angular momentum decreases the centrifugal force and brings the electron closer to the core. Emission or absorption of radiation according to Eq. (2) does not occur for all pairs of levels but is subject to the *selection rule* $\Delta l = \pm 1$. Transitions from P levels to the lowest S level form the *principal series*. Its lines can also be observed in absorption since the lower level is the ground level; the first member is the well-known yellow *resonance* line. Transitions from D or higher S levels to the lowest P level form the *diffuse* and *sharp* series, those from F levels to the lowest D level, the Bergmann or *fundamental* series.

A feature that cannot be explained by this model is the *doublet* structure, a doubling of all except the S levels. It is due to the fact that the electron possesses a *spin*, i.e., an intrinsic angular momentum $\mathbf{S}$ of fixed absolute value given by $|\mathbf{S}|^2 = s(s + 1)\hbar^2$, where $s = \frac{1}{2}$, and connected with a magnetic dipole moment μ. The interaction of μ with the magnetic field due to the

orbital motion, the *spin-orbit coupling*, causes any one energy level of given n and l (except for $l = 0$) to split into two levels. They are characterized by a new quantum number j associated with the total angular momentum resulting from vector addition of $\mathbf{L}$ and $\mathbf{S}$. It can have the two values $j = l \pm s = l \pm \frac{1}{2}$. Optical transitions are subject to the selection rule $\Delta j = \pm 1$ or 0. The width of the doublet splitting increases with core penetration and thus with decreasing l; it is most prominent in P terms. It decreases rapidly with increasing n and increases from Li to Cs. In the term symbol, j is written as suffix and the doublet character is indicated by superscript 2. For example, two transitions forming the yellow resonance doublet of Na are written $3^2 S_{1/2}$ – $3^2 P_{1/2}$ and $3^2 S_{1/2}$ – $3^2 P_{3/2}$. The absolute value of n (= 3 in this case) can be deduced by comparison with hydrogen (Fig. 1).

Since for all term values $T_n \to 0$ for $n \to \infty$, the extrapolation of a series $T_n - T_{n'}$ for $n' \to \infty$ gives the term value T_n. If this is the ground term, chT_n is the ionization energy of the atom. A convenient conversion formula is 8066 cm^{-1} = 1 eV.

Under high resolution, hydrogen-like spectra are found to have a rather complex structure known as *fine structure* (the same name is often applied to the much wider doublet or multiplet structures); it can be explained by a relativistic velocity dependence of the electron mass removing the degeneracy of states of different l, and by magnetic spin-orbit coupling causing a doublet splitting. In fact, these two effects are related since the spin itself is relativistic in origin. The theory gives the result that a hydrogen level of given n depends on j only, so that, e.g., $n = 2, l = 0, j = \frac{1}{2}$ should coincide with $n = 2, l = 1, j = \frac{1}{2}$. In fact, such terms show a small difference known as *Lamb shift*. Its existence can be explained by quantum electrodynamics.

A more complete description of the state of an alkali atom has to treat the core as a dynamical system of many particles. This cannot be done rigorously, but as a useful zero-order approximation, quantum numbers n and l can be assigned to individual electrons; in extension of the symbolism used before, values $l = 0, 1, 2 \cdots$ for individual electrons are described by small letters $s, p, d \cdots$, and the number of electrons of the same n and l, called *equivalent* electrons, by a superscript. Thus two $2p$-electrons ($n = 2, l = 1$) are said to form the *configuration* $2p^2$. The number of equivalent electrons in one atom is limited by the *Pauli principle* to $2(2l + 1)$, i.e., to 2 for s-electrons, 6 for p-electrons and 10 for d-electrons. When this limiting number is completed, a closed *subshell* is said to be formed. Thus the 10 electrons of the atom Ne form the three closed subshells $1s^2$, $2s^2$, and $2p^6$, and the entire atom contains the two closed shells $n = 1$ ($1s^2$) and $n = 2$ ($2s^2 2p^6$). The same applies to the 10 electrons forming the core of the atom of Na.

In a complete subshell or shell the orbital angular momenta of the electrons cancel one another out, as do the spins of the individual elec-

trons; the total charge distribution has spherical symmetry. In an alkali atom the quantum numbers l and s of the outer electron therefore determine the orbital- and spin-angular momentum of the entire electron structure of the atom. The ground level of Na, e.g., can be described either as an s-level or an S-level, since $L = l = 0$.

The classical concept of the core as a *rigid* charge distribution is expressed by the assumption that the quantum numbers of the core electrons remain constant during the excitation of the outer electron.

Other Simple Spectra Helium, and also Li$^+$, Be^{++}, $\cdots$, have two electrons, and the atoms in the second column of the periodic table Be, Mg (also B$^+$, Al$^+$, $\cdots$) have two electrons outside closed shells. The analysis of the spectra leads to two systems of terms, *singlets* and *triplets*, with only weak intercombinations; the S terms are single also in the triplet system. These facts can be formally described, in analogy to alkali spectra, by vector addition of the two spins to form the two possible resultant spin quantum numbers $S = 0$ and 1. The first alternative produces singlets ($j = l$), the second triplets ($j = l - 1, l, l + 1$) unless $l = 0$. This implies a strong interaction forming the resultant S of the two spins and a weaker interaction forming j. The latter interaction is the same magnetic spin-orbit interaction that causes doublet splitting in alkali atoms, but the former is, in a less obvious way, due to the electrostatic repulsion between the two electrons. In all the terms concerned, the symbol for the configuration shows only *one* electron to be excited, e.g., $1s2p$ in He, but owing to the identity of the electrons, it is not possible to attribute the excited state $2p$ to one particular electron. The situation is analogous to that of two identical, coupled, linear oscillators showing two normal modes of vibration, each involving both oscillators in a *symmetrical* and *antisymmetrical* way. Application of Pauli's principle to the wave mechanical description of this two-electron system leads to two energy states, one with parallel and one with anti-parallel spins, $S = 1$ and 0 respectively. Elements in the subgroup (Zn, Cd, Hg) show similar singlet and triplet spectra; in the heavier elements, however, the magnetic spin-orbit interaction is no longer weak compared with the electrostatic repulsion, and the division into singlet and triplet terms has a very restricted meaning.

In the elements of the third column, B, Al, Ga, In, Tl, the single electron outside a closed subshell produces doublet spectra, but in contrast to the alkali spectra, the ground term is a P term.

Complex Spectra The assumption that the quantum numbers n and l of only one of the electrons outside closed shells change in emission or absorption of a spectral line forms a good approximation for most of the strongest spectra in the optical range, from near infrared to near ultraviolet. Somewhat arbitrarily but conveniently one can define complex spectra as those in which more than one electron outside closed subshells assumes a value of $l > 0$. One then has to consider the interaction of more than two

angular momentum vectors of orbits and spins, and a simple interpretation in terms of a vector model is meaningful only in certain limiting conditions. Very often, especially in low-lying levels, a description in terms of the Russell Saunders coupling scheme (L, S coupling) is possible because the electrostatic interaction predominates over the magnetic spin-orbit interaction. As a result, we can define terms, each of which is characterized by a set of values L, S (or a multiplicity $2S + 1$), and each term is split into levels, each characterized by a value of j, the highest of which is equal to $L + S$. The classification and terminology are obvious generalizations of those for two-electron spectra. For configurations of 3; 4; 5 electrons the possible multiplicities are respectively: doublets and quartets; singlets, triplets and quintets; doublets, quartets and sextets, etc. The strongest lines arise from transitions between terms of the same multiplicity. Such line multiplets are often recognizable by their characteristic groupings of the lines and their intensity ratios. The level spacings are governed by the *interval rule*: they are in the ratio of the j values, e.g., the levels of $^4D_{7/2,5/2,3/2,1/2}$ have spacings in the ratio $7:5:3:1$.

Other, often much more complex forms of coupling occur, especially in the higher levels, and L and S then lose their meaning. One important property of any level which always remains well defined is the *parity*, and the *Laporte rule* states that even terms combine only with odd terms and vice versa. If the configuration is defined, a level is *even* or odd if Σl is even or *odd*. As one proceeds to higher levels or to heavier elements the concept of the configuration becomes less distinct. A given energy level may still be said to belong to a certain configuration, but a more accurate description often requires the inclusion of one or more other configurations of the same parity in the form of a *perturbation*. In other cases the *configuration interaction* is so strong that even the lowest approximation has to be based on the concept of mixed configurations.

Hyperfine Structure (hfs) and Isotope Shift These structures are usually of the order of fractions of 1 cm^{-1} and generally require interferometric methods for their study. Hyperfine structure is primarily due to the magnetic interaction of the nuclear magnetic moment μ_N with the field produced by spins and orbital motions of the electrons. A level of given j splits into hyperfine levels, each characterized by a quantum number F, where F can assume the values $j+I$, $j+I-1$, $\cdots$, $|j-I|$. The nuclear spin I is a characteristic property of each nucleus and has integral or half-integral values for even or odd values of the atomic number. The structure of hyperfine multiplets is similar to that of fine structure multiplets, with F, I, j taking the place of j, S, L. However, there is often also an electrostatic interaction between the electrons and the nucleus if the nuclear charge distribution has no spherical symmetry. Deviations from the interval rule in hyperfine multiplets have led to the discovery of such nuclear deformations described mainly by the *quadrupole moment Q*. Hyperfine structures in ground states can be measured very accurately by methods of atomic beam resonance. Hyperfine structure studies lead to values of I, approximate values of μ_N and Q, and accurate values for the ratio of the two latter for different isotopes.

For different isotopes of an element, the spectral lines—or the centers of gravity of their hyperfine multiplets—are often displaced against each other. This *isotope shift* is due to two causes: in the light elements, it is due to the difference in nuclear mass, though this *mass effect* is not as easy to calculate as that causing the difference in the Rydberg constant in hydrogen-like spectra. In the heavier elements, differences in size and shape of isotopic nuclei can cause quite appreciable isotope shifts. Studies of this *volume* or *field effect* have contributed to our knowledge of nuclear volumes and the dependence of nuclear deformations on neutron numbers.

Magnetic and Electric Effects The effects caused by magnetic fields play a great part in research on atomic spectra, particularly in magnetic resonance methods. An external magnetic field removes the degeneracy due to the spherical symmetry of atomic force fields and causes the energy to depend on the magnetic quantum number m. This leads to the formation of the *Lorentz triplet* or *normal Zeeman effect* in singlet spectra and to the more complex structures of *anomalous Zeeman effects* in multiplet lines. Zeeman effects in hyperfine structures are especially important for the determination of nuclear spins. The *Stark effect*, due to electric fields, is of somewhat less importance. It causes the energy to depend on $|m|$ only, thus not removing the degeneracy completely. While magnetic splittings are proportional to the field strength, Stark splittings are generally proportional to the square of the electric field.

Radiofrequency Spectra Hyperfine structures of atomic energy levels are now generally measured by radiofrequency methods involving transitions between hf components of one level, usually in a magnetic field. Such transitions between states of the same parity are due to magnetic interaction with the radiofrequency field. Though the techniques differ widely from those of optical spectroscopy, they are a form of atomic spectroscopy in which the frequency ν of the *resonance* between radiation field and atomic system is measured and gives the small energy differences between magnetic sublevels of the hf structure by the relation $\Delta E = h\nu$, often to a high degree of accuracy.

The principal methods, characterized by the form of detection of the resonance, are: (1) *atomic beam resonance* (see ATOMIC AND MOLECULAR BEAMS), based on the difference of the magnetic moments of different states

causing different deflections in inhomogeneous magnetic fields; (2) *double resonance* and *optical pumping* (see OPTICAL PUMPING), where changes in the population of magnetic sublevels are detected by changes of polarization and intensity of fluorescent light or by changes of absorption of light; (3) a related method, though not using radiofrequency, known as *level crossing* (see OPTICAL PUMPING). Level crossing in zero field, known as *Hanle effect*, has proved to be a powerful method for measurement of *lifetimes* of excited states.

The above-mentioned *Lamb shift*, first observed in optical spectra, has been accurately measured by radiofrequency methods.

Far Ultraviolet and X-ray Spectra Atomic spectra of frequencies about 1000 times those of optical spectra have long been known as *characteristic* x-ray spectra (see ENERGY LEVELS). Though generally observed in condensed matter, they are characteristic of the constituent atoms, only slightly modified by chemical bonds or crystal structure. They are due to the inner electrons of the atom which are very tightly bound by the strong attraction of the nuclear charge, only partly screened by the other electrons of the same or lower n. The energy of the inner electrons depends primarily on n, as in hydrogen-like spectra, and in x-ray terminology one classifies electrons and shells by the value of n as K-, L-, M-, $\cdots$ electrons and shells for $n = 1, 2, 3, \cdots$. Since the inner shells are filled in atoms of not too small Z, the absorption spectrum shows mainly continuous bands, due to the removal of an electron from one of these shells. The photoionization energies for electrons of $n = 1, 2, \cdots$ mark the low-frequency edges of the K-, L- $\cdots$ bands. The state of an atom with a "hole" in one of the inner shells, caused by x-ray absorption or electron bombardment, represents a highly excited state of the atomic ion. It leads to emission of the x-ray line spectra by transition of an electron from a higher shell to the vacant state of the inner shell.

Spectra in the gap between x-rays and the near ultraviolet have recently received increasing attention, partly owing to their importance to astrophysics. Work in this *far* and *extreme* ultraviolet requires vacuum spectrographs, usually with gratings used at grazing incidence. *Emission* spectra of highly ionized atoms (*stripped* atoms) can be observed in the solar corona and in stellar nebulae, and in the laboratory in condensed sparks and high-temperature plasmas. Their strongest lines are in the extreme ultraviolet; e.g., in work ranging down to about 20 Å, all the spectra of the isoelectronic sequence from NaI ($Z = 11$) to Cu XIX ($Z = 29$) are known. The study of *absorption* spectra of neutral atoms has been extended into the extreme ultraviolet, partly by the use of the continuous background radiation from synchrotrons. Such spectra are mainly due to two kinds of processes: either the excitation of one of the

electrons in closed shells, e.g., of one of the electrons $1s$, $2s$, or $2p$ in Na, or the simultaneous excitation of two electrons. A simple example of the second type is the absorption series $1s^2\ ^1S - 2snp\ ^1P$ in He between 206 and 165 Å. In both types of absorption spectra, many lines show a peculiar, strongly asymmetric profile known as *Fano profile*. It can be explained by configuration interaction in the following way. The same energy as that of the two-electron excitation state $2snp\ ^1P$ can be reached from the normal atom by removal of a single electron with excess kinetic energy, i.e., the absorption line falls in the range of the continuous absorption extending towards higher frequencies from the limit $n = \infty$ of the absorption series $1s^2\ ^1S - 1snp\ ^1P$. Configuration interaction between the discrete state and the continuous state of the same energy and parity causes the anomalous line profile by a kind of interference effect. The absorption of light within this line leads either to re-emission of the same frequency or to nonradiative transition to the ionized state, a process known as *autoionization*. In x-ray spectroscopy, the analogous process had been detected by the appearance of fast, free electrons and is known as *Auger* effect (see AUGER EFFECT). The process of autoionization is closely related to the inverse process of *resonance capture* of electrons by ions.

H. G. KUHN

References

Kuhn, H. G., "Atomic Spectra," 2nd ed., London, Longmans, and New York, Academic Press, 1971.
Woodgate, G. K., "Elementary Atomic Structure," New York, McGraw-Hill, 1970.

Cross-references; ATOMIC AND MOLECULAR BEAMS, AUGER EFFECT, ELECTRON SPIN, ENERGY LEVELS, OPTICAL PUMPING, SCHRÖDINGER EQUATION, SPECTROSCOPY, X-RAYS, ZEEMAN AND STARK EFFECTS.

AUGER EFFECT

Definition and History The Auger effect is the filling of an electronic vacancy in the atom by one electron from a less tightly bound state, with the simultaneous emission not of a photon but of a second electron from another less tightly bound state.

Following experiments by Barkla (1909) and Sadler (1917) in which the number of characteristic K x-rays emitted by material absorbing higher-energy x-rays appeared to be substantially less than the number of x-rays absorbed in the K shell, Kossel (1923) suggested that the remaining vacancies might be filled by a radiationless transfer of the excess energy to an emitted electron. This interpretation was reiterated by Barkla and Dallas (1924), who observed

an increase in the number of electrons emitted when x-rays were absorbed. Wilson (1923) had observed in a cloud chamber, simultaneous ejection of two electrons from the same atom. It remained for Auger (1925, 1926) to make systematic investigations of this phenomenon in argon. The effect has since been called the Auger effect, and the ejected electrons have been called Auger electrons.

Principal Features Auger showed that:

(1) The photoelectron and its Auger electron arise at the same point.

(2) The Auger-electron track length is independent of the wavelength of the primary x-rays, but the photoelectron track length increases with x-ray energy.

(3) The direction of ejection of the Auger electron is independent of that of the photoelectron.

(4) Not all photoelectron tracks show a coincident Auger track.

Filling of vacancies by the Auger effect can occur for any vacancy for which there are two electrons in the atom sufficiently less tightly bound that a net positive energy is available for the ejected Auger electron. Because photon emission is more easily detected and has played such an important role in the development of quantum theory, it is not generally realized that Auger emission is much more probable. Only for vacancies in the K shell in atoms with atomic number above 32 and in vacancies in the outer two electron states of an atom does photon emission dominate. The Auger effect also occurs after capture of a negative meson by an atom. As the meson changes energy levels in approaching the nucleus, the energy released may be either emitted as a photon or transferred directly to an electron which is emitted as a fairly high-energy Auger electron (keV for hydrogen, MeV for heavy elements). Finally we note that each Auger process increases the positive ionization of the atom by changing one initial vacancy into two final vacancies.

Energy Spectra of Auger Electrons Auger spectroscopy is the measurement of the number, energy, and intensity of lines present. The spectrum of Auger electrons resulting from a given vacancy is more complex than the corresponding photon spectrum. The energy of the Auger electron resulting from the filling of a vacancy V of energy $E(V)$ by production of vacancies X_i and Y_j of energies $E(X_i)$ and $E(Y_j)$ is $E(V - X_iY_j) = E(V) - E(X_i) - E(Y_j) - \Delta Ex_iy_j$, where ΔEx_iy_j can be interpreted as either the increase in binding energy of the Y_j electron due to an X_i vacancy, or vice versa. Experimental energy determination in Auger spectra then consists of determining ΔEx_iy_j for each transition. Exact calculation of the number of possible Auger transitions, their energies, and their relative probabilities necessitates the use of a relativistic intermediate-coupling theory. In the above notation, X and Y refer to the total quantum number of a group of levels, and i and j to the individual substates within the group.

At low resolution the Auger spectrum from a vacancy with initial total quantum number n always consists of at least three well separated groups which can be characterized by vacancies as $n \to (n + 1)(n + 1)$, $n \to (n + 1)(n + m)$, and $n \to (n + m)(n + m)$, where $(n + m)$ represents all final vacancies with total quantum numbers greater than or equal to $(n + 2)$. Thus for an initial K vacancy we have K-LL, K-LX, and K-XY groups where X and Y stand for all vacancies with quantum numbers equal to or greater than $n + 2$ (in this case 3). Similarly, for an L_3 primary vacancy we have L_3-MM, L_3-MX, and L_3-XY, and similarly for L_1 and L_2. But for the L shell the groups do not appear well separated because the L_1 and L_2 groups overlap each other and the L_3 groups.

When a higher resolution is used each band is seen to be composed of numerous lines of which many are ordinary lines resulting from a single initial vacancy and others are satellites resulting from multiple initial vacancies, multiple Auger processes, and other complex phenomena.

Complete interpretation of the ordinary lines necessitates relativistic-intermediate coupling which is a combination of L-S coupling (small binding energies) and j-j coupling (very large binding energies). As an example of these interpretations we show in Table 1 the designations for the K-LL group.

Auger spectra also enable the relative intensities of the lines or groups of lines to be determined. At high resolution the K-LL intensities of all the ordinary lines can be accurately measured. No theoretical calculation gives the correct relative intensities for all values of atomic number but relativistic j-j coupling gives quite good agreement above 80. K-LX and K-XY lines are less well resolved and theories are less developed. For L-MM spectra the experimental intensities are much less precise due to the much lower energies and the overlapping of the bands. Nonrelativistic L-S and j-j coupling theoretical intensities have been calculated, and crude agreement is obtained with the former for low atomic numbers and with the latter for high atomic numbers. Very little good data exist for L-MN and L-NN spectra. Considerable medium resolution data exist for M and N Auger spectra.

While the global K-Auger intensity is easy to obtain by integrating under the spectrum, the total L_1, L_2, and L_3 intensities are difficult to obtain because of the overlap of the three bands.

Relative Probability of Auger and X-ray Emission The evaluation of the relative probability of x-ray and Auger emission for different initial vacancies, and the determination of the relative intensities of various Auger lines constitute one of the most important aspects of Auger effect research.

The fluorescence yield, ω_i, for any initial vacancy i is defined as the fraction of vacancies filled by emission of photons. The Auger yield is defined correspondingly as the fraction filled

TABLE 1

L-S Coupling (light elements)	Intermediate Coupling	j-j Coupling (heavy elements)
$K - 2s2s \ ^1S_0$	K-$L_1L_1 \ ^1S_0$	K-L_1L_1
$^1P_1$	K-$L_1L_2 \ ^1P_1$	
$K - 2s2p$	K-$L_1L_2 \ ^3P_0$	K-L_1L_2
$^3P_{0,1,2}$	K-$L_1L_3 \ ^3P_2$	K-L_1L_3
	K-$L_1L_3 \ ^3P_2$	
$^1S_0$	K-$L_2L_2 \ ^1S_0$	K-L_2L_2
$^1D_2$	K-$L_2L_3 \ ^1D_2$	
$K - 2p2p$	K-$L_2L_3 \ ^3P_1$ parity forbidden	K-L_2L_3
$^3P_{0,1,2}$	K-$L_3L_3 \ ^3P_0$	K-L_3L_3
	K-$L_3L_3 \ ^3P_2$	

For K-Auger electrons, measurements and comparison with theory are extensive.

by emission of Auger electrons. The Auger yield is divided into two parts, one (denoted by a_i) which transfers the vacancy to a level with a higher total quantum number, and the other (denoted by f_{ij}) which transfers the vacancy to a lower-energy vacancy with the same total quantum number. The latter process is called the Coster-Kronig effect.

For the K shell the following equation holds

$$1 = \omega_K + a_K.$$

Although in principle $\omega_K(Z)$ should be readily calculable, the number of (frequently relativistic) electron wave functions which must be known for each Z, and the number of permutations and combinations of these functions which must be handled in order to calculate the individual probability of every line and, by summing, the total K-Auger probability per unit time, present a formidable problem even with the aid of a sophisticated computer. The K fluorescence yield is therefore normally found by fitting theoretical expressions for ω_K containing empirical constants to the experimental values. For $20 < z < 55$, ω_K is given to a few per cent by

$$\omega_K = (1 + 7.8 \times 10^5 \ Z^{-4})^{-1}$$

and somewhat less accurately for $10 < z < 20$. For $z < 10$ the experimental errors are large because of solid state and molecular effects, and the theoretical estimates may also be considerably in error.

For $Z > 50$ it is better to estimate a_K since relativity has an important effect on a_K but not on ω_K which is very close to unity. The following equation probably predicts a_K to 10 to 15 per cent and hence ω_K to a per cent or better for $z > 50$:

$$a_K = [1 - (1 + 7.8 \times 10^5)^{-1}] (1 + 3.5 \times 10^{-5} \ Z^2 + 3 \times 10^{-8} \ Z^4).$$

For the L shell in the j-j coupling limit the following equations hold:

$$1 = \omega_3 + a_3$$
$$1 = \omega_2 + a_2 + f_{23}$$
$$1 = \omega_1 + a_1 + f_{12} + f_{13}.$$

In addition, the average L-fluorescence yield $\overline{\omega}_L$ for an atom with an L vacancy, having probability n_1, n_2, and n_3 of being in each of the three subshells, is

$$\overline{\omega}_L = 1 - \overline{a}_L = n_1(\omega_1 + f_{12}\omega_2 + f_{13}\omega_3 + f_{12}f_{23}\omega_3) + n_2(\omega_2 + f_{23}\omega_3) + n_3\omega_3.$$

The values of the nine L-shell constants are much less well known than the two constants for the K shell. Below atomic number 50 the ω_i are all less than 6 per cent and appear to be less than 50 per cent for all elements. ω_3 is given reasonably accurately by

$$\omega_3 = (1 + 0.82 \times 10^8 \ Z^{-4})^{-1} \quad Z > 65$$
$$\omega_3 = (1 + 1.08 \times 10^8 \ Z^{-4})^{-1} \quad Z > 50.$$

ω_2 is much less accurately known but the agreement between theory and experiment is fairly good. The knowledge of ω_1 is relatively poor. The Coster-Kronig yields go through sudden changes in value as certain transitions become energetically possible or impossible. For example, $L_2 - L_3 \ M$ transitions are forbidden for Z from 50 to 73. Experimental values for f_{13} and f_{23} have precisions ranging from 5 to 20 per cent, while f_{12} has only a precision of about 30 per cent. Agreement with theory is not very good. The $\overline{\omega}_L$ and $\overline{a}_L$ clearly depend on the type of excitation.

Although initial interest in the Auger effect arose through creation of vacancies by ejection of photoelectrons by x-rays, there has been a strong recent upsurge in interest in several other

types of experimental work which involve Auger spectra closely:

(1) Vacancies created in radioactive decay.

(2) Vacancies created in electron-ion and ion-ion collisions in gases.

(3) Auger electrons emitted from the surface layers of solid targets in ultrahigh vacuum when the surface is bombarded by electrons up to 3 keV and sometimes by ions.

When radioactive decay occurs, internal conversion, shake-off, accompanying beta-decay, and electron capture all create vacancies. In fact, the only method of studying the relative probability of orbital capture in the various shells and subshells of a nuclide involves the study of the x-ray or Auger spectrum of the product nuclide. The interpretation of these spectra necessitates the knowledge of the constants discussed above.

The importance of the Auger effect for radioactive nuclei, as well as the almost 100 per cent probability of Auger and Coster-Kronig emission for the M and higher levels, is indicated by measurement of the total charge accumulated by certain radioactive nuclei. For example, a vacancy produced in xenon $131m$ by internal conversion gives rise in some cases to as many as 21 Auger processes, leaving a xenon ion with a charge of $-22e$.

The highest-resolution Auger spectra are those from vacancies created in gaseous atoms or molecules at low pressure by bombardment by electrons or other ions. Such spectra are particularly rich in lines (satellites) arising from multiple vacancies, and their interpretation has contributed to our understanding of the processes which take place in such collisions.

Since about 1967 there has been great interest in the study of surface impurities by means of the Auger spectra of solid surfaces in ultrahigh vacuum bombarded by low energy, up to 3 keV, electrons. The experiments are usually done by modifying a Low Energy Electron Diffraction (LEED) apparatus to provide it with a retarding grid. By varying the retarding voltage, an integral spectrum of the scattered and secondary electrons is obtained. By applying a small alternating voltage to this grid and tuning the detector amplifier to twice the frequency, a very sharp differential line spectrum of scattered and Auger electrons is obtained. Impurity detection of better than $\frac{1}{50}$ of a monolayer is claimed in some cases. Although it can be shown that a deflection-type spectrometer with an alternating voltage on the detector has in principle a better signal-to-noise ratio than the retarding grid, the combination of the latter with electron diffraction studies of the same surface constitutes an extremely powerful tool for the study of surface physics and chemistry.

SHERWOOD K. HAYNES

References

Burhop, E. H., "The Auger Effect and Other Radiationless Processes," Cambridge, The University Press, 1952.

Listengarten, M. A., "The Auger Effect" (a Review), *Bull. Acad. Sci. USSR*, **24** (9), 1050 (1960).

Burhop, E. H. S., and Asaad, W. H., "The Auger Effect," in "Advances in Atomic and Molecular Physics," New York, Academic Press 1972.

Chang, C. C., "Auger Electron Spectroscopy," *Surface Sci.*, **25**, 53–79 (1971).

Sevier, K., "Low Energy Electron Spectroscopy," New York, John Wiley & Sons Inc., 1972.

Haynes, S. K., "Phenomenological Systematics of L-Auger Spectra," Summary of the IUPAP Conference on Inner Shell Ionization Phenomena, Atlanta, Georgia, April 1972.

Cross-references: ATOMIC PHYSICS, PHOTOELECTRICITY, X-RAYS.

AURORA AND AIRGLOW

The visual aurora consists of luminous forms (arcs, rays, bands) in the night sky, usually confined to high latitudes, and based in the ionospheric E region (see IONOSPHERE). The airglow consists of faint relatively uniform luminosity which is world wide in occurrence, and, except under unusual conditions, can only be observed instrumentally.

The luminosity arises from emissions by the atmospheric constituents in atomic, molecular, or ionized forms. Table 1 shows the chief emissions in the visible regions, with approximate intensities in Rayleighs, for a bright aurora and temperate latitude airglow. There are many other emissions in the infrared and ultraviolet. In bright aurorae the colors can be seen visually; faint aurorae appear grayish white since the color vision threshold of the human eye (except in the red) is above the visual threshold.

An auroral arc is a narrow horizontal band of light up to a thousand or more kilometers long, lying approximately geomagnetic east-west. The term arc derives from its appearance from the earth's surface due to perspective. A band is a portion of an arc showing distortion normal to its length. Auroral rays have been likened to searchlight beams; they lie along the geomagnetic field direction and may be several hundred kilometers long. Arcs and bands may be homogeneous or rayed.

The visual aurora is caused by the precipitation of energetic charged particles (mainly electrons) along the geomagnetic field lines into the ionosphere, where they excite and ionize the atoms and molecules. On the night side of the earth the energetic particles originate from near the inner edge of the plasma sheet of the magnetosphere, and the aurora appears at about $65°$ to $70°$ geomagnetic latitude in both hemispheres; on the day side from the vicinity of the neutral points on the nose of the magnetosphere, and the aurora appears at $75°$ to $80°$ geomagnetic latitude (see SPACE PHYSICS). The net result is that the instantaneous distribution of the aurora over the earth approximates two ovals, called the auroral ovals, surrounding the north and south geomagnetic poles. This pat-

TABLE 1. CHIEF AURORAL AND AIRGLOW EMISSIONS IN THE VISIBLE REGION[a]

Emission	Spectral Region or Wavelength	Approximate Height (km)	Approximate Intensity (Rayleighs)	
			Bright Aurora[b]	Nightglow
[OI]	5577Å	90–110	100 000	250
	6300, 6364Å	>160	50 000	50–100
NII	Blue to red		25 000	
H (Balmer series)	Red, blue	E layer	10 000	
N_2 (1st positive)	Red	D layer	50 000	
(2nd positive)	Violet	D layer	100 000	
N_2^+ (1st negative)	Blue-violet		165 000	
O_2^+ (1st negative)	Red-yellow	D layer	10 000	
NaI	5890, 5896Å	80–90		100 (winter)
				20 (summer)
OH	Red-yellow	60–100		100
O_2 (Herzberg)	Blue-violet	90–100		15

[a]Adapted from Chamberlain (see References) which should be consulted for information including ultraviolet and infrared emissions.

[b]International Brightness Coefficient III (brightness of moonlit cumulus clouds).

NOTE: Emissions are highly variable or absent with type and latitude of aurora. Heights are given only when well defined. 1 Rayleigh = apparent emission rate of 10^{10} photons m^{-2} (column) sec^{-1}. 1 Å (Ångstrom unit) = 10^{-10} m.

tern is fixed relative to the sun, and the earth rotates beneath. The auroral zones are the loci on the earth of the midnight portions of the ovals, where the aurora is brightest and where the ovals extend to their lowest latitude. The auroral zones are hence approximately symmetrical about the geomagnetic poles, and reach their lowest geographic latitudes over eastern Canada and over the ocean south of Australia.

Associated with the aurora are strong electric fields which drive electric currents in the ionospheric E region. The strongest current flows on the night side of the auroral oval, and is called the auroral electrojet. The magnetic effects of the electrojet are easily observed at the ground. The general association between aurora and magnetic disturbance has been known for over 200 years.

The instantaneous position of the auroral oval is directly related to the distortion of the magnetosphere by the solar wind (see SPACE PHYSICS). In a large disturbance the midnight aurora may extend to well below $50°$ geomagnetic latitude; cases are on record of it having been observed from the tropics. The associated magnetic disturbance is called a storm (see GEOPHYSICS).

On the time scale of an hour or two the intensity, position, and dynamic behavior of the aurora vary in an irregular manner. Typically there is a sudden brightening of an auroral arc on the midnight meridian, and this is followed by characteristic dynamic features expanding poleward, and westward and eastward often to beyond the dusk and dawn meridians. The main auroral forms are quite distinct each side of the midnight meridian. The display decays to a series of quiet arcs round the auroral oval in about three hours. This dynamic sequence is called an auroral substorm. The frequency and intensity of substorms increases during magnetic storms.

Other important phenomena associated with aurorae and magnetic storms are auroral radio absorption, the radio aurora, and VLF radio emissions. The more energetic precipitating particles (predominantly electrons >10 keV) penetrate to the D region where the consequent excess ionization causes HF radio absorption (see IONOSPHERE). The radio aurora consists of irregularities in electron density that have gradients sufficiently large to reflect VHF and UHF radio waves. It is now believed that the irregularities are due to longitudinal plasma waves produced by one or more types of instability that develop when the rate of interpenetration of positive ions by electrons (constituting electric current) exceeds certain limits (see PLASMAS). VLF radio emissions in the audio range consisting of discrete tones (chorus) or noise (hiss) are produced by various charged particle-wave interactions in the magnetosphere.

There is a general relationship between the various phenomena but details are obscure. The whole auroral process is extremely complicated electrodynamically, and much is yet unknown about such features as the triggering, development, and decay of substorms, the acceleration of charged particles to auroral energies, the discrete structure of visual forms, and the origin of the electric fields.

The airglow is subdivided into dayglow, nightglow, and twilightglow. The original energy source is solar radiation and the dayglow is the prompt emission. The stored energy is released in the nightglow by a variety of processes many of which are not fully understood. In the D and lower E regions complex chemical reactions involving atomic, molecular, and ionized species, including oxides of nitrogen, occur. In the iono-

spheric F region a significant part of the oxygen red emission arises through electron-ion recombination, and photoelectrons migrating from higher altitudes are sometimes important. The well known sodium twilight emission is due to resonance scattering of sunlight. There are marked seasonal and latitude effects, and distinct patchiness, in the intensities of some emissions, which are probably related to the wind systems and vertical motions in the neutral atmosphere.

Our understanding of the aurora and airglow has developed enormously in the last decade; solution of many of the outstanding problems may be expected in the next.

R. S. UNWIN

References

Akasofu, S–I., "Polar and Magnetospheric Substorms," Dordrecht-Holland, D. Reidel, 1968.
Chamberlain, J. W., "Physics of the Aurora and Airglow," New York and London, Academic Press, 1961.
McCormac, B. M. (ed.), "The Radiating Atmosphere," Dordrecht-Holland, D. Reidel, 1971.
Stormer, C., "The Polar Aurora," Oxford, Clarendon Press, 1955.

Cross-references: GEOPHYSICS, IONOSPHERE, MAGNETIC FIELD, PLASMAS, SOLAR PHYSICS, SPACE PHYSICS.

B

BALLISTICS

Ballistics is an applied science dealing with the position, velocity, and acceleration of bodies in space and the forces influencing them. It is considered a branch of applied physics or MECHANICS and was formerly concerned primarily with military projectiles such as rifle bullets, field artillery shells, bombs, and rockets, but now has a bearing upon missiles, space vehicles, and orbiting satellites. Interior ballistics is concerned with the motion generated within the gun barrel or container, exterior ballistics is concerned with the motion in free air, and terminal ballistics is concerned with the effects at the point of impact (hopefully, at the target). Some bodies in motion will not involve all three divisions of this subject, for some are not launched from a gun barrel and some have no definite target or impact point (such as a vehicle which ends up orbiting the sun).

In designing a gun and a bullet, an attempt is made to obtain the highest velocity with the lowest possible maximum gas pressure. The burning rate of the propellant is important and this can be controlled by the shape and size of the pieces of propellant used. The erosion of the inside of the barrel must be held at a minimum in order to retain accuracy and keep down the heating of the barrel. It is said that some of the large German guns in World War I could be fired only once a day because they got so hot it was necessary to allow them to cool off in between firings. The smoke and the flash should be held at a minimum. Early inventors struggled with the problem of measuring projectile velocity and gas pressure in the gun barrel. The first crude method of indicating gas pressure was merely to note whether or not the gun barrel burst. When it did burst, the gas pressure had been increased too much! Great progress was made when Benjamin Robins developed the ballistic pendulum, a description of which he presented before the Royal Society of England in 1742. This involved computing the velocity of a projectile by measuring the swing of a large pendulum catching the shot. It was possible to estimate the velocity at the target as well as near the muzzle. Other methods involved the Boulengé chronograph, which measured the time elapsed between the breaking of two wire screens in the path of the shot, and the use of a magnetized projectile fired through two coils in series which recorded the induced voltage as a function of time. Improvements came through the use of strain gauges cemented to gun barrels and x-rays to locate the position of the projectile in the barrel as a function of time, and by comparing emissivities in two spectral regions to measure or estimate the temperature of the gas.

In exterior ballistics an effort is made to trace or plot the entire trajectory of the projectile. When the target is fixed, errors of firing can be observed and corrected quickly; but when bombing is done from a plane or when the interception of a missile is attempted by launching another missile, errors of sighting or launching cannot be corrected as quickly, for the plane cannot return to its former position exactly and a second missile to be intercepted is not apt to follow the same trajectory as the first one. The first attempts to predict trajectories of shells were made on an assumption that gravity was the only force acting upon the shell, but as muzzle velocity became greater, the air resistance became many times more important than gravity. The shape of the shell became more important, and as pointed noses were designed, it became necessary to devise some way to stabilize the projectile. The shells were spun by spiral grooves inside the barrel while bombs, rockets, and missiles were equipped with fins.

As missiles became larger and more powerful, they left the atmosphere of the earth sufficiently to be affected by the motion of other planets. It was difficult to record their trajectories. One method used in 1956 was to mount powerful strobe lights on the missiles and program them to flash in certain patterns. A radio signal was sent to the earth simultaneously with the flashes of the lights. Large ballistic cameras were set, some on islands, along the path of the missiles and their shutters were left open during the entire flight of the missiles. The camera plates recorded the flashes of the strobe lights and also the star trails. The flights were made at night and it was important to have a clear night with no clouds. The star trails aided in the exact orientation of the cameras. An electronic computer program was devised to synchronize the timing records of the ground receiving stations and the light flashes so that the position, velocity, and acceleration of the missile were quickly computed. Computer programs were

even developed to the point where the computer would predict the point of impact from the early observations before the missile landed, usually in the ocean. Multiple warheads for missiles have been designed to contain atomic bombs which can be independently directed, each with a different trajectory, to specified targets.

Terminal ballistics, which is concerned with fragmentation, blast, and penetration of armour and concrete, cannot be covered in detail in this brief article.

HARRY PELLE HARTKEMEIER

References

Barr, J., and Howard, W. E., "Polaris!", New York, Harcourt, Brace and Company, 1960.

Bliss, G. A., "Mathematics for Exterior Ballistics," New York, John Wiley & Sons, Inc., 1944.

Davis, L., Jr., Follin, J. W., Jr., and Blitzer, L., "Exterior Ballistics of Rockets," New York, Van Nostrand Reinhold, 1958.

Hartkemeier, H. P., "Synchronization of Trajectory Images of Ballistic Missiles and the Timing Record of the Ground Telemetry Recording System," RCA Data Reduction Technical Report No. 31, AFMTC-TN-56-80, ASTIA Doc. No. 96634, 5 Nov. 1956, Patrick Air Force Base, Cape Canaveral, Florida.

Hymans, J. S. C., "Guns, Shells, and Rockets: A Simple Guide to Ballistics," London, 1950.

Lowry, Edward, "Interior Ballistics," New York, Doubleday & Co., 1968.

McShane, E. J., Kelly, J. L., and Reno, F. V., "Exterior Ballistics," Denver, 1953.

Nelson, W. C., Ed., "Selected Topics on Ballistics," New York, Pergamon Press, 1959.

Moulton, F. R., "Methods in Exterior Ballistics," New York, Dover Publications, 1962.

Rosser, J. B., Newton, R. R., and Gross, G. L., "Mathematical Theory of Rocket Flight," New York McGraw-Hill Book Co., Inc., 1947.

Schwiebert, E. G., "A History of the U. S. Air Force Ballistic Missiles," New York, Frederick A. Praeger, 1965.

Wimpress, R. N., "Internal Ballistics of Solid Fuel Rockets, New York, McGraw-Hill Book Co., Inc., 1950.

Cross-reference: DYNAMICS.

BATTERIES*

The term "battery" generally denotes an assembly of one or more electrochemical cells which exhibit a voltage difference between their two electrodes, so that they will deliver usable current when connected to an external circuit. Some authorities apply the term "galvanic" or "voltaic" cells to this family, to distinguish them from cells to which current is fed from an

*Editor was unable to locate author. Article is reprinted from first edition.

outside source for purposes such as electroplating or extraction of metals. There are many ways in which a voltage difference can be produced in an electrochemical cell. The simplest cell, thermodynamically speaking, is the "concentration cell" in which electrolyte or electrode materials are incorporated into half-cells in differing concentrations; a "half cell" is a system involving an electrolyte and a single electrode. When the half-cells are connected, the free energy change accompanying the transfer of one substance from high to low concentration results in the liberation of electrical energy. Concentration cells, though interesting theoretically, are not important commercially.

The majority of economically important cells consists of two dissimilar electrodes of metal or metal compounds, immersed in an aqueous solution of an acid, base, or in some cases a salt. The negative of a fresh cell is typically in the metallic state, while the positive is usually an oxide, or occasionally, a salt of the metal. During discharge, the negative electrode is oxidized as electrons leave it via the external circuit, and the positive is reduced. Since by definition an anode is an oxidation electrode, in the literature the negative is generally called the "anode" and the positive the "cathode"; this conforms to accepted electrochemical terminology, though it is the cause of some confusion.

Theoretically, galvanic cells might look more attractive than heat engines as sources of electric power, since the energy changes are not subject to the limitations of the Carnot cycle. In actuality, however, the cost of public-utility-produced power is 3¢ to 5¢ per kWh, as compared with roughly $2 per kWh for the power delivered throughout the life of a sealed rechargeable nickel-cadmium cell, and $50 per kWh for a nonrechargeable Leclanché flashlight cell. This is because of inefficiencies in electrochemical operation, high material costs, high cost of the tightly controlled production operations necessary, etc. Galvanic cells have grown in importance because of the strength of other needs such as the need for a portable supply of power, for power at a place far distant from the prime power source or at a different time than can be supplied by the prime source, for a reserve supply of power to cover peak demands which are beyond the capacity of the prime source or to supply power in the event of failure of the prime source. There are also needs for a source of pure direct current or for a stable reference voltage which are filled by galvanic cells.

Taking the familiar lead-acid storage battery and the conventional Leclanché flashlight-type cell as examples, cell systems are schematized in the literature as follows, the vertical lines denoting phase boundaries between the solid active materials and the electrolyte:

$$Pb \,|\, H_2SO_4 \,|\, PbO_2$$

$$Zn \,|\, NH_4Cl, \, ZnCl_2 \,|\, MnO_2, \, C$$

Abbreviations denoting the state and the concentration of the materials may appear beside the chemical symbols. Some cells are shown as containing more than three phases; e.g., those with a different electrolyte at each electrode. In all cases, the oxidation electrode, the negative, is given on the left, and the reduction electrode on the right, with the electrolyte phase or phases between. Cell reactions are written in the conventional chemical fashion, the charged reactants on the left and the discharged products on the right. For example,

$$Pb + PbO_2 + 2H_2SO_4 \underset{\text{charge}}{\overset{\text{discharge}}{\rightleftharpoons}} 2PbSO_4 + 2H_2O.$$

References which discuss cell reactions in any detail will include also the half-cell reactions for each individual electrode.

The basic thermodynamics of a galvanic cell operating reversibly at constant temperature and pressure is described by the equation

$$\Delta G = - nF\xi \qquad (1)$$

where ΔG is the change in the Gibbs free energy, n is the valence change in the cell reaction, F is the Faraday (96 487 coulombs), and ξ is the reversible emf of the cell. In terms of ΔH, the heat of the reaction,

$$\xi = - \frac{\Delta H}{nF} + T\left(\frac{\partial \xi}{\partial T}\right)_P \qquad (2)$$

where T is the absolute temperature, and the derivative is the voltage-temperature coefficient of the cell at constant pressure.

Expressing the basic cell reaction as

$$xA + yB \rightarrow vL + wM \qquad (3)$$

a practical expression for ξ may be written:

$$\xi = \xi^0 - \frac{RT}{nF} \ln \frac{(a_L) \, v(a_M)^w}{(a_A)^x \, (a_B)^y} \qquad (4)$$

where R is the gas constant, a_z the activity of species Z and ξ^0 is the standard emf; the latter term, ξ^0, may be expressed as

$$\xi^0 = \frac{RT}{nF} \log K \qquad (5)$$

where K is the equilibrium constant of the cell reaction. Alternatively, ξ_0 may be calculated in terms of the oxidation potentials of the negative and positive electrodes; the potentials of many electrode reactions may be obtained from standard sources.[1] A rough calculation of ξ may be made by using the concentrations of the several species as approximations of their activities; the activity of a pure phase, such as a solid, is considered to be unity.

In actual operation, a discharging cell does not behave reversibly, and therefore does not obey Eq. (1). Hence it is useful to define the electrochemical efficiency ϵ as the ratio of the chemical energy expended to the electrical energy delivered during the time t_D necessary to completely discharge the cell; i.e.,

$$\epsilon = - \int_0^{t_D} \xi_D i_D \, dt / \Delta G \qquad (6)$$

where ξ_D in this case is the cell terminal voltage, and i_D the current, during discharge. With rechargeable cells, it is also useful to define the storage efficiency ϵ_s as the ratio of the energy delivered during discharge to that returned in the subsequent recharge (denoted by subscript c); i.e.,

$$\epsilon_s = \int_0^{t_D} \xi_D i_D \, dt \left/ \int_0^{t_c} \xi_c i_c \, dt \right. \qquad (7)$$

In the definition of ϵ_s, it is assumed that the cell is charged until it is returned to its original condition.

Both ϵ and ϵ_s are considerably less than unity in practical operating cells, for a number of reasons. Not all the current that theoretically could be delivered by the quantity of active material in the cell will actually be produced, due to incomplete chemical reactivity, imperfect electrical contact between the active material and the conductive grid, and other factors. Further, observed cell voltage will be less than that predicted from thermodynamic data, due to competing reactions occurring spontaneously within the cell and to "polarization" effects. (Polarization is the term given to any process, such as the accumulation of products of the discharge reaction at the reaction sites, which causes a reduction in the potential of an electrode as current is being passed through it.)

Typically, ϵ will range from 75 to 90 per cent (the latter figure pertaining to alkaline cells with low internal resistance, operating at low discharge rates); ϵ_s will generally range from 55 to 75 per cent, depending, as one factor, on the rate at which charging is done and the consequent spread between charge and discharge voltage. With practical cells, the degree to which the change in free energy of the cell reactants can be realized in terms of electrical energy is not of as much importance as is the electrical energy produced per unit weight or unit volume of the cell.

For the sake of providing some comparison between galvanic cells and thermal converters, consideration might be given to thermal efficiency. This can be approximated by substituting ΔH for ΔG in Eq. (6). Thermal efficiency in many modern cells is 50 per cent to 80 per cent, as compared with 40 per cent to 45 per cent for the better thermal converters. Thermal converters may, however, be superior on a watt-hour per pound basis, particularly when operated over long periods of time.

Physical Configurations, Plate Types Cells are commonly made in three basic configurations: cylindrical, rectangular, (sometimes called "prismatic," particularly in Europe), and small disk-shaped "button" cells. Each of these has distinct advantages and disadvantages, and each is made with plates of specialized design, tailored to fit that shape. Cylindrical cells make optimum use of internal volume and contain internal pressures well (a necessity with sealed cells). When assembled into multicell batteries, however, they are wasteful of battery internal volume. Further, they require specialized, and often costly, production techniques. Plates for cylindrical cells are frequently molded as slugs of the desired cylindrical shape, or they may be cut from sheet material into long strips which then are rolled, with an intervening strip of separator, into a coil. This sheet plate material may be made by a wide variety of methods including sintering, electroplating, pasting of active materials onto some suitable support, impregnating active materials into a porous matrix, or forming sheet metal. In rare cases, flat rectangular plates may be assembled into a cylindrical cell container.

Rectangular cells are easily assembled; the cases are easily fabricated of a variety of materials. They make acceptable use of battery internal volume. They do not, however, contain well the force of plate expansion or internal gas pressure. And usually a lesser proportion of cell internal volume can be filled with plate material than can be done with cylindrical cells. Button cells lend themselves to automatic production techniques; the assembly operations are relatively simple and inexpensive; the cells are easily stacked into batteries of any required voltage. As disadvantages, they do not contain internal pressures well; they cannot easily be made in sizes much larger than 1.0 ampere hour in capacity; and they involve considerable waste of cell internal volume. Plates for both rectangular and button cells are almost invariably flat. Button cell plates are usually molded or stamped from sheet stock into the required disk shape. Plates for rectangular cells may be sheet material made by any of the methods given in the previous paragraph. Or they may be cast or molded.

"Primary" and "Secondary" Types Galvanic cells of commercial importance fall into two classes, "primary" and "secondary." Primary cells are said to be nonreversible; at the end of discharge, the active materials are in such state that they cannot be returned to their original condition by charging. Secondary cells are said to be reversible; they can be recharged by applying current to the cell terminals in opposite polarity to that produced by the cell during discharge. As normally used, these cells are not truly reversible in the thermodynamic sense: keeping charge-discharge times within acceptable limits, it takes considerably more than an "infinitesimal increase" in opposing force to drive the cell reaction in the opposite "charging" direction. Ordinarily, primary cells yield higher energy densities (ratios of power output to weight or volume) than do secondary cells. One reason for this is that providing rechargeability involves considerable sacrifice in the amount of reactive material that can be packed into a given unit weight or volume, due to the need to incorporate relatively massive grid structures within or around the plates, plus space-and weight-consuming separators between the plates. Providing rechargeability may even require incorporating the active materials in a form which offers less than optimum electrochemical reactivity.

Primary Cells. Until recent years, zinc was used as the anode of almost every primary cell known. The metals above zinc in the electromotive series (aluminum, magnesium, calcium, potassium, etc.) react so readily with the water of the aqueous electrolytes (the only electrolytes judged practical in the past), that much of their energy is consumed in wasteful side reactions. The metals below zinc provide inadequate cell voltage and, in several instances, are costly (chromium, cadmium, cobalt). Zinc is still the only common primary anode, although magnesium, calcium, lead, silver, and indium have been used for some special military and experimental cell types. A considerably greater variety of materials has been used as cathodes, including, in the older cells, manganese dioxide, oxygen, cuprous oxide and copper, carbon, and mercuric oxide. More recently, primary cells have been built with cathodes of mercuric oxide, silver (I) and silver (II) oxide, lead dioxide, zinc chloride, lead chromate, copper halides, silver chloride, and, in experimental cells, such materials as bismuth trioxide, vanadium pentoxide, and a variety of organic compounds such as the nitrobenzenes, nitropropanes, and N-halogens which promise high energy yield per unit weight.

Secondary Cells. Far fewer secondary than primary systems have been developed to a practical level. The difficulties in providing acceptable cost, satisfactory physical, electrical, and environmental characteristics, together with rechargeability, are so severe that today there are only six secondary systems of any practical importance. Five of these—the nickel-cadmium, nickel-iron (Edison), silver-zinc, silver-cadmium, and zinc-manganese dioxide—are alkaline. (In Europe, particularly the Soviet Union, another alkaline system, the nickel-zinc, is used.) The remaining system, the familiar lead-acid, is the cheapest storage battery type, and is by far the most important commercially. Total sales of all secondary types in 1962 were reported to be $460 million; of this, $425 million was for lead-acid batteries, the preponderant majority of which were ordinary car or truck starting batteries.

Standard Cells Standard cells are galvanic cells that are used to provide a stable, known

voltage for calibration of other equipment, rather than for supplying electric power. The only type in general use now is the "Weston," or mercury-cadmium cell. The "saturated" cell type is: Cd, Hg|3CdSO$_4$·8H$_2$O|CdSO$_4$|Hg$_2$SO$_4$|Hg. The anode is a 10 per cent cadmium amalgam; the CdSO$_4$ is a saturated aqueous solution. The emf at 20°C is 1.01864 volts. It has a fairly large temperature coefficient (0.00004 volt/°C at 20°C). A more generally used type, the "unsaturated" cell (assembled without cadmium sulfate crystals) has a temperature coefficient of 0.00001 volt/°C.

Fuel Cells Fuel cells, though operating as galvanic cells at the electrodes, are in a class by themselves in that they provide direct, single-site conversion of original raw materials into electrical power, obviating the boiler-turbine-transmission-rectifier chain that precedes the production and use of ordinary batteries. The raw materials, usually involving hydrogen and oxygen, are fed into the cell in a constant flow, as long as power is needed; when the fuel flow is stopped, the cell is inert. The fuels react at the electrodes, forming H$_2$O as the exhaust in most cells, and liberating electricity. Calculating actual power output versus theoretical free energy change of the original fuels, efficiencies of 65 to 85 per cent have been achieved in prototype and laboratory models. The technological problems remaining to be solved before practical fuel cells appear on the market are formidable, and include elimination of the water from the pores of the electrodes, preventing contamination of the electrochemical system by impurities carried in with the cheaper fuels, achieving workable energy densities, simplifying the necessary control and supporting equipment, and providing adequate electrode life. For an excellent general discussion of various fuel cell types, see reference 2.

WM. W. JAKOBI

References

1. Latimer, W., "The Oxidation States of the Elements and Their Potentials in Aqueous Solutions," second edition, New York, Prentice-Hall, Inc., 1952.
2. Mitchell, Will, Jr., Ed., "Fuel Cells," New York, Academic Press, 1963.
3. "Batteries and Electric Cells" in "Encyclopedia of Chemical Technology," second edition, Vol. 3, New York, John Wiley & Sons, Inc., 1964.

Cross-references: ELECTRIC POWER GENERATION, ELECTROCHEMISTRY, POTENTIAL.

BETATRON

The betatron is a particle accelerator using a sustained induced voltage to accelerate the particles to full energy during the whole period of acceleration of the particle. Since this method of acceleration seemed most applicable to electrons, the name "betatron" was used to indicate that it was the agency for producing high-speed electrons. The action of the betatron is similar to the action of an electrical TRANSFORMER in which a high-voltage winding of many turns is used. In a transformer, the voltage can be stepped up from the primary voltage, V_1, to the secondary voltage, V_2.

$$V_2 = V_1 N_2 / N_1$$

where N_2 is the large number of turns of the secondary and N_1 is the small number of turns in the primary. For example, x-ray transformers having high voltage, such as 100 000 volts, have very many turns of fine wires and consequently raise the primary voltage by a large factor.

The main structure of the betatron is really a transformer, and focusing magnets are arranged around the transformer core where a secondary winding might be put. A vacuum tube instead is placed between these focusing magnets so that it can conduct electrons hundreds of thousands of times around the core. Each time the electron circulates around the core it acquires an energy equivalent to the voltage which would have been induced in one turn of wire at that instant.

In order to guide the electrons on many revolutions the focusing magnet can be such that the magnetic field decreases with increasing radius. Then the lines of force bulge outwardly about the orbit, providing vertical focusing forces back to a horizontal orbit in case the particle strays above or below the orbital plane. This bulging field is the requirement for vertical focusing, and it is used in cyclotrons too. However, it is necessary that the magnetic field decrease less rapidly than $1/r$, where r is the radius of the orbit. If this latter requirement is met, then radial focusing will be insured; because the required centripetal force to hold the particle in the circle going around the core decreases as $1/r$. Consequently, if the magnetic force decreases less rapidly than this, it will be too strong at large radii to permit the orbit to remain circulating at a large radius, and it will be too weak at small radii to maintain the particle circulating at a small radius. The particle thus will hunt about the so-called equilibrium orbit by means of this radial focusing action in addition to the previously mentioned vertical focusing action. The oscillations of the particle about this orbit are called betatron oscillations, and the name appears in the scientific literature referring to particle motions in other accelerators such as synchrotrons, because this focusing was first worked out for the case of the betatron.

It is possible to have strong focusing magnets with much more rapid variation of field with radius to provide the focusing. In this case, a succession of focusing and de-focusing magnets must be used which alternately focus vertical and radial motion and which are called alternate gradient focusing magnets. Such strong focusing

magnets can limit the oscillation of the particle about the equilibrium orbit to a very small amplitude.

The usual betatron has a magnetic field which rises proportionately with the increase in the transformer's magnetic flux within the orbit. By means of this proportionality, the strength of the guiding field rises along with momentum gained by tranformer action, and hence the guiding field provides sufficient centripetal force to hold the particle at the same radius.

The first betatron of this type produced 2 MeV and radiation equivalent to 2 grams of radium. It is now in the Smithsonian Museum in Washington, D.C. This accelerator is the size of a typewriter. The largest betatron can generate beams of 320 MeV. The x-rays and electrons can be used to produce mesons and numerous nuclear disintegrations. The most commonly used betatrons are for 25 to 35 MeV. These provide x-rays of maximum penetration in iron for industrial radiography, and they provide x-rays and electrons with optimum depth dose characteristics for x-ray or electron therapy of the human body.

The intensity of radiation from the 25-MeV betatron is of the order of 100 to 200 roentgen/min at a meter from the target for x-rays. With the extracted electron beam, the ionization doses would depend on how widely the electrons are spread at the point of treatment, but comparable doses are obtained. The large 320-MeV betatron at the University of Illinois produced intensities of the order of 20 000 roentgen/min at a meter or, in other terms, of the order of 5 watts.

It is possible to make what are called fixed-field alternating-gradient betatrons (FFAG). In this case, the focusing field is constant in time, and the particle orbit can be caused to spiral either outwardly or inwardly with increasing energy between the focusing poles of a direct current magnet or a permanent magnet. These FFAG betatrons are capable of giving a beam of x-rays up to 20 per cent of the time, whereas the betatrons with time-varying focusing fields just give one pulse of electrons in every cycle, and these pulses are only of the order of a microsecond in duration. Because of the large duty factor available with FFAG betatrons, it should be possible to achieve intensities of 10 000 watts. Although FFAG combination betatrons and synchrotrons have been made, full advantage has not been taken of a large duty factor achievable by incorporating a full-size transformer core within the betatron orbit.

In the case of the conventional betatron with constant orbit radius, the relation between the strength of guiding field and the total flux change within the orbit can be found as follows:

The momentum of the orbit

$$p = \frac{e}{c} BR$$

while the rate of change of momentum

$$\frac{dp}{dt} = eE$$

where e is the charge of the electron, c is the velocity of light, B is the magnetic field in gausses, R is the radius in centimeters, and E is the electrical field in the electrostatic units.

$$2\pi RE = \frac{1}{c} \frac{d\Phi}{dt}$$

the volts per turn where Φ is the flux linking the orbit. Combining the last two equations

$$\frac{dp}{dt} = \frac{e}{2\pi Rc} \frac{d\Phi}{dt}.$$

Thus, after a lapse of time

$$p = \frac{e}{2\pi Rc} (\Phi_2 - \Phi_1)$$

Combining this with the first equation

$$2\pi R^2 B = \Phi_2 - \Phi_1$$

Thus the flux change within orbit $\Phi_2 - \Phi_1$ is twice as big as the flux would be if the flux density, B, were constant within the orbit. Therefore, the transformer core must be adjusted so that the proper excess flux density provided within the orbit meets the conditions of this last relation if the orbit is to be at a constant radius, the assumption made in the above derivation.

D. W. KERST

Cross-references: ACCELERATORS, LINEAR; ACCELERATORS, PARTICLE; CYCLOTRON; SYNCHROTRON; ACCELERATORS, VAN DE GRAAFF.

BIONICS

Bionics is defined as the branch of knowledge pertaining to the functioning of living systems and the development of nonliving systems which function in a manner characteristic of, or resembling, living systems. The definition of bionics infers the use of scientific skills and techniques from biological, physical, mathematical, and applied sciences in carrying out research in which: (1) the functions of chosen biological components and systems are studied and analyzed to determine underlying principles and processes that may lead to methods for improving physical components or systems, and (2) the theories and techniques of chemistry, physics, and mathematics are applied to advance our knowledge of the principles upon which these functions are based.

Bionics research depends on the acceptance of certain postulates. These postulates are of two types—one essentially operational, the other

essentially technical. The important operational postulates are: (1) Common experience shows that biological systems perform operations that no nonbiological system can now perform efficiently, e.g., operations such as pattern recognition and identification, discrimination, and learning; (2) biological components perform such functions as detection, filtering, and information transfer more efficiently and with greater certainty over broader bandwidths than do present nonbiological components; (3) intensive study, analysis, and application of the principles that make superior biological performance possible can lead to nonbiological systems that equal or may, in some cases, exceed biological systems capabilities. The technical postulates are: (1) The functional advantages of biological systems are implied in the unique methods for information transfer, memory storage, and retrieval, united with unique ways of correlating and integrating data from many sensors or sensor systems. These unique methods depend mainly on: (a) many converging and diverging information transfer channels and many connections between channels, and (b) the special properties of biological components at the points where these channels are interconnected. (2) The superior capabilities of biological components or particular elements of the components (e.g., receptor cells or nerve muscle junctions) are derived from specific ways of interconnection and probably as well from specific molecular properties. (3) The relevant data describing biological systems that will represent major improvements over existing physical and engineering hardware are analyzed and studied. (4) The present rapid advances in microminiaturization techniques suggest that, for the first time, the possibility exists for the development of physical components or systems that incorporate these superior biological principles and processes.

The definition of bionics suggests the methodology of procedure. We design, grow, or in some way obtain nonbiological systems that function in a way "resembling" living systems. The physical component simulates the biological way of doing or carrying out its function. To obtain this objective, we first choose the biological components that perform the desired function; second, we compile the descriptive biological data; third, we translate these data into engineering terms; and fourth, we apply the translated data for the physical simulation of the function.

This process requires application of relevant mathematics to describe clearly, and as rigorously as possible, the biological function by some mathematical theory or model. This process may also require various techniques from the physical sciences to arrive at the necessary data defining the biological function of interest.

While the bionics research procedure requires the description, mathematically, of the function to be performed by the nonbiological system, it may also require mathematical and physical descriptions of the properties of the materials used to construct the nonbiological analog.

Gaining enough data to describe the given biological function may require study of the biological component or one of its elements at the molecular level. Similarly, solid-state or molecular techniques may be required to construct the physical system that is the appropriate simulation of the desired biological function.

Successful bionics activity may be modified by several factors. These include the complexity of the biological functions; the kind, quality, and quantity of data available to describe the functions; and the existence of relevant mathematical and physical techniques essential to the simulation of the functions.

In terms of the bionics objectives, the scope of the work must include research on the following components and/or systems: (a) receptors or sensors; (b) receptor systems—including central interconnections and interconnections among receptor systems; (c) central nervous system networks and the interconnections among parts of the nerve network; (d) effectors and actuators; (e) effector systems—including the feed-back and feed-forward connectors to and from the central processor; (f) the integrated system made up of sensors and their input channels, the central correlating, control, and computing networks, and the channels from the central system to the effectors and actuators.

This complete research program will extend over a long period of time. However, progress has been made. Data have been acquired, analyzed, and put into engineering terms to provide a set of specifications for the functional properties of several types of neurons. The neuron is presumed to be that physiological component underlying observed psychological parameters such as learning and adaptation. Therefore, the construction of a network of artificial neurons should, to some extent, simulate these observed behavioral parameters. In contrast, data have been acquired and analyzed from the field of experimental psychology on functions such as learning. These data can be translated into engineering and can suggest types of components which can simulate the learning function directly. This example illustrates a procedure which is common in bionics research. One can start at the operational level with an observed set of functional parameters and attempt to synthesize the class of mechanisms that could simulate these functions, or one can start with the biological component which is presumed to give rise to these functions and attempt to simulate this component. The choice of one method over the other depends greatly on the assurance one has of the validity of the data at one level or the other.

Applications, using the former (functional simulation) type of component, have been successfully made to flight control systems, variable

geometry jet engine control, radar detection and search problems, and various industrial process control problems. A few of the relevant papers are listed in the references under *Applications*.

CECIL W. GWINN
LEONARD M. BUTSCH, JR.

References

General

"Bionics Symposium 1960," Wright Air Development Division, U.S. Air Force, Technical Documentary Report 60-600.
"Biological Prototypes and Synthetic Systems," New York, Plenum Press, 1962.
"Bionics Symposium 1963," Aeronautical Systems Division, U.S. Air Force, Technical Documentary Report 63-946.
Thompson, D'Arcy W., "On Growth and Form," Cambridge, Cambridge University Press, 1942.
Sommerkoff, G., "Analytical Biology," London, Oxford University Press, 1950.
Ashby, W. R., "Design for a Brain," New York, John Wiley & Sons, Inc., 1960.
Ashby, W. R., "Introduction to Cybernetics," New York, John Wiley & Sons, Inc., 1958.
"Cybernetic Problem in Bionics," London, Gordon and Breach, 1968.
Beer, S., "Decision and Control," New York, John Wiley & Sons, 1966.
"Modern Systems Research for the Behavioral Scientist," Chicago, Aldine, 1968.
"Systems Thinking," London, Penguin Books, 1969.
Rosen, R., "Optimality Principles in Biology," New York, Plenum Press, 1967.

Applications

Barron, R. L., and Gwinn, C. W., "Applications of Self Organizing Control to Aeronautical and Industrial Systems," Design Engineering Conference ASME, New York, April 1971.
Gwinn, C. W., and Barron, R. L., "Recent Advances in Self-Organizing and Learning Controllers," paper in NATO AGARD Symposium, AGARD-CP-68-70 on "Application of Digital Computers to Guidance and Control," London, 1970.
Young, G. O., and Howard, J. E., "Adaptive AMTI Radar Techniques Investigation," Hughes Aircraft Corp. under Contract F33615-70-C-1754 with U. S. Air Force Avionics Laboratory, AFAL-TR-71-201, July, 1971.
Adaptonics, Inc., "Design, Fabrication and Flight Testing of Self-Organizing Flight Control System," under Contract AF33615-5141 with U.S. Air Force Flight Dynamics and Avionics Laboratories, AFFDL-TR-70-77, May 1970.
Barron, R. L., and Cleveland, D., "Self-Organizing Control of Advanced Turbine Engines," under contract F33615-68-C-1606 with U. S. Air Force Propulsion Laboratory, AFAPL-TR-69-73, August 1969.

Cross-references: BIONICS, CYBERNETICS, MATHEMATICAL BIOPHYSICS.

BIOPHYSICS*

Just as biochemistry was born slowly and painfully out of general physiology over a period of fifty years centered at the turn of the century, so biophysics is now emerging as a major, distinguishable part of science. Disciples of this youngest daughter of general physiology, biophysicists apply the new and developing techniques of physics and physical chemistry to biological subject matter; in addition, they develop new methods to examine, and theories to describe, biological processes.

Because of its biological and physical origins, the subject cuts into, or overlaps with, several other "branches" of science. However, like all these other disciplines, the boundaries are not too well defined, nor can they be in a classification which is essentially a subjective one. The various subdivisions of biophysics—mathematical, physical, physicochemical, physiological and psychological—intrude on and overlap with the corresponding established disciplines whenever those disciplines make a physically oriented attack aimed at the fundamental description and understanding of living matter.

Certain men in history focused the experience of their time. Biophysics might be said to have begun immediately after Isaac Newton was hit on the head with the falling apple: effects of gravitational attraction and the psychological results of the impulse to his head doubtless drew his immediate attention! Interest in impulse and momentum-transfer to living matter persists for obvious pathological reasons.

The discovery of animal electricity by Luigi Galvani in 1778 opened up, in Allesandro Volta's words 20 years later, "a very wide field for reflection." The development of electrophysiology and the more fundamental biophysical studies of the molecular and ionic mechanisms associated with irritability of tissue are a distant consequence.

The anatomist, Adolf Fick, considered by some to be the father of biophysics, showed the way to quantitative studies of diffusion and mass transport. Recognizing immediately the interdisciplinary nature of his studies, he thoughtfully published his work simultaneously in a journal of physics and a journal of physiology in 1855. Modern familiarity with exchange processes, membrane processes and the like, stems from his pioneering work. Meanwhile Thomas Young was completing a long career during which he formulated important ideas on the physics of color vision and heart action. Young was followed later into studies on these and many other topics of biophysical interest by one of the intellectual giants of the nineteenth century, the ubiquitous scientific explorer, Hermann Ludwig Ferdinand von Helmholtz, who put color vision, hearing and energy

*Editor was unable to locate author. Article is reprinted from first edition.

conversion, on a physical foundation which was firm enough to withstand nearly a century's further progress.

The basic principles of fluid flow through blood vessels, and pipes in general, were described quantitatively in 1884 by Jean Louis Poiseuille. It was only a few years later that that last fruitful quarter-century was completed in rousing fashion by three other discoveries which were to lead to later very important developments in biophysics. First, Svante Arrhenius, Hans Kohlrausch, and others characterized the electrical and osmotic properties of *ionic* solutions. Second, Henri Becquerel discovered natural radioactivity in 1895; and third, Wilhelm Roentgen discovered the penetrating and ionizing radiation which he named x-rays in 1898. From the new fundamental knowledge of electrolytes, have proceeded electrochemical studies on the origin and nature of electric currents in living tissue, and studies on the subtleties of water balance in cells and tissues. In a similar development, further knowledge of the origin, physical properties and the physical effects of particulate and electromagnetic ionizing radiations has formed the basis for studies of their biophysical effects, which are closely interwoven with those being studied in radiation chemistry, radiobiology and radiology. For example, studies on the time and spatial distribution of the energy absorbed by living tissues from gamma-ray beams have led to some understanding of the mechanisms of (a) changes induced in mass-transport processes in blood plasma, (b) changes in chemical reactivity, and (c) subtle changes in the electrochemical processes which form the basis of transmission of information along nerve membranes. The psychological effects of an increased background of ionizing radiation on the noise level in human nerve transmission may be one of man's important problems in the future.

The continuing development of fast, sensitive electronic equipment—fast dc amplifiers, electron microscopes of high resolving power, ultraviolet microscopes, mechanoelectrical transducers, etc.—has encouraged more and more physicists to become interested in the properties of biological material. Conversely, students of biology have become increasingly more familiar with properties of fundamental particles, physical measurements, kinetic techniques and analyses, etc., and are applying them to their focus of interest when feasible. For instance, during the 1930's some very clever experimental and theoretical studies were begun by A. V. Hill and others on the transformation of the energy from chemical reactions into the mechanical energy of muscle contraction and the attendant electrochemical energy for nervous control. Although the process is unbelievably complicated on the molecular scale, research is now able to be centered on myosin, the remarkable contractile protein-enzyme molecule, and its molecular associate, actin. Chemical activity of myosin as a specific hydrolytic enzyme is accompanied by conformational changes, which permit both sliding and folding processes to occur at the macromolecular level during contraction of the bulk muscle. The energy balances (heat, mechanical, electrochemical, chemical) and the power balances are slowly being worked out in detail. They are devious, reflecting the complexity of the basic molecular system. Although still only partly quantitative, a comprehensive molecular theory is becoming more and more satisfying.

Since the early 1950's, a concerted study of the interaction of matter waves (sound and ultrasound) with living tissues has been apparent, with contributions from several disciplines: electrical engineering studies on the production, focusing and measurement of radiated sonic energy; physiological studies on the reception by the ear and other mechano-receptors; electrochemical studies of interfaces irradiated with acoustic beams, associated with the receptor-nerve junction; physical studies of the mechanisms of absorption by watery polymeric solutions. From these has emerged a flourishing part of biophysics not only concerned with the fundamental processes of absorption and transduction, but also providing knowledge useful in the diagnosis and location of brain disorders and subcutaneous lesions, and even therapy by acoustic irradiation.

A mathematical description of selected biophysical concepts was made in 1938 by Nicholas Rashevsky, and in the years since, he and one group of biophysicists have been actively developing mathematical descriptions of current ideas on growth, cancer, energy and mass transfer in cell respiration, cell movements and, more recently, nerve conduction and the stability (steady-state) of living organisms (see MATHEMATICAL BIOPHYSICS for Rashevsky's account of this research). Inherent in this work are developments of new mathematical concepts, or algebraic models, which at least in principle can describe the detailed behavior of living tissue when stimulated with certain forces. Perhaps the greatest contribution of this kind of work is that it presses the experimental biophysicist continually to refine his techniques, to measure yet more parameters of the living material he is studying, for the models developed usually contain explicit functions of parameters which are not or cannot yet be measured. The difficulty in this work is to be able to relate the theory, at sufficiently small intervals in its development, to reality as found by the experimentalist.

The quantitative concepts so successfully used in the electrical and electronic engineering of guided missiles have recently been applied with useful results to processes occurring in the brain, and to the better understanding of the principles of organization of the physical apparatus which forms the physical basis of memory, emotions, and instinct. Even without

complete knowledge about how a neuron works, in terms of atoms and molecules of which it is composed, certain properties of cell assemblies, or neural nets, are beginning to show in research on electronic models, and the systems concept is suggesting where else we should look for other properties of other subsystems, or assemblies. This biophysical approach may, in another twenty years, enable man to give a better physiological as well as psychological account of neuroses and anxieties. Maintenance of the steady-state, assessment of the kind of and time of response to given inputs or feedbacks—in short, problems in stability of the system—occupy an important group of biophysicists today. Even the teaching of biophysics has received benefit from the early introduction of the systems concept into the course: it is a good framework on which the teacher can hang the details of the course.

Meanwhile a considerable number of biophysicists concern themselves with two very new and modern topics: molecular biophysics and the biophysics of weightlessness. This work seems to have to be done by big teams, in which the biophysicist has his role. Evidence was presented in 1961 that a coding of genetic and hereditary information in the chromosome may be carried in the arrangement of the four pyridine and pyrimidine bases which occur in desoxyribonucleic acid (DNA), and since then other macromolecules have become suspect. Further on macromolecules: for many years certain vague variants of composition and structure had been associated with specific so-called molecular diseases. As a result of these two developments, the subject of "molecular biology" has become loosely circumscribed as a special very important interest in science; and as part of this circumscribed interest has sprung "molecular biophysics"—loosely (yet) defined as the study of structure and physical properties of macromolecules as they affect their physicochemical roles in living tissue.

With man now entering the space age, the problems he and his living ancillary equipment will have to face are already becoming apparent. Lessening of elasticity in the major arteries of the astronauts—an accommodation to less stress on the walls in the absence of gravitational force—has recently been proven, and its mechanism is being sought. Plant cells fixed and stained in space showed distortions of the cell membranes, as well as disorder in the normally well-organized nucleus, mitochondria, and other cell components. The absence of gravitational force apparently has new and unpredictable effects on heretofore earthbound biological material. It probably should be mentioned in passing that we can only guess now about what changes will occur in living tissues as they leave the electromagnetic field of the earth with which so many biological rhythms seem to be bound.

In the words of A. V. Hill, biophysics is the study of biological function, organization, and structure by physical and physicochemical ideas and methods. The application of techniques and fundamental principles in studies of living tissues and the recognition of new principles and the development of new methods from them comprise biophysics.

An International Union of Pure and Applied Biophysics recognizes the scope of the subject, and many countries have national Biophysical Societies. Learned journals devoted to research, and review papers in biophysics include: *Advances in Biological and Medical Physics, Progress in Biophysics and Biophysical Chemistry, Biophysical Journal, Acta Biophysica, Physics in Medicine and Biology*, and *Archives in Biochemistry and Biophysics*. The *Proceedings of the Institute of Electrical and Electronic Engineering* has had notable issues on biophysical topics. Among the contributed volumes designed to broaden the view of the specialist is "Biophysical Science—A Study Program," edited by J. L. Oncley *et al.*, John Wiley & Sons, Inc., New York, 1959.

Textbooks at various levels of study, and reflecting the individual authors' experience and viewpoints of this broad and not too well-defined interdisciplinary subject include: "Biophysical Science," by E. Ackerman, Prentice-Hall, Inc., Englewood Cliffs, N.J., 1962; "Biophysics—Concepts and Mechanisms," by E. J. Casey, Van Nostrand, New York, 1962; "Molecular Biophysics," by R. B. Setlow and E. C. Pollard, Addison-Wesley Publishing Co., Inc., Reading, Mass., 1962; "Mathematical Biophysics. Physico-mathematical Foundations of Biology," by N. Rashevsky, 3rd Revised Edition, Vol. I, Dover Publications, Inc., New York, 1960.

E. J. CASEY

Cross-references: COLOR, MATHEMATICAL BIOPHYSICS, RADIOACTIVITY, VISION AND THE EYE.

BOLTZMANN'S DISTRIBUTION LAW*

Let us consider a system composed of molecules, of one or more kinds, able to exchange energy at collisions but otherwise independent of one another. Evidently we cannot say anything useful or interesting about the state of a particular molecule at a particular time. We can however, make useful statements about the average fraction of molecules of a given kind in a given state, or, what is the same thing, the fraction of time spent by each molecule of a given kind in a given state. If the system is maintained at a definite temperature, for example by keeping it in a thermostat, then the frac-

*Author deceased. Article is reprinted from first edition.

tion of molecules of a given kind in a given state is determined by the energy of this state and by the temperature. In particular, if we denote by i and k two completely defined states of a molecule of a given kind and by E_i and E_k the energies of these two states, then the average numbers N_i and N_k of molecules in these two states are related by

$$N_i/N_k = \exp \{-\beta(E_i - E_k)\} \qquad (1)$$

where β is a parameter having a positive value determined entirely by the thermostat; i.e., β has the same value for all states of a given kind of molecule and for all kinds of molecules. In other words β has all the characteristics of temperature except that it decreases as temperature increases. If we write

$$\beta = 1/kT \qquad (2)$$

then it can be shown that T is identical with thermodynamic (or absolute) temperature and k is a universal constant whose value determines the unit of T called the degree. When k is given the value 1.38041×10^{-23} joules/degree, the temperature scale becomes the Kelvin scale defined by $T = 273.16$ K at the triple point of water. Substitution of Eq. (2) into Eq. (1) leads to

$$N_i/N_k = \exp \{- E_i - E_k)/kT\} \qquad (3)$$

This fundamental relation is called Boltzmann's distribution law after the creator of STATISTICAL MECHANICS, Ludwig Boltzmann (1844/1906), Professor of Physics in Leipzig, and k is called Boltzmann's constant (see also KINETIC THEORY).

We must now discuss the meaning of the words used above, "completely defined state." These words have one meaning in classical mechanics and a different, but related, meaning in quantum mechanics. Since the quantal definition is the simpler we shall discuss it first. We begin by considering a system of highly abstract "molecules" having only a single degree of freedom, for example linear oscillators. The quantum states form a simple series specified by consecutive integers called the quantum numbers. In this simple example there is no ambiguity in the meaning of "completely defined state"; each state i is completely defined by the integral value of a single quantum number. Let us now consider a "molecule" with three degrees of freedom such as a structureless particle moving in three-dimensional space. The complete specification of this particle's state requires not one but three integral quantum numbers. If the particle moves freely in a cubical box, the three quantum numbers may be associated with motion along the three directions normal to the faces of the box. The subscript labels i and k in the previous formulas are abbreviations for sets of three quantum numbers. For example i might mean (2, 5, 1) and

k might mean (3, 4, 2). There can now be several states having the same energy. For a particle moving freely in a cubical box, it follows from symmetry that the states (2, 5, 1), (1, 2, 5), (5, 1, 2), (1, 5, 2), (2, 1, 5), and (5, 2, 1) all have the same energy; such an energy level is called sixfold degenerate. (One should *not* speak of a p-fold degenerate *state*, but of a p-fold degenerate energy level.) It is sometimes desirable to consider the fraction of molecules having a given energy rather than the fraction in a given state. If N_r and N_s denote the average number of molecules of a given kind having energy E_r and E_s then evidently

$$N_r/N_s = (p_r/p_s) \exp \{- (E_r - E_s)/kT\} \qquad (4)$$

Alternatively, if f_r denotes the average fraction of molecules of a given kind having energy E_r, then

$$f_r = p_r \exp (- E_r/kT)/\Sigma_s p_s \exp (-E_s/kT) \qquad (5)$$

The sum Σ_s occurring in the denominator is called the partition function.

It may happen that certain degrees of freedom are completely independent of other degrees of freedom. We call such degrees of freedom "separable." The partition function can then be separated into factors relating to the several sets of separable degrees of freedom, and Boltzmann's distribution law is applicable separately to each set of separable degrees of freedom. For example, for an electron moving freely in a rectangular box, the translational motions normal to the three pairs of faces and the fourth degree of freedom due to spin are all separable.

We shall now consider briefly the meaning of completely specified state according to classical mechanics. We know that classical mechanics is merely an approximation, sometimes good but sometimes bad, to quantum mechanics. Motion in each separable degree of freedom can be described classically by a coordinate x and its conjugate momentum p_x. If x and p_x are plotted as Cartesian coordinates, the diagram is called the phase plane. There is a simple correlation between the quantal and the classical descriptions: the density of quantum states is one per area h (Planck's constant) in the phase plane. This may be extended to several degrees of freedom. If there are f degrees of freedom, the motion is described by f coordinates $q_1, \ldots q_f$ and the conjugate momenta $p_1, \ldots p_f$. We can imagine these plotted in a $2f$ dimensional Cartesian space called phase space. There is then one quantum state per $2f$ dimensional volumes h^f of phase space. In the classical as in the quantum description there can be degenerate energy values and there can be separable degrees of freedom. The classical description is a good approximation to the quantal description when the spacing between energy levels is small compared with kT. An example of an effectively classical separable degree of freedom

is the motion in a given direction of a free particle. If the linear coordinate is denoted by x and the linear momentum by p_x, then the fraction of molecules at a position between x and $x + dx$ and having a momentum between p_x and $p_x + dp_x$ is

$$\frac{\exp(-p_x{}^2/2mkT)\,dx\,dp_x}{\int dx \int_{-\infty}^{\infty} dp_x \exp(-p_x{}^2/2mkT)} \qquad (6)$$

where m is the mass of the particle so that its (kinetic) energy is $p_x{}^2/2m$. In the classical treatment, the kinetic and potential factors are separable. Consequently the fraction of molecules, anywhere or everywhere, having momentum between p_x and $p_x + dp_x$ is

$$\frac{\exp(-p_x{}^2/2mkT)\,dp_x}{\int_{-\infty}^{+\infty} \exp(-p_x{}^2/2mkT)\,dp_x} \qquad (7)$$

Equation (7) is called Maxwell's distribution law after Clerk Maxwell (1831/79), Professor of Physics at Cambridge (England), who obtained it in 1860 before Boltzmann in 1871 obtained his wider distribution law. Maxwell derived his distribution law from the conservation of energy together with the assumption that the motion is separable in three mutually orthogonal directions. The latter assumption was violently attacked by mathematicians, but we now recognize that the assumption is both reasonable and true.

In conclusion we must mention that a necessary condition for the validity of Eq. (3), and consequently of other formulas derived from Eq. (3) is that $N_i \ll 1$ for the state (or states) of lowest energy and *a fortiori* for all other states. When this inequality does not hold, Boltzmann's distribution law must be replaced by a more general and more precise distribution law, either that of Fermi and Dirac or that of Bose and Einstein according to the nature of the molecules.

E. A. GUGGENHEIM

References

Guggenheim, "Boltzmann's Distribution Law," Amsterdam, North Holland Publishing Company, 1955.
Mayer and Mayer, "Statistical Mechanics," New York, John Wiley & Sons, 1940.
Tolman, "The Principles of Statistical Mechanics," London, Clarendon Press, 1938.

Cross-references: BOSE-EINSTEIN STATISTICS; FERMI-DIRAC STATISTICS; KINETIC THEORY; QUANTUM THEORY; STATISTICAL MECHANICS; RADIATION, THERMAL.

BOND, CHEMICAL

The chemical bond is a concept used to account for the close association of atoms in neutral or charged molecules. In molecules with more than two atoms, the concept attempts to describe the stability and other properties in terms of the aggregate effect of several bonds. The description of the bonds may then be either *localized*, i.e., confined to attraction between pairs of atoms, or *delocalized*, where the attraction is thought to extend over larger groups of atoms. Various idealized types of bonds are customarily recognized: *ionic* or electrostatic bonds, *covalent* or electron-pair bonds, and metallic bonds. An additional bonding concept, the hydrogen bond, is used to describe certain attractions *between* molecules.

Ionic bonding exists, e.g., in solid and fused salts. Electrons here are localized in one or the other ion giving rise to charged particles whose mutual attractions and repulsions can be calculated from simple electrostatic theory. Since electrostatic forces do not diminish rapidly with distance, significant interactions still exist beyond nearest ionic neighbors in the crystal lattice. Nevertheless, the *lattice energy*, or the total ionic bonding energy referred to an ideal ionic gas as zero, can be calculated as the sum of the Coulomb energy terms for all possible ion pairs at their equilibrium distances. Empirical corrections for short-range repulsions between electronic envelopes of the ions must be made, and polarization and van der Waals energies can be taken into account.

Covalent bonding is described qualitatively according to the ideas of Lewis and Kossel as being due to the sharing of electron pairs between bonded atoms. The valence-bond treatment of Heitler and London, elaborated by others, applies quantum mechanical theory to this idea. Approximate wave functions for bonding electron pairs are constructed as products of atomic wave functions. The energy of the covalent bond, referred to the isolated atoms as zero, can then be calculated. A major portion of this energy is the quantum mechanical *exchange energy*, which arises from the fact that either electron may reside on either atom with equal probability.

In certain molecules, e.g., benzene, two or more plausible pairing schemes can be combined in the same calculation; bond energies calculated this way indicate molecular stability is enhanced by the so-called *resonance energy*.

Polar covalent bonds, where electron pairs are not shared equally, are described by including ionic wave functions in the calculation. Among chemical substances, one can find a more or less continuous variation of bond polarity, ranging from purely ionic bonds to nonpolar covalent bonds. The polarity of a bond can be judged qualitatively by the electronegativity difference of the bonded atoms.

Alternately, covalent bonds may be described

in terms of the molecular orbital (MO) method, in analogy to the description of electrons in atoms by means of atomic orbitals. Electrons are assumed to be delocalized throughout the molecule consistent with the overall molecular geometry, their motion being described by means of wave functions obtained as *linear* combinations of *atomic orbitals* (LCAO approximation).

These wavefunctions (MO's) describe the distribution of electrons one at a time (one-electron MO's), and each molecular orbital can accommodate two electrons, which differ only in their spin; each orbital corresponds to a certain level of binding energy for the electron. On occasion, different MO's may have the same energy (degenerate levels). The most stable electron configuration corresponding to the molecule in the ground state (lowest energy) is then obtained by filling of MO's with electron pairs in the order of increasing energy, in analogy to the building-up of electron configurations in isolated atoms.

Refinements of the approach consider explicitly the interactions between electrons, e.g., by considering the effect on the motion of one electron of the average electrostatic field produced by the remaining electrons. Successive approximations eventually lead to optimum results (self-consistent-field, SCF).

When there are one or more valence electrons per atomic valence orbital, the description can often be reduced to an equivalent series of MO's localized between two atoms, and thus represents conventional covalent bonds. On occasion, some bonding electrons still remain delocalized as in benzene, the boron hydrides, or carbonate ion; in such situations, molecules tend to be more stable then expected from a conventional view as a consequence of the *delocalization energy*. In this context, the delocalization energy corresponds to the resonance energy of the valence bond description. Molecular orbitals may be classified by the symmetry of the electron distribution in them, e.g., as σ bonds (bond direction is an axis of symmetry) or as π bonds (one symmetry plane containing the bond direction). Multiple bonds always consist of one σ bond and one or two π bonds.

Recently δ bonds have been proposed in order to account for the properties of certain transition-metal complexes. The orbitals describing such bonds are analogous to d-orbitals in atomic orbital theory. Another distinction is based on relative energy: a bonding MO has lower energy than the constituent atomic orbitals, an antibonding MO has higher energy. Orbitals having the same energy as the constituent atomic orbitals are called nonbonding. As the name implies, electron pairs in them contribute no net binding to the molecule and are equivalent to lone pairs in the Lewis description.

In metals where there are commonly few valence electrons per atom, the MO description is completely delocalized. The valence MO's form, on an energy scale, bands of closely spaced energy levels many of which are degenerate. For lack of electrons, the bands are only partially filled, the electrons are not all paired and are free to move throughout the solid in this so-called conduction band. In semiconductors, the valence band is completely filled but an empty band, slightly higher in energy, can receive electrons by thermal excitation or other energy input, thus becoming a conduction band. Bonding in semiconductors can be viewed as intermediate between the metallic and the covalent type. Graphite, condensed aromatic hydrocarbon derivatives and molecules with conjugated multiple bonds can also be placed in this intermediate category as evidenced by recent research. Examples of bond type intermediate between metallic and ionic are the alloys and interstitial compounds of transition metals and hydrogen, carbon and nitrogen, and perhaps the nonstoichiometric oxides and sulfides of the transition metals.

Properties which have found use in the systematic discussion of bonding are the strength, length, force constant, and polarity of bonds. The strength of chemical bonds is measured in terms of *bond energies* and bond dissociation energies. Bond energies are defined so that the sum of the energies of the bonds broken in completely atomizing a molecule or complex ion is equal to the energy of atomization of the substance. Bond energies depend on the order of the bond and typically range from 30 to about 100 kcal mole for single bonds, up to about 150 kcal for double bonds and up to about 220 kcal for triple bonds. Bonds of a given type between a fixed atom and a series of other atoms generally decrease in strength as the principal quantum number of the valence electrons of the other atoms increases.

The *bond dissociation energy* is defined as the energy required to break one given bond in a molecule yielding, in general, atoms and/or smaller molecules. Bond dissociation energies and bond energies are identical only in diatomic molecules. Significant differences in more complex cases may occur, particularly when delocalization or resonance is involved in the broken bond, or in the molecular fragments. This implies that the energy of a given bond may depend on the environment in the remainder of the molecule. Nevertheless, the concept has proved invaluable in the correlation of molecular structure with thermodynamic and kinetic stability. Bond energies and bond dissociation energies are derived from heats of formation and reaction, activation energies in reaction kinetics, appearance potentials in mass spectrometry, and from electronic spectra, or from photoionization studies.

Bond lengths, or equilibrium internuclear distances, are determined from x-ray, electron, and neutron diffraction patterns, from rotational spectra and the fine structure of Raman and infrared spectra. They depend on the identity of

the bonded atoms and are a function of the bond strength and the bond polarity. Sets of atomic radii have been developed for the various bond types such that radius sums duplicate normal bond lengths. Comparisons of computed and observed bond lengths can thus be made to characterize the bonds. Bond stretching *force constants* are obtained from vibrational spectra and serve as an additional index of bond character. Force constants are a measure of the curvature of the potential energy surface at the equilibrium distance; they increase with bond strength and decrease with bond length.

Bond dipole moments are a quantitative measure of the polarity of bonds and permit calculation of the distribution of charge between bonded atoms, if bond lengths are known. Bond dipole moments are estimated by expressing the molecular electric dipole moment (obtained from dielectric or Stark effect measurements) as the vector sum of the constituent bond moments. This method should be used with caution since nonbonding electron pairs in directional hybrid orbitals may make significant contributions to the molecular moment. The presence of a net dipole in the molecule commonly leads to enhancement of intermolecular interactions and thus to stabilization of the condensed states of matter by means of attraction between dipoles.

Hydrogen bonds may exist between molecules (intermolecular) or between portions of the same molecule (intramolecular). Bonding of this type involves on the one side a hydrogen atom already bonded to another atom and on the other an atom with nonbonded electron pairs which is fairly electronegative (e.g., F, O, N, or Cl). The simplest theoretical description involves electrostatic attractions between the positive charge of an electron-deficient hydrogen atom and the negative charge represented by a lone electron pair, but more sophisticated models involving the resonance or the MO approach have been more successful. The strength of hydrogen bonds is much weaker than of covalent or ionic bonds, typically 5 to 20 kcal/mole, but since this bonding is superimposed on the other bonds it may exert profound perturbations on molecular structure and properties. For example, bond stretching force constants are decreased, heats of vaporization are increased, and the temperature range over which the solid or liquid state may exist is extended beyond the values expected in the absence of such bonding. Finally, intermolecular hydrogen bonding often determines the structure of aggregations of molecules, e.g., in liquid water or in ice, while intramolecular hydrogen bonding may fix the orientation of portions of large molecules relative to each other (molecular conformation). Thus the long-range structure of enzymes, proteins, and of the molecular carriers of genetic information, the nucleic acids, is critically influenced by the existence of a large number of hydrogen bonds per molecule.

G. E. RYSCHKEWITSCH

References

Ryschkewitsch, G. E., "Chemical Bonding and the Geometry of Molecules," New York, Van Nostrand Reinhold, 1963.

Gray, H. B., "Electrons and Chemical Bonding," New York, W. A. Benjamin, Inc., 1964.

Cartwell, E., and Fowles, G. W. A., "Valency and Molecular Structure," New York, Academic Press, 1956.

Pauling, L., "The Nature of the Chemical Bond," Third edition, Ithaca, N.Y., Cornell University Press, 1960.

Coulson, C. A., "Valence," 2nd ed., London, Oxford University Press, 1961.

Coulson, C. A., and Streitweiser, A., "Dictionary of π Electron Calculations," San Francisco, W. H. Freeman, 1965.

Pimentel, G. C., and A. L. McClellan, "The Hydrogen Bond," San Francisco, W. H. Freeman, 1960.

Coulson, C. A., "Valence," London, Oxford University Press, 1952.

Cross-references: DIELECTRIC THEORY, ENERGY LEVELS, MOLECULES AND MOLECULAR STRUCTURE, POLAR MOLECULES, SEMICONDUCTORS.

BOSE-EINSTEIN STATISTICS AND BOSONS

Bose-Einstein statistics is a type of quantum statistics concerned with the distribution of particles of a particular kind among various allowed energy values taking into account the quantization of the energy values. Quantum statistics is a branch of STATISTICAL MECHANICS which treats the average or statistical properties of a system composed of a large number of particles using standard mathematical techniques and the properties of the constituent particles. It is different from classical statistical mechanics only in that the particles of the system are described quantum mechanically.

Let us consider a system of N non-interacting particles. Three different distributions of the particles among the various energy levels are possible depending upon the assumptions that are made about the particles. If it is assumed that each arrangement or distribution which conserves energy is equally probable and also that the particles are distinguishable, and if each permutation of particles among the possible levels is counted as a different distribution, one obtains an average for the relative number of particles in the various levels known as the Maxwell-Boltzmann distribution. If the particles are treated as indistinguishable and only the number of different combinations of particles is counted, the Bose-Einstein distribution is obtained. A third distribution, known as the Fermi-Dirac distribution, results if, in addition to indistinguishability, it is required that the particles obey the Pauli exclusion principle which permits no more than one electron in each quantum state.

These three distributions may be expressed mathematically as follows where $n(\epsilon)$ gives the

number of particles per energy level at energy ϵ when the particles are in thermal equilibrium at temperature T:

(1) $n(\epsilon) = \dfrac{1}{e^{(\epsilon - \epsilon_0)/kT}}$ \quad Maxwell-Boltzmann

(2) $n(\epsilon) = \dfrac{1}{e^{(\epsilon - \epsilon_0)/kT} - 1}$ \quad Bose-Einstein

(3) $n(\epsilon) = \dfrac{1}{e^{(\epsilon - \epsilon_0)/kT} + 1}$ \quad Fermi-Dirac

where k is the Boltzmann constant and ϵ_0 is related to the number of particles present and depends on the temperature in such a way that for energies large compared to kT (so that the probability of occupation for a level becomes considerably less than unity), all three distributions reduce to the Maxwell-Boltzmann distribution.

The appropriate form of statistics to apply to an assembly of particles can also be discussed in terms of the symmetry properties of the wave functions describing the particles. Two classes of wave function ψ (a solution of the SCHRÖDINGER EQUATION for two or more identical particles) result from interchanging all the coordinates, both spatial and spin, in the wave function. It should be noted that this symmetry class does not change as a function of time. The wave functions for particles obeying Fermi-Dirac statistics (fermions) are antisymmetric, while those for bosons (Bose-Einstein statistics) are symmetric. Therefore, for a system of bosons, if all the coordinates of any pair of identical particles are interchanged in the wave function, the new wave function will be identical with the original.

Photons, pi mesons, and all nuclei of even mass number are bosons, while nucleons, electrons, neutrinos, mu mesons and all nuclei of odd mass number are fermions. All known bosons have angular momentum $nh/2\pi$, where n is an integer or zero and h is Planck's constant. The statistics of some nuclei have been determined experimentally by the observation of the relative intensities of successive lines in the band spectra of homonuclear, diatomic molecules.

One application of Bose-Einstein statistics to a physical situation is the treatment of a "photon gas." It is possible to obtain the Planck distribution law for blackbody radiation by treating the electromagnetic radiation inside an enclosure at constant temperature as a gas of particles of zero rest mass which obey the Bose-Einstein distribution law. This treatment provides an interesting example of the wave-particle duality found in nature, since it is in marked contrast to the original derivation which was based on the wave nature of electromagnetic radiation.

Another interesting application is the explanation of the superfluid properties of liquid helium which occur below the so-called λ point of 2.18 K. Natural helium is composed mostly of ^{4}He which has zero spin angular momentum and hence is a boson. A qualitative explanation of the superfluid properties of liquid helium is obtained if care is taken not to follow the usual procedure of assuming that the energy states for the bosons are continuously distributed. At low temperatures, the discrete nature of the lowest levels can be important. If one takes account of the fact that an appreciable number of helium atoms will be in the lowest energy state as the temperature is reduced below the λ point, and if one associates these atoms, which have no thermal energy, with the superfluid component, many of the interesting superfluid properties can be understood. It is significant to note that no such properties are observed for ^{3}He which is a fermion.

ROBERT L. STEARNS

References

1. King, A. L., "Thermophysics," San Francisco, W. H. Freeman Co., 1966.
2. Mandl, F., "Statistical Physics," New York, John Wiley & Sons, 1971.
3. Landau, L. D., and Lifshitz, I. M., "Statistical Physics," Reading, Mass., Addison-Wesley Pub. Co., 1958.

Cross-references: FERMI-DIRAC STATISTICS AND FERMIONS, PHOTON, SCHRÖDINGER EQUATION, STATISTICAL MECHANICS, SUPERFLUIDITY.

BREMSSTRAHLUNG AND PHOTON BEAMS*

An electron can suffer a very large acceleration in passing through the Coulomb field of a nucleus, and in this interaction the radiant energy (photons) lost by the electron is called bremsstrahlung,[1] (bremsstrahlung† sometimes designates the interaction itself). If an electron whose total energy $E_0 \gtrsim 800/Z$ MeV traverses matter of atomic number Z, the electron loses energy chiefly by bremsstrahlung. This case is considered here.

Bremsstrahlung in the coulomb fields of the *atomic electrons* is adequately included by replacing Z^2 in the formulas by $Z(Z + 1)$. For $Z \lesssim 5$, more complicated correction is required.[1]

Protons and heavier particles radiate relatively little because of their large masses (radiation rate is proportional to the square of the acceleration, inversely proportional to the square of the mass). If a very energetic electron traverses

*This work was supported by the U.S. Atomic Energy Commission.
†"Bremsstrahlung"–German; bremsen, to brake and Strahlung, radiation.

one radiation length (X_0) of any matter, bremsstrahlung reduces the electron's energy to $1/e$ of its incident value on the average. Some examples are:

Element	Air	C	Al	Fe	Cu	W	Pb
Radiation length X_0 cm	29800	20	9.1	1.7	1.42	0.32	0.51

The energy dependence of radiation loss per centimeter by an electron of energy E_0, traversing matter of density n atoms/cm³ is given by $dE/dx = -nE_0\phi_{rad}$ where ϕ_{rad} is given by the curves in Fig. 1.

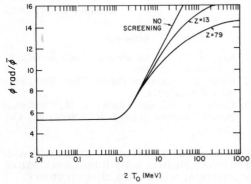

FIG. 1. Dependence of the total radiation cross section $\phi_{rad} = (1/E_0) \int_0^{E_0} k \, d\sigma$ on the initial electron kinetic energy, E_0. The parameter $\bar{\phi} = Z^2 r_0^2/137$.[1]

A beam of energetic electrons incident upon a radiator produces a bremsstrahlung beam that is directed sharply forward. Photon angular distributions for typical "thick" tungsten targets are shown in Fig. 2. Curves for other heavy elements are similar if all radiator thicknesses are measured in units of the radiation length. In such thick radiators, the incident electrons scatter appreciably, as well as radiate, making any observed photon distribution actually an average over electron scattering angles of the basic bremsstrahlung distribution. The basic bremsstrahlung angular distribution has a zero at $\alpha = 0$, which is quite different from the curves of Fig. 2. The basic spectral shape is a weak function of photon angle and, in thick radiators, electron scattering modifies this shape slightly (Fig. 3). Examples of thick radiator spectra are shown in Fig. 4 for various incident electron energies. The bremsstrahlung spectra depend upon screening of the nuclear coulomb field by atomic electrons through the parameter

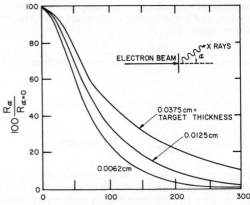

FIG. 2. Theoretical bremsstrahlung angular distributions from thick tungsten targets for relativistic energies. These data are obtained from the Natl. Bur. Std. Handbook, 55. R_α is defined as the fraction of the total incident electron kinetic energy that is radiated per steradian at the angle α.[1]

The angle α is measured with respect to the incident electron's direction. Since the electron may scatter before it radiates, $\alpha \neq \theta$ where α is shown in Fig. 3.

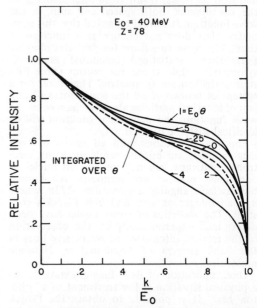

FIG. 3. Dependence of the spectral shape (Schiff's calculation) on the photon emission angle, θ. k is the photon energy in MeV. These curves are from reference 1. E_0 is the incident electron energy in MeV.

$\gamma = 51k/[E_0(E_0 - k)Z^{1/3}]$, where k is the photon energy in million electron volts. For complete screening ($\gamma \approx 0$), the thick radiator spectrum is given by

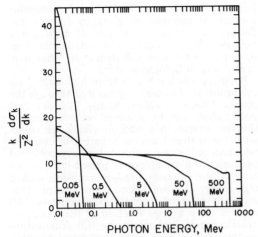

PHOTON ENERGY, Mev

FIG. 4. Dependence of the Born-approximation absolute cross section (integrated over photon directions) on the photon and electron energy. These curves are from reference 1.

$$\frac{d\sigma_b}{dk} = \frac{4Z^2 r_0^2}{137k} \left\{ \left[1 + \left(\frac{E}{E_0} \right)^2 - \frac{2}{3} \frac{E}{E_0} \right] \right.$$
$$\left. \cdot \ln \left(183 Z^{-1/3} \right) + \frac{1}{9} \frac{E}{E_0} \right\} \text{cm}^2/\text{MeV}$$

where E is the final electron total energy in million electron volts and r_0 is 2.82×10^{-13} cm. For no screening ($\gamma \gg 1$),

$$\frac{d\sigma_b}{dk} = \frac{4Z^2 r_0^2}{137k} \left[1 + \left(\frac{E}{E_0} \right)^2 - \frac{2}{3} \frac{E}{E_0} \right]$$
$$\cdot \left[\ln \frac{2E_0 E}{0.51k} - \frac{1}{2} \right] \text{cm}^2/\text{MeV}$$

Intermediate screening ($2 < \gamma < 15$) leads to much more complicated formulas.[1]

A remark concerning formulas is in order. Generally, expressions for a given cross section are very different depending upon whether the electron energy is small or very large, upon whether the screening is zero, intermediate, or complete, and upon whether one is dealing with the most usual electron-nucleus collisions or with purely electron-electron collisions. Most calculations have been done in Born approximation. The reader is referred to Koch and Motz[1] for an excellent review article on the subject.

The absolute number of bremsstrahlung photons in the photon energy interval dk radiated by a single electron of energy E_0 traversing a radiator of thickness dt and n atoms/cm³ is given by $(d\sigma_b/dk)n \, dt \, dk$, where $d\sigma/dk$ can be found from Fig. 4.

It must be noted that photon-electron showers begin developing in approximately one radiation length, and these formulas and curves

apply only to the basic bremsstrahlung interaction itself or to radiators somewhat thinner than one radiation length.

Conventional bremsstrahlung beams are partially polarized only from extremely thin radiators ($< 10^{-3}$ radiation lengths) because the angular region of polarization is sharply peaked about the angle $\theta = m_0 c^2 / E_0$. Electron scattering in the radiator broadens the peak and shifts the maximum to larger angles. Polarization is defined by

$$P(\theta, E_0, k) = \frac{d\sigma_\perp(\theta, E_0, k) - d\sigma_\parallel(\theta, E_0, k)}{d\sigma_\perp(\theta, E_0, k) + d\sigma_\parallel(\theta, E_0, k)}$$

where an electron of energy E_0 radiates a photon of energy k at angle θ. $\perp$ and $\parallel$ directions are with respect to the plane defined by the incident electron and the radiated photon. When the electron is relativistic before and after the radiation, the electric vector is most probably

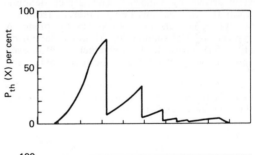

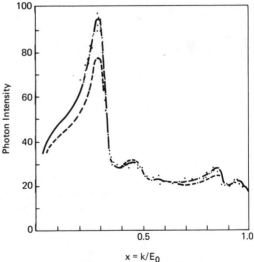

x = k/E₀

FIG. 5. Photon intensity and photon polarization from a diamond target; experimental spectra compared with the averaged intensity and theoretical polarization for photon angle equal to 50 mrad and electron energy $E_0 = 4.8$ GeV. The solid line represents Hartree potential, the dashed line shows exponential potential.

in the $\perp$ direction. Polarization in conventional beams is difficult to observe because thin, low-yield radiators are required. Practical thick-target bremsstrahlung shows no polarization effects whatever. One usually deals with this unpolarized bremsstrahlung and therefore averages over all possible states of polarization of the incident photons.

It is clear that if one makes use of polarized photons when investigating electromagnetic interactions, additional information on spin and angular momentum states can be obtained. The need for this additional information is so compelling that special techniques are frequently employed at the highest-energy electron accelerators (e.g., SLAC, DESY*) to generate polarized photons. Unfortunately, yields are low by normal intensity standards, but not unusably so.

Coherent bremsstrahlung from an electron incident upon a properly oriented single crystal (e.g., diamond) is discussed in a definitive review article by Palazzi.[2] This effect depends upon the interactions being coherent from the scattering centers in a given crystal plane. A typical spectral shape (Fig. 5) and polarization (Fig. 5a) prove to be extremely useful even though the spectrum is not monochromatic and

*SLAC—Stanford Linear Accelerator Center, Stanford, California; DESY—Deutsches Elektronen-Synchrotron, Hamburg, Germany.

free from background. Techniques for orienting the crystal radiator are given by Luckey and Schwitters.[3] Typical examples of high-energy polarized photon beams and their applications to physics are found in Ballam et al.,[4] Bingham et al.,[5] and in Bologna et al.[6]

Polarized photon beams from high-energy accelerators are frequently generated through the inverse Compton effect. Nearly 100 per cent polarization can be achieved with reasonable spectral shapes, but photon yields are somewhat lower than from the coherent bremsstrahlung process discussed above. Linearly polarized photons from a high-power pulsed laser are directed into a nearly head-on collision with a high-energy electron beam. Those photons that are back-scattered through approximately 180 degrees carry a large fraction of the electron's kinetic energy and retain the full polarization of the original laser photons. Several hundred photons of $\approx$ 95 per cent polarization and 5 GeV energy are routinely obtained from each pulse of a two-joule ruby laser in conjunction with the linear accelerator electron beam at SLAC.[7] (See Fig. 6.)

Kinematics of these "laser beams" are given by

$$k = \frac{E_0(1 - a)}{1 + a(\Gamma\theta)^2} \qquad \theta \ll 1$$

where k = scattered photon energy in the

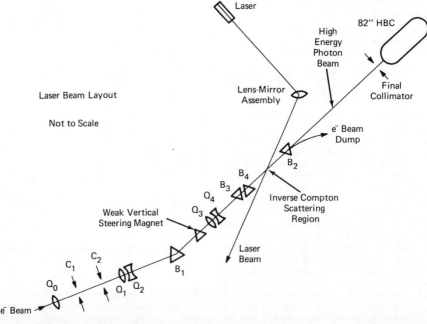

FIG. 6. A nearly-head-on collision of a high energy electron and a laser photon is accomplished at SLAC in the manner shown schematically here. The electron beam employed is part of the central beam facility at SLAC. Angles are exaggerated and there is no scale. Practical considerations eliminated the possibility of crossing the two beams at angles much less than 3 mrad. The high energy photon beam finally enters the 82" hydrogen bubble chamber where its interactions with hydrogen are studied.

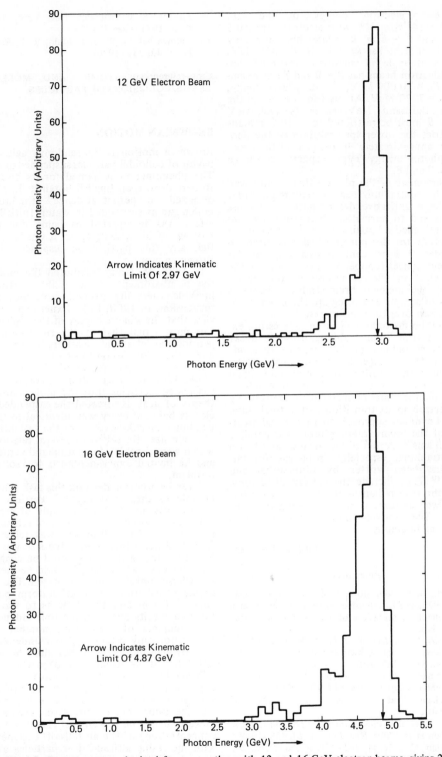

FIGS. 7 and 8. Energy spectra obtained from operation with 12 and 16 GeV electron beams, giving 2.97 and 4.87 GeV scattered photons respectively. These spectra were obtained by measuring e^+e^- pairs produced in the bubble chamber along the known beam line.

lab, E_0 = electron energy in the lab, $a = [1 + (4\Gamma k_i/m)]^{-1}$, m = electron mass (0.5 MeV), and $\Gamma = E/m$. k_i = laser photon energy (ruby laser light has $k_i = 1.786 \times 10^{-6}$ MeV) and θ = lab angle (in radians) of scattered photon. (Electron beam has $\theta = 0$ rad.) For example, if $E_0 = 20.000$ MeV, k_i = ruby laser energy, then $k = 7070$ MeV. At photon energies in the several thousand MeV range (several GeV range), θ must be restricted to $\approx 10^{-5}$ radians to restrict the lower spectral limit of the photons to approximately 90 per cent of the maximum photon energy. Typical spectra are shown in Figs. 7 and 8.

Measurement of the photon flux in an accelerator bremsstrahlung beam is required in order to make quantitative determinations of cross sections and to normalize observations. An instrument called a "quantameter"[8] is used quite successfully for this purpose and is accurate to the order of 1 per cent. It basically provides sufficient matter (copper plates) to contain the entire electron photon shower volume generated by the incident bremsstrahlung beam as well as to sample and integrate the intensity of the showers over their entire extent.

"Inner bremsstrahlung" is an interesting example of true bremsstrahlung. In beta decay interactions and in orbital electron capture, one sees, on the average, a low-intensity photon continuum, the quantum limit of which is equal to the transition energy of the interaction. These photons are bremsstrahlen emitted by the electron in its transition to the final state.

The Feynman approach to theoretical treatment of the bremsstrahlung process is detailed by Williams.[9] A definitive review article on bremsstrahlung, especially from gaseous targets, has been written by Blumenthal and Gould.[10] They include the closely allied topic of synchrotron radiation and Compton scattering as well as some other interesting radiative effects. They provide an excellent and quite current bibliography.

ROBERT W. KENNEY

References

1. Koch, H. W., and Motz, J. W., *Rev. Mod. Phys.* **31**, 920, 1959. Extensive survey of formulas and excellent presentation of curves for numerical calculation.

2. Palazzi, G. D., *Rev. Mod. Phys.*, **40**, 611 (1968).

3. Luckey, D., and Schwitters, R. F., *Nucl. Inst. Meth.*, **81**, 164 (1970).

4. Ballam et al., *Phys. Rev. Letters*, **24**, 1364 (1970); **24**, 960 (1970); **23**, 498, 817 (E) (1970).

5. Bingham et al., *Phys. Rev., Letters*, **24**, 955 (1970).

6. Bologna et al., *Nuovo Cimento*, **42A**, 844 (1966).

7. Ballam et al., *Phys. Rev. Letters*, **23**, 499 (1969); Sinclair, C. K. et al., *IEEE Trans. Nucl. Sci.*, **16**, 1065 (1969).

8. Yount, D., *Nucl. Ins. Meth.*, **52**, 1 (1967).

9. "An Introduction to Elementary Particles," 2nd Ed., W. S. C. Williams, New York, Academic Press, 1971 (page 313 ff.).

10. Blumenthal, G. R., and Gould, R. J., *Rev. Mod. Phys.*, **42**, 237 (1970).

Cross-references: ATOMIC AND MOLECULAR BEAMS, COLLISIONS OF PARTICLES.

BROWNIAN MOTION

Brownian motion is the randomly agitated behavior of colloidal particles suspended in a fluid. The phenomenon is named for its discoverer, Robert Brown, an English botanist. In 1828 he observed the "perpetual dance" of microscopic pollen grains suspended in water. Initially, this effect was interpreted as being due to the motions of living matter, but it was later found that any tiny particles in suspension exhibit Brownian motion.

In 1888, M. Gouy attributed the motion to the bombardment of the visible particles by invisible thermally excited molecules of the suspension. In 1900, F. M. Exner expressed the view that the kinetic energy of the visible particles must equal that of the surrounding suspension particles, and he attempted to estimate molecular velocities on this basis.

In a series of papers published from 1905 to 1908, Einstein[1] successfully incorporated the suspended particles into the molecular-kinetic theory of heat. He treated the suspended particles as being in every way identical to the suspending molecules except for the vast difference of their size. He set forth several relationships which were capable of experimental verification and he invited experimentalists to "solve" the problem.

Several workers undertook this task. The most notable of these was Perrin.[2] Perrin's special success was due to his technique of preparing particles to suspend which were of uniform and known size. The uniformity was achieved by fractional centrifuging, and the size was established by noting that they could be coagulated into "chains" whose length could be measured and whose "links" could be counted. The microscopic observation of these uniform particles enabled Perrin and his students to verify the Einstein results and to make four independent measurements of Avogadro's number. These results not only established our understanding of Brownian motion, but they also silenced the last critics of the atomic view of matter.

Probably the simplest example of Perrin's experiments was his test of the Law of Atmospheres. If we assume that the air is at rest and has the same temperature from ground level upward, it can be shown that the pressure (and concentration) of the air falls off exponentially with increasing altitude. For particles of mass m and density ρ suspended in a medium of density ρ' at absolute temperature T, the ratio of the particle concentrations n_1 to n_2 at

heights h_1 and h_2 is given by

$$\frac{n_1}{n_2} = exp\left[-\frac{mg(\rho - \rho')N_0(h_1 - h_2)}{\rho RT}\right]$$

where N_0 is Avogadro's number, g is the acceleration of gravity, and R is the universal gas constant. Although the concentration of air varies slowly with height, the concentration of the relatively heavy particles varied significantly over a height change of a few millimeters. By observing the concentration variation as a function of height, all quantities in the given equa-tion were known except Avogadro's number which could therefore be determined.

JAMES A. RICHARDS, JR.

References

1. Einstein, Albert, "Investigation of the Theory of the Brownian Movement," A. D. Cowper, trans-lator, New York, Dover Publications, 1956.
2. Perrin, Jean, "Atoms," D. L. Hammick, translator, London, Constable, 1923.

Cross-references: ATOMIC PHYSICS.

C

CALCULUS OF PHYSICS

To label a topic as the "calculus of physics" is not intended to imply the establishment of some new type of mathematics, but rather that a point of view different from that comfortable to the professional mathematician is to be employed in its discussion. Concepts are introduced for the immediacy of their application to the description of physical phenomena, and a heuristic approach is used to introduce them. We shall not hesitate to ignore interesting but uncommon exceptions to our statements and shall make use of pictorial representations and special cases to illustrate our points.

Functions Since many of the processes of physics are continuing, with the state of things at a given instant developing smoothly out of the state of things in the previous instant, the means of describing these processes compactly is with the help of continuous functions. In some sense, any way of naming the members of a set of objects when given a member of another set comprises a functional relationship. Thus if one is given the set of numbers

$$x = 1, 2, 3, 4 \cdots$$

and the relation

$$y = x^3, \tag{1}$$

then one immediately knows that

$$y = 1, 8, 27, 64, \cdots.$$

Eq. (1) is one way of representing the function. Another would be to tabulate x and y side by side:

x	1	2	3	4
y	1	8	27	64

and another is to draw a graph of y against x, as in Fig. 1. The points contain exactly the same information as the table; the curve contains much more information, but not as much as Eq. (1). Thus it would be a hypothesis to say from the table alone that to $x = \frac{1}{2}$ there corresponded $y = \frac{1}{8}$. The curve (if it could be read accurately enough) would allow one to make that assignment, but would not allow one to conclude that $x = 5$ corresponds to $y = 125$. Equation (1) contains all of this information, and more. We understand from it that to *any*

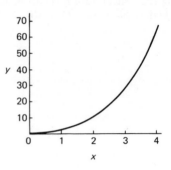

FIG. 1

value of x one may obtain y by multiplying x by itself and the result by x again. In this case, x is the independent variable, y the dependent variable. The concept of continuity is contained in the idea that between any two values of x another can be found; and the concept of continuous function, that to all such values of x a value of y can be assigned according to the prescription in Eq. (1).

Our example is one of the simplest types of function: an algebraic function. Functions of several variables may be considered: functions of complex variables, trigonometric functions, exponential functions, etc. Because of their importance in representing physical processes, let us consider the trigonometric functions a little more closely.

The trigonometric functions are functions of the variable θ (or x or y, or any other symbol you choose), which need not be an angle in the narrow sense, although in physics applications we shall insist that the variable be dimensionless as an angle is. (The distinction between *units* in which the size of a quantity is expressed relative to some standard and dimensions, which are fundamental attributes of a quantity in terms of mass, length, and time, will not hold us here. Suffice to say that, e.g., a *second* is a unit for the dimension time, and the ratio of an arc length to a radius of the arc, which may be expressed in the unit *radian*, is dimensionless.) The tables of trigonometric functions provide a discrete representation, and the familiar graphs are even more useful in visualizing their properties. Figure 2 is a graph of the function $y = \sin \theta$ and Fig. 3 of $y = \cos \theta$. The horizontal scale of each of Figs. 2, 3 should be thought of

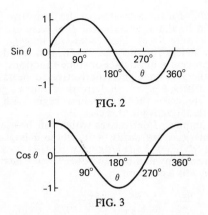

FIG. 2

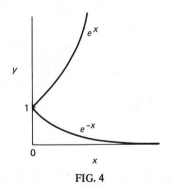

FIG. 3

$$e^x = 1 + x + \frac{x^2}{2!} + \frac{x^3}{3!} + \cdots + \cdots$$

$$e^{-x} = 1 - x + \frac{x^2}{2!} - \frac{x^3}{3!} + \cdots + \cdots.$$

Derivative We can now introduce a few of the concepts of the branch of mathematics which deals with functions and their properties, the calculus. To be specific, we should like to mention the *derivative* and the *integral* of a function. The reader will know something of these already: e.g., the speed of an automobile is the time derivative of its position. This is shown in Fig. 5. The slope of each line repre-

as extending to the left and right indefinitely with the curves repeating the behavior as shown every 360°. The vertical scales for the sine and cosine functions need be no larger than shown, since their curves oscillate between plus and minus one.

These are examples of continuous functions of a single variable (θ in these illustrations). They are *periodic* functions, i.e., they repeat their values periodically as the independent variable continuously changes. It is the property of periodicity which makes these functions suitable for representing certain physical phenomena.

In Fig. 4 we represent two more useful functions for physics applications: the exponential curve, $y = e^x$ and its inverse, $y = e^{-x} = 1/e^x$.

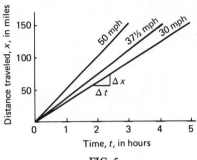

FIG. 5

sents the speed with which the automobile traveled from New Haven to Boston: 50 mph, $37\frac{1}{2}$ mph, 30 mph. The speed, v, is given by $\Delta x/\Delta t$, where Δt is the time required to traverse the distance Δx. From the graph, one sees that the slope is also the tangent of the angle made by the line with the horizontal axis. These are general properties of the derivative.

The question arises as to what happens if the line is not straight. Then one defines the derivative in the same way, but expects its value to change from point to point along the curve. At each point, one draws the tangent line and calculates its slope. This is the derivative. The abstract definition of derivative is based on the notion of *limit*. In mathematical language, if a function approaches a fixed value as close as one pleases while the independent variable approaches a given value arbitrarily, the function is said to approach a limit as the parameter approaches its value. The notation is $\lim_{x \to a} f(x) = f(a)$, to be read as "the limit of $f(x)$ as x approaches a is $f(a)$." For simple algebraic functions the concept is rather obvious: If $f(x) = ax + bx^2$, then $\lim_{x \to 2} f(x) = 2a + 4b$. The reader should be warned, however, that the situation is not always so obvious. For example, let $f(x) = (ax + bx^2)/cx$. As $x \to 0$, both numerator and denominator approach 0, so $\lim_{x \to 0} f(x)$ seems to be 0/0, which is indeterminate. However, the limit is actually finite; namely, it is a/c. The derivative has been heuristically defined as $\Delta f(x)/\Delta x$, but this has signifi-

FIG. 4

As a matter of notational convenience, one frequently replaces y by $f(x)$, to be read as "function of x." As a rule, continuous functions can be represented by sums of *algebraic* functions of the independent variable. For example:

$$\sin \theta = \theta - \frac{\theta^3}{3!} + \frac{\theta^5}{5!} - \frac{\theta^7}{7!} + \cdots + \cdots$$

$$\cos \theta = 1 - \frac{\theta^2}{2!} + \frac{\theta^4}{4!} - \frac{\theta^6}{6!} + \cdots + \cdots$$

where θ must be expressed as a dimensionless ratio; i.e., in radians rather than degrees, and

cance only so long as the ratio remains determinate as $\Delta x \to 0$. Formally, one says

$$\frac{df(x)}{dx} = \lim_{x_2 \to x_1} \frac{f(x_2) - f(x_1)}{x_2 - x_1}, \text{ or}$$

$$\frac{df(x)}{dx} = \lim_{\Delta x \to 0} \frac{\Delta f(x)}{\Delta x}$$

For all the cases we shall be interested in discussing, the limit exists, is equal to the derivative, and is equivalent to the tangent to a curve of $f(x)$ vs x at the point in question. This is illustrated in Fig. 6, which is a graph of $s = 16t^2$.

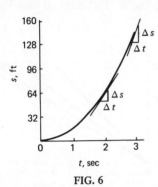

FIG. 6

At 2 sec, the tangent has a slope of 64 ft/sec, and at 3 sec it is 96 ft/sec. Since the speed is changing with time, we can graph it and find its rate of change or derivative, as shown in Fig. 7.

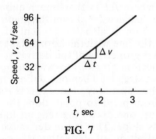

FIG. 7

The slope is seen to be a constant: 32 ft/sec². What is its meaning? This is the *acceleration* of the object which is moving according to the graph in Fig. 6. Thus the acceleration is defined as the time derivative of the speed. For an object moving with constant speed, the acceleration is zero—as it should be to conform with common sense.

While speed and acceleration are among the most familiar examples of derivatives, we should note that the derivative of a function need not be taken with respect to time. If f is a function of an arbitrary variable, x, then the derivative is equal to $\Delta f(x)/\Delta x$, where Δf and Δx are measured on the tangent drawn at point x. The notation, which we shall have occasion to employ, is df/dx for the derivative, and

d^2f/dx^2 for the derivative of the derivative (this would be the acceleration if $f(x)$ were distance and x were time). The reader will imagine that more derivatives may be taken, and wonder if the process is limitless. For some functions, e.g., e^x, there is no highest derivative to be taken. For others, e.g., x^3, all derivatives above a given one are zero—the zero values begin with the fourth derivative in this case.

Examples of derivatives which can be used in calculations are $da/dx = 0$, where a is a constant, $dx/dx = 1$, $dx^2/dx = 2x$, $dx^n/dx = nx^{n-1}$ where n is any number, and $d(ax^n)/dx = nax^{n-1}$, where a is a constant.

$$\frac{de^x}{dx} = e^x, \frac{de^{-x}}{dx} = -e^{-x},$$

$$\frac{d \sin \theta}{d\theta} = \cos \theta, \frac{d \cos \theta}{d\theta} = -\sin \theta.$$

Integral The other important operation of the calculus is *integration*. It may be simply defined as the inverse of taking the derivative, although such a definition has only limited usefulness—mainly it lulls the unwary into thinking he may know something of the process. An operational definition, lacking elegance, may be more nearly indicative of the true nature of the integral: It is a function so constructed that its derivative yields the function whose integral was to be found. From our examples of derivatives, the curve of Fig. 7 may be written as

$$dx/dt = 32t, \tag{2}$$

and of Fig. 6 as

$$x = 16t^2. \tag{3}$$

We have been at some pains to show that $dx/dt = 32t$, so by our definition of integral, x is the integral of dx/dt. The notation for integral is shown in Eq. (4):

$$x = \int (dx/dt) \, dt. \tag{4}$$

Although this is rather a special case, it contains a number of interesting features. If it were a legitimate operation to "multiply" dx/dt by dt, the expected product would be dx, and Eq. (4) would become

$$x = \int dx, \tag{5}$$

which somehow looks like an identity. In fact, if we think of dx replaced by Δx and $\int$ by "sum of," then

$$x = (\text{``sum of''}) \, \Delta x$$

is pretty obvious. Pictorially, we may think of

the integral of a function as the area under a curve giving the graphical representation of the function. In the general case, the notation reads

$$\int f(x)\,dx,$$

where the dx performs some of the functions in the derivative notation: It identifies the independent variable and implies how the operation is to be carried out.

To give an example, let us return to Fig. 7 and calculate the area under the curve. Table 1

TABLE 1

t Interval	0 to 1 sec	0 to 2 sec	0 to 3 sec
Area	16	64	144

contains the results for the area up to 1 sec, up to 2 sec, etc. It is clear that the numbers in the "area" row can be obtained from Eq. (3) by evaluating it for $t = 1, 2, 3$ sec, respectively.

What of the integral as area when the curve is not as simple as our example? Even the case graphed in Fig. (6) appears to be beyond the definition. We are rescued from this dilemma by recalling that we deal with continuous functions, so we may employ as small a Δx as we please. Thus the integration becomes the summation of many areas whose bases are Δx and heights the values of $f(x)$ at the point in question. Some error will remain: The lined areas shown in Fig. 8 will not always cancel as they

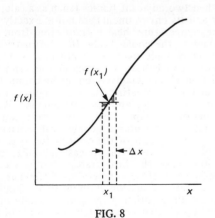

FIG. 8

must for exact total area calculation. That is, our calculation of the area of the strip as $f(x) \cdot \Delta x$ omits the piece with vertical shading lines and incorrectly includes the piece with horizontal shading. However, as Δx becomes smaller, these two pieces will come nearer and nearer to canceling for each strip. The penalty for increased accuracy is increasing the number of strip areas to obtain and sum.

In fact, for the simpler functions it is possible to obtain the integral without adding areas: The means we have already used of looking for a function whose *derivative* is the function in hand is one method of doing so. Of course, with the advent of high-speed digital computers, the task of adding up many little strips to calculate the integral numerically is reduced to preparing a program to control the computer—and the program will work for any function which can be tabulated.

Sample integral formulas which can be used are

$$\int dx = x + c, \quad \int x\,dx = \frac{1}{2}x^2 + c,$$

$$\int ax\,dx = \frac{ax^2}{2}, \quad \int x^n\,dx = \frac{1}{n+1}x^{n+1} + c,$$

$$(n \neq -1)$$

$$\int \cos\theta\,d\theta = -\sin\theta + c, \quad \int \sin\theta\,d\theta = \cos\theta + c,$$

$$\int e^x\,dx = e^x + c, \quad \int e^{-x}\,dx = -e^{-x} + c,$$

where c is a constant which cannot be determined in the integration.

MCALLISTER H. HULL, JR.

References

1. Hull, M. H., "The Calculus of Physics," New York, W. A. Benjamin, 1969.
2. Henriksen, M., and Lees, M., "Single Variable Calculus with an Introduction to Numerical Methods," New York, Worth, 1970.
3. Mizel, V. J., and MacCamy, R. C., "Linear Analysis and Differential Equations," New York, Macmillan, 1969.

Cross-references: DIFFERENTIAL EQUATIONS IN PHYSICS, MATHEMATICAL PRINCIPLES OF QUANTUM MECHANICS.

CALORIMETRY

Calorimetry is the science of measuring the quantity of heat absorbed or evolved by matter when it undergoes a change in its chemical or physical state. The apparatus in which the measurement is performed is a calorimeter, and the experimenter is frequently referred to as a calorimetrist.

When matter is involved in a chemical or physical process, its total energy content is usually altered. The difference in energy between its initial and final states, ΔE, must be transferred to, or from, the environment of the system. This energy exchange between the system and its environment is in the form of heat or work or both. In calorimetry, the energy exchanged as

heat is quantitatively evaluated. The heat absorbed by the system, q, is related to the work done by the system on its environment ω, and the increase in internal (total) energy of the system, ΔE, by the thermodynamic relationship

$$q = \Delta E + \omega \qquad (1)$$

When calorimetric measurements are performed at constant pressure and only pressure-volume work is involved, q is equal to the increase in heat content or enthalpy, ΔH. Most calorimetric measurements are performed under these conditions, but when other conditions are imposed, appropriate consideration must be made in the thermodynamic treatment of the data.

The process selected for calorimetric study may be a simple change in the physical state of matter, such as a change in temperature of the material, or it may consist of a series of complex chemical reactions such as are encountered in the combustion of many fuels. In fact, nearly any process involving a chemical or physical change in matter might well become a necessary subject for calorimetric investigation.

Calorimetric determinations of energy changes are essential in many theoretical and practical problems. Heat capacity or specific heat data are vital to the design of heat exchange equipment. The thermal properties of steam and certain metals are major considerations in the design of modern boilers and turbines. The heats of combustion of fuels are essential in rocket, engine and gas turbine design. The heat liberated by chemical reactions must be considered in the development of chemical process equipment. Often the required equilibrium constant of a process is most conveniently obtained by a simple calculation from the free energy change, ΔF. For a great many processes, numerical values of ΔF can be obtained from the change in heat content, ΔH, and the entropies of the participating substances, S, using the thermodynamic relationship

$$\Delta F = \Delta H - T \Delta S \qquad (2)$$

where T is the absolute temperature. The entropies of the individual substances can generally be evaluated from heat capacity measurements that extend to very low temperatures.

The design and constructional details of calorimeters vary widely because of the diversified nature of the processes suitable for calorimetric study. However, the basic principles are general, and their consideration constitutes a common requirement in practically all designs. Suitable devices and procedures for three essential measurements are usually required, but one or two can sometimes be omitted by operating under certain restrictions. The measurements are: (1) the temperature of the calorimeter and its contents, (2) the quantity of energy that is added to the calorimeter from an external source, and (3) the quantity of heat that is exchanged between the calorimeter and its environment.

Most calorimetric operations involve a temperature change, since the heat liberated (or absorbed) during the process is stored in the calorimeter and its contents by virtue of their combined heat capacity. Thermocouples, thermopiles and resistance thermometers are commonly used for temperature measurements. The quantity of energy liberated or absorbed in a calorimetric process is evaluated in terms of electrical energy. This is done by three similar methods. (1) In an exothermic process where heat is liberated, the calorimeter is cooled to the original temperature; the temperature rise is then duplicated using an electrical resistance heater. (2) The heat absorbed in an endothermic process is supplied by an electrical heater at such a rate as to keep the temperature constant. (3) In heat-capacity measurements, the electrical energy is supplied directly by a heater. Electrical energy and temperature can be measured very accurately by modern methods. Very sensitive methods have also been developed that can detect the changes in temperature of quite small samples containing typically 10^{-4} moles of material. These new methods rely upon phase-sensitive detection of the thermal response to an alternating or cyclic input of heat into the sample, and make it possible to investigate small single crystals and other samples of difficult to produce, or rare materials. The problem of heat transfer between the calorimeter and its environment is more difficult. The minimization of, and accurate correction for, heat exchange is the major problem to be reckoned with in modern calorimetry.

When two adjacent bodies (such as a calorimeter and its environment) are not at exactly the same temperature, heat is transferred from the warmer to the cooler body. In calorimetry the transfer is made by three major processes: (1) gaseous convection, (2) conduction, and (3) radiation. Gaseous convection can be completely avoided by evacuating the space between the calorimeter vessel and its environment. When evacuation is impractical, convection can be minimized by suitable geometrical considerations in the design of the calorimeter. It is very important to avoid or at least minimize convection, since the heat transported is a complex function of the temperature difference and an accurate evaluation is impossible. Conduction by air or other gases is also usually minimized by evacuating as much as possible of the space between the calorimeter proper and its environment. Conduction in solid materials, used for supporting the calorimeter and for electrical leads, is minimized by proper choice of materials and geometrical design. For small temperature differences, radiation is usually not a serious problem at low temperatures but is a major contributor to heat exchange at elevated temperatures. Heat exchange by radiation can be limited to a few per cent of the blackbody

(maximum) values by the use of suitable reflecting surfaces on the outside of the calorimeter and on the adjacent environment. In the absence of convection and for small temperature differences, the heat transferred, Q, is essentially proportional to the temperature difference, ΔT, and time, t, in accordance with Newton's law of cooling.

$$Q = k \Delta T t \qquad (3)$$

It is apparent that anything that can be done in calorimeter design and operation to minimize the terms on the right hand side of Eq. (3) will aid in decreasing the quantity of heat exchanged. Adiabatic calorimeters are operated on the principle that there is no heat exchange and thus no correction to evaluate, if the calorimeter and its environment are maintained at the same temperature.

In calorimeters containing liquids, there is a possibility of a fourth mechanism for transporting heat. This method involves the transport of matter from the calorimeter and its subsequent condensation on the surrounding surfaces. The effect can be avoided by keeping the environment warmer than the liquid or by completely enclosing the liquid. However, even in a completely enclosed system the possibility of vaporization into the space above the liquid with increasing temperature must be considered for volatile liquids.

There are many different varieties of calorimeters, each being particularly suited for a specific type of measurement. Some general features of several representative types are discussed below.

Low-temperature calorimetry, used down to the temperatures available with liquid and solid hydrogen, ~ 10 K, has become an important source of heat capacity data for the evaluation of entropies of substances from measurements extending from near the absolute zero to room temperature or slightly above. The calorimetric vessel consists of a vacuum-tight metal container in good thermal contact with an electrical resistance heater and a thermocouple or resistance thermometer. The sample under study is sealed in the container along with a small amount of gaseous helium. The helium aids in attaining thermal equilibrium at low temperatures because of its high thermal conductivity. The calorimetric vessel is suspended in an evacuated chamber by some material, such as a strong thread, having low thermal conductivity. This chamber is often within a massive copper block which provides a uniform and stable thermal environment. The temperature of the protective block is kept at a temperature near that of the calorimetric vessel. The heat exchanged is evaluated by observing the temperature difference, ΔT, as a function of time and applying Eq. (3) in an integrated form. The constant, k, is evaluated by observing the change in temperature of the calorimeter vessel

and its contents under equilibrium conditions. During this rating period the temperature change is due entirely to heat exchanged with the environment. Some calorimetrists use the adiabatic principle and maintain the temperature of a protective shield as near as possible to that of the calorimeter. This procedure results in the elimination of heat exchange corrections but is not entirely free from objections. Although low-temperature calorimeters are used chiefly for heat capacity determinations, heats of transition, heats of fusion, and heats of vaporization are also measured.

At very low temperatures, calorimetry is used to measure energies associated with the ordering of the magnetic moments of nuclei, transitions into the superconducting state of metallic elements and compounds, and other phenomena which require only small amounts, or quanta, of energy to be activated. A decade decrease in temperature means a decade decrease in the size of the energy quanta which can be studied, and in this sense the range from 0.1 to 0.01 K covers a range equivalent to that between 1000 K and 100 K (i.e., from far above, to far below room temperature at 300 K). Temperatures down to 1 K are achieved by reducing the pressure over liquid helium. Temperatures below 1 K have been available for some time by adiabatic demagnetization of a magnetic salt such as potassium chromium sulfate (chrome alum). The sample is placed in contact with the salt, which is cooled to 1 K by reducing the pressure over a bath of liquid helium. The salt is magnetized in thermal contact with the bath, then contact is broken by means of a thermal or mechanical switch and the salt plus sample are cooled by slowly turning off the magnetic field. The cold sample is then isolated from the salt by a second heat switch, and its heat capacity is then measured by the methods described above. Recently a very convenient helium dilution refrigerator has been developed which works on a continuous basis down to 0.01 K by simply evaporating the isotope of helium, of mass 3, ^{3}He, into a solution of ^{3}He dissolved in the normal isotope ^{4}He. The sample can be cooled by placing it in contact with the ^{3}He "boiler" and then proceeding as already described.

The dropping method is the most common of the accurate high-temperature procedures for measuring heat contents. This apparatus consists of a carefully regulated furnace and a suitable calorimeter, such as a Bunsen ice calorimeter, operating near room temperature. The sample under investigation is sealed inside of a container that will not undergo chemical reaction at the highest temperature of the measurements. The sample and container are thermally equilibrated with the furnace and then dropped into the calorimeter. The empty container is studied in an identical manner and the difference in the two measurements gives the heat content of the sample relative to the room temperature reference. Heat capacities are derived from a series

of such measurements as a function of temperature and the thermodynamic relationship:

$$C_p = \frac{\partial(H)}{(\partial T)_p} = \left[\frac{\partial H - H_0}{\partial T}\right]_p \qquad (4)$$

where C_p is the heat capacity at constant pressure, H the heat content, H_0 the heat content at the reference temperature, and T the absolute temperature.

The Bunsen ice calorimeter is an example of an isothermal calorimeter that is operated at a fixed temperature. The calorimeter is usually surrounded by ice, making it also adiabatic and thus free from heat exchange. Bunsen's design makes use of the very large difference between the specific volume of ice and water. The calorimeter contains a closed chamber which is full of ice and water. A pool of mercury is maintained in the bottom of the chamber, and as the ice melts, additional mercury enters and keeps the chamber full. The calorimeter has a universal calibration in the form of energy per unit mass of mercury. In early versions, the quantity of ice melted was used as a measure of the heat liberated in the calorimeter. By replacing the ice with other suitable substances, the restriction of operating at one fixed temperature can be removed.

Quantitative measurements of the heat liberated (or absorbed) during the solution of a solid or of another liquid by a solvent are performed in solution calorimeters. Heats of solution, dilution and mixing are common determinations of this type. In addition to participating in the process under investigation, the solvent is used as a means of attaining uniform temperature and composition throughout the calorimeter. This feature necessitates stirring, which is usually accomplished with mechanically or magnetically driven stirrers. Sometimes, however, the calorimeter itself is rotated. Regardless of the method used, the quantity of heat introduced by the stirring must be determined either directly or indirectly and a suitable correction must be applied. Another feature characteristic of solution calorimeters is the method of adding the sample. Either it must be equilibrated with the solvent in the calorimeter, or its heat content relative to the calorimeter temperature must be determined. A common method for solids is immersing a capsule containing the sample in the solvent and breaking it at the desired time.

The heat of combustion of fuels and similar materials is usually measured by bomb calorimetry. The solid or liquid sample is contained in a bomb (pressure vessel) containing excess oxygen or other suitable gas under pressure. The bomb is immersed in a calorimeter containing a liquid, usually water. The reaction is initiated by igniting the sample with a measured amount of electrical energy, and the heat evolved is measured in terms of the temperature rise of the calorimeter. Electrical energy is usually used to duplicate the temperature rise and thus evaluate the heat liberated. However, sometimes a standard sample of a substance having a known heat of combustion such as benzoic acid, is used to calibrate the apparatus. In bomb calorimetry, corrections to standard conditions must be applied (Washburn corrections) since the system is under pressure and because solutions are usually formed.

There are many other important types of calorimeters, such as flow calorimeters, microcalorimeters, flame calorimeters, etc. Nearly any process can be studied by the investigator who is ingenious enough to devise the appropriate apparatus and who has the resources and patience to undertake an extensive project. Although calorimetric measurements are in general time-consuming and tedious, they are essential for a fundamental and practical understanding of many important chemical and physical processes.

T. H. GEBALLE
J. E. KUNZLER

Cross-references: ENTROPY, HEAT CAPACITY, HEAT TRANSFER, THERMODYNAMICS.

CAPACITANCE

Definition and Fundamental (Quasi) Static Properties If a constant voltage V[V = volts] is applied between two conductors insulated from each other, electrical charges Q [As = coulomb] are so distributed that the conductors form equipotentials. The measure for the charges stored is the capacitance C [F = farad = 10^6 μF = 10^9 mμF = 10^{12} pF] of the capacitor so formed.

$$Q = C \cdot V \qquad (1)$$

(Q in coulombs, C in farads, V in volts.) It is often more convenient to express this storing capacity in terms of energy

$$E = (\tfrac{1}{2}) V^2 C \qquad (2)$$

(E in watts.) C is defined by

$$C = \frac{1}{V} \int i \, dt \quad \text{or} \quad C = I \left| \frac{dv}{dt} \right. \qquad (3)$$

For capacitor discharge (E_0 = starting voltage),

$$e_c/E_0 = \epsilon^{-t/\tau} \qquad (4a)$$

and for capacitor charge (E_b = battery voltage)

$$e_c/E_b = 1 - \epsilon^{-t/\tau} \qquad (4b)$$

with the time constant τ

$$\tau = CR \qquad (5)$$

where R is the resistor through which the capacitor is being (dis)charged.

For sinusoidal excitation of angular frequency ω, the reactance of the lossless capacitor is

$$V[\text{V}]/I[\text{A}] = (-)jX[\Omega] = 1/j\omega C[\Omega] \quad (6)$$

If, in electrical circuits, capacitors are connected in parallel, their capacitances add

$$C = \sum_{k=1}^{n} C_k \quad (7a)$$

If capacitors are connected in series, their elastances (the reciprocal of capacitance, S) add

$$S = \sum_{k=1}^{n} S_k \quad (7b)$$

Losses in the dielectric may be expressed by a complex relative dielectric constant

$$\varepsilon = \varepsilon' - j\varepsilon'' \quad (8)$$

where $\varepsilon'/\varepsilon'' = Q_e$ determines the dielectric quality factor. For $Q_e > 10$, the loss resistance of the capacitor is given by

$$(1/\omega C)/r_s = Q_e = R_p/(1/\omega C) \quad (9)$$

where r_s is the equivalent series and R_p is the corresponding parallel loss resistance. $Q_e = 1/DF$ (DF = dissipation factor). The power factor is related to DF by

$$PF = DF \sqrt{1/(1 + DF^2)} \quad (10)$$

The loss factor $= (DF) \cdot \varepsilon$ is proportional to the energy loss/cycle/voltage^2/volume.

Capacitors are used for: (1) frequency determining or selective networks [LC circuits and filters; cf. Eq. (6)]; (2) energy storage [Eq. (2)], for instance, the capacitor being slowly charged and quickly discharged [Eqs. (9) and (10)] in a short burst of energy; and (3) integrators and differentiators [in conjunction with R; cf. Eq. (3)].

Geometry *Uniform Fields.* For a uniform field as, for instance, given between two closely spaced parallel metallic plates (area A in square meters, distance l in meters) and disregarding edge effects

$$C[\text{F}] = \varepsilon_0 \varepsilon A/l \quad (11)$$

with $\varepsilon_0 \varepsilon =$ dielectric constant of free space $= (36\pi \times 10^9)^{-1}$ [F/m] and $\varepsilon =$ the relative dielectric constant (dimensionless) of the material between the plates.

Discontinuity in Uniform Fields. If, in the above case, the dielectric consists of two sheets of different materials with ε_1 (having thickness l_1) and ε_2 (having thickness l_2)

$$\frac{E_1}{E_2} = \frac{\varepsilon_2}{\varepsilon_1} \quad (12)$$

where E_n is electric field strength $= V_n/I_n$. (13)

Equation (12) is of great practical significance if one of the ε's is very high, since then the sheet with the low ε carries nearly all voltage (for this reason, for example, higher-ε ceramic capacitors have to have fired-on electrodes).

Nonuniform Fields. The most common capacitance with nonuniform fields is the coaxial capacitor (inside diameter d, outside diameter D). Its capacitance is

$$C'[\text{pF/m}] = 55.6\varepsilon/\ln (D/d) \quad (14)$$

Extreme cases of nonuniformity, often causing corona, exist on the sharp edges of plate capacitors. Remedy: For field equalization, deform plates to follow equipotential lines of half potential in a capacitive field with twice the spacing of the original, flat plates (Rogowski profile).

Dielectrics The dielectric "constant" is often not constant but a function of crystal orientation (anisotropy), temperature, voltage, and frequency (dispersion).

The objective of developing a good fixed capacitor is to have the largest capacity in the smallest possible volume for a given operating voltage. Ideally, the capacitance is not to change with voltage, temperature, time, mechanical stress, humidity, and frequency, and (in most cases) is to have a minimum of losses. The greatest capacitance can be achieved by maximizing ε (Case a) and A (Case b), and minimizing l (Case c) [cf. Eq. (11)].

Typical for *Case (a)* are *ceramic* capacitors made in discoidal or tubular form (and now recently also as coaxially laminated capacitors). There are four classes of ceramic dielectrics:

(1) Semiconducting, so-called layerized, ceramics with dielectric constants above 10^5. These can be used only for very low voltages (transistor circuits), are quite lossy, and have a strong dispersion of ε in the megacycle range.

(2) High-ε' dielectrics (mostly barium titanates) with ε' in the order of 6000. These are quite temperature- and voltage-sensitive (nonlinearity and hysteresis) and are used as guaranteed-minimum-value capacitors (GMV).

(3) So-called stable dielectric capacitors with an ε' of 2000 or, if doped with rare-earth materials, with an ε' of 3000 to 4000. These are much less dependent on temperature and applied dc voltage.

(4) Linear, high-Q (in the order of several thousand) temperature-compensating capacitors made with a prescribed (P positive, N negative, or NPO) temperature coefficient of the capacity for incorporation in temperature-stable tuned circuits (compensation of the temperature coefficient of the inductance). The ε of such materials lies between 10 and 100.

Case (b) (large A) is exemplified best by stacked plates [silvered mica (for military use; excellent Q, temperature coefficient about -100 ppm) or ceramic (monolithic)] or rolled dielectric strips [polystyrene (excellent Q; com-

mercial use; also about −100 ppm T.C.); "Mylar"; oil-impregnated paper; "Teflon" etc.].

Case (*c*) (small *l*) is represented by polarized capacitors (to make them unpolarized, two capacitors are connected in series in polarity opposition, usually in the same housing), and it includes the older, larger, and cheaper types like the aluminum foil electrolytics. The newer, more costly, but much smaller, types (having much less leakage current) are tantalum oxide capacitors. Ta_2O_5 stands continuously the extraordinary field strength of 3×10^6 V/cm with an ε' of 25, *l* being measured in angstroms. The Q is about 100. For microminiaturization, silicon monoxide or dioxide or tantalum oxide films of very small *l* are utilized.

Rating The reliability of a capacitor is predominantly determined by the dielectric and the seal of the housing. One has to distinguish between failure value and withstand value. The failure value of dielectric strength is the voltage at which the material fails and is conventionally given as the average failure voltage. In contrast, the withstand value is a voltage below which no failure can be expected.

Deterioration of capacitors with time (aging) can be greatly reduced by systematic "physics of failure" investigations. Typical failure mechanisms are, for instance, precorona discharge in adsorbed air layers, or silver migration.

Non-ideal Behavior at Higher Frequencies Equation (6) presumes ideal conditions. An actual capacitor, particularly if considered over many decades of frequency, and more so, if used as a shunting element across lines, is much more aptly describable as a three-terminal network. Figure 1 marshals the four key deviations from the ideal behavior:

a. At very high frequencies, inductive input-output coupling may override the shunting effect of the capacitor. Remedy: use feed-through capacitors where input and output leads are separated by a shield.

b. Again, at high frequencies, unless as a remedy a feed-through configuration is selected, a series L in the shunt branch results in the capacitor behaving as an inductor above the resonance frequency thus determined ($\omega = (LC)^{-1/2}$).

c. If the capacitive reactance at high frequencies becomes very small, the resulting transfer impedance may be determined by the series loss resistance. A typical case is a tantalytic capacitor behaving this way. Remedy: It must be paralleled by a smaller capacitor of less high frequency losses.

d. At very high frequencies, let us say 100 MHz and above, even ceramic feed-through capacitors start to resonate internally (transmission line effect) rendering them useless above certain frequencies. Remedy: See, for instance, bibliography 1.

Nonlinear Capacitance The dielectric of highly nonlinear capacitors is the depletion layer formed at the *p-n* junction by application of proper bias. These back-biased diodes have a reasonable Q and are widely used as nonlinear reactances in parametric amplifiers for VHF and higher frequencies and for varactor tuning in TV receivers. Nonlinear ceramics are less suitable for this purpose because of their high losses and great temperature dependency.

H. M. SCHLICKE

Reference

1. H. M. Schlicke's chapter on filtering in "Practical Design for Electromagnetic Compatibility," edited by R. Ficchi, Hayden, 1971.

Cross-references: DIELECTRIC THEORY, POTENTIAL.

CARNOT CYCLES AND CARNOT ENGINES

Description The Carnot cycle is often represented, as shown in Fig. 1, by a device which uses an ideal gas as its working substance. A quantity of gas is confined in a cylinder with a wall so well insulated that no heat can flow through it. The cylinder's heat-conducting base rests on the first reservoir, whose constant temperature is T_h, and the gas assumes this temperature. A weighted insulating piston holds the pressure of the gas at P_1 at which pressure its volume is V_1. The gas is then said to be in thermodynamic state 1 characterized by P_1, V_1, and T_h. Little by little the weight on the piston is now set aside until the pressure is reduced to P_2 and the volume is expanded to V_2. The gas is now in state 2 characterized by P_2, V_2, and T_h. The transition from one thermodynamic state to another is called a thermodynamic process. A process is called reversible if done so slowly that no temperature differences arise within the gas and if the piston moves without friction. The cylinder base is kept at temperature T_h, so during this process the temperature of the gas remains at T_h; that is, it is an isothermal process. When this is shown on a pressure-volume diagram, the process appears as a portion of the T_h isotherm. To hold the temperature constant, some heat energy Q_h must

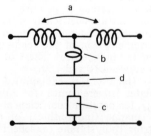

FIG. 1. High-frequency behavior of capacitors.

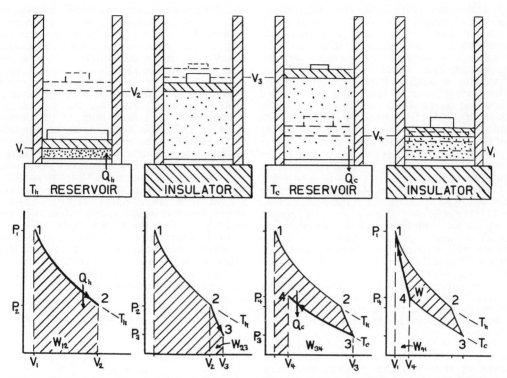

FIG. 1. The steps of a Carnot cycle and the corresponding pressure-volume diagrams. The piston location at the start of each process is shown in solid lines; at the end, in dashed lines. The pressure on the gas can be estimated by the area of the weight shown on top of the piston. The dots indicate that the molecules of the ideal gas are close together when the volume is small and are farther apart when the volume is large.

flow from the reservoir into the gas. In expanding against the weight on the piston, the gas does work W_{12} which is represented on the P-V diagram by the crosshatched area. The cylinder is next moved to an insulated pad where the pressure is further decreased by setting aside more weights, and the gas again expands. No heat energy flows into the gas from the outside during this expansion, and this is called an adiabatic process. The temperature decreases and when it reaches T_c, the temperature of the second reservoir is stopped. The gas is now in state 3 characterized by P_3, V_3, and T_c. During this process the gas does work W_{23} against the load. The cylinder is then moved to the second reservoir where enough weights are slowly replaced to bring the gas to state 4, the point on the T_c isotherm from which state 1 can be reached by an adiabatic process. During this isothermal compression, heat energy Q_c flows from the gas into the reservoir, and the piston does work W_{34} on the gas. To show that this work is done on the gas while previously the work was done on the piston, the appropriate portion of the crosshatched area has been removed. The cylinder is finally placed on an insulated pad, the remaining weights are slowly added, and the gas returns adiabatically to state 1. Again the fact

that the piston does work W_{41} on the gas, is shown by the removal of the cross-hatched area. One Carnot cycle is now completed.

Definition and Characteristics A Carnot cycle is any reversible cyclic thermodynamic operation composed of four processes which are alternately isothermal and adiabatic. (The working substance need not be an ideal gas, but traditionally this is used in discussions.) Since no natural process is strictly reversible, the Carnot cycle is an idealization.

Although heat energy has entered and left it and work has been done on it, the gas undergoes no detectable physical changes for having passed through the Carnot cycle. Heat energy Q_h was removed from the hotter reservoir, and a smaller amount Q_c flowed into the cooler reservoir so that the heat energy budget of the gas increased by $Q = Q_h - Q_c$. The net work done by the gas on the piston is $W = W_{12} + W_{23} + W_{34} + W_{41}$, and the mechanical energy budget of the gas decreased by W which is represented on the P-V diagram by the area enclosed by the phase lines. The first law of thermodynamics requires that $W - Q = 0$ so no energy residue is left in the gas. If the cycle is traversed as described, heat energy Q_h is removed from the higher-temperature reservoir. Part of this remains in the form of heat energy

Q_c as it flows into the cooler reservoir, and part of it is converted to mechanical energy as the work W done on the piston. A Carnot cycle operated in this direction is called a Carnot engine. If the direction of operation were reversed, the cycle would be called a Carnot refrigerator. In such a device mechanical energy, the work W done by the piston, is converted into heat energy which combines with the heat energy Q_c which flows from the cooler reservoir into the gas. All this heat energy Q_h flows out of the gas into the hotter reservoir.

The efficiency η of any engine is the fraction of the heat energy input Q_h which is converted into mechanical energy W; that is, $\eta = W/Q_h$. The following properties of Carnot engines are derived in many textbooks of thermodynamics.

(1) The efficiency of a Carnot cycle depends only on the temperatures of the two reservoirs.

(2) No heat engine operating in cycles between two reservoirs can have a greater efficiency than a Carnot engine operating between those reservoirs.

The Carnot engine is thus a standard against which other heat engines can be compared. Historically it was the source of a number of ideas that are now basic to the study of thermodynamics.

History of the Carnot Cycle In 1824 Sadi Carnot[1] (1796–1832) analyzed a heat engine assuming that heat can perform mechanical work in falling from a higher temperature to a lower just as water can do work falling from a higher level to a lower, and assuming that no heat would be lost just as no water was lost. (His work preceded by more than 20 years the theory of Joule and Helmholtz on the mechanical equivalence of heat.) In his study he proposed an ideal heat engine that operated in a continuous cycle and was reversible. He then showed that it is impossible in a cyclic operation to obtain work from a single constant-temperature heat source and that no more work can be obtained from any process than is required to reverse it.

His ideas escaped notice until 1834 when Clapeyron[2] recognized their merit, suggested some of the details of the device described above, and plotted its behavior on a P-V diagram. Again the ideas were neglected until William Thomson (later Lord Kelvin) learned of Carnot's work through Clapeyron's memoir. In 1848, Thomson described[3] how a Carnot engine could be used to define a temperature scale that was absolute in the sense that it did not depend on what thermometric substance was used. It was based on a series of Carnot engines, each of which did the same amount of work. This was the first important idea drawn from a study of the Carnot cycle. In 1850 Clausius[4], who learned of Carnot's ideas through Thomson and Clapeyron, showed how Carnot's assumption (no loss of heat) could be reconciled with the newer views of Joule

and Helmholtz (which now form the basis of the first law of thermodynamics). It was only required that the engine exhaust less heat energy, by the amount of the work done, than it accepted. Thomson independently reached the same conclusion[5] in 1851.

In 1854 Clausius[6] in his study of the Carnot cycle identified the physical property he later named "entropy." This was the second important idea drawn from study of the Carnot cycle. In 1877 Boltzmann[7] took the principle of Clausius that real processes evolve naturally toward states of higher entropy (which is the second law of thermodynamics) as a basic point in his theory and thus had no need to consider the Carnot cycle from which that principle was derived. It is now common practice to discuss thermodynamics axiomatically rather than historically so that the Carnot cycle no longer plays the important role it once did. The most complete discussions are found in the older volumes,[8] but some recent books do describe the cycle in detail.[9] An historical account with an elementary presentation of the theory is also available.[10]

ROBERT A. LUFBURROW

References

1. Carnot, S., "Reflexions sur la Puissance Motrice du Feu," Paris, Bachelier, 1824. Reprinted (together with references 2 and 4, below) by Dover Publications, New York.
2. Clapeyron, E., reprinted in *Pogg. Ann.*, **59**, 446–451, 566–586 (1843). See reference 1.
3. Thomson, W., "Mathematical and Physical Papers," Vol. I, pp. 100–106, Cambridge, University Press, 1882.
4. Clausius, R., *Pogg. Ann.*, **79**, 368–397, 500–524 (1850). See reference 1.
5. Thomson, W., *Pogg. Ann.*, **79**, 174–316 (1850).
6. Clausius, R., *Pogg. Ann.*, **93**, 481–506 (1854); **125**, 390 (1865).
7. Boltzmann, L., "Lectures on Gas Theory" (translated by S. G. Brush) Berkeley, University of California Press, 1964.
8. Britwistle, G., "The Principles of Thermodynamics," Cambridge, University Press, 1925. Preston, T., "The Theory of Heat," Third edition, London, The Macmillan Co., 1919.
9. Shortley, G. H., and Williams, D. E., "Principles of College Physics," Englewood Cliffs, N.J., Prentice-Hall, Inc., 1959.
   Zemansky, M. W., "Heat and Thermodynamics," Fourth edition, New York, McGraw-Hill Book Co., Inc., 1957.
10. Sandfort, J. F., "Heat Engines," Garden City, N.Y., Doubleday & Co., Inc., 1962.

Cross-references: HEAT, THERMODYNAMICS.

CAVITATION*

Cavities may form, grow, and collapse in a liquid when variational tensile stresses are superimposed on the prevailing ambient pressure. Pure liquids have theoretical tensile strengths which are estimated on various grounds to be of order 300 to 1500 atmospheres (bars), but the observed tensile strengths of real liquids are much lower. It is presumed, therefore, that the observed tensile strength is a measure of the stress required to enlarge the minute cavities, or cavitation nuclei, which already exist in the liquid rather than the stress required to form new interior interfaces.

The transient cavities formed by tensile stress are unstable and would grow indefinitely if the stress were maintained. After the cavitation nuclei have been expanded to many times their original size, however, they may collapse violently if the stress is reduced or removed. The kinetic energy of the liquid that follows each inwardly collapsing interface becomes highly concentrated as the cavity collapses. If such transient cavities contain very little permanent gas, the peak pressures at collapse may reach thousands of bars, the temperature may reach thousands of degrees, and strong SHOCK WAVES may be radiated to a distance of several cavity radii. Similar cavities formed in saturated liquids will usually contain more gas and their collapse will be less violent, but the peak pressures attained are still sufficient to produce unique mechanical effects such as the corrosion and pitting of metallic surfaces (as in marine propellers and sonar projectors) and the beneficial removal of embedded dirt (as in ultrasonic cleaners). In the latter case, the soil to be removed provides a prolific source of cavitation nuclei at exactly the sites where cavitation is desired.

In hydrodynamic cavitation, the tensile stress is of relatively long duration and plenty of cavitation nuclei are usually available. As a result, cavitation occurs when the total net pressure, or the stagnation pressure, becomes approximately equal to the vapor pressure of the liquid. In acoustic cavitation, the cyclic pressure required to produce cavitation is a function of the frequency, the partial pressure of any dissolved gas, and the population of cavitation nuclei. For frequencies above about 200 kHz, the threshold pressure for cavitation increases with the square of the frequency and is almost independent of the degree of gas saturation. For frequencies below 200 kHz, the threshold pressure is a function of the partial pressure of the dissolved gas. In saturated liquids, at sound pressures less than a few bars, stable bubbles can grow from cavitation nuclei by the process of rectified diffusion. At higher levels of acoustic excitation, transient cavities can be formed. The threshold

*Author deceased. Article is reprinted from first edition.

sound pressure at which they appear and the violence of their collapse increase as the partial pressure of the dissolved gas is lowered.

The physical nature of the cavitation nucleus, the details of its dynamic growth from submicroscopic to visible size, and the peak pressures and temperatures achieved at the climax of collapse are current topics of active research interest.

F. V. HUNT

References

Flynn, H. G., "Cavitation," in Mason, W. P., Ed., "Physical Acoustics," Vol. 1B, Ch. 9, New York, Academic Press (1964).

Apfel, R. E., "The Role of Impurities in Cavitation Threshold Determination," *J. Acoust. Soc. Am.*, 48, 1179–1186 (1970).

Cross-references: ACOUSTICS, ULTRASONICS, LIQUID STATE.

CENTRIFUGE

A centrifuge is a device consisting of a rotating container in which substances with different densities are separated by the centrifugal forces on the substances.

In most cases, the centrifuge is used for producing sedimentation in fluids, i.e., for the concentration and purification of materials.[1,2] However, it also has been used extensively as an analytical tool for determining particle or molecular weights and sizes,[1,3,4] as a means of determining the strength of materials, and numerous other research and practical problems.[1] Centrifugal fields of 10^9 times gravity have been employed in some experiments. The effective centrifugal force, F, on a particle of mass m and density ρ in a fluid of density ρ' is given by the relation $F = m(\rho - \rho')\omega^2 r/\rho$. This force is opposed by the frictional force of the fluid on the particle. If the speed of sedimentation v is not too large, i.e., the Reynolds number, $v\rho d/\eta$ does not exceed the order of unity, where d is the diameter of the particle and η the coefficient of viscosity, and if the wall effects are neglected, the force of friction f is given by Stokes' law. In the case of sedimentation in a liquid for a particle of effective radius a

$$4/3\pi a^3(\rho - \rho')\omega^2 r = 6\pi\eta a v \qquad (1)$$

Since ω, r, ρ, ρ' and η are measurable, a and hence the mass of the particle m can be determined. If we are concerned with a substance of molecular weight M, partial specific volume $\overline{V}$, molar frictional constant f, density of solution ρ, and diffusion constant D, the corresponding equation is[3]

$$M(1 - \overline{V}\rho)\omega^2 r = f \frac{dr}{dt} \qquad (2)$$

For a dilute solution $f = RT/D$ where R is the gas constant and T is the absolute temperature. Hence,

$$v = \frac{dr}{dt} = \frac{MD(1 - \rho \overline{V})}{RT}\omega^2 r \qquad (3)$$

The velocity of sedimentation in a unit field $s = (dr/dt)/\omega^2 r$. If M is known s can be calculated since the other factors in the equation can be determined, or if s is measured, M can be found. The quantity s is called the sedimentation constant and is expressed in Svedberg units $(10^{-13} \text{ sec})^{-1}$ named in honor of the great pioneer in the field of molecular weight measurement by ultracentrifugation. It is a very important quantity for characterizing a substance in solution.[3,4]

From the above equations alone, one might expect a substance would completely settle out of the solution even with very weak centrifugal fields or gravity alone if the field is applied for sufficient time. This, of course, is not the case because of thermal agitation of BROWNIAN MOTION of the molecules or particles, which gives rise to back diffusion. It can be shown[5] that the average displacement of a particle in time τ due to Brownian motion is $\overline{\Delta} X = 2D\tau$ and for a spherical particle of radius a the average velocity for a time τ is

$$v_\tau = \frac{\overline{\Delta} X}{\tau} = \left(\frac{RT}{N} \frac{1}{3\pi\eta a\tau}\right)^{1/2}$$

where N is the Avogadro number. It is clear that when v_τ becomes very much larger than the settling velocity v nothing can sediment out of the solution. When this is the case, it can be shown[3,4] that when equilibrium is reached between sedimentation and back diffusion

$$\log_e \frac{C_1 f_1}{C_2 f_2} = \frac{M(1 - \rho \overline{V})\omega^2 (r_2^2 - r_1^2)}{2RT} \qquad (4)$$

where C_1 and f_1 are the concentration and activity coefficient, respectively, at the radius r_1 and C_2 and f_2 are the corresponding quantities at the radius r_2. If the substance is in dilute solution in a sector-shaped centrifuge cell, the weight-average molecular weight M_w is given by[3,4]

$$M_w = \frac{2RT}{(1 - \overline{V}\rho)\omega^2(r_b^2 - r_a^2)} \frac{C_b - C_a}{C_0} \qquad (5)$$

where C_a is the concentration at the radius of the miniscus r_a, C_b is the concentration at the peripheral radius r_b and C_0 is the average concentration.

In deriving the above equations, the effect of electrical charges has been neglected. Usually, the solutions are kept near the isoelectric point, but in many important cases this is not possible. The effects of charges on the above equations have been investigated and in some cases found to be quite large.[3,4,6]

For the separation, purification, or concentration of materials in solution or suspension in a liquid, the centrifugal field is made high enough so that the sedimentation velocity v is appreciable. Equations (1), (2) and (3) are used for estimating the sedimentation. However, these equations hold strictly only when the sedimentation is radial, and no turbulence, radial flow, or re-mixing occurs. In most centrifuges used commercially (the cream separator, for example), the liquid flows through the machine during the sedimentation. Any radial flow stream is acted upon by coriolis forces which usually produce mixing. Also, the temperature may not be uniform throughout the sedimenting column. This gives rise to convection if the temperature change produces greater densities near the axis. The driving force which generates thermal convection is roughly proportional to the density gradient times the centrifugal field. Since the latter is large in most centrifuges, the temperature gradient must be small. For a detailed discussion of commercial type centrifuges, both flow-through and batch-type and their operation, reference should be made to Keith and Lavanchy[2] and others.[7] In addition to the use of the centrifuge in industry, it is widely used in research and testing laboratories for the purification and preparation of many different substances. As should be expected from theory, high speed centrifuges do not deactivate most molecular species. Even molecular species such as are often encountered in biology and medicine which are stable only over a few degrees of temperature and a small range of pH are not appreciably effected by a comparatively large centrifugal field. For this reason, high speed centrifuges are widely used in biochemistry and molecular biophysics. The rotors of these high speed centrifuges usually spin in a good vacuum (below 10^{-5} torr) to avoid heating and thermal gradients in the rotor. Such centrifuges with push-button control are readily obtainable commercially.

Analytical Centrifuges The centrifuge is employed as an analytical tool in one of two general methods.[3,4] The first method makes use of Eqs. (1), (2) and (3), while the second is based upon Eqs. (4) and (5). Sometimes combinations of these two methods are used.[3,4] When a centrifuge is employed in analytical work, it is usually called an ultracentrifuge.[3] The first method has been more widely used, at least, until recently. In this method, comparatively high rotor speeds with the resulting high centrifugal fields are employed in order to produce an easily measurable rate of sedimentation v. The value of v is usually measured by optical means and s is computed. The high centrifugal field quickly produces a small density gradient across the centrifugal cell which stabilizes the sedimenting column. As a result, very high accuracy in rotor temperature and speed control are not mandatory, although desirable. Another important factor is that the time of centrifugation

is comparatively short ($\sim$ hours). Furthermore, if the solution contains a number of molecular species, each species sediments at its characteristic rate and the value of its sedimentation constant s is easily determined. The effect of ionic charge and the pH of the solution on the values of s and the effect of concentration of one species on the other during sedimentation, etc., have been quantitatively investigated, both theoretically and experimentally, by a number of workers.[3,4,7,8] The rate-of-sedimentation method has the disadvantage of not being an absolute method and requiring a knowledge of the diffusion constant D as well as the shape of the sedimenting particle or molecule. Often these factors introduce large uncertainties in the value of M.

The second method, known as the equilibrium method, is based upon Eqs. (4) and (5). It is a reliable, absolute method since it is based upon equilibrium thermodynamics. Also, it is not necessary to know the value of the diffusion constant or the shape of the molecule to get the value of M. As pointed out above, no actual sedimentation on the walls of the centrifuge cell occurs in the equilibrium method so that the rotor speed and resulting centrifugal field are relatively low. Consequently, if the concentration of the solute in the solvent is low, the density gradient in the cell is small which in turn makes the sedimenting column sensitive to small rotor temperature and rotor speed variations. Recently, considerable effort has gone into designing and adapting ultracentrifuges to equilibrium measurements and the centrifuging time has been reduced from several days to several hours.[1,3,4,9] An over-all precision in the measurement of the molecular weights of between 0.1 and 1 per cent over the molecular weight range from 100 to 10^8 has been obtained.[9] The determination of molecular weight distributions, etc., can be carried out.

Gas Centrifuging The centrifuge has been used for removing fine particles suspended in gases and for the separation of gaseous mixtures. The fine particles sediment on the inner wall of the centrifuge where they are removed while the centrifuge is spinning or when it is stopped. In the separation of gases and vapors a tubular type centrifuge is usually used in which the gases flow out of the centrifuge in a light and heavy fraction. Such tubular centrifuges have been used for the separation of isotopes.[7,10-12]

When a centrifugal field is applied to a gas it sets up a pressure gradient

$$dp/dr = \frac{Mp}{RT} \omega^2 r$$

where p is the pressure, M the molecular weight of the gas, R the gas constant and T the absolute temperature. In a binary mixture of two ideal gases with molecular weights M_1 and M_2 and with mole fraction N of the lighter gas of molecular weight M_1, it has been shown both theoretically and experimentally that at equilibrium where r_2 is the radius of the inside periphery of the centrifuge tube

$$\left(\frac{N}{1-N}\right)_{r=r_2} = \left(\frac{N}{1-N}\right)_{r=0} \exp \frac{(M_2 - M_1)\omega^2 r_2^2}{2RT}$$

In order to determine the value of a centrifuge or cascade of centrifuges for separating isotopes or gases, it is customary to calculate the separative work or separative power which is a measure of separation produced by a single centrifuge or a number of centrifuges used in a cascade. Cohen[13] has shown that the separative power of a single centrifuge is

$$\delta U = \frac{Dp}{RT} \left[\frac{(M_2 - M_1)\omega^2 r_2^2}{2RT}\right]^2 \frac{\pi Zf}{2} \text{ moles/sec}$$

where Z is the centrifuge tube length, D the diffusion constant, and f the flow factor which depends upon the flow pattern in the centrifuge and has a maximum value of one. The number of centrifuges required to carry out a given amount of separation in a time t is $U/t\delta U$ where U is the total separative work and is defined as[14]

$$U = W(2N_w - 1) \log_e \frac{N_w}{1-N_w} P(2N_p - 1)$$

$$\cdot \log_e \frac{N_p}{1-N_p} - F(2N_F - 1) \log_e \frac{N_F}{1-N_F}$$

where F is the number of moles of feed material of mole fraction N_F and W and N_w and P and N_p are the corresponding values for the waste and the product. It will be observed that the effectiveness of a centrifuge for gaseous or isotope separation increases directly as the fourth power of the peripheral speed as the length of the centrifuge, and as $(M_2 - M_1)^2$.

J. W. BEAMS

References

1. Beams, J. W., *Science*, **120**, 619 (1954); *Physics Today*, **12**, 20 (1959) (see for other references).
2. Keith, F. W., Jr., and Lavanchy, A. C., in Kirk-Othmen's "Encyclopedia of Chemical Technology," second edition, New York, Interscience Publishers, 1964.
3. Svedberg, T., and Pederson, K. O., "The Ultracentrifuge," Clarendon Press, 1940.
4. Schachman, H. K., "Ultracentrifugation in Biochemistry," New York, Academic Press, 1959.
5. Burton, E. F., "The Physical Properties of Colloidal Solutions," London, Longmans, Green and Co., 1938.
6. MacInnes, D. A., "Principles of Electrochemistry," New York, Van Nostrand Reinhold, 1939.
7. Beams, J. W., *J. Appl. Phys.* **8**, 795 (1937); *Rev.*

Mod. Phys., **10**, 245 (1938); *J. Wash. Acad. Sci.*, **37**, 221 (1947) (see for other references).

8. Williams, J. W., "Ultracentrifugal Analysis in Theory and Experiment," New York, Academic Press, 1963.
9. Beams, J. W., Boyle, R. D., and Hexner, P. E., *J. Polymer Chem.*, **57**, 161 (1962).
10. Beams, J. W., Snoddy, L. B., and Kuhlthau, A. R., *Proc. 2nd U.N. Geneva Conf.* **4**, 428 (1958).
11. Beyerle, K., Groth, W. E., Nann, E., and Welge, K. H., *Proc. 2nd U.N. Geneva Conf.*, **4**, 439 (1958); *Proc. Intern. Symp. Isotope Separation, Amsterdam*, (1956).
12. Kistemaker, J., Los, J., and Veldhuyzen, E. J., *Proc. Intern. Symp. Isotope Separation, Amsterdam* (1956).
13. Cohen, K., "Theory of Isotope Separation," New York, McGraw-Hill Book Co., Inc., 1951.
14. Benedict, M., and Pigford, T. H., "Nuclear Chemical Engineering," New York, McGraw-Hill Book Co., Inc., 1957.

Cross-references: BROWNIAN MOTION, MOLECULAR WEIGHT, ROTATION–CIRCULAR MOTION.

ČERENKOV RADIATION

This is a feeble radiation in the visible spectrum, which occurs when a fast charged particle traverses a dielectric medium at a velocity exceeding the velocity of light in the medium. It is thus a shock-wave phenomenon, the optical analog of the "supersonic bang." The radiation arises from the local and transient polarization of the medium close to the track of the particle. Consider, Fig. 1(a), an arbitrary element S of the medium to one side of the track AB of a fast electron, the track defining the z-axis. At a particular instant of time, when the electron is at say e_1, the local polarization vector P_1 will be directed along S e_1', to a point e_1' slightly behind e_1, owing to the retarded fields. As the particle goes by, the vector P_2 will turn over and, when the electron reaches e_2, will be directed to a point e_2'. The variation of P with time, may be resolved into radial and axial components P_ρ and P_z, as shown in Fig. 1(b). Owing to cylindrical symmetry, this polarization, viewed at a point distant from the particle, appears as an elementary dipole lying along the axis z, Fig. 1(c). As the particle plunges through the medium, radiation arises from the coherent growth and decay of this sequence of elementary dipoles. Two essential features of the radiation become at once apparent. First, since it is only the P_z component which is important, the field variation, Fig. 1(b), is that of a double δ-function. Thus, from Fourier analysis, if the circular frequency is ω, we will expect a spectrum of the form $\omega \cdot d\omega$, i.e., radiation which is bluer than that from an equi-energy spectrum. Secondly, since the radiating element is an axial dipole, the angular distribution, for this element alone, will be of the form $\sin^2\theta$, Fig. 1(c). It is impor-

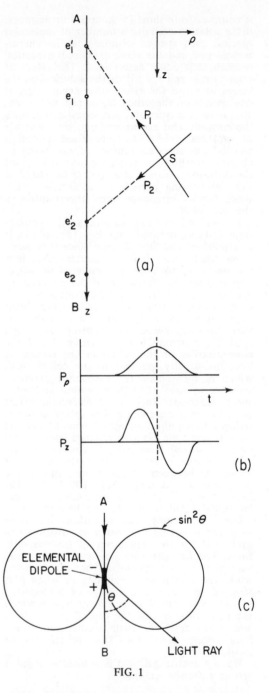

(a)

(b)

(c)

FIG. 1

tant to realize that the radiation arises from the medium itself, not directly from the particle. Since the medium is stationary, the intensity and angular distributions do not contain the relativistic factor (mc^2/E); in this respect, it is essentially different from Bremsstrahlung or synchrotron radiation.

The description above applies only to one

element along the track. The most characteristic feature of Čerenkov radiation, its coherence, is at once apparent when we now consider an extended region of track. In Fig. 2(a) it is easily seen that there is only one angle θ at which it is possible to obtain a coherent wave front. If the velocity of the particle is v ($=\beta c$, where c is the velocity of light in vacuo), and n is the refractive index of the medium, the particle travels a distance AB in a time Δt, given by AB $= \beta c \cdot \Delta t$; in the same time the radiation, emitted at A, travels a distance AC $= (c/n)\Delta t$, from which we

obtain the Čerenkov relation:

$$\cos \theta = (1/\beta n) \qquad (1)$$

From Eq. (1) it is at once evident that there is a threshold velocity given by $\beta = (1/n)$, below which no radiation takes place. At ultrarelativistic velocities, as $\beta \to 1$, the Čerenkov angle θ tends to a maximum value $\theta(\max) = \cos^{-1}(1/n)$. The polarization vectors E and H of the radiation which, owing to symmetry, takes place over the surface of a cone, are shown in Fig. 2(b).

The radiation yield, from the theory of Frank and Tamm, is

$$\frac{dW}{dz} = \frac{e^2}{c^2} \int_{\beta n > 1} \left[1 - \frac{1}{\beta^2 n^2} \right] \omega \cdot d\omega, \text{ ergs/cm path}$$

$$(2a)$$

or

$$\frac{dN}{dz} = 2\pi \left(\frac{e^2}{hc} \right) \cdot \left[\frac{1}{\lambda_2} - \frac{1}{\lambda_1} \right] \cdot \sin^2 \theta$$

photons/cm path   (2b)

between wavelength limits λ_1 and λ_2 (in cm). The spectral distribution is $(dW/d\omega) \propto \omega$ or $(dW/d\lambda) \propto \lambda^{-3}$, expressed as energy per unit circular frequency or per unit wavelength, respectively. The radiation has, therefore, a continuous spectrum toward the blue and ultraviolet. There is no radiation in the x-ray region, for which $n < 1$. For example, in the case of a fast electron in water, $n = 1.33$, we find from Eq. (2b), that when $\beta \to 1$ and $\theta(\max) = 41°$, the yield (dN/dz) is ~ 200 photons/cm, between λ_1 and λ_2 of 3500 and 5500Å, respectively,

The phenomenon has found considerable application in the fields of high-energy nuclear physics and cosmic-ray research; in almost all practical Čerenkov counters, the light is detected by means of a photomultiplier. The unique directional and threshold properties of the radiation may be used in a number of different ways. For example, by velocity selection, it is possible to distinguish between particles of different mass having the same energy, and it is also possible to measure particle velocities directly, by measuring θ. Other examples may be cited: The e^2 dependence, Eq. (2) above, has been used to determine the charge spectrum of the primary cosmic rays, and transparent lead-loaded glasses have been developed as total-absorption spectrometers for high-energy γ-rays.

Čerenkov radiation in gaseous media is now used extensively in high-energy physics, light flashes from the night-sky associated with cosmic ray showers have been attributed to the effect, and microwaves have been produced by the Čerenkov process.

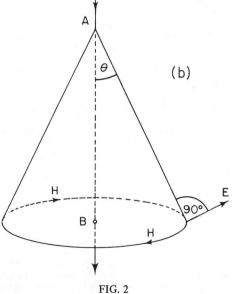

FIG. 2

J. V. JELLEY

References

Čerenkov, P. A., *C.R. Acad. Sci. (USSR)*, **2**, 451 (1934).
Frank, I. M., and Tamm, Ig, *C.R. Acad. Sci.* (USSR), **14**, (3), 109 (1937).
Jelley, J. V., "Čerenkov Radiation and Its Applications," London, Pergamon Press, 1958.
Bolotovskii, B. M., *Usp. Fiz. Nauk.*, **67**, 201 (1957).
Hutchinson, G. W., *Progr. Nucl. Phys.*, **8**, 197 (1960).

Cross-references: DIELECTRIC THEORY, DIPOLE MOMENTS.

CHEMICAL KINETICS

Besides offering useful rate equations to describe the speeds of chemical reactions, chemical kinetics attempts to describe exactly how each reaction occurs. It does so in terms of one or more elementary steps, which are reactions having no observable intermediate chemical species. The ultimate goal is a theory interrelating energy, structure, and time for these single chemical events. Many of the ideas, developed since 1850 when the first quantitative rate study was made, have been extended by analogy to explain electron-hole processes in semiconductors, various solid-state processes, and thermonuclear reactions.

Reaction rates depend on the nature of the reactants, temperature, pressure, kind and intensity of radiation, nature of catalyst or solvent, and many other factors. The extent of a reaction can be followed by withdrawal of samples for early chemical analysis. It is more common, however, to analyze the main reaction mixture continuously and nondestructively by spectroscopic means or by observing physical properties like density, electrical conductivity, optical activity, dielectric constant, and so on.

The rate v of a reaction $aA + bB \rightarrow eE + fF$ is best related to the rate of change of the concentrations $[A]$ and $[B]$ of reactants by rewriting the equation as $0 = eE + fF - aA - bB$. If the change is an elementary step, its rate is

$$v = -\frac{1}{a}\frac{d[A]}{dt} = -\frac{1}{b}\frac{d[B]}{dt} = +\frac{1}{e}\frac{d[E]}{dt} =$$

$$+ \frac{1}{f}\frac{d[F]}{dt} = k[A]^a[B]^b$$

Here k is a rate constant independent of concentration. If the step is not elementary, its rate is often presumed to be expressible as proportional to certain empirically observed powers $m, n, \cdots$ of the concentrations of species present in the reaction vessel. The values of $m, n, \cdots$ need not be integers and cannot be predicted from the balanced chemical equation if the step is not elementary. The over-all order of a reaction is the sum of these exponents, and the order with respect to a particular species is its own exponent. The order of a reaction can be determined in several ways. In the method of initial rates, concentrations of all but one reactant are held constant, if possible at great values, and v is observed at the start of reaction for several values of $[A]$. The order with respect to A is the slope of a graph of log v vs. log $[A]$.

The first major reaction rate theory was founded on the kinetic theory and classical mechanics. It still is very useful when reactants approach each other in an attractive potential field (e.g., ions), when the distribution of energies is nonequilibrium (e.g., electrical discharge in gases), or when the molecules involved are tremendous in size. In general, however, the collision theory suffers from its inability to satisfactorily predict effective cross sections (molecular sizes for reaction) or the effect of isotopic substitution.

Most modern theories suppose the existence of an undetectable transition state of high energy and fleeting existence. The configuration of this activated complex lies, as it were, atop the mountain pass of lowest height between energy-valleys of reactants and products. It is mechanically stable to all vibrations except the one that describes the progress of reaction over the saddle-point at the pass. This one motion is assigned a very low (sometimes imaginary) frequency, but otherwise the activated complex is just another molecule. It is supposed to be in dynamic equilibrium with reactants and its free energy can be calculated from its partition function by the usual methods of STATISTICAL MECHANICS. The rate constant k_n then takes the form $(kT/h) \exp(-\Delta A/kT)$ where k is the gas constant per molecule, T is the absolute temperature, h is Planck's constant, and ΔA is the increase in free energy on going from reactants to activated state. This resembles the well-known relation $k_n = s \exp(-E/kT)$ discovered empirically in 1889 by Arrhenius. In it, s and E are approximately independent of T, and E is called the activation energy.

A recent theory of promise treats reactants as a wave packet that gradually spreads in time. The rate of reaction is taken to be the probability that the packet will be found in a configuration that is indentified with products.

Thermal decomposition of an initially pure gas is seemingly a simple change, yet its order often changes gradually from first to second as the pressure falls. Moreover, there is always the question why like molecules do not all decay at once. The answers lie in understanding the mechanism, which is presently taken to be collision with any other molecule M ($0 = A^* + M - M - A$ with rate constant k_2') to yield an energized molecule A^* that may suffer a stabilizing collision ($0 = A + M - M - A^*$, with k_2) or internal change ($0 = A^\ddagger - A^*$, with k_1) that leads to the activated state $A^\ddagger$. The reaction is called unimolecular because the activated complex $A^\ddagger$ contains only one reactant molecule. The rate of decomposition of A at any instant is $v = k_2'[M][A] - k_2[M][A^*]$, and the rate of

decomposition of A^* is $v^* = k_1 [A^*] - k_2'[M][A] + k_2[M][A^*]$. Since the v's are time derivatives, these are simultaneous differential equations.

It is generally impossible to solve the simultaneous differential equations that describe a mechanism. The least restrictive and most useful simplification is generally the steady-state approximation, wherein the concentration of a species of low concentration is assumed to reach an effectively constant value after a certain reasonable time (induction period) has passed. If $[A^*]$ reaches a steady-state concentration, $v^* = 0$ and the v^* differential equation becomes an algebraic one for $[A^*]$. Moreover, the rate of decomposition of A then is $v = k_1[A^*] = k_1k_2'[M][A](k_1 + k_2[M])^{-1}$. This rate equation becomes second order if $k_2[M] \ll k_1$; this occurs at low pressure or when A^* changes rapidly into $A^\ddagger$. If A is a simple molecule of few atoms, the activation energy easily becomes effective in one bond to cause decay. On the other hand, the order becomes first if $k_2[M] \gg k_1$; this corresponds to high pressure or an A with many degrees of freedom to accommodate the activation energy.

A generally more restrictive way to simplify the mathematics of a sequence of reactions is to assume that one step is so much slower than the others that it alone limits the rate. All steps besides the rate-limiting one are assumed to be at equilibrium in this approximation. If, in unimolecular decomposition, the rate-limiting step is $A^* \rightarrow A^\ddagger$, then the rate is $k_1[A^*]$. The reaction is then first order in A because $v = 0$ for the equilibrium $A + M = M + A^*$. If, however, the rate-limiting step is $A + M \rightarrow A^* + M$, then the rate is $k_2'[M][A]$.

Bimolecular reactions, wherein the activated state consists of two reactant species, are very common. The rates of the fastest of these are limited by the rates of diffusion of reactants and have rate constants of the order of 10^{10} liter mole^{-1} sec^{-1} in aqueous solution. Typical examples are the aqueous neutralizations $NH_4^+ + H_2O \rightarrow NH_3 + H_3O^+$ and $H_3O^+ + F^- \rightarrow HF + H_2O$. Typical bimolecular gaseous reactions are the linear chain reactions $X + H_2 \rightarrow HX + H$ and $H + X_2 \rightarrow HX + X$ where X is H, D, Cl, Br, or I. A nice way to initiate these reactions of H_2 and X_2 is by a photon: $X_2 + \text{photon} \rightarrow X + X$. Thermal dissociation of X_2 is also sufficient to start reaction.

Carbon compounds undergo many reactions, but most of them can be classified into a few types. Nucleophilic substitution, wherein a basic reactant replaces another initially on C by a net reaction $X + RY \rightarrow XR + Y$, may be first order in RY alone or in both X and RY. If first order in just RY, the mechanism is labeled S_N1 and the rate-limiting step is conceived as production of the active carbonium ion R^+ by the process $RY \rightarrow R^+ + Y^-$. If second order (S_N2), the rate-limiting step is considered to be production of the bimolecular activated complex $X \cdots R \cdots$ Y. Elimination reactions typically yield a double bond with loss of part of the organic reactant RCH_2CH_2Y. If first order in organic reactant (type E_1), the rate-limiting step is said to be production of the carbonium ion $RCH_2CH_2^+$, which then swiftly eliminates H^+ to become $RCH = CH_2$. If first order in both base and organic reactant (type E_2), the rate-limiting step is thought of as production of a bimolecular complex which eliminates H^+ and Y^- almost simultaneously. A fifth class of organic reaction (S_{Ni}) describes how an electrophilic reagent (e.g., NO_2^+ in mixed HNO_3 and H_2SO_4 or Br^+ in Br_2 with $FeBr_3$) may attack an aromatic ring like that in benzene to form a positively charged intermediate that soon loses H^+ to a base in the solution.

A catalyst is a species that changes the rate of a reaction and yet is regenerated by that reaction so that it seems to be unchanged in the net reaction. Catalysts do not affect the equilibrium state but they do lower the activation energy and sometimes may provide a needed steric arrangement. The most general mechanism of catalysis is $A + C_1 \rightarrow D + C_2$ followed by $B + C_2 \rightarrow E + C_1$ to give the net change $A + B \rightarrow D + E$. Many so-called catalysts of industry need regeneration ($C_2 \rightarrow C_1$) by a reaction other than that catalyzed. For example, silica-alumina cracking catalysts used in making gasoline must be cyclically burned free of carbon deposited during cracking. A catalyzed reaction is almost always first order in catalyst concentration (or surface area) and usually has an order that is less than the true order by unity.

Enzymes are biological catalysts. Many act by the well-known Michaelis-Menten mechanism $E + S \rightleftarrows C \rightarrow P + E$, where enzyme E attacks substrate S with a rate $k_A[E][S]$ to form a complex C that may yield products P at a rate $k_P[C]$ or may revert to S with rate $k_R[C]$. The rate of disappearance of S is $v_S = k_A[E][S] - k_R[C]$ and the rate of appearance of C or disappearance of E is $v_E = k_A[E][S] - k_R[C] - k_P[C]$. The total concentration of enzyme in the system is $[E]_0 = [C] + [E]$. In the steady state, $v_E = 0 = k_A([E]_0 - [C])[S] - (k_R + k_P)[C]$ so that

$$v_S = k_P[C] = \frac{k_P k_A[S][E]_0}{(k_R + k_P) + k_A[S]}.$$

The rate of disappearance of S is always first order in total enzyme but may change from first to zero order in S as $[S]$ increases. The maximum rate at which E can act occurs when $[S]$ is great and $v_S = k_P[E]_0$.

WILLIAM F. SHEEHAN

References

Most physical chemistry textbooks contain introductions to chemical kinetics. Some of their many authors are: G. M. Barrow, G. W. Castellan, F. Daniels

and R. A. Alberty, S. Glasstone, E. A. Moelwyn-Hughes, W. J. Moore, and W. F. Sheehan.

Benson, S. W., "The Foundations of Chemical Kinetics," New York, McGraw-Hill Book Co., Inc., 1960.

Glasstone, S., Laidler, K. J., and Eyring, H., "The Theory of Rate Processes," New York, McGraw-Hill Book Co., Inc., 1941.

Hinshelwood, C. N., "The Kinetics of Chemical Change," London, Oxford University Press, 1940.

Slater, N. B., "Theory of Unimolecular Reactions," Ithaca, N.Y., Cornell University Press, 1959.

There are several timely review articles in various volumes of "Advances in Chemical Physics," I. Prigogine, Ed., London and New York, John Wiley & Sons, Ltd. (1958).

Values of rate constants for specific reactions are listed in National Bureau of Standards Circular 510, its two supplements, and in NBS Monograph 34.

For critically evaluated rate constants and mechanisms, see S. W. Benson and H. E. O'Neal, "Kinetic Data on Gas Phase Unimolecular Reactions," NSRDS–NBS 21 (Feb, 1970), Washington, D.C., U.S. Government Printing Office.

Cross-references: CHEMISTRY, PHYSICAL CHEMISTRY, STATISTICAL MECHANICS.

CHEMICAL PHYSICS

It is difficult to define each of the traditional fields in science. It is more difficult to define in-between fields. This article will consist mostly of a description of chemical physics that follows brief historical descriptions of chemistry and physics.

During the nineteenth century chemistry dealt with atoms and molecules. It was the science of atoms and their combination. Chemistry was largely empirical and descriptive. Chemists devoted great effort to chemical synthesis and analysis. They made use of precipitation, titration, color changes, weighing, vapor pressure measurements, melting point measurements, and the like. On the other hand, physics dealt with mechanics, electricity and magnetism, wave motion, large-scale properties of matter and so forth. Its tools were those for measuring forces, velocities, electric fields, etc. Physicists had not learned how to treat small-scale mechanics. During this period chemistry and physics seemed to be far apart.

During the early part of the twentieth century physical science leaped ahead. Chemists began to make general use of classical thermodynamics and they became more interested in microscopic phenomena. By 1927 the basic structure of quantum mechanics had been erected and subsequently statistical mechanics was correspondingly modified and expanded.

By 1930 the separation between chemistry and physics no longer existed. The advent of statistical and quantum mechanics and of new, mostly physical, experimental methods and tools wrought great changes in chemistry and physics. The two sciences were able to help each other greatly, and the distinction between them became largely meaningless. It is perhaps unfortunate that chemistry and physics were ever separated. Surely it is true today that chemists need to know much about "physics" and vice versa.

There are many physical problems in which the concepts and methods of the two separate sciences are mixed so that this area may be called chemical physics. A wide range of study is common to both chemistry and physics. The basic problems in chemical physics concern properties of atoms and molecules and the behavior of statistical ensembles of atoms and molecules. Chemical physics is the study of the detailed spatial structures of atoms and molecules, the properties of matter on an atomic and molecular scale, and the application of results to macroscopic properties of matter. Physical chemistry, another interdisciplinary field, is more often concerned with the physical and thermodynamic properties of matter in bulk. Physical chemistry is usually regarded as a branch of chemistry.

We may use *The Journal of Chemical Physics* to explore chemical physics further. The fact that research men chose this journal for publication and that the editors of the journal did publish their papers would seem to indicate that the articles appearing in them "operationally define" chemical physics. Volume 54 of *The Journal of Chemical Physics* was issued during the first half of 1971. During this interval 711 papers and 166 notes appeared.

The Journal of Chemical Physics lists 30 areas within chemical physics that appeared 20 times or more. Six and one-half per cent were on the kinetics of chemical reactions. Within the top 50 per cent there were also, in descending order, molecular and atomic wave functions, molecular structure and constants, crystalline state, luminescence, liquids, isotope effects, gases, molecular interactions, thermodynamic properties, energy transfer, radiation chemistry, surface phenomena, photochemistry, phase transitions, free radicals, ionization, and polymers. Each of these topics might well be listed in one or several journals devoted to chemistry, physics, physical chemistry, solid-state physics, etc. It is this combination of topics that is characteristic of the area of chemical physics.

The Journal of Chemical Physics indicates 20 tools or methods that were used by chemical physicists in carrying on their research. Twenty-five per cent used electron paramagnetic, nuclear magnetic, or nuclear quadrupolar resonance spectroscopy. Nineteen per cent used infrared, visible, or ultraviolet absorption spectroscopy. The remaining phenomena in the top 75 per cent used as tools were in order: particle scattering, luminescence, mass spectroscopy, atomic and molecular beams, Raman spectroscopy, and microwave absorption spectroscopy.

One should note that all of these methods have been developed since 1910. Five have been developed since 1945.

Thirty per cent of the papers were theoretical, according to their authors, and 9 per cent were theoretical and experimental. Statistical mechanics was employed in 77 per cent of the papers, followed by quantum mechanics, with classical mechanics a distant third. Theoretical analyses of microscopic systems and phenomena play a major role in chemical physics.

Compared to seven years ago (see first edition) the study of luminescence has appeared; Mössbauer spectroscopy has come into use; statistical mechanics was used more often than quantum mechanics.

Other articles in this book discuss in detail some of the major areas in chemical physics.

J. W. McGRATH

Cross-references: CHEMISTRY; MATHEMATICAL PHYSICS; PHYSICAL CHEMISTRY; PHYSICS; THEORETICAL PHYSICS.

CHEMISTRY

Chemistry is the branch of natural science that includes knowledge about the nature, composition, and transformation of matter and the particular structure of substances and compounds. Because every chemical change always involves one or more physical interactions, chemistry is very closely allied to physics. In fact, current knowledge of atomic structure, both nuclear and extranuclear, was derived almost entirely by using physical concepts and techniques.

Material creativity is dramatically manifested in chemistry, because in this field only is man able to synthesize new combinations of elements, substances and materials. Actually, chemists have created in the laboratory several chemical elements (43, 61, 87, and 93 to 105 inclusive) that apparently are not normally present in or on our planet. Even a cursory examination of the concept of isomerism (the existence of two or more different compounds that have identical compositions) yields the conclusion that literally trillions and trillions of different compounds of carbon could be synthesized by man. In fact, there are possible at least 62×10^{12} different compounds (called isomers) all having an identical composition indicated by the formula $C_{40}H_{82}$. This specific combination of atoms is just one of millions of other possible combinations, and some of these would have thousands of isomers. The current chemical literature contains documented evidence for either the existence, or the synthesis by man, of well over a million different compounds of carbon. And carbon is only one of the 105 known chemical elements. No wonder, therefore, that chemical nomenclature and no-

tation is of more than a little concern to modern chemists.

Because of the magnitude and latitude of chemistry, several specialized branches have arisen over the years. Some of these divisions are inorganic, organic, analytical, physical, physical organic, chemical physical, quantum chemistry, food chemistry, geochemistry and astrochemistry.

The chemical industry is now a significant part of our economy. The abundance of coal, petroleum and natural gas is one prominent reason for the growth of this branch of commerce. The continually increasing need for commodities such as structural materials, fabrics, fertilizers, pesticides and pharmaceuticals will enhance the chemical industry. The consumption of sulfuric acid, for instance, has for several decades been considered a significant indication of general industrial activity.

Historical Background The history of alchemy is a fascinating record of man's earliest investigations of matter. However, the alchemist's productivity was seriously hampered by absence of such factors as logical reasoning, unbiased observations and interlaboratory communications. The presence of greed, in some cases, was detrimental.

Robert Boyle and Antoine Lavoisier, two of the earliest proponents of exact quantitative experimentation, exerted profound influences on late eighteenth and early nineteenth century chemistry. Their techniques were mainly physical.

Around the middle of the nineteenth century, Friedrich Kekulé and Archibald Couper independently proposed a system for writing graphic formulas for chemical compounds. Their concepts were based apparently on the notion that physical forces held together the atoms in compounds. About the same time, general acceptance was finally accorded Amedeo Avogadro's hypothesis (proposed about 50 years earlier) which stated that equal volumes of gases at the same temperature and pressure contain equal numbers of molecules. Acceptance of this physical concept and those of Kekulé and Couper was a marked stimulus to nineteenth century chemical research.

During the period 1860-1900 organic chemistry flourished, and hundreds of compounds were prepared, correctly analyzed and identified, and logically classified as to structure and reactivity. And yet, throughout this period, chemists had no knowledge whatsoever about the structure and composition of atoms. Also they had a rather shallow conception of chemical bonding and molecular geometry. The growth of organic chemistry during the nineteenth century is an epic example of the productivity of sound inductive and deductive reasoning.

Some discoveries in physics that greatly accelerated the growth of chemistry are: Henri Becquerel's discovery of radioactivity (1896)

which ultimately led to our current knowledge of atomic nuclear composition and phenomena; the belief in the significance of the electron (Stoney, 1894) which led to the acceptance of the existence of ions; Max Planck's quantum concept (1900); the concepts of probability and the equivalence of mass and energy by Albert Einstein (1905); Niels Bohr's atomic theory (1913); and the duality of the wave and particle character of matter by Louis DeBroglie (1924).

Since 1940 there has been phenomenal growth in the use of spectroscopy in the elucidation of the structure of molecules. The major types of spectra are, in order of seniority, ultraviolet, infrared, nuclear magnetic resonance, electron spin resonance, and Mössbauer. Mass spectrometry is valuable in the determination of molecular as well as atomic structure.

During and following World War II there was considerable investigation of the transuranic elements, and of technetium, francium and promethium in relation to their production and use. All these radioactive elements were produced by extraordinary nuclear reactions, whereas all ordinary chemical reactions involve only the electrons outside the nucleus. Ordinary chemical reactions are, in a sense, extranuclear.

The extension, since 1940, of the techniques of column chromatography to other types such as paper, vapor phase (gas), salting-out, liquid, and thin layer has made much easier the separation of the components of complex mixtures. The use of ion-exchange in the resolution of ionic mixtures and in the removal of ions from solutions has been extended during the past twenty years.

The applications of the molecular orbital, crystal-field and ligand-field concepts have been highly successful in the description of the bonding in and geometry of complex molecules. These concepts have firm physical bases.

The decision made by chemists and physicists in 1961 to use a common standard, carbon-12, to assign atomic masses to the chemical elements is a notable landmark in the history of chemistry.

The discovery in 1962 by Neil Bartlett of a stable compound of xenon, $Xe^+(PtF_6)^-$, was an epic event. Since the discovery of the noble gases during the period, 1894-1900, most chemists had assumed or believed that these elements were either chemically inert or could form only unusual compounds or complexes. Therefore, Bartlett's discovery prompted much activity to produce other noble gas compounds. Several stable binary fluorides, such as XeF_2, XeF_4, XeF_6 and KrF_4 are ordinary solid compounds produced by ordinary chemical reactions. Xenon oxy-compounds such as XeO_3, $XeOF_3$ and $XeOF_4$, although less stable than the binary fluorides, seem to be ordinary compounds.

The importance of chemistry in modern biology, and especially in medicine, has been reemphasized by knowledge of the role of the nucleic acids, such as DNA and RNA, in the genetic scheme. The increased use of chemotherapy in medicine is common knowledge.

Inorganic Chemistry This branch of chemistry is mainly that of all forms of noncarbonaceous matter. Although its potential scope is huge, it has attracted, until recently, much less attention than have organic and physical chemistry. The major minerals (except coal, petroleum and lignite) are essentially inorganic. The use of inorganic compounds, especially those of boron and of nitrogen, as fuels and the growth of nonferrous (other than iron) metallurgy are major developments in inorganic chemistry.

Organic Chemistry This division of chemistry is essentially that of the compounds of carbon. Originally organic chemistry was confined to materials in or from living organisms, probably because nearly every compound either isolated from or produced by a living organism is a compound of carbon. Although there are more compounds of hydrogen than of any other element, the compounds of carbon are next in line. The property of catenation (ability of identical atoms to bond together) is exhibited most extensively by carbon. The hundreds of different carbon-atom skeletons of the thousands of known organic compounds attest this fact. All foods, nearly every fabric, every ordinary commercial fuel, and almost all pharmaceuticals are organic in the sense they contain compounds of carbon.

Analytical Chemistry The qualitative and quantitative determination of the elemental composition of matter resides in the branch of chemistry called analytical chemistry. Any means of determining molecular structure is often called an analytical technique. Until relatively recently most analyses were performed by using specific chemical reactions and techniques in liquid solutions. Recent advances in spectroscopy and other physical techniques have yielded a variety of instruments that greatly facilitate chemical analyses.

Physical Chemistry The quantitative measurements of the properties and behavior of the elements and their compounds are the major concern of the physical chemist. Nearly every technique and concept has been adopted from physics. The development of new chemical concepts follows logical consideration of quantitative data.

The major branches of physical chemistry are spectroscopy, nuclear chemistry, kinetics, thermodynamics, quantum and statistical mechanics, and solution and surface chemistry. Physical organic and inorganic chemistry have gained prominence during the past 25 years.

Biochemistry Investigations of the chemical phenomena in, and the constituent compounds of, living organisms are performed mainly by biochemists. Because every chemical reaction in

any living organism involves compounds of carbon, biochemistry is essentially the application of organic chemistry to investigations of vital systems. However, both physical and analytical chemistry are essential to biochemistry.

DONALD C. GREGG

Cross-references: BOND, CHEMICAL; ELEMENTS; ISOTOPES; MOLECULAR WEIGHT; MOLECULES; PHYSICAL CHEMISTRY; SPECTROSCOPY.

CIRCUITRY*

Basic Concepts As with very many concepts relating to electricity and magnetism, that of the electric circuit very properly may be attributed to James Clerk Maxwell. It was he who took the bold step to ascribing a dual role to the quantity I, which he identified with the current. In perfect conductors, it is the rate of flow of electric charge. In perfect dielectrics, it is proportional to the time rate of change of electricity intensity. Above all, however, it has the typical property that it always flows in closed paths. It is this last property upon which the whole concept of electric circuitry is based.

To be more explicit, consider an elementary circuit composed of a resistor R, a capacitor C, and an inductor L, all three connected together end-to-end so that a closed ring or loop is formed. Open this ring at some point and insert a source of electric energy, such as a battery or an alternator that causes an electric current to flow around the closed loop. At any point in the loop the value of the current is equal to its value at any other point. It is this property of the current that determines the configuration of the circuit. The relation of the current to the electromotive force, or voltage, V generated by the energy source is given by the familiar differential equation

$$V = RI + L\frac{dI}{dt} + \frac{1}{C}\int I\,dt \qquad (1)$$

In a very general sense V may be expressed in the form of the sum of a number of exponentials

$$V = \sum b_m e^{p_m t} \qquad (2)$$

where at least one of the b_m's may be zero. This suggests trying to find solutions of Eq. (1) by expressing the current in the analogous form

$$I = \sum a_n e^{p_n t} \qquad (3)$$

When Eqs. (2) and (3) are substituted in Eq. (1) it is seen that the p_n's must be paired with identical p_m's. This gives a set of equations each

*Author deceased. Article is reprinted from first edition.

having the form:

$$b_m = Ra_m + Lp_m\,a_m + \frac{a_m}{Cp_m} \qquad (4)$$

There will be one such equation for each value of b_m in Eq. (2). They can be solved to give

$$a_m = \frac{b_m}{R + Lp_m + \dfrac{1}{Cp_m}} \qquad (5)$$

As remarked above, at least one of the b_m's may be zero. For this case, the denominator of Eq. (5) must also be zero. Thus, in Eq. (5) there are two values of p_m which apply, namely

$$p_{01} = -\frac{R}{2L} + j\sqrt{\frac{1}{LC} - \frac{R^2}{4L^2}} = \alpha + j\beta \qquad (6)$$

$$p_{02} = -\frac{R}{2L} - j\sqrt{\frac{1}{LC} - \frac{R^2}{4L^2}} = \alpha - j\beta \qquad (7)$$

When these are reintroduced into Eq. (2), the corresponding values of the a_m's are determined by the known conditions existing at a given time, for instance at $t = 0$.

From this approach it is easy to generalize. A periodic voltage is the sum of two exponentials $b_1 e^{j\omega t}$ and $b_1 e^{-j\omega t}$. The resulting current is correspondingly the sum of two exponentials

$$\frac{b_1 e^{j\omega t}}{R + j\omega L + \dfrac{1}{j\omega C}} \quad \text{and} \quad \frac{b_1 e^{-j\omega t}}{R - j\omega L - \dfrac{1}{j\omega C}}$$

Since the second of these is merely the complex conjugate of the first, both for the voltage and the current, it is convenient for circuit analysis to deal only with the first in both cases. However, the convention breaks down in handling nonlinear systems. There it is necessary to carry the conjugate terms throughout the analysis.

A further step in the generalizing process is to regard Eq. (2) as a Fourier series where the p_m's are now the imaginaries $\pm jn\omega_0$. The quantity $R + j\omega L + 1/j\omega C$ is called the impedance Z. Hence, in a very simple way, for each of the exponentials comprising V, we can express Eq. (1) in the form

$$V = IZ \qquad (8)$$

whence

$$I = \frac{V}{Z} \qquad (9)$$

The solution of the elementary single-loop circuit is thus reduced to that of a simple algebraic equation.[1]

The extension to multi-loop networks follows immediately. It is based on the concept that currents always flow in closed loops and that

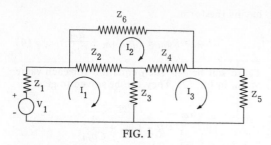

FIG. 1

the values of the loop currents are always the same at any two points in the loop. Figure 1 gives a typical configuration.* This shows a three-loop network where the loops are identified by the three currents, I_1, I_2 and I_3. In applying Eq. (8) to these three loops, it is necessary to take cognizance of the fact that some of the impedance elements, Z_3 for instance, are subjected to the influence of more than one of the individual loop currents. The current I_1 flows down through Z_3 and the current I_3 flows up through it. The net contribution of Z_3 to the right-hand side of Eq. (8) is $(I_1 - I_3)Z_3$. Thus, the complete description of the network of Fig. 1 is given by the three equations, one for each loop, as follows:

$$V_1 = I_1(Z_1 + Z_2 + Z_3) - I_2 Z_2 - I_3 Z_3$$

$$0 = -I_1 Z_2 + I_2(Z_2 + Z_4 + Z_6) - I_3 Z_4 \quad (10)$$

$$0 = -I_1 Z_3 - I_2 Z_4 + I_3(Z_3 + Z_4 + Z_5)$$

Solution yields the currents in the form

$$I_n = \frac{V_{1n}}{Z_{1n}} \quad (11)$$

where Z_{1n} is the transfer impedance from V_1 to the nth current loop. Matrix methods of handling combinations of such networks immediately suggest themselves and these methods have been developed in considerable detail in the literature.[2,3]

Another generalization involves extending Eq. (2) beyond the Fourier series form to the Fourier integral. Thus, instead of Eq. (2) we have

$$V(t) = \frac{1}{2\pi}\int_{-\infty}^{\infty} A(j\omega)e^{j\omega t}\, d\omega \quad (12)$$

where

$$A(j\omega) = \int_{-\infty}^{\infty} V(t)e^{-j\omega t}\, dt \quad (13)$$

*Certain complications occur when circuit networks are of such a topological character that they cannot be represented on a plane surface, as well as when magnetic couplings are involved. However, appropriate extensions of the simple concepts are available for handling these cases.

In this context, Eq. (8) takes the form

$$I(t) = \frac{1}{2\pi}\int_{-\infty}^{\infty} \frac{A(j\omega)}{Z(j\omega)} e^{j\omega t}\, d\omega \quad (14)$$

and here all of the matrix generalizations indicated by Eq. (11) may be carried along. In this environment, many of the fundamental properties of the impedance function may be derived.[4] For example, the fact that a real voltage produces only real currents insures that the real portion of the impedance function is an even function of ω, while the imaginary portion is an odd function. Consideration of the behavior of Eqs. (11), (12) and (13) over the entire complex plane of

$$p = \alpha + j\omega \quad (15)$$

yields further insight into the interesting and useful properties of the impedance function and the entire impedance concept in the environment of Fourier and Laplace transforms.[4,5]

One of the more important of these expresses the current response of a network to any arbitrary voltage in terms of its response to a vanishingly short pulse of voltage. The response may be measured either in the same loop where the voltage is applied or in a different one. In this aspect, Eq. (11) takes the form

$$I(t) = \int_{-\infty}^{\infty} V(\tau)J(t-\tau)\, d\tau \quad (16)$$

where $J(t - \tau)$ is the current resulting from a very short pulse of voltage of unit amplitude injected at time $(t = \tau)$. The integral in Eq. (16) is known as the convolution of $V(\tau)$ and $J(t-\tau)$.

Other important properties derivable from consideration of the whole complex plane involve the properties of active† vs passive networks, stability requirements for active networks, and requirements for physical realization imposed on the impedance elements and their properties.[4,6,7]

Nonlinear Circuits Solution of circuits involving nonlinear relations is in nowhere near as satisfactory a condition. This is not to deny that many of their properties have been discovered and analyzed in rather complete fashion. Those cases where the nonlinearity can be considered as a perturbation on the linear situation have been dealt with satisfactorily. Even in cases involving mixers and modulators, analysis and interpretation is quite straightforward.[8] However, handling of such situations as the buildup and leveling off of transients in self-oscillatory circuits has made little progress since the investigations of such pioneers as Balth Van der Pol.[9]

†Active networks are those that contain energy sources such as electron tubes or transistors.

Systems with Time-varying Elements A number of years ago, interest was aroused in the properties of circuits containing time-varying elements.[10] It was then shown that some of these had amplifying properties. Since no very simple way of producing such elements developed at that time, interest lagged until a few years ago. Now it is realized that modern parametric amplifiers may be handled in this same manner. Moreover, many of the properties of masers and lasers may be interpreted in analogous terms.

Other New Circuit Elements Of special interest in recent years are circuits that transmit signals differently in different directions. Of course, circuits with vacuum tubes had been known to have this property for many years. Under some conditions, circuits with transistors can be given the same property. These all require sources of power to realize their properties. Some configurations such as those of gyrators, isolators and circulators, possess the property without requiring such sources. True, they do demand the presence of a magnetic field but this need not necessarily require power consumption. The initial application of circuits containing isolators was to prevent changes in the neighborhood of a radio antenna from reacting backwards and affecting the properties of circuitry that was feeding signal energy into the antenna. Later applications allowed multistage parametric amplifiers to be built without encountering backward flow of signal energy in sufficient quantities to produce instabilities in the form of self-oscillations.

Physical Embodiments While these advances and developments were taking place in the theoretical analysis and technical applications of circuitry, changes of far-reaching significance were in progress in their physical aspects and in materials composing the impedance elements themselves. Originally, resistors, inductors, and capacitors were distinct and separate entities of rather bulky form and unique appearance. Resistors required long lengths of german silver wire, wound so as to reduce the inductive effects, or else lengths of graphite or of volcanic material that went by the name of lavite. Inductors were coils of wire wound on an insulating form either with air core or a core of magnetic material such as soft iron. Capacitors were multi-layer affairs of metallic plates separated by dielectric material which might be either solid or air. Paper was often used for the dielectric.

Nowadays, complicated circuits consisting of many elements in different combinations are formed by various techniques of depositing, spraying or printing materials of many kinds on sheets or cards. Capacitors are formed with much higher capacitance values compressed into volumes much smaller than ever before. Similar advances have been made with inductors. Very thin films of metallic material have contributed to improvements in reliability, stability and accuracy of resistors also.

Switching circuitry has developed very rapidly in connection with electronic telephone exchanges and digital computers. Circuit elements involve many new devices such as ferreed switches, ferrite memory storage and twistors. Also, it should be noted that optical methods are increasingly being adapted to perform the functions of the older types of circuitry including even such applications as filtering and equalizing. It is probable that the next few years will see remarkable developments and applications along these lines as well as in other directions as yet not even thought of.

F. B. LLEWELLYN

References

1. Carson, J. R., "Electric Circuit Theory and Operational Calculus," New York, McGraw-Hill Book Co., 1926.
2. Guillemin, A. E., "Communication Networks," New York, John Wiley & Sons, 1931; "Theory of Linear Physical Systems," John Wiley & Sons, 1963.
3. Weinberg, Louis, "Network Analysis and Synthesis," New York, McGraw-Hill Book Co., 1962.
4. Bode, H. W., "Network Analysis and Feedback Amplifier Design," New York, John Wiley & Sons, 1945.
5. Brown, W. M., "Analysis of Linear Time-Invariant Systems," New York, McGraw-Hill Book Co., 1963.
6. Nyquist, H., "Regeneration Theory," *Bell System Tech. J.*, **11**, 126–147 (January 1932).
7. Llewellyn, F. B., "Some Fundamental Properties of Transmission Systems," *Proc. I.R.E.*, **40**, 271–283 (March 1952).
8. Llewellyn, F. B., and Peterson, L. C., "The Performance and Measurement of Mixers in Terms of Linear Network Theory," *Proc. I.R.E.*, **33**, No. 7, 458–476 (July 1945).
9. Van der Pol, B., "Selected Scientific Papers," Amsterdam, North-Holland Publishing Co., 1960.
10. Hartley, R. V. L., "Oscillations in Systems with Non-linear Reactance," *Bell System Tech. J.*, **15**, 424–440 (July 1936).

Cross-references: ALTERNATING CURRENTS; CAPACITANCE; CONDUCTIVITY, ELECTRICAL; FEEDBACK; INDUCTANCE; LASER; MASER.

CLOUD PHYSICS

Gross Dynamics of Clouds Atmospheric clouds consist of small drops of water condensed from atmospheric water vapor by cooling of the air below its saturation temperature (dew point). Cooling may be induced by radiation near the surface or by temperature contrasts between the air and underlying surface to form clouds near the surface (fog.) Clouds in the upper atmosphere are mostly caused by more-or-less adiabatic cooling due to lifting of the air. Gradual upward vertical motions induced

by large-scale atmospheric circulations (~100 km or more in diameter) usually lead to stratiform clouds, whereas small-scale turbulent motions usually induced by heating from below may result in bunchy dense clouds called cumulus (~100 meters to several kilometers in diameter and height).

In meteorological work, a thermodynamic chart with pressure and temperature as the ordinate and abscissa, respectively, is often used to relate the presence of clouds to the vertical temperature and humidity structure of the atmosphere at a given radiosonde station. On such a chart, the adiabatic behavior of an imaginary air parcel may be followed in an imaginary lifting process from any level, particularly the surface, to establish the condensation level (cloud base). The atmosphere's vertical stability may also be evaluated based on whether or not the parcel is negatively (stable) or positively buoyant (unstable) with respect to the atmospheric sounding.

A more realistic representation of convection in the atmosphere may be made by allowing mixing in proper proportions between the parcel and its environment. Observations with a properly instrumented aircraft may eventually be used to relate temperature, liquid water content, drop size and vertical velocity in cumulus clouds by a physically consistent turbulent mixing process between cloud and environment. The relationship of cumulus convection to large-scale atmospheric motions and of the smaller-scale mixing process to the microphysical aspects of cloud drop growth and coalescence are understood only in a rough qualitative sense.

Microphysics of Clouds Clouds of liquid drops can be formed in a pure atmosphere free of dust or charged particles only by supersaturations of three or four times that over a flat water surface. So many particles are suspended in the earth's atmosphere that maximum initial supersaturations of the order of 1 per cent are all that is required to start the condensation process, which proceeds without appreciable supersaturation once the drops are past a critical size. Computations of the early stages of drop growth indicate that the initial number of drops is established by the initial upward velocity and the number of extremely active condensation nuclei available. Over the oceans the active nucleus spectrum is dominated by sea salt particles of the order of 1μ in diameter (giant salt nuclei).

As a cloud grows, its top may cool below freezing. The cloud drops do not freeze immediately on reaching a temperature of $0°C$ but tend to supercool to considerably lower temperatures before freezing. Just as condensation is induced with difficulty in pure air, similarly freezing of pure water is also helped by the presence of impurities.

Particles in the air itself may become nuclei for sublimation (condensation from the vapor to the ice phase). Similarly particles in the cloud drops may induce freezing at certain temperatures of supercooling. The results of laboratory experiments indicate that large water samples or drops tend to freeze at higher supercooling temperatures than small drops. The size dependence of average freezing temperature has been explained as a sampling effect based on the greater probability of having an active nucleus in a large volume.

Ice-forming nuclei producing ice crystals at temperatures warmer than $-20°C$ have a concentration of the order of one per liter of air. Therefore cloud tops as a rule do not become glaciated until the temperature of $-20°C$ is reached.

The Formation of Rain A cloud consisting of drops less than 40μ in diameter is quite stable in the sense that they grow only by condensation, not by coalescence. Recent work on the aerodynamics of small droplets indicates that collision of droplets less than 36μ in diameter is impossible. The collision efficiency of clouds consisting of droplets greater than 40μ in diameter rises rapidly as the drop size and drop concentration increase.

The presence of relatively few ice crystals in a supercooled cloud causes it to become unstable regardless of the drop size, since ice crystals at the temperature of supercooled water have a lower vapor pressure. Thus the ice crystals grow at the expense of drops and eventually fall through the cloud growing by coalescence.

Cloud Seeding and Weather Modification The marginal stability of clouds, consisting of large numbers of small drops, has led to many natural cloud modification experiments. Most of these experiments have been aimed at locally increasing precipitation from supercooled clouds by introducing a relatively small concentration of ice crystals or ice-forming nuclei to increase the rate of rain or snow formation.

Early cloud seeding experiments were done with dry ice pellets which leave an obvious trail of ice crystals as they fall. Seeding of supercooled stratiform clouds from aircraft by this method resulted in holes obviously shaped like the airplane's path configuration from which light snow showers were observed. The effect, although obvious, was not particularly useful.

Silver iodide released in the form of smoke was later introduced as a seeding agent because of the similarity of its crystal structure to that of ice, its effectiveness in ice nucleation as proven in laboratory experiments, and its relative ease of application. Other ice-nucleating agents, both natural and artificial, have been and are still being investigated in the laboratory.

Various methods of applying silver iodide nuclei have been explored. The continuously operated smoke generator used for application over a large area has been operated on the ground, but in recent years has been mostly applied with aircraft because of greater flexibility

and control in application. More recently developed methods of delivery are pyrotechnics (smoke bombs) to be dropped by aircraft and rockets and artillary shells to be fired from the ground. These methods are used to concentrate silver iodide in a particular towering cumulus cloud.

The haphazard efforts of individual commercial cloud seeders have given way to the more carefully designed, government-financed, statistical experiments because of the difficulties involved in untangling the effects of natural variability of precipitation from cloud-seeding effects. The picture has been further complicated by statistical evidence of inadvertently induced rainfall related to urban air pollution. The area type of cloud seeding has shown some promise in clouds formed over mountain ranges in contrast to negative results over level terrain. Carefully designed experiments on individual towering cumulus clouds seeded by pyrotechnics and monitored by radar have yielded statistically significant dynamic development (increase in size and intensity of upward motion).

The overseeding of severe thunderstorms with rockets and shells has been tried to suppress hail. The heavy seeding is designed to freeze most of the supercooled water drops before they can be collected by small hail particles to form large ones. Although this method is being used operationally in some areas, the statistics on effectiveness are not yet adequate.

Attempts to increase the coalescence of cloud drops to form rain in warm clouds (above freezing) have been made also. The seeding agents for this purpose are salt or urea particles applied at cloud base to increase the size of the initially formed cloud drops or large water drops dropped in at cloud tops to promote coalescence by a sort of chain reaction. The latter process is supposed to occur when drops grow larger than 0.9 cm in diameter, become unstable, and break up, thus increasing the number of large rain drops at the expense of the cloud-sized drops. The restriction of such seeding to relatively small clouds has made the statistical verification problem considerably more difficult and marginal.

The significant effects achieved by seeding individual cumulus clouds have led to seeding of hurricanes to weaken them. Both the statistics and physical logic of these experiments are still too weak to justify routine operational seeding.

Even the use of black topping on the earth's surface is being considered as a way of stimulating cumulus convection by increased solar heating of the surface to increase rainfall along normally arid coastal regions.

The case for purposeful or inadvertent weather modification by the effect of small particles on clouds is somewhat stronger than it was several years ago. Therefore, legal problems have arisen concerning possible destructive effects of weather modification efforts in spite of the marginal and tentative nature of the positive results. However, weather modification is so inextricably intertwined with weather forecasting that our ability to do the former is, at best, no better than our skill in the latter.

JOSEPH LEVINE

References

Battan, L. J., "Cloud Physics and Cloud Seeding," Garden City, N.Y., Doubleday & Co., Inc., 1962.

Battan, L. J., "The Thunderstorm," New York, Signet Science Library, 1964.

Fletcher, N. H., "The Physics of Rainclouds," Cambridge, Cambridge University Press, 1962.

Mason, B. J., "Clouds, Rain, and Rainmaking," Cambridge, Cambridge University Press, 1962.

Mason, B. J., "The Physics of Clouds," London, Oxford University Press, 1971.

Cross-references: CONDENSATION, METEOROLOGY, THERMODYNAMICS.

COHERENCE

Basic Definitions The term coherence as it is used in electromagnetic radiation studies is best explained by a discussion of Young's interference experiment. Referring to Fig. 1, we consider a self-luminous radiating source S (like a mercury arc lamp) placed a distance l_1 from an opaque screen A. In the screen A two pinhole openings P_1 and P_2 are made a distance d apart. The radiation passing through the pinholes impinges upon and is recorded upon a photographic plate B a distance l_2 from screen A.

If l_1 is a very large distance from A (say $l_1 \gg bd/\bar{\lambda}$, $\bar{\lambda}$ being the average radiation wavelength) and the spectral width of the radiation is made very narrow by filtering, then the fringes observed on B in the neighborhood of O will be very sharp, and we say that the radiation fields impinging upon P_1 and P_2 are very coherent. This is in accord with our usual notions about the radiation from a point source. If, on the other hand, we use the same source and l_1 is taken to be small (say of the order of b) and the dimension b is large compared to d then fringes will not be observed on B, and we say that the radiation fields impinging upon P_1 and P_2 are incoherent. Again this is to be expected since in this case we observe the radiation just as it emerges from the lamp. As the distance l_1 is increased from the order of b, faint fringes will begin to appear upon B. As l_1 increases, the fringes will become progressively stronger until they become very pronounced when $l_1 \gg bd/\bar{\lambda}$. The intermediate states, when the fringes are present but not necessarily very strong, are termed states of partial coherence. This experiment may be performed using a variety of sources. The experiment, as we have empha-

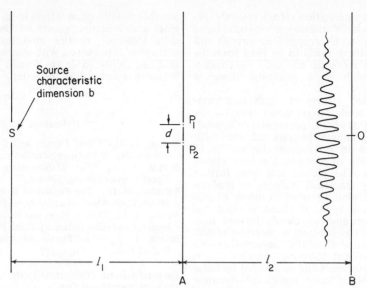

FIG. 1. Young's interference experiment.

sized, measures the coherence of the radiation when it reaches P_1 and P_2; it does not measure the coherence of the source.

A quantitative measure of the fringe strength called the visibility $\mathcal{V}$, was given by Michelson.[7] It is defined as

$$\mathcal{V} = \frac{I_{\max} - I_{\min}}{I_{\max} + I_{\min}} \qquad (1)$$

where $I_{\max}$ is the maximum intensity recorded in the vicinity of O and $I_{\min}$ is the minimum intensity. $\mathcal{V}$ varies between 0 and 1 and, roughly, we term radiation fields at two points coherent when $\mathcal{V} = 1$ (strong fringes) and incoherent (no fringes) when $\mathcal{V} = 0$.

In the above introduction, d was held fixed but it is most important to realize that the fringe visibility at O is a function of the spacing d and that $\mathcal{V}$ may be close to 1 for one spacing of d and close to zero for another spacing of d. For example, if we fix l_1, we will generally decrease the visibility of fringes at O by making d larger (more precisely it will decrease and then increase in a succession of oscillations with the successive peaks being reduced in magnitude.) The visibility may be thus viewed as a measure of the correlation (coherence) between the radiation at P_1 and the radiation at P_2. To give a more precise definition of coherence, Wolf[9] considered the correlation function $\Gamma(P_1, P_2, \tau)$, commonly termed the mutual coherence function, defined as

$$\Gamma(P_1, P_2, \tau) = \langle V(P_1, t + \tau) V^*(P_2, t) \rangle \qquad (2)$$

where $V(P_1, t)$ is the radiation field at P_1 and time $t + \tau$ (in a scalar approximation), V^* is the radiation field at P_2 at time t and the brackets $\langle \rangle$ denote a time average. For convenience Wolf

used a complex notation (V^* is the complex conjugate of V), but this need not concern us here.

It can be shown that the magnitude of the normalized form of $\Gamma(P_1, P_2, \tau)$, $\gamma(P_1, P_2, \tau)$, where

$$\gamma(P_1, P_2, \tau) = \frac{\Gamma(P_1, P_2, \tau)}{\sqrt{\Gamma(P_1, P_1, 0)\Gamma(P_2, P_2, 0)}} \qquad (3)$$

is equal to the visibility $\mathcal{V}$ when the radiation is quasi-monochromatic (narrow spectral width) and all path lengths in the problem are small compared to $c/\Delta v$ (where c is the velocity of light and Δv is a characteristic spectral spread). In this case it is appropriate to fix τ at some value τ_0 usually taken to be zero.

The definition given by Eq. (2) was intended to consider polychromatic fields in addition to the quasi-monochromatic fields so often studied using the visibility $\mathcal{V}$. Beran and Parrent[1] have shown that the full function $\Gamma(P_1, P_2, \tau)$ is, in principle, measurable by an extension of the techniques used in a Young's interference experiment. Modern discussions of coherence now center on the calculation and measurement of the mutual coherence function $\Gamma(P_1, P_2, \tau)$. For calculation it is convenient to note that Wolf[9] has shown that $\Gamma(P_1, P_2, \tau)$ satisfies the pair of wave equations

$$\nabla_i^2 \Gamma(P_1, P_2, \tau) = \frac{1}{c^2} \frac{\partial^2 \Gamma(P_1, P_2, \tau)}{\partial \tau^2} \quad (i = 1, 2) \quad (4)$$

The vector properties of the electromagnetic field may easily be introduced into the mutual coherence function. In general one must consider the tensor

$$\mathcal{E}_{ij}(P_1, P_2, \tau) = \langle E_i(P_1, t + \tau)E_j^*(P_2, t)\rangle \quad (5)$$

where $E_k(P_s, t)$ is the kth component of the electric field at the space point P_s and time t. In general, this function has proved most useful in the study of polarization effects for fields in which the radiation has a principal direction of propagation. The form of $\mathcal{E}_{ij}(P_1, P_2, \tau)$ has, however, been derived for the radiation in a black body cavity.

The above considerations have been for radiation fields that are stationary in time. That is, the statistical parameters, as opposed to the detailed structure of the radiation field, are independent of the absolute scale of time. For fields in which this is not true we must introduce the concept of an ensemble average (similar to that used in statistical mechanics). The mutual coherence function $\mathcal{E}_{ij}(P_1, P_2, \tau)$ must be replaced by the function $\mathcal{E}_{ij}{}^E(P_1, t_1; P_2, t_2)$ defined as

$$\mathcal{E}_{ij}{}^E(P_1, t_1; P_2, t_2) = \overline{E_i(P_1, t_1)E_j(P_2, t_2)} \quad (6)$$

where the overbar denotes an average over an ensemble of systems.

Higher-order Coherence Functions and Quantum Aspects As the concept of coherence grew and the statistical formulation of the theory came more into the fore it was realized that a two-point moment like $\mathcal{E}_{ij}(P_1, P_2, \tau)$ or $\mathcal{E}_{ij}{}^E(P_1, t_1; P_2, t_2)$ was inadequate to completely describe the radiation field. Two fields could have the same mutual coherence function and yet differ in the statistical content of the field. To completely describe the field, it was necessary to consider higher-order moments like $L_{ijkl}(P_1, t_1; P_2, t_2; P_3, t_3; P_4, t_4)$ defined as

$$L_{ijkl}(P_1, t_1; P_2, t_2; P_3, t_3; P_4, t_4) =$$

$$\overline{E_i(P_1, t_1)E_j(P_2, t_2)E_k(P_3, t_3)E_t(P_4, t_4)} \quad (7)$$

and, in fact, for a complete description it was necessary to consider the probability density function $P[E_i(P_1, t_1)]$ defined roughly as the probability of the occurrence of a particular realization of the field.

There are a number of problems that require consideration of higher-order moments. These moments are necessary in intensity interferometry, the study of laser radiation and the study of the radiation from turbulent gases. The measurement of the contracted fourth-order moment

$$R_{ik}(P_1, P_2, 0) = \langle |E_i(P_1, t)|^2 |E_k(P_2, t)|^2 \rangle \quad (8)$$

(called intensity interferometry) has received considerable attention since it entailed consideration of the quantum aspects of the electromagnetic field. This moment may be thought of as the correlation of instantaneous intensities

$$I_i(P_1, t) \equiv |E_i(P_1, t)|^2$$

at two points and was originally studied as an alternate method to the measurement of $\Gamma(P_1, P_2, 0)$ for determining the angular diameter of visible and radio stars.[4,5] In measuring $\Gamma(P_1, P_2, 0)$, we may use the Young's interference experiment described above; the quantum nature of the field rarely explicitly enters since averaging times are usually long enough to permit a classical analysis. To measure R_{ik}, however, we need to correlate the two signals $I_i(P_1, t)$ and $I_k(P_2, t)$ which are recorded using photomultipliers or coincidence counters. Since the relationship between the impinging electric field and the ejected photoelectron is a statistical one, classical considerations did not suffice for a deep understanding of the problem or for consideration of the very important signal-to-noise problems resulting from inadequate averaging times.

A quantum field formalism for coherence theory has been studied by a number of authors in the last decade. Klauder and Sudarshan[6] summarize and reference most of the basic work. Optical correlation phenomena have been studied extensively and particular consideration has been given to the fundamental differences between laser light and thermal light. Laser models have been developed using coherence concepts. In addition it is possible to study the basic interaction between light and matter from a coherence point of view. For example, the Kramers-Heisenberg dispersion formula may be generalized to include the effects of partially coherent incident electromagnetic fields, and spontaneous radiation may be studied when the initial atomic states are correlated.

Applications (Measurement of the Angular Diameter of Stars) Coherence theory is of great use in the treatment of imaging and mapping problems. It is especially convenient for treating problems involving the effects of the turbulent atmosphere on resolution.[2] To present the reader with a definite example of the use of the coherence theory formalism, we will conclude this brief discussion with an outline of the measurement of the angular diameter of visible stars.

Let us suppose that the source in Fig. 1 is a visible star so that l_1 is many light-years. There is no telescope big enough to resolve any star, and to make direct measurements of the angular diameter of a star, Michelson introduced the use of interference experiments to essentially give one a bigger effective aperture.

For purposes of visible star measurement we can replace the star of diameter D by a circular disk of diameter D lying in a plane parallel to A. The radiation leaving the star is assumed to be incoherent so that for all points on the disk we may take $\Gamma(P_1, P_2, 0) = c\delta(P_1 - P_2)$. Using Eq. (4) this allows us to solve for $\Gamma(P_1, P_2, 0)$ on the earth (screen A) if we filter the starlight to insure the validity of the quasi-monochromatic approximation. We find

$$\Gamma(P_1, P_2, 0) = \text{const.} \frac{J_1\left[\dfrac{\bar{k}dD/2}{l_1}\right]}{\dfrac{\bar{k}dD/2}{l_1}} \quad (10)$$

where $\bar{k}$ is the average wave number of the light and J_1 is a first-order Bessel function.

If we define the angular diameter of the star as $\theta = D/l_1$, we see that J_1 equals zero when $\theta = 1.22\bar{\lambda}/d$, where $\bar{\lambda} = 2\pi/\bar{k}$. When J_1 equals zero, there are no fringes on the screen B. Hence to find the angular diameter of the star, we need only increase d from zero, when there will be high contrast fringes, to the separation d when there are no fringes. Putting this latter value into our expression for θ gives us the angular diameter of the star. The effects of turbulence may be taken into account in this problem if Eq. (4) is generalized to include a variable index of refraction.

Basic References For a fundamental treatment of coherence theory we refer the reader to the following basic texts: Born and Wolf,[2] O'Neill,[8] Beran and Parrent,[1] Klauder and Sudarshan.[6]

MARK J. BERAN

References

1. Beran, M., and Parrent, G., Jr., "Theory of Partial Coherence," Englewood Cliffs, N.J., Prentice Hall, 1964.
2. Beran, M., and Whitman, A., *J. Opt. Soc.*, **61**, 1044 (1971).
3. Born, M., and Wolf, E., "Principles of Optics," London, Pergamon Press, 1959.
4. Hanbury Brown, R., and Twiss, R., *Proc. Royal Soc. London Ser. A*, **242**, 300 (1957).
5. Hanbury Brown, R., and Twiss, R., *Proc. Royal Soc. London Ser. A*, **243**, 291 (1957).
6. Klauder, J., and Sudarshan, E., "Fundamentals of Quantum Optics," New York, W. J. Benjamin, 1968.
7. Michelson, A., *Phil. Mag.* (5), **30**, 1 (1890).
8. O'Neill, E., "Introduction to Statistical Optics," Reading, Mass., Addison-Wesley, 1963.
9. Wolf, E., *Proc. Royal Soc. London Ser. A*, **230**, 246 (1955).

Cross-references: INTERFERENCE AND INTERFEROMETRY, LASER, MASER.

COLLISIONS OF PARTICLES

Introduction Scattering experiments provide the principal technique by which physicists attempt to understand the structure and interactions of matter on a microscopic scale. Scattering theory provides the basis for analyzing and interpreting scattering experiments.

A description of the development of scattering theory may be divided into several topics.

The oldest and simplest branch of scattering theory is that of potential scattering, or scattering of two particles which interact through a *local potential*[1]. Potential scattering was studied extensively in the first two decades following the development of quantum mechanics in the analysis of elastic scattering of particles by atoms and of nucleon-nucleon scattering. The latter topic, in particular, led to the introduction of an elaborate theory of scattering by noncentral interactions[2]. The development of nuclear physics, with the observation of resonance reactions, indicated the need for more general descriptions of scattering. The resulting theory of resonance reactions[3,4] has leaned only rather lightly on the details of the Schrödinger equation. Quantum field theory was developed to describe electromagnetic phenomena.[5] Of major importance in the development of scattering theory was the introduction of renormalization techniques into FIELD THEORY.[6]

It might be claimed that modern scattering theory began with the integral equation formulation of Lippmann and Schwinger[7] and the introduction of S-matrix theory by Heisenberg[8] and others[9]. This work has stimulated much of the development of theoretical physics in the last decade. Of particular significance are the clarification of the study of rearrangement collisions and the development of the so-called dispersion theoretic techniques.

The Scattering Cross Section The properties of scattering interactions are usually expressed most conveniently in terms of the *scattering cross section*. To define this term, we consider the following scattering experiment: A beam of particles (called *beam particles*) is directed on a scatterer consisting of *target particles*. As a result of collisions between beam and target particles, there are particles which emerge from the reactions (called *reaction products*) and these are detected in *particle detectors*. To describe this quantitatively, we suppose that the scatterer contains N_t target particles and that this is uniformly illuminated by a flux F_B (expressed as the number of beam particles per unit area per unit time arriving at the target) of beam particles. We suppose also that the scatterer is sufficiently small that the beam is negligibly attenuated in passing through it. Then, if there are δN_s scattering interactions per unit time which lead to detected particles, we define the scattering cross section $\delta\sigma$ as[10]

$$\delta\sigma = \frac{\delta N_s}{N_t F_B} \quad (1)$$

In the limit that the detectors subtend very small solid angles, as seen from the target, we define the *differential* scattering cross section $d\sigma$. When a single detector, subtending a solid angle $\delta\Omega$, is used to define $\delta\sigma$, we may define the cross section per unit solid angle as

$$\frac{d\sigma}{d\Omega} = \lim_{\delta\Omega\to 0} \frac{\delta\sigma}{\delta\Omega} \qquad (2)$$

The total scattering cross section σ is obtained by summing $\delta\sigma$ over all scattering events:

$$\sigma = \sum \delta\sigma \qquad (3)$$

[Equation (3) does not exist for scattering by a coulomb force.]

The scattering cross section may be expressed in terms of the square of the magnitude of a scattering amplitude (or S-matrix, or T-matrix element) and is completely described as a function of the momenta and internal states of the particles in the initial and final states. Thus, for the two particles prior to collision[11] we may take the momenta p_1 and p_2 and the internal state quantum numbers s_1 and s_2 as variables. (For example, s_1 and s_2 may describe spin orientation, isotopic spin, etc. For colliding molecules these variables will describe vibrational, rotational and electronic states). We may suppose there to be μ particles in the final state following the collision and specify this state by the momenta and internal variables $k_1, \cdots k_\mu$, $s_1' \cdots s_\mu'$. The scattering cross section may be expressed in terms of these variables. Because of symmetries, the number of variables required to describe $\delta\sigma$ may ordinarily be reduced. The most commonly encountered of these symmetries are: (1) energy and momentum conservation; (2) rotational invariance; (3) the Lorentz invariance of the scattering cross section $\delta\sigma$.[12] The Lorentz invariance of $\delta\sigma$ permits one to describe the scattering in the *barycentric* coordinate system—the coordinate system in which the total momentum of the interacting particles is zero.

This may be illustrated for the special case for which there are only two particles in the initial and two in the final state and an average has been performed over all spin orientations. Then the twelve components of p_1, p_2, k_1 and k_2 may be replaced by only two variables. These may be taken, for example, as the barycentric energy and angle between p_1 and k_1. Convenient variables in relativistic analyses are often chosen to be the Lorentz invariants

$$s \equiv (p_1 + p_2)^2 = (k_1 + k_2)^2$$
$$t \equiv (p_1 - k_1)^2 = (p_2 - k_2)^2 \qquad (4)$$

where we have written p_1, etc., for the four-component energy-momentum vector.

Potential Scattering We briefly illustrate the discussion of the preceding section with the example of nonrelativistic scattering by a local central potential $V(r)$. The SCHRÖDINGER EQUATION for scattering in the barycentric coordinate system is

$$[\nabla_r^2 + \kappa^2 - v(r)]\psi_\kappa^+(\mathbf{r}) = 0 \qquad (5)$$

Here $\hbar\kappa$ is the momentum of particle "1" in the barycentric system and $v(r) = \frac{2M_r}{\hbar^2} V(r)$, with M_r the reduced mass of the two particles. In the limit of large separation r between the particles the wavefunction ψ_κ^+ has the asymptotic form [our notation is such that we represent a unit vector in the direction of κ by $\hat{\kappa}$]

$$\psi_\kappa^+(\mathbf{r}) \to (2\pi)^{-3/2}\left[e^{i\kappa\cdot\mathbf{r}} + \frac{e^{i\kappa r}}{r}f(\hat{\kappa}\cdot\hat{\mathbf{r}})\right] \qquad (6)$$

Here $f(\hat{\kappa}\cdot\hat{\mathbf{r}})$ is the scattering amplitude for scattering particle "1" from the direction $\hat{\kappa}$ into the direction $\hat{\mathbf{r}}$. The corresponding cross section per unit solid angle is

$$\frac{d\sigma}{d\Omega} = |f(\hat{\kappa}\cdot\hat{\mathbf{r}})|^2 \qquad (7)$$

The wave function ψ_κ^+ may be expanded into partial waves as follows:

$$\psi_\kappa^+(\mathbf{r}) = \sum_{l=0}^{\infty} \frac{(2l+1)}{4\pi\kappa r} P_l(\hat{\kappa}\cdot\hat{\mathbf{r}})i^l e^{i\delta l} w_l(\kappa;r) \qquad (8)$$

Here P_l is the Legendre polynomial of order l, δ_l is the scattering phase shift [see Eq. (10) below], and $w_l(\kappa;r)$ satisfies the differential equation [Eq. (13)]

$$\left[\frac{d^2}{dr^2} + \kappa^2 - \frac{l(l+1)}{r^2} - v(r)\right]w_l = 0 \qquad (9)$$

This is to be integrated subject to the condition that w_l is regular at $r = 0$. For large r, w_l has the asymptotic form

$$w_l(\kappa;r) \to \sqrt{\frac{2}{\pi}}\sin\left(\kappa r - \frac{\pi l}{2} + \delta_l\right) \qquad (10)$$

It is Eq. (10) which permits the determination of the phase shift δ_l. The quantity

$$S_l(\kappa) = \exp[2i\delta_l(\kappa)] \qquad (11)$$

is an eigenvalue of Heisenberg's S-matrix.[8]

For scattering by noncentral forces, the potential $V(\mathbf{r}, \mathbf{S}_1, \mathbf{S}_2)$ is a function of $\mathbf{r}$ (and sometimes the orbital angular momentum operator) and the spin operators $\mathbf{S}_1$ and $\mathbf{S}_2$ of the two colliding particles (if either has no spin, we consider its spin operator to be zero). Spin eigenfunctions $u(\nu_1, \nu_2)$ may be introduced as depending on the orientations ν_1 and ν_2 of the respective spins of magnitudes S_1 and S_2. Then the wave function $\psi_{\kappa,\nu_1,\nu_2}^+$ is to be labeled with the initial spin orientations ν_1 and ν_2. The asymptotic form corresponding to Eq. (6) is

$$\psi_{\kappa,\nu_1,\nu_2}^+ \to (2\pi)^{-3/2}\left[e^{i\kappa\cdot\mathbf{r}}u(\nu_1, \nu_2)\right.$$
$$\left. + \frac{e^{i\kappa r}}{r}\sum_{\nu_1',\nu_2'}\langle\nu_1', \nu_2'|f(\hat{\kappa},\hat{\mathbf{r}})|\nu_1, \nu_2\rangle u(\nu_1', \nu_2')\right]$$
$$(12)$$

Here $\langle \nu_1', \nu_2' | f(\hat{k}, \hat{r}) | \nu_1 \nu_2 \rangle$ is the scattering amplitude for scattering to a final spin orientation ν_1', ν_2'. The cross section per unit solid angle is in this case

$$\frac{d\sigma}{d\Omega} = |\langle \nu_1', \nu_2' | f(\hat{k}, \hat{r}) | \nu_1, \nu_2 \rangle|^2 \qquad (13)$$

For an unpolarized initial state, corresponding to a uniform mixture of the $(2S_1 + 1)(2S_2 + 1)$ spin states, the cross section for scattering particle "1" into the direction $\hat{r}$ with any spin orientation is

$$\frac{d\bar{\sigma}}{d\Omega} = \frac{1}{(2S_1 + 1)(2S_2 + 1)}$$

$$\times \sum_{\nu_1', \nu_2'} \sum_{\nu_1, \nu_2} |\langle \nu_1', \nu_2' | f | \nu_1, \nu_2 \rangle|^2 \quad (14)$$

where the sums extend over all spin orientations.

Following scattering by noncentral forces, the particles will in general have preferred spin orientations, or be *polarized*. When, for example, particle "1" has spin one-half with a spin operator σ_1, we define its polarization vector $\mathbf{P}(\nu_1, \nu_2)$ by the equation

$$\mathbf{P}(\nu_1, \nu_2) = \left\{ \sum_{\nu_1'', \nu_1', \nu_2'} [\langle \nu_1'', \nu_2' | f | \nu_1, \nu_2 \rangle]^* \right.$$

$$\times \langle \nu_1'' | \sigma_1 | \nu_1' \rangle \langle \nu_1', \nu_2' | f | \nu_1, \nu_2 \rangle \Big\}$$

$$\times \left\{ \sum_{\nu_1', \nu_2'} |\langle \nu_1', \nu_2' | f | \nu_1, \nu_2 \rangle|^2 \right\}^{-1}$$

$$(15)$$

For an unpolarized initial state, the polarization is

$$\bar{\mathbf{P}} = \frac{1}{(2S_1 + 1)(2S_2 + 1)} \sum_{\nu_1, \nu_2} \mathbf{P}(\nu_1, \nu_2) \quad (16)$$

The study of polarization following scattering has provided an important tool for analyzing nuclear and elementary particle reactions.[14,15] In particular, the role of noncentral interactions in nucleon-nucleon scattering has been studied in great detail.[16]

Formal Scattering Theory To describe a general scattering reaction Lippmann and Schwinger[7,17] introduced a scattering matrix $\mathcal{T}_{ba}$ to describe scattering from an initial state χ_a to a final state χ_b[18]. This is defined as

$$\mathcal{T}_{ba} = (\chi_b, V\psi_a^+) \qquad (17)$$

where ψ_a^+ is the steady-state wave function for the event and V is the scattering interaction. Since momentum is conserved for an isolated scattering, we may write

$$\mathcal{T}_{ba} = \delta(\mathbf{P}_b - \mathbf{P}_a)T_{ba} \qquad (18)$$

where $\mathbf{P}_a$ and $\mathbf{P}_b$ are the total momenta of the particles in the initial and final states, respectively, and T_{ba} is defined only for states b and a corresponding to $\mathbf{P}_b = \mathbf{P}_a$.

The scattering cross section $\delta\sigma$ [Eq. (1)] is expressed in terms of T_{ba} as[12]

$$\delta\sigma = \frac{(2\pi)^4}{v_{rel}} \sum_b \delta(\mathbf{P}_b - \mathbf{P}_a)\delta)(E_b - E_a)|T_{ba}|^2$$

$$(19)$$

Here v_{rel} is the relative velocity of beam and target particles, E_b and E_a are the respective total energies of the particles in states b and a, and the sum on b extends over those states which lead to the reaction products striking the detectors and thus to register an event. We emphasize that Eq. (19) is Lorentz invariant.[12]

The Heisenberg S-matrix[8] is given by the expression

$$S_{ba} = \delta_{ba} - 2\pi i\delta(E_b - E_a) \mathcal{T}_{ba} \qquad (20)$$

where δ_{ba} is a Dirac δ-function. The S-matrix is unitary, so

$$\sum_b S_{cb}^\dagger S_{ba} = \delta_{ca} \qquad (21)$$

On substituting Eq. (20) into this, we obtain the equivalent expression of unitarity

$$i[\mathcal{T}_{ca} - \mathcal{T}_{ca}^\dagger] = 2\pi \sum_b \mathcal{T}_{cb}^\dagger \delta(E_b - E_a)\mathcal{T}_{ba}$$

$$(22)$$

which is defined only for states c and a on the same *energy shell* (corresponding to $E_c = E_a$).

The fundamental problem of scattering theory is to determine the $\mathcal{T}$-matrix on the energy shell (or, equivalently, the S-matrix). The first step in doing this is to make use of general symmetry principles (such as Lorentz invariance) to limit the functional forms allowed. Following this a dynamical principle is needed. Such dynamical principles (reviewed in Chapters 5 and 10 of reference[10]) have been proposed in a great variety of forms including integral equations, variational principles, and conditions of functional analyticity.

Scattering from Composite Systems Scattering from systems composed of two or more particles is generally very complex. This is in part due to the occurrence of sequential interactions, in part due to the dynamics of the scattering system, and in part due to the possibility of rearrangement phenomena.

Description of sequential interactions can be given in terms of the multiple scattering and optical model equations.[19]

Rearrangement collisions (i.e., collisions in which bound particles rearrange themselves) have been studied extensively following the development of formal scattering theory. Much of

the early work[20] was stimulated by the observance of apparent paradoxes. Later work has tended to be directed toward specific applications. The formulation of Feshbach, for example, has led to a variety of applications in nuclear and atomic physics.[21] The eikonal approximation has been used in the description of rearrangement collisions of slow ions, atoms, and molecules.[22]

The careful description of three-body scattering given by Fadeev[23] has led to active study of this and related phenomena.[24]

Variational principles have also been developed for application to several-body collisions.[25]

Field Theory Quantum field theory was originally developed to describe electromagnetic phenomena. It was applied in a promising context during the 1930's to β-decay and to the meson theory of nuclear forces. The great optimism following the development of renormalization theory[6] faded quickly for want of adequate mathematical techniques for handling strong interactions. The most successful applications to strong interactions were the semiphenomenological calculations of Chew and others.[5,26]

An interesting and novel attempt to revive field theory has been initiated by Weinberg.[27]

S-matrix Theory Heisenberg suggested in 1946[8] that a proper quantum theory of scattering would deal with only observable quantities such as the S-matrix and should not require off-the-energy-shell matrix elements of such quantities as $\mathcal{T}$ [Eq. (18)]. Considerable impetus for this point of view has been given by the development of *dispersion theory*, following early suggestions of Wigner and others.[28] The first attempt at a systematic formulation of a dispersion relation within the context of quantum field theory was made by Gell-Mann, Goldberger, and Thirring.[29] Further development followed applications of formal scattering theory to quantum field theory.[30] The development of the Mandelstam representation[31] provided an important step toward obtaining a "dynamical principle." A further important step was the proposal by Chew and Frautschi and Blankenbecler and Goldberger,[33] who suggested that the only singularities of the S-matrix are those required by the unitarity condition [Eq. (22)] and that families of particles should be associated with Regge Trajectories.[34]

KENNETH M. WATSON

References

1. The early development of scattering theory is well described in the classic work of Mott, N. F., and Massey, H. S. W., "The Theory of Atomic Collisions," Oxford, Clarendon Press, 1933.
2. Rarita, W., and Schwinger, J., *Phys. Rev.*, **59**, 436 (1941). Christian, R. S., and Hart, E. W., *Phys. Rev.*, **77**, 441 (1950). Christian, R. S., and Noyes, H. P., *Phys. Rev.*, **79**, 85 (1950).
3. Breit, G., and Wigner, E. P., *Phys. Rev.*, **49**, 519, 642 (1936).
4. Wigner, E. P., *Phys. Rev.*, **70**, 15, 606 (1946); Wigner, E. P., and Eisenbud, L., *Phys. Rev.*, **72**, 29 (1947).
   Sachs, R. G., "Nuclear Physics," Reading, Mass., Addison-Wesley Publishing Co., 1953.
5. See, for example, Mandl, F., "Introduction to Quantum Field Theory," New York, Interscience Publishers, 1959. The older work is admirably described in G. Wentzel, "Quantum Theory of Fields," New York, Interscience Publishers, 1949.
6. Feynman, R. P., *Phys. Rev.*, **76**, 749 (1949). Dyson, F. J., *Phys. Rev.*, **75**, 486 (1949). Tomonaga, S., *Progr. Theoret. Phys. (Kyoto)*, **1**, 27 (1946). Schwinger, J., *Phys. Rev.*, **74**, 1439 (1948).
7. Lippmann, B., and Schwinger, J., *Phys. Rev.*, **79**, 469 (1950).
8. Heisenberg, W., *Z. Naturforsch.*, **1**, 608 (1946).
9. Wheeler, J. A., *Phys. Rev.*, **52**, 1107 (1937). Møller, C., *Kgl. Danske Videnskab. Selskab, Mat. Fys. Medd.*, **23**, 1 (1948).
10. This is a much abbreviated version of the discussion given in Ch. 3 of Goldberger, M. L., and Watson, K. M., "Collision Theory," New York, John Wiley & Sons, Inc., 1964.
11. The case that more than two particles collide is important for the discussion of chemical reactions in gases and liquids. This is discussed, for example, in Ch. 5 and Appendix B of reference 10.
12. See, for example, p. 90 of reference 10.
13. Following the notation of Section 6.3, reference 10.
14. Wolfenstein, L., and Ashkin, J., *Phys. Rev.*, **85**, 947 (1952). Simon, A., and Welton, T., *Phys. Rev.*, **93**, 1435 (1954). Wolfenstein, L., *Am. Rev. Nucl. Sci.*, **6**, 43 (1956).
15. A comprehensive account of the theory is given in Ch. 7 of reference 10.
16. Moravcsik, M. J., and Noyes, H. P., "Theories of Nucleon-Nucleon Elastic Scattering," *Ann. Rev. Nucl. Sci.*, **11**, 95 (1961).
17. Gell-Mann, M., and Goldberger, M. L., *Phys. Rev.*, **91**, 398 (1953).
18. We are here following the notation of Chs. 3 and 5 of reference 10.
19. Watson, K. M., *Phys. Rev.*, **89**, 575 (1953); **105**, 1388 (1957); Francis, N. C., and Watson, K. M., *Phys. Rev.*, **92**, 291 (1953); See also, Chapter 11 of reference 10.
20. Foldy, L., and Tobocman, W., *Phys. Rev.*, **105**, 1099 (1957); Epstein, S., *Phys. Rev.*, **106**, 598 (1957); Lippmann, B., *Phys. Rev.*, **102**, 264 (1956); Brening, W., and Haag, R., *Fortschr. Physik.* **7**, 183 (1959); Cook, J., *J. Math. Phys.*, **6**, 82 (1957). A somewhat more flexible interpretation has been made in Chapter 4 of reference 10.
21. Feshbach, H., *Ann. Phys.* (New York), **5**, 357 (1958); ibid., **19**, 287 (1962); Hahn, Y., and Spruch, L., *Phys. Rev.*, **153**, 1159 (1967); Hahn, Y., *Phys. Rev., C1*, 12 (1970); Chen, J. C. Y., *Phys. Rev.*, **156**, 150 (1967).
22. Chen, J. C. Y., and Watson, K. M., *Phys. Rev.*, **174**, 152 (1968); ibid., **188**, 236 (1969).

23. Fadeev, L. D., *Zh. Eksperim. i Teor. Fiz.*, **39**, 1459 (1960) [English trans.: *Soviet Phys.-JETP*, **12**, 1014 (1961)].

24. Weinberg, S., *Phys. Rev.*, **133**, B 232 (1964); Newton, R. G., *Nuovo Cimento*, **24**, 400 (1963); Watson, K. M., and Nuttall, J., "Topics in Several Particle Dynamics," San Francisco, Holden-Day, 1967.

25. Schwartz, C., *Phys. Rev.*, **124**, 1468 (1961). O'Malley, T. F., Sprach, L., and Rosenberg, L., *J. Math. Phys.*, **2**, 491 (1961) and earlier references. Sugar, R., and Blankenbecler, R., *Phys. Rev.*, **136**, B472 (1964).

26. This subject is reviewed by Wick, G. C., *Rev. Mod. Phys.*, **27**, 339 (1955).

27. Weinberg, S., *Phys. Rev.*, **130**, 776 (1963).

28. The history of this subject is reviewed in Ch. 10 of reference 10.

29. Gell-Mann, M., Goldberger, M. L., and Thirring, W., *Phys. Rev.*, **95**, 1612 (1954).

30. Lehmann, H., Symanzik, K., and Zimmerman, W. *Nuovo Cimento,* **1**, 205 (1955).

31. Mandelstam, S., *Phys. Rev.*, **112**, 1344 (1955); **115**, 1741, 1759 (1959).

32. Chew, G. F., and Frautschi, S. C., *Phys. Rev. Letters*, **8**, 41 (1962).

33. Blankenbecler, R., and Goldberger, M. L., *Phys. Rev.*, **126**, 766 (1962).

34. Reviews of the S-matrix theory of scattering can be found in Chew, G. F., "S-Matrix Theory of Strong Interactions," New York, Benjamin, 1961.
   Omnes, R., and Froissart, M., "Mandelstam Theory and Regge Poles," New York, Benjamin, 1963.

Cross-references: ATOMIC AND MOLECULAR BEAMS, CONSERVATION LAWS AND SYMMETRY, CROSS SECTIONS AND STOPPING POWER, FIELD THEORY, SCHRÖDINGER EQUATION.

COLOR

Definition Color is the property of light by which an observer may discriminate between two structure-free patches of light of identical size and shape. If two such patches cannot be distinguished by eye from each other, they are said to match in color.

Conditions for a Color Match Two patches of light defined physically by their spectral concentrations $(dL/d\lambda)$ of radiance L (radiant energy per unit time, unit solid angle, and unit of orthogonally projected area) color match provided that simultaneously:

$$\int \bar{x}_\lambda (dL/d\lambda)_1 \, d\lambda = \int \bar{x}_\lambda (dL/d\lambda)_2 \, d\lambda$$

$$\int \bar{y}_\lambda (dL/d\lambda)_1 \, d\lambda = \int \bar{y}_\lambda (dL/d\lambda)_2 \, d\lambda$$

$$\int \bar{z}_\lambda (dL/d\lambda)_1 \, d\lambda = \int \bar{z}_\lambda (dL/d\lambda)_2 \, d\lambda$$

where $\bar{x}_\lambda, \bar{y}_\lambda, \bar{z}_\lambda$ are the color-matching functions of wavelength λ characterizing the observer. Values of these functions customarily used for observers of average normal color vision are those recommended in 1931 by the International Commission of Illumination (CIE); with trivial exceptions any weighted mean of $\bar{x}_\lambda, \bar{y}_\lambda, \bar{z}_\lambda$, may be substituted for any of them without changing the meaning of Eq. (1). If the two light patches have identical spectral concentrations of radiance, Eq. (1) is satisfied for all observers and describes a nonmetameric match. If Eq. (1) is satisfied even though $(dL/d\lambda)_1$ is different from $(dL/d\lambda)_2$ for some parts of the visible spectrum, Eq. (1) describes a metameric match. Such a color match will usually be a mismatch for observers not characterized by $\bar{x}_\lambda, \bar{y}_\lambda, \bar{z}_\lambda$.

Deviations from normal color vision are of three types depending on the number of requirements for a color match that have to be satisfied. Anomalous trichromatic vision (protanomalous vision, deuteranomalous vision), like normal trichromatic vision, requires satisfaction of three conditions. Dichromatic vision (protanopia, deuteranopia, and tritanopia) requires satisfaction of but two conditions, and monochromatic vision (characterizing total color blindness and also characterizing normal vision in sufficiently dim light) requires satisfaction of but one condition. The color-matching function for the usual type of monochromatic vision is the CIE scotopic luminous-efficiency function recommended in 1951. The color-matching functions for the other forms of deviant color vision are related to those $(\bar{x}_\lambda, \bar{y}_\lambda, \bar{z}_\lambda)$ for normal daylight vision as given in Table 1. To make clear this relation, the color-matching functions for normal vision are stated, as is admissible, in terms of $-0.460\bar{x}_\lambda + 1.359\bar{y}_\lambda + 0.101\bar{z}_\lambda$ instead of $\bar{x}_\lambda$. An alternate statement, to be discussed later, is also given. Figure 1 shows all of these color-matching functions.

Measurement of Color The integrals of Eq. (1), called tristimulus values, X, Y, Z, serve as specifications of the color of the light patch defined physically by the values of spectral concentration of radiance $(dL/d\lambda)$ throughout the visible spectrum. The tristimulus values may be determined visually by having the observer adjust a mixture of three lights, called working primaries, to produce a color match for the specimen light patch. The required amounts of working primaries, R, G, B, are tristimulus values relative to the working primaries. The tristimulus values, X, Y, Z, relative to the CIE primaries may then be computed from the tristimulus values $(X_r, Y_r, Z_r; X_g, Y_g, Z_g; X_b, Y_b, Z_b)$ of the working primaries, thus:

$$X = X_r R + X_g G + X_b B$$
$$Y = Y_r R + Y_g G + Y_b B \qquad (2)$$
$$Z = Z_r R + Z_g G + Z_b B$$

TABLE 1. COLOR-MATCHING FUNCTIONS FOR VARIOUS TYPES OF TRICHROMATIC AND DICHROMATIC VISION

Type of Vision	Color-matching Function		
	Long-wave Sensitive	Middle-wave Sensitive	Short-wave Sensitive
Trichromatic			
Normal (1, 5, 7)*	$(.639\bar{x}_\lambda + .490\bar{y}_\lambda - .129\bar{z}_\lambda)$	$(-.509\bar{x}_\lambda + 1.410\bar{y}_\lambda + .099\bar{z}_\lambda)$	$\bar{z}_\lambda$
(4, 5, 7)*	$\bar{y}_\lambda$	$(-.460\bar{x}_\lambda + 1.359\bar{y}_\lambda + .101\bar{z}_\lambda)$	$\bar{z}_\lambda$
Protanomalous (2, 5, 7)*	$(.32\bar{x}_\lambda + .25\bar{y}_\lambda - .07\bar{z}_\lambda)^n$**	$(-.460\bar{x}_\lambda + 1.359\bar{y}_\lambda + .101\bar{z}_\lambda)$	$\bar{z}_\lambda$
Deuteranomalous (2, 3-4, 7)*	$(.32\bar{x}_\lambda + .25\bar{y}_\lambda - .07\bar{z}_\lambda)^n$**	Intermediate to $\bar{y}_\lambda$ and $(.312\bar{x}_\lambda + .757\bar{y}_\lambda + .069\bar{z}_\lambda)$	$\bar{z}_\lambda$
Dichromatic			
Protanopic (5, 7)*	None	$(-.460\bar{x}_\lambda + 1.359\bar{y}_\lambda + .101\bar{z}_\lambda)$	$\bar{z}_\lambda$
Deuteranopic (3-4, 7)*	Intermediate to $\bar{y}_\lambda$ and $(.312\bar{x}_\lambda + .757\bar{y}_\lambda - .069\bar{z}_\lambda)$	None	$\bar{z}_\lambda$
Tritanopic (4, 5)*	$\bar{y}_\lambda$	$(- .460\bar{x}_\lambda + 1.359\bar{y}_\lambda + .101\bar{z}_\lambda)$	None

*Numbers of the curves of Fig. 1 showing these color-matching functions.

**The number, n, greater than one, characterizes each individual anomalous trichromatic observer.

Photoelectric color measurement may be accomplished by providing a photocell with three filters such that its spectral sensitivity may be made proportional in turn to $\bar{x}_\lambda$, $\bar{y}_\lambda$, $\bar{z}_\lambda$. When the light patch of color to be determined is projected onto the photosensitive surface with the X-tristimulus filter interposed, the response of the cell will be proportional to $\int (dL/d\lambda) \bar{x} d\lambda = X$; and by inserting the Y-tristimulus filter and the Z-tristimulus filter in turn, Y and Z may be found for the unknown color.

Color Perception and Chromatic Adaptation The color perception of a spot of light against a dark surround may be described in terms of hue, brightness and saturation. Hue refers to red, orange, yellow, green, blue, purple, back to red, and their intermediates. Brightness determines whether the patch appears to be emitting more or less light per unit area; it varies from very dim to dazzling. Saturation refers to the amount of difference between the color perception to be described and the neutral color perception (exhibiting no hue) of the same brightness; it varies from neutral to very vivid. Average daylight usually yields a neutral color perception. The color perception of an object illuminated by daylight may be described in terms of hue, saturation (see above) and lightness. Lightness determines whether the object appears to be reflecting a greater or lesser fraction of the incident light; it varies from a minimum for black to a maximum for white.

The color perception of a spot of light viewed against a dark background correlates well with the tristimulus values of the spot. For example, brightness corresponds to the tristimulus value Y, also known as luminance, but with nonlinear scaling. The cube-root of luminance $Y^{1/3}$ correlates well with estimates of brightness.

The color perception of an object illuminated by average daylight and viewed by a daylight-adapted observer against a white background correlates well with the tristimulus values of the light reflected toward the observer's eye from the object relative to that from the surround. For example, lightness corresponds to Y/Y_s, but with nonlinear scaling where Y_s refers to the surround. The function $(Y/Y_s)^{1/3}$ correlates well with estimates of lightness.

If the light patch or object is viewed by an observer adapted to a color quite different from darkness or daylight (such as by use of a vivid red surround) the color perceptions are markedly changed. If the tristimulus values of the color which appears gray to the observer in his changed state of adaptation be X_a, Y_a, Z_a, and that of the color which appears gray in daylight adaptation be X_c, Y_c, Z_c, the ratios X_c/X_a, Y_c/Y_a, and Z_c/Z_a serve as measures of the changed state of adaptation. The color perceptions then correlate to a first degree of approximation to $(X_c/X_a)X$, $(Y_c/Y_a)Y$, and $(Z_c/Z_a)Z$, instead of to X, Y, Z. Still better approximations are obtained if primaries different from the CIE primaries are used, such as those implied by curves, 3, 5, and 7 of Fig. 1. The approximate correlation so achieved is known as the v. Kries coefficient law.

Control of Color by Pigments and Dyes Objects owe their color to materials (colorants) incorporated in them or spread over their surfaces. Objects viewed by transmitted light usually owe their colors to soluble colorants (dyes). The spectral concentration, $dE/d\lambda$, of the radiant flux incident per unit area is changed to $T_\lambda(dE/d\lambda)$ on passage through the dyed object, where T_λ is the spectral transmittance of the object. Objects viewed by reflected light usually owe their colors to insoluble colorants (pigments) which scatter as well as transmit the incident light. The light penetrates the object, and after multiple scattering emerges from the illuminated side. The spectral concentration, $dE/d\lambda$, is changed to $R_\lambda(dE/d\lambda)$, where R_λ is the spectral reflectance of the object.

The colors of objects may be specified by the

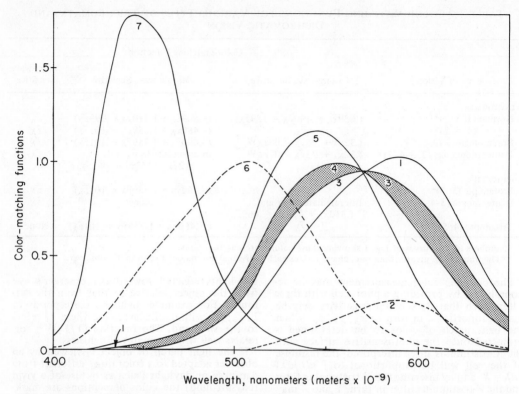

FIG. 1. Color-matching functions for normal and various forms of deviant vision:

Curve 1 = $(.639\bar{x}_\lambda + .490\bar{y}_\lambda - .029\bar{z}_\lambda)$, product of spectral transmittance of eye media by spectral absorptance of photo-pigment presumed to exist in the retina.

Curve 2 = $(.32\bar{x}_\lambda + .25\bar{y}_\lambda - .07\bar{z}_\lambda)^2$, long-wave-sensitive function for both protanomalous and deuteranomalous vision ($n = 2$).

Curve 3 = $(.312\bar{x}_\lambda + .757\bar{y}_\lambda - .069\bar{z}_\lambda)$, long-wave extreme of the range (shown crosshatched) or deuteranopic long-wave functions; also the long-wave extreme of the deuteranomalous middle-wave functions.

Curve 4 = $\bar{y}_\lambda$, photopic luminous-efficiency function, which is the long-wave-sensitive function for normal and tritanopic vision, and the short-wave extreme of the range (shown crosshatched) of long-wave-sensitive deuteranopic functions and of the middle-wave deuteranomalous functions.

Curve 5 = $(-.460\bar{x}_\lambda + 1.359\bar{y}_\lambda + .101\bar{z}_\lambda)$, long-wave-sensitive protanopic function, middle-wave-sensitive function for protanomalous and normal color vision, and short-wave-sensitive function for tritanopic vision; also close to $(-.509\bar{x}_\lambda + 1.410\bar{y}_\lambda + .099\bar{z}_\lambda)$, the product of spectral transmittance of eye media by spectral absorptance of photo-pigment presumed to exist in the retina.

Curve 6 = scotopic luminous-efficiency function, the color-matching function for the usual type of total color blindness.

Curve 7 = $\bar{z}_\lambda$, short-wave-sensitive function for all types of vision except tritanopic and scotopic; also product of the spectral transmittance of the eye media by the spectral absorptance of photo-pigment presumed to exist in the retina.

tristimulus values of the light leaving them toward the observer's eye compared to the tristimulus values of the incident light.

Color Scales A series of color standards whose colors are suitably spaced over a color range form a color scale. Perhaps the most common example of a one-dimensional color scale is a series of solutions of different colors produced by different concentrations of a known colorant. By visual comparison of a solution of unknown concentration of this colorant with the color standards making up the scale, the

concentration of the unknown may be evaluated. Another one-dimensional color scale is a series of grays ranging from black to white, and still another is the scale of color temperature, defined as the temperature of a blackbody required to make it match the color of an unknown light source to be evaluated.

If the color range is two dimensional, a two-dimensional color scale consisting of a family of one-dimensional scales is required. An example is the range of colors producible by mixing in various proportions paints of any three colors,

say black, white, and red. The colors produced by mixing black paint with white paint in various proportions form one of the series of one-dimensional scales, and the other one-dimensional scales might be produced with 10 per cent red paint, 20 per cent, and so on.

If the color range is three dimensional, a three-dimensional color scale is required. The color standards of the Lovibond, the Ostwald, and the Munsell color systems are examples of three-dimensional color scales; the Arny solutions form another.

Automatic Production of Pictures in Color Pictures produced automatically in color as in television, photography, or multiple printing, depend on the principle of photoelectric color measurement. A record of the tristimulus values of each picture element is made either by the television camera or by a camera with photographic film. The final picture is synthesized by the information stored in this record. The synthesis is made by averaging the colors of small spots (television), by addition of colorant layers through which light passes in succession on its way to the observer's eye (most color photography), or by a combination of the two (process printing). The tristimulus values X_a, Y_a, Z_a, of the average color of a group of juxtaposed spots too small to be resolved by eye can be computed simply as the averages of the corresponding tristimulus values of the spots, thus:

$$X_a = (X_1 + X_2 + X_3 \cdots + X_n)/n \qquad (3)$$

and similarly for Y_a and Z_a.

The tristimulus value of the light transmitted by three layers of colorants (say magenta, lemon yellow, and cyan) are integrals like those of Eq. (1), where the spectral radiance distribution $dL/d\lambda$ of the source is supplanted by: $T_m T_{1y} T_c (dL/d\lambda)$, where T_m, T_{1y}, and T_c are the spectral transmittances of the magenta, the lemon yellow, and the cyan layers, respectively.

Theories of Color It is generally supposed that change in the incidence of radiant energy on an element of the retina is detected by four photopigments present there; one of these (rhodopsin) serves for twilight vision yielding gray perceptions (see curve 6, Fig. 1); the other three (chemical composition unknown) in combination, serve for daylight vision yielding chromatic perceptions (see curves 1, 5, and 7).

Rhodopsin is found in the retinal rods (duplicity theory). The other three photopigments are found in the retinal cones, either segregated full strength (curves 5 and 7), segregated at low concentration (curve 2), or integrated (either curve 3 or curve 4). Normal vision is explained by triads of receptors (curves 3, 5, 7, or curves 4, 5, 7) according to the three-components or Young-Helmholtz theory.

The signals from the retinal cones are processed on their way to the visual center of the cortex in the occipital lobe of the brain. It is generally supposed that the red, green, and blue signals leaving the retinal cones are converted by this processing into light-dark, yellow-blue, and red-green signals at the occipital lobe. These processes correlate with the following functions of the tristimulus values: Y (light-dark), Y-Z (yellow-blue), and X-Y (red-green). The explanation of normal color vision in terms of these processes is the opponent-colors, or Hering, theory of vision.

Explanations of color vision in terms of a photopigment stage, a receptor stage, and an optic-nerve or cortical stage, are called stage theories of vision (Müller, Adams).

DEANE B. JUDD

References

Evans, Ralph M., "An Introduction to Color," New York, John Wiley & Sons, 1948.

LeGrand, Y., "Light, Colour and Vision," New York, John Wiley & Sons, 1957.

Judd, Deane B. and Wyszecki, Günter, "Color in Business, Science, and Industry," New York, John Wiley & Sons, 1963.

Wright, W. D., "The Measurement of Colour," London, Hilger & Watts, 1963.

Wyszecki, G., and Stiles, W. S., "Color Science: Concepts and Methods, Quantitative Data and Formulas," New York, John Wiley & Sons, 1967.

Cross-references: LIGHT, VISION AND THE EYE.

COLOR CENTERS

The term "color center" is broadly used to describe those microsopic defects that produce a change in the optical transparency of materials. The prototypes of these defects are found in crystals of the alkali halides which consist of positive alkali ions, e.g., K^+, and negative halide ions, e.g., Cl^-, which are arranged alternately in a three-dimensional array. If a negative halide ion is removed from its lattice site and put at some other position in the crystal, such as on the surface or into the space between other normal ions, thereby forming an "interstitial ion," a negative ion vacancy results. An electron can be trapped by the positive electric field that arises from the positive ions that surround the negative ion vacancy, thereby forming what may be crudely considered as the analog of the hydrogen atom with the positive field arising from the surrounding alkali ions replacing the positive field of the nucleus. This crystal defect—an electron trapped at a negative ion vacancy—is known as the "F-center." The F-center may be in its lowest energy state—the ground state—or it may be excited to higher states by the absorption of a photon of a characteristic frequency. The electron interacts strongly with the positive ions which are neighbors to the vacancy. Since the position of these positive ions determines the strength of this interaction, any motion of these ions alters

the characteristic frequency which is necessary to excite the F-center. There is, therefore, a "band" of frequencies that can be absorbed by a crystal containing F-centers. As the temperature of the lattice is decreased, the motion of the atoms decreases—thereby decreasing the width of the band of frequencies which can be absorbed. Cooling below the temperature of liquid nitrogen (– 196°C) results in little further change in the width of the band since the vibration of the atoms in the lattice is almost entirely a result of zero-point vibrations below this temperature. As can be seen in Table 1, the wavelength (or frequency) of the maximum of the absorption band is characteristic of F-centers in a particular alkali halide crystal.

Following the absorption of a photon, the center is in an excited state. It can return to its ground state by luminescing (i.e., emitting a photon), by ionization of the electron thereby freeing it from the defect, or by a non-radiative process in which the excess energy appears as heat. The relative probability of each of these processes depends upon such parameters as the temperature, the concentration, and the types of defects. At low temperatures and for low concentrations of defects, the probability that the F-center luminesces approaches unity. As the temperature is raised, the probability for luminescence decreases while the probability for ionization increases. Since the electron distribution in the excited state is different from that in the ground state, the ions in the neighborhood of the F-center shift to a new equilibrium position in the excited state following the absorption of a photon. Energy is therefore given to the lattice with the resulting emitted photon having an energy less than that of the absorbed photon. This is called the Stokes shift of the luminescence. A band of frequencies is emitted when excited F-centers luminesce.

The ionization of the electron may be detected by observing the current that flows in the presence of an electric field when light is absorbed by the F-center. The disappearance of this photoconductivity at low temperatures is evidence that the first excited state of the center is bound. That is, the electron can be freed from, or ionized out of, the first excited state only if additional energy is provided by the thermal vibrations of the lattice. It is also observed that a strong electric field can provide sufficient energy to "field ionize" the electron out of the first excited state.

The microscopic models of a number of the prominent electron excess centers in the alkali halides are as follows: *F-center*—an electron trapped at a negative ion vacancy. The principal optical absorption band arises from an electronic transition that may be qualitatively classified as $1s \to 2p$. *M-center*—two F-centers which occupy nearest-neighbor positions. The center resembles a hydrogen molecule. The principal optical absorption band corresponds to a $^1\Sigma_g^+ \to {}^1\Sigma_u^+$ transition. *R-center*—three F-centers that occupy nearest-neighbor positions in a plane. Two distinct absorption bands are associated with this defect. *F'-center*—two electrons trapped at a negative ion vacancy, i.e., an F-center that has trapped an electron.

Alkali halide crystals exhibit strong optical absorptions in the ultraviolet region of the spectrum. The lowest energy of these transitions can be visualized as arising from the transfer of an electron from a negative halide ion to a positive alkali ion thus producing what is called an "exciton." The energy of this transition is perturbed by crystal defects and gives rise to the so-called Greek absorption bands. The *α-band* arises from an exciton transition in the neighborhood of a negative ion vacancy. The *β-band* arises from an exciton transition in the neighborhood of an F-center.

In addition to the defects that have trapped an electron, there also exist defects that have a

TABLE 1.   Color Centers Characteristic in
Some Alkali Halides

	Wavelength of the Maximum of the Absorption Bands (Angstroms)						
	F	M	R_1	R_2	V_k	H	α
KCl							
20°C	5600	8220	6800	7400	–	–	
–196°C	5400	8010	6590	7290	–	–	1770
–269°C	5370	7980	–	–	3650	3350	
LiF							
20°C	2490	4470	3100	3800	3480	–	
KI							
–269°C	6590	10100	8100	9050	4040	–	2380
RbBr							
–196°C	6770	9570	8050	8590	–	–	

deficiency of electrons—the so-called hole traps. The V_k-*center* consists of a hole that is shared by two negative halide ions. No vacancies are involved in this center. It may be pictured as a X_2^- molecule that occupies two normal halide ion lattice sites in the crystal. X^- is here a negative halide ion in an alkali halide crystal. The *H-center* consists of a hole that is shared by four negative halide ions that occupy three normal halide ion lattice sites in the crystal. Although this center is also molecular in nature, it may be conveniently pictured as an interstitial halide *atom*.

Impurities, such as Tl^+, Pb^{++}, Ag^+ and Cu^+, introduce one or more absorption bands into the alkali halides when they are substituted for the alkali ion. The nature of these absorption bands depends upon the specific impurity. Impurities can also modify the properties of some of the color centers described above. If a lithium ion replaces a potassium ion that is the nearest neighbor of an F-center in KCl, it is found that two distinct absorption bands appear instead of the single absorption band that arises from the F-center in the pure crystal. This defect—an F-center with a foreign alkali ion impurity as a nearest neighbor—is called the F_A-*center*.

Color centers may be readily generated by the following three techniques:

(1) Irradiation with x-rays, fast electrons, neutrons, or high-energy protons generate defects which trap electrons in equal numbers with holes. The temperature at which the irradiation is made determines the type of defects that are produced. At room temperature, F-, M- and R-centers are the principal electron excess centers that are formed. At $-196°C$, F-, F'-, V_k- and α-centers are formed. At the temperature of liquid helium ($-269°C$), F-, H-, V_k- and α-centers are formed.

(2) Heating of a crystal to several hundred degrees centigrade in an atmosphere of the alkali metal produces crystals with a stoichiometric excess of alkali metal. If the crystal is rapidly cooled from this temperature, the F-center is the prominent defect. Absorption of light by the F-centers generates M- and R-centers if the optical irradiation is made at room temperature and F'-centers if the crystal is at about $-100°C$.

(3) Passage of a dc electrical current through samples held at several hundred degrees centigrade generates color centers. F-centers are generated at the cathode and move into the crystal under the action of the applied electric field.

Many of the properties of the host crystal are strongly affected by the presence of color centers. The density decreases when F-centers are introduced, the thermal conductivity at low temperatures is reduced, the crystal exhibits paramagnetic properties, and an enhanced electrical conduction is observed when the crystal is irradiated with light. Irradiation with x-rays enhances the hardness of the crystal.

Although the microscopic models of the color centers and their interactions with the host lattice and with other defects are best understood in the alkali halides, a considerable amount of information is available on similar defects in other materials. In many cases, the defects have been introduced by irradiation. Studies have been particularly intensive on the alkaline earth halides and oxides, crystalline quartz, fused silica, aluminum oxide, and diamond. Recent studies of radiation-induced defects in semiconductors, particularly germanium and silicon, have revealed defects that may also be properly classified as color centers.

W. DALE COMPTON

References

Books

Schulman, J. H., and Compton, W. D., "Color Centers in Solids," London, Pergamon Press, 1962.

Mott, N. F., and Gurney, R. W., "Electronic Processes in Ionic Crystals," Oxford, Clarendon Press, 1940.

Przibram, K., "Irradiation Colours and Luminescence," London, Pergamon Press, 1956.

"Radiation Effects in Inorganic Solids," *Discussions Faraday Soc.*, **31** (1961).

Fowler, W. B., Ed., "Physics of Color Centers," New York, Academic Press, 1968.

Markham, J. J., "F-Centers in Alkali Halides," Supplement No. 8, *Solid State Physics*, F. Seitz and D. Turnbull, Eds., New York, Academic Press, 1966.

Review Articles

Seitz, F., *Rev. Mod. Phys.*, **18**, 384 (1946); **26**, 7 (1954).

Compton, W. D., and Rabin, H., *Solid State Phys.*, **16**, 121 (1964).

Pick, H., *Nuovo Cimento*, 7 (2), 498 (1958).

Crawford, J. H., *Advances in Solids*, **XVII** (65), 93 (1968).

Henderson, B., and Wertz, J. E., *Advances in Solids*, **XVII** (70), 749 (1968).

Cross-references: EXCITONS; LUMINESCENCE; PHOTOCONDUCTIVITY; RADIATION, IONIZING, BASIC INTERACTIONS.

COMPRESSIBILITY, GAS

(a) The *compressibility* of a gas is defined as the rate of volume decrease with increasing pressure, per unit volume of the gas. The compressibility depends not only on the state of the gas, but also on the conditions under which the compression is achieved. Thus, if the temperature is kept constant during compression, the compressibility so defined is called the isothermal compressibility β_T:

$$\beta_T = -\frac{1}{V}\left(\frac{\partial V}{\partial P}\right)_T = \frac{1}{\rho}\left(\frac{\partial \rho}{\partial P}\right)_T. \qquad (1)$$

If the compression is carried out reversibly without heat exchange with the surroundings, the adiabatic compressibility at constant entropy, β_S, is obtained:

$$\beta_S = - \frac{1}{V} \left(\frac{\partial V}{\partial P} \right)_S = \frac{1}{\rho} \left(\frac{\partial \rho}{\partial P} \right)_S. \quad (2)$$

The two compressibilities are related by

$$\beta_S/\beta_T = C_V/C_P. \quad (3)$$

Here P is the pressure, V the volume, ρ the density, T the temperature, S the entropy, and C_V, C_P specific heats at constant volume and pressure, respectively.

The *compressibility factor* of a gas is the ratio PV/RT (cf. GAS LAWS). This name is not well chosen since the value of the compressibility factor is no indication of the compressibility.

(b) The *experimental behavior* of the compressibility as a function of pressure and temperature is as follows: dilute gases obey the laws of Boyle and Gay-Lussac, $PV=RT$, to a good approximation. The compressibilities β_T and β_S of a dilute gas are then given by

$$\beta_T = \frac{1}{P}; \beta_S = \frac{(C_V/C_P)}{P}. \quad (4)$$

Compressed gases, however, show large deviations from the behavior predicted by Eq. (4). This is demonstrated in Fig. 1, where the isothermal compressibility of argon, divided by the corresponding value for a perfect gas at the same density, Eq. (4), is pictured as a function of density for various temperatures. At all temperatures the compressibility at high densities falls to a small fraction of the value for a perfect gas. As the critical temperature is approached from above, a large maximum occurs in β_T at densities near critical. The isothermal compressibility diverges strongly at the critical point (just like C_P, see Ref. 1d) and is infinite everywhere in the two-phase region, where the pressure does not rise on isothermal compression. The adiabatic compressibility, however, diverges only weakly (like C_V, see Ref. 1d) when the critical point is approached, and it is finite in the two-phase region.

(c) Simple notions taken from *molecular theory* can be used to explain the general features of the compressibility in its temperature and density dependence. The pressure of the gas is caused by the impact of the molecules on the wall. If the volume is decreased at constant temperature, the average molecular speed and force of impact remain constant, but the number of collisions per unit area increases and thus the pressure rises. If the gas is compressed adiabatically, the heat of compression cannot flow off, thus the average molecular speed and force of impact increase as well, giving rise to an extra increase on pressure. Therefore $\beta_S < \beta_T$. The actual magnitude of the temperature

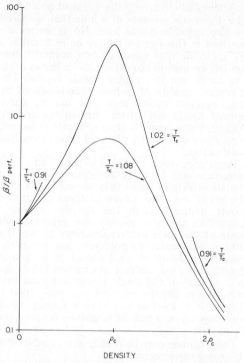

FIG. 1. The ratio $\beta/\beta_{perf.}$ of the isothermal compressibility of argon to that of a perfect gas at the same density, as a function of the density, at 0.91, 1.02, and 1.08 times the critical temperature. The critical density is indicated by ρ_c.

rise depends on the internal state of the molecules; the more internal degrees of freedom available, the more energy can be taken up inside the molecule and the smaller the temperature rise on adiabatic compression. If molecules have many internal degrees of freedom, the difference between β_T and β_S, just like the difference between C_P and C_V, becomes small.

Molecular theory also shows that if the molecules have negligible volume and do not interact with each other, the gas follows the perfect gas laws of Boyle and Gay-Lussac so that Eq. (4) holds for the compressibilities β_T and β_S. However, in real gases the molecular volume is not negligible. Consequently, in states of high compression little free space is left to the molecules and thus the real gas and the liquid have low compressibilities as compared to the perfect gas (Fig. 1). On the other hand, the mutual attraction molecules experience as they approach each other makes a real gas easier to compress than a perfect gas. This explains the initial rise of $\beta_T/\beta_{perf.}$ at temperatures not too far above critical.

(d) *Experimental values* for the compressibility could be obtained in principle by measuring the pressure increase on a small volume decrement. In practice a measurable pressure increase is obtained only in regions of low com-

pressibility, i.e., in the dense gas. Usually, compressibilities are determined in indirect ways. Thus, the isothermal compressibility, being proportional to $(\partial V/\partial P)_T$, can be deduced from experimental PVT data if these data are sufficiently accurate and densely spaced. For obtaining the adiabatic compressibility from PVT data, some additional information is needed, for instance SPECIFIC HEAT data in the perfect gas limit. For reviews of experimental methods for determining PVT relations and deriving thermodynamic properties see Refs. 1a, b.

The adiabatic compressibility is readily obtained from speed-of-sound data through the relation

$$v^2 = \frac{1}{\rho \beta_S} \qquad (5)$$

Eq. (5) is valid only when compressions and expansions of the sound wave are truly reversible and adiabatic, i.e., if the frequency is low and the amplitude small. Experimental techniques for determining the speed of sound are discussed in Ref. 1c.

The isothermal compressibility, through the fluctuation theorem of statistical mechanics, is related to the density fluctuations in the system.[2,3] These density fluctuations are responsible for the scattering of light. Thus, the isothermal compressibility can be directly obtained from the intensity of scattered light.[2] In gases, sufficient intensity is obtained only in regions of large density fluctuations, i.e., near the critical point. The rapid development of laser optics and electronics has made this method a promising one in the critical region. For references to recent literature, see Ref. 1d.

(e) *Theoretical predictions* for the isothermal compressibility can be made in those circumstances that the equation of state is known from first principles. Thus, at low densities, the compressibility follows from the virial expansion of the equation of state; this expansion expresses the ratio PV/RT in a power series in the density, the coefficients being related to interactions of groups of two, three, etc. particles.[2,3]

The virial expansion is not useful for dense gases, because convergence is slow and higher virials are hard to calculate. For dense systems, powerful methods have been developed for evaluation of the radial distribution function $g(r)$, which is the ratio of the average density of molecules at a distance r from any given molecule, to the average density in the gas. The compressibility is related to $g(r)$ by the fluctuation theorem

$$kT\beta_T = 1/\rho + \int [g(r) - 1] \, 4\pi r^2 \, dr \qquad (6)$$

Approximate evaluations of the radial distribution function in dense systems are being obtained as solutions to integral equations for $g(r)$ under well-defined approximations.[3]

Many semiempirical equations of state with varying degrees of theoretical foundation have been developed and can be used with Eq. (1) to calculate the compressibility. Van der Waals' equation, a two-parameter equation which gives a qualitative picture of the PVT relation of a gas and of the gas-liquid transition, is an example. For surveys of useful semiempirical equations see Refs. 1b and 2.

J. M. H. LEVELT SENGERS

References

1. Vodar, B., and Le Neindre, B., Eds., "Experimental Thermodynamics" (I.U.P.A.C.), Volume II: "Experimental Thermodynamics of Non-reacting Fluids," New York, Plenum Press; London, Butterworths, 1973/74.
   a. Trappeniers, N. J. and Wassenaar, T., "PVT relationships in gases at high pressure and moderate or low temperatures."
   b. McCarty, R. D., "Determination of thermodynamic properties from the experimental PVT relationship."
   c. Van Dael, W., "Measurement of the velocity of sound and its relation to the other thermodynamic properties."
   d. Levelt Sengers, J. M. H., "Thermodynamical properties near the critical state."
2. Hirschfelder, J. O., Curtiss, C. F., and Bird, R. B., "Molecular Theory of Gases and Liquids," New York, John Wiley & Sons, 1954.
3. Münster, A., "Statistical Thermodynamics," Vol. 1, Berlin, Springer-Verlag, 1969.

Cross-references: GAS LAWS, KINETIC THEORY.

COMPTON EFFECT

Introduction The Compton effect refers to the collision of a photon and a free electron in which the electron recoils and a photon of longer wavelength is emitted as indicated in Fig. 1. It is one of the most important processes by which x-rays and γ-rays interact with matter and is also one which is accurately calculable theoretically.

A discussion of the effect is found in most textbooks on atomic physics. Particularly complete presentations have been made by Evans.[1,2]

History Barkla and others (1908) made many observations on the scattering of x-rays by different materials. The diffuse scattering was interpreted qualitatively by J. J. Thomson in terms of the interaction of electromagnetic waves with electrons which he had shown to be a constituent of all atoms. As more experiments were carried out with light elements, it was established by J. A. Gray (1920) that the diffusely scattered x-rays were less penetrating. This implied that the scattered radiation had a longer wavelength than the incident radiation. This could not be reconciled with Thomson's theory which represented x-rays as continuous

electromagnetic waves with wavelengths unchanged by scattering.

The effect which now bears his name was established quantitatively by Arthur Holly Compton (1923) when he published careful spectroscopic measurements of x-rays scattered at various angles by light elements. He found that x-rays scattered at larger angles had systematically larger wavelengths. In searching for an explanation of the data, he discovered that the observations were accounted for by considering the scattering as a collision between a single photon and a single electron in which energy and momentum are conserved.

The important place which the effect occupies in the development of physics lies in his interpretation of the effect in terms of the newly emerging quantum theory. The essential duality of waves and particles was demonstrated in an especially clear way, since the collision conserved energy and momentum while both the incident and scattered x-rays revealed wave-like properties by their scattering from a crystal. In recognition for this contribution, Compton was awarded the Nobel Prize in 1927.

A complete theory for the effect was worked out in 1928 by Klein and Nishina using Dirac's relativistic theory of the electron. The calculation was one of the brilliant successes of the Dirac theory. It represents quantitatively, within the experimental uncertainties, all phenomena associated with the scattering of photons by electrons for energies up to several billion electron volts. Because of the confidence with which photon interaction with electrons can be interpreted, the Compton effect has been important in the analysis of the energy and the polarization of gamma rays from many sources.

Kinematics The relations between the energies and directions of the incident and scattered photons and the recoil electron are determined by the conservation of energy and of the components of momentum parallel and at right angles to the incident beam. In the usual case, where the electron is initially at rest and the energy and momentum of the incident photon are $h\nu$ and $(h\nu/c)$, the equations are:

$$h\nu = h\nu' + T \tag{1}$$

$$\frac{h\nu}{c} = \frac{h\nu'}{c} \cos \theta + p \cos \phi \tag{2}$$

$$0 = \frac{h\nu'}{c} \sin \theta - p \sin \phi \tag{3}$$

where c is the velocity of light, h is Planck's constant, and the angles are those indicated in Fig. 1. The relativistic relation between the kinetic energy T of the recoiling electron and its momentum p is

$$pc = \sqrt{T(T + 2mc^2)} \tag{4}$$

where m is the mass of the electron. These equations can be combined to obtain relations

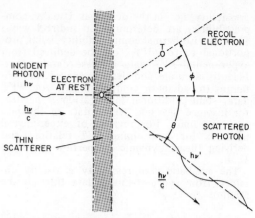

FIG. 1. Diagram showing the initial and final energies and momenta for Compton scattering.

which are useful in the interpretation of data. The Compton shift is

$$\lambda' - \lambda = \frac{c}{\nu'} - \frac{c}{\nu} = \frac{h}{mc}(1 - \cos \theta) \tag{5}$$

This relation was first found experimentally by Compton, who noted that the shift in wavelength ($\lambda' - \lambda$) depended on the angle, but not on the wavelength, of the incident photon. The quantity (h/mc), which is the shift at $90°$, is called the Compton wavelength of the electron and is one of the useful constants (2.4262×10^{-10} cm).

$$h\nu' = \frac{mc^2}{1 - \cos \theta + \dfrac{mc^2}{h\nu}} \tag{6}$$

In this form, the energy of the scattered photon is seen to vary from that of the incident photon at $0°$ to less than $(mc^2/2)$ at $180°$. At high energies the angle θ for which $h\nu'$ is $(h\nu/2)$ is approximately $2(mc^2/h\nu)$ radians.

The kinetic energy of the recoiling electron is

$$T = \frac{h\nu(1 - \cos \theta)}{(1 - \cos \theta) + \dfrac{mc^2}{h\nu}} \tag{7}$$

The relation between the scattering angles of the electron and photon is

$$\cot \phi = \left(1 + \frac{h\nu}{mc^2}\right)\left(\frac{1 - \cos \theta}{\sin \theta}\right) \tag{8}$$

Graphs of these kinematic relations and of the scattering cross section are given by Evans[2] and by Nelms[3].

Scattering of Unpolarized Radiation The differential cross section for the scattering of unpolarized radiation at an angle θ is given by the Klein and Nishina equation.

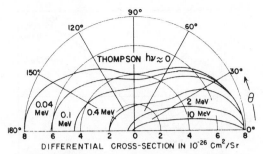

FIG. 2. Differential cross section for photons scattered at angles, θ, for a number of incident energies.

$$\frac{d\sigma}{d\Omega} = \frac{r_0^2}{2} \left(\frac{\nu'}{\nu}\right)^2 \left(\frac{\nu}{\nu'} + \frac{\nu'}{\nu} - \sin^2\theta\right) \quad (9)$$

where r_0 is the electron radius $= e^2/mc^2 = 2.8177 \times 10^{-13}$ cm, and ν' is obtained from Eq. (6). The cross section is shown as a function of θ for several energies in Fig. 2. The classical Thomson cross section $r_0^2 (1 + \cos^2\theta)/2$ can be seen to hold for low energies where $\nu' \approx \nu$.

The total cross section obtained by integrating this cross section over angle is important in the attenuation of well-defined beams in passing through a material. The relative importance of Compton scattering as compared to the photoelectric effect and pair production is illustrated for aluminum in Fig. 3 where the attenu-

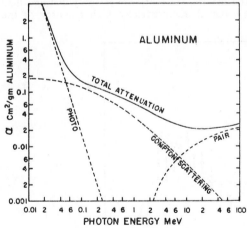

FIG. 3. The attenuation coefficients, α, for the absorption of photons in aluminum as a function of energy. The broken lines represent the separate contributions of the photoelectric effect, the Compton effect, and pair production to the absorption.

ation coefficient α is shown as a function of energy. The fraction of the photons surviving without an interaction upon passing through x g/cm^2 of aluminum is $e^{-\alpha x}$. The Compton effect is the major one between 0.5 and 2 MeV.

Extensive tables and graphs for other elements are available.[2,4]

In detectors whose response is proportional to the energy deposited by the recoil electrons, the distribution of electron energies associated with a photon of known energy is of interest. The distribution is given by the relation

$$\frac{d\sigma}{dT} = \frac{\pi r_0^2 mc^2}{(h\nu)^2} \left\{ 2 + \left(\frac{T}{h\nu - T}\right)^2 \right.$$
$$\left. \left[\frac{(mc^2)^2}{(h\nu)^2} + \frac{h\nu - T}{h\nu} - \frac{2mc^2(h\nu - T)}{h\nu T}\right] \right\}$$

where T varies from 0 to $T_{max} = 2(h\nu)^2/(2h\nu + mc^2)$. A number of these distributions are shown in Fig. 4.

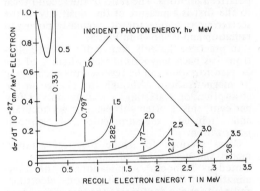

FIG. 4. The energy distribution of the Compton recoil electrons for several values of the incident photon energy $h\nu$. Based on figure in "Compton Effect" by R. D. Evans in "Handbuch der Physik," Vol. XXXIV, pp. 234–298, 1958, J. Fluge, Ed., by permission of Springer-Verlag, publishers.[2]

Scattering of Plane Polarized Radiation The differential cross section for the scattering of plane polarized radiation by unoriented electrons was also derived by Klein and Nishina. It represents the probability that a photon, passing through a target containing one electron per square centimeter, will be scattered at an angle θ into a solid angle $d\Omega$ in a plane making an angle η with respect to the plane containing the electric vector of the incident wave.

$$\frac{d\sigma}{d\Omega} = \frac{r_0^2}{2} \left(\frac{\nu'}{\nu}\right)^2 \left(\frac{\nu}{\nu'} + \frac{\nu'}{\nu} - 2\sin^2\theta\cos^2\eta\right) \quad (9)$$

The cross section has its maximum value for $\eta = 90°$, indicating that the photon and electron tend to be scattered at right angles to the electric vector of the incident radiation.

This dependence is the basis of several instruments for determining the polarization of photons. For example, it was used by Wu and Shaknov[5] to establish the crossed polarization of the two photons emitted upon the annihilation of a positron electron pair; by Metzger and Deutsch[6]

to measure the polarization of nuclear gamma rays; and by Motz[7] to study the polarization of bremsstrahlung.

Scattering of Circularly Polarized Radiation
The scattering of circularly polarized photons by electrons with spins aligned in the direction of the incident photon is represented by

$$\frac{d\sigma}{d\Omega} = r_0{}^2 \left(\frac{\nu'}{\nu}\right)^2 \left[\left(\frac{\nu}{\nu'} + \frac{\nu'}{\nu} - \sin^2 \theta\right) \\ \pm \left(\frac{\nu}{\nu'} - \frac{\nu'}{\nu}\right) \cos \theta\right] \quad (10)$$

The first term is the usual Klein-Nishina formula for unpolarized radiation. The + sign for the additional term applies to right circularly polarized photons. The ratio of the second term to the first is a measure of the sensitivity of the scattering as a detector of circularly polarized radiation and is shown in Fig. 5.

In practice, the only source of polarized electrons has been magnetized iron where 2 of the 26 electron spins can be reversed upon changing its magnetization. Although the change in the absorption or scattering is usually only a few per cent, this is often sufficient to get accurate and reliable measurements of circular polarization.

Cross sections for some practical arrangements and discussions of earlier work are presented by Tolhoek.[8] Applications to the determination of the helicities of photons, electrons, and neutrinos in confirming the two-component theory of the neutrino are reviewed in considerable detail by L. Grodzins.[9]

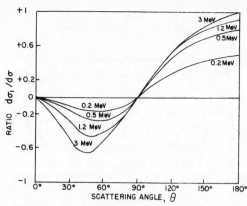

FIG. 5. The ratio of the partial cross section dependent on the spin orientation of the electrons to the average cross section as represented by the second and first terms of Eq. (10). Based on figure in "Compton Effect" by R. D. Evans in *Handbuch der Physik*, Vol. XXXIV, pp. 234–298, 1958, J. Fluge, Ed., by permission of Springer-Verlag, publishers.[2]

Proton and Deuteron Compton Effect Particle-like scattering of high-energy photons by protons and deuterons has been observed and has been referred to as the proton and deuteron Compton effect. The kinematic equations are identical to those for electrons except that the mass is that of the proton or deuteron.

Although the cross sections are smaller than that for electrons, by the square of the ratio of the masses, the scattering is easily distinguished by the characteristically higher energy of the

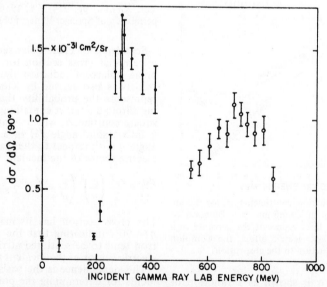

FIG. 6. The differential cross section for the scattering of high-energy photons by protons at 90° in the center of mass system. Based on figure in Steining, Loh and Deutsch, *Phys. Rev. Letters*, **10**, 536 (1963).[10]

radiation at large angles. At energies above the pion threshold, the cross section is dominated by pion nucleon resonances. The experimental cross sections for the scattering by protons, as presented by Steining, Loh, and Deutsch,[10] are shown in Fig. 6. Some experimental results and calculations on the coherent scattering from deuterium are described by Jones, Gerber, Hanson, and Wattenberg.[11]

Measurements at photon energies up to 7 and 16 GeV and comparisons with theoretical predictions of the vector dominance model have been reported by groups from Hamburg[12] and Stanford.[13]

A. O. HANSON

References

1. Evans, R. D., "The Atomic Nucleus," Chapter 23, New York, McGraw-Hill Book Co., 1955.
2. Evans, R. D., "Compton Effect," In Flugge, S., Ed., "The Encyclopedia of Physics," Vol. 34, pp. 234–298, Berlin, Springer-Verlag, 1958.
3. Nelms, A. T., "Graphs of the Compton Energy-Angle Relationship and the Klein-Nishina Formula from 10 keV to 500 MeV," *Natl. Bur. Std. Circ.*, **542** (1953).
4. White, G. R., "X-Ray Attenuation Coefficients form 10 keV to 100 MeV," *Natl. Bur. Std. Rept.*, **1003** (1952).
5. Wu, C. S., and Shaknov, I., "Angular Correlation of Scattered Annihilation Radiation," *Phys. Rev.*, **77**, 136 (1950).
6. Metzger, F., and Deutsch, M., *Phys. Rev.*, **78**, 551 (1950).
7. Motz, J. W., "Bremsstrahlung Polarization Measurements for 1 MeV Electrons," *Phys. Rev.*, **104**, 557 (1956).
8. Tolhoek, H. A., "Electron Polarization Theory and Experiment," *Rev. Mod. Phys.*, **28**, 277 (1956).
9. Grodzins, L., "Measurement of Helicity," in Frisch, O. R., Ed., "Progress in Nuclear Physics," New York, Pergamon Press, 1959.
10. Steining, R. F., Loh, E., and Deutsch, M., "The Elastic Scattering of Gamma Rays by Protons," *Phys. Rev. Letters*, **10**, 536 (1963).
11. Jones, R. S., Gerber, H. J., Hanson, A. O., and Wattenberg, A., "Deuteron Compton Effect," *Phys. Rev.*, **128**, 1357 (1962).
12. Buschhorn, G., Criegee, L., Franke, G., Heide, P., Kotthaus, R., Poelz, G., Timm, U., Vogel, G., Wegener, K., Werner, H., and Zimmerman, W., Proton Compton Scattering between 2.2 and 7 GeV," *Phys. Lett.*, **37B**, 207 (1971).
13. Boyarski, A. M., Coward, D. H., Ecklund, S., Richter, B., Sherden, D., Siemann, R., and Sinclair, C., "Forward Compton Scattering from Hydrogen and Deuterium at 8 and 16 GeV," *Phys. Rev. Lett.*, **26**, 1600 (1971).

Cross-references: COLLISIONS OF PARTICLES, CONSERVATION LAWS AND SYMMETRY, QUANTUM THEORY, X-RAYS.

COMPUTERS

Introduction A computer may be defined as a device capable of solving problems by accepting data (input), performing prescribed operations on the data (processing), and providing the results of these operations (output). The basic distinction between electronic calculators, which also fit this definition, and computers is that the latter provide speed in performing complex operations, virtually infinite program and data storage, and the ability to interact with the environment (including other computers) on a real time basis.

Computers may be hydraulic, mechanical, electromechanical, or electronic devices. They are broadly classified as being *digital*, *analog*, or *hybrid*, i.e., analog and digital linked together. The first two types differ fundamentally in the manner in which data are stored and operated upon. Analog computers operate on continuous variables, in the form of voltage or current (the electrical analog of a number or physical quantity), that represent continuous data. Digital computers operate on discrete numerical data represented by a series of binary digits. The data and instructions are stored internally and are indistinguishable in memory. Digital computers perform calculations by adding binary numbers according to instructions derived from coding an arithmetical expression or series of expressions (an algorithm) that represent the problem to be solved. Even though the problem may include differential or trigonometric expressions, each is reduced to simple addition or subtraction (addition of the complement) since addition is the only direct operation a digital computer can perform. Instructions, which are written sequentially, are executed sequentially (one at a time). Calculations usually culminate in a numerical display or graphical representation of the results. Because of the sequential nature of the digital process, the amount of time spent in solution is proportional to the problem complexity. Analog computers, on the other hand, are composed of elements which perform summation, integration, multiplication and differentiation directly. Rather than a serially coded algorithm, the instructions are in the form of basic modifications of the analog computer's circuitry by a user-wired patch board panel. There is no internal data or program storage as such. Instructions are executed effectively simultaneously (in parallel) while the solution is displayed in graphical form in continuous fashion. Since operations are performed in parallel, increased problem complexity demands more computer components, not more time. Solution time is therefore a function of the time characteristics of the problem, not the machine. The speed of the analog computer, therefore, is orders of magnitude faster than the digital computer in solving complex problems that involve calculus. This speed is paid for by a precision of results that is orders of magnitude less than for a digital computer. Hybrid computers

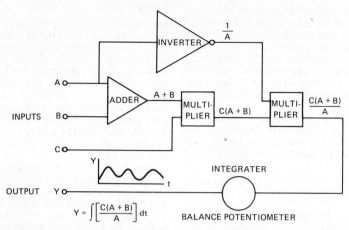

FIG. 1. Typical analog computer configuration to solve the equation for y. Requires: 1 adder, 1 inverter, 2 multipliers, 1 integrator.

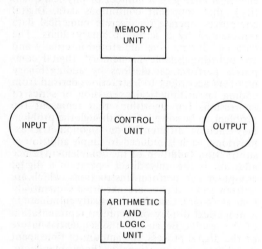

FIG. 2. Basic configuration of a digital computer. Problems are of the form

Input A = 3.0, B = 4.0
Output C = SQRT (A * A + B * B)

attempt to combine the best features of both types i.e., the speed of the analog with the precision of a digital. This is brought about through a digital "front-end" which is used to set up and check out the analog computer and its program. The actual computation time is equivalent to that of a pure analog machine, but the total time (including set-up time) is significantly reduced. Indeed, problems may be solved that would be cost prohibitive on a digital computer and, for all practical purposes, impossible to set up on an analog computer.

As described below, in physics all three types of computers are utilized. Digital computer applications range from theoretical calculations to pure data collection and experiment control. Applications of analog computers involve primarily solutions of differential equations which serve as models of physical systems. Hybrid systems come into play for extremely complex simulation. Examples include determination of tactical envelopes for missiles, optimization of control settings in a nuclear power plant, and development of chemical kinetic models. Whatever the branch of physics, one can be sure that computers today play some significant role.

Computers of the Past The abacus has been called the earliest computing machine. For more than 3000 years after the recording of its invention, this was the sole device available to aid in arithmetic calculations. Finally, in the year 1642, a Frenchman, Blaisé Pascal, invented the first mechanical adding machine. His stylus operated "arithmetic machine" had the ability to handle carry overs from one column to the next. Nearly 200 more years elapsed before C. X. Thomas, also a Frenchman, working on a concept proposed by the German, Gottfried Wilhelm Leibniz, built an "arithmometer" in 1820 which, besides addition and subtraction, could perform multiplication and division using the concept of repeated addition and subtraction.

While this was going on, an independent development in the weaving industry saw Frenchmen Jacques de Vaucanson, in 1741, and Joseph Marie Jacquard, in 1804, use holes punched, first in metal drums, later in punched cards, as the control or programmer for textile looms. On a more esoteric plane, Englishman Charles Babbage, in 1823, began construction of his "difference engine." This device, based on the fact that an equation of degree n will have a constant nth difference, was used to make calculations for trigonometric and logarithmic tables. Babbage succeeded in constructing a machine to solve a second degree equation. But his "analytical engine," which

had a memory, control, an arithmetic unit, and an input/output section could not be built at that time with sufficient precision to produce reliable results. Earliest analog computers of the type designed by Vannevar Bush and others in the 1930's actually followed these same mechanical principles until electronics began to take over in the late forties. This activity was culminated perhaps by the Maddida, which appeared in 1951. Analog computers since that time have differed mainly in the application of advanced modular electronics and in linkages with digital computers. Developments of calculators after Pascal and Thomas are not reliably documented. Two American mechanical adders, which spawned present day companies, are worthy of mention, however. These include the Felt "macaroni box" made in 1885 by a firm which later became the Victor Comptometer Corporation, and the "listing accountant" made by a forerunner of the Burroughs Corporation.

The real push behind the development of modern digital computers came about because of U. S. Government requirements, first to count people and tabulate corresponding data; later, during World War II, for developing artillery trajectory tables and performing calculations for the Manhattan project. In preparation for the 1890 census, it became clear that, using available counting and sorting techniques, it would be nearly time to perform the 1900 census before 1890 figures could be determined. Herman Hollerith, who had worked for the census office and was a mechanical engineer, solved the problem by devising a punched card, which could contain all pertinent data, and a series of machines for punching, counting and sorting. Using this equipment, census figures were published in less than three years with unheard-of accuracy. Hollerith revised his punched cards in 1894. They contained 80 columns, each with holes for 0 through 9; this is exactly the format in predominant use today. Hollerith's efforts eventually led to the formation of the International Business Machines Corporation, the world's largest manufacturer of computers. Tremendous quantities of work have been accomplished and are still possible using punch card techniques. However, this methodology is practical only for sorting, counting and selecting in a limited number of ways.

Electronic and electrical techniques were required to make practical, accurate computations of the vast quantities of data to solve problems and prove theories which today serve as the cornerstone of modern science. These machines are based upon the foundations laid by George Boole, who pioneered in the field of symbolic logic, and Allan Turing, who hypothesized a universal computer. George Boole's algebra provides a mechanism for representing logic in mathematical symbols and rules for calculating the truth or falsity of statements.

Digital computers carry out these operations an infinite number of times. Allan Turing's paper, "Computable Numbers," in 1937, described a hypothetical Turing machine that can solve any type of mathematical problem which can be reduced to coding in a given set of commands within the memory capacity of the machine.

First application of these principles resulted in the Bell Telephone Laboratories relay computer in 1939. Five years later, in 1944, the second significant relay computer, which was also the first general purpose digital machine, was constructed at Harvard by Professor Howard Aiken, with funds provided partially by IBM. Known as the Mark I, this machine was really a huge electro-mechanical calculator. The Electronic Numerical Integrator and Calculator, "ENIAC," the first electronic computer, was developed in 1946 by J. P. Eckert and J. W. Mauchly of the Moore School of Engineering in Philadelphia. Funds were provided by the U. S. Army with the promise that the machine would be suitable for calculating ballistic tables. This machine contained 18,000 vacuum tubes which replaced the former mechanical relays as switching elements. As might be expected, it was huge, weighing over 30 tons, and terribly unreliable. Nevertheless, it existed until 1955 after over 80,000 hours of operation had been logged.

Development proceeded thereafter at a much more rapid rate. IBM continued work, producing the Selective Sequence Electronic Calculator (SSEC) in 1947. The Moore School developed a second machine known as the Electronic Discrete Variable Computer (or EDVAC) which became operational in 1952. EDVAC is accepted as the first stored program computer. Unlike earlier machines which were programmed at least partially by setting switches or using patch boards, this machine and all others which were to follow, stored instructions and data in identical fashion. EDVAC used acoustical delay lines, which were simply columns of mercury through which data passed at the speed of sound, as the main memory. This type of storage has given way to magnetic core memory and semiconductor memory in computers of today.

In 1946, John Von Neumann, a mathematician at the Institute of Advanced Study (IAS), Princeton, New Jersey, presented a paper entitled "Preliminary Discussion of the Logical Design of an Electronic Computing Instrument." This paper, which was prepared jointly under a contract with the U. S. Army, suggested the principles under which all digital computers which followed would be built. This included internal program storage, relocatable instructions, memory addressing, conditional transfer, parallel arithmetic, internal number base conversion, synchronous internal timing, simultaneous computing while doing input/output, and magnetic tape for external storage. An IAS computer, employing most of these concepts, actually went into operation in the early fifties. All

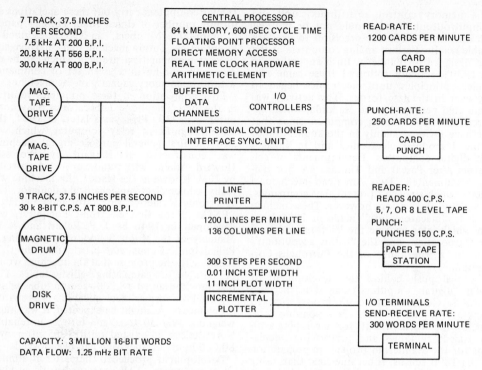

7 TRACK, 37.5 INCHES
PER SECOND
7.5 kHz AT 200 B.P.I.
20.8 kHz AT 556 B.P.I.
30.0 kHz AT 800 B.P.I.

MAG.
TAPE
DRIVE

MAG.
TAPE
DRIVE

9 TRACK, 37.5 INCHES PER SECOND
30 k 8-BIT C.P.S. AT 800 B.P.I.

MAGNETIC
DRUM

DISK
DRIVE

CAPACITY: 3 MILLION 16-BIT WORDS
DATA FLOW: 1.25 mHz BIT RATE

CENTRAL PROCESSOR
64 k MEMORY, 600 nSEC CYCLE TIME
FLOATING POINT PROCESSOR
DIRECT MEMORY ACCESS
REAL TIME CLOCK HARDWARE
ARITHMETIC ELEMENT

BUFFERED
DATA
CHANNELS

I/O
CONTROLLERS

INPUT SIGNAL CONDITIONER
INTERFACE SYNC. UNIT

LINE
PRINTER

1200 LINES PER MINUTE
136 COLUMNS PER LINE

300 STEPS PER SECOND
0.01 INCH STEP WIDTH
11 INCH PLOT WIDTH

INCREMENTAL
PLOTTER

READ-RATE:
1200 CARDS PER MINUTE

CARD
READER

PUNCH-RATE:
250 CARDS PER MINUTE

CARD
PUNCH

READER:
READS 400 C.P.S.
5, 7, OR 8 LEVEL TAPE
PUNCH:
PUNCHES 150 C.P.S.

PAPER TAPE
STATION

I/O TERMINALS
SEND-RECEIVE RATE:
300 WORDS PER MINUTE

TERMINAL

FIG. 3. Typical 3rd generation, medium size computer.

machines which followed used virtually the same principles. UNIVAC I (Universal Automatic Computer) was the first commercially available digital computer (circa 1950). This machine was a direct descendent of ENIAC and EDVAC, having been built by Remington Rand following acquisition of the Echert-Mauchly Computer Corporation. Eventually, 48 UNIVAC I's were built making Remington Rand the number one computer manufacturer until International Business Machines (IBM) began in earnest in 1954 with the introduction of its 700 line. This machine and its successor, the 650, made IBM the number one computer manufacturer in the world with well over half of the market, a position which it holds today.

Digital Computer Hardware As shown in Figs. 2 and 3, general-purpose digital computers are comprised of four basic components: an arithmetic or computing unit, a high speed internal storage unit, input-output devices, and a control unit. Data and instructions are indistinguishable within the computer; both are represented by binary patterns of semiconductor or magnetic core states. Each binary unit is called a "bit". A fixed number of bits is referred to as a computer "word". A word is, generally, the smallest directly addressable whole unit of memory. The number of bits in the word determines the accuracy of the basic machine and its cost. Small word machines are employed in real world applications to control

processes and make basic decisions. These small machines are referred to as minicomputers. Large word computers serve as theoretical number crunchers, often with smaller machines preprocessing input data or controlling output devices. Computer word size ranges from eight bits, or a single word accuracy of one part in 256, to sixty bits for an accuracy of one part in 2^{60} or a maximum positive decimal number of about 1 152 921 504 000 000 000.

In setting (programming or coding) instruction sequences, the user arranges for the control unit to determine, through an instruction decoder, whether the instruction itself refers to some memory location where data resides or calls for some basic arithmetic or logical operation to be performed. These operations are performed between data registers. Registers always provided include: an accumulator, a program counter, a memory address indicator, and an overflow indicator. Operations themselves may modify the stored instructions by performing calculations on them, branch to a new set of instructions, and/or cause the machine to interact with the outside world. Response from this interaction may cause the machine to "decide" what operations to perform next depending upon the options built into the program. The computer can make no decision of its own accord; it is simply directed to "conclude" which one of a given set of alternatives best fits a given situation. This being the case, it is impor-

tant to remember that computers don't solve problems, people that program them do. The advantage possessed by the computer is speed of operation. Even the slowest machines can perform an addition of two numbers in less than 3 microseconds. Using special circuitry, multiplication of any two numbers takes less than ten microseconds. These arithmetic functions, plus logical operations like AND, OR, XOR, repeated thousands of times in one second enable the machine to use iterative techniques to do all operations necessary for calculating mathematical tables, as well as to keep up with the real world in monitoring and control applications where data at rates of up to 100,000 characters per second are encountered.

Figure 3 shows the configuration of a typical third generation, medium size machine (first introduced after 1968, and employing medium scale integrated circuitry with a multiprogramming operating system). Its purpose is to show the diversity of peripheral gear which is tied to a computer and the speed at which this equipment operates. The numbers shown are representative and by no means show the highest capacities available. This configuration will support a dedicated operation (one user at a time) or several users simultaneously in a multiprogramming or time shared mode. These latter terms refer to the ability of the system to run more than one user program simultaneously. The difference between time sharing and multiprogramming, as the terms are usually used, is that several users are connected simultaneously to the system in time sharing, while more than one program is run at the same time under multiprogramming. This assumes, of course, that no single program requires total system resources for more than a small time period. Hardware controllers have been optimized to take advantage of this usual case and permit virtually simultaneous user access to the central processor.

Digital Computer Software Computer *software* refers to all programs which direct machine activities. This software can be generally divided into three classes: an operating or executive system; language assemblers, translators and compilers; user applications programs, mathematical program libraries, and data analysis packages. The first class generally goes under acronyms similar to Disk Operating System (DOS), Mass Storage Operating System (MSOS), Real Time Executive (RTE), or other such names. It is the function of this master software to schedule users and users' programs, allocate processor and peripheral resources, perform internal "housekeeping," and handle emergencies. It is the operating system that permits time sharing and multiprogramming to be carried out. All but the most basic systems offer this software. The second software class operates within or is subject to the OS. It includes such things as FORTRAN (Formula Translator) compilers, BASIC (Beginners All-Purpose Symbolic Instruction Code) interpreters, a system editor, and an assembler. These and other conversion programs reside within the machine and are used to change English language statements or data to machine bit patterns which are decoded internally. Standards have been devised for FORTRAN, BASIC, ALGOL, COBOL, PL/I and other languages so that a program written on one manufacturer's machine will (almost) run on another. Assembly languages, however, are machine independent and in no way compatible. The final class of software includes those programs designed and written to accomplish a specific task. For example: find the roots of a polynomial expression of a certain type; or given a set of data describing the elongation versus temperature and load of an alloy specimen, as well as known constants, calculate stress and strain values at the break point. On small dedicated computer systems a single application package may be the only software loaded other than input/output drivers which communicate with peripheral devices. This is true of minicomputers used as communications processors, experiment controllers, front-end machines and, in general, all computers that have less than 8000 words of central memory. Software clearing houses that supply computer programs worldwide for exclusive manufacturers, as well as for general use, have gone into business to meet the demand for application programs.

Scientific Applications The evolution of the digital computer and modern scientific knowledge are closely linked. We have seen that development of the ENIAC was the direct result of the need to perform millions of calculations on the Manhattan Project that would have taken years during a time when years were not available. A second example is the fact that no attempt was made to find a rigorous solution of the "3-Body Problem" of celestial mechanics until the advent of the modern digital computer. Today these servants of scientists and engineers are found in their smaller versions in more physics laboratories than not. Theoretical data or that produced by passive data acquisition devices is then transmitted to larger systems for further processing. Where theoretical studies are involved, large systems perform computations that would simply not be practically possible otherwise. Examples of typical applications or user software now in use to solve particular scientific problems include programs to: calculate Cartesian coordinates for all atoms in a molecule, compute numerical eigenvalues and matrix elements for the quantum mechanical radial equation, and determine the coulomb lattice energy of an ionic crystal. There is also a complete system of programs for quantitative theoretical chemistry. In the area of direct data acquisition and instrument control, small computer systems of the configuration shown in Fig. 4 are most often employed. These systems are built as part of electron spin and nuclear

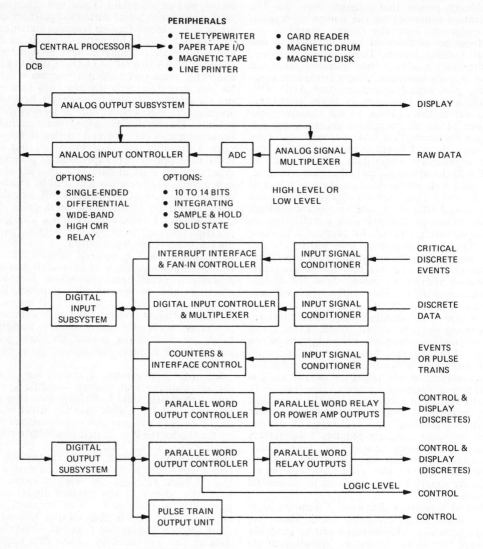

FIG. 4. Typical data acquisition and analysis configuration.

magnetic resonance spectrometers, all types of optical spectrophotometers, real time Fourier analyzers, and x-ray spectrometers, to name only a few. They are used to control and acquire data in applications ranging from remote seismic stations to laboratory spark chamber monitoring. In physics education they find uses ranging from teaching basic principles to performing semiautomatic pattern recognition for bubble chamber film data analysis.

Future Developments As we have shown, the computer industry has yet to celebrate its silver anniversary, but there is almost no area of our life which it has not affected. Today the world population of computers exceeds 70 000 units. In terms of dollars, the hardware, soft-

ware and manpower investment is on the order of 100 billion dollars. Despite these impressive figures, which point to success, many serious shortcomings in computer technology and its application are evident. Most experts agree that hardware advances at the component level will slow down. Peripheral devices such as line printers, card readers, etc., appear to be approaching their capacity limits. These devices must give way to new technologies or be reduced in cost to the extent that they can proliferate infinitely. It seems more reasonable that they will give way to more direct user involvement through input/output terminals and direct data transfer. The direction of central and mass memory supports this contention since costs,

speed, and density continue to improve drastically. This trend will continue for some time with mechanical devices giving way to new approaches employing chemical and basic molecular phenomena. Real future advances will occur as a result of changes in arithmetic and control elements and in the software systems which drive computers. Micro-processors made possible by large scale integrated circuitry (LSI) will allow "intelligence" to be built into all computer peripherals and make possible special purpose modules to be employed for handling a single arithmetic or control function. This will permit many more operations to be performed in parallel, thus decreasing time to solution. The low cost of these modules will cause them to begin to appear almost everywhere. Few scientific instruments will be built where they are not employed as control elements or to provide at least intermediate results directly. Software development will respond to make use of this distributed internal processing and permit better machine and manpower utilization. More emphasis will be placed on high level languages similar to PL/I and on the development of applications packages which will handle a given problem from start to finish. Less distinction will be made between systems and language routines. A single tool will be available to accomplish a given objective. Problems like code conversions between units will be handled by hardware. Modular programming techniques and top-down software management will harness software development making distributed intelligence and application of automatic data processing a reality in all fields.

DENNIS E. WISNOSKY

References

Weik, Martin H., "Standard Dictionary of Computers and Information Processing," New York, Handen Book Co., 1969.

Davis, Gordon B., "An Introduction to Electronic Computers," New York, McGraw-Hill Book Co., 1965.

Bernstein, Jeremy, "The Analytical Engine: Computers, Past, Present, and Future," New York, Random House Inc., 1963.

Boole, George, "An Investigation of the Laws of Thought," New York, Dover Publications, 1954.

Quantum Chemistry Program Exchange, Indiana University, Bloomington, Indiana 47401.

Korn, Granizo Arthur, "Minicomputers for Engineers and Scientists," New York, McGraw-Hill Book Co., 1973.

Perone, Sam P. and Jones, David O., "Digital Computers in Scientific Instrumentation," New York, McGraw-Hill Book Co., 1973.

"Digital Products and Applications," Digital Equipment Corporation, Maynard, Massachusetts, 1971.

"CDC System 17 Computer Systems Applications Guide," Control Data Corporation, Minneapolis, Minnesota, 1973.

Petrocelli, O. R., Ed., "The Best Computer Papers of 1971," Princeton, Auerbach Publishers Inc., 1972.

Cross-references: MEASUREMENTS, PRINCIPLES OF; CYBERNETICS.

CONDENSATION

The condensation of a vapor to form a liquid, other amorphous phase, or crystal generally occurs by the mechanisms of nucleation and subsequent growth. Nucleation is a thermally activated process which leads to a stable fragment of the condensed phase. In the absence of surfaces of certain condensed phases, reactive foreign molecules, or other potent catalysts to the nucleation process, it is usually the slower step and occurs at an appreciable rate only under conditions considerably removed from equilibrium. For the usual case where nucleation catalysts are present, the process is characterized as heterogeneous nucleation, but if there are no such catalysts at all, it is called homogeneous nucleation.

In principle, statistical thermodynamics would appear to offer the most attractive approach to nucleation rate theory. For example, Band[1] and Hill[2] have given formal treatments for the equilibrium concentration of clusters of molecules in a vapor. However, the internal partition functions have thus far eluded quantitative evaluation. Further, in the case of metallic systems, there is at present little knowledge of the electronic energy states in clusters containing only a few atoms.

Accordingly, even to the present day, most treatments follow that of Volmer[3] and co-workers who evaluated the free energy of formation of clusters by ascribing macroscopic thermodynamic properties to them. Thus the free energy of a droplet is described as the sum of a surface term (area times surface tension) and a volume term (volume times the negative bulk free energy change). An attractive feature of this approach is that it permits ready visualization of the origin of the free energy barrier to nucleation in terms of the maximum in the above sum as a function of size. However, a very unattractive aspect is that the calculated size of the critical nucleus, i.e., the cluster size at the top of the free energy barrier, is only about 100 molecules, which leads one to doubt the applicability of macroscopic concepts in the present examples. Nevertheless, following standard methods,[4] this spherical-drop model leads directly to a rather simple expression for the rate of homogeneous nucleation of droplets from supersaturated vapor.

The remarkable agreement[3,5] of this macroscopic theory with observations of the critical supersaturations for appreciable nucleation rates of various liquids in cloud chambers stood for many years as the basis of our knowledge of nucleation. For example, referring to the data

of C. T. R. Wilson[6] and of C. F. Powell[7] who reported a "fog limit"* for homogeneous nucleation of water droplets at a supersaturation ratio of about 5.0 at 275K,† agreement with the macroscopic theory is excellent.[8] However, in recent years it has been pointed out[4,5,8,9,10] that the external partition functions for free translation and rotation had been neglected in the macroscopic theory. When these contributions are included, the theory predicts a critical‡ supersaturation ratio of about 3.0 for water vapor at 275K, in poor quantitative agreement with Powell's observations. This situation stimulated a great deal of experimental and theoretical work in the field. On the experimental side, two new techniques were developed to measure critical supersaturation ratios for homogeneous nucleation: (1) the diffusion cloud chamber[11,12] and (2) the supersonic nozzle method.[13] Work is still in progress, but it appears that there are some substances, e.g., ammonia and chloroform, which follow the revised formulation of the macroscopic theory, which includes the contributions from free translation and rotation.[14,15] On the theoretical side, much effort has been directed toward ascertaining the magnitude of another correction to the macroscopic theory, which tends to counterbalance the effects of free translation and rotation. This is termed the replacement partition function, and it describes the free energy due to the six internal degrees of freedom the isolated cluster does not have because it is not a part of the bulk phase. Efforts to calculate this quantity by classical phase integral methods[10,16] have not been entirely successful because of the great difficulty in defining an embedded cluster in a liquid. However, real progress has been made through normal mode computer calculations of the vibrational free energy of isolated crystallites.[17,18,19] Results available at the present time show that the replacement free energy, though quite appreciable, by no means offsets the contributions from free translation and rotation. Monte Carlo computer calculations will be needed to determine the replacement free energy for the case of liquids.

Interesting insights into the nucleation process are afforded by observations of critical supersaturations for heterogeneous nucleation on gaseous ions.[3,20,21] It is believed that there is, in general, a large electrostatic contribution which tends to reduce the free energy of formation of droplets on ions; indeed, gaseous ions are thought to be coated with an adsorbed layer of condensable molecules, even in unsaturated systems. However, it is a remarkable fact that the presence of gaseous ions does not greatly reduce the critical supersaturation required for condensation. This is tentatively explained by the circumstance that, unlike the case of homogeneous nucleation, there is a negligible contribution from free translation and rotation in the case of heterogeneous nucleation on ions because the external partition function for the ion with its "liquid shell" and for the critical nucleus nearly cancel. Thus the presence of electrostatic effects is thought to be nearly offset by the absence of any appreciable negative contribution from free translation and rotation.

A considerable amount of work has been done on the heterogeneous nucleation of metal crystals from thermal vapor beams onto substrates.[5] Most theoretical approaches follow a macroscopic treatment similar to that outlined above. In view of the high supersaturation ratios, typically 10^6 to 10^{33}, and resulting small critical nucleus sizes (1 to 5 atoms) involved in this case, an "atomistic" theory[22,23] has been introduced to replace the older macroscopic theory. However, quantitative agreement with observed supersaturations for appreciable nucleation rate is not good for either the old or the new theory. Nevertheless it has been established that in most cases nucleation occurs by the processes of adsorption, surface diffusion, and statistical fluctuation to form the crystalline nuclei. Also, the qualitative relationships between nucleation and epitaxial deposition are thought to have been reasonably well established. Finally, the field emission microscope has yielded interesting information on nucleation of metals in deposition from the vapor onto clean tungsten field emitter tips.[24,25] Some metals, e.g., copper and gold, form critical adsorbed coverages of several monatomic layers before nucleation of crystals occurs.

Growth is the process by which the stable nuclei continue to grow and thereby consume the supersaturated vapor. In general, several mechanisms are involved in the growth process, and some of these are thermally activated. However, the free energies of activation are usually low, and hence most growth processes proceed at an appreciable rate even under conditions close to equilibrium where the gross evaporation flux almost equals the gross condensation flux. The first step in growth from the vapor is thought to be adsorption of the impingent molecule. The overwhelming bulk of both experimental and theoretical work[5] indicates that the impingent atoms or molecules are in most cases thermally accommodated and adsorbed at the surface before being either reevaporated or integrated into the liquid or crystalline structure. In the case of liquids with asymmetric molecules, Eyring[5] and co-workers have shown that there is an entropy contribution to the free energy of activation which tends to reduce the adsorption efficiency* and

---

*Denoting production of many droplets, i.e., of the order of 10^7 cm^{-3}.

†Meaning the ratio of actual to equilibrium partial pressure of vapor.

‡Critical for a given, usually high, nucleation rate.

*Ratio of molecules which become adsorbed to those which impinge.

hence the condensation coefficient[†] to somewhat below unity.

In the case of liquids, it is thought that the molecular mobility is sufficiently high that the adsorbed molecules are taken almost immediately into the liquid structure. However, the situation is quite different for crystals, whose surfaces are still most conveniently visualized in terms of the original "atomic building block" model of Kossel[26] and Stranski.[27] Thus, in the case of certain surfaces of high index, the kinks in the steps of the atomically rough surface provide ready sinks for adsorbed molecules. In fact, experiment shows that such planes grow so rapidly that they quickly eliminate themselves from the crystal growth form, leaving the smoother surfaces of low index. These closely packed planes contain no steps and kinks to serve as sinks for the admolecules diffusing on the surface. Accordingly, for a perfect crystal, it is thought that growth can proceed only by nucleation of new monomolecular layers, whose edges provide the sinks, and their lateral propagation. A typical supersaturation ratio for appreciable growth by this mechanism is of the order of 1.5 for molecular substances, and there is a large amount of theoretical and experimental evidence[28] for the general occurrence of this type of growth from the vapor at high supersaturations.

The fact that real crystals do indeed grow at much lower supersaturation ratios, of the order 1.01, continued to present a theoretical problem for many years. Then in 1949 Burton, Cabrera, and Frank[29] showed that certain emergent dislocations of the screw orientation[*] must provide a source of monomolecular steps for growth at low supersaturations. Further, they demonstrated that the resultant growth form on the close-packed surface, the growth spiral, cannot exterminate itself as do other types of steps or ledges. In the usual case, crystal growth by this mechanism is thought to be controlled by surface diffusion of the admolecules. Experimental verification of these predictions is now voluminous.[30] In recent years it has been possible to simulate the motion of the monatomic steps in growth or evaporation of crystals with the aid of computers.[31] In effect, a very difficult boundary value problem is thereby solved, and it is found that the monatomic steps are in general so closely spaced in the stationary state that the condensation or evaporation coefficient, insofar as it is controlled by surface diffusion, lies below but is close to unity. This result is consistent with many experimental observations.

In the interests of brevity, the complex and interesting effects relating to diffusion in the vapor,[5] adsorption of impurities,[5] chemical reaction,[28] and dissipation of the heat of condensation[8] have been omitted from the above discussion. The subject of crystal growth morphologies is, of course, huge and beyond the scope of the present article.[5,28]

G. M. POUND

References

1. Band, W., "Quantum Statistics," New York, Van Nostrand Reinhold, 1955.
2. Hill, T. L., "Statistical Mechanics," New York, McGraw-Hill Book Co., 1956.
3. Volmer, M., "Kinetik der Phasenbildung," Dresden and Leipzig, Steinkopff, 1939.
4. Frenkel, J., "Kinetic Theory of Liquids," London, Oxford University Press, 1946.
5. Hirth, J. P., and Pound, G. M., "Condensation and Evaporation, Nucleation and Growth Kinetics," Oxford, Pergamon Press, 1963.
6. Wilson, C. T. R., *Phil. Trans. Roy. Soc. London*, **192**, 403; **193**, 289 (1899).
7. Powell, C. F., *Proc. Roy. Soc. London*, **119**, 553 (1928).
8. Feder, J., Russell, K. C., Lothe, J., and Pound, G. M., *Adv. Phys.*, **15** (57), 111 (1966).
9. Dunning, W. J., "Nucleation," Edited by A. C. Zettlemoyer, p. 1, Marcel Dekker, New York, 1969.
10. Lothe, J., and Pound, G. M., "Nucleation," Edited by A. C. Zettlemoyer, p. 109, Marcel Dekker, New York, 1969.
11. Franck, J. P., and Hertz, H. G., *Z. Physik*, **143**, 559 (1956).
12. Katz, J. L., *J. Chem. Phys.*, **52**, 4733 (1970).
13. Wegener, P. P., and Parlange, Jean-Yves, *Naturwissenschaften*, **57**, 525, (1970).
14. Jaeger, H. L., Willson, E. J., Hill, P. G., and Russell, K. C., *J. Chem Phys.*, **51**, 5380 (1969).
15. Dawson, D. B., Willson, E. J., Hill, P. G., and Russell, K. C., *J. Chem. Phys.*, **51**, 5389 (1969).
16. Kikuchi, R., *J. Statistical Phys.*, **1**, 351 (1969).
17. Burton, J. J., *J. Chem. Phys.*, **52**, 345 (1970).
18. Nishioka, K., Shawyer, R., Bienenstock, A. I., and Pound, G. M., *J. Chem. Phys.*, **55**, 5082 (1971).
19. Abraham, F. F., and Dave, J. V., *J. Chem. Phys.*, **55**, 1587 (1971).
20. Thomson, J. J., "Conduction of Electricity Through Gases," Cambridge, The University Press, 1906.
21. Russell, K. C., *J. Chem. Phys.*, **50**, 1809 (1969).
22. Walton, D., *J. Chem. Phys.*, **37**, 1282 (1962).
23. Rhodin, T. N., in "Proceedings of a Conference on Single Crystal Films at Bluebell, Pennsylvania," Edited by M. H. Francombe and H. Sato, p. 31, London, Pergamon, Oxford, 1964.
24. Jones, J. P., *Proc. Roy. Soc. (London)*, **284A**, 469 (1965).
25. Moazed, K. L., and Pound, G. M., *Trans. Metall. Soc. of AIME*, **230**, 234 (1964).
26. Kossel, W., *Nachr. Akad. Wiss. Göttingen, Math, Physik Kl.*, **1**, 135 (1927).
27. Stranski, I. N., *Z. Phys. Chem.*, **136**, 259 (1928).
28. Strickland-Constable, R. F., "Kinetics and Mechanism of Crystallization," London, Academic Press, 1968.
29. Burton, W. K., Cabrera, N., and Frank, F. C.,

[†]Ratio of net condensation to impingent fluxes.

[*]Or edge dislocations with a component of the Burgers vector perpendicular to the surface.

Phil. Trans. Roy. Soc. London Ser. A., **243**, 299 (1950).

30. Dekeyser, W., and Amelinckx, S., "Les Dislocations et la Croissance des Cristaux," Paris, Masson, 1956.
31. Surek, T., Pound, G. M., and Hirth, J. P., *J. Chem. Phys.*, **55**, 5157 (1971).

Cross-references: CRYSTALLIZATION, FIELD EMISSION, STATES OF MATTER, VAPOR PRESSURE AND EVAPORATION.

CONDUCTIVITY, ELECTRICAL

The electrical conductivity of a substance is an intrinsic property denoting the ability with which electric charge can flow through the substance. The meaning of a definite conductivity is most commonly associated with solids, although electrical conduction also occurs in liquids, electrolytes, and ionized gases. Electrons are the usual charge carriers in solids, but ionic conduction can be important for some materials, such as the alkali halides and compounds of the KAg_4I_5 class, while proton conduction has been demonstrated for ice.

A suitable definition for the electrical conductivity of an isotropic material is provided by *Ohm's law*. This is the statement that the direct-current density **J** within a conductor is proportional to the dc electric field **E**. At a given temperature and pressure, the constant of proportionality is the electrical conductivity σ, thus:

$$\mathbf{J} = \sigma \mathbf{E}$$

If the material is *anisotropic*, the magnitude of **J** depends not only on the magnitude of **E** but on its direction as well. **J** and **E** are then non-parallel for some orientations of the material, and σ is a tensor of the second rank. Since the ability of a material to conduct electricity is influenced by the mechanisms resisting the flow of charge, it is also helpful to work in terms of the *specific electrical resistivity* ρ, which is the reciprocal of σ.

If a voltage V between the ends of a conductor of length ℓ and uniform cross-sectional area A maintains a current I through the conductor, Ohm's law may be set in a practical form by combining the relations:

$$\mathbf{J} = \sigma \mathbf{E}, \quad \mathbf{E} = \frac{V}{\ell}, \quad \mathbf{J} = \frac{I}{A}, \quad \sigma = \frac{1}{\rho}.$$

Hence, $I/A = (1/\rho)(V/\ell)$ or $V = I(\rho\ell/A)$, so that $V = IR$. The ratio $\rho\ell/A$ is called R, the *electrical resistance* of the conductor. It is a property of a particular sample because it involves the dimensions A and ℓ, whereas ρ and σ are intrinsic properties of the constituent material. With V in volts and I in amperes, R is measured in ohms. The electrical resistivity $\rho = RA/\ell$ is then given in ohm-meters if A is in square meters and ℓ in meters, while σ is given in (ohm-meters)$^{-1}$ or mhos per meter.

The major factors determining the magnitude of the electrical conductivity for a material are the conduction electron, or ion, density, and the nature of the interatomic forces (which decide the mobility of the charge carriers). The actual current flow also depends on the size of the electric field. Part of the energy carried by the current is inevitably consumed as Joule heat, but there are many commercial devices in which such heat or light conversion is put to good use (electric fires, toasters, cookers, light filaments, fuses, etc.). The rate per unit volume at which energy is converted is I^2R or VI, in units of watts or joules per second. Where it is required to add resistance to an electrical circuit, resistors made of carbon, graphite, or metallic alloys are often selected. When wires of low resistance are needed, copper is the most common material ($\rho \sim 1.7 \times 10^{-8}$ Ωm) although at ordinary temperatures silver is the best conductor ($\rho \sim 1.6 \times 10^{-8}$ Ωm).

In alternating current circuits, the conductivity or resistivity depends on the frequency of the applied electric field. Deviations from the dc value are not appreciable at low frequencies but may become significant for microwave or higher frequencies.

Gases can conduct electricity if they are ionized. Practical applications include discharge tubes, electronic vacuum tubes, and the arc discharge. Natural ionization of the atmosphere results from cosmic rays or radioactive sources in the ground. The conductivity of the atmosphere is quite low at ground level but it increases rapidly with altitude up to 50 km because of the greater cosmic radiation and the lower density of scattering centers.

Many liquids or solutions known as electrolytes (besides a few solids) can be decomposed by an electric current into charged particles called anions and cations. Such processes involve a transfer of matter through the conductor. The conductance of a solution is defined as the current flowing per unit charge applied to the electrodes immersed in the solution and per unit concentration of electrolyte between the electrodes. It is dependent on the number and mobilities of the ions in the solution. In geophysics there is an important field of activity involving electrical conductivity measurements of the surface layers of the crusts of the earth and the moon. But in laboratory physics a principal area of activity lies in solid-state physics, and the remainder of this article will be devoted to such work.

Solids may be classified in various ways (according to their binding, ductility, crystalline or amorphous nature, etc.) but a particularly convenient one considers their conduction properties. Two distinctive qualities are of interest: (i) the magnitude of σ or ρ at a suitable comparison temperature (say, room temperature), and (ii) the temperature variation of

σ or ρ. Three broad classes of solids may thus be characterized:

(1) *Metals* having high conductivities (when pure) with specific resistivities at room temperature lying in the range 1.6×10^{-8} Ωm (for silver) to 140×10^{-8} Ωm (for manganese and plutonium). Less pure metals and alloys may have resistivities up to 1000 times bigger than these, while very pure metals at liquid helium temperatures may have resistivities 10^5 times smaller. In general, the resistivities of metals increase with temperature. Also the effect of adding small amounts of impurities is that of adding a temperature-independent contribution to the resistivity (*Matthiessen's rule*). If ρ_T is the thermal resistivity and ρ_0 is the impurity contribution, the total resistivity $\rho = \rho_T + \rho_0$.

(2) *Semiconductors* which have much lower conductivities than do metals, with resistivities in the range 10^{-5} to 10^5 Ωm. In contrast to metals, their resistivities decrease with rising temperature and very rapidly with the addition of impurities.

(3) *Insulators* whose electrical conductivities are lower still, with resistivities ranging from 10^6 to 10^{16} Ωm. The feeble conductivity is little affected by impurity additions, but it improves rapidly as the temperature is raised.

The basic differences between these classes can be understood in terms of atomic and quantum-mechanical principles which explain the varying degree of availability of free electrons or mobile ions for conduction purposes. The main features are outlined below. An additional distinct class, that of superconductivity, which is a spectacular quantum situation in which the low-temperature state of a number of metals and a few semiconductors is one of zero resistance, is not dealt with here (see SUPERCONDUCTIVITY).

Metals are characterized by their high density of free conduction electrons which transport negative charge $(-e)$ through the interstices of the crystal lattice composed of positive ions. The origin of the conduction electrons is some or all of the valence electrons from the previously neutral atoms. In the absence of an electric field the conduction electrons have high-speed random motions $(\sim 10^6 \text{ ms}^{-1})$, and there is no directed charge flow in any particular direction. But when a field is applied, they acquire a steady net drift, of much lower speed than their kinetic speeds, in exactly the opposite direction to the field. Part of the kinetic energy gained in this way is just as steadily returned to the lattice as Joule heat via collision processes with it. The current density $\mathbf{J}$ is then $-ne\mathbf{v}$ for an electron density of n per unit volume and drift velocity $\mathbf{v}$. The mean-free path between collisions commonly exceeds 100 interatomic spacings at room temperature, or even 10^7 spacings in pure metals at low temperatures. An assumption that the collisions are elastic permits the use of a relaxation time τ, at least under the conditions pertaining at high temperatures for thermal scattering or at low temperatures for impurity scattering. τ is a quantity inversely related to the probability per unit time of an electron undergoing a collision. A basic equation of the form $\rho = m/(ne^2\tau)$, in which m is closely related to the electron mass, can be derived without undue difficulty, so that the major barrier to calculating the magnitude of ρ or σ of a metal revolves about understanding and evaluating τ and its temperature dependence.

A conceptual hurdle here is how can an electron proceed more than a few atomic spacings without being scattered by the massive, closely spaced lattice ions? The reason is that the lattice is the source of a periodic electrostatic field and that the electron waves are modulated by a function having the same period. It can then be shown that such waves are propagated with no loss of energy if the lattice is perfectly periodic. In practice, the lattice potential is never perfect, for it is disturbed by both thermal vibrations and impurity atoms or physical defects. The thermal vibrations are quantized with discrete energy values called *phonons*. For temperatures exceeding the Debye temperature, the phonon density and hence the electron-phonon scattering and the resistivity increase almost in proportion to T. At very low temperatures, $\rho_T \propto T^5$. This is directly related to the T^3 variation in the Debye phonon spectrum which gives a T^3 specific heat at low temperatures. Obtaining realistic estimates of the resistivity magnitudes for metals other than the alkali metals remains a matter of considerable complexity. A useful semiempirical equation is the Grüneisen-Bloch relation because it facilitates the analysis and discussion of experimental data. It represents the variation of the thermal resistivity of a wide selection of metals rather well. In some multivalent metals, but more importantly in semiconductors, electrons behave in a way which can be described by the displacement of positive charge carriers called *holes*. Experimental results are sometimes discussed as if the current arises from the flow of electrons and holes.

Magnetic metals have additional resistive effects due to scattering from localized-spin assemblies. An important field is *dynamic cooperative phenomena* using the divergence of $d\rho/dT$ at magnetic critical points as a tool. Another active field is the *Mott transition* whereby certain materials can be switched from a metallic to an insulating condition using small changes of pressure, temperature, or electron-to-atom ratio. Resistivity is also used to study atomic order-disorder and crystal phase transitions, and in the study of defect production and migration. Its temperature dependence is used for *thermometry* and its strain dependence for strain gauges. Its magnetic-field dependence is the basis of the major field of *magnetoresistivity*. When used together with the related Hall effect, valuable information is

provided on the effective sign, number, and mobility of the charge carriers in semiconductors, while in metal single crystals certain details of the FERMI SURFACE can be deduced.

Insulators and pure semiconductors have no free electrons available at 0 K for conduction. Diamond, silicon, and germanium are typical examples. All their four valence electrons are fully occupied in forming chemical bonds in the solid. Raising the temperature energizes, and frees for conduction duties, a small fraction of these electrons. The empty energy states left behind (holes) also aid in conduction. The fraction of carriers is ~1 in 10^9 for Si and Ge at room temperature; the number varies approximately as $T^{3/2} \exp(-\Delta E/2kT)$ where ΔE is the energy to excite a bound electron and k is the Boltzmann constant. ΔE is ~5.2, 1.2, and 0.75 eV for diamond, silicon, and germanium respectively. The chief difference between the behavior of diamond (a typical insulator) and pure Si and Ge (typical semiconductors) is the greater ease with which temperature can induce conduction in the latter. The conduction of semiconductors, but not of insulators, is readily improved by adding certain impurities. This has the effect of introducing electrons (n-type) or of producing holes (p-type). Such materials are termed extrinsic, or impurity, semiconductors. Their great practical application is in transistors and diodes. (See SEMICONDUCTORS and SOLID-STATE PHYSICS.) Conduction in many semiconductors and insulators is also increased by the photoelectric action of incident light radiation (see PHOTOCONDUCTIVITY).

G. T. MEADEN

References

Blatt, F., "Physics of Electronic Conduction in Solids," New York, McGraw-Hill, 1968.

Kittel, C., "Introduction to Solid State Physics," Fourth Edition, New York, Wiley, 1971.

Meaden, G. T., "Electrical Resistance of Metals," New York, Plenum, 1965; London, Iliffe, 1966.

Meaden, G. T., "Conduction Electron Scattering and the Resistance of the Magnetic Elements," Contemporary Physics, **12**, 313–337 (1971).

Ziman, J. M., "Electrons and Phonons," Oxford, Clarendon Press, 1960.

Cross-references: ELECTRICITY, FERMI SURFACE, HALL EFFECT AND RELATED PHENOMENA, PHOTOCONDUCTIVITY, SEMICONDUCTORS, SOLID STATE PHYSICS, SUPERCONDUCTIVITY.

CONSERVATION LAWS AND SYMMETRY

Among the most basic of the laws of nature are the conservation laws. A conservation law is a statement saying that in a given physical system under specified conditions, there is a certain measurable quantity that never changes regardless of the actions which go on within the system. One of the tasks of physics is to determine which properties of a given system are actually conserved during the course of specific types of interactions.

In classical (pre-quantum and pre-relativity) physics the following conservation laws were known:

(1) Conservation of Mass. In a closed system the total mass is constant.

(2) Conservation of Energy. In a closed system the total amount of energy is constant. (In relativistic physics these two laws are identical due to the equivalence of mass and energy.)

(3) Conservation of Momentum. The total momentum of a system is constant if there is no outside force acting on the system. (The momentum of an object is defined as the mass multiplied by the velocity; the total momentum of a system is the vector sum of all the individual momenta of the parts.) This means that the internal forces within the system have no effect on the total momentum.

(4) Conservation of Angular Momentum. The total angular momentum of a system is constant if there is no torque acting on the system from without. (The angular momentum of an object relative to a point O is its momentum multiplied by the perpendicular distance between its line of travel and the point O.)

Historically these laws arose out of a philosophical belief that the universe was created with a definite amount of motion which remained unchanged following the original creation. As a result of the attempt to clarify what kind of "motion" was conserved, the concepts of momentum and kinetic energy were developed. As early as the seventeenth century Huygens recognized that both momentum and kinetic energy were conserved in the collisions of elastic balls. During the nineteenth century the existence of various "forms" of energy was recognized, and the more general law of conservation of energy arose out of measurements involving reactions in which energy was transformed from one form to another (e.g., mechanical, thermal, electrical). The measurements showed that within certain limits of accuracy, the total amount of energy in a closed system was unchanged by any of the reactions tested.

From the modern point of view, it is not necessary to make measurements involving large-scale systems, for the macroscopic behavior of matter results from the interactions between relatively few types of elementary particles. Therefore it is sufficient to investigate the conservation laws as they apply to the basic interactions between fundamental particles.

At present only four fundamental types of interactions have been recognized: the gravitational, the weak nuclear, the electromagnetic, and the strong nuclear force. Each of these interactions individually obeys the classical

conservation laws. As a result those laws must be obeyed in any kind of action involving interactions between particles. This rule, of course, applies to every activity in the universe.

For example, when we compress a spring, the potential energy of the spring is increased. The modern picture visualizes the energy as stored in the electric fields between the atoms of the spring as they are pushed closer together. Thus, the spring's potential energy is ultimately of an electrical nature.

The development of a conservation law is seen to depend on a combination of theoretical concept and experimental measurement: The scientist forms in his mind an abstract concept of a physical quantity such as energy which can be measured by a given set of operations. Measurements then show that (within limitation of error) this quantity is conserved under a given set of conditions. Modern measurements have been able to verify the conservation laws to very high degrees of accuracy. Conservation of energy has been verified to within 1 part out of 10^{15}, using the Mössbauer effect. (See Reference 1.)

An important function of the conservation laws is that they allow us to make many predictions about the behavior of a system without going into the mechanical details of what happens during the course of a reaction. They give us a direct connection between the state of the system before the reaction and its state after the reaction. In particular we can say that any action which violates one of the conservation laws must be forbidden. For example, many problems involving rotational or orbital motion are solved very simply by noting that the motion must be such that the angular momentum of the system remains constant. No further information concerning the forces or accelerations are required.

With the development of the Hamiltonian method of solving physical problems, and particularly with the growth of importance of quantum mechanics, it has become clear that the conservation laws are closely connected with the concept of symmetry in nature. This is based upon the fact that the interaction between two or more objects can be described in terms of a potential energy function (more precisely a mathematical function called the Hamiltonian of the system). If the potential energy of the system is known for any position of these objects in space, then we can predict the future motion of the objects in the system.

A detailed solution of the equations of motion will describe the position and velocity of each particle in the system at any time during their interaction. However, certain general predictions can be made without going through the complete solution of the problem, if there exist certain symmetries of space and time. The following examples illustrate the various geometrical or space-time symmetries encountered in classical physics.

(1) If the potential energy function does not depend explicitly on one of the space coordinates, then the component of momentum associated with that coordinate never changes—it is a constant of the motion, and thus obeys a conservation law. Particular situations most frequently encountered are as follows:

(a) An object moves in a three-dimensional space where its potential energy is a constant. That is, the expression describing the potential does not explicitly contain the coordinates x, y, or z, so it does not make any difference where the origin of the coordinate system is located. This means that the description of the system is invariant with respect to a translation of the origin of the coordinate system in any direction. As a result of this symmetry the momentum of the object in all three dimensions is constant. In technical terms, conservation of linear momentum is associated with translational symmetry (or homogeneity) of space.

(b) An object moves in a world which is flat, so that the force of gravity is in the vertical (z) direction. The potential energy depends on the height of the object above the ground, but does not depend on its location in the horizontal plane. That is, the description of the system is invariant with respect to a translation of the coordinate system in the x-y plane. Since there is symmetry in the x-y plane, the object's momentum is conserved as far as motion in that plane is concerned, but is not conserved in the z direction.

(c) Two spherical bodies interact in such a way that the potential energy depends only on the distance between the two bodies. This interaction has spherical symmetry, and the system is invariant with respect to a rotation of the coordinate system about any axis; i.e., it is isotropic. In spherical coordinates there are two angle variables, so there are two components of angular momentum to be conserved. As a result the two bodies orbit around their common center of mass in such a way that the magnitude of the total angular momentum is constant, while the plane of the orbit in space never changes. In other words, conservation of angular momentum is due to the isotropy of space.

(2) If the interaction between two objects does not depend explicitly on the time coordinate, then the actions which take place do not depend on when we start measuring time. That is, the properties of the system are invariant with respect to a translation of the origin along the time axis. As a result of this symmetry it is found that the total energy of the system is conserved. In other words, conservation of energy is associated with a symmetry in the time dimension.

Use of a four-dimensional coordinate system in accordance with Einstein's principle of relativity allows us to combine both space and time symmetries into a single space-time symmetry. With this scheme the three dimensions of space and the one dimension of time make

up a single four-dimensional space. Analogously, energy is regarded as the fourth component of a four-dimensional vector whose first three components are the three components of momentum. The symmetries associated with translation and rotations in this space-time continuum are called Poincaré symmetries.

With the rise in importance of elementary particle physics, a new type of symmetry has proven very valuable. These are "internal symmetries"—symmetries involving the internal properties of particles. The general philosophy underlying the study of elementary particle interactions is that anything can happen as long as it is not expressly forbidden by a law of nature. Among elementary particles there are a vast number of conceivable reactions that might take place. However, most of these reactions are forbidden by "selection rules," which are essentially conservation laws. For example, the total electric charge during any reaction cannot change. This rule immediately forbids such reactions as the conversion of a neutron into a proton plus a neutrino. An electron must also be created to balance the charge.

The study of symmetries and conservation laws is especially important in elementary particle physics because the exact nature of the strong and weak nuclear interactions is not known, so one cannot make detailed predictions concerning the results of reactions involving these forces. However, a knowledge of symmetry principles gives one a great amount of general information concerning these reactions, so one can estimate the probability of each reaction taking place.

While a law such as conservation of energy is true for all interactions, a number of the internal symmetries lead to conservation laws that do not apply to all of the four fundamental interactions. Such symmetries are therefore called "approximate" or "broken" symmetries. The implication of the term is that undistorted nature would be completely symmetrical, but that the presence of certain forces leads to an asymmetry, or breaking of the symmetry.

One important class of conservation laws has to do with the constancy of certain essential numbers during the course of particle reactions. These "number laws" are as follows:

(1) *Conservation of Electric Charge.* If P is the number of positive charges in a system, and N is the number of negative charges, then $Q = P - N$ is the net number of charges. The charge number Q is unchanged by any reaction. For example, the creation of a positive charge must always be accompanied by the formation of an equal negative charge (e.g., an electron-positron pair is created by a high-energy photon). Conservation of electric charge is associated with a symmetry property of Maxwell's equations known as gauge invariance, which states that the absolute value of the electric potential (as opposed to the relative value) plays no part in physical processes. In quantum field theory conservation of electric charge is connected with the fact that the properties of a system of particles do not depend on the phase of the wave function describing the system.

(2) *Baryon Conservation.* Baryons are a class of elementary particles including the proton, the neutron, and several heavier particles such as the lambda, the sigma (plus, minus, and neutral), and the omega (minus). Baryons are particles that interact with the strong nuclear force. Each baryon is given a baryon number 1, each corresponding antibaryon is given a baryon number -1, while the light particles (photons, electrons, neutrinos, muons, and mesons) are given baryon number 0. The total baryon number in a given reaction is found by algebraically adding up the baryon numbers of the particles entering into the reaction. During any reaction among particles the baryon number cannot change. This rule ensures that a proton cannot change into an electron, even though a neutron can change into a proton. Similarly, to create an antiproton in a reaction, one must simultaneously create a proton or other baryon. Baryon conservation ensures the stability of the proton against decaying into a particle of smaller mass. Both conservation of charge and baryon conservation are absolute selection rules.

(3) *Lepton Conservation.* Leptons are a class of light particles that include electrons, neutrinos, and muons, as well as their antiparticles: the positrons, antineutrinos, and antimuon. Each lepton is assigned a lepton number +1, while each antilepton has a lepton number -1. All other particles have lepton number zero. In any reaction the algebraic sum of lepton numbers is conserved. This rule determines the course of beta decay, muon decay, and other reactions governed by the weak interaction.

(4) *Isospin Conservation.* Since the strong nuclear force acting between two neutrons is found to be the same as the force acting between two protons, as well as between a neutron and a proton, it is found useful to consider the neutron and proton as two states of the same particle (the *nucleon*). These two states are considered to differ only by the different positions of a vector property called the *isospin* (or isotopic spin). This concept arises by analogy from the fact that two electrons in an atom can exist in a state of spin "up" and spin "down." These two states are indistinguishable in the absence of an external magnetic field because of symmetry of space with respect to rotations around an arbitrary axis. Similarly, a proton is a nucleon with isospin "up" and the neutron is a nucleon with isospin "down." In particle physics, whenever a system can exist in a discrete state, characterized by a definite quantum number, there exists a property (in this case isospin) that is conserved. In the absence of electromagnetic interactions there is no difference between the two isospin states because of

symmetry with respect to rotation in "isospin space." Electromagnetic interactions make a difference because of the charge on the proton. Isospin conservation implies equality of p-p, n-n, and n-p forces, except for the effect of the electromagnetic force. Thus isospin conservation is only an approximate symmetry.

(5) *Strangeness Conservation. Strangeness* is a property of elementary particles found useful to classify hyperons (particles more massive than nucleons) into families. Each particle is assigned a strangeness quantum number S which is related to the electric charge Q, the isospin number T, and the baryon number B by the formula $Q = T + (S + B)/2$. ($T = \frac{1}{2}$ for a proton and $-\frac{1}{2}$ for a neutron; other particles may have $T = 0$ or 1, depending on the type.) Strangeness is conserved in reactions involving the strong interaction. The selection rules resulting from strangeness conservation are very important in explaining why some reactions take place much more slowly than others.

A very important set of conservation laws is related to symmetries involving parity (P), charge conjugation (C), and time reversal (T). Parity is a property that is important in the quantum-mechanical description of a particle or system of particles. It relates to the symmetry of the wave function that represents the system. If the wave function is unchanged when the coordinates (x, y, z) are replaced by ($-x$, $-y$, $-z$) then the system has a parity of $+1$. If the wave function has its sign changed from positive to negative (or vice versa) when the coordinates are reversed, then the system is said to have a parity of -1. During a reaction in which parity is conserved, the total parity number does not change.

Changing the coordinates (x, y, z) into ($-x$, $-y$, $-z$) converts a right-handed coordinate system into a left-handed coordinate system. In terms of symmetry, the meaning of conservation of parity is that in any situation where parity is conserved, the description of the reaction will not be changed if the word "left" is changed to the word "right" and vice versa. This means that such reactions can provide no clue that will distinguish between the directions right and left.

Prior to 1956 it was believed that all reactions in nature obeyed the law of conservation of parity, so that there was no fundamental distinction between left and right in nature. However, in a famous paper by C. N. Yang and T. D. Lee it was pointed out that in reactions involving the weak interaction, parity was not conserved, and that experiments could be devised that would absolutely distinguish between right and left. This was the first example of a situation where a spatial symmetry was found to be broken by one of the fundamental interactions.

The principle of charge conjugation symmetry states that if each particle in a given system is replaced by its corresponding antiparticle, then nobody will be able to tell the difference. For example, if in a hydrogen atom

the proton is replaced by an antiproton and the electron is replaced by a positron, then this antimatter atom will behave exactly like an ordinary atom, if observed by people also made of antimatter. In an antimatter universe the laws of nature could not be distinguished from the laws of an ordinary matter universe.

However, it turns out that there are certain types of reactions where this rule does not hold, and these are just the types of reactions where conservation of parity breaks down. For example, consider a piece of radioactive material emitting electrons by beta decay. The radioactive nuclei are lined up in a magnetic field which is produced by electrons traveling clockwise in a coil of wire, as seen by an observer looking down on the coil. Because of the asymmetry of the radioactive nuclei, most of the emitted electrons travel in the downward direction. If the same experiment were done with similar nuclei composed of antiparticles and the magnetic field were produced by positron current rather than an electron current, then the emitted positrons would be found to travel in the upward, rather than in the downward, direction. Interchanging each particle with its antiparticle has produced a change in the experiment.

However, the symmetry of the situation can be restored if we interchange the words "right" and "left" in the description of the experiment at the same time that we exchange each particle with its antiparticle. In the above experiment, this is equivalent to replacing the word "clockwise" with "counterclockwise." When this is done, the positrons are emitted in the downward direction, just as the electrons in the original experiment. The laws of nature are thus found to be invariant to the simultaneous application of charge conjugation and mirror inversion.

Time reversal invariance describes the fact that in reactions between elementary particles, it does not make any difference if the direction of the time coordinate is reversed. Since all reactions are invariant to simultaneous application of mirror inversion, charge conjugation, and time reversal, the combination of all three is called *CPT* symmetry and is considered to be a very fundamental symmetry of nature.

A new type of space-time symmetry has been proposed to explain the results of certain high-energy scattering experiments. Called "scale symmetry," it pertains to the rescaling or "dilation" of the space-time coordinates of a system without changing the physics of the system. (See Reference 5.) Other symmetries, such as chirality, are of a highly abstract nature, but aid the theorist in his effort to bring order into the vast array of possible elementary particle reactions.

It is a temptation to say that "nature likes symmetries" in order to prove the theoretical necessity of a conservation law. However it must be realized that only human beings can

like anything. The search for symmetries in nature leads to experiments that test the theory. While a symmetry idea may suggest a conservation law, the conservation law must be tested by experiment to see if nature really behaves that way in a given situation.

MILTON A. ROTHMAN

References

1. Rothman, M. A., "Discovering the Natural Laws: The Experimental Basis of Physics," New York, Doubleday & Co., Inc., 1972.
2. Rothman, M. A., "The Laws of Physics," New York, Basic Books, Inc., 1963.
3. Swartz, C. E., "The Fundamental Particles," Reading, Mass., Addison-Wesley Publishing Co., 1965.
4. Sakurai, J. J., "Invariance Principles and Elementary Particles," Princeton, N.J., Princeton University Press, 1964.
5. Jackiw, R., "Introducing Scale Symmetry," *Physics Today* (January, 1972).

Cross-references: ANTIPARTICLES; ELEMENTARY PARTICLES; IMPULSE AND MOMENTUM; IRREVERSIBILITY; PARITY; POTENTIAL; ROTATION—CIRCULAR MOTION; WEAK INTERACTIONS; WORK, POWER, AND ENERGY.

CONSTANTS, FUNDAMENTAL

It is basic to the structure of modern physical theory that physical quantities such as the rest mass of the electron or the speed of light in vacuum have fixed and unchanging numerical values. It is also true that our knowledge of the numerical magnitude of these values is variable and, in general, changes with each new measurement which is made. For example, measurements of the velocity of light made over the past century have yielded results which have varied over wide ranges. This has even led some theorists to suggest that the velocity of light may in fact not be an exact constant but might have periodic variations with periods of several years. Not only does such a suggestion violate established theories of relativity, but it also violates the experimental evidence of a host of well-established indirect experiments. As a result of these indirect experiments, one can only conclude that it must be the experimental technique which is variable, rather than the speed of electromagnetic radiation. The uniqueness of the magnitudes of such quantities as the charge and mass of the electron or of Planck's constant of action has been well established by various indirect measurements and is fundamental to the current structure of physical theory. It is, in fact, the existence of unique magnitudes which is characteristic of the fundamental nature of these concepts.

Fundamental Units The numerical values of the fundamental constants are closely related to the question of units and standards, and it has long been suggested that fundamental physical constants be used as standards for physical units. It has been recognized that a fundamental physical quantity as a unit of length, for example, would be conceptually much better than the arbitrary unit of the foot or the meter. It is possible to consider as an appropriate fundamental atomic unit of length the Bohr radius $h^2/4\pi^2 me^2$, or alternately the Compton wavelength of the electron, h/mc. Because of the limitations of physical measurement, the use of such microscopically small standards of length would sacrifice accuracy in the comparison of the standard with macroscopic lengths. However, the use of a physical unit rather than a completely arbitrary one (such as a standard meter bar) has the advantage of unique reproducibility and universal availability. The optical interferometer allows one to compare lengths in terms of wavelengths of a monochromatic light source. The unit of length is now defined in terms of the wavelength of the electromagnetic radiation arising from the optical transition $2p_{10} - 5d_5$ in the isotope of krypton of mass ·86. In terms of the wavelengths of this radiation, the meter is now defined as 1650763.73 wavelengths, and the foot is defined by international agreement among all of the English-speaking nations to be exactly 0.3048 meters (1 inch = 2.54 cm).*

The unit of time (the second) is ordinarily defined as 1/86400 part of a day. As the available precision of measurement increased and the demands of science and technology became more stringent this definition proved inadequate since the time between successive occurrences of local noon varies through the year. This arises because the speed of the earth in its orbit around the sun is not constant. The second was then defined astronomically in terms of the length of the mean solar day. However, this definition also proved inadequate and the second was redefined as a specified fraction of an astronomical year. In its turn this definition proved inadequate and the second has been defined, according to a resolution of the XIIth General Conference on Weights and Measures (Oct. 6, 1964) in terms of an "atomic clock." The second is now defined as 9192631770 cycles of the radiation of transition between the hyperfine levels $F = 4$, $m_F = 0$ and $F = 3$, $m_F = 0$ of the ground state $^2S_{1/2}$ of the atom of cesium 133 undisturbed by external fields.

The unit of mass and the unit of temperature, however, are still defined in a completely arbitrary manner—the unit of mass, in terms of the mass of the prototype kilogram, and the unit of temperature, as 1/273.16 of the absolute thermodynamic temperature of the triple point of pure water.

*Thus the English-speaking world uses the metric system for standards, if not for units.

Experimental Determinations The experimental determination of the numerical values of the physical constants is uncertain and variable if we confine our attention to the limits of experimental capabilities. The difficulties inherent in measuring physical constants to an accuracy of a few parts per million are great. Direct measurements of the mass of the electron or of the electronic charge are not as accurate as measurements which determine instead various combinations of these quantities. Whereas Millikan was able to measure the elementary charge on an electron in 1912 to one part in a few thousand (and this experiment can hardly be improved upon today), our current knowledge of the electronic charge, with an accuracy of approximately 1 part in 300 000, comes from combining measurements of the Sommerfeld fine structure constant with the gyromagnetic ratio of the proton, the Faraday constant, the magnetic moment of the proton relative to the Bohr magneton, and a half-dozen or so other measurements which affect the final result to a greater or lesser degree. In fact, the present knowledge of the numerical values of all of the so-called fundamental constants of physics come from such indirect measurements. Of these physical constants, only the universal gravitational constant, G, is measured independently of the others. In the first place, no theoretical relation is known which relates G to the other physical constants, and in the second place, the accuracy with which G is known is several orders of magnitude poorer than the accuracy of the atomic constants.

With the growth in our knowledge of natural laws and of the technical means of making precise physical and chemical measurements, an increasing number of relationships have been discovered between the fundamental constants of physics and chemistry. The situation regarding our knowledge of these constants can be considered as resembling a spiderweb of interconnected data or a bridge truss made up of elastic members, in which the length of each member represents the experimentally measured relationship between constants, and the stiffness is a measure of the accuracy of this measurement. The problem is to determine the positions of the nodes of this network. Furthermore, the alteration of any one member will produce an effect which will be transmitted throughout the entire structure. This will be true whether we change the length of a member, or its stiffness, or remove it entirely.

In order to determine the values of the physical constants from such an overdetermined set of data, it has become common to use the method of least squares. This can be considered as equivalent to the problem of minimizing the stored potential energy in our multidimensional framework. The fundamental requirement, however, is basically one of establishing a method of analysis which is consistent and independent of the choice of variables used to describe the situation. The method of least squares not only does this but also provides a procedure which yields "best" values of the constants in the sense that these values are the most accurate. For these reasons, least squares adjustment has been used for all of the significant determinations of the values of the fundamental physical constants over the past 25 years.

Numerical Values The numerical values given in Tables 1, 2, and 3 are based on the most accurate and consistent measurements available as of June 1973. The velocity of light, c, has been determined by measuring the wavelength and frequency of a methane-absorption-stabilized helium-neon laser; the product of these two quantities is the velocity of light. Other significant measurements are the frequency voltage relation in a superconducting Josephson junction which determines the ratio $2e/h$; the Faraday constant, $N_A e$; the ratio of the magnetic moment of the proton to the magnetic moment of the electron, μ_p/μ_e, or to the magnetic moment of the muon, μ_p/μ_μ; the proton magnetic moment measured in units of the Bohr magneton μ_p/μ_B, or in units of the nuclear magneton $\mu_p/\mu_N = (m_p/m_e)\mu_p/\mu_B$; the conversion factor from milliangstroms (10^{-13} m) to x-units, Λ; and the determination of the density,

TABLE 1. DEFINED VALUES AND
EQUIVALENTS

Meter (m)	1650763.73 wavelengths of the transition $2p_{10} - 5d_5$ in ^{86}Kr
Kilogram (kg)	Mass of the international kilogram
Second (sec)	9192631770 cycles of the radiation of the hyperfine transition F = 4, m_F = 0 to F = 3, m_F = 0 of the ground state of the atom ^{133}Cs.
Degree Kelvin (K)	In the thermodynamic scale, 273.16 K = triple point of water $T(^\circ C) = T(K) - 273.15$ (freezing point of water, $0.0000 \pm 0.0002\,^\circ C$)
Unified atomic mass unit (u)	1/12 the mass of an atom of the ^{12}C nuclide
Standard acceleration of free fall (g_n)	9.80665 m/sec^2 980.665 cm/sec^2
Normal atmosphere (atm)	101325 N/m^2 1013250 dyne/cm^2
Thermochemical calorie (cal$_{th}$)	4.184 J 4.184 × 10^7 erg
Liter	0.001000028 m^3 1000.028 cm^3 (recommended by CIPM, 1950)
Inch (in.)	0.0254 m 2.54 cm
Pound (advp) (lb)	0.45359237 kg 453.59237 g

TABLE 2. GENERAL PHYSICAL CONSTANTS[a]

Constant	Symbol	Value
Speed of light in vacuum	c	299792458 m $\cdot$ s^{-1}
Gravitational constant	G	6.672×10^{11} N $\cdot$ m^2 $\cdot$ kg^{-2}
Elementary charge	e	1.60219×10^{-19} C
Avogadro constant	N_A	6.0220×10^{23} mole^{-1}
Mass unit	u	1.66057×10^{-27} kg
Electron mass	m_e	9.1095×10^{-31} kg
	M_e	5.4858×10^{-4} u
Proton mass	m_p	1.67265×10^{-27} kg
	M_p	1.0072765 u
Neutron mass	m_n	1.67495×10^{-27} kg
	M_n	1.008665 u
Faraday constant	F	96485 C mole^{-1}
Planck constant	h	6.6262×10^{-34} J $\cdot$ s
	$\hbar = h/2\pi$	1.05459×10^{-34} J $\cdot$ s
Fine structure constant	α	0.00729735
	α^{-1}	137.0360
Josephson frequency	$2e/h$	483.594 THz/μV
Magnetic flux quantum	Φ_0	2.06785×10^{-15} T $\cdot$ m^2
	h/e	4.1357×10^{-15} J $\cdot$ s $\cdot$ C^{-1}
Quantum of circulation	$h/2m_e$	3.63695×10^{-4} J $\cdot$ s $\cdot$ kg^{-1}
	h/m_e	7.2739×10^{-4} J $\cdot$ s $\cdot$ kg^{-1}
Rydberg constant	R_∞	109737312 m^{-1}
Bohr radius	a_0	5.29177×10^{-11} m
Compton wavelength	$\lambda_c = h/m_e c$	2.42631×10^{-12} m
	$\lambdabar_c = \lambda_c/2\pi$	3.86159×10^{-13} m
Electron radius	r_e	2.81794×10^{-15} m
Thompson cross section	$8\pi r_e^2/3$	6.6524×10^{-29} m^2
Compton wavelength of	$\lambda_{c,p} = h/m_p c$	1.32141×10^{-15} m
the proton	$\lambdabar_{c,p}/2\pi$	2.10309×10^{-16} m
Gyromagnetic ratio of	γ_p'	2.67513×10^8 s^{-1}T^{-1}
protons in H$_2$O	$\gamma_p'/2\pi$	42.5760 MHz T^{-1}
Gyromagnetic ratio of	γ_p	2.67520×10^8 s^{-1}T^{-1}
the free proton	$\gamma_p/2\pi$	42.5771 MHz T^{-1}
Bohr magneton	μ_B	9.2741×10^{-24} J $\cdot$ T^{-1}
Nuclear magneton	μ_N	5.0508×10^{-27} J $\cdot$ T^{-1}
Proton magnetic moment	μ_p'/μ_B	1.520993×10^{-3}
in H$_2$O	μ_p'/μ_N	2.792774
Free proton magnetic moment	μ_p/μ_B	1.5210322×10^{-3}
	μ_p/μ_N	2.792846
	μ_p	1.41062×10^{-26} J $\cdot$ T^{-1}
First radiation constant	$8\pi hc$	4.9926×10^{-24} J $\cdot$ m
	$2\pi hc^2$	3.7418×10^{-16} W $\cdot$ m^2
Second radiation constant	hc/k	1.4388×10^{-2} m $\cdot$ K
Gas constant	R	8.314 J^{-1} mole^{-1}
Boltzmann constant	k	1.3807×10^{-23} J $\cdot$ K^{-1}
Standard volume of a perfect gas	V_0	22.414×10^{-3} m^3

[a]Based on an analysis of the data available June 1973. The numerical values are expected to be accurate to within a few units in the last digit given. All quantities are in SI (Systeme Internationale) units:

C	= coulomb	T	= tesla
G	= gauss	W	= watt
Hz	= hertz (cycles per second)	Wb	= weber
J	= joule	u	= unified atomic mass unit
N	= newton	K	= kelvin (degrees).

molecular weight, and lattice spacing of a crystal which measures $N_A\Lambda^3$. The spectroscopy of the energy levels of one-electron atoms (positronium, muonium, hydrogen, deuterium, and ionized helium) provide a means of determining the fine structure constant, α, or serve as an experimental verification of the theoretical predictions of quantum electrodynamics (QED).

TABLE 3.   ENERGY CONVERSION FACTORS

1 eV	= 1.60219 10^{-19} J
	= 8065.48 cm^{-1}
	= 2.41797 10^{14} Hz
$\nu\lambda$	= 12398.5 10^{-8} eV-cm
1 eV/particle	= 11604 K
	= 23060 cal$_{th}$ mole^{-1}
1 amu	= 931.50 MeV
1 electron mass	= 511003 eV
Rydberg	= 13.6058 eV
Gas constant	= 8.314 J K^{-1} mole^{-1}
	82.06 cm^3 atm K^{-1} mole^{-1}
	1.9612 cal$_{th}$ mole^{-1} K^{-1}

These quantum-electrodynamic measurements include the anomalous moment of the electron, the fine structure separation in hydrogen, hyperfine structure separation in positronium, muonium, and hydrogen, and the Lamb shift in hydrogen and deuterium. Some of these experiments are of such high accuracy that they outstrip the present state of the theory. The comparison of theory and experiment in these cases cannot give us any information on the numerical values of the fundamental physical constants but can serve only to highlight the areas of further theoretical calculations. All of the data in these tables which depend upon molecular weights are expressed on the unified scale adopted in 1960 by the International Union of Pure and Applied Physics and the International Union of Pure and Applied Chemistry. This scale is defined by the arbitrary assignment of the mass of exactly 12 units to the isotope ^{12}C. As such, this definition replaces both the physical scale of atomic weights based on the assignment of mass 16 to the isotope ^{16}O and the chemical scale of atomic weights which assigns the mass 16 to the "natural" isotopic mixture of oxygen isotopes.

All values are truncated or rounded off to the point where the uncertainty is at most ± one or two in the last digit quoted.

E. RICHARD COHEN

Cross-references: SYMBOLS, UNITS AND NOMENCLATURE IN PHYSICS; MEASUREMENTS, PRINCIPLES OF.

CORIOLIS EFFECT

A marksman fires his rifle due north. In the absence of wind, he might well expect it to travel in a straight line and land due north of him. But will it? The physicist would, in general, answer no on the basis that the earth is rotating and is not, therefore, an inertial frame of reference (see ROTATION—CIRCULAR MOTION). G. G. Coriolis first analyzed this effect in 1844, and he is acknowledged in its name. For large artillery projectiles this effect may be significant, but for hand carried weapons it is usually negligible. For instance, a typical .22-caliber rifle bullet might be horizontally deflected 0.2 meter in traveling one kilometer.

That a projectile will normally follow a path which is curved in the horizontal leads conversely to the idea that to follow a straight path over the rotating earth requires the application of a sidewise force. Even though this appears to violate Newton's first law (see DYNAMICS), it is perfectly true in a non-inertial system—hence, the reason that this force is sometimes called "fictitious."

A body which is moving with constant speed in a straight line in an inertial system is not accelerating and is subject to no net force. An observer in a rotating coordinate system will, however, observe the same object to follow a curved path. The observer may treat this apparent deflection from a straight line as an acceleration which is always perpendicular to the path of the object. It is called the Coriolis acceleration. The apparent force applied to the body to cause the deflection from a straight path into a curve is called the Coriolis force.

The true acceleration of a body moving with constant speed in a straight line in a rotating coordinate system is equal in magnitude to the apparent acceleration just described. An expression for it may be derived simply and quite rigorously, but not generally, for the case of a body moving with constant radial speed in a rotating system. It consists of two distinct components both easily evaluated for the case mentioned. One component arises from the change in direction of the radial velocity of the body, the other from its change in tangential velocity due to changing distance from the center of rotation (see ROTATION—CIRCULAR MOTION).

Suppose the rotating system has a constant angular velocity ω, and the body moves radially with constant speed v. It is initially at distance r_1 from the center of rotation with velocity $\bar{v}_1$. After a small time interval Δt, it is at distance r_2 with velocity $\bar{v}_2$ (see Fig. 1). The two velocities $\bar{v}_1$ and $\bar{v}_2$ are related since the final velocity $\bar{v}_2$ is the vector sum of the initial velocity $\bar{v}_1$ and the change in velocity $\Delta\bar{v}$. Refer to Fig. 2 for a vector diagram of the preceeding statement (see STATICS). If we consider instantaneous values, Δt approaches zero, the angle $\omega\Delta t$ approaches zero, and the chord Δv approaches its arc in length. We may then use the well known angle-arc relationship (arc length) = (radius) (angle in radians), and write

$$\Delta v = v\omega \Delta t, \text{ or } \Delta v/\Delta t = \omega v$$

Now $\Delta v/\Delta t$ is the acceleration component (a_1) resulting from the change in direction of $\bar{v}$.

The tangential velocity of a body equals the product of its angular velocity and its radius of rotation. Equating changes in these quantities yields

$$\Delta v_t = \omega(r_2 - r_1) = \omega \Delta r$$

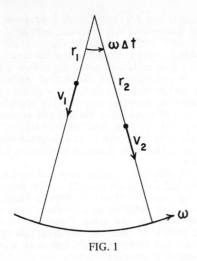

FIG. 1

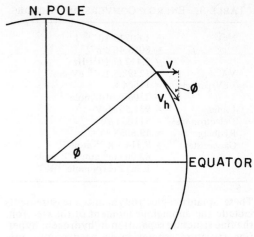

FIG. 3

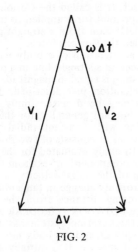

FIG. 2

Or, dividing by Δt

$$\Delta v_t/\Delta t = \omega \, \Delta r/\Delta t$$

Now $\Delta v_t/\Delta t$ is the acceleration component (a_2) arising from changing tangential velocity, and $\Delta r/\Delta t$ is the radial speed v. Hence a_2 also equals ωv.

Since both a_1 and a_2 lie in the same direction, being perpendicular to the radial velocity and to the right in the figure, their magnitudes may be added together with the sum equaling the magnitude of the Coriolis acceleration a_c

$$a_1 + a_2 = a_c = 2\omega v$$

Using Newton's second law $F = ma$, the Coriolis force is

$$F_c = 2m\omega v$$

The earth is not, of course, a rotating plane. The Coriolis acceleration reaches a maximum at the poles and vanishes at the equator. If v_h de-

notes horizontal velocity on the earth's surface, the resulting Coriolis acceleration may be evaluated by reference to Fig. 3 where ϕ is the latitude and v is the true radial speed with respect to the earth's axis.

$$v/v_h = \sin \phi$$

$$v = v_h \sin \phi$$

and the Coriolis acceleration becomes

$$a_c = 2\omega v_h \sin \phi$$

and the Coriolis force is

$$F_c = 2m\omega v_h \sin \phi$$

The Coriolis effect applies to any object moving on the surface of the earth, and a more general treatment will show it to be completely independent of the direction of motion. The quantity $2\omega \sin \phi$ is commonly known as the Coriolis parameter. Since the earth rotates 2π radians in 24 hours, or at a rate of 7.27×10^{-5} radians/sec, the parameter is quite small, and equals exactly 10^{-4} sec^{-1} at about $43\frac{1}{2}°$ latitude. This small value for the Coriolis parameter means that in everyday life its effects are small and go largely unnoticed. For instance, the Coriolis force on an automobile driving at turnpike speeds might typically be five newtons. The acceleration can cause considerable deflection of long range artillery, however, and appropriate corrections must be made.

The Coriolis effect plays a large role in the great mass movements of the oceans and atmosphere. In the northern hemisphere, the apparent deflection is always to the right of the direction of motion. For example, air drawn toward a center of low pressure is deflected to the right and eventually flows *around* the low pressure area in a counterclockwise motion. This motion characterizes frontal storms typical of temperate climates. If the pressure force and

Coriolis force are equal, the resulting wind velocity is said to be geostrophic (i.e., "turned by the earth"). Above one kilometer, the winds are closely geostrophic.

Though it has been only a little over a century since the first analysis of this effect, the Coriolis force has through the centuries influenced man's environment through its control of the motions of winds and waters, and hence the distribution of the sun's heat over the earth. Ancient man, not aware of the motion of his planet, was nevertheless profoundly influenced by it.

JULIAN M. PIKE

References

Byers, Horace Robert, "General Meteorology," third edition, New York, McGraw-Hill Book Co., 1959.
Coriolis, G. G., "Traite de la Mecanique de Corps Solides," Paris, 1844.
Fowles, Grant R., "Analytical Mechanics," New York, Holt, Rinehart and Winston, 1962.
Stephenson, Reginald J., "Mechanics and Properties of Matter," second edition, New York, John Wiley & Sons, Inc., 1960.

Cross-references: DYNAMICS, MECHANICS.

COSMIC RAYS

Cosmic rays are conventionally divided into two classes: primary and secondary. The former are, for the most part, energetic charged particles of extraterrestrial origin, while the latter are the products resulting from collisions of the primary cosmic rays with atoms of the earth's atmosphere.

The Primary Radiation The primary cosmic radiation is quite striking in four respects: the primary intensity is essentially constant in time, isotropic in space, anomalous in composition, and it contains very energetic particles indeed.

Present-day measurements indicate that with the exceptions of the local perturbations discussed under solar effects, the primary cosmic-ray intensity exhibits less than 1 per cent variation in time. In fact, measurements of radioactivity produced in meteors by cosmic rays show that the intensity has not appreciably changed in the last several million years.

Isotropy simply means that there is no direction or directions in the sky from which the bulk of cosmic radiation emanates; this includes the direction of the sun. Since there are magnetic fields of varying magnitude and directtion throughout interstellar space which deflect charged particles, the isotropic nature of the primary intensity is not too surprising. For one can say that, owing to "collisions" of the cosmic rays with these fields, the primary particles lose their "memory" of the directions to their source. Magnetic fields also act in other ways. For example, the earth's field effectively prevents

particles of less than 10^8 eV energy from reaching the earth at all (1 eV $= 1.6 \times 10^{-19}$ joule). Moreover, there is some indication that cosmic rays between 10^{14} and 10^{18} eV may be very slightly guided along the field lines of the local spiral arm of our galaxy. It should be remarked that the diameter of the orbit of a proton of 10^{18} eV moving in the galactic magnetic field would be comparable with the thickness of the galactic disc, so that above 10^{18} eV such guidance is impossible.

The total number of primary cosmic rays striking the earth's atmosphere is roughly 1 cm^{-2} sec^{-1}. These particles are mostly protons, but decreasing proportions of heavier atomic nuclei are present ranging from helium (15 per cent of the proton intensity for the same momentum-to-charge ratio) all the way to iron. Although there are many interesting features of the primary composition, one of the most notable is that the abundance of the elements in cosmic rays is very different from the chemical composition of the sun. Not only are cosmic rays relatively rich in heavy nuclei, but there is roughly one million times as much lithium, beryllium, and boron in cosmic rays as in the sun. These light elements presumably arise from collisions of heavy nuclei with interstellar matter. Such considerations determine a value of a few grams per square centimeter for the average amount of matter traversed by cosmic rays before reaching the earth. This, in turn, gives a mean lifetime of cosmic rays in the galaxy (density $\sim 10^{-26}$ g/cm^3) on the order of 10^8 years or $\sim 10^6$ years in the spiral arms.

The spectrum of cosmic ray energies between 10^{10} and 10^{20} eV is a power law relation given by $N(>E) = A E^{-\alpha}$ where A is about 10^{-9} (cm^2 sec steradian)$^{-1}$ and E is the energy in 10^{15} eV. Between 10^{10} eV and 10^{15} eV the exponent, α, is roughly 1.6, while beyond 10^{15} eV the exponent increases to 2.2. The maximum particle energies which have been detected are well in excess of 10 joules. These are truly phenomenal energies, equivalent to taking all of the kinetic energy of an apple dropped a distance of several meters and giving it to just one proton of the apple's atoms. Not only are some cosmic rays individually energetic, but because of their high spatial density, cosmic rays represent a large fraction of the total energy associated with astrophysical phenomena. The energy density of cosmic rays, optical photons, interstellar magnetic fields, and the turbulent motions of interstellar matter are each about equal to 1 eV/cm^3.

The Origin of Cosmic Rays In the half-century since their discovery by Hess in 1911, the problem of the origin of cosmic rays has remained largely unsolved. The major difficulty has been that of finding a satisfactory mechanism whereby charged particles can be accelerated to the very high energies just discussed. Our sun is wholly inadequate in this respect;

the sun fails on all four counts mentioned previously to be considered as the sole source of cosmic rays.

Present-day speculation considers the sources to be violently active celestial objects; exploding galaxies and exploding stars or supernovae. There are several reasons why such objects may indeed be the long-sought sources. For one thing, supernovae are known to be rich in heavy elements. For another, both types of explosive phenomena involve huge amounts of energy. This is inferred from the presence of synchrotron radiation (the emission of electromagnetic waves by electrons moving in magnetic fields) which implies in some instances electron energies as high as 10^{13} eV. These electrons are most likely the decay products of mu-mesons which are again the decay products of charged pi-mesons. The pi-mesons are created in nuclear interactions, thereby suggesting the presence of very energetic nuclei, some of which could escape from the magnetic fields of the supernovae to become cosmic rays. There are possibilities of verifying such a model, for neutral pi-mesons should also be produced in the nuclear interactions. These mesons decay into gamma rays which travel in straight lines unaffected by magnetic fields. Thus, experiments to detect high-energy gamma rays coming from supernovae and radiogalaxies will be of much aid in solving the long-standing problem of cosmic-ray origin.

High-energy photons have already been observed in the primary cosmic rays. Gamma and x-rays produced by interaction of primary particles with interstellar matter and photons of the universal 3°K blackbody radiation (by the process of inverse Compton scattering) give information on the distribution and composition of matter in our galaxy. Also, more than 100 point sources of x-rays have been discovered. These include pulsars, supernovae, binary systems, and several galaxies. The processes whereby these x-rays are created are not definitely established in each case but may be either blackbody radiation, thermal bremsstrahlung, or magnetic bremsstrahlung (synchrotron radiation).

All high-energy interactions lead ultimately to the production of neutrinos. Although the detection of primary neutrinos is terribly difficult, neutrino astronomy may yet become a useful tool for the study of astrophysical phenomena.

Solar Effects Although the sun has little effect on the high-energy cosmic-ray flux, it strongly influences the low-energy flux during the occurrence of solar flares. At such periods of solar activity protons may be emitted by the sun with kinetic energies of nearly 10^{11} eV. The accompanying increase in the sea-level cosmic-ray intensity can be as much as fifty times larger than the normal value of about 1.0 cm^{-2} min^{-1}.

The earth is surrounded by electron ring currents circulating in the earth's magnetic field. These ring currents, which are named Van Allen belts after their discoverer, contain electrons with energies ranging from 10^3 to 10^5 eV. Occasionally, the sun emits an ionized gas which moves outward with a velocity of 10^3 km/sec. These particles do not have enough energy to penetrate the earth's magnetic field but they do modify the field, thereby releasing electrons trapped in the Van Allen belts. When the electrons strike the atmosphere, the resultant ionization produces auroras. The magnetic fields associated with the ionized gas also prevent low-energy galactic cosmic rays from reaching the earth. The accompanying decreases in the sea-level cosmic-ray intensity are known as Forbush decreases. Since these fluctuations in intensity are related to solar activity, their occurrence is periodic and associated with the 11-year solar sunspot cycle.

The Secondary Radiation If it were not for the secondary cosmic rays, high-energy primaries would never have been discovered. Consider a particle detector of area 1 cm^2 and aperture 1 steradian. With such a detector one must wait nearly 10^{10} years, the lifetime of the universe, before registering the passage of a 1-joule particle. As we shall now see, the detection frequency is enormously enhanced by the earth's atmosphere.

The layer of air above the earth represents about 13 collision mean free paths for an incident proton. After the inevitable interaction of a primary particle with some atom high in the atmosphere, the nuclear debris so produced undergoes successive interactions with air atoms further down in the atmosphere. In each collision pi-mesons are created which decay as described earlier into mu-mesons and gamma rays. Owing to their large Lorentz factors commensurate with their high energies, the mu-mesons continue on down to sea level before decaying. The gamma rays, on the other hand, produce electron-positron pairs which, in turn, radiate more gamma rays. The huge number of electrons created in this way is called an extensive air shower (EAS). After reaching a maximum at an atmospheric depth dependent on the energy of the primary particle, the EAS slowly decays by ionization losses. Even so, energetic primaries can give rise to EAS which contain billions of electrons at sea level. The total number of EAS particles reaching sea level is nearly proportional to the primary energy, the relation being roughly 10^9 to 10^{10} primary eV per secondary electron.

As they cascade down through the atmosphere, the electrons are scattered by air atoms so that, upon reaching sea level, the EAS electrons and positrons are distributed over a large area. The density distribution of these secondaries is peaked around the shower axis (the direction of motion of the primary particle) and decreases monotonically with distance in a plane perpendicular to the shower axis. For example, a 1-joule primary can create detectable numbers of electrons per square meter even at distances

of 1 km from the shower axis. Thus, a small number of detectors spread out in a plane can (a) detect EAS produced by energetic primaries, (b) give information concerning the primary energy from knowledge of the secondary electron density distribution, and (c) be used to determine the incidence angle of the primary particle. The last measurement involves timing the arrival of the shower front (the nearly plane surface containing the majority of the secondaries and propagating along the shower axis with the velocity of light) at several distances from the shower axis. By spreading a dozen or so detectors over an area of 10^6 square meters, several showers representing primaries of 1 joule or more can be detected per year.

In order to extend the detectable upper limit of primary cosmic-ray energies, other techniques are in which effectively increase the sensitive area of the individual detectors. One of these methods involves the detection of the atmospheric fluorescence produced isotropically (hence detectable over a wider area than the electrons themselves) by the secondary electrons as they pass through the atmosphere. A more successful method has been the detection of EAS by means of the Čerenkov light that the high-energy secondary electrons radiate in the air owing to their extremely relativistic velocities.

Among the many uses of the secondary radiation has been the discovery of new particles, notably the positron and the various mesons, and the study of their interactions with matter. At present the secondary radiation is being searched for many bizarre particles such as magnetic monopoles, and more intensively, quarks, the postulated fundamental building blocks of nuclear matter. In addition, some of the interactions provide remarkable clocks for finding the age of many terrestrial features. For example, the collisions of secondary neutrons with atmospheric nitrogen produce carbon-14 which combines with oxygen to form radioactive CO_2, thus facilitating the familiar technique of radiocarbon dating developed by Libby.

JOHN P. DELVAILLE

References

Progress in Cosmic Ray Physics, 1–3, and subsequent volumes entitled *Progress in Elementary Particle and Cosmic Ray Physics,* Amsterdam, North Holland Publishing Co.

Annual Review of Astronomy and Astrophysics, 1 (1963) and subsequent volumes, Palo Alto, Ann. Revs. Inc.

"Proceedings of the 12th International Conference on Cosmic Rays," Hobart, 1971 *Conference Papers* (University of Tasmania), Vols. 1 through 8.

Greisen, K., "Cosmic Ray Showers," *Ann. Rev. Nucl. Sci.,* **10,** 63 (1960).

Greisen, K., "The Physics of Cosmic X-ray, γ-ray, and Particle Sources," New York, Gordon and Breach, 1971.

Ginzberg, V. L. and Syrovatskii, S. I., "The Origin of Cosmic Rays," New York, Pergamon Press, 1964.

Cross-references: ASTROPHYSICS; ELEMENTARY PARTICLES; ELEMENTS, CHEMICAL; RADIATION BELTS; RADIO ASTRONOMY.

COSMOLOGY

Cosmology is the study of the structure and evolution of the universe in the large. The observable universe consists of a hierarchy of stars, galaxies and clusters of galaxies, the latter having typical dimensions of about 1.6 megaparsecs* (Mpc) or 5 million light-years, and containing a few hundred members. It is still in dispute as to whether there are clusters of clusters of galaxies or even higher-order structure. It is generally considered that the space between galaxies and clusters is permeated with a tenuous gas. However, this has not been directly observed and only crude limits can be put on the amount and physical state of the intergalactic medium. The smoothed-out density of the matter which is observable in the form of galaxies is about 5×10^{-30} g/cm^3. The total density, including the unobserved intergalactic matter could be two or three orders of magnitude higher than this.

It was discovered about forty years ago that the lines in the spectra of galaxies are redshifted with respect to their terrestrial wavelengths and that the red shift increases linearly with increasing distance. It is generally supposed that this is due to the Doppler effect and that, consequently, the universe is expanding. It is held by a minority that the universe is static and that photons lose energy while traversing the intergalactic medium by physical processes which are not yet understood. The rate at which the apparent velocity of recession increases with increasing distance is known as Hubble's constant, H. Current observations indicate that H is about 100 km/sec/Mpc; this value could be wrong by as much as a factor of two. The most distant known galaxies have redshifts $\Delta\lambda/\lambda \approx 0.5$ and lie at distances of roughly 1000 Mpc, or 3 billion light-years.

Theoretical cosmologists investigate the properties of idealized "world models" in which, for example, the observed patchy distribution of matter is replaced by a smoothed-out distribution. In order to construct the mathematical models, simplifying assumptions must be made, and the uniqueness of the universe, coupled with the fact that we have only been able to survey a small part of it, means that these assumptions are only partly based on observation. The most generally adopted assumption is the "cosmological principle"—that the universe has the same general character as seen from any point

*A parsec is the distance at which the radius of the earth's orbit around the sun subtends an angle of one second of arc. It approximately equals 3×10^{18} cm.

within it at a given time. A more powerful assumption, the "perfect cosmological principle," that the universe has the same general character as seen from any point *at any time*, forms the starting point of the steady-state cosmology proposed by Bondi and Gold in 1948. In this theory, matter is supposed to be continually created throughout the universe so as to exactly balance that lost by the observed expansion. Thus, cosmology is not, strictly speaking, a branch of physics because although the predictions of a particular cosmology must be consistent with the laws of physics as we know them locally, the cosmologist does not always start by extrapolating these known laws to the large scale.

Probably the first attempt to apply modern ideas to the universe as a whole was made by Olbers in 1826. Olbers assumed that space is Euclidean, that it is filled with stars whose average number per unit volume and whose average luminosity are constant throughout space and time, and that there are no large-scale systematic motions of the stars relative to one another. He was then able to show that if the universe has infinite extension in space and time, the radiation density at any point should equal that at the surface of a typical star! This result was a paradox to Olbers and the paradox remained unresolved until the discovery of the expansion of the universe one hundred years later.

The first dynamical models of the universe were derived after the publication of Einstein's General Theory of Relativity in 1915. This theory, with its idea that space is only locally Euclidean and that the presence of matter influences the curvature of space, made it possible to devise world models which are isotropic and finite in volume but which have no boundary in the sense that a light ray can travel on and on indefinitely. It is also possible to construct expanding or contracting models in which the density of matter and radiation remains uniform but a function of the time and in which there is no preferred center of expansion. Thus the space between clusters of galaxies is imagined to expand or contract in a manner similar to the behavior of a uniform distribution of points on the surface of an expanding or contracting ballon.

We now describe some of the main world models which have resulted from solutions of the field equations of general relativity. In 1916, Einstein devised a static model of the universe in which the density is uniform and in which space is so curved that the universe has a finite volume. In order to obtain this solution and to overcome certain mathematical difficulties, Einstein had to incorporate an additional term, known as the cosmological constant, into his equations. This term represents a repulsive force between masses which increases with their separation. This term has a negligible effect on terrestrial phenomena and on the motions of the planets, but it can have an important effect on the cosmic scale and, in Einstein's static universe, the repulsive term just balances the gravitational attraction.

In 1917, de Sitter found a further solution of Einstein's equations for a universe of vanishingly small density. It represented an expanding universe in which test particles of negligible mass would recede from one another with ever increasing velocity. It was just at this time that astronomers were discovering the red shift of the galaxies, and de Sitter's model, although it represented a universe having zero mass, helped to establish the idea of an expanding universe.

In Einstein's static model, the equilibrium between the gravitational attraction and the cosmical repulsion is unstable. Thus a slight contraction of the universe would lead to the gravitational attraction dominating the repulsion and the universe would continue to contract, and vice versa. On this basis, Lemaître and Eddington were able to devise a universe having an infinite past in the unstable Einstein state until some unknown effect started off the expansion which would then go on at an ever increasing rate.

In all the theories, with the exception of the steady-state theory, the age of the universe (i.e., the time which has elapsed since the beginning of the expansion) is of the order of the reciprocal of Hubble's constant. The currently adopted value of $H = 100$ km/sec/Mpc leads to a "Hubble time" of about 10^{10} years. The measurement of the Hubble constant is technically very difficult and depends in essence on measuring the *apparent* luminosity of an object of known *intrinsic* luminosity. Distances to galaxies within a few megaparsecs can be measured by using cepheid variable stars for which there is a relation between the period of light variation and the intrinsic luminosity; this relation can be calibrated using cepheids in our own galaxy. Unfortunately, distances within our own galaxy are difficult to measure accurately; hence, until recently, the adopted value of Hubble's constant was about 500 km/sec/Mpc. This led to a "Hubble time" of less than 2×10^9 years whereas the earth is known to be about 3.5×10^9 years old! In order to avoid a situation in which the solar system is older than the whole universe, cosmological theories have been devised, principally by Dirac, by Jordan, and by Dicke, in which the universal constants (for example, G, the constant of gravitation) are functions of time. The time-scale problem is now less serious, but the astrophysically determined ages of the oldest star clusters in our galaxy come out to be about 16×10^9 years, or almost twice the Hubble time. This discrepancy is generally not considered serious in view of the large uncertainties in the age dating of star clusters and the measurement of Hubble's constant.

However, if the age discrepancy persists it will be strong evidence in favor of the steady-state

theory of Bondi and Gold, in which the universe has an infinite past and infinite future. In this theory, the loss of matter by the expansion of the universe is exactly compensated by the creation of new matter so that the formation of new galaxies is always going on and only the *average* galaxy need have an age equal to the Hubble time. The steady-state theory has also been vindicated to some extent by recent work on the origin of the elements. It is known that most of the mass of the universe is in the form of hydrogen, the simplest and lightest element, and until about 1950, it was generally considered that conditions necessary for the synthesis of the heavier elements could only have existed in some primeval compact state of the universe before the expansion began. However, it has now been shown that element building can go on inside stars during the normal course of their evolution and that, indeed, the primeval gas out of which our galaxy formed was almost pure hydrogen.

The original form of the steady-state theory was later elaborated by Hoyle who added additional terms to the field equations of general relativity to represent the creation of matter. In 1963, Hoyle and Narlikar advanced a new version of the theory which is claimed to incorporate Mach's principle—the idea that the inertia of a body is due to its interaction with distant parts of the universe. Failure to incorporate Mach's principle has long been considered to be a major drawback to the cosmologies based on the conventional field equations.

On the observational side the major step forward in recent years has been the discovery that many of the radio astronomical sources are extremely distant abnormal galaxies. This has led to the discovery of the most distant known galaxies and to attempts to decide between the various cosmological models by examining the way in which the number of sources increases with decreasing luminosity. The first indications were that the data favor an evolutionary rather than the steady-state cosmology, but this cannot be confirmed until more is known about the intrinsic distribution in luminosity of the radio galaxies.

W. L. W. SARGENT

References

Bondi, H., "Cosmology," Second edition, London and New York, Cambridge University Press, 1961.

Hubble, E. P., "The Realm of the Nebulae," New Haven, Conn., Yale University Press, 1936; reprinted by Dover Publications, Inc., New York, 1958.

Sciama, D. W., "The Unity of the Universe," Garden City, N.Y., Doubleday Anchor Press, 1961.

Cross-references: ASTROMETRY; ASTROPHYSICS; DOPPLER EFFECT; ELEMENTS, CHEMICAL; RELATIVITY; SOLAR PHYSICS; SPACE PHYSICS.

CRITICAL MASS*

The mass of fissionable material required to produce a self-sustaining sequence of fission reactions in a system (a reactor, for example) is the *critical mass* for that system.

The chain of reactions will be self-sustaining if, on the average, the neutrons released in each fission event initiate one new fission event. The system is said to be *critical* when that condition exists.

Neutrons released from fissioning nuclei may escape from the system; they may be captured in non-fissioning reactions, or they may produce new fissions. The critical mass depends on the relative probabilities of these processes and on the average number of neutrons released per fission. Evaluation of these probabilities is the concern of criticality calculations which are important in the design of neutron chain reactors.

The escape probability becomes larger for smaller systems, inasmuch as the ratio of surface to volume increases as a system is made smaller. Thus, there is a *critical size* below which the chain reaction in a given system cannot be made self-sustaining. The concept of critical size is often discussed along with critical mass.

Neutrons colliding with non-fissionable nuclei in the system may be absorbed and thus lost to the chain reaction. In fact, not every neutron absorption by a fissionable nucleus results in a fission. Non-fission absorption must be taken into account in calculating the critical mass. For example, a system containing pure ^{235}U can be made to have a low critical mass. If the same configuration were loaded with a sufficient quantity of natural uranium (0.0057 per cent ^{234}U, 0.72 per cent ^{235}U, and 99.27 per cent ^{238}U) to contain the same total amount of ^{235}U, it would not be critical because at certain energies the ^{238}U readily absorbs neutrons without fissioning.

The probability that a neutron striking a fissionable nucleus will cause it to fission depends on the fission cross section (see FISSION) which in turn depends on the energy of the neutron, increasing as the neutron energy gets lower. Thus the addition of a moderator, that is, a material which takes up energy from the neutrons without absorbing them, will lower the critical mass of a system. Water and carbon are good moderators.

The critical mass also depends on the average number of neutrons released per fission. This number changes slightly with neutron energy. For ^{235}U it is about 2.45 for thermal neutrons and about 2.65 for 1 MeV neutrons. The numbers are slightly higher for ^{233}U.

A complete criticality calculation must take into account the fission cross section as a function of neutron energy and the average neutron

*Research sponsored by the USAEC under contract with Union Carbide Corporation.

yield per fission as a function of neutron energy. Also to be considered are the geometrical distributions in the system of the fissionable nuclei, the absorbing nuclei, and the moderator, and how the neutrons scatter from them. Furthermore, the configuration of reflecting material outside of the fuel volume has a marked influence on the critical mass. A complete calculation would construct the spatial and energy distributions of neutrons in the system through the use of a mathematical procedure that models the history of neutrons from their release to their capture or escape. Neutron diffusion theory or transport theory is usually used for such calculations. Actual calculations use idealizations and produce approximate results. Often, criticality experiments are required to verify results.

Finally, as example of critical masses, a sphere 32 cm in diameter containing ^{235}U dissolved in water has a critical mass of about 2.1 kg. The same sphere with ^{233}U has a critical mass of about 1.1 kg.[1] The Oak Ridge National Laboratory graphite reactor was loaded with 31 tons of natural uranium. This contains about 203 kg of ^{235}U.

A thorough discussion of neutron chain reactors is given in reference 2.

C. D. GOODMAN

References

1. Callihan, A. D., Morfitt, J. W., and Thomas, J. T., *Proc. Intern. Conf. Peaceful Uses At. Energy*, Geneva, **5**, 145 (1956).
2. Weinberg, A. M., and Wigner, E. P., "The Physical Theory of Neutron Chain Reactors," Chicago, University of Chicago Press, 1958.

Cross-references: CROSS SECTIONS AND STOPPING POWER; FISSION; NUCLEAR REACTIONS; NUCLEAR REACTORS.

CRITICAL PHENOMENA

Introduction The field of phase transitions and critical phenomena has seen extraordinary developments within the past few years,[1] and in this brief account we shall attempt to provide an overview of some of these, concentrating our discussion on the concepts of scaling and universality.

We shall organize the introduction to critical phenomena about three simple questions: (1) "What happens?", (2) "Why study?", and (3) "What do we actually do?"

"What Happens?" What happens near the critical point is easily explained by means of the example of a simple magnet. The most striking macroscopic property of a magnet is that it is in fact "magnetized"—it can, for example, pick up thumb tacks! Suppose we measure the number of thumbtacks or magnetization as we heat the magnet at a uniform rate. As we heat,

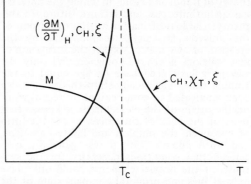

FIG. 1. Behavior (schematic) of some common physical quantities near the critical point.

the tacks fall off one by one, but the rate of falloff suddenly diverges to infinity at a certain temperature (see Fig. 1) and there are no thumbtacks left for temperatures higher than this temperature. We call this temperature the *critical temperature*, T_c, and we call phenomena associated with the critical point *critical phenomena*.

Examples of other critical phenomena are the singularities in two important *"response functions"*:

(1) the constant-field specific heat (see Fig. 2(a))

$$C_H \equiv \text{response in heat content to a change in temperature}$$

$$\equiv T\left(\frac{\partial S}{\partial T}\right)_H, \qquad (1)$$

where here $S = S(T, H)$ denotes the entropy of the system, and

(2) the isothermal susceptibility (see Fig. 2(b))

$$\chi_T \equiv \text{response of magnetization to a change in magnetic field}$$

$$= \left(\frac{\partial M}{\partial H}\right)_T, \qquad (2)$$

where $M = M(T, H)$ is the magnetization and H is the magnetic field.

Thermodynamic functions are *macroscopic* in nature. What is happening at a *microscopic* level to account for the anomalies in the thermodynamic functions? Simply said, the motion of increasing numbers of particles is becoming correlated; e.g., the correlation function,

$$C_2(T, H, \underset{\sim}{r}) \equiv \langle s_0 s_{\underset{\sim}{r}} \rangle - \langle s_0 \rangle \langle s_{\underset{\sim}{r}} \rangle, \qquad (3)$$

which describes the degree of correlation among the constituent magnetic moments s_r of our magnet, is becoming long-range. Here the angular brackets denote thermal averages.

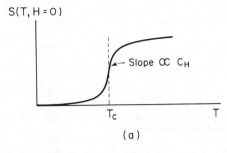

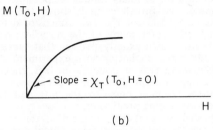

FIG. 2. Definitions of two response functions, the constant-field specific heat $C_H(T, H = 0)$, and the isothermal susceptibility evaluated in zero field $\chi_T(T, H = 0)$. Both functions are singular at the critical point of a simple magnet.

In fact, the "moments" of the correlation function,

$$\mu_a(T, H) \equiv \int |\underset{\sim}{r}|^a \, C_2(T, H, \underset{\sim}{r}) \, d\underset{\sim}{r}, \quad (4)$$

are found to diverge for all positive a and even for a limited range of negative a (roughly $a \gtrsim -2$)! In particular, the zero-field isothermal susceptibility is directly proportional to the zeroth moment

$$\chi(T, H = 0) \propto \mu_0 \, (T, H = 0) = \int C_2(T, 0, \underset{\sim}{r}) d\underset{\sim}{r}, \quad (5)$$

so the divergence of the susceptibility can be seen to be directly related to the increase in range of $C_2(T, H, \underset{\sim}{r})$.

A particularly useful measure of the range of the correlation function is the correlation length, $\xi(T, H)$, defined by the equation

$$\xi^2(T, H) = \mu_2(T, H)/\mu_0(T, H) \quad (6)$$

This quantity can be measured experimentally, e.g., by light scattering, and it is found to diverge near the critical point (see Fig. 1).

"Why Study?" There are, of course, many answers to the question "why study critical phenomena," but certainly the simplest answer is that there exist rather striking discrepancies between the predictions of closed-form theories and our findings in the real world. For example, in Fig. 3 we compare, in a qualitative fashion, the experimentally observed temperature de-

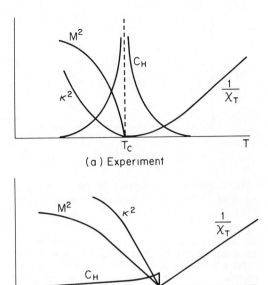

FIG. 3. Behavior (schematic) of common physical quantities near the critical point, (a), compared with the predictions of the mean field theory, (b). Here $\kappa \equiv 1/\xi$.

pendences of the functions discussed above with the predictions of the *mean field theory* (mft) of cooperative phenomena. The mean field theory corresponds to a model in which each magnetic moment interacts with all other magnetic moments in the entire system with an *equal* exchange interaction. Such a model is unlikely to be a realistic model for the task of describing the effects noted above, and indeed we know that interaction energies in a system fall off with distance between the magnetic moments. Thus one reason for studying critical phenomena is that it provides a testing ground for theories that concern the microscopic interactions in matter.

A second reason for the burgeoning interest in critical phenomena is that a wide variety of seemingly disparate physical systems are found to behave quite similarly near their "critical points." For example, phenomena analogous to those shown in Fig. 1 are found in a liquid-gas system (see LIQUID STATE), in a ferroelectric, in a superfluid, in a superconductor, and in a binary alloy or mixture. Accordingly, workers from a variety of disciplines have been drawn together by the problem of critical phenomena, adding to the interdisciplinary flavor of the field.

"What Do We Actually Do?" The answer to this question may be given on many different levels, but basically it is that we simply want to understand on a microscopic level what forces exist between the constituent particles in mat-

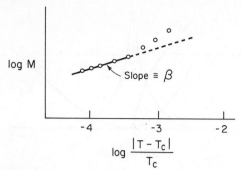

FIG. 4. Sketch of definition of the critical-point exponent β [$M \sim |\tau|^\beta$] to illustrate the general definition (8).

ter, and how they "contrive" to produce the anomalies discussed above and sketched in Fig. 1. As a first step in this direction, it is useful to provide a quantitative measure of the phenomena.

It is found that in almost all systems the limiting behavior of the functions of interest is well described by a simple power law—so that if one plots one's data on log-log paper, the data fall on a straight line sufficiently near the critical point (see Fig. 4). It is important to emphasize that the power law behavior sets in for some systems only quite near the critical point, and when we write

$$f(x) \sim x^\theta, \qquad (7)$$

meaning "$f(x)$ varies as x to the θ power for x near zero," we mean, formally, that

$$\theta \equiv \lim_{x \to 0} \frac{\log f(x)}{\log x}. \qquad (8)$$

There is in general a different exponent for each function and each path of approach to the critical point. The thermodynamic functions considered above all concern approaches to the critical point ($T = T_c$, $H = 0$) in which $H = 0$ and $\tau \equiv T - T_c \to 0$. Accordingly, we define the three exponents α, β, and γ in Table 1 to describe, respectively, the behavior of the specific

heat, the spontaneous magnetization, and the isothermal susceptibility along this path.

The second column gives a typical range of experimental values for the exponents, while the third column gives the values predicted by the mean field theory. The reader would do well to verify from inspection of Fig. 3 that the mean field exponents are correctly listed. That the agreement is far from perfect is consistent with the discrepancies between Figs. 3(a) and 3(b) (experiment and mft).

Theorists have endeavored to calculate the exponents for as many models as possible. For example, the fourth column shows the exponents calculated for the two-dimensional Ising model, for which many of the zero-field properties are known exactly. We see that these exponents agree no better with experiment than do the mean field exponents—in fact, they err in the opposite direction, with the experimental numbers lying in between the mft and two-dimensional Ising predictions.

We shall subsequently argue that the reason that the two-dimensional Ising model disagrees with experiments on three-dimensional systems is that the system dimensionality plays a crucial role in determining critical-point exponents. Indeed, the fifth column, showing the results of numerical approximation procedures for the three-dimensional Ising model, is seen to agree rather better with the experimental results.

Scaling Hypothesis One could continue discussing exponents for other systems, for other functions, or for other paths of approach to the critical point. Until a few years ago this discussion would serve to summarize most of the research activity in critical phenomena. However, we are sooner or later going to seek a deeper understanding of the exponents, and this understanding is just beginning to arise. It is coming not from the exact solutions of model systems—for which the complexity of the derivation all but totally obscures any physical insights concerning the magnitude of the exponent obtained—but rather from an altogether different approach.

This approach began historically with the introduction of rigorous relations among the critical-point exponents—these relations took the form of inequalities, and generally involved

TABLE 1. DEFINITIONS AND TYPICAL VALUES OF SELECTED
CRITICAL-POINT EXPONENTS FOR A SIMPLE MAGNET.

Exponent	Definition	Experiment	Mean Field Theory (mft)	$d = 2$ Ising	$d = 3$ Ising
α', α	$C_H \sim (-\tau)^{-\alpha'}$ $\sim \tau^{-\alpha}$	−0.1 to 0.2	0	0	$\simeq 1/8$
β	$M \sim (-\tau)^\beta$	0.2 to 0.4	1/2	1/8	$\simeq 5/16$
γ', γ	$\chi_T \sim (-\tau)^{-\gamma'}$ $\sim \tau^{-\gamma}$	1.1 to 1.5	1	7/4	$\simeq 5/4$
$\alpha' + 2\beta + \gamma'$		$\simeq 2$	2	2	$\simeq 2$

three exponents. The inequality involving α', β, and γ' is simply

$$\alpha' + 2\beta + \gamma' \geqslant 2, \qquad (9)$$

and is generally called the Rushbrooke inequality.[2] That model systems appeared to satisfy Eq. (9) (and most of the other "rigorous" inequalities) as *equalities* (Table 1), and that most experimental systems were not inconsistent with the possibility that (9) is an equality, did not go unnoticed. However, all attempts to rigorously prove (9) as an equality have been singularly unsuccessful.

It is in the finest tradition of theoretical physics that when one cannot solve the original problem, one seeks to replace it with a simpler problem that one can solve. In this instance, the "breakthrough" occurred in 1965—two years after Rushbrooke proposed the Rushbrooke inequality—by many investigators working independently.[3] Their work generally goes by the name of the *"homogeneity"* or *"scaling"* hypothesis, and is perhaps most easily formulated in terms of a class of functions called *generalized homogeneous functions* (GHFs). A function $f(x, y, z, \cdots)$ is a GHF if we can find functions $g_x(\lambda)$, $g_y(\lambda)$, $\cdots$, $g_f(\lambda)$ such that for all positive λ,

$$f[g_x(\lambda)x, g_y(\lambda)y, \cdots] = g_f(\lambda)f[x, y, \cdots], \quad (10)$$

where the functions $g_i(\lambda)$ are arbitrary except that they possess inverses. It is elementary to show[3] that (10) is equivalent to the statement that there exist numbers a_x, a_y, $\cdots$, af such that

$$f(\lambda^{a_x} x, \lambda^{a_y} y, \cdots) = \lambda^{af} f(x, y, \cdots). \quad (11)$$

The scaling hypothesis is just that—a hypothesis. It involves GHFs, and because of the properties of GHFs, it can be made about a variety of functions. One can make a scaling hypothesis about three different classes of functions: thermodynamic functions (TF), static correlation functions (SCF), and dynamic correlation functions (DCF).

TF hypothesis: Close to the critical point $\tau = H = 0$, the singular part of the Gibbs potential per spin $G(\tau, H)$ is "asymptotically" a GHF.

SCF hypothesis: Close to the critical point

and for large $|r|$, the static correlation function $C_2(\tau, H, \underset{\sim}{r})$ is a GHF.

DCF hypothesis: Close to the critical point and for large $|r|$ and t, the dynamic correlation function $C_2(\tau, \underset{\sim}{H}, \underset{\sim}{r}, t)$ is a GHF.

One can show that these statements are not entirely independent of one another and that in fact:

DCF hypothesis $\Rightarrow$ SCF hypothesis

$\Rightarrow$ TF hypothesis.

The TF hypothesis predicts that Eq. (9) holds as an equality, and thus is consistent with the numbers shown in Table 1. However, it also makes other predictions, not anticipated before. For example, it predicts that all data taken near the critical point can be made to "collapse" onto a single curve providing the data are plotted in the correct units. The single curve is called a "scaling function," and examples of scaling functions are shown in Fig. 5 and defined in Table 2. The scaling function has just recently been calculated directly for the Heisenberg model, and agreement with experimental data on magnetic systems is striking.[4]

Universality Hypothesis The universality hypothesis has arisen from attempts to answer the question "On what features of a model do critical properties (exponents, scaling functions, etc.) depend?" Universality states that the only properties are the dimensionality d and the "symmetry" D, where D actually denotes that dimensionality of the "order parameter" or spin space.

To make this concept more precise, let us introduce a general Hamiltonian which encompasses, as special cases, a very large proportion of the models that exhibit critical phenomena. This Hamiltonian utilizes the concept of classical spin vectors, situated on sites $\underset{\sim}{r}$ and $\underset{\sim}{r}'$ in a d-dimensional lattice, and interacting with energy parameters $J_{r-r'\alpha}$ that depend upon the vector $(\underset{\sim}{r} - \underset{\sim}{r}')$. The important thing is that the spin vectors are taken to be unit vectors spanning a D-dimensional space, i.e.,

$$\underset{\sim}{S} \equiv (S^1, S^2, \cdots, S^D), \qquad (12a)$$

with

$$(S^1)^2 + (S^2)^2 + \cdots (S^D)^2 = 1. \qquad (12b)$$

TABLE 2. SUMMARY OF SCALING FUNCTIONS PREDICTED BY THE SCALING HYPOTHESIS FOR THE *M-H-T* EQUATION OF STATE. HERE δ IS DEFINED BY $H \sim M^\delta$. SKETCHES OF THE THREE FUNCTIONS ARE SHOWN IN FIG. 5

Function	Dependent Variable	Independent Variable
$H_\tau = \mathcal{J}_{\mathrm{sgn}\,\tau}{}^{(1)} (M_\tau)$	$H_\tau \equiv H/|\tau|^{\beta\delta}$	$M_\tau \equiv M/|\tau|^\beta$
$H_M = \mathcal{J}_{\mathrm{sgn}\,M}{}^{(2)} (\tau_M)$	$H_M \equiv H/|M|^\delta$	$\tau_M \equiv \tau/|M|^{1/\beta}$
$M_H = \mathcal{J}_{\mathrm{sgn}\,H}{}^{(3)} (\tau_H)$	$M_H \equiv M/|H|^{1/\delta}$	$\tau_H \equiv \tau/|H|^{1/\beta\delta}$

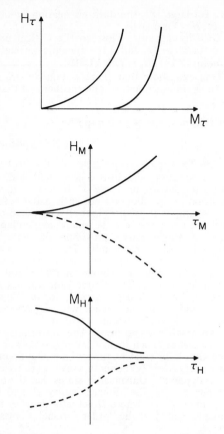

FIG. 5. Sketches of the three possible "scaling functions" for interpretation of MHT equation of state data near the critical point. A dashed line indicates that data are not taken for this "branch" of the scaling function due to MH symmetry.

Thus the Hamiltonian under consideration is[5]

$$\mathcal{H} = - \sum_{\underset{\sim}{r},\underset{\sim}{r}'} \sum_{\alpha=1}^{D} J_{\underset{\sim}{r}-\underset{\sim}{r}'}(\alpha) \, S_{\underset{\sim}{r}}{}^{\alpha} S_{\underset{\sim}{r}'}{}^{\alpha} . \quad (13a)$$

Note that when $D = 1$, this Hamiltonian reduces to the Ising model, since the spins become simply one-dimensional "sticks" capable of assuming the two discrete orientations $+1$ (up) and -1 (down).

For $D = 2$, the Hamiltonian (13a) describes a system of two-dimensional vectors, and is generally called the XY of "plane rotator" model. It has also been called the Vaks-Larkin model, because Vaks and Larkin have considered it a lattice model for the superfluid transition in a Bose fluid.

For $D = 3$, (13a) describes the general anisotropic Heisenberg model, which has proved particularly useful in describing a variety of magnetic materials near their critical points.

For $D \to \infty$, (13a) reduces to the spherical model.[6]

A study that has recently been done concerns which parameters in the general model Hamiltonian (13a) are important for determining the values of critical-point exponents, and which are "irrelevant." To this end, one considers

(1) the lattice dimensionality, d;
(2) the spin dimensionality, D;
(3) the "lattice anistropy" or "nonuniformity of the interaction"—i.e., the dependence of $J_{r-r'}{}^{\alpha}$ upon the direction of $\underset{\sim}{r} - \underset{\sim}{r}'$.[7] There are many important materials for which the interaction strength in one crystal direction is different than in another direction, so this is not "of merely academic interest."
(4) the "spin space anistropy," or dependence of $J_{r-r'}{}^{\alpha}$ upon α. Probably no material is *perfectly* isotropic and there are certainly some materials for which the anistropy is believed to play a very important role.[8]
(5) the range of interaction, or dependence of $J_{r-r'}{}^{\alpha}$ upon $\underset{\sim}{r} - \underset{\sim}{r}'$. Again, there are probably no materials for which the commonly made assumption that only nearest neighbors of one another interact, and that all other pairs of spins are completely coupled, is valid.[9]
(6) the spin quantum number, S.[10] The Hamiltonian (13a) was for classical spins, and corresponds to the $S = 1/2$ Ising model and the $S \to \infty$ limits of the other systems. Materials in nature have a wide range of spin quantum number S, and accordingly we must consider what happens to these models for general quantum number S.

The conclusion of this work is that the only features of Eq. (13a) that are important are lattice dimensionality d and the symmetry of the ground state (which can be measured by an "effective dimensionality" of the spin). This conclusion is sometimes called "*the universality hypothesis*," and it has the implication—if believed—that one need only consider *two* parameters, d and D.[11,12] Hence (13a) may be replaced by[5]

$$\mathcal{H}_U(d, D) \equiv -J \sum_{\underset{\sim}{r}, \delta} \sum_{\alpha=1}^{D} S_{\underset{\sim}{r}}{}^{\alpha} S_{\underset{\sim}{r}+\delta}{}^{\alpha} \quad (13b)$$

where here δ denotes a vector between nearest-neighbor pairs of lattice sites.

Conclusion and Outlook In this all-too-brief introduction to the subject of critical phenomena we have perforce concentrated our discussion on a single type of system, namely a simple magnet. One principal attraction, as noted above, is that a great variety of physical systems appear to behave quite similarly near their critical points. Indeed, the role of cooperative phenomena (and the proposed role of phase transitions) in certain biological systems has long been a subject of fascination for many, and it may be that the concepts that are even-

tually uncovered in our attempts to understand physical systems near their critical points will prove useful in elucidating biological behavior.[13-16]

H. EUGENE STANLEY

References

1. Stanley, H. E., "Introduction to Phase Transitions and Critical Phenomena," London and New York, Oxford University Press, 1971. Second Edition scheduled for 1974.
2. Rushbrooke, G. S., *J. Chem. Phys.*, **39**, 842 (1963).
3. See, e.g., the recent GHF approach of A. Hankey and H. E. Stanley, *Phys. Rev.*, **B6**, 3515 (1972); a comprehensive list of references to all earlier work is found therein.
4. Milošević, S., and Stanley, H. E., *Phys. Rev.*, **B5** 2526 (1972); **B6**, 986 (1972); **B6**, 1002 (1972).
5. Stanley, H. E., *Phys. Rev. Letters,* **20**, 589 (1968).
6. Stanley, H. E., *Phys. Rev.*, **176**, 718 (1968).
7. Paul, G., and Stanley, H. E., *Phys. Rev.*, **B5**, 2578 (1972).
8. Jasnow, D., and Wortis, M., *Phys. Rev.,* **176**, 739 (1968).
9. Paul, G., and Stanley, H. E., *Phys. Rev.*, **B5**, 3715 (1972).
10. Lee, M. H., and Stanley, H. E., *Phys. Rev.,* **B4**, 1613 (1971).
11. Kadanoff, L. P., in "Proceedings of the Varenna Summer School on Critical Phenomena," M. S. Green, Ed. London and New York, Academic Press, 1972.
12. Griffiths, R. B., *Phys. Rev. Letters,* **24**, 1479 (1970).
13. Herzfeld, J., and Stanley, H. E., *J. Mol. Biol.* (in press).
14. Stanley, H. E., in "Proceedings of the Enrico Fermi Summer School on Phase Transitions," K. A. Müller, Ed., London and New York, Academic Press, 1973.
15. Stanley, H. E., Ed. "Cooperative Phenomena near Phase Transitions: A Bibliography with Selected Readings," Cambridge, Mass., MIT Press, 1973.
16. Stanley, H. E., Ed., "Biomedical Physics and Biomaterials Science," Cambridge, Mass., MIT Press, 1972.

Cross-references: ANTIFERROMAGNETISM, COMPRESSIBILITY, FERRIMAGNETISM, FERROELECTRICITY, GAS LAWS, GASES: THERMODYNAMIC PROPERTIES, HEAT, HEAT CAPACITY, LIGHT SCATTERING, LIQUID STATE, MANY BODY PROBLEM, MATHEMATICAL BIOPHYSICS, POLYMER PHYSICS, SUPERCONDUCTIVITY, SUPERFLUIDITY.

CROSS SECTION AND STOPPING POWER

Cross section, σ, is a conceptual quantity widely used in physics, particularly in nuclear physics, to represent the probability of collision between particles. For example, if a beam of neutrons ⓝ is incident from the left on a nucleus Ⓐ, a certain fraction of the neutrons will be removed from the beam by interaction with A.

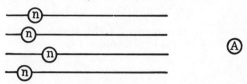

By definition, σ is the fraction of neutrons, contained in 1 cm² of beam, that interact with A.

For a thin layer of material of thickness dx containing N nuclei/cm³ the number of nuclei/cm² is $N \, dx$. If the flux of incident neutrons is ϕ/cm², the fractional decrease in traversing the thin layer will be:

$$- (d\phi/\phi) = N\sigma \, dx \qquad (1)$$

or for a finite thickness x and incident flux ϕ_0:

$$\phi = \phi_0 e^{-N\sigma x} \qquad (2)$$

For a given type of nucleus there are, in general, a number of possible interactions, $a, b, c, \cdots$. The total cross section σ_t is the sum of the cross sections for the individual interactions:

$$\sigma_t = \sigma_a + \sigma_b + \sigma_c \cdots \text{etc.} \qquad (3)$$

A convenient unit for nuclear cross sections is the *barn*, an area of 10^{-24} cm², which is approximately equal to the cross-sectional area of medium weight nuclei.

The *stopping power, Sp*, of a material for an incident particle is the quantity $- dT/dx$, i.e., the energy loss per unit length of path, generally expressed in ergs per centimeter. This type of attenuation is used primarily in considerations of the passage of heavy charged particles, such as protons, deuterons and alpha particles, through matter. For example, for a particle of any spin having a rest mass $M(\gg m_0$, the rest mass of an electron), charge ze, and velocity $V(=\beta c)$, the energy loss (as excitation and ionization) per element of path $- dT/dx$ to a homogeneous medium containing N atoms/cm³, each of atomic number Z, is given by:

$$-\frac{dT}{dx} = \frac{4\pi e^4 z^2}{m_0 V^2} NZ \left[\ln \frac{2m_0 V^2}{I} - \ln(1 - \beta^2) - \beta^2 \right] \qquad (4)$$

where I is the mean atomic excitation potential calculable from the Thomas-Fermi electron distribution function to be $I = kZ \approx 11.5 \, Z$ electron volts.

The *relative stopping power S* is the inverse ratio of the length of a material to the length of a standard substance having equivalent stopping

power (usually referred to aluminum as $S_0 = 1$) at 15°C and 76 cm pressure:

$$S = \frac{(dT/dx)_1}{(dT/dx)_0} = \frac{N_1 B_1}{N_0 B_0} = \frac{\rho_1 B_1 A_0}{\rho_0 B_0 A_1} \qquad (5)$$

where ρ is the density, A the atomic weight, and $B = Z \ln 2m_0 V^2 / I$ from Eq. (4).

CLARK GOODMAN

Cross-references: COLLISIONS OF PARTICLES.

CRYOGENICS

Cryogenics is the production and study of phenomena which occur at very low temperatures, i.e., below about 80 K. The first step in attaining the required temperature generally involves the liquefaction of a gas or gases. Liquids can exist over a range of temperatures limited by the critical point at the higher end and the triple point at the low-temperature end. It is thus possible to compress a gas to the liquid phase at the critical point and to cool it by boiling under reduced pressure to its triple point. A series of gases having their critical and triple points overlapping can thus be used in a cascade process each being used as the refrigerant for the next in the series. Pictet used this method to liquefy oxygen, using methyl chloride and ethylene as refrigerants. There are however no liquids which cover the range from 77 K to the critical point of hydrogen or from 14 K to the critical point of helium (5.2 K). Thus liquid hydrogen and helium cannot be produced by the cascade method.

A gas may also be cooled by making it do work in the course of an expansion. When an ideal gas is expanded through an aperture into a constant volume, no work is done, since there are no interactions between the molecules and the molecules themselves occupy no volume. When a nonideal gas is so expanded, however, an amount of internal work ($W = (PV)_{final} - (PV)_{initial}$) is done against the intermolecular forces; this work may be positive or negative, resulting in a cooling or heating of the gas. Air is cooled by this Joule-Thomson expansion at room temperature, but hydrogen and helium must be precooled to 90 and 15 K to obtain further cooling upon expansion. Using this method, Kamerlingh Onnes first succeeded in liquefying helium in 1908. Compressed gases may also be made to do external work, for example by expansion against a movable piston. In this case the work is always positive and helium may be cooled and liquefied without any precooling by liquid hydrogen. The marketing of a machine of this type designed by Collins has given a great impetus to low-temperature research.

With liquid helium readily available in the laboratory, research in the temperature range 5 to 0.8 K has become commonplace. By using the isotope of helium ^{3}He, it is possible to attain temperatures down to about 0.3 K. Since ^{3}He is relatively rare it is used in small closed systems and is pre-cooled by ^{4}He which is at about 1 K. Reduction of the pressure over the liquid ^{3}He can cool it to about 0.3 K since it has a lower boiling point than ^{4}He. This is about the lowest temperature that can be attained by boiling liquids at reduced pressure, and to reach lower temperatures it is necessary to use magnetic phenomena.

It was pointed out by Debye and Giauque that at 1 K the entropy of paramagnetic salts was still fairly large and, moreover, that it was almost all due to nonalignment of magnetic moments and that the entropy of lattice vibrations was very small. If the electron spins are aligned by application of a magnetic field, the entropy of the salt drops to a low value and the heat of magnetization can be extracted isothermally. The salt can then be thermally isolated and demagnetized adiabatically and its temperature will fall. Temperatures in the order of 0.01 K can readily be reached by this method, and the lower limit for a single demagnetization would seem to be about 10^{-3} K. When demagnetization occurs, the spin system reaches equilibrium temperature in about 10^{-10} seconds. It is found that equilibrium is achieved between the spin temperature and the lattice temperature by spin-orbit coupling in times in the order of a few seconds. Paramagnetic salts have relatively high specific heats at low temperature, and hence the cold salt can be used to cool other bodies; however, making good thermal contact to the cooled salt can be difficult.

Kurti, Simon and Gorter suggested that a further reduction in temperature could be attained if adiabatic demagnetization was performed on nuclear moments rather than the electron spin. The temperature which can be reached in an adiabatic demagnetization is determined by the point at which the entropy of the system in zero external field decreases sharply with decrease in temperature due to the alignment of magnetic moments, i.e., the point at which the interaction energy μh equals kT (h = internal field, μ = magnetic moment). Since the interaction energies of nuclear moments are much smaller than electron-spin interactions, much lower temperatures should result. The materials used experimentally were metals cooled to 10^{-2} K by contact with a paramagnetic salt. The thermal isolation of the nuclear spins during demagnetization was achieved naturally by the nuclear spin-conduction electron relaxation time ($\sim$ 100 seconds). Thus while the nuclear spins cooled to between 10^{-5} and 10^{-6} K, the conduction electrons and lattice remained in thermal contact with the cooling salt at 10^{-2} K. Kurti postulates that cooling of the lattice to 10^{-4} K might be possible if suitable thermal switches can be devised.

Another method of attaining temperatures below 1 K is to use the fact that the entropy of

a superconducting metal is less than that of the metal in its normal state. Quenching of a superconductor by the application of a magnetic field can cause a cooling to about 0.1 K. However, since the specific heat of metals is very small at these temperatures, they are not very suitable for cooling other bodies.

Measurements of low temperatures are usually carried out using secondary thermometers which have been calibrated at certain fixed points previously determined on the absolute scale by a standard instrument. This instrument is generally a constant-volume gas thermometer used at low pressures. When the readings of this instrument are extrapolated to zero pressure, the scale coincides with the thermodynamic scale. In the range 0.8 to 5.2 K, the vapor pressure of ^{4}He provides the most commonly used secondary scale and it agrees with the absolute scale to within 2 millidegrees over this range. The use of ^{3}He instead of ^{4}He increases the coverage of 0.3 K.

Resistance thermometers are useful over a wide range; for example, platinum is used from 273 to 15 K, and carbon covers the range 20 to 2 K and has the advantage of being quite insensitive to magnetic field. The above are examples of secondary standards where the scales are interpolated between fixed points. For temperatures below 0.3 K the susceptibility of a paramagnetic salt can be measured and the temperature calculated by extrapolation from Curie's Law $\chi = C/T$. This method gives true values for the temperatures as long as Curie's Law holds. Beyond this region, it is necessary to perform a thermodynamic cycle to determine the relationship between the magnetic temperature T^* and the absolute temperature T. The method of Kurti and Simon is to demagnetize adiabatically from a known temperature on the absolute scale, using a number of different field intensities, and hence to determine the relationship between T^* and the entropy S over the required range of temperature. Measurement of the amount of heat Q necessary to raise the temperature from T^*_1 to T^*_2 gives the absolute value of the average temperature T_{12} from the relationship $\Delta Q = T \Delta S$. The heat is generally supplied to the salt by gamma rays, thus ensuring even heating of the sample, a necessary precaution since the thermal conductivity is poor. The problem of nonlinearity does not arise in the case of nuclear spin demagnetization since in this case the susceptibility obeys Curie's Law down to 10^{-7} K.

One of the most interesting phenomena of cryogenics is that of SUPERCONDUCTIVITY, which was also discovered by Kamerlingh Onnes. When metals are cooled from room temperature, their resistivities decrease and at low temperature, they attain low values which are fairly independent of temperature. Some metals, however, have a critical temperature below which their resistance goes to zero. Such a metal is known as a superconductor. In a single crystal

of tin, for example, the transition from normal to superconducting may take place in less than a milli-degree. If a current is induced in a loop of a normal metal, it decays with a time constant determined by the inductance and the resistance of the loop. In the case of a superconductor, induced currents have been observed to flow for years without any measurable decrease. Since the resistance of a superconductor is zero, the electric field inside it must be zero; hence, from Maxwell's equation Curl $\mathbf{E} = -\partial \mathbf{B}/\partial t$, we know that $\mathbf{B}$ cannot change inside a superconductor. In fact it has been shown that $\mathbf{B}$ is zero throughout a superconductor. When a superconductor is placed in a magnetic field, supercurrents flow in such a way as to exclude the magnetic field, hence a superconductor is a perfectly diamagnetic body with $\chi = -1/4\pi$. A superconducting material below its critical temperature can be returned to the normal state by a magnetic field (which may be externally applied or may be due to a current flowing in the superconductor). Another property of superconducting metals is the fact that their thermal conductivity is about 1000 times less than that of the same metal in the normal state. Thus superconductors can be used as thermal switches by quenching them with magnetic fields.

An interesting phenomenon which takes place at low temperature is that of superfluidity in liquid helium. As liquid helium is cooled below 2.18 K, it undergoes a sudden discontinuity of specific heat and a second-order transition to the superfluid state. In this state the viscosity of the helium becomes a function of the method used to measure it. Measured by an oscillating disc method, the viscosity falls from 23×10^{-6} poise just above the transition to 1×10^{-6} poise at 1.3 K. Measured by passage through very fine capillaries the viscosity is very nearly zero in the superfluid state. Hence, it is postulated that there are two coexisting non-interacting fluids, one having the properties of non-"superfluid" helium and the other having virtually zero viscosity and zero entropy. It is interesting to note that the thermal conductivity of superfluid helium is about 2000 times greater than that of copper; this is the result of motion of the entropy-free superfluid rather than normal thermal conductivity (see SUPERFLUIDITY).

The use of magnetic properties in cooling has already been mentioned. There are several fundamental experiments on the magnetic properties of materials which become possible as a result of the low-temperature environment available. The first of these was discovered by deHaas and Van Alphen in 1930. They found that at low temperatures, the susceptibility of bismuth single crystals rose and fell periodically as the magnetic field was increased. Later work has shown that the periodicity occurs in all metals at low temperatures and is the result of quantization of electron motion perpendicularly to

the applied field. This effect has recently been used to determine the Fermi surface of metals.

The method of alignment of nuclear moments has been used to study radioactive decay as a function of nuclear orientation. The aligning field in this case can be either an externally applied magnetic field or an internal crystal field. One of the more striking of these experiments has been the test of the Lee-Yang theory of non-conservation of parity in weak interactions. A third fundamental experiment of interest was the confirmation of London's idea that flux through a superconducting ring is quantized. The ring was in fact a lead tube of 10^{-3}-cm diameter, and it was suspended from a torsion balance. The tube was made superconducting in the presence of longitudinal magnetic fields, and the frozen-in flux was measured and found to be quantized.

In addition to the fundamental aspects of cryogenics, several practical applications of low-temperature phenomena have recently been developed. The most striking of these is the superconducting magnet. To achieve magnetic fields in the order of 70 kilogauss by normal methods calls for the expenditure of about a megawatt of power for as long as the field is maintained. The necessity of removing this power by circulation of cooling fluids adds to the inefficiency. When a superconducting coil is used in the persistent current mode, no energy is needed to maintain fields of this magnitude. These magnets have been made possible by the discovery of alloys such as Nb_3Sn and Nb-Zr which have the capacity to remain superconducting while they are subjected to high magnetic fields and are carrying the current necessary to produce the field. A second practical result has been the development of superconducting circuitry. The basic device in this area has been the cryotron, a switch in which the field resulting from current in a superconductor can quench another superconducting superconductor to its normal state. When made in the form of deposited thin films, cryotrons have switching times less than 10^{-8} seconds. The use of thin-film cryotron circuits represents the first attainment of the all-thin-film integrated circuit.

JOHN L. MILES

References

Jackson, L. C., "Low Temperature Physics," Fifth edition, London, Methuen, 1962.

Gorter, C. J., Ed., "Progress in Low Temperature Physics," Vol. 1-5, 1957-1967.

Mendelssohn, K., "Cryophysics," New York, Interscience Publishers, 1960.

Cross-references: CONSERVATION LAWS AND SYMMETRY, DE HAAS-VAN ALPHEN EFFECT, ENTROPY, HEAT TRANSFER, LIQUEFACTION OF GASES, HEAT, SUPERCONDUCTIVITY, SUPERFLUIDITY.

CRYSTAL STRUCTURE ANALYSIS

Diffraction of radiation by the ordered, periodic arrangement of atoms in a crystal yields mainly information about: (1) the nature of the radiation (spectrum); (2) the geometry of the crystal (repeat unit and symmetry); and (3) the distribution of the scattering material in the repeat unit of the crystal. In the last category lies the powerful technique of *crystal structure analysis* as revealed primarily by x-ray diffraction, and also by neutron and electron diffraction. With x-rays the electron density distribution is determined, and from this rather precise information about atomic locations (± 0.005 Å), as well as thermal motions, polarization effects, and disorder phenomena, is obtained. Neutrons yield information about positions and thermal motions of atomic nuclei, and also about distributions of magnetic and spin vectors in the crystal.

Experimental Aspects When atomic properties are of primary importance, the radiation used is monochromatic, usually generated as characteristic x-radiation from a specified target material in a Coolidge tube (typically $CuK\alpha$, $\lambda = 1.5405$ Å, or $MoK\alpha$, $\lambda = 0.7107$ Å). The diffraction effects are observed by various photographic methods, or by means of a goniometer or diffractometer fitted with a pulse counter.

The geometry of a crystal can be determined by routine methods, in which the diffraction effects observed are interpreted in terms of the reciprocal lattice (see CRYSTALLOGRAPHY). Various single-crystal film cameras are arranged to show separately the x-ray spectra produced by as many gratings in the crystal as possible (each spectrum corresponds to a node in the reciprocal lattice), and if the x-rays are monochromatic, each spectrum (or "reflection") appears as a spot-image of the crystal on the photographic film, or a sharp peak on the diffractometer trace. Within the limitations of Friedel's Law $|F(hkl)|^2 = |F(\bar{h}\bar{k}\bar{l})|^2$, so that a center of symmetry is always present in the diffraction effects when the scattering is purely elastic), such observations show the crystal system, point symmetry, and dimensions of the unit cell of the crystal. Further information about glide and screw symmetries may lead to a unique assignment to one of the 230 space groups (such as the common $P2_1/c$, $Pcab$ or $P2_12_12_1$), but may leave a 2- to 4-fold ambiguity. The space group assignment and unit cell dimensions place severe, often crucial restrictions on the atomic arrangement in the crystal, and are a necessary prerequisite for any crystal analysis.

The *intensities* of the spectra, or reflections,

form the basis of the determination of the atomic arrangement. The determination (using x-rays) is based on the development of the electron density distribution in the unit cell by means of the relationship:

$$\rho(x,y,z) =$$

$$\frac{1}{V}\sum_h \sum_k \sum_l F(hkl)\, e^{-2\pi i(hx+ky+lz)} \quad (1)$$

in which V is the volume of the unit cell. The structure amplitudes $F(hkl)$ are obtained experimentally from

$$|F(hkl)|^2 = \frac{Kz}{ALp}\, I(hkl) \quad (2)$$

where A is an absorption factor, L is a geometric correction (Lorentz) factor and p is the polarization factor; $I(hkl)$ is the total intensity in the reflection peak (integrated intensity). The scale factor K is not usually determined, and so the observed data set consists of the relative structure amplitudes $|F(\text{obs})| = |F|/K$, each indexed and identified by the Miller indices h, k, and l.

Though the number of terms in (1) is theoretically infinite, the actual number is always limited by the wavelength and the angular range available. With x-rays (but not with neutrons) the average $|F|$ values decrease rapidly with Bragg angle, so that often no intensities can be measured at higher angles. Within these limitations, an effort is generally made to collect all of the independent relative amplitudes that can be produced by a crystal. Such a data set may contain about 1000 (for simple inorganic structures) or as many as 30 000 (for proteins) observations.

The Crystal Structure Problem A computation of the electron density distribution in the unit cell by Eq. (1) will clearly provide all the crystal structure information that can be extracted from the measured data. Unfortunately, there is one link missing between this desired result and the experimental observations, namely, the relative phases of the terms in Eq. (1). These phase angles cannot be determined experimentally and must be derived indirectly. This situation constitutes the notorious "phase problem" of crystal structure analysis, a major stumbling block in the procedure for the first 50 years following the discovery by Laue of x-ray diffraction in 1912, and one which strongly affected the character of crystal structure research during all that time. In the 1960s powerful theoretical arguments showed how the phase information was contained in and could be extracted from the intensity distributions within the data set itself. Thus, the chasm of the phase problem was finally bridged, so that there is no longer any limit on the complexity of structures that can be determined,

and crystal structure analysis has become a standard and exceedingly powerful tool in the service of chemistry and physics.

Trial and Error Methods Formerly, an empirical trial structure model served as a starting point of an iterative procedure that was used to try to converge on a true set of phases for equation (1). From such a model, theoretical amplitudes and phases can be directly calculated by:

$$F(hkl) = \sum_n t_n f_n e^{2\pi i(hx_n+ky_n+lz_n)} \quad (3)$$

in which f_n is the form (scattering) factor of the atom n (a tabulated function of the Bragg angle), t_n is a thermal parameter of the form $\exp\left[-(2\pi\bar{u}_n \sin\theta)^2/\lambda^2\right]$ ($\bar{u}_n$ is the root-mean-square amplitude of vibration of atom n), and x_n, y_n, and z_n are the coordinates of the atom n. F is thus a complex quantity

$$F(hkl) = A(hkl) + iB(hkl) \quad (4)$$

where $A = F(hkl)\cos\alpha$ and $B = F(hkl)\sin\alpha$. In general, the phase angle α may have any value, but if the origin of coordinates is a center of symmetry, F must be an even function and therefore $B = 0$. In that case the phase problem reduces to a choice of sign for each term in the equation

$$\rho(x,y,z) =$$

$$\frac{1}{V}\sum_h \sum_k \sum_l \pm |F(hkl)|\cos 2\pi(hx+ky+lz) \quad (5)$$

This condition enormously simplifies the phase problem.

The quality of a given model is judged by comparison of $|F(\text{obs})|$ with $|F(\text{calc})|$ obtained from equation (3). The traditional figure of merit commonly used in crystal structure analysis is a relative first moment coefficient

$$R = \frac{\sum \|F(\text{obs})| - |F(\text{calc})\|}{\sum |F(\text{obs})|} \quad (6)$$

known as the "R factor," "reliability index," etc. For analytical purposes a so-called "weighted R factor" is also used:

$$R_w \text{ or } R_2 = \frac{\sum w\,(|F(\text{obs})| - |F(\text{calc})|)^2}{\sum w\,|F(\text{obs})|^2} \quad (7)$$

where $\sqrt{w}$ is the weight of the observation $|F(\text{obs})|$. In structure analysis where the observations often outnumber the parameters by more than 10 to 1, the two R indices follow each other closely.

If R for the initial model is < 0.50, the model may be at least partly correct, and is then tested by forming an electron density synthesis from

Eq. (1) or (5), using only F(obs) terms whose phases are strongly indicated by Eq. (3). This map will show the starting partial model plus other features in the structure not included in that model (additional atoms, shifts in assumed atom positions, etc.), from which an improved model can be derived. This model is then used to calculate new values of F(calc), leading favorably to substantially reduced R, and thus initiating an iterative process of structure refinement.

Vector Maps Considerable information about the structure can be gained from another type of Fourier synthesis that does not depend on knowledge of phase angles, the so-called "Patterson function":

$$P(x, y, z) =$$

$$\frac{1}{V}\sum_h\sum_k\sum_l |F(hkl)|^2 \cos 2\pi(hx + ky + lz) \quad (8)$$

It was shown by A. L. Patterson in 1935 that this function contains maxima at the points in crystal space which represent interatomic vectors in the crystal structure standing at the origin, and that the height of these maxima is proportional to the product of the electron densities of the two atoms forming these vectors. Thus, if there are n atoms in the unit cell, there will be $n(n - 1)$ peaks in the Patterson map, the remaining n peaks being superposed at the origin representing self-vectors for each atom. The Patterson map is a convolution of the electron density over every point in space, or essentially every atom in the structure, and many highly ingenious techniques have been devised to effect a deconvolution. Nevertheless, when n becomes very large, interpretation becomes impossible. The Patterson map and its various convolutions are called generally "vector maps."

Obviously, the task of interpretation of a vector map is greatly simplified if there is one or a very few relatively heavy atoms in the structure (with large f in Eq. (3)), because these will be identified easily in the mapping, and will tend to dominate the distribution of phases in Eq. (1). This is the basis of the so-called "heavy-atom method." Where it is applicable, it can avoid much of the labor involved with more direct methods, and it is still of primary importance in protein structure analysis.

Statistical Methods of Phase Determination D. Sayre in 1952 first noted that when large F terms are concerned, there is a strong tendency for

$$S[F(h_1 \pm h_2, k_1 \pm k_2, l_1 \pm l_2)] \approx$$

$$S[F(h_1 k_1 l_1)] \cdot S[F(h_2 k_2 l_2)] \quad (9)$$

where S signifies $+1$ or -1 according to the centrosymmetric phase of F. This relationship, which depends on the required positivity of the function (1), is the root of the most powerful phase-determining procedures in modern use,

notably the "symbolic addition procedure" evolved by Karle and Karle (see ref. 6). These techniques, consisting of the analysis of vector combinations of the strongest F terms (usually normalized to emphasize the trigonometric part of equation (3)), have been extended to noncentrosymmetric cases with considerable general success, so that the phase problem may now confidently be said to be for the most part overcome.

Refinement of the Crystal Structure Once a satisfactory model structure has been evolved, defined by a given set of parameters (which may amount to hundreds or even thousands), the refinement of these parameters is carried out by differential methods. The least squares analysis of the F(obs) data set (in which a function based on Eq. (7) is minimized) is the most easily adapted to computers and is most widely used. Methods based on minimization of $\Delta\rho$ (using "difference maps" calculated by Eq. (1) with ΔF as coefficients instead of F) are also commonly used. Convergence when $R \sim 0.15$ is considered satisfactory (with standard error of bond lengths ~ 0.03 Å), but as the quality of data measurement and techniques of refinement have improved, R often nowadays reaches 0.05 or lower (standard error of bond lengths < 0.005 Å).

Crystal Structure Data The most important information yielded by crystal structure analysis, namely, the configuration of atoms in molecules and the solid state, and the distances between the atoms, forms a vast body of critical data on the properties of substances which is expanding at a rapid rate. Compilations of these and of unit cell geometry data are published with a lag usually of 10 years or more, so that reference to the journal literature is usually necessary to find reliable and recent data concerning a particular substance. Reference to original papers is also very desirable to answer the important question of the reliability and distribution of errors in a given structure determination.

Data compilations and treatments of techniques of crystal structure analysis are given in a list of selected references below.

HOWARD T. EVANS, JR.

References

1. Bacon, G. E., "Neutron Diffraction," 2nd ed., Oxford, Clarendon Press, 1962.
2. Buerger, M. J., "Vector Space," New York, John Wiley & Sons, Inc., 1959.
3. Buerger, M. J., "Crystal-Structure Analysis," New York, John Wiley & Sons, Inc., 1960.
4. Donnay, J. D. H., and Ondik, H. M., eds., "Crystal Data," 3rd ed., 2 vols., Nat. Bur. of Stand. and Jt. Comm. on Powder Diffr. Stand., 1973 (compilation of unit cell data, references to structure determinations).
5. Ewald, P. P., and Hermann, C., eds., "Strukturbericht," vol. 1-7, Leipzig, Akademische Verlags-

gesellschaft M.B.H., 1931–43 (detailed compilation of crystal structure determinations, 1913–1939).

6. Karle, J., and Karle, I. L., *Acta Cryst.*, **21**, 849 (1966) (symbolic addition procedure).

7. Lipson, H., and Cochran, W., "The Determination of Crystal Structures," 3rd ed., Ithaca, N.Y., Cornell Univ. Press, 1966.

8. Stout, G. H., and Jensen, L. H., "X-ray Structure Determination," London, The Macmillan Co., 1968.

9. Warren, B. E., "X-Ray Diffraction," Reading, Mass., Addison-Wesley Publ. Co., 1969.

10. Wilson, A. J. C., and Pearson, W. B., eds. "Structure Reports," vol. 8–26, Utrecht, N.V.A. Oosthock's Vitgenvers Mij. 1956–1969 (continuation of "Strukturbericht" (ref. 5), covering literature 1940–1961).

11. Woolfson, M. M. "Direct Methods in Crystallography," Oxford, Clarendon Press, 1961.

12. Wyckoff, R. W. G., "Crystal Structures," 2nd ed., vol. 1–6, New York, John Wiley & Sons, Inc. 1963–1969. (compilation of results of crystal structure determinations).

Cross-references: CRYSTALLOGRAPHY, DIFFRACTION BY MATTER AND DIFFRACTION GRATINGS, NEUTRON DIFFRACTION, PARACRYSTALS, X-RAY DIFFRACTION, X-RAYS.

CRYSTALLIZATION

The forms of natural crystals have been studied by mineralogists for many years and have been classified by symmetry, interfacial angles, perfection of shape, and more detailed criteria. These forms are often related to the molecular structure and growth of the crystals. The equilibrium shape of a crystal is that for which the surface energy is a minimum. Since atomic planes of densest packing usually have the lowest surface energy, these planes predominate in the surface facets of equilibrium crystals, resulting in a correspondence between the atomic structure and shape of the crystal. However, natural and even synthetic crystals rarely have the equilibrium shape, because for crystals larger than about 10μ in dimension, the differences in surface energy between faces are too small to transport enough material over the distances required. Therefore the morphology of crystals is usually determined by the rate of crystal growth, rather than by the equilibrium shape.

A crystal is bounded by those faces whose rate of growth is slowest, since fast-growing faces grow out of existence. Close-packed planes frequently grow most slowly, so even when kinetic factors control the crystal shape there is usually a relation between the faces of a crystal and its molecular structure.

Unusual crystalline morphologies result from particular conditions, Dendritic, or tree-like, shapes result when crystals grow with high driving force, or with rapid transfer of heat

or material. These shapes may result from instabilities in growth processes (see Refs. 5 and 6). Spherulitic crystals, which are actually clusters of crystals growing out from a common center, are found in minerals, liquid crystals, polymers, and glasses, and can have a complex structure including helical, twisted strands (see A. Keller in Ref. 4, p. 499). Very regular laminar or rod-like crystals can be solidified from eutectics.

Crystals form initially in tiny regions of the parent phase and then propagate into it by accretion of material. The formation of such regions in a parent phase below its transformation temperature is driven by the difference between the actual and the transformation temperature; however, this formation is opposed by the necessary creation of surface between the crystal and the parent phase. When the volume of a crystalline embryo fluctuates to a value large enough so that this opposing surface energy is overcome, the resulting crystalline nucleus grows. Crystals almost always nucleate on foreign material, such as container walls or impurity particles, because a foreign surface reduces the surface energy for nucleation.

Since crystallization proceeds by propagation of the nucleus into the parent phase, the surface separating these phases is the site of incorporation of molecules into the crystal. If this surface is perfectly smooth, incorporation of molecules into the crystal is difficult; however, if there is a monomolecular step on the surface, incorporation will occur preferentially at the step. Such a step contains kinks or jogs, which are the final sites for incorporation. Thus the progress of a molecule from the parent phase into the crystal is: (1) transport through the parent phase to the crystal surface, (2) adsorption onto the crystal surface, (3) movement on the surface to a step (surface diffusion), (4) adsorption onto a step, (5) transport along the step to a kink, and (6) incorporation at the kink. Steps (2), (4) and (6) can involve reorientation and desolvation of the molecules. The rates at which crystals grow can be controlled by any one or several of these steps. The rate of removal of the heat of transformation from the crystallizing interface can also influence the over-all growth rate.

Under certain extreme conditions the surface of a crystal is "rough," so that molecules can be incorporated anywhere on it. However, these conditions are unusual, and normally molecules are incorporated only at steps. If the crystal surface is molecularly perfect, a pillbox of material must be nucleated on it to create a step, which then grows to another perfect surface. Under these circumstances, continued surface nucleation is required, and growth occurs only below a certain undercooling. However, experimentally, crystals often grow at much smaller undercoolings than this calculated one, so that a continuous source of steps must exist. For this source F. C. Frank postulated a screw

dislocation in the crystal that emerges at the crystal surface. This emergent dislocation provides a step pinned at one end, so that as it propagates it winds up into a spiral and is always available for incorporation of molecules. Many spirals have been observed on crystal surfaces; one is shown in Fig. 1. The surface nucleation and screw dislocation mechanisms for crystal growth were definitely confirmed by the elegent experiments of G. W. Sears on the growth of perfect metallic filaments ("whiskers"), metallic platelets, and paratoluidine crystals.[10]

Impurity molecules can modify the morphology and growth rate of crystals by their effects on the relative surface energies and growth rates of different crystal faces. These molecules can poison growth on certain planes by adsorption at kinks in steps on these planes, slowing the growth of these steps. Impurities can also change the rates of adsorption and surface diffusion of incorporating molecules. The rate of pillbox nucleation can be increased by the lowering of surface tension by impurity adsorption. There-

fore impurities can produce different crystal habits and either faster or slower growth rates.

To make crystals for laboratory and industrial use a great variety of techniques have been used. Growth by either condensation or chemical reaction from the vapor phase can give crystals with high purity and special structures and forms. For large-scale industrial use, this method is too costly, although it is valuable for certain special applications. Luminescent crystals of zinc and cadmium sulfides are grown from the vapor for industrial use. Metallic crystals with few impurities and defects, and in the special forms of thin films or whiskers, can readily be grown from the vapor. Other crystals made in this way are silicon, germanium, iodine, selenium, phosphorus, and a variety of organic crystals. The study of the growth of ice crystals from water vapor has special importance in meteorology.

The most common method of growing metallic and semiconducting crystals is by solidification of their melts. Special techniques have been

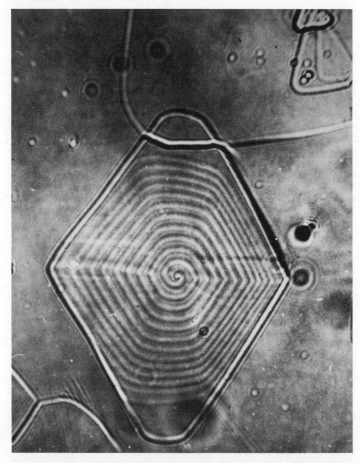

FIG. 1. Growth spiral on a paraffin crystal, observed by C. M. Heck. From Doremus, Roberts and Turnbull "Growth and Perfection of Crystals," by permission of John Wiley & Sons, Inc., New York.[4]

developed to grow single crystals of these materials and many others. In the Czochralski method, a seed crystal is touched to the melt, and the crystal is "pulled" from it by slowly withdrawing the seed. In the Bridgman technique, the melt is slowly moved through a temperature gradient in a furnace, so that crystallization starts at one point in the melt and propagates through it relatively slowly. In the Verneuil method, powder is added to the molten surface of a crystal so that a crucible of other material is not needed. This method is used for materials with high melting temperatures, such as alumina, spinels, rutile, mullite, ferrites, and yttrium-iron garnet. A new method of growing sapphire crystals from the melt, called "edge-defined film-fed growth," has been announced by Tyco Laboratories. The crystal is pulled rapidly from a die, to which molten alumina is transported as a film. Solid crystals are often purified by zone melting, in which a molten zone is moved through the crystal. Segregation of impurities into the melt purifies the crystal.

Precipitation from liquid solution is a common method of growing crystals. Ionic salts are grown from aqueous solutions both industrially and in the laboratory. Sugar is crystallized from water solution. Other organic crystals, including polymers, are grown from a variety of solvents. Quartz crystals are grown from aqueous solution at elevated temperatures and pressures ("hydrothermal growth"). Various crystals have been grown from more exotic solvents, for example: garnets, titanites, and ferrites from molten salts ("fluxes"); tin, iron, and phosphorous from mercury; and diamond from a molten metal under pressure.

Crystallization from the solid phase is also possible. Growth of grain size in a single-phase solid, called recrystallization, is often used to improve the properties of polycrystalline materials, particularly metals. Crystalline compounds can be made from high-melting materials by pressing together mixtures of their powders and diffusing them together at high temperature ("sintering"). Crystals can be grown from a solid solution. This type of precipitation is frequently used to improve the properties of metals, for example, to harden them.

R. H. DOREMUS

References

1. Holden, A., and Singer, P., "Crystals and Crystal Growing," Garden City, New York, Doubleday and Co., 1960. A simple, nonmathematical discussion of crystal growth and structure.
2. Strickland-Constable, R. F., "Kinetics and Mechanism of Crystallization," London and New York, Academic Press, 1968. Emphasis on nucleation, and crystallization from the vapor.
3. Laudise, R. A., "The Growth of Single Crystals," Englewood Cliffs, N.J., Prentice-Hall, 1970. A guide for persons wanting to grow crystals, with

accent on practical methods together with some background material.

Papers from Symposia

4. Doremus, R. H., Roberts, B. W., and Turnbull, D., Eds., "Growth and Perfection of Crystals," New York, John Wiley & Sons, 1958.
5. Frank, F. C., Mullin, J. B., and Peiser, H. S., Eds., "Crystal Growth in 1968," in *J. Crystal. Growth*, 3 and 4, 1968.
6. Laudise, R. A., Mullin, J. B., Mutaftschiev, B., "Crystal Growth 1971," Amsterdam, North-Holland, 1972.

Special Techniques

7. Bockris, J. O., and Razumney, G. A., "Fundamental Aspects of Electrocrystallization," New York, Plenum Press, 1967.
8. Henisch, H. K., "Crystal Growth in Gels," University Park, The Pennsylvania State University Press, 1970.

Review Article

9. Parker, R. L., "Crystal Growth Mechanisms: Energetics, Kinetics, and Transport," in "Solid State Physics," Vol. 25, New York, Academic Press, 1970 (p. 152).

Research Paper

10. Sears, G. W., *J. Chem. Phys.*, **24**, 868 (1956) and other references by the same author.

Cross-references: CONDENSATION, CRYSTALLOGRAPHY, PARACRYSTALS, VAPOR PRESSURE AND EVAPORATION.

CRYSTALLOGRAPHY

Crystallography is the science of the geometric properties of matter in the ordered solid state. When atoms or molecules condense into a solid phase from a liquid or gaseous phase, the lowest energy state is achieved if they become arranged in as regular a way as possible, usually by forming a small basic unit of structure which is repeated indefinitely in three dimensions throughout the solid to form a *crystal*. The geometric properties of this unit and its manner of regular repetition are highly characteristic of the substance in question, and constitute an exceedingly useful subject of study in connection with any field of science involving the solid state. Occasionally, no extended, regular repetition of structure is present in the solid phase, but this glassy state has many properties of a liquid and lies outside the realm of crystallography. In other cases, extended order may occur in one direction only (as in fibres) or in two directions (as in some clays), but by far the most common condition of the solid state is full three-dimensional order, and it is with this type of order that crystallography is primarily concerned.

The familiar outward manifestation of the three-dimensional order of the atomic structure

of the solid is the polyhedral shape commonly exhibited by crystals. These remarkable shapes were admired for centuries (see, for example, Albrecht Dürer's engraving "Melancholia," 1514), but the underlying principle governing them was first discovered by Steno in 1669. This principle is expressed as the Law of the Constancy of Interfacial Angles, according to which the dihedral angles between the faces of all crystals of a given substance remain unchanged regardless of how the relative sizes and shapes of the faces may vary. René Just Haüy in the late eighteenth century was the first to present a systematic account of the characterization of substances by the measurement of interfacial angles, that is, crystallography, and thus establish it as a science. Haüy was a mineralogist, and through his influence crystallography was subsequently developed and applied by workers mainly in mineralogy, and to a small extent in chemistry. The link between external form and internal structure was dramatically completed by M. von Laue's discovery of x-ray diffraction in 1912, and from then on crystallography was rapidly developed and advanced in physics laboratories, and later more and more in chemistry.

A crystal may or may not exhibit external faces, but if it does, these may be studied in terms of their distribution and development, which constitutes the *morphology* of the crystal, by special techniques of *crystallometry*, usually making use of an instrument that reflects beams of light from the crystal faces into a telescope, the *two-circle goniometer*. If the crystal has no faces, its internal geometric properties may be studied by its interaction with radiation, by the methods of *optical crystallography* if refraction of infrared, visible or ultraviolet light is involved, or by *x-ray crystallography* if diffraction of x-rays (also neutrons or electrons) is studied.

The crystal can be defined completely (except for chance irregularities and defects) in terms of the arrangement of the atoms within a finite unit of volume called the *unit cell* (whose size is usually of the order of 10Å on an edge) and the way this unit is repeated in three dimensions to fill up the volume of the crystal. The shape and dimensions of the unit cell provide parameters characteristic of the substance and constitute the first primary geometrical property of crystals. The most general unit cell (triclinic case) is a parallelopiped which can be defined by six constants, three edge lengths (a, b and c) and three interedge angles (α, β and γ). This unit cell is repeated by *translation*, a shift along each of the cell edges by an integral number of edge lengths. If the unit cell and its contents are represented by a point in space, the crystal consists of a regular array of such points called a *lattice*, in which each point is related to every other by an integral number of vectorial translations corresponding to the unit cell edges. The lattice should be distinguished from the *crystal struc-*

ture, which refers to the arrangement of atoms within the unit cell, although the term "lattice" is sometimes loosely used in reference to the structure.

The atoms within the unit cell may be related to each other by a number of geometric operations called *symmetry*, and this phenomenon constitutes the second chief geometric property of crystals. The unit cell must embrace all of the different types of atoms related by symmetry that are not related by simple translation. On the other hand, the symmetry operations which apply to one unit cell are also operated on by the lattice translations, so that these symmetry operations must also apply to the entire crystal. Thus, the morphology of the crystal and all its other properties must obey this symmetry. The detection and definition of the symmetry also serve to characterize the substance and are equally as important in crystallography as the measurement of the lattice parameters.

The way in which symmetry operations can interact consistently with each other is strictly limited by the geometry of coincidence and can be rigorously analyzed by the mathematical methods of group theory, both as to what symmetry operations are possible and how they may be combined. The problem is usually approached by constraining all symmetry operations to pass through a single point in space, but special restrictions are introduced by the requirement that this point must be consistent with any point in the crystal lattice, that is, the symmetry groups must be consistent with the translational operations of the lattice. An important symmetry operation is the axis of rotation by which any motif is reproduced by a rotation around an axis of $360/n$ degrees, where n is the order of the axis; n successive operations then superimpose the object on itself. In crystals, because of the requirements of the lattice, n can only have the values 1, 2, 3, 4 and 6. A 5-fold axis is not possible, for example, for the same reason that it is not possible to fit regular pentagons into a regular two-dimensional pattern which will fill all space. Further, there are only 11 ways to combine the 5 axes together at a point; these are called the 11 axial point groups. These form a convenient basis for classifying all crystals into 6 *crystal systems*, which, while not strictly rational in their definition, provide a fundamental link between the symmetry of the crystal and its dimensional properties. Reference axes are generally chosen parallel to lattice translation directions, of course, but further, they are customarily taken parallel to prominent symmetry axes. Four of the axial point groups, for example, have a single 3-fold axis or 6-fold axis, with or without a number of 2-fold axes at right angles to them. In all these, the reference c axis is customarily set parallel to the unique 3- or 6-fold axis, and the other two axes a_1, and a_2, which are equivalent by symmetry, are taken normal to the c axis along lattice directions 120° apart, coinci-

dent with the 2-fold axes if present. These groups are all included in the hexagonal system.

The axial symmetry operations are operations of the first kind, that is, they reproduce left-hand motifs as left-hand motifs. Other symmetry elements of the second kind, that is, which reproduce left-hand motifs as right-hand motifs, are the center of symmetry and the mirror plane of symmetry. When these operations are added to the axial groups, 32 *point groups* are produced.

Referring to the lattice, the introduction of symmetry gives rise to a number of lattice groups in which various rational relationships exist between the lattice parameters. One important result of this interaction is the appearance of *centered lattices*, in which the lattice unit cell chosen according to the rules used to set up the 6 crystal systems contains additional lattice points on body or face diagonals. There are 14 such "Bravais lattices." The symmetry groups so far mentioned can in favorable circumstances all be detected from the external morphology of the crystal.

When the combinations of lattice translations and symmetry operations, that is, the symmetry properties of the crystal structure, are analyzed, new symmetry operations are evolved (screw axes and glide planes) and each of the point groups contains many such combinations, adding up to a total of 230 *space groups*. These are detected by diffraction methods. Table 1 summarizes the relations between the crystal systems and the symmetry groups.

A fundamental concept of great importance to all aspects of crystallography is that of the *reciprocal lattice*. If the unit vectors of the direct lattice are a, b, and c, then a reciprocal lattice exists whose unit vectors are $a^* = b \times c$, $b^* = c \times a$, $c^* = a \times b$, with lengths given by $a^* = (1/V) \, bc \sin \alpha$, $b^* = (1/V) \, ca \sin \beta$, $c^* = (1/V) \, ab \sin \lambda$; the reciprocal unit cell volume $V^* = 1/V$. Because the Bragg diffraction angle 2θ is a function of the reciprocal of spacings in the direct lattice ($2 \sin \theta = \lambda/d$), the various orders of diffraction are associated with nodes in the reciprocal lattice. These nodes are designated by their integral coordinates in the lattice h, k, and l, known as *Miller indices*. Each node in the reciprocal lattice corresponds to a set of net planes in the direct lattice, and vice versa; the duality is complete. Crystal faces, which are parallel to the direct lattice net planes are therefore designated by Miller indices. This duality of direct and reciprocal space is exactly parallel to that represented by the Fourier transform:

$$f(x,y,z) = \iiint g(h,k,l)e^{-2\pi i(hx+ky+lz)} \, dxdydz$$

where h, k, and l may now be continuously variable (nonintegral). The potential $f(x, y, z)$ at any point x, y, z in direct space (e.g., electron density) is thus a synthesis of all the reciprocal potential $g(h, k, l)$ (e.g., x-ray scattering) in reciprocal space (and vice versa). In a crystal, the reciprocal potential is sampled at the reciprocal lattice points (vanishing for nonintegral h, k, l) and the above integral becomes a triple summation. The concept is used also in the interpretation of electron momentum space in a crystal, in which the Brillouin zones are defined by the reciprocal lattice (see FERMI SURFACE).

HOWARD T. EVANS, JR.

References

deJong, W. F., "General Crystallography," San Francisco, W. H. Freeman and Co., 1959.

Phillips, F. C., "An introduction to Crystallography," New York, Longmans, Green and Co., 1946.

Terpstra, P., and Codd, L. W., "Crystallometry," New York, Academic Press, 1961.

Buerger, M. J., "Elementary Crystallography," New York, John Wiley & Sons, Inc., 1956.

Hilton, H., "Mathematical Crystallography and the Theory of Groups of Movements," Oxford, Clarendon Press, 1903; New York, Dover Publications, Inc., 1963.

TABLE 1.   THE SIX CRYSTAL SYSTEMS

System	Independent Lattice Parameters	Axial Relationships	Number of Symmetry Groups			
			Axial Point Groups	Point Groups	Bravais Lattices	Space Groups
Triclinic	$a, b, c, \alpha, \beta, \gamma$	none	1	2	1	2
Monoclinic	a, b, c, β	$\alpha = \gamma = 90°$	1	3	2	13
Orthorhombic	a, b, c	$\alpha = \beta = \gamma = 90°$	1	3	4	59
Tetragonal	a, c	$b = a$ $\alpha = \beta = \gamma = 90°$	2	7	2	68
Hexagonal	a, c	$b = a$ $\alpha = \beta = 90°$ $\gamma = 120°$	4	12	2	52
Cubic (isometric)	a	$b = c = a$ $\alpha = \beta = \gamma = 90°$	2	5	3	36

Cross-references: CRYSTALLIZATION, DIFFRAC-
TION BY MATTER AND DIFFRACTION GRAT-
INGS, CRYSTAL STRUCTURE ANALYSIS, X-RAY
DIFFRACTION.

CURRENT ALGEBRA

Current algebra is a study of hadronic matter,
(i.e., strongly interacting particles like protons,
neutrons, and π mesons), through their electromagnetic and weak interaction properties. This
study leads to a degree of unification of the
three different forms of elementary particle
interactions: strong, weak, and electromagnetic.
The electromagnetic four current density
$J_{e.m.}{}^{\mu}(x) \equiv (\rho(x), \vec{J}(x))$, with $\vec{J}$ and ρ respectively the densities of electric current and
charge, is long familiar from Maxwell's equations. The conservation of this current, of
course, leads to charge conservation in nuclear
reactions. Mathematically this is expressed by
saying $Q = \int d^3 x \rho(x)$ is a time-independent
constant. In 1958 it was established that the
weak decays of hadrons are also described by
currents. This led to the highly successful (V-A)
theory of weak interactions, proposed by Marshak and Sudarshan and independently by
Feynman and Gell-Mann. (Here V is a vector
current and A is an axial vector current.) Soon
after the successful proposal of SU(3) symmetry for classification of hadrons (suggested
by Gell-Mann and Ne'eman in 1961) Gell-Mann
laid down the foundations of current algebra.
In attempting to interpret in precise terms the
notion of symmetry violated by the strong interactions, Gell-Mann suggested that SU(3) symmetry operators be identified with charges associated with the weak and electromagnetic
currents. In particular he emphasized the equal
time commutation rules of these charges, and
suggested that they may remain unchanged
even in the presence of SU(3) breaking interactions, showing how this leads to a precise notion of universality of weak and electromagnetic interactions.

In the SU(3) scheme, one can define eight
vector currents, with the charges corresponding
to these operators being the generators of the
group. These charges obey the equal time commutator algebra.

$$[F_i, F_j] = i f_{ijk} F_k \qquad i, j, k = 1 \cdots 8 \quad (1)$$

where f_{ijk} are antisymmetric structure constants of the group SU(3). One may also define
an octet of axial currents, and the charges associated with these currents, $F_i{}^5$, obey the algebra

$$[F_i, F_j{}^5] = i f_{ijk} F_k{}^5 \qquad i, j, k = 1 \cdots 8. \quad (2)$$

Gell-Mann further postulated that axial generators among themselves obey a similar algebra,

$$[F_i{}^5, F_j{}^5] = i f_{ijk} F_k \qquad i, j, k = 1 \cdots 8. \quad (3)$$

Such an algebra leads to an abstract group
SU(3) $\times$ SU(3). Although such a group is in
fact not a symmetry group of particle states,
nevertheless the generators at equal time are assumed to obey the commutator algebra. Thus
the axial charges are not constants of motion,
nor are all the vector charges constants of motion. The charges that play a role in electromagnetic and weak interactions are respectively

$$Q = F_3 + F_8 / \sqrt{3} \quad (4)$$

and

$$J^{\pm} = \cos \theta \, (F_1 \pm i F_2) + \sin \theta \, (F_4 \pm i F_5)$$
$$- \cos \theta \, (F_1{}^5 \pm i F_2{}^5) - \sin \theta \, (F_4{}^5 \pm i F_5{}^5). \quad (5)$$

Here θ is a parameter called the Cabibbo angle,
and experimentally $\theta \cong 15°$.

Gell-Mann suggested that the current algebra
be used in the same way as the familiar quantum condition, i.e., $[q, p] = i\hbar$, to derive sum
rules as in atomic physics. His proposal remained dormant until use was made of another
concept called the partial conservation of axial
current hypothesis (PCAC). This postulate connects the pseudoscalar pion field to the divergence of the axial current. This hypothesis was
used to obtain a value for the weak decay of
the π meson from the known strong interaction
pion-nucleon coupling constant (Goldberger-
Treiman relation) and is known to be accurate
to about 10 percent.

Among the successful applications of current
algebra are prediction of weak decay rates of
hyperons [e.g., $\Sigma^- \rightarrow n + e^- + \bar{\nu}$]. Such decays
involve vector and axial parts; the vector parts
are predicted to be just Clebsch-Gordon coefficients of the group SU(3), while the axial parts
are also predicted in terms of two unknowns
(f and d type couplings). As for the meson de-
cay rates, the $K \rightarrow \pi \, e \, \nu$ decay is predicted accurately, although in meson systems symmetry-
breaking corrections have to be made in general
before predictions can be compared.

Application of current algebra leads to *sum
rules* between different observables, as was the
case in atomic physics. To illustrate the use of
commutators in atomic physics, we give a derivation of the Thomas-Reiche-Kuhn sum rule.
One starts with the fundamental quantum-
mechanical assumption

$$[\vec{\epsilon} \cdot \vec{q}_i, \; \vec{\epsilon} \cdot \vec{p}_j] = i\hbar \delta_{ij} \quad (6)$$

where i and j label different electrons and $\vec{\epsilon}$ is
an arbitrary unit vector. Assuming that forces
are velocity-independent, we may write

$$p_i = im \, [H, q_i] \, \hbar \quad (7)$$

Using Eqs. (1) and (2) we may take the expec-
tation value between the ground state $|0\rangle$ of an
atom with Z electrons.

$$\sum_{ij} \langle 0 | \, [\vec{\epsilon} \cdot \vec{q}_i, [H, \vec{\epsilon} \cdot \vec{q}_j]] \, | 0 \rangle = \frac{Z}{m} \hbar^2 \quad (8)$$

Now inserting a complete set of intermediate states one gets

$$\sum_n |\langle 0| \sum_{i=1}^{Z} \vec{\epsilon} \cdot \vec{q}_i \ |n\rangle|^2 (E_n - E_o) = \frac{Z\hbar^2}{2m} \quad (9)$$

The usefulness of the sum rule arises from the fact that the left-hand side of the equation involves matrix elements of dipole operators that are observable in the transition spectrum of an atom. Very similar methods can be used with current algebra to obtain sum rules.

A sum rule obtained by Adler and Weisberger for the axial vector coupling in β-decay is among the triumphs of the axial-charge algebra. Use was made of the commutation relation

$$[F_1{}^5 + iF_2{}^5, F_1{}^5 - iF_2{}^5] = 2 F_3 \quad (10)$$

to derive

$$1 = \left[\frac{G_A}{G_V}\right]^2 + \frac{F_\pi}{\pi} \int_\mu^\infty \frac{d\nu \sqrt{\nu^2 - \mu^2}}{\nu^2} [\sigma_{\pi^- p}(\nu)$$

$$- \sigma_{\pi + p}(\nu)] \quad (11)$$

Here G_A is the axial vector coupling, G_V is the vector coupling, F_π is the pion decay constant, ν is the laboratory pion energy, and σ is the pion-nucleon total cross-section. G_A calculated from this relation is in good agreement with experiment. Other results include: *Adler's neutrino sum rule*, which relates neutrino to antineutrino scattering on protons at high energy; *Cabibbo-Radicati sum rule*, which relates anomalous magnetic moments of nucleons to cross-sections for absorption of isovector photons on nucleons; and *photoproduction sum rules*. These sum rules, wherever tested, are in good agreement with experiment.

Another class of applications leads to derivation of *low-energy theorems*. These theorems especially relate to processes where pions are emitted. It was shown that the Adler-Weisberger sum rule could be obtained as a low-energy theorem relating (G_A/G_V) to s-wave pion-nucleon scattering lengths. Other theorems deal with leptonic decays of K-mesons. A theorem due to Callan and Treiman for the decay $K \to \pi e \nu$ states that the two form factors that enter this decay are related to the K and π decay constants.

$$f + (m_K{}^2) + f - (m_K{}^2) = F_K/F_\pi \quad (12)$$

Other theorems due to Weinberg relate form factors in the $K \to \pi \pi e \nu$ decay and obtain $\pi \pi \to \pi \pi$ scattering lengths. Low-energy theorems that combine PCAC and current algebra are not tested as well by experiment and some corrections may have to be made.

Other applications of the current algebra lead to a value of the electromagnetic mass difference of $\pi^+ - \pi^0$ mesons. Current algebra has

been further extended by assuming that the currents are proportional to vector fields, like ρ, ω, K^* mesons. This hypothesis, called the current-field identity, has led to predictions for a large number of strong interaction decay rates of mesons. Such applications, however, involve a large number of free parameters. Nevertheless this enables calculations to be made where no method existed before.

In recent years current-algebra assumptions have been further enlarged to include commutators of charges and divergences of currents. Such models lead to a better understanding of the precise nature of symmetry-breaking interactions. Low-energy theorems with small corrections can be obtained in this way.

During 1971 the equal time algebra was extended to regions on the light cone $x^2 + y^2 + z^2 = c^2 t^2$. Such assumptions led to new predictions about certain inelastic processes.

To conclude, fairly good evidence exists for the validity of current algebra. The question as to the deep meaning of why this algebra is a property of nature is not fully understood. If the hadrons are composed of "quarks" as has been proposed, there may be a simple explanation of the algebra in terms of the quark currents. The search for quarks has not yet been successful, however.

N. G. DESHPANDE

References

1. Adler, S. L., and Dashen, R. F., "Current Algebras and Applications to Particle Physics," New York, Benjamin, 1968.
2. Bernstein, J., "Elementary Particles and Their Currents," San Francisco, W. H. Freeman, 1968.
3. Gasiorowicz, S., "Elementary Particle Physics," New York, John Wiley & Sons, 1966.

Cross-references: CONSERVATION LAWS AND SYMMETRY, ELECTROMAGNETIC THEORY, ELEMENTARY PARTICLES, MATRIX MECHANICS, QUANTUM THEORY, STRONG INTERACTIONS, WEAK INTERACTIONS.

CYBERNETICS

Cybernetics can be described as "the science of control in machines and animals," but the connotation of the word (or its equivalent in other languages) shows a difference of emphasis between *control* in the United States and *the handling of information* in continental Europe. For the science of control involves three streams of work: closed-loop feedback systems (sometimes called goal-seeking systems); manipulation of the information which guides these systems; and processes of filtering to exclude casual disturbances from the information channel as far as possible. The second of these, obviously, and the third, less obviously, can lead on to a consideration of communication, control and thought processes in animals.

One of the earliest applications of closed-loop feedback was to the power steering of ships, and a successor to this application is the power-aided steering of automobiles (see FEEDBACK). As soon as the steering wheel is turned, producing a temporary discrepancy between the setting of the steering wheel and the angle of the road wheels, power is applied to the steering linkage in the appropriate direction and maintained until the two agree once more. The qualification "as soon as" is important, because if there were a noticeable delay in response, conditions might have changed so that the position originally demanded would be incorrect by the time it was reached. It can be shown mathematically that the occurrence of delay within the closed loop may cause the system to oscillate about the desired position without coming to rest ("hunting"); moreover, there is always a tendency for the magnitude of the delay round the loop to increase with the amount of amplification in the loop; and hence a high-gain loop (one designed to provide a large driving power in response to a small input signal) is particularly susceptible to this type of instability. The general principles involved for linear systems have been outlined by Bode,[1] and one of the tasks of the "servo" designer is to ensure by analysis (for which there are several mathematical techniques) that the system is free from this type of instability. Later developments in control theory have been concerned with systems which are nonlinear, or in which stochastic (random) phenomena are predominant, or in which information is transmitted in sampled form.

Closed-loop control systems are often designed to respond to signals which may be regarded as a kind of "information." For example, in the push-button controlled elevator the passenger informs the machine of the floor to which he wishes to travel by pushing a button, and the elevator continues in motion until the desired floor is reached; or in the programmed control of machine tools, information may be fed in via punched cards, punched paper or magnetic tape. "Information" is then an essential part of cybernetics, and the idea of information as a quantity which can be measured in physical terms dates effectively from Shannon's work on the information-capacity of communication channels.[2] To be measurable, the information must be finite. If there is a finite group of n different signals of which the ith occurs with probability (or relative frequency) p_i, the quantity

$$I = \sum_{i=1}^{n} p_i \log p_i$$

is the information conveyed by the group of signals. There are physical as well as mathematical arguments for stating that information is the negative of ENTROPY, the latter quantity being as defined in STATISTICAL MECHANICS.

The essence of Shannon's work, the germ of which lay unperceived in the earlier work of the telegraphists Kelvin, Carson and Nyquist, is that information can be defined as a quantity which is invariant to transformations of the wave forms by which it is conveyed. Such transformations are known as "coding" of information. Shannon showed further that there is a maximum rate (to be achieved by "ideal coding") at which information can be communicated without error through a physical channel of specified bandwidth and signal-to-noise ratio.

Communication is increasingly being carried out through the use of binary signals, telephony being converted to this form by pulse-code modulation (p.c.m.) and a great deal of effort has been devoted to the design of binary codes with which one can detect and correct any errors which may occur in transmission. Particular forms of such codes are also used in large electronic computors to overcome possible imperfections in the storage and reading of information from the memory.[3]

The third line of work in cybernetics is the study of methods of minimizing interference, of separating signals from noise, and the classic work in this field is that of Norbert Wiener. Following his work on generalized Fourier series,[4] Wiener showed[5] the relationship between the auto-correlation function of a random waveform and its power spectrum, the Wiener-Khintchine theorem:

$$W(f) = 2 \int \psi(\tau) \cos 2\pi f \tau \, d\tau$$

where $W(f)$ is the power spectrum (spectrum of squared amplitudes) and $\psi(\tau)$ is the autocorrelation function for lag τ. He also showed how related mathematical techniques could be used to design a filter which for given statistical characteristics of signal and of noise will give an output having least mean square error (the Wiener-Hopf equation). Similar mathematical techniques are widely used to determine the internal characteristics of automatically controlled systems (e.g., chemical process plants) without interrupting their operation: either a small random disturbance is superimposed on the control signals, or naturally occurring disturbances are utilized, and comparison of the signals at the input and output of the system allows its internal characteristics to be evaluated.

From the evaluation of the characteristics of a system one proceeds to their improvement and there is a whole class of *adaptive control systems* whose characteristics are automatically modified in accordance with current conditions. One application is to the adjustment of the filtering characteristics of a control system to suit the types of signal and noise being applied to it at any time. Another application is to the optimization of performance of plant such as chemical process control and distillation plant. In this type of plant the function of automatic

control was originally to maintain specified conditions of temperature, pressure, flow, etc.; but in optimizing control, the automatic equipment finds and maintains optimum conditions which it can vary in response to changes in external circumstances such as change in the raw material at the input, and it can be used to find experimentally optimum conditions which are not known in advance.

Adaptive systems are more sophisticated than automatic controls having fixed characteristics and in addition to their superficial resemblance at least to the instinctive behavior of animals, they have other relationships with biological systems, the two most remarkable characteristics of which are the ability to learn and the ability to transfer functions from one physical channel to another in case of damage. It must first be said that the idea of coding of information has made a decisive contribution to knowledge of the mechanism of the nervous systems of animals. Much is now known about the forms of pulse code by which information is sent along nerve channels, and the neuron of biology is coming to be regarded as the prototype element for performing the operations of Boolean algebra, so that the designer of digital computers uses the neuron symbol to denote schematically an elementary circuit which will be constructed from electronic components. The adaptive control system shows some of the characteristics of learning, and electronic models of the type known as "conditional probability machines"[6] can be made to exhibit behavior resembling that of conditioned reflexes in animals. Attempts have been made to press the analogy further in two directions. Ross Ashby devised a model which he called the "homeostat" which made a random search to find a stable position which it could then maintain constant, and the constancy bears some analogy to the homeostasis (constancy) of temperature, chemical constitution of blood stream, etc. in the higher animals. Then various workers, such as W. G. Walter[7], constructed mechanical toy animals which could apparently exhibit elementary forms of animal behavior such as the search for "food," and of which the more sophisticated versions could learn to thread a simple maze.[8] The relevance of the behavior of these devices to the mechanisms of animal behavior is debatable. Finally, familiarity with the concept of coding of information makes it easier to understand "the genetic code," i.e., the way in which genetic information can be stored in the pattern of chemical groups along the length of a complex molecule, and in some ways, this is the most spectacular contribution of cybernetics to human knowledge.

D. A. BELL

References

1. Bode, H. W., "Network Analysis and Feedback Amplifier Design," New York, Van Nostrand Reinhold, 1945.

2. Shannon, C. E., "A Mathematical Theory of Communication," *Bell Syst. Tech. J., 27,* 379 and 623 (1948).

3. Hsiao, M. Y., "A Class of Optimal Minimum Odd-weight-column SEL-DED Codes," *I.B.M.J., Res. & Dev.*, **14,** 395 (July, 1970).

4. Wiener, N., "The Fourier Integral and Certain of its Applications," Cambridge, Cambridge University Press, 1933.

5. Wiener N., "The Extrapolation, Interpolation and Smoothing of Stationary Time Series with Engineering Applications," New York, John Wiley & Sons, 1949.

6. Uttley, A. M., "Conditional Probability Machines and Conditioned Reflexes," in Automata Studies," Princeton, N.J., Princeton University Press, 1956.

7. Walter, W. G., "An Electromechanical 'Animal'," *Discovery,* **11,** 90 (March, 1950).

8. Deutsch, J. A., "The Insightful Learning Machine," *Discovery,* **16,** 515 (December, 1955).

Bibliography of Introductory Books

Bell, D. A., "Information Theory and its Engineering Applications," London, Pitman, 1968.

Porter, A., "An Introduction to Servo-Mechanisms," London, Methuen, 1953.

Bellman, R., "Adaptive Control Processes: a Guided Tour," Princeton, N.J., Princeton University Press, 1961.

Laning, J. H., Jr., and Battin, R. H., "Random Processes in Automatic Control," New York, McGraw-Hill Book Co., 1956.

Anfinsen, Christian B., "The Molecular Basis of Evolution," London, Chapman & Hall, 1959.

Cross-references: BIONICS, FEEDBACK, SERVO-MECHANISMS.

CYCLOTRON*

The cyclotron is an accelerator of ions widely used to study the nucleus, to produce radioactive substances, and to study the interactions of ionizing radiation with living systems and with inert matter. It is equally important as the first of a class—*Magnetic Resonance Accelerators*—which includes the various kinds of synchrotron (see SYNCHROTRON) as well as synchrocyclotrons and sector focused cyclotrons. The essential feature of this type of accelerator is that acceleration of charged particles to high energies is achieved by a successive application of small accelerations in synchronization with the rotational period of the particles in a magnetic field. The condition for synchronization is simple and can be derived as follows: A charged particle moving perpendicularly to the lines of force in a magnetic field will describe a circle which is defined by the equilibrium between the Lorentz force $F_{\varrho} = eBv$ and the centrifugal force $F_c = mv^2/r$. Equating these gives the rotational frequency of the particles which is set

*Effort supported by U.S. Atomic Energy Commission.

equal to the frequency of the accelerating field. This is the *Cyclotron Resonance Condition:*

$$f_a = f_0 = \frac{eB}{2\pi m} \qquad (1)$$

where

f_a = frequency of accelerating field
f_0 = rotational frequency
e = charge of ion
m = mass of ion
B = magnetic field strength.

The important fact is that the rotational frequency is independent of the energy of the particle and depends only on quantities which are (approximately) constant. In 1929 the possibility of using this relationship as the basis for an accelerator occurred to Ernest O. Lawrence, who like many other physicists at the time had been inspired by Rutherford's success in disintegrating atoms with alpha particles from natural sources to seek a means of producing a controlled beam of high energy particles. The practicability of the idea was demonstrated, and most of the essential features of the Cyclotron were developed by Lawrence, M. Stanley Livingston, N. E. Edlefsen, and others during the next few years.

Figure 1 is a schematic diagram showing the principle components of a cyclotron. The dees are two hollow semicircular electrodes in a vacuum tank located between the poles of an electromagnet which provides an approximately uniform magnetic field over the entire region. The dees are part of an electrical resonant circuit which may be excited by an oscillator whose frequency is adjusted to the rotational frequency given by Eq. (1). Ions are produced by an electric discharge in a source located at the center. They are drawn from the source and accelerated into a dee while it is negative, they follow a semicircular path in the (electrostatic) field free interior of the dee and again arrive at the gap between the dees where, by that time,

the voltages are reversed in sign and they are accelerated again. The ions describe semicircles of increasing radius as their velocity and energy increase as a result of repeated accelerations. When they reach the maximum radius of the dee, they enter a channel between a septum in one of the dees and the deflector. The deflector is charged negatively and draws the particles out where they may strike a target in the target chamber or they may travel some distance as a beam outside the cyclotron before they are used.

The kinetic energy of the accelerated particles is given by:

$$T = \frac{1}{2} \frac{B^2 R^2 e^2}{m} \qquad (2)$$

where T is the kinetic energy and R is the radius of ion path at point of extraction. For protons, Eq. (1) reduces to $f = 1.52B$ MHz and Eq. (2) to $T = 0.484\, B^2 R^2$ MeV with B in kilogauss and R in meters. The usual values of B are from 15 to 22 kilogauss.

In addition to the resonance condition, a successful cyclotron requires that the orbits be stable, i.e., they must remain in the median plane and at the appropriate radius. The first is achieved by introducing in the magnetic field a small negative gradient with respect to radius. The field lines are then bowed as shown in Fig. 2, and the Lorentz force on a particle off the median plane has a vertical focusing component. Radial stability results from the fact that the orbit of the particle is an equilibrium orbit with the inward Lorentz force predominating at radii larger than the equilibrium orbit and the centrifugal force predominating at smaller radii. Ions which are displaced either vertically or radially then execute oscillations about the equilibrium orbit. If the magnetic field is described by the index,

$$n = -\frac{r}{B} \frac{\partial B}{\partial r} \qquad (3)$$

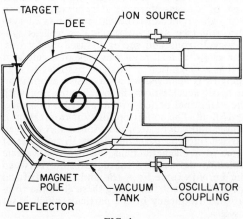

FIG. 1

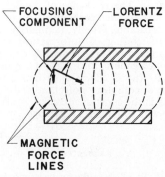

FIG. 2

where r is the radius, then it can be shown that for $0 < n < 1$ stable oscillations occur with frequencies:

$$f_z = f_0 \sqrt{n}$$

$$f_r = f_0 \sqrt{1 - n} \qquad (4)$$

where f_z is the frequency of vertical oscillations and f_r is the frequency of radial oscillations.

The negative gradient in the magnetic field results, however, in the situation where the rotational frequency, Eq. (1), is not exactly the same at all radii. In addition, it must be noted that the mass in Eq. (1) is the relativistic mass, $m = m_0 + T/c^2$ and increases with energy. The result of these two discrepancies is that the rotational frequency of the ion decreases as it is accelerated and there is an accumulated phase lag between the ion and the accelerating field which when it approaches π radians, results in no further acceleration. The energy limit of the conventional cyclotron can be shown to be proportional to the square root of the accelerating potential and to be about 30 MeV for protons with a dee-to-dee potential of 200 kV. It has not been possible to reach the theoretical maximum energy in practice, and for reasons made clear in the next sections, the incentive to do so has disappeared. The maximum energy which has been attained with protons is 22 MeV and that required about 500 kV on the dees. Currents in cyclotrons are usually of the order of 100 μA but up to 1 mA has been attained. The most commonly used ions are protons, deuterons, and alpha particles, although heavier ions such as carbon, nitrogen and oxygen ionized to +3 or +4 have also been accelerated.

A possibility of achieving higher energies with cyclotrons was opened up in 1945 when V. Veksler and E. M. McMillan independently pointed out the phase stable characteristic of the cyclotron resonance condition [Eq. (1)] which is apparent if the equation is rewritten in terms of particle energy:

$$f_0 = \frac{Be\,c^2}{2\pi(E_0 + T)} \qquad (5)$$

where E_0 is the rest energy of the particle.

Consider a particle rotating in a cyclotron at the resonant frequency and crossing the accelerating gap at a phase such that it gains no energy and that a later arrival causes it to lose energy. If this particle is perturbed by an excess of energy, f_0 decreases and the particle loses energy. If the particle is perturbed in phase so that it arrives at the accelerating gap too early, it gains energy, f_0 decreases, and the phase slips back. Perturbations in energy or phase thus result in oscillations about the equilibrium phase. Under these conditions, if the accelerating frequency of a cyclotron is slowly decreased, the ions will execute stable oscillations about that phase which will give sufficient energy gain so that the radius and energy are matched as the orbits

expand. This is the *Principle of Phase Stability* as applied to the Synchrocyclotron. It completely removes the energy limitation of the cyclotron previously discussed. This principle was immediately exploited and synchrocyclotrons (also sometimes called Frequency Modulated or FM Cyclotrons, and in the U.S.S.R., Phasotrons) have been built which give protons up to 700 MeV. The only limit is the economic one due to the large size of the magnet.

The important structural difference between a synchrocyclotron and a conventional cyclotron is in the provision for a variable frequency. This is accomplished by placing a variable capacitor in the resonant dee circuit. Rotary blade capacitors have been in common use for this purpose, but in more recent designs, vibrating blade capacitors have been preferred. The required frequency swings are about two to one, and the usual modulation frequencies are about 60 to 100 Hz. The ions are accelerated in pulses as the accelerating frequency sweeps through its modulation cycle in contrast to the continuous acceleration in a conventional cyclotron. The result is that average currents in synchrocyclotrons are about 1 per cent of cyclotron currents, thus removal of the energy limit has been accomplished at the expense of a current limitation.

Another method of circumventing the energy limit of the cyclotron was proposed by Thomas in 1938, seven years before the principle of phase stability was enunciated. In the Thomas proposal, the average magnetic field increases with radius so that the resonance condition may be exactly matched by a constant accelerating frequency as the ion gains energy. The axial focusing force is supplied by an azimuthal variation of the magnetic field which may be obtained by using sectored magnet poles, Fig. 3. The ion orbits are then no longer circular, and the radial component of velocity interacting with the azimuthal component of magnetic field produces an axial focusing force. This is the "edge focusing" which occurs when an ion crosses a fringe field obliquely, and it has long been used in mass spectrometers and other devices.

This idea was well in advance of the theory and practice of the cyclotron art at the time and was not immediately exploited. Development beginning in 1949 and extending to recent years has resulted in a whole subclass of cyclotrons characterized by a fixed rotational frequency and focusing forces derived from spatial variation in the magnetic field. For example, if the sectors are spiral shaped as in Fig. 3, additional focusing forces of alternating gradient type are developed. These cyclotrons are variously called Sector Focused, Isochronous, and AVF (azimuthally varying field) cyclotrons. They have energies well beyond the energy limit of the conventional cyclotron and, at the same time, are capable of high average currents because they operate at a constant frequency. Pro-

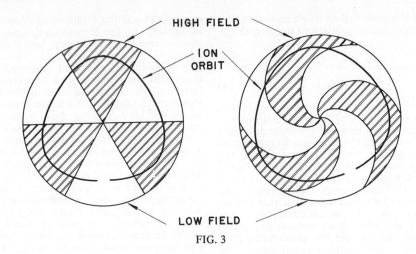

FIG. 3

TABLE 1

	CYCLOTRON 60-inch Cyclotron, University of Washington, Seattle	SYNCHROCYCLOTRON 184-inch Cyclotron Lawrence Radiation Laboratory, Berkeley	SECTOR FOCUSED CYCLOTRON 88-inch Cyclotron, Lawrence Radiation Laboratory, Berkeley	SECTOR FOCUSED CYCLOTRON (Under Construction) SIN, Swiss Institute for Nuclear Research
Magnet	1.52 m diameter, 19 kG max. field, 197,000 kg	4.8 m diameter, 23.4 kG max. field, 3,900,000 kg	2.24 m diameter, 3 sector, 20 kG max. field, 272,000 kg	9.2 m diameter, 8 separated sectors, 20 kG max. field, 2,000,000 kg
RF	Fixed frequency, 11.6 MHz, two dees, 250 kV	Variable frequency, 18–36 MHz for protons, Modulation frequency 64 Hz, single dee, 9 kV	Fixed frequency, adjustable 5.5–16.5 MHz for various particles, single dee, 70 kV	Fixed frequency, 50 MHz, 4 cavities, 500 kV/cavity
Beam	Protons 11 MeV, deuterons 22 MeV, alpha particles 44 MeV, 1 mA max. current	Protons 730 MeV, deuterons 460 MeV, alpha particles 910 MeV, 1.5 μA max. current.	Protons 60 MeV, deuterons 65 MeV, alpha particles 130 MeV, 3 mA max. current.	Protons 580 MeV, 100 μA design current.

vision of auxiliary magnet coils on the pole tips, to trim the field shape over a range of values of average field, and adjustable frequency oscillators, to provide for different ions and a variation in maximum energy, have made the modern cyclotron of this type very flexible.

In a further application of the Thomas principle, the magnet assembly is made up of individual sectors with field-free spaces between them. Fixed-frequency accelerating cavities are located between the sectors. This design variation of the sector focused cyclotron results in higher energies, but at a sacrifice of the features permitting easy variation of energy and ion species. Cyclotrons of this type will soon be in operation and are intended to be sources of in-tense pion beams; they are sometimes called "meson factories."

Table 1 gives a comparison of the salient design features and performance of typical examples of a classical cyclotron, a synchrocyclotron, a sector focused cyclotron designed for high intensity and variable ion and energy, and a sector focused cyclotron designed for high intensity and energy.

EDWARD J. LOFGREN

References

Livingood, John Jacob, "Principles of Cyclic Particle Accelerators," New York, Van Nostrand Reinhold, 1961.

Livingston, M. Stanley, and Blewett, John P., "Particle Accelerators," New York, McGraw-Hill Book Co., 1962.

Kolomensky, A. A., and Lebedev, A. N., "Theory of Cyclic Accelerators," New York, John Wiley & Sons, 1966.

Cross-references: ACCELERATORS, LINEAR; ACCELERATORS, PARTICLE; BETATRON; SYNCHROTRON; ACCELERATOR, VAN DE GRAAFF.

CYCLOTRON RESONANCE (DIAMAGNETIC RESONANCE)†

The term cyclotron resonance is used to designate the resonant coupling of electromagnetic power into a system of charged particles undergoing periodic orbital motion in a uniform static magnetic field. The frequency of the electric field at resonance is simply related to the orbital frequency of the electron in the magnetic field. The effect has been observed and studied extensively in gases and in solids.

One important application of the cyclotron resonance principle is made in the acceleration of charged particles, as in a cyclotron. In a uniform magnetic field, H, a charged particle of mass, m_c, undergoes orbital motion with an angular velocity

$$\omega_c = \frac{eH}{m_c c}, \tag{1}$$

in which e is the charge and c the velocity of light. Energy from the electromagnetic fields, i.e., from the alternating electric and magnetic fields, is transferred into kinetic energy of the particle, and the radius of the particle orbit is increased with no change in angular velocity. Particle acceleration takes place *in vacuo* in order to prevent energy transfer to the gas by means of collisions.

In solids, cyclotron resonance has been successfully applied to studies of electronic energy band structure. The perfectly periodic array of atoms in an ideal solid scatters electrons coherently. An electron experiencing such coherent scattering can be described by the same equations of motion as the free electron, except that the free electron mass is replaced by an effective mass, m^*. Incoherent scattering from crystalline imperfections causes electronic collisions which limit the number of completed electron orbits, thus giving rise to a frequency bandwidth for the cyclotron resonance absorption. The observation of cyclotron resonance requires that the charged particle execute about one complete cyclotron orbit without collisions, or $\omega_c \tau \gtrsim 1$, in which the collision time, τ, is the mean time between incoherent scatterings. A long collision time is achieved by using samples of the highest possible purity and lattice per-

†Support of U.S. Air Force is acknowledged.

fection and by cooling to very low temperature (usually liquid He temperature, 4 K) to eliminate the thermal motion of the atoms. The condition for cyclotron resonance can also be satisfied by increasing ω_c through the use of high magnetic fields, e.g., 100-kilogauss static fields are currently available which for free electrons results in $\omega_c \approx 1.5 \times 10^{12}$ rad/sec or an electromagnetic wave length of about 1 mm.

Electrons moving in the periodic lattice of a solid occupy energy levels which are specified by the wave vector quantum number, $\mathbf{k}$, or by the crystal momentum, $\hbar \mathbf{k}$. Since the number of electrons is very large, the wave vectors assume an almost continuous range of values. A knowledge of the functional form of the dependence of the energy on wave vector is necessary for a complete description of the behavior of electrons in solids. The simplest form of the relation between energy and wave vector valid for energy bands in cubic crystals is

$$E(\mathbf{k}) = \frac{\hbar^2 k^2}{2m^*}. \tag{2}$$

In this case, the constant energy surfaces in wave vector space are spheres, and the cyclotron mass of Eq. (1) is just the effective mass, m^*. For energy extrema located at general points in wave vector space, Eq. (2) becomes

$$E(\mathbf{k}) = \frac{\hbar^2}{2} \left(\frac{k_x{}^2}{m_x} + \frac{k_y{}^2}{m_y} + \frac{k_z{}^2}{m_z} \right) \tag{3}$$

in which the extremal point is taken as the origin, and m_x, m_y, and m_z are three components of an effective mass tensor. This generalization is also necessary in describing the energy bands for crystals with symmetry lower than cubic.

An expression for the cyclotron effective mass which is valid for an electron orbiting on a constant energy surface of energy E for an arbitrary $E(\mathbf{k})$ is

$$m_c(E, k_H) = 2\pi\hbar^2 \left(\frac{\partial A}{\partial E} \right)_{k_H} \tag{4}$$

in which k_H is the wave vector component parallel to the magnetic field, A is the area of the electron orbit in wave vector space, and $(\partial A/\partial E)_{k_H}$ is the derivative of this area with respect to energy evaluated at constant k_H. For spherical or ellipsoidal constant energy surfaces, the cyclotron mass is independent of both energy and k_H, and for these two simple cases, m_c is given, respectively, by $m_c = m^*$, and

$$\left(\frac{1}{m_c} \right)^2 = \frac{\alpha^2}{m_y m_z} + \frac{\beta^2}{m_x m_z} + \frac{\gamma^2}{m_x m_y} \tag{5}$$

in which α, β, γ are the direction cosines of the magnetic field with respect to the axes of the ellipsoidal constant energy surface.

For solids which have relatively low carrier density (e.g., insulators, semiconductors, and semimetals) the electronic states which are important in the transport properties are located near energy band extrema. For nondegenerate extremal points in wave vector space, $E(\mathbf{k})$ can be expanded in a Taylor's expansion. The leading term of such an expansion would be given by Eq. (3). For degenerate points (positions where two or more levels have the same energy), a simple generalization of a Taylor's expansion must be used. In solids with relatively high carrier density (e.g., metals), the transport properties are determined by electronic states which are far from the energy extrema and the $E(\mathbf{k})$ relation is not adequately described by a Taylor's expansion.

Cyclotron resonance experiments have been particularly successful in the quantitative determination of the band parameters of the semiconductors silicon and germanium. The successful application of this technique in these semiconductors is attributed to the high quality of the available material, and to the complete classification of the possible forms of the theoretical band structure model. Since in these materials the intrinsic carrier concentration is extremely small at low temperatures, electrons are optically excited out of filled valence levels in the crystal in order to produce sufficient carriers to obtain a measurable signal. Resonances are observed both for the excited electrons and for the holes left behind in the empty levels in the valence band.

In metals, the high carrier density requires modification of the conventional cyclotron resonance experiment. Two important consequences of this high carrier density are the nonuniform penetration of the electromagnetic field in the skin depth and the inapplicability of the simple effective mass theory to describe the electronic states. To overcome the problem of the small electromagnetic penetration depth, the geometrical arrangement suggested by Azbel and Kaner is used. The static magnetic field is applied in the plane of a flat sample, so that the electrons near the surface can be accelerated by the electromagnetic fields, and the orbits described by a cyclotron radius which is large compared with the skin depth. In this way, whenever the applied frequency is a multiple of the cyclotron frequency, a resonant condition is satisfied. This type of cyclotron resonance experiment yields an effective mass at the Fermi energy given by Eq. (4), which is, in general, dependent on the wave vector component parallel to the magnetic field. The interpretation of these experiments is not simple but when coupled with experiments which measure the shape of the Fermi surface, such as DE HAAS-VAN ALPHEN EXPERIMENTS, a fairly complete determination of the electronic band structure is possible. These techniques have been successfully applied in the study of copper.

Cyclotron resonance in ionic crystals allows the measurement of polaron effects. The POLARON denotes the charge carrier together with its local lattice distortion. Cyclotron resonance observed in AgBr has been interpreted as a polaron orbiting in the applied magnetic field.

G. DRESSELHAUS

References

Kittel, C., "Introduction to Solid State Physics," sec. ed. p. 371, New York, John Wiley & Sons, Inc., 1956.

Lax, B., and Mavroides, J. G., "Solid State Physics," Vol. XI, p. 261, New York, Academic Press Inc., 1960.

Cross-references: CYCLOTRON, DE HAAS-VAN ALPHEN EFFECT, DIAMAGNETISM, FERMI SURFACE.

D

DE HAAS-VAN ALPHEN EFFECT

In 1930, W. J. de Haas and P. M. van Alphen observed an anomalous behavior in the magnetic susceptibility of a pure bismuth single crystal at very low temperatures. Subsequent studies showed that the susceptibility oscillated with changing magnetic field and was in fact periodic in the reciprocal field. This effect was thought for some years to be peculiar to bismuth; however, in 1947 it was found in zinc and, shortly afterwards, in a number of other metals. The effect has now been observed in most metals (including ferromagnetic elements), as well as intermetallic compounds and ordered alloys. Related magneto-oscillatory behavior is observed in the electrical resistance, Hall effect, specific heat, ultrasonic attenuation and velocity, and the thermoelectric power. While originally thought to be somewhat of a scientific curiosity, the de Haas-van Alphen effect has become one of the most powerful tenchiques for studying the FERMI SURFACE in metals.

A basis for an understanding of this effect was provided in 1930 by Landau who showed that for a system of free electrons in a magnetic field, the motion of the electrons parallel to the field is classical while the motion perpendicular to the field is quantized. These ideas were shown by Peierls in 1933 to hold for free electrons in a metal (spherical Fermi surface). As a consequence, the free energy F of the system and, hence, the magnetic moment $M = - \partial F/\partial H$ oscillate with magnetic field H. These results were extended by Blackman in 1938 to the case of ellipsoidal energy surfaces, accounting quite well for the experimental results obtained on Bi.

The importance of the de Haas-van Alphen effect as a tool in studying the Fermi surface was perhaps not fully appreciated until Onsager (1952) showed that the frequencies of the oscillations are directly proportional to extremal cross-sectional areas of the Fermi surface perpendicular to the magnetic field. Onsager arrived at this result by applying the Bohr-Sommerfeld quantization condition to the electron orbits normal to the field. If $\mathbf{p}$ is the electronic momentum and if $\mathbf{A}$ is the vector potential, then

$$\oint \left(\mathbf{p} - \frac{e\mathbf{A}}{c} \right) \cdot d\mathbf{l} = (n + \gamma)h,$$

where $[\mathbf{p} - (e/c)\mathbf{A}]$ is the canonical momentum, n is an integer, γ is a phase factor, and h is Planck's constant. From the Lorentz force equation $\dot{\mathbf{p}} = (e/c) (\mathbf{v} \times \mathbf{H})$, it follows that electron paths in momentum space have the same shape as those in real space but changed in scale by a factor $(e/c)H$ and turned through $90°$. We note

that $\oint \mathbf{A} \cdot d\mathbf{l} = \int \nabla \times \mathbf{A} \cdot d\mathbf{S} = HS$, where S is

the area of the orbit in real space. Furthermore, the area of the orbit in momentum space $\mathfrak{A}_p$ is just $(eH/c)^2$ times the area in real space, so it follows that $\mathfrak{A}_p = (n + \gamma) (ehH/c)$. Since the momentum is related to the wave number k by $p = \hbar k$, the area in k-space is given by $\mathfrak{A}_k = (n + \gamma) (2\pi eH/c\hbar)$.

If one now considers a free electron metal near absolute zero, the surfaces of constant energy ($E \propto k^2$) in k-space will be a quasi-continuous set of spheres up to some maximum size corresponding to the Fermi energy E_F. When a magnetic field is applied in the z direction, these surfaces will degenerate into a discrete set of cylinders, a consequence of the quantization of states in the x-y plane. This is shown schematically in Fig. 1. As indicated above, the cross-sectional area of the nth cylinder will be given by $\mathfrak{A}_k(n)$. Each of these permitted states is highly degenerate, but as the field is increased, and the cylinders expand through the Fermi surface, they must give up their electrons to inner cylinders of lower quantum number. For the inner cylinders, this leads to a rather smooth variation in the free energy of the system, but for the outer cylinder, the occupied length decreases very rapidly as the cylinder approaches the extremal cross section of the Fermi surface ($\mathfrak{A}_0$). This rapid depopulation of the nth cylinder at a critical field given by $1/H_n = 2\pi(n + \gamma)e/\hbar c\ \mathfrak{A}_0$ completes an oscillation in the free energy of the system. As the field is increased further, the process is repeated, giving oscillations in the energy and hence the susceptibility $\chi = - (1/H)\ (\partial F/\partial H)$ which are periodic in $(1/H)$ with period $\Delta\ (1/H) = 2\pi e/c\hbar\ \mathfrak{A}_0$. The same result occurs for a Fermi surface of more complicated shape, and if the surface consists of several pieces or sections, there will be oscillations related to the extremal cross-sectional area of each section. Observed de Haas-van Alphen periods found in different metals range in value from $\approx 10^{-5}$ to

205

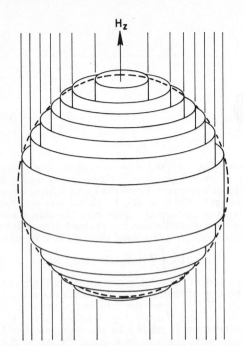

FIG. 1. Quantized orbits in a free electron metal illustrating the origin of the de Haas-van Alphen effect. The dashed sphere denotes the Fermi level.

$\approx 10^{-9}$ gauss^{-1} corresponding to Fermi surface cross sections from $\approx 10^{+13}$ to $\approx 10^{+17}$ cm^{-2}. A study of the de Haas-van Alphen effect frequencies (proportional to $\mathfrak{A}_0$) for various directions of the applied field relative to the crystal axes can thus be of great value in mapping out the geometrical shape of the Fermi surface.

At temperatures above absolute zero, the quantized orbits or energy levels (Landau levels) are not sharp but are "smeared out" over an energy range of $\approx kT$ by electron collisions with lattice vibrations. This results in a rapid decrease in the amplitude of the oscillations with increasing temperature. The effect of electron collisions with impurities results in a further reduction in amplitude. A general requirement for the observation of the effect is that $\omega\tau \geqslant 1$, where ω is the cyclotron frequency, related to the time for an electron to complete an orbit, and τ is the mean time between collisions. For this reason, experiments are generally carried out at liquid-helium temperatures (≈ 4.2 K) on ultrahigh-purity crystals.

A detailed theoretical treatment of the de Haas-van Alphen effect was carried out by Lifshitz and Kosevich.[4] The result for the free energy can be expressed as

$$F \propto TH^{3/2} \exp\left\{- 2\pi^2 k(T + x)cm^*/e\hbar H\right\}$$

$$\cos\left\{c\hbar\ \mathfrak{A}_0/eH \mp \frac{\pi}{4} - \delta\right\}$$

for the case $2\pi^2 k(T + x)cm^*/e\hbar H \gg 1$. Here k is the Boltzmann constant, δ is a phase factor, T is the absolute temperature, and x is a factor which takes into account the impurity collision broadening and is related to the relaxation time of the electron (or hole). The quantity m^* is the "effective mass" or "cyclotron mass" of the electron (or hole) for the extremal cross section and is related to the curvature of the energy surface. It can be seen from the above expression that by determining the temperature and field dependences of the amplitude of the oscillations, one can find the effective mass m^* and the scattering factor x.

Of the various techniques for observing the de Haas-van Alphen effect, the torsion balance method and the pulsed field method have been most common. In the former, the sample is suspended in a uniform transverse field (usually from 0 to 40 kilogauss) and the torque exerted on the sample is recorded as a function of field strength. This method has the advantages of high sensitivity and accuracy, but it cannot detect oscillations arising from spherical Fermi surface segments. Furthermore, available transverse field intensities place limitations on its use for very high de Haas-van Alphen frequencies (corresponding to large Fermi surface areas). In the pulsed field method, the specimen is situated inside of a balanced coil system which detects the changing magnetization in a varying field. Magnetic fields rising to 100 to 200 kilogauss in times on the order of 10 msec are produced through discharge of a large condenser bank into a copper-wound solenoid. The high fields enable one to study very high de Haas-van Alphen frequencies. In addition, the method detects isotropic surface segments.

Another technique which combines some of the advantages of both of the above methods uses a dc magnet modulated by a sinusoidally varying field with amplitude smaller than the period of the de Haas-van Alphen oscillations. A signal proportional to the de Haas-van Alphen effect is detected by means of a small balanced coil system surrounding the sample as in the pulsed field method. This technique is particularly suited for use with superconducting solenoids which produce extremely large, high-stability fields with low power requirements.

A. C. THORSEN

References

1. Shoenberg, D., in Gorter, C. J., Ed., "Progress in Low Temperature Physics," New York, Interscience Publishers, 1957.
2. Chambers, R. G., *Can. J. Phys.*, **34**, 1395 (1956).
3. Pippard, A. B., in Stickland, A. C., Ed., *Rept. Progr. Phys.*, **23**, 176 (1960).
4. Lifshitz, I. M., and Kosevich, A. M., *J. Exp. Theoret. Phys.*, **29**, 730 (1955).
5. Shoenberg, D., in Ziman, J. M., Ed., "Physics of Metals," London, Cambridge University Press, 1969 (p. 62).

6. Stark, R. W., and Windmiller, L. R., *Cryogenics*, 8, 272 (1968).

Cross-references: FERMI SURFACE, MAGNETISM.

DENSITY AND SPECIFIC GRAVITY

Density is a fundamental property of matter which is a measure of the compactness of its particles. Density is expressed as the ratio of mass to volume and depends on the composition of the specimen, its homogeneity, temperature, and especially in the case of gases, on pressure. Density is a property used to identify elements, compounds, and mineral specimens. In the case of minerals where homogeneity varies, a range of densities may be cited as typical of samples of the mineral.

Gases One way to determine the density of a gas is to weigh an evacuated bulb and then weigh it again filled with the gas, both weighings at known temperature and pressure. The bulb must be dry and free from condensed moisture. The weighing must be corrected for the buoyant force of the air on the bulb. If a two-pan balance is used, an evacuated counterpoise bulb of the same volume may be used. On a single-pan balance, the buoyancy of the air must be calculated for accurate work.

The buoyant effect is the basis for a sensitive method of finding the density of a gas. In the Edwards gas density balance[3,4] a sealed glass cylinder is at one end of a balance beam and a counterweight at the other. This equipment is mounted within a gastight chamber which is attached to a manometer. Gases are introduced into the chamber—first air and then, after complete removal of the air, the gas whose density is to be measured. The pressure exerted to restore the beam to equilibrium is read in each case. The densities of the two gases are inversely proportional to the pressures required to attain equal buoyant force on the beam within the chamber. A relatively large sample of gas is needed for this method.

The Schilling effusion method for determining the density of a gas[5] involves measuring the time for a given gas sample of given volume and temperature to escape through a known orifice. This time is compared with the time for an equal volume of dry air under the same conditions. The density of the sample is proportional to the square root of the time of escape.

Liquids The simplest method of finding the density of a liquid at a specified temperature is to float a hydrometer of suitable range in it and to read the value of the density from the graduations on the hydrometer stem. Such testing is used for the electrolyte in automobile and boat storage batteries and for antifreeze fluids in automobile radiators.

More precise measurement can be made with a Westphal balance. A sinker is weighed in air and again while it is suspended in water. It is then weighed while it is suspended in the liquid to be measured. Since the same volume of liquid is displaced by the sinker in both cases, the buoyant forces are proportional to the densities of the liquids.

A pycnometer is a small glass bottle fitted with a ground-glass stopper through which a capillary hole extends lengthwise. When the bottle is filled with liquid at a given temperature and the contents fill the capillary tube completely (or in some cases to a mark), the pycnometer holds the volume marked on it, or it may be calibrated with a liquid of known density. The pycnometer must first be weighed dry at the specified temperature, and the weighing must be corrected for the buoyancy of the air. The mass of the contents divided by the volume of the pycnometer is the density of the liquid. Other designs of pycnometers are available, many of them refined for special purposes.

Solids A wide-mouthed pycnometer allows the introduction of a solid whose density is to be measured. In the Russell form, the stopper has a long graduated tube attached to it and a reservoir above that which can be filled with a dense liquid such as mercury. The apparatus is placed upright and the mass of mercury in the tube is measured. The apparatus is inverted so that the mercury runs into the reservoir. A solid of known mass is placed within the pycnometer, the stopper is inserted, and the liquid is permitted to return. The new and higher readings of the mercury in the stem subtracted from the original reading gives the volume of the solid within the pycnometer. Air bubbles must be avoided.

Mixtures of "density liquids" such as methylene iodide (3.325 g/ml) and benzene (0.87901 g/ml) or similar pairs of miscible liquids are made in such proportions that their densities range between the values given. An insoluble solid has the same density as that of the liquid in which it fails to float or sink. The density of the liquid mixture is checked by the pycnometer or other method.

Both methods depend on the principle of Archimedes that a solid immersed in a liquid has a buoyant force exerted on it proportional to the mass of the volume of the displaced liquid. A simple density measurement can be made by weighing an object in air and then in water. The mass in air divided by the loss of weight in water (density 1 g/ml) is the density of the solid. In case a liquid other than water is used, the volume can be found by dividing the loss of weight of the solid by the density of the liquid in which it is immersed, thus extending the usefulness of the method to solids which are soluble in water but which are insoluble in benzene and other liquids.

A density gradient tube consists of two liquids mixed so that the density gradually and regularly increases from top to bottom. A sample is dropped into the tube, and its density is estimated from the position where it rests within the tube.

Specific Gravity Specific gravity is the ratio between the density of a specimen and the density of a standard material. For liquids and solids, that standard is ordinarily pure water at 4°C (precisely 3.98°C). Mercury has a density of 13.6 g/ml; water has a density of 1.00 g/ml. Their ratio 13.6 to 1.00 or 13.6, is the specific gravity of mercury. Notice that specific gravity has no units of measurement while density requires measurement units. In the English system, densities are 62.4 times as great as those for solids and liquids in the metric system. Water is 1 g/ml in the metric system, but 62.4 lb/ft^3 in the English system. Specific gravities come out numerically the same if English units are used for the density measurements, as they do for metric units.

For gases, hydrogen (0.08988 g/ml at 760 torr, and 273 K) and air are the standards. If air is the standard (1.29 g/liter at STP), the specific gravity of hydrogen is 0.0656 and that of carbon dioxide is 1.53.

The specific gravity of sulfuric acid of one concentration is expressed as $1.834_4{}^{20}$. This means that sulfuric acid at 20°C is 1.834 times as dense as water at 4°C. The density of this acid is 1.834 g/ml at 20°C.

Density measurements are readily made to four significant figures, and with refinements to seven or eight. Density measurements are sufficiently precise to follow the distribution of isotopes in the course of the electrolysis of lithium fluoride.[6] The per cent of D_2O in H_2O can be found readily by measuring the density of the mixture.

ELBERT C. WEAVER

REFERENCES

1. Weissberger, A., "Technique of Organic Chemistry," New York, Interscience Publishers, 1959.
2. Weaver, Elbert C., "Specific Gravity," in Hampel and Hawley, Eds., "Encyclopedia of Chemistry," p. 1029, New York, Van Nostrand Reinhold, 1973.
3. Edwards, J. D., *Natl. Bur. Std. Tech. Paper*, 89, 1917.
4. Smith, F. A., *et al.*, *Natl. Bur. Std. Misc. Publ.* 177, 1947.
5. Kunberger, A. F. (Ch.) "Gas Analysis and Testing of Gaseous Materials," 3rd ed., p. 321, Am. Gas Ass., 1929.
6. Hutchinson and Johnston, *J. Am. Chem. Soc.*, **62**, 3165 (1940).

DIAMAGNETISM

Magnetic susceptibility is defined as $\chi_m = M/H$, where M is the magnetic moment per gram (gram susceptibility) or per mole (mole susceptibility) that is induced by an external magnetic field strength H. If $M > 0$, the susceptibility is *paramagnetic*; if $M < 0$, the susceptibility is *diamagnetic*. Whereas most magnetic phenomena, including PARAMAGNETISM, are manifestations of ELECTRON SPIN, diamagnetism reflects electron angular momentum.

If an external field strength H is applied to a conductor so as to change the number of lines of flux that thread through it, there is induced in the conductor an electric current whose associated magnetic field opposes the change (*Faraday's Law of Induction* and *Lenz's Law*). In most conductors the current I that is thus induced is rapidly dissipated as heat through the I^2R loss, where R is the electrical resistance. These currents are known as *eddy currents*, and they are of great practical interest in ac applications. However, such transients do not influence the dc measurement of χ_m. There are three other classes of electron-momentum change induced by H that are not dissipated: electron currents in SUPERCONDUCTORS, where the resistance is $R = 0$; currents of atomic dimension induced in atoms or molecules or the atomic "core" electrons of solids; and microscopic conduction-electron helical currents having quantized helical radii.

In a superconductor, switching on of an H induces eddy currents that permanently shield the inside of the conductor from penetration by the magnetic-field lines. Therefore the superconductor is an ideal diamagnet, except for a small skin depth at the surface. If a superconductor is cooled through the normal-conducting ⇌ superconducting transition temperature in the presence of H and after the eddy currents induced in the normal-conducting state have been dissipated, the field lines are rapidly expelled from the superconductor (*Meissner effect*). This proves that the ideally diamagnetic state is thermodynamically stable.

An external field H superposes on the motion of atomic or molecular electrons (or the atomic core electrons in solids) a common circular motion about H of angular frequency $\omega_L = eH/2mc$, where e/m is the electronic charge-to-mass ratio (*Larmor's theorem*). This atomic current produces an atomic moment that is proportional to the square of the distance of a classical electron from the nucleus, $r_i \sim 1\text{Å}$. Therefore the diamagnetic contribution from electrons localized about an atomic nucleus is

$$\chi_m{}^{core} = -(Ne^2/6mc^2) \sum_i \overline{r_i{}^2},$$

where N is the number of atoms per gram (or mole).

In addition to macroscopic eddy currents, conduction electrons tend to move in microscopic helical paths in the presence of an H. The contribution to χ_m from this helical motion is a purely quantum mechanical effect. The radii of the H-induced helical paths are quantized, which leads to a "bunching" of the energy levels within an energy band of conducting states, and at large H these "bunches" can be resolved. They are known as *Landau levels* because Landau[1] first presented the quantum mechanical theory of conduction-electron diamagnetism,

which for single parabolic energy bands gives

$$\chi_m{}^{cond} = -\frac{2}{3}\mu_B{}^2 N(E_F),$$

where μ_B is the *Bohr magneton* and $N(E_F)$ is the density of energy levels at the *Fermi energy* E_F. Since $N(E_F)$ oscillates with H as successive Landau levels pass through E_F, $\chi_m{}^{cond}$ shows oscillations in large H (DE HAAS-VAN ALPHEN EFFECT). Transitions between Landau levels, which are split by an energy $\hbar\omega_p = eH/m^*c$, may be induced by an electromagnetic field of angular frequency ω_p. This gives rise to resonance power absorption as ω passes through ω_p (*cyclotron or diamagnetic resonance*). These two effects are used to map out the contours in momentum space of the Fermi energies in metals.

JOHN B. GOODENOUGH

Reference

1. Landau, L. D., *Z. Physik*, **64**, 629 (1930).

DIELECTRIC THEORY

A dielectric is a material having electrical conductivity low in comparison to that of a metal. It is characterized by its dielectric constant and dielectric loss, both of which are functions of frequency and temperature. The dielectric constant is the ratio of the strength of an electric field in a vacuum to that in the dielectric for the same distribution of charge. It may also be defined and measured as the ratio of the capacitance C of an electrical condenser filled with the dielectric to the capacitance C_0 of the evacuated condenser:

$$\epsilon = C/C_0$$

The increase in the capacitance of the condenser is due to the polarization of the dielectric material by the applied electric field. Since the dielectric constant is not a constant, it is frequently called the "dielectric permittivity." The relative permittivity or dielectric constant is the ratio ϵ/ϵ_0, where ϵ_0 is the permittivity or dielectric constant of free space. In the mks system of units, the dielectric constant of free space is 8.854×10^{-12} farad/m, while in the esu system the relative and the absolute dielectric constants are the same. The relative dielectric constant, which is dimensionless, is the one commonly used. When variation of the dielectric constant with frequency may occur, the symbol is commonly primed. When a condenser is charged with an alternating current, loss may occur because of dissipation of part of the energy as heat. In vector notation, the angle δ between the vector for the amplitude of the charging current and that for the amplitude of the total current is the loss angle, and the loss tangent, or dissipation factor, is

$$\tan\delta = \frac{\text{Loss current}}{\text{Charging current}} = \frac{\epsilon''}{\epsilon'}$$

where ϵ'' is the loss factor, or dielectric loss, of the dielectric in the condenser and ϵ' is the measured dielectric constant of the material.

At low frequencies of the alternating field, the dielectric loss is normally zero and ϵ' is indistinguishable from the dielectric constant ϵ_{dc} measured with a static field. Debye has shown that

$$\frac{\epsilon_{dc} - 1}{\epsilon_{dc} + 2} = \frac{4\pi N_1}{3}\left(\alpha_0 + \frac{\mu^2}{3kT}\right) \quad (1)$$

where N_1 is the number of molecules or ions per cubic centimeter; α_0 is the molecular or ionic polarizability, i.e., the dipole moment induced per molecule or ion by unit electric field (1 esu = 300 volts/cm); μ is the permanent dipole moment possessed by the molecule; k is the molecular gas constant, 1.38×10^{-16}, and T is the absolute temperature. An electric dipole is a pair of electric charges, equal in size, opposite in sign, and very close together. The dipole moment is the product of one of the two charges by the distance between them.

In Eq. (1) $\mu^2/3kT$ is the average component in the direction of the field of the permanent dipole moment of the molecule. In order that this average contribution should exist, the molecules must be able to rotate into equilibrium with the field. When the frequency of the alternating electric field used in the measurement is so high that dipolar molecules cannot respond to it, the second term on the right of the above equation decreases to zero and we have what may be termed the optical dielectric constant ϵ_∞, defined by the expression

$$\frac{\epsilon_\infty - 1}{\epsilon_\infty + 2} = \frac{4\pi N_1}{3}\alpha_0 \quad (2)$$

ϵ_∞ differs from n^2, the square of the optical refractive index for visible light, only by the small amount due to infrared absorption and to the small dependence of n on frequency, as given by dispersion formulas. It is usually not a bad approximation to use $\epsilon_\infty = n^2$. The general Maxwell relation $\epsilon' = n^2$ holds when ϵ' and n are measured at the same frequency. The Debye equation may be written in the form

$$\frac{\epsilon_{dc} - 1}{\epsilon_{dc} + 2} - \frac{\epsilon_\infty - 1}{\epsilon_\infty + 2} = \frac{4\pi N_1}{9kT}\mu^2 \quad (3)$$

A much better representation of the dielectric behavior of polar liquids is given by the Onsager equation

$$\frac{\epsilon_{dc} - 1}{\epsilon_{dc} + 2} - \frac{\epsilon_\infty - 1}{\epsilon_\infty + 2}$$
$$= \frac{3\epsilon_{dc}(\epsilon_\infty + 2)}{(2\epsilon_{dc} + \epsilon_\infty)(\epsilon_{dc} + 2)}\frac{4\pi N_1\mu^2}{9kT} \quad (4)$$

Anomalous dielectric dispersion occurs when the frequency of the field is so high that the molecules do not have time to attain equilibrium with it. One may then use a complex dielectric constant

$$\epsilon^* = \epsilon' - i\epsilon'' \tag{5}$$

where $j = \sqrt{-1}$. Debye's theory of dielectric behavior gives

$$\epsilon^* = \epsilon_\infty + \frac{\epsilon_{dc} - \epsilon_\infty}{1 + j\omega\tau} \tag{6}$$

where ω is the angular frequency (2π times the number of cycles per second) and τ is the dielectric relaxation time. Dielectric relaxation is the decay with time of the polarization when the applied field is removed. The relaxation time is the time in which the polarization is reduced to $1/e$ times its value at the instant the field is removed, e being the natural logarithmic base.

Combination of the two equations for the complex dielectric constant and separation of real and imaginary parts gives

$$\epsilon' = \epsilon_\infty + \frac{\epsilon_{dc} - \epsilon_\infty}{1 + \omega^2\tau^2} \tag{7}$$

$$\epsilon'' = \frac{(\epsilon_{dc} - \epsilon_\infty)\omega\tau}{1 + \omega^2\tau^2} \tag{8}$$

These equations require that the dielectric constant decrease from the static to the optical dielectric constant with increasing frequency, while the dielectric loss changes from zero to a maximum value ϵ''_m and back to zero. These changes are the phenomenon of anomalous dielectric dispersion. From the above equations, it follows that

$$\epsilon_m'' = (\epsilon_{dc} - \epsilon_\infty)/2 \tag{9}$$

and that the corresponding values of ω and ϵ' are

$$\omega_m = 1/\tau \tag{10}$$

and

$$\epsilon_m' = (\epsilon_{dc} + \epsilon_\infty)/2 \tag{11}$$

The symmetrical loss-frequency curve predicted by this simple theory is commonly observed for simple substances, but its maximum is usually lower and broader because of the existence of more than one relaxation time. Various functions have been proposed to represent the distribution of relaxation times. A convenient representation of dielectric behavior is obtained, according to the method of Cole and Cole, by writing the complex dielectric constant as

$$\epsilon^* = \epsilon_\infty + \frac{\epsilon_{dc} - \epsilon_\infty}{1 + (j\omega\tau_0)^{1-\alpha}} \tag{12}$$

where τ_0 is the most probable relaxation time and α is an empirical constant with a value between 0 and 1, usually less than 0.2. When the values of ϵ'' are plotted as ordinates against those of ϵ' as abscissas, a semicircular arc is obtained intersecting the abscissa axis at $\epsilon' = \epsilon_\infty$ and $\epsilon' = \epsilon_{dc}$. The center of the circle of which this arc is a part lies below the abscissa axis, and the diameter of the circle drawn through the center from the intersection at ϵ_∞ makes an angle $\alpha\pi/2$ with the abscissa axis. When α is zero, the diameter lies in the abscissa axis, there is but one relaxation time, and the behavior of the material conforms to the simple Debye theory. When, as may arise from intramolecular rotation, a substance has more than one relaxation mechanism, or, when the material is a mixture, the observed loss-frequency curve is the resultant of two or more different curves and, therefore, departs from the simple Debye or Cole-Cole curve.

The behavior of a good many materials which have been found, mostly at low temperatures, to depart from the symmetrical arc given by Eq. (12) has been well represented by the empirical equation of Cole and Davidson, in which the exponent $1 - \alpha$ in Eq. (12) is replaced by β. The corresponding curve is a skewed arc and the empirical parameter β, which has values between 0 and 1, measures the degree of skewness. Glarum has accounted for skewed-arc behavior in terms of the diffusion of lattice defects. Anderson and Ullman have treated the reorientation probability of a molecule as a function of the free volume, which fluctuates as the result of random thermal motion. If the rate of free-volume fluctuation is slow compared with that of molecular reorientation, the Cole-Cole plot is symmetrical, but flatter, the greater the dependence of the relaxation rate on the free volume. When the rate of change of free volume is much greater than that of reorientation, all of the molecules have the same environment and a single relaxation time should be observed. For an intermediate situation a skewed-arc plot is to be expected. These and other approaches to the problems of dielectric behavior have been described by Hill, Vaughan, Price, and Davies. Nee and Zwanzig have recently formulated a theory of dielectric relaxation involving dielectric friction on the rotating dipole, which leads to a frequency-dependent relaxation time. Frequency-dependent dynamic viscosity has recently been used by Johari and Smyth to explain an apparent wide distribution of the relaxation times of supercooled solutions of rigid polar molecules as well as the seemingly low dielectric relaxation times found for polar molecules at high frequencies or high viscosities. The complexity of molecular behavior in condensed matter is such that no molecular theory of dielectrics is completely satisfactory at the present time.

If the dielectric material is not a perfect dielectric, and has a specific dc conductance k' (ohms^{-1} cm^{-1}), there is an additional dielectric loss

$$\epsilon_{dc}{}'' = \frac{3.6 \times 10^{12} \pi k'}{\omega} \qquad (13)$$

The effective specific conductance is given by

$$k' = \frac{1}{4\pi} \frac{(\epsilon_{dc} - \epsilon_\infty)\omega^2 \tau}{1 + \omega^2 \tau^2} \qquad (14)$$

It is evident from this equation that k' increases with ω, approaching a limiting value, k_∞, the infinite-frequency conductivity, which is attained when 1 can be neglected in comparison with $\omega^2 \tau^2$, so that

$$k_\infty = \frac{\epsilon_{dc} - \epsilon_\infty}{4\pi\tau} \qquad (15)$$

In a heterogeneous material, interfacial polarization may arise from the accumulation of charge at the interfaces between phases. This occurs only when two phases differ considerably from each other in dielectric constant and conductivity. It is usually observed only at very low frequencies. It is, but, if one phase has a much higher conductivity than the other, the effect may increase the measured dielectric constant and loss at frequencies as high as those of the radio region. This so-called Maxwell-Wagner effect depends on the form and distribution of the phases as well as upon their real dielectric constants and conductances. Each type of form and distribution requires special treatment. For a commercial rubber, for example, the observed loss may be

$$\epsilon''(\text{observed}) = \epsilon_{dc}{}'' + \epsilon''(\text{Maxwell-Wagner})$$

$$+ \epsilon''(\text{Debye}) \qquad (16)$$

Charles P. Smyth

References

Böttcher, C. J. F., "Theory of Electric Polarization," Second edition, revised by O. C. Van Belle, P. Bordewijk and A. Rip, Vol. I, New York, Elsevier, 1973.

Debye, P., "Polar Molecules," reprinted by Dover, New York, 1945.

Fröhlich, H., "Theory of Dielectrics," Second edition, London, Oxford University Press, 1958.

Hill, N. E., Vaughan, W. E., Price, A. H., and Davies, M., "Dielectric Properties and Molecular Behavior," New York, Van Nostrand Reinhold Co., 1969.

Johari, G. P., and Smyth, C. P., *J. Am. Chem. Soc.*, **91**, 5168 (1969); also results to be published.

Nee, T.-W., and Zwanzig, R., *J. Chem. Phys.*, **52**, 6353 (1970).

Smyth, C. P., "Dielectric Behavior and Structure," New York, McGraw-Hill Book Co., 1955; *Ann. Rev. Phys. Chem.*, **17**, 433–456 (1966).

Cross-references: DIPOLE MOMENTS, POLAR MOLECULES, REFRACTION, RELAXATION.

DIFFERENTIAL EQUATIONS IN PHYSICS

Because of their high frequency of occurrence and importance in the physical sciences it is fitting to introduce some of the more common differential equations that arise and to use these as a basis for discussion and development.

(i) When a given mass of a radioactive substance disintegrates it is well known that if at any time t the mass remaining is m, then the rate of decay of mass, $-dm/dt$, is proportional to the amount remaining. This implies that

$$- \frac{dm}{dt} = km \qquad (k = \text{positive constant}). \quad (1)$$

(ii) Suppose that an alternating voltage $E \cos \omega t$ is applied to an electrical circuit consisting of a resistance R, inductance L, and capacitance C in series connection, t specifying time. If i denotes the current flowing in the circuit at time t and q the charge on the capacitance plate into which it flows, then $i = dq/dt$ and so the potential differences across the three components are respectively $Ri, L\,di/dt, q/C$. Equating their sum to the applied voltage gives

$$R \frac{dq}{dt} + L \frac{d^2 q}{dt^2} + \frac{q}{C} = E \cos \omega t. \qquad (2)$$

(iii) When heat is conducted along a metal bar the temperature $u(x, t)$ at time t at a distance x from one end is known to satisfy

$$\frac{\partial u}{\partial t} = k \frac{\partial^2 u}{\partial x^2}, \qquad (3)$$

in the case when there are no radiation losses. For homogeneous material and constant cross section, k is a positive constant.

(iv) If $y(x, t)$ denotes the lateral displacement at time t of a point distant x from one of the fixed ends of a string set in vibration, then it can be shown that

$$\frac{\partial^2 y}{\partial t^2} = c^2 \frac{\partial^2 y}{\partial x^2}, \qquad (4)$$

where c is a constant for a uniform string of constant cross section.

The equations (1) through (4) are examples of *differential equations*. In each case it is seen that a relation exists between a quantity or function whose value is sought, i.e., the *dependent variable*, one or more *independent variables*, and the derivatives of the dependent variables with respect to the independent ones. Equations (1), (2) are examples of *ordinary differential* equations and they involve only total derivatives as there is but one independent variable. Equations (3), (4), however, involve partial derivatives and are called *partial differential equations*. Partial differential equations involve two or more independent variables. In both cases the *order* of the differential equation is that of the highest-order derivative it contains. (1) is of

first order, but (2), (3), (4) are all of second order.

In many physical problems which are formulated as differential equations auxiliary conditions are imposed upon the dependent variable and possibly also on certain of its derivatives. These conditions compounded with the partial differential equation constitute a *boundary value problem*. If, as often happens, such conditions are prescribed at $t = 0$, where t is an independent variable specifying time, the compound problem is called an *initial value problem*.

(1) Ordinary Differential Equations We now consider the ordinary differential equation of order n

$$a_n \frac{d^n y}{dx^n} + a_{n-1} \frac{d^{n-1} y}{dx^{n-1}} + \cdots + a_1 \frac{dy}{dx} + a_0 y = f(x)$$

or

$$L(D)y = f(x)$$

$$(5)$$

where $L(D) \equiv a_n D^n + a_{n-1} D^{n-1} + \cdots + a_1 D + a_0$ and $D^r \equiv d^r/dx^r$. The coefficients $a_0, a_1, \cdots, a_n$ may be either constants or functions of x only. Note that y and all its derivatives in (5) occur only to the power unity and that there are no products of these quantities. Such an equation is said to be *linear*. Suppose that (5) is satisfied by the particular value $y = Y(x)$ so that $L(D)Y(x) = f(x)$. Then $Y(x)$ is called a *particular integral* of (5). Further suppose that the equation $L(D)y = 0$ has n linearly independent solutions $y_1(x), y_2(x), \cdots, y_n(x)$. Then it is easily seen that

$$L(D)(A_1 y_1 + A_2 y_2 + \cdots + A_n y_n) = 0,$$

where $A_1, \cdots, A_n$ are arbitrary constants, and so $y = A_1 y_1 + \cdots + A_n y_n$ satisfies the homogeneous equation $L(D)y = 0$. This solution of the homogeneous equation is called the *complementary function* of the nonhomogeneous equation (5). The number of constants in it is equal to the order of the differential equation. Since

$$L(D)\{Y(x) + A_1 y_1 + A_2 y_2 + \cdots + A_n y_n\}$$

$$= L(D)Y + 0 = f(x),$$

Eq. (5) is satisfied by

$$y = Y(x) + A_1 y_1(x) + \cdots + A_n y_n(x). \quad (6)$$

This form can be shown to be the most general form of solution to (5) and it is called the *complete primitive*. Thus the task of finding the complete primitive to (5) consists of finding the complementary function, obtained by taking $f(x) = 0$, and adding to this a particular integral.

For the special case when the coefficients $a_0, a_1, \cdots, a_n$ in (5) are all constants—and this assumption will be made from now on—the general solution to the equation $L(D)y = 0$ is obtained by making the trial substitution $y = e^{mx}$, where m is an undetermined constant. We find

$$a_n m^n + \cdots + a_1 m + a_0 = 0. \quad (7)$$

Let $m = m_1, m_2, \cdots, m_n$ be the n roots of the *auxiliary equation* (7). Then $L(D)y = 0$ has the n solutions $e^{m_1 x}, e^{m_2 x}, \cdots, e^{m_n x}$ and it can be shown that its most general solution is

$$y = A_1 e^{m_1 x} + A_2 e^{m_2 x} + \cdots + A_n e^{m_n x}, \quad (8)$$

where $A_1, \cdots, A_n$ are constants and the m's are all distinct. As an example the differential equation (1) is a first-order homogeneous equation, and by putting $m = e^{\lambda t}$ we find $\lambda = -k$. Thus the general solution is $m = Ae^{-kt}$, involving but one arbitrary constant. If it is given that $m = m_0$ when $t = 0$, we find $A = m_0$ and so the solution of this initial value problem is $m = m_0 e^{-kt}$.

By way of further example, consider the second-order homogeneous equation

$$\frac{d^2 y}{dx^2} + (a + b) \frac{dy}{dx} + ab\, y = 0$$

$$(a, b \text{ unequal constants}).$$

Putting $y = e^{mx}$ gives the auxiliary equation $m^2 + (a + b)m + ab = 0$ having roots $m = -a, -b$. Hence the general solution is

$$y = Ae^{-ax} + Be^{-bx} \quad (a \neq b).$$

This form is suggested immediately if the differential equation is written in the operator form

$$(D + a)(D + b)y = 0 \quad (a \neq b),$$

since $y = Ae^{-ax}$ and $y = Be^{-bx}$ satisfy $(D + a)y = 0$ and $(D + b)y = 0$ respectively. In the case when $a = b$, it can easily be verified that xe^{-ax} is a second solution to $(D + a)^2 y = 0$ and so its general solution is

$$y = Ae^{-ax} + Bxe^{-ax}.$$

For the general solution of (5), it follows that the main task is the finding of a particular integral. Various techniques are available. Here we describe two methods using suitable examples.

The first is called the method of *variation of parameters*. Suppose it is required to solve for $y(t)$ the differential equation

$$\frac{d^2 y}{dt^2} + \omega^2 y = \cos \omega t. \quad (9)$$

This is the resonance equation and we observe that when $R = 0$ and $\omega^2 = 1/LC$, Eq. (2) is of this form. The complementary function, found from the auxiliary equation $m^2 + \omega^2 = 0$ is clearly $y = ae^{i\omega t} + be^{-i\omega t}$. This may be more simply expressed in the form $y = A \cos \omega t + B \sin \omega t$ using the relations $e^{\pm i\omega t} = \cos \omega t \pm i \sin \omega t$, the constants A, B being given by $A = a + b, B = i(a - b)$. To obtain a particular integral of (9) take

$$y(t) = A(t) \cos \omega t + B(t) \sin \omega t; \quad (10)$$

then

$$\dot{y}(t) = -\omega A(t) \sin \omega t + \omega B(t) \cos \omega t, \quad (11)$$

provided A and B are so chosen that

$$0 = \dot{A}(t) \cos \omega t + \dot{B}(t) \sin \omega t. \quad (12)$$

Differentiating $\dot{y}$ in (11),

$$\ddot{y}(t) = -\omega^2 A(t) \cos \omega t - \omega^2 B(t) \sin \omega t, \quad (13)$$

provided A and B are so chosen that

$$\cos \omega t = -\omega \dot{A}(t) \sin \omega t + \omega \dot{B}(t) \cos \omega t. \quad (14)$$

Solving equations (12), (14) for $\dot{A}$ and $\dot{B}$ we find

$$\dot{A}(t) = -\frac{1}{\omega} \sin \omega t \cos \omega t, \quad \dot{B}(t) = \frac{1}{\omega} \cos^2 \omega t$$

$$= \frac{1}{2\omega} (1 + \cos 2\omega t)$$

and so integrating these,

$$A(t) = -\frac{1}{2\omega^2} \sin^2 \omega t,$$

$$B(t) = \frac{1}{2\omega} \left(t + \frac{1}{2\omega} \sin 2\omega t \right).$$

Thus on substituting these into (10) and simplifying we obtain the particular integral $y = (t/2\omega) \sin \omega t$. Hence the complete primitive is

$$y = A \cos \omega t + B \sin \omega t + \frac{t}{2\omega} \sin \omega t$$

$$(A, B \text{ constants}).$$

As a second method we introduce the *Laplace transform*. This device is eminently suited to solving initial value problems and it is consequently favored by electrical and control engineers. The Laplace transform of $f(t)$ is denoted either by $\mathcal{L}\{f(t)\}$ or by $\overline{f}(s)$ and it is defined to be

$$\mathcal{L}\{f(t)\} = \overline{f}(s) = \int_0^\infty e^{-st} f(t)\, dt.$$

By elementary integration one can compile the following useful table of Laplace transforms for different forms of $f(t)$:

$f(t)$	1	e^{at}	$\cos at$	$\sin at$	t^n
$\overline{f}(s)$	$\dfrac{1}{s}$	$\dfrac{1}{s-a}$	$\dfrac{s}{s^2+a^2}$	$\dfrac{a}{s^2+a^2}$	$\dfrac{n!}{s^{n+1}}$

Here a is constant and $n = 1, 2, 3, \cdots$. Also it is easy to show by integration by parts that

$$\mathcal{L}\left\{ \frac{df(t)}{dt} \right\} = s\,\overline{f}(s) - f(0),$$

$$\mathcal{L}\left\{ \frac{d^2 f(t)}{dt^2} \right\} = s^2 \overline{f}(s) - s f(0) - \dot{f}(0).$$

Let us use this method to solve again equation (9), subject to the initial conditions $y(0) = 0$, $\dot{y}(0) = 0$. Let $\overline{y}(s) = \mathcal{L}\{y(t)\}$. Then, using the initial conditions, $\mathcal{L}\{dy/dt\} = s\,\overline{y}(s)$, $\mathcal{L}\{d^2 y/dt^2\} = s^2 \overline{y}(s)$. Also the table shows that $\mathcal{L}\{\cos \omega t\} = s/(s^2 + \omega^2)$. Hence on taking the Laplace transform of both sides of (9),

$$(s^2 + \omega^2)\overline{y}(s) = s/(s^2 + \omega^2)$$

and so

$$\overline{y}(s) = s/(s^2 + \omega^2)^2.$$

Now

$$\frac{s}{s^2 + \omega^2} = \int_0^\infty e^{-st} \cos \omega t\, dt,$$

and so differentiating both sides of this partially with respect to ω,

$$-\frac{2\omega s}{(s^2 + \omega^2)^2} = \int_0^\infty \frac{\partial}{\partial \omega} (e^{-st} \cos \omega t)\, dt,$$

$$= \int_0^\infty (-t\, e^{-st} \sin \omega t)\, dt.$$

Dividing through by -2ω, we have

$$\frac{s}{(s^2 + \omega^2)^2} = \int_0^\infty e^{-st} \left(\frac{t}{2\omega} \sin \omega t \right) dt.$$

Thus

$$\overline{y}(s) = \mathcal{L}\left\{ \frac{t}{2\omega} \sin \omega t \right\},$$

and so

$$y(t) = \frac{t}{2\omega} \sin \omega t.$$

(2) Partial Differential Equations The simplest methods of solution are based on the technique of *separation of variables* and on the use of an *integral transform* such as the Laplace transform. These are illustrated by means of examples.

Suppose it is desired to solve the one-dimensional heat conduction equation (3) holding along a uniform rod of length ℓ, being given that when $t = 0$, $u = u_0 x$ and, for all $t \geq 0$, $\partial u/\partial x = 0$ at $x = 0$ and $x = \ell$ (i.e., both ends are thermally lagged). Making the trial solution $u = X(x) T(t)$, we find

$$X''(x)/X(x) = T'(t)/kT(t).$$

As the left side of this equation is a function of x only and the right one of t only, each is constant. The physical nature of the problem implies that as t increases, u decreases for any particular value of x. Hence T decreases as t increases and so $T' < 0$. Thus we take the constant to be negative, say $-m^2$, and obtain the ordinary differential equations

$$\begin{cases} X''(x) + m^2 X(x) = 0, \\ T'(t) + m^2 kT(t) = 0. \end{cases}$$

These have the general solutions

$$\begin{cases} X(x) = A \cos mx + B \sin mx, \\ T(t) = C \exp(-m^2 kt). \end{cases}$$

Thus, writing $E = AC$, $F = BC$, a solution for $u(x, t)$ is

$$u(x, t) = XT$$

$$= \exp(-m^2 kt)(E \cos mx + F \sin mx).$$

Since, for all t, $\partial u/\partial x = 0$ when $x = 0$ and when $x = \ell$,

$$F m \exp(-m^2 kt) = 0,$$
$$m \exp(-m^2 kt)(-E \sin m\ell + F \cos m\ell) = 0.$$

The first of these equations implies that $F = 0$ and the second that $m\ell = n\pi$, where n is an integer. Thus a solution satisfying the end conditions is

$$u(x, t) = E \exp(-n^2 \pi^2 kt/\ell^2) \cos(n\pi x/\ell),$$

where n is an integer. A more general solution may be obtained by superposition (as (3) is linear) in the form

$$u(x, t) = \sum_{n=0}^{\infty} E_n \exp(-n^2 \pi^2 kt/\ell^2) \cos(n\pi x/\ell)$$

Using the initial condition $u(x, 0) = u_0 x$, the last form leads to the half-range Fourier series representation

$$\sum_{n=0}^{\infty} E_n \cos(n\pi x/\ell) = u_0 x \quad \text{for} \quad 0 < x < \ell.$$

Determining the coefficients by the usual method,

$$E_0 = \frac{1}{\ell} \int_0^{\ell} u_0 x \, dx = \frac{1}{2} u_0 \ell,$$

and for $n = 1, 2, 3, \cdots$,

$$E_n = \frac{2}{\ell} \int_0^{\ell} u_0 x \cos\left(\frac{n\pi x}{\ell}\right) dx$$

$$= -\frac{2u_0 \ell}{n^2 \pi^2} [1 - (-1)^n].$$

Thus the solution to the boundary value problem is

$$u(x, t) = \frac{1}{2} u_0 \ell$$

$$- \frac{4u_0 \ell}{\pi^2} \sum_{n=1}^{\infty} \frac{\exp\{-(2n-1)^2 k\pi^2 t/\ell^2\}}{(2n-1)^2}$$

$$\cdot \cos \frac{(2n-1)\pi x}{\ell},$$

where $t \geq 0$ and $0 \leq x \leq \ell$. It can be shown that the solution is unique.

To illustrate the Laplace transform technique, consider the boundary value problem of solving for $f(x, y)$ the partial differential equation

$$\frac{\partial^2 f}{\partial x \partial y} = f(x, y)$$

in the region $x \geq 0$, $y \geq 0$ and subject to the boundary conditions

$$\begin{cases} f(x, 0) = 0, \\ f(0, y) = a \ (= \text{const.}). \end{cases}$$

The first boundary condition suggests taking the Laplace transform with respect to y. To this end write

$$\overline{f}(x, s) = \int_0^{\infty} e^{-sy} f(x, y) \, dy.$$

Then

$$\mathcal{L}\{\partial f/\partial y\} = s \, \overline{f}(x, s) - f(x, 0) = s \, \overline{f}(x, s),$$

and

$$\mathcal{L}\left\{\frac{\partial^2 f}{\partial x \partial y}\right\} = \frac{\partial}{\partial x} \mathcal{L}\left\{\frac{\partial f}{\partial y}\right\} = s \frac{d\overline{f}(x, s)}{dx}.$$

Thus the partial differential equation transforms into

$$\frac{d\overline{f}(x, s)}{dx} = \frac{1}{s} \overline{f}(x, s)$$

and this ordinary differential equation has the general solution

$$\overline{f}(x, s) = \overline{f}(0, s) \exp(x/s).$$

Since $f(0, y) = a$, $\overline{f}(0, s) = a/s$ and so

$$\overline{f}(x, s) = \frac{a}{s} \exp\left(\frac{x}{s}\right)$$

$$= a\left[\frac{1}{s} + \frac{x}{s^2} + \frac{x^2}{2! \, s^3} + \frac{x^3}{3! \, s^4} + \cdots\right].$$

From the table, $\mathcal{L}\{y^n\} = n!/s^{n+1}$ for positive integral n, and so

$$f(x, y) = a \left[1 + xy + \frac{x^2 y^2}{(2!)^2} + \frac{x^3 y^3}{(3!)^2} + \cdots \right].$$

In terms of the modified Bessel function this may also be written as $f(x, y) = a I_0 (2\sqrt{xy})$.

FRANK CHORLTON

References

1. Carslaw, H. S., and Jaeger, J. C., "Operational Methods in Applied Mathematics," London, Oxford University Press, 1947.
2. Chorlton, F., "Boundary Value Problems in Physics and Engineering," New York, Van Nostrand Reinhold, 1969.
3. Courant, R., and Hilbert, D., "Methods of Applied Mathematics," New York, Interscience, 1962.
4. Churchill, R. V., "Fourier Series and Boundary Value Problems," New York, McGraw-Hill, 1941.
5. Forsyth, A. R., "Differential Equations," London, Macmillan, 1921.
6. Ince, E. L., "Ordinary Differential Equations," New York, Dover, 1956.
7. Piaggio, H. T. H., "Differential Equations," London, Bell, 1942.
8. Sneddon, I. N., "Elements of Partial Differential Equations," New York, McGraw-Hill, 1957.

Cross-references: CALCULUS IN PHYSICS, FOURIER ANALYSIS.

DIFFRACTION BY MATTER AND DIFFRACTION GRATINGS

According to the principle of Huygens (1629–1695) each point in the space which is touched by a wave gives rise to a spherical secondary wave, which again produces tertiary waves, and so on. Every wave interferes with the next one and quite generally gives rise to diffraction phenomena (see OPTICS, PHYSICAL). Such phenomena in the case of visible light first were observed by F. M. Grimaldi (1618–1663) and mathematically explained by J. Fresnel (1788–1827). G. R. Kirchhoff (1824–1887) gave the first exact mathematical solution of the scalar wave differential equation in terms of a boundary integral. If both the primary and the diffracted rays are parallel (e.g., small source, large distances between diffracting sample and source and detector), we have the experimental conditions of Fraunhofer (1787–1826). With two lenses L_1 and L_2, a collimator pinhole P in the focal plane of L_1, and a photographic plate F in the focal plane of L_2, this condition is fulfilled even for short distances (Fig. 1). Monochromatic light is produced by a Hg lamp with a Schott filter S and an aqueous solution of $CuSO_4$. If s_0 and s are unit vectors in the direction of the primary and the diffracted beam, and λ is the wavelength of the source, then the

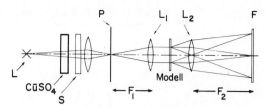

FIG. 1. Equipment for Fraunhofer diffraction.

diffracted intensity I is proportional to

$$I(\mathbf{b}) \cong f_e^2 f_\theta^2 |R|^2 \; ; \; R(\mathbf{b}) = F(\rho) \qquad (1)$$

where

$$\mathbf{b} = \frac{\mathbf{s} - \mathbf{s_0}}{\lambda} \qquad (2)$$

and

$$F = \int e^{-2\pi i (\mathbf{bx})} \, dv_x \qquad (3)$$

is the symbol of the Fourier transform, $\mathbf{x}$ is a vector in physical space, $\rho^2 (\mathbf{x})$ is the transparency of the object M at the end point of the vector $\mathbf{x}$, which lies in the plane of the object, dv_x is a surface element of the object, f_θ^2 and f_e^2 are explained in Table 1 and $\mathbf{b}$ is given by Eq. (2). Figure 2(a) shows an object $\rho(\mathbf{x})$ in the form of a parallelogram with the edge vectors L_1 and L_2, and Fig. 2(b) give its Fraunhofer pattern:

$$|R|^2 = |S|^2 \; ;$$

$$S(\mathbf{b}) = |\, L_1 \wedge L_2 \,| \frac{\sin \pi(\mathbf{bL_1})}{\pi(\mathbf{bL_1})} \cdot \frac{\sin \pi(\mathbf{bL_2})}{\pi(\mathbf{bL_2})} \qquad (4)$$

Fraunhofer used assemblies of N parallel oriented metal wires with an intermediate distance d and the distance a (from center to center), in the direction s_1. Hence

$$\rho(x_1) = \begin{cases} 1 \text{ for } na - \dfrac{d}{2} \leqq x_1 \leqq na + \dfrac{d}{2} \\ 0 \text{ for all other } x_1 \end{cases} \qquad (5)$$

and

$$I(b_1) = \frac{1}{a} f^2 \widehat{Z|S|^2} \qquad (6)$$

$$f = \frac{\sin \pi b_1 d}{\pi b_1} \; ; \quad Z = \frac{1}{a} \sum_n^\infty P(b_1 - n/a) \; ;$$

$$S = \frac{\sin \pi b_1 Na}{\pi b_1} \qquad (7)$$

f is the Fourier transform of a single slit, S that of the shape of the whole lattice (length Na). Z is the "reciprocal" lattice point function (lattice factor) of the centers of the wire, since

TABLE 1. FACTORS fe^2 AND $f\theta^2$ FOR DIFFERENT RADIATIONS

		fe^2	$f\theta^2$	
1	Visible light	$1/\lambda^2$	$\dfrac{1 + \cos^2 2\theta}{2}$	2θ scattering angle
2	X-rays	$\left(\dfrac{e^2}{m_0 c^2}\right)^2$	$\dfrac{1 + \cos^2 2\theta}{2}$	e electric charge of an electron m_0 rest mass of an electron
3	Electrons	$\dfrac{m_0 e^2 \lambda^2}{2h^2}$	$1/\sin^4 \theta$	c velocity of light h Planck's constant
4	Neutrons	Cross section	Polarization factor	λ (de Broglie) wavelength

(a)

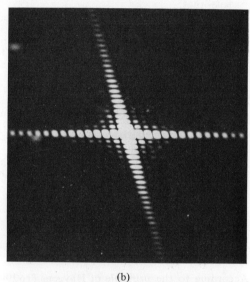
(b)

FIG. 2. (a) Parallelogram as diaphragm. (b) Fraunhofer pattern. Secondary maxima of the shape factor S^2 (Eq. (4)).

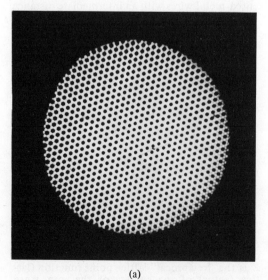
(a)

(b)

FIG. 3. (a) Steel balls in a crystalline lattice. (b) Bragg reflections with shape factor S^2.

$P(b_1 - 0)$ is a normalized point function at $b_1 = 0$. The symbol of convolution $\frown$ is defined for both functions $G_1(\mathbf{b})$ and $G_2(\mathbf{b})$ in Fourier space, and $g_1(\mathbf{x})$ and $g_2(\mathbf{x})$ in physical space by

$$\widehat{G_1(\mathbf{b})G_2}(\mathbf{b}) = \int G_1(\mathbf{c})G_2(\mathbf{b} - \mathbf{c})dv_c \qquad (8)$$

$$\widehat{g_1(\mathbf{x})g_2}(\mathbf{x}) = \int g_1(\mathbf{y})g_2(\mathbf{x} - \mathbf{y})dv_y \qquad (9)$$

In the one-dimensional case of Eq. (8) $\mathbf{c}$ is to be replaced by the scalar quantity c_1 and dv_c by dc_1. Two-dimensional gratings are of high interest, since their Fraunhofer pattern gives all the information we need to understand the more complicated structural theories of three-dimensional matter. This will be shown below.

The technique of preparing such models is quite easy: in the examples of Figs. 4, 5, 6, 7, 8, 10 and 12, the objects were painted with india ink on paper 15 X 15 inches and then photographed on fine-grained films 0.5 X 0.5 inch with steep gradation characteristics (for instance Peruline film F 10). The black ink points now become transparent on a black background. In the models of Figs. 3, 9 and 11, steel balls of 2 to 3 mm diameter were placed into the focal plane of a lens system and photographed with a linear reduction 1 : 15 on the same film material mentioned above.

By defocusing the system, one obtains diaphragms, where the single balls do not touch each other (Figs. 3 and 9, but not Fig. 11). This is quite advantageous, since the width of the atom-factor f^2 [see Eq. (6)] is larger and more reflections are visible.

Fig. 3(a) shows a model of a two-dimensional ideal periodic "point lattice," and Fig. 3(b) represents its Fourier transform.

$$\rho(\mathbf{x}) = \sum_r^\infty P(\mathbf{x} - \mathbf{x}_r); \, \mathbf{x}_r = p_1\mathbf{a}_1 + p_2\mathbf{a}_2 \qquad (10)$$

$$R^2 \sim Z(\mathbf{b}) = \frac{1}{|\mathbf{a}_1 \wedge \mathbf{a}_2|}\sum_h^\infty P(\mathbf{b} - \mathbf{b}_h);$$

$$\mathbf{b}_h = h_1\mathbf{A}_1 + h_2\mathbf{A}_2 \qquad (11)$$

where $\mathbf{a}_1$ and $\mathbf{a}_2$ are the vectors of a lattice cell of the model, and $\mathbf{A}_1$ and $\mathbf{A}_2$ are those of the "reciprocal" lattice cell (in $\mathbf{b}$-space)

$$\mathbf{A}_1 = \frac{\mathbf{a}_2 \wedge \mathbf{a}_3}{\mathbf{a}_1(\mathbf{a}_2 \wedge \mathbf{a}_3)} \, ; \, \mathbf{A}_2 = \frac{\mathbf{a}_3 \wedge \mathbf{a}_1}{\mathbf{a}_2(\mathbf{a}_3 \wedge \mathbf{a}_1)} \qquad (12)$$

$\mathbf{a}_3$ is an arbitrary vector orthogonal to $\mathbf{a}_1$ and $\mathbf{a}_2$, and p_1, p_2, h_1 and h_2 are integers. Since the lattice of Fig. 3(a) is bounded if one multiplies $\rho(\mathbf{x})$ by the shape function $s(\mathbf{x})$ of the lattice (which is 1 inside the lattice, and zero out of it) the p-summation can be extended to infinity. From the convolution theorem one obtains

generally

$$Fg_1g_2 = \widehat{G_1G_2} \, ; Fg_1\widehat{g_2} = G_1G_2 \qquad (13)$$

Hence the Fourier transform of the bounded lattice $\rho(\mathbf{x}) \cdot s(\mathbf{x})$ is given again by the convolution product of Eq. (6), where $S(\mathbf{b})$ is the Fourier transform of $s(\mathbf{x})$ and $Z(\mathbf{b})$ is the Fourier transform of Eq. (11). $f^2 = 1$ applies only for "point-like" atoms, otherwise f is the Fourier transform of the shape of each "point."

M. v. Laue in 1911 prepared an article "Wellenoptik" for the "Encyclopedie der Math. Wissenschaften" and found that Eq. (11) can be easily developed to the Fourier transform of three-dimensional point lattice, where $\mathbf{a}_3$ is a third lattice vector, non-coplanar to $\mathbf{a}_1$ and $\mathbf{a}_2$. Then $\mathbf{b}_h$ in Eq. (11) must be replaced by

$$\mathbf{b}_h = h_1\mathbf{A}_1 + h_2\mathbf{A}_2 + h_3\mathbf{A}_3;$$

$$\mathbf{A}_3 = \frac{\mathbf{a}_1 \wedge \mathbf{a}_2}{\mathbf{a}_3(\mathbf{a}_1 \wedge \mathbf{a}_2)} \qquad (14)$$

Together with W. Friedrich and P. Knipping using x-rays of a wavelength of the same order of magnitude as that of the atomic distances, M. v. Laue (1912) found three-dimensional diffraction effects in single crystals. $f(\mathbf{b})$ then is the atom form amplitude

$$f(\mathbf{b}) = F(\rho_0) \qquad (15)$$

where $\rho_0(\mathbf{x})$ is the electron density distribution of one atom, whose center lies at $\mathbf{x} = 0$.

C. J. Davisson and L. H. Germer (1927) observed the same diffraction phenomena using electron beams. $\rho(\mathbf{x})$ must then be understood as density distribution of both the electrons (negative) and protons (positive). If single diffraction processes occur, Eq. (6) remains unchanged.

D. P. Mitchell, P. N. Powers, H. v. Halban and P. Preiswerk (1936) found the same diffraction phenomena using thermal neutrons. In this case $\rho(\mathbf{x})$ is the density distribution of the nuclei, each one weighted by the mean of the square root of its respective cross section. The proportional factors f_e^2, f_θ^2 of Eq. (1) for the different radiations are given in Table 1.

The vector $\mathbf{b}$ defined by the integral of Eq. (3) expands the three-dimensional Fourier space and is connected with the unit vectors $\mathbf{s}$, $\mathbf{s}_0$ of the diffracted and primary beam by Eq. (2). This is the construction of Ewald (1914). For a fixed λ and $\mathbf{s}_0$ all values $R(\mathbf{b})$ are in reflection positions, which lie on a sphere with radius $1/\lambda$ and the center at $\mathbf{b}_0 = \mathbf{s}_0/\lambda$.

P. Debye (1915) found that the molecules in the gaseous state give rise to diffraction patterns depending on the structure of the single molecules, without any intermolecular interferences.

In 1927, F. Zernike and I. A. Prins discussed quantitatively diffraction phenomena of liquids and laid down the fundamentals of the structure analysis of amorphous matter. Moreover, P.

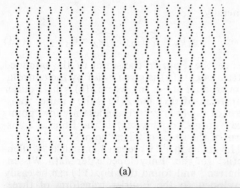

(a)

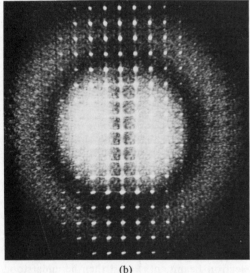

(b)

FIG. 4. (a) Linear thermal oscillations without correlations. (b) Debye factor and thermodiffuse background.

Debye (1913) and I. Waller (1927) found that real crystals never have a periodic lattice similar to that of Fig. 3(a), since the atoms show thermal oscillations around their ideal positions. All these different phenomena can be studied quite easily with the help of two-dimensional statistical models and their Fraunhofer patterns, since Eq. (1) holds for all diffraction phenomena. In Fig. 4(a) we have the "frozen" structure of a point lattice with thermal oscillations. They are quite anisotropic and occur only in the horizontal direction. If $H(\mathbf{x})$ is the frequency of the center of an atom being at the distance x from its ideal position and if the atoms oscillate independently from each other, then R^2 is given by

$$R^2(b) = Nf^2(1 - D^2) + \frac{1}{v_r} f^2 D^2 \widehat{Z|S|^2};$$

$$D(\mathbf{b}) = F(H) \quad (16)$$

(v_r = volume of a lattice cell). In Fig. 4(b) can be clearly recognized the first term of Eq. (16)

as a diffuse background. It has a structure in the horizontal direction. The "Bragg reflections" are weakened by the "Debye-Waller factor" D^2, the more, the stronger is the diffuse background $(1 - D^2)$. In nature there exist correlations between the different oscillations and "elastic waves" with an "acoustical" and "optical" frequency creep through the lattice.

Fig. 4(a) gives a single undamped longitudinal and sinusoidal wave with a horizontal wave vector $\mathbf{b}_t$ and a wavelength λ_t and amplitude $\mathbf{a}_t$

$$\lambda_t = \frac{1}{|b_t|} = 8a; \; |a_t| = \frac{1}{4}\,a \quad (17)$$

According to the theories of M. v. Laue (1927) and Laval (1941) in Fig. 5(b) at the reciprocal

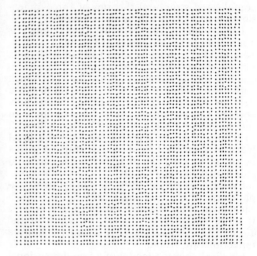

(a)

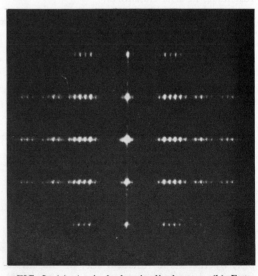

FIG. 5. (a) A single longitudinal wave. (b) Extra Laue spots.

lattice points

$$\mathbf{b} = \mathbf{b}_h + m\mathbf{b}_t \qquad (18)$$

"Extra Laue spots" ("Laval spots") occur. According to conventional theories, $m = 1$ is called one-phonon scattering, $m = 2$ is two-phonon scattering and so on; and it is said that the frequency ν_0 of the incident radiation is changed into $\nu_0 + m\nu_t$ ("inelastic scattering," ν_t-frequency of the phonons).

In Fig. 6(a) we have again a horizontal wave with the same wave vector [Eq. (17)], which now is transverse. From Laue's theory it follows, that the intensity of a Laue spot of the mth order is proportional to the square of the Bessel function

$$I_m(2\pi(\mathbf{b}\mathbf{a}_t))$$

where m is the order of the Bessel function and $\mathbf{a}_t$ is the amplitude vector of the elastic wave. Hence in Fig. 6(b), strong Laval spots occur only in the vertical $\mathbf{b}_h$ direction; in Fig. 5(b), in the horizontal $\mathbf{b}\mathbf{a}_t$ direction. Since $I_1(I_2)$ has its maximum at $\mathbf{b}\mathbf{a}_t = 0.25\ (0.5)$, in Figs. 5(b) and 6(b), the Laval spot $m = 1$ at the reflection h_1, $h_2 = 1.0\ (0.1)$ is much stronger and in the 2.0 (0.2) reflection, much weaker, than the Laval spot $m = 2$.

In nature, one never finds such sharp Laval spots, but a completely smooth "thermodiffuse" scattering, and it is said that a "white" spectrum of undamped elastic waves exists.

In Fig. 7(a) strongly damped transverse waves according to Eq. (17) consisting only of two

(a)

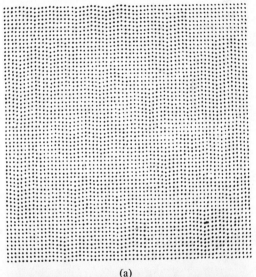

(a)

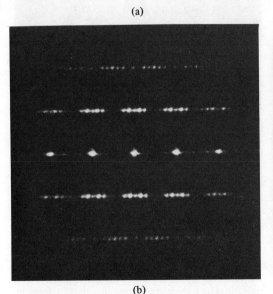

(b)

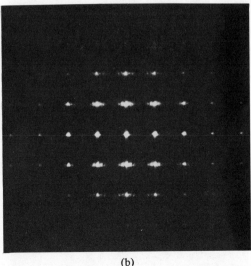

(b)

FIG. 6. (a) A single transversal wave. (b) Extra Laue spots.

FIG. 7. (a) Twelve damped transversal waves. (b) Diffuse extra Laue spots.

maxima and minima are introduced. Now in Fig. 7(b) quite diffuse spots appear. Hence, in nature, such damped waves could also occur, and if they had a spectral distribution, they could give rise to the same observable thermo-diffuse scattering. According to Debye's theory of heat capacity, every wave has a different amplitude a_t, following a Boltzmann statistic. Then in certain regions of a single crystal, the atoms oscillate statistically with different amplitudes than in others. As a result, the lattice cells exhibit different sizes and paracrystalline distortions occur.

Close to the melting point, the amplitudes a_t of the elastic waves become so large that the electron clouds of the atoms suffer large deformations, which damp these waves more and more.

Another physical reason for paracrystalline distortions below the melting point exists if the "motives" in the single lattice cells have different shapes. Such phenomena have been observed in the "macrolattices" of natural and synthetic high polymers.

Figure 8(a) shows a paracrystalline model, where both coordination statistics H_k are horizontal line functions. Figure 8(b) represents its Fraunhofer pattern and Fig. 8(c) the x-ray small-angle pattern of the β-keratin of the quill of a sea gull (Bear and Rugo (1951)). The cell edge a_2 in the vertical direction parallel to the fiber axis has a constant length of 185Å but statistically changes its direction (with respect to the macroscopic fiber axis) within ±5°, while the orthogonal edge length a_1 has an average value of 34Å and changes its length statistically within ±2.5Å. As a result of the van der Waals forces, which allow a variation of the length a_1 orthogonal to the fiber axis, the homopolar forces along a_2 have freedom to change their direction

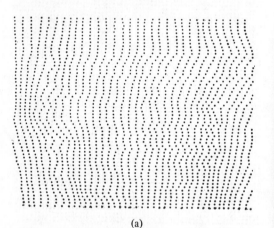

(a)

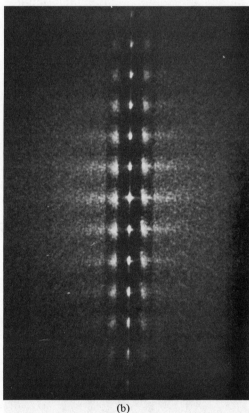

(b)

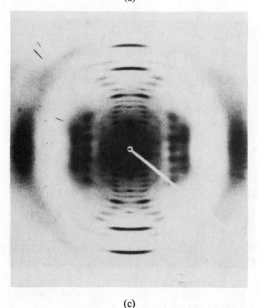

(c)

FIG. 8. (a) Monoparacrystal with linear horizontal coordination statistics. (b) Its Fraunhofer pattern. The reflections (o, h_2) are crystalline, all others are more or less diffuse. (c) Small-angle x-ray pattern from β-feather-keratin (Bear-Rugo, 1951).

of the molecular chain, within one paracrystal. This paracrystal itself, therefore, shows a flexible character in atomic dimensions.

Equation (6) holds again, if one replaces the crystalline lattice factor Z of Eqs. (7) and (11) by the paracrystalline lattice factor

$$Z(\mathbf{b}) = \frac{1}{v_r} \prod_{k=1}^{3} Re \; \frac{1 + F_k(\mathbf{b})}{1 - F_k(\mathbf{b})} \qquad (19)$$

$$F_k(\mathbf{b}) = F(H_k) \qquad (20)$$

H_k is a so-called coordination statistic. $H_k(\mathbf{x})$ is the "a priori" probability of finding a cell edge vector $\mathbf{a}_k = \mathbf{x}$ in a certain paracrystalline lattice cell.

For the same reason, in mixed crystals consisting of atoms of different sizes, paracrystalline distortions can also occur.

Figure 3(a) showed a model of steel balls of the same size, building up a crystalline lattice. Figure 3(b) represents its Fourier transform. In Fig. 9(a) steel balls of different sizes built up a paracrystalline lattice, whose Fraunhofer pattern [Fig. 9(b)] exhibits characteristic features of a paracrystalline lattice [cf. Fig. 8(b)].

In Fig. 10(a) another model of a mixed crystal is given without paracrystalline lattice distor-

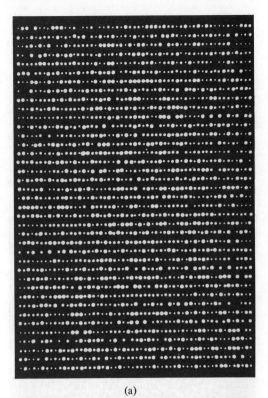

(a)

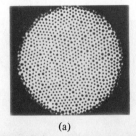

(a)

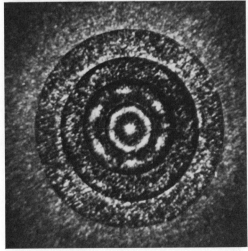

(b)

FIG. 9. (a) Mixed single paracrystal (steel balls). (b) Intensity function (Eq. (6) and (19)).

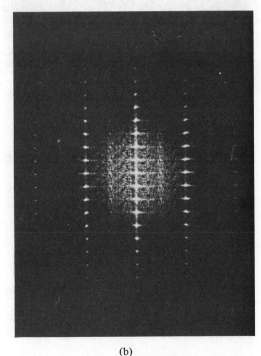

(b)

FIG. 10. (a) Mixed single crystal with "cooperative forces." (b) Background with diffuse walls (*Nahordnung*).

tions. Now the two kinds of atoms are not distributed totally randomly to the lattice points. Hence the Fraunhofer pattern of Fig. 10(b) shows a diffuse background, which is not given by

$$N(\overline{f^2} - \overline{f}^2) \qquad (21)$$

and which presents "diffuse walls" in the vertical direction at $h_1 = \pm\frac{1}{2}$ of a width $\delta b_1 \sim \frac{1}{8}A_1$. This means that in the horizontal direction, rows of about 8 atoms show a kind of "superstructure" (*Nahordnung*, "cooperative order"). This "superstructure" has a psychological background: The technician, painting the models

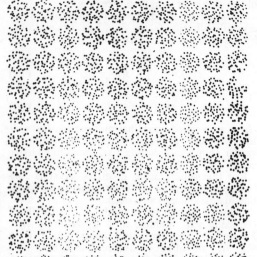

(a)

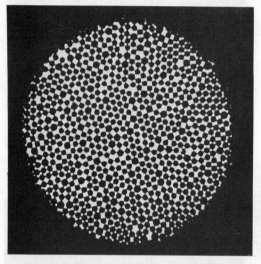

(a)

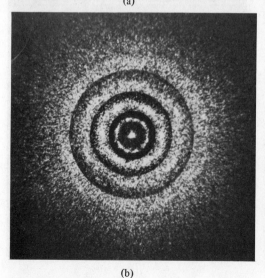

(b)

FIG. 11. (a) Polymicroparacrystalline assembly of steel balls. (b) Intensity function of "amorphous" matter.

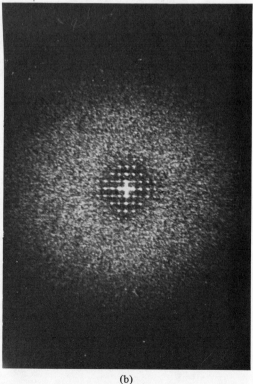

(b)

FIG. 12. (a) Zirconium crystal with discrete electrons. (b) Rayleigh scattering of the electrons.

row by row in the horizontal direction was anxious to choose thick and thin atoms quite arbitrarily. However, he did not use a Monte Carlo Method, but tried as arbitrarily as possible to draw statistical sequences. Unfortunately, after he painted a thick atom he tended to choose a thin one, etc. Unconsciously, he introduced "cooperative forces."

Similar diffuse walls are observed in ferroelectric $NaNO_2$ above the Curie point: In this case, rows of about six $NaNO_2$ molecules have parallel oriented polar axes, and have built up microferroelectric domains in a statistically paraelectric matrix (M. Canut and R. Hosemann, 1964).

In Fig. 11(a), similar to Fig. 9(a), steel balls of different sizes which now built up a structure of single small paracrystallites were used. The Fraunhofer pattern, Fig. 11(b), shows the typical features of a liquid or melt or "amorphous" solid. Hosemann and Lemm (1964) have proved, that in molten gold and lead such paracrystals can be found with average diameters of 12Å to 40Å.

After having completed the step from crystals to amorphous matter, Fig. 12(a) gives an example of a special gas and Fig. 12(b) at larger b-values, the gas-interferences. Lord Rayleigh (1842–1919) proved that here phase relations between the single scattering centers are destroyed in the average as a consequence of their irregular positions. Since in Fig. 12 only 5200 centers were used, "ghosts" remain in the Fraunhofer pattern. Besides this fluctuation the intensity at large b-values is given by the shape of the single points. Moreover in Fig. 12(a) every 40 points cluster together. The clusters are arranged in a crystalline lattice. Hence, at small angles in Fig. 12(b), "Bragg-reflections" whose intensity is proportional to the squared transform Eq. (15) do occur. ρ_0 is now a forty-point function different for each cluster, and in Eq. (6), f must be replaced by the average $\bar{f}$. The diffuse background of Fig. 12(b), which now is the statistical fluctuation of the density distribution ρ_0 is given again by Eq. (21). If we replace the word "cluster" by zircon atom and "point" by electron, Fig. 12(a) gives an instantaneous picture of the electron configuration in a zirconium crystal. The Bragg reflections give in this case information about Schrödinger's wave functions for electrons

$$\overline{\rho_0(x)} = \psi\psi^*$$

and the fluctuation term of Eq. (21) gives some information about the structure of a single electron. In reality, Compton processes disturb the diffraction. There is some hope for further detailed studies.

ROLF HOSEMANN

Cross-references: ABERRATION, DIFFRACTION THEORY OF; CRYSTALLOGRAPHY; ELECTRON DIFFRACTION; NEUTRON DIFFRACTION; OPTICS, PHYSICAL; PARACRYSTAL POLYMER PHYSICS; SCHRÖDINGER EQUATION; X-RAY DIFFRACTION.

DIFFUSION IN LIQUIDS

Diffusion, in a macroscopic sense, is a universal process that leads to the eliminating of concentration gradients in gases, solids, or liquids. At the molecular level, it arises because atoms or molecules undergo small, essentially random displacive movements as a result of their thermal energy. Such motions of individual particles may be likened to a kind of aimless three-dimensional *random walk*. If we limit our attention to the displacement of a single particle in a given direction from its position at some arbitrary zero of time, the *probability* that it will be found at a distance, $\pm x$, from its origin after a time, t, is given by:

$$P(x, t) = \frac{1}{2(\pi Dt)^{1/2}} \exp(-x^2/4Dt) \qquad (1)$$

In this equation, the parameter D, called the *diffusion coefficient*, is a measure of the average rate with which the displacement of the particle occurs.

If, instead of attempting to follow the random motion of an individual particle, we introduce a large number of particles C_0 at a point within the system, their concentration $C(x, t)$ will vary with time and distance in a given direction according to:

$$C(x, t) = \frac{C_0}{2(\pi Dt)^{1/2}} \exp(-x^2/4Dt) \qquad (2)$$

Both equations have the form of the well-known Gaussian error curve, which gives the distribution of random errors to be expected in a large set of measurements. Figure 1 illustrates these equations, showing the probability of finding a single particle at a distance from its origin (or the concentration distribution of a finite quantity of a substance) after times, t_1 and t_2.

Equation (2) is a particular solution of a pair of more general differential equations known as Fick's laws. Consider a plane of unit cross-sectional area in a system, across which a concentration gradient, $\partial C/\partial x$, exists. There will be a net flux of matter, J_x, through the plane from the region of higher to lower concentra-

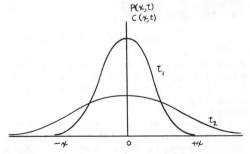

FIG. 1. Concentration or probability profiles for one-dimensional diffusion for times t_1 and t_2.

tion given by Fick's first law:

$$J_x = -D \frac{\partial C}{\partial x} \qquad (3)$$

In principle, it is possible to determine the coefficient of diffusion on the basis of Eq. (3) by measuring the net quantity of matter that crosses through unit area of the plane in unit time. This proves to be difficult in liquids or solids, however, and an additional complication is that the concentration gradient $\partial C/\partial x$ is not constant but decreases with time.

For this reason, it is more feasible to measure the accumulation of matter in a small volume element after a measured period of time. We may consider such a volume element to be bounded by parallel planes of unit area, separated from one another by a distance dx, as shown in Fig. 2. The rate of change of concentration within the volume element is expressed by Fick's second law:

$$\frac{d}{dx}\left[J_x - \left(J_x + \frac{\partial J}{\partial x} \cdot dx \right) \right] = \frac{dC}{dt} = D \frac{\partial^2 C}{\partial x^2}$$

$$(4)$$

This is the fundamental equation, upon which all experimental studies of diffusion depend.

One of the most widely used of the absolute methods for measuring diffusion coefficients of liquids is the "open capillary" technique, devised by Anderson and Saddington.[1] A capillary tube, usually less than 1 mm in diameter and 2–3 cm in length, is filled with an isotopically labeled substance and immersed in a thermostatted bath of the unlabeled liquid. Interdiffusion of the labeled and unlabeled molecules occurs across the open end of the capillary, and at the end of the experiment, the average concentration of labeled substance remaining in the capillary is determined by suitable radiochemical or mass spectrometric techniques. The relation between the diffusion coefficient and the initial and final concentration of labeled substance in the capillary is given by a series solution of Fick's second law:

$$\frac{C_{av}}{C_0} = \frac{8}{(\pi)^2} \sum_{n=0}^{\infty} \frac{1}{(2n+1)^2}$$

$$\exp\left(-(2n+1)^2 \pi^2 D t / 4L^2\right) \quad (5)$$

In this equation, for which L and t are, respectively, the capillary length and time, the series converges rapidly and as a rule may be terminated after the first or second term with negligible error.

A completely different method for the measurement of diffusion coefficients in the liquid state is based upon nuclear magnetic resonance (NMR). An assembly of atomic nuclei which have been excited to some nonequilibrium spin distribution will return to thermal equilibrium

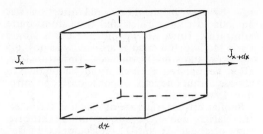

FIG. 2. Diffusive flux across parallel planes.

by a mechanism that involves the coupling of the nuclear spins with their local molecular environment. The rate of the return to equilibrium is characterized by a *relaxation time* (T_1, the spin-lattice relaxation time), and is governed by the variations in the local magnetic field at nuclei which are induced by the translational motions of neighboring molecules. In favorable circumstances the spin-lattice relaxation time may be obtained from the width of the NMR resonance line. Bloembergen, Purcell, and Pound[2] developed the basic theory which relates the spin-lattice relaxation time to the diffusion coefficient of molecules, and made the first measurements on water and a series of hydrocarbons to test its validity. A more direct determination of the self-diffusion coefficient of liquids is provided by NMR spin-echo experiments. These techniques employ rf pulses and either steady or pulsed magnetic field gradients to determine the rate of decay of the induced nuclear spin polarization. Spin echo measurements of the self-diffusion coefficients of liquid lithium and liquid sodium, as well as of H_2O and D_2O, are in excellent agreement with the results of isotope labeled diffusion experiments.[4]

A completely different approach to the study of the dynamics of atom motion in liquids is based upon slow neutron scattering. The angular and energy dependence of the cross section for inelastic scattering of neutrons by the nuclei of atoms in a liquid metal, for example, may be used to deduce the Van Hove space-time correlation function.[5] This function contains information about the diffusive motions of nuclei, and experiments on liquid metals indicate that a transition from the gas-like free motion of particles to solid-like diffusive displacements occurs on a time scale of 10^{-13} sec.

Studies of the temperature dependence of the diffusion coefficient of liquids generally lead to an empirical relationship of the form:

$$D = D_0 \exp\left(-(Q/RT)\right) \qquad (6)$$

where D_0 and Q are experimental parameters that are essentially temperature-independent and characterize the diffusion process in the system at hand. Because of the exponential form of Eq. (6), the mechanism of diffusion in

liquids is often assumed to be an activated process, by analogy with other kinetic processes to which the *absolute reaction rate theory*[3] has been applied with much success. According to this theory, the rate-limiting step of a kinetic process is determined by the frequency with which atoms or molecules acquire sufficient energy through thermal fluctuations to surmount an energy barrier identified by the parameter Q. It has not yet proved possible to make accurate *a priori* calculations of D_0 and Q on the basis of the activated state theory, however, and the exponential form of Eq. (6) is no proof that the mechanism of atom transport in liquids is a thermally activated process in any simple sense. In fact, the prevailing view is that diffusion in the liquid state is a highly cooperative process involving the correlated motions of many particles, for which no simple activated state is an adequate description. At this time, it appears that a more fundamental insight into the structure and dynamic interactions of molecules in the liquid state will emerge from theories[6] which concern themselves with the cooperative motions of particles that exchange momenta with one another during collisions. The success of such efforts will depend upon more accurate knowledge of intermolecular potentials.

The range over which diffusion coefficients of liquids[7] vary is much more limited than that of solids (see DIFFUSION IN SOLIDS). As a rule, experimental values lie between 10^{-4} and 10^{-6} cm²/sec, but despite this relatively narrow compass, they contain information that must lead to a more complete description of the disordered liquid state.

NORMAN H. NACHTRIEB

References

1. Anderson, J. S., and Saddington, K., *J. Chem. Soc.*, 381 (1949).
2. Bloembergen, N., Purcell, E. M., and Pound, R. V., *Phys. Rev.*, **73**, 679 (1948).
3. Glasstone, S., Laidler, K. J., and Eyring, H., "The Theory of Rate Processes," p. 477, New York, McGraw-Hill Book Co., 1941.
4. Murday, J. S., and Cotts, R. M., *J. Chem. Phys.*, **53**, 4274 (1970).
5. Van Hove, L., *Phys. Rev.*, **95**, 249 (1954).
6. Rice, S. A., and Allnatt, A. R., *J. Chem. Phys.*, **34**, 2144 (1961).
7. Jost, W., "Diffusion," p. 436, Academic Press, 1960.

Cross-references: BROWNIAN MOTION, DIFFUSION IN SOLIDS, KINETIC THEORY, MAGNETIC RESONANCE, RELAXATION.

DIFFUSION IN SOLIDS

The term "diffusion" refers to the random motion, generally activated by local fluctuations of thermal energy, of particles through a medium. The particles with which we shall be concerned are atoms and molecules; the medium can be various types of solids. Of special interest will be crystalline solids—these include all metals, most ionic substances, and many covalent ones—in which the atoms occupy periodic and well-defined sites.

The migrating particles may themselves be uniformly distributed constituents of the host solid; this is called self-diffusion. When the diffusing system contains chemical inhomogeneities or when a foreign substance diffuses in from the surface, we speak of chemical or of impurity diffusion. Diffusion processes are technologically important in the oxidation and tarnishing of metals, where one reactant must migrate through the layer of reaction product, and in the annealing of deformed or radiation-damaged materials. Self-diffusion is an essential step in the photographic process in silver halides, and impurity diffusion is widely used in the fabrication of semiconductor devices such as transistors. Many metals, such as steel and duralumin, are hardened by solid-state precipitation and reaction, in which diffusion plays a dominant role. It is also significant in the powder metallurgy technique of fabrication of parts from high-melting metals.

If, in the medium, there are variations in the concentration of the migrating atoms—perhaps chemically different atoms or, in the case of self-diffusion, radioactive tracer isotopes—then there occurs a net drift of the diffusing species from regions of high concentration to those of lower concentration. This flow takes place even though each individual atom may migrate completely at random. It is a statistical result of the fact that if there are more atoms per unit volume of, say, A to the left of a given plane than to the right, then even with random, non-directed motion, more A atoms will cross the plane from the left than from the right. We can define the flux of A as the net excess of A atoms crossing a plane of unit area in unit time. Experimentally, this flux is found to depend on the chemical natures of the medium and the diffusing species. If the medium is isotropic or is a crystal of cubic symmetry, the flux is along the direction of the concentration gradient. Moreover, if the system is not too thermodynamically nonideal, the flux is proportional to the concentration gradient; the constant of proportionality is called the diffusion coefficient, D. Thus, we write the flux $J = -D \, dc/dx$, where the negative sign indicates that the net flow is toward the region of lower concentration. This statement is known as Fick's law. If lengths are measured in centimeters and time in seconds, D is in units of square centimeters per second. It follows from Fick's law that at any given point in the medium, the concentration of the diffusing entity A will change with time at a rate governed by the variation of the flux with distance [$\partial c/\partial t = \partial/\partial x(D\partial c/\partial x)$; for the particularly simple case where D is independent of distance, as in

self-diffusion, then $\partial c/\partial t = D\partial^2 c/\partial x^2$]. Also, from the theory of random flights, it can be shown that the root-mean-square displacement of atoms resulting from diffusion for a time t increases as the square root of the product Dt; $R_{rms} = (6Dt)^{1/2}$.

It is observed that for any given system, D increases rapidly with increasing temperature, almost invariably following the Arrhenius relation $D = D_0 \exp(-H/RT)$. Here, D_0 and H are positive constants for a given system and R is the universal gas constant. The parameter H is called the activation energy and generally increases as the melting point of the host crystal increases. Typically, in crystals which melt at 400 to 500°C, H is about 20 000 to 25 000 cal/mole, or 1 eV/atom, for self-diffusion or diffusion of substitutionally dissolved impurities. In crystals which melt near 1000°C, such as the noble metals, the activation energy is approximately 2 eV/atom. The value of the parameter D_0 is usually in the range 0.01 to 100 cm²/sec. It is interesting that for a large number of metals and simple ionic crystals, the diffusion coefficients for self-diffusion and for most impurities lie near to 10^{-8} cm²/sec at temperatures approaching the melting point. Thus, after diffusing for one day at such a temperature, the value of R_{rms} is about 1 mm, rather a large distance when compared to the spacing between atoms in a crystal.

Because of the three-dimensional regularity of atomic positions in a crystalline solid, the unit step in diffusion must be the jump of an atom from one site to a neighboring, crystallographically equivalent site. Large-scale diffusion is the result of random superposition of many such jumps, all of the same length λ but distributed among the various jump directions allowed by the crystal. It is readily shown that the relation between the macroscopic diffusion coefficient D and the microscopic atomic jump frequency Γ is $D = 1/6\lambda^2\Gamma$. This equation may be compared with that given above for R_{rms} by noting that for random jumps $R_{rms} = \lambda(\Gamma t)^{1/2}$. Now λ will depend on the details of the mechanism of diffusion but it must be of the order of the interatomic spacing, about 3 × 10^{-8} cm. Then the typical high-temperature diffusion coefficient of 10^{-8} cm²/sec requires each atom to make 10^7 to 10^8 jumps each second.

In most crystals the atoms are rather densely packed; thus the means whereby such a high frequency of jumps can be accomplished is not obvious. Conceptually, the simplest possibility is the simultaneous exchange of sites between two atoms, but this is ruled out because of the excessive activation energy that would be required to push aside the mutual neighbors of the pair. A dramatic demonstration that diffusion must proceed by a mechanism which allows independent motion of individual atoms is the Kirkendall effect. Two mutually soluble specimens of differing composition, say A and B, are welded together with inert markers imbedded at the interface. Subsequent interdiffusion of A and B results in a drift of the markers relative to the ends of the specimen, indicating that more atoms have left one side of the couple than have entered it from the other. Clearly a pair exchange mechanism cannot be operative here.

Extensive evidence is now available that in most cases of self-diffusion or of substitutionally dissolved impurities, migration proceeds as a result of the presence and mobility of vacant lattice sites. These vacancies exist in the crystal in thermodynamic equilibrium, at concentrations which increase with temperature as exp $(-H_f/RT)$, where H_f is the energy required to form a vacancy (about 1 eV in the noble metals). At temperatures near the melting point, the fraction of sites vacant is typically 0.01 to 0.1 per cent. Vacancies move by the jumping of adjacent atoms, at a rate which varies as exp $(-H_m/RT)$. H_m is the activation energy for the migration process. The average jump frequency of an atom must then be the product of the jump frequency of a vacancy and the fraction of atomic sites that are vacant. Comparing the temperature dependence of the diffusion coefficient with that of these two factors, it follows that H must equal the sum of H_m and H_f. Quantitative experimental verification of this equality in a number of substances has firmly established the vacancy mechanism for diffusion in such crystals.

Other mechanisms, however, are also known to operate. For example, linear or planar defects within the crystal can provide paths for easier and more rapid diffusion. Thus, along boundaries between crystal grains, on the external surfaces, and along the linear defects known as crystal dislocations, the atomic regularity is interrupted and binding energies are correspondingly decreased. As a result, the activation energy for diffusion is locally smaller and the diffusion coefficients are therefore larger; one speaks of a "short-circuiting" effect. Along dislocations and internal boundaries, the diffusion activation energy is typically only about half that for diffusion within the bulk crystal, and short-circuiting contributions become especially important at temperatures below about half of the melting point. Diffusion along external surfaces appears to depend strongly on the nature of the ambient atmosphere, and the details of the process are not well understood at present.

Another mechanism which is found in some systems involves the diffusing atom (or ion) migrating from one interstitial position (i.e., squeezed in between proper atom sites) to another. This process is not surprising in those cases in which a very small impurity ion is already dissolved interstitially, such as for carbon in iron; its occurrence is perhaps unexpected, however, in cases where the migrating ion is present primarily substitutionally (i.e., in

normal atomic sites of the crystal). Thus, in the silver halides, self-diffusion of silver and the diffusion of several cationic solutes proceed primarily via the interstices of the lattice; perhaps the "softness" of the silver halides encourages such a mechanism. Also, in the loosely packed crystals of germanium and silicon, some solutes (such as copper or gold) diffuse interstitially, although they are dissolved mainly substitutionally. And more recently, it has come to be appreciated that in many polyvalent metals such as lead and tin, the noble metals and their divalent neighbors diffuse by some sort of interstitial process. In all such cases the diffusion coefficients at high temperatures are much larger, by several factors of ten, than would be expected for ordinary substitutional diffusion by means of vacancies.

LAWRENCE SLIFKIN

References

The first reference describes experimental techniques for determining diffusion coefficients; those following are recent brief reviews in order of increasing sophistication or date of publication. References to more detailed discussions are given in these. The last reference is quite extensive.

Tomizuka, C. T., in Lark-Horovitz, K., and Johnson, V., Eds., "Methods of Experimental Physics," Vol. 6A, p. 364, New York, Academic Press, 1959.
Girifalco, L. A., "Atomic Migration in Crystals," New York, Blaisdell, 1964.
Shewmon, P. G., "Diffusion in Solids," New York, McGraw-Hill Book Co., 1963.
Lazarus, D., "Diffusion in Metals," in Seitz, F., and Turnbull, D., Eds., *Solid State Phys.*, **10**, 71 (1960).
Peterson, N. L., "Diffusion in Metals," in Seitz, F., and Turnbull, D., Eds., *Solid State Phys.*, **22**, 409 (1968).
Crawford, J. H., Jr., and Slifkin, L., "The Structure of Defects in Solids," in Huggins, R. S., Ed., *Ann. Rev. Materials Sci.* **1**, 139 (1971).
Neumann, G., and Neumann, G. M., "Surface Self-Diffusion of Metals," in Wöhlbier, F. H., Ed., Diffusion Monograph Series, No. 1; Solothurn (Switzerland), The Diffusion Information Center, 1972.
Various chapters in: Crawford, J. H., Jr., and Slifkin, L., Eds. "Point Defects in Solids," New York, Plenum Press, 1972 and 1973.
Adda, Y., and Philibert, J., "La Diffusion dans les Solides," Paris, Presses Universitaires de France, 1966.

Cross-references: CRYSTALLIZATION, CRYSTALLOGRAPHY, DIFFUSION IN LIQUIDS, SOLID-STATE PHYSICS, SOLID-STATE THEORY.

DIMENSIONS

When describing natural phenomena, certain physical attributes or characteristics, such as mass or length, are distinguished. To these are assigned numerical *magnitudes* by prescribed measuring procedures, in which selected *scales* are employed. The length of a Foucault pendulum might be measured with a meter stick and found to equal 64 *units* of measurement, namely 64 meters. The length is called a physical *quantity*.

Customarily, certain quantities, such as length and time, are chosen to be primary or fundamental. Other quantities, like velocity, can then be expressed in terms of these. They are termed secondary or derived quantities. When the meter and the second are taken as units of length and time, the magnitude of a velocity can be expressed in meters per second. The exponent of the power of any primary quantity is called the *dimension* of the secondary quantity in that primary quantity. The dimensions of a secondary quantity are then written in terms of the primary quantities from which they are constituted and the powers to which they are raised. Thus the dimensions of a velocity v, here written as $[v]$, with length L and time T as primary dimensions, are LT^{-1}.

Most physical statements, such as those relating to the conservation of energy or mass, or to equilibrium of forces, can be considered as accounting statements, certifying that there is to be neither a gain nor a loss of a certain quantity. The terms in the equations, in which such statements are expressed, then must all refer to the same quantity: The equations must be *dimensionally homogeneous*.

Consider Bernoulli's equation for steady, nonviscous, incompressible flow in a gravity field. It may be written as

$$p/\rho + v^2/2 + gz = \text{const.}$$

where p is the pressure, ρ the mass density, v the fluid velocity, g the acceleration of gravity, and z the vertical distance measured from some arbitrary level. When mass M, length L, and time T are selected as primary quantities, the dimensions of a force can be derived from Newton's second law as that of mass times acceleration: $[F] = MLT^{-2}$. Therefore the dimensions of pressure, being force per unit area, are $[p] = ML^{-1}T^{-2}$. Further

$$[\rho] = ML^{-3}, \quad [v] = LT^{-1}, \quad [g] = LT^{-2}, \quad [z] = L.$$

All terms in Bernoulli's equation have the dimensions L^2T^{-2}, which are those of the square of a velocity, but also of energy per unit mass. Dimensional homogeneity can be used as a check against errors.

Dimensional Analysis Mathematical relations, with which one attempts to describe nature's order, cannot depend on arbitrary units of measurement (meter, second, etc.). These relations must be expressible in dimensionless form by means of dimensionless parameters. Dimensional analysis, making it possible to find such parameters and to say something about the relation between them, is useful particularly in dealing with complex problems not amenable

to direct analysis. It provides the rationale for all model experiments.

To perform dimensional analysis, one must have an insight into the quantities which are relevant to the problem in question. Typically, one lists these relevant quantities and selects the primary quantities in which their dimensions are to be expressed.

For example, assume that a homogeneous body of arbitrary shape and having a characteristic dimension ℓ, having been kept at uniform temperature, is suddenly subjected, over a portion of its surface, to a temperature which is greater by the amount θ_0. The remainder of the surface is to be insulated. What can be said about the temperature rise θ at any point, designated by some radius vector $\mathbf{r}$, after a time t has elapsed?

Heat conduction being a geometric phenomenon, the heat-absorbing capacity per unit volume is judged to be relevant. With the specific heat c of the material being defined as the heat energy which raises the temperature of a unit mass by one degree, and designating the mass density by ρ, the heat capacity per unit volume is $c\rho$. Another relevant quantity must be the thermal conductivity k of the material, defined as the heat transmitted per unit time per unit cross section per unit temperature gradient.

For this problem heat energy $[E]$, length $[L]$, time $[T]$, and temperature $[\theta]$ are convenient primary quantities. The quantities judged to be significant, with their exponents in terms of these primary dimensions are listed in Table 1. The number of dimensionless parameters to be obtained is determined by Buckingham's PI theorem. Formal ways to determine them are given in references 1 through 5. In this case, inspection shows that there are three dimensionless parameters, which can be written as:

$$\pi_1 = \theta/\theta_0, \quad \pi_2 = \mathbf{r}/\ell, \quad \pi_3 = kt/c\rho\ell^2$$

The result can be stated as: $\theta/\theta_0 = f(\mathbf{r}/\ell, kt/c\rho\ell^2)$. The temperature rise θ at any point and at any time is proportional to θ_0. The time t needed to attain a temperature rise which is a specified fraction of θ_0 is proportional to the square of the characteristic dimension ℓ (the size of the body). The material is fully described by the quantity $k/c\rho$, known as the thermal diffusivity.

Particularly in fluid mechanics and heat transfer, some dimensionless parameters have gained general significance. The Mach number is the ratio of local fluid velocity to local velocity of sound. The Reynolds number is $v\ell\rho/\mu$, where v is a characteristic velocity, ℓ a characteristic dimension, ρ the fluid density, and μ the viscosity of the fluid.

Dimensions and Physical Constants Physical constants appear when relations are established among quantities which are already dimensionally connected. For example, Newton's second law when written as $F = md\mathbf{v}/dt$ fixes the dimensions of force as $[F] = MLT^{-2}$. But Newton's law of gravitation also relates a force (that of gravitation) with masses and their distance. With MLT dimensions taken to be independent, the gravitational law is written $F = Gm_1 m_2/r^2$ where G is a dimensional gravitational constant. It is possible to write the gravitational law $F = m_1 m_2/r^2$, but then M, L, T can no longer be independent. For example, the mass dimensions could be expressed in terms of L and T: $[M] = L^3 T^{-2}$. Since physical constants are dimensional, they can be expected to be constant only when the operational methods with which the fundamental units are defined are properly correlated. They then take on the character of conversion factors. The velocity of light, having the dimensions LT^{-1}, can be universally invariant only when the operational definitions of L and T make it so, as can be done by making use of radiation phenomena.

In thermal problems E, L, T, and θ can be selected as primary quantities. But, as $[E] = ML^2 T^{-2}$, obviously M, L, T, θ can also be chosen where convenient. When physical constants are relevant to a particular problem with the dimensions selected, they must be listed among the relevant quantities. When the gas law $p = \rho R\theta$ applies to the problem, the gas constant R must thus be listed. Alternatively, R can be taken to be dimensionless, making $[\theta] = L^2 T^{-2}$. Then θ would no longer appear as a primary quantity.

In electricity, a variety of primary quantities can be used, based on the manner in which the electrostatic and electromagnetic laws are stated. Often M, L, T, and Q (electric charge) are employed.

REINOUT P. KROON

TABLE 1.

| Quantities | Exponents of Dimensions | | | |
	E	L	T	θ
ℓ		1		
$\mathbf{r}$		1		
θ_0				1
θ				1
$c\rho$	1	-3		-1
k	1	-1	-1	-1
t			1	

TABLE 2. SOME QUANTITIES AND THEIR TYPICAL DIMENSIONS

Physical Quantity	MLT	Primary Quantities $MLT\theta$	$MLTQ$
Velocity	LT^{-1}		
Acceleration	LT^{-2}		
Force	MLT^{-2}		
Energy, Torque	ML^2T^{-2}		
Momentum	MLT^{-1}		
Density	ML^{-3}		
Viscosity	$ML^{-1}T^{-1}$		
Heat, Energy		ML^2T^{-2}	
Specific Heat		$L^2T^{-2}\theta^{-1}$	
Conductivity		$MLT^{-3}\theta^{-1}$	
Entropy		$ML^2T^{-2}\theta^{-1}$	
Electric Current			$T^{-1}Q$
Electric Potential			$ML^2T^{-2}Q^{-1}$
Impedance			$ML^2T^{-1}Q^{-2}$
Capacitance			$M^{-1}L^{-2}T^2Q^2$

References

1. Buckingham, E., "Dimensional Analysis," *Philosophical Magazine*, 48, 141 (1924).
2. Bridgman, P. W., "Dimensional Analysis," Cambridge, Mass., Harvard University Press, 1931.
3. Huntley, H. E., "Dimensional Analysis," London, MacDonald and Co., Ltd., 1958.
4. Sedov, L. I., "Similarity and Dimensional Methods in Mechanics," New York, Academic Press, 1959.
5. Kline, S. J., "Similitude and Approximation Theory," New York, McGraw-Hill, 1965.
6. Kroon, R. P., "Dimensions," *J. Franklin Inst.*, 292 (July 1971).

Cross-references: CONSTANTS, FUNDAMENTAL; SYMBOLS, UNITS, AND NOMENCLATURE IN PHYSICS.

DIODE (SEMICONDUCTOR)

There exists a class of two-terminal devices which have the property of permitting current to flow with practically no resistance in one direction and offer nearly infinite resistance to current flowing in the opposite direction. These devices are called *diodes*. The applications of diodes to electronic circuits are numerous. To mention a few, they include rectification of alternating current to a unidirectional current, detection of radio waves, and gating circuits used in digital computers.

The basic materials utilized for making semiconductor diodes are germanium (Ge) and silicon (Si). These elements are included in column IV of the periodic table (see PERIODIC LAW AND PERIODIC TABLE). Both Ge and Si are *tetravalent* elements, i.e., they have 4 valence electrons. Elements in their pure state are said to be *intrinsic*.

Each element under column III of the periodic table has 3 valence electrons and is referred to as *trivalent*. Examples of trivalent elements include indium (In) and gallium (Ga). Elements in column V of the table have 5 valence electrons and are called *pentavalent*. Arsenic (As) and antimony (Sb) are examples of pentavalent elements.

The process of introducing one of the elements from column III or V into intrinsic Ge or Si is called *doping*. The doped material becomes impure or *extrinsic*. If a trivalent impurity is introduced in Ge or Si (trivalent elements have one less valence electron than Ge or Si) holes are created and the material is said to be *p*-type. Introduction of a pentavalent impurity (pentavalent elements have one more valence electron than Ge or Si) creates free electrons and the material is *n*-type.

Because of thermal effects, free electrons and holes are always being produced in Ge and Si (intrinsic generation of electron-hole pairs). Consequently, there will be some electrons in the *p*-type material and some holes in the *n*-type material. These carriers are referred to as *minority* carriers. Electrons in *n*-type material and holes in *p*-type material are termed *majority* carriers. The most widely used diode is the *p-n junction diode*. Imagine a single crystal of Ge (or Si) doped so half the material is *p*-type and the other half, *n*-type. The internal boundary between the two extrinsic regions is a *p-n* junction, and the resulting device is a junction diode (Fig. 1). The electrical symbol for the junction diode is illustrated in Fig. 2.

What are the characteristics of the *p-n* junction? To answer this question, three possible conditions are considered. Referring to Fig. 3, these are:

(1) *Unbiased:* *p*- and *n*-sides are connected by a wire.

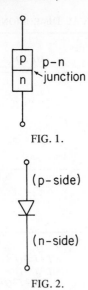

FIG. 1.

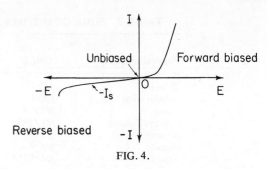

FIG. 4.

FIG. 2.

(2) *Reverse biased:* the *p*-side is connected to the negative terminal of battery E, and the *n*-side connected to the positive terminal.

(3) *Forward biased:* the *p*-side goes to the positive terminal of E, and the *n*-side to the negative terminal.

Simple energy diagrams for the three conditions are shown in Fig. 3 for the electron. Similar diagrams can be generated for holes. When the diode is unbiased, no net flow of electrons takes place across the junction. Assuming that some electrons on the *n*-side have sufficient energy to overcome the potential hill, electrons on the *p*-side (minority carriers) "slide down" the hill making the net current flow zero. For the reverse biased case, the potential hill is raised and only the few minority carriers from the *p*-side "slide down." This results in a minute reverse saturation current. When the diode is forward biased, the potential hill is lowered. This enables electrons to climb over the hill and current flow occurs. The same considerations apply

to holes. In fact, the total diode current is equal to the sum of the electrons and holes flowing across the junction.

The characteristic curve of a semiconductor diode is shown in Fig. 4. An equation for this curve, called the *rectifier equation*, is expressed as:

$$I = I_s(e^{-11600E/T} - 1)$$

where

I = diode current, amperes
I_s = reverse saturated current (which is temperature dependent), amperes
E = diode biasing voltage ($+E$ for forward bias; $-E$ for reverse bias), volts
T = absolute temperature ($^\circ C + 273^\circ$), degrees Kelvin

At room temperature (300 K) and $E > 0.1$ volt:

$$I \cong I_s e^{39E}$$

When E is more negative than 0.1 volt:

$$I \cong -I_s$$

An example of a simple rectifier employing a *p-n* junction diode is given in Fig. 5. During the positive half-cycle (0° to 180°) of the ac sinusoidal waveform v_s, the diode is forward-biased and conducts. The voltage v_L across load resistor R_L is therefore nearly identical to that of v_s for the positive half-cycle. For the negative half-

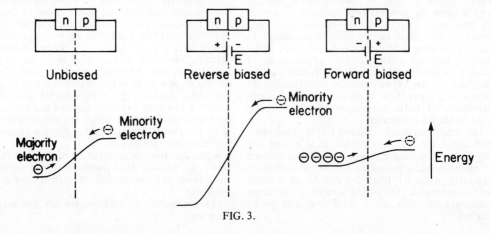

FIG. 3.

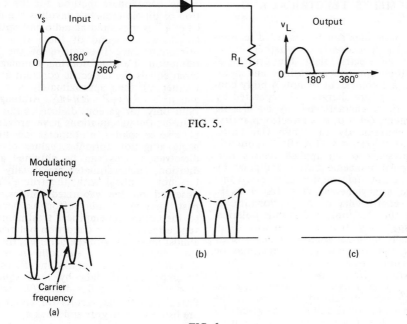

FIG. 5.

FIG. 6.

cycle (180° to 360°) the diode is reverse-biased and does not conduct. No current flows in R_L, and $v_L = 0$ during the negative half-cycle. Because the diode conducts for only one-half cycle, the circuit of Fig. 5 is called a *half-wave rectifier*.

The waveform of v_L is only unidirectional. To obtain steady dc, like that from a battery, a filter is required. An example of an elementary filter is a large-valued capacitor placed across the load resistor.

The circuit of Fig. 5 can also be used as a detector of amplitude-modulated (AM) radio waves. Figure 6(a) illustrates the components of an AM wave. If this is applied to the input of Fig. 5, the wave is rectified and the output appears as shown in Fig. 6(b). Placing a small-valued capacitor across R_L filters out the carrier frequency and the desired modulating signal is obtained (Fig. 6(c).

Besides the *p-n* junction diode, there are a number of other diode types which find use in specialized applications. These include the following diodes:

Gunn: used for the generation of microwave power.

Hot carrier (*Schottky* barrier): used for fast switching of waveforms, such as found in computers.

IMPATT: used for the generation of microwave power.

Injection: used for the generation of laser frequencies.

Light-emitting (LED): used for alpha-numeric displays.

Varactor: a reverse-biased junction diode that behaves like a variable capacitor, as a function of the applied voltage across the device.

Zener: a reverse-biased junction diode that exhibits a dc voltage which is nearly independent of a specified range of current flowing in the device. The *Zener* diode finds wide use as a voltage reference in regulated power supplies.

ARTHUR H. SEIDMAN

References

Ghaznavi, C., and Seidman, A. H., "Electronic Circuit Analysis," New York, The Macmillan Company, 1972.

Hunter, L. P., "Handbook of Semiconductor Electronics," 3rd Ed., New York, McGraw-Hill Book Company, Inc., 1970.

Seidman, A. H., "Solid-State Principles," *Electro-Technol.* (Dec. 1964).

Seidman, A. H., and Marshall, S. L., "Semiconductor Fundamentals: Devices and Circuits," New York, John Wiley & Sons Inc., 1963.

Sowa, W. A., and Toole, J. M., "Special Semiconductor Devices," New York, Holt, Rinehart and Winston, Inc., 1968.

Streetman, B. G., "Solid State Electronic Devices," Englewood Cliffs, N.J., Prentice-Hall, Inc., 1972.

Cross-references: ENERGY LEVELS, POTENTIAL, SEMICONDUCTOR, SEMICONDUCTOR DEVICES, SOLID-STATE PHYSICS, SOLID-STATE THEORY, TRANSISTOR.

DIPOLE MOMENTS (ELECTRICAL AND MAGNETIC)

Uncharged molecules can be classified as nonpolar or polar dependently on whether, in the absence of an electric field, the centers of gravity of their constituent positive and negative charges are coincident or not. A body containing two opposite charges, $\pm Q$, separated by a distance d, is characterized by an electric dipole moment, $Qd = \mu$; μ is a vector quantity, expressed conveniently in debye (D) units: 1 debye $= 10^{-18}$ esu $= 3.33 \times 10^{-30}$ [coul m].

In the presence of an applied field a normally nonpolar molecule becomes dipolar by induction, i.e., by deformation of its electronic and atomic arrangements: $m = (\alpha_e + \alpha_a)E$, where the coefficients of proportionality α_e and α_a are the electronic and atomic polarizabilities, respectively. In the general case of an anisotropically polarizable molecule, α_e and α_a are tensors, the components of which may be evaluated from observations of electric birefringence (Kerr effect), the depolarization of (Rayleigh) scattered light, refractive index dispersion, etc. An estimate of the mean of the three principal polarizabilities is given by $3R/4\pi N$, where R is a molecular refraction by the Lorenz-Lorentz formula; when R is extrapolated to infinite wavelength the mean polarizability obtained refers to the electronic deformations alone. Polarizabilities are expressed in volume units (cubic centimeters) (N = the Avogadro number).

A field E exercises a torque on an electric dipole μ, tending to align it in the field direction in opposition to the randomness caused by thermal agitation. In a large assembly of molecules, therefore, a statistical and temperature-dependent equilibrium is achieved which corresponds to a slight excess of molecules having their permanent dipoles oriented antiparallel to the field so that the average moment $\overline{m}$ of one molecule is apparently proportional to the field intensity, i.e., an orientation polarizability α_0 is exhibited.

The electric dipole moment per unit volume of a dielectric material is the polarization vector P, understandable in magnitude as the charge density bound at the electrodes by a polarized dielectric. Based on the arguments of Mossotti (1850) and Clausius (1879), the polarization per mole is related to the dielectric constant ϵ by $M(\epsilon - 1)/d(\epsilon + 2) = 4\pi N\alpha/3$, where M/d is the molecular volume, N is the Avogadro number, and α is the over-all polarizability. Debye (1912) showed α_0 to be $\mu^2/3kT$ (k = Boltzmann's constant, T = absolute temperature) so that $\alpha = \alpha_e + \alpha_a + \alpha_0$, and the total polarization per mole $_TP$ is the sum of the electronic, atomic, and orientation polarizations: $_TP = _EP + _AP + _OP$. A possible fourth polarization mechanism, the blocking or trapping of migrating charge carriers in a dielectric, although ignored in the classical molecular theory, may also contribute to the apparent ϵ of solid or macromolecule-containing systems.

The commonest method for the determination of dipole moments involves the dispersion of ϵ: $_TP$ is measured at radio and optical wavelengths (the second of these is a molecular refraction since the square of the index of refraction of a nonabsorbing, nonmagnetic material equals the dielectric constant at the same frequency), then approximately $R = _EP + _AP$, and $\mu^2 = 9kT(_TP - R)/4\pi N$. Although strictly valid only for gaseous dielectrics the Mossotti-Clausius-Debye equations have proved applicable also to solutes in nonpolar solvents, and by using alligation formulas, values of $_TP$ for a dissolved species can be obtained at infinite dilution; such estimates are usually close to, but not identical with, the true $_TP$'s directly observed on the vaporized solutes. Over the past thirty years, much effort has been devoted to theoretical or empirical treatments of "solvent effects." Since distortion polarizations are almost invariant with temperature, the temperature dependence of $_TP$ follows as $(_TP)_T = A + B/T$; the constants A and B, when fitted to experimental data by least squares, give $A = _EP + _AP$ and $B = 4\pi N\mu^2/9k$, whence $\mu = 0.012812B^{0.5}$ esu; results for about 350 gases are listed by Marryott and Buckley.

Practical details concerned with the measurement of dielectric constants, and other properties, necessary for the deduction of μ's of solutes or vapors, are described fully in the books (cited below) by Le Fèvre, Smith, and Smyth, wherein also references are made to other, but less simple, techniques by which dipole moments can be determined (e.g., Stark splitting in microwave spectra of gases at low pressures, the dielectric losses or power factors of dilute solutions, molecular beam studies, etc.); the first two of these are useful since they can detect very small moments which the ordinary dielectric constant methods cannot reveal accurately; the third technique—involving the deviation undergone by a thin ribbon of gaseous molecules in passing through an intense nonhomogeneous electric field—is applicable to substances, such as metal salts, which through insolubility or low volatility would be otherwise unexaminable.

By the end of 1961, some 7000 dipole moment values for more than 6000 substances had been recorded (see McClellan's Tables); they fall mostly in the range 0 to 5 debyes.

Chemical interest is largely due to the relationships between polarity and molecular structure. Monatomic molecules, diatomic molecules of the type AA, and centrosymmetric polyatomic molecules, are nonpolar; a linear triatomic molecule ABA is nonpolar, but if bent or constructed as AAB it is polar; pyramidal tetratomic molecules AB_3 are polar, etc. A more quantitative approach supposes that characteristic polarities are associated with covalent chemical bonds, e.g., that two bonds, having "bond moments" μ_1 and μ_2, mutually inclined at $\theta°$, produce a resultant of $(\mu_1^2 + \mu_2^2 + 2\mu_1\mu_2 \cos \theta)^{0.5}$. On this basis, bond moments de-

duced from the resultant moments of molecules with known structures, often permit the discovery or testing of stereo specifications of further molecules. However, caution is necessary since bond moments are not independent of bond environments, but may be modified by induced moments—determined by the fields of neighboring polar bonds or centers and the (anisotropic) polarizabilities of the bonds under consideration—or by other internal electronic effects (c.f. resonance, mesomerism, hybridization, etc.). Completely successful calculations of dipole moments from *a priori* theory have yet to be made.

Some concepts developed for electrostatic fields have magnetic counterparts; thus in place of polarization $\mathbf{P}$ there is magnetization $\mathbf{I}$, the magnetic dipole moment per unit volume caused in a material by an externally applied field $\mathbf{H}$; internally the magnetic flux density (the magnetic induction) is $\mathbf{B} = \mathbf{H} + 4\pi\mathbf{I}$; the ratio $\mathbf{I}/\mathbf{H}$ is the volume susceptibility κ ordinarily measured. Individual magnetic monopoles are not known to exist in nature, but movements and spins of electrons in atoms and molecules—if viewed classically as direct currents flowing in closed circuits—can create fields identical with those expected from magnetic dipoles having moments dimensionally equivalent to products of pole strengths and distances. The elementary magnetic moment is the "Bohr magneton," 9.273×10^{-21} [erg gauss^{-1}], assumed to be the magnetic moment of an electron "spinning" on its own axis. Atoms may possess orbital moments (due to mechanical angular movements of electrons) and spin moments (one for each electron). Magnetic moments can be induced or permanent. A unit volume containing ν particles each of magnetizability α_m, subjected to a field $\mathbf{H}$, displays a magnetization $\mathbf{I} = \nu\alpha_m\mathbf{H} = \nu\overline{m}$, where $\overline{m}$ is the average magnetic dipole moment per particle; thus $\kappa = \nu\alpha_m$, and the molar susceptibility $\chi = \kappa V = N\alpha_m$ (where V is the molar volume and N the Avogadro number); α_m can be split into $\alpha_i + \alpha_p$, to correspond with the contributions to $\mathbf{I}$ made by the induced and permanent moments respectively.

An electron in an orbit of radius r represents a current loop; application of a magnetic field H perpendicularly to the loop plane will induce a voltage tending to create a field opposing that applied; the effect will be manifest as an apparent induced moment antiparallel to $\mathbf{H}$ and—by classical calculations—of the value $-e^2r^2\mathbf{H}/6mc^2$ (here e is the electronic charge, m is the electronic mass, c is the velocity of light); hence $\alpha_i = -e^2r^2/6mc^2$, and for a monatomic substance with spherical atoms the molar diamagnetic susceptibility $\chi = -(Ne^2/6mc^2)\sum n r_i^2$, where r_i^2 is the mean value of r^2 for the ith electron and the sum is taken over n electrons. The χ's observed for the inert gases, the C atoms in diamond, the Cl atoms in Cl_2, etc. have agreed with reasonable magnitudes of $\sum r^2$. Pascal (1910) showed diamagnetic susceptibility

to be an "additive-constitutive" property, so that the χ's of polyatomic molecules can be approximately predicted by summing "atom" and "bond" susceptibilities in numbers and kinds appropriate to the molecular structure under consideration. The diamagnetic susceptibility of an individual molecule is a tensor quantity; χ/N by experiment is an average of three principal magnetic susceptibilities directed along three mutually perpendicular principal axes of magnetic susceptibility; these can be investigated through torsional movements of crystals in magnetic fields (Krishnan's method) or from magnetic birefringence measurements (Cotton-Mouton effects) in conjunction with data for χ_{mean} secured with a Gouy balance.

A permanent magnetic dipole will experience a torque in a magnetic field. Langevin (1905) showed that the mean moment $\overline{m}$ of a gaseous molecule in the field direction (provided that H is not too large) is $\overline{m} = (m_p^2/3kT)H$, where m_p is the actual moment of each molecule; therefore the molar paramagnetic susceptibility χ_p is $N\overline{m}/H = N\alpha_p = Nm_p^2/3kT$. In practice χ_p is extracted from the observed χ by treating this as the algebraic sum of a negative diamagnetic susceptibility (estimated from Pascal's constants) and a positive paramagnetic susceptibility; thus m_p follows as $(3kT\chi_p/N)^{0.5}$ [erg gauss^{-1}] or as $2.84(T\chi_p)^{0.5}$ [Bohr magnetons]. Molar diamagnetic susceptibilities are independent of temperature, while molar paramagnetic susceptibilities in general vary as $1/T$ or $1/(T - T_c)$. The small paramagnetisms of alkali metals, Cu, Ag, etc., or of certain salts (e.g., $KMnO_4$ or $K_2Cr_2O_7$), attributable respectively to uncompensated spins of conduction electrons, or to uncompensated paramagnetisms of complex ions, are temperature invariant.

Normally any atom or molecule with unpaired electrons shows paramagnetism and possesses a magnetic moment. Magnetic properties can therefore provide important information on valency states in free radicals, molecules containing first period elements with unpaired p electrons, transition elements having unpaired d electrons, lanthanides with unpaired $4f$ and actinides with unpaired $5f$ electrons. Theoretical expressions exist to calculate paramagnetic moments in terms of atomic structures and spin and orbital angular momenta of unpaired electrons. Simple examples are the ions of transition metals where, if n is the number of unpaired electrons, m_p is approximately predicted as $[n(n + 2)]^{0.5}$ Bohr magnetons (for a full discussion of such relations see Nyholm's review). Determination of m_p thus gives n, which is often of value in deciding the three-dimensional arrangements and bond types involved in molecules, especially those built around a central metal atom.

For most substances χ is independent of field strength, but a few paramagnetic compounds can, below the characteristic temperature T_c (see above), show "ferromagnetism" due to spontaneous parallel alignments of spins of atomic magnets. Materials which are ferromag-

netic at ordinary temperatures (e.g., soft iron) have nonlinear magnetization-field characteristics, develop large magnetizations in weak fields, rapidly approach saturation conditions, exhibit hysteresis, etc.; whole domains about 0.01 mm in diameter and magnetically saturated are thought to be undergoing orientation during such processes. Ferromagnetism—and related phenomena such as "antiferromagnetism" and "ferrimagnetism"—have at present few applications in chemistry; in electronics (e.g., ferrites in antennas and in magnetic tape), they are frequently important.

R. J. W. LE FÈVRE

References

Debye, P., "Polar Molecules," New York, The Chemical Catalog Co., Inc., 1929.

Hippel, A. R. von, "Dielectrics and Waves," New York, J. Wiley & Sons, Inc., 1954.

Le Fèvre, R. J. W., "Dipole Moments," Third edition, London, Methuen and Co., Ltd., 1953.

Le Fèvre, R. J. W., "Molecular Refractivity and Polarizability" in "Advances in Physical Organic Chemistry," London and New York, Academic Press, 1965.

Le Fèvre, R. J. W., "Polarization and Polarizability in Chemistry," *Rev. Pure and Applied Chem.* (Aust.), **20**, 67 (1970).

Le Fèvre, C. G., and Le Fèvre, R. J. W., in "Physical Methods of Chemistry," Vol. I, Weissberger, A. and Rossiter, B., Eds., New York, Wiley-Interscience, 1972 (part IIIc, pp. 399–452).

McClellan, A. L., "Tables of Experimental Dipole Moments," San Francisco and London, Freeman and Co., 1963.

Maryott, A. A., and Buckley, F., "Table of Dielectric Constants and Electric Dipole Moments of Substances in the Gaseous State," *Natl. Bur. Std. Circ.*, **537** (1953).

Nyholm, R. S., *Quart. Rev. London*, **7**, 377 (1953).

Selwood, P. W., "Magnetochemistry," New York, Interscience Publishing, 1956.

Smith, J. W., "Electric Dipole Moments," London, Butterworth's Scientific Publications, 1955.

Smyth, C. P., "Dielectric Behavior and Structure," New York, Toronto, London, McGraw-Hill Book Co., Inc., 1955.

Van Vleck, J. H., "The Theory of Electric and Magnetic Susceptibilities," Oxford, Clarendon Press, 1932.

Cross-references: BOND, CHEMICAL; DIELECTRIC THEORY; FERROMAGNETISM; MAGNETISM.

DOPPLER EFFECT

The wave effect by which astronomers measure the radial velocities of galaxies, and policemen determine the speeds of approaching automobiles, was in spite of its simplicity not discovered until the nineteenth century. In 1842, Christian Doppler predicted that the frequencies of received waves were dependent on the motion of the source or observer *relative to the propagating medium*. His predictions were promptly checked for sound waves by placing the source or observer on one of the newly developed railroad trains.

In his original article on the special theory of relativity (see RELATIVITY), Einstein[1] developed the expression for the Doppler shift of light waves which was dependent upon the velocity of the source *relative to the observer*. From the photon hypothesis for light, Schrödinger[2,3] obtained the same results. Thus, the Doppler effect provides one of the illustrations of the equivalence of the wave and particle descriptions of light.

Classroom demonstrations of the Doppler effect for water waves are made in shallow glass-bottom ripple tanks. Instead of giving the vibrating source a constant velocity, one lets the sheet of water as medium flow continuously by the source.

The circles of Fig. 1 are snapshots of the crests of a water wave or compressions in a sound wave observed when the source is moving at constant velocity v to the right relative to the medium. Points 1 and 2 are positions of the source one and two periods after passing O. The largest circular crest originated at O, the next at 1 and the smallest at 2. A crest is about to leave point 3 at the time the snapshot is taken. If the position P of the observer is a large distance from the source compared to the distance the source moves in one period, then with good approximation we may assume that two successive crests are moving in the same direction as they pass P. If v is the velocity of the source in the direction OA, the source moves a distance vT in one period T. In one period, the source

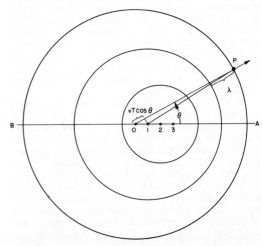

FIG. 1. The source is moving relative to the medium along the line BA. The circles represent crest of the wave at an instant. (Andrews, C. L., "Optics of the Electro-Magnetic Spectrum", Englewood Cliffs, N.J., Prentice-Hall, Inc., 1960).

comes closer to P by the amount $vT\cos\theta$, where θ is the angle between the direction of the velocity of the source and the line from the source to the observer at P. Now λ_0 is the wavelength and ν_0 the frequency when the source is at rest; λ is the observed wavelength and ν the observed frequency when the source is in motion. Because of the motion of the source, the wavelength received at P is reduced by $vT\cos\theta$.

$$\lambda = \lambda_0 - vT\cos\theta$$

If c is the velocity of the wave, $T = \lambda_0/c$ and $\lambda = \lambda_0[1-(v/c)\cos\theta]$, but $\lambda = c/\nu$ and $\lambda_0 = c/\nu_0$. Therefore,

$$\frac{\nu}{\nu_0} = \frac{1}{1-\dfrac{v}{c}\cos\theta} \qquad (1)$$

when the *source is in motion relative to the medium.*

In Fig. 2 the source is at rest, but the observer at P has a velocity v with respect to the medium. The velocity of the wave relative to the observer is equal to the vector sum of the velocity of the wave relative to the medium and the velocity of the medium relative to the observer. In Fig. 2, c is the velocity of the wave and v the velocity of the observer relative to the medium. Let λ_0 be the wavelength, ν_0 the frequency of the source, and ν the frequency received by the moving observer. The radial velocity of the wave relative to the observer is $c + v\cos\theta$ so that

$$\nu\lambda_0 = c + v\cos\theta$$

For an observer at rest $\nu_0 = c/\lambda_0$. Substituting for λ_0, we obtain

$$\frac{\nu}{\nu_0} = 1 + \frac{v}{c}\cos\theta \qquad (2)$$

when the *observer is in motion relative to the medium.*

By a postulate of relativity, the velocity of light is the same relative to all observers. The theory of relativity yields the frequency

$$\frac{\nu}{\nu_0} = \frac{1 + \dfrac{v}{c}\cos\theta_0}{\sqrt{1-\dfrac{v^2}{c^2}}} \qquad (3)$$

in which $v\cos\theta_0$ is the component of the velocity of the source toward the observer. The angle θ_0 is measured in the source system. If θ is the angle measured in the observer's system, then

$$\cos\theta_0 = \frac{\dfrac{v}{c}-\cos\theta}{\dfrac{v}{c}\cos\theta - 1} \qquad (4)$$

Figure 3 is a graphical plot of ν/ν_0 against v/c for the radial motion in the three cases we have

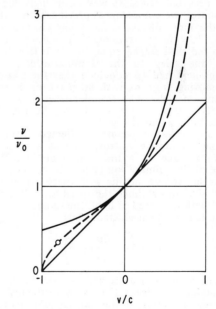

$$\frac{\nu}{\nu_0}$$

$$v/c$$

FIG. 3. Graphical plots of the ratio of the observed frequency to the frequency at the source against the ratio of radial velocity to the velocity of the wave for three cases: (1) sound waves from a moving source, (2) sound waves to a moving receiver, (3) electromagnetic waves. The circle represents the red shift of light received from the most distant galaxies observed.

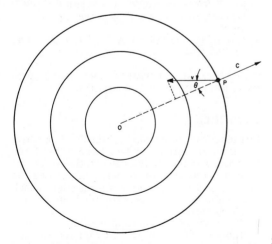

FIG. 2. The source is at rest at point O and the observer at point P is moving with velocity v relative to the medium. (Andrews, C. L., "Optics of the Electro-Magnetic Spectrum," Englewood Cliffs, N.J., Prentice-Hall, Inc., 1960).

treated. (1) The linear relation is that for the observer in motion relative to the medium that propagates sound or other mechanical waves. (2) The other solid curve is for the source of sound in motion. (3) The broken curve represents the Doppler effect for electromagnetic waves such as x-rays, light, and radio waves.

By comparing several spectral lines of elements observed in a star with a laboratory spectrum of the same elements, astronomers use the Doppler effect to measure the radial components of velocity of astronomical bodies toward or away from the earth. Spectra of the edges of the sun's disk are measured to determine the velocities toward and away from the earth. The radial velocities of the principal stars of our galaxy have been recorded. The spectral lines of some of the stars are doublets which periodically come together and separate again indicating that the light comes from two stars revolving about a common center of gravity (see ASTROMETRY).

In the expanding universe, the radial velocities of other galaxies away from our galaxy are proportional to their distances from the observer. Thus, the Doppler red shift provides a means of determining the dimensions of the observed universe. In 1964, some of the most intense radio sources (see RADIO ASTRONOMY) were located with high precision by observing these sources when the moon passed in front of them. With this knowledge of position, the same sources were located with a light telescope.[4] The measured red shift was surprisingly high. The sources were not stars as previously thought but the most distant galaxies known. One of them, 3C-9 in the catalogue of radio sources had a red shift $\Delta\lambda/\lambda_0$ equal to 2.0. If this shift were due soley to the Doppler effect, the astronomers had to conclude that the source was moving from us with 80 per cent of the velocity of light. The Doppler frequency and velocity of this source is indicated by a circle on the broken line of Fig. 3.

If a microwave beam is reflected from a moving microwave mirror, such as a person, an automobile or a man-made satellite, the image of the primary source may be considered as another source moving with twice the velocity of the mirror. Since the speed is small compared with the speed of light, the squared terms of Eq. (3) may be neglected. Thus

$$\nu = \nu_0 \left(1 + \frac{2v}{c}\cos\theta\right)$$

Direct frequency measurements cannot be made to enough significant figures to distinguish ν from ν_0. However, if the two frequencies are combined they give beats or the difference frequency

$$\Delta\nu = \nu_0 \frac{2v}{c}\cos\theta$$

Since the beat frequency is porportional to the radial velocity, a frequency meter may be cali-brated in miles per hour. The precision of such a speed detector depends upon the frequency of the source being so stable that it varies less than the Doppler frequency shift during the time that the wave travels from the source to the mirror and back. The same phenomena of beats between the direct wave from the source and the wave reflected from a moving mirror may be observed with light. If one of the mirrors of Michelson's interferometer is moved at constant speed, the frequency with which dark bands pass the cross hair is the difference in frequency of the two waves.

The numerator of Eq. (3) contains a term for the radial component of velocity. However, the second-order term in the denominator is independent of direction. Thus, as v/c approaches unity, one may expect to detect a *tangential Doppler effect*. Ives and Stilwell[5] have measured the predicted value for the Doppler shift in frequency due to a stream of radiating molecules for which v/c was 10^{-2}. This experiment was a direct proof of time dilatation (see RELATIVITY) for the transverse case. In order to separate the tangential from the radial effect, Ives and Stilwell produced a sharply collimated beam of molecules. In order that θ be precisely 90°, they set a mirror accurately normal to the line of observation and altered the line of observation until nearly the same wavelengths were given by direct and reflected light.

C. L. ANDREWS

References

1. Einstein, A., *Ann. Physik*, **17**, 891 (1905).
2. Schrödinger, E., *Physik. Z.*, **23**, 301 (1922).
3. Michels, W. C., *Am. J. Phys.*, **15**, 449 (1947).
4. Burbage, G., and Burbage, M., "Quasi-Stellar Objects," San Francisco, W. H. Freeman Co., 1967; Schmidt, M., and Billo, F., *Sci. Amer.*, p. 60 (May 1971).
5. Ives, H. E., and Stilwell, A. R., *J. Opt. Soc. Am.*, **31**, 369 (1941).

Cross-references: ASTROMETRY, RADIO ASTRONOMY, RELATIVITY, WAVE MOTION.

DYNAMICS

Introduction *Dynamics*, a branch of mechanics, is often defined in two basic parts. First, *kinematics* is the study of the motion of bodies with no consideration of what has caused the motion, and second, *kinetics* is the study which relates the action of forces on the bodies to the resulting motion.

This order of presentation is often utilized in textbooks and other treatises on the subject. With various interpretations of the word *bodies*, the subject has also been divided into the areas of particle dynamics, rigid body dynamics, and fluid dynamics. As needs have developed, various specializations have been created and new theories have been formulated. These special

areas include mechanical vibrations, flight dynamics, space dynamics, gas dynamics, magnetohydrodynamics, dynamic systems,[1] and relativistic dynamics, to mention a few.

The present state of knowledge recognizes all motion as relative, since no fixed reference is known for finding the absolute motion of any body. The earth, which is frequently used as a frame of reference is rotating about its own axis and is also revolving about the sun. The solar system, which consists of the sun and its planets, is a minute part of the Milky Way galaxy that is known to be revolving in space[2]. Beyond this, there is limited knowledge of the nature of motion that exists.

In the field of astronomy, measurements are evaluated in a coordinate system that is located relative to the *fixed* stars. These stars are located at such a vast distance from the earth that they appear as points of light that are almost motionless in space. In this frame of reference, the motions of celestial bodies are described with extremely great precision, and the motions of bodies within the solar system can be predicted accurately over periods of hundreds of years.

Some applied areas of dynamics, exemplified by the space exploration program, also require the degree of extreme accuracy that is possible with a celestial frame of reference. In many other areas, this extreme accuracy is not essential and measurements based upon this frame of reference would be tedious and impractical. In such cases, motion may often be adequately described in a coordinate system located relative to the earth.[3]

Kinematics A particle is a body having dimensions that are small, relative to other dimensions of the system, so that its motion may be considered equivalent to the motion of a point at its mass center with rotational effects neglected. Thus, particles may be either small or large. In the solar system, it would be possible to assume the earth to be a particle but, in a terrestrial system, this assumption could be totally unjustifiable.

A rigid body is a group of particles having unvarying external and internal configuration. The size of the rigid body would be appreciable in comparison to the other dimensions of the system, so that the rotational effect would have to be considered.

A fluid body is a group of particles with varying external and or internal configuration. The analysis of this type of system will not be considered in this article. (See FLUID DYNAMICS.)

The kinematic analysis of the motion of a particle may be approached through the establishment of a position VECTOR **r**, directed from the origin of a specified fixed coordinate system to the point representing the position of the particle, to give

$$\mathbf{r} = x\mathbf{i} + y\mathbf{j} + z\mathbf{k} \qquad (1)$$

where **i**, **j**, and **k** are unit vectors along the $x, y,$ and z axes, respectively. Differentiating Eq. (1)

with respect to time yields a velocity equation of the form

$$\mathbf{v} = \frac{d\mathbf{r}}{dt} = \frac{dx}{dt}\mathbf{i} + \frac{dy}{dt}\mathbf{j} + \frac{dz}{dt}\mathbf{k} \qquad (2)$$

where the instantaneous velocity, **v**, of the particle at any position on its path is the instantaneous time rate of change of displacement. A second differentiation with respect to time yields the acceleration of the particle in the form

$$\mathbf{a} = \frac{d\mathbf{v}}{dt} = \frac{d^2\mathbf{r}}{dt^2} = \frac{d^2x}{dt^2}\mathbf{i} + \frac{d^2y}{dt^2}\mathbf{j} + \frac{d^2z}{dt^2}\mathbf{k} \qquad (3)$$

where the instantaneous acceleration, **a**, of the particle at any position on its path is the instantaneous time rate of change of velocity.

If $x, y,$ and z are scalar functions of time, then Eqs. (1), (2), and (3) may be used to trace the path of the particle and determine the velocity and acceleration at any instant. These equations may be easily adapted to the cases of rectilinear translation and curvilinear translation of a particle in plane motion.

The kinematic analysis of a rigid body moving in a plane often involves the trace of two points, which may be called A and B, that are located on the body. These points move with the body and remain a fixed distance apart. Two coordinate systems may be used to define the position of the body in the plane. An X-Y coordinate system, with origin O, is a fixed reference, and an x-y coordinate system, with origin o located at A, is attached to the body so that it moves and rotates with the body. In the fixed reference system, a position vector **R** is directed from O to point A on the body and a second position vector ρ is directed from O to point B. In the moving coordinate system, a vector **r** is directed from A to B. An equation relating the position of the two points may be written as

$$\rho = \mathbf{R} + \mathbf{r} \qquad (4)$$

Using the **I**, **J**, **K** unit vectors for the X-Y-Z coordinate system and the **i**, **j**, **k** unit vectors for the x-y-z coordinate system, Eq. (4) may be rewritten as

$$\rho = X\mathbf{I} + Y\mathbf{J} + x\mathbf{i} + y\mathbf{j} \qquad (5)$$

Differentiating Eq. (5) with respect to time yields the velocity of B in the form

$$\mathbf{v}_B = \frac{d\rho}{dt} = \frac{dX}{dt}\mathbf{I} + \frac{dY}{dt}\mathbf{J}$$

$$+ \frac{dx}{dt}\mathbf{i} + x\frac{d\mathbf{i}}{dt} + \frac{dy}{dt}\mathbf{j} + y\frac{d\mathbf{j}}{dt} \qquad (6)$$

Noting that $dx/dt = dy/dt = 0$, Eq. (6) simplifies to

$$\mathbf{v}_B = \mathbf{v}_A + \mathbf{v}_{B/A} \qquad (7)$$

where v_B and v_A are the velocities of points B and A, respectively, and $v_{B/A}$ is the velocity of point B relative to point A.

A second differentiation of Eq. (5) with respect to time yields the acceleration of B in the form

$$a_B = a_A + a_{B/A} \qquad (8)$$

where a_B and a_A are the accelerations of points B and A, respectively, and $a_{B/A}$ is the acceleration of point B relative to point A.

A second important case of rigid body motion exists when point B is not attached to the same body as point A but is moving along a constrained path on this body. For the analysis of this motion, it is convenient to designate the fixed reference as body 1, the body to which point A is attached as body 2, and the body to which point B is attached as body 3. The same general arrangements of coordinate systems are used but in this case, the fixed X-Y coordinate system may be considered as attached to body 1 while the moving x-y coordinate system is attached to body 2. In the general case, vector r within the x-y coordinate system is varying in both magnitude and direction. Differentiating the position expression

$$\rho = R + r \qquad (9)$$

once with respect to time and simplifying yields

$$v_{B3} = v_{A2} + v_{B2/A2} + v_{B3/2} \qquad (10)$$

where v_{B3} is the velocity of point B on body 3, v_{A2} is the velocity of point A on body 2, $v_{B2/A2}$ is the velocity of point B on body 2 relative to point A on body 2, and $v_{B3/2}$ is the velocity of point B on body 3 relative to body 2.

A second differentiation with respect to time gives

$$a_{B3} = a_{A2} + a_{B2/A2} + a_{B3/2} + 2\omega_2 \times v_{B3/2}$$

$$(11)$$

where a_{B3} is the acceleration of point B on body 3, a_{A2} is the acceleration of point A on body 2, $a_{B2/A2}$ is the acceleration of point B on body 2 relative to point A on body 2, $a_{B3/2}$ is the acceleration of point B on body 3 relative to body 2, ω_2 is the angular velocity of body 2, and $v_{B3/2}$ is the velocity of point B on body 3 relative to body 2. The term $2\omega_2 \times v_{B3/2}$ is often referred to as the CORIOLIS component of acceleration.

Equations 7 and 8 may be adapted to the case of rotation of a rigid body about a fixed axis at point A by considering point A to be fixed. Thus, v_A and a_A are both zero and

$$v_B = v_{B/A} \qquad (12)$$

$$a_B = a_{B/A} \qquad (13)$$

For a body rotating about a fixed axis, analysis of the rotational motion yields

$$\frac{d\theta}{dt} = \omega \qquad (14)$$

$$\frac{d\omega}{dt} = \alpha \qquad (15)$$

where θ is the angular displacement in radians, ω is the angular velocity in radians per second, and α is the angular acceleration in radians per second per second. It should be noted that time may be expressed in other units.

Kinetics *Newton's Laws of Motion* The laws of Newton are based upon the motion of a particle relative to a fixed frame of reference in which the particle can be made completely free of all outside influences. Under such a condition, the particle at rest will remain at rest and a particle in motion will continue to move at a constant velocity. This ideal frame of reference is often referred to as a Newtonian or as an inertial frame of reference.[4]

Since it is not possible to actually establish the Newtonian frame of reference, Newton's laws of motion are used in a celestial or a terrestrial frame of reference. The gyroscopic instruments and the stabilized platforms represent attempts to achieve a fixed or stabilized frame of reference for aircraft or space vehicles.

In modern terminology, Newton's laws of motion for a particle may be interpreted as

(1) A particle tends to remain at rest or continues to move at a constant velocity if there is no unbalanced force acting upon it.

(2) An unbalanced force acting on a particle will produce a time rate of change of momentum, $d(mv)/dt$, which, at any instant, will be proportional to the force and will be in the same direction as the force.

(3) The forces that exist between two contacting particles are equal in magnitude, are opposite in direction, and are collinear.[5]

The concept of the first law is the fundamental principle used for the analysis of forces acting on stationary particles and also for the analysis of forces acting on particles moving with a constant velocity. The concept has been expanded to include rigid bodies and fluid bodies.

The second law is the foundation of the analysis of forces acting on particles moving with accelerations, and again it has been extended to include rigid bodies which involve rotary motion and to include fluid bodies.

The third law is fundamental to the force analysis of interconnecting systems of particles under both static and dynamic conditions. It has also been extended to include simple contact between any pair of bodies and, with some modification, to include any type of interaction between bodies.

Force and Acceleration In general, Newton's second law is stated as

$$\sum F = k \frac{d(mv)}{dt} \qquad (16)$$

where $\sum \mathbf{F}$ is the net unbalanced force on the particle; k is a constant of proportionality, consistent with the units used, that is determined experimentally; m is the mass of the particle; and $\mathbf{v}$ is the instantaneous velocity of the particle.

For a particle that is not shedding or accumulating mass, Newton's second law reduces to

$$\sum \mathbf{F} = km\mathbf{a} \qquad (17)$$

where $\sum \mathbf{F}$, k, and m are as previously defined and $\mathbf{a}$ is the instantaneous acceleration of the particle. By the proper choice of units in Eq. (16) and (17), the constants of proportionality can be made equal to unity.

For a rigid body in plane motion, both translational and rotational acceleration must be considered. By extending the concept of Newton's second law, it may be stated that

$$\sum \mathbf{F} = k_1 m\mathbf{a} \qquad (18)$$

$$\sum \mathbf{T} = k_2 \bar{I}\alpha \qquad (19)$$

where $\sum \mathbf{F}$ and $\sum \mathbf{T}$ are the unbalanced force and unbalanced torque, respectively, acting on the body; k_1 and k_2 are constants of proportionally, consistent with the units used, that are determined experimentally; m is the mass of the body; $\bar{I}$ is the mass moment of inertia of the body about a centroidal axis that is perpendicular to the plane of the motion; $\mathbf{a}$ is the linear acceleration of the center of mass of the body; and α is the angular acceleration of the body. Again, with proper choice of units, k_1 and k_2 can be made equal to unity.

The concepts and equations presented herein can be applied for the solution of a wide variety of problems which involve systems of particles, systems of bodies, or combinations thereof. The usefulness of this approach may be further broadened by the introduction of the closely related concepts of energy and impulse—momentum.

It should be noted that, in Newtonian mechanics, the fundamental property of the particle is an unvarying mass and time is absolute. It should also be noted that when the speed of the particle approaches the speed of light, this theory becomes inaccurate in compariosn to a theory based upon a more exact mathematical model attained through the application of the principles of RELATIVITY.[6]

GLENN L. DOWNEY

References

1. Cannon, Robert H., Jr., "Dynamics of Physical Systems," New York, McGraw-Hill, 1967.
2. Robertson, H. P., "The Universe," *Sci. Am.*, **195** (3), 73–81 (September 1956).
3. Kane, Thomas R., "Dynamics," New York, Holt, Rinehart and Winston, Inc., 1968.
4. Goodman, L. E., and Warner, W. H., "Dynamics," Belmont, California, Wadsworth, 1964.
5. Smith, G. M., and Downey, G. L., "Advanced Engineering Dynamics," 2nd ed., Scranton, Pa., International Textbook, 1968.
6. Synge, J. L., and Griffith, B. A., "Principles of Mechanics," 3rd ed., New York, McGraw-Hill, 1959.

Cross-references: ASTRODYNAMICS, CORIOLIS EFFECT, FLUID DYNAMICS, IMPULSE AND MOMENTUM, MECHANICS, STATICS.

E

ELASTICITY*

Elasticity is the part of mechanics dealing with deformations that vanish entirely once the forces that have caused them are removed. Most solid bodies behave elastically for sufficiently small deformations, and we will be concerned here with the infinitesimal theory of elasticity. Also we will consider only isotropic bodies, that is, bodies whose elastic properties are the same in all directions.

The fundamental quantities in elasticity are second-order tensors, or dyadics: the deformation is represented by the *strain dyadic*, and the internal forces are represented by the *stress dyadic*. The physical constitution of the deformable body determines the relation between the strain dyadic and the stress dyadic, which relation is, in the infinitesimal theory, assumed to be linear and homogeneous. While for anisotropic bodies this relation may involve as much as 21 independent constants, in the case of isotropic bodies, the number of elastic constants is reduced to two.

Let $s(r)$ be the displacement vector, due to the deformation, of a particle that before the deformation was situated at point P having r as position vector with respect to some arbitrary origin. A neighboring point Q, whose position vector was $r + dr$ before the deformation, will suffer a displacement $s(r + dr)$ which will differ from $s(r)$ by the quantity

$$ds = dr \cdot \nabla s$$

The hypothesis of small deformations means that ds, the change in the displacement vector when we go from P to the neighboring point Q, is very small compared to dr, the position vector of Q relative to P. Consequently, the scalar components of the dyadic ∇s are all very small compared to unity. The geometrical meaning of the dyadic ∇s is obtained by separating it into its symmetric part $S = \frac{1}{2} (\nabla s + s \nabla)$ and its antisymmetric part $R = -\frac{1}{2} 1 \times (\nabla \times s)$, where 1 is the unity dyadic. The antisymmetric part is interpreted as follows: if at some point M the symmetric part vanishes, then we have for the neighborhood of M the relation

$$ds = dr \cdot R_M = \omega_M \times dr$$

*See MECHANICAL PROPERTIES OF SOLIDS for a less mathematical introduction to elasticity.

where $\omega_M = \frac{1}{2} (\nabla \times s)_M$ is an infinitesimal vector. This means that the neighborhood of point M undergoes an infinitesimal rigid rotation, without any change in shape or size. Consequently, the deformation is represented by the symmetric part S, which is called the *strain dyadic*.

In a Cartesian orthonormal basis, in which we have $r = \sum_{i=1}^{3} x_i a_i$, we write $s = \sum_{i=1}^{3} s_i a_i$, and obtain

$$S = \sum_{i,j=1}^{3} a_i a_j S_{ij}$$

where $S_{ij} = \frac{1}{2} \left[\frac{\partial}{\partial x_i} s_j + \frac{\partial}{\partial x_j} s_i \right]$. The diagonal components S_{11}, S_{22}, and S_{33} are the coefficients of linear extension in the directions a_1, a_2, and a_3, respectively, while the non diagonal components $S_{12} = S_{21}$, $S_{13} = S_{31}$, and $S_{23} = S_{32}$ are called shear strains. For instance, $2S_{12}$ is the change in the angle of the dihedron formed by the planes that before the deformation were respectively normal to the directions a_1 and a_2. The shear strains are not essential for the complete representation of a deformation since they can be made to vanish by expressing S in the basis of its principal axes.

If an infinitesimal element of the body occupies the volume dV before the deformation and the volume dV' after, the relative increase of volume, or volumetric dilatation, is given by

$$\frac{dV' - dV}{dV} = S_{11} + S_{22} + S_{33} = |S| = \nabla \cdot s$$

The forces applied to a finite deformable body are either body forces acting on every volume element dV and represented by the notation $dV F = dV \rho K$, where F is the force per unit volume, K is the force per unit mass, and ρ is the density, or surface forces acting on every element dS of the bounding surface and represented by $dS T$, where T is the surface stress, or surface force per unit area. The effect of these applied forces is transmitted throughout the body, so that through any surface element inside the body, there is a force exerted by the matter on one side of the element upon the matter on the other side. Such forces are called

240

internal stresses and are defined as follows: let dS be a surface element completely inside the body, and let us choose arbitrarily the positive sense of the normal n to this surface element; this defines for dS a positive side, the one containing n, and a negative side. Then $\mathbf{T_n}$, the stress vector on the positive side of dS is defined as a vector such that $dS\mathbf{T_n}$ is the surface force on the positive side of dS—i.e., the resultant of all the forces exerted through dS by the matter on the positive side of dS upon the matter on the negative side. In general there is a normal component $\mathbf{T_n} \cdot \mathbf{nn}$, which is a pressure or a traction depending upon whether the sign of $\mathbf{T_n} \cdot \mathbf{n}$ is negative or positive, and a tangent component $\mathbf{n} \times \mathbf{T_n} \times \mathbf{n}$ called the shear stress. The value of stress vector $\mathbf{T_n}$ depends upon the orientation of the normal n, so that we can characterize the state of stress at a point by defining the *stress dyadic* $\mathbf{T}$ through the relation

$$\mathbf{T_n} = \mathbf{n} \cdot \mathbf{T}$$

The mechanical equilibrium conditions applied to an arbitrary volume V, bounded by the closed surface S, and completely inside the deformable body give

$$\int_V dV\mathbf{F} + \int_s dS\mathbf{n} \cdot \mathbf{T} = 0$$

and

$$\int_V dV\mathbf{r} \times \mathbf{F} + \int_s dS\mathbf{r} \times (\mathbf{n} \cdot \mathbf{T}) = 0$$

By the use of the divergence theorem, the first condition gives the equation

$$\nabla \cdot \mathbf{T} + \mathbf{F} = 0$$

at any point inside the body, and the second condition implies that $\mathbf{T}$ is a symmetric dyadic. On the external surface of the body, we have usually to fulfill the boundary condition

$$\mathbf{n} \cdot \mathbf{T} = \mathbf{T}$$

where $\mathbf{T}$ is the applied external force per unit area. Other boundary conditions can also be met, such that the value of the displacement be prescribed.

For infinitesimal deformations, we assume that the relation between strain and stress is expressed by Hooke's law: the deformation is proportional to the applied force. For isotropic bodies, this linear relation is

$$\mathbf{S} = \frac{1}{E} [(1 + \nu)\mathbf{T} - \nu|\mathbf{T}|\mathbf{1}]$$

where E is Young's modulus and ν is Poisson's ratio. These two elastic constants can be defined by considering the stretching of a cylindrical bar by normal traction forces uniformly distributed on the end sections; then we have

Young's modulus =

$$\frac{\text{Normal traction force/unit cross sectional area}}{\text{Relative longitudinal extension}}$$

and

$$\text{Poisson's ratio} = \frac{\text{Relative lateral contraction}}{\text{Relative longitudinal extension}}$$

We can also write

$$\mathbf{T} = 2\mu\mathbf{S} + \lambda|\mathbf{S}|\mathbf{1}$$

where $\mu = E/2(1 + \nu)$ and $\lambda = \nu E/(1 + \nu)(1 - 2\nu)$ are Lamé's constants. μ is the rigidity modulus, the only constant necessary when the volumetric dilatation vanishes everywhere.

Substituting the preceding relation into the equilibrium equations, we transform them into

$$2\mu\nabla \cdot \mathbf{S} + \lambda\nabla|\mathbf{S}| + \mathbf{F} = 0 \text{ inside the body}$$

and

$$2\mu\mathbf{n} \cdot \mathbf{S} + \lambda\mathbf{n}|\mathbf{S}| = \mathbf{T} \text{ on the bounding surface.}$$

These vector relations are not sufficient for the complete determination of the symmetric dyadic $\mathbf{S}$. To insure that a solution of the above equations corresponds to a possible displacement vector s, we must be able to integrate the relation

$$\mathbf{S} = \tfrac{1}{2} (\nabla s + s\nabla)$$

i.e., from a given expression for $\mathbf{S}$, obtain the value of s. From the vanishing of the curl of a gradient, it is easily seen that this integrability condition, also called the compatibility equation, is

$$\nabla \times \mathbf{S} \times \nabla = 0$$

By elimination of the vector products, we obtain the equivalent form

$$\nabla\nabla \cdot \mathbf{S} + \nabla \cdot \mathbf{S}\nabla - \nabla\nabla|\mathbf{S}| - \nabla \cdot \nabla\mathbf{S} = 0$$

Using the stress-strain relation and the equilibrium conditions, we obtain the Beltrami-Michell form of the compatibility equation:

$$\nabla \cdot \nabla\mathbf{T} + \frac{1}{1 + \nu} \nabla\nabla|\mathbf{T}| = -\frac{\nu}{1 - \nu} \nabla \cdot \mathbf{F}\mathbf{1}$$

$$- (\nabla\mathbf{F} + \mathbf{F}\nabla)$$

Finally, by expressing the strain dyadic in terms of the displacement vector, we obtain Navier's form of the equilibrium equations:

$$\mu\nabla \cdot \nabla s + (\lambda + \mu)\nabla\nabla \cdot s + \mathbf{F} = 0 \text{ inside the body}$$

and

$$\lambda n\nabla \cdot s + 2\mu\mathbf{n} \cdot \nabla s + \mu\mathbf{n} \times (\nabla \times s) = \mathbf{T}$$

$$\text{on the bounding surface.}$$

Dealing here directly with the displacement vector, there is no need of considering the compatibility equation.

The propagation equation for elastic disturbances is obtained by adding the inertia force to the body force. We get then

$$\mu \nabla \cdot \nabla \mathbf{s} + (\lambda + \mu) \nabla \nabla \cdot \mathbf{s} + \rho \mathbf{K} = \rho \frac{\partial^2}{\partial t^2} \mathbf{s}$$

inside the body.

The stress-strain relation and the boundary conditions are not affected, but we generally have to take into account initial conditions.

The energy density u, or energy per unit volume, is given by

$$u = \frac{1}{2} \mathbf{S} : \mathbf{T} + \frac{1}{2} \rho \frac{\partial \mathbf{s}}{\partial t} \cdot \frac{\partial \mathbf{s}}{\partial t}$$

where the first term is potential, or strain energy, and the second term is kinetic energy. The energy flux density vector

$$\mathbf{S} = -\frac{\partial \mathbf{s}}{\partial t} \cdot \mathbf{T}$$

is a vector such that $dS \mathbf{n} \cdot \mathbf{S}$ gives the quantity of energy that flows per unit time through the surface element dS in the positive direction of $\mathbf{n}$, the normal to dS. At any point the energy continuity equation

$$\frac{\partial u}{\partial t} + \nabla \cdot \mathbf{S} - \rho \frac{\partial \mathbf{s}}{\partial t} \cdot \mathbf{K} = 0$$

expresses the conservation of mechanical energy.

GÉRARD NADEAU

References

Godfrey, D. E. R., "Theoretical Elasticity and Plasticity," London, Thames and Hudson Co., 1959.
Green, A. E., and Zerna, W., "Theoretical Elasticity," New York, Oxford University Press, 1954.
Jaunzemis, W., "Continuum Mechanics," New York, Macmillan, 1967.
Nadeau, G., "Introduction to Elasticity," New York, Holt, Rinehart and Winston, Inc., 1964.
Pearson, C. E., "Theoretical Elasticity," Cambridge, Mass., Harvard University Press, 1959.
Sokolnikoff, I. S., "Mathematical Theory of Elasticity," New York, McGraw-Hill Book Co., Inc., 1956.

Cross-references: MECHANICAL PROPERTIES OF SOLIDS, POLYMER PHYSICS, VECTOR PHYSICS, VISCOELASTICITY.

ELECTRIC POWER GENERATION

About 95 per cent of the electric power produced in this country is by 3-phase generators. It is transmitted and distributed this way. Advantages of 3-phase generators lie in economy of apparatus, lower transmission losses, inherent starting torque for polyphase motors, and constant running torque for balanced loading. A generator is built with axial slots for armature coils in a stationary hollow cylindrical iron core called the stator. The windings are placed in the slots so that when carrying current they produce a chosen even number of alternate magnetic poles. The coils over each magnetic pole are grouped in 3 equal bands to give a 3-phase balanced system of terminal voltages.

An inner rotor has coils which carry direct current to give the same number of alternate magnetic poles as on the stator. Rotor current strength is controlled by a rheostat or voltage from a dc generator. Voltages are produced in the stator windings by flux cutting as the rotor magnetic flux sweeps by them, and currents flow when the generator terminals are connected to a 3-phase load impedance. The 3-phase stator line voltages are equal in magnitude and 120 electrical degrees apart in time sequence. So also are the line currents for a balanced 3-phase load. Generator voltages are of the order of 12 000 to 30 000 volts for large machines.

Generator frequency is the product of the pairs of magnetic poles and the speed in revolutions per second. At 60 Hz (cycles per sec.), a 2-pole generator runs at 3600 rpm and a 6-pole generator at 1200 rpm. The maximum speed of 3600 rpm has been increasingly adopted even for very large machines because high speed means decreased size and weight for a given kilowatt rating and better steam-turbine performance. Waterwheels and water turbines show best characteristics at much lower speeds—roughly a range of 100 to 600 rpm. Sixty Hz is the prevailing frequency in this country for public utility power generation. Because of weight and space limitation, 400 Hz is found in the aircraft industry. Europe is basically on 50 Hz.

In the large central station steam power plants, single generators may reach, or go somewhat beyond, 250 000 kW in rating. Some "units" (so-called) will have ratings up to a million kilowatts. Very large units are usually 2 separate single-shaft turbine-generator sets with one or two turbines on each shaft. One turbine takes steam at high pressure and the others at intermediate or low pressure.

Direct-current generators are built with their dc magnetic poles in the stator. Armature conductors on the rotor have ac voltages induced in them as they are rotated; the same principle of flux cutting holds as before. An automatic mechanical switching device, called a commutator, is placed on the shaft. It carries fixed brushes, and with its many insulated copper bars connected to the armature coils, it inverts every other alternation of the voltage to give unidirectional, or dc, voltage at the 2 armature terminals. It is the commutator that requires the rotor to be the armature so that coils and

their switching arrangement always move exactly together. Direct-current generators are generally limited to several thousand kilowatts, and their application lies mainly in industrial plants.

Generators in stations of electric utility companies are driven by steam turbines, water wheels, or water turbines. The ratio of steam to hydropower is 4 to 1. Industrial production of steam plus hydro is about one-twelfth that of utility steam alone. The installed generating capacity in this country is over 500 million kW, about one-third of the world total. The United States produces about four times the energy in kilowatt-hours as the rest of the world.

In addition to power generation by steam and hydro, electric power also is obtained from gasoline- and diesel-driven motor-generator sets; from BATTERIES, fuel cells, and solar cells; by THERMOELECTRICITY and PHOTOELECTRICITY; and by wind motion. Most of these are described elsewhere in this volume. Power production by these last methods is small compared with steam and water power. Windmills are used to charge batteries, but use of wave motion or tides has never proved feasible.

The only fuels of consequence used by steam plants are coal, oil, and gas. Coal has predominated in the eastern part of the United States, with oil and natural gas used in the western states. Burners for oil or gas plants may be adaptable for either type of fuel, or they can be interchanged quickly. In some instances, provision is also made for coal burning.

Nuclear steam plants have now demonstrated safety, economy, reliability, and excellent performance. They are competitive with conventional plants and indicate better capabilities. They give less air pollution, and in small sizes have applications not possible with other forms, but there is a problem with radioactive by-products of fuel processing. There are now over 10 million kW installed in civilian reactor plants, and by 1980, 40 million kW are expected, about 17 per cent of the total required capacity in the United States. Expansion here and in Europe is rapidly advancing, with 1 million kW in a single plant.

Geothermal production of electric power uses natural steam obtained from the earth through steam wells and piped to turbines. Italy produces about one-third of a million kW in this manner and New Zealand has slightly less installed capacity of this kind. The only U.S. installation is about 175 000 kW on the West Coast. Geothermal power is limited. Temperatures and pressures are low, but there is a lower capital investment and absence of fuel cost. A serious problem lies in elimination of contamination in the steam.

Major problems today include improvement of over-all characteristics and economy of existing apparatus, development of materials to withstand increasing temperatures and stresses, the disposal of combustion products and radioactive wastes, and finding new and enlarged power sources. Some envision the elimination of the conventional plant with its rotating machinery, associated equipment, noise, and maintenance.

Among new methods currently studied for power generation are the magnetohydrodynamic (MHD) generator, fuel cell, thermionic converter, thermoelectric generator, fusion reactor, and solar power. None are yet practical and economic for a utility company even though there have been a few minor applications. Of this group, the first and the last appear to be most promising.

The limited efficiency of steam turbines imposed by the thermodynamic properties of steam has stimulated the development of methods to convert heat directly into electricity. The MHD generator is one in which a thermally ionized gas is forced at high temperature, pressure, and velocity through a duct situated in a transverse magnetic field. An induced voltage appears in the third mutually perpendicular direction (the Hall effect), and this voltage may be tapped by electrodes within the duct (see MAGNETO-FLUID-MECHANICS).

If the exhaust gas from the MHD generator is used to heat steam for a conventional generator, a larger portion of the thermal spectrum will be utilized and the system efficiency may be raised from the present 40 per cent to possibly 50 or 55 per cent. Heat for the system may come from the use of fossil fuel, nuclear reactors, or as expected in the future, fusion reactors.

B. L. ROBERTSON

References

Robertson, B. L., and Black, L. J., "Electric Circuits and Machines," Second Edition, New York, Van Nostrand Reinhold, 1957 (three-phase circuits, machine construction and performance).
Federal Power Commission yearly reports (power production and utilization in the United States).

Cross-references: BATTERIES, ELECTRICITY, HALL EFFECT AND RELATED PHENOMENA, MAGNETO-FLUID-MECHANICS, NUCLEAR REACTORS, PHOTOELECTRICITY, THERMOELECTRICITY.

ELECTRIC PROPULSION

Electric propulsion is a form of rocket propulsion in which electric power, generated on board the propelled vehicle, is used to eject propellant rearward at high velocity to produce thrust. Electric propulsion systems can be considered to be made up of two major components: (1) the *electric power generation system*, which converts power from a basic power source (such as a nuclear reactor or the sun) into electric power, and (2) *the thruster*, which uses this electric power to produce thrust by ejecting the propellant.

The primary potential advantage of electric

rockets over chemical rockets or solid-core nuclear rockets is that much higher propellant ejection velocities can be attained. Higher ejection velocities, in accordance with Newton's law, produce higher thrust per unit mass of propellant, so that the total mass of propellant needed for space missions can be greatly reduced. The mass of the required electric power generation equipment is appreciable, however, so that some of the saving in propellant mass is offset by the mass of the power generation system. The net mass saving possible using electric propulsion, therefore depends strongly on the performance parameters of the system.

One of the most important of these performance parameters is the propulsion-system specific mass α, which is defined as

$$\alpha = \frac{m_{ps}}{P_j} \quad \frac{kg}{kW} \tag{1}$$

where m_{ps} is the total propulsion system mass (in kilograms) and P_j is the jet power produced (in kilowatts). If this parameter is less than about 25 kg/kW, electric propulsion systems can be employed to advantage over nuclear or chemical rockets for many unmanned interplanetary exploration missions. For such missions, typical required power levels range from several hundred kilowatts to a megawatt, to propel vehicles having initial mass in earth orbit in the range of 10 000 to 100 000 kg.

If α is less than about 5 kg/kW, electric propulsion is superior to nuclear rockets, with regard to required initial weight and trip time, for manned expeditions to the near planets.[1] For these missions, power levels of several megawatts will be needed for vehicle weights (in orbit) of the range of 100 000 to 1 000 000 kg. In other possible applications, such as providing small amounts of thrust for attitude control or orbit control of satellites, the specific mass is less important, since the required electric power is small and can usually be obtained from the power supply used by the other on-board equipment.

Most of the mass of an electric propulsion system resides in the electric power generation system; however, the performance of the other major component, the thruster, is of equal importance in determining the over-all specific mass. The most important parameter for the thruster is the efficiency η with which the electric power is converted into jet power. If this efficiency is low, the required electric power, and therefore the power-plant mass, is correspondingly high.

Another important parameter for the thruster (as for all rockets) is the specific impulse I. This parameter is defined as the thrust F produced per unit weight flow of propellant:

$$I = \frac{F}{\dot{m}_p g_0} \quad sec \tag{2}$$

where $\dot{m}_p$ is the mass flow rate of propellant and g_0 is the acceleration of gravity at the earth's surface (9.8 m/sec^2) which relates mass to weight. The relation of thrust, specific impulse, and propellant ejection velocity is

$$F = \dot{m}_p g_0 I = \dot{m}_p v_j \quad newtons \tag{3}$$

where v_j is the mean propellant ejection velocity (more commonly called *effective jet velocity*). The first and last terms in Eq. (3) express Newton's law that force is equal to the time rate of change of momentum. The last two terms show that specific impulse is directly proportional to effective jet velocity.

The *jet power* is the time rate of change of jet kinetic energy, or

$$P_j = \tfrac{1}{2} \dot{m}_p v_j^2 = \tfrac{1}{2} F v_j = \tfrac{1}{2} g_0 I F \quad newton\text{-}m/sec$$

or, in kilowatts,

$$P_j = \frac{g_0 I F}{2000} \quad kW \tag{4}$$

For constant thrust and jet velocity, the total propellant mass m_p needed for a mission can be written [from Eq. (3)] as

$$m_p = \frac{Ft}{g_0 I} \quad kg \tag{5}$$

where t is the total propulsion time and Ft is the total impulse required for the mission. From Eq. (1) and (4), the propulsion system mass can be written:

$$m_{ps} = \alpha P_j = \frac{\alpha g_0 I F}{2000} \quad kg \tag{6}$$

These equations show that, although propellant mass can be reduced indefinitely by increasing the specific impulse [Eq. (5)], the power required (and therefore the power-plant mass) is increased when this is done [Eq. (6)]. It is, therefore, desirable to use that value of specific impulse for which the *sum* of the masses of propellant and propulsion system is lowest. This optimum specific impulse will yield the least total mass for the mission, or the highest payload mass for a given total mass. For lunar and interplanetary missions and for specific weights likely to be obtained, calculations show that the optimum specific impulses range from about 1500 to 15 000 seconds (corresponding to jet velocities of about 15 to 150 km/sec). These specific impulses compare with values of about 450 seconds that are typical for high-energy chemical rockets and about 900 seconds that may be possible with solid-core nuclear rockets.

Another characteristic feature of electric propulsion systems is the very low thrust generated in comparison with chemical or nuclear rockets. This can be seen from Eq. (6) which can be written:

$$\frac{F}{m_{\text{ps}}g_0} = \frac{2000}{\alpha I g_0^2} \qquad (7)$$

For a specific mass α of 10 kg/kW, and a specific impulse I of 5000 seconds, Eq. (7) yields a thrust-to-weight ratio of about 4×10^{-4}. This very low value results partly from the higher specific impulse typical of electric rockets, but mostly from the specific mass, which is of the order of 1000 or more times higher than that obtainable with solid-core nuclear rockets or chemical rockets. The low thrust-weight ratio means that electric propulsion systems cannot be used for launching from planetary surfaces. They are best suited for propelling vehicles between orbits about the planets or between orbits about the earth and the moon.

Because the thrust-weight ratio is so low, electric rockets must operate for much longer periods of time (of the order of 1000 times longer) than chemical or nuclear rockets to produce the same total impulse. Typically, for interplanetary missions to the near and far planets, these required operating times range from many months to several years. The removal of limitations on jet velocity, therefore, is obtained at the expense of greatly increased propulsion system mass and required operating lifetime.

Power Generation Systems The need for low specific mass dominates the selection of suitable methods for generating electric power for primary propulsion of space vehicles. The requirement that power be generated with very little consumption of mass dictates that either nuclear or solar energy must be used as the basic energy source.

Among the possible methods of converting this energy into electric power, the most direct are photovoltaic solar cells and radioisotope cells. Considerable progress has been made in reducing the thickness, and hence the weight of photovoltaic solar cells;[2] eventual achievement of a specific mass near 5 kg/kW appears possible. A lightweight radioisotope cell, in the range of 1 kg/kW, has been proposed and analyzed[3] but not yet demonstrated. This cell is basically a very high-voltage, low-current device, which converts a large fraction of the kinetic energy of the isotope decay particles directly into electric power. This system matches the requirements with respect to voltage and current, of colloidal-particle thrusters (see "Thrusters," p. 246).

Somewhat less direct in energy conversion are systems that use thermionic cells

$$\left(\begin{array}{c}\text{nuclear} \rightarrow \\ \text{solar} \rightarrow\end{array}\text{heat} \rightarrow \text{electricity}\right)$$

A nuclear reactor or solar concentrator is used to heat a suitable material (such as tungsten) to temperatures high enough to produce thermal emission of electrons. These electrons traverse a gap to a cooled collector electrode, thereby producing electric power at a potential of the order of 1 volt. Many thousands of these thermionic cells must be connected in series-parallel combinations to achieve the required power levels and voltages. Also, to produce useful power densities, emitter temperatures must be in the range 1500 to 2000 K. Conversion efficiencies (heat into electric power) of 15 to 30 per cent are possible. The remaining 70 to 85 per cent of the thermal power must be radiated into space. The collector electrodes, where this waste heat appears, must be adequately cooled by a heat-transfer fluid that is pumped past the collector to pick up the waste heat and carry it to a radiator. In order that the radiator be of adequately low size and weight, it must operate at temperatures of about 1000 K or higher. Analyses for a complete nuclear thermionic system yield specific masses of the order of 4 to 10 kg/kW, but numerous severe performance, design, and engineering problems remain to be solved before such systems can be developed to mission status.[4]

Still more indirect, in the conversion of energy, are the turboelectric systems

$$\left(\begin{array}{c}\text{solar} \rightarrow \\ \text{nuclear} \rightarrow\end{array}\text{heat} \rightarrow \text{mechanical} \rightarrow \text{electric}\right)$$

For these, as well as the thermionic systems, the nuclear reactor appears to be a better basic energy source than the sun, because it provides a more compact and versatile system, suitable for operation in shaded regions and at any distance from the sun.

A nuclear turboelectric system for electric propulsion (as illustrated in Fig. 1) is basically a lightweight adaptation to space conditions of ground-based nuclear power stations.[5] The chief differences result (as for the thermionic systems) from the lack of means other than radiation to eliminate the waste heat resulting from inescapable conversion inefficiencies. To produce specific mass below 10 kg/kW, the waste-heat radiator must operate at temperatures above 900 K, which in turn requires that the nuclear reactor operate at temperatures in excess of 1200 K.

The most suitable working fluid, at these temperatures, is potassium, if a liquid-vapor thermodynamic cycle (Rankine cycle) is used. In a single-loop version of this cycle, the liquid metal is vaporized in the nuclear reactor; the resulting vapor drives the turbine, which in turn drives the generator to produce electric power. The vapor passes from the turbine through the radiator, where it is recondensed, and the liquid is then recirculated through the reactor. A major problem is to develop materials with adequate corrosion resistance during long periods of high-temperature operation with alkali liquid metals. As illustrated in Fig. 1, the radiator is the largest and heaviest part of the system.

A possible alternative to the turboelectric system is an MHD (magnetohydrodynamic) gener-

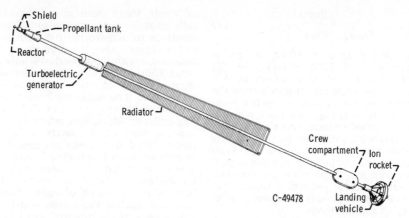

FIG. 1. Conceptual design of space vehicle for manned Mars mission. Nuclear turboelectric propulsion system.

ator, which replaces the turbogenerator with a duct through which a hot, electrically conducting fluid is passed. The duct is embedded in a strong magnetic field which must be produced by superconducting coils to minimize the power consumption. The most suitable fluid seems to be a noble gas seeded with cesium to make it electrically conducting.[6] When this fluid, heated by the nuclear reactor, is forced through the magnetic field, electric currents are induced, and power can be extracted by electrodes embedded in the duct. Such a system can tolerate higher temperatures than turbines, and should be particularly attractive for required power levels in the multi-megawatt range.

Thrusters A large number of methods are possible to eject propellant by use of electric power. These are generally divided into three categories: (1) *electrostatic thrusters*, in which atoms (or heavier particles) are electrically charged and then accelerated rearward by means of an electrostatic field; (2) plasma thrusters, in which the propellant is made into an electrically conducting gas and accelerated rearward by application of electromagnetic forces; (3) electrothermal thrusters, which use the electric power to heat the propellant, and then accelerate it rearward by thermal expansion through a nozzle.

Electrostatic thrusters that accelerate atomic

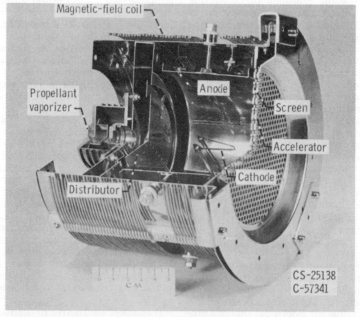

FIG. 2. Cutaway photograph of electron-bombardment ion thruster. With about 1 kW of power, this unit produces a thrust of 0.025 Newtons grams at a specific impulse of 5000 sec.

ions (ion rockets) have received the most research and development attention, as a result of early demonstrations of good efficiencies in the range of specific impulses needed for major space missions. Typical of these ion rockets is an electron-bombardment thruster (such as that shown in Fig. 2) which uses mercury vapor as propellant.[7] The propellant atoms are ionized by collision with electrons emitted by the cathode and attracted toward the anode. A weak axial magnetic field is maintained in the ionization chamber to make the electrons spiral around on their way to the anode, thereby increasing their path length and their probability of colliding with propellant atoms. The resulting positive ions are extracted through a screen grid by means of an accelerating grid that is maintained at the proper voltage difference (usually several thousand volts) to produce the desired ejection velocity (specific impulse). A second electron emitter (not shown) is placed adjacent to the ion beam, downstream of the accelerator, to neutralize both the ion space charge and the net current leaving the thruster. Experimental efficiencies in converting electric power into jet power range from 60 to 80 per cent at specific impulses in the range 2500 to 9000 seconds. Thrusters in sizes up to 150 cm in diameter, with jet powers near 180 kW have been successfully operated.[7]

Other ion thrusters, using contact ionization of cesium atoms on hot tungsten to produce the ions (rather than electron bombardment), have achieved somewhat lower performance. In these thrusters, cesium vapor is passed through porous tungsten, which must be heated to about 1500 K to evaporate enough cesium ions from the ionizer surface. The high work function of tungsten and the low ionization potential of cesium make these two substances the most promising for contact ionization thrusters.

Atomic-ion thrusters tend to become less efficient at low ejection velocities (low specific impulse), because a certain fixed amount of energy is needed to ionize the propellant atoms. As the ejection velocity decreases, the jet power approaches the power required for ionization, and the efficiency decreases. A possible way to increase the efficiency is to increase the mass of each charged particle so that its kinetic energy, at a given jet velocity, is higher. This approach leads to use of colloidal particles in place of atomic ions. Because of the much higher mass per unit charge, voltages in the hundreds of kilovolts are needed to produce the desired jet velocities.

Although the efficiencies attainable with electrostatic thrusters are high, there remains a limitation which, although not crucial, is undesirable, namely, a low thrust (or power) per unit beam area, due to limitations on ion beam current density. These limitations result from two sources: (1) space charge and (2) accelerator electrode erosion. The space-charge limited current is determined by the accelerating voltage and the distance between accelerator electrode and ion source. The voltage, in turn, is approximately fixed by the desired specific impulse, and the accelerator spacing is limited by electrical breakdown and thermal warping. The erosion limitation appears to be even more restrictive on thrust per unit area than space charge. As the current density is increased, there is greater impingement of ions on the accelerator electrode. For an accelerator lifetime of the order of 1 year, estimates indicate a limit for thrust per unit beam area of about 2 newtons (0.2 kg) per square meter (about 50 kW/m^2) at a specific impulse of 5000 seconds. Higher values are allowable as specific impulse increases.

Plasma thrusters, which operate on the principle of accelerating an electrically conducting gas (plasma) are not subject to the space charge limitation, and require no accelerator grid. Consequently, a higher thrust per unit area with adequate lifetime may be achievable. A variety of plasma thruster types have been investigated during the past decade,[8] but so far the efficiencies have been much lower than those of ion thrusters. Sizable effort has been devoted to the magnetoplasmadynamic (MPD) arc jet, which consists of a coaxial discharge between a central cathode and a surrounding anode in the presence of a magnetic field.[9]

Electrothermal thrusters are primarily of two types—the electric-arc jet and the electrically powered hydrogen heater (also called resistojet). The hydrogen heater is limited to specific impulses less than about 1000 seconds, because of the limitation on the wall temperature of the heater. High efficiencies, however, have been achieved.[10] The arc jet, which heats the propellant by means of continuous electric discharge as the propellant flows by, can achieve somewhat higher specific impulses (up to about 2000 seconds), but the efficiency is generally less than 50 per cent, due to losses involved in dissociation and ionization of the propellant atoms, and losses to the walls of the arc chamber and nozzle. Because of the lower specific impulse range, electrothermal thrusters are not useful for interplanetary missions, but may be used for more limited applications such as satellite orientation control and orbit correction.

History and Status The possibility of reducing propellant consumption by ejecting the propellant electrically at high velocities was recognized by early space flight and rocket pioneers, such as Goddard[11] and Oberth,[12] but the practical feasibility of such propulsion systems was not demonstrated. With the advent of nuclear-electric power and large rockets during and after World War II, more interest in electric propulsion was aroused, and between 1946 and 1956, a number of preliminary analyses of nuclear and solar electric systems were published.[13,14]

Comparative studies of the applicability of electric, nuclear, and chemical propulsion to future space missions, together with an engineering study of large electric power systems for

FIG. 3. Artist's drawing of SERT-II Spacecraft.

space use were completed in 1957.[15] These and similar studies led to the initiation of major research programs in electric propulsion and power generation at U.S. government and industrial laboratories. Low-thrust trajectory studies and mission analyses[1,16,17] have further clarified the role of electric propulsion in future space missions.

The use of cesium-tungsten constant ionization for electrostatic thrusters was proposed by Stuhlinger,[14] and early experimental work in the United States, beginning in 1957, was concentrated on this approach.[18-20] However, the invention and development of the electron bombardment ion thruster[21] showed that it could achieve higher efficiencies with less sensitivity to fabrication techniques and materials. In 1964, the first successful space flight test of ion thrusters was accomplished with the launching of SERT-I (Space Electric Rocket Test I).[22] One cesium-tungsten and one electron bombardment thruster were launched into a 20-minute ballistic space trajectory. The cesium-tungsten thruster developed a high-voltage breakdown, but the electron bombardment thruster operated successfully. The test demonstrated that ion beam neutralization in space was no problem, and that the thrust level was the same as in ground test vacuum facilities. After further research and development of the electron bombardment thruster, a long-duration satellite orbital test (SERT II) was launched in February 1970 (Fig. 3).[23] One of the two thrusters operated continuously for five months and the other for three months. Power source was a 1.5 kW solar cell array. These tests showed that ion thrusters were ready for mission application. Since solar-cell arrays with adequately low specific mass have also been developed, complete solar-electric propulsion systems appear technologically ready for application. Nuclear-electric propulsion systems, however, must await development of suitable nuclear power systems.

W. E. MOECKEL

References

1. Moeckel, W. E., "Comparison of Advanced Propulsion Concepts for Deep Space Exploration," *J. Spacecraft and Rockets*, 9 (12), 863–868 (December, 1972).

2. Rappaport, P., "Photovoltaic Power," *J. Spacecraft and Rockets*, 4 (7), 838–841 (July 1967).

3. Mickelsen, W. R., and Low, C. A., Jr., "Potentials of Radioisotope Electrostatic Propulsion," *Astronautics Aerospace Eng.*, 1 (9), 52–57 (October 1963).

4. Becker, R. A., "Thermionic Space Power Systems Review," *J. Spacecraft and Rockets*, 4 (7), 847–851 (July 1967).

5. Zipkin, Morris A., "Alkali-Metal Rankine-Cycle Power Systems for Electric Propulsion," *J. Spacecraft and Rockets*, 4 (7) 852–858 (July 1967).

6. Nichols, Lester, D., "Comparison of Brayton and Rankine Cycle Magnetogasdynamic Space Power Generation Systems," NASA TN D-5085, 1969.

7. Richley, Edward A., and Kerslake, William R., "Bombardment Thruster Investigations at the

Lewis Research Center," *J. Spacecraft and Rockets*, **6** (3), 289–295 (March 1969).

8. Seikel, George R., "Generation of Thrust–Electromagnetic Thrusters," NASA SP-11, 1962, pp. 171–176.

9. Connolly, D. J., Sovie, R. J., Michels, C. J., and Burkhart, J. A., "Low Environmental Pressure MPD Arc Tests," *AIAA J.*, **6** (7), 1271–1276 (July 1968).

10. Jack, John R., "NASA Research on Resistance-Heated Hydrogen Jets," "Advanced Propulsion Concepts," Vol. I, Gordon and Breach Science Pub., Inc., 1963 (pp. 75–89).

11. Lehman, Milton, "This High Man," New York, Farrar, Straus, and Co., 1963.

12. Oberth, H., "Wege zur Raumschiffahrt," Munich and Berlin, Verlag von Oldenbourg, 1929 (reprinted by Edwards Bros. Inc., 1945).

13. Shepherd, L. R., and Cleaver, A. V., "The Atomic Rocket," Pt. I, *J. Brit. Interplanet. Soc.*, 7, 185–189 (1948); Pt. II, ibid., 7, 234–241 (1948); Pt. III, ibid., 8, 23–37 (1949); Pt. IV, ibid., 8, 59–70 (1949).

14. Stuhlinger, E., "Electrical Propulsion System for Space Ships with Nuclear Power Source," *J. Astronautics*, 2 (4), 149–152 (1955); 3 (1), 11–14 (1956); 3 (2), 33–36 (1956).

15. Moeckel, W. E., Baldwin, L. V., English, R. E., Lubarsky, B., and Maslen, S. H., "Satellite and Space Propulsion Systems," NASA TN D-285, 1960. (Unclassified versions of material presented at NACA Flight Propulsion Conference, November 22, 1957.)

16. Irving, J. H., and Blum, E. K., "Comparative Performance of Ballistic and Low-Thrust Vehicles for Flight to Mars," *Vistas Astron.*, 2, 191–218 (1959).

17. Sauer, C. G., and Melbourne, W. G., "Optimum Earth-to-Mars Trip Trajectories Using Low-Thrust, Power-Limited Propulsion Systems," Rep. TR 32-376, Jet Prop. Lab., C.I.T., 1963.

18. Forrester, A. T., and Spenser, R. C.: "Cesium-Ion Propulsion," *Astronautics*, 4 (10), 34–35 (October 1959).

19. Childs, J. H., "Design of Ion Rockets and Test Facilities," Paper 59-103, Inst. Aero. Sci., Inc., 1959.

20. Brewer, G. R., Etter, J. R., and Anderson, J. R., "Design and Performance of Small Model Ion Engines," Paper 1125-60, ARS, 1960.

21. Kaufman, Harold R., "An Ion Rocket with an Electric Bombardment Ion Source," NASA TN D-585, 1961.

22. Cybulski, R. J., Shellbauer, D. M., Lovell R. R., Domino, E. J., and Kutnik, J. J., "Results from SERT-I Ion Rocket Flight Test," NASA TN D-2718, March 1965.

23. Kerslake, W. R., Goldman, R. G., and Neiberding, W. C., "SERT-II: Mission, Thruster, and In-Flight Measurements," *J. Spacecraft and Rockets*, 8 (3), 223–224 (March 1971).

Cross-references: ASTRODYNAMICS; ASTRONAUTICS, PHYSICS OF; DYNAMICS; FLIGHT PROPULSION FUNDAMENTALS; IMPULSE AND MOMENTUM; MAGNETO-FLUID-MECHANICS; PHOTOELECTRICITY; PLASMA.

ELECTRICAL DISCHARGES IN GASES

Motion of Slow Electrons in Gases Suppose that a swarm of electrons traverses a gas in which a uniform electric field X exists. In general the distribution of energy among the electrons will depend on the distance x which they have traveled in the field. However, provided x is sufficiently large, the energy distribution attains a steady value independent of x. In this steady state, the average rate of supply of energy to an electron from the field is equal to the average rate of loss of energy in collisions with gas molecules.

Many important quantities in this subject are related to $eX\lambda$, the energy gained by an electron of charge e in traveling the mean distance λ between two successive collisions with gas molecules. Since λ is inversely proportional to the gas density, the above quantity can be expressed in the form X/P_0 where P_0 is the gas pressure reduced to some standard temperature.

The mean energy of an electron in the swarm, $\bar{\epsilon}$, is a function only of X/P_0 for a particular gas. Figure 1 shows the form of this variation for a

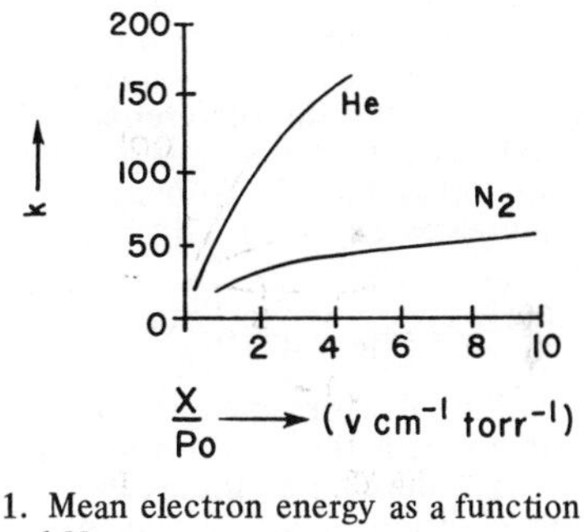

FIG. 1. Mean electron energy as a function of X/P_0 for He and N_2.

monatomic gas (He) and a diatomic gas (N_2). Here $k = \bar{\epsilon}/\bar{\epsilon}_g$, where $\bar{\epsilon}_g$ is the mean kinetic energy of a gas molecule at $15°C$ (0.037 eV). It is seen that the mean electron energy greatly exceeds the mean energy of a gas molecule even when X/P_0 is small. This is due to the inefficient energy exchange in collisions between electrons and gas molecules. If the collisions are elastic, it is readily shown that f, the mean fractional energy lost by an electron in a collision, is $\sim 2m/M$ where m is electron mass and M is molecular mass. Clearly $f_{el} \ll 1$. At a given X/P_0, $\bar{\epsilon}$ is generally lower in polyatomic than in monatomic gases. Owing to the possibility of inelastic collisions involving vibrational or rotational excitation of the molecule, $f \gg 2m/M$ in the former case. In the latter case, only electronic excitation of the atom can occur and this requires much higher energies in general.

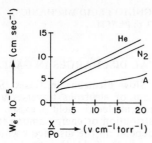

FIG. 2. Electron drift velocity as a function of X/P_0 for He, A and N_2.

In addition to their random motion, the electrons must obviously possess a superimposed drift motion in the direction of the applied field. Figure 2 shows the variation of the drift velocity W_e with X/P_0; normally W_e is small compared to the mean random speed of the electrons.

Ionization by Electron Collision When the energy of an electron exceeds a certain critical value ϵ_i, ionization can occur at a collision with a gas molecule. As X/P_0, and hence $\bar{\epsilon}$, is increased, an increasing fraction of electrons in the swarm will have energies exceeding ϵ_i. The size of the electron swarm will then increase with the distance x traveled in the field direction.

This growth is most conveniently studied under conditions where $\bar{\epsilon}$ is kept constant. This can be done by releasing electrons from the cathode of a plane-parallel system and varying the electrode gap d and potential difference V in such a way that the electric field $X(=V/d)$ is fixed. It is then found that the electron current at the anode, i, increases exponentially with d or V. That is

$$i = i_0 \exp (\eta V) \qquad (1)$$

where i_0 is the electron current released from the cathode and η is the electron ionization coefficient: this is defined as the average number of ionizing collisions made by an electron in moving through a 1-volt potential difference. η is also a function only of X/P_0 for a given gas (Fig. 3).

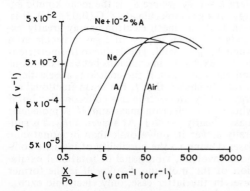

FIG. 3. Electron ionization coefficient as a function of X/P_0 for air, Ne, A, and Ne + 10^{-2} per cent A.

It is important to note that the curve of η against X/P_0 passes through a maximum. The decrease in η at low X/P_0 is due to the increasing importance of excitation compared with ionization as X/P_0 decreases; since the excitation energy losses are larger in polyatomic than in monatomic gases, as remarked earlier, the decrease in η occurs more rapidly in air than in neon. The decrease in η at high X/P_0 (300 volts cm^{-1} torr^{-1}), where excitation losses are comparatively unimportant, is due to the fact that an increasingly large fraction of the energy supplied from the field is used in maintaining the kinetic energy of the swarm.

The curve for the gas mixture Ne + 10^{-2} per cent A is of great interest. Since the excitation potential of the most important metastable state of Ne (16.5 volts) exceeds the ionization potential of A (15.8 volts), the process Ne* + A → Ne + A$^+$ + e can occur. This reaction has a very high probability, of the order unity per collision, and causes a great increase in η at low X/P_0 above the value for pure neon, since the effective excitation energy losses are now considerably reduced. The double maximum in the curve of η vs X/P_0 arises from the fact that the direct and indirect ionization processes have their maximum efficiencies at different X/P_0 values (~70 and 2 volts cm^{-1} torr^{-1}, respectively).

Secondary Ionization Processes It is found that Eq. (1) no longer holds at larger values of V; i now increases more rapidly leading ultimately to spark breakdown. This is due to the occurrence of secondary ionization processes, in addition to ionization by collision between electrons and gas molecules. In general, the most important secondary process is the release of electrons from the cathode surface. If various simplifying assumptions are made, it can be shown that the ionization current is now given by:

$$i = \frac{i_0 \exp (\eta V)}{1 - \gamma [\exp (\eta V) - 1]} \qquad (2)$$

where γ is a generalized secondary ionization coefficient. This is defined as the probability of a secondary electron being released from the cathode per positive ion arriving at the cathode. Included in γ are contributions to the secondary emission arising from radiation quanta and metastable molecules.

Since γ depends largely on the mean energies of the electrons and ions, it is, like η, a function only of X/P_0 though the function now depends on the nature of the cathode as well as on the gas.

Spark Breakdown It is clear from the above equation that the ionization current tends to become very large as the potential difference across the gap approaches the value V_s given by:

$$\eta V_s = \log \left(1 + \frac{1}{\gamma} \right) \qquad (3)$$

This is the condition for spark breakdown and can be best explained in the following manner.

Suppose that a primary electron current i_0 is released from the cathode when $V = V_s$. The electron current reaching the anode is then i_0 exp (ηV_s). Hence, the positive ion current reaching the cathode due to the current i_0 is i_0 [exp $(\eta V_s) - 1$]. This will give rise to a secondary electron current of value γi_0 [exp $(\eta V_s) - 1$]. If V_s is given by Eq. (3), then γ [exp $(\eta V_s) - 1$] = 1 and the secondary current is equal to the original primary current i_0. Hence it is clear that the process can continue even if the initiating current ceases. When V is less than V_s, however, the discharge current i is proportional to i_0 [Eq. (2)]. Thus $i = 0$ when $i_0 = 0$. It follows that $V = V_s$ marks the transition from a non-self-maintained to a self-maintained discharge. V_s is best defined as the potential difference required to maintain a small discharge current i when the primary current $i_0 = 0$. V_s is independent of i provided this is sufficiently small to avoid space charge distortion of the field.

Since η and γ are both functions only of X/P_0 and $X = V_s/d_s$ at breakdown, it follows from Eq. (3) that

$$V_s = F(P_0 d_s) \qquad (4)$$

Thus, for a given gas and cathode material, the breakdown potential between large plane-parallel electrodes depends only on the product of the reduced gas pressure and electrode separation. This result, which is known as Paschen's law, has been confirmed experimentally over a wide range of P_0 and d_s.

The variation of V_s with $P_0 d_s$ for a number of gases and cathode materials is shown in Fig. 4. It should be noted that the curves all exhibit a minimum; this corresponds to the maximum in the curve of η vs X/P_0. It will be seen that the rise of V_s at high values of $P_0 d_s$ is most marked in air, less in pure Ne, and less still in the Ne + A mixture. This is readily understood by reference to the decrease in η at low X/P_0 ($=V_s/P_0 d_s$) in these gases (Fig. 3).

Time Lag of Spark Breakdown If a potential difference $\geqslant V_s$ is suddenly applied to a discharge gap, a finite time elapses before the ini-

tial current i_0 has increased to a self-maintained discharge current $\sim 10^{-7}$ ampere/cm^2. This time lag consists of two parts. First of all, there is a statistical lag which arises from the fact that the primary and secondary ionization processes are both subject to statistical fluctuations. Thus, although $V > V_s$ where γ [exp $(\eta V_s) - 1$] = 1 implies that on the average one electron leaving the cathode will give rise to one secondary electron, this may not happen in any particular case. Clearly the mean statistical lag t_s will decrease as the initial current is increased and it may be shown that

$$t_s = \frac{1}{PN_0} \qquad (5)$$

where N_0 is the number of primary electrons leaving the cathode per second and P is the probability that any particular electron leads to breakdown. The latter quantity is zero at the sparking threshold V_s but increases rapidly for $V > V_s$. $P \simeq 1$ provided $V > 1.25\ V_s$.

The second component of the total time lag is the formative lag t_F. This can be regarded as the time that must elapse after the appearance of a suitable initiatory electron before the various ionization processes generate a self-maintained current of any given magnitude. This current can be chosen arbitrarily to specify breakdown of the gap and is generally taken to be $\sim 10^{-7}$ ampere/cm^2. Clearly t_F will depend on the relative importance of the various secondary mechanisms mentioned earlier; positive ion transit times are typically $\sim 10^{-6}$ second, while the time lags involved in the contribution of radiation quanta and metastable molecules to γ are $\sim 10^{-8}$ and 10^{-3} second, respectively. The observed variation of t_F with overvoltage ΔV ($= V - V_s$) for various fixed values of X/P_0 in H$_2$ is shown in Fig. 5. Comparison with theory enables an estimate to be made of k, the relative contribution of photons at the cathode to the

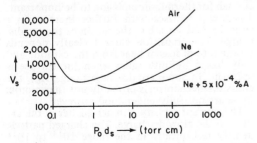

FIG. 4. Breakdown potential as a function of the product of the reduced gas pressure and electrode separation, $P_0 d_s$ for air, Ne, and Ne + 0.0005 per cent A with an iron cathode.

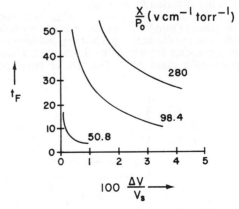

FIG. 5. Variation of formative time lag with overvoltage for various fixed values of X/P_0 in H$_2$ with copper electrodes.

total γ. This ranges from 0.75 at $X/P_0 = 50$ to 0.50 at $X/P_0 = 300$ volts cm^{-1} torr^{-1}.

Glow Discharge We have seen that any small current i can be maintained even in the absence of initiatory electrons when the potential difference between the electrodes reaches a value V_s given by Eq. (3). V is only independent of i when the latter is less than ~ 1 μA. At higher currents the space charge concentration becomes sufficient to cause X and hence η to vary across the gap, and ηV_s in Eq. (3) must be replaced by $\int \eta \, dV$. The static V-i characteristic is normally negative since the field redistribution produced by the space charge effects increases the over-all ionization efficiency. Once breakdown has taken place, the current increases to a value determined by the impedance of the voltage supply.

If the current density is sufficiently small (< 0.1 ampere/cm^2), the cathode is not heated to a high enough temperature for thermionic emission to be a significant factor in the maintenance of the discharge. This regime is termed a glow discharge and the field variation across the gap in a long cylindrical tube is indicated in Fig. 6. We can distinguish five main regions here:

(1) The cathode fall, in which the field decreases from a high value at the cathode to approximately zero.

(2) The negative glow, in which ionization and excitation are due largely to fast electrons arriving from the cathode fall. The length of this region is normally controlled by the distance traveled by the electrons before their energy is reduced below the minimum required for excitation.

(3) Faraday dark space. In many cases the ionization in the negative glow is so intense that the electron current here exceeds the total discharge current. A region is therefore required where electrons are lost by diffusion and not replenished by ionization; usually $X \leqslant 0$ here.

(4) The positive column, where X has a small constant value such that the corresponding electron energy distribution gives an ionization rate which just balances the loss of electrons and ions by radial diffusion to the walls.

(5) The anode fall, where X again increases.

Regions (1) and (2) are the most important regions of the discharge; the primary and secondary ionization by which the discharge is maintained take place here. The fall of potential

across region (1), usually termed the cathode fall (V_c) is clearly an important parameter of the discharge.

It should be noted that the section extending from the negative glow to the anode has only a small field strength and small resultant space charge with $| n_i - n_e | \ll n_e$, where n_i and n_e are the ion and electron concentrations. This region is generally called a plasma. In many cases, the electrons here have a random motion which is large compared to their drift motion in the field direction. Our earlier discussion on electron swarms is valid here. On the other hand, the regions which occur near the cathode and the walls have a high field strength and resultant space charge with $n_i \gg n_e$. The electrons and ions behave here as a beam rather than as a swarm.

Ambipolar Diffusion The radial diffusion of ions and electrons to the wall in the plasma region (4), above, does not occur at the same rate as when only one type of carrier is present. Clearly, the electrons will tend to diffuse to the walls much more rapidly than the ions leaving an excess of positive charge. A space charge field is set up which retards electrons and accelerates positive ions so that their effective diffusion rates are equalized. This process can be described in terms of the ambipolar diffusion coefficient D_a which is given approximately by:

$$D_a \doteq D_i \left[1 + \frac{T_e}{T_i} \right] \qquad (6)$$

where D_i is the normal ion diffusion coefficient and T_e and T_i are the effective electron and ion temperatures, respectively.

Cathode Fall When the current is sufficiently small (< 10 mA for a cathode of area ~ 1 cm^2), the discharge does not occupy the entire cathode area. The current density in the covered portion j_n is approximately constant, and the cathode fall of potential V_c is nearly independent of current and pressure. This is termed the normal cathode fall. The abnormal cathode fall occurs when $i > j_n S$, where S is the total cathode area. V_c now increases with current.

Arc and High Current Discharges If i is increased sufficiently, a stage will eventually be reached where the cathode temperature is high enough for thermionic emission to be important. V_c now decreases with further increase in i (Fig. 7), and we are in the region of the arc discharge. The transition current clearly depends on the rate of loss of heat from the cathode and only has a definite value when the surface is uniform. In some arc discharges (e.g., Hg), the emission mechanism is probably not thermionic; these are not fully understood however.

The current density is much higher in the arc than in the glow discharge. The charged particle density is typically in the range 10^{14} to 10^{18} electrons cm^{-3} in the core of the arc when the pressure is approximately atmospheric. Because of the very high frequency of collisions between the electrons, positive ions, and neutral mole-

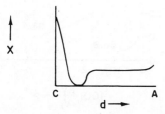

FIG. 6. Variation of axial field with distance from the cathode for a glow discharge in a long cylindrical tube.

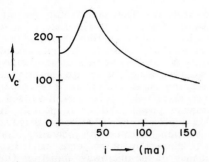

FIG. 7. Variation of cathode fall of potential with current for discharge in A at 30 torr pressure with spherical tungsten electrodes, 1.8 mm diameter.

cules, thermal equilibrium is often established for all the groups of particles present in the arc positive column. The temperature at the axis of the arc is typically in the range 4 000 to 10 000 K. At high pressures the temperature diminishes laterally very quickly whereas at low pressures it remains constant over a large portion of the cross section.

We have assumed hitherto that the current is always sufficiently low for the magnetic field produced by the current to play an unimportant role in the discharge mechanism. At high currents this is no longer true, and the interaction of the self-magnetic field of the discharge and the current produces forces on the ionized gas comparable to the other forces acting. The required currents increase with the gas pressure p; at normal temperatures, $i > 10^3$ amperes and $p < 1$ torr are required. The force due to the magnetic field tends to constrict the discharge, and a column so constricted is said to be pinched. This pinch effect offers a possible method of confining the hot gas to a channel remote from the walls of the containing vessel. However, a major obstacle to the achievement of a steady pinched discharge is the inherent instability of such a channel to lateral perturbations. This causes the pinched column to leave the axis of the containing tube and take up a helical path in contact with the walls. It is, however, possible that a suitable arrangement of magnetic fields may help to stabilize the discharge, leading to the prospect of continuous operation of a pinched discharge.

J. D. SWIFT

References

Craggs, J. D., and Meek, J. M., "Electrical Breakdown of Gases," London, Oxford University Press, 1953.
Loeb, L. B., "Basic Processes of Gaseous Electronics," Berkeley, Cal., University of California Press, 1955.
Jones, F. Llewellyn, "Ionisation and Breakdown in Gases," London, Methuen & Co., Ltd., 1957.
Acton, J. R., and Swift, J. D., "Cold Cathode Discharge Tubes," London, Heywood and Co., Ltd., 1963.

von Engel, A., "Ionized Gases," London, Oxford University Press, 1965.
Somerville, J. M., "The Electric Arc," London, Methuen & Co., Ltd., 1959.
Nasser, E., "Fundamentals of Gaseous Ionization and Plasma Electronics," New York, John Wiley & Sons, 1971.
Llewellyn-Jones, F., "The Glow Discharge and an Introduction to Plasma Physics," London, Methuen & Co., Ltd., 1966.
Raether, H., "Electron Avalanches and Breakdown in Gases," London, Thornton Butterworth, 1964.
Hoyaux, M., "Arc Physics," Berlin, Springer-Verlag, 1968.
Brown, S. C., "Introduction to Electrical Discharges in Gases," New York, John Wiley & Sons, 1966.

Cross-references: IONIZATION, POTENTIAL

ELECTRICAL MEASUREMENTS

In an *electrical measurement*, one is concerned with the evaluation of an electrical quantity—resistance, capacitance, inductance, current, voltage, power, energy—or of a quantity or relationship that depends on some combination of them. The measurement means may be a ratio device, such as a potentiometer or bridge in which generally similar quantities are compared; or it may be an electromechanical system in which a force is developed to produce a displacement proportional to the electrical quantity to be measured. Electrical indicating instruments, such as ammeters, voltmeters and wattmeters, use this principle. In still other measuring systems, the heating effect of an electric current is utilized.

The basis of any meaningful electrical measurement must ultimately be the *National Reference Standards* maintained by the National Bureau of Standards in Washington, D.C. The magnitudes of these National Reference Standards are assigned in terms of *absolute* measurements in which certain electrical quantities are determined in terms of appropriate mechanical quantities—the electrical system of units being related to the metric system of mechanical units in such a way that both systems have identical units of power and energy. In 1954 it was agreed internationally that the "practical system of units of measurement" should be based on the *meter, kilogram, second,* and *ampere,* together with the unit of thermodynamic temperature (the *kelvin*) and the unit of luminous intensity (the *candela*). The name—International System, or Système International, abbreviated SI—was assigned in 1960 to this "practical" system of units, now in use throughout the world.

Two *absolute* measurements are needed to assign values to the National Reference Standards. Historically, these have been: (1) an *ohm* determination and (2) an *ampere* determination. In the ohm determination, a resistance is com-

pared to the reactance of an inductor or capacitor at a known frequency. The magnitude of the inductor or capacitor is calculated from its measured dimensions, and the resistance value is thus assigned in terms of the mechanical units of length and time—the meter and the second. In the ampere determination, the value of a current carried by two coils is measured in terms of the force with which the coils interact. The force between the coils is opposed by the force of gravity acting on a known mass, and the ampere is assigned in terms of the mechanical units of length, mass, and time—the meter, kilogram and second. When the ampere experiment is performed, the measured current is passed through a resistor of known value, and the potential drop is used to assign the electromotive force of a *standard cell*.

The basic National Reference Standards, in terms of which the *legal* electrical units are maintained, are groups of 1-ohm resistors and of standard cells of the cadmium sulfate type—the "Weston" saturated cell—whose values are assigned by *absolute* measurements. At the National Bureau of Standards, the national reference standard of resistance consists of ten 1-ohm resistors, fully annealed and mounted strain-free, out of contact with the air in sealed containers. The national reference standard of voltage consists of several groups of Weston cells maintained in closely controlled constant temperature enclosures. In the past, maintenance of the units was based on the means of these groups, which were assumed constant. The *legal* ohm continues to be maintained in terms of this group mean; but, since July 1, 1972, the *legal* volt has been maintained directly in terms of an atomic constant, by a method described below.

The stability of the standards that represent the *legal* units for measurement purposes can be examined in a number of ways. Individuals within the reference group are routinely intercompared to detect any drift of individuals with respect to the group mean; and members of the group are compared with units maintained by the national laboratories of other countries to measure differences among their "as-maintained" units. This international comparison is carried out at 3-year intervals by the International Bureau of Weights and Measures in France (Bureau International des Poids et Mesures at Sèvres, abbreviated BIPM). A better way of monitoring the stability of the *National Reference Standards* is through the use of experiments that relate an electrical unit directly to some atomic constant—a natural invariant. In one such experiment the *ampere* is related to *proton gyromagnetic ratio*. Since there is associated with protons a characteristic magnetic moment and spin, this elementary particle behaves both as a magnet and a gyroscope—it tends to align itself in a magnetic field and to precess about the field direction if the alignment is disturbed. In fact, proton precession frequency has become a widely used method for measuring magnetic field strength. The repeatability of proton precession frequency in the field of a stable solenoid excited by a current measured in terms of the *legal* volt and ohm, is a measure of the stability of the *legal* ampere. In another experiment use is made of the voltage appearing across a Josephson junction (made up of two superconductors separated by a barrier), irradiated with microwave power, and simultaneously biased with a direct current. The direct voltage across the junction increases with increasing bias current in discrete quantum jumps related to the frequency of the microwave radiation. Quantitatively this relation is $Nh\nu = 2eV_N$, where N is step number, h is Planck's constant, ν is the microwave frequency, e is the elementary electron charge, and V_N is the voltage across the junction. In this experiment the stability of the *legal* volt is monitored in terms of a frequency and the ratio of Planck's constant to electron charge by comparing the Josephson voltage to that of the National Reference Standard.

A reassignment of the *legal* volt (USA) was made on January 1, 1969 based on recent *absolute-ampere* determinations. The decrease in the volt assignment was such that the number describing the emf of a standard cell must be increased by 8.6 microvolts over its previous (1948–1968) assignment. Other national laboratories made similar adjustments such that all national reference standards of emf, including the standard at the International Bureau (BIPM), were in agreement at that time. With the refinement of the Josephson volt experiment, it became apparent that the emf of the group of standard cells used to maintain the *legal* volt, was slowly drifting in value (perhaps by 0.3 microvolt per year). It was therefore decided that the emf of these cells would be reassigned from time to time to keep the *legal* volt at a constant value. Thus, since July 1, 1972 the *legal* volt has, in effect, been maintained in terms of an assumed constant frequency/voltage ratio obtained from the Josephson experiment rather than in terms of the group average of a particular group of standard cells. Recent *absolute-ohm* determinations, based on a calculable capacitor, have indicated that the value assigned to the National Reference Standard of resistance is correct within a microhm, and the value of the *legal* ohm continues to be maintained by the average of a group of 1-ohm standards on the basis of their 1948 assignment.

The *voltage divider* is the basis of many precise measurement networks. In general, it consists of a group of series-connected resistors or impedors (using resistance, capacitance, inductance, or some combination of them). Its operating principle is as follows: When the series circuit is tapped at an intermediate point but no current is drawn from the tap, the ratio of the voltage between the tap point and one terminal of the divider to the voltage impressed across the whole divider equals the ratio of the tapped resistance. (or impedance) to the total resistance

(or impedance) of the divider. Modern dc potentiometers operating on this principle achieve an accuracy of a few parts in a million in comparing direct voltages and, with appropriate range-extending voltage dividers, can be used to measure voltages up to 1500 volts with an accuracy—referred to the legal volt—of 10 parts in a million. Standard cells can be intercompared to 1 to 2 parts in 10^7, using special potentiometers designed to eliminate or minimize parasitic voltages. Direct currents can also be measured to a few parts in a million with a potentiometer, by comparing the voltage drop that the current produces in a known resistance with a known reference voltage.

In any measurement network using voltage-divider techniques, a sensitive detector such as a galvanometer must be included in the circuit element containing the tap point, to indicate the absence of current in this branch. Although a number of electronic detectors have been developed for dc measurements, which are rugged and convenient to use, the D'Arsonval galvanometer, operated to make optimum use of its design characteristics, is still the most sensitive detector of voltage unbalance in potentiometers and in the usual dc bridge networks. In fact, unbalance detection at the nanovolt level in circuits having resistances up to a few hundred ohms is quite possible with the D'Arsonval galvanometer. A galvanometer consists basically of a coil of wire suspended by very fine metallic filaments—usually flat ribbons—in a radial magnetic field. Current in the coil introduced through the suspension filaments, interacts with the magnetic field to produce a torque tending to rotate the coil. The suspension stiffness opposes the coil rotation. A light beam, reflected from a mirror fixed to the moving system, indicates the magnitude of the rotation and hence the current in the coil. The light beam can be focused on a scale for direct observation, or may be shared by two differentially connected photocells whose output is supplied to a second galvanometer, producing a greatly amplified deflection. Such a photoamplifier system may be used to achieve nanovolt response in the detector system.

Two voltage dividers may be connected in parallel to the same voltage source to form a *bridge*. Equality of divider ratios—indicated by zero voltage difference at their tap points—permits the accurate comparison of impedances and generally is relatively insensitive to minor variations in the level of the supply voltage. The best known bridge for dc resistance determination is the Wheatstone network. It incorporates two dividers, one of which provides a known ratio, the other includes the unknown resistor and a known resistor with which it is compared. The Wheatstone bridge is used for resistors, usually of value greater than 1 ohm, which have only two terminals, i.e., whose potential and current connections coincide. An alternate network, the Kelvin bridge, is used for resistors which have

four terminals, i.e., whose potential and current terminals are separated. Two known ratios of identical magnitude must be provided in addition to the "divider" which incorporates the unknown and reference resistors. By employing one or the other of these bridges, and using a direct substitution method, nominally equal resistors can be compared to a few parts in a million or better in the resistance range from 10^4 to 10^{-4} ohm; at the 1-ohm level the comparison can be made to a part in 10^7.

The more general impedance bridge is usually a 4-arm network similar to the Wheatstone bridge—or a more complicated network which, by appropriate star-delta transformations, can be reduced to an equivalent 4-arm network—in which, by proper choice of components, inductances can be intercompared or measured in terms of a combination of capacitance and resistance, or capacitances can be intercompared or determined by a combination of inductance and resistance. The accuracy of such bridges is usually limited by the stability of the reference components and the other elements of the bridge, and by how well their values are known. Additional limits may be imposed by intercoupling between bridge elements or by their coupling to nearby objects or to ground. Such coupling may consist of an ambient magnetic field inducing a parasitic emf in an inductive bridge element or even in open loops formed by connectors between bridge elements, or by capacitance or leakage resistance between elements or to a neighboring source of potential or to ground. Such effects can be reduced or eliminated by choice and arrangement of inductive elements to avoid inductive coupling and by the use of shields maintained at appropriate potentials, to eliminate the effects of stray capacitance and leakage resistance on the bridge balance. Thus, no statement of bridge capability is possible except in the context of the individual components and their arrangement. As an extreme example of state-of-art measurements, 10-pF, 3-terminal capacitors can be compared to a part in 10^8, in a completely shielded bridge whose ratio arms are formed of closely coupled transformer windings.

Indicating instruments are commonly used to measure current, voltage, and power, and with special circuit arrangements or transducers, they can be used to indicate other electrical quantities —resistance, frequency, phase—or nonelectrical quantities such as speed, temperature, pressure, level of illumination—in fact any quantity for which an appropriate transducer can be devised that will convert the measurand into a usable electric signal.

Direct-current instruments are usually of the permanent-magnet moving coil type, sometimes called D'Arsonval-type instruments because their operating principle is identical with that of the D'Arsonval galvanometer. A coil, suspended or pivoted in a radial field between the polepieces of a permanent magnet, tends to rotate from the

mechanical interaction between its current and the field of the magnet. The turning moment of the coil is opposed by spiral springs in the case of a pivoted coil (or by the suspensions in a taut-band construction), and the equilibrium position of the coil is indicated by a pointer attached to it and moving across the instrument scale, which is marked in units of the quantity being measured. In a milliammeter, the entire current may be taken by the moving coil; in an ammeter, where the current is too large for the coil and connecting springs, a parallel circuit or shunt carries the bulk of the current, and only a fraction of it is taken by the moving coil; in a voltmeter, a large series resistance (or multiplier) is used to limit the coil current, and the indicated voltage is the product of coil current by total resistance between the instrument terminals.

In a permanent-magnet moving-coil instrument, the direction of the torque reverses with the direction of current in the moving coil. Therefore, this arrangement cannot be used for alternating-current indication. An arrangement is required for which the direction of torque is independent of current direction. A number of such arrangements are possible, and a variety of types of ac ammeters and voltmeters are used.

(1) The *rectifier* instrument makes use of four semiconductor rectifier elements arranged in a square with the input across one diagonal and a permanent-magnet moving-coil instrument connected across the other diagonal, the rectifier elements being arranged with their direction of conduction such that current in the permanent-magnet moving-coil instrument is in the same direction for either polarity at the input terminals. This arrangement can be used either for a voltmeter or for a low-range current meter (a milliammeter), but its use for a high-range current meter (ammeter) is generally impractical. The *average* value of current or voltage over a half cycle of the alternating current is indicated. Since usually one is concerned with the effective (rms) value of current or voltage, the scale is marked in terms of the rms quantity for a sine-wave input, and wave-form errors are present for a non-sinusoidal input. Use of this type of instrument is restricted to relatively low frequencies, such as those used for transmitting power or those in the low audio-frequency range.

(2) *Thermocouple* instruments utilize the heating effect of an electric current. A fine wire or thin-walled tube is heated by the current to be measured; a thermocouple is attached to the heater element, and the temperature rise produces an emf whose value is indicated on a low-range permanent-magnet moving-coil millivolt-meter. Since the rate of heat production (and the consequent temperature rise in the heater element) is proportional to the square of the current, the indication is of *effective* (rms) value and there is no wave-form error. This type of instrument may be used for current measurement (milliammeters and ammeters) from dc to

the rf range (with some constructions to 200 megahertz or more) without serious frequency errors. As a voltmeter, the use of this instrument is usually restricted to audio frequencies but, with multipliers of special design having low distributed capacitance, the useful range of thermocouple voltmeters can be extended upwards to a megahertz or more.

(3) *Electronic* instruments are used as voltmeters over a wide frequency range, extending upwards in some instances to several hundred megahertz. A variety of circuit arrangements is used. In one common arrangement, the voltage to be measured is rectified, reduced to an appropriate level by means of an attenuator, and impressed on the grid of a vacuum tube to control plate current. The magnitude of the plate current is a function of the grid voltage and is read on a dc milliammeter whose scale is marked directly in volts. In this instance, the response is to the peak value of the impressed alternating voltage, although the scale is generally marked in terms of rms volts for a sine-wave input. Thus, a substantial wave-form error may be present if the impressed voltage is not sinusoidal. In other circuit arrangements, peak, average or even rms values may be directly indicated, and it is important to know the response law of the instrument so that appropriate allowance may be made for wave-form errors if the response is not truly rms. Vacuum-tube voltmeters form an important class of instruments because of their wide frequency range and because, generally, their input impedance is quite high. In many electronic voltmeter circuits the power required for operation and indication is supplied from an auxiliary source, and negligible power is taken from the circuit whose voltage is measured.

(4) In *moving-iron* instruments, a soft-iron piece forms the moving element. It is immersed in the field of a coil that carries the current to be measured, and its motion in the field is such as to increase the inductance of the system with increasing coil current. Since the energy stored in the magnetic field can be written $E = \frac{1}{2} I^2 L$ where L is the inductance of the system, its derivative—the torque—is $T = \partial E / \partial \theta = \frac{1}{2} I^2 \ \partial L / \partial \theta$, and the system's response is proportional to I^2; the instrument indicates rms (effective) current or voltage. By suitably shaping and arranging fixed and movable irons in the field of the coil, the instrument scale can be made very nearly linear over as much as 80 per cent of its range. Alternatively, the upper range of the scale can be greatly compressed, and a small portion of the total range can be expanded to cover much of the scale. The latter arrangement is particularly appropriate in a voltmeter that is used to monitor a voltage which is nearly constant most of the time, e.g., a line voltage.

(5) *Electrodynamic* ammeters and voltmeters have both a fixed and a moving-coil system, each of which carries the current to be measured or a fraction of it. The interaction of their fields produces a torque proportional to the square of

the current if the coils are connected in series (in a voltmeter), or proportional to the product of the fixed and moving-coil currents in a parallel arrangement (in an ammeter). Thus the scale indication is of rms (effective) voltage or current as in the moving-iron instrument. Here, however, eddy-current errors are much less, and electrodynamic instruments are generally useful over an extended range of power- and low audio-frequencies. In addition, the dc response can be substantially error-free, and electrodynamic instruments are used extensively as ac-dc transfer standards to determine the ac performance of other instruments which cannot be calibrated reliably on dc.

This transfer function is an important one, since the basic standards of resistance and emf, and the potentiometer techniques for accurately measuring current and voltage, are available only on direct current. This function of electrodynamic instruments—ac-dc transfer standards—is generally confined to frequencies below a kilohertz. Over a more extended frequency range—to 20 kilohertz or more—thermocouple elements with appropriate shunts and series resistors are used as current and voltage transfer standards. With special multipliers, thermoelements can be used to extend ac-dc voltage transfer measurements to frequencies into the megahertz region.

Electrodynamic instruments are also used as wattmeters to measure power at low frequencies, generally below 1 kilohertz. For this purpose, the moving coil with an appropriate series resistance is connected across the supply lines as the voltage circuit of the wattmeter. The fixed coils are connected to carry the load current. The instrument torque is proportional to the product of the currents in the fixed and moving-coil systems at any instant, and is therefore proportional to the instantaneous product of line voltage and load current. The time integral of this product over a cycle (divided by the period) is the average power in the load, and since the moving system cannot follow variations within so short a time interval, it takes up a position that indicates average power—in effect, it performs the required integration. Thermoelement arrangements have been used to a limited extent in some laboratories to measure power through the audio-frequency range, but such instruments are not available commercially. In the rf and microwave regions, the precise measurement of power is difficult. Arrangements are available in which the power output of a circuit is absorbed in a calorimeter or bolometer, and its magnitude indicated by temperature rise, resistance change, or voltage developed across a fixed resistance.

Digital voltmeters convert a direct voltage input to a digital output, which may either be displayed in a numeric readout or further processed, for example by a computer. With an appropriate signal conditioner ahead of the voltmeter input, the system can be used for a variety of measurements, direct or alternating current, alternating voltage, resistance, ratio,

and even nonelectrical quantities from which electrical signals can be generated, such as temperature, pressure, etc. Basically the input signal is compared to an internally generated reference voltage, and the accuracy of the system is always limited by this internal reference as well as by critical network components in the voltmeter and the signal conditioner. There are a number of ways in which the input signal may be processed. It may be served or approached by successive approximations as in an automatic self-balancing potentiometer; the reference voltage may be used to generate a ramp function that may open a counting gate when the ramp voltage equals the input signal and close the gate when the ramp voltage is zero, resulting in a voltage-to-time conversion; or, in a dual-slope instrument, the input signal may be made to charge a capacitor at a constant rate, which is then discharged at a linear rate by the reference voltage, the discharge being gated for a voltage-to-time conversion. Reference voltage sources are available with five-place accuracy, and digital voltmeters may have advantages in accuracy, resolution, and speed of response over analog instruments. However, in the measurement of ac quantities, those signal conditioners which present average or peak rather than rms values to the instrument input, are subject to the same waveform errors as the similar analog instrument.

The range of current, voltage or power that can be measured directly with indicating instruments is practically limited to a few amperes, or a few hundred volts or watts. *Instrument transformers* are used at power frequencies to extend the range of measurement capability almost indefinitely. For example, *current* transformers rated at 10 000 amperes are used in some installations, as are *voltage* transformers rated at 350 000 volts. Instrument transformers, consisting of a primary and a secondary winding coupled by a magnetic core, are designed specifically to accurately reproduce the primary current (or voltage) on a reduced scale in the secondary circuit. They are quite different from power transformers in details of design and operation, although their basic operating principle is the same. The usual *current* transformer, designed for use with a 5-ampere ammeter, or to supply the current circuit of a wattmeter or watt hour meter, is capable of delivering only a few watts to these instrument circuits, and generally operates under nearly short-circuit conditions with its magnetic circuit at very low flux density. The usual *voltage* transformer, designed for use with a 120-volt voltmeter, or to supply the voltage circuit of a wattmeter or watt-hour meter, also generally has a relatively low power rating and operates under nearly open-circuit conditions with its magnetic circuit approaching saturation. Instrument transformers of good design can be expected to have errors of only a few hundredths or at most tenths of a per cent when operated within their design limits.

The *current comparator* is a recently developed means of comparing two currents by a balance of their current-linkages with a common core. It has been incorporated into a number of very precise measurement networks capable of a ppm or better resolution. Applications include the following: networks for determining the ratio and quadrature errors of instrument transformers; bridges for the evaluation of high-voltage power cables and energy-storage capacitors; (in d-c versions) potentiometers; and bridges for the comparison of resistance standards or the evaluation of current-carrying shunts. In addition to the windings whose ampere-turns are to be compared, the common core is linked by a detection winding to determine when no magnetic flux is present in the core (i.e., when ampere-turn balance is achieved), and generally by an auxiliary winding into which a current can be injected to compensate the difference in ampere-turns between the main windings. It must be protected from external fields by a magnetic shield. The comparator differs from a transformer in that, at balance, no flux is present in the core, so that no energy is transferred from one winding to another and no power is required for core excitation. Thus, the comparator is free from the principal errors associated with instrument transformers. The advantage of incorporating a current comparator, as a ratio component, into a bridge or potentiometer is that its ratio depends solely on the arrangement of core and windings. Thus the ratio is a question of geometry only, and is therefore stable and independent of ambient conditions and of drift with time, which can affect the value of a resistance ratio.

The *induction watthourmeter*, for the measurement of electrical energy, is probably the most familiar and widely used of all electrical instruments. More than 8×10^7 of them are in continuous use to meter the electrical energy consumed in the United States, representing revenue to the power companies of the nation approaching 25 billions of dollars in 1971. The essential features of an induction watthourmeter are indicated schematically in Fig. 1. The voltage winding has many turns of fine wire and carries a current that is almost in quadrature with the line voltage; special lag arrangements are used to ensure that the magnetic field of the voltage pole V lags the line voltage by precisely

90°. The current coils (a few turns of coarse wire) carry the current of the load being measured, and the field of the current poles C is in phase with the load current. The eddy currents produced in the disk by the alternating field from the current poles are in quadrature with this field and hence have a component in phase with the field from the voltage pole, corresponding to the in-phase (or power) component of the load current. The reaction between this component of the current-pole-induced eddy currents in the disk and the field from the voltage pole produces a driving torque on the disk. Similarly, the eddy currents in the disk, induced by the voltage pole, are in phase with the field associated with the power component of the load current in the current poles; and again a driving torque results which is proportional to the power through the meter. A braking torque proportional to disk speed results from interaction of the brake-magnet field with the eddy currents it produces in the moving disk. As a result, the disk speed is proportional to load power; and the total number of disk revolutions (read from a counter geared to the disk) is a measure of the total energy consumed by the load.

FOREST K. HARRIS

References

"Precision Measurement and Calibration (Selected NBS Papers on Electricity–Low Frequency)," National Bureau of Standards Special Publication 300, Vol. 3 (1968), U.S. Govt. Printing Office, Washington, D.C.

"The International System of Units (SI)," National Bureau of Standards Special Publication 330 (1971), U.S. Govt. Printing Office, Washington, D.C.

Drysdale, C. V., Jolley, A. C., and Tagg, G. F., "Electrical Measuring Instruments," New York, Wiley, 1952.

Stout, M. B., "Basic Electrical Measurements," Englewood Cliffs, N.J., Prentice-Hall, 1960.

Harris, F. K., "Electrical Measurements," New York, Wiley, 1952.

Hague, B., "Alternating Current Bridge Methods," New York, Pitman, 1957.

Canfield, D. T., "Measurement of AC Energy," New York, McGraw-Hill, 1939.

Kusters, N. L., "The Precise Measurement of Current Ratios," *IEEE Trans.*, I and M13, 197–209 (1964).

Harris, F. K., Fowler, H. A., and Olsen, P. T., "Accurate Hamon-Pair Potentiometer for Josephson Frequency-to-Voltage Measurements," *Metrologia*, 6 134–142 (1970).

Driscoll, R. L., and Olsen, P. T., "Application of Nuclear Resonance to the Monitoring of Electrical Standards" (Precision Measurement and Fundamental Constants), National Brueau of Standards Special Publication 343, pp 117–121 (1971), U.S. Govt. Printing Office, Washington, D.C.

Thompson, A. M., "An Absolute Determination of Resistance Based on a Calculable Standard of Capacitance," *Metrologia*, Vol. 4 (January 1968).

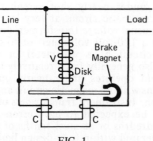

FIG. 1.

Field, B. F., *et al.*, "Volt Maintenance at NBS via 2e/h; A New Definition of the NBS Volt," *Metrologia*, Vol. 11 (October 1973).

Cross-references: ALTERNATING CURRENTS; ELECTRICITY; INDUCTANCE; SYMBOLS, UNITS, AND NOMENCLATURE.

ELECTRICITY

The history of electricity and magnetism goes back to ancient times. The Greeks knew that rubbed amber attracts small particles, while the lodestone was used as a magnetic compass for navigation by the Chinese in the eleventh century and possibly much earlier. Qualitative understanding of the phenomena began in a substantial way with Gilbert's great work "De Magnete," published in 1600. Quantitative study came with Franklin's appreciation in 1747 of the law of conservation of electric charge, Priestley's formulation in 1767 of the inverse square law of force between electric charges, and Michell's similar discovery in 1750 for magnetism. The nineteenth century saw the full development of the "classical" account of electromagnetism, notable discoveries being the magnetic effect of an electric current (Oersted, 1820) the force between currents (Ampère, 1820), the relation between potential difference and current for a metal (Ohm, 1826), electromagnetic induction (Faraday, 1831), and electromagnetic waves (Maxwell, 1861–1862, and Hertz, 1886). At the end of the century came the discovery of the electron (J. J. Thomson, 1897) and the beginning of modern ideas about the nature of electricity. We now know that an isolated atom consists of a small nucleus, itself composed of protons and neutrons, surrounded by a cloud of electrons. The proton and the electron are the ultimate stable particles of electricity. Their charges are equal and opposite, the proton being regarded, by convention, as positive. A normal atom with its full complement of electrons is thus uncharged.

Electrostatics It is easy to detach electrons from atoms. For instance, by rubbing a piece of plastic with woollen cloth, electrons are removed from one substance, which is then positively charged to the other, which then has an excess of electrons and is negatively charged. (To produce marked effects, only one electron need be removed for every hundred thousand *surface* atoms.) These separated charges give rise to electrostatic effects. Charges of the same kind repel one another, unlike charges attract each other. During dry (frosty) weather, pulling off one garment over another can give small sparks visible in the dark; the huge electric fields that build up during a thunderstorm are electrostatic in origin. In a television tube the electrons that strike the viewing screen have been accelerated by an electrostatic field. Elec-

trons can be separated from atoms by other means, e.g., by chemical action in a battery, but unless many batteries are used the electrostatic effects, though present, are not obvious.

Since positive and negative charges attract, any such charges tend to move towards and neutralize one another. The movement of charges, usually the electrons, is called an electric current and gives rise to various effects; heat is produced and a magnetic field is found near the current.

By using batteries the current can be maintained in a wire and it can be detected by the deflection of a pivoted magnet placed near the wire. Usually the conductors of such currents are metals, but current can flow through some liquids (electrolytes), such as an aqueous solution of common salt, and through rarefied gases as in neon advertising signs. It can flow through *any* substance if the electrical stresses are large enough to disrupt the atoms of the substance— as happens when a lightning bolt passes through air, which is normally a very good insulator.

Two electric currents in adjacent wires exert a force upon one another, an effect we can think of as the force on one current due to the magnetic field of the other. This force can be greatly augmented by the presence of magnetic materials such as iron, as in electromagnets and electric motors.

If a magnetic field near a closed loop of wire is changed either by moving the wire or the field, or by altering the strength of the field, a current will flow in the wire; an *electromotive force* has been produced causing the electrons in the wire to move. This phenomenon, *electromagnetic induction*, is utilized in dynamos and alternators.

If a current of electrons in a wire moves backwards and forwards sufficiently rapidly, energy is radiated as electromagnetic (radio) waves. If these waves fall on another wire, currents can be detected in it. By controlling the strength of the original current, we can transmit sound and pictures by radio and television.

Electricity is an exact branch of science and is governed by the laws given below. Between two positively charged bodies (or two negatively charged ones) there is a repulsive force; between positively and negatively charged ones, an attractive force. The nature of these forces is subsumed in Coulomb's law*

$$\mathbf{F} = \frac{1}{4\pi\epsilon_0} \frac{Q_1 Q_2}{r^2} \mathbf{r}_1 \qquad (1)$$

where $\mathbf{F}$ is the force between two charges Q_1 and Q_2 carried on bodies very small compared with their separation r (i.e., between "point" charges); $\mathbf{r}_1$ is a unit vector along the line joining Q_1 and Q_2, and indicates that the force is directed along that line; and ϵ_0 is a constant

---

*We consider only systems which do not include dielectrics. For such see DIELECTRIC THEORY.

that depends on the units used and takes the value $1/(36\pi \times 10^9)$ for the SI system of units. The forces between extended distributions of charge can be calculated by adding together (vectorially) the forces between the very small elements of charge into which the charge distributions can be imagined to be divided.

We can speak of the *electric field* of force **E** at a point due to a system of charges and define it by means of the force **F** on a *small* test charge q placed at the point:

$$\mathbf{E} = \mathbf{F}/q \tag{2}$$

For a point charge Q, the field at a distance r from it is then

$$\mathbf{E} = Q\mathbf{r}_1/4\pi\epsilon_0 r^2 \tag{2a}$$

If we slowly move a small charge q a small distance $d\mathbf{x}$ in a field **E**, the electric system does work *against* the force **F** holding the small charge in place, so the work done *on* the electrical system *by* the force is

$$dW = -\mathbf{F} \cdot d\mathbf{x} = -q\mathbf{E} \cdot d\mathbf{x} \tag{3}$$

We define *electric potential difference* dV by

$$dV = dW/q = -\mathbf{E} \cdot d\mathbf{x} \tag{4}$$

The *electric flux* through a small geometrical (not necessarily material) surface of size dA is $\mathbf{E} \cdot d\mathbf{A}$ where $d\mathbf{A}$ is the vector normal to the surface. Then from equation (2a) for a surface A enclosing a charge Q, we have

$$\int_A \epsilon_0 \mathbf{E} \cdot d\mathbf{A} = \int_Q \int_A \frac{dQ\mathbf{r}_1 \cdot d\mathbf{A}}{4\pi r^2}$$

$$= \frac{1}{4\pi}\int_Q \int_\omega dQ\, d\omega = Q \tag{5}$$

where $d\omega = \mathbf{r}_1 \cdot d\mathbf{A}/r^2$ is the solid angle subtended by dA at the element of charge dQ.

This is Gauss' theorem, one often of great assistance in solving electrostatic problems, for which the most difficult part can be to obtain the distribution of the charge on a system of conductors (which cannot sustain an electric field unless an emf is present or energy continuously supplied). For example, consider two parallel conducting plates of area S, a small distance t apart. Then ignoring edge effects, by symmetry **E** is constant between the plates and perpendicular to them. Applying Gauss' theorem to a small cylinder with one end of area a in the positively charged plate (so for this end $\mathbf{E} = 0$) and the other between the plates, we have, by Gauss' theorem, since **E** is parallel to the sides (and so $\mathbf{E} \cdot d\mathbf{A}$ zero for the sides),

$$\int \epsilon_0 \mathbf{E} \cdot d\mathbf{A} = \epsilon_0 Ea = Qa/S.$$

Then from Eq. (4) the potential difference between the plates is $V = Et = Qt/\epsilon_0 S$ and so the CAPACITANCE of the plates, defined as $C = Q/V$, is $\epsilon_0 S/t$.

The laws of electrostatics underly many phenomena such as thunderstorms and the behavior of electrons in radio and cathode-ray tubes.

Current Electricity If two bodies at different potentials are connected by a conductor, such as a metal wire in which there are free electrons, the electrons in the wire drift under the influence of the electric field. Such movement of electrical charges gives rise to further phenomena and we speak of an *electric current*. This we can define quantitatively as the rate at which charge is passing:

$$I = dQ/dt \tag{6}$$

The current may be one of electrons only, as in a metal, in semiconductors or in electron tubes; of positive nuclei, as in an isotope-separator; or of both positive and negative charges, as in the conduction by ions (atoms that have gained or lost an electron) in liquids or in gaseous electrical discharges. (see CONDUCTIVITY, ELECTRICAL; ELECTRIC DISCHARGES IN GASES). Note that *electrons* flowing in the *positive* direction give rise, by our convention of signs, to a *negative* current and that in a metal, semiconductor, or conducting liquid, the velocity at which the electrons or ions drift is quite slow, less than 1 cm/sec even for current densities in a metal as high as 10^4 amperes/cm^2. In vacuum devices, such as cathode-ray tubes, the speed of the electrons approaches that of light.

If a wire joins two electrostatic charges, the current lasts for a short time only, but it may be maintained by means of some source of energy, such as a battery, a generator, a thermocouple, or a solar photoelectric cell.

When a current I flows under the influence of a potential difference V, the moving charges—electrons in metals, ions in solutions—are impeded by collision with the atoms in the conducting metal or liquid. The charges give up to the atoms the energy they acquired as they moved in the electric field, and electrical power is converted into other forms,—for instance, into heat in the case of a metal wire. From Eqs. (4) and (6), this power P is given by

$$P = \frac{dW}{dt} = \frac{d(VQ)}{dt} = V\frac{dQ}{dt} = VI \tag{7}$$

A metal wire at constant temperature (but not all conductors) obeys Ohm's law: that is, $V = RI$, where R is a constant for the wire known as its resistance (in ohms if V and I are in volts and amperes). In this case

$$P = RI^2 = V^2/R \tag{8}$$

and this is the rate at which heat is generated. The heat in most forms of electric heaters (including filament lamps) is generated in this way. (For an explanation of how current flows in more complicated circuits see "CIRCUITRY.")

Accompanying a current I there is always a magnetic field $\mathbf{H}$ which shows itself by the force exerted between the current-carrying conductor and a magnet or another electric current. At a point P a distance a from a long, thin, straight wire carrying current I, the field $\mathbf{H}$ is perpendicular to both the wire and the radius from the wire to P, so that the "lines of force" are circles concentric with the wire and perpendicular to it. The field is of magnitude

$$H = I/2\pi a \qquad (9)$$

For a long cylindrical coil, $H = nI$, where n is the number of turns per unit length. In general, we have the relation that

$$\oint \mathbf{H} \cdot d\mathbf{s} = NI \qquad (10)$$

where N is the total number of turns, each carrying current I, enclosed by the path s. This holds true whether or not the path traverses magnetic materials. Associated with the field $\mathbf{H}$, there is a magnetic flux density $\mathbf{B}$,

$$\mathbf{B} = \mu_0\mu_r\mathbf{H} \qquad (11)$$

where μ_0 is a constant of value $4\pi \times 10^{-7}$ in SI units and μ_r is the relative permeability. μ_r is not necessarily a constant, but it has the value 1 for free space and is of the order of 1000 for magnetic materials.

The magnetic flux density satisfies Gauss' theorem [see Eq. (5)], but because magnetic poles cannot be isolated in the way electric charges can be, the theorem takes the form

$$\int_A \mathbf{B} \cdot d\mathbf{A} = 0 \qquad (12)$$

where the integral is taken over the geometrical surface A. Equations (10), (11) and (12) are sufficient, in principle, for the calculation of the magnetic field of any steady current.

The force between a current I, traversing a short length $d\mathbf{l}$ in a magnetic field of flux density $\mathbf{B}$, and the field is

$$I\,d\mathbf{l} \times \mathbf{B} \qquad (13)$$

so for a wire of length l in a field perpendicular to it, the force is IlB perpendicular to both wire and field. The force between two long parallel wires in free space, each carrying a current I and distance a apart, is, from Eqs. (9) and (13),

$$F = 2 \times 10^{-7}I^2/a \text{ newtons/m} \qquad (14)$$

For currents in the same direction it is an attraction. This equation defines the SI unit of current though that unit is *established* by means of the larger force between coils carrying a common current I, for which $F = KI^2$, where K is a factor that can be calculated accurately from the geometry of the coils. The force between a current-carrying coil and magnetic material, or another current, is the basis of many electrical instruments such as ammeters, of electric motors and of other electromechanical devices.

If we think of the current as consisting of electrons, or ions, of charge Q, moving with velocity $\mathbf{v}$ along a wire or in a vacuum, these experience a force in a magnetic field $\mathbf{B}$ given by

$$F = Q\mathbf{v} \times \mathbf{B} \qquad (15)$$

a relation that is required for the explanation of the behavior of electrons in a magnetic electron microscope, of ions in a mass spectrometer, and of cosmic rays in the earth's magnetic field. Further, if a wire, with its electrons free except in so far as they are confined to the wire, and a magnetic field $\mathbf{B}$ are caused to move relative to one another with velocity $\mathbf{v}$, by virtue of Eq. (15) the electrons will suffer a force *along* the wire; an INDUCED ELECTROMOTIVE FORCE is set up. If the ends of the wire are connected by a conductor, a current will flow. This is the phenomenon of *electromagnetic induction* and the basis of equipment such as transformers and electric generators.

When an electric current changes rapidly, electromagnetic waves are radiated. If the current is an alternating one, the power radiated, for a current of given size, increases as the square of the frequency. Such waves, at frequencies of 100 kHz or more, are the basis of radio communication.

Though electrostatic phenomena are important—in radio tubes, for instance—current electricity is vital in the modern world. Small currents can be maintained by batteries and secondary cells, but the very large amounts of power used in a modern industrial state must be obtained mainly by electromagnetic machinery (see ELECTRIC POWER GENERATION), usually as ALTERNATING CURRENTS.

E. S. SHIRE

References

Shire, E. S., "Classical Electricity and Magnetism," Cambridge, Cambridge University Press, 1960.

Panofsky, W. K. H. and Phillips, M., "Classical Electricity and Magnetism," 2nd Ed., 1962 Adison-Wesley, Reading, Mass.

Gibson, W. M., "Basic Electricity," London, Penguin Books, 1969.

Lewis, J. L., and Heafford, P. E., "Electric Currents," London, Longman, 1969.

Shire, E. S., "Rutherford and the Nuclear Atom," London, Longman, 1972.

Lewis, J. L., "Electrons and Atoms," London, Longman, 1971.

Cross-references: CAPACITANCE; CIRCUITRY; CONDUCTIVITY, ELECTRICAL; DIELECTRIC THEORY; ELECTRIC POWER GENERATION; ELECTRICAL DISCHARGES IN GASES; ELECTRON; INDUCED ELECTROMOTIVE FORCE; INDUCTANCE; POTENTIAL; STATIC ELECTRICITY.

ELECTROACOUSTICS

Introduction Electroacoustics is concerned with the principles (transduction processes) and devices (transducers) by which electrical energy may be converted into acoustic energy and vice versa. Consider the familiar electrodynamic transducer. A periodic electric current passing through a coil interacts with a steady radial magnetic flux causing the coil to vibrate. The coil in turn drives a diaphragm which radiates sound waves from one side. (The other side is usually enclosed to avoid cancellation of the acoustic output.) The entire process is reversible since sound waves striking the diaphragm set up a periodic variation in air pressure adjacent to the diaphragm causing it to vibrate. As the moving coil cuts the magnetic flux, an emf is generated which causes a current to flow when a load is connected to the coil terminals.

Many, but not all, types of transducer are similarly reversible. A reversible transducer may be made to perform sending and receiving functions successively in such a manner that an absolute sensitivity may be determined (reciprocity calibration).

The electrodynamic transducer may further be classified as passive since all of the energy appearing in the acoustic load is derived from the electrical input energy, and linear in the sense that there is a substantially linear relationship between the input and output variables (electric current and acoustic pressure in this case).

Transduction Processes *Irreversible Transducers.* These depend on a variety of special effects of which the best known is (a) the variation of surface-contact electrical resistance with pressure (carbon microphone). Other effects are (b) variation of bulk resistance with elastic strain (piezoresistance), (c) variation of transistor parameters with strain, (d) cooling effect of periodic air movement (hotwire microphone), (e) pressure wave generated by an electrical spark, (f) dependence of air pressure on level of corona discharge (ionophone).

Reversible Transducers. An important class of reversible transducer depends on relative movement of suitable components linked by an electric or magnetic field traversing a gap. Examples are (a) the electrodynamic transducer already described; (b) electrostatic, depending on the relative movement of charged condenser plates; (c) magnetic or variable reluctance, depending on relative movement of magnetic poles in a magnetic circuit linked with a fixed coil.

Other reversible transducers are dependent on dimensional changes connected with the state of magnetic or electric polarization of certain crystalline materials (piezomagnetism and piezoelectricity). Since strain may be longitudinal or shear and since both strain and polarization are directional quantities, many possible relationships between strain and polarization exist. The behavior of an X-cut quartz disk may serve as an illustration. When such a disk is axially compressed, electric charges appear on the plane surfaces. Conversely, if a potential difference is established between the two surfaces, contraction or expansion occurs depending on the direction of the electric field. Other important single-crystal piezoelectric materials are ammonium dihydrogen phosphate (ADP) and Rochelle salt. During the past decade, polycrystalline ceramic materials based on barium titanate and lead zirconate titanate have replaced single-crystal materials in many applications. These materials are ferroelectric, and when prepolarized, exhibit piezoelectric behavior.

Until recently (see below) only polycrystalline piezomagnetic materials had been used for transduction. Examples of these are the magnetostrictive metals and alloys such as nickel and permendur. Others are the ferrite ceramics [basic composition: $(NiO)(Fe_2O_3)$] which have such a high electrical resistivity that eddy current losses are negligible making lamination unnecessary.

Electromechanical Coupling Transducer performance is closely connected with the tightness of coupling between mechanical and electrical aspects. Consider a piezoelectric disk which is compressed by putting in mechanical energy W_m. The appearance of surface charges shows that electrical energy W_e is stored in the self-capacitance and is available when an external circuit is connected to suitable electrodes. The ratio $W_e/W_m = k^2$ sets a limit to the efficiency for a given bandwidth (frequency range). The value of k (electromechanical coupling coefficient) may reach 75 per cent for lead zirconate titanate.

Transducer Design Impedance matching is of primary importance in electroacoustics. It may be likened to the choice of gear ratio and wheel size in automobile design. Impedance matching is generally closely related to transducer parameters such as beam width of projected or received sound and frequency response, as well as efficiency. The many available matching techniques include (a) resonance, (b) horn systems (acoustic transformers), (c) lever systems (mechanical transformers). In the direct radiator electrodynamic loudspeaker, the diaphragm is made large enough to interact with the acoustic medium (air) and yet small enough

in relation to the sound wavelength (at low frequencies, at least) to ensure uniform projection of sound over a wide angle. In the condenser loudspeaker, a large transducer area compensates for the weakness of electrostatic forces. In the underwater sonar projector, slabs of piezoelectric ceramic may be sandwiched between metal plates to form a resonant device which radiates a narrow beam of sound with high efficiency over a narrow frequency range.

Recent Advances Discoveries in the solid-state field have led to many new electroacoustic materials, techinques, and devices.

Microwave acoustics is concerned with the use of acoustic waves in solids for signal storage, amplification, and processing in the frequency range above 50 MHz. A piezoelectric transducer thin enough to operate in the fundamental mode at several hundred MHz can be formed by evaporating a thin film of piezoelectric material such as Cds onto a suitable substrate or by forming a semiconductor *depletion layer* of the correct thickness. More recently, *magnetoelastic transducers* have been formed of materials such as yttrium iron garnet (YIG) which operate, for example, in the resonance mode of the ferromagnetic spin system and generate longitudinal acoustic waves.

A sound-transmitting bar and a pair of transducers provides a very compact *delay line*. Furthermore, the interaction of free charges with elastic waves in piezoelectric materials can provide acoustic amplification. This is achieved with a longitudinal electric field sufficient to establish a carrier drift velocity greater than the elastic wave velocity. *Traveling-wave amplifiers* with 40 dB gain and 10 per cent bandwidth at 1 GHz for a 1 mm transmission path have been built with semiconductors such as cadmium sulfide.

The *interdigital transducer* is an array of parallel conducting strips with $\lambda/2$ spacing deposited on a piezoelectric substrate such as lithium niobate which provides efficient excitation of acoustic surface waves (e.g., Rayleigh waves). Surface waves generated in this fashion can be guided and selectively delayed by grooves and metallic film boundaries, and can be coupled in and out at many points along the path. Surface waves can also be amplified by drifting charge carriers in the substrate or in a semiconductor layer above the wave-carrying surface. These properties are highly compatible with integrated circuit techniques.

The newly developed *electret microphone* uses an electrostatic transducer in which a polarizing field is maintained by a quasi-permanent charge layer embedded in a thin plastic film. Recently, fluoroethylene propylene and other plastic materials have been prepared with estimated charge storage half-lives of 100 years or more. The electret transducer, which has a very high electrical impedance, is usually combined with an integrated field effect transistor (FET) amplifier. Complex array properties can

readily be built into electret microphones. Two examples are the second-order-gradient "toroidal" microphone proposed for conference use and a 200×200 square array proposed for acoustic holography.

The *parametric acoustic array* has provided a means of obtaining a narrow beam of low-frequency underwater sound using a small primary transducer. Due to the non-linearity of the equations of fluid motion, a pair of highly collimated high-frequency sound beams can be made to act as a very large end-fire array launching a directional sound beam at a comparatively low difference frequency. Since the liquid medium rapidly absorbs the primary beams, the array is "tapered."

Intense coherent sound waves can be generated at several GHz by the electrostrictive processes which accompany the passage of intense laser beams through liquids and solids (*stimulated Brillouin scattering*).

E. A. G. SHAW

References

Hunt, F. V., "Electro-acoustics," Cambridge, Harvard University Press, and New York, John Wiley & Sons, Inc., 1954.

Beranek, L. L., "Acoustics," New York, McGraw-Hill Book Co., Inc., 1954.

Westervelt, P. J., "Parametric Acoustic Array," *J. Acoust. Soc. Amer.*, **35**, 535–537 (1963).

Ultrasonics Symposium: 1965, *Proc. IEEE*, **53**, 1290–1635 (1965). (See particularly: Jaffe, H., and Berlincourt, D. A., "Piezoelectric Transducer Materials," pp. 1372–1386; May, J. E., "Ultrasonic Traveling Wave Amplifier," pp. 1465–1487; Strauss, W., "Elastic and Mangetoelastic Waves in YIG," pp. 1485–1495).

Beecham, D., "Ultrasonic Transducers for Frequencies above 50 MHz," Ultrasonics, **5**, 19–28 (1967).

Sessler, G. M., and West, J. E., "Foil Electrets and Their Use in Condenser Microphones," *J. Electrochem. Soc.*, **115**, 836–841 (1968).

Special Issue on Microwave Acoustics, *IEEE Transactions on Microwave Theory and Techniques*, MTT **17**, 798–1052 (1969). (See particularly: Stern, E., "Microsound Components, Circuits and Applications," pp. 835–844; Lakin, K. M., and Shaw, H. J., "Surface Wave Delay Line Amplifiers," pp. 912–920, Reeder, J. M., and Winslow, D. K. "Microwave Acoustic Transducers," pp. 927–941).

Taylor, R. G. F., and Pointon, A. J. "Microwave Ultrasonics," *Contemporary Physics*, **10**, 159–178 (1969).

Gayford, M. L., "Electroacoustics: Microphones, Earphones and Loudspeakers," London, Butterworth, 1970.

Reedyk, C. W., "Electret Transducers Applied to the Telephone," *IEEE Trans. on Audio and Electroacoustics*, AU-**19**, 1–5 (1971).

Mason, W. P., "Use of Solid-State Transducers in Communications," *IEEE Transactions on Audio and Electroacoustics*, AU-**19**, 13–18 (1971).

Sessler, G. M., and West, J. E., "Directional Transducers," *IEEE Transactions on Audio and Electroacoustics*, AU-19, 19–23 (1971).

Cross-references: ACOUSTICS, CRYSTALLOGRAPHY, DIELECTRIC THEORY, LASER, MAGNETISM, RESONANCE, SOLID-STATE PHYSICS, ULTRASONICS.

ELECTROCHEMISTRY

Electrochemistry is that branch of science which deals with the interconversion of chemical and electrical energies, i.e., with chemical changes produced by electricity as in electrolysis or with the production of electricity by chemical action as in electric cells or batteries. The science of electrochemistry began about the turn of the eighteenth century. In 1796 Alessandro Volta observed that an electric current was produced if unlike metals separated by paper or hide moistened with water or a salt solution were brought into contact. Volta used the sensation of pain to detect the electric current. His observation was similar to that observed ten years earlier by Luigi Galvani who noted that a frog's leg could be made to twitch if copper and iron, attached respectively to a nerve and a muscle, were brought into contact.

In his original design Volta stacked couples of unlike metals one upon another in order to increase the intensity of the current. This arrangement became known as the "voltaic pile." He studied many metallic combinations and was able to arrange the metals in an "electromotive series" in which each metal was positive when connected to the one below it in the series. Volta's pile was the precursor of modern batteries (see BATTERIES).

In 1800 William Nicholson and Anthony Carlisle decomposed water into hydrogen and oxygen by an electric current supplied by a voltaic pile. Whereas Volta had produced electricity from chemical action these experimenters reversed the process and utilized electricity to produce chemical changes. In 1807 Sir Humphry Davy discovered two new elements, potassium and sodium, by the electrolysis of the respective solid hydroxides, utilizing a voltaic pile as the source of electric power. These electrolytic processes were the forerunners of the many industrial electrolytic processes used today to obtain aluminum, chlorine, hydrogen, or oxygen, for example, or in the electroplating of metals such as silver or chromium.

Since in the interconversion of electrical and chemical energies, electrical energy flows to or from the system in which chemical changes take place, it is essential that the system be, in large part, conducting or consist of electrical conductors. These are of two general types—electronic and electrolytic—though some materials exhibit both types of conduction. Metals are the most common electronic conductors. Typical electrolytic conductors are molten salts and solutions of acids, bases, and salts.

A current of electricity in an electronic conductor is due to a stream of electrons, particles of subatomic size, and the current causes no net transfer of matter. The flow is, therefore, in a direction contrary to what is conventionally known as the "direction of the current." In electrolytic conductors, the carriers are charged particles of atomic or molecular size called *ions*, and under a potential gradient, a transfer of matter occurs.

An electrolytic solution contains an equivalent quantity of positively and negatively charged ions whereby electroneutrality prevails. Under a potential gradient, the positive and negative ions move in opposite directions with their own characteristic velocities and each accordingly carries a different fraction of the total current through any one solution. Each fraction is referred to as the ionic transference number. Furthermore, the velocity increases with temperature causing a corresponding increase in electrolytic conductivity. This characteristic is opposite to that observed for most electronic conductors which show less conductivity as their temperature is increased.

The concept that charged particles are responsible for the transport of electric charges through electrolytic solutions was accepted early in the history of electrochemistry. The existence of ions was first postulated by Michael Faraday in 1834; he called negative ions "anions" and positive ones "cations." In 1853, Hittorf showed that ions move with different velocities and exist as separate entities and not momentarily as believed by Faraday. In 1887, Svante Arrhenius postulated that solute molecules dissociated spontaneously into *free ions* having no influence on each other. However, it is known that ions are subject to coulombic forces, and only at infinite dilution do ions behave ideally, i.e., independently of other ions in the solution. Ionization is influenced by the nature of the solvent and solute, the ion size, and solute-solvent interaction. The dielectric constant and viscosity of the solvent play dominant roles in conductivity. The higher the dielectric constant, the less are the electrostatic forces between ions and the greater is the conductivity. The higher the viscosity of the solvent, the greater are the frictional forces between ions and solvent molecules and the lower is the electrolytic conductivity.

In 1923 Debye and Hückel presented a theory which took into account the effect of coulombic forces between ions. They introduced the concept of the ion atmosphere, or continuous charge distribution, which is a continuous function of r, the radial distance from a central or reference ion rather than a discrete or discontinuous charge distribution. The ion atmosphere acts electrostatically somewhat like a sphere of charge $-\epsilon$ at some average distance from a central or reference ion of charge $+\epsilon$, with the value of the average distance approximating that of

the ionic radii of ionic crystals. This interionic attraction leads to two effects on the electrolytic conductivity. Under a potential gradient, an ion moves in a certain direction. However, the ion cloud, being of opposite sign will tend to move in the opposite direction, and because of its attraction for the central ion, will have a retarding effect on the ion velocity and thereby lead to a lowering in the electrolytic conductivity. On the other hand, the central ion will tend to pull the ion cloud with it to a new location. The ion atmosphere will adjust to its new location in time, but not instantaneously, and the delay results in a dissymmetry in the potential field around the ion. This also causes a lowering in the conductance of the solution. These effects become more pronounced as the concentration of the solution is increased; for dilute solutions, below about 0.1 molal, the equivalent conductance decreases with the square root of the concentration. For more concentrated solutions, the relation between conductivity and concentration is much more complex and depends more specifically on individual solute properties.

Interionic attraction in dilute solutions also leads to an effective ionic concentration or activity which is less than the stoichiometric value. The *activity* of an ion species is its thermodynamic concentration, i.e., the ion concentration corrected for the deviation from ideal behavior. For dilute solutions the activity of ions is less than one, for concentrated solutions it may be greater than one. It is the ionic activity that is used in expressing the variation of electrode potentials, and other electrochemical phenomena, with composition.

When electricity passes through a circuit consisting of both types of electrical conductors, a chemical reaction always occurs at their interface. These reactions are electrochemical. When electrons flow from the electrolytic conductor, oxidation occurs at the interface while reduction occurs if electrons flow in the opposite direction. These electronic-electrolytic interfaces are referred to as *electrodes*; those at which oxidation occurs are known as *anodes* and those at which reduction occurs, as *cathodes*. An anode is also defined as that electrode by which "conventional" current enters an electrolytic solution, a cathode as that electrode by which "conventional" current leaves. Positive ions, for example, ions of hydrogen and the metals, are called *cations* while negative ions, for example, acid radicals and ions of nonmetals are called *anions*.

In 1833, Michael Faraday enunciated two laws of electrolysis which give the relation between chemical changes and the product of the current and time, i.e., the total charge (coulombs) passed through a solution. These laws are: (1) the amount of chemical change, e.g., chemical decomposition, dissolution, deposition, oxidation, or reduction, produced by an electric current is directly proportional to the quantity of electricity passed through the solution; (2) the amounts of different substances decomposed, dissolved, deposited, oxidized, or reduced are proportional to their chemical equivalent weights. A chemical equivalent weight of an element or a radical is given by the atomic or molecular weight of the element or radical divided by its valence; the valence used depends on the electrochemical reaction involved. The electric charge on an ion is equal to the electronic charge or some integral multiple of it. Accordingly, a univalent negative ion has a charge equal in magnitude and of the same sign as a single electron, and its chemical equivalent weight is equal to its atomic weight, if an element, or to its molecular weight, if a radical. A trivalent ion has +3 or −3 electronic charges, depending on whether it is a positive or a negative trivalent ion. For trivalent ions, then, the equivalent weight would be equal to its atomic weight, if an element, or to its molecular weight, if a radical, divided by three.

The quantity of electricity required to produce a gram-equivalent weight of chemical change is known as the *faraday*. A faraday corresponds, then, to an *Avogadro number of charges*. The most accurate determination of the faraday has been made by a silver-perchloric acid coulometer in which the amount of silver electrolytically dissolved in an aqueous solution of perchloric acid is measured. This method gives 96487 coulombs (or ampere-seconds) per gram-equivalent for the faraday on the unified C^{12} scale of atomic weights.

The *electrochemical equivalent* or, preferably, the *coulomb equivalent* of an element or radical is that weight in grams which is equivalent to one coulomb of electricity and is given by the gram-equivalent weight divided by the faraday (96487 coulombs per gram-equivalent); for example, the electrochemical equivalent of silver is given by 107.870/96487 or 0.00111797 g/coulomb where 107.870 is the atomic weight of silver based on the unified C^{12} scale. The electrochemical equivalents of other elements may be calculated in like fashion.

In electrolysis and in any electric cell or battery, there is an electromotive force (emf) or voltage across the terminals. This emf is expressed in the practical unit, the volt, which is equal to the electromagnetic unit in the meter-kilogram-second system. In any one cell, the emf is the sum of the potentials of the two electrodes and of any liquid-junction potentials that may be present. Neither of the individual electrode potentials can be evaluated without reference to a chosen reference electrode of assigned value. For this purpose, the hydrogen electrode has been universally adopted and is arbitrarily assigned a zero potential for all temperatures when the hydrogen ion is at unit activity and the hydrogen gas is at atmospheric pressure. A hydrogen electrode consists of a stream of hydrogen gas bubbling over platinized platinum or gold foil and immersed in a solution containing

hydrogen ions; the electrochemical reaction is: $1/2H_2$ (gas) = H^+(solution) + ϵ, where ϵ represents the electron. The potential of the hydrogen electrode, E_H, as a function of hydrogen-ion concentration and hydrogen-gas pressure is given by

$$E_H = E_H^0 - (RT/nF) \ln (a_{H^+}/p_{H_2}^{1/2})$$

$$= E_H^0 - (RT/nF) \ln (c_{H^+}f_{H^+}/p_{H_2}^{1/2}).$$

where E_H^0 is the standard quantity assigned a value of zero, R is the gas constant, T the absolute temperature, n the number of equivalents, F the faraday, p_{H_2} the pressure of hydrogen, and a_{H^+}, c_{H^+} and f_{H^+}, respectively, the activity, concentration, and activity coefficient of hydrogen ions. When a_{H^+} and $p_{H_2}^{1/2}$ equal one, $E_H = E_H^0$. For very dilute solutions below 0.01 molal f_{H^+} may be taken as unity without appreciable error.

The standard potentials, E^0, of other electrodes are obtained by direct or indirect comparison with the hydrogen electrode. Values thus obtained at 25°C for some typical elements are listed in Table 1.

The reducing power of the elements decreases on going down the column. These values are for the ions at unit activity, and reversible or thermodynamic values as a function of metal or radical concentration are given by equations similar to the one above. For the general reaction: $M = M^{n+} + n\epsilon$, the potential is given by $E_M = E_M^0 - (RT/nF) \ln a_M^{n+}$.

In electrolysis, at very low current densities, the potentials of the electrodes approximate in magnitude their reversible values and deviate somewhat from these values because of an *IR* drop in the solution and possible concentration polarization (the concentration at the electrode surface may differ from that in the bulk of the solution). Also for high current densities, especially for the generation of gases such as hydrogen, oxygen or chlorine, the voltage required exceeds the reversible voltage; the excess voltage is known as overvoltage, or overpotential for a single electrode, and arises from energy barriers

at the electrode. Overpotential, in general, increases logarithmically with an increase in current density.

In addition to the above topics, it is frequently customary to include under electrochemistry: (1) processes for which the net reaction is physical transfer, e.g., concentration cells; (2) electrokinetic phenomena, e.g., electrophoresis, electroosmosis, streaming potential; (3) properties of electrolytic solutions if determined by electrochemical or other means, e.g., activity coefficients and hydrogen-ion concentration; (4) processes in which electrical energy is first converted to heat which in turn causes a chemical reaction to occur that would not do so spontaneously at ordinary temperature. The first three are frequently considered a portion of physical chemistry, and the last one is a part of electrothermics or electrometallurgy.

The passage of electricity through gases is sometimes included under electrochemistry. However, in electrical discharges in gases, the principles are entirely different from what they are in the electrolysis of electrolytic solutions. Whereas in the latter, ionic dissociation occurs spontaneously as a result of forces between solvent and solute and without the application of an external field, for gases relatively high voltages must be applied to accelerate the electrons from the electrode to a velocity at which they can ionize the gas molecules they strike. In this case, the resulting chemical reaction taking place between ions, free radicals, and molecules occurs in the gas phase and not at the electrodes as in the electrolysis of solutions. Studies of the electrical conduction of gases, accordingly, are generally considered under the physics of gases.

Electrochemistry finds wide application. In addition to industrial electrolytic processes, electroplating, and the manufacture and use of batteries already mentioned, the principles of electrochemistry are used in chemical analysis, e.g., polarography, and electrometric or conductometric titrations; in chemical synthesis, e.g., dyestuffs, fertilizers, plastics, insecticides; in biology and medicine, e.g., electrophoretic separation of proteins, membrane potentials; in metallurgy, e.g., corrosion prevention, electrore-

TABLE 1. SOME STANDARD ELECTRODE POTENTIALS AT 25°C

Electrode	Potential (V)	Electrode	Potential (V)
Li = Li$^+$ + ϵ	−3.045	Cu = Cu^{++} + 2ϵ	+0.337
Ca = Ca^{++} + 2ϵ	−2.87	Cu = Cu$^+$ + 1ϵ	+0.521
Na = Na$^+$ + ϵ	−2.714	2I$^-$ = I$_2$ + 2ϵ	+0.536
Mg = Mg^{++} +2 ϵ	−2.37	2Hg = Hg$_2^{++}$ + 2ϵ	+0.789
Al = Al^{+++} + 3ϵ	−1.66	Ag = Ag$^+$ + ϵ	+0.799
Mn = Mn^{++} + 2ϵ	−1.18	Pd = Pd^{++} + 2ϵ	+0.987
Zn = Zn^{++} + 2ϵ	−0.763	Pt = Pt^{++} + 2ϵ	+1.20
Fe = Fe^{++} + 2ϵ	−0.440	2Cl$^-$ = Cl$_2$ + 2ϵ	+1.36
Ni = Ni^{++} + 2ϵ	−0.250	Au = Au$^+$ + ϵ	+1.68
H$_2$ = 2H$^+$ + 2ϵ	0.000	2F$^-$ = F$_2$ + 2ϵ	+2.87

fining; and in electricity, e.g., electrolytic rectifiers, electrolytic capacitors, Josephson junctions.

WALTER J. HAMER

References

Bockris, J. O'M., and Reddy, K. N., "Modern Electrochemistry; An Introduction to an Interdisciplinary
Area," 2 Vols., New York, Plenum Press, 1970.
Delahay, Paul, "New Instrumental Methods in Electrochemistry," New York, Interscience Publishers, Inc.,
1954.
Heise, G. W., and Cahoon, N. C., "The Primary Battery," Vol. 1, New York, John Wiley & Sons, Inc.,
1971.

Cross-references: BATTERIES; CONDUCTIVITY, ELEC-
TRICAL; DIELECTRIC THEORY; ELECTRICAL
DISCHARGES IN GASES; IONIZATION; MOLECU-
LAR WEIGHT; POTENTIAL; VISCOSITY.

ELECTROLUMINESCENCE

Electroluminescence is a process which generates
light in crystals by conversion of energy supplied
by electric contacts, in the absence of incan-
descence, cathodo- or photoluminescence.

It occurs in several forms. The first observation of the presently most important form,
"radiative recombination in p-n junctions," was
made in 1907 by Round, then more thoroughly
by Lossev from 1923 on, when point electrodes
were placed on certain silicon carbide crystals
and current passed through them. Explanation
and improvement of this effect became possible
only after the development of modern solid-
state science since 1947.

If minority carriers are injected into a semiconductor, i.e., electrons are injected into a p-
type material, or "holes" into n-type material,
they recombine with the majority carriers,
either directly via the bandgap, or through exciton states, or via impurity levels within the
bandgap, thereby emitting the recombination
energy as photons. Part of the recombinations
occur nonradiatively, producing only heat.

Exploitation of the effect was strongly dependent on progress in compound semiconductor crystal preparation and solid-state electronics, since crystal perfection (absence of
defects) is of prime importance. At present,
single-crystalline dome-shaped p-n diodes made
of gallium arsenide, GaAs, a "III-V compound"
(from groups III and V of the periodic system),
yield the highest efficiencies (40 percent of the
electrical power input converted into optical
power output) in the near-infrared, and diodes
made of gallium phosphide, GaP, doped with
oxygen and zinc, yield red and infrared light,
efficiency peaked at 8 percent. GaP diodes
doped with nitrogen emit green light, with
.5 percent efficiency. Very important are alloys

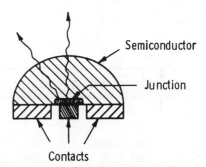

FIG. 1. Light-emitting diode.

such as $In_x Ga_{1-x} P$, $Al_x Ga_{1-x} As$, and especially
$GaAs_x P_{1-x}$ (red-emitting), where the color of
luminescence can be changed by changing the
composition. For high efficiency, it is important
that the material have a "direct" bandgap, allowing electron-hole recombination without phonon participation. Wavelengths of light emitted
by III-V crystals range from 6300 Å to 30 μ.

An important phenomenon, "injection laser
action," was discovered in GaAs diodes in 1962.
The crystal faces at the ends of a p-n junction
are made optically parallel so as to form a
Fabry-Perot optical cavity. Beyond a certain injection current density, (the "threshold current") the individual recombination processes
no longer occur randomly and independently of
each other, but in phase, so that a near-parallel
beam of coherent light (~9000 Å) of enormous
intensity (10^7 W/cm² in pulsed operation) is
emitted. The efficiency has been improved by
using graded bandgap $Al_x Ga_{1-x} As$ heterojunc-
tions and special doping profiles so that the
lasing region near the p-n junction acts as a
"light pipe," preventing light straying out sideways. AlAs has the same lattice constant as
GaAs, yet higher bandgap. Therefore, these
junctions are free of strain-generated imperfections. The current threshold for lasing is now
reduced to 800 A/cm² at room temperature,
allowing continuous operation at low total
power, to prevent heating.

These coherent or incoherent electroluminescent p-n diodes are small point sources used
for pilot lights, alpha-numeric readouts, optoelectronic processing, ranging systems, direct-
sight communication, and as IR-lamps for night
vision devices.

Another kind of electroluminescence, discovered by Destriau in 1936, uses inexpensive
powders consisting of small particles of essentially copper-doped zinc sulfide, ZnS, a II-VI
compound, embedded in an insulating resin and
formed into a large flat plate capacitor with one
plate transparent (e.g., SnO_2-coated glass). If
an ac voltage is applied, light is emitted (blue,
green, red, depending on the exact material
composition) twice per cycle, with brightnesses
up to thousands of foot-lamberts. Brightness
increases linearly with drive frequency, and ex-

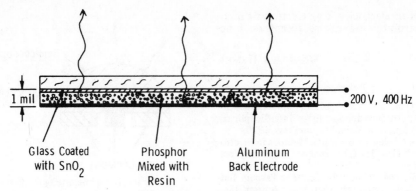

FIG. 2. Destriau-type EL panel.

ponentially with voltage, until saturation occurs. The efficiency is about 1 percent but it decreases with increasing brightness.

Microscopic examination of the interior of an individual particle reveals that the light is emitted inhomogeneously, in the form of two sets of comet-like striations which light up alternatingly, each set once per cycle. These comets coincide with long, thin conducting copper sulfide precipitates which form along crystal imperfections. The applied field relaxes in these needles and concentrates at the tips, so that electrons and holes are alternatingly field-emitted into the surrounding insulating luminescent ZnS. The holes are trapped there until they recombine with the more mobile electrons, emitting the typical luminescent spectra. The local brightness can be as high as 10^5 foot-lamberts.

Low-voltage dc-driven-electroluminescence of polycrystalline films of ZnS on glass, doped with copper and manganese, has also been achieved. The mechanism involves high-field-aided hole injection. The operation with DC simplifies the addressing of multi-element display panels.

Among applications of this large-area, thin light source are safety lights for home use, luminous instrument faces, alpha-numeric and other information display panels. The deterioration of these light sources is more rapid than that of p-n junction diodes (claimed half-life for these is 10^5 years), but the time to half-brightness has been improved to usable intervals (10 000 hours).

Compared to p-n junction recombination electroluminescence, the main advantage of this type is low cost and large area.

Even lower cost is possible with electrochemiluminescence; for example using the organic dye rubrene dissolved in an organic solvent and driven with low-voltage AC between transparent electrodes. Intense yellow light is emitted, with little deterioration.

Still another type of electroluminescence is acceleration-collision electroluminescence. In back-biased p-n junctions, Schottky barriers,

and near conducting inclusions, the local field can become high enough (10^5 V/cm or more) so that electrons acquire sufficient kinetic energy to impact-ionize luminescent centers of the host lattice, creating secondaries. Electroluminescence occurs upon recombination. The efficiency is low, because only a small fraction of the electrons can attain sufficient energy; the others create only heat.

A. G. FISCHER

References

Fischer, A. G., "Electroluminescence in II-VI Compounds," in "Luminescence of Inorganic Solids," P. Goldberg, Ed., New York, Academic Press, 1966 (pp. 541–602).

Dean, P. J., "Junction Electroluminescence," in "Applied Solid State Science," R. Wolfe and C. J. Kriessman, Eds., New York, Academic Press, 1969 (pp. 1–151).

Bergh, A. A., and Dean, P. J., Proc. IEEE, 60, 156–223 (1972) (LEDs).

ELECTROMAGNETIC THEORY

The task of electromagnetic theory is to account for the effects of electrical charges in various states of motion. Although historically electromagnetic theory was developed from Coulomb's celebrated law, it is at present more economic to develop it differently[9,10]. The macroscopic effects are described with remarkable accuracy by the following set of equations (rationalized mks system of units)

$$\mathbf{F} = q\mathbf{E} + q\mathbf{v} \times \mathbf{B} \qquad (1)$$

$$\nabla \cdot \mathbf{J} + \frac{\partial \rho}{\partial t} = 0 \qquad (2)$$

$$\nabla \times \mathbf{H} = \frac{\partial \mathbf{D}}{\partial t} + \mathbf{J} \qquad (3)$$

$$\nabla \times E = -\frac{\partial B}{\partial t} \qquad (4)$$

$$D = f_1(E) \qquad (5)$$

$$B = f_2(H) \qquad (6)$$

$$J = f_3(E, H) \qquad (7)$$

provided the functional relationships indicated in Eqs. (5), (6), and (7) are known explicitly. With these equations and the laws of mechanics, classical electromagnetic theory becomes essentially a branch of applied mathematics.

Equation (1), sometimes known as the Lorentz force equation, defines the field quantities, E, the electric field intensity, and B, the magnetic induction, in terms of an observable, the force F on a charge q. In Eq. (1), v is the velocity of the charge relative to the observer. Equation (2) is a statement of the law of conservation of electric charge in terms of the charge density ρ and the total current density J. Equation (3) is the differential form of Ampère's law,

$$\oint_{c \text{ of } s} H \cdot dl = \iint_s J \cdot dS = I$$

which relates the magnetic field intensity H to the current, including in addition the displacement current density term $\partial D / \partial t$, which was added by Maxwell to make the law applicable to time-varying fields. The term J represents the total current density. Equation (4) is the differential form of Faraday's law of electromagnetic induction. Equations (5), (6), and (7) are functional relationships, for the most part determined experimentally, by means of which the effects of different materials are accounted for. Mathematically, these equations are employed to reduce Eq. (3) and (4) to a pair of equations in only two unknowns. In free space, Eq. (5), (6) and (7) take their simplest form, respectively, $D = \epsilon_0 E$, $B = \mu_0 H$, $J = 0$ (or $J = J_s$, a source current independent of E and H), where ϵ_0 and μ_0 are constants whose value depends on the system of units (in the mks system $\epsilon_0 = 8.854 \times 10^{-12}$ farad/meter, $\mu_0 = 4\pi \times 10^{-7}$ henry/meter). Since matter itself is a relatively dilute collection of charged particles, it is always theoretically possible to define terms so that the theory is a description of the effects and interactions of charges in free space, with consequently no essential distinction between D and E or between, B and H, as indicated above. In practice however effects of materials are usually best handled in another way.[6,7,9,10] Dielectric polarization effects are accounted for by making the D vector include the electric dipole moment density P, $D = \epsilon_0 E + P$, and then introducing a material constant, the permittivity ϵ, such that $D = \epsilon E$. The relative permittivity of a dielectric material is then equal to one plus the electric susceptibility. Magnetic polarization effects are handled similarly by

defining the field vector B so that it includes the magnetic dipole moment density M, $B = \mu_0(H + M)$. The material permeability is then introduced so that it depends upon the magnetic susceptibility analogously, and $B = \mu H$. Effects of conductors are represented by a material conductivity σ, such that $J_c = \sigma E$. With these simple forms for Eq. (5), (6) and (7), Eq. (3) and (4) take on the useful form

$$\nabla \times H = \epsilon \frac{\partial E}{\partial t} + \sigma E + J_1 \qquad (8)$$

$$\nabla \times E = -\mu \frac{\partial H}{\partial t} \qquad (9)$$

provided μ and ϵ are constant in time. The term J_1 here includes currents arising from charges in free space plus any (source) currents which are independent of E and H. If there are no free charges in the region, J_1 includes only the source currents; these latter are known, so Eq. (8) and (9) may be solved for E and H. Since the equations are partial differential equations, boundary conditions over closed surfaces are required for unique solutions. Boundary conditions on the field quantities, which must hold at any boundary between two regions, may be derived from these equations. The conditions are: across a boundary (a) tangential E must be continuous, (b) tangential H must be continuous, (c) normal D and normal B must be continuous. Idealizations of material properties are sometimes helpful. For example, a perfect conductor has no non-static fields inside it, and at its surface, tangential E and normal B are zero, tangential H is equal and perpendicular to any surface current density, and normal D is equal to any surface charge density.

Two additional equations, especially useful in static problems, may be deduced from Eq. (2), (3) and (4):

$$\nabla \cdot D = \rho \qquad (10)$$

$$\nabla \cdot B = 0 \qquad (11)$$

Solutions to the field equations are most readily obtained by imposing a restriction on the time dependence. If the fields are assumed to be independent of time (static), then Eq. (3) and (4) or (8) and (9) decouple. One of the equations becomes $\nabla \times E = 0$. This means that E is irrotational and may be represented by a scalar potential function ϕ, $E = -\nabla\phi$. Combining this with Eq. (10) gives the fundamental equation of electrostatics,

$$\nabla^2 \phi = -\rho/\epsilon \qquad (12)$$

Poisson's equation. This equation for the electrostatic potential is solved by the standard methods of partial differential equations. The boundary conditions on the potential may be found from the boundary conditions on the fields.[9,10] In practice, it is frequently necessary

to solve for the potential and electric field in a restricted region in which the charge density is zero, but the potential at the boundary is held at some particular value(s). The problem then is to solve Laplace's equation, $\nabla^2 \phi = 0$, subject to the stated boundary conditions. The standard techniques for solving boundary value problems are employed. However, if the region of interest is partially open, known analytical techniques are sometimes inadequate to solve the problem. In two-dimensional problems of such a difficult type, the method of conformal transformations (conjugate functions) is often helpful.[8,10]

The main applications of electrostatic theory are in (a) the theory of material properties, (b) the calculation of charged particle trajectories in electron guns, deflection systems, and accelerators (here in conjunction with magnetostatic theory), (c) the calculation of circuit component values, such as capacitance, and (d) the determination of voltage gradients in connection with voltage breakdown problems.

Magnetostatic theory is developed from Eq. (11) and (8). Since $\mathbf{B}$ is divergenceless, it can be represented by the curl of a vector $\mathbf{A}$, which is known as the magnetic vector potential. Equation (8) can usually be written in terms of this potential as follows:

$$\nabla^2 \mathbf{A} = -\mu \mathbf{J} \qquad (13)$$

Taken one rectangular component at a time, this equation is of the same form as Poisson's equation [Eq. (12)] and may be solved in the same way. The boundary conditions on $\mathbf{A}$ may be found from those on $\mathbf{B}$ and $\mathbf{H}$. In regions with no current, Eq. (8) becomes $\nabla \times \mathbf{H} = 0$ so that $\mathbf{H}$ may be represented by a scalar potential function $\mathbf{H} = -\nabla \phi_m$. In such regions then, in view of Eq. (11), the magnetic scalar potential, ϕ_m, must satisfy Laplace's equation

$$\nabla^2 \phi_m = 0 \qquad (14)$$

provided $\nabla \mu = 0$ in the region. The techniques and solutions of electrostatics are applicable to many magnetostatic problems. Unfortunately, however, in practice many of the systems designed to establish a given magnetic field incorporate ferromagnetic materials. For such materials, the magnetic susceptibility (and hence the permeability) is not independent of the field intensity and the field equations become nonlinear. Present mathematical techniques for handling nonlinear problems are severely limited. Practical magnetostatic problems are, therefore, frequently solved by some approximation. One of the simplest and most useful approximations is a representation by a magnetic circuit.[6, 8,10] Series and parallel branches of the magnetic circuit may be recognized, and the techniques of linear and nonlinear circuit analysis can be applied to obtain a solution.

Magnetostatic theory is applicable to a myriad of magnetic devices, including deflection systems, motors, generators, relays, magnetic pickup devices, permanent magnets, memories, transducers and coils. To date, the need for particular solutions has frequently arisen before sound analytical methods have been available, so many devices are developed empirically.

Energy is required to establish electric and magnetic fields, and such energy is associated with the fields. The field energy in a given volume may be computed in most cases from a volume integral of one or both of the following energy density expressions $W_e = \frac{1}{2} \epsilon E^2$, $W_m = \frac{1}{2} \mu H^2$, respectively the electrostatic and magnetostatic values.

When the fields are time varying, Eq. (8) and (9) are coupled and must be solved simultaneously. Almost invariably, a potential function such as a vector potential or a Hertz potential is introduced.[9,10] For example, Eq. (11) implies that $\mathbf{B}$ may be replaced by a vector potential such that $\mathbf{B} = \nabla \times \mathbf{A}$. Equation (9) implies the following equation for $\mathbf{E}$

$$\mathbf{E} = -\nabla \phi - \frac{\partial \mathbf{A}}{\partial t} \qquad (15)$$

so that $\mathbf{H}$ and $\mathbf{E}$ may be replaced in Eq. (8), and with the condition on $\mathbf{A}$, $\nabla \cdot \mathbf{A} = \mu \epsilon \partial \phi / \partial t$, the following equations may be obtained for $\mathbf{A}$ and ϕ (σ assumed zero here)

$$\nabla^2 \mathbf{A} - \mu \epsilon \frac{\partial^2 \mathbf{A}}{\partial t^2} = -\mu \mathbf{J} \qquad (16)$$

$$\nabla^2 \phi - \mu \epsilon \frac{\partial^2 \phi}{\partial t^2} = -\rho / \epsilon \qquad (17)$$

That is, both the vector potential $\mathbf{A}$ and the scalar potential ϕ satisfy a differential equation known as the inhomogeneous wave equation.

Because of their simplicity and practical importance, solutions for those sources and fields which simply oscillate at a single frequency have been studied extensively.[2,9,10] In this case, the time is eliminated as an independent variable, as if by a transform operation. (In fact, transform methods are often the best means of obtaining transient field solutions.) In the equations, the time derivatives are replaced by frequency multipliers so that the resulting equations are functions of the space variables only. The vector potential may then be found by standard techniques of partial differential equations and boundary value problems. Having $\mathbf{A}$, the field quantity $\mathbf{B}$ is found from $\mathbf{B} = \nabla \times \mathbf{A}$ and $\mathbf{E}$ is found from Eq. (8). In practice, a theorem which can be derived from the field equations, called the reciprocity theorem,[2,4,10] is often helpful. The theorem relates the fields $\mathbf{E}_a$ and $\mathbf{E}_b$ produced respectively by a pair of current distributions $\mathbf{J}_a$ and $\mathbf{J}_b$. The theorem is

$$\iiint \mathbf{E}_a \cdot \mathbf{J}_b \, dv = \iiint \mathbf{E}_b \cdot \mathbf{J}_a \, dv \qquad (18)$$

For example, if J_b is selected to be a point current at point P, directed along x (represented mathematically by a Dirac delta function), then Equation (18), $E_{ax}(P) = \iiint E_b \cdot J_a dv$, gives a formula for the computation of the field due to J_a which is equivalent to a superposition integral involving a Greens function.

Perhaps the most fundamental problem of electromagnetic theory is the determination of the fields of a point charge, at rest, in oscillation, or in some general state of motion. For a point charge q, at rest in free space, the solution may be obtained by solving Eq. (12) in spherical coordinates. With the point charge at the origin, symmetry conditions may be employed to eliminate the angular variation, and the remaining differential equation in r can be solved subject to Eq. (10) to give $\phi_G = q/4\pi\epsilon_0 r$ for the potential associated with the point charge. A superposition integral

$$\phi = \iiint \frac{\rho \, dv}{4\pi\epsilon_0 r} \qquad (19)$$

may then be employed to find the potentials associated with more complicated distributions. The field of an oscillating dipole, which is equivalent to a point alternating current, is also of great interest. This solution may be obtained from Eq. (16) (single frequency version). If the point current is directed along z, the z-component of the vector potential may be found by a procedure similar to that employed for a point charge. The final result is

$$A_{zG} = \frac{I\Delta z}{4\pi\mu_0 r} \cos \omega(t - \sqrt{\mu_0\epsilon_0}r) \qquad (20)$$

where $I\Delta z$, the current moment, is equal to $\omega q\Delta z$, the maximum dipole moment of the oscillating dipole. The factor $(t - \sqrt{\mu_0\epsilon_0}r)$ exhibits the time delay required for the effects of the oscillating charges to propagate to distant points. The electric and magnetic fields may be computed from Eq. (20) as indicated above. The magnetic field strength produced by an oscillating dipole (point current) is, for example, in the spherical coordinate system (r, θ, φ)

$$H_\varphi = \frac{I\Delta z}{4\pi} \sin \theta \left[\frac{\cos \omega(t - \sqrt{\mu_0\epsilon_0}r)}{r^2} \right.$$
$$\left. - \frac{\omega\sqrt{\mu_0\epsilon_0}}{r} \sin \omega(t - \sqrt{\mu_0\epsilon_0}r) \right]$$

This form, like Eq. (20), shows that the crests and valleys of the field oscillations are propagated in spherical waves at the speed of light $v = (\mu_0\epsilon_0)^{-1/2}$. The solution for a point current may be employed in an integral similar to Eq. (19) to find the vector potential of a more complicated distribution of current. Such solutions may also be employed to find the radiation patterns and input impedances of antennas.[11]

The potentials and fields produced by a charge moving in an arbitrary way may also be obtained.[3,9] The results may be found in Stratton.[9, pp. 475-476]

In regions free of source currents and charges, the fields and potential satisfy the homogeneous wave equation [for example Eq. (16) with $J = 0$]. Then one of the simpler solutions which can be obtained is that of the plane electromagnetic wave. With appropriate orientation of the rectangular coordinate system, the solutions show that plane waves may progress along z, with components as follows:

$$E_x = E_0 \cos \omega(t - \sqrt{\mu_0\epsilon_0}z)$$
$$H_y = E_0 \sqrt{\frac{\epsilon_0}{\mu_0}} \cos \omega(t - \sqrt{\mu_0\epsilon_0}z)$$

where E_0 is an arbitrary constant amplitude. Note that E, H and the direction of propagation are all perpendicular to one another. The Poynting vector, $S = E \times H$, points in the direction of propagation. Moreover, the power carried through a closed surface by an electromagnetic field may be computed from a surface integral of the Poynting vector.

With single frequency fields in source free regions, both H and E can be represented by vector potentials,[2,9,10] $H_1 = \nabla \times A_1$, $E_2 = \nabla \times A_2$, and moreover the coordinate systems may be oriented so that A_1 and A_2 each have a single component.[10] In cylindrical systems, this single component is commonly along z. H_1 is then transverse to z (TM) and the set of fields, E_1, H_1, derivable from A_1', are called TM fields. E_2 is likewise transverse to z and the set of fields, E_2, H_2, derivable from A_2, are called TE fields. This procedure is particularly helpful in problems involving transmission lines and WAVEGUIDES and is developed in detail in Weeks[10, Ch. 4-6].

Some of the most interesting and fundamental problems of electromagnetic theory are concerned with the scattering and diffraction of electromagnetic waves.[2,3,8-10] For example, exact solutions are available for the scattering by cylinders and spheres, as well as an infinitely long slit. Approximate solutions are available for many other shapes. The methods are those outlined above, supplemented by generalizations of the principles of Huygens and Babinet.

Another topic of wide interest is the nature of fields in ionized gases or plasmas. The applications range from ionospheric propagation to microwave devices to nuclear apparatus to magneto-hydrodynamics to satellite re-entry problems. The simplest theory for these effects is developed from Eq. (3) and (4) (single frequency version) by separating the ion current term $J_e = \rho v$ from J, and employing Newton's law to eliminate v in favor of E, H and whatever mechanical constraints are applicable[4,9,10] (see PLASMAS).

Effects peculiar to charges moving with very

high velocities have not been included in this discussion (see RELATIVITY THEORY). Quantum effects are also discussed elsewhere (see QUANTUM ELECTRODYNAMICS and QUANTUM THEORY).

W. L. WEEKS

References

1. Hayt, W. H., "Engineering Electromagnetics," New York, McGraw-Hill Book Co., 1958.
2. Harrington, R. F., "Time-Harmonic Electromagnetic Fields," New York, McGraw-Hill Book Co., 1961.
3. Jackson, J. D., "Classical Electrodynamics," New York, John Wiley & Sons, 1962.
4. Javid, M., and Brown, M., "Field Analysis and Electromagnetics," New York, McGraw-Hill Book Co., 1963.
5. Panofsky, W., and Phillips, M., "Classical Electricity and Magnetism," Reading, Mass., Addison-Wesley, 1955.
6. Peck, E. R., "Electricity and Magnetism," New York, McGraw-Hill Book Co., 1953.
7. Plonsey, R., and Collin, R., "Principles and Applications of Electromagnetic Fields," New York, McGraw-Hill Book Co., 1962.
8. Smythe, W. R., "Static and Dynamic Electricity," Second edition, New York, McGraw-Hill Book Co., 1950.
9. Stratton, J. A., "Electromagnetic Theory," New York, McGraw-Hill Book Co., 1941.
10. Weeks, W. L., "Electromagnetic Theory for Engineering Applications," New York, John Wiley & Sons, 1964.
11. Weeks, W. L., "Antenna Engineering," New York, McGraw-Hill Book Co., 1968.

Cross-references: ELECTRICITY, PLASMAS, POTENTIAL, QUANTUM ELECTRODYNAMICS, QUANTUM THEORY, RELATIVITY, STATIC ELECTRICITY, WAVEGUIDES.

ELECTRON

The electron is the smallest known electrically charged particle. Its existence and characteristics were inferred from many experiments clustered in and around the last decade of the nineteenth century. In the 1830's, Faraday had tentatively suggested that his experiments in ELECTROCHEMISTRY could be interpreted in terms of a small unit of charge attached to ions. This notion of individual "atoms of charge" was somewhat eclipsed, however, by the enormous success of Maxwell's theory of electromagnetism, which was generally interpreted, by 1880, as favoring a view that electrical phenomena were due to continuous charge distributions and motions. G. Johnstone Stoney, in 1874, and Helmholtz, in 1881, had suggested again an atomic interpretation of electricity, but it was not until the brilliant experiments of Perrin, J. J. Thomson, Zeeman, and others in the 1890's

that the concept of the electron received firm experimental foundation. Later experiments and theory (Millikan, Bohr, etc.) established the constancy of the electronic charge and interwove the concept of an electron of definite charge and mass into the basic structure of the atom.

The Cathode Ray Controversy After the discovery of the cathode ray in high-vacuum discharge tubes by Plücker in 1858, there developed, with the experiments of Goldstein, Crookes, Hertz, Lenard, and Schuster, a controversy over the nature of the rays. A predominately German school held that the rays were a peculiar form of electromagnetic rays. The British physicists thought they were negatively charged particles. The controversy provides a classic "case history" of the typical scientific controversy in which two quite different models both explain most, but not all, of the observable facts. The proponents of each model designed ingenious experiments and in some cases were so trapped in their preconceptions that they badly misinterpreted their observations. The Germans were especially impressed by the fact that the rays could go through thin foils—something no known particles could do. The British were firm in pointing out that the rays could be deflected by magnetic fields—something not possible with electromagnetic waves. Hertz, in what he thought was a crucial experiment, was unable to detect deflection of the rays by electric fields, but this very phenomenon was demonstrated by J. J. Thomson and made the basis for his conclusive experiments that the rays had velocities less than that of light. Thomson showed, further, that if one assumed that the rays were composed of particles, then the particles had the same ratio of charge to mass regardless of the cathode material or the nature of the residual gas. Perrin's classic experiment, meanwhile, proved that the rays did indeed convey negative charge. In the decade between 1896 and 1906, Thomson and others showed that negatively charged particles from sources other than cathode rays had the same ratio of charge to mass: the negative particles emitted by hot filaments in the Edison effect, the beta rays emitted by some radioactive materials, and the negative particles emitted in the photoelectric effect that had so ironically been discovered by Heinrich Hertz in his great experiment which demonstrated the electromagnetic rays predicted by Maxwell's equations.

Thomson's Determination of, e/m In 1897 Thomson devised an apparatus in which he could deflect a beam of cathode rays with a magnetic field of induction B and also with an electric field of strength E. If the fields are perpendicular to each other, and to the original path of the beam, and if they occupy the same region, then (with proper polarities and magnitudes of fields) the electric force on the beam can equal the magnetic force, so that the beam hits the same point on a fluorescent screen as when no fields are applied. If e is the charge of a

given particle, m its mass, and v its velocity, $v = E/B$. Thus, velocities of typical cathode ray beams could be measured. If the magnetic field is used alone, and the curvature R of the beam is measured, then one can equate centripetal and magnetic field forces $mv^2/R = Bev$, and then deduce $e/m = v/BR$. With v known from the previous experiment, e/m can be calculated. Thomson's early values were not very precise, but later experiments of a similar type gave values close to 1.76×10^{11} coulomb/kg. More recent evaluations, drawing on measurements of many kinds, give $e/m = 1.7588 \times 10^{11}$ coulombs/kg as a 1973 value calculated from values for e and m given under CONSTANTS, FUNDAMENTAL, in this book.

The Zeeman Effect In 1896 Zeeman discovered the broadening of spectral lines when a light source was in a strong magnetic field. Experimental refinements of Zeeman and others, and theoretical work by Lorentz and Zeeman, permitted the interpretation of this effect as due to the influence of the magnetic field on oscillating or orbiting negatively charged particles within the light-emitting or absorbing atoms. From the spectroscopic data, the ratio of charge to mass of these hypothetical particles could be shown to be equal to that of cathode rays. The Zeeman effect thus provided the first experimental evidence that the negative particles emitted by atoms when heated (Edison effect) or subject to high fields and/or ionic bombardment (cathode rays) or bombarded by short-wavelength light (photoelectric effect) were, indeed, actual constituents of the atoms and were probably responsible for the emission and absorption of light.

The Charge on the Electron In the decade following 1897, many different methods were evolved for determination of ionic charges. Some methods depended upon measuring the total charge of a number of ions used as nuclei for cloud droplet formation. Other methods were more indirect—experiments, for example, which, combined with the kinetic theory of gases, could give crude values for avogadro's number, N (see MOLE CONCEPT). By dividing the Faraday constant (the charge carried in electrolysis by ions formed from one gram-atom of a univalent element) by N, one could determine the average charge per ion. Similarly, the constants in Planck's theory of blackbody radiation, when evaluated experimentally, could provide a numerical value for N, as could certain experiments in radioactivity. All such methods gave values of N of the order of 6×10^{23}, and hence 1.6×10^{-19} coulomb for the ionic charge. None of these methods measured individual charges; strictly speaking, the value for the ionic charge could be thought of only as an average value.

Millikan's experiments with single oil drops, beginning in 1906, provided a method for measuring extremely small charges with precision. He was able to show that the charge on his drops was *always ne*, with $e = 1.60 \times 10^{-19}$ coulomb (modern value) and n a positive or negative integer.

He observed the motions of very small charged oil drops in uniform vertical electric fields. The drops were so small that they moved with constant velocity (except for Brownian fluctuations) for a given force. The force in each case was due to gravity acting on the mass of the drop and to the electric field (if any) acting on the charge, q, on the drop. The charge on a given drop could be changed by shining x-rays upon it. Using Stokes' Law, in a form modified to correct for the fact that the drops were *not* large in comparison to the inhomogenieties of the surrounding air, and the velocity of a drop in free (gravitational)fall, Millikan could infer the diameter and mass of a given drop, and then calculate its charge. The charge q always equaled ne. (See reference 1 or 2 for experimental details.) A few other physicists, in similar experiments, thought they had detected electric charges smaller than Millikan's e, but their experimental techniques were probably faulty.

Millikan's experiment did not prove, of course, that the charge on the cathode ray, beta ray, photoelectric, or Zeeman particle was e. But if we call all such particles electrons, and assume that they have $e/m = 1.76 \times 10^{11}$ coulomb/kg, and $e = 1.60 \times 10^{-19}$ coulomb (and hence $m = 9.1 \times 10^{-31}$ kg), we find that they fit very well into Bohr's theory of the hydrogen atom and successive, more comprehensive atomic theories, into Richardson's equations for thermionic emission, into Fermi's theory of beta decay, and so on. In other words, a whole web of modern theory and experiment defines the electron. (The best current value of e (June, 1973) $= 1.60219 \times 10^{-19}$ coulomb (see CONSTANTS, FUNDAMENTAL).

The Wave Nature of the Electron In 1924, L. DeBroglie suggested that the behavior of electrons within atoms could be better understood if it were assumed that the motion of an electron depends upon some sort of accompanying wave, the length of which would be h/p (h = Planck's constant and p the momentum of the electron). This suggestion led to the development of QUANTUM MECHANICS by Schrödinger, Heisenberg, and others. The concept of electron waves provided an explanation for experiments on reflection of electron beams by metallic crystals, carried out from 1921 onward by Davisson and others, and provided an impetus for the experiments of G. P. Thomson on the diffraction of electron beams by thin films (see ELECTRON DIFFRACTION).

Other Characteristics of Electrons In applying quantum mechanics to certain problems in atomic spectroscopy, in 1925 and 1926, Pauli, and Goudsmit and Uhlenbeck found that electrons must possess angular momentum of amount $\pm \frac{1}{2}(h/2\pi)$. Dirac's work on a generalized quantum theory of the electron showed that it possessed a related magnetic dipole moment of magnitude $eh/4\pi mc$ (see ELECTRON SPIN). The ratio of the dipole moment to the angular momentum (e/mc) is larger than can be accounted

for in classical terms with any homogeneous wholly negative model. The concept of electronic dipole magnetic moment is essential not only in spectroscopy but in theories of ferromagnetism (see MAGNETISM).

One may speak of the "classical radius of the electron," $a = e^2/mc^2$, derived by setting the self-energy of the coulomb field of a charge e contained at a radius a equal to the relativistic rest energy, mc^2 of the electron. This $a = 2.82 \times 10^{-13}$ cm, comfortably smaller than any atom, but larger than the usual estimates of sizes of protons and neutrons.

Positive Electrons Dirac's paper in 1928 could be interpreted as predicting the existence of electrons that are positive. But until such particles were found experimentally by C. D. Anderson in 1932 in cloud chamber pictures of cosmic ray particle tracks, most physicists preferred other interpretations of Dirac's paper. Positive electrons, or POSITRONS are now known (1) to occur as decay products from certain radioactive isotopes, (2) to be produced (paired with a negative electron) in certain interactions of high-energy gamma rays with intense electric fields near nuclei, and (3) to be the product of certain decays of certain mesons. In principle, positrons could form anti-atoms with nuclei made from anti-protons and anti-neutrons, but in practice almost all positrons produced in ordinary matter quickly meet their end by annihilating themselves together with some hapless negative electron. The end product of a positron-electron annihilation is a pair of gamma rays.

Recent Theoretical Developments The relativistic quantum mechanical theory of the electron, in its earlier forms, led to embarrassing predictions of infinite electronic mass and charge. Schwinger and others have developed methods for coping with these infinities, so the theory, in general, now satisfactorily agrees with observations. Further developments are not unlikely. (See QUANTUM ELECTRODYNAMICS).

Experiments and theory, first in radioactive decay, and more recently in elementary particle physics, have made it clear that electrons can be thought of as members of a class of particles called "leptons." These particles, which include neutrinos (see NEUTRINO) and muons (see ELEMENTARY PARTICLES) interact with each other and with other particles in so-called "weak interactions," apart from whatever other reactions they may share, such as gravitational, magnetic, and electrical interactions.

Applications of Electrons Aside from their inherent usefulness in physical theories of magnetic, electrical, optical, and mechanical properties of matter, electrons either in beams or in conductors can be made to do all sorts of useful things. Cathode ray oscilloscopes, electron microscopes, image converters, certain memory devices for computers, television picture tubes, and most "radio tubes" depend upon beams of electrons controlled by electric or magnetic fields (see ELECTRON OPTICS). In ordinary

metallic conductors, electricity is carried primarily by electrons. The behavior of electrons in SEMICONDUCTORS and in superconductors (see SUPERCONDUCTIVITY) has in recent years been the basis both of intense theoretical interest and of interesting and useful devices.

DAVID L. ANDERSON

References

1. Millikan, R. A., "The Electron," edited with an introduction by J. W. M. DuMond, Pheonix, Science Series, PSS523, University of Chicago Press, 1963.
2. Anderson, D. L., "The Discovery of the Electron," New York, Van Nostrand Reinhold, 1964.
3. Shankland, R. S., "Atomic and Nuclear Physics," Second edition, New York, The Macmillian Company, 1960.
4. Condon, E. U., and Odishaw, H., "Handbook of Physics," pp. 7–169, New York, McGraw-Hill Book Co., Inc., 1958.
5. Borowitz, S., and Bornstein, L. A., "A Contemporary View of Physics," Chapter 12, New York, McGraw-Hill Book Co., 1968.

Cross-references: ELECTROCHEMISTRY, ELECTRON DIFFRACTION, ELECTRON OPTICS, ELECTRON SPIN, ELEMENTARY PARTICLES, MAGNETISM, MOLE CONCEPT, NEUTRINO, PHOTOELECTRICITY, POSITRON, QUANTUM ELECTRODYNAMICS, QUANTUM MECHANICS, SUPERCONDUCTIVITY, ZEEMAN AND STARK EFFECTS.

ELECTRON DIFFRACTION

The discovery of electron diffraction independently by C. J. Davisson and L. H. Germer (1927) and G. P. Thomson (1927) verified L. de Broglie's earlier hypothesis (1924) that matter exhibits both corpuscular and wavelike characteristics. This hypothesis served as a stimulus for the formal development of quantum mechanics by E. Schrödinger, M. Born, W. Heisenberg, and others. Following this momentous discovery, which eventually resulted in the award of a Nobel Prize to Davisson and Thomson, electron diffraction was immediately utilized as a tool for the study of the structure of matter.

Electron, x-ray and neutron diffraction are all used for structure studies. Electron diffraction is used particularly for those structural studies that involve small numbers of atoms. This is due to the strong interaction of electrons with matter. Thus the principal area of application of electron diffraction is for the study of thin films, surfaces, gases and small samples.

The different energy ranges that were used in the Davisson-Germer and Thomson experiments provide a natural division for a description of

the types of equipment, areas of application, and analytical techniques that have evolved since 1927. These experiments were performed with electrons having energies in the vicinity of 150 eV and 15 keV, respectively. De Broglie's relationship $\lambda = h/mv$, where h is Planck's constant and λ is the wavelength associated with a mass m traveling with a group velocity v, reduces to $\lambda = \sqrt{150/V}$ for electrons in the nonrelativistic limit, where V is the accelerating voltage and λ is expressed in Angstroms. The two experiments thus used electrons having a wavelength of approximately 1 and 0.1 Å. The longer wave-length is comparable to the spacing between atoms in crystals.

While 50-keV electrons, which are used in most commercial electron diffraction instruments, penetrate to a depth of about 10^3 Å into a crystal, 150-eV electrons penetrate only about 10 Å. Since the higher-energy electrons are capable of passing through the several layers of adsorbed foreign material that normally are present on the surface of a crystal, surface cleanness and therefore the vacuum requirements for 50-keV electron diffraction are not as stringent as those for low-energy electron diffraction. This factor, in addition to the relative ease in focusing intense high-voltage beams, and individual interests, resulted in the wide application of high-energy electron diffraction for structure studies. A typical instrument of this type operates at about 50 keV, has provisions for producing and focusing the electrons, contains specimen manipulators, photographic means to record the diffraction patterns and is contained in a chamber capable of being evacuated to 10^{-5} torr. Diffraction patterns are obtained either by transmission of the beam through very thin films or by working at grazing incidence and reflection. The grazing incidence technique is potentially capable of resolving structures having a monolayer thickness.

One of the most common uses of 50-keV electron diffraction by transmission or reflection is for the study of films on amorphous, polycrystalline and single crystal substrates. This includes films that have been formed by the oxidation or corrosion of a surface, as well as those formed by the deposition of material on a substrate. In many instances these films consist of crystallites having an orientation that is related to the structure and orientation of the substrate material.

In the past few years, the transmission ELECTRON MISCROSCOPE has become widely used for the study of atomic arrangements at lattice imperfections, such as dislocations and stacking faults. Image contrast is obtained by local differences in the intensities of diffracted beams. In addition, many electron microscopes are constructed in such a way that it is possible to obtain the diffraction pattern associated with the material in the area being studied.

Electron diffraction in this energy range is especially useful for the determinaiton of the atomic arrangements, bond distances, bond angles, and mean square atomic vibrational amplitudes in gaseous molecules.

Low-energy electron diffraction was used by only a few groups until approximately 1960. Improved diffraction equipment, which enabled the direct display of the diffraction pattern on a fluorescent screen by accelerating the diffracted electrons after they had passed through grids, and the commercial availability of ultrahigh (10^{-10} torr) vacuum equipment, resulted in a resurgence of interest in this field. The structure of clean surfaces, the arrangements of foreign atoms on these surfaces at a monolayer or less coverage, and many aspects of the initial stages in the oriented overgrowth of thin films have been studied with electrons having energies in the range of 2 to 10^3 eV. It has been revealed that the atomic arrangement at the clean surfaces of semiconductors such as germanium and silicon is quite unlike that found in the bulk of these materials. At low coverages, foreign atoms are normally adsorbed in structures that have a symmetry and dimensions that are simply related to the orientation of the substrate plane. A multitude of such structures has been found on semiconductors and metals. Their atomic array is dependent on many parameters, such as the amount of adsorbed material, the temperature, orientation and cleanness of the substrate. This same equipment is also used to determine the presence of impurity atoms on the surface by the technique of Auger spectroscopy. The secondary electrons have energy that is characteristic of the surface atoms and can be used to make a quantitative identification of surface impurities, which can assume an important role in affecting surface structures.

Fundamental properties of solids, such as characteristic energy losses, atomic mean square vibrational amplitudes, and electron range, have also been investigated by both high- and low-energy electron diffraction.

ALFRED U. MAC RAE

References

Pinsker, Z. G., "Electron Diffraction," London, Butterworth's Scientific Publications, 1953.

Heidenreich, R. D., "Fundamentals of Transmission Electron Microscopy," New York, John Wiley & Sons, 1964.

Cross-references: DIFFRACTION BY MATTER AND DIFFRACTION GRATINGS, ELECTRON, ELECTRON MICROSCOPE, ELECTRON OPTICS.

ELECTRON MICROSCOPE

The electron microscope is a device that forms magnified images by means of electrons. The electrons are usually accelerated to between 50

and 100 kV. The microscope magnifies in two or three stages by means of electromagnetic or electrostatic lenses.

In 1878 Ernst Abbe proved that the resolution of the optical microscope is limited by the wavelength of light. No matter how perfect and free of aberrations the optical system is, the image of a geometrical point is not a point but a disc, the "Airy disc." Regardless of any further magnification, two separate points cannot be resolved as separate unless their centers are the distance d apart, whereby d is the radius of the Airy disc referred to the object plane:

$$d = \frac{0.5 \, \lambda}{n \sin \alpha} \qquad (1)$$

where

λ = wavelength of the illuminating light
n = index of refraction of medium between object and lens (in air, $n = 1$)
α = aperture of lens, i.e., half-angle of collected light beam
$n \sin \alpha = NA$ = numerical aperture of lens (in air, $NA_{max} = 0.95$).

Even if we go to the extreme of using the ultraviolet line of mercury ($\lambda = 253.7$ nm*), oil immersion optics ($NA = 1.4$), quartz lenses and microphotography, the best resolution obtainable is still:

$$d = 110 \text{ nm}$$

The electron microscope makes use of the wave properties of the moving electron. Its "de Broglie" wavelength is:

$$\lambda = \frac{h}{mv} = \frac{1.23}{V^{1/2}} \text{ [nm]} \qquad (2a)$$

for nonrelativistic electrons (below 20kV) and

$$\lambda = \frac{1.23}{(V + 10^{-6} \, V^2)^{1/2}} \text{ [nm]} \qquad (2b)$$

for relativistic electrons,
where

h = Planck's constant
m = mass of electron
v = velocity of electron
V = accelerating voltage in volts.

For electrons of $V = 50$ kV the wavelength is therefore:

$$\lambda_{50kV} = 0.00535 \text{ nm}$$

Objective lenses for electrons, unlike those for light optics cannot be made free of spherical aberrations. They have to operate with numerical apertures that are 500 to 1000 times lower. The best theoretical resolution for magnetic

*1 nanometer (nm) = 1 millimicron (mμ) = 10 angstrom units (Å).

lenses working with electrons of 50 kV energy is:[1]

$$\ddot{\delta} = 0.21 \text{ nm}$$

The best practical resolution is between 0.5 and 1 nm.

The first electron microscope was built by M. Knoll and E. Ruska at the Technical University of Berlin early in 1931[2]. It had two electromagnetic lenses in series and achieved a modest magnification of 17. Knoll and Ruska improved the electron microscope step by step. They added a condenser lens and built an iron shield with a narrow center gap around their magnetic lens. Ruska, working from 1932 by himself, equipped the magnetic lenses with narrow pole pieces and was able to demonstrate in 1934 a resolution of 50 nm (magnification of 12,000)[3], better than the best obtainable optical resolution. Figure 1 shows a functional diagram of his supermicroscope. Figure 2 shows the details of one of his lenses.

Parallel to the development of the magnetic electron microscope went the development of an electrostatic one. In 1931, Brüche and Johannson of the Research Institute of A.E.G. of Berlin imaged the emitting surface of the cathode with an electrostatic immersion objective. In 1932, they employed unipotential or Einzel-lenses.

Magnetic Lenses A charged particle entering a uniform magnetic field perpendicular to the lines of force will describe a circle; moving parallel to them, it will not be deflected. The radius of the circle that the particle describes, the "cyclotron radius," is:

$$\rho = \frac{m}{e} \frac{v}{B} \qquad (3)$$

where

m = mass of particle
e = charge of particle
v = velocity
B = magnetic field intensity (gauss).

The circle described by an electron is

$$\rho_e = 3.372 \frac{\sqrt{V}}{B} \text{ [cm]} \qquad (4a)$$

for nonrelativistic electrons,

$$\rho_e = \frac{1}{B} \sqrt{11.3V + 1.11 \times 10^{-5} V^2} \text{ [cm]} \qquad (4b)$$

for relativistic electrons,

where V is in volts and B is in gauss.

The time it takes a particle to describe a cyclotron circle is:

$$\tau = \frac{2\pi\rho}{v} = 2\pi \frac{m}{e} \frac{1}{B} \text{ [sec]} \qquad (5)$$

A charged particle entering a uniform magnetic field at an angle will describe a cycloid.

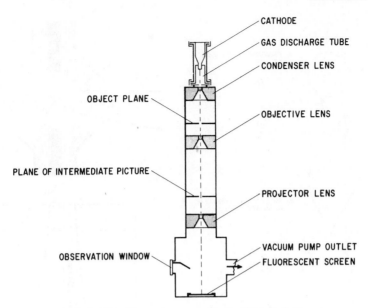

FIG. 1. First Supermicroscope (Ruska 1934, Ref. 3).

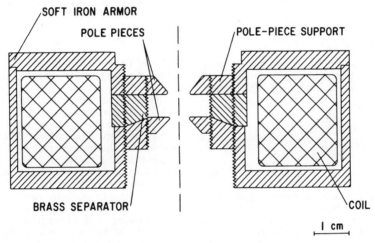

FIG. 2. Magnetic Lens (Ruska 1934, Ref. 3).

While its velocity component normal to the field lines causes it to describe a circle, the velocity component parallel to the field lines remains unchanged. Since the time required to describe a circle is independent of the normal velocity, all circles, large or small, are traversed in the same time interval. In an electron beam with low divergence where, therefore, the velocities parallel to the magnetic field (v_z) are identical, all electrons leaving one point P on the axis will meet downstream at another point P' at a distance

$$d = \frac{v_z}{\tau} \tag{6}$$

with angles to the axis identical to those they had at point P (see Fig. 3).

A "long" magnetic lens, having a uniform magnetic field extending from the object to the image point, will form an upright picture of the object with an image to object ratio of 1 to 1.

A "thin" magnetic lens is a lens with a magnetic field short compared to the object-to-image distance. A "weak" thin lens is a lens with the focal length large compared to the axial length of the magnetic field. The refractive power, i.e., the reciprocal of the focal length, of such a lens is determined by:

$$\frac{1}{f} = \frac{0.022}{V} \int_{-\infty}^{+\infty} B_z{}^2 dz \ [\mathrm{cm^{-1}}] \tag{7}$$

It images according to the general optical equation:

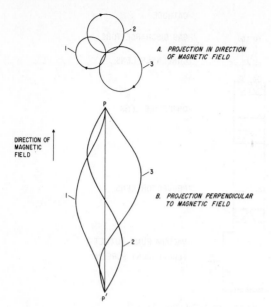

FIG. 3. Cycloids, described by electrons in uniform magnetic field.

$$\frac{1}{f} = \frac{1}{a} + \frac{1}{b} \qquad (8)$$

where a is the object distance and b is the image distance. The picture is turned around from the position of the object. The angle it is turned is determined by:

$$\theta_1 = \frac{0.149}{\sqrt{V}} \int_{-\infty}^{+\infty} B_z dz \ [\text{radians}] \qquad (9)$$

The objective and projector lenses of the electron microscope require extremely short focal lengths in order to obtain high magnifications without going to extremely long microscopes. These lenses have, therefore, pole pieces which limit the extent of the magnetic field, both in the axial and radial dimensions. The treatment of strong, thin magnetic lenses can be found in references 4 and 5.

Electrostatic Lenses *Immersion lenses* consist of two apertures or two coaxial cylinders at different potentials. They are important as lenses for television or oscillograph cathode-ray tubes. The lenses used in electrostatic transmission electron microscopes are usually *unipotential* or *Einzel-lenses*. They have the same potential on either side of the lens. They consist of three apertures: the two outer apertures are at ground or anode potential, and the center electrode can have either a positive or negative potential. Regardless of whether a positive or a negative potential is applied, the lens will always be convergent. Figure 4(a) shows the equipotential lines of such a lens; Fig. 4(b) shows the focal length vs V_L/V_0 for this lens, where

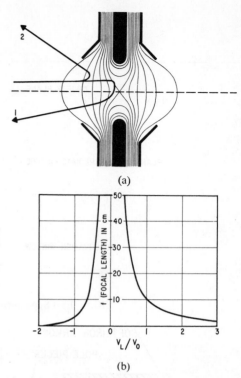

(a)

(b)

FIG. 4. Unipotential or Einzel-lens: (a) equipotential lines (Ref. 6); (b) focal length vs V_L/V_0 (Ref. 7).

V_L is the voltage applied to the center electrode and V_0 the cathode potential. Figure 5 shows the design of a typical electrostatic lens.

The Standard Transmission Microscope The best known electron microscope is the magnetic transmission microscope where the image is formed by electrons which have passed through the specimen. It is composed of the following major sections: electron gun, condenser lens, specimen chamber, objective lens, projector lens, viewing and photographing chamber. It has the following ancillary equipment: (1) power supplies for high voltage, heater voltage, and focusing currents; (2) vacuum systems.

The *electron gun* generates the electron beam which illuminates the object. It has to provide the required electron density within a certain limited divergence. It consists of a hairpin tungsten filament enclosed in a cup-shaped electrode at cathode or a more negative potential. While the anode facing the cathode is at ground potential, the cathode is maintained at a high negative potential, usually between 50 and 100 kV.

The *condenser lens* or lenses increase the electron density reaching the specimen by concentrating the beam. An aperture in the condenser lens of 0.25 to 0.5 mm diameter reduces the amount of stray electrons reaching the specimen.

The *objective lens* provides the first magnification. It is a strong, thin lens with a high re-

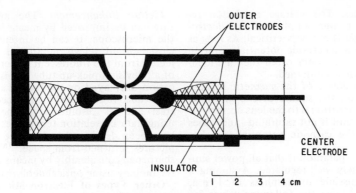

FIG. 5. Typical electrostatic lens (see ref. 8).

fractive power. It has, therefore, narrow precision pole pieces. An aperture of 25 to 100μ diameter is usually inserted in the gap of this lens to limit the beam divergence. The specimen is mounted above and very close to this magnetic gap.

The *projector* or *image lens* selects a small portion of the intermediate image produced by the objective lens and magnifies it again. A third electron-optical magnification is in some cases produced by a second projector lens.

The *specimen chamber* is located above the objective lens. It can be opened for inserting the specimen without disturbing the vacuum in the main column. It has adjustments that permit shifting the specimen in the object plane in order to locate the area of interest. Some models have special facilities to keep the specimen at certain high or low temperatures.

The *viewing chamber* at the bottom of the microscope column contains the fine-grain fluorescent screen that can be observed through glass windows either directly or through a telescope. If a permanent record is desired, the fluorescent screen is moved aside and a photographic plate inside a plate holder is exposed. The electrons produce a latent image directly. Each plate can be removed from the vacuum separately.

In some cases when an extremely high magnification, for instance 100 000 times, is desired, it may pay to magnify electron-optically to a somewhat lower magnification and to add a final photographic enlargement later; the adjustment of the electron microscope is then much easier, since the field of vision is so much larger.

A photographic film is used sometimes, instead of plates, if a series of pictures is to be taken and if extremely high resolution is not required.

The *vacuum system*, generally maintaining a vacuum of 10^{-4} to 10^{-5} torr (1 torr = 1 mm Hg), consists usually of an oil diffusion pump backed by a mechanical forepump. A second mechanical pump is sometimes used to purge the specimen chamber and the photographic plate lock before they are opened to the main

vacuum column. A water or liquid-nitrogen-cooled baffle is used to reduce backstreaming of oil vapor into the chamber.

While this type of vacuum system may be satisfactory for a great number of applications, it proved to be unsatisfactory for more demanding investigations. It is impossible to prevent completely the backstreaming of diffusion pump oil into the system. The electron beam interacts with the oil molecules, causing hydrocarbon "varnish" to be deposited on the specimen and on critical apertures. This limits the exposure time and requires frequent cleaning of apertures. Heating or cooling the specimen stage will improve the situation, but the vacuum may still not be satisfactory, especially in cases where film depositions are studied in the microscope.

When a dry vacuum is desired, ion pumps or turbomolecular pumps are used, often in conjunction with titanium sublimation pumps. To bring the system down to the pressure where these pumps take over, rotary oil pumps or nitrogen-cooled zeolite molecular sieve traps are used.

Scientists who converted their system from oil diffusion pumps to dry pumps report a longer cathode life, reduced exposure time, sharper pictures, and practically the elimination of the varnish problem. They report a reduction in varnish build-up from .5 to 1 nm sec^{-1} down to .1 to .5 nm min^{-1}.*)

To reduce the contamination from elastomer o-rings, they are sometimes replaced in critical locations, for instance in the specimen chamber, by metal gaskets—usually oxygen-free copper rings. Viton A o-rings are used for less critical seals. These o-rings have to be outgassed for many hours in vacuum at a temperature of 150°C before they can be installed in the system. Photographic plates must be outgassed too before they can be placed in the chamber.

*The build-up is measured by observing the decrease in the radius of a small hole, approximately 1 μ in diameter, in a carbon film deposited on a thin substrate.

Power Supplies. The voltage regulation required for the power supplies of the *electrostatic* microscope is not very critical. As long as the lens voltage and cathode potential maintain the same linear ratio—very often they are identical—a good image is obtained.

The refractive power of the *magnetic* lens depends directly on the square of the magnetic flux, which is proportional to the lens current—if the magnetic circuit is not saturated—and varies inversely with the cathode potential [see Eq. (7)].

It is, therefore, paramount that all power supplies be extremely well-regulated. Assuming a maximum permissible unsharpness of 1 nm, Zworykin et al.[9] give the following values for maximum permissible instabilities:

High-voltage power supply: $\dfrac{\Delta V}{V} = 1.1 \times 10^{-4}$

Objective lens: $\dfrac{\Delta I_1}{I_1} = 0.55 \times 10^{-4}$

Projector lens: $\dfrac{\Delta I_2}{I_2} = 1.3 \times 10^{-4}$

Condenser lens: $\dfrac{\Delta I_3}{I_3} = 1 \times 10^{-3}$

The values guaranteed by various manufacturers are often considerably lower, especially during short exposure times.

Image Formation. In the transmission electron microscope, the image is formed by the scattering of electrons during their passage through the specimen. The absence of the scattered electrons produces the lighter or darker appearance of each spot in the image. Three types of electrons emerge after transit through the specimen: unscattered electrons, elastically scattered electrons, and inelastically scattered electrons. The *unscattered* electrons are those that did not interact with the atoms of the specimen. They traversed it without deviating from their trajectory. The *elastically scattered* electrons interacted with the nuclei of atoms in their path. The interaction is especially strong with heavy nuclei. The number of elastically scattered electrons is proportional to the $\frac{4}{3}$ power of Z, the atomic number of the atoms. The elastically scattered electrons did not lose kinetic energy but changed their direction significantly. *Inelastically scattered* electrons did interact with the electrons of the atoms in their path. They emerge within a narrow angle but have given up some of their energy. Their number is proportional to the $\frac{1}{3}$ power of Z. Elastically scattered electrons are removed, to a large extent, by the limiting aperture in the gap of the objective lens. Inelastically scattered electrons cause chromatic aberrations. They are focused in a plane other than the image plane of the unscattered electrons. They degrade the image.

Picture Enhancement. The microscope picture can be improved by means independent of the microscope. It can be intensified by using closed-circuit television. In this case it is projected from the fluorescent screen onto the face of a television pick-up tube and is, after amplification, displayed on the face of a television picture tube. It can also be enhanced; e.g., its contrast and its resolution can be improved by using data correlation techniques, methods that have been developed to improve the quality of pictures returned from space.[10a] It can also be sharpened considerably by means of holographic technology using optical deblurring filters.[10b]

Other Types of Electron Microscopes *Electrostatic Electron Microscope.* Its development is as old as the development of the magnetic electron microscope.[11] It uses mostly unipotential lenses. Electrostatic transmission electron microscopes are used where a high resolution is not required. Since electrostatic lenses do not require highly regulated power supplies, they are in general less costly than magnetic microscopes.

Emission Electron Microscope. It has been used to study various surface phenomena. The first electrostatic and one of the first magnetic microscopes were used to study thermionic emission. Secondary emission and photo emission have also been studied. For the *field emission microscope* see FIELD EMISSION.

Million Volt Electron Microscope. The first extra high voltage microscope went into operation in 1960. It was built by Dupouy and Perrier at the Laboratoire d'Optique Electronique, Toulouse, France.[12] It was designed for 1.5 MV operation. The first 1 MV microscope in the United States started operation in 1967 at the U. S. Steel Corp. Research Center at Monroeville, Pennsylvania. By the end of 1972 there were supposed to be five such instruments in the United States, eight in Great Britain, seven in Japan, four in France, and one each in West Germany and Sweden. Development is under way in the U.S.S.R., East Germany and Canada. A number of 500 to 750 kV instruments are also in operation at the present time. Dupouy and the Hitachi Company have each built and tested 3 MV microscopes and designs for a 6 to 10 MV instrument are reported to be under consideration by the Hitachi Company.

The ever increasing number of these rather expensive instruments indicates that they are able to provide information that is not obtainable in any other way. The MV microscope has the advantage of a higher resolution due to the shorter wavelength of the electrons at the higher voltage. It has a five to eight times greater penetration power than the conventional transmission microscope. It permits, therefore, the investigation of specimens of greater thickness. Biological specimens can be examined that could not be penetrated and that had to be sectioned before. Bulk properties of various materials, for instance of crystalline

materials, can be investigated that may be different from those of thin foils. Materials can be studied that could not be sliced thin enough or that would be affected or contaminated by the slicing process. Another advantage is that, at the higher voltage, the electrons have a lower cross section for inelastic scattering. This leads to lower radiation damage in materials such as polymers that are easily damaged at voltages between 15 and 100 kV. The reduced inelastic scattering leads also to reduced chromatic aberration.

Mirror Microscope.[13] If we were to apply to the unipotential lens in Fig. 4(a) a potential much more negative than that of the cathode, a zero potential line would cross the center of the lens, which the electrons cannot penetrate. They would have to turn back. The unipotential lens is then turned into a mirror. If the electrons are able to penetrate into the convergent center section of the lens, the mirror will act as a convergent mirror [electron path 1 in Fig. 4(a)]. If the potential of the center electrode is so highly negative that the electrons can penetrate only into the divergent outer section, the mirror is divergent (electron path 2).

If the center electrode of the unipotential lens is closed and is kept at cathode or a somewhat more negative than cathode potential, the unipotential lens would be transformed into a divergent immersion mirror. By keeping the potential of this electrode very close to cathode potential, the electrons will penetrate close to its surface before they turn around. At the lowest point, they will have only a very small tangential energy. They are, therefore, easily influenced by various parameters of the specimen surface, e.g., by weak magnetic fields, by electrostatic charges or by distortions in the electrostatic field close to the surface due to surface roughness. They form, therefore, an enlarged image of certain surface features if a fluorescent screen is mounted some distance away from the mirror, e.g., on the underside of the preceding lens. This screen has a small aperture in order to admit the electron beam to the mirror.

Scanning Electron Microscope. While in the standard transmission electron microscope the total area under observation is irradiated at the same time by the electron beam, only a single element of this area is irradiated at any one time by the "probe" in the scanning electron microscope (SEM). This probe is a very fine electron beam that has been demagnified by magnetic lenses. It scans the specimen in a television-type raster. The finer the probe, the higher is the resolution of the microscope. The signal originating from each element while it is under irradiation modulates the electron beam of a display tube. The beam of the display tube is deflected synchronously with the probe scan.

A system of this type without probe demagnification, and therefore, with low resolution was first used by M. Knoll in 1936.[14] A demagnified probe was used by M. von Ardenne in 1938. The SEM has been developed since that time into an extremely useful tool through the work of many researchers. Various models are now commercially available.

The SEM can operate in a number of different modes that will supply different information about the specimen. The SEM can make use of:

(a) Secondary electrons from the surface of a thick specimen.
(b) Backscattered electrons from the surface.
(c) Transmitted electrons.

In some cases cathodo-luminescence and x-rays are used.

The SEM operates in its most common form at a voltage between 5 kV and 50 kV. It has a tungsten hairpin cathode and two demagnifying lenses that are built like the lenses of the standard transmission microscope (see Fig. 6). The final lens has built inside its inner cylinder two sets of vertical and horizontal scanning coils. One set near the top of the lens deflects the beam away from the axis, while the second set deflects it in the opposite direction towards the axis, so that the beam crosses the axis in the exit aperture of the lens. Stigmators are used to correct imperfections of the lens.

The specimen is held several millimeters be-

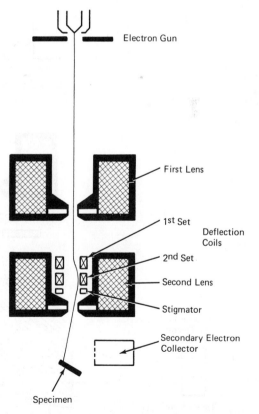

FIG. 6. Typical scanning electron microscope.

low the exit aperture, at a tilting angle between 30° and 60°. The distance has to be great enough to prevent the magnetic field of the lens from interfering with the measurement. Backscattered electrons are collected by a ring electrode mounted below the exit aperture of the lens. Secondary electrons are collected by a collector mounted on the side, facing the specimen. The collector is at a high enough positive potential to attract the secondary electrons that leave the specimen with an energy of a few volts. Inside the collector box is a scintillation crystal at a still higher positive potential. The light flashes produced by the impinging electrons are conducted through a light pipe to a photomultiplier tube located outside the vacuum chamber. The signal from the photomultiplier is amplified and used to modulate the beam of the display cathode ray tube. The display tube has, usually, a long-persistent phosphor screen. The micrograph is taken photographically from the face of the display tube. It is possible to display different signals side by side that are obtained from different types of collectors. Storage tubes may be used in place of ordinary display tubes. The signal can also be stored on magnetic tape or on a magnetic drum and can be fed to a computer for image

enhancement. The magnification of the SEM is determined by the size of the raster on the specimen. The number of scanning lines per frame can be varied between 250 and 1000 lines or more. The time per scan can be varied from a fraction of a second, for observation, to several minutes for recording. Since the probe currents are very small, on the order of 10^{-12} to 10^{-10} A, long exposure times are necessary in order to obtain a good signal-to-noise ratio. The exposure time is limited by the stability of the voltage supplies and the difficulty of eliminating mechanical vibrations completely.

The SEM has a very small beam-convergence angle—between .005 and .01 radian. This means that it has a great depth of focus, much greater than that of optical or standard transmission microscopes. This accounts for the three-dimensional qualities of its pictures.

In the secondary emission mode the contrast in the picture is generated by a change in the composition of the specimen, causing a change in the secondary emission ratio. Where the composition of the specimen surface is so uniform that the secondary emission ratio varies very little, the contrast can be produced by the topography of the surface. The reason for this is that the secondary emission ratio increases as

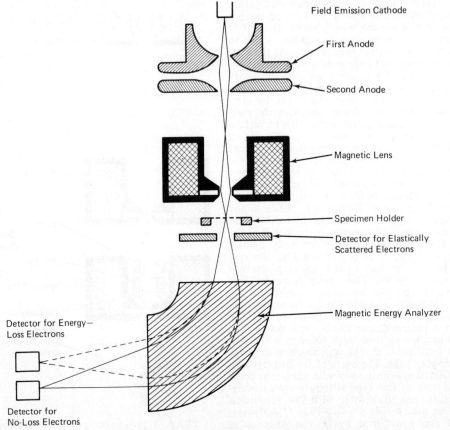

FIG. 7. Crewe-type scanning electron microscope.

the angle of incidence of the primary electron increases.

The resolution of the SEM described above is limited to 10 to 25 nm (100 to 250 Å). This limitation is determined by the size of the electron probe. This in turn is determined by the limiting aperture near the cathode, by the demagnification of the electron optical system, and by the increase in spot size due to the range in kinetic energy of the electrons emerging from the cathode. The hot tungsten cathode has a low emission density even when operated at the highest temperature compatible with a useful life. Owing to its high temperature, the emitted electrons have a great range in kinetic energy (approximately 0.9 V). A different cathode at a lower temperature and higher emission density would permit a smaller limiting aperture for the same optical system and the same probe current. The lanthanum hexaboride cathode introduced by A. N. Broers[15] is a great improvement over the tungsten filament. A greater improvement was achieved by A. V. Crewe of the University of Chicago by introducing a field emission electron source.[16] The field emission technique was invented in 1937 by E. W. Müller (see FIELD EMISSION). In Crewe's SEM (see Fig. 7) the field emission cathode, which requires a vacuum of 10^{-10} torr, consists of a fine tungsten point, 100 nm in diameter. A negative potential of 3 kV is applied to the cathode against a spherical first anode. A second anode at ground potential is at a potential of 30 kV against the cathode. The two anodes together form an immersion lens. Emission currents of several microamperes emanating from a virtual spot as small as 3 nm are possible. Since the tungsten tip is at room temperature, the range of kinetic energy of the emitted electrons is less than 0.2 V. By adding a magnetic lens, a probe diameter of 0.5 nm (5 Å) is possible with a probe current of 10^{-11} to 10^{-10} A.

Crewe collects separately the three types of electrons that emerge after passing through the specimen, namely: unscattered, elastically scattered, and inelastically scattered electrons. A ring electrode mounted underneath the specimen collects essentially all elastically scattered electrons that have changed their direction significantly. The opening in the ring permits the unscattered and the inelastically scattered electrons to pass. A magnetic—or electrostatic—analyzer separates the two types. In a homogeneous magnetic field perpendicular to the electron path, the inelastically scattered electrons will describe a circle of smaller radius than the unscattered electrons due to their lower energy. Two different detectors can then collect the two types separately. Since the number of elastically scattered electrons increases much faster than the number of inelastically scattered electrons with increasing atomic number, the signals can be used to determine the atomic number of the atoms at the spot under investigation.

MARTIN M. FREUNDLICH

References

1. Ruska, E., "Fifth International Congress for Electron Microscopy," New York, Academic Press, 1962.
2. Freundlich, M. M., "Origin of the Electron Microscope," *Science,* 142 (3589), 185–188 (1963).
3. Ruska, E., "Uber Fortschritte im Bau und in der Leistung des Magnetischen Elektronenmikroskops," *Z. f. Physik,* 87 (9 & 10), 580–602 (1934).
4. Ruska, E., *Arch. Elektrotechn.,* 38, 102–130 (1944).
5. Hall, C. E., "Introduction to Electron Microscopy," Chapter 5, New York, McGraw-Hill Book Co., 1953.
6. Mahl, H., and Pendzich, A., *Z. Tech. Physik,* 24, 38–42 (1943).
7. Johannson, H., and Scherzer, O., *Z. f. Physik,* 80, 183–202 (1933).
8. Mahl, H., *Jahrb. AEG Forsch.,* 7, 43–56 (1940).
9. Zworykin, V. K., Morton, G. A., Ramberg, E. G., Hillier, J., and Vance, A. W., "Electron Optics and the Electron Microscope," New York, John Wiley & Sons, 1945 (pg. 214).
10a. Andrews, H. C., Tescher, A. G., and Kruger, R. P., "Image Processing by Digital Computers," *IEEE Spectrum,* 9 (7), 20–32 (July 1972).
10b. Stroke, G. W., "Sharpening Images by Holography," *New Scientist* 23 Sept. 1971; "Optical Computing," *IEEE Spectrum,* 9 (12), 24–41 (December 1972).
11. Brüche, E., "Elektronenmikroskop," *Naturw.,* 20, 49 (1932).
    Brüche, E., and Johannson, H., "Elektronenoptik und Elektronenmikroskop," *Naturw.,* 20, 353–358 (1932).
12. Dupouy, G., and Perrier, F., *J. Microscopie,* 1, 167–192 (1962).
13. Hottenroth, G., *Ann. Physik,* 30 (5), 689–711 (1937).
14. Knoll, M., "Aufladepotential und Sekundäremission Elektronenbestrahlter Körper," *Z. Techn. Physik,* 16 (11), 467–475 (1935); "Aenderung der Sekundären Elektronenemission von Isolatoren und Halbleitern durch Elektronenbestrahlung," *Naturw.,* 24 (22), 345 (1936).
15. Broers, A. N., *Rev. Sci. Instr.,* 40, 1040 (1969).
16. Crewe, A. V., "Scanning Electron Microscopes: Is High Resolution Possible?" *Science,* 154 (3750), 729–738 (1966).
    Crewe, A. V., "A High Resolution Scanning Electron Microscope," *Sci. Amer.,* 224 (4), 26–35 (1971).

Cross-references: ELECTRON OPTICS, FIELD EMISSION, MICROSCOPE.

ELECTRON OPTICS

The invention of wave mechanics in 1926 by Heisenberg and Schrödinger saw a revolution in physics. It became apparent that the ideas of classical dynamics could be formally replaced when a stream of particles was considered. According to the well-known De Broglie hy-

pothesis, a wavelength λ can be assigned to any material particle such that

$$\lambda = h/mv \qquad (1)$$

where h is Planck's constant, m is the particle mass, and v is the particle velocity.

As one of the many consequences of these ideas, the new science of electron optics emerged. In the same year, Busch demonstrated that the action of a short axially symmetrical magnetic field on a beam of electrons was similar to that of a glass lens on light. Terms used before then in optics found their use in describing electron devices. Electron "lenses" and "mirrors" having "focal lengths" and "resolutions and aberrations" were described. This analogy has proved useful in the study of the behavior of electrons in electronic valves, magnetrons and klystrons, traveling wave tubes, cathode ray tubes, and electron microscopes, to name only a few devices. The original concept of the electron microscope was evolved by direct analogy with the light microscope.

An electron which has fallen through a potential V has a kinetic energy $\Gamma = \frac{1}{2}mv^2 = eV$. Hence $v = (2eV)^{1/2}/m^{1/2}$, and using Eq. (1), we obtain the useful formula expressing electron wavelength in terms of volts

$$\lambda = \left(\frac{150}{V}\right)^{1/2} \qquad (2)$$

where λ is in angstroms.

In light optics, the least resolvable distance S between two objects is given by the Abbe expression $S = \lambda/(2n \sin i)$, where n is the refractive index of the material between object and lens and $2i$ is the angle subtended at the lens by the object; $n \sin i$ is called the numerical aperture. In the case of white light of equivalent $\lambda = 5600$ Å,

$$S_{(\text{minimum, light})} = 1800 \text{ Å, i.e., } 1.8 \times 10^{-5} \text{ cm.}$$

Using the same expression and Eq. (2), which gives λ for an electron $= 0.04$ Å for $V = 100 \text{ kV}$,

$$S_{(\text{minimum, electrons})} \simeq 0.04 \text{ Å}$$

i.e., small fractions of an angstrom can be resolved. However, the theory does not take into account the fact that lenses are imperfect. Spherical aberrations drastically affect the situation. In addition, certain diffraction defects and scattering impose limitations. These facts and others make it impossible to obtain resolutions near the theoretical maximum. Instead, 2.0 Å is a better theoretical value. Practical limiting resolutions obtained are of the order of 2.5 Å to 3.0 Å.

Source of Electrons The basic source of electrons in electron tubes is the heated filament or disk. The well-known equation $J = AT^2 \exp(-\phi/kT)$ describes the emission, where J is the current density, T is the temperature, ϕ is the work function of the emitting material, A is a constant, and k is Boltzmann's constant. J is enhanced by increasing T or reducing ϕ. Typical cathode materials used are tungsten, tantalum, and the oxides of barium and strontium.

A voltage is applied to accelerate the emitted electrons, and the current density is given by $J = AT^2 \exp(-\phi/kT)$ if they are removed to the anode. However, many electrons stay near the cathode and repel other emitted electrons back to the cathode. Most devices operate in this "space-charge limited" way. For any electrode configuration, the current density is then $J = GV$ where V is the applied voltage and G is a constant for the particular electrode configuration. G is roughly equivalent to electrical conductance and is called the "perveance." The constant is fundamentally important. The higher G is in value, the greater is the efficiency of the beam system.

In simple designs, the axial portion of the cathode is overloaded, producing excessive emission and cathode burn-out. To avoid this situation, carefully shaped electrodes must be used, but the acceptable design depends upon the application. A bent hairpin point cathode is used in, for example, the electron microscope. It produces low perveance but high emission density. Since G is low, the field at the cathode can be high, and this tends to reduce ϕ, giving emission at lower temperature. The electron guns for klystrons, traveling wave tubes, and metallurgical applications such as vacuum melting and welding require higher efficiency and current density. Hence they are high-perveance guns.

Beam Control Electrostatic and magnetic fields control the motion of an electron according to the following equation:

$$\overline{F} = m\frac{dv}{dt} = e\,(\overline{E} + \overline{v} \times \overline{B}) \qquad (3)$$

where

$\overline{F}$ = force
$\overline{E}$ = electrostatic field
$\overline{B}$ = magnetic field
$\overline{v}$ = electron velocity
e = electronic charge

The electron must travel in a vacuum if it is not to be scattered and lose its kinetic energy by collision with relatively massive gas molecules. Nuclear particles such as protons and neutrons are each about 1837 times larger in mass than the electron.

Electrostatic Electron Lenses If in Eq. (3), $\overline{B} = 0$, then $\overline{F} = e\overline{E}$. The equation says that an electron in a field $\overline{E}$ experiences a force $\overline{F}$ in the direction of the field. Thus in the system shown in Fig. 1 where there is a voltage V_1 on cylinder 1 and V_2 on cylinder 2, and where $V_2 > V_1$, the field and the path of an electron are as shown. The electron moving from left to right increases its velocity and is deflected

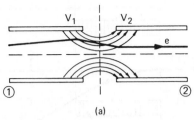 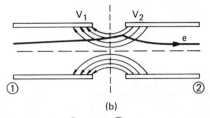

(a)   (b)

FIG. 1. Electrostatic focusing of electron beam by cylinder lenses ① and ②. (a), voltage $V_2 > V_1$; (b), voltage $V_2 < V_1$.

towards the axis. After passing the median, the force is away from the axis, but since velocity is increased, the electron spends less time in this part of the field. Therefore, deflection away from the axis is less than it was towards it, and there is a net convergence. If $V_2 < V_1$, as in Fig. 1 (b), then for an electron beam traveling from left to right the lens will still be convergent because maximum deflection will occur after the electrons have slowed down. All such lenses are convergent for $\overline{E} = 0$ on both sides of the lens.

Magnetic Electron Lenses If in Eq. (3) $\overline{E} = 0$, then $\overline{F} = e\overline{v} \times \overline{B}$. This says that the force $\overline{F} = e|\overline{v}||\overline{B}| \sin \theta \, \overline{\epsilon}$ where $|\overline{v}|$ and $|\overline{B}|$ are the numerical values of the vectors and θ is the angle between them; $\overline{\epsilon}$ is a unit vector perpendicular to both, and indicates the direction of the force. For $\overline{F}$ to be greater than 0, $\overline{v}$ must be greater than 0. The force constrains the electron to move in a circle of radius $\rho = (\overline{v} \sin \theta)/(\overline{B} \, e/m)$. At the same time it moves in a perpendicular direction with velocity $\overline{v} \cos \theta$, and therefore, it traces the path of a helix and returns to the axis in a time $T = 2\pi/(\overline{B} \, e/m)$ which is independent of both $\overline{v}$ and θ. The net effect is that all electrons are focused by $\overline{B}$ to produce an image of the source from which they diverge.

The simple magnetic lens consists of a short coil of wire contained in a surrounding shield of magnetic material. A small gap in the case material concentrates the escaping field when the coil is energized. The electron microscope (shown in Fig. 2) illustrates the use of magnetic lenses. The coils are wound in opposite sense to cancel the spiral distortion of the electron beam which is introduced by the individual lenses.

Electrostatic Deflection If in Fig. 3(a) a voltage V_d exists between the plates $x_1 \, x_2$ and an electron enters along the axis with a constant velocity $v = (2 \, Ve/m)^{1/2}$, then because of the field $\overline{E}_y$ caused by V_d, a transverse force $\overline{F}_y$ causes a motion in this direction to be impinged on the electron, i.e., $m \, (d^2y/dt^2) = V_d e/d$, from which $dy/dt = (V_d/d) \, (e/m) \, t$ and $y = \frac{1}{2} \, (V_d/d) \, (e/m) \, t^2$. The force acts for time $t = \ell/v$; thus deflection $y = \frac{1}{2} \, (V_d/d) \, (e/m) \, (\ell/v)^2 = \frac{1}{4} \, (V_d/d) \, (\ell^2/V)$. The additional deflection, after $\overline{F}$ has ceased to act on the electron, is $y^1 = (V_d/V) \, (\ell L/2d)$.

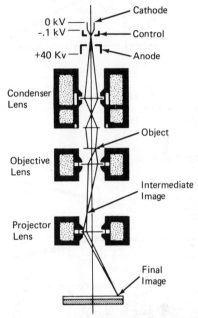

FIG. 2. Schematic diagram illustrating the general arrangement of a transmission electron microscope.

Magnetic Deflection See Fig. 3(b). If $\overline{B}$ is a sharply defined field, then the deflection on leaving the field is given by $y = \ell^2/2\rho$. Total deflection $D = L \tan \alpha + y$. To a good approximation

$$D = \frac{\overline{B} L \ell}{v} \frac{e}{m} \left(1 + \frac{1}{2L}\right).$$

It should be emphasized that these considerations are only approximate. In practice, factors such as the inability to sharply define a field edge in space cause added complications.

Cathode Ray Tubes A device worthy of brief consideration is the cathode ray display tube. Its basic components are as follows: an electron gun, an acceleration and focus system, a deflection, and a display system which is normally a phosphor screen. Depending on the type of tube the applied voltage causes electrostatic or magnetic deflection. In the oscilloscope tube electrostatic deflection is used while in the large display tube, such as the television

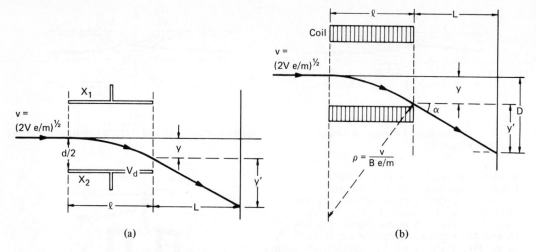

FIG. 3. (a) Deflection of electron beam by electric field between parallel plates X_1X_2. (b) Deflection of electron beam by magnetic field. Electron path is an arc of a circle only while it is influenced by field. After leaving the field the path is linear.

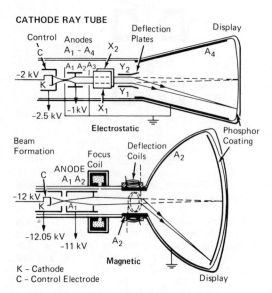

FIG. 4. Schematic diagram of cathode ray tubes.

tube, magnetic deflection is used because of the large scan angles which are required. The tubes are illustrated in Fig. 4.

Advanced Oscilloscope Tubes The instrument tube shown in Fig. 4 is of low cost and has limited frequency performance to 5 to 10 MHz. If voltage on A_4 is increased, then it becomes increasingly difficult to deflect the beam in such a tube. In recent years performance of the comparatively low-cost tube has been increased to greater than 50 MHz by the introduction of post-deflection acceleration systems, the most successful of which is shown in the tube illustrated in Fig. 5. Here a grid of

fine wires placed over the end of the gun assembly shields the deflection area from the effect of the high acceleration field required for high brightness and high writing speed. The electrons pass through the grid and those which collide with it cause low energy emission of secondary electrons which can be collected readily by placing a small positive voltage on a neighbouring electrode such as A_4, and therefore they do not cause background illumination of the image produced by the primary beam.

Table 1 illustrates the operating features and performance of the tube. The display envelope is commonly rectangular and an external magnetic coil is needed to align the beam axes with those of the display face. Plate capacitances are reduced by the use of side pins. Nevertheless these capacitances and transit time phenomena contribute to the main limitations for use at higher frequencies. However, other tubes operating at frequencies greater than 500 MHz have been developed.

Color Television Tube In the television tube the beam must be deflected to trace each part of the screen in sequence while it is simultaneously intensity modulated. The resulting picture is a mosaic of dark and light elements. Three primary red, green and blue pictures must be displayed in exact registration to obtain a a high-quality color picture. Color mixing to produce the wide range of colors required is obtained subjectively and depends on the relative brightnesses of the three primary light yields at a particular point on the screen. There are numerous ways of achieving the color picture, but the "shadow mask tube" has been developed to provide the most economical method. There are three primary guns

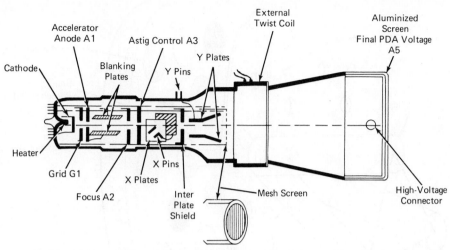

FIG. 5. Advanced Instrument Cathode Ray Tube. Mesh screen, held near mean plate potential, prevents PDA field from reducing deflection plate sensitivity. Note other features such as side pin connection to plates to reduce capacitance; also the blanking arrangement for blanking the beam during time-base flyback. (The method has advantages over using grid G1.) See Table 1 for other information.

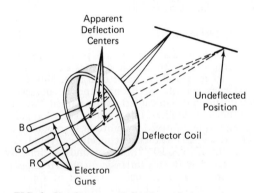

FIG. 6. Simultaneous deflection of three electron beams in shadow mask color tube.

in the tube, each tilted to converge to a central point near the screen. A single deflection coil is used to scan the beams in registration (as shown in Fig. 6. Additional deflection yokes carry currents derived from the main deflection waveform to introduce convergence corrections as needed to maintain registration over the complete screen.

The screen must emit red light when bombarded by electrons from the red gun, green from the green gun, and blue from the blue gun. To enable this to occur a perforated metal mask is positioned about 12 mm from the screen and the beams in fact converge to its central point rather than that of the screen. Electrons must pass through the mask holes to reach the screen as shown in Fig. 7. The beams appear to originate from three apparent deflection centers in the deflection field. Thus, they will strike the face in three points of a triangle when passing through a particular hole. Red, green, or blue emitting phosphor "dots" are deposited at these points as appropriate. The plate is called a shadow mask because when one gun is switched on, the unwanted dots are

TABLE 1. PERFORMANCE OF MESH PDA TUBE (See Reference 5)

Beam deflection plate potential	1250 V[a]	1500 V
First acceleration plate potential	1250 V	1500 V
Focusing plate potential	160–80 V	200–100 V
PDA voltage	12.5 KV	12.5 KV
Typical screen current	10 μA	10 μA
Line width 10 μA	0.36 mm	0.32 mm
Linearity	2 per cent	2 per cent
Y sensitivity	4.8 Vcm^{-1}	5.8 Vcm^{-1}
X sensitivity (time base)	9 Vcm^{-1}	11 Vcm^{-1}
Y scan	80 mm	
X scan	100 mm	
Tube length	350 mm	

[a]Voltages w.r.t. cathode.

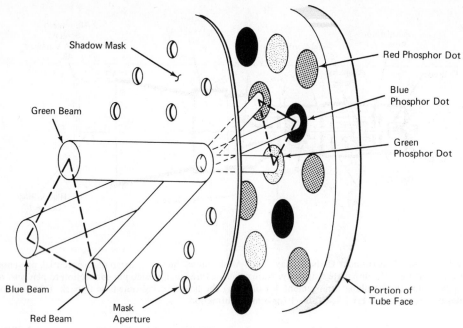

Shadow Mask

Green Beam

Blue Beam

Red Beam

Mask
Aperture

Red Phosphor Dot

Blue
Phosphor Dot

Green
Phosphor Dot

Portion of
Tube Face

FIG. 7. Operation of shadow mask in color television tube.

not energized since they lie in its shadow. Typical mask holes are 0.5 mm in diameter and about 0.7 mm apart. The total number of holes is about 400 000 for a 25-inch tube.

During manufacture the mask itself is used to process the screen. The phosphor is deposited with a photosensitive lacquer and a UV light source is placed at the appropriate deflection center. The screen is exposed through the mask, developed, and the process repeated for the other two colors. The deflection centers move slightly towards the screen for large deflection angles, and a correction lens has to be used to compensate during exposure. The accurate positioning of the million or more phosphor dots is achieved in this way.

BARRY A. GEORGE

References

1. Klemperer, "Electron Optics," Cambridge, The University Press, 1953 (for a rigorous treatment of electron optics).
2. Bakish, R., "Introduction to Electron Beam Technology," New York, John Wiley & Sons, 1962 (for the practical applications of electron optics).
3. Bakish, R., Ed., "Electron and Ion Beams in Science and Technology," New York, John Wiley & Sons, 1965.
4. Pierce, J. R., "Theory and Design of Electron Beams, New York, Van Nostrand Reinhold, 1949.
5. "Performance data relates to modern German CRT," AEG Telefunken D14-131, Table 1.

Cross-references: ELECTRON; ELECTRON MICROSCOPE; ELECTRON TUBES; OPTICS, GEOMETRICAL; OSCILLOSCOPE; THERMIONICS.

ELECTRON SPIN

The electron is an elementary particle of essential importance to atomic physics and, in addition to its stability, basic charge e, and small rest mass m, it has been found to possess a quantum mechanical attribute named "spin." As the name implies, this is a mechanical angular momentum of fixed magnitude (projected) of $\frac{1}{2}\hbar$ (one-half Planck's constant divided by $2\pi = 0.52729 \times 10^{-34}$ joule-second). Intimately associated with this intrinsic quantized angular momentum is a magnetic moment of approximate value $e\hbar/2m$ (this quantity is called the *Bohr magneton*, μ_B, and has the value 0.92741 $\times 10^{-23}$, ampere-meter^2). While these concepts have a classical analogy in an imagined spinning or rotational motion of the charge and mass of the electron (assumed to be not a point), nevertheless, it is not possible to treat the electron spin wholly classically. For instance, the electron *gyromagnetic ratio* (ratio of the magnetic moment to the mechanical moment) is twice the classical value. Also, since the spin quantum number is limited to $\frac{1}{2}$, the spin disappears in the classical limit of $\hbar \to 0$. The fact that these properties are quantized implies their quantum nature, and indeed, the spin and magnetic moment are natural consequences of the relativistically invariant Dirac equation.

The hypothesis of the electron spin was first proposed in 1925 by Uhlenbeck and Goudsmit to explain the spectroscopic fine structure. The spin can be introduced as a vector $\mathbf{S}$ such that the square of the spin has the eigenvalue $\mathbf{S} \cdot \mathbf{S} = s(s + 1)\hbar^2$ where $s = \frac{1}{2}$ so that $S = \sqrt{\frac{3}{4}}\hbar$. The component of $\mathbf{S}$ in a specified direction, such as

the z axis, is $S_z = m_s \hbar$ where $m_s = +\frac{1}{2}$ or $-\frac{1}{2}$. This implies a spin angular momentum component of absolute value $\frac{1}{2}\hbar$. It is further necessary to postulate that the intrinsic magnetic moment of the electron (due to its spin) is $\mu = -e/m\mathbf{S}$. The component of μ along the z axis is then $\mu_z = m_s(e\hbar/m)$ or $+\mu_B, -\mu_B$.

Direct experimental evidence for quantized electron angular momentum and magnetic moment was presented by the Stern-Gerlach experiment in 1922. As shown in Fig. 1, a collimated beam of neutral silver atoms was directed through an inhomogeneous magnetic field. This field acted on the magnetic moment of the unpaired valence electron of the silver atom to produce a transverse force and, hence, a lateral deflection. In contrast to the classical expectation of a continuous spread of deflections due to many possible orientations of the electron magnetic moment, it was observed that only two opposite deflections occurred. This implied only two possible values of μ_z leading to the space quantization of spin, $m_s = \pm\frac{1}{2}$. Similar molecular beams have provided Rabi and Kusch and their colleagues with a supply of free atoms and molecules whose orientation in magnetic fields could be varied with magnetic resonance. Considerable information on atomic hyperfine structure has resulted from these measurements as well as recognition of the anomalous magnetic moment of the electron.

It had been thought that the magnetic moment of the *free* electron could not be directly measured due to the overwhelming force associated with the motion of the charge in the magnetic field. However, Crane and his colleagues have trapped electrons into helical orbits in a magnetic field and have accurately compared the cyclotron orbital frequency to the spin precessional frequency. This makes possible a highly precise measurement of the *electron magnetic moment* and its value was found to be slightly larger than a Bohr magneton, $\mu_e = 1.00115939\ \mu_B$. This anomaly is now understood as a consequence of the uncertainty jittering or pulsation in which

the electron exchanges virtual photons with the radiation field and experiences a sort of radiation reaction which increases its effective inertial mass. The spinning motion should not be affected by this change and, hence, the magnetic moment should be slightly greater when measured in units of Bohr magnetons using the apparent inertial mass of the electrons. The theory has been worked out in adequate detail and the electron magnetic moment is predicted to be $\mu_e = \mu_B(1 + \alpha/2\pi - 0.327\alpha^2/\pi^2)$ in good agreement with experiment. This more precise value is 0.92848×10^{-23} ampere-meter^2.

An important consequence of the spin concept occurs when the Pauli exclusion principle is applied to polyelectronic atoms using the spin quantum number $m_s = \pm\frac{1}{2}$ in addition to the principle quantum number n, the azimuthal quantum number $l \leq n-1$, and its projection $m_l \leq l$. The Pauli exclusion principle, based on the symmetry properties of the wave functions appropriate to the electron as a Fermi particle (i.e., spin $\frac{1}{2}$ particle), limits the number of electrons in an atom to those which can be differentiated by unique sets of quantum numbers. The possible combinations of the integral quantum numbers n, l, m_l with the two possible values of m_s determine the number and structure of the electrons in the atom. The recurring similarities in the orbital characteristics of the outer electrons produced by the quantum numbers determine the valencies and chemical characteristics of the atoms in a periodic fashion as exemplified in the periodic table.

Since the electron spin can have two orientations with respect to the axis of the orbital motion of the electron, a difference in energy will result from the interaction of the spin magnetic moment with the magnetic field produced by the orbital motion. This energy difference can be evaluated and leads to a *fine structure separation* energy which is less than the electronic level separations by a factor of the order of α^2 where $\alpha = e^2/4\pi\epsilon_0 c\hbar$ is the fine structure constant, approximately $1/137$. This

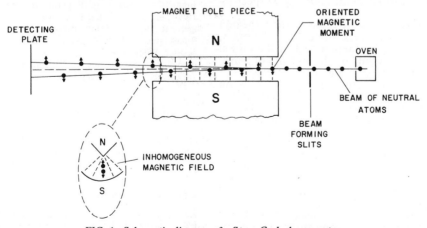

FIG. 1. Schematic diagram of a Stern-Gerlach apparatus.

is the origin of the well-known sodium yellow doublet.

The imposition of an external magnetic field gives rise to further splittings called *Zeeman effects*. The spin couples with the orbital motion giving rise to *splitting factors*, *g*, which are complicated because of the different gyromagnetic ratios of the spin and orbital motions. If the magnetic field is strong enough, it can uncouple the spin from the orbital motion giving a somewhat simpler Zeeman splitting called the complete Paschen-Back effect.

The magnetic effects of the electron's spin magnetic moment as well as their orbital moment are reduced by the tendency of electrons in atoms to pair spins of opposite direction and to complete shells of compensating orbital motion. This is even more pronounced in molecules since the chemical binding force is essentially the result of pairing electrons and completing shells. Nevertheless, when an unpaired electron exists, its magnetic moment is available for detection and can be measured by determining the aggregate magnetic moment of the sample. However, a more sensitive method, with considerably better accuracy and resolution, involves a magnetic resonance measurement (see MAGNETIC RESONANCE). When applied to the electron spin magnetic moment the measurement is often called ESR, or *electron spin resonance*, but more widely, EPR, or *electron paramagnetic resonance*. These techniques extend the earlier atomic and molecular beam resonance measurements of Rabi and his school.

The detection can be described, quantum mechanically, in terms of the absorption of photons of frequency f and photon quantum energy hf by excitation of transitions between neighboring quantum states of the atom or molecule separated by the Zeeman splitting due to an imposed external magnetic field. Since the energy difference is primarily $g\mu B = hf$, the frequency for reasonable fields of the order of a thousand gauss (i.e., $B \approx 0.1$ weber/m^2) is in the microwave region, i.e., $f \approx 10^{-10}$ cps. Consequently, the techniques appropriate to these measurements are associated with microwave spectroscopy.

The simplest cases are those in which the odd electrons are in S states with no orbital motion, or in which the magnetic effect of the orbital motion is "quenched" by the presence of neighboring atoms. Then, "spin-only" effects occur and the splitting factor g is close to 2. When quenching does not occur, the orbital motion magnetic field complicates the Zeeman splittings and gives rise to more complex patterns of resonance. In solids, the crystalline electric field affects the orbital motion and, hence, the pattern which then varies with crystal orientation. Interaction of the electron magnetic moments with the nuclear magnetic moments gives hyperfine splittings with even greater detail.

A large number of atoms which show paramagnetic or electron spin effects are those in the transition groups, i.e., iron group, rare earth, palladium group, platinum group and actinide group in which inner electron shells are being filled.

Other situations where the electron magnetic moment effects are useful for analysis or detection involve the presence of free radicals, molecules with broken bands from irradiation or heating, etc., conduction electrons in some metals, and defects and impurities in crystals.

In solids composed of elements of the iron group (occasionally the rare earths), the long-range cooperative effects between electron spin magnetic moments give rise to ferro-, ferri-, and antiferromagnetism.

WILLIAM E. STEPHENS

References

Electron Spin

Harnwell, G. P., and Stephens, W. E., "Atomic Physics," p. 74, New York, Dover Publications, Inc., 1966.

Leighton, R. B., "Principles of Modern Physics," pp. 89, 184, 667, New York, McGraw-Hill Book Co., 1959.

Van Vleck, J. H., "Electric and Magnetic Susceptibilities," Oxford, Clarendon Press, 1932.

Ramsey, N. E., "Molecular Beams," Oxford, Clarendon Press, 1956.

Uhlenbeck, G. H., and Goudsmit, S. A., *Physica*, **5**, 266 (1925); *Nature* **117**, 264 (1926).

Stern, O., and Gerlach, W., *Ann. Physik*, **74**, 673 (1924); *Z. Physik*, **41**, 563 (1927); **8**, 110; **9**, 349 (1922).

Wilkinson, D. T., and Crane, H. R., *Phys. Rev.* **130**, 852 (1963).

Electron Spin Resonance

Pake, G. E., "Paramagnetic Resonance," New York, W. A. Benjamin, Inc., 1962.

Low, W., "Paramagnetic Resonance in Solids," New York, Academic Press, 1960.

Bleaney, B., and Stevens, K. W. H., *Rept. Progr. Phys.*, **16**, 108 (1953).

Bowers, K. D., and Owen, J., *Rept. Progr. Phys.*, **18**, 304 (1955).

Orton, J. W., *Rept. Progr. Phys.*, **22**, 204 (1959).

Poole, C. P. Jr., "Electron Spin Resonance: A Comprehensive Treatise in Experimental Techniques," New York, Interscience, Wiley, 1967.

Alger, R. S., "Electron Paramagnetic Resonance: Techniques and Applications," New York, Interscience, Wiley, 1968.

Abragam, A., and Bleaney, B., "Electron Paramagnetic Resonance of Transition Ions," Oxford, Clarendon Press, 1970.

Swartz, Bulton, and Borg, "Biological Applications of Electron Spin Resonance," New York, Wiley, 1972.

Cross-references: ELECTRON, MAGNETIC RESONANCE, ZEEMAN AND STARK EFFECTS.

ELECTRON TUBES

The electron tube can be considered to consist of a cathode, which emits electrons, and one or more additional electrodes in a sealed envelope.

The operation of an electron tube depends upon an electron flow or gas ion plasma flow within the enclosed space between these electrodes. The generic term "electron tube" is applicable to thermionic (hot-cathode) vacuum tubes and gas-filled tubes.

The thermionic vacuum tube classification includes such types as receiving tubes, transmitting tubes, klystron tubes, magnetron tubes, traveling wave tubes, oscilloscopes, and television picture tubes.

The gas-filled tube classification includes such types as two-electrode hot-cathode mercury vapor rectifier tubes, two-electrode cold-cathode glow tubes, three-electrode hot-cathode thyratron tubes, three-electrode cold-cathode grid glow tubes, and single-anode multi-electrode mercury pool rectifier tubes such as the ignitron.

An electron tube, designed as a thermionic (hot oxide-coated cathode) vacuum tube usually consists of a heater for kinetic energy excitation of electrons, a cathode which acts as a transfer electrode source of electrons, controlling grid electrodes, and an anode that is maintained electrically positive with respect to the cathode. These elements are insulated from each other and enclosed within an evacuated envelope made of either glass, metal, ceramic, or a combination of these materials. A getter is flashed within the tube to absorb any residual gas molecules which could have a harmful effect—electrically and chemically—on the operation of the tube.

When the device has only two electrodes, a cathode and an anode, it is called a *diode*. With the anode maintained electrically positive with respect to the cathode, an electric field results which causes the electrons to move toward the anode. In the external circuit, the electrons flow from the anode through the load impedance and then through the voltage source to the *oxide*-coated cathode, which acts as a low-work function transfer medium, and so back to the anode. In this discussion, the work function is considered to be the total amount of work necessary to free an electron from a solid.

Other electrodes are often introduced between the cathode and the anode in the form of grids. By varying the voltages on these intervening electrodes, it is possible to modify the electric field between the cathode and the anode, and thus to control the current in the external circuit. Tubes having one grid in addition to the cathode and anode are called *triodes*. Tubes with two grids are called *tetrodes*; tubes with three grids are called *pentodes*. In general, tubes are labeled in accordance with the total number of active electrodes in a linear arrangement using a common electron stream. Sometimes, two or more sections are enclosed within the same envelope (e.g., a diode-triode or a triode-pentode); these tubes are not referred to in terms of the total multi-electrode structure, but they are designated in terms of the respective tube units.

Oxide-coated Cathode Oxide-coated filamentary cathodes can operate at relatively low temperatures of 1000 K because of the low-work-function surface layer. However, they are sub-

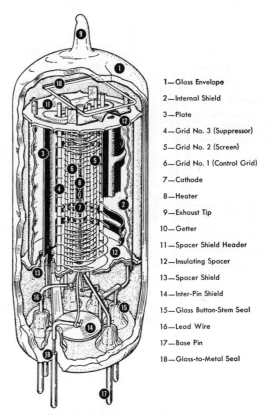

1—Glass Envelope
2—Internal Shield
3—Plate
4—Grid No. 3 (Suppressor)
5—Grid No. 2 (Screen)
6—Grid No. 1 (Control Grid)
7—Cathode
8—Heater
9—Exhaust Tip
10—Getter
11—Spacer Shield Header
12—Insulating Spacer
13—Spacer Shield
14—Inter-Pin Shield
15—Glass Button-Stem Seal
16—Lead Wire
17—Base Pin
18—Glass-to-Metal Seal

FIG. 1. Structure of a miniature tube.

ject to sputter effects and can also evaporate substantial amounts of material that deposit onto adjoining electrodes and lead to harmful grid-emission and contact-potential phenomena. Such oxide-coated filaments are high-efficiency emitters at low-wattage inputs and are used successfully in low-current pulsed high-voltage rectifiers for scanning systems in television receivers.

The indirectly heated cathode consists of a nickel alloy sleeve coated with alkaline earth oxides of barium and strontium, and, inside the sleeve, a heater of alumina-coated tungsten or molybdenum-tungsten alloy wire. The heater wire is in the form of a helical coil or folded strands; it is coated with alumina to insulate the heater wire from the cathode nickel sleeve. In addition, this insulating coating prevents adjoining helix turns or strands of wire from short-circuiting each other. The cathode sleeve is heated by conduction and radiation from the heater. Because the oxide-coated cathode is electrically isolated from the heater, it is called a *unipotential cathode*, since unlike the filamentary type, there is no voltage drop along its length due to heater current.

The use of the indirectly heated unipotential cathode offers two advantages, Firstly, the heater voltage does not appear as a component of the grid-to-cathode bias, as is the case with a directly heated filamentary cathode. Secondly,

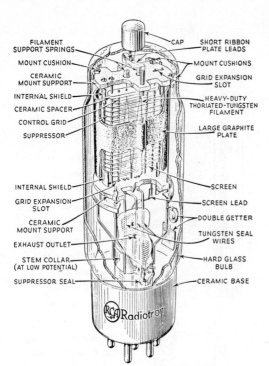

FILAMENT
SUPPORT SPRINGS
CAP
SHORT RIBBON
PLATE LEADS
MOUNT CUSHION
MOUNT CUSHIONS
CERAMIC
MOUNT SUPPORT
GRID EXPANSION
SLOT
INTERNAL SHIELD
HEAVY-DUTY
THORIATED-TUNGSTEN
FILAMENT
CERAMIC SPACER
CONTROL GRID
SUPPRESSOR
LARGE GRAPHITE
PLATE

INTERNAL SHIELD
SCREEN
GRID EXPANSION
SLOT
SCREEN LEAD
CERAMIC
MOUNT SUPPORT
DOUBLE GETTER
EXHAUST OUTLET
TUNGSTEN SEAL
WIRES
STEM COLLAR
(AT LOW POTENTIAL)
HARD GLASS
BULB
SUPPRESSOR SEAL
CERAMIC BASE

RCA Radiotron

FIG. 2. Structure of a transmitting pentode (RCA-803).

the use of a cylindrical nickel sleeve cathode permits the control grid to be more closely spaced to the cathode which, in turn, results in higher transconductance. In addition, the use of close cathode-to-anode spacing design in rectifier service creates low tube-voltage drops and better voltage regulation.

Because of these advantages, electron tube manufacturers make extensive use of the indirectly heated cathode system. The oxide coating formed on the nickel alloy cathode is derived from alkaline earth carbonates, either 50/50 mole per cent barium-strontium carbonate or 49/45/6 mole per cent barium-strontium-calcium carbonate. The presence of this activated oxide coating lowers the work function of the substrate nickel.

The electron emission performance of the indirectly heated cathode is influenced by three basic factors: (1) the effects of the low work function, (2) an n-type semiconductor method of electron transfer, and (3) the electron transfer efficiency involved in the porous nature of the alkaline earth oxide matrix coating. These three factors are discussed in the following paragraphs.

The usefulness of materials having low work functions is limited by their high rate of evaporation which tends to deposit material onto adjoining electrodes as well as to shorten the life of the system under vacuum-tube condi-

tions. Accordingly, balance of work function and rate of evaporation is a desired feature in effective cathode design. The barium/barium oxide component of the alkaline earth oxide matrix meets this requirement by having the lowest usable work function consistent with a minimum rate of evaporation and long life at the operating temperature (1025 K) of such cathode systems.

Normally, barium oxide is an insulator. In vacuum-tube technology, however, the oxide is made to act as a semiconductor material by an activating process which uses physical chemical reactions to form barium and associated donor sites in the oxide lattice. In addition to having a low work function, the barium oxide now exhibits properties similar to an n-type semiconductor which allows it to transfer electrons at temperatures below 575 K. Furthermore, a relatively thick oxide coating of 0.5 to 2.0 mil thickness will result in favorable coating porosity and electron pore gas transfer at temperatures above 575 K. Although electron pore gas transfer does not reduce the work function of the system, it does improve the conductivity of the oxide layer at 1025 K. The resulting decrease in voltage drop across the oxide coating permits a greater effective applied voltage gradient to exist between the cathode and the anode; the magnitude of the potential barrier due to the space charge is reduced so that more of the slower-moving electrons emerging from the cathode can reach the anode and improve the emission performance.

Barium and the associated donor centers are produced by the chemical reduction of barium oxide by elemental agents of carbon, magnesium, silicon, and tungsten present within the cathode nickel alloy. This reproductive action is a function of the effective concentration of the elements, as well as their rate of diffusion through the metal, and their rate of reaction with the emission oxides at the interface region.

In conclusion, the operating characteristics of the oxide cathode system itself are determined by a number of physical chemical factors including: the porosity of the applied coating; the conversion of the carbonates to the oxide crystal lattice form; the minimum sintering action induced by the eutectic phase of barium carbonate/barium oxide; the rate of electrolytic transport of the barium ions; the evolution of oxygen gas; the rate of evaporation of barium/barium oxide; and the formation of films on adjoining electrodes. Thus, the oxide-coated cathode system operates in a dynamic equilibrium involving solid, ion, and gas phase changes across the interface region of the cathode metal-to-oxide layer as well as the phase boundary between the oxide layer and the residual gases and vapors in the vacuum regions of the tube. These equilibria are dependent upon the noninjurious trace concentrations of carbon dioxide, oxygen, water vapor, sulfur, halogens, and volatile metal oxides in the environmental

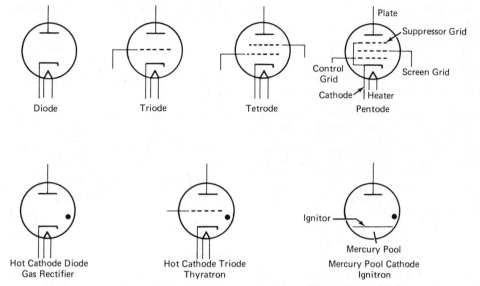

FIG. 3. Schematic representation of tube types. (Dot represents gas-filled tube, or mercury vapor in tubes with mercury.)

vacuum region for the best electron transfer performance and long life of the cathode system.

Diodes As previously mentioned, the diode is the simplest form of vacuum tube having a cathode system and anode together with a flashed getter. In well-degassed tube structures, the reducing element content of the cathode nickel alloy creates sufficient active barium sites in the emission oxide matrix so that the unit itself can function as a getter at high operating temperatures. Diodes are used as rectifiers, detectors, dampers, and limiters. These tubes are high-vacuum types in which the internal voltage drop is proportional to the dc load current. When a low constant-voltage drop is desired, mercury vapor tubes are used. The constant-voltage drop of 15 volts is a function of the ionization potential of the mercury vapor since the positively charged mercury ions neutralize the space charge effect. In general, for diodes, when the current demand is less than the temperature-limited value, the current I will vary as the three-halves power of the applied voltage E as given by the following equations. For the plane parallel system: $I/A = 2.34 \times 10^{-6} E^{3/2}/S^2$ amperes/cm^2 where S is the cathode to anode spacing, and A is the cathode area. For the concentric cylindrical system: $I = (14.65 \times 10^{-6} E^{3/2})/(b^2 \times r_a)$ where b is the ratio of the anode radius r_a to the cathode radius r_c. For very low anode voltages, the above approximations are not accurate because the effects of the initial electron velocity and the contact potential result in currents larger than calculated.

Not all electrons leaving the cathode reach the anode. Some electrons remain in the space above the cathode and produce a cloud of electrons or "space charge" which repels other electrons back to the cathode and thus impedes the flow of electrons to the anode. The extent of this action and the amount of the space charge are dependent upon the temperature of the cathode, the cathode-to-anode spacing, and the anode potential.

Under fixed temperature conditions, the maximum number of electrons that are emitted is also fixed. The higher the anode potential, however, the lower is the number of electrons remaining in the space charge region; as a result, an increase of the anode voltage results in an increase in current until saturation is reached. Beyond this condition additional anode (plate) voltage will only increase the plate current slightly because of the reduction of the work function at the cathode due to the electrostatic effect of the applied field.

The Richardson-Dushman equation yields information pertaining to the work function ϕ of cathode systems and the zero field current I_{s0} with respect to temperature T. The emission current density for a cathode of surface area S is denoted in the equation $J_{s0} = A_0 S T^2 e^{-(11610\,\phi_0/T)}$, where A_0 is a constant in terms of units of area used, T is the temperature in degrees Kelvin, and ϕ_0 is the work function in electron volts. The zero field saturated current I_{s0} is extrapolated from a plot of the log I_s (saturated current) as a function of the square root of the applied voltage of the anode V_a. The work function with an external field E is a function of the square root of the external field strength such that $\phi_E = \phi_0 - 3.78 \times 10^{-5} E^{1/2}$.

Triode When a third electrode, called a grid, is placed between the cathode and the anode, the tube is called a triode. This grid consists of a

fine wire wound on two support side rods; the spacing between the turns of the wire is relatively large so that electrons are able to pass from the cathode to the anode. When the tube is used as an amplifier, a varying signal imposed on a negative dc voltage on the grid controls the plate current. As the grid voltage becomes more negative, the plate current decreases while the plate voltage increases back to the original applied potential as a result of the decrease in the voltage drop across the load impedance. In other words, the grid voltage and the plate current are in phase, but the plate voltage is 180° out of phase with the grid voltage. The cathode, grid, and plate of the triode form an *electrostatic system* such that it is possible to equate the plate current I_b to a three-halves power law similar to that for diodes, i.e.,

$$I_b = k \left[\frac{C_{gk}}{C_{pk}} \times E_g + E_b \right]^{3/2}$$

where K is a constant (the perveance) which depends upon the geometry of the tube, and C_{gk} and C_{pk} are the effective grid-to-cathode and the plate-to-cathode capacitance, respectively. It should be noted that these values of capacitances are not the externally measured values or the published values of tube capacitances. This equation assumes a negligible effect for the initial velocity of electrons from the cathode. Actually, the initial electron velocity creates the space-charge effect so that the cathode is slightly negative (instead of zero) and a potential minimum exists a short distance in front of the cathode. The effect of this shift is to increase the plate current slightly. Because the initial electron velocity distribution depends upon cathode temperature, the plate current will also be influenced by the cathode temperature even though it is limited by the space charge.

The electrical characteristics of triodes are described in terms of three parameters: the amplification factor (μ), the dynamic plate resistance (r_p), and the transconductance (g_m) as given by the following relationships:

$$\mu = - \frac{C_{gk}}{C_{pk}} = - \frac{\partial e_b}{\partial e_g} = - \frac{de_b}{de_g} \bigg|_{i_b \text{ constant}}$$

$$r_p = \frac{\partial e_b}{\partial i_b} = \frac{de_b}{di_b} \bigg|_{e_g \text{ constant}}$$

$$g_m = \frac{\partial i_b}{\partial e_g} = \frac{di_b}{de_g} \bigg|_{e_b \text{ constant}}$$

These relationships are applicable within the region where the family of curves is straight, parallel, and equidistant for equal increments in the parameter. The triode tube can be considered a linear circuit element within small variations, and the quantities μ, r_p, g_m may be used as constants in the analysis of tube performance. A useful *approximation* for the calculation of plate current I_b is the expression

$$I_b \doteq \frac{2.34 \times 10^{-6} (E_g + E_b/\mu)^{3/2}}{(S_{gk})^2}$$

where S is the distance between grid and cathode.

The interrelationship among the three quantities i_b, e_g, and e_b can be shown as follows:

$$di_b = \left(\frac{\partial i_b}{\partial e_b} \right)_{E_g} \times de_b + \left(\frac{\partial i_b}{\partial e_g} \right)_{E_b} \times de_g$$

as $r_p = \left(\frac{\partial e_b}{\partial i_b} \right)_{E_g}$ or $\frac{1}{r_p} = \left(\frac{\partial i_b}{\partial e_b} \right)_{E_g}$

and $g_m = \left(\frac{\partial i_b}{\partial e_g} \right)_{E_b}$

Therefore:

$$di_b = \frac{1}{r_p} \times de_b + g_m \times de_g$$

and when the plate current is constant such that di_b equals zero:

$$g_m \times de_g = - \frac{1}{r_p} \times de_b$$

or $g_m \times r_p = - \left(\frac{de_b}{de_g} \right)_{I_b} = \mu.$

Tetrodes The effects of interelectrode capacitances between the grid and the plate and between the grid and the cathode sometimes result in coupling between the input and output circuits. Such coupling and impedance mismatching can cause instability and low output performance. The grid-to-plate capacitance can be sufficiently reduced by the introduction of an additional grid electrode, called the screen grid, between the control grid and the plate, and such tubes are known as tetrodes. In practice, the control grid-to-plate capacitance is reduced from several picofarads for a triode to less than 0.01 pF for a screen grid tube when a rf capacitor is connected between the grid circuit and the cathode.

The screen grid operates at a positive voltage and supplies an electrostatic force which pulls electrons from the space charge region, through its widely spaced turns of wire, and onto the plate. The plate is shielded from the cathode and exerts insignificant force on the space charge region. The plate current in a tetrode is almost independent of the plate voltage and depends mainly upon the screen grid voltage. With tetrodes, moderately high amplification can be obtained without capacitive feedback from the plate to the control grid. However, for operation in amplifiers where linearity is required between the control grid voltage and the plate current,

the transconductance must be constant. To achieve this condition, the tetrode must be operated in the region where the plate voltage is higher than the screen voltage, i.e., where the family of curves is nearly straight, parallel, and equidistant for equal increments.

Tetrodes are not useful for amplification of very large signals because the proximity of the positive screen grid to the plate (at equal or slightly higher positive voltage) permits the capture of secondary electrons emitted from the plate. The capture of the lower-velocity secondary electrons by the screen grid is more pronounced when the plate voltage swings lower than the screen grid voltage. This condition occurs when large signal variations cause an increased voltage drop across the load impedance in the plate circuit.

Pentodes The effects of secondary emission from the plate in a tetrode configuration are minimized when a fifth electrode is used. This fifth electrode (a third grid) is made of widely spaced turns of wire between the screen grid and the plate, and is known as the *suppressor grid*; it is usually connected to the cathode at zero potential. A tube with five electrodes in a linear arrangement, a cathode, three grids, and a plate, is called a pentode. The suppressor grid is negative with respect to the plate and can divert secondary electrons of low velocity back to the plate. Pentodes are capable of high voltage amplification and high power output at low levels of driving voltage on the control grid. When large signal inputs are placed on the control grid, large load impedance voltage drops result in the plate circuit which cause the plate voltage to become momentarily lower than the screen grid voltage without the loss of secondary electrons from the plate.

Instead of a suppressor grid, the interelectrode region between the screen grid and the plate can be virtually used as a space charge region to minimize the loss of secondary electrons from the plate. In practice, a suppressor grid or a beam-confining plate is used to enhance the effect of the electron cloud density. This effect is created primarily by designing the tube electrodes in such a way that the electron stream from the cathode is confined and concentrated in the region between the screen grid and the plate. The space potential is depressed at some point in the interelectrode region in front of the anode to a value below the anode potential to prevent secondary electrons from reaching the screen grid. A tube with this feature of construction is called a *beam-power tube*.

In beam-power tubes, the pitches of the helical turns of the lateral wire of the control grid and the screen grid are made equal and the wires are aligned to confine the passage of electrons into flat beams. A focusing beam plate, or optional use of a wide-spread suppressor grid electrode, is used to maintain this high electron density. Because of the alignment of the control grid and the screen grid, very few electrons are captured by the screen grid; thus, a beam power tube draws low current in the screen grid circuit. Effective suppressor grid action and low screen grid current permit beam power tubes of moderate size and voltages to operate efficiently at high power outputs with large values of transconductance. The large values of transconductances obtained with beam power tubes make them useful in the design of wide-band amplifiers for television service.

In both tetrodes and pentodes, the control grid is sometimes constructed in a non-uniform manner. The spacing between the adjoining helix turns of the grid lateral wire is made closer at the ends than at the center of the grid. In tubes with such variable pitch grids, the amplification factor decreases when the plate current decreases. Such grid structures also require large negative voltages to produce cut off conditions. These tube types are known as remote cutoff or variable-mu tubes. Tubes having uniform grids are called sharp cutoff tubes. Remote cutoff tubes are used in automatic-volume-control circuits in which the dc component of the control grid voltage is varied in such a manner that the amplification of the tube is made smaller for large signal voltages.

Multifunction Tubes In addition to the single function multigrid tube such as a tetrode amplifier 6CY5 or a pentode amplifier 6BC5, there are other multi-electrode tubes that perform more than one function, e.g., an oscillator and mixer in a superheterodyne receiver. The term pentagrid converter represents a tube with five grid structures that lie in the electron stream between the cathode and the plate. Two of the grids function as control grids; the remaining grids function as screen or suppressor grids to shield the control grids from the plate, e.g., pentagrid converters 6BE6 and 6SA7 or the 6BY6, a pentagrid amplifier used in color television receivers as a sync separator and sync clipper as part of a gated amplifier circuit.

There are also multi-unit tubes consisting of combinations of diodes, triodes and pentodes in one envelope which use more than one cathode and/or plate. For example, the twin triode 12AX7A used in resistance coupled amplifiers; the 8AW8A in which the triode unit is used in a sync separator circuit and the pentode unit is used as an i.f. or video amplifier; and the triple triode 6EZ8 used in oscillator mixer and AFC circuits in FM receivers.

Transmitting Tubes Electron tubes known as "power transmitting tubes" are designed for high power output circuits. The smaller versions of these power tubes using triode or beam power tetrode construction are designed for operation at frequencies below 500 MHz, where the transit time of electrons is long compared to the anode voltage cycle. These tube types are capable of moderate power outputs up to five kilowatts. The constructional features of the small power tubes are identified with indirectly heated, unipotential cathodes having oxide-

coated emitter surfaces (or with thoriated tungsten filaments, when the dc anode voltages are greater than 900 V), conventional design features of side rod and lateral wire construction for control grids and screen grids, beam plates, anodes, glass bulbs, mica or ceramic insulators, and getters. Materials used for the grids may be tungsten, molybdenum, tantalum, or alloys of phosphor bronze. Grid wires may be plated with gold to minimize the effect of primary grid emission (i.e., negative grid current) because the gold-plated surface absorbs the barium–barium oxide films evaporated from the oxide cathode. Grids may be coated with carbon to improve the dark body radiation of the grid, and thus, lower its temperature; lower temperatures reduce the level of grid emission. The product of the positive grid current and the peak positive grid-to-cathode voltage is the driving power in watts (minus some circuit losses) that circulates in the grid circuit.

The anode electrode (plate) of a transmitting tube is the major difference between a transmitting tube and the horizontal output tube used in television receivers. Because plates in transmitting tubes collect large currents, the heat build-up resulting from the high wattage dissipation must be radiated or conducted away in order to keep the plate temperature at a controlled level. Were the anode allowed to operate at high temperatures, back radiation from the anode would cause the cathode temperature to vary with the load (and dissipation) in the plate circuit. Typical plate design construction ranges from internal oval or cylindrical metal barrels with flanged fins for air-cooled tubes to ingenious, external solid radial or louvered axial fins, integrally connected to the anode and joined externally with glass-to-metal vacuum seals for use with forced-air or water-jacketed cooling. Materials used for anodes are nickel, tantalum, molybdenum, formed carbon blocks, zirconium-coated nickel-steel, and copper. Heat conduction and heat-radiating capability as well as hot strength determine the choice of the material. Further considerations of internal and external capacitance effects between the anode and other electrodes as well as design requirements of weight, shape, and supporting structures determine the final selection of the material.

The term "plate power input" refers to the total amount of dc power in watts supplied to the plate circuit. It is the product of the average rms plate voltage and the plate current, $E_b \times I_b$. It is from this input wattage that the output signal power delivered to the load in the plate circuit is derived—i.e., the square of the plate current times the load resistance, $I_b^2 \times R_L$. The difference between the power input and the power output is the power lost in the circuit and is mainly dissipated as heat in the plate. Transmitting tube types are rated in terms of peak envelope power, PEP; the PEP input is equal to $E_b \times 1.414 I_b$. In the output circuit,

the average dc plate voltage is at a minimum when the average plate current is at a maximum because of the voltage drop across the load resistance, I_b max $\times R_L$. Thus, the PEP output is equal to $(E_b - E_b \text{ min}) \times I_b$ max $/4$ for a triode at zero bias grid drive condition.

Transmitting tubes are designed in different ways depending upon the circuit application, the rf frequency, the duty cycle, and the plate dissipation requirements. Ratings, based on operating conditions, are given to these tubes for selection of service.

A further requirement for the application of transmitting tubes depends upon the proportion of the plate voltage cycle during which the plate current flows at output circuit load conditions. The classes of operation are as follows:

The class A amplifier is an amplifier in which the grid bias and the rf grid input voltages are such that the plate current flows during the complete grid voltage cycle.

The class AB amplifier is an amplifier in which the grid bias and the rf grid input voltages are such that the plate current flows for more than half but less than the complete grid voltage cycle.

The class B amplifier is an amplifier in which the grid bias is almost equal to the cutoff value such that the plate current is almost zero when no rf grid input voltage is applied; the plate current will flow during one-half of the grid voltage cycle when the rf signal voltage is applied to the grid.

The class C amplifier is an amplifier in which the grid bias is equal to or greater than the cutoff voltage so that the plate current is zero when no rf input voltage is applied to the grid; the plate current will flow for less than one-half of the grid voltage cycle when rf input voltage is applied to the grid.

Microwave Tubes The above-mentioned multigrid tubes are used normally in amplification circuits at frequencies up to 500 MHz. However, above this frequency, the transit time of electrons is short when compared to the plate voltage cycle, and as a result, the phase angle between the plate current and the plate voltage becomes less than 180°. Accordingly, an increase occurs in the power dissipated at the plate for a given designed power output. At these very high frequencies, electron loading can occur at the control grid because of the short transit time of the electrons from the cathode to the plate. Certain pencil-type triode tubes are made to operate in the 500 MHz region with conventional tube constructional arrangement except that the interelectrode spacing between the cathode and the grid, and between grid and plate, is made very small (about 1-mil clearance) in order to accommodate the short transit time of electrons.

Superpower gridded transmitting tubes are especially designed to operate at 1 000 000 W peak plate–pulsed power output at 940 MHz and a pulse width of 20 μsec. These tubes are

large, specially shaped, and use sturdy metal grids and anodes arranged with extensive liquid jacketed cooling. Other types are designed to operate at 65 000 W peak plate–screen pulsed power output at 1215 MHz with pulse width of 10 μsec; forced-air cooling is used. These superpower gridded tubes are designed to mate the rugged ceramic-to-metal construction for high-power capability with the close spacing needed for high-frequency performance. The superpower gridded tubes make use of a symmetrically aligned ring of unitized matrix cathodes with *closely spaced concentric rings of grid assemblies and anode in a triode or tetrode design.* The nickel-matrix alkaline earth oxide is strongly bonded to the substrate cathode element to resist positive-ion bombardment, flaking, and sputtering; its matrix reservoir is designed for 50 000 hours of operational service. These matrix cathodes have excellent structural strength and dimensional stability to permit the close-spaced construction of grids and anode and so reduce internal losses caused by space charge effects and electron transit time. Superpower gridded tubes are relatively small and light in weight for their power-handling capability; focusing magnets are not required to contain the electron beams as is required in other types of high-frequency, high-power tubes.

A successful approach to superpower rf amplification has been engineered into a special triode construction consisting of a *concentric* arrangement of double-tuned plate-cavity resonators, and a close-spaced grid assembly surrounding a core matrix filamentary cathode, all contained in a vacuum enclosure. This type of superpower triode is known as the *coaxitron*; it operates with coaxial input of rf power to the grid assembly and waveguide delivery of the rf power output from the tuned plate-cavity resonators. Broadband amplifier performance is obtained with high efficiency and high gain. For example, a coaxitron tube with several integral cavities designed for short-pulse operation from 385 to 465 MHz, using a 2-V, 2000-A matrix filament, can deliver 5 000 000 W peak plate-pulsed power at a duty factor of 0.008.

For those applications where extremely high gain, high frequency, and high peak power are required, and operating voltages are of secondary consideration, special microwave tubes have been designed to make use of the transit time of the electrons as well as avoid the effects of interelectrode capacitances at these high frequencies. Klystrons, traveling wave tubes, and magnetrons are special-purpose tubes designed to operate in the microwave region.

Klystrons In conventional electron tube construction, wherein the electrons pass from the cathode through the grid to the anode, the grid, in effect, controls and changes the intensity of the constant-velocity electron beam. In a velocity-modulated electron tube, the input voltage on the grid changes the velocity of the electrons in a constant current electron beam. Thus, in the *klystron*, the electrons leaving the cathode are accelerated and focused by an electron gun arrangement into a beam. The electron beam then passes between two grids between which a high-frequency voltage is applied. Some of the electrons in the beam current are accelerated and other electrons are decelerated—i.e., their velocities are modulated. The electrons are given velocities that are a function of the time at which they passed through the grids. The grids are placed very close together so that the electron transit time is very small compared to the time cycle of the rf voltage supplied to the grids. Because the rf impressed voltage is much smaller than the dc anode voltage applied to the electron beam current, no density modulation of the beam current is produced at this point. Equal numbers of electrons are accelerated as are decelerated so that the process of velocity modulation avoids losses in the input circuit which usually occur at high frequencies in conventional tube construction.

The resulting velocity-modulated electron beam emerging from the first pair of grids travels through a field-free "drift space" in groups or *bunches* in the direction of the beam current. The bunches of electrons pass through a second pair of parallel grids in the "catcher cavity." The rf current created by the bunching of the electrons in the beam current induces an rf voltage between the catcher grids. This conversion is a result of the transit time required for the electron bunches to be formed when faster electrons overtake slower electrons in their passage through the field-free space. Thus, the undesirable feature of transit time in conventional triodes now becomes the means of obtaining density modulation from velocity modulation within the interval distance of the field-free drift space. The catcher cavity is made resonant at the frequency of the new density-modulated electron beam so that an oscillating field is set up within it by the passage of the electron bunches through the catcher grid aperture. With proper design, losses in the circuit are made small; the current impulses occurring with each bunch cycle will sustain oscillation. The electron bunches of the beam current, after transferring some of their energy to the resonant circuit, continue to move along the tube to be collected by the anode. External magnetic focusing, permanent or electromagnetic, is used to confine the narrow electron beam.

The quarter-wavelength section of the catcher cavity resonator induces standing waves and associated high magnetic flux densities. A loop located in the region of variable high magnetic flux density will have a high-frequency voltage induced in it. The power obtained from such a resonant circuit is greater than is required to produce the sequential velocity modulated-to-density modulated electrons which feed the resonant output circuit. Thus, the klystron tube can serve as an oscillator or amplifier. The interaction between the initially velocity-modu-

lated electrons and the density-modulated electron bunches occurs over a very short distance of "field-free" space between the "buncher grids" and the "catcher grids." Therefore, a high-impedance narrow-band frequency-resonant circuit response is needed to extract the rf energy.

Klystrons are used where very high gain, high frequency, and high peak power are required—i.e., the TV klystron for UHF-TV applications, the CW klystron for scatter communications in the 4.5 to 5.0 GHz band, and the linear-pulsed rf amplifiers used in linear accelerators for high-energy physics applications.

Traveling Wave Tube The traveling wave tube, TWT, is designed to convert dc energy of a velocity-modulated electron beam current into an ac energy output by interacting the velocity-modulated beam with an rf energy field. An electron beam is formed and focused to travel down a long internal interaction zone of a helical coil region and arrive at a collector anode. The electron beam is prevented from spreading by a strong magnetic field applied by a coaxially located external permanent magnet or electromagnet. More recently developed TWT types use lightweight periodic permanent magnet focusing or electrostatic magnetic focusing structures encapsulated onto the helix tube to provide even higher coercive forces.

The periodic permanent magnet structures develop very uniform high coercive fields for the helix of the TWT. The small-diameter ring magnets are made of ferroceramics, and more recently of samarium-cobalt ceramics, having large coercive forces. They are encapsulated around the helix tube in an arrangement wherein the magnet disks are stacked between steel shims with similarly polarized faces of each pair of disks adjacent to each other—i.e., NS:SN:NS:SN:NS. A periodic magnitic field is produced around the helix tube through which the electron beam will spiral around its mean free path. No auxiliary focusing power is required; the need for solenoid energizing field currents and associated cooling structures is eliminated. Thus, lightweight TWT packages can be assembled that weigh about 2 to 12 pounds in contrast to former types that weighed about 50 to 100 pounds.

In the traveling wave tube, the rf energy to be amplified is applied to the helical coil. The acutal progress of the electromagnetic wave down the axis of the helix is slower than straight-line propagation because of the helical winding. The reduced speed of wave propagation is called phase velocity. The beam current from the electron gun is adjusted to match the unloaded wave phase velocity by adjusting the collector voltage. For optimum interaction and efficiency, the electron beam must travel at a slightly faster velocity than the phase velocity in order to allow for energy losses as the wave zone approaches the output load coupling.

The rf signal field surrounding the helical coil interacts with the dc electron beam current. The velocity of some beam electrons is increased in an accelerating field region while other beam electrons have their velocities decreased in the decelerating field regions. Higher-velocity electrons overtake slower-velocity electrons; bunching and debunching take place in the beam current. This velocity-modulated beam of electrons travels down the axis of the helix and arrives at the collector anode. Electrons that have been slowed down add energy to the rf signal in the helix circuit and induce an amplified rf current in the helix. The amplified signal is transferred through a waveguide connection to the external circuit.

The basic concept of the TWT, as described above, refers to the *forward-wave* traveling wave tube amplifier. The electron beam current and the electro-magnetic wave in the helix both travel in the same direction and at almost the same velocity. When the electron beam velocity is made slightly greater than the rf phase velocity in the helix coil, more beam current electrons are decelerated than are accelerated so that the net transfer of the kinetic energy from the beam current to the rf circuit is increased. Where the rf energy increase is extracted from the kinetic energy of the beam electrons, the traveling wave tube is classified as an "O" type. Some TWT designs are arranged to extract the potential energy of the beam current electrons; these types are known as cross-field devices or "M" types.

The forward-wave TWT is designed for use in oscillator and amplifier circuits operated at frequencies over 1000 MHz. The design features make use of the transit time of electrons wherein "bunches" are formed in the accelerating and decelerating rf field along the axis of the helix. Because the helix circuit in the TWT is nonresonant and the zone of interaction with the electron beam current is relatively long, the tube can amplify a broad band of rf signals that can be tuned to yield the desired slow-wave phase velocity. Traveling wave tubes can be designed and tuned to operate at 3000 MHz with gains as high as 20 dB over a bandwidth of 600 to 800 MHz. Developmental types using periodic magnetic focusing obtained by electrostatic means have been operated in the 9000 MHz range with power outputs in excess of five kilowatts.

A variation of the TWT in which the electron beam current travels in one direction and the slow-wave phase velocity of the rf energy travels in the opposite direction is called the *backward-wave TWT*. The backward-wave TWT is useful for signal generator or local oscillator output because it is tunable over a small range of frequencies merely by changing the collector voltage of the beam current.

Magnetrons The magnetron electron tube consists of a filamentary cathode surrounded by longitudinal segmented sections of a coaxial cylindrical anode. The anode is maintained at a

positive potential with respect to the cathode. A magnetic field parallel to the axis of this cylindrical diode is superposed upon the cathode-to-anode electric field.

An electron leaving the cathode is accelerated radially outward toward the anode, but the magnetic field causes the electron to deflect away from the anode and assume a curved path. At a critical magnetic field strength, the electron path will become tangential to the surface of the anode. When the magnetic field is increased beyond this critical value, the electron does not reach the anode but continues along a curved path to return eventually and bombard the filament. The anode current is zero at this magnetic field strength under static dc anode voltage conditions.

In practical magnetrons, the anodes are usually of the multicavity type with four to twenty segments. The resonant cavities (waveguide structures) between the anode segments are electronically coupled into the common central cathode region by slots of critical size and shape. A high-frequency voltage is superimposed on the dc anode-to-cathode voltage such that alternate anode segments vary (more or less positive) about the average dc value. The rf frequency is selected so that the time for one cycle of rf voltage is equal to the time for an electron leaving the cathode to complete its curved trajectory path back to the cathode without ever reaching the anode. Thus, the rf component of the anode voltage reverses direction twice with each electron rotation—i.e., transit time. The electric field is considered to be the circuit capacitance; it is concentrated across the gap between each anode segment. The magnetic field is considered to be the circuit inductance; it is concentrated in the resonant cavities.

When successive segments of the anode are at different potentials (by reason of the applied rf voltage superimposed on the dc anode potential), there are conditions of magnetic and potential fields such that current flow is greater in that anode electrode segment that is less positive. Electrons which are accelerated by the more positive anode segment are magnetically deflected toward the less positive anode segment. In effect, the magnetron exhibits negative-resistance characteristics. Thus, oscillations can be generated in the resonant cavity between adjoining anode segments. The electrons emitted by the filamentary cathode normally follow curved trajectory paths under the influence of the magnetic field. The motion of these electrons is modified by the potential fields generated at the slotted openings of the oscillating resonant cavities. Some electrons will lose energy to these fields and never return to the space cloud region around the cathode, and thus continue to gyrate around the cathode cavity. Other electrons gain energy from the resonant cavity fields and ultimately return to the cathode. The resultant effect of all force fields and electron energies is to transfer energy from the moving electrons to the electric fields and maintain oscillations in the resonant cavities.

The circuit is considered to be continuously shifting its phase relation between adjoining anode segments and returning upon itself. A steady-state condition exists when the phase shift in radians per segment is equal to π; the anode pole faces alternate in polarity and the electric fields across the gaps reverse polarity twice per electron cycle. When a steady state exists, the phase shift β, in radians, is equal to $2\pi n/N$, where N is equal to the number of pole segments, and n is the number of electron cycles around the cathode. Thus, at $n = N/2$, β is equal to π. This state is called the π mode.

The magnetron device transfers the electron energies into standing waves in the resonant cavities at high efficiencies ranging from 35 to 50 per cent for four-cavity resonators and up to 70 per cent for a twenty-cavity device. Frequencies of operation can be designed to range from 1000 MHz (30 cm) to 30 000 MHz (1 cm) by using greater multiples of anodes and a higher order of harmonic modes. Commercial applications range from a fixed-tuned, electromagnetically focused, liquid-cooled magnetron generating continuous rf power of 30 kW at 915 MHz at 80 per cent efficiency for industrial processing to tunable magnetrons operating at 8500 to 9600 MHz with peak power outputs of 250 kW for pulsed oscillator service.

Mercury Vapor Rectifier The gaseous thermionic rectifier is a two-element tube (diode) consisting of a filament or an indirectly heated cathode and an anode (plate) in a glass envelope. A small amount of liquid mercury is back-filled into the tube after the getter is flashed at the end of the vacuum pump-down schedule; the tube is then sealed off. The rectifier tube with liquid mercury is known as the mercury vapor rectifier because the liquid mercury is vaporized when the hot filament or cathode raises the temperature of the tube. Mercury vapor diodes are used as half-wave rectifiers.

In operation, electrons are emitted from the surface of the hot cathode and form a space cloud of electrons around the cathode. This space cloud which normally surrounds the cathode is the cause of a large variable voltage drop from anode to cathode which contributes to poor voltage regulation in regular rectifiers. However, when the cathode in the mercury vapor rectifier is heated, some mercury is vaporized and raised to this operating temperature. High-velocity electrons leaving the space cloud region under the influence of the anode potential collide with some mercury atoms to create positive ions. The positive ions are drawn to the negative space cloud region and partially neutralize it. The positive ions remain in the vicinity as a *positive ion sheath* around the surface of the cathode. In effect, the space cloud voltage drop is lowered and is maintained at an average of 15 V (12 to 20 V depending

upon the load current) over a wide range of load current in a properly designed rectifier circuit.

When the mercury vapor rectifier is in operation, a positive ion sheath exists within one mil (0.00254 cm) distance of the surface of the cathode. The region between this positive ion sheath and the anode surface consists of electrons, positive mercury ions, and mercury atoms; this region is called the *plasma*. A relatively constant potential exists across the plasma region, i.e., the anode potential; the voltage drop across the positive ion sheath near the cathode surface is essentially equal to the voltage drop across the tube. Electrons leaving the cathode enter the plasma region within a mil distance at almost the full anode potential. Because spacing between cathode and anode is not of importance for determining the tube voltage drop, thermionic oxide-coated cathodes are formed in broad ribbon widths, folded and convoluted, to minimize radiant heat losses. Emission efficiency can be designed to yield as much as 1200 mA per watt of heater power input in contrast to conventional oxide-cathode construction in high-vacuum tubes which yield about 100 mA per watt of heater power. Operating conditions for two half-wave mercury vapor rectifiers in a single-phase, 60-cycle full-wave rectifier circuit can be as high as 22000 peak inverse volts with 7000 V dc output to the filters at a maximum dc output current of 20 A.

Thyratron A thermionic gas rectifier containing a grid is known as a thyratron. In this instance, the grid structure consists of a metal electrostatic shield insulated from and surrounding the cathode and the faceplate of the anode. A series of integral shields with holes and slots is constructed within the grid to act as baffle plates between the cathode and anode surfaces. In operation, this gas triode has a thermionic cathode from which electrons are emitted, a dynamic gas plasma when the anode voltage is applied, and the grid which prevents the plasma from being formed before a specified time interval in the anode voltage cycle. The massive shielding action of the grid permits the use of a small negative grid voltage to neutralize the effects of the much greater anode voltage.

Similar to the thermionic gas rectifier, the conducting thyratron operates with a hot gas plasma. Thus, the cathode must be permitted to reach the operating temperature because of the injurious effects of positive ion bombardment on a cold cathode. The oxide-coated cathode is designed for high heat efficiency with broad convoluted or spiral ribbon features to minimize heat radiation losses. In addition, the solid mass of the grid structure surrounding the cathode contributes to heat efficiency by acting as a reflector and minimizing heat losses.

It is necessary that both external anode and grid circuits incorporate limiting series impedances to prevent the flow of higher-than-rated currents which would destroy the cathode.

Large mercury vapor thyratrons can handle switching currents (peak forward currents) of 200 A and surge currents of 2000 A. Small thyratrons using krypton-argon gas mixtures handle low currents of 100 mA. Thyratrons are used for pulse type or on-off type current-voltage switching in applications for pulsing radar modulator-magnetron circuits, speed controllers for meters, oscilloscope sweep circuits, voltage-regulated rectified power supplies, and control of servomechanisms.

In operation, after due warm-up time to permit the hot cathode to produce a space cloud of electrons, the negative grid potential prevents any grid or anode current to flow when the anode circuit is switched on. As the grid becomes less negative, some high-velocity electrons escape from the space cloud region and enter the grid-to-anode region to collide with some gas atoms to produce some positive ions. When the still negative grid potential reaches a value (not necessarily positive) wherein sufficient positive ions are being formed in the gas plasma, the existing anode potential takes control and starts the gas discharge. The negative grid voltage cannot shut off the anode current because the tube voltage drop (anode-to-cathode) now assumes the value of 10 to 20 V, representing the average ionization voltage of the gas, a value somewhat lower than can be calculated because of the catalytic action of some metastable atoms and double step ionization reactions.

The conducting thyratron tube now acts like a hot gaseous rectifier tube in that a positive ion sheath forms around the cathode; the negative grid maintains a less intense positive ion sheath while being surrounded by the gas plasma. Returning the grid potential to the negative value it had before the tube fired does not stop the anode current. In order for the grid to regain control, the anode voltage must be reduced to zero or made negative with respect to the cathode in order to interrupt the plasma current. This switching action can be accomplished by using an alternating anode voltage supply wherein the anode voltage periodically becomes negative for a sufficient time to permit the plasma current to be cut off. In conjunction with an alternating grid voltage supply, there will be a point in the grid voltage cycle as it is becoming less negative which will determine some point in the positive half of the anode voltage cycle at which the tube plasma will be fired and conduct. During the negative half of the anode cycle, the plasma current will be stopped and the negative grid cycle voltage will again take control. Where the grid voltage becomes positive with respect to the cathode during its cycle, large positive grid current will flow, so the grid circuit must incorporate limiting series impedances to prevent excessive grid currents from destroying the cathode and the tube.

Gas tubes using hydrogen, argon, krypton,

and xenon are not temperature-sensitive. Their gas plasma concentrations are a function of the dosing pressure when the tube is filled with the respective gas mixtures. However, the concentration of the gas in these tubes slowly decreases during life because of the adsorption of the gas on the glass walls of the tube as well as on the metal electrodes during the plasma conduction when the tube is fired. In practice, enough gas is introduced initially to allow for such clean-up and permit a usable life performance capability. The inert "noble" gases are used in low anode voltage applications. Mercury vapor and hydrogen thyratrons can handle high-voltage applications. A large, negative-control, mercury vapor thyratron used in welder control service can handle peak forward voltages of 10 000 V, with peak anode currents of 16 A at an average anode amperage of 4 A. A hydrogen thyratron, a positive-control triode type, used in pulsed modulator service at 2000 pps at peak anode voltages of 3000 V and peak currents of 35 A (average current is only 0.035 A) can supply 43000-W pulses to the output transformer. The anode-to-cathode voltage drop in the tube is about 150 V for the hydrogen thyratron.

Ignitron   The ignitron type of mercury vapor rectifier diode is constructed with a mercury pool cathode and a massive graphite anode assembly. An internal arrangement of baffle shields, electrically insulated from anode and cathode, prevents the direct splash of mercury onto the anode. The mercury pool cathode has a pointed auxiliary electrode of silicon carbide or boron carbide, called the ignitor, dipping into it. The mercury does not wet this refractory material but rises about the pointed tip with the meniscus curled away from the surface. The ignitron tube is in a nonconducting state until the ignitor circuit is switched on to pass microsecond pulses of high-amperage current from the tip of the ignitor electrode to the pool of mercury during the positive cycle of the anode voltage.

An auxiliary circuit provides the ignitor with activating currents ranging from 10 A at 400 V to 50 A at 100 V for several microseconds of time so that the average power requirement is small. It is believed that the voltage gradient existing at the tip of the ignitor may be of the order of 20 000 to 50 000 V per mil spacing to the mercury meniscus surface; this high voltage is great enough to induce high field emission output sufficient to create the glow plasma in the mercury meniscus surrounding the tip of the ignitor rod. This tiny spark gap expands into a conduction plasma arc between the mercury pool cathode and the anode during the cycle when the anode is positive. It is necessary to energize the ignitor to generate the spark gap on the mercury pool cathode at the beginning of each conducting cycle of the anode voltage.

Ignitrons are constructed as half-wave rectifiers with one anode and not as full-wave rectifiers with two anodes in order to eliminate the problem of backfiring. When one anode would be conducting while at the positive peak of the cycle, the other anode would be nonconducting at the large negative peak of the cycle with respect to the other anode. Consequently an arc-back condition would be created between the two anodes. Ignitrons are built as permanently evacuated and sealed metal units; high-power units are water-jacketed for cooling. For rectifier service, ignitrons can be rated as high as 1500 A at 2000 V instantaneous; the mercury vapor conduction tube drop is, of course, 12 to 20 V. Such large ignitrons can be arranged in multiple array with auxiliary 150-V anodes closer to the mercury pool cathode in order to provide plasma generation to the main anode. For extended life in heavy-duty service, some ignitrons are provided with three ignitors—only one of the ignitors is used at a time, because the high surge currents passing through the ignitor tips for some 50 to 100 μsec of time cause the tips to sputter and deteriorate. Ignitors are used mainly in heavy-duty rectifier service, and in intermittent control switching of ac current in resistance welding control. A typical ignitron rating would specify ignition requirements of 200 peak volts at peak currents of 30 A for a 100-μsec starting time for use in resistance welding control applications delivering 2800 peak amperes at 600 V, the average current being 75 A.

CARL H. MELTZER

References

Spangenberg, K. R., "Vacuum Tubes," New York, McGraw-Hill Book Co., 1948.

Deketh, J., "Fundamentals of Radio Valve Techniques," Eindhoven, N. V. Phillips, 1949.

Loosjes, R., and Vink, H., "Properties of Pore Conductors," *Phillips Res. Rep.*, 4, 449 (1949).

Pierce, J. R., "Traveling Wave Tubes," New York, Van Nostrand Reinhold, 1950.

Millman, J., and Seely, S., "Electronics," New York, McGraw-Hill Book Co., 1951.

Nergaard, L. S., "Oxide Cathode," *RCA Rev.*, 13, 464 (1952); "Physics of the Cathode," *RCA Rec.*, 18, 486 (1957); "Thermionic Emitters," *RCA Rec.*, 20, 191 (1959).

Cobine, J. D., "Gaseous Conductors," New York, Dover Publications, Inc., 1958.

Knoll, M., "Materials and Processes of Electron Devices," Berlin, Springer-Verlag, 1959.

Langford-Smith, Ed., "Radiotron Designers Handbook," 4th Ed. RCA, 1960.

Hutter, R. G. E., "Beam and Wave Electronics in Microwave Tubes," New York, Van Nostrand Reinhold, 1961.

Reich, H. J., "Microwave Theory and Techniques," New York, Van Nostrand Reinhold, 1961.

Harvey, A. F., "Microwave Engineering," New York, Academic Press, 1963.

Rowe, J. E., "Non-Linear Electron Wave Interaction Phenomena," New York, Academic Press, 1965.

Collin, B. E., "Microwave Engineering," New York, McGraw-Hill Book Co., 1966.

Gewartowski, J. W., and Watson, H. A., "Principles of Electron Tubes," New York, Van Nostrand Reinhold, 1966.

Publications

Siekanowicz, W. W., and Sterzer, F., "A Developmental Wide Band, 100 watt 20 db S-band, TWT Using PPM-periodic Permanent Magnetic Focusing," *Proc. IRE* (January 1956).

Cuccia, C. L., and Johnson, W., "Periodic Electrostatically Focused TWT for L and S Bands," *National Electronics Conf.* (October 1959).

Shimada, T., "Periodic Electrostatic Focusing of High Perveance Electron Beams for High Power Klystrons," *Electron. and Commun. Jap.* (USA), 53 (8), 76–79 (August 1970).

Mancebo, L., "100 KV Hydrogen Thyratron without Gradient Grids," *IEEE Trans. Electron Devices,* **ED-18** (10), 920–24 (October 1970).

Lebacqz, J. V., "High Power Klystron Development at Stanford Linear Accelerator Center," *8th Int. Conf. Microwave and Optical Generation and Amplification,* **MOGA-70,** Eindhoven, Netherlands (September 1970).

Bacal, M., and Cristescu, M., "The Effect of Electron Reflection on Magnetron Cut-off Characteristics," *Surface Science* (Netherlands), 26 (1), 230–54 (June 1971).

Heynisch, H., "Microwave -200 MHz to Sub mm Tube Developments," *Siemens Review* (Ger.), 38 (11), 483–90 (November 1971).

Doring, H., "State of the Art and Research Trends in Microwave Tubes," *Ingenieur* (Netherlands), 82 (52), 183–191 (December 1971).

Neugebauer, W., "A 10-stage Electrostatic Depressed Collector for Improved Klystron Efficiency," *IEEE Trans. Electronic Devices* (USA), **ED-19** (1), 111–121 (January 1972).

Grant, J. E., "A 2-Kw Multi-octave TWT PPM Focused with Samarium Cobalt Magnets," *IEEE Trans. Electronic Devices* (USA), **ED-19** (1), 86–9 (January 1972).

Lind, B. I., and Askne, J. I. H., "Energy Flow Relation in Multiwave TWT Systems with Absorption and Dispersion," *IEEE Trans. Electronic Devices* (USA), **ED-19** (2), 239–245 (February 1972).

Cross-references: CIRCUITRY, DIODE (SEMICONDUCTOR), POTENTIAL, THERMIONIC EMISSION, TRANSISTOR.

ELECTRONICS

The term "electronics" (Ger. *Elektronik*) was first used to describe the branch of physics now generally called physical electronics; that usage goes back almost to the discovery of the electron in 1897, as witness the names of two early journals in the field, *Jahrbuch der Radioaktivität und Elektronik* (founded in 1904) and *Ion: A Journal of Electronics, Atomistics, Ionology, Radioactivity and Raumchemistry* (1908).

In the currently prevalent technological context, the adjective "electronic" and the noun "electronics" (Ger. *technische Elektronik*) date back only to the 1920s and did not achieve wide circulation until after the foundation of the journal *Electronics* by McGraw-Hill Publishing Co. in 1930. (The older meaning also survives: as an example, the Institute of Physics and Physical Society in Britain has an Electronics Group concerned with physical electronics.)

Electronics in the technological sense has been variously subdivided into categories that encompass most of the profession of electrical engineering. For instance, since the American Institute of Electrical Engineers and the Institute of Radio Engineers combined in 1962 to form the Institute of Electrical and Electronics Engineers, the new organization has subdivided into 32 specialized groups, most of them pertaining to electronics, as follows:

> Aerospace and
>   Electronic Systems
> Antennas and
>   Propagation
> Audio and
>   Electroacoustics
> Automatic Control
> Biomedical Engineering
> Broadcast and Television Receivers
> Broadcasting
> Circuit Theory
> Communications
> Computers
> Education
> Electrical Insulation
> Electromagnetic
>   Compatibility
> Electron Devices
> Engineering Management
> Geoscience Electronics
> Industrial Electronics and
>   Control Instrumentation
> Industry Applications
> Information Theory
> Instrumentation and
>   Measurement
> Magnetics
> Manufacturing
>   Technology
> Microwave Theory
>   and Techniques
> Nuclear Science
> Plasma Science
> Parts, Hybrids, and
>   Packaging
> Power Apparatus
>   and Systems
> Professional Communication
> Reliability
> Sonics and Ultrasonics

Systems, Man, and
Cybernetics
Vehicular Technology

Such grouping points up the increasing penetration of electronics into various branches of technology and science, a process that is by no means as yet complete. Few educated people remain unaware of the role that electronics has played not only in the communications industry and in the development of computers (both with regard to military and to space applications), but also in industrial instrumentation and control (automation). Less generally appreciated is the part that electronics is coming to play in such diverse fields as food technology, geophysical exploration, medical instrumentation, materials processing, and a host of other endeavors not usually associated with electronics.

Research scientists depend on electronics *qua* technology to a surprisingly large extent. Many of the scientist's conventional instruments have been replaced by electronic devices of greater capabilities. Even more important, the advent of electronics has sparked the development of entire new branches of science such as microwave spectroscopy, electron microscopy, radio astronomy, and other fields that depend on processes such as amplifying weak signals; transmitting, recording, and analyzing large amounts of rapidly acquired data at high rates; and investigating phenomena at frequencies extending from the audio to the visible range.

Electronics is certainly repaying its large debt to physics, in numerous ways. Not only have cathode-ray oscilloscopes, vacuum tubes, and scintillation counters been joined by transistors and other semiconductor devices to provide an ever-increasing range of complex instruments, but the very devices that have been developed as a result of certain discoveries in physics have, in turn, been used in physics research in a very direct way. A few instances will suffice to illustrate the point.

Discovery of the physical phenomenon of secondary emission of electrons has led to the development of the *photomultiplier*, an instrument that has revolutionized nuclear physics by its ability to enhance otherwise imperceptible signals and to make it possible to register extremely large numbers of discrete events.

Photoelectronic *image intensifiers*, developed in the first instance for television camera tubes, have found application in astronomy, to increase the efficiency of optical instruments and to detect faint objects against relatively bright backgrounds; in nuclear physics, to record the passage of fast nuclear particles through transparent phosphor blocks and perhaps to detect Čerenkov radiation from fast particles passing through a dense medium; in spectroscopy, to enhance ultraviolet radiation that could be otherwise detected through glass or quartz windows only with difficulty; and in the detection of x-ray patterns, both where it is necessary to detect radiation down to the shot-noise level of the x-ray quanta and in medical radiology, where the patient must be protected from excessive dosage. The applications related to nuclear physics depend on a further property of the device—its ability to be switched on or off within nanoseconds, so that one specific event out of a multitude of uninteresting events can be recorded.

The high-resolution *electron spectrometer*, derived from the electron microscope (which in turn is a descendant of the cathode-ray tube), has been used to investigate the characteristic losses of electrons transmitted through thin films of metals and alloys, providing information of basic importance for metallurgy.

Various physical principles of importance to electronics, and the corresponding devices, are described elsewhere in this book. Additional information on electronics is available in the writer's "The Encyclopedia of Electronics" (Van Nostrand Reinhold, 1962), a companion volume to the present work.

CHARLES SÜSSKIND

Reference

Süsskind, C., "The Encyclopedia of Electronics," New York, Van Nostrand Reinhold, 1962.

Cross-references: ANTENNAS, CAPACITANCE, CIRCUITRY, DIELECTRIC THEORY, DIODE (SEMICONDUCTOR), ELECTRICITY, ELECTROMAGNETIC THEORY, INDUCTANCE, MICROWAVE TRANSMISSION, OSCILLOSCOPES, PHOTOMULTIPLIER, RECTIFIERS, SEMICONDUCTORS, SERVOMECHANISMS, THERMIONICS, TRANSISTOR, WAVEGUIDES.

ELEMENTARY PARTICLES

The search for the elementary constituents of matter is as old as physics itself, but any quantitative attempt at such a theory had to await the experimental discoveries of this century. Such a search is prompted by two considerations: the identification of the basic building blocks of nature and the hope that their laws of interaction would be essentially simple.

The atom had to yield its claim to be indivisible when it was found that electrons were constituents of all atoms; moreover, the electrons from various species of atoms were identical. Light, with its particle properties, seemed another universal entity connected with matter, since the photons (light quanta) which were emitted in atomic transitions appeared identical apart from their momenta. The electron and the photon were the first two elementary particles to be discovered, and a quantitative theory of the emission and absorption of photons by the electrons in an atom was possible only after the invention of quantum mechanics. The corre-

sponding picture of the atom regarded the electrons in an atom as being subject to electrostatic attraction of the positively charged nucleus (and the mutual repulsion of other electrons), the photons having only a transitory existence being either emitted or absorbed in the transitions between the atomic states. The search for the structure of matter now became a search for the constituents of the nucleus.

A quantum theory of the nucleus (or rather nuclei) was made possible by the discovery of the proton and the neutron. The nuclear interaction which was responsible for holding the nucleus together (against the disruptive electrostatic repulsion of the protons) was found to be of an entirely new kind, much stronger than the electric interaction at short distances but decreasing very much more rapidly with distance. The various complex nuclei differ in the number of protons and neutrons they contain.

By that time, the theory of the interaction between electrons and photons had developed to the point where the electrostatic repulsion or attraction between electrically charged particles could be understood in terms of the exchange of photons between them. In the lowest non-trivial approximation, it gave the Coulomb law for small velocities. The basic interaction was the emission and absorption of "virtual" photons by charged particles. A similar mechanism could be invoked to explain the short-range nuclear interaction; and essentially our present picture of the nuclear interaction is that it is due to the exchange of particles, which have nonzero masses which are a fraction of nuclear mass—the same approximation procedure used for deducing the static Coulomb force (from the electron-photon interaction) is no longer valid here; and the nuclear force has a rather complicated form. However, these theoretical considerations did predict the existence of a set of three particles called pions, which have since been discovered.

Another kind of particle and another kind of interaction were discovered from a detailed study of beta radioactivity in which electrons with a continuous spectrum of energies are emitted by an unstable nucleus. The corresponding interactions could be viewed as being due to the virtual transmutation of a neutron into a proton, an electron and a new neutral particle of vanishing mass called the neutrino. The theory provided such a successful systematization of beta decay data for several nuclei that the existence of the neutrino was "well-established" more than twenty years before its experimental discovery. The beta decay interaction was very weak even compared to the electron-photon interaction.

Meanwhile, the electron was found to have a positively charged counterpart called the positron; the electron and positron could annihilate each other, with the emission of light quanta. The theory of the electron did in fact "predict" the existence of such a particle. It has, since

then, been found that the existence of such "opposite" particles (antiparticles) is a much more general phenomenon (see below and also see ANTIPARTICLES).

Our present catalog of elementary particles and decay modes contains many more entries. These particles fall into five families: the photon family, the electron family, the muon family, the meson family and the baryon family. Most of these particles are unstable and decay within a time which is often very small by normal standards but which is many orders of magnitude larger than the time required for any of these particles to traverse a typical nuclear dimension. There is a wide variety of reactions between them, but they could be understood in terms of three basic interactions—the strong (or nuclear) interactions, the electromagnetic interactions and the weak interactions. The nuclear forces and the interaction between pions and nucleons belong to the first, the electron-electron and electron-photon interactions to the second, and the beta decay interaction to the third. The present theoretical framework enables us to handle more or less quantitatively the electromagnetic and weak interactions only. Despite this, it is possible to understand many aspects of strong (as well as the other) interactions in terms of conservation laws and invariance principles (see CONSERVATION LAWS AND SYMMETRY).

The classical conservation laws of energy, momentum and angular momentum are valid in the relativistic quantum theory of elementary particles also. The particles may possess intrinsic angular momentum or "spin" which expressed in natural units $h/2\pi$ of angular momentum is restricted to an integer or a half-odd integer. Angular momentum conservation holds only when this spin angular momentum is included. But one finds that to every particle, there corresponds an antiparticle with the same mass, same spin and same lifetime. (In the case of the photon and the neutral pion, they are their own antiparticles; they are strictly neutral particles.) The particle and antiparticle have equal and opposite electric charges, and the antiparticle of the antiparticle is the original particle. The conservation of electric charge is another familiar (although non-classical) conservation law satisfied by all known interactions. It is the prototype of a set of "additive" conservational laws which include the conservation of the baryon number, the muon number and the electron number. To the best of our knowledge, these conservation laws are still exact. Incidentally, the conservation of baryon number is the refinement of the classical law of conservation of matter, and may be thought of as the fundamental law guaranteeing the stability of the physical universe.

In addition to these additive conservation laws which arise from continuous symmetries, there is a set of "multiplicative" conservation laws which are associated with discrete symmetries.

It is possible to examine the invariance of the physical laws under space inversion, i.e., using a left-handed coordinate system instead of a right-handed coordinate system or vice versa; if the statement of the law is unaffected by this interchange, it is possible to show that a quantum number having the two values ± 1 can be assigned to classify the quantum-mechanical states such that a state with the label $+1$ will not change to one with the label -1 due to any interaction. This quantum number is called "parity." Just as particles may possess intrinsic angular momentum (spin), particles may also have intrinsic parity. Table I lists the particles (and their corresponding antiparticles) with their respective additive quantum numbers, intrinsic parities and lifetimes. General principles of relativistic quantum theory imply that antiparticles of integral spin particles have the same parity as the particles; for half-odd-integral spin particles the antiparticle has the parity opposite that of the particle. All experimental checks are in accordance with this prediction.

In addition to invariance under space inversion, we may consider particle conjugation (replacement of particles by antiparticles), invariance, and time reversal invariance, or combinations of these transformations. It turns out that strong and electromagnetic interactions are invariant under each of these three transformations (and hence any product of these), but weak interactions are invariant only under combined inversion (product of particle conjugation and space inversion) and under time reversal. It can be shown that all interactions are invariant under the product of the three transformations of space inversion, particle conjugation and time reversal if some very general principles of the relativistic quantum theory of these particles are valid.

Even the statement that weak interactions are invariant under combined inversion has turned out not to be strictly true. In the decay of the neutral K meson we should have expected a short-lived particle (even under combined inversion) called K_1^0 and a longer-lived particle (odd under combined inversion) called K_2^0, provided combined inversion were strictly valid. We do observe such short- and long-lived components; but we also expect that the long-lived component K_2^0 cannot decay into two pions. Experimentally we find a small amount of decay into two pions. This violation of combined inversion (and, hence, of time reversal invariance) is only two-tenths of a percent, but it is definitely present. Thus none of the discrete symmetries (except the product of the three) seems to be strictly valid.

One notices that the various particles belonging to a family have the same spin and the same values of the additive quantum numbers except the electric charge. The photon has a universal interaction with all charged particles; it has been found possible to connect the conservation of electric charge and this universal interaction

structure, on the one hand, to the vanishing mass and unit spin of the photon, on the other. The electron and muon partake of both electromagnetic and weak interactions, but do not exhibit any strong interaction. In fact the muon family appears to be simply a duplicate of the electron family except for a change in the unit of mass. At the present time, no basic reason has been found for this doubling, and it is perhaps the most fascinating puzzle of current elementary particle physics. The members of these two families are collectively known as leptons and they all have spin one-half. The neutral members (the electron neutrino, the muon neutrino, and their antiparticles) have extremely weak interaction with matter since they do not participate even in electromagnetic interactions.

The meson family consists of eight members which fall into a triplet of pions, a singlet eta, a doublet of kaons, and a doublet of antikaons. They are all pseudoscalar (spin zero and odd parity) and exhibit strong interactions. The charged particles are of course coupled to the photon, but even the neutral members can participate in electromagnetic interaction by virtue of the large probability for virtual dissociation into charged particles. They participate in a variety of weak interactions including the nuclear beta decay interaction.

It is found that the kaons, the hyperons (baryons other than the neutron and proton) and their antiparticles, collectively known as "strange particles," can decay by weak interactions not involving leptons or photons with a lifetime which is large compared to the natural periods appropriate to strong interactions. On the other hand, these particles are produced copiously in high-energy nuclear collisions. These two circumstances can be understood in terms of the existence of another additive quantum number, called hypercharge, which is conserved in strong and electromagnetic interactions but violated in weak interactions.

The meson-baryon system exhibits further regularities as far as strong interactions are concerned. The neutron and the proton have very nearly the same mass and similar nuclear interactions although their electromagnetic properties are quite different. The three pions have different electric charges, but again they have approximately equal masses and similar nuclear interactions. This kind of multiplet structure is evident for other strongly interacting particles: the kaons form a doublet, the sigma hyperons form a triplet, the xi hyperons form a doublet, and the lambda hyperon remains a singlet. In view of the relative weakness of the electromagnetic interaction, it is tempting to ascribe all deviations from exact equality of the masses to the indirect action of the electromagnetic interaction. In this framework, it is possible to consider the members of a multiplet to be different states of the same particle corresponding to the values of a new quantum number. What is remarkable is that if one takes this point of view,

TABLE 1. CATALOG OF ELEMENTARY PARTICLES

Particle	Family[a]	Spin	Mass (MeV)	Lifetime[b] (sec)	Antiparticle	Parity[c]	Charge	Hyper-charge	Baryon Number	Electron Number	Muon Number
Photon, γ	Photon	1	0	Stable	Photon, γ	-	0	0	0	0	0
Electron neutrino, ν_ϵ	Electron	$\frac{1}{2}$	0	Stable	Antielectron neutrino, $\bar{\nu}_\epsilon$	Undefined	0	0	0	1	0
Electron, e^-	Electron	$\frac{1}{2}$	0.51098	Stable	Positron, e^+	+	-1	0	0	1	0
Muon neutrino, ν_μ	Muon	$\frac{1}{2}$	0	Stable	Antimuon neutrino $\bar{\nu}_\mu$	Undefined	0	0	0	0	1
Muon, μ^-	Muon	$\frac{1}{2}$	105.66	2.20×10^{-6}	Positive muon, μ^+	+	-1	0	0	0	1
Neutral pion, π^0	Meson	0	135.0	0.84×10^{-16}	Neutral pion, π^0	-	0	0	0	0	0
Positive pion, π^+		0	139.6	2.60×10^{-8}	Negative pion, π^-	-	+1	0	0	0	0
Neutral kaon, K^0		0	497.8	0.86×10^{-10}	Neutral antikaon, $\bar{K}^0$	-	0	+1	0	0	0
Positive kaon, K^+		0	493.8	1.24×10^{-8}	Negative antikaon, $\bar{K}^-$	-	+1	+1	0	0	0
Proton, p	Baryon	$\frac{1}{2}$	938.3	Stable	Antiproton, $\bar{p}$	+	+1	+1	1	0	0
Neutron, n		$\frac{1}{2}$	939.6	$0.93 \times 10^{+3}$	Antineutron, $\bar{n}$	+	0	+1	1	0	0
Lambda, Λ		$\frac{1}{2}$	1115.6	2.5×10^{-10}	Antilambda, $\bar{\Lambda}$	+	0	0	1	0	0
Positive sigma, Σ^+		$\frac{1}{2}$	1189.4	0.8×10^{-10}	Negative antisigma, $\bar{\Sigma}^-$	+	+1	0	1	0	0
Neutral sigma, Σ^0		$\frac{1}{2}$	1192.5	1×10^{-14}	Neutral antisigma, $\bar{\Sigma}^0$	+	0	0	1	0	0
Negative sigma, Σ^-		$\frac{1}{2}$	1197.4	1.5×10^{-10}	Positive antisigma, $\bar{\Sigma}^+$	+	-1	0	1	0	0
Neutral xi, Ξ^0		$\frac{1}{2}$	1314	3.0×10^{-10}	Neutral antixi, $\bar{\Xi}^0$	+	0	-1	1	0	0
Negative xi, Ξ^-		$\frac{1}{2}$	1321	1.7×10^{-10}	Positive antixi, $\bar{\Xi}^+$	+	-1	-1	1	0	0
Omega, Ω^-		$\frac{1}{2}$	1672	1.3×10^{-10}	Antiomega, $\bar{\Omega}^+$	+	-1	-2	1	0	0

[a] Electron and muon families are collectively known as the lepton family. The proton and neutron are both nucleons; other members of the baryon family are the hyperons.

[b] The neutral kaon has a long-lived component K_2^0 and a short-lived component, which are quantum mechanical superpositions of the neutral kaon and the neutral antikaon.

[c] Electron, muon, proton, neutron and lambda parities are defined by convention. Antifermions have opposite parity from fermions. Antibosons have same parity as bosons.

TABLE 2.   STRONGLY INTERACTING PARTICLES AND RESONANCES (AS OF APRIL 1971)

Particle or Resonance	Spin	Mass (MeV)[a]	Width (MeV)[b]	Parity	Electric Charge	Hyper-charge	Isotopic Spin	G-parity	Unitary Symmetry Assignment
Pion, π	0	138.5	0	−	0, +1	0	1	−	
Kaon, K	0	495.8	0	−	0, +1	+1	$\frac{1}{2}$	Undefined	Pseudoscalar meson octet
Antikaon, $\overline{K}$	0	495.8	0	−	0, −1	−1	$\frac{1}{2}$	Undefined	
Eta, η	0	548.8	0	−	0	0	0	+	
Nucleon, N	$\frac{1}{2}$	938.9	0	+	0, +1	+1	$\frac{1}{2}$	Undefined	
Lambda, Λ	$\frac{1}{2}$	1115.6	0	+	0	0	0	Undefined	Baryon octet
Sigma, Σ	$\frac{1}{2}$	1193.4	0	+	0, +1, −1	0	1	Undefined	
Xi, Ξ	$\frac{1}{2}$	1318.4	0	+	0, −1	−1	$\frac{1}{2}$	Undefined	
Rho resonance, ρ	1	765	125	−	0, +1, −1	0	1	+	
Koan resonance, K^*	1	893	50	−	0, +1	+1	$\frac{1}{2}$	Undefined	Vector meson octet
Antikaon resonance, $\overline{K}^*$	1	893	50	−	0, −1	−1	$\frac{1}{2}$	Undefined	
Phi resonance, ϕ	1	1019	4	−	0	0	0	Undefined	
Omega resonance, ω	1	784	11	−	0	0	0	−	Vector meson singlet
Nucleon resonance, N^*	$\frac{3}{2}$	1236	120	+	0, +2, +1, −1	+1	$\frac{3}{2}$	Undefined	
Y resonance, Y^*	$\frac{3}{2}$	1385	36	+	0, +1, −1	0	1	Undefined	Baryon resonance decuplet
Xi resonance, Ξ^*	$\frac{3}{2}$	1530	7	+	0, −1	−1	$\frac{1}{2}$	Undefined	
Omega minus resonance, Ω		1672	0		−1	−2	0	Undefined	

[a]The average mass of the members of the isotopic multiplet is tabulated.
[b]Since the unstable particles of Table 1 live "practically forever" on the nuclear time scale, the corresponding widths are several orders of magnitude smaller than one MeV; these are quoted here as "0".

it is possible to show that the strong interactions exhibit a remarkable invariance under a group of continuous transformations which may be viewed as the group of rotations in a fictitious three-dimensional space (or more correctly as the special unitary group SU(2) of transformations on two variables). The transformations act as follows: the singlet is unchanged, the doublet components transform like the components of a spinor, and the triplet components transform like the components of a vector. This property of strong interactions is called "charge independence"; and the corresponding conserved dynamical variable (with three components) is called the isotopic spin. It then turns out that hypercharge conservation is a consequence of isotopic spin conservation and electric charge conservation. While the conservation of isotopic spin is violated by the electromagnetic (and weak) interactions, the charge independence of nuclear interactions is still expected to be satisfied to within a few per cent and experimental tests confirm this. Since the symmetry associated with invariance under isospin transformations is not directly related to space-time properties, one often refers to it as an "internal symmetry."

On might now raise the question: Which of these particles are basic constituents of matter? For the case of the atom, say the simplest of them all, the hydrogen atom, it seems easy to say that it is a composite system made up of an electron and proton bound together by an electrostatic force. However, this answer is not completely satisfactory since the electrostatic force itself is due to the exchange of light quanta, and in the process of atomic transitions photons are emitted or absorbed. Yet we do not include them as constituents of the atom. In beta radioactivity, electrons and neutrinos emerge from the nucleus, yet the nucleus is not pictured as containing either of these varieties of particles but rather as made up of protons and neutrons. The beta electron and neutrino are rather assumed to be created at the moment of emission. With the mesons taking part in strong interactions, however, such distinctions are no longer obvious, and the question of whether a particle is elementary or is composed of several other particles cannot be answered except perhaps within the context of a more quantitative but limited model. A point of view that has gained some acceptance is that *none* of these particles are elementary and that each is a composite of several particles (including perhaps itself)!

This view, while by no means inevitable or even well-established, is a possible picture, because in the realm of elementary particles we can not only add particles together to construct a composite system, we can also "subtract" particles by adding antiparticles. The claim that particles A and B go to make up the particle C is difficult to distinguish from the claim that particles $\bar{B}$ (antiparticle to B) and C go to make

up the particle A. Further, particles play a dual role. On the one hand, they are constituents of a composite system; on the other hand, they are the objects which are exchanged to generate forces between the constituents. In any case, in view of the very large number of entries in Table 1, it is not desirable to accept all of them as the ultimate constituents of matter.

This is even more forcefully brought to our attention by the recent discovery of a very large number of ultra short-lived particles. They appear as sharp resonances in multiparticle systems. Since these "resonances" disintegrate within a short time (even on the nuclear scale!), it is difficult to view them as elementary particles, but they seem to play an important role in interaction phenomena and are produced as often as the more stable (and familiar) mesons and baryons included in Table 1. It appears at the present time that they ought to be included on more or less the same footing. A list of the better established resonances is given in Table 2 along with the mesons and baryons from Table 1. Since an unstable particle lives only for a very short time, its energy and consequently its mass cannot be sharp, and from elementary quantum mechanical considerations we should expect this "width" in the mass of a resonance to be inversely proportional to its lifetime. Since the width is what is measured experimentally, the width (rather than the lifetime) is usually quoted in connection with resonances.

Since these particles are coupled in the strong interactions, one would expect them to occur in isospin multiplets. This is in fact observed. It turns out that since strong interactions are invariant under particle conjugation and are charge independent, we could define a multiplicative quantum number called G-parity which has definite values ±1 for mesons and meson resonances. These values are also included in Table 2.

With these resonances included among the "elementary particles" we have a situation somewhat parallel to atomic spectroscopy *before* the discovery of quantum mechanics. The catalogue of the strongly interacting particles (collectively known as "hadrons") now contains well over a hundred entities and it would be difficult to consider a hundred plus "elementary" constituents. Yet how are we to select the genuine subset of elementary constituents? We have already remarked about the picture in which *every* hadron is a composite system. We should then look for regularities among them including groupings into families, multiplets etc., as well as for systematic relations between masses, spins, multiplet sizes, etc.

There are also practical questions regarding the identification and interpretation of resonances. How wide a resonance is to be included? When a number of different reaction channels are open, a resonance may not be easily visible as a pronounced peaking in cross section or mass plot. When resonances overlap the problem

is aggravated. A particularly curious example is given by the so-called A_2 resonance, which corresponds to a meson with spin 2, even parity, isospin 1, and odd G-parity in the neighborhood of 1300 MeV. The generally accepted picture views this as a double resonance, approximately coincident in mass and variable width. For example, the data could be fitted with one resonance of width 80 MeV and another of width 10 MeV, both at 1300 MeV. It could be fitted equally well with two resonances, both with width 25 MeV, but one at 1290 MeV and another at 1310 MeV. Yet other experiments do not find any splitting at all! This is admittedly an extreme case, yet it highlights the kind of problem involved.

One notes also that the meson and baryon multiplets seem to fall into further supermultiplets. Following the analogy of the isospin group, we may now ask what internal symmetry group is responsible for this interaction. We must also remember that whatever is responsible for the violation of this higher symmetry must itself be a part of the strong interaction. A scheme in which invariance under the special unitary group on three variables SU(3) holds approximately has been successful in correlating and predicting the spectrum of particles and their interactions. The isospin group SU(2) is a subgroup of this unitary group. Just as for charge independence, no basic reason has been found for the origin of this "unitary symmetry." Still other symmetry groups, even wider than SU(3) and generally incorporating it, and which are even more significantly violated, are being studied. It appears that the complete understanding of these higher internal symmetries would involve not only their origin, but also the origin of their violation.

The hadron multiplets appear to have other regularities. We can discern, in analogy with atomic physics, subfamilies consisting of a lowest-spin "ground state" and successively higher spin "excited states." The states listed in Table 2 may be viewed as the ground states. If we plot the masses squared versus the spin for several of these subfamilies, we find them to lie approximately on straight lines with a universal slope of about $1 \ (\text{GeV})^{-2}$. These may be thought of as the generalization of the bound state energy versus spin relation for potentials to the domain of resonances, and thus, as orbital excitations; and in this context they are known as Regge families.

The ground states themselves may be understood in terms of a generalization of the "internal symmetry" to include a spin aspect also, so that instead of SU(3) we consider SU(6). The spin $\frac{1}{2}$ even parity baryon octet and spin 3/2 even parity baryon decuplet resonances together then form a single 56-dimensional representation of SU(6). The nine spin 0 odd parity mesons and the nine spin 1 odd parity vector meson resonances form a mixture of the 35-dimensional and the 1-dimensional representa-

tion of SU(6). We can combine this SU(6) structure together with the orbital excitations mentioned above to bring about a phenomenological SU(6) $\times$ O(3) classification for hadrons.

It is very tempting to think of this SU(6) $\times$ O(3) structure as pointing to a substructure of the hadrons in terms of 3 hypothetical entities with spin $\frac{1}{2}$ and even parity which transform as a 3 $\times$ 2-dimensional representation of this group called "quarks." The simplest baryon resonances are then to be viewed as three-quark compounds and the meson resonances as quark-antiquark compounds. The spin, parity, and SU(3) quantum numbers of most hadrons are consistent with this picture and some quantitative understanding of the resonance masses and decay parameters can be obtained within this framework, sometimes referred to as the "quark model." It should be pointed out that so far no quarks have been discovered and physicists are not sure if they even expect them to exist.

We should also remark that the particles so far discovered all have either finite mass (Class I particles or tardyons), or zero mass (Class II particles or luxons). It is an interesting question to ask if particles of imaginary mass (Class III particles or tachyons) can and do exist. It used to be thought that such particles could not exist, since their existence would violate the principle of relativity, but now we know that such is not the case. If hadronic tachyons exist, the quantum theory of tachyons predicts that they will show up as fixed resonances in momentum transfer; experimentally the situation has not been conclusive. Leptonic tachyons (and photon-like tachyons) could probably be best detected in astronomical phenomena. If they exist they would provide for a substantial pressure in the interior of hot stars and thus provide a balancing force to alleviate gravitational collapse. Whether the concept of particles of imaginary mass, which is the relativistic counterpart of geometric size used in simpler nonrelativistic physics, is useful in elementary particle physics is not yet clear.

The theoretical description of the interaction of electrons and photons involves a relativistic quantum theory of the electron and photon fields (QUANTUM ELECTRODYNAMICS). While fundamental difficulties still remain, the computational techniques developed have enabled the accurate prediction of even the finer details of the electron's electromagnetic properties. Such a method of calculation completely fails for strong interactions, although there are reasons to believe that the correct theory should involve interacting quantized relativistic fields. The immediate correspondence between each kind of particle and a field as obtained in quantum electrodynamics is unlikely for the strongly interacting particles. On the other hand the answer to the question "What are the primitive fields?" is not obvious. The problem is made much more difficult by the appearance of meaningless divergent quantities in direct calculations.

At the present time we have a number of ad hoc theoretical devices to extract some meaningful quantitative predictions in perturbation theory, but at the loss of much physical intuition. Thus we are faced with a frustrating situation: there are reasons to believe that the basic theory should involve relativistic interacting quantized fields, but there is no immediate way of deciding the number or nature of the fields or of the law of their interaction.

The problem of divergences in local relativistic quantum theory may be seen to be a reappearance of the Rayleigh-Jeans divergence of the specific heat of the vacuum in the context of interacting fields. Basically it stems from the unqualified availability of the infinite number of degrees of freedom of a local field. Just as Planck's hypothesis of quanta was a drastic departure from usual theory, such a natural, yet drastic, departure is indicated to eliminate the divergences. To do this without departing from local interaction structure we may generalize the notion of the vector space of states to a mathematical space with indefinite metric. Within such an indefinite metric quantum field theory the various scattering and transition amplitudes can be calculated to a desired degree of approximation without the appearance of infinities. However, we do have to deal with generalized probabilities which may be positive or negative. Negative probabilities cannot be reconciled with the physical interpretation of probabilities in quantum theory. This logical hurdle has been overcome with the discovery of shadow states. These are mathematical states which have no physical counterpart. They enter the dynamical theory but the probability is conserved among physical states only; there is no transition between physical states and shadow states. Quantum field theory with shadow states is the realization of a finite relativistic field theory. So far only perturbation theory has been worked out within this framework.

Since the quantum field theory framework has not so far yielded acceptable computational techniques for strong interactions, in recent years increasing effort has gone into attempts to make a theory of the reaction amplitudes ("scattering matrix elements") directly. The hope is that from the general principles of quantum field theory together with sufficient clues provided by the scattering experiment one can directly construct a theory for the scattering amplitude. This point of view has triggered a systematic effort to scan transition amplitudes in various kinematical regions and to higher and higher accelerator energies, and a substantial amount of data has been accumulated. As an intermediate step in the groping for fundamental building blocks of the theory the investigation often appears to be the direct interpretation of scattering phenomena. We have gained some qualitative (and partially quantitative) understanding; but the goal is still beyond the horizon. Eventually, of course, we expect that this

approach would include also an understanding of the leptons and the photon.

To sum up, we find that we have now a very large number of "elementary" particles which, by their very number, forfeit their claim to be considered ultimate constituents of matter. We have some understanding of the regularities observed in their spectrum and their interactions, and we have discovered a variety of conservation laws. However, we still do not understand the multiplicity of these particles, nor do we have a quantitative theory of their interactions. Perhaps yet another level of discovery awaits us in our search for the constitution of matter.

E. C. G. SUDARSHAN

References

Ford, K. W., "The World of Elementary Particles," New York, Blaisdell Publishing Co., 1964.

Marshak, R. E., and Sudarshan, E. C. G., "Introduction to Elementary Particle Physics," New York, Interscience Publishers, 1962.

Bernstein, J., "Elementary Particles and Their Currents," San Francisco, W. H. Freeman, 1968.

Marshak, R. E., Riazzuddin, and Ryan, C. P., "Theory of Weak Interactions in Particle Physics," New York, John Wiley, 1969.

Streater, R. F., and Wightman, A. S., "TCP Theorem and All That," W. A. Benjamin, New York, 1964.

Chew, G. F., "S-Matrix Theory of Strong Interactions," New York, W. A. Benjamin, 1961.

Schwinger, J., "Particles, Sources, and Fields," Reading, Mass., Addison-Wesley, 1970.

Bilaniuk, O. M. P., and Sudarshan, E. C. G., "Particles Beyond the Light Barrier," *Physics Today*, 22, 43–51 (1969).

Sudarshan, E. C. G., "The Nature of Faster-Than-Light Particles and Their Interactions," *Arkiv för Fysik*, 39, 585 (1969).

Sudarshan, E. C. G., "Action-at-a-distance," *Fields and Quanta*, 2, 175–216 (1972).

Particle Data Group, "Review of Particle Properties," *Rev. Mod. Phys.*, 43, 51 (1971).

Cross-references: ANTIPARTICLES; CONSERVATION LAWS AND SYMMETRY; QUANTUM ELECTRODYNAMICS; STRONG INTERACTIONS; WEAK INTERACTIONS.

ELEMENTS, CHEMICAL

The idea of simplicity underlying the bewildering complexity of nature has always been a conceptual thread underlying man's view of the world. The Greek philosophers of antiquity were among the first to record their speculations, and we are to this day influenced in an unconscious way by their thoughts on the elements, which they supposed to be the ultimate components of matter and chemical change. Thus we speak of "man's battle with the ele-

ments" and "the raging elements" in unconscious reflection of the ideas of Thales, Anaximenes, Heraclitus and Empedocles of the fifth century B.C. who believed that all matter was made of one or more of the elements earth, air, fire and water. These ideas did not prove particularly fruitful in advancing our understanding of the nature of matter and chemical change. Nevertheless, it was not until van Helmont (1648) that they were challenged on a rational basis.

In 1662, Robert Boyle, in the *Sceptical Chymist* gave a reasonably clear definition of a chemical element with operational overtones which we can accept today. "I mean by elements, . . . certain Primitive and Simple, or perfectly unmingled bodies; which not being made of any other bodies, or mingled bodies, are the Ingredients of which all those called perfectly mixt bodies are immediately compounded, and into which they are ultimately resolved." He gave no list of elements, however, this being left to Lavoisier who published a naturally incomplete, but remarkably accurate list in 1789, in his justly famous, *Traité de Chimie*.

The Definition of "Element" In modern language, Boyle can be paraphrased in the following way: an *element* is a chemical species that cannot, by ordinary chemical manipulation be decomposed into a number of simpler chemical species. It is the entity that survives intact the infinite variety of transformations that a sample of matter can be caused to undergo. Every *compound* is composed of two or more of these species and can be decomposed into them by suitable chemical procedures. This definition provides an operational means of identifying an element in terms of laboratory procedure, and by it, any species that defies decompositional efforts must be classified as an element. Such an assignment must of course be somewhat tentative, since in a number of cases, substances that have stubbornly resisted decomposition and therefore carried the classification, have ultimately yielded as new techniques developed.

With the recent growth in detailed knowledge of atomic structure, it became possible to define an element in terms of the submicroscopic structure of matter. Such a definition is relieved of the ambiguities mentioned above. Thus an element is a sample of matter that consists of only one kind of atom, the atoms being identified in terms of their atomic number, or nuclear charge. Each element is composed of atoms having characteristic nuclear charge and an equivalent number of electrons. This nuclear charge can be determined by the charged-particle scattering technique first employed by Rutherford or by the simpler and more precise method of Moseley which relates the frequency of the characteristic x-rays produced by the element upon electron bombardment to the nuclear charge z by means of the equation

$$w = R(z - b)^2$$

where w is the wave number of the x-ray, z is the nuclear charge, and b and R are constants.

This definition removes the ambiguities created by such observations as the decomposition of elemental molecular hydrogen or nitrogen by high temperatures into atomic species, or the decomposition of the rare gases into charged species in an electric discharge. This type of decomposition, which does not effect the underlying nuclear structure is thus excluded from the operational definition originating with Boyle.

Numbers and Kinds of Elements The number of substances recognized as chemical elements has steadily increased since the publication of Lavoisier's list which included about thirty of the true elements. Today it is recognized that there are some 90 naturally occuring elements, the exact number depending upon the level of abundance considered limiting. There are also about 15 artificial ones with this latter number possibly increasing as the techniques of nuclear science improve. The artificial elements include those with atomic numbers above 92 as well as promethium and technetium. Technetium is also observed in stars, and in that sense is naturally occuring. (See table in the article ISOTOPES).

The 105 presently known elements represent distinct chemical species differing by integral units of positive charge (corresponding to the charge of the proton) beginning with element number 1, hydrogen, and progressing through element number 105. Species having nuclear charges between 1 and 105 have all been identified, so it can be said that the list of elements is complete, except for the possibility of adding new ones with atomic numbers greater than 105. Considerable effort, both experimental and theoretical, is currently being expended in the effort to find super-heavy elements of unusual stability. With the discovery of element 103, the actinide series was completed. Both 104 and 105 are quite unstable; however, islands of stability are predicted to occur between atomic numbers 114 and 126 and again between 164 and 194.

Most of the elements exhibit variations in mass, due to the varying numbers of neutrons present in their nuclei. Atoms having the same nuclear charge but differing in mass number or atomic weight are referred to as ISOTOPES. If all of these are considered, then there are approximately 1000 different atomic species represented in the list of chemical elements. Only 18 of the elements existing in nature exhibit a single mass number, and some, tin being a good example, have as many as ten naturally occurring stable species differing only in their neutron number or mass. All of the elements exhibit a variety of mass modifications which are artificially produced, but these are unstable or radioactive. These artificially produced species, of course, make up the bulk of the previously mentioned 1000 different entities. The *natu-*

TABLE 1. THE THIRTEEN MOST ABUNDANT ELEMENTS IN THE EARTH'S CRUST

Element	Abundance (%)
Oxygen	49.52
Silicon	25.75
Aluminum	7.51
Iron	4.70
Calcium	3.39
Sodium	2.64
Potassium	2.40
Magnesium	1.94
Chlorine	1.88
Hydrogen	0.88
Titanium	0.58
Phosphorus	0.120
Carbon	0.087

rally occuring radioactive isotopes, in addition to those beyond bismuth, include carbon 14, chlorine 36, vanadium 50, potassium 40, rubidium 87, indium 115, lanthanum 138, neodymium 144, samarium 147, lutetium 176, tantalum 180, rhenium 187, and platinum 190.

The Natural Distribution of Elements The relative abundance of the elements is quite different for the earth's crust from what it is thought to be for the universe as a whole. These terrestrial abundances are listed in Table 1 from which it can be seen that only thirteen elements comprise over 98 per cent of the earth's crust, the oceans and the atmosphere. It will be noted that many of the common and important elements of commerce are not included in this list, but rather belong to the remaining 2 per cent of the earth's crust. Copper, lead, and nitrogen are especially conspicuous by their absence.

If we turn our attention now to cosmic abundances, the list has quite a different make up (see Table 2). This list of course is known with

TABLE 2. THE THIRTEEN MOST ABUNDANT ELEMENTS IN THE UNIVERSE

Element	Relative Abundance[a]
Hydrogen	3.5×10^8
Helium	3.5×10^7
Oxygen	2.2×10^5
Nitrogen	1.6×10^5
Carbon	8×10^4
Neon	2.4×10^4
Iron	1.8×10^4
Silicon	1×10^4
Magnesium	9×10^3
Sulfur	3.5×10^3
Nickel	1.3×10^3
Aluminum	8.8×10^2
Calcium	6.7×10^2

[a]These abundances are relative to silicon taken as 1×10^4.

considerably less accuracy since it is our attempt to guess at the relative abundance of the chemical elements in the entire universe: our galaxy, all the other galaxies, and the vast, but not entirely empty spaces in between. This information has largely been gathered by spectroscopic studies of the light emitted by the luminous bodies in these galaxies and by careful analysis of the samples of off-planet material (meteorites) that constantly shower the earth, as well as lunar-samples.

It can readily be seen that this list is quite different from the terrestrial abundance list. For the universe as a whole, the elements hydrogen and helium far outrank all others, while on the earth, hydrogen is only tenth in abundance and helium doesn't even appear on the list. Oxygen remains high, and nitrogen, absent from the terrestrial list, is the fourth most abundant element when cosmic abundances are considered. In Fig. 1, some of the interesting variations in abundance are displayed. The relative abundance is plotted against mass number.

It will be noted that elements with atomic weights that are multiples of four and two are more abundant than nearby elements with relatively similar atomic weights. Examination shows that those elements having *proton or neutron* numbers 8, 50, 82, and 126 also exhibit maxima. These numbers are so-called magic numbers confering an especially high degree of nuclear stability.

The Origins of the Elements Considerable speculation has been devoted to the question of the origin of the particular atomic weight distribution of elements thought to represent cosmic abundances. Examination of Fig. 1 suggests that this distribution is related to nuclear stability so that it would seem fruitful to consider what kind of an environment and sequence of events might lead to the observed distribution.

It should first of all be clear that in none of these theories is an attempt being made to truly consider *origins*, but only to explain the present distribution of atomic weights relative to some rather arbitrarily chosen point of time in the past. Nothing is postulated concerning the events preceding the zero time chosen.

One of the earliest and most popular theories, due mainly to Gamow, assumes that at time zero, the universe consisted of a dense mass of neutrons and radiation which at that time began a rapid expansion. During the early period, the temperature and density rapidly fell to values prevalent today. In the first five minutes, the universe was converted to a mixture of protons, neutrons, and electrons; in the next five minutes, sufficient cooling had occurred to permit thermonuclear reactions to occur, leading predominantly to the light elements. By the end of thirty minutes, the temperature of the expanding universe had dropped below that required for thermonuclear reactions in light elements and the distribution that we observe today, in which about 99 per cent of the universe is com-

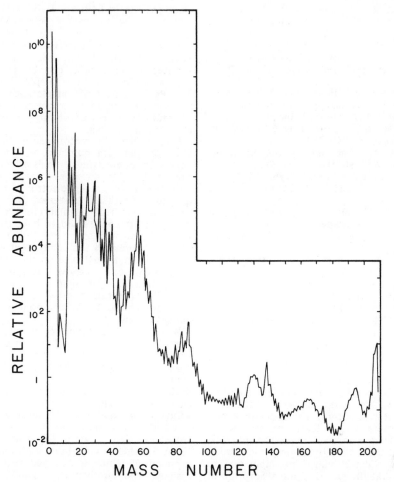

FIG. 1. [From Cameron, A. G. W., *Sky and Telescope*, 254 (May, 1963).]

posed of hydrogen and helium, was achieved. The buildup of the heavier elements is somewhat less clear. This theory assumes that the buildup was generally by neutron capture, but the absence of any stable nucleus of mass 5 throws some doubt on this general mechanism.

A theory based on equilibrium arguments involving the relation of binding energies of the nuclei to their abundance, predicts a much higher initial density of matter than the preceding kinetic theory and suggests that all of the elements were formed in exploding novae. While this theory is adequate in predicting abundances up to about mass 60, it seems quite inadequate for the heavier elements.

The most recent theory of formation of the elements, which is also the most detailed, assumes a steady-state process, without beginning or end. Matter is continuously formed and condenses into new stars and galaxies which undergo a series of evolutionary changes as a result of internal nuclear reactions and eventually

again distribute their matter into interstellar space.

The observational and experimental basis for this theory is mainly the *variations* in elemental distribution that are known for various types of stars in our galaxy. These variations suggest that the heavier elements, especially, are the natural consequence of stellar evolution. Detailed reaction schemes have been developed which account quite well for the high abundance of hydrogen and helium, and the low abundance of carbon, nitrogen and oxygen. The peak in mass number around 56 is also quite adequately explained. These reaction schemes suggest an age for our galaxy between 10 and 15 billion years.

RUSSELL H. JOHNSEN

References

1. Cherdyntsev, V. V., "Abundance of Chemical Elements," Chicago, University of Chicago Press, 1961 (translated by W. Nichiporuk).

2. Choppin, G. R., and Johnsen, R. H., "Introductory Chemistry," Reading, Mass., Addison-Wesley Inc., 1972.

3. Haissinsky, M., "Nuclear Chemistry and Its Applications," Reading, Mass., Addison-Wesley Publishing Company, Inc., 1964 (translated by D. G. Tuck).

4. Johnsen, R. H., and Grunwald, E., "Atoms, Molecules and Chemical Change," Third edition, Englewood Cliffs, N.J., Prentice-Hall, Inc., 1971.

5. Cameron, A. G. W., "Birth of the Elements," *Sky and Telescope*, 254 (May 1963).

6. Fowler, W. A., "The Origin of the Elements," *Chem. Eng. News*, 90 (March 16, 1964).

7. Herrmann, G. and Karl-Erich Seyb, "De Schwersten Chemischen Elemente," *Naturwiss.*, 590 (December 1969).

8. Keller, O. K., Jr., Burnett, J. L., Carlsen, T. A., and Nestor, C. W., Jr., "Predicted Properties of the Super Heavy Elements I., Elements 113 and 114," *J. Phys. Chem.*, **74**, 1127 (1970).

9. Seaborg, G. T., "From Mendeleev to Mendelevium and Beyond," *Chemistry*, **43**, 6 (1970).

Cross-references: COSMOLOGY, ELECTRON, ISOTOPES, NEUTRON, PERIODIC LAW AND PERIODIC TABLE, PROTON, RADIOACTIVITY.

ENERGY LEVELS

The term "energy level" is used in referring to discrete amounts of energy which atoms and molecules can have with respect to their electron or nuclear structure. The concept of permissible discrete energy levels was first introduced by Planck in explaining the physical basis for the spectral distribution of blackbody radiation. A second related principle due to Planck was that the emission and absorption of radiation are associated with transitions between these energy levels, the energy thereby lost or gained being equal to the energy, $h\nu$, of the quantum of radiation. Here h is Planck's constant and ν is the frequency of the radiation.

The first application of energy levels in the electron structure of atoms to explain optical spectra was made by Bohr. The original Bohr atom had as its basis that the only allowable states of an atom were those in which the electronic angular momentum was an integral multiple of $h/2\pi$. Circular orbits suggested by Bohr were extended by Sommerfeld to include the quantization of momentum in elliptic orbits, and to provide an improved explanation of optical spectra.

These early concepts were modified by the development of the theory of wave mechanics, in which it was shown that the allowable "stationary" states for the electrons in an atom must represent solutions of the Schrödinger wave equation. These solutions are conveniently represented by a set of "quantum numbers" for each electron. On this basis the electron structure of an atom containing any number of electrons can be built up. Two further concepts which are essential to this picture, however, are electron spin proposed by Uhlenbeck and Goudsmit, and the exclusion principle due to Pauli. In addition to the angular momentum of the electron in its orbit, each electron possesses angular momentum due to spin about an axis. The Pauli exclusion principle specifies that no two electrons in an atom can exist in the same quantum state, corresponding to the same set of quantum numbers.

Each electron in an atom can be characterized by four quantum numbers, n, l, m_l, m_s. The energy of an electron depends principally upon the positive integer n, and larger values of n correspond to larger electronic orbits. The quantum number l possesses physical significance in terms of angular momentum in the orbit, and is constrained to have the values of zero or positive integers less than n. The number, m_l, represents the component of l along a given axis, and must take on the values of zero or positive and negative integers whose absolute values are less than or equal to the value of l. The quantum number, m_s, can be $+\frac{1}{2}$ or $-\frac{1}{2}$, and represents the component of the spin along the axis.

Within a given atom, electrons having the same value of the principal quantum number, n, form a definite group or "shell." Those electrons possessing the same value of l for a given value of n are in the same subgroup or "subshell." The possible number of electrons in a shell or subshell depends upon the possible values of m_l and m_s. Whenever a subshell is filled, the total angular momentum of the electrons involved is zero. Electrons outside of filled subshells contribute additional angular momentum which is summed vectorially and assigned the numbers J, L and S. Here J is representative of the total angular momentum, L the orbital angular momentum, and S the spin angular momentum.

An atom is stable only when it exists in the state for which the quantum numbers of its electrons give the lowest total energy. The energy of the atom may be increased to a higher level by having an electron "excited" to another state represented by a different set of allowed quantum numbers. Transitions back again to the "ground" state will be accompanied by the emission of radiation. Wave mechanics indicates, however, that only certain transitions from one quantum state to another can be probable. These "selection rules" specify that $\Delta L = \pm 1$ and that $\Delta J = 0$ or ± 1.

Following the principles just given, an electron energy-level diagram can be constructed for the excited states of the atoms of any particular isotope. Discrete energy levels will exist for the allowed quantum states of excited electrons. The spectrum of radiation which can be emitted from the isotope will be determined by the energy differences between these states, where the transitions involved are allowed by

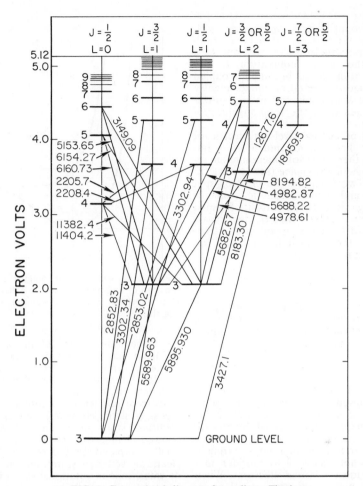

FIG. 1. Energy-level diagram for sodium. The large
numbers are wave lengths in A of radiation emitted or
absorbed during the indicated transitions. Principal
quantum numbers are shown as integers.

selection rules. Figure 1 illustrates such an
energy-level diagram for sodium.

This diagram indicates that very little difference in energy level results from changes in the
electron spin orientation. These orientations
correspond to different values of J for the same
value of L. No attempt is made to show a
separation in the diagram for the cases of $L = 2$
and $L = 3$. Such closely spaced energy levels
due to the effect of the coupling of the electron
spin give rise to "fine structure" in spectra.

Many spectral lines, when examined with high
resolving power instruments, are found to exhibit a still finer structure of several lines very
close together. This is termed "hyperfine structure" and has been found to be due to two
causes. One is the isotope effect in which atoms
of different isotopes of the same element
possess slightly different excited electron energy
levels. The other cause of hyperfine structure

has been determined to be due to the fact that
the atomic nucleus also possesses angular momentum, which is vectorially added to the electronic angular momentum and quantitized. Differences in the resultant states of the atom
correspond to very small differences in the
energy levels and hence in the observed
spectrum.

Another source of structure in spectra results
when the atoms emitting or absorbing the radiation are in a magnetic or an electric field. In a
field, space quantization in the direction of the
field takes place. The values of the magnetic
moment or electric moment of the atom associated with the various possible components of
angular momentum as quantitized in the field
direction result in different energy levels. This
splitting of levels is referred to as the Zeeman
effect in the case of an applied magnetic field,
and the Stark effect in the case of an applied

electric field (see ZEEMAN AND STARK EF-FECTS). The amount of splitting increases with the intensity of the superposed field. In addition, the spectral structure can vary due to a tendency for the orbital momentum, L, and the spin momentum, S, to become uncoupled and undergo space quantization independently in high fields. In weak fields, the space quantization is determined from the total angular momentum J.

The splitting of energy levels in electric or magnetic fields has become much more important in another type of phenomenon referred to as magnetic resonance (see MAGNETIC RESONANCE). Two examples are electron spin resonance (esr) and nuclear magnetic resonance (nmr). If a single level is split into its Zeeman components by a magnetic field H, electromagnetic radiation of frequency ν will induce transitions between the Zeeman levels if the following condition is satisfied:

$$h\nu = g\mu H$$

Here g is energy level "splitting factor" and μ is the appropriate "magneton" (Bohr magneton μ_B for esr and nuclear magneton μ_N for nmr). (See reference 1.) For magnetic field strengths conveniently available in the laboratory, the resonance frequencies are in the short radio or microwave regions.

Any electron of an atom may be excited to some higher allowed energy level by absorption of the amount of energy specified by the difference in the energy levels involved. By absorption of a sufficient amount of energy, any electron can be removed from an atom, resulting in ionization. It is not necessary to consider only the outermost loosely bound electrons. When electrons from inner shells are excited or removed, the process of returning to the "ground" or lowest energy state involves the emission of "characteristic" x-rays. They are "characteristic" in that the x-ray spectrum produced is typical of the particular atom producing the radiation. Atoms of higher atomic number and transitions involving electrons in innermost shells produce higher-energy radiation. Absorption, as well as emission, of characteristic x-ray radiation is observed between allowed electronic energy levels. For further information on atomic spectra and energy levels, see reference 2.

In addition to the energy levels associated with particular types of atoms, wave mechanics shows that discrete quantum states and energy levels are associated with molecular structure. New energy levels arise from vibration and rotation of molecules. To illustrate the allowable vibrational states for a diatomic molecule, consider Fig. 2, which shows the mutual force, F, and the potential energy, V, plotted as a function of the separation, r, between the two atoms. Possible energy levels are indicated by the dotted lines. Even the lowest state corresponds to an energy greater than V_0, where

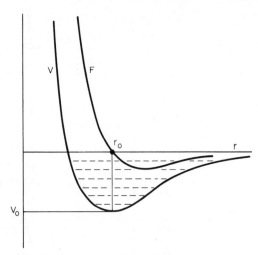

FIG. 2. Mutual potential energy V and force F as a function of atomic separation in a diatomic molecule. F is repulsive when positive and attractive when negative.

the force between the atoms would be zero, and hence has some associated kinetic energy.

The rotation of a molecule has a quantitized angular momentum which can be vectorially combined with that of the electrons. Transitions from one level to another usually involve a change in the electronic state as well as in the rotational state. Since energy differences due to allowed changes in rotational motion are very small compared to the energy differences in electronic states or vibrational states, the effect of transitions in rotational states is to produce bands of very closely spaced frequencies in the emission and absorption spectra. Such "rotational" bands are observed in molecular spectroscopy, depending upon what other transitions may be simultaneously involved, in the ultraviolet region, the visible, the infrared, and even the microwave region. See reference 3 for further details on molecular energy levels and associated spectra.

An atom may not only combine with others to form a molecule, but may be one of a large number of atoms forming a crystal. Here solutions to the wave equation show that within the solid, the individual energy levels of the free atom broaden into bands of overlapping levels. This is illustrated in Fig. 3. The bulk electrical and optical properties of solids are determined by the nature of these energy-level bands. Metals have the highest occupied energy band unfilled, while satisfying the exclusion principle that no two electrons occupy the same state. This permits electrons to gain energy under the application of an electric field and flow freely through the solid. Insulating crystals have the highest occupied energy band filled and appreciably separated from the next

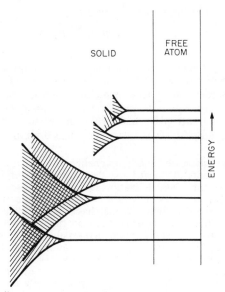

SOLID

FREE
ATOM

ENERGY ⟶

FIG. 3. The electron levels of a free atom split into bands when the atom enters a solid.

Cross-references: ATOMIC PHYSICS, ELECTRON SPIN, MAGNETIC RESONANCE, MOLECULES AND MOLECULAR STRUCTURE, NUCLEAR STRUCTURE, SCHRÖDINGER EQUATION, SEMICONDUCTORS, SPECTROSCOPY, X-RAYS, ZEEMAN AND STARK EFFECTS.

ENTROPY

The word "entropy" was coined from the Greek by Rudolf Clausius in 1865 to mean "transformation". He applied it to a thermodynamic function, S, defined by the differential equation

$$dS = dQ/T \quad \text{(reversible)} \quad (1)$$

where dQ is the element of heat added reversibly to a system at absolute temperature T. In the classical macroscopic approach to thermodynamics, no meaning is assignable to entropy. The classical view is that thermodynamics is a machine into which some facts are put and other facts emerge.

In 1948, Claude Shannon[3] demonstrated that the change in the function defined by

$$S_I = -k \sum_i p_i \log p_i \quad (2)$$

measures the amount of information in any message (p_i = probability that the receiver assigns to the receipt of the ith possible). The sum is over all possible messages. It has been shown that the entropy of Clausius is derivable from that of Shannon.[1] Before considering this derivation, a simple example of the meaning of entropy will be considered. Suppose you are asked to guess which number from 1 to 100 has been secretly written on a piece of paper. Taking each p_i equal to 1/100, it is found that in the above equation, $S_I = k \log (100)$. Letting k equal 1 and taking the logarithm to the base 2 gives $S = 6.67$ "bits." This means if each question has only two possible answers (i.e., "yes" or "no"), it will take between 6 and 7 questions to find the number. The questioner begins by asking, "Is the number between 1 and 50?" Depending on the answer, he continues by reducing the possible numbers by a factor of 2 with each question. Since $2^6 = 64$ and $2^7 = 128$, the questioner will surely find the number in 7 questions and 1/3 of the time he will find it in 6 questions. Entropy may therefore be said to measure the state of ignorance of a person relative to a well-defined question, if the person only knows a probability distribution. It measures the expected number of questions he will have to ask in order to go from his state of partial knowledge to a state in which he knows everything about the well-defined question. According to the Shannon derivation,[3] S_I represents the amount of information in a message telling the actual number written on the paper (for someone for whom $p_i = 1/100$). This interpretation of entropy is used in information

higher band. Semiconductors represent an intermediate situation where electrons can be injected into an unfilled band to contribute to conduction.

If the solid crystal is not completely regular but contains imperfections or impurity atoms, specific electron energy levels will be associated with these sites. This condition is responsible for luminescence and phosphorescence in certain solids. Additional information on energy bands in solids is given in reference 4.

Finally, it should be mentioned that in addition to energy levels associated with the electronic structure of atoms and the motion of atoms in molecules, there are energy levels associated with the structure of nucleii. Such levels evidence themselves in various ways, particularly through the different energies of the electromagnetic radiation, or gamma rays, emitted from excited nucleii.

WILLIAM E. PARKINS

References

1. Kittel, Charles, "Introduction to Solid State Physics," Third edition, New York, John Wiley & Sons Inc., 1966.
2. White, Harvey E., "Introduction to Atomic Spectra," First edition, New York, McGraw-Hill Book Co., 1934.
3. Herzberg, Gerhard, "Molecular Spectra and Molecular Structure," Second edition, New York, Van Nostrand Reinhold, 1950.
4. Seitz, Frederick, "The Modern Theory of Solids," First edition, New York and London, McGraw-Hill Book Co., 1940.

theory in the design of codes and in the analysis of information transmission systems.

To make the connection with classical thermodynamics, consider a physical system and ask the question "In what quantum state is this system?" Of course one can never say in which quantum state a system resides but rather can only give a probability for the system being in a particular state. The probability distribution for the states must be consistent with the observer's knowledge. The information theory principle of maximum entropy says to choose a set of probabilities which agrees with the available data and maximizes the entropy, for, in accordance with the meaning of entropy, this is the most non-committal view. A state of equilibrium is, by the definition given by Gibbs,[4] a state of maximum entropy. From the information theory point of view, it is a state in which all of the random motions which can take place are, in fact, taking place so that the observer knows as little about the systems as it is possible to know beyond his knowledge of the "constants of the motion." If we describe a system by giving only the pressure, temperature and volume (or other gross properties), we omit many details. Entropy measures how much more there is to be said before the quantum state is specified.

As an illustration, consider a closed system of particles. From quantum mechanics, we know the system is in some state, i, with energy ϵ_i. If we make an observation of ϵ, the best we can do is infer that it represents the expectation energy, $\langle \epsilon \rangle$, for this is a repeatable quantity associated with the motion. To generate the appropriate probability distribution, we maximize S_I defined in Eq. (2), with the following constraints on the p_i:

$$\sum p_i = 1 \text{ (the system is in some state)} \quad (3)$$

$$\sum p_i \epsilon_i = \langle \epsilon \rangle \text{ (the system has an expectation energy)} \quad (4)$$

Maximization of the entropy subject to the two equations given leads to the probability distribution

$$p_i = e^{-\psi - \beta \epsilon_i} \quad (5)$$

The resultant entropy, $S_{I,\max}$, is, by Gibbs[1] definition, the equilibrium entropy. The probability distribution is known as the Boltzmann distribution. It is easy to demonstrate that the parameter β is equal to $1/kT$ where k is the Boltzmann constant and T is the absolute temperature. If the observer is limited to macroscopic observations concerned with the energy of a body, the above derivation leads to laws which connect the observations to one another. That is, the quantities ψ, β, $\langle \epsilon \rangle$, S and various combinations are related to one another by equations from which p_i and ϵ_i have been eliminated. These relations are known as the "Laws of Classical Thermostatics".

For example, since, from Eq. (4)

$$d \langle \epsilon \rangle = \sum_i \epsilon_i dp_i + \sum_i p_i d\epsilon_i$$

it is clear that the changes in the energy of a body may be divided into two classes: (a) those of the type $\sum \epsilon_i dp_i$ which *necessarily* change the probabilities and therefore the entropy (non-isentropic) and (b) those in which $\sum_i \epsilon_i dp_i = 0$ (i.e., isentropic). This division into two classes of energy exchange gives rise to the concepts of "heat" and "work." For a detailed account of the derivation see reference 2.

Entropy, as a logical device for generating probability distributions, has been applied in reliability engineering, decision theory, and the theory of steady-state irreversible processes. (See list of references with reference 5.) The generalized approach to entropy usage was initiated by Jaynes.[6] Applications of the entropy principle in engineering are given in reference[7].

M. TRIBUS

References

1. Tribus, M., "Information Theory as the Basis for Thermostatics and Thermodynamics," *J. Appl. Mech.*, B (March 1961).
2. Tribus, M., "Thermostatics and Thermodynamics," New York, Van Nostrand/Reinhold, 1961.
3. Shannon, Claude, "A Mathematical Theory of Communication," *Bell System Tech. J.* (July and October 1948).
4. Gibbs, J. W., "Collected Works," Vol. I, p. 56, New Haven, Conn., Yale University Press.
5. Tribus, M., and Evans, R., "The Probability Foundations of Thermodynamics," *Appl. Mech. Rev.*, 765 (October 1963).
6. Jaynes, E. T., "Information Theory and Statistical Mechanics," *Phys. Rev.*, **106**, 620; **108**, 171 (1957).
7. Tribus, M., "Rational Descriptions, Decisions and Designs," Oxford, Pergamon Press, 1969.

Cross-references: BOLTZMANN'S DISTRIBUTION LAW, IRREVERSIBILITY, PHYSICAL CHEMISTRY, STATISTICAL MECHANICS, THERMODYNAMICS.

EQUILIBRIUM

In the elementary sense of the macroscopic (visible to the naked eye) system, equilibrium is obtained if the system does not tend to undergo any further change of its own accord. Any further change must be produced by external means.

Mechanical and Electromagnetic Systems Equilibrium in mechanical and/or electromagnetic systems is reached when the vectorial summation of generalized forces applied to the system is equal to zero. In any potential field,

that is, gravitational or electric potential or magnetic vector potential, force can be expressed as gradient of potential (magnetic force however, is a curl of a vector potential). The potential energy therefore has an extremum at the equilibrium configuration. For example, a system such as a mass suspended by a string against the gravitational force (or its weight) is at mechanical equilibrium if the tensile force in the string is equal to the weight of the mass it supports. The d'Alembert principle further states that the condition for equilibrium of a system is that the virtual work of the applied forces vanishes.

Thermodynamic Systems When a hot body and a cold body are brought into physical contact, they tend to achieve the same warmth after a long time. These two bodies are then said to be at thermal equilibrium with each other. The zeroth law of thermodynamics (R. H. Fowler) states that two bodies individually at equilibrium with a third are at equilibrium with each other. This led to the comparison of the states of thermal equilibrium of two bodies in terms of a third body called a thermometer. The temperature scale is a measure of state of thermal equilibrium, and two systems at thermal equilibrium must have the same temperature (see THERMODYNAMICS).

Generalization of equilibrium consideration by the second law of thermodynamics specifies that the state of thermodynamic equilibrium of a system is characterized by the attainment of the maximum of its ENTROPY. Thermodynamic coordinates are defined in terms of equilibrium states.

Equilibrium between two phases of a system is reached when there is no net transfer of mass or energy between the phases. Phase equilibrium is determined by the equality of the Gibbs functions (also called free enthalpy, free energy, or chemical potential) of the phases in addition to equality of their temperatures and stresses (such as pressure and/or field intensities—intensive properties). Equilibrium of first-order phase change requires continuity of slope or first derivative of the Gibbs function with respect to an intensive property and is generalized as the Clapeyron relation. Second- and higher-order phase changes are given by the condition of continuity of curvature or second derivative of the Gibbs function and so on.

Chemical or nuclear equilibrium of a reactive system is reached when there is no net transfer of mass and/or energy between the components of a system. At chemical or nuclear equilibrium, the Gibbs function of the reactants and the products must be equal according to stoichiometric proportions, in addition to uniformity in temperature and stresses. Chemical equilibrium is summarized in the form of the Law of Mass Action. The trend for the displacement from an equilibrium state is specified by Le Châtelier's principle.

Thermodynamic equilibrium is reached when the condition of mechanical, electromagnetic, thermal, phase, and chemical and nuclear equilibrium is reached.

Stability of Equilibrium A process or change of state carried out on a system such that it is always near a state of equilibrium is called a quasi-stationary equilibrium process. This requires that the process be carried out slowly. If a mechanical system is initially at the equilibrium position with zero initial velocity, then the system will continue at equilibrium indefinitely. An equilibrium position is said to be stable if a small disturbance of the system from equilibrium results only in small, bounded motion about the rest position. The equilibrium is unstable if an infinitesimal displacement produces unbounded motion. In the gravitational field, a marble at rest in the bottom of a bowl is in stable equilibrium, but an egg standing on its end is in unstable equilibrium. When motion can occur about an equilibrium position without disturbing the equilibrium, the system is in neutral (or labile, or indifferent) equilibrium, an example being a marble resting on a perfectly flat plane normal to the direction of gravity. It is readily seen that stable equilibrium is the case when the extremum of potential is a minimum.

When dealing with general thermodynamic systems, the fact that entropy tends to a maximum in the trend toward equilibrium of a natural process generalizes the above mechanical consideration with respect to stability. An equilibrium state can be characterized as a stable equilibrium when the entropy is a maximum; neutral equilibrium when displacement from one equilibrium state to another does not involve changing entropy; and unstable equilibrium when entropy is a minimum. Any slight disturbance from an unstable equilibrium state of a system will lead to transition to another state of equilibrium.

Statistical Equilibrium In the microscopic sense, that is, treating systems in terms of elemental particles such as molecules, atoms, and other material or quasi-particles (such as photons in radiation, phonons in solids and liquids, rotons in liquids), equilibrium states are recognized as the most probable states. An equilibrium state of a system is therefore defined in terms of most probable distributions of its elements among microscopic states which may be defined in terms of energy states. In this sense, statistical equilibrium is a condition for macroscopic equilibrium and an equilibrium state of a system is one of its extremal states. In the methods of STATISTICAL MECHANICS, the probability of distribution is expressed in terms of the density of distributions in the phase space. Based on the Liouville theorem, if a system is in statistical equilibrium, the number of the elements in a given state must be constant in time; which is to say that the density of distribution

at a given location in phase space does not change with time. For an isolated system, the distribution is represented by a microcanonical ensemble. At equilibrium, no phase point can cross over a surface of constant energy, and the density of distribution is preserved. In this case individual molecules of a system can be represented by phase points. Any part of an isolated system in statistical equilibrium can be represented by a canonical ensemble. A subsystem of a large system in thermal equilibrium also behaves like the average system of a canonical ensemble. A system and a constant temperature bath together can be considered as an isolated system. A phase point in a canonical ensemble can represent a large number of molecules, thus accounting for strong interactions. A canonical ensemble is characterized by its temperature and is therefore pertinent to the concept of thermal equilibrium. When applied to equilibrium of systems involving mass exchange, such as a chemical system, we have a "particle bath" in addition to a constant temperature bath. The pertinent representation for equilibrium including mass exchange as well as energy exchange is known as a grand canonical ensemble, which accounts for the chemical potentials of its elements.

When applied to a system with a large number of elements, the distributions are measured by thermodynamic probability (W); the most probable distribution is such that W is a maximum. This optimal principle is consistent with the condition of maximum entropy (S) given in the above. The Boltzmann hypothesis states that $S = k \ln W$, where k is the Boltzmann constant.

Depending on the specifications of W, namely, those of Maxwell-Boltzmann (for low concentration of distinguishable particles, weak interaction and high temperature, such as a dilute perfect gas), Fermi-Dirac (for elemental particles with antisymmetric wave functions at high concentrations of indistinguishable particles and low temperatures, such as electrons in metal), or Einstein-Bose (for elemental particles with symmetric wave functions, such as He^4 at high concentration of indistinguishable particles and low temperature), equilibrium distributions take different forms (see BOSE-EINSTEIN STATISTICS and FERMI-DIRAC STATISTICS). The Maxwellian speed distribution in a dilute perfect gas is a distribution based on Maxwell-Boltzmann statistics.

As a consequence of molecular considerations, when two systems are connected for transfer of mass without significant transfer of energy, such as two containers at different temperatures connected by a capillary tube, we have the relation of thermal transpiration.

Trend toward Equilibrium The mechanism by which equilibrium is attained can only be visualized in terms of microscopic theories. In the kinetic sense, equilibrium is reached in a gas when collisions among molecules redistribute the velocities (or kinetic energies) of each molecule until a Maxwellian distribution is reached

for the whole bulk. In the case of the trend toward equilibrium for two solid bodies brought into physical contact, we visualize the transfer of energy by means of free electrons and phonons (lattice vibrations).

The Boltzmann H-theorem generalizes the condition that with a state of a system represented by its distribution function f, a quantity H, defined as the statistical average of $\ln f$, approaches a minimum when equilibrium is reached. This conforms with the Boltzmann hypothesis of distribution in the above in that $S = -kH$ accounts for equilibrium as a consequence of collisions which change the distribution toward that of equilibrium conditions.

Consideration of perturbation from an equilibrium state leads to methods for dealing with rate processes and methods of irreversible thermodynamics in general.

Fluctuation from Equilibrium A necessary consequence of the random nature of elemental particles in a body is that the property of such a body is not at every instant equal to its average value but fluctuates about this average. A precise meaning of equilibrium can only be attained from consideration of the nature of such fluctuations. In the above, we have repeatedly considered a "large" number of particles. It is important to know how large a number is "large." When considering fluctuation of energy from an average value in an isolated system, the ratio of the two is given to be proportional to $1/\sqrt{N}$, where N is the total number of elements in the system. This is also the magnitude of the fluctuation of number of particles in a system involving transformation of phases and chemical and nuclear species. An equilibrium state is one at which the longtime mean magnitude of fluctuation from the average state is independent of time and this magnitude has reached a minimum value.

Large perturbation from a given state of fluctuation leads to a relaxation process toward a state of equilibrium. The relaxation time, for instance, measures the deviation from quasi-stationary equilibrium of a process which is carried out at a finite rate.

S. L. Soo

References

Goldstein, H., "Classical Mechanics," Cambridge, Mass., Addison-Wesley Publishing Co., Inc., 1956.

Soo, S. L., "Analytical Thermodynamics," Englewood Cliffs, N.J., Prentice-Hall, Inc., 1962.

Cross-references: BOSE-EINSTEIN STATISTICS, ENTROPY, FERMI-DIRAC STATISTICS, IRREVERSIBILITY, THERMODYNAMICS.

EXCITONS

Excitons are neutral and mobile modes of electronic excitation in insulating crystals and may be regarded as quanta of the classical polarization field in a dielectric medium. They are fun-

damental in the description of the interaction of light with nonmetals and play an important role in energy transport.

The original model of an exciton, developed by Frenkel in 1931, is based on the tight-binding description of a solid. In this description, applicable primarily to molecular crystals, excitons are to be identified with excited states of the constituent molecules; because of the Coulomb interaction between electrons on adjacent molecules, such excited states cannot remain localized but spread through the solid as a "wave of excitation." Frenkel's model does not take into account the possibility that an excited electron may transfer to a nearby lattice site, in effect leaving behind it a positive hole. So long as the attraction between electron and hole keeps the two from drifting apart, the resulting entity will still be a neutral form of electronic excitation, i.e., an exciton. Thus a more general picture of an exciton is that of a bound electron-hole pair; the tight-binding exciton simply has the two bound at a single site so that the separate identities of electron and hole are lost. It is not, however, strictly accurate to describe the tightly bound exciton in terms of a *single* electron-hole pair, as many electrons may participate in a given excited state. The single-pair picture works well in materials with large dielectric constant and/or small reduced electron-hole mass, particularly in semiconductors. In such solids, the electron-hole separation may attain the size of many lattice cells, and it becomes appropriate to describe the exciton as a positronium-like "atom" embedded in a smooth dielectric medium (Wannier-Mott model). This weak-binding model is improved by taking into account the band structure of the solid: an electron from a conduction band, characterized by parameters describing this band (symmetry, effective mass, etc.), is bound to a hole from a valence band, with the resulting exciton energy lying within the band-gap. Typically, the exciton levels are within tenths of an electron volt below the conduction band edge, out of total gap energies of several electron volts. When the electron-hole separation is of the order of a few lattice spacings, as is the case in alkali halides and solid rare gases, neither description of the exciton is quantitatively accurate, and more elaborate but less successful schemes have been devised (electron transfer model, excitation model). The great variety of properties of excitons of the various types is best illustrated by the enormous range of effective masses: these vary from as much as hundreds of electron masses for tightly bound triplet excitons (excitons in which electron and hole have parallel spin; the necessary spin flip impedes the propagation of triplet excitons) down to tenths and even hundredths of an electron mass for sums of conduction and valence band masses in some weakly bound cases.

Excitons in molecular crystals, primarily in crystals of aromatic hydrocarbons, have undergone extensive studies. In these materials, exciton band structure can often be elucidated with the aid of the Davydov splitting of spectral lines: a given excited state of a molecule gives rise to as many different exciton branches (differing in energy, coupling to light, polarization) as there are translationally inequivalent sites in a unit lattice cell. One method of investigating energy transport via excitons is to study optical spectra when foreign ("guest") molecules are embedded dilutely in a "host" crystal. Excitons can explore large regions of the crystal during their lifetime and thus are sensitive to very dilute concentrations of "guests." Triplet excitons, whose lifetimes may be as long as tenths of a second, can detect certain impurities as dilute as one part per billion. They can moreover detect other triplet excitons: in many organic crystals, the collision of two triplet excitons can result in a fusion process leading to the production of a more energetic singlet exciton which can then decay optically, producing a phenomenon known as delayed fluorescence. The study of this phenomenon has in recent years been a productive source of information on triplet excitons (see Ref. 6). Their diffusion can be determined by studying the effects on delayed fluorescence of a spatially inhomogeneous exciton distribution. Magnetic fields are found to influence delayed fluorescence, despite the fact that appreciable polarization of the exciton spins is not possible at room temperature. The effect arises from the existence of spin restrictions on the fusion process coupled with the fact that during the short time that two excitons can interact their relative spin orientation cannot thermalize but evolves coherently, depending on the fine structure interactions of the excitons and on the external field. The fission of a singlet exciton into two triplets has also been observed and is similarly magnetic-field dependent.

The most striking evidence for the weakly bound model of an exciton is observed in hydrogen-like series of absorption lines—notably in Cu_2O, also in CdS and PbI_2—which the simplest form of this model predicts. The model can be further probed by subjecting the excitons to electric and magnetic fields, also to strain fields. Such studies have yielded understanding of much of the band structure of Cu_2O and CdS, materials in which this structure was not so accessible otherwise.

Absorption of light in insulating materials (in pure crystals, also emission) is directly related to the production (in pure crystals, also decay) of excitons. Only excitons with very small wave vectors couple to visible light since the latter has wavelengths of hundreds of lattice constants; yet the exciton wave vector is not so small as to escape detection, and the mobile character of optically produced excitons has been verified via the Lorentz force acting on a moving exciton in a magnetic field. Another selection rule important in exciton-photon coupling comes about from the fact that the matrix element for the production of an exciton contains in lowest order a vector quantity, the transition moment μ. Only excitons with

wave vector perpendicular to μ couple to light. The interaction with photons results in mixed exciton-photon modes, often called polaritons. The finite mass of the exciton part of a polariton gives rise to effects associated with spatial dispersion, e.g., anomalous modes of light propagation. In Raman scattering experiments the fact that light inside the crystal propagates as a polariton can lead to a resonant enhancement of phonon-scattering cross sections as the light frequency approaches an exciton frequency.

To obtain bonafide absorption of light, an energy sink is needed for the excitons; except for possible re-emission at lower frequencies, phonons provide the main sink of energy. The exciton-phonon interaction may bring about the formation of "self-trapped excitons," which carry along a region of self-produced lattice distortion. Such self-trapped excitons have indeed been identified in alkali halide crystals. Phonons have important effects on the line shapes of optical exciton spectra, particularly in the alkali halides where absorption peaks may attain widths of tenths of an electron volt even at low temperatures. Phonons make possible the optical production of "indirect" excitons, excitons which have wave vectors large compared to those of light. Excitons can bind not only to phonons, but also to crystal imperfections, magnons, and even to other excitons, forming "excitonic molecules." Excitonic molecules have been shown to provide an efficient channel for stimulated emission (in CuCl). Exciton densities which are sufficiently high to observe excitonic molecules are achieved via laser illumination at low temperatures and have yielded a variety of other interesting phenomena involving exciton-exciton interactions. Experiments demonstrating the formation of microscopic droplets of exciton "liquid" in Ge and Si are particularly fascinating. Another kind of exciton condensation has been proposed theoretically; if the electron-hole binding energy can be made to exceed the band gap, a spontaneous collapse of a semiconductor into an "excitonic insulator" is expected to occur.

An important exciton-related effect which is virtually universal in the absorption spectra of insulators is the empirical Urbach law: absorption below the absorption edge decreases exponentially with energy. Many theories for special instances of this law have been proposed, and a unified understanding is now emerging in terms of the interaction of excitons with fluctuating electric microfields caused by phonons or imperfections.

Excitons, though intrinsically non-current-carrying entities, are instrumental in photoconductivity and photoemission; the necessary charge carriers are produced from ionization of impurity states by excitons or from ionization of the excitons themselves. Excitons have also been studied in the x-ray region. Other related topics include vibrational excitons, propagating vibrational states in molecular crystals which are not strictly electronic in nature yet share the properties of Frenkel excitons. Excitons are also of interest in long-chain organic molecules which act like one-dimensional crystals; thus they may even have biological significance.

Acknowledgements The original article was written at the University of California, Berkeley, where the support of the National Science Foundation and discussions with Professor J. J. Hopfield and Dr. B. Halperin are acknowledged. Discussions with Professor Hopfield and with Dr. P. Avakian during the present revision are also appreciated.

A. SUNA

References

Space limitations prevent quoting original references to ideas presented. Some useful review articles are given below. Of these, 1 is a general introduction to the subject, 2 is a comprehensive review covering the literature relevant to inorganic solids up to mid-1963, and 3 contains a short review of more recent work. For literature on molecular excitons, see the review articles 4 through 6 and the exhaustive bibliographies 7.

1. Dexter, D. L., and Knox, R. S., "Excitons," New York, Interscience, 1965.
2. Knox, R. S., "Theory of Excitons," Suppl. 5 of *Solid State Physics*, Academic Press, New York (1963).
3. Toyozawa, Y., in "Proceedings of Tenth International Conference on the Physics of Semiconductors," Cambridge, Mass., USAEC Div. of Technical Information (1970), p. 5.
4. McClure, D. S., *Solid State Physics*, **8**, 1, Academic Press, New York (1959).
5. Wolf, H. C., *Solid State Physics*, **9**, 1, Academic Press, New York (1959).
6. Avakian, P., and Merrifield, R. E., *Mol. Cryst.*, **5**, 37 (1968).
7. Morozova, A. I., and Sheka, E. F., *Mol. Cryst. Liq. Cryst.*, **14**, 329 (1971); Lipsett, F. R., ibid, **6**, 175 (1969), and references to preceding bibliographies contained therein.

Cross-references: PHONONS, PHOTON, SOLID-STATE PHYSICS, SOLID-STATE THEORY.

EXPANSION, THERMAL

Definition and General Remarks All substances change their shapes as a consequence of undergoing changes in temperature. A measure of this change is the thermal coefficient of expansion. In most cases the result is an increase in the length, area, or volume of a sample. The effect is by no means negligible but for moderate changes in the temperature a first-order correction suffices. The prevention of thermal expansion requires very large mechanical stresses. For example, a compressive stress of order 5×10^8 dynes/cm^2 is necessary to prevent a steel bar from expanding when the temperature is increased by 20°C. For solids in the form of a

thin rod or cable, this change is confined (to first order) to a change in length, and a linear coefficient of expansion is thus defined by

$$\alpha_0 = \frac{1}{L_0}\left(\frac{\partial L}{\partial t}\right)_P \qquad (1)$$

where L_0 is the length of the specimen at $0°C$ and the subscript P implies that the pressure is kept constant. Correspondingly, for fluids and for solids of arbitrary shape, one defines a cubical or volume coefficient of expansion, β_0, by the relation

$$\beta_0 = \frac{1}{V_0}\left(\frac{\partial V}{\partial t}\right)_P \qquad (2)$$

with V_0 being the volume at the reference temperature (usually chosen to be $0°C$). It may readily be shown that $\beta_0 = 3\alpha_0$. Thus for solids one usually tabulates values of α_0 while, of course, only β has meaning for fluids. Whereas β_0 is simply $1/273$ for all ideal gases (this follows from the equation $PV = nRT$), there exists a wide variation for β values among liquids. Table 1 gives α and β values for several sub-

TABLE 1. LINEAR COEFFICIENTS OF EXPANSION, α, FOR SOME SOLIDS AND CUBICAL COEFFICIENTS OF EXPANSION, β, FOR SOME LIQUIDS AT ROOM TEMPERATURE

	α (/C°)	β (/C°)
Aluminum	25.0×10^{-6}	
Copper	16.8×10^{-6}	
Nickel	12.8×10^{-6}	
Sodium	77.0×10^{-6}	
Mercury		18.2×10^{-5}
Glycerin		48.5×10^{-5}
Water (0–4°C)		-3.2×10^{-5}

stances. The negative value of β for water below 4°C is anomalous and is caused by the comparatively open lattice structure of ice. In the case of nonisotropic crystals, the coefficient of linear expansion differs for different directions in the crystals and may even have opposite signs along different directions as is the case for $CaCO_3$.

Thermodynamic Relationships The cubical coefficient of expansion plays an important role in relating the molar specific heat at constant pressure, C_P, (which is usually measured directly in the laboratory) to the molar specific heat at constant volume (which is most often obtained from theory). This relationship, based solely on the laws of thermodynamics is[1]

$$C_P - C_V = (\beta^2 VT)/X \qquad (3)$$

where T is the absolute temperature and X the compressibility defined by

$$X = -\frac{1}{V}\left(\frac{\partial V}{\partial P}\right)_T \qquad (4)$$

To obtain this result we write the first law of thermodynamics (see THERMODYNAMICS):

$$\delta Q = dU + P\,dV \qquad (5)$$

Since

$$C_V = \left(\frac{\delta Q}{\delta T}\right)_V = \left(\frac{\partial U}{\partial T}\right)_V \qquad (6)$$

$$dU = \left(\frac{\partial U}{\partial V}\right)_T dV + \left(\frac{\partial U}{\partial T}\right)_V dT \qquad (7)$$

and

$$dV = \left(\frac{\partial V}{\partial P}\right)_T dP + \left(\frac{\partial V}{\partial T}\right)_P dT \qquad (8)$$

we obtain

$$\delta Q = \left[\left(\frac{\partial U}{\partial V}\right)_T + P\right]\left(\frac{\partial V}{\partial P}\right)_T dP$$
$$+ \left\{C_V + \left[\left(\frac{\partial U}{\partial V}\right)_T + P\right]\left(\frac{\partial V}{\partial T}\right)_P\right\}dT \qquad (9)$$

Thus

$$C_P = \left(\frac{\delta Q}{\delta T}\right)_P = C_V + \left[\left(\frac{\partial V}{\partial T}\right)_P\right]\left[P + \left(\frac{\partial U}{\partial V}\right)_T\right] \qquad (10)$$

By the second law of thermodynamics, we have

$$dS = \frac{dU}{T} + \frac{P}{T}dV \qquad (11)$$

On using Eq. (7) again this becomes

$$dS = \frac{1}{T}\left[\left(\frac{\partial U}{\partial V}\right)_T + P\right]dV + \frac{1}{T}\left(\frac{\partial U}{\partial T}\right)_V dT \qquad (12)$$

Since

$$dS = \left(\frac{\partial S}{\partial V}\right)_T dV + \left(\frac{\partial S}{\partial T}\right)_V dT \qquad (13)$$

one obtains on comparing Eqs. (12) and (13)

$$\left(\frac{\partial S}{\partial V}\right)_T = \frac{1}{T}\left[P + \left(\frac{\partial U}{\partial V}\right)_T\right] \qquad (14)$$

$$\left(\frac{\partial S}{\partial T}\right)_V = \frac{1}{T}\left(\frac{\partial U}{\partial T}\right)_V \qquad (15)$$

Since

$$\frac{\partial}{\partial T}\left(\frac{\partial S}{\partial V}\right)_T = \frac{\partial}{\partial V}\left(\frac{\partial S}{\partial T}\right)_V \qquad (16)$$

we get from Eqs. (14) and (15)

$$\frac{1}{T}\frac{\partial^2 U}{\partial V \partial T} = -\frac{1}{T^2}\left[P + \left(\frac{\partial U}{\partial V}\right)_T\right]$$
$$+ \frac{1}{T}\left[\left(\frac{\partial P}{\partial T}\right)_V + \frac{\partial^2 U}{\partial T \partial V}\right] \quad (17)$$

or

$$\left(\frac{\partial U}{\partial V}\right)_T = T\left(\frac{\partial P}{\partial T}\right)_V - P \quad (18)$$

Inserting Eq. (18) into Eq. (10), yields

$$C_P - C_V = T\left(\frac{\partial V}{\partial T}\right)_P\left(\frac{\partial P}{\partial T}\right)_V \quad (19)$$

Now

$$\left(\frac{\partial P}{\partial T}\right)_V\left(\frac{\partial T}{\partial V}\right)_P\left(\frac{\partial V}{\partial P}\right)_T = -1 \quad (20)$$

Thus on replacing $(\partial P/\partial T)_V$, the final form of Eq. (19) becomes

$$C_P - C_V = -\frac{T\left(\frac{\partial V}{\partial T}\right)_P^2 V^2}{\left(\frac{\partial V}{\partial P}\right)_T V^2} \quad (21)$$

or Eq. (3) when the definition of compressibility [Eq. (4)] is employed.

Thus for a substance where β and X are experimentally known C_V may be established from a measurement of C_P.

Grüneisen Relation[2] Grüneisen introduced the parameter $\gamma = \beta V/XC_V$ and on the basis of simple models reached the conclusion that γ is independent of temperature. This implies that the thermal expansion coefficient is proportional to the specific heat and has the same type of temperature dependence. This is true for many substances and has, in fact, been employed as a means for predicting values for C_V at low temperatures. To illustrate the physical basis of the Grüneisen relation, we will work with a crystal model of N oscillators of identical frequency, ν, and each having equilibrium energy, ϵ. In the region of $h\nu \ll kT$, the free energy is given by:

$$F = N\left(\epsilon + 3kT \log \frac{h\nu}{kT}\right) \quad (22)$$

Since this must be a minimum at equilibrium, we obtain:

$$N\frac{d\epsilon}{dV} = -3NkT\frac{d(\log \nu)}{dV} \quad (23)$$

To obtain the thermal expansion coefficient, one expands $d\epsilon/dV$:

$$\frac{d\epsilon}{dV} = \left(\frac{d\epsilon}{dV}\right)_{V=V_0} + (V - V_0)\left(\frac{d^2\epsilon}{dV^2}\right)_{V=V_0} \quad (24)$$

But the compressibility is given by

$$\frac{1}{X_0} = NV_0\left(\frac{d^2\epsilon}{dV^2}\right)_{V=V_0} \quad (25)$$

and thus

$$\frac{V - V_0}{V_0} = -3NkTX_0\frac{d(\log \nu)}{dV} \quad (26)$$

Differentiating with respect to T and realizing that $3NkT$ is the thermal energy, we obtain:

$$\frac{\alpha V_0}{C_V X_0} = -\frac{d(\log \nu)}{d(\log V)} \quad (27)$$

More exact crystal models yield values for

$$\gamma_i = -\frac{d(\log \nu_i)}{d(\log V)}$$

where ν_i is the ith frequency of a set of normal modes of vibration.[3] These and other refinements give rise to modifications of the simple Grüneisen theory.

Source of Thermal Expansion The dynamical basis for thermal expansion is the presence of an anharmonic component for the interaction potential. A qualitative argument for this is based on the property of typical potential energy of atoms in a lattice.[4] Figure 1 represents such a curve and it will be observed that the curve is not symmetrical about r_0, the equilibrium distance between atoms. As the internal energy E increases with an increase in temperature, the average value of r shifts to larger values. Clearly if the potential curve were perfectly parabolic about r_0, we would not have thermal expansion. This argument can be made qualitative as follows.[5] Taking x as the displacement of a lattice atom from its equilibrium neighbor separation, the potential energy has the form

$$V(x) = cx^2 - gx^3 \quad (28)$$

Then $\bar{x}$, the average displacement using the Boltzmann distribution function becomes

$$\bar{x} = \frac{\displaystyle\int_{-\infty}^{\infty} xe^{-V(x)/kT}\,dx}{\displaystyle\int_{-\infty}^{\infty} e^{-V(x)/kT}\,dx} \quad (29)$$

Assuming that the anharmonic term is much less than the harmonic contribution, we expand $V(x)$ to yield

$$\int xe^{-V/kT}\,dx = \int e^{-cx^2/kT}\left[x + \frac{gx^4}{kT}\right]dx \quad (30)$$

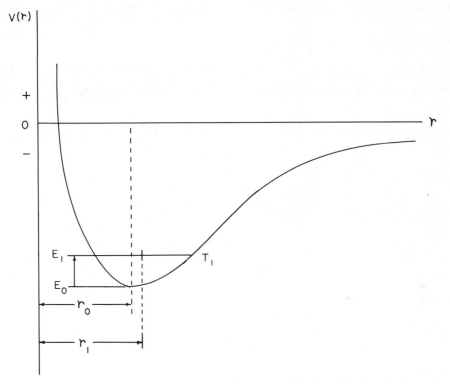

FIG. 1. Potential energy curve for atoms in crystalline solid as a function of interatomic separation.

and

$$\int e^{-V/kT} = \int e^{-cx^2/kT} \, dx \qquad (31)$$

Both integrals are readily evaluated to give

$$\bar{x} = \frac{3kTg}{4c^2} \qquad (32)$$

or a constant temperature coefficient for thermal expansion. This simple derivation may be amplified to include specific interaction forces for the atoms of a lattice.[6]

Thermal Expansion and Curie Temperature
The Curie-Weiss law for both ferroelectrics and ferromagnets may be shown to be connected with the thermal expansion coefficient.[7] Consider a region where the dielectric constant, ε, is large. If we let N be the cell density and A a constant, the Clausius-Mosotti formula is

$$\frac{\varepsilon - 1}{\varepsilon + 2} = AN \qquad (33)$$

Differentiating with respect to T, the temperature, and making use of the assumption that $\varepsilon \gg 1$, one finds that

$$\frac{3d\varepsilon}{\varepsilon^2 dT} = \frac{1}{N} \frac{dN}{dT} = -\beta \qquad (34)$$

On integrating between T and θ, the Curie temperature, one obtains

$$\varepsilon = \frac{3/\beta}{T - \theta} \qquad (35)$$

which is a typical Weiss law and indicates the Curie constant is of the order of the reciprocal of the thermal expansion. The special electronic structure of ferromagnetic materials also gives rise to anomalous thermal expansion coefficients in the transition region. For some materials β values are depressed and for others β values increase more rapidly with temperature. Both magnetostriction and the variation of the energy of magnetization with the atomic size account for the anomalous behavior of different substances.

JACOB NEUBERGER

References

1. Any text in thermodynamics such as:
   Zemansky, M. W., "Heat and Thermodynamics," New York, McGraw-Hill Book Company, Inc., 1951.
2. Mott, N. F., and Jones, H., "The Theory of the Properties of Metals and Alloys," New York, Dover Publications, 1936.
3. Arenstein, M., Hatcher, R. D., and Neuberger, J.,

"Equation of State of Certain Ideal Lattices," *Phys. Rev.*, **13**, No. 5, 2087–2093 (1963).

4. Halliday, D., and Resnick, R., "Physics," Part I, New York, John Wiley & Sons, 1968 (p. 537).

5. Kittel, C., "Introduction to Solid State Physics," New York, John Wiley & Sons, 1971.

6. Peierls, R. E., "Quantum Theory of Solids," New York, Oxford Press, 1955. (Reprinted in 1964.)

7. Dekker, A., "Solid State Physics," Englewood Cliffs, N.J., Prentice Hall, 1957; Sinnott, M., "The Solid State for Engineers," New York, John Wiley & Sons, 1958.

Cross-references: BOLTZMANN'S DISTRIBUTION LAW, DIELECTRIC THEORY, HEAT CAPACITY, MAGNETISM, THERMODYNAMICS.

F

FALLOUT

The term fallout generally has been used to refer to particulate matter that is thrown into the atmosphere by a nuclear process of short time duration. Primary examples are nuclear weapon debris and effluents from a nuclear reactor excursion. The name fallout is applied both to matter that is aloft and to matter that has been deposited on the surface of the earth. Depending on the conditions of formation, this material ranges in texture from an aerosol to granules of considerable size. The aerodynamic principles governing its deposition are the same as for any other material of comparable physical nature that is thrown into the air, such as volcanic ash or particles from chimneys. Therefore, many of the principles learned in studies of fallout from nuclear weapons can be applied to studies of other particulate pollution in the atmosphere.

The topographic distribution of fallout is divided into three categories called local (or close-in), tropospheric (or intermediate), and stratospheric (or world wide) fallout. No distinct boundaries exist between these categories. The distinction between local and tropospheric fallout is a function of distance from source to point of deposit, while the primary distinction between tropospheric and stratospheric fallout is the place of injection of the debris into the atmosphere, above or below the tropopause. Whether radioactive debris from a nuclear weapon becomes tropospheric or stratospheric fallout depends on yield, height, and latitude of burst (the height of the tropopause is a function of latitude).

Because air acts as a viscous medium, a drag force is developed to oppose the gravitational force that acts on airborne particulate matter. This makes the velocity of fall dependent on particle size. The larger particles (diameters greater than about $20\mu m$) have a higher rate of settling and create local fallout. Smaller particles injected below the tropopause are carried by prevailing winds over large regions of the surface of the earth and create the tropospheric fallout. Tropospheric fallout particles larger than about 0.1-μm diameter continually mix through the circulating air mass that is in contact with the surface of the earth and gradually settle to the ground, or are washed down by rain or snow. Many smaller particles form nuclei for raindrops. Parts of the tropospheric fallout many remain in the atmosphere for a month or more, long enough to circle the earth several times. The mean residence time above the tropopause of stratospheric fallout is from 5 to 30 months, during which time it completely encircles the earth. It gradually returns through the tropopause, primarily in certain regions where mixing between the two layers is more probable.

The exact characteristics of the radiation associated with fallout depend on the nature of the nuclear processes from which its radioactivity originates. Generally these radioactive nuclides are fission products formed from the fissioning of uranium or plutonium, but, under appropriate circumstances, considerable quantities of radioactivity can be formed through nuclear reactions induced by neutrons that are produced by the weapon or reactor. The radiation problems associated with local fallout are usually those of high-intensity gamma-ray radiation fields resulting from the relatively large quantities of radioactive material that fall back to earth within a few tens of miles from the point of origin. The important radioactive materials consist in this case of short-lived fission products and neutron-induced radioactive nuclides. The hazards of worldwide fallout come more from the problems of the long-lived radionuclides, such as ^{134}Cs, ^{137}Cs, and ^{90}Sr, that can enter the human food chain and ultimately be absorbed by the body.

For a nuclear weapon burst in air, all materials in the fireball are vaporized. Condensation of fission products and other bomb materials is then governed by the saturation vapor pressures of the most abundant constituents. Primary debris can combine with naturally ocurring aerosols, and almost all of the fallout becomes tropospheric or stratospheric. If the weapon detonation takes place within a few hundred feet of (either above or below) a land or water surface, large quantities of surface materials are drawn up or thrown into the air above the place of detonation. Condensation of radioactive nuclides in this material then leads to considerable quantities of local fallout, but some of the radioactivity still goes into tropospheric and stratospheric fallout. If the burst occurs sufficiently far underground, the surface is not broken and no fallout results.

C. SHARP COOK

References

Brunner, H., and Prêtre, S., Eds., "Radiological Protection of the Public in a Nuclear Mass Disaster," Proceedings of symposium at Interlaken, Switzerland, 26 May–1 June, 1968, Bern, Bundesamt für Zivilschutz, 1968.

Cook, C. S., "Initial and Residual Ionizing Radiations from Nuclear Weapons," in Attix and Tochilin, Eds., "Radiation Dosimetry," Vol. III, New York, Academic Press, 1969 (pp. 361–399).

Freiling, E. C., Ed., "Radionuclides in the Environment," Washington, D.C., American Chemical Society, 1970.

Cross-references: ATOMIC ENERGY, FISSION, FUSION, ISOTOPES, NUCLEAR REACTIONS, RADIOACTIVITY.

FARADAY EFFECT

This effect was the first demonstration of a connection between magnetism and light. Faraday found in 1845 that when plane polarized light was transmitted through glass in a direction parallel to an applied magnetic field, the plane of polarization was rotated. Since Faraday's original discovery, the phenomenon has been observed in many solids, liquids, and gases. It is important in the interaction of electromagnetic radiation with the ionosphere and in the study of charge carrier behavior in the laboratory. These effects may all be regarded as acting on the electric field associated with the wave. There is a second class of Faraday rotation phenomena in which the effect acts on the magnetic-field component of the wave. These effects are very large in ferromagnetic insulators and have made possible the development of a class of nonreciprocal microwave devices, which are described briefly in the concluding paragraph. Cgs units are used throughout this article.

Electric-field Effects. *Optical Rotation from Spectral Transitions.* In the region of the spectrum close to an absorption line, the dielectric properties of the medium are dominated by the absorption and its associated dispersion. In those cases of interest, the absorption line is broadened or split by an applied magnetic field. One can show by quite general arguments that for every spectral component displaced linearly in the applied field, there must be a second component that is displaced in the opposite direction. The simplest case is one in which the original spectral line splits into two lines with frequencies

$$\omega^- = \omega_0 - \omega_L \qquad \omega^+ = \omega_0 + \omega_L$$

where $\omega_L = geH/4mc$ is the Larmor frequency and g is called the spectroscopic splitting factor. One can again show by general arguments that in an isotropic medium, a positively circularly polarized wave will be absorbed only at ω^+ and similarly a negative wave only at ω^-. With this theoretical background, we may now consider the mechanism of rotation. Let us imagine that a linearly polarized wave at frequency ω is directed into the medium along the magnetic field. We can expect that if we decompose the incident wave into two waves of opposite circular polarization, the waves propagate independently. Each wave is characterized by its own dielectric constant and, therefore, its own phase velocity. If the dielectric constant of the positive component is larger than that of the negative component at frequency ω, then the positive component has the lower phase velocity and is rotated through a larger angle on passing through the medium. If we recombine the waves after a path length l, we will find the plane of polarization to be rotated through an angle.

$$\theta = \pi l(n^- - n^+)/\lambda_0$$

where λ_0 is the free-space wavelength and n^+ and n^- are the refractive indices for the two polarization directions. It is occasionally inconvenient to decompose the incident field into circular components. One can alternatively characterize the medium by a dielectric tensor. The off-diagonal elements of the tensor are given by

$$\mathcal{E}_{xy} = -\mathcal{E}_{yx} = (\mathcal{E}^+ - \mathcal{E}^-)/2j$$

By comparison with the earlier expression, the rotation angle may be written approximately as

$$\theta = -j\pi\mathcal{E}_{xy}l/n\lambda_0$$

For the particular case considered here we have

$$\mathcal{E}_{xy} = 2j\omega\omega_p^2\omega_L/(\omega_0^2 - \omega^2)^2$$

where $\omega_p = (4\pi Ne^2/m)^{1/2}$ is the plasma frequency. One of the important advantages of Faraday rotation as a technique for studying optical spectra is that it permits a determination of the Larmor frequency under circumstances where it may not be possible to resolve the splitting directly. This technique is also of very considerable importance in the determination of internal magnetic fields in ferromagnetic materials.

Carrier Rotation. One can apply an analysis similar to the above in the case of free charge carriers. It is convenient to discuss the rotation by charge carriers in two limits. At frequencies low compared with the collision frequency of the carriers and to first order in the magnetic field, we obtain

$$\mathcal{E}_{xy} = 4\pi\sigma_0\mu H/j\omega c$$

where $\mu = e\tau/m$ is the carrier mobility and σ_0 is the low-frequency conductivity. The low-frequency Faraday effect and the Hall effect (*q.v.*) are closely related. At high frequencies the rotation is proportional to

$$\mathcal{E}_{xy} = j\omega_c\omega_p^2/\omega^3$$

where $\omega_c = eH/mc$ is the cyclotron frequency. The Faraday effect is particularly important in the study of semiconductivity, where carriers move with an effective mass that may be considerably different from their free mass.

Magnetic-field Effects In addition to the high-frequency Faraday effect, which is usually associated with electric dipole transitions, there are a number of low-frequency rotation phenomena, which are associated with magnetic dipole transitions. Here the rotation is associated with the tensor properties of the magnetic permeability. The rotation angle is given by

$$\theta = -j\pi\mu_{xy}l/n\lambda_0$$

Paramagnetic Rotation. In a paramagnetic material the rotation is associated with the paramagnetic resonance absorption in much the same way that optical rotation is associated with optical absorption. For a paramagnetic material, the rotation is proportional to

$$\mu_{xy} = -4j\pi\chi_0\gamma H/\omega$$

where γ is the magneto-mechanical ratio.
Ferromagnetic Rotation. In a ferromagnetic material, very large rotations may be achieved because of the very large effective susceptibility $\chi_0 = M/H$. For magnetically saturated material we obtain

$$\mu_{xy} = -4j\pi\gamma M/\omega$$

Antiferromagnetic Rotation. Antiferromagnetic materials are characterized by resonance absorption even in the absence of a field. Applying the magnetic field along the symmetry axis we obtain

$$\mu_{xy} = -8j\pi\chi_\perp\omega\gamma H\omega_0{}^2/(\omega_0{}^2 - \omega^2)^2$$

where ω_0 is the zero-field resonance frequency and $\chi_\perp$ is the susceptibility perpendicular to the axis.

Applications The principal application of the Faraday effect to electronics has been in the development of nonreciprocal microwave devices. Because of the nonsymmetric character of the permeability tensor in a magnetic field, it is possible to fabricate devices that permit the nearly unattenuated passage of microwaves in one direction but will effectively block microwave transmission in the reverse direction. These devices, which make use of ferromagnetic insulators like ferrite or garnet, are of reduced effectiveness at high frequencies because of their inverse dependence on ω. Attention is being given to antiferromagnetic materials for use at high frequencies because of their increased transverse permeability in this range.

A. M. PORTIS

Cross-references: HALL EFFECT AND RELATED PHENOMENA, LIGHT, MAGNETISM, POLARIZED LIGHT, PROPAGATION OF ELECTROMAGNETIC WAVES, SEMICONDUCTORS.

FEEDBACK*

The notion of "feedback" is central to the theory of information and control, christened by the late mathematician N. Wiener in 1948 as "cybernetics," and *a fortiori* it occupies a pivotal position in the technical aspects of "automation," the latter term being coined by the American industrialist D. S. Harder in 1936. To date, "feedback," the return of "output" signals to the "input" of any device for the purpose of correcting or improving the characteristics of the device, has had greater influence within technology than within science. Within the design philosophy of modern systems, whether analogue or digital, it has become a criterion for the physical "richness" of those systems; systems not utilizing "feedback" being too simple.

The concept of the "ultrastability" of a dynamical system, i.e., the additional provision in a classical dynamical system to alter the kinds of its characteristics or to adapt to its environment, makes crucial use of secondary "feedback" to adjust other primary "feedbacks." The idea of "ultrastability," conceived by W. R. Ashby, the other principal pioneering cyberneticist, makes frequent appearance in the study of models to simulate and realize intellectual activities such as checker playing on electronic machines and theorem proving on electronic machines.

Perhaps, the oldest and simplest scheme employing "feedback" is the question-and-answer giving of ordinary conversation. If only one party does all the talking, or, more generally, all of the transmitting of signs, then there is no guarantee that the alleged message has been received, or if so, whether or not it has been understood. By continually monitoring one another, critical scientific conversation becomes possible.

Other simple, but more technical, examples of "feedback" for automatic control occur in the governor of steam engines, in thermostats, and in the automatic volume controls of radios. When more steam is fed to a steam engine its shaft accelerates. Automatic control can be realized by using a centrifugal device to tend to close off steam with greater shaft velocities. With such a scheme of "negative feedback" the engine acquires stability, i.e., it runs at an optimal velocity determined by the characteristics of the governor. On the other hand, if the centrifugal device had been installed (incorrectly) so as to supply more steam with greater shaft velocities, then this scheme of "positive feedback" would produce an instability that would either destroy the steam source or the steam engine, or both. Similarly, the automatic volume controls of radios provide "negative feedback" of a continuous or analogue variety.

*Editor was unable to locate author. Article is reprinted from first edition.

However, the thermostat provides "negative feedback" of a continual or discrete variety. If the local temperature exceeds a certain value, the furnace is turned off, and if the local temperature is below a certain value the furnace is turned on. Thus, unlike a steam engine and governor, the thermostat is an "on-off" device.

During and after the 1950's, even the digital computers have become components of complex sampled-data, feedback control systems. A basic idea behind sampled-data systems is that statistical sampling of signals, rather than continuous sampling, is sufficient in many cases for reliable control systems. Indeed, by the so-called Sampling Theorem, if time sampling is often enough, but not necessarily continuous, and there is an upper bound to the electrical frequencies considered, then there is *no* loss of information.

Finally, the presently available models for the study of sequential switching circuits, which includes important parts of digital computers, all have explicit provisions for the "feedback" of informational signals.

ALBERT A. MULLIN

References

Wiener, Norbert, "Cybernetics," New York, The M.I.T. Press and John Wiley & Sons, 1961.

Wiener, Norbert, "The Human Use of Human Beings," Garden City, N.Y., Doubleday & Co., 1954.

Ashby, W. R., "An Introduction to Cybernetics," New York, John Wiley & Sons, 1956.

de Latil, P., "Thinking by Machine," Boston, Houghton Mifflin Co., 1957.

Truxal, J. G., "Control System Synthesis," New York, McGraw-Hill Book Co., 1955.

Fogel, L. G., "Biotechnology," Englewood Cliffs, N.J., Prentice-Hall, 1963.

Cross-references: CIRCUITRY, COMPUTERS, CYBERNETICS, MECHANICS.

FERMI-DIRAC STATISTICS AND FERMIONS

Solid metals are good conductors of heat and electricity because about one electron per atom is free to migrate through the volume of the conductor. These electrons were once thought to behave like gas molecules which obey Maxwell-Boltzmann statistics in which the number of particles at higher energies falls off exponentially according to a relation of the form

$$n_{E,T} = \frac{1}{e^{E/kT}}$$

where E is the energy, k the Boltzmann Constant and T the absolute temperature. This electron gas theory was qualitatively useful in explaining many metallic properties, but it was never quantitatively successful. One notable failure was its prediction that electrons should contribute to the specific heats of metals.

Bohr had shown that the electron in hydrogen is not free to assume any energy, but is restricted to certain permitted energies called quantum states or energy levels. When this quantum view of atomic electron structure was extended to more complex atoms, it was found that electrons obey the Pauli exclusion principle—only two electrons in any one atom having oppositely directed spin can occupy the same energy state. Thus in an atom with many electrons, no more than two can have the lowest permitted energy, no more than two may have the next higher permitted energy, etc. An unexcited atom with all its electrons in their lowest possible energy states includes many electrons whose energy is well above the energy of the lowest two. The old electron gas theory of metals recognized that the inner electrons associated with each atom were quantized but assumed that the electrons that were not bound to particular atoms were entirely free to migrate through the metal with no *a priori* restrictions on their energy. Fermi-Dirac statistics describes the behavior of the electron gas under the assumption that *all* electrons within the conductor have their energies quantized and obey the Pauli principle. This new viewpoint leads to a distribution of electron energies according to a relation of the form

$$n_{E,T} = \frac{1}{e^{(E-E_i)/kT} + 1}$$

where the new symbol, E_i, is a critical energy characteristic of the metal more fully described below. If the metal is at high temperature, this function approaches the Maxwell-Boltzmann distribution. We can see this by noting that if $T \to \infty$, the exponent of e approaches zero regardless of E. Thus, in both cases, the number of electrons of each energy tends to become uniform. The high-temperature electrons have so many states available to them that quantum restrictions make little difference. If we let the temperature approach absolute zero, the difference between these distributions becomes extreme. If T is very small, the Maxwell-Boltzmann distribution is strongly dependent on E with most particles having low E and few having high E. Indeed for $T = 0$, the number of particles with $E \neq 0$ becomes zero—in a Maxwell-Boltzmann gas all particles come to rest at absolute zero. A Fermi-Dirac gas behaves very differently at absolute zero. The exponent of e is plus or minus infinity depending upon whether E is greater or less than E_i. The exponential term is either infinity or zero. The denominator is either infinity or one. All energy states below E_i are filled whereas all those above E_i are empty. Thus, consistent with the assumptions, at absolute zero the electrons do not crowd into one state of zero energy but are

uniformly distributed among those states which are below the critical energy E_i called the Fermi energy or the Fermi level. Fermi energies depend on the kind of metals but they are of the order of several electron volts. Thus, even at absolute zero, some electrons have energies which would be typical of a Maxwell-Boltzmann electron gas only if that gas were at several thousand degrees.

The contrast may be dramatized by the following analogy. If grains of sand are spilled on an open floor, they will spread out so they are only one deep and each has zero potential energy. If the grains are poured into a drinking straw, the straw will fill to a certain height and some grains will have considerable potential energy.

Heating a metal from absolute zero to room temperature adds only .025 eV to the average energy of its particles. Since the electrons already have a *much* greater average energy, heating a metal has but a slight effect on the energy distribution of the electrons. This accounts for the fact that electrons make a negligible contribution to the specific heats of metals, and it also explains why metals must be glowing hot before electrons acquire enough additional energy to escape from the metal surface as in the filaments of radio tubes. Since the quantum view of electrons in a metal provides both a qualitative and quantitative picture of many metallic properties, we know metallic electrons are quantized Fermi particles rather than unquantized Maxwell particles. The application of Fermi-Dirac statistics to semi-conductors accounts for their special properties as demonstrated by transistors.

From the standpoint of wave mechanics, all particles which are confined in any way are quantized. Those whose spin is integral have symmetric wave functions and do not obey the Pauli principle. If they are so numerous that they must be treated statistically, they are called *bosons* and are described by Bose-Einstein statistics. Photons are the most common bosons. Those particles whose spins are odd multiples of $\frac{1}{2}$ have antisymmetric wave functions and obey the Pauli principle. They are called *fermions* and obey Fermi-Dirac statistics. Although electrons are the most common example, protons, neutrons, and μ-mesons are all fermions with spin $\frac{1}{2}$. At high temperatures, the quantum nature of both bosons and fermions becomes insignificant and both obey the classical statistics of Maxwell-Boltzmann. The technique of deriving these distributions is called statistical mechanics.

To convey the over-all method of STATISTICAL MECHANICS, we note that it is a probability theory in which the basic technique is to compute the number of possible ways in which a system can arrange itself subject to restrictions as to the number and total energy of the particles. These ways are all assumed equally likely. (There are 52 factorial, 52!, different arrangements which might result from the shuffling of a deck of playing cards. Each is equally likely.) Then, depending on the nature of the particles, bosons or fermions, the number of distinguishable ways is computed. (In the game of bridge, there are many fewer deals $52!/(13!)^4$, than there are shuffles because the order in which a player receives his cards does not change his "hand.") The probability of any particular distinguishable distribution is proportional to the number of ways in which it can be achieved. (If we flip a coin five times, there are $2^5 = 32$ orders in which the coin can fall. Of these, there are ten ways to get two heads and only one way to get five heads. We therefore find getting two heads ten times more probable than getting five heads.) The actual expected distribution is the one which can be achieved in the largest number of ways.

JAMES A. RICHARDS, JR.

Reference

Leighton, Robert B., "Principles of Modern Physics," New York, McGraw-Hill Book Co., 1959.

Cross-references: BOLTZMANN'S DISTRIBUTION LAW, BOSE-EINSTEIN STATISTICS AND BOSONS, ELECTRON SPIN, STATISTICAL MECHANICS.

FERMI SURFACE

The Fermi surface of a metal, semi-metal, or semiconductor is that surface of constant energy in momentum space which separates the energy states which are filled with free or quasi-free electrons from those which are unfilled. [Momentum space is defined in terms of three orthogonal axes, the components of the momentum vector, p_x, p_y, and p_z (or alternatively, the components of the wave vector, k_x, k_y, and k_z: $\mathbf{p} = \hbar\mathbf{k}$, where $\hbar$ = Planck's constant divided by 2π). The components of momentum of an electron at a given instant of time may be thought of as the coordinates of a point in momentum space which then moves about as various forces act on the electron.] The Fermi surface exists simply because the electrons obey Fermi-Dirac statistics.

Consider first an elementary model of a metal consisting of a lattice of fixed positive ions immersed in a sea of conduction electrons which are free to move through the lattice. Every direction of electron motion is equally probable. Since the electrons fill the available quantized energy states starting with the lowest, a three-dimensional picture in momentum coordinates will show a spherical distribution of electron momenta and, hence, will yield a spherical Fermi surface. In this free electron model, no account has been taken of the interaction between the fixed positive ions and the electrons; indeed the only restriction on the move-

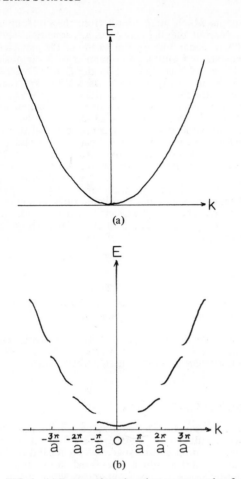

(a)

$$-\frac{3\pi}{a} \quad -\frac{2\pi}{a} \quad -\frac{\pi}{a} \quad O \quad \frac{\pi}{a} \quad \frac{2\pi}{a} \quad \frac{3\pi}{a}$$

(b)

FIG. 1. (a) Energy plotted against wave number for the free electron model. (b) Energy plotted against wave number for the "quasi-free" electron model, showing energy discontinuities at Brillouin zone boundaries.

ment or "freedom" of the electrons is the physical confines of the metal itself.

A short derivation starting with the Schrödinger equation shows that the total energy of an electron (and thus also its kinetic energy) is given by

$$E = \hbar^2 k^2 / 2m = p^2 / 2m$$

where m is the mass of the electron. A plot of E against k is then a parabola, as shown in Fig. 1(a). The Cartesian components of those values of k which are possible solutions to the Schrödinger equation are $k_i = 2\pi n_i / L$, where the n_i's are integers and L is a physical dimension of the metal. Since for each energy value so defined there are actually two states (one for an electron with spin up, one with spin down), it can be shown that the density of energy states available to the electrons is

$$g(E) = \frac{(2m)^{3/2}}{2\pi^2 \hbar^3} E^{1/2}$$

where $g(E) \, dE$ is the number of states in the energy range E to $E + dE$. Then $n(E)$, the number of electrons per unit volume occupying energy states in this energy range, is

$$n(E) \, dE = g(E) f(E) \, dE$$

where $f(E) = \{\exp [(E - E_f)/bT] + 1\}^{-1}$, a function characteristic of particles which obey Fermi-Dirac statistics. In this expression, T is the absolute temperature, b is Boltzmann's constant, and E_f is a parameter depending on the number of electrons involved and indeed turns out to be the Fermi energy. E_f can be evaluated by integrating $n(E) \, dE$ from $E = 0$ to $E = \infty$ and recognizing that the integral is equal to N, the total number of electrons per unit volume. The result (at $T = 0$ K) is

$$E_f = \frac{\pi^2 \hbar^2}{2m} \left(\frac{3N}{\pi}\right)^{2/3}$$

At $T = 0$ K, for $E < E_f$, $f(E) = 1$, while for $E > E_f$, $f(E) = 0$. Physically this means that the probability of a state below the Fermi level being occupied is one; whereas for states with $E > E_f$ the occupancy probability drops abruptly to zero. For temperatures greater than absolute zero, the occupancy probability drops smoothly from 1 to 0 in a range of energy of width approximately equal to bT. This shell of partially filled states gives rise to the following definition: The Fermi level is the energy level at which the probability of a state being filled is just equal to one half.

A numerical evaluation of the Fermi energy for a simple metal having one or two conduction electrons per atom yields a value of approximately 10^{-11} erg, or a few electron volts. The equivalent temperature, E_f/b, is several tens of thousands of degrees Kelvin. Thus, except in extraordinary circumstances, when dealing with metals, $bT \ll E_f$; i.e., the energy range of partially filled states is small, and the Fermi surface is well defined by the statement above. It must, however, be noted that this is not necessarily true for semiconductors where the number of free electrons per unit volume may be very much smaller.

The foregoing treatment gives a qualitative insight into the physics of metals and, under some circumstances, semi-metals and semiconductors. A more detailed analysis requires that the effects of the ions in the lattice be recognized. This can be accomplished by introducing the periodic potential due to the lattice through which the electrons must move. Then the electrons are no longer "free," but, depending on the strength and character of the potentials and the approximations used in solving the Schrödinger equation, act as "quasi-free" particles. Another approach is the "tight-binding approximation"; occasionally a combination of the two approaches is used. In any case, introduction of lattice effects changes the characteristics of the model; the total energy and kinetic energy of an electron are no longer equivalent.

The periodic lattice can be described conveniently in terms of Brillouin zones, each of which is large enough (in momentum space) to accommodate two electrons per atom. The Brillouin zone boundaries appear to the electrons as Bragg reflection planes or energy discontinuities, resulting in an energy versus wave number plot as shown in Fig. 1(b).

For many metals, the "nearly free" electron description corresponds quite closely to the physical situation. The Fermi surface remains nearly spherical in shape. However, it may now be intersected by several Brillouin zone boundaries which break the surface into a number of separate sheets. It becomes useful to describe the Fermi surface in terms not only of zones or sheets filled with electrons, but also of zones or sheets of holes, that is, momentum space volumes which are empty of electrons. A con-

ceptually simple method of constructing these successive sheets, often also referred to as "first zone," "second zone," etc., was demonstrated by Harrison.[1] An example of such a construction is shown in Fig. 2. This construction works quite well, for example, for aluminum which has three valence electrons per atom. Experiments, and indeed more elegant theoretical calculations, show that the fourth zone is totally unoccupied and that the third zone monster is not multiple-connected in the manner shown. The recipe for constructing these figures, some of which may even be pleasing to art connoisseurs, cannot be developed in the limited space of this article but will be found in the references.[1,2]

The intense research effort of the last 15 years on the Fermi surfaces of metals and semimetals originated, to a great extent, with Pip-

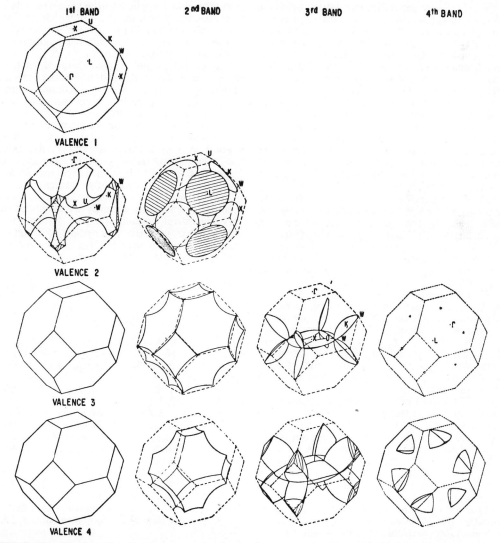

FIG. 2. Fermi surfaces in several zones or bands, for face-centered cubic metals having various numbers of "quasi-free" electrons per atom, as constructed by Harrison.[1]

pard's ingenious deductions, based on anomalous skin-effect experiments, concerning the Fermi surface of copper.[3] Prior to Pippard's work, it was taken for granted that in copper, with one quasi-free electron per atom, the first Brillouin zone would be only half filled and, hence, would have a nearly spherical Fermi surface. His work suggested that a series of eight necks pull out and touch the Brillouin zone boundaries in the [111] crystallographic directions. This shape has now been confirmed and precisely mapped, not only for copper but also for silver and gold.

A variety of experimental techniques has been developed, capable of yielding both overlapping and complementary information concerning Fermi surfaces of metals. Some of these techniques are described briefly:

(1) The DE HAAS-VAN ALPHEN EFFECT[4] is an oscillatory behavior of the magnetic susceptibility (or more generally, oscillatory behavior of any electronic property) due to the quantization of magnetic flux through an electron orbit in units of hc/e (where h = Planck's constant, c = speed of light, and e = electron charge). Measurements of the periods of the oscillations can be directly related to extremal cross-sectional areas of the Fermi surface.

(2) Cyclotron resonance[5] refers to oscillations in the magnetic field dependence of high-frequency surface impedance arising when the electron's cyclotron frequency is an integral multiple of the rf frequency. The periods of these oscillations measure dA/dE, the rate of change of cross-sectional area with energy at extremal cross sections.

(3) Magnetoresistance[6] refers to extra resistance in a metal in the presence of a magnetic field. This magnetoresistance may be changed by changing the direction of the magnetic field and/or its magnitude. This direction and field dependence gives information about Fermi surface topology, particularly regions of contact with Brillouin zone boundaries.

(4) The magnetoacoustic effect[7] refers to oscillations in the magnetic field dependence of ultrasonic attenuation. The oscillations occur when dimensions of cyclotron orbits of electrons in extremal states on the Fermi surface are equal to integral multiples of the ultrasonic wavelength so that measurements of these oscillations give extremal linear dimensions of the Fermi surface.

(5) The anomalous skin effect[3] occurs when the electron mean free path is long compared to the rf skin depth. In this circumstance, electrons moving nearly parallel to the sample surface will dominate the conductivity. A measurement of surface impedance then gives an integral of the radius of curvature over that part of the Fermi surface containing the effective electrons.

(6) Positron annihilation in metals[8] gives directly the number of electron states in various cross sections of the Fermi surface.

Because a positron impinging upon a metal is quickly thermalized, when it annihilates with an electron the resulting gamma rays must carry off the annihilated electron's momentum. Thus gamma ray angular correlation measurements can be related to the distribution of electron momenta.

(7) The Gantmakher effect[9] (or radio frequency size effect) occurs in thin samples when a magnetic field parallel to the sample surface is adjusted so that extremal electron orbits just fit in the sample thickness. RF energy can then be transported across the thickness of the sample by the electrons. Observation of these Gantmakher resonances, like the magnetoacoustic resonances, gives extremal linear dimensions of the Fermi surface.

These techniques have been used primarily to measure extremal properties of the Fermi surface geometry. More recently considerable effort has been applied to the measurement of nonextremal properties[10, 11] which can do much to elucidate Fermi surface geometry. A second new area of Fermi surface measurement involves experiments on alloys.[12]

The precision and applicability of each of these techniques is dependent on the material under investigation. Among pertinent factors are number of quasi-free electrons per atom, crystallographic structure, magnetic properties, purity, and practicality of sample preparation.

Paralleling this experimental work has been a good deal of theoretical activity. Attention has been concentrated on the calculation of Fermi surfaces for a number of metals and semi-metals, most frequently through the use of orthogonalized or augmented plane wave techniques and more recently by means of the very powerful pseudopotential technique[13] which brings into the description of a metal a realistic approximation of the effects of the electrons in the positive ion core.

H. V. BOHM
NORMAN TEPLEY

References

1. Harrison, W. A., *Phys. Rev.*, **118,** 1190 (1960).
2. Ziman, J. M., "Electrons in Metals; A Short Guide to the Fermi Surface," London, Taylor and Francis, 1963.
3. Pippard, A. B., *Phil. Trans. Roy. Soc. London Ser. A*, **250,** 323 (1957).
4. Shoenberg, D., in "Proceedings of the Ninth International Conference on Low Temperature Physics," J. G. Daunt, D. O. Edwards, F. J. Milford, and M. Yaqub editors, New York, Plenum Press, 1965 (p. 665).
5. Kip, A. F., in "The Fermi Surface," W. A. Harrison, and M. B. Webb editors, New York, John Wiley & Sons, 1960 (p. 146).
6. Pippard, A. B., "The Dynamics of Conduction Electrons," New York, Gordon and Breach, 1965 (p. 90).

7. Tepley, N., *Proc. I.E.E.E.*, **53**, 1586 (1965).
8. Stewart, A. T., in "Positron Annihilation," A. T. Stewart and L. O. Roellig editors, New York, Academic Press, 1967 (p. 17).
9. Gantmakher, V. F., *Zh. Eksperim, i Teor. Fiz.*, **43**, 345 (1962). (English Transl.: *Soviet Physics JETP*, **16**, 247 (1962).)
10. Dooley, J. W., and Tepley, N., *Phys. Rev.*, **187**, 781 (1969).
11. Henrich, V. E., *Phys. Rev. Letters*, **26**, 891 (1971).
12. Saito, Y., and Maezawa, K., in "Proceedings of the Twelfth International Conference on Low Temperature Physics," E. Kanda editor, Kyoto, Academic press of Japan, 1971 (p. 583).
13. Harrison, W. A., "Pseudopotentials in the Theory of Metals," New York, W. A. Benjamin, 1966.

Cross-references: CYCLOTRON RESONANCE; DE HAAS–VAN ALPHEN EFFECT; ENERGY LEVELS; SOLID STATE PHYSICS; SOLID STATE THEORY; TRANSPORT THEORY.

FERRIMAGNETISM

Snoek's publication (1946) of his wartime work on ferrites established the existence of new ceramic magnetic materials capable of combining the resistivity of a good insulator (10^{12} ohm-cm) with high permeability. (see MAGNETISM.) In 1948, Néel introduced the term ferrimagnetism to describe the novel magnetic properties of these materials. A simple ferrite is composed of two interpenetrating FERROMAGNETIC sublattices with magnetizations $M_a(T)$ and $M_b(T)$ which decrease with increasing temperature and vanish at the Curie point, T_c. In a ferromagnetic material, the resulting saturation magnetization, M, would be $M_a + M_b$; however, in a ferrite, strong antiferromagnetic interaction between sublattices results in antiparallel alignment, and $M = M_a - M_b$. In general $M_a(T) \neq M_b(T)$, and the material behaves in most respects like a ferromagnet, exhibiting domains, a hysteresis loop, and saturation of the magnetization at relatively low applied magnetic fields. Practical values for saturation magnetization and Curie temperature range from 250 to 5000 oersteds and from 100 to 600°C.

Ferrimagnetic materials have spinel, garnet, and hexagonal structures. A typical spinel ferrite is $NiFe_2O_4$. Other ferrites may be obtained by substituting magnetic (Co, Ni, Mn) or nonmagnetic (Al, Zn, Cu) ions for some of the Ni or Fe ions, e.g., $Ni_{1-y}Co_yAl_xFe_{2-x}O_4$, where x and y may be varied to modify M and T_c. Yttrium iron garnet (YIG), $Y_3Fe_5O_{12}$, is the classical ferrimagnetic garnet which combines very low magnetic loss with high resistivity. Substitution of magnetic RARE EARTH ions (Gd, Yb, Ho, etc.) for Y and of nonmagnetic ions (Ga, Al) for some of the Fe ions leads to many different ferrite compositions with a wide range of M and magnetic loss. The rare earth ions form a third magnetic sublattice with at-tendant magnetization M_c antiparallel to the resultant magnetization $M_{a,b}$ of the two Fe sublattices. Since M_c and $M_{a,b}$ exhibit different variations with temperature, the net magnetization may vanish twice, at T_c and at an intermediate temperature called the compensation point, T_{comp}, where $M_c = M_{a,b}$.

A typical hexagonal ferrite is $BaFe_{12}O_{19}$. Again, other magnetic ions such as Mn, Co, and Ni may be introduced to produce wide variations in M and T_c. Hexagonal ferrites are characterized by large anisotropy fields with an axis of symmetry which may be either a direction of hard (planar ferrites) or easy (uniaxial ferrites) magnetization.

To distinguish among major fields of applications, ferrites can be separated into five groups: soft, square-loop, hard, microwave, and single-crystal ferrites.

Soft ferrites have a slender, S-shaped hysteresis loop with low remanence and low coercive force permitting easy magnetization and demagnetization with little magnetic loss. Mn-Zn and Ni-Zn ferrites with spinel structure exhibit these properties and permit adjustment of M, and permeability, μ_i, over a wide range of values through variations in composition. Ni ferrite has $\mu_i = 15$ and $M = 3000$ G, whereas Ni-Zn ferrite may have as much as $M = 5000$ G combined with a permeability of several thousand. Mn-Zn ferrites have values of $\mu_i = 500$ to 5000 depending on composition. These ferrites are uniquely suited to low-loss inductor and transformer cores for radio, television, and carrier telephony.

Square-loop ferrites are materials exhibiting an almost rectangular hysteresis loop with two distinct states of remanence and with a coercive force of a few Oe. All practical square-loop ferrites have a spinel structure. The Mg-Mn (Zn) system has retained its preeminent position in computer memory applications two decades after its discovery in 1951. More recently, Li-Ni ferrites and more complex systems containing Li, Mn, and Al have become competitive in applications requiring stability and fast switching over a wide range of temperatures.

Hard ferrites are characterized by hexagonal structure, a hysteresis loop enclosing a large area, and a coercive force of several thousand Oe. These ferrites can store a significant amount of magnetic energy, and have found widespread application as permanent magnets in hi-fi loudspeakers, small motors, generators, measuring instruments, etc.

Microwave ferrites have garnet, spinel, or hexagonal crystal structure, and very low electric and magnetic loss factors. In general, the required M increases with the frequency, f, of application. Substituted and pure garnets, Mg-Mn-Al ferrites and Mg-Mn ferrites are used at the lower part of the microwave spectrum where $M = 200$ to 3000 G is adequate. In the millimeterwave region, $f = 30$ to 100 GHz, one uses Ni-Zn ferrites ($M = 5000$ G) and hexagonal ferrites of various compositions.

All microwave ferrite devices such as isolators, circulators, switches, phase shifters, limiters, parametric amplifiers, and harmonic generators are based on interactions of rf signals with the ferrite magnetization. Aligning M with an external biasing magnetic field, H_{dc}, and applying a microwave signal in an orthogonal direction leads to strong interaction and gyromagnetic resonance. On a microscopic scale, this is explained as application of a torque to the unpaired ELECTRON SPINS of the magnetic ions which causes them to precess at the rf frequency much like so many spinning tops. The precessional motion has a microwave RESONANCE frequency f_r dependent upon H_{dc} and the gyromagnetic splitting factor g_{eff}. In ferrimagnets with spinel structure, g_{eff} is related to the g-factors of the sublattices as follows:

$$g_{eff} = M/[(M_a/g_a) - (M_b/g_b)]$$

On a macroscopic scale, this interaction modifies the rf magnetic field in a manner which is described by introducing an antisymmetric permeability tensor $[\mu]$ whose complex components depend on M, H_{dc}, and frequency. When the frequency approaches f_r, one observes a resonance absorption line whose width, ΔH, is determined by the magnetic loss of the material. Values for ΔH cover a range from <1 oersted for single-crystal YIG to >1000 oersteds for some polycrystalline Ni-ferrites. The interaction of rf fields and electron spins becomes a maximum if the rf field is circularly polarized in the same sense as the precessional motion of the spins. Circular polarization in the opposite direction produces almost no interaction and no gyromagnetic resonance. This permits design of nonreciprocal ferrite devices. At high levels of microwave power, nonlinear coupling between microwave signal and precessional spin motion causes the parametric excitation of higher order modes of spin motion (magnetostatic modes and spin waves). This effect has been exploited in limiters and parametric amplifiers.

Single-crystal ferrites of practical importance are rare-earth garnets grown in a flux of molten lead oxide. Some of these are optically transparent permitting direct observation of magnetic domains. Interaction of infrared and visible light with the electron spins is called the magneto-optic effect. It permits electronic modulation of a beam of light which propagates through a single-crystal garnet. Devices of this type are of great potential interest in the rapidly developing laser technology.

Single-crystal, rare-earth garnet sheets have been grown on a substrate with a preferred direction of magnetization perpendicular to the plate. In these plates, tiny round magnetic domains called "bubbles" can be formed by an applied magnetic field. These bubbles can be propagated, erased, and manipulated to perform binary functions in computers including logic, memory, counting, and switching.

W. H. von Aulock

References

Standley, K. J., "Oxide Magnetic Materials," Oxford, Clarendon Press, 1962.

Smit, J., and Wijn, H. P. J., "Ferrites," New York, John Wiley & Sons, Inc., 1959.

Lax, B., and Button, K. J., "Microwave Ferrites and Ferrimagnetics," New York, McGraw-Hill Book Co., Inc., 1962.

von Aulock, W. H., "Handbook of Microwave Ferrite Materials," New York, Academic Press, 1965.

von Aulock, W. H., and Fay, C. E., "Linear Ferrite Devices for Microwave Applications," New York, Academic Press, 1968.

Snelling, E. C., "Soft Ferrites," London, Iliffe Books, Ltd., 1969.

Helszajn, J., "Principles of Microwave Ferrite Engineering," London, Wiley Interscience, 1969.

Cross-references: FERROMAGNETISM, MAGNETISM, RESONANCE, TRANSFORMER.

FERROELECTRICITY

Ferroelectricity is recognized as a special case of ferroicity. A crystal is said to be ferroic when it has two or more orientation states in the absence of magnetic, electrical, and mechanical forces, and can shift from one to another of these orientation states by the application of an appropriate magnetic, electrical, or mechanical force or combined forces. Here any two of the orientation states are identical or enantiomorphous in crystal structure, but differ with respect to direction of arrangement of the atoms which may bear an electric charge, an electric dipole moment, and/or a magnetic dipole moment.

In a ferroic crystal, a state shift (or a change in orientation state) which is accompanied by a turn of the spontaneous magnetization vector, spontaneous electric polarization vector, or spontaneous mechanical strain tensor is said to be ferromagnetic, ferroelectric, or ferroelastic, respectively; or the crystal is said to be ferromagnetic, ferroelectric, or ferroelastic with respect to this state shift, respectively. There are two kinds of ferroelectric crystals—full ferroelectrics and partial ferroelectrics—which are distinguished according as all or not all but some of their state shifts are ferroelectric. The situation is the same for ferromagnetic crystals and ferroelastic crystals. A ferromagnetic, ferroelectric, or ferroelastic state shift can be accomplished by a magnetic field, an electric field, or a mechanical stress, respectively.

However, state shifts accomplishable by mechanical stresses are not all ferroelastic, since among them there are ones which are accompanied by a change of elastic compliance tensor but no change of spontaneous strain tensor; an example is the state shift in quartz. Likewise, state shifts accomplishable by electric (or magnetic) fields may not all be ferroelectric (or ferromagnetic), since among them there may be ones which are accompanied by a change of

electric (or magnetic) susceptibility tensor but no change of spontaneous polarization (or magnetization) vector.

Specimens of a ferroic crystal may often consist of several domains; each domain, as a whole, is in an orientation state, and the orientation states of any two adjacent domains are different. A specimen which as a whole is in an orientation state is said to be unidomain or a single domain. When we try to shift a specimen from an orientation state S to another orientation state S' by applying a magnetic, electrical, or mechanical force or combined forces, we cannot usually accomplish the state shift without passing through intermediate stages at which domains being in S' appear and grow, and simultaneously, domains being in S dwindle and vanish. This is the reason why, for example, in a ferroelectric crystal the electric polarization versus electric field curve is hysteretic.

In particular, if the transition between orientation states S and S' is ferroelastic, the domains being in S and the domains being in S' differ not only in mechanical strain but also in optical refractivity, since refractivity is the same kind of tensor as strain—a second-rank polar tensor. This difference in refractivity enables us to see the domain pattern directly with transmitted light.

The room-temperature phases of Rochelle salt, $Gd_2(MoO_4)_3$, $BaTiO_3$, and $NaBa_2Nb_5O_{15}$, for example, are not only (fully or partially) ferroelectric but also (fully or partially) ferroelastic.

For a crystal to become ferroic, it is not sufficient that some orientation states can be assigned to the crystal. Any two of these orientation states, in addition, must be able to change to each other through only slight movements of the atomic nuclei. So, every ferroic crystal may be regarded as a slight modification of a certain nonferroic ideal crystal, which is called the prototype of that ferroic crystal. On varying temperature, a ferroic crystal commonly (not necessarily) makes a phase transformation to a nonferroic phase having the same symmetry as the prototype. This phase is designated as the prototypic phase of that ferroic crystal, or sometimes as the paramagnetic, paraelectric, or paraelastic phase of that ferroic crystal when the ferroic crystal is ferromagnetic, ferroelectric, or ferroelastic, respectively. The temperature at which the ferroic-prototypic phase transformation takes place is called Curie temperature.

Ferroelectrics are divided into normal ferroelectrics and faint ferroelectrics according to the mechanism of the transformation from the paraelectric phase to the ferroelectric phase. In normal ferroelectrics, the phase transformation is caused by the lowering to zero of the eigenfrequency of a certain infrared-active mode of lattice vibration with zero wave number, so that the principal electric susceptibility (or the element of electric susceptibility tensor in the direction in which the spontaneous polarization

vector is to appear) increases rapidly as the Curie temperature is approached in the paraelectric phase. Usually, this increasing is in proportion to $(T - T_0)^{-1}$, and is known as the Curie-Weiss law, where T stands for temperature and T_0 stands for the temperature at which the eigenfrequency becomes zero. In faint ferroelectrics, the phase transformation is caused by the lowering to zero of the eigenfrequency of other kinds of vibration modes than that mentioned above, so that the principal electric susceptibility varies little as the Curie temperature is approached in the paraelectric phase. The ferroelectricity in $BaTiO_3$ is an example of normal ferroelectricity. The ferroelectricity in $Gd_2(MoO_4)_3$ is an example of faint ferroelectricity.

KÊITSIRO AIZU

References

Aizu, K., *Phys. Rev. B*, **2**, 754 (1970).
Cochran, W., *Adv. Phys.*, **9**, 387 (1960).
Aizu, K., *J. Phys. Soc. Japan*, **31**, 802 (1971).

Cross-references: CRYSTALS AND CRYSTALLOGRAPHY, DIELECTRIC THEORY, POLAR MOLECULES.

FERROMAGNETISM

Ferromagnetism is an example of cooperative phenomena in solids. It is characterized by a spontaneous macroscopic magnetization M (magnetic moment per unit volume) in the absence of an applied magnetic field at temperatures below a critical value known as the Curie temperature, T_C. This property is exhibited by the transition metals, Fe, Co, and Ni; the rare earth metals, Gd, Tb, Dy, Ho, Er, and Tm; and by a variety of alloys, compounds, and solid solutions involving the transition, rare earth, and actinide elements. Ferromagnetic Curie temperatures range from a fraction of a degree to hundreds of degrees Kelvin.

Cooperative magnetic behavior results from the exchange interaction between electrons, which is qualitatively described as follows. Electrostatic coulomb repulsion between like electric charges acts to keep two electrons apart, a separation which is also favored by the Pauli exclusion principle if the electrons have parallel spins. Thus if two electrons are farther apart when their spins are parallel than they would be if their spins were antiparallel, the parallel state will have lower mutual electrostatic energy. However, the kinetic energies increase if the electrons are separated, and consideration of this energy may lead to lower total energy for antiparallel spins. In other words, the exchange interaction is electrostatic in nature, but is modified by details of kinetic energy and the exclusion principle, and is highly dependent on the spatial distribution of the electrons. The

exchange energy between two electrons, though electrostatic, is usually expressed in the mathematically equivalent form, $-2J\mathbf{s}_1 \cdot \mathbf{s}_2$, where J is the quantum mechanical exchange integral, related to the overlap of the charge distributions 1, 2; and $\mathbf{s}_1$ and $\mathbf{s}_2$ are the spin angular momentum vectors of the two electrons. The value of J is usually expressed in energy units, such as ergs, when the angular momentum vectors are assigned nondimensional values, i.e., spin quantum numbers. When J is positive, parallel spins represent a lower energy state than antiparallel spins. Since each electron has a magnetic moment proportional to its spin angular momentum, a state of parallel spins corresponds to a state of parallel magnetic moments.

The principal effect of the exchange interaction is embodied in the empirical Hund's rules, which describe the combination of electron spins in an atom to form the atomic spin. The principal interaction between magnetic atoms, i.e., between atoms with magnetic moments as a consequence of spin angular momenta, is thought to be of exchange character also, and there has been considerable success in describing magnetic properties by assuming this interaction to have the form,

$$\mathcal{H} = -\sum_{i,j} J_{ij} \mathbf{S}_i \cdot \mathbf{S}_j.$$

Here $\mathbf{S}_i$ and $\mathbf{S}_j$ are the spin angular momentum vectors of atoms i and j; the exchange integral, J_{ij}, may vary for different pairs and is usually regarded as a phenomenological parameter to be evaluated by means of experimental data. When J_{ij} is positive, parallel ordering or alignment of the atomic spins in a common direction is favored, and so there is a large spontaneous magnetization even in the absence of an applied field. For negative J_{ij}, antiparallel spins result in lower energy (see ANTIFERROMAGNETISM, FERRIMAGNETISM).

Maximum ordering obtains at the absolute zero of temperature where the randomizing effect of thermal agitation disappears. The initial decrease of the magnetization as the temperature is increased from zero is well represented by a superposition of wavelike disturbances known as spin waves. At the Curie temperature the magnetic ordering is destroyed by thermal agitation and the spontaneous magnetization is zero (Fig. 1). Above the Curie temperature a ferromagnetic material behaves paramagnetically and has a net magnetization only in the presence of an applied field (see MAGNETISM and PARAMAGNETISM).

At temperatures below T_C a sample of ferromagnetic material is usually divided into small regions called domains, which vary in size and shape with a typical dimension from 0.1 to 1000 μm. Within each domain the magnetization is uniform and has the maximum or saturation value, M_S, characteristic of the temperature of the material (Fig. 1), but the direction of

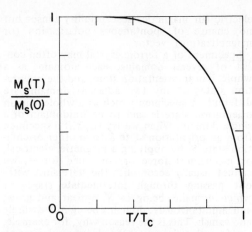

FIG. 1. Typical variation of spontaneous domain magnetization, M_S, as a function of temperature, T.

alignment of the individual moments in each domain changes from one domain to the next. The magnetization of the sample, which is the resultant of the magnetization of all the domains, may be much less than the saturation value (of a single domain), or it may even be zero in a completely demagnetized state.

The magnetization of a sample increases when a magnetic field, H, is applied. The value of H required to saturate the magnetization may be as small as 0.01 oersted or as large as several thousand oersteds, depending on the material. The magnetization process for a previously demagnetized material is represented by the 0-to-a portion of the magnetization curve in Fig. 2. When the applied field is subsequently removed, the magnetization exhibits the phe-

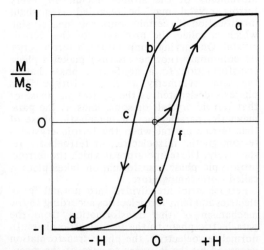

FIG. 2. Typical variation of sample magnetization, M, as a function of applied field strength, H; the magnetization curve depends on the magnetic history of the sample.

nomenon of hysteresis, or lagging behind, tracing the path a-b and retaining a finite value, called the remanence, when the field is zero. The coercive force is the value of the field which must be applied opposite to the direction of the magnetic moment to trace the path b-c and reduce the magnetization to zero. Further increase of the field in this direction, followed by its removal, traces the path c-d-e. Repetition of the cycle then traces the curve e-f-a-b-c-d-e-, etc. Permanent magnets are characterized by a large coercive force; i.e., a large reverse field (typically thousands of oersteds) is necessary to destroy the magnetization However, in soft magnetic materials the coercive force may be less than one oersted.

Domains exist in a ferromagnetic material because their formation results in a lower total energy for the sample than it would have if the entire sample were a single domain. Total alignment of the magnetic moments is favored by the exchange forces, but these are usually short range forces acting between an atom and its neighbors. The dipole-dipole forces, although weaker, are long range and, alone, would orient the atomic moments like bar magnets, north pole to south pole, in closed chains to minimize the external field of the magnet (see DIPOLE MOMENT and MAGNETISM). One additional factor is required for the formation of domains. This factor is anisotropy, a result of the crystal structure of most solid materials. The structure of a crystal is not the same in all directions; consequently its physical properties depend on direction. It is easier to magnetize a magnetic material in some directions, called easy axes, than in other directions. When the effect of anisotropy is superimposed on the effects of exchange and dipolar coupling, the ordered atomic moments break up into segments or domains, so that in each domain the magnetization is uniform and lies along or near one of the easy axes. There is a large change in the direction of magnetization from one domain to the next, with the reorientation occurring gradually (on an atomic scale) in a narrow transition region known as the domain wall.

The initial part of the magnetization process, 0-a in Fig. 2, is represented schematically in Fig. 3. In the demagnetized state the domains are arranged to minimize the external field due to the magnetization and to give zero net moment for the sample (Fig. 3a). In low fields the domain boundaries move so that the domains with magnetization direction near the direction of the applied field grow in size while other domains are depleted (Fig. 3b). As the field strength is increased, the domain boundaries are swept out of the sample (Fig. 3c), and finally the (single) domain magnetization rotates into the direction of the applied field until saturation is reached (Fig. 3d). When the field is removed, domains re-form in varied orientation along the easy axes, but there is a prefer-

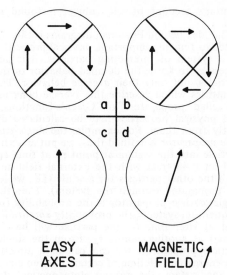

EASY AXES $+$ MAGNETIC FIELD $\nearrow$

FIG. 3. Schematic representation of the change of domain structure and magnetization with applied field.

ence for domains whose magnetization vectors lie in the easy directions nearest the direction in which the field was applied, and consequently the sample as a whole has a magnetic moment (remanent magnetization).

R. J. JOENK

References

Bozorth, R. M., "Ferromagnetism," New York, Van Nostrand Reinhold Co., 1951.

Chikazumi, S., "Physics of Magnetism," New York, John Wiley & Sons, Inc., 1964.

Craik, D. J., "Structure and Properties of Magnetic Materials," London, Pion Ltd., 1971.

Morrish, A. H., "The Physical Principles of Magnetism," New York, John Wiley & Sons, Inc., 1965.

Cross-references: DIPOLE MOMENTS, FERRIMAGNETISM, MAGNETISM, PARAMAGNETISM.

FEYNMAN DIAGRAMS

I. Introduction Feynman diagrams provide one of the most powerful methods known for finding the physical properties of systems of interacting particles, i.e., particles interacting with an external field and/or with each other. Since all physical systems—solids, liquids, gases, molecules, plasmas, atoms, nuclei, elementary particles—are composed of interacting particles, the Feynman diagram method is now used extensively in all branches of modern physics. In this article, the examples are from solid-state physics; the reader is referred to the References for examples from other branches. A very ele-

mentary account of the subject is found in Ref. 1.

The idea behind Feynman diagrams is this: In order to find the important physical properties of a system of interacting particles, it is not necessary to know the detailed behavior of the particles, but only their *average* behavior. The quantities which describe this average behavior are called "propagators" or "Green's functions," and physical properties may be calculated directly from them. For example, the *single-particle propagator* is defined thus: we put an extra particle into the system at point r_1 at time t_1, and let it interact with the external field and with the other particles for a while (i.e., we let it "propagate" through the system). Then the single-particle propagator is the probability (or in quantum systems, the probability *amplitude*) that at later time t_2, the particle will be observed at another point, r_2. From the single-particle propagator, we can calculate directly the energy and lifetime of certain excited states of the system, the ground state energy, etc. Similarly, there are the two-particle propagator, the no-particle propagator or "vacuum amplitude"), etc., which yield other physical properties (see Ref. 1).

Feynman diagrams give us a method of calculating propagators by means of pictures. We shall first show how this is done in a simple classical example from "liquid-state" physics, i.e., the drunken man propagator, then give a couple of illustrations from solid-state physics.

II. Classical Example: The Drunken Man Propagator A man who has had too much to drink (Fig. 1), leaves a party at point 1 and on the way to his home at point 2, he can stop off at one or more bars—Alice's Bar (A), Bardot Bar (B), Club 6 Bar (C), $\cdots$ etc. We ask for the probability, $P(1, 2)$, that he gets home. This probability, which is just the propagator here

(with time omitted for simplicity), is the sum of the probabilities for all the different ways he can propagate from 1 to 2 interacting with the various bars. Assuming, for simplicity, that the various processes involved are independent, this is just $P_0(1, 2)$ (= probability that he will go "freely" from 1 to 2, i.e., without stopping at any bar), plus $P_0(1, A) \times P(A) \times P_0(A, 2)$ (= probability he will go freely from 1 to bar A, times the probability that he stops off at A for a drink, times the probability that he then proceeds freely to 2), plus $P_0(1, B) \times P(B) \times P_0(B, 2)$ (= probability for route 1–bar B–2) plus etc. $\cdots$ plus $P_0(1, A) \times P(A) \times P_0(A, A) \times P(A) \times P_0(A, 2)$ (= probability for route 1–A–A–2) plus etc. $\cdots\cdot$. This gives us an infinite series for the propagator:

$$P(1, 2) = P_0(1, 2) + P_0(1, A)P(A)P_0(A, 2)$$
$$+ P_0(1, B)P(B)P(B, 2) + \cdots$$
$$+ P_0(1, A)P(A)P_0(A, A)P(A)P_0(A, 2) + \cdots. \quad (1)$$

Now this series is a complicated thing to look at. To make it easier to read, we draw a "picture dictionary" to associate diagrams with the various probabilities as shown in Table 1. Using this dictionary, series (1) can be drawn as in Fig. 2(a). Since, by Table 1, each diagram element stands for a factor, Fig. 2(a) is completely equivalent to series (1). However, Fig. 2(a) has the great advantage that it also reveals the physical meaning of the series, giving us a "map" which helps us to keep track of all the sequences of interactions the drunken man can have in going from 1 to 2.

The series may be evaluated approximately by selecting the most important terms in it and summing them. This is called "*partial summation.*" For example, suppose the man's favorite

FIG. 1. Propagation of drunken man.

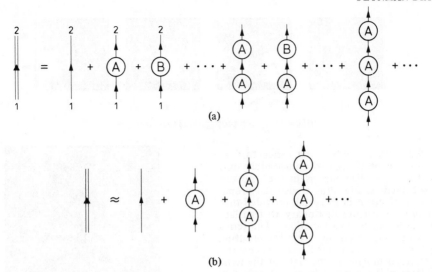

(a)

(b)

FIG. 2. (a) Feynman diagram series for drunken man propagator, or for electron propagating in crystal. (b) Approximate series ("partial sum") for drunken man propagator.

TABLE 1. FEYNMAN DIAGRAM DICTIONARY FOR DRUNKEN MAN PROPAGATOR

Word	Picture	Meaning
$P(1, 2)$		Probability of propagation from 1 to 2.
$P_0(\mathbf{r}, \mathbf{s})$		Probability of free propagation from $\mathbf{r}$ to $\mathbf{s}$.
$P(X)$		Probability of stopping off at bar X for a drink.

bar is Alice's bar, so that $P(A)$ is large and all other $P(x)$'s are small. Then Fig. 2(a) becomes approximately Fig. 2(b). Assuming for simplicity that all $P_0(\mathbf{r}, \mathbf{s}) = c$ (a constant) we have, using Table 1:

$$P(1, 2) \approx P_0(1, 2) + P_0(1, A)P(A)P_0(A, 2) + \cdots$$

$$= c + c^2 P(A) + c^3 P^2(A) + \cdots$$

$$= c\,[1 + cP(A) + c^2 P^2(A) + \cdots]$$

$$= c/[1 - cP(A)] \qquad (2)$$

where we have used the fact that the expression in brackets is a geometric series. This same technique is used in the quantum case.

III. Single Electron Propagating in a Crystal
The example here is just like the previous one,

except that instead of a propagating drunken man interacting with various bars, we have a propagating electron interacting with various ions in a crystal. A crystal consists of a set of positively charged ions arranged so they form a regular lattice, as in Fig. 3. An electron interacts with these ions by means of the Coulomb force. The single-particle propagator here is the sum of the quantum-mechanical probability amplitudes for all the possible ways the electron can propagate from point $\mathbf{r}_1$ in the crystal, at time t_1, to point $\mathbf{r}_2$ at time t_2, interacting with the various ions on the way. These are: (1) freely, without interaction; (2) freely from $\mathbf{r}_1, t_1$ (= "1" for short) to the ion at $\mathbf{r}_A$ at time t_A, interaction with this ion, then free propagation from the ion to point 2; (3) from 1 to ion B, interaction at B, then from B to 2, etc. Or we could have the routes 1–A–A–2, 1–A–B–2, etc. We can now use the dictionary in Table 1 to translate this into diagrams, provided the following changes are made: change "probability" to "probability amplitude," and change the meaning of the circle with an X to "probability amplitude for an interaction with the ion

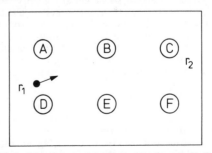

FIG. 3. Electron propagating among ions A, B, C $\cdots$ in crystal.

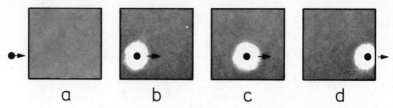

FIG. 4. Electron propagating in electron gas.

at X." When this is done, the series for the propagator can be translated immediately into exactly the same diagrams as in the drunken man case! That is, Fig. 2(a) is also the propagator for an electron in a crystal, provided that we just use a quantum dictionary to translate the lines and circles into functions. The series can be partially summed, and from the resulting propagator we obtain immediately the energy of the electron moving in the field of the ions.

IV. Electron Propagating in an Electron Gas

We now look at the problem of many interacting particles, taking as an example a large number of electrons interacting with each other by

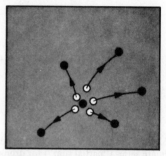

FIG. 5. "Hole" picture of empty space around electron in electron gas.

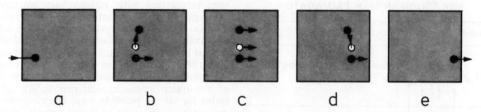

FIG. 6. One possible way in which an electron can propagate through the electron gas.

means of the Coulomb force. It is assumed that there is a uniform, fixed positive charge "background" present which keeps the whole system electrically neutral. This system is called the "electron gas" and is used as a simple model for electrons in a metal. The propagation of an added electron through this system is shown in Fig. 4. Figure 4(a) shows the uniform charge distribution in the undisturbed system, with an extra electron entering from the left. In 4(b) the extra electron has entered, repels other electrons away from it (Coulomb repulsion between like charges), so we get an "empty space" near the extra electron and repelled electrons further away. The extra electron surrounded by the empty space is called the "*quasi electron*" and it propagates through the system as shown in Fig. 4(c), (d). It is convenient to view the empty space around the extra electron as composed of "holes" in the electron gas. That is, the Coulomb repulsion "lifts out" electrons from the electron gas in the immediate vicinity of the extra electron, thus creating "holes" in the charge distribution of the gas, and puts these lifted-out electrons down again further away. This picture is shown in Fig. 5.

Using this picture, we can decompose the propagator into the sum of the probability amplitudes for all possible ways that the extra electron can propagate through the system interacting with the other electrons. The simplest way is free propagation without interaction. Another way is shown in the "movie" in Fig. 6. Figure 6(a) shows the extra electron entering the electron gas. In 6(b) we see the extra electron interacting with a nearby electron in the gas, creating a hole nearby and a lifted-out electron further away. The extra electron, the hole, and the lifted-out electron then propagate freely through the gas as in 6(c). In 6(d), the extra electron interacts with the lifted-out electron, causing it to fall back into the hole, thus annihilating both the lifted-out electron and the hole. Figure 6(e) shows the extra electron propagating out of the system. (It should be noted that unlike the drunken man case, the processes

FIG. 7. Feynman diagram for interaction between two electrons.

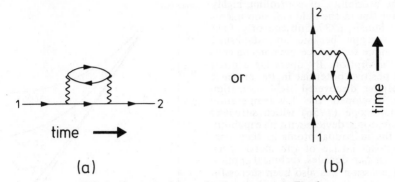

or

FIG. 8. Feynman diagram for the sequence in Fig. 6.

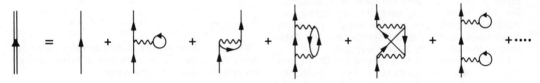

FIG. 9. Feynman diagram series for electron propagator in the electron gas.

shown in Fig. 6 are not physical but rather "virtual" or "quasi-physical" processes, since they do not conserve energy and they may violate the Pauli exclusion principle.)

Let us represent the Coulomb interaction between an electron at point **r** and one at **r'** by a wiggly line as in Fig. 7. Then the sequence of processes in Fig. 6 may be represented by the Feynman diagram shown in Fig. 8(a) or 8(b). Note that hole lines are drawn as electron lines with a direction opposite to the direction of increasing time. By analyzing the other possible processes which can take place, we find the series for the electron propagator shown in Fig. 9. Again, these diagrams may be evaluated by writing the appropriate factor for each free electron and hole propagator and each interaction, and carrying out a partial sum. The resultant expression for the propagator yields directly the energy and lifetime of the quasi electron.

For a more extensive and detailed account of Feynman diagrams, see Ref. 1.

R. D. MATTUCK

References

1. Mattuck, R. D., "A Guide to Feynman Diagrams in the Many-Body Problem," London, McGraw-Hill, 1967. (Most elementary account, examples from solid-state and nuclear physics.)
2. Fetter, A. L., and Walecka, J. D., "Quantum Theory of Many-Particle Systems," New York, McGraw-Hill, 1971. (Advanced, examples from solid state and nuclear physics.)
3. Mandl, F., "Introduction to Quantum Field Theory," New York, Interscience Publishers, 1959. (Elementary account, examples from elementary particle physics.)

FIELD EMISSION

Field emission of electrically charged particles occurs when a sufficiently high electric field is applied to the surface of a conductor. Specifically, field emission of electrons from cold metals into a vacuum is a basic physical effect comparable to thermionic, photoelectric, or secondary emission. Field electron emission is also termed "cold emission" or "autoelectronic emission." Field emission of electrons from metals at room temperature requires an electric field of an order of magnitude of 3×10^7 volts/cm which can be obtained by applying a few thousand volts to a sharply curved cathode, which may be either a fine wire, a sharp edge, or a needle tip. From such cathodes, field emission was first observed by R. W. Wood in 1897, and technical application in high-voltage rectifiers and x-ray tubes was attempted by J. E. Lilienfeld in the early 1920's. He failed because of the inadequate vacuum techniques available at that time. The quantum mechanical theory of field emission was given by R. H. Fowler and L. W. Nordheim in 1928, which agreed with the current-voltage relationship measured by R. A. Millikan and C. C. Lauritsen, but experimental work to further verify the predictions advanced

only with the possibility of controlling highly perfect emitter tips in the field emission microscope by E. W. Müller, 1937. Subsequently, field emission microscopy became an established research technique for surface phenomena connected with adsorption. By operating a point emitter at a positive potential in the presence of a gas, Müller discovered field ionization (1951) and developed the low-temperature field ion microscope (1956) which surpasses all other microscopic devices with its capability of showing the individual atoms as they constitute the crystal lattice of the metal specimen. In the last two decades, technical application of field emission has also been successful with the development of powerful flash x-ray tubes (W. P. Dyke, 1955). The extremely large current densities of up to 10^8 amperes/cm² make a field emission cathode very attractive for mm wave tubes, cathode ray tubes, and electron microscopes, but the sensitivity to contamination and cathode sputtering are detrimental to stability and long lifetime.

Field emission can be explained with the concepts of quantum mechanics. The conduction electrons of a metal are moving in a potential trough, from which they can escape ordinarily only by addition of thermal energy (thermionic emission), by an energy transfer from photons (photoelectric emission), or by collision with other energetic particles (secondary emission). If the barrier of the trough is narrowed by the application of an external electric field to be comparable with the wavelength of the electrons inside the metal, then a small amplitude of the electron wave will be noticeable outside the barrier, or in an equivalent interpretation, there is a finite probability of the electron penetrating through the potential barrier, even if its kinetic energy is insufficient to go over it. According to the Fowler-Nordheim theory of field emission, the current density J (in amperes/cm²) as a function of field strength F (volts/cm) and of the work function ϕ (electron-volts) is approximately given by

$$J = 1.55 \times 10^{-6} \frac{F^2}{\phi} e^{-\frac{6.85 \times 10^7 \phi^{3/2}}{F}}$$

A more refined theory takes into account the effect of the image force on the electron, which reduces the exponent of the above equation by a factor slightly smaller than unity and which depends upon $\phi/\sqrt{F}$. The field required for a given current density is thus reduced by some 10 to 20 per cent. The temperature dependence of field emission is found to be very small below about 1000 K (Fig. 1). Considerable increase in emission is observed when both the temperature and the field are high. This effect is called T-F emission.

Field emission of positive ions can occur when an adsorption layer is removed from the positive emitter tip by the electric field (field desorption,

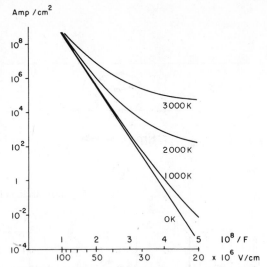

FIG. 1. Current density of field emission for a tungsten cathode plotted as a function of reciprocal field strength, for various temperatures.

Müller, 1941) or at still higher field strength when the metal atoms of the emitter are coming off after single or multiple ionization (field evaporation, Müller, 1956). These ion currents are only transients since the source of the ions,

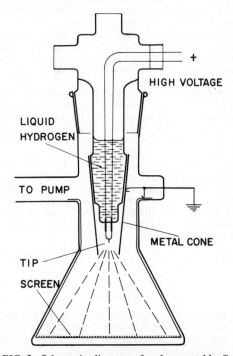

FIG. 2. Schematic diagram of a demountable field ion microscope. The hemispherical cap of the tip, having a typical radius of 500 Å, is radially projected onto the fluorescent screen with the help of helium ions.

one monoatomic adsorption layer or the tip surface itself, is soon consumed. Continuous field ion emission is obtained by operating the positive emitter in a gas of low pressure. Gas molecules attracted to the tip surface by polarization are ionized when their valence electron tunnels out into the metal while the molecule is a few angstroms above the surface. Ion currents are small (less than 10^{-8} ampere) due to the limited supply of the gas molecules, and the fields necessary for ionization are very high, about 2.5×10^8 volts/cm for hydrogen and 4.5×10^8 volts/cm for helium.

In spite of its limited technical application, field emission has been a subject of intensive investigations, and the field electron and the field ion microscopes have become productive tools of basic research in the study of metal surfaces. The specimen of the field emission microscope is a needle-shaped field emitter with a hemispherical tip of a radius of some 10^{-5} to 10^{-4} cm, arranged in a vacuum tube opposite to a fluorescent screen. With a few thousand volts applied, field emitted electrons move away from the tip in a radial direction, displaying on the screen an enlarged projection image of the distribution of electron emission at the emitter. The magnification of this microscope is approximately equal to the ratio of screen distance to tip radius and can exceed a million diameters. The lateral resolution is limited to 25 Å by a random tangential velocity component of the electrons due to the Fermi distribution inside the metal and by diffraction due to the de Broglie wavelength. As even traces of adsorption layers change the work function and, thereby, the emission, the presence of such layers can be readily detected on the screen. The imaged tip cap usually represents a single crystal, so that the behavior of adsorption layers can be studied in its dependence on crystallographic orientation of the substrate. As little as 10^{-3} of a monolayer of oxygen is clearly discernible on many metals. Because of the small temperature dependence of field emission, such layers, their surface migration, adsorption and desorption

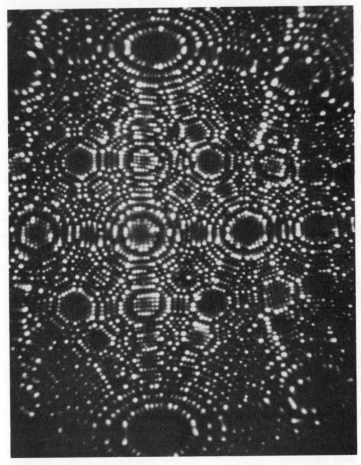

FIG. 3. Field ion micrograph of a platinum-cobalt alloy crystal (50 per cent, ordered at 700°C), showing the individual atoms as single dots. Original magnification on the 5-inch screen was 1.5 million diameters.

rates, and the activation energies of these processes can be measured in a wide temperature range. This is done by immersing the entire microscope into a cryogenic bath and by heating the emitter to any desired temperature up to near its melting point. Most studies have been done with the high-melting metals, W, Re, Ta, Mo, Nb, Ir, Pt, Rh, Pd, V, Ni, Fe, Ti, Cu, and various alloys and with adsorption layers of H_2, N_2, O_2, CO, CO_2, and the noble gases. Detailed patterns of individual organic molecules, such as phthalocyanine or similar aromatic compounds, cannot yet be fully explained. The interpretation of thermal desorption experiments is often difficult because of the occurrence of surface migration, while the well-defined field strength obtained in field desorption experiments cannot be fully utilized because of the complex polarization conditions at the various adsorption sites.

The field ion microscope (Fig. 2) was developed to overcome the limitation of resolution of the field electron microscope. In contrast to the case of electrons, the undesirable tangential motion of the imaging ions can be reduced by lowering the emitter temperature. The shorter de Broglie wavelength of ions is also an advantage. Usually operated with helium as the imaging gas and the tip cooled by liquid nitrogen, or better by liquid hydrogen, the ions image the field distribution over the emitter tip in a resolution of up to 2.5 Å (Fig. 3). The specimen is atomically cleaned and shaped to an evenly curved, highly perfect surface by field evaporation. Helium atoms ionize above each atomic protrusion of the specimen and are then accelerated towards the screen. Each protruding surface atom is imaged by about 10^5 helium ions/sec. The surface stays atomically clean as all impurity gases have a lower ionization potential than helium and thus are ionized in the lower field region in space before they can reach the tip. Vacuum requirements are, therefore, very modest, and an unbaked demountable system can be used. Image stability requires that the evaporation field be above the ionization field of the imaging gas. Field ion microscopy with helium is, therefore, limited to the refractory metals. Using lower ionization potential gases, such as Ne, Ar, or H_2, imaging with some loss of resolution can be done with reduced fields, and the common transition metals become accessible. Difficulties of observing and photographically recording the images, which are extremely weak and may be transient due to the instability of the surface near the evaporation field, are overcome by photoelectronic image intensification, or more

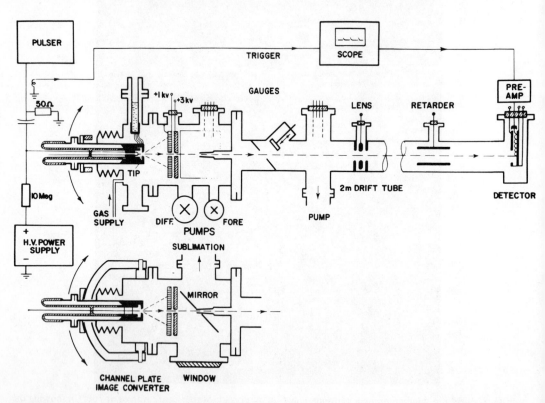

FIG. 4. In the atom-probe FIM the tip is tilted with the help of an external gimbal mount and a metal bellows seal. The ion image is displayed on a microchannel plate and seen as a 1000 times amplified electron image on the phosphor screen at 3 kV. The image is viewed through the 45° inclined mirror.

effectively by converting the ion image into an amplified electron image with the help of microchannel plates. Thus even metals as soft as Au, Cu, and Al have been successfully imaged. However, imaging at a reduced field does not eliminate all difficulties with the lower-strength metals, since one always has to go up to the evaporation field in order to produce a perfect hemispherical tip shape required for the radial projection imaging. Many metals yield to the associated mechanical stress $F^2/8\pi$, which amounts to nearly 1000 kg/mm^2 at the helium image field of 4.8×10^8 volts/cm.

The most promising application of field ion microscopy is the direct observation of lattice imperfections in metal crystals. Single vacancies produced by quenching, cold working, or irradiation can be counted and localized. Interstitials resulting from radiation damage as well as from impurities can be seen, and their thermally activated migration to the tip surface can be measured. The core structure of dislocations and the matching of the lattices along grain boundaries can be studied in atomic details, including their interaction with impurity atoms. Controlled field evaporation permits the removal and inspection of subsequent surface layers, so that the depth of the crystal can be searched for bulk defects. The mechanical field stress can affect the motion of lattice defects, but it may also be utilized for the study of slip and fatigue. Short-range and long-range order in alloys can also be investigated.

The atom-probe FIM adds a new dimension to field ion microscopy by identifying mass-spectrometrically a single atom or the atoms of a small region of the tip surface. The new instrument (Fig. 4) allows the observer to select one atom by tilting the tip until its image falls onto a small probe hole in the screen. By superimposing a 10-nanosecond field evaporation pulse, the selected atom is ripped off and travels through the probe hole and subsequently through a 2 m long drift tube, at the end of which is a detector of single ion sensitivity. Its signal is displayed on an oscilloscope screen, so that the time-of-flight and the known voltage energy of the ion can be used to determine its mass. With this microanalytical tool of ultimate sensitivity, the nature of single impurity atoms, of adsorbate gases, and of alloy constituents can be readily identified. At the same time, the atom probe provides new insights into the mechanism of the FIM, as well as in surface physics, since it has turned out that field ionization preferably occurs through a field-adsorbed, imaging, noble gas atom, and that many metal atoms field evaporate with two, three, or four charges, often forming compound molecule ions with hydrogen and even helium.

E. W. MÜLLER

References

Good, R. H., Jr., and Müller, E. W., "Field Emission," in "Handbuch der Physik," Second Edition, Vol. XXI, pp. 176–231, Springer, Berlin, 1956.

Müller, E. W., "Field Ionization and Field Ion Microscopy," Adv. Electron. Electron Physics, 13, 83–179 (1960).

Gomer, R., "Field Emission and Field Ionization," Cambridge, Mass., Harvard University Press, 1961.

Müller, E. W., and Tsong, T. T., "Field-Ion Microscopy, Principles and Applications," New York, London, Amsterdam, Elsevier, 1969.

Bowkett, K. M., and Smith, D. A., "Field-Ion Microscopy," Amsterdam-London, North Holland Publishing Co., 1970.

Müller, E. W., "Investigations of Surface Processes with the Atom-Probe FIM," Ber. d. Bunsenges, 75, 979 (1971).

Swanson, L. W., and Bell, A. E., "Recent Advances in Field Electron Microscopy of Metals," Adv. Electron. Electron Physics 32, 193–309 (1973).

Müller, E. W., and Tsong, T. T., "Field Ion Microscopy, Field Ionization and Field Evaporation," Progr. Surface Sci. 4, part I (1973).

Cross-references: ADSORPTION AND ABSORPTION, ELECTRON MICROSCOPE, POTENTIAL, SOLID-STATE PHYSICS, SOLID-STATE THEORY, THERMIONICS.

FIELD THEORY

The description of the physical world has evolved profoundly through the ages, at times because of, at other times being the cause of, sweeping changes in our philosophical, mathematical and experimental knowledge. Greek geometry concerned itself essentially with properties of "objects as such," a triangle or a cube being studied, for example, without any thought of their spatial environment; the Ptolemaic system enhanced this view into a clockmaker's dream, where celestial bodies parade around the earth, rigidly driven in circular motions. Only with Descartes' analytical geometry did objects become "portions of space" and the properties of space itself the main object of study; with Galileo and Newton, a correct science of dynamics was born, which permits the prevision of an amazing number of mechanical phenomena in that space from a few first principles.

Field theory studies the phenomena of the physical world as due to interactions which propagate through space; the "geometrical emptiness," which is the space of mathematics, becomes the medium into and through which actions take place or, even more drastically, a structure which is itself determined by the properties of matter, as in general relativity (which will not be discussed in this article).

Suppose two bodies interact in space, e.g., the sun and the earth with Newton's law, or two electric charges with Coulomb's law. Two pictures of this situation are equally possible and correct. One is that this interaction cannot be conceived if *both* bodies are not there and that we should study primarily its effects without looking for a detailed mechanism for its propagation from one body to the other; this is the description of "action at a distance", in which

forces are the main concepts and space is a vacuum into which bodies follow trajectories determined by the forces acting upon them. The other picture consists of imagining that each body, whether alone or not, modifies the structure of the space which surrounds it, geometrically or because in each point of that space there is now potentially a force, which becomes active if another body occupies that point, but should be conceived as existing there in any case; the main objective here is to study how these "fields of force" are created in space by material objects and how they propagate; this is the point of view of "action with contact," which finds its full development in field theory.

Mathematically, a field is characterized by assigning to each point of space a quantity which is *intrinsically* associated with it; a temperature, for instance, or a velocity, or a tensor or a spinor of arbitrary rank. "Intrinsic" means that if we change our frame of observation, this quantity does *not* change; supposing, e.g., that our field is that of the velocities at a given instant of all the points of a moving fluid, if we rotate our coordinate system we shall observe different values for the components of those velocities, just because we, not the velocities, have changed position. It is therefore essential that, together with the specification of the field quantities, their transformation laws also be assigned under changes of the reference frame; these laws are indicated by the description of the field quantity as a "scalar" (which does not change), a "vector" (which changes with the same law as the coordinates), a "tensor," etc.; the complete specification of all such possible laws is a standard chapter of group theory.

Physically, we have to account for the creation or the existence of the field, by describing the field quantities as generated by "sources," such as positive or negative charges for the electromagnetic field, or the sources and sinks of hydrodynamics. Moreover, we have to describe in which way the values of the field quantities change when the point at which they are considered, or the time, is changed. In the absence of discontinuities, for instance in vacuum, one expects these values to differ by infinitesimal amounts if the corresponding points are infinitesimally close, in some way which is typical of the field considered; in other words, that the rates of change of the field quantities with respect to the space coordinates and time be connected by relations which specify both how these changes can occur compatibly with the geometrical properties of space, and how they are related to the sources. Group theory determines all the possible forms which are permissible for these relations, which take the name of *field equations*; each field theory is characterized by a special set of field equations, which are clearly *partial differential equations*.

RELATIVITY and QUANTUM THEORY have played a great rôle in the development of field theory; we shall briefly discuss, later, their influence both in the explanation of new physical phenomena and in the mathematical formulation of the theory.

Field theory has taken an entirely new shape with the so-called second quantization, which has led to several modern developments, of which some embody faithfully the concepts outlined thus far and others instead represent new views in natural philosophy; this is still a matter of controversy at present, and it is yet unpredictable whether a reasonably lasting description of nature will come out of such attempts or whether a new drastic turn in human thought will be necessary before we can hope to understand the fundamental laws of physics. Be that as it may, the ideas and the computational techniques of field theory have proved already of invaluable help in the description of many phenomena, from particle physics to superconductivity.

It is convenient to examine first the theories in which the field quantities are ordinary functions of space and time points, regardless of whether they have a direct physical meaning (as with the velocities of hydrodynamics and the electromagnetic forces) or not (as with the wave function which obeys a Schrödinger equation). This comprises of course most of classical and modern physics; mathematics permits again, however, a tremendous conceptual simplification. In the study of continuous media or fields one is, most often, interested in one of the following classes of phenomena:

(1) Phenomena which consist of the propagation of some action; the medium itself is not transported from one place to another; typical is the propagation of waves, whether they be seismic, fluid or electromagnetic;

(2) Phenomena in which there is transport or diffusion of a quantity in a medium: of heat in a wall, of solute in a solvent, of neutrons in a pile;

(3) Equilibrium phenomena: deformations of strained elastic bodies, electro- or magnetostatic fields as determined by charges and boundaries.

Each class is ruled by essentially one type of equation. Let $\Delta = \partial^2/\partial x^2 + \partial^2/\partial y^2 + \partial^2/\partial z^2$ denote the Laplace operator; $\phi = \phi(x, y, z, t)$ the field quantity; F some function of x, y, z, t, ϕ and, at most, of the first-order derivatives of ϕ; v a velocity; and D a diffusion constant. The corresponding equations can be brought into the standard forms:

$$\Delta\phi - \frac{1}{v^2}\frac{\partial^2\phi}{\partial t^2} = F \text{ (hyperbolic partial differential}$$

$$\text{equation) (1)}$$

$$\Delta\phi - \frac{1}{D}\frac{\partial\phi}{\partial t} = F \text{ (parabolic partial differential}$$

$$\text{equation) (2)}$$

$$\Delta\phi = F \text{ (elliptic partial differential equation)}$$

$$(3)$$

If the field quantity has more than one component, one may deduce for each of its components an equation which is essentially of the same type, although it may be difficult or impossible to obtain an independent equation for each component.

This classification of physical phenomena according to the type of equation to which their study can be reduced is of the greatest importance: Eqs. (1), (2) and (3) are called in fact "the equations of mathematical physics"; more specifically, Eq. (1) is also called the wave equation, Eq. (2) the heat equation, and Eq. (3) the Laplace or potential equation. The study of their mathematical properties gives complete information on all the physical phenomena which they describe.

The equations of quantum mechanics can also be brought, at least formally, into the form of Eq. (1) or (2); the intervention of complex quantities modifies the situation somewhat, in a way which we cannot discuss here.

Electromagnetic phenomena fall typically into the category of Eq. (1): each of the components of the electric field $\mathbf{E} \equiv (E_x, E_y, E_z)$ and of the magnetic field $\mathbf{H} \equiv (H_x, H_y, H_z)$ satisfies, in vacuum, Eq. (1), with $F = 0$; the connections between $\mathbf{E}$ and $\mathbf{H}$ are given by the Maxwell equations, which characterize completely the theory, and lead in vacuum to the result just mentioned. When $\mathbf{E}$ or $\mathbf{H}$ does not vary with time, Eq. (1) reduces to Eq. (3), thus yielding electro- or magnetostatics.

The electromagnetic field, i.e., the vectors $\mathbf{E}$ and $\mathbf{H}$, generated by a distribution of moving charges or currents confined within a limited volume has a part which becomes dominant at a large distance from that volume, because it decreases only with the inverse of that distance (instead of the inverse-square law of static fields); this part constitutes the *radiation* field, which is responsible for the transmission of energy and signals (the radiated energy is, of course, supplied by the mechanism which drives the generating charges or currents). This is easy to understand: the energy radiated through a large sphere around the source is proportional to the area of the sphere times the square of E; it vanishes therefore with increasing radius for all but the radiative component, for which it stays constant: energy is actually removed from the source and radiated away to all distances. The study of radiation is a most important part of the theory, both macroscopically (telecommunications, radar) and microscopically (atoms, nuclei, elementary particles).

Relativity and quantum mechanics have extended and modified profoundly the classical picture presented so far. The very concepts of space and time change with special relativity: events which are simultaneous for an observer are not such when seen by another observer in uniform motion with respect to the first, because time and space are mixed together by the Lorentz transformations which relate the reference frames associated with the two observers. As a consequence, the laws of nature can retain their universal validity only if they are formulated in the same form by any such observer, i.e., if their form is not altered by a Lorentz transformation—technically speaking, if they are "Lorentz covariant." This requirement becomes a stringent dogma; it suffices to determine, with the help of group theory, the possible equations for any conceivable relativistic field theory; it is of invaluable help, when computations are made, in checking or correcting them.

The nonrelativistic Schrödinger equation for the wave function of a particle is, but for the appearance of complex quantities, of the type (2) described before: this is not acceptable in a relativistic world, because time and space are not treated alike. One needs either an equation which contains only second-order derivatives, or one with only first-order derivatives; for a free particle, this leads either to the Klein-Gordon equation, which is of type (1), or to the Dirac equation, which contains linearly only the first-order derivatives of the wave function, but has a mathematical structure which necessarily assigns special physical properties to the particles described by it. It was one of the greatest triumphs theoretical physics ever witnessed, to discover that such properties are actually displayed by all particles which obey the Dirac equation: spin, and the existence for each Dirac particle of a corresponding *antiparticle*, i.e., a particle having the opposite mechanical and electrical properties. (See article on ANTIPARTICLES.)

The requirement of relativistic covariance has thus led to fundamental physical discoveries; for each particle obeying the Dirac equation, the corresponding antiparticle has been experimentally found in nature; electron and positron, proton and antiproton, neutron and antineutron, etc. What is more, the theory predicts that a particle-antiparticle pair can be created in a collision phenomenon, if sufficient energy is available, or can annihilate itself, giving away its energy in the form of electromagnetic radiation or other particles.

The classical theory allowed only for the electromagnetic radiation emitted by moving charges or currents; the creation or absorption of particles in collision phenomena, as well as the creation or annihilation of pairs, were outside its scope and possibilities. A new formulation of the theory was needed, which could account consistently for all such phenomena, handling situations in which particles can be created and destroyed in any numbers. The formalism devised for this purpose is that of quantum field theory.

The basic idea is to describe each type of particle by means of a field which is not any more an ordinary numerical function of space and time, but an "operator," i.e., a quantity which changes the number of particles existing in any given state of the system. If the field operator is known, one can then evaluate the probability

of a given state (so many particles, with determined energies and momenta) changing into an equally determined, different state. If the particles do not interact among themselves or with other particles, no change is possible; if there is interaction, the field operator has a structure which can cause such transitions. The field equations appear to be essentially the same as those of the classical Maxwell, Klein-Gordon, Dirac theories, etc.; their structure is however fundamentally different, because they now must be equivalent to infinite sets of ordinary equations, which couple states with different and ever-increasing numbers of particles.

Fields which are associated with particles obeying Bose-Einstein statistics (of which any number can be found in any given state) have radically different mathematical properties from fields associated with particles obeying Fermi-Dirac statistics (of which at most one can be found in any given state); examples of the first are photons (the massless neutral quanta of the electromagnetic field), pions (massive particles, with or without electric charge, which are believed to be responsible for nuclear forces), etc.; examples of the second are electrons and positrons, protons and antiprotons, etc.

The passage from numerical fields to operator fields is called "second quantization"; quantum field theory deals with operator fields.

Striking successes have been met with this approach. From a quantitative point of view, they are confined mostly to electrodynamics, where very small deviations from the values predicted by the non-quantized theory, which were observed in the measurement of the magnetic moment of the electron and in the so-called Lamb shift, were accounted for with amazing accuracy by quantum field theory. Qualitatively, the new conceptual framework has proved extremely useful in understanding elementary phenomena, especially with the help of the diagrams devised by R. P. Feynman, which give a simple intuitive picture of collision and radiation processes involving elementary particles. Very little has been achieved quantitatively, though, for theories other than electrodynamics, because of the tremendous mathematical difficulties which arise as soon as the simplest approximation techniques are not applicable because the interaction is too strong; nevertheless, these ideas have proved greatly helpful in many ways, in combination with general principles of symmetry, Lorentz invariance and causality.

A beautiful consequence of this conception, which assumes that particles are the quanta of a field (as photons were recognized by Einstein to be the quanta of the electromagnetic field) was the discovery of H. Yukawa, that whenever such quanta have a mass different from zero, the force they create between two bodies which interact by exchanging such quanta with each other must be an exponentially decreasing function of distance; this force can become of a coulombian type only if the mass of the quanta vanishes. Thus, the Coulomb force can be explained as due to the exchange of photons among electric charges, the nuclear forces (which have typically short ranges) as due to the exchange of massive particles among nucleons. Exchanges of this nature are not observable in the laboratory, because this runs against Heisenberg's indeterminacy principle; if enough energy is supplied, however, such quanta can actually break loose and do appear as the particles created in collision processes.

The mathematical difficulties encountered in quantum field theory are many, and there is as yet lack of agreement as to the best way to circumvent some of them. Besides mathematical complexity, which prevents all but the simplest calculations, there are many unsolved problems of mathematical rigor and apparent inconsistencies which can be removed only by delicate analyses. Typical of the latter is the fact that unsophisticated calculations give infinite values for masses and charges of interacting particles, and a painstaking analysis is required to retrieve from them the significant physical values; this is the so-called renormalization procedure, which copes with infinities which partly are already present in the classical theory (such as the infinite electromagnetic contribution to the mass of a point-like charged particle, when computed from Maxwell's equations) and partly originate from the new formalism (which permits, for instance, pair creation).

It is not yet certain whether such difficulties are due to the lack of adequate mathematical techniques or are the expression of a fundamental inadequacy of the theory to describe ultimate laws of nature. For this reason, while, on the one hand, the attention of some theoreticians has been directed to perfecting the mathematical foundations of quantum field theory (giving rise to axiomatic field theory and to more rigorous methods of obtaining and studying the quantum field equations, etc.), on the other hand, most physicists have been trying new avenues, such as the S-matrix theory, dispersion relations, the so-called Regge poles, etc.; these approaches have certainly led to very useful results, but they leave altogether at least as many doubts as hopes.

Whatever may be the future prospects of field theory as the correct means for describing the fundamental laws of nature, its tremendous usefulness in providing a conceptual framework, in inspiring new ideas, and in suggesting computational techniques has been overwhelmingly demonstrated in the last decades. It has now found a new, very fertile ground of application in the study of systems containing a very large number of particles, where it has already provided a reasonably good quantitative understanding of superconductivity and superfluidity, and promises many other results of interest in the study of solids and liquids.

E. R. CAIANIELLO

Cross-references: ANTIPARTICLES, ELEMENTARY PARTICLES, QUANTUM THEORY, RELATIVITY, SCHRÖDINGER EQUATION, VECTOR PHYSICS.

FISSION*

Nuclear fission is the breakup of a heavy nucleus, such as that of uranium, into two medium-weight nuclei, with the release of a considerable quantity of energy. Also produced are a few neutrons, some gamma rays, and a number of beta-particles (electrons) from the radioactive decay of the two fragments. Fission occurs spontaneously in some cases, or may be induced by bombardment of the fissionable material with neutrons, protons, or other particles.

Discovery of Fission Although fission was not discovered until 1939, it had been realized, ever since Einstein published his theory of relativity in 1905, that there was a theoretical possibility of releasing tremendous energy from matter.

Fission is now known to have been first produced by Enrico Fermi and his co-workers in 1934, when they irradiated many elements, including uranium, with the newly discovered neutrons. They found a number of different β-activities to be produced from uranium, but believed that these were due to neutron capture. Later radiochemical work indicated that some of the new activities were from elements chemically similar to the much lighter elements Ba, La, etc.

Fission remained unrecognized until O. Hahn and F. Strassmann, German radiochemists, showed by very careful work that these products were not merely chemically similar to lighter elements, but *were* lighter elements. They published their startling results in the January 6, 1939 issue of *Naturwissenschaften*. On January 16, Lise Meitner and O. Frisch sent in to *Nature* (from Stockholm and Copenhagen) a paper in which they named the new process "fission," predicted that the fragments should have large kinetic energies, and explained the process in terms of a liquid-drop model. On the same date, Frisch sent in to *Nature* another paper in which he reported that he had observed the large electrical pulses from fission fragments in an ionization chamber.

Niels Bohr in the meantime had taken the news of the discovery of fission, and the prediction of large energies, to a conference on physics in Washington, D.C. During the conference physicists in a number of laboratories independently verified the tremendous kinetic energies of fission fragments, unaware as yet of Frisch's results.

During the months following the discovery of fission, there was feverish activity in laboratories around the world. It was soon discovered

*Work performed under the auspices of the U.S. Atomic Energy Commission.

that neutrons were being produced by fission, and that almost all of the fission of U was taking place in the relatively rare isotope, ^{235}U. In that same year (1939), Bohr and Wheeler published their theory of fission, based on the liquid-drop model, which is still basic to modern fission theory.

Development of Atomic Energy On the date of publication of the Bohr-Wheeler paper, September 1, 1939, Germany invaded Poland, the Second World War was underway, and fission suddenly had a new importance. It was realized by many that a chain reaction was possible for fission, with the neutrons from each fission producing more fissions, resulting in the release of very large amounts of energy.

The fission process results in the conversion of 0.09 per cent of the mass of the original nucleus into kinetic energy. This amounts to about 200 MeV per fission, or 3.20×10^{-11} joules. The fission of 1 kilogram of ^{235}U thus releases a total energy equal to 8.21×10^{13} joules, or 2.28×10^7 kilowatt-hours. This is roughly equal to the daily output of Hoover Dam, and very much greater than the energy released in chemical reactions. One kg of ^{235}U is equivalent in energy release to the burning of 3.45×10^6 kg of coal (C) by 9.20×10^6 kg of oxygen. This chemical process releases 7.2×10^{-11} of the mass as heat energy, more than 10 million times smaller than for fission.

The fission of 1 kg of ^{235}U is also equivalent in energy released to the detonation of 19.6×10^6 kg (19.6 kilotons) of high explosive. A kiloton, 1000 metric tons, is conventionally taken to be equivalent to 10^{12} calories, or 4.186×10^{12} joules; a megaton is 1000 times larger.

Thus it was known to many people in 1939 that it might well be possible to produce the destructive effect of many thousands of tons of high explosive with a single bomb containing a relatively small amount of fissionable material. It seemed probable that Germany would press ahead with this development. Aware of this danger, scientists in the rest of the world largely ceased publishing fission results by 1940.

Work on fission was continued quietly at an increasing rate. In June 1942, the Manhattan Project (under U.S. Army direction) was set underway in the United States, with the objective of producing nuclear weapons, if possible. The first chain reaction was produced on December 2, 1942, under the direction of Enrico Fermi, who had arrived from Fascist Italy in January 1939. Fermi and his co-workers had piled up blocks of ordinary uranium and extra-pure graphite (carbon) to produce a nuclear reactor, under Stagg Field Stadium of the University of Chicago. The carbon was used to slow down fission neutrons and thus increase the likelihood of fission. Cadmium rods inserted in the reactor (at that time called a "pile") were used to control the chain reaction by capturing a certain fraction of the neutrons.

Thus, by December 1942, a fission chain reaction had been achieved. In the following years, research vital to the Manhattan Project was carried on at many laboratories. In order to produce the fissionable material for nuclear weapons, two tremendous industrial plants were set up beginning in 1943, at Oak Ridge, Tennessee, and Hanford, Washington.

The Oak Ridge plant was for the purpose of separating the more fissionable isotope, ^{235}U, from the much more common isotope, ^{238}U, which accounted for 99.3 per cent of the mass of ordinary uranium metal. The most successful separation process, which is still in use at Oak Ridge, was that of gaseous diffusion. Uranium in the form of a gas, uranium hexafluoride, is passed through a long series of porous barriers. The lighter isotope ^{235}U can diffuse more readily than ^{238}U, and the result of the process is enriched uranium, the ^{235}U content having been increased from 1 part in 140 to around 95 per cent.

The Hanford plant consists of giant nuclear reactors to produce a new element, plutonium, from ordinary uranium by neutron capture. It was thought, and eventually proved, that plutonium should be fissionable by slow neutrons in the same way as ^{235}U. Capture of a neutron by ^{238}U produces the heavier isotope ^{239}U, which then decays by beta-emission to the new element ^{239}Np (neptunium), and then by another beta-decay to ^{239}Pu.

The work of designing and building nuclear weapons was carried out at a laboratory set up at Los Alamos, New Mexico. This laboratory, under the direction of J. Robert Oppenheimer, began its work in early 1943. Before the end of the war, a good fraction of the world's most eminent nuclear physicists had come to work at Los Alamos, including Bohr, Fermi, Frisch, and many British scientists.

One of their most basic problems was to find a way to assemble the fissionable components of a weapon rapidly enough to produce a powerful chain reaction, lasting less than one μsec. The individual masses of enriched uranium or plutonium had to be of such a size and shape as not to be capable of a chain reaction; i.e., they had to be of less than critical mass. If these pieces were not assembled at sufficient speed, the result would be only a minor explosion, or perhaps the melting of the device. Two approaches were tried. One involved firing one piece of fissionable material at another in a short "gun." The other was the implosion method, in which the fissionable material is assembled into a highly compressed mass by the explosion of a surrounding spherical shell of high explosive.

Both methods of achieving a nuclear explosion were ultimately successful, but it was not known whether either method would work until July 16, 1945, when the first nuclear device ("atomic bomb") was set off in a desert area near Alamogordo, New Mexico. On August 6 a weapon was exploded over Hiroshima, Japan,

and on August 9 another was detonated over Nagasaki. Each weapon had a yield equivalent to about 20 kilotons of high explosive and caused tremendous destruction. On August 10, the Japanese first offered to surrender, and accepted Allied terms on August 15; the mobilization of the massive United States invasion force was called off. Germany, which had surrendered on April 8, 1945, was found to have made little progress toward nuclear weapons during the war.

Following the end of the war, the work on nuclear weapons and nuclear power in the United States were placed under the newly created (1946) Atomic Energy Commission. Similar agencies have since been set up in many countries. On August 29, 1949, the U.S.S.R. detonated its first nuclear device. During the next several years, enormous production plants for ^{235}U were built at Paducah, Kentucky, and Portsmouth, Ohio, as well as facilities for producing ^{239}Pu and hydrogen isotopes on the Savannah River in South Carolina. On November 1, 1952, the Los Alamos Scientific Laboratory exploded the first thermonuclear device ("hydrogen bomb"), with a yield equivalent to many megatons of high explosive. Such a weapon uses nuclear fission to trigger nuclear fusion, in which light elements (such as the various isotopes of hydrogen) are combined at exceedingly high temperature to give heavier nuclei, with considerable release of energy. On August 12, 1953, the Russians set off their first thermonuclear weapon. In the years since then, the British, French, and Chinese have all developed their own nuclear weapons.

Nuclear reactors and nuclear power have been developed extensively since the war, in many countries. Nuclear-powered submarines, aircraft carriers, and other vessels have revolutionized naval strategy. Nuclear-propelled rockets (the "Rover" program at Los Alamos) may soon be used in space exploration. The possible use of nuclear explosives for earth-moving, increasing gas-well yield, and other engineering purposes has been an extensive project ("Plowshare") of the Lawrence Livermore Laboratory, as well as of the Los Alamos Scientific Laboratory. Nuclear power plants are rapidly becoming more economical, and already account for a significant fraction of electrical power production.

Chain Reactions The basic feature which makes both nuclear reactors and nuclear weapons possible is the "chain reaction," in which each fission produces another fission, or several, by means of the several neutrons emitted from fission. If there is not enough fissionable material, or it is not arranged compactly enough, no chain reaction will be possible. The fission neutrons emitted in such a situation will have too great a chance of escaping from the fissionable material, or of being absorbed in non-fissionable material, to continue the chain of fissions should one fission occur.

There is thus a "critical mass," or minimum amount of fissionable material, necessary for a

chain reaction in any given arrangement. For a spherical mass of metal in air, the critical mass of highly enriched (94 per cent) ^{235}U, for instance, is 52 kg; the critical mass for ^{233}U or ^{239}Pu metal is lower, about 16 kg. The critical mass can be lowered by mixing fissionable material with graphite or other material as a "moderator" to slow down the neutrons, or by surrounding the fissionable material with a reflector to scatter neutrons back.

The smallest critical masses are achieved by water (or heavy water) solutions of fissionable material, since H and D are most effective in slowing down neutrons. The "Water-Boiler" thermal reactor at Los Alamos operated ordinarily with about 1100 grams of enriched uranium in water solution, and has gone critical with less than 600 grams.

The energy of the neutrons producing most of the fissions in a reactor determines whether it is called "fast," "intermediate," or "thermal." Fast reactors use neutrons only slightly slowed down from the 2-MeV average energy with which they are emitted. Thermal reactors use neutrons slowed down, by collision with moderator atoms, almost to the velocities corresponding to thermal motion at the temperature of the reactor. At 294 K, about room temperature, the most probable velocity is 2200 meters/sec., which corresponds to a neutron energy of 0.0253 eV. Intermediate reactors use partially slowed down neutrons, with less than 100-keV energy.

In order for a chain reaction to continue, it is necessary that each fission produce, on the average, at least one more fission. The average number of fissions produced by the neutrons from one fission is called k, the criticality factor or multiplication constant. If k is less than 1.0 (the critical value), a chain reaction, even if begun with many fissions, will soon die out.

A reactor must have $k = 1.0$ during normal, steady, operation, and must have k greater than 1.0 during the start-up operation. These changes in criticality factor can be brought about by introducing or removing from the reactor control rods made of neutron-absorbing elements, such as cadmium or boron.

This regulation of reactor power is made much easier by the phenomenon of delayed neutrons, which are emitted from some fission products for a few seconds after the fission. In the case of thermal-neutron fission of ^{235}U, 0.7 per cent of the neutrons produced (0.017 out of 2.43 neutrons per fission) are delayed in this way. Only if k were increased above 1.007 in this case could the reactor power increase rapidly, since each fission would then, on the average, produce one more fission promptly. Reactors are of course designed to avoid this "prompt critical" condition, since this can lead to overheating and destruction of the reactor. In any case, reactors cannot possibly achieve the high values of the criticality factor needed for a true nuclear explosion.

A "breeder" reactor is one which produces as much nuclear fuel as it consumes, as by using the capture of neutrons in ^{238}U to produce thermally fissionable ^{239}Pu. Breeder reactors are now being developed for more efficient power production.

The Fission Process The fission of a nucleus can be understood on the basis of the liquid-drop model, which was first discussed by Meitner and Frisch and later greatly extended by Bohr and Wheeler. This model explains many features of fission, but others are still not fully understood, and the complete theory of fission is still awaited.

On the basis of this model, the nucleus is assumed to be similar to a uniformly charged drop of incompressible liquid. It will then be normally spherical, kept in this shape of minimum energy by the effect of surface tension. However, the individual parts of the positive charge, actually protons, tend to repel each other and to lessen the effective surface tension. It has been calculated that the two effects will cancel each other out for a value of Z^2/A equal to about 45 (Z is the atomic number or the number of protons; A is the mass number or total number of nucleons in the nucleus). The ratio of Z^2/A to this critical value is called the fissionability parameter x.

For a fissionability parameter equal to 1.0, the nucleus should have no effective surface tension and no stability against distortion, so that it should promptly elongate to a point where the coulomb (electrostatic) forces can blow it apart. Such a nucleus would have no "fission barrier" and could not exist long. Known nuclides have lower values of the fissionability parameter; for ^{235}U the value of x is about 0.8. For such nuclei, it takes 5 or 6 MeV of energy to deform the nucleus to the point where coulomb forces can cause fission. However, such a fission barrier may be overcome by the capture of a neutron, which adds an excitation energy of 5 or 6 MeV.

For the even-Z, odd-N nuclides ^{233}U, ^{235}U, and ^{239}Pu (N is the number of neutrons in the nucleus), fission can be induced by the capture of even a low-energy neutron. Even-even target nuclides require more energy, so that ^{238}U is very unlikely to fission upon capture of a thermal neutron, but needs about 1 MeV additional neutron energy to overcome the fission barrier. Even-even *compound* nuclei (i.e., after neutron capture) are evidently more likely to undergo fission. Even-even nuclei are also much more likely to undergo spontaneous fission, in which an occasional nucleus manages to overcome the fission barrier without any added energy. Fission may also be induced by gamma rays of energy equal to the fission barrier or by energetic particles of many kinds such as protons or alpha particles.

The probability that particles passing through a target of fissionable material will induce fission is measured by the fission cross section. The "cross section" is the effective area of a nucleus for a given process. For a thin target of

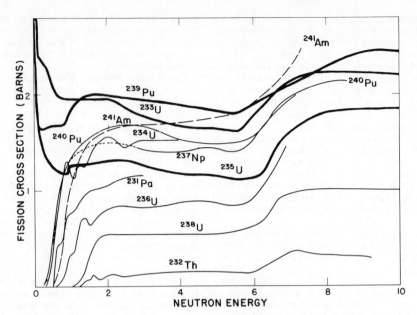

FIG. 1. Dependence of fission cross section (a "barn" is 10^{-24} cm^2) on inducing neutron energy (in MeV) for 11 different fissionable nuclei (reprinted with permission from R. L. Henkel, "Fission by Fast Neutrons," in J. B. Marion and J. L. Fowler, Eds., "Fast Neutron Physics, Part II," New York, Interscience Publishers, 1963).

thickness l cm having n nuclei per cubic centimeter, each with fission cross section σ_f cm^2, the probability that a particle passing through the target will induce a fission is $nl\sigma_f$.

Figure 1 shows the fission cross section for 11 fissionable nuclei, as a function of the energy (in MeV) of the neutron inducing fission. For those nuclides (^{233}U, ^{235}U, ^{239}Pu) which lead to even-even compound nuclei, the cross sections are very high for low-energy neutrons; these are "fissile" nuclides. For the other target nuclides, the fission cross section is extremely small until the neutrons have energy in excess of a threshold energy. All the cross sections may be seen to increase noticeably at about 7 MeV. This increase is due to the added possibility of fission following low-energy neutron emission, which becomes energetically possible here.

The energy released when fission takes place amounts to about 200 MeV. This is the difference in mass between a heavy fissionable nucleus and the two medium-weight nuclei, plus neutrons, into which it breaks up. This energy release of 200 MeV amounts to 21.3 per cent of the mass of a single proton or neutron. Most of the energy appears in the form of kinetic energy of the two fission fragments, which are sent flying apart with an average total of 167 MeV in the case of thermal fission of ^{235}U.

The two fragments share the kinetic energy in the inverse ratio of their masses, since they have equal and opposite momenta. The mass division is usually asymmetrical, as may be seen in Fig. 2. The probability that neutron fission of ^{235}U

will produce two given fragments of nearly equal mass (symmetrical fission) is about 600 times lower than that of the most probable case of asymmetrical division into light and heavy fragments. The initial fragments (before neutron emission) in this case have masses averaging 96 and 140 mass units. The lighter fragment has on the average about 99 MeV of kinetic energy, and the heavy fragment about 68 MeV. These energies correspond to initial velocities of 1.4 and 1.0×10^9 cm/sec, or 4.7 and 3.2 per cent of the speed of light, respectively. The total fragment energy is rather closely given, on the average, by $0.121\, Z^2/A^{1/3}$ MeV.

Such fragment energies are due to the Coulomb interaction between the two fragments, and would be expected on the basis of any fission theory. The asymmetrical mass division, however, would not be predicted by liquid-drop theory and has so far resisted detailed explanation. The liquid-drop model would, in its simplest form, predict primarily symmetrical fission, which is rarely observed.

The fragments, as we have seen, carry away most of the 200-MeV energy release in the form of kinetic energy. The rest of the energy is released in the form of neutron energy, gamma rays, and beta decay. The prompt neutrons, which are emitted within 10^{-14} sec. following fission, will be discussed below. The fission fragments are strong sources of prompt gamma rays, emitting about 8 within a microsecond or less following fission. The gamma rays have a broad spectrum of energies, up to as much as 7 MeV, but they average about 1 MeV apiece, so

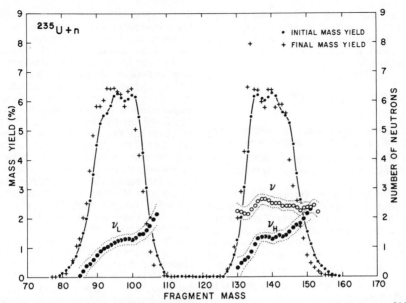

FIG. 2. Dependence of neutron yield on initial fragment mass for thermal-neutron fission of ^{235}U. Average numbers of neutrons emitted by light and heavy fragments are given the symbols ν_L and ν_H; the total from both fragments is ν. Standard deviations are indicated by dotted lines. Also shown are the initial and final mass yields [reprinted from J. Terrell, *Phys. Rev.*, **127**, 880–904 (1962)].

that the total energy emitted in prompt gamma rays is about 8 MeV. This is more than simple theories would predict.

Immediately after the emission of neutrons and prompt gamma rays, the fragments (now called "fission products") begin the process of beta decay, which ultimately accounts for perhaps 22 MeV of fission energy release. The fission products have neutron-to-proton ratios which are nearly the same as that of the heavy nucleus from which they were formed (about 1.55). This is too many neutrons for stability in the fission-product mass region, where non-radioactive nuclei have neutron-proton ratios in the range 1.3 to 1.4. Since there is thus energy to be released by changing neutrons to protons, the result is a long sequence of beta decays averaging 3 or 4 for each fission product. Each beta decay results in the emission of a negative electron, a neutrino, and usually gamma rays, and an increase of the charge of the nucleus by one unit. The neutrinos ultimately carry away about 10 MeV of the energy released, and for all practical purposes this energy is not detectable and is never seen again. The fission products are intensely radioactive immediately after fission, as the beta decays having the shortest half-life are completed, and gradually become less radioactive with the passage of time.

For a small fraction of the fission products it is energetically possible for a neutron to be emitted at some stage in the chain of beta decays. These delayed neutrons, amounting on the average to 0.017 per thermal-neutron fission of ^{235}U, are very useful in stabilizing the opera-

tion of nuclear reactors, as mentioned above. Because they are emitted immediately following beta decays, they appear to follow the same radioactive decay curves as some of the beta decays, and have varying half-lives, of the order of seconds.

In rarer cases—about one fission out of 400—an alpha particle (^{4}He) is emitted during the fission process, in addition to the two fragments. This process is usually called ternary fission, as distinguished from the usual binary fission. Because of the high energy (averaging 15 MeV) and direction (roughly perpendicular to fragment motion) of the alpha particle, it is probably formed at the same time as the two heavier fragments, and between them. In still rarer cases, other light charged particles such as nuclei of tritium (^{3}H) or of ^{6}He are seen. There seems even to be evidence that, in perhaps one fission out of 100 000, three fragments of roughly equal mass are formed.

In the vast majority of fissions, however, two fragments and several neutrons are the result. For low-energy fission it is clear that most, or perhaps all, of the neutrons are emitted by the fragments. The average number of neutrons per fission ($\bar{\nu}$) ranges from 2.0 to 4.0 for various nuclides. Fission at high energies, such as that induced by 100-MeV alpha particles, produces many more neutrons, most of which are emitted before fission.

In the typical case of thermal-neutron fission of ^{235}U, $\bar{\nu}$ is 2.43, including delayed neutrons. For individual fissions the number ν can vary from zero to 5 or 6, the standard deviation

from the average being ±1.10. The prompt neutrons in this case have an average energy of 1.94 MeV. The neutron energy spectrum in this and other cases is well described by a Maxwellian distribution,

$$N(E) = (2/\sqrt{\pi T^3}) \sqrt{E} e^{-E/T}$$

in which $N(E)$ is the number of neutrons per unit energy E, and T is a parameter equal to two-thirds of the average energy $\bar{E}$. Such a spectrum is predicted from nuclear temperature theory.

Of the roughly 2-MeV average energy per neutron, about 0.75 MeV is contributed by the motion of the emitting fragments. There is evidence that the average neutron energy increases with increasing number of neutrons. This would be expected from considerations of nuclear temperature, which lead to the relation $\bar{E} = 0.75 + 0.65 \sqrt{\bar{\nu} + 1}$, in MeV, in agreement with experimental data.

The total kinetic energy carried away by the typical 2 or 3 neutrons per fission is thus about 5 MeV, of which 2 MeV is taken from fragment energy. The fragments after neutron emission thus have a total energy reduced (in the case of ^{235}U) from 167 to 165 MeV, and lower mass numbers.

The final fragment masses may be determined by radiochemical data on fission products. The final mass yields for ^{235}U are shown in Fig. 2, as crosses. The initial mass yields may be determined from simultaneous measurement of the velocities of the two fragments and are also shown in the Figure. The differences between initial and final mass yields are accounted for by emission of neutrons and may be used to determine the numbers of neutrons. The average numbers of neutrons emitted by individual fragments are shown (ν_L and ν_H) as functions of fragment mass; the total $\nu(= \nu_L + \nu_H)$ is also shown.

As may be seen in Fig. 2, the average number of neutrons emitted by a fission fragment depends strongly on the fragment mass; it is near zero for the lightest of the light fragments, and also for the lightest of the heavy fragments, and rises to high values elsewhere. Thus the two fragments from a fission will usually emit quite different numbers of neutrons, which implies quite different initial excitation energies. This phenomenon came as quite a surprise when it was first reported by Fraser and Milton in 1954. It has since been found to be a common and perhaps universal feature of fission.

It seems now that this "sawtooth" dependence of neutron number on fragment mass may be understood on the basis of varying stiffness of the fragments against deformation. The fragments having "magic" numbers of neutrons or protons would be expected to be stiff and to be exceptionally resistant to deformation and the consequent excitation. The magic number of neutrons, $N = 50$, will occur for fragments in the vicinity of mass 82, at the lower boundary of the light fragment peak. Similarly, two magic numbers ($Z = 50$ and $N = 82$) occur at the lower edge of the heavy fragment peak, near mass 130. The low neutron yields seen at these magic-number positions may be quantitatively explained on the basis of the effects of magic numbers on the deformation parameters. It is hoped that this "fragment deformation" theory will be able to account quantitatively for the little-understood spectrum of fragment masses, since the mass yields and neutron yields tend to vanish near the same magic numbers.

Fission isomers have been of much interest recently. These are excited states of fissionable nuclides, produced by bombardment with energetic particles or nuclei, which exist for times of the order of 10^{-2} to 10^{-9} seconds before fissioning. Such quasi-stable states, lying a few MeV above the unexcited ground states, are believed to be "shape isomers" explainable by a double-humped fission barrier, for which there is other evidence in the intermediate structure of resonances in the fission cross sections. Such a fission barrier has a minimum at some deformation in the energy required to deform the nucleus from the ground state. It is thought now that all fission barriers have such a double-humped structure, explained in terms of variation of magic numbers with deformation.

JAMES TERRELL

References

Fraser, J. S., and Milton, J. C. D., "Nuclear Fission," *Ann. Rev. Nuclear Sci.*, **16**, 379–444, 1966.

Gindler, J. E., and Huizenga, J. R., "Nuclear Fission," Chapter 7 in "Nuclear Chemistry," Vol. II, New York, Academic Press, 1968.

Glasstone, S., and Sesonske, A., "Nuclear Reactor Engineering," New York, Van Nostrand Reinhold, 1963.

Glasstone, S., Ed., "The Effects of Nuclear Weapons," revised edition, U.S.A.E.C., U.S. Government Printing Office, 1964; especially Chapter 1.

Hyde, E. K., "The Nuclear Properties of the Heavy Elements III: Fission Phenomena," Englewood Cliffs, N.J., Prentice-Hall, Inc., 1964.

I.A.E.A., "Physics and Chemistry of Fission," Proceedings of the Second I.A.E.A. Symposium, Vienna, I.A.E.A., 1969.

Keepin, G. R., "Physics of Nuclear Kinetics," Reading, Mass., Addison-Wesley Publishing Co., 1965.

Terrell, J., "Prompt Neutrons from Fission," in Proceedings of the I.A.E.A. Symposium on the Physics and Chemistry of Fission; I.A.E.A., Vienna (1965).

Cross-references: ATOMIC ENERGY, FUSION, NUCLEAR RADIATION, NUCLEAR STRUCTURE, NUCLEONICS.

FLIGHT PROPULSION FUNDAMENTALS

Propulsion is not a science in itself, and has no unique basic principles of its own. The fundamentals of propulsion really are selected from the basic laws of MECHANICS, THERMODYNAMICS, and CHEMISTRY; certain special types of propulsion require also some principles of ELECTRICITY or NUCLEONICS.

Propulsion is defined here as the act of changing the natural state of motion of a vehicle flying in air or in space. Thus a propulsion mechanism applies a force to a flying body and so changes the momentum of the body, or, in the case of maintaining steady, level equilibrium flight, the force of propulsion overcomes or equals the atmospheric drag. To propel a vehicle, it is necessary to accelerate another mass (usually a gaseous fluid) in the opposite direction. Hence, not only Newton's basic laws of motion, but also the conservation of momentum (change of momentum of vehicle equals change of momentum of ejected high-velocity masses) and the perfect gas laws are important here (see CONSERVATION LAWS AND SYMMETRY and IMPULSE AND MOMENTUM).

The acceleration of a *gaseous working fluid* (often called propellant) to high exhaust velocities requires the supply and expenditure of energy. Thus, it is possible to classify flight propulsion systems according to their energy sources and the types of propellants (see Table 1). The device which creates and/or converts the energy into the form which is useful for propulsion is called an *engine*. It is the purpose of this section to summarize some of the most important propulsion relationships and to describe briefly the principal engine types.

Fundamental Relations Assume an ideal engine inside of which the fluid receives energy and is heated and accelerated as shown schematically in Fig. 1. The acceleration of a mass

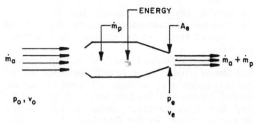

FIG. 1. Simple engine.

flow of air or fluid $\dot{m}_a$ from an initial velocity v_0 (which equals the forward flight velocity of of the vehicle) to the jet velocity at the exit v_e will result in a net thrust F, which is equal to the mass flow rate multiplied by the velocity increment. Additional terms are added to this momentum relation in order to correct for the additional mass flow rate of the fuel or propellant ($\dot{m}_p$) (the fuel is carried in the vehicle) and for any difference in static pressure of the jet exit of the engine (p_e) and the atmospheric or ambient pressure p_0.

$$F = \dot{m}_a(v_e - v_0) + \dot{m}_p v_e + A_e(p_e - p_0)$$

The last term in this equation is called the pressure thrust; it is positive if $p_e > p_0$ (which occurs when there is incomplete expansion of the gases in the engine exit nozzle) or negative if $p_e < p_0$ (which occurs when there is over-expansion in the engine exit nozzle). For a rocket engine, the air mass flow $m_a = 0$, and the thrust is equal to the last two terms of the equation only. In the case of a propeller engine, there are really two different air flows, and the first term in the above equation is split into two separate terms: one flow which crosses the plane of the propeller and is accelerated by the propeller blades and a second smaller airflow which goes through the engine

TABLE 1. ENERGY SOURCES AND PROPELLANT TYPES FOR SEVERAL DIFFERENT PROPULSION ENGINES

Type of Propellant	Type of Energy Source		
	Chemical	Nuclear	Solar
Surrounding medium used as working fluid	Aircraft piston engine with propeller	Nuclear turbojet Nuclear ramjet Nuclear submarine with propeller	−
Surrounding medium plus stored propellant or fuel	Turbojet Ramjet Ducted rocket	Nuclear turbojet with afterburning of chemical fuel	−
Propellant stored within vehicle	Liquid and/or solid propellant rocket Chemical battery with electric propulsion	Nuclear H_2 fission rocket Nuclear reactor power source with electrical propulsion	Solar heated hydrogen rocket
No propellant expelled	−	Future photon rocket	Solar sail

to furnish oxygen for combustion. In the case of a nuclear reactor energy source, $\dot{m}_p = 0$ and the second term can be omitted. In a vacuum $p_0 = 0$.

Consider a winged vehicle in equilibrium rectilinear flight in a two-dimensional (fixed plane) trajectory; assume all control forces, lateral forces and turning moments to be zero and the flight direction to be the same as the thrust direction. In the direction of the flight, the instantaneous vehicle mass m_v times the vehicle acceleration dv/dt has to equal the sum of all the forces, namely a component of the thrust F, the aerodynamic drag D, and a component of the gravitational attraction or the weight $m_v g$. The angles are as defined in Fig. 2.

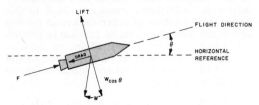

FIG. 2. Simple free body diagram of flying vehicle.

$$m_v \, dv/dt = F - D - m_v g \sin \theta \qquad (2)$$

The vehicle mass m_v multiplied by the acceleration in a direction perpendicular to the flight path $(v \, d\theta/dt)$ must equal the sum of all forces perpendicular to the flight direction; here, the lift force L must be considered.

$$m_v v \frac{d\theta}{dt} = L - m_v g \cos \theta \qquad (3)$$

The solution to these two equations results in the determination of a two-dimensional trajectory, maximum flight velocity, range, and other flight performance parameters. The actual solution is three-dimensional, and must usually be a numerical integration since m_v decreases with time, L and D vary with speed and altitude, and the direction of thrust is not the same as the flight direction; also, both the flight angle and the angle of attack are usually changing. For the case of a linear, simplified horizontal equilibrium flight, $\theta = 0$, $dv/dt = 0$, and thus Eq. (2) reduces to $F = D$. The vehicle mass m_v consists of the vehicle dry mass or final vehicle mass after expenditure of all propellant $(m_v)_f$ plus the propellant or fuel mass m_p. For steady fuel flow, $m_p = \dot{m}_p t$. For the case of gravity-free flight in a vacuum (true space environment), Eq. (1) can be rewritten for a rocket:

$$\frac{dv}{dt} = \frac{F}{m_v} = \frac{\dot{m}_p v_e}{(m_v)_f + \dot{m}_p t}$$

Integration gives

$$v_v = -v_e \ln \frac{m_v - m_p}{m_v} = v_e \ln \frac{(m_v)_i}{(m_v)_f}$$

Thus the maximum velocity attained by a rocket-space vehicle operating in a gravitationless vacuum is equal to the product of the average effective rocket exhaust velocity v_e and a logarithmic function of the initial vehicle mass $(m_v)_i = (m_v)_f + m_p$ (fully fueled vehicle) at start of the engine operation, divided by the final vehicle mass (with all the fuel expanded) $(m_v)_f$ at the end of engine operation. This velocity v_v will be large when v_e is large, i.e., high energy is available from the propellant or the engine and when $(m_v)_i$ is small, i.e., when the dry mass of the vehicle (dry engine mass, tanks, payload, or structure) is small and no unnecessary mass is designed into the vehicle. This means that m_p is large and the initial vehicle mass $(m_v)_i$ consists largely of propellant.

The *specific impulse* of an engine can be defined as the thrust force obtained from a unit propellant weight flow.

$$I_s = \frac{F}{\dot{w}} = \frac{F}{\dot{m}g} \text{ (kg force/kg mass per second)}$$

Since the propellant usually refers to the fuel stored in the vehicle and not to the air flow, the values of I_s for air-breathing engines are generally very high.

The *specific fuel consumption* (sfc) is usually expressed as the fuel flow rate (pounds per hour) per engine shaft brake horsepower. Both of these parameters are an indication of the quality of design and operation of an engine; a high value of I_s or a low value of (sfc) indicates efficient use of propellant or fuel.

Some of the most significant types of engines are described briefly in the remainder of this section.

Rocket Engines These engines use both a fuel and oxidizing propellant and both are stored within the flying vehicle, making it independent from its surrounding fluid. Thus a rocket can operate in space, air, or under water. The supersonic nozzle jet exit velocity v_e of a rocket using ideal gas laws can be derived to be

$$v_e = \sqrt{\frac{2gkR}{(k-1)} \frac{T}{M} \left[1 - \left(\frac{p_e}{p_c} \right)^{(k-1)/k} \right]}$$

where

v_e = nozzle exit velocity
g = gravitational constant
k = ratio of specific heats of gas
R = universal gas constant
M = molecular weight of hot gas
T = absolute combustion temperature
p_e = nozzle exit gas pressure
p_c = combustion chamber pressure.

The exhaust velocity (or the specific impulse which is $I_s = v_e/g$) increases as the molecular weight M is decreased or as the combustion temperature T is increased. Because of the pressure ratio effect, there is actually a slight (10 to 20 per cent) increase in specific impulse as the

altitude is increased (lower ambient pressure) or as chamber pressure is increased. Air-breathing engines, in comparison, lose specific impulse with altitude. Values of v_e or I_s calculated for a given propellant and engine from thermochemical and thermodynamic data are usually very close to actual performance (usually within 5 to 10 per cent), because rocket combustion efficiencies are usually high and nozzle losses are usually low. Schematic diagrams of several liquid and solid propellant systems are shown in Figs. 3 to 7, and some important applications are shown in Table 2.

In *liquid propellant rocket engines* the propellants are fed under pressure from tanks in the vehicle into a thrust chamber where they are injected, mixed, and burned at high pressures and very high temperatures to form the gaseous reaction products, which in turn, are accelerated in a nozzle and ejected at high velocities. The feed system for transferring the propellants into the thrust chamber includes valves and controls.

The principal components of a *thrust chamber* (Figs. 3 and 4) are the *nozzle*, the *chamber*, and the *injector*. An injector introduces and meters the flow of the liquid propellants and also atomizes and mixes them in the correct proportions in such a manner that they can be readily vaporized and burned. In the combustion chamber, the burning of the liquid propellant takes place at high pressure, usually between 5 and 150 atmospheres.

The *gas pressure feed system* (Fig. 3) offers one of the simplest and most common means of transferring propellants by displacing them with a high-pressure gas which is fed into the tanks under a regulated pressure. In a *turbopump feed system*, the propellant is pressurized by means of pumps driven by one or more turbines (Fig. 4) which derive their power from the expansion of hot gases. A separate gas generator ordinarily produces these gases in the required quantities and at a temperature which

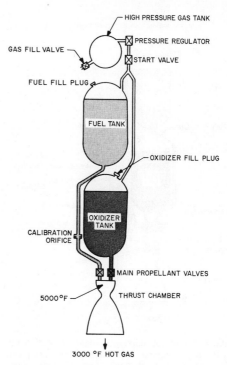

FIG. 3. Simplified schematic diagram of liquid propellant rocket engine with pressurized gas feed system and uncooled thrust chamber (reproduced by permission from McGraw-Hill Encyclopedia of Science and Technology, Vol. II, New York, McGraw-Hill Book Co.)

will not hurt the turbine buckets (1200 to 2000°F).

Liquid Propellants. A *bipropellant rocket* unit has two separate propellants, a fuel and an oxidizer (such as kerosene and liquid oxygen), which are not mixed until they come in contact with each other in the combustion cham-

TABLE 2. TYPICAL DATA FOR VARIOUS ROCKET ENGINES

Type	Typical Range of Thrusts (lbs)	Typical Range of Duration	Application
High thrust liquid propellant rocket	1 000 000 to 4 000 000 for each engine with several engines in a cluster	1 to 5 min	Booster and sustainer stages of large missiles and space vehicles
Large solid propellant rocket	5 000 to 3 000 000	1 to 60 sec	Large and small missiles (surface to surface, surface to air, air to surface)
Prepackaged storable liquid propellant	100 to 100 000	1 to 60 sec	Special applications of small missiles, lunar landing and takeoff
Jet assisted takeoff (solid propellant)	200 to 10 000	5 to 30 sec	Assist takeoff of airplanes
Space vehicle attitude control	1 to 150	0.01 to 10 sec/cycle; accumulate up to an hour	Control position, angle and orientation of spacecraft

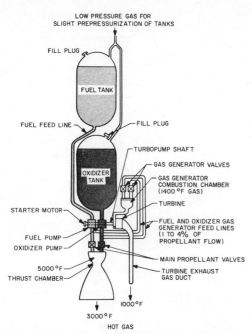

LOW PRESSURE GAS FOR
SLIGHT PREPRESSURIZATION OF TANKS

FILL PLUG

FUEL TANK

FUEL FEED LINE — FILL PLUG

TURBOPUMP SHAFT

GAS GENERATOR VALVES

OXIDIZER TANK

GAS GENERATOR
COMBUSTION CHAMBER
(1400°F GAS)

TURBINE

STARTER MOTOR

FUEL AND OXIDIZER GAS
GENERATOR FEED LINES
(1 TO 4% OF
PROPELLANT FLOW)

FUEL PUMP
OXIDIZER PUMP

MAIN PROPELLANT VALVES

5000°F
THRUST CHAMBER

TURBINE EXHAUST
GAS DUCT

1000°F

3000°F

HOT GAS

FIG. 4. Simplified schematic diagram of liquid propellant rocket engine with turbopump feed system and regeneratively cooled thrust chamber (reproduced by permission from McGraw-Hill Encyclopedia of Science and Technology, Vol. II, New York, McGraw-Hill Book Co.)

ber. Most liquid propellant rockets have been of this bipropellant type. A *monopropellant* contains oxidizing agent and combustible matter in a single substance. It can be a mixture of compounds, such as hydrogen peroxide with liquid alcohol, or it may be a homogeneous chemical agent, such as nitromethane. Certain types of liquid fuels and oxidizers are self-igniting and start burning when they come in contact with each other. Other types of propellants, for example, oxygen and alcohol, are not spontaneously ignitable, but require an igniter to furnish thermal energy for starting their combustion reaction. Typical values for liquid and solid propellants are given in Table 3.

Solid Propellants. In a *solid propellant rocket engine* all the propellant is contained within the combustion chamber. The hardware includes, in addition to the combustion chamber nozzle, an igniter and provisions for mounting the rocket (Figs. 6 and 7). Solid propellants themselves usually have a plastic, cakelike appearance (specific gravity is approximately 1.6) and burn at high pressure (10 to 150 atmospheres) on their exposed surfaces to form hot exhaust gases which are ejected through the nozzle. The physical mass or body of the propellant is called the *grain*. In some rockets, there is more than one grain inside the same combustion chamber.

The solid propellant grain contains all the material necessary for sustaining combustion. It can be a mixture of several chemicals, e.g.,

FIG. 5. F-1 rocket engine used in booster stage of advanced Saturn space vehicle.
(Courtesy of Rocketdyne, A Division of North American Aviation, Inc.)

TABLE 3. TYPICAL PERFORMANCE OF SEVERAL CHEMICAL ROCKET PROPELLANTS

Propellant	Theoretical Thrust Chamber Specific Impulse at 500 psi Chamber Pressure, sec.		Bulk Specific Gravity lb/ft³	Optimum Mixture Ratio (Oxidizer–Fuel)	Combustion Temperature, F	Molecular Weight of Exhaust Gas lb/mole	Burning Rate in/sec
	At Sea Level, Area Ratio = 8	In Vacuum, Area Ratio = 25					
Cryogenic Liquid							
Oxygen and kerosene	261	324	63	2.25	5800	22	
Oxygen and 92.5% ethyl alcohol	249	311	61	1.5	5370	23	
High Energy Liquid							
Fluorine and hydrogen	364	447	19	4.0	4700	9	
Fluorine and hydrazine	303	372	80	1.75	7300	18	
Oxygen and hydrogen	358	440	8	4.0	4500	8	
Storable Liquid							
Nitric acid and dimethyl hydrazine	246	304	76	2.4	5100	22	
90% hydrogen peroxide and kerosene			79	7.0	4600	22	
Monopropellant (Liquid)							
90% hydrogen peroxide and hydrazine	137	167	87	0	1365 1800	21	
Solid							
Double base solid	190–250	235 to 315	100	—	3000–5000	24	.2 to .9
Composite perchlorate	180–250	220 to 315	100	—	3000–5000	24	.1 to .8
Nitrate composite	175–210	210 to 255	100	—	2400–3000	21	.03 to .15

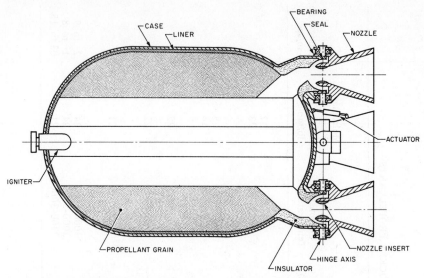

FIG. 6. Simplified schematic diagram of solid propellant rocket engine (reproduced by permission from G. P. Sutton, "Rocket Propulsion Elements," Third edition, New York, J. Wiley & Sons, Inc., 1963).

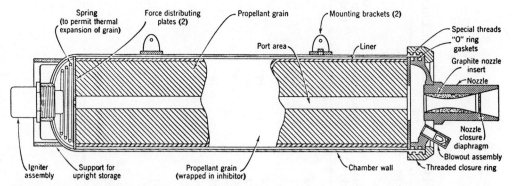

FIG. 7. Solid propellant rocket (reproduced by permission from G. P. Sutton, "Rocket Propulsion Elements," Third edition, New York, J. Wiley & Sons, Inc., 1963).

a mixture of ammonium perchlorate in a matrix of organic polymeric fuel such as rubber. Or it can be a homogeneous charge of special oxidizing organic chemicals such as nitrocellulose or nitroglycerine. Once the propellant is ignited, the grain burns smoothly on all of its exposed surfaces in a direction normal to the burning surface.

Compared to liquid propellant, the solid propellant requires no pump or pressurization for the fuel tank, and hence is mechanically simpler. The combustion chamber with solid propellant is larger, especially for large rockets, and is frequently operated at higher pressure than for a liquid engine. Solid rockets are simpler, more storable, and are usually more immediately ready for use, but are generally lower in performance when compared to liquid propellant units.

Most solid propellant grains are somewhat sensitive to variations in the ambient temperature and have a tendency to become soft on very hot days or brittle on very cold days; for certain propellants, therefore, it is necessary to restrict the temperature range over which they may operate. If the propellant should crack from too great a temperature variation (which induces thermal stresses) or from rough handling, additional burning surfaces would be created in the cracks and an unregulated increase in the pressure would cause failure of the chamber.

There is a maximum pressure above which smooth combustion can no longer be sustained and detonations may occur, and a minimum pressure below which stable, consistently smooth burning does not seem possible. Because of the active nature of the chemicals, some propellants deteriorate in storage. This can often be prevented by the addition of chemical stabilizers or inhibitors to the propellant.

In addition to producing a thrust force, solid and liquid propellant engines can be used also for producing auxiliary power and control torques to be applied to the vehicle. This latter is called *thrust vector control* and basically it is usually a mechanical means for altering the direction of the engine's thrust during flight.

Air-breathing Engines As shown by Figs. 8 to 11, there exists a variety of different types of air-breathing propulsion engines. The range of performance values shown in Table 4 for different types of air-breathing engines is representative and does not correspond to data for specific engines. Each engine is optimized for a specific flight operating condition of speed (Mach number) and altitude. For example the turbojet engine listed in Table 4 for a specific fuel consumption of 1 pound of thrust per pound of fuel flow at a Mach number of $M = 0.8$, is a different engine from the one operating at $M = 3.0$ with a fuel consumption of 1.5; also it operates at different altitudes.

In an aircraft or missile engine, the atmospheric air is usually first compressed (by a mechanical rotary compressor or by a diffuser); then heated by burning with fuel; sometimes sent through a turbine (which provides the rotary power for driving the compressor and accessories, such as electrical generators or hydraulic pumps); and then ejected at high velocities (usually supersonic) through a nozzle. The process in air-breathing engines approaches an ideal thermodynamic cycle (such as the Otto cycle for reciprocating engines or the Brayton cycle for a turbojet) which limits their maximum theoretical efficiency. The inlet duct serves to scoop up the desired air mass flow and to convert some of the kinetic energy of the flow into pressure, thus reducing the velocity. After heating the flow in a combustion chamber, the reverse process occurs adiabatically in the nozzle, where it is desired to attain a maximum exhaust velocity. The efficiency of energy conversion in the inlet duct, nozzle, combustors, compressors, and turbines is a very

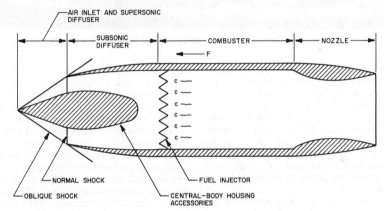

FIG. 8. Simplified schematic diagram of ram jet (reproduced by permission from H. H. Koelle, "Handbook of Astronautical Engineering," New York, McGraw-Hill Book Co., 1961).

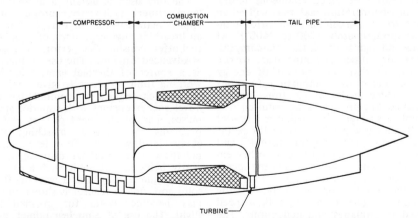

FIG. 9. Simplified schematic diagram of turbojet (reproduced by permission from H. H. Koelle, "Handbook of Astronautical Engineering," New York, McGraw-Hill Book Co., 1961).

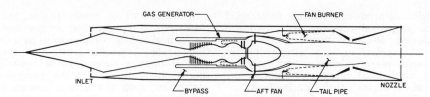

FIG. 10. Simplified Schematic diagram of advanced turbojet with bypass (reproduced by permission from H. H. Koelle, "Handbook of Astronautical Engineering," New York, McGraw-Hill Book Co., 1961).

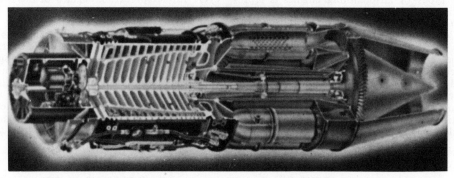

FIG. 11. Photo of J-47 turbojet engine. (Courtesy of General Electric Company.)

important factor, and becomes a predominant criterion at supersonic and hypersonic velocities, when compression is achieved usually by a series of oblique shock waves commencing at an inlet spike. To maintain good efficiency and the desired airflow, some diffusers and nozzles incorporate a variable wall contour or cross-section geometry. In general, air-breathing engines have been well developed to a high state of reliability and have given millions of hours of good service.

The available oxygen from the air limits the combustion process. For example, at constant flight speed, the thrust thus decreases with altitude (or oxygen density) and below a combustion pressure of approximately 3 psi, combustion is not easily sustained (flameout limit). Available high-temperature materials will set an upper limit to the maximum combustion temperature at approximately 1700 to 2400°F. At high speeds and high altitude, the ram-compression of the air causes its temperature to rise substantially, so that the amount of energy that can be added by combustion (without damaging turbine materials) is thus limited; also, special cooling provisions are required.

The simplest air-breathing engine is a *ramjet* (Fig. 8). It does not produce static thrust (at zero flight speed, such as during takeoff) and thus needs a rocket engine or some other engine to bring it to its minimum operating speed.

The *reciprocating piston engine with a propeller* was the very first engine to fly. It is the most economic engine for subsonic flight speed and is used in airplanes and helicopters. The hot gases do work against a piston (not a turbine), which in turn requires a crank mechanism to convert the reciprocating piston motion into shaft rotation. The use of a variable pitch propeller and superchargers for precompression of of the inlet air further increases the economy.

The *turbojet* (Figs. 9 and 11) can be designed for a variety of speeds, altitudes and thrust ranges. It often includes special design features such as afterburners (increases the thrust) or bypass duct arrangements with and without a separate compressor called the fan (this improves the fuel economy over certain performance ranges of speed and altitude). This may also include a secondary set of combustion chambers which add heat to the bypass air. An advanced bypass turbojet is shown in Fig. 10.

The *fuel* used is usually a narrow-cut petroleum refinery hydrocarbon product, having the approximate formula of $CH_{1.95}$. For advanced air-breathing engines, the use of liquid hydrogen fuel offers considerable performance gains.

Advanced Engines The use of nuclear fission as a source of thermal energy for heating a working fluid promises to give ramjets, turbojets (which require no combustible fuel) and novel rocket engines with superior specific impulses. The development of such engines faces problems in materials, matching of reactor energy level with the flow level, shielding of radiation, and afterheat disposal, and is currently being investigated. Such a rocket engine using liquid hydrogen as a working fluid and a solid core fission reactor is shown in Fig. 12; it may become useful for manned planetary flight. The use of a nuclear ramjet, now being experimentally investigated, will permit the

TABLE 4. TYPICAL DATA FOR AIR-BREATHING ENGINES

Engine Type	Flight Speed (mph)	Altitude (feet)	Cruise Specific Fuel Consumption or Specific Thrust	Thrust to Weight or Power to Wt. Ratio	Typical Applications
Reciprocating piston engine with propeller	0–400 mph	0–40 000	0.37 to 0.52 lb/hp-hr	1.0 to 2.0	Transport aircraft Small airplanes Helicopters Target drones
Turbojet	0–2500	0–100 000	1.0 lb/lb–hr at M = 0.8 1.5 lb/lb–hr at M = 3.0	0.8 to 5.0 (100 to 400% increase with afterburner)	Bomber Fighter Transport aircraft Target drones
Turboprop	0–550	0–50 000	0.8 lb/hp–hr at M = 0.6 0.25 lb/hp–hr at M = 0	2.0	Fast transport aircraft Small airplanes Helicopters
Ramjet	700 to 4200	0–120 000	1.5 lb/lb–hr at M = 2 2.0 lb/lb–hr at M = 6	up to 20.0	Target drones Anti-aircraft missiles

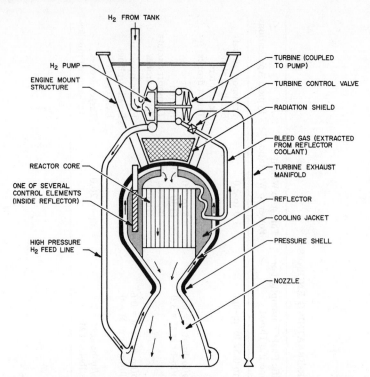

H₂ FROM TANK

H₂ PUMP

ENGINE MOUNT
STRUCTURE

REACTOR CORE

ONE OF SEVERAL
CONTROL ELEMENTS
(INSIDE REFLECTOR)

HIGH PRESSURE
H₂ FEED LINE

TURBINE (COUPLED
TO PUMP)

TURBINE CONTROL VALVE

RADIATION SHIELD

BLEED GAS (EXTRACTED
FROM REFLECTOR
COOLANT)

TURBINE EXHAUST
MANIFOLD

REFLECTOR

COOLING JACKET

PRESSURE SHELL

NOZZLE

FIG. 12. Simplified schematic diagram of nuclear rocket with a solid core fission reactor (reproduced by permission from G. P. Sutton, "Rocket Propulsion Elements," Third edition, New York, J. Wiley & Sons, Inc., 1963).

eventual development of aircraft with theoretically unlimited endurance.

Fusion reactions may someday allow the development of a second type of nuclear engine. They avoid undesirable by-products and could release their energy directly to the working fluid. However, techniques for controlled fusion are yet to be developed.

The use of electrical energy offers further potential increases in rocket engine performance. Electrical propulsion units are discussed separately in ELECTRIC PROPOLSION.

Photon Propulsion. Solar sail engines rely on the reflection of photons from the sun (radiation pressure at the distance of the earth from the sun is about 5×10^{-7} kg/m²). Although this force is limited by being directed only "away" from the sun, solar "sailing" can provide low thrusts, and attitude control, turning a spaceship completely around in a few hours. No working fluid is carried in the vehicle.

For the vehicle to carry its own light source, a photon rocket engine of adequate thrust would necessitate energies and techniques far beyond present capabilities.

G. P. SUTTON

References

1. Koelle, H. H., "Handbook of Astronautical Engineering," New York, McGraw-Hill Book Co., 1961.

2. Sutton, G. P., "Rocket Propulsion Elements," Third edition, New York, J. Wiley & Sons, 1963.

3. Morgan, H. E., "Turbojet Fundamentals," Second edition, New York, McGraw-Hill Book Co., 1958.

Cross-references: AERODYNAMICS; ASTRODYNAMICS; ASTRONAUTICS, PHYSICS OF; DYNAMICS; ELECTRIC PROPULSION; IMPULSE AND MOMENTUM; MECHANICS.

FLUID DYNAMICS

Fluid dynamics is study of the motion of matter in the gas, liquid, plastic or plasma state. When restricted to flow of incompressible (i.e., constant density) fluids, it is called *hydrodynamics;* when dealing with electrically conducting fluids with magnetic fields present, it is called *magneto-fluid dynamics;* when dealing with practical problems of air flow past airplane wings, through ventilating equipment, etc., it is called *aerodynamics.*

Basically two fundamental approaches are employed: (1) continuum or field dynamics and (2) kinetic theory and nonequilibrium statistical mechanics.

In continuum dynamics, fluid properties—namely, velocity u_i, density ρ, pressure p (more generally stress), temperature T, viscosity, conductivity, etc.—are assumed to be physically meaningful functions of three spatial variables

x_1, x_2, x_3 and time t. Two of the four basic equations relating these continuum variables (no electrical current, linear relation between residual stress and rate of strain with viscosity coefficients μ and η') are:

Continuity

$$\frac{\partial(\rho u_i)}{\partial x_i} + \frac{\partial \rho}{\partial t} = 0$$

Motion

$$\rho \frac{\partial u_i}{\partial t} + \rho u_j \frac{\partial u_i}{\partial x_j} = -\frac{\partial p}{\partial x_i} + \eta' \frac{\partial^2 u_k}{\partial x_i \partial x_k}$$

$$+ \mu \frac{\partial}{\partial x_j}\left(\frac{\partial u_i}{\partial x_j} + \frac{\partial u_j}{\partial x_i}\right) + \frac{\partial u_k}{\partial x_k}\frac{\partial \eta'}{\partial x_i}$$

$$+ \frac{\partial u_i}{\partial x_j}\frac{\partial \mu}{\partial x_j} + \frac{\partial u_j}{\partial x_i}\frac{\partial \mu}{\partial x_j}$$

In the above equations, the index notation used for subscripts is that i, j, k may be 1, 2 or 3 representing components of vectors along axes 1, 2 or 3, respectively, and in any term where an index occurs twice, a sum over products is implied. Two additional equations expressing the heat transfer and viscous transfer of energy in forms involving statements of the first and second laws of thermodynamics and the equation of state of the material are required. The four equations, together with boundary conditions, constitute formally a complete set of equations determining p, T, ρ and u_i. For complete discussion and additional equations pertaining to the more general case, see reference 1.

These partial differential equations are nonlinear and have no general solutions even for the most restrictive boundary conditions. Solutions are carried out for very idealized flows. Examples of particular solutions for selected geometrical boundaries are given below.

In Fig. 1, the special flow called Couette flow is indicated schematically. The flow is between parallel plates, lower plate at $y = 0$ at rest, upper plate at y_B moving with constant speed u_B in the x direction. Stress throughout the fluid is constant, given by $P_{xy} = \mu(du/dy) = \mu(u_B/y_B)$. This is pure shear flow and experimentally is often considered to define and measure the viscosity coefficient μ assumed constant for the homogeneous fluid. The velocity profile appearing at the right in the figure shows by velocity arrows of different length at the various positions y how the velocity varies with

position. Steady flow (no dependence of any quantity on time), constant pressure, constant density and laminar flow are additional assumptions for Couette Flow. The flow is realized experimentally by confining the fluid in the narrow annulus between rotating concentric cylinders of nearly equal radius; the cylinders rotate at different speeds.

In Fig. 2, the special flow is in a pipe of uniform cross section, pressure is assumed to be constant across each cross section but to vary linearly with distance x along axis of pipe so $dp/dx = (p_1 - p_2)/L$. Pistons driving the flow are assumed to be infinitely far away, so that the flow velocity, parallel to pipe axis, has the same dependence upon y and z for all x. The velocity profile is parabolic in both the two-dimensional case (infinite parallel plates) and in the circular cross-section case. Mean flow velocity u_m and viscosity coefficient μ are assumed constant; the flow is assumed steady and laminar. For a circular cross-section pipe of radius a, at any distance r from the center, $u = 2u_m(1 - r^2/a^2)$, and the volume passing a cross section per second is $Q = \pi a^2 u_m = \pi a^4(p_1 - p_2)/8\mu L$. Since these formulas do not apply near pipe entrances, caution in applying them to pipes of finite length is necessary even when the flow is steady and laminar. (See later discussion of turbulent and laminar flows.)

Other examples of idealized solutions are one-dimensional flow of an ideal gas through a normal shock wave, flow of an ideal gas without viscosity through a pipe of slowly changing cross section (wind tunnel), and one-dimensional finite waves in an ideal gas. Many other solutions involve making whatever approximations and assumptions are necessary to obtain descriptions of observed flows.

In kinetic theory and nonequilibrium statistical mechanics, fluid properties are associated with averages of properties of microscopic entities. Density, for example, is the average number of molecules per unit volume times the mass per molecule. While much of molecular theory in fluid dynamics aims to interpret processes already adequately described by the continuum approach, additional properties and processes are presented. The distribution of molecular velocities (i.e., how many molecules have each particular velocity), time-dependent adjustments of internal molecular motions, and momentum and energy transfer processes at boundaries are examples.

When motion of the fluid consists of only small fluctuations about a state of near-rest, the

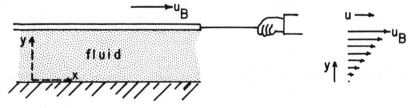

FIG. 1. Couette flow.

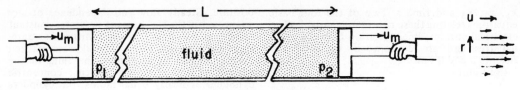

FIG. 2. Poiseuille flow.

continuum equations are linearized by neglecting nonlinear terms and become the equations of acoustics[2]. A large variety of fluid motions are described as sound waves; when the small-motion or acoustic description can be used, the *principle of superposition* is valid. This powerful principle allows addition of simple simultaneous motions to represent a more complex motion, such as the sound reaching the audience from the instruments of a symphony orchestra. The superposition principle does not apply to large-scale (nonacoustical) motions, and the subject fluid dynamics (in distinction from acoustics) treats nonlinear flows, i.e., those which cannot be described as superpositions of other flows. The description of small motions in a small region of even a nonlinear flow is useful; at each place in the flow, there is a "local sound speed."

Since sound waves travel with a speed relative to the fluid, waves moving in a moving fluid can sometimes be carried off in a direction opposite to the direction of sound travel. The flow where such a thing happens is called *supersonic*; the flow speed is greater than the sound speed at the spot where the flow is supersonic. Supersonic flow occurs around high-speed vehicles and missiles, and in pipes when high pressure gas escapes through a nozzle into a region of sufficiently lower pressure. A steady supersonic flow always must pass through a *shock front* to slow down to subsonic flow again.

The continuum description of flow fails to describe nearly all actual flows because actual flows when looked at carefully are *turbulent*. Turbulent flows have violent and erratic fluctuations of velocity and pressure which are not associated with any corresponding fluctuations of the boundaries containing or driving the fluid. Turbulence is generally considered to be the manifestation of the nonlinear nature of the fundamental equations. Under certain conditions as mentioned earlier in describing Couette and Poiseuille flows, nonturbulent or *laminar* flow exists. A common example is cigarette smoke rising from a cigarette held at rest; near the cigarette, the stream is smooth and straight, or laminar, and further up the flow breaks into turbulence.

Reynolds showed that Poiseuille flow in a pipe occurs when $\rho u_m a/\mu$ is smaller than 2000. The combination of variables is dimensionless and is called the *pipe Reynolds number*. Blood flow in capillaries is laminar, but water flow in household pipes is turbulent unless the flow is about that allowed by a leaky faucet or less. Other types of flow have Reynolds numbers

characterizing transition from laminar to turbulent; for example a sphere falling in a fluid of viscosity μ obeys *Stokes' Law*

$$mg = 6\pi a\mu u$$

where u is the constant speed of fall, m is the sphere mass, a its radius, and g the weight per unit mass, but the law is obeyed only if the *sphere Reynolds number* $\rho u a/\mu$ is smaller than about 1.

Because of turbulence and viscosity, the very simple and useful *Bernoulli formula* is not valid; it can be derived as applying to a constant-density fluid with zero viscosity in laminar flow. However, under certain conditions, the formula applies approximately even when the flow is turbulent, predicting properties within 5 to 20 per cent of the observed values. The Bernoulli formula states

$$p + \rho gh + \tfrac{1}{2}\rho u^2 = \text{same constant in all places in the fluid}$$

where p is the fluid pressure, ρ is the fluid mass density (which must be treated as constant), u is the fluid speed, h is the vertical height above some convenient reference level, and g is the weight per unit mass.

When combined with the equation of continuity, the Bernoulli formula gives a simple description of the Venturi, used in the automobile carburetor (see Fig. 3). Continuity states $u_1 A_1 =$

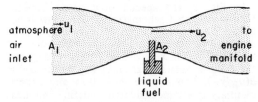

FIG. 3. Pipe flow with a constriction; carburetor employing Venturi.

$u_2 A_2 =$ volume crossing any cross section of the pipe per second. $u_1/u_2 = A_2/A_1$ is small so u_1 is smaller than u_2. The Bernoulli formula states $p_1 + \tfrac{1}{2}\rho u_1^2 = p_2 + \tfrac{1}{2}\rho u_2^2$, and since u_1 is smaller than u_2, p_1 is larger than p_2. The atmospheric pressure p_1 pushes the liquid up into the lower pressure region p_2.

Another common situation described by the Bernoulli formula is the discharge of (constant density) fluid from a small hole. For the cylindrical bucket of water in Fig. 4, equate the sum

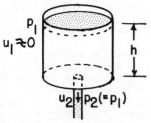

FIG. 4. Discharge through a small hole in a bucket.

of the quantities in the Bernoulli formula at the top surface to the sum at the hole: $p_1 + \rho g h + 0 = p_2 + 0 + \frac{1}{2} \rho u_2{}^2$. The pressure at both top and bottom is atmospheric pressure p_1; the speed at the top is approximately zero because the hole is considered to be very small. The predicted speed of the emerging water is therefore $(2gh)^{1/2}$ regardless of the size of the hole (as long as the hole is small).

A valuable instrument in the form of a probe for observing fluid speed is the Pitot tube; its operation is described by the Bernoulli formula. A glass or metal tube with an open end points into the flow, and the pressure difference Δp between the stagnant fluid in the tube and the moving fluid allows calculation of the fluid speed at the place where the tube tip is inserted by $u = (2\,\Delta p/\rho)^{1/2}$ where ρ is the fluid mass density. When observing air speed, the pressure difference Δp is easily measured by connecting the open ended tube via rubber hose to a glass U-tube water manometer. Errors as much as 50 per cent may easily occur in various practical situations, but order-of-magnitude measurements at least are usually possible.

RAYMOND J. EMRICH

References

1. Landau, L. D., and Lifshitz, E. M., "Fluid Mechanics," London, Pergamon Press, 1959.
2. Hunt, F., "Propagation of Sound in Fluids," "American Institute of Physics Handbook," Article 3c, New York, McGraw-Hill Book Co., 1972.
3. Lamb, H., "Hydrodynamics," First American Edition, New York, Dover Publications, 1945.
4. Hirschfelder, J., Curtiss, C. F., and Bird, R. B., "Molecular Theory of Gases and Liquids," New York, John Wiley & Sons, 1954.
5. Gaydon, A. G., and Hurle, I. R., "The Shock Tube in High-Temperature Chemical Physics," New York, Van Nostrand Reinhold, 1963.

Cross-references: FLUID STATICS, KINETIC THEORY, MAGNETO-FLUID-MECHANICS, STATISTICAL MECHANICS.

FLUID STATICS

Statics involves a study of the conditions under which a body remains at rest. If a body of fluid is at rest, the forces are in equilibrium or the fluid is in static equilibrium. The types of force which may act on a body are shear or tangential force, tensile force, and compressive force. Fluids move continuously under the action of shear or tangential forces. Thus, a fluid at rest is free in each part from shear forces; one fluid layer does not slide relative to an adjacent layer. An example is a quantity of water or other liquid at rest in a bottle.

Fluids can be subjected to a compressive stress which is commonly called "pressure." The term pressure will be used to designate a force per unit area; pressure units may be dynes per square centimeter, newtons per square meter, or pounds per square foot.

Atmospheric pressure is the force acting on a unit area due to the weight of the atmosphere. "Gage" pressure is the difference between the pressure of the fluid measured (at some point) and atmospheric pressure. The term vacuum refers to pressures below atmospheric. "Absolute" pressure, which can be measured by a mercury barometer, is the sum of gage pressure plus atmospheric pressure.

Pascal's law states that the pressure in a static fluid is the same in all directions. This condition is different from that for a stressed solid (as steel) in static equilibrium; in such a solid, the stress on a plane depends on the orientation of that plane. A liquid in contact with the atmosphere is sometimes called a "free surface." A static liquid has a horizontal free surface if gravity is the only type of force acting.

Imagine a body of static fluid in a gravitational field. The mass of the fluid is m (as in grams or kilograms) and the weight of the fluid is mg (as dynes or newtons) where g is the local gravitational acceleration. Figure 1 indicates a large region of any static fluid with a very small or infinitesimal element. Figure 2 indicates the element in detail. The vertical distance z is

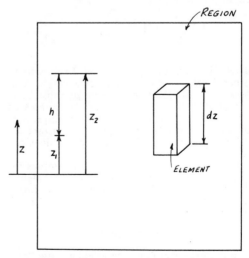

FIG. 1. Large region of any static fluid.

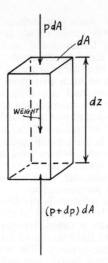

FIG. 2. Vertical forces on infinitesimal element.

measured positively in the direction of decreasing pressure (up), dA is an infinitesimal area, p is the pressure acting on the top surface, and $(p + dp)$ is the pressure acting on the bottom surface; the pressure difference is due only to the weight of the fluid element. Let ρ represent density, which is mass per unit volume (as grams per cubic centimeter or kilograms per cubic meter). Thus the weight of the element is $\rho g\, dz\, dA$. Considering the element as a free body, an accounting of forces in the vertical direction gives

$$dp\, dA = -\rho g\, dz\, dA \qquad dp = -\rho g\, dz \qquad (1)$$

As z is measured positively upward, the minus sign indicates that the pressure decreases with an increase in height. This fundamental equation of fluid statics can be applied to all fluids. In integral form, Eq. (1) becomes

$$\int_1^2 \frac{dp}{\rho g} = -\int_1^2 dz = -(z_2 - z_1) \qquad (2)$$

where 1 refers to one level and 2 refers to another level. The functional relation between pressure p and the combination ρg must be established before Eq. (2) can be integrated. There are two major cases: (a) incompressible fluids, in which the density ρ is constant and (b) compressible fluids, in which the density ρ varies.

Liquids can be considered as incompressible in many cases. For small differences in height, a gas might be regarded as incompressible. For an incompressible fluid, with constant g, Eq. (2) becomes

$$p_2 - p_1 = -\rho g(z_2 - z_1) \qquad (3)$$

The term $(z_2 - z_1)$ may be called a static "pressure head," and it can be expressed in feet, inches, or meters of water, or some height of any liquid. For example, barometric pressure can be expressed in inches or centimeters of mercury.

A "manometer" is a device that measures a static pressure by balancing the pressure with a column of liquid in static equilibrium. A large variety of manometers is used, such as differential, vertical, and inclined. The common mercury barometer is essentially a manometer for measuring atmospheric pressure; a mercury column in a glass tube balances the weight of the air above the mercury. Figure 3 illustrates a

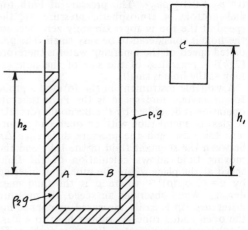

FIG. 3. Manometer.

manometer in which the left leg is open to the atmosphere; the liquid has a specific weight (weight per unit volume) $\rho_2 g$. In the other leg is a liquid of specific weight $\rho_1 g$. Starting with the left leg, the gage pressure p_A at point A is

$$p_A = h_2 \rho_2 g$$

Since the fluid is in static equilibrium, the pressure p_B at point B equals the pressure at point A. Thus

$$p_A = p_B = h_2 \rho_2 g$$

The pressure p_C at point C is less than at B. Thus

$$p_B - p_C = h_1 \rho_1 g$$

Then the gage pressure at point C is

$$p_C = g(h_1 \rho_2 - h_1 \rho_1)$$

When a body of any kind is partly or completely immersed in a static fluid, every part of the body surface in contact with the fluid is pressed on by the fluid; the pressure is greater on the areas more deeply immersed. The resultant of all these fluid pressure forces is an upward or buoyant force. The pressure on each part of the body is independent of the body

material. Archimedes' principle states that the buoyant force equals the weight of the displaced fluid.

Equation (3) is for the special case of an incompressible fluid. As an example of a compressible fluid, consider an isothermal or constant-temperature layer of gas. The equation of state for such a gas can be written

$$p = \rho R T_1 \qquad (4)$$

where T_1 is the given absolute temperature and R is a gas constant or gas factor depending on the gas. Assuming a constant g, Eq. (2) gives

$$\frac{R T_1}{g} \int_1^2 \frac{dp}{p} = -(z_2 - z_1)$$

$$z_2 - z_1 = \frac{R T_1}{g} \log_e \frac{p_1}{p_2} \qquad (5)$$

Equation (5) is sometimes called a "barometric-height" relation. For an isothermal atmosphere a measurement of the temperature T_1 and the static pressure (as with a barometer) at two different levels will provide data for the calculation of the height difference.

RAYMOND C. BINDER

References

Binder, R. C., "Fluid Mechanics," Englewood Cliffs, N.J., Prentice-Hall, 1973.

Prandl, L., and Tietjens, O. G., "Fundamentals of Hydro- and Aeromechanics," New York, McGraw-Hill Book Co., 1934.

Cross-references: FLUID DYNAMICS, MECHANICS, STATICS.

FOURIER ANALYSIS

Fourier analysis is the mathematical representation of functions as linear combinations of sine, cosine, or complex exponential harmonic components. Such representations take their name from Jean Baptiste Fourier (1768–1830), French mathematician and physicist, who used them extensively in developing a mathematical theory of heat conduction. They continue to be widely used in mathematical physics and engineering, finding application in the study of such diverse subjects as diffraction, diffusion, image formation, spectroscopy, electrical networks, x-ray crystallography, and the theory of probability.

Fourier Series Let $f(x)$ be a periodic function with period L, i.e., $f(x)$ satisfies

$$f(x) = f(x - L) \qquad (1)$$

for all x. For a wide class of such functions, we can represent $f(x)$ by an infinite summation of sine and cosine harmonic components

$$f(x) = a_0 + \sum_{n=1}^{\infty} a_n \cos \frac{2\pi n x}{L} + \sum_{n=1}^{\infty} b_n \sin \frac{2\pi n x}{L}, \qquad (2)$$

known as the *Fourier series* representation of $f(x)$. If the left and right hand sides of Eq. (2) are multiplied by $\cos 2\pi m x/L$ or by $\sin 2\pi m x/L$, and the resulting equation is integrated with respect to x over one period L, the orthogonality of the harmonic sine and cosine components on this interval implies the following formulas for the *Fourier coefficients* a_0, a_n, b_n:

$$a_0 = \frac{1}{L} \int_{-L/2}^{L/2} f(x) \, dx$$

$$a_n = \frac{2}{L} \int_{-L/2}^{L/2} f(x) \cos \frac{2\pi n x}{L} \, dx \qquad n = 1, 2, \cdots$$

$$b_n = \frac{2}{L} \int_{-L/2}^{L/2} f(x) \sin \frac{2\pi n x}{L} \, dx \qquad n = 1, 2, \cdots$$

$$(3)$$

Other equivalent forms of the Fourier series can be obtained from Eq. (2). For example, $f(x)$ may be written

$$f(x) = a_0 + \sum_{n=1}^{\infty} C_n \cos \left(\frac{2\pi n x}{L} - \phi_n \right) \qquad (4)$$

where

$$C_n = \sqrt{a_n^2 + b_n^2}$$

$$\phi_n = \tan^{-1} \frac{b_n}{a_n}. \qquad (5)$$

Another widely used representation is the exponential (or complex) form of the Fourier series,

$$f(x) = \sum_{n=-\infty}^{\infty} \alpha_n e^{i(2\pi n x/L)} \qquad (6)$$

where

$$\alpha_n = \frac{1}{2} (a_n - i b_n) = \frac{1}{L} \int_{-L/2}^{L/2} f(x) e^{-i(2\pi n x/L)} \, dx. \qquad (7)$$

For a real-valued $f(x)$, α_{+n} and α_{-n} are not independent, since $\alpha_{-n} = \alpha_{+n}^*$, where * indicates complex conjugate. However, when $f(x)$ is complex-valued, α_{+n} and α_{-n} are in general not related.

An important property of Fourier series, known as *Parseval's theorem*, states that the mean quadratic content of $f(x)$ (which often has the physical interpretation of average power) may be found by summing the squares of the Fourier coefficients. Thus, for the three representations used,

$$\frac{1}{L}\int_{-L/2}^{L/2}|f(x)|^2\,dx=\begin{cases}a_0{}^2+\displaystyle\sum_{n=1}^{\infty}\frac{a_n{}^2+b_n{}^2}{2}\\[2ex]a_0{}^2+\displaystyle\sum_{n=1}^{\infty}\frac{C_n{}^2}{2}\\[2ex]\displaystyle\sum_{n=-\infty}^{\infty}|\alpha_n|^2\qquad(8)\end{cases}$$

No discussion of Fourier series would be complete without some mention of the conditions under which the series actually converge to the functions they are to represent. Conditions which are both necessary and sufficient are not known. However, for the series to converge to $f(x)$ at each point of continuity, it is known to be a sufficient condition that $f(x)$ have only a finite number of maxima and minima in the interval $-L/2\leqslant x\leqslant L/2$. Under this same condition, at points of discontinuity of $f(x)$ the series converges to the arithmetic mean of the values of $f(x)$ immediately to the left and right of the discontinuity.

Fourier Integrals Just as a periodic function can be represented by the sum of harmonic components in a Fourier series, so too an aperiodic function may be represented by an integral over a continuous spectrum of complex-exponential components. In this case we write

$$f(x)=\int_{-\infty}^{\infty}F(\nu)e^{i2\pi\nu x}\,d\nu\qquad(9)$$

which is referred to as the *Fourier integral* representation of $f(x)$. Here $F(\nu)$, known as the *Fourier transform* (or Fourier spectrum) of $f(x)$, is given by

$$F(\nu)=\int_{-\infty}^{\infty}f(x)e^{-i2\pi\nu x}\,dx.\qquad(10)$$

The variable ν is generally referred to as the *frequency* variable.

Note that a simple expansion of the exponential in Eq. (10) yields $F(\nu)$ in terms of sine and cosine integrals,

$$F(\nu)=\int_{-\infty}^{\infty}f(x)\cos 2\pi\nu x\,dx$$

$$-i\int_{-\infty}^{\infty}f(x)\sin 2\pi\nu x\,dx.\quad(11)$$

If $f(x)$ is an even function of x, the sine integral vanishes, leaving $F(\nu)$ expressed as a *Fourier cosine integral*,

$$F(\nu)=2\int_{0}^{\infty}f(x)\cos 2\pi\nu x\,dx.\qquad(12)$$

Other forms of the Fourier integral and Fourier transform are often found in the literature. For example, frequency ν is often replaced by angular frequency $\omega=2\pi\nu$, in which case Eqs. (9) and (10) become

$$f(x)=\frac{1}{2\pi}\int_{-\infty}^{\infty}F(\omega)e^{i\omega x}\,d\omega$$

$$F(\omega)=\int_{-\infty}^{\infty}f(x)e^{-i\omega x}\,dx.\qquad(13)$$

Alternatively, the forms

$$f(x)=\frac{1}{\sqrt{2\pi}}\int_{-\infty}^{\infty}F(\omega)e^{i\omega x}\,d\omega$$

$$F(\omega)=\frac{1}{\sqrt{2\pi}}\int_{-\infty}^{\infty}f(x)e^{-i\omega x}\,dx\qquad(14)$$

are sometimes found. Here we shall continue to use the forms of equations (9) and (10).

As in the case of Fourier series, the Fourier integral representation will converge to $f(x)$ only for a certain class of functions. Convergence at points of continuity is assured if $f(x)$ satisfies the following set of sufficient conditions:

(i) $f(x)$ is absolutely integrable;
(ii) $f(x)$ has only a finite number of maxima and minima in any finite interval; and
(iii) $f(x)$ has no infinite discontinuities.

Under these conditions, at points of discontinuity of $f(x)$, the Fourier integral converges to the arithmetic mean of the values of $f(x)$ immediately to the left and right of the discontinuity. In general, any one of the above sufficient conditions can be slightly relaxed at the price of strengthening one or both of the additional conditions.

While the class of functions encompassed by the above conditions is wide, there do exist certain functions important in mathematical physics which are not included, such as $\sin x$, $\cos x$, and $f(x)=1$. These may be included if the concept of the Dirac delta function, $\delta(\nu)$, is introduced, having the properties

$$\delta(\nu)=0\quad\nu\neq 0,$$

$$\int_{-\infty}^{\infty}\delta(\nu)\,d\nu=1.\qquad(15)$$

TABLE 1. FOURIER TRANSFORM PAIRS

$f(x) = \exp(-\pi x^2)$ $F(\nu) = \exp(-\pi \nu^2)$

$$f(x) = \begin{cases} 1 & |x| \leqslant \frac{1}{2} \\ 0 & |x| > \frac{1}{2} \end{cases} \qquad F(\nu) = \frac{\sin \pi \nu}{\pi \nu}$$

$$f(x) = \begin{cases} 1 - |x| & |x| \leqslant 1 \\ 0 & |x| > 1 \end{cases} \qquad F(\nu) = \left[\frac{\sin \pi \nu}{\pi \nu}\right]^2$$

$f(x) = 1$ $F(\nu) = \delta(\nu)$

$f(x) = \cos \pi x$ $F(\nu) = \frac{1}{2}\delta(\nu - \frac{1}{2}) + \frac{1}{2}\delta(\nu + \frac{1}{2})$

$f(x) = \exp(i\pi x^2)$ $F(\nu) = \exp\left[-i\pi(\nu^2 - \frac{1}{4})\right]$

$$f(x) = \sum_{n=-\infty}^{\infty} \delta(x - n) \qquad F(\nu) = \sum_{m=-\infty}^{\infty} \delta(\nu - m)$$

Strictly speaking, $\delta(\nu)$ is not a function in the usual mathematical sense. However, it can be treated rigorously using the theory of distributions.

In Table 1 are presented the Fourier transforms of a number of the more important functions encountered in mathematical physics and engineering. From the basic Fourier transform pairs listed in the table, many other pairs may be derived with the help of the following Fourier transform theorems.

Linearity: If $f(x) = a\,g(x) + b\,h(x)$, then $F(\nu) = a\,G(\nu) + b\,H(\nu)$, where $G(\nu)$ and $H(\nu)$ are the Fourier transforms of $g(x)$ and $h(x)$, respectively.

Similarity: If $f(x) = g(ax)$, then $F(\nu) = (1/|a|)G(\nu/a)$.

Shift: If $f(x) = g(x - a)$, then $F(\nu) = G(\nu)\exp(-i2\pi a\nu)$.

Convolution: If $f(x) = \displaystyle\int_{-\infty}^{\infty} g(\xi)h(x - \xi)\,d\xi$,

then $F(\nu) = G(\nu)H(\nu)$.

A relation entirely analogous to Parseval's theorem of Fourier series is *Plancherel's* theorem,

$$\int_{-\infty}^{\infty} |f(x)|^2\,dx = \int_{-\infty}^{\infty} |F(\nu)|^2\,d\nu. \quad (16)$$

In many physical applications this theorem leads to the interpretation of $|F(\nu)|^2$ as the energy spectrum of the function $f(x)$.

The Fourier integral representation (and the Fourier series representation) can be generalized to apply to functions of two or more independent variables. Most important are functions defined over a plane or over three-dimensional space. In the case of two independent variables we have

$$f(x,y) = \iint_{-\infty}^{\infty} F(\nu_X, \nu_Y)$$
$$\cdot \exp\left[i2\pi(\nu_X x + \nu_Y y)\right]\,d\nu_X d\nu_Y$$

$$F(\nu_X, \nu_Y) = \iint_{-\infty}^{\infty} f(x,y)$$
$$\cdot \exp\left[-i2\pi(\nu_X x + \nu_Y y)\right]\,dx dy. \quad (17)$$

For the most part, the properties of one-dimensional Fourier transforms carry over directly to the N-dimensional case. There is extra richness in the theory for the multidimensional case, however. For example, if $f(x,y)$ exhibits circular symmetry, i.e., is a function of only radius r in the plane, then Eqs. (17) can be reduced to the form of the so-called *Fourier-Bessel transform* (or Hankel transform of zero order),

$$f(r) = 2\pi \int_0^{\infty} \rho F(\rho)J_0(2\pi r\rho)\,d\rho$$

$$F(\rho) = 2\pi \int_0^{\infty} r f(r)J_0(2\pi r\rho)\,dr \quad (18)$$

where $r = (x^2 + y^2)^{1/2}$, $\rho = (\nu_X^2 + \nu_Y^2)^{1/2}$, and J_0 is a Bessel function of the first kind, zero order.

Applications The applications of Fourier analysis are so widespread throughout physics and engineering that to summarize them adequately in a brief space is nearly impossible. At best we can only outline some of the most important classes of applications, illustrating with a simple mention some of the particular branches of science that benefit from Fourier analysis in each case.

The applications of Fourier analysis can be

conveniently divided into two major categories. Within the first category we find Fourier analysis used purely as an analytical tool, for the calculation and prediction of the results of experiments not yet performed, or for the explanation of experimental results already obtained. For example, in certain important cases the wave amplitude produced by a diffracting structure may be calculated using Fourier transforms, a consequence of the fact that the complete diffraction integrals may be reduced to Fourier transforms.

As a second example of this category, it might be desired to predict the image obtained when a certain object is viewed through an imaging system. The characteristics of such a system are often most easily specified in terms of its effects on spatial sine wave objects of various spatial frequencies. To predict the image obtained for a nonsinusoidal object, that object may be decomposed, by means of a Fourier integral, into sine wave (or complex exponential) components. The image is then found by synthesizing, again with a Fourier integral, the various sine wave image components, after their amplitudes and phases have been modified by the known properties of the imaging system. A similar approach is used in the analysis of linear, time-invariant electrical networks. It can also be used to calculate the diffusion of heat through a conducting plate when a known temperature distribution is impressed across one edge of the plate.

A second major category of applications utilizes Fourier analysis as an experimental tool, applied to experimental data to derive related physical information. For example, in Fourier spectroscopy the interferogram obtained from a scanned Michelson interferometer may be Fourier-analyzed to yield the spectral intensity distribution of the radiation source. In x-ray crystallography, the x-ray diffraction pattern produced by a crystal may be Fourier-analyzed to yield information about the crystal lattice structure. In radio astronomy the correlation coefficients produced when the signals collected by various elements of an array are cross-correlated may be Fourier-analyzed to yield a map of the radio brightness distribution of the sky. In all of these latter examples, Fourier analysis plays a fundamental role in transforming data which are readily collected by experiment into data which are more directly related to the physical properties of interest.

JOSEPH W. GOODMAN

References

1. Bracewell, R. N., "The Fourier Transform and Its Applications," New York, McGraw-Hill Book Co., 1965.
2. Goodman, J. W., "Introduction to Fourier Optics," New York, McGraw-Hill Book Co., 1968.
3. Papoulis, A., "Systems and Transforms with Applications in Optics," New York, McGraw-Hill Book Co., 1968.
4. Arsac, J., "Fourier Transforms and the Theory of Distributions," Englewood Cliffs, N.J., Prentice-Hall, Inc., 1966.
5. Titchmarsh, E. C., "Introduction to the Theory of Fourier Integrals," Oxford, Oxford University Press, 1937.

Cross-references: CALCULUS OF PHYSICS, DIFFERENTIAL EQUATIONS IN PHYSICS.

FRICTION

Introduction Friction is the resistance to motion which exists when a solid object is moved tangentially with respect to the surface of another which it touches, or when an attempt is made to produce such motion. Friction thus takes its place as one of the general systems of force which are considered in MECHANICS (others being GRAVITY, ELASTICITY, etc.). Unfortunately friction depends to a marked extent on the material properties of the contacting surfaces, and even more importantly, on any surface contaminants which may be present, so that it is very difficult to estimate values of the friction force theoretically, with an uncertainty of less than about 20 per cent. In many calculations in solid mechanics, this uncertainty in the friction constitutes the limiting factor in determining the accuracy of the over-all calculation.

The friction force arises from the fact that, when two solids are pressed together, bonding between their surface atoms occurs, and these bonds have to be broken before sliding can commence. Bonding of any considerable strength occurs only in places where the surface atoms come within range of each other's strong force-fields (i.e., closer than about 3×10^{-10} m); thus, when ordinary solids with appreciable roughness are used, bonding is confined to a few small patches (called junctions) over their interface, where the high spots (or asperities) of one material have made contact with asperities on the other material.

The energy used up in the friction process appears almost entirely in the form of heat. Generally this consists of a moderate temperature rise over the contacting bodies, and superposed on this there are higher "flash temperatures" at the junctions. At high sliding speeds, softening or even melting of the tips of the asperities may occur.

In addition to the bonding or "adhesion" effect, which is the principal cause of friction, there are four other mechanisms which use up energy during sliding; energy which must be supplied by the friction force. These mechanisms are:

(1) A roughness effect, caused by the interlocking of asperities and the need to lift one surface over the high spots of the other;

(2) A ploughing effect, whereby an asperity on a hard material can dig a groove in a softer material;

(3) A hysteresis effect, whereby there is

elastic and plastic deformation of the material at or near the junctions, and not all the deformation energy is recoverable;

(4) An electrostatic effect (with electric insulators), where work must be done to separate electrically charged regions on the sliding surfaces.

In a great majority of applications these four mechanisms do not account for as much as 20 percent of the total resistance to sliding. The widely held belief that friction is due mainly to a roughness effect does not find experimental support. Cleaved mica (smooth to an atomic scale) shows very high friction.

Laws of Friction If a normal load L presses two surfaces together, then we may apply a tangential force up to some limiting value F_s, and the surfaces will remain at rest. Sliding occurs when the tangential force exceeds the static friction force F_s, and almost as soon as motion starts the tangential force takes on a characteristic value, F_k, and always acts in a direction opposite to the relative velocity of the surfaces. F_s is often some 30 per cent larger than F_k, but sometimes they are equal.

The ratio F_s/L is the static friction coefficient f_s(or μ_s), while the ratio F_k/L is the kinetic friction coefficient f_k. We may cite quite general statements, or "laws," involving these coefficients of friction. The three classical laws, dating back to the seventeenth and eighteenth centuries, are:

(1) The friction coefficient is independent of the load.

(2) The friction coefficient is independent of the contact area.

(3) The kinetic friction coefficient is independent of the sliding velocity.

More recently, it has been found possible to make another general statement about the friction coefficient:

(4) The friction coefficient is independent of the surface roughness.

We may summarise these laws in the comprehensive statement.

(5) The friction coefficient is essentially a material property of the contacting surfaces, and of the contaminants and other films at their interface.

Although in practice these "laws" are reasonably well obeyed, there are often systematic divergencies, some of which have important consequences. In the rare cases in which the friction coefficient varies with load, it is often because of some special effect (e.g., a surface coating which is broken up at heavy loads); however, materials with a high elastic limit (e.g., polymers) generally show a friction coefficient which goes down somewhat as the load is increased. The fourth law applies closely to the intermediate ranges of surface roughness, but it is found that very smooth surfaces have higher friction because they tend to seize, and very rough surfaces have higher friction because of asperity interlocking.

Velocity and Time Effects in Sliding Violations of the third friction law are important because they can lead to friction-induced oscillations. With some materials f_k is almost independent of velocity over a very wide range; however, with hard materials the friction generally goes down as the speed goes up (a so-called negative characteristic), while soft materials show a negative characteristic at high sliding speeds and a positive characteristic at low sliding speeds. Often, f_k changes by about 10 per cent during a factor-of-ten change of velocity. In a sliding system which has elastic compliance, a negative characteristic introduces an instability, and at high speeds this takes the form of harmonic oscillations (e.g., a violin string), while at low speeds relaxation oscillations occur (e.g., a creaking door). The relaxation oscillations are usually referred to as stick-slip, because during a part of each cycle the surfaces are at rest. The severity of the stick-slip is enhanced because, while the surfaces are at rest, f_s increases somewhat with time of stick (about 10 per cent for every factor-of-ten increase in time of stick above 10^{-3} seconds).

Value of the Friction Coefficient In most situations the total real area of contact, or sum of all the asperities, is produced by plastic deformation of the asperities, and if we assume that strong bonds are formed joining the materials across the interface we find that the friction coefficient is given by

$$f = s/p$$

where s is the plastic shear stress, and p the plastic indentation hardness, of the softer of the two contacting materials. Since s and p are similar plastic strength parameters, their ratio tends to be constant, within the range 0.3 to 0.6, for a wide variety of materials. With some materials the real area of contact increases during sliding, and friction coefficients above 1.0 are then commonly observed. Especially bad in this connection are materials with a high ratio of surface energy to hardness, namely clean soft metals such as lead, aluminum and copper.

A lubricant acts by introducing a layer of lower shear stress s_1 at the interface, and lowers the friction coefficient accordingly, down to 0.05 in favorable cases. Many nominally clean materials also give low friction, as result of contamination during manufacture or handling. Slight differences in the degree of contamination can produce drastic differences in the friction.

Some typical friction values are given in Table 1.

Materials with Unusual Frictional Properties In this category we may place the hard non-metals (diamond), which give low friction (~ 0.1); the elastomers (natural rubber) which give very high friction (~ 0.9); the layer-lattice substances (graphite, molybdenum disulfide,

TABLE 1. COEFFICIENTS OF FRICTION

Materials	Surface Conditions	f_s	f_k
Metals on metals (e.g. steel on steel, copper on aluminum)	Carefully cleaned	0.4–2.0	0.3–1.0
	Unlubricated, but not cleaned	0.2–0.4	0.15–0.3
	Well lubricated	0.05–0.12	0.05–0.12
Nonmetals on nonmetals (e.g., leather on wood, rubber on concrete)	Unlubricated	0.4–0.9	0.3–0.8
	Well lubricated	0.1–0.2	0.1–0.15
Metals on nonmetals	Unlubricated	0.4–0.6	0.3–0.5
	Well lubricated	0.05–0.12	0.05–0.12

cadmium iodide) which give low friction ($\sim$0.1) and are used as solid film lubricants; the hexagonal close-packed metals (rhenium, magnesium, titanium, cobalt) which when clean give lower friction coefficients ($\sim$0.5) than do other metals; "Teflon," which adheres very poorly to other solids and accordingly gives very low friction ($\sim$0.05); and metals in group IVa of the periodic table (titanium, zirconium, hafnium) which cannot be well lubricated by any known liquid substances. Generally, the frictional anomalies of solids may be traced to peculiarities in their structure or surface properties.

Related Fields of Interest Friction is considered one of a group of mechanical surface interaction phenomena, and research in the other members of the group is of great interest to workers in the friction field. There is an extensive common literature. The other interaction phenomena are wear (the removal of surface material as result of mechanical action), lubrication (the properties of surface films which reduce friction and wear), and adhesion (the tendency of solid objects pressed together to remain together).

ERNEST RABINOWICZ

References

Bowden, F. P., and Tabor, D., "Friction and Lubrication of Solids," Oxford, Clarendon Press, Part I, 1950, Part II, 1964.

Rabinowicz, E., "Friction and Wear of Materials," New York, Wiley, 1965.

Ku, P. H., Ed., "Interdisciplinary Approach to Friction and Wear," NASA Report SP-181, National Aeronautics and Space Administration, Washington, D.C., 1968.

Cross-references: DYNAMICS, MECHANICS, STATICS.

FUSION

Introduction When nuclei of certain light elements fuse together, an excess binding energy is liberated. This is the energy source of both the sun and the hydrogen bomb, and it is the object of fusion research to liberate the energy in a controlled manner on earth. Because of the abundance of these elements, the energy source is virtually unlimited.

In order to promote nuclear fusion, the reacting nuclei must have sufficient energy to overcome their mutual coulomb repulsion. Thus nuclei with a high ratio of mass to charge, such as deuterium (D) and tritium (T), heated to a high temperature are most suitable. The reaction of interest is

$$D + T = {}^4He\,(3.5\ MeV) + n\,(14.1\ MeV)$$

where the reaction products are helium (^4He) and a neutron (n), and the numbers in parentheses are the kinetic energies of the reaction products. The probability of this reaction is a maximum for a deuteron energy of 107 KeV and the corresponding ratio of nuclear energy liberated to the deuteron energy is 160. The magnitude of the energy available is emphasized by noting that 36 m^3 of natural water contains 1 kg of deuterium, which yields a maximum of 1.7×10^{15} joules of nuclear energy on fusion, equivalent to the energy available from $\sim 5 \times 10^4\ m^3$ of gasoline or 400 kilotonnes of TNT.

Although the cross section peaks at a directed deuteron energy of 107 KeV, it is possible to use a much lower mean energy if the nuclei are thermalized. This is because there is an exceedingly sharp rise of cross section with energy, so most of the fusion reactions are produced by nuclei with energies far in the tail of the Maxwellian distribution. Even so, the temperature required is extremely high, typically near 10^8 K.

Plasma in a Fusion Reactor At such high temperature, atoms are ionized by collisions and the electrons are not bound to any particular nucleus; this state of matter is called a plasma. Since stars are in the plasma state, plasmas are by far the most common form of matter in the universe (though they are rare on earth) and the problems of controlled thermonuclear fusion are closer to astrophysical plasma physics than to nuclear physics.

Because of the unbound electrons, plasmas are good electrical conductors and a magnetic field cannot easily diffuse through them. While the diffusion proceeds there is a current induced in the plasma surface which interacts with the

field to cause a pressure perpendicular to the field lines of $\sim 5 \mu_0 B^2$ atmospheres where B is the field in kiloamperes per meter and $\mu_0 = 4\pi \times 10^{-7}$; effectively the plasma pressure is balanced by the field pressure which is supported by the magnetic coils generating the field. Thus the magnetic field affords the means of insulating the plasma from the material walls against which it would rapidly cool.

Often, as the result of the method of forming the plasma or because of field diffusion, magnetic field becomes mixed with the plasma. The confining magnetic field pressure must then balance the sum of the plasma pressure and the pressure of the field in the plasma. In this connection, an important parameter of the plasma is β, the fraction of the confining field pressure that supports the plasma pressure, which varies from 0 to 1 as the field inside the plasma goes from the confining field to zero.

Operating Regime The operating regime of a fusion reactor is determined by the variation of the reaction cross section with temperature, the economics of energy conversion into useful work, and material properties such as the strength of the magnet metal, vaporization of the wall of the containment vessel, etc. Energy balance in the reactor gives a minimum requirement for the product nt where t is the reaction time and n is the number of nuclei per cubic meter. If the total energy released in the reaction vessel (the nuclear energy plus the energy of the plasma particles plus energy radiated) is returned with an efficiency of 1/3 to maintain the plasma temperature and make up the radiation losses, the nt must be greater than 10^{20} and the minimum temperature is about 3×10^7 K. For this minimum condition, 1 per cent of the nuclei fuse together. Also, since the reaction rate depends on n^2, too high an n rapidly leads to wall vaporization and too low an n to a negligible rate. It is assumed that a power density of 30 MW/m³ can be handled continuously (compared to present fission reactor levels of about 100 MW/m³) and n must be approximately equal to 10^{20} nuclei/m³ so that t greater than about 1 sec is required.

If the helium from the fusion reaction is trapped in the plasma, its energy can maintain the plasma temperature against losses by radiation. This avoids the inefficiency of recycling the fusion energy to heat more plasma. The minimum temperature for this approach, called the "ideal ignition temperature," is 4.6×10^7 K. All the energy of the neutrons from the fusion reaction can then be applied to produce useful power.

Radiation One of the many problems to be solved in devising a fusion reactor is that of radiation at these high temperatures. Fortunately, the plasma required is so diffuse that it does not act as a blackbody which would follow a fourth-power law of temperature for the radiant energy and produce unacceptably high energy loss. Instead, the radiation mean free path is larger than the plasma dimensions and the dominant radiation process is caused by electrons deflected in the coulomb field of the nuclei. This is called bremsstrahlung and has a maximum intensity in the soft x-ray region at a wavelength of around 1 Å. The power radiated is proportional to $Z^2 n_e n_i T^{1/2}$ (Z = nuclear charge; n_e and n_i are the electron and ion density, and $T[K]$ is the temperature), which depends on the square root rather than the fourth power of the temperature, and for reasonable-sized reactors, is far less than blackbody radiation. For hydrogen, bremsstrahlung radiation is not very important; an increase of two orders of magnitude is needed before energy balance is threatened. However, because of the $n_e Z^2$ factor, ionized impurities could produce a serious radiation loss. Impurities also absorb energy during ionization, not only because of the ionization potential of the electrons, but also in the excitation of the partially ionized atoms by free electrons with insufficient energy to produce complete ionization; this excitation energy is radiated a few nanoseconds after excitation. It is therefore very important to ionize impurities rapidly.

A further important mechanism of energy loss in the plasma is charge exchange produced between a neutral impurity molecule (liberated, for instance, at the wall of the vacuum vessel by the radiation) drifting into the plasma and donating an electron to a hot ion. The hot ion now becomes neutral, is no longer held by the magnetic field, and is lost from the plasma. Meanwhile the cold impurity ion absorbs plasma energy in being further ionized and heated, and the hot neutral particle bombards the wall to liberate further impurities.

Therefore because of both radiation and charge exchange every effort is made to produce a highly pure plasma, typically with an impurity level of less than 0.1 per cent. This is difficult considering the low operating density and the high temperature involved.

Plasma Heating For temperatures up to a few million degrees, the conductivity of the plasma is sufficiently small for ohmic heating to be effective. Also, particularly at low particle densities and high applied electric fields, instabilities can cause an enhanced heating rate. Above these temperatures and densities other forms of heating must be used.

A common method of heating is to compress the plasma with the magnetic field; the energy put into the plasma is then

$$\int_{v_1}^{v_2} \beta p \, dv$$

where p is the magnetic field pressure and $v_1 - v_2$ is the volume change. The volume change is limited by the size of the magnet, so it is desirable to use a high value of p. In the "theta" and "Z" pinch experiments the gas is heated in

a cylindrical tube first ohmically, then by the powerful magnetic pressure. The magnetic field is produced by current from a very low inductance, high-voltage capacitor energy store. The compression is then so rapid that shock fronts develop in the plasma; subsequent isentropic compression is produced by raising the field still further. Temperatures of the order of 10^7 K are commonly quoted, and even 10^8 K has been claimed for late in the life of the plasma. A method of obtaining high plasma compressions without large volumes of magnetic field is to transfer the plasma into successively smaller magnets as the compression increases. The transfer was achieved in an experiment called "toy top" by using a larger field at one end of the plasma than at the other.

Another method of heating the plasma by magnetic compression without large volume changes is magnetic pumping. The plasma is alternately compressed and decompressed at one point on its length, and the problem is to choose conditions in which the plasma does not cool on decompression (i.e., an irreversible cycle is required). The heating depends on the pumping period compared to the ion/ion collision time and the transit time of an ion through the pumping region. If the pumping period is of the order of the transit time and much shorter than the collision time, the ions gain energy while the field is increasing and leave the region before decompression. The heating is then proportional to $T^{3/2}$ and becomes more effective at high temperatures.

Both ohmic and compression methods of heating plasma are limited by collision processes and by the duration an electric field can be applied to the plasma. They may be regarded as methods of bringing the plasma temperature up towards the ignition temperature; above the ignition temperature the plasma can be sustained by heating from the energetic helium produced by thermonuclear reactions.

A third important means of forming the plasma is to accelerate individual nuclei in an electrostatic field, then inject them into the confining magnetic field. This has the advantage that high particle energies (of the order of tens of keV) are relatively easy to produce, but the problem of injecting the nuclei is difficult because it is not possible in general to trap the nuclei in a static magnetic field under conservative conditions. The procedure is to change the particle orbit discontinuously either by a collision against background plasma or by altering the charge-to-mass ratio. In the "D.C.X. mirror" experiment, fast D_2^+ molecules are injected, and dissociated in an arc. In the "Phoenix mirror" and "Alice mirror" experiments, excited neutral atoms are injected which are ripped apart when they reach the magnetic field because, due to the difference in charge, the negative electrons and positive ions in the atom gyrate in opposite directions (this is called "Lorentz trapping"). These methods of heating

have the advantage of being continuous, but the disadvantages that highly anisotropic velocity distributions are produced leading to instabilities especially at low densities, and the difficulty of obtaining sufficient beam intensity.

Confinement, Equilibrium, and Stability Single charged particles move in circular orbits perpendicular to a uniform magnetic field; thus, if the radius of gyration does not intersect the container wall, the particles are confined perpendicular to the field direction. To confine particles parallel to the field lines either "magnetic mirrors" or closed toroidal magnetic field lines are used.

The principle of magnetic mirrors is to increase the magnetic field strength at the ends of the system. When the particles reach the high field (or mirror) region there is a component of magnetic force which, if the initial axial energy of the particle is not too great, will reflect the particle back into the main body of the plasma. In contrast with the uniform magnetic field where the particles are only in neutral equilibrium, the gradient of magnetic field associated with magnetic mirrors causes the particles to drift around the axis of the system in a direction depending on the sign of the charge. For an axisymmetric system like a magnetic mirror, this does not cause charge separation and a consequential electric field which would cause plasma to move radially, and so equilibrium is maintained. However, the system is magnetohydrodynamically unstable to small surface perturbations because charges can build up at the edge of the perturbation. This has been overcome by applying another magnetic field perpendicular to the main field to create a field minimum into which the plasma falls. This solution tends to be expensive in magnetic field, reducing the potential of mirror systems as a reactor. Another problem is that there is always a certain fraction of particles with sufficient axial energy to penetrate the mirrors and this fraction will be continually replenished by coulomb collisions within the plasma. Unfortunately the confinement time varies only as the logarithm of the ratio of the magnetic field in the mirror to the magnetic field in the plasma, so large ratios are needed. One suggestion to overcome this problem is to recover the energy of the particles which escape by a diode electrode structure placed in the low-density plasma far outside the mirrors. A further problem is the non-Maxwellian anisotropic velocity distribution caused by the escape of particles through the mirrors. Some of the potential energy of the trapped particles can then appear as "microinstabilities"; these are electrostatic waves which cause an enhanced radial diffusion of particles across the magnetic field. Against the disadvantages, the low-β open-ended mirror has the attractions over closed-line systems of small size and good accessibility.

Like magnetic mirrors, closed-line toroidal confinement systems must involve magnetic

field gradients since, because of flux continuity, the field increases as the major axis is approached. A simple toroidal solenoidal field has a gradient in which electrons and ions drift in opposite directions perpendicular to the major radius, and the resulting electric field causes the plasma to drift outwards, so the system is not in equilibrium. Broadly, three different experimental approaches are used to overcome this: the Stellarator, Tokamak, and Multipole.

In Stellarators, the magnetic field lines are twisted about the minor axis by adding a helical magnetic field coil outside the plasma. This causes the particles to drift in alternate directions at regular regions of the major circumference so that the tendency for charges to separate is reduced, and within a particular minor radius, the plasma is in equilibrium (a similar effect was obtained in early Stellarators by twisting the torus into a figure eight). Because of the fall of helical magnetic field with distance from the field coil towards the minor axis, the twist or shear of the field lines is a function of position. Such a system is magnetohydrodynamically stable if the correct shear conditions are present (in the linear approximation this is known as the Suydam condition). The system is rather complicated and many details remain to be explored. For instance, there is the possibility of microinstabilities. These may arise because the flux tubes form helices around the minor axis, and the field strength in a particular flux tube varies from a maximum when the tube is closest to the major axis to a minimum when the tube is furthest from the major axis. Thus one can conceive of a class of trapped particles reflected between the high field regions which, like the open-ended mirror, can have an anisotropic velocity distribution producing microinstabilities and enhanced diffusion. A further complication is that the helical field windings produce asymmetric flux surfaces. These windings also create field nonuniformities which may considerably reduce the confinement properties.

Another type of toroidal confinement geometry is the Tokamak. The helical field is generated by a plasma current flowing parallel to the minor axis in combination with a much stronger toroidal field produced by solenoidal coils. The Tokamak has the advantage over Stellarators in that the flux surfaces are symmetric, but the disadvantage that the magnitude and configuration of the helical field cannot be precisely defined since it is determined by plasma currents. A further and more obvious disadvantage is that the current for the helical field must be induced by transformer action, and an efficient pulsed Tokamak fusion reactor is difficult to conceive. It has, however, been shown theoretically that if the ignition temperature is reached, radial diffusion of plasma can automatically cause the current required to produce the required helical field so, if fresh plasma can continuously be injected near the minor axis, a continuous Tokamak seems feasible; this possibility requires experimental verification. Tokamaks have been studied intensively in Russia and their success at producing plasmas approaching fusion interest has led to similar experiments being started in many other countries. At higher β the early experiments on Zeta in England showed that under certain conditions it is possible to find stable regions using plasma currents to create the shear field, and this work is being developed using a more flexible apparatus, the HβTX.

Another method of preventing magnetohydrodynamic instabilities is to use a magnetic well. Although it is not possible to create a magnetic well over a continuous region of the toroid, an average well may be made where the stabilizing effect of one region more than overcomes the destabilizing effect of an adjacent region if there is good electrical connection between the two regions. An appropriate magnetic field configuration can be made by immersing one or more current-carrying ring conductors in the plasma. This is the Multipole class of experiments. Current can be supplied via small leads or induced while the conductors are supported on fine wires (e.g., in the Climax experiment). Magnetic field gradients in the minor cross section cause plasma to drift parallel to the minor axis and eventually on to the wires. The containment time is too short for a practical reactor, and such experiments are used to investigate plasma stability. Longer times may be obtained by using a superconducting levitated ring (the Levitron and Spherator experiments). Even so, there still may be difficulty in using the Multipole in a reactor because of the heat loading on the ring.

Diffusion Because of the complex interaction between plasma and magnetic field, one of the foremost problems is to understand the possible instabilities of plasma with parameters as close as possible to fusion reactor conditions. The main parameters are density, temperature, β, and containment time and in experiments only one (or occasionally two) approaches reactor values. Apart from the physics problems, cost at present prohibits attempts to obtain all the values simultaneously. The overall effect of the instability on the containment time is usually expressed in terms of a coefficient of diffusion (D) across the magnetic field [this is related to the confinement time and characteristic length of density gradients (x) by $x^2 \approx D_t$]. After each collision, the particle center of gyration shifts by a distance of $\sim$ Larmor radius to a lower density region. The minimum diffusion rate (D_c) is determined by the "classical" electron-ion coulomb collision rate giving $D_c \propto nT^{-1/2}B^{-2}$ [in toroidal geometry this must be multiplied by the Pfirsch-Schluter factor, $1 + (rB_z/RB_\theta)^2$ where r and R refer to the minor and major radii, B_θ is the field parallel to the minor circumference, and B_z is the field parallel to the major circumference]. However, insta-

bilities can generate random electric fields which enhance the collision rate, increasing the diffusion up to a maximum. This maximum occurs when there is one collision during each gyration period because greater collision rates impede the diffusion of particles down a given density gradient (i.e., when the mean free path becomes less than the radius of gyration). The maximum diffusion coefficient $D_B \propto T/B$, and with a suitable numerical factor, is known as the Bohm coefficient. Thus $D_c \leqslant D \leqslant D_B$. The range of possible diffusion rates, expressed by the ratio $D_B/D_c \sim T^{3/2}B/n$, becomes much larger at high temperatures and low densities (i.e., when the classical electron-ion collision time $\gg$ the gyration time). This is the state of plasma in a fusion reactor: e.g., with $T \sim 10$ KeV, $n \sim 10^{22} m^{-3}$, and $\beta \sim 0.3$, $D_B/D_c \sim 10^5$. Also, the required containment time for efficient operation leads to the condition $D/D_B > 10^{-2}$.

In the late 1950s many experiments were magnetohydrodynamically unstable; typical examples were z pinches, early Zeta operation, and mirrors. When the magnetohydrodynamic stability conditions had been understood and the apparatus modified, a wide range of diffusion rates was observed. The open-ended mirror, Phoenix II using a plasma formed from 10 KeV injected particles, produced a low density of $\sim 10^{15} m^{-3}$ and $\beta \sim 10^{-5}$. Then $D_B/D_c \sim 10^5$ and $D/D_B \sim 10^{-2}$, so the temperature and containment were satisfactory but the density was too low. Attempts to increase the density were frustrated by losses and microinstabilities. The toroidal experiment, Stellarator C gave $T \sim 100$ eV, $n \sim 10^{19} m^{-3}$ with $D_B/D_c \sim 400$, but only reached $D/D_B \sim 0.2$, and again microinstabilities were detected with electrostatic probes. Thus both the temperature and containment times were unsatisfactory. On the other hand, a very low temperature, low-density Stellarator, Wendelstein II, obtained the lowest possible diffusion rate, D_c, and $D/D_B \sim 10^{-2}$. This used a barium plasma with $T \sim 0.2$ eV and $n \sim 10^{15} m^{-3}$. Encouraging results have been obtained at higher densities of up to $10^{19} m^{-3}$ with a high-shear Stellarator, Proto-Cleo. The plasma temperature is still low, 5 to 30 eV and $\beta \sim 10^{-4}$, but the containment time is 10^{-2} to 10^{-3} sec and $D/D_B \sim 0.2$ to 0.02. This experiment is important in that it has given a good insight into various possible regimes of diffusion that can occur as the collision rate is varied. Experiments with this apparatus and larger developments are continuing.

Currently, the machine that is exciting a great deal of interest is the Tokamak because it produces plasma with parameters approaching reactor requirements. Typically $T \sim 1$ KeV, $n \sim 2.10^{19} m^{-3}$, and containment time ~ 20 msec, and the results show $D/D_B \sim 0.02$ and $D_B/D_c \sim 300$. Work is proceeding on Tokamaks and their variants in many countries.

Lastly, mention should be made of another interesting machine in which the classical diffusion rate is observed, the long open-ended Theta pinch. This gives $n \sim 10^{22} m^{-3}$, $T \sim 200$ eV, $\beta \sim 0.4$, but a containment time of only ~ 30 μsec because of end loss. However, before the ends influence the loss, the radial loss was shown to be classical. This supports theories which predict that high-β plasmas should not exhibit microinstabilities. Further high-β work is proceeding using high-shear toroids.

Engineering Many feasibility studies have been made of fusion reactors assuming that the broad plasma physics problems can be overcome. A typical scheme is a toroidal plasma 6-m major radius, 1-m minor radius surrounded by a molybdenum vacuum vessel 2-m minor radius. The vacuum vessel must have ports for fresh plasma injection and a scraping ("divertor") device to remove spent fuel that has diffused to the wall. Most of the energy is in the neutrons produced. The energy is absorbed in a 1-m thick blanket of molten lithium salt surrounding the vacuum vessel. This thickness is determined by the neutron mean free path, and the salt is continuously pumped through external heat exchangers to produce steam. Lithium is chosen so that tritium fuel can be "bred" by the $^6Li(n, \alpha)T$ reaction, so that the reactor burns the raw material lithium and deuterium. Outside the blanket there are further neutron and γ-ray shields, and then dc superconducting magnets cooled to 4 K. Some of the major problems are:

(a) Injection of fresh fuel on the axis of the plasma.

(b) The material of the vacuum wall. This must withstand large atmospheric forces, neutron and γ-ray bombardment yet not liberate impurities into the plasma, and the divertor must not perturb the magnetic field in the plasma to produce instabilities.

(c) Magnets. The bigger the reactor, the more efficient it is, since the same surface density of superconducting winding contains a greater plasma volume. This can lead to a problem of rather large sizes; Current designs show that economical toroidal reactors should generate a few gigawatts of electrical power [GW(E)]. [The present-day maximum-power station size is about one GW(E). However, the larger amount of power will probably be accommodated by distribution networks by the year 2000, the earliest date that a commercial fusion reactor could be in operation assuming there are no unforseen delays.]

(d) To use the magnets as efficiently as possible, the plasma β must be high and there must be no wasted space between the magnets and the plasma.

Conclusions Overall, it seems that a fusion reactor could produce power for a cost of about 0.3 cents/KWh by the turn of the century. The present work is concentrated to a large extent on investigating the physics feasibility, mainly with larger and larger toroidal systems, and the efforts of the next ten years should yield a

sufficient understanding of the scaling of containment, n, t, and β with the size of the system for an experimental reactor to be built to investigate engineering problems. The research is expanding, being at present about 150 million dollars per year (approximately equally divided between the United States, Western Europe and Russia).

J. A. REYNOLDS

References

Glasstone, S., and Lovberg, R. H., "Controlled Thermonuclear Reactions," New York, Van Nostrand Reinhold, 1960.

Pease, R. S. "Research on Controlled Nuclear Fusion," Rivista del Nuovo Cimento, Series 1, Vol. 1 (1969) Numero Speciale, 184–213.

Rose, D. J., "Engineering Feasibility of Controlled Fusion, A Review," *Nuclear Fusion*, 9, 183–203 (1969).

Cross-references: BREMSSTRAHLUNG, FISSION, NUCLEAR REACTIONS, NUCLEAR REACTOR, NUCLEONICS, PLASMAS.

G

GAS LAWS

The term "gas law" refers to the thermodynamic equation of state of a gas, which is an equation relating the pressure p, the volume V, the absolute temperature T, and the number of moles ν. The equation of state is a valid relation when and only when the gas is in a state of thermodynamic equilibrium; the pressure and temperature are then constant and uniform throughout the volume occupied by the gas.

Ideal or Perfect Gas The ideal or perfect gas is defined thermodynamically by the two conditions: (1) it obeys the equation of state: $pV = \nu RT$ where R is the gas constant per mole ($R = 8.3169 \times 10^7$ erg mole^{-1}°C^{-1}), and (2) the internal energy U is independent of pressure and volume and is a function only of the temperature ($(\partial U/\partial V)_T = 0$). The statistical-mechanical definition of an ideal gas is that it is a gas of noninteracting molecules, i.e., the molecules exert no appreciable forces of attraction or repulsion on each other. Since the notion of a finite "size" of a molecule connotes the existence of a repulsion which prevents two molecules from overlapping each other, the molecules of an ideal gas must be of negligible "size." The two thermodynamic properties can be deduced from the statistical mechanical definition.

The ideal gas equation: $pV = \nu RT$ embodies the experimental laws of Boyle, Charles and Gay-Lussac. It can be derived either from kinetic theory or from statistical mechanics. It is often written in the form: $p = nkT$ where n is the molecular number density and k is Boltzmann's constant ($k = 1.3804 \times 10^{-16}$ erg °C^{-1}). In the case of a mixture of inert, ideal gases, each gas obeys the equation: $p_i = n_i kT$ where p_i and n_i are, respectively, the partial pressure and partial density of the ith component gas. Boyle's law will not hold if the gases in the mixture react chemically since a change in p or V will in general change the value of ν.

Real or Imperfect Gas The ideal gas law is, of course, only an approximation which holds at temperatures sufficiently far above the critical temperature and at sufficiently low densities. The ordinary properties of bulk matter in the liquid and solid states require the existence of strong intermolecular repulsions which endow the molecules with a finite "size" and also require the existence of attractive forces to hold the molecules together. The equation of state

of a real gas is therefore determined by the nature of the intermolecular forces. One of the earliest, simplest, and most useful equations is that of van der Waals

$$\left(p + \frac{a}{V^2}\right)(V - b) = RT \text{ (for 1 mole)} \quad (1)$$

where a and b are constants, determined empirically for each gas, which are related to the attractive and repulsive forces, respectively. This equation can be related theoretically, in first approximation, to a molecular model in which the molecules are represented by rigid elastic spheres that weakly attract each other. The van der Waals equation accounts qualitatively for the liquid-vapor phase transition. The constants a and b can be determined from critical point data.

Other equations of state for an imperfect gas have been proposed which are more accurate than the van der Waals equation, e.g., the equations of Dieterici, Berthelot, Beattie-Bridgeman, and Benedict-Webb-Rubin. These empirical equations are useful in treating the thermodynamic properties of gases at high densities. At low densities, the empirical equations have been superseded by *the virial equation of state*

$$\frac{pV}{RT} = 1 + \frac{B(T)}{V} + \frac{C(T)}{V^2} + \frac{D(T)}{V^3} + \cdots \text{ (for 1 mole)} \quad (2)$$

where $B(T)$, $C(T)$, and $D(T)$ depend on the nature of the gas and are called the second, third and fourth virial coefficients, respectively. The departures of a gas from ideality are represented in this case by a power series in the density. We may rewrite Eq. (2) as

$$p/kT = n + \hat{B}(T)n^2 + \hat{C}(T)n^3 + \hat{D}(T)n^4 + \cdots \quad (3)$$

where $\hat{B}, \hat{C}, \hat{D}$ are the virial coefficients referred to one molecule.

The basic experimental problem in this field is to measure the virial coefficients of different gases as functions of the temperature. The higher-order coefficients beyond $B(T)$ and $C(T)$ are very difficult to measure. The basic theoretical problem is to calculate the virial coefficients

from an assumed form for the intermolecular potential energy and, ultimately, to derive the intermolecular potential from quantum mechanics.

Statistical Mechanics of the Imperfect Gas

The derivation of the virial equation of state from the intermolecular potential involves several steps which may be summarized as follows:

Intermolecular Forces and the Equation of State

In order to calculate the cluster integrals and virial coefficients, one must first choose a form for the intermolecular potential $u(r)$. In principle, the potential $u(r)$ is determined by quantum mechanics for any pair of molecules and could be found by solving the Schrödinger equation. In practice, this is virtually impossible,

Virial Equation   ←Helmholtz Function   ←Canonical Partition Function
                  ←Grand Potential (PV) ←Grand Partition Function

←Configuration Integral   ←Cluster Integrals   ←Intermolecular Potential

The two routes indicated are via the canonical and the grand ensembles. The most difficult step is the evaluation of the configuration integral:

$$Q_N = \int \cdots \int \exp\left[-\Phi(\mathbf{r}_1, \mathbf{r}_2, \cdots \mathbf{r}_N)/kT\right]$$

$$d\tau_1 \, d\tau_2 \, \cdots d\tau_N \quad (4)$$

where Φ is the total intermolecular potential energy of the gas of N molecules. The proper way to evaluate Q_N was first sketched by Ursell and later carried through by Mayer who assumed central forces that were pairwise additive, i.e.,

$$\Phi = \sum_{i<j} u(r_{ij})$$

where $u(r_{ij})$ is the potential between molecules i and j. Neither of these assumptions is correct, but they appear to be good approximations, and with their aid, it is possible to evaluate Q_N rigorously in terms of the so-called cluster integrals, b_l, which are integrals over the coordinates of l molecules only. $B(T)$ is obtained directly from b_2, $C(T)$ is obtained from b_3 and b_2, and the lth virial coefficient requires evaluation of the cluster integrals up through b_l. Explicit formulas for $\hat{B}(T)$ and $\hat{C}(T)$ are:

$$\hat{B}(T) = -\frac{1}{2V} \iint f_{12} d\tau_1 \, d\tau_2 \quad (5)$$

$$\hat{C}(T) = -\frac{1}{3V} \iiint f_{12} f_{23} f_{13} \, d\tau_1 d\tau_2 d\tau_3 \quad (6)$$

where $f_{ij} \equiv \exp\left[-u(r_{ij})/kT\right] - 1$. Higher coefficients in the virial series are increasingly more difficult to evaluate.

The calculations just described are based on the classical Maxwell-Boltzmann statistics and are sufficiently accurate for most gases at ordinary temperatures. However, in the case of the lightest gases H_2 and He and especially at low temperatures, it is necessary to introduce quantum corrections in the equation of state.

and quantum-mechanical calculations have been made only for the very simplest molecules. In the case of interactions between neutral, nonpolar, spherical molecules, e.g., noble-gas atoms, the quantum-theoretical interaction energy can be approximately decomposed into several parts, of which the two most important are the *dispersion energy* and the *valence repulsion energy*. The former corresponds to the van der Waals attraction and the latter to the van der Waals repulsion. The dispersion energy varies inversely with the sixth power of the distance. The valence-repulsion energy takes account of the short-range repulsion that sets in when the electron distributions of the two molecules begin to overlap, and it is associated with the Pauli exclusion principle. There is no simple, general form for the dependence of the valence repulsion potential on the distance: it is often empirically represented by Ae^{-ar} or by μr^{-n} where $n = 12$ is commonly used. In the case of molecules that possess permanent electric dipole or quadrupole moments, there are additional contributions to the van der Waals attraction but these are usually less important than the dispersion energy (H_2O is an exception).

In the absence of a complete quantum-mechanical expression for the intermolecular potential, it is necessary to approximate the potential by a semi-empirical formula, containing one or more adjustable constants, which is chosen on the grounds of physical plausibility and mathematical convenience. The semi-empirical force law is then used to calculate macroscopic properties that are known from experiment, and the parameters in the force law are adjusted to give the best agreement with experiment. Given the form of the intermolecular potential, it is possible to calculate not only the virial coefficients in the equation of state but also the kinetic-theory transport coefficients (i.e., the viscosity coefficient, the thermal conductivity, and the various diffusion coefficients of the gas) and the density, compressibility, and sublimation energy of the solid. A particular functional representation of the intermolecular potential can be considered satisfactory only if it is possible to secure agreement with all experimental data involving a particular pair of molecules with a single choice of the parameters that appear in the law of force.

The semiempirical law that is most frequently used to represent the interaction between non-polar molecules is the *Lennard-Jones* (12, 6) *potential:*

$$u(r) = 4\epsilon[(\sigma/r)^{12} - (\sigma/r)^6] \qquad (7)$$

where ϵ and σ are parameters characterizing the particular pair of molecules. This simple two-parameter function, when inserted in Eq. (5), predicts a temperature variation of the second virial coefficient in good agreement with experiment. The same potential with slightly different values of ϵ and σ also explains the temperature variation of the viscosity coefficient over a substantial temperature range. Third virial coefficients calculated from Eq. (6) do not agree with experiment at low temperatures near the critical point. The large discrepancies have been attributed to three-body forces which invalidate the assumption of pairwise additivity. Calculations of virial coefficients and transport coefficients of gases and of equilibrium properties of the crystal lattices have also been made for other semiempirical potential functions, but the results are not very different from those found with the (12, 6) potential. Nevertheless, there is accumulating evidence both from experiment, e.g., atomic beam scattering, and from theory, e.g., quantum-mechanical calculations of the dispersion energy, that the (12, 6) potential has serious defects, and it has been replaced in recent work by more complicated multiparameter potential functions.

Further advances in this field will come, on the theoretical side, from a more detailed knowledge of the intermolecular forces, and on the experimental side, from more accurate ways of extracting virial coefficients from thermodynamic data. Current values of $C(T)$ are not only subject to experimental errors in the p, V, T measurements but also to substantial uncertainties incurred in fitting the data with polynomials in the density.

Dense Gases High-density gases cannot be conveniently represented by the virial equation of state because of the slow convergence of the virial series. Furthermore, the theoretical evaluation of the higher virial coefficients on the basis of any plausible molecular model would meet with great computational difficulties. Other approaches are therefore needed, e.g., the empirical equations of state already mentioned and the principle of corresponding states. In the latter method, one introduces the reduced, dimensionless variables: $p_r = p/p_c$, $V_r = V/V_c$, and $T_r = T/T_c$ where the subscript c refers to the critical point. The principle of corresponding states then asserts that all substances obey the same equation of state in terms of the reduced variables. The variables may also be reduced in terms of intermolecular potential parameters.

A promising theoretical approach to the equation of state of a dense gas or liquid is provided by the method of the radial distribution function $g(r, n, T)$. Because of intermolecular forces,

the actual density at a small distance r from a given molecule is different from the bulk density n and is represented by $ng(r, n, T)$. Thus the radial distribution function measures the effect of intermolecular forces on the probability of finding two molecules close together. While it is difficult to determine $g(r, n, T)$ theoretically, it can be found experimentally from the diffraction pattern observed when x-rays are scattered by the fluid.

R. D. PRESENT

References

Cowling, T. G., "Molecules in Motion," London, Hutchinson & Co., Ltd., 1950 (for the general reader).

Hill, T. L., "Statistical Mechanics," Ch. 5 and 6, New York, McGraw-Hill Book Co., 1946 (statistical mechanics of imperfect gases and dense fluids).

Hirschfelder, J. O., Curtiss, C. F., and Bird, R. B., "Molecular Theory of Gases and Liquids," Chs. 3 and 4, New York, John Wiley & Sons, 1954 (covers all aspects of the subject and is the standard reference in this field).

Present, R. D., "Kinetic Theory of Gases," Ch. 6 and 12, New York, McGraw-Hill Book Co., 1958 (kinetic theory of the second virial coefficient; intermolecular forces).

Rushbrooke, G. S., "Introduction to Statistical Mechanics," Ch. 16, London, Oxford University Press, 1949 (good introduction to imperfect-gas theory).

Levelt Sengers, J. M. H., Klein, M., and Gallagher, J. S., "Pressure-Volume-Temperature Relationships of Gases, Virial Coefficients," AEDC-TR-71-39, 1971, and American Institute of Physics Handbook.

Cross-references: COMPRESSIBILITY, GAS; GASES: THERMODYNAMIC PROPERTIES; INTERMOLECULAR FORCES; KINETIC THEORY; THERMODYNAMICS.

GASES: THERMODYNAMIC PROPERTIES

Fundamental Principles The thermodynamic properties of a substance may be classified as either reference properties, energy functions, or derived properties.[1] The reference properties of a single-component system with their symbols and units are pressure, p, Pa or Nm^{-2}; volume, V, m^3; temperature, T, K; and entropy, S, JK^{-1} mol^{-1}. For a specific amount of a pure gas, it is necessary to specify only two of these reference properties to fix the state of the system and its properties. For mixtures of gases, the composition must also be specified to fix the system completely. The energy functions with their symbols and units are internal energy, U, J mol^{-1}; enthalpy, H, J mol^{-1}; Helmholtz energy, A, J mol^{-1}; and Gibbs energy, G, J mol^{-1}. These functions represent the energy available for performing useful work under various process conditions. Derived properties with their symbols and units include heat

capacity, C, JK^{-1} mol^{-1}; fugacity, f, Pa or Nm^{-2}; compression factor, Z, unitless; and the Joule-Thomson coefficient, μ, K Pa^{-1} or Km^2 N^{-1}.

Properties are termed intensive if they are independent of the amount of the material. Examples are pressure and temperature. Properties such as volume and entropy, which are dependent on the amount of material, are termed extensive.

Absolute values may be determined for the reference properties, but the energy functions must be determined relative to an arbitrary zero reference point. The internal energy, U_0°, of the ideal gas at the absolute zero of temperature is generally taken as the zero reference point of the enthalpy and free energy functions. Other reference points include a zero value for the enthalpy of the ideal gas at the ice point, $H_{273.15}^\circ$, and another in which the sensible enthalpies are combined with chemical energies.[2] In the latter base, the value of $H_{298.15}^\circ$ is zero for the assigned reference elements so that the values of $H_{298.15}^\circ$ for the various compounds are equal to their heats of formation from the assigned reference elements.

Thermodynamic properties of gases are calculated for both the ideal gas state and the real gas state. A gas is defined to be ideal if it follows the simple equation of state, $pV = RT$, for 1 mole of gas. Gases behave in this manner only at very low pressure, but the ideal gas state is a convenient reference state for the calculation of the thermodynamic properties. Thus, the thermodynamic standard state[3] is defined as the ideal gas at 1 atmosphere (= 101 325 Pa) pressure at each temperature, and it is denoted by a superscript degree mark as in H° and S°. The ideal gas properties have been calculated for many substances, but the real gas properties are known for relatively few substances.

Thermodynamic properties are used in the calculation of energy balances, reaction compositions at chemical equilibrium, reaction temperatures, and the work involved in the compression or expansion of gases in various systems.

Ideal Gas Properties The thermodynamic properties of an ideal gas such as heat capacity at constant pressure, C_p°, enthalpy function, $(H^\circ - H_0^\circ)/T$, entropy, S°, and Gibbs energy function, $(G^\circ - G_0^\circ)/T$, in units of JK^{-1} mol^{-1}, are calculated from theoretical equations and from an analysis of spectroscopic and molecular structure data.[4-6] These complex calculations are based upon the contributions from all of the energy states available to the molecule, such as translational, electronic, vibrational, and rotational. Contributions from excited electronic states are important for diatomic molecules at higher temperatures but are entirely negligible for most polyatomic molecules. Vibrational energy levels are obtained from an analysis of infrared and Raman spectroscopic data by applying the principles of wave mechanics and

group theory.[4,7] The interpretation of the spectra includes the assumption of a model for the molecule with parameters such as bond lengths, bond angles, and force constants. The parameters are varied within certain limits until the best agreement with observed spectra is obtained. Rotational energy levels are observed in infrared, Raman, and microwave spectra. The rotational energy includes not only the rotation of the molecule as a whole but also internal rotations by groups of atoms within the molecule and a pseudorotation in some ring molecules.[8]

For higher orders of accuracy in the calculation of the thermodynamic properties, additional contributions may be determined that are caused by the interaction between vibrational and rotational motions, centrifugal distortion of the molecule during rotation, and anharmonicity of the vibrations. Another contribution due to nuclear spin can be, and generally is, neglected for all molecules except H_2 and D_2 since it causes a detectable effect on measurable quantities only at very low temperatures. Adjustments are made for the presence of isotopes in some diatomic and polyatomic molecules.

The calculation of the thermodynamic properties of an ideal gas is based not only on theory but also on accurate experimental vapor heat capacity, heat of vaporization, and low-temperature calorimetric data.[8] The ideal gas heat capacity C_p° and entropy S° are derived from these data and are compared to theoretical values. When differences are found, the theoretical calculations are revised until there is good agreement. In this manner, new information is gained about the conformation of the molecule, its frequencies of vibration, etc. Thus, experimental data provide a firm base to test theoretical calculations and improve the calculation of all of the thermodynamic properties.

Theoretical calculations become increasingly complex as the molecular size increases. Thus, a method of increments has been devised to calculate the thermodynamic properties of large molecules based on an "anchor compound" for a given homologous series.[1,9]

Real Gas Properties The thermodynamic properties of real gases are determined primarily from experimental compressibility (pressure-volume-temperature) measurements (see COMPRESSIBILITY, GAS). All other properties are calculated either from equations of state or from a correlation of the individual experimental data points. In addition, the properties may be estimated from generalized correlations of the compression factor ($Z = pV/RT$). Here and in the equations that follow, V denotes molar volume in m^3 mol^{-1} and R denotes the molar gas constant, in JK^{-1} mol^{-1}.

Experimental compressibility measurements have been made by a variety of methods[10,11] such as constant volume cells (Eucken and Meyer), variable volume cells (Beattie and

Douslin, Michels, and Sage and Lacey), expansion systems with variable sample mass (Burnett), and differential systems (Whytlaw-Gray). The apparatus of Beattie and Douslin is used to measure both isometrics and isotherms up to 350°C and 400 atmospheres. The Michels apparatus may be used up to 3000 atmospheres but is limited to a temperature of 150°C. Sage and Lacey have made extensive measurements on both gas and liquid systems up to 240°C and 670 atmospheres.

Equations of state have been derived from compressibility data to represent the behavior of a gas over wide ranges of temperature and pressure.[10,12] Numerous equations have been published but one of the most important is the virial equation,

$$pV = RT(1 + B/V + C/V^2 + D/V^3 + \cdots)$$

(1)

It is quite important because the parameters B, C, D, etc., are related to the interactions between molecules according to the intermolecular potential energy theory. Other equations having wide applications are those of Beattie and Bridgeman and of Benedict, Webb, and Rubin (see GAS LAWS).

The energy functions, entropy, and heat capacity of a real gas are calculated as the sum of the ideal gas properties and a correction for the nonideality of the gas. The corrections for the nonideality of the gas are called difference or departure functions. For example, S-$S°$ is the entropy of the gas in the real state less that of the gas in the standard state at the same temperature. Theoretical equations needed for the computation of the thermodynamic properties have been derived in terms of pressure, volume, temperature, and the first derivatives $(\partial V/\partial T)_p$ or $(\partial p/\partial T)_v$.[12]

For example:

$$H - H° = \int_v^\infty [p - T(\partial p/\partial T)v] dV + pV - RT$$

(2)

The neat capacity differences $C_p - C_p^°$ and $C_v - C_v^°$ are functions also of the second derivatives $(\partial^2 V/\partial T^2)_p$ or $(\partial^2 p/\partial T^2)_v$ depending upon whether the equations are written in terms of p and T, or V and T. The quantities appearing in Eq. (2) are usually evaluated from equations of state. However, the most accurate properties are those which are calculated from an analysis of isometric and isothermal p-V-T data.[13] The slopes of the isometrics $(\partial p/\partial T)_v$ are found by analytical, residual, and graphical techniques. The integrals as in Eq. (2) are integrated graphically or numerically.

Extensive correlations of data have been made to develop methods for estimating the properties of gases.[1,12] One method based on the theory of corresponding states presents the thermodynamic properties as a function of reduced temperature $(T_r = T/T_c)$, reduced pressure $(p_r = p/p_c)$, and the compressibility factor, Z_c. The subscript c refers to the critical state.

Gas Mixtures The thermodynamic properties of a mixture of gases may be calculated, but the procedures are only approximate unless compressibility data are available for the particular mixture[10-12] Since few data for mixtures are available, the properties must be estimated from: (a) the equations of state of the pure gases assuming either additive volumes or additive pressures, (b) an equation of state for the mixture, or (c) generalized correlations of the compressibility factor based on pseudo-reduced conditions.[1]

ROLAND H. HARRISON

References

1. Hougen, O. A., Watson, K. M., and Ragatz, R. A., "Chemical Process Principles, Part Two: Thermodynamics," New York, John Wiley & Sons, Inc., 1959.
2. Guggenheim, E. A., "Thermodynamics," pp. 244–248, Amsterdam, North Holland Publishing Co., 1967.
3. "Selected Values of Properties of Hydrocarbons and Related Compounds," American Petroleum Institute Research Project 44, Chemical Thermodynamic Properties Center, Texas A&M University, College Station, Texas, 2652 loose-leaf sheets extant December 31, 1971.
4. Herzberg, G., "Molecular Spectra and Molecular Structure II. Infrared and Raman Spectra of Polyatomic Molecules," New York, Van Nostrand Reinhold Co., 1945.
5. Stull, D. R., Westrum, E. F., Jr., and Sinke, G. C., "The Chemical Thermodynamics of Organic Compounds," New York, John Wiley & Sons, Inc., 1969.
6. Stull, D. R., and Prophet, H., "JANAF Thermochemical Tables," National Standard Reference Data Series, National Bureau of Standards (U.S.), 37, 1141 pp. (June 1971), U.S. Government Printing Office, Catalog No. C 13.48:37, Washington.
7. Wilson, E. B., Jr., Decius, J. C., and Cross, P. C., "Molecular Vibrations—The Theory of Infrared and Raman Vibrational Spectra," New York, McGraw-Hill Book Co., Inc., 1955.
8. McCullough, J. P., Pennington, R. E., Smith, J. C., Hossenlopp, I. A., and Waddington, G., "Thermodynamics of Cyclopentane, Methylcyclopentane, and 1,cis-3-Dimethylcyclopentane: Verification of the Concept of Pseudorotation," J. Am. Chem. Soc., 81, 5880 (1959).
9. Scott, D. W., and McCullough, J. P., "The Chemical Thermodynamic Properties of Hydrocarbons and Related Substances," U.S. Bur. Mines Bull., 595 (1961).
10. Rowlinson, J. S., in Flugge, S., Ed., "Encyclopedia of Physics," Vol. XII, pp. 1–72, Berlin, Springer-Verlag, 1958.

11. Douslin, D. R., Harrison, R. H., and Moore, R. T., "Pressure-Volume-Temperature Relations in the System Methane-Tetrafluoromethane. I. Gas Densities and the Principle of Corresponding States," *J. Phys. Chem.*, **71**, 3477–3488 (1967).

12. Beattie, J. A., and Stockmayer, W. H., in Taylor, H. S., and Glasstone, S., Eds., "Treatise on Physical Chemistry," Vol. 2, pp. 187–290, New York, Van Nostrand Reinhold Co., 1951.

13. Harrison, R. H., and Douslin, D. R., "Tetrafluoromethane–Thermodynamic Properties of the Real Gas," *J. Chem. Eng. Data*, **11**(3), 383–388 (1966).

Cross-references: COMPRESSIBILITY, GAS; GAS LAWS; HEAT CAPACITY; KINETIC THEORY; THERMODYNAMICS.

GEODESY

Geodesy comprises the determination of the earth's external form and gravitational field, and the location of points with respect to earth-fixed reference systems. The earth's external form is customarily defined by the geoid: the equipotential of the earth's gravity field which most closely approximates the mean sea level.

The geoid is irregular in form, so that the mathematical representation thereof is necessarily an approximation. The most important approximation is an oblate ellipsoid of revolution, which is conventionally defined by its equatorial radius, a, and the flattening, f, equal to $(a - b)/a$, where b is the polar semidiameter. Location is conventionally expressed in coordinates referred to such an ellipsoid, in terms of the latitude ϕ, the angle between the normal to the ellipsoid and the equator; the longitude λ from the reference meridian, Greenwich; and altitude h above or below the ellipsoid.

If the ellipsoid is considered to be rotating with rate ω, and to be an equipotential for the combined effects (called gravity) of centrifugal and gravitational acceleration, additional parameters customarily required are γ_e, the acceleration of gravity at the equator; and m, the ratio of the centrifugal acceleration at the equator, $\omega^2 a$, to γ_e. γ_e and m are connected to the total mass M contained in the ellipsoid by:

$$GM = a^2 \gamma_e [1 - f + 3m/2 - 15mf/14$$
$$+ O(f^3)] \quad (1)$$

where G is the constant of GRAVITATION $(6.67 \times 10^{-8} \, cm^3 \, g^{-1} \, sec^{-2})$. The customary formula for the acceleration of gravity γ at geodetic latitude ϕ is:

$$\gamma = \gamma_e [1 + (5m/2 - f - 17mf/14) \sin^2 \phi$$
$$+ (f^2/8 - 5mf/8) \sin^2 2\phi + O(f^3)] \quad (2)$$

The customary formula for the gravitational potential external to the ellipsoid is:

$$V = \frac{GM}{r} \left[1 - J_2 \left(\frac{a}{r} \right)^2 P_2 (\sin \phi) \right.$$
$$\left. - J_4 \left(\frac{a}{r} \right)^4 P_4 (\sin \phi) - O(f^3) \right] \quad (3)$$

In Eq. (3), V is written as positive, which is the convention of astronomy and geodesy, contrary to that of physics. In Eq. (3), P_2 and P_4 are Legendre polynomials, and

$$J_2 = 2f(1 - f/2)/3 - m(1 - 3m/2 - 2f/7)/3$$
$$+ O(f^3) \quad (4)$$

while J_4 is usually taken as a quantity determined observationally from satellite orbits.

The discrepancies in location of the actual geoid and a well-fitting ellipsoid are nearly always 10^{-5} or less of the radius vector, while the discrepancies in intensity of the gravitational acceleration from that of the standard ellipsoid are nearly always 10^{-4} or less of the total intensity. The mathematical representation of these discrepancies may either be in the form of spherical harmonic coefficients or in the form of mean values for areas; the former being preferable for effects on satellites in orbit, and the latter for use of terrestrial data. The potential theory dealing with the relationship between variations in the location of the geoid and the intensity of gravitational acceleration is known in geodesy as Stokes' theorem.

There are five principal systems of measurement in geodesy.

(1) Horizontal control comprises the determination of the horizontal components of position—latitude and longitude—starting from fixed values for a certain point. It includes measurement of distances over the ground by metal tapes or by pulsing or modulating radio or light signals, and measurement of angles about a vertical axis by theodolites. Over the land, the relative horizontal position of points is obtained either by triangulation—a system of overlapping triangles with nearly all angles measured, but only occasional distances measured; or by traverse—a series of measured distances at measured angles with respect to each other; or by trilateration—a system of overlapping triangles with all sides measured. Much of the land area of the world is covered by triangulation, which gives the difference in latitude and longitude between points in the same network with a relative error of about 10^{-5}.

(2) Vertical control comprises the determination of heights, which is performed separately from horizontal control because of irregularities in atmospheric refraction. The most accurate method, leveling, measures successive differences of elevation on vertical staffs by horizontal lines of sight taken at intermediate points over short distances (less than 150 meters) balanced so as to minimize differential refraction effect. The datum to which vertical control

TABLE 1. GEODETIC PARAMETERS

Parameter	Standard Value	Current Estimate and Standard Deviation
Mean sidereal rotation rate, ω	$.7292115085 \times 10^{-4}$ sec^{-1}	$.7292115085 \times 10^{-4}$ sec^{-1}
Gravitational constant $\times$ mass, $\lambda_e\, GM$	3.986032×10^{14} m^3/sec^2	$3.986013\ (\pm.000003) \times 10^{14}$ m^3/sec^2
Equatorial radius, a	6378165 meters	6378140 ± 3 meters
Flattening, f	1/298.25	$1/298.26 \pm .01$

refers is mean sea level as determined by tide gages. The accuracy is such that the error in difference of elevation between points on the same principal network should be a few tens of centimeters or less.

(3) Geodetic astronomy comprises the determination of the direction of the gravity vector and the direction of the north pole at a point on the ground. Astronomic longitude is the angle between the meridian of the gravity vector and the Greenwich meridian and is determined by measuring the time of intersection of a line of sight by a star. Astronomic latitude is the angle between the gravity vector and the equatorial plane, and is determined by measuring the maximum altitude attained by a star. In these types of astronomic observation, several stars are normally observed which are selected so as to minimize error due to atmospheric refraction. Astronomic azimuth is determined by the measurement of the horizontal angle between a target and Polaris or other reference star.

(4) Gravimetry comprises the determination of intensity of gravitational acceleration. Most gravimetric observations are made differentially, by determining the change, with change in location, of the tension on a spring supporting a constant mass. These measurements are connected through a system of reference stations to a few laboratory determinations of absolute acceleration of gravity. The relative accuracy of gravimetry is about $\pm.001$ cm/sec^2 on land and $\pm.005$ cm/sec^2 at sea. The principal difficulty in its geodetic application is irregular distribution of observations.

(5) Satellite tracking comprises the determination of the directions, ranges, or range rates of earth satellites (including the moon) from ground stations or other satellites. These observations will be affected both by errors in positions of the station with respect to the earth's center of mass and by perturbations of the orbit by the earth's gravitational field; hence, in conjunction with a dynamical integration of the orbit, they are used to determine the position of tracking stations and the variations of the gravitational field. To minimize refraction effect, directions are determined by photographs of the satellite against the background of fixed stars. Satellites can also be used as elevated targets by simultaneous observations from several ground stations.

The principal practical application of geodesy is to provide a distribution of accurately measured points to which to refer mapping, navigation aids, engineering surveys, geophysical surveys, etc. The principal scientific interests in geodesy are the indications of the earth's internal structure from the variations of the gravity field and surface motions.

Numerical values of the leading geodetic parameters are given in Table 1.

WILLIAM M. KAULA

References

Bomford, G., "Geodesy," Third edition, London, Oxford University Press, 1971.

Gaposchkin, E. M., "Satellite Geodesy: Results," *Trans. Amer. Geoph. Un.*, 52, IUGG 30–33, 1971.

Garland, G. O., "The Earth's Shape and Gravity," Oxford, Pergamon Press, 1965.

Heiskanen, W. A., and Moritz, H., "Physical Geodesy," San Francisco, Freeman, 1967.

Jeffreys, H., "The Earth," Fifth edition, London, Cambridge University Press, 1970.

Kaula, W. M., "Theory of Satellite Geodesy," Waltham, Mass., Blaisdell, 1966.

Cross-references: ASTRODYNAMICS, ASTRONOMY, ASTRONAUTICS, GEOPHYSICS, GRAVITATION, POTENTIAL, ROTATION–CIRCULAR MOTION.

GEOPHYSICS

Geophysics is the physics of the earth and the space immediately surrounding it and the interactions between the earth and extraterrestrial forces and phenomena. It consists of a number of interlocking sciences dealing with physical properties of the earth, its interior and atmosphere, its age, motions and paroxysms, and their practical applications. All of these sciences use the methods of physics for measurements and analysis. From observational material, often of an indirect nature, attempts are made to derive abstract models of states and processes through advanced mathematical concepts, and, in some cases, through statistical relations.

Geophysics is an ancient science. In its early stages it was developed by the Greeks who at-

tempted to determine the shape and size of the Earth (Eratosthenes, 275–194 B.C.). Among its most illustrious contributors have been Galileo Galilei (1564–1642); Sir Isaac Newton (1642–1727) who dealt with the motions of the earth and its gravitational field; Karl Friedrich Gauss (1777–1855), who developed the theory of the magnetic field; and Vilhelm Bjerknes (1862–1951) who laid the foundation for the hydrodynamic theories of the atmosphere and the oceans. During the current century, its roster of distinguished scientists includes: L. Vegard (polar aurora); Sidney Chapman (aeronomy); C.-G. Rossby (meteorology); H. U. Sverdrup (oceanography); Sir Harold Jeffreys; F. A. Vening-Meinesz (structure of the earth); and B. Gutenberg and J. B. Macelwane (seismology).

A major milestone in the development of the science was the International Geophysical Year (IGY), followed by the International Geophysical Cooperation, from 1957–1959, when over 8000 scientists of 66 nations collaborated in a coordinated attack on the remaining physical mysteries of our planet. The IGY gave birth to man's most spectacular ventures to date: the launching of artificial earth satellites and the conquest of the icy wastes of the Antarctic continent in the quest for solutions of important geophysical problems. IGY took place during an interval of high solar activity and was followed in 1964–65 by the year of the quiet sun (IQSY) to cover the whole range of solar influences on the earth (see INTERNATIONAL GEOPHYSICAL YEAR AND INTERNATIONAL YEARS OF THE QUIET SUN).

A brief survey of the various subfields of geophysics follows:

Geochronology is the study of the age of the earth and its various geological formations. Inadequate earlier methods of sedimentology have been replaced by the use of radioactive decay constants and isotope ratios. This has made it possible to date approximately all major geological eras. For the oldest rocks, the decay of ^{238}U to ^{206}Pb has led to ages of around 3×10^9 years.

GEODESY deals with the size and shape of the earth and its gravitational field. Because of the rotation of the earth, its lack of absolute rigidity, crustal mass distribution, and tidal forces, the shape is not spherical but approximates that of a triaxial ellipsoid. The polar diameter is shorter than the equatorial. This polar flattening has been determined by measurements on the surface, lunar observations and, since, 1958 satellite motions. The best estimate of the flattening is 1 : 298. The actual figure of the earth, which is irregular, is referred to as the *geoid*, which represents an isopotential surface. The undulations of the geoid have been determined by gravity measurements. The measured values of gravity depend on latitude because of the flattening and the variation of the centrifugal force from pole to equator. The normal value of gravity at the earth's surface in centimeters per

second per second, is represented by

$$\gamma = 978.0318[1 + 0.0053024$$
$$\sin^2 \phi - 0.0000059 \sin^2 2\phi]$$

where ϕ is latitude, and referred to as The Geodetic Reference System of 1967.

Gravity measurements have shown that in spite of large mass differences at the surface, the earth is nearly in isostatic equilibrium. Various crustal blocks act as if they floated in a dense subcrustal material. The undulations of the geoid do not exceed 80 meters. Approximate dimensional figures for the earth are: surface area 510.1×10^6 km²; volume $1,083 \times 10^9$ km³; average density 5.517 g/cm³; mass 5.975×10^{27} grams; equatorial radius $6,378.163$ km.

The deformations of the solid earth by tidal forces form a specialty. The twice daily occurring *tides* are observed by deflections of the vertical or variations of gravity. For the lunar tide, the variations amount to about 0.168 milligal, for the sun to 0.075 milligal. (One milligal equals 10 microns per sec per sec.) The maximal elevation of the geoid is 36 cm, the largest depression 18 cm, for the lunar effect; the total solar tide can reach 25 cm. The combined total at new and full moon is 79 cm.

Geomagnetism deals with one of the most important physical characteristics of the earth. Its magnetic field is about 1/2 gauss in strength. It consists of an internal part, about 9/10 of the total and an external part of 1/10. The internal part is assumed to originate from electromagnetic fields caused by differential rotation between the earth's core and its mantle. The external part is caused by an ionospheric ring current. The field can be represented by a dipole, which fluctuates in direction both in time and space. Short-periodic fluctuations are brought about by solar disturbances which cause invasions of protons and electrons into the high atmosphere. These disturbances, which follow broadly solar activity as expressed by sunspots, cause minor and major fluctuations of the earth's magnetic field. The major disturbances, called magnetic storms, can be observed worldwide. The same particle bombardments cause *polar aurorae* through excitation of oxygen, hydrogen, and nitrogen atoms in the high atmosphere. Much slower variations of the magnetic field are tied to the internal field and possibly connected with convective currents. Paleomagnetic evidence indicates that the magnetic poles are not fixed and that the field has reversed direction several times during the earth's history. In the present era, the magnetic poles and poles of rotation do not coincide.

It has been hypothesized that the migration of the magnetic poles is also an indication of migrations of the inertial axis of the earth. The distribution of the field over the surface of the earth has been mapped in form of the total intensity, the horizontal and vertical intensity, the inclination and declination. The latter is of

great practical importance for use of magnetic compasses in direction finding. The influence of the earth's magnetic field extends outward into space for many earth radii. It influences the path of invading particles and is responsible for the configuration of the van Allen belts.

SEISMOLOGY deals with the study of earthquakes. Most of them can be attributed to breaks in the earth's crust. A few may be subcrustal and caused by phase transformations. Some minor ones are associated with collapse of cavities and volcanic eruptions. All of them are characterized by sudden release of elastic waves. These are longitudinal, transverse, Rayleigh or Love (surface) waves. Through analysis of their travel time from the point of origin to receiving seismograph stations, they permit deduction of the layering and elastic constants of the interior of the earth. Like other waves, earthquake waves can be reflected and refracted upon entering a different medium. The internal constitution of the earth has been derived primarily from seismic evidence. This reveals an upper and lower crust, an upper and lower mantle, and the core. The boundary between crust and mantle was first discovered by A. Mohorovičić in 1909. The depth is variable. In some oceanic areas, it may be only 5 km; in continental areas, it is usually 30 to 40 km and the maximum is estimated at 60 km. The quest for knowledge about the petrographic constitution of the mantle has led to the project attempting to drill in one of the suboceanic thin crustal areas to the Mohorovičić discontinuity, the so-called Mohole. The boundary of the core is about 2900 km deep. The density in the mantle is from 3 to 6 g/cm^3, that of the core from 10 to 17 g/cm^3. The temperature of the interior has been variously estimated at 1500 to 4000°C. Earthquakes are primarily tied to areas of geologically recent mountain formation, the great island arcs, and the adjacent great rifts. The same areas usually show also the greatest contemporary volcanic activity.

Volcanology deals with some of the most spectacular phenomena in geophysics. They include explosive eruptions, lava flows, gaseous exhalations, magma intrusions, geysers and hot springs. Study of the earth's active volcanoes revealed that release of tectonic pressure may lead to volcanic eruptions, but no reliable systems of forecasting impending volcanic activity have yet been devised. The greatest eruption within human memory was that of Krakatoa on May 20, 1883 which threw about 4 km^3 of dust into the air up to stratospheric levels. This dust stayed in suspension for over two years, interfering with the earth's heat balance. Some hypotheses of climatic fluctuations are based on the varying intensity of eruptive volcanism during the earth's history.

METEOROLOGY and *Aeronomy* are concerned with the physical state and the motions of the atmosphere, which is divided into a number of layers. The lowest is the troposphere with an average thickness of 7 to 8 km in polar regions and 13 km in the equatorial zone. Temperatures decrease to the interface, called tropopause, with the next layer the stratosphere. At the tropopause, polar temperatures average around -55°C, in equatorial regions -80°C. In the stratosphere, temperatures stay nearly isothermal with height and increase again above 25 km. Above the stratosphere are the mesosphere and ionosphere, and the outermost layer, the exosphere, gradually fades into the plasma continuum between earth and sun. In these higher layers of the atmosphere, complex interactions between the fluxes of electromagnetic radiation of various wavelengths and corpuscular radiation from the sun on one side and the low-density concentrations of atmospheric gases on the other side take place. The particulate radiations are also governed by the earth's magnetic field. Radiations of short wavelength cause a variety of photochemical reactions, the most notable of which is the creation of a layer of ozone acting as an effective absorber of solar ultraviolet and thus causing a warm layer at 30 km in the atmosphere. The upper atmosphere as an absorber of primary cosmic rays shows many interesting nuclear reactions and is an important natural source of radioactive substances including tritium and carbon 14 which are used as tracers of atmospheric motions and as criteria of age.

Most manifestations of weather take place in the troposphere. They are governed by the general atmospheric circulation which is stimulated by the differential heating between tropical and polar zones. The resulting motions in the air are subject to the laws of fluid dynamics on a rotating sphere with friction. They are characterized by turbulence of varying time and space scale. Evaporation of water from the ocean and its transformation through the vapor state to droplets and ice crystals, forming clouds and precipitation, are important symptoms of the weather-producing forces (see METEOROLOGY).

Hydrology studies the water cycle on the earth in detail. It includes the runoff from precipitation, the surface courses of water and their floods, the deposited forms of water as snow and ice, and the return of water to storage underground or the ocean. The study of glaciers and their mass budget is an important phase of this field and contributes to the as yet speculative hypotheses about ice ages.

Oceanography has a broad overlap with both meteorology and hydrology. It 'includes the study of wind-driven waves and currents, and the storage and release of heat to the atmosphere. The tidal motions and their dependence upon configuration of ocean basins and coastal lines were among the earliest geophysical phenomena observed and analyzed by man. They were also the first to be predicted by a computer. The density differences of ocean waters, predicated on temperature and salinity, cause three-dimensional internal circulations in the deeper ocean layers. Much of this remains to be

observed and explained. Of great practical importance to inhabitants of shore lines are the *tsunamis* which are gravity waves caused by underwater earthquakes. Because their movement is much slower than that of elastic seismic waves, warnings can be issued through prompt evaluation of seismic records.

Geophysical prospecting is based on physical methods derived from the study of earthquakes and magnetic and gravitational fields. These procedures, highly refined, are being used in the discovery of mineral resources. Inhomogeneities in the crust caused by inclusions of different physical characteristics can be noted from the surface by local anomalies of the magnetic or the gravitational field. Miniature earthquakes produced by explosions will disclose layering, salt domes and other geological features. Distortion of artificially created electric fields also can lead to ore bodies or similar anomalies. Interpretation of radioactivity observed at the surface or in boreholes also permits geological deductions. Extremely sensitive apparatus, especially for magnetometric mapping, can be used from the air and permits rapid surveying of vast areas.

H. E. LANDSBERG

References

Chamberlain, J. W., "Physics of the Aurora and Airglow," New York, Academic Press, 1961.
Flügge, S., Ed., "Handbuch der Physik" (Encyclopedia of Physics); Bartels, J., group editor, "Geophysics," Vols. 47 and 48, Berlin, Springer, 1956 and 1957.
Israël, H., "Einführung in die Geophysik," Berlin, Springer, 1969.
Jacobs, J. A., Russel, R. D., and Wilson, J. Tuzo, "Physics and Geology," New York, McGraw-Hill Book Co., 1959.
Jeffreys, Harold, "The Earth," Fifth edition, Cambridge, Cambridge University Press, 1970.
Landsberg, H. E., and van Mieghem, J., Eds., *Advan. Geophys.*, **1–16** (1952–1973).
Valley, Shea L., Ed., "Handbook of Geophysics and Space Environments," Air Force Cambridge Research Laboratories, Office of Aerospace Research, USAF, 1965.

Cross-references: FLUID DYNAMICS, GEODESY, GRAVITATION, INTERNATIONAL GEOPHYSICAL YEAR AND INTERNATIONAL YEARS OF THE QUIET SUN, MAGNETISM, METEOROLOGY, PLANETARY ATMOSPHERES, SEISMOLOGY.

GRAVITATION

Gravitation is the phenomenon characterized by the mutual attraction of any two physical bodies. This universal character of the gravitational force was first recognized by Sir Issac Newton who also gave its quantitative expression. For point masses or spherical bodies a simple expression results:

$$F = \frac{GM_1 M_2}{R^2} \tag{1}$$

In addition to the masses M_1, M_2 of the two bodies and their distance apart R, the force depends only on a constant $G = 6.670 \times 10^{-8}$ dyne cm^2 which is independent of all properties of the particular bodies involved. The same force law describes the motion of the planets around the sun, of the moon around the earth, as well as the falling of an apple to the earth. A body moving under an inverse square law as given in Eq. (1) satisfies the three laws established by Kepler for the motion of the planets around the sun:

(1) The planets move in elliptical orbits with the sun at one focus (the general orbit is a conic section) (Fig. 1).

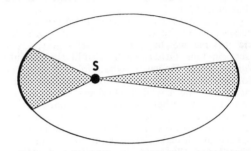

FIG. 1. An elliptical orbit for a planet around the sun. The shaded areas indicate equal areas swept out in equal times at different parts of the orbit. Clearly, the speed of the planet varies with its position in its orbit.

(2) The radius vector sweeps out equal areas in equal times.
(3) The square of the period of revolution is proportional to the cube of the semimajor axis: $a^3 = (2\pi)^{-2} GM_\odot T^2$. Here $M_\odot$ is the mass of the sun and T is the period of the planet. These results together with a detailed analysis of anomalies in the motion of the moon established the correctness of the Newtonian theory of gravitation (see KEPLER'S LAWS).

Recently, careful calculations have been carried out to determine the orbits of the artificial satellites which have been launched by the United States and the Soviet Union. These have required modifications in the force law Eq. (1) to take into account the deviation of the earth's figure from a sphere and the anistropy of the earth's density as well as the atmospheric drag. The success of the space program to date is an additional tribute to Newton's genius. Other calculations study powered space flight in order to examine possible orbits for exploration of the solar system. There is every reason to believe that Newton's gravitational theory is sufficiently accurate for this purpose. Einstein's

modification of the theory, to be described below, will probably have little effect on our space program for some time to come.

The weight of a body of mass M on the earth is the force with which it is attracted to the center of the earth. On the surface of the earth the weight is given by

$$W = Mg$$

where the acceleration due to gravity is obtained from Eq. (1):

$$g = \frac{GM_E}{R_E{}^2} = 980 \text{ cm/sec}^2 = 32 \text{ ft/sec}^2$$

All freely falling bodies near the surface of the earth are accelerated at the same rate g. It is for this reason that Galileo found that both light and heavy objects take the same time to reach the ground when dropped from the Leaning Tower of Pisa.

An astronaut is said to be in a state of weightlessness when he is in orbit. Strictly speaking, he still has weight, for the earth's gravity still acts on him. Otherwise he would fly off into outer space. However, when in free fall, the local effects of the gravitational field are eliminated for the astronaut. Objects which are released fall together with him and hence remain in his vicinity, unlike the situation on the ground. Therefore, the organs of the body respond as though the gravitational field were absent and this gives the sensation of weightlessness. Conversely, we sense the earth's gravity and feel weight because we are supported by the earth's surface.

Gravitational Field According to Newtonian theory, the sun exerts the gravitational force directly on the earth without an intervening medium for transmitting that force. The behavior of such forces is called "action at a distance." To overcome the conceptual difficulty of a force acting directly over large distances, one assumes that a gravitational field fills all space. The force acting on any mass is determined by the gravitational field in its neighborhood. Thus, at the point P a distance R from the center of the earth, the gravitational field has the magnitude

$$\mathcal{G} = \frac{GM_E}{R^2}$$

and magnitude of the force on a mass M at P is simply $F = M\mathcal{G}$. Note that the field is to exist at P even in the absence of the mass M.

It is sometimes convenient to introduce the gravitational potential which determines the field through its gradient. For a spherical earth, it is defined as

$$\phi = -\frac{GM_E}{R}, \quad \mathcal{G} = -\text{ grad } \phi$$

In general ϕ will satisfy Poisson's equation

$$\frac{\partial^2\phi}{\partial x^2} + \frac{\partial^2\phi}{\partial y^2} + \frac{\partial^2\phi}{\partial z^2} = 4\pi\rho \tag{2}$$

ρ is the density of matter. The potential energy of a mass M, in the field is simply expressed in terms of ϕ,

$$V = M\phi$$

A body has enough speed to escape from the earth's attraction if its total energy, kinetic plus potential, is zero or greater. From the definition of potential energy above, the *escape velocity* at a distance R from the center of the earth is given by

$$v_{es}{}^2 = \frac{2GM_E}{R} \tag{3}$$

At the surface of the earth the $v_{es} = 11$ km/sec. It is interesting to note that when $R = R_s$, the Schwarzschild radius, the escape velocity is just equal to the velocity of light, $c (3 \times 10^5$ km/sec.):

$$R_s = \frac{2\,GM}{c^2} \tag{4}$$

The subscript E has been dropped from M because the *Schwarzschild radius* R_s is defined for any mass. For the earth, $R_s = 0.9$ cm while for the sun, $R_s = 3$ km. Now, according to special relativity, the speed of light is a limiting speed for matter and cannot be exceeded by any signal. Therefore, it is fortunate that the Schwarzschild radii of the sun and the earth are interior to their surfaces. Otherwise we would receive no energy from the sun and we could not explore the solar system.

Although one can introduce the gravitational field, it is an auxiliary concept in Newtonian theory for the field has no independent dynamical behavior as is true of the electromagnetic field (e.g., electromagnetic waves). At any time, the Newtonian gravitational field is determined by the configuration of masses at that instant and does not depend on previous history or state of motion. Thus, if the sun were to vanish, the gravitational force on the earth would immediately be removed. This property may be thought of in terms of an infinite velocity of propagation for the gravitational field. Letting the velocity of light become infinite in Maxwell's equations eliminates all independent dynamical behavior for the electromagnetic field. In that case there could be no radio or television. The special theory of relativity which is based on the velocity of light in vacuum being the maximum velocity for the transmission of energy, implies that Newton's theory requires modification.

Principle of Equivalence The mass of a body may be measured either by weighing $W = Mg$

(gravitational mass) or by observing its motion under a known applied force using Newton's second law of motion $F = MA$ (inertial mass). The equality of these two differently defined masses has been measured by R. H. Dicke to an accuracy of 1×10^{-11} improving an earlier measurement by Eötvös. It is this equality which distinguishes the gravitational force from all other forces in giving all bodies the same acceleration. The discussion of weightlessness pointed out that local effects of the gravitational field are eliminated for an observer in free fall precisely because all bodies fall at the same rate. It follows that the gravitational field measured by an observer will depend on his state of motion. In a sense there is an equivalence between a gravitational field down and an acceleration up for the observer. However, the equivalence is not complete, for real gravitational fields converge on their sources so that two particles released at the same time will drift closer together as they fall. On the other hand, acceleration fields have no effect on the separation of particles moving on parallel paths (Fig. 2). In a curved space, initially parallel

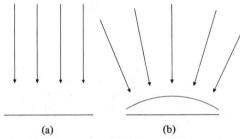

(a)   (b)

FIG. 2. The paths of particles released in: (a) an acceleration field (the acceleration is up, the apparent force is down); (b) a gravitational field showing convergence toward the source.

geodesics—the "straight lines"—do not maintain a constant separation (e.g., great circles on a sphere). Thus, the gravitational field may have its explanation in the geometry of a curved space-time.

Red Shift According to the quantum theory, a photon of frequency ν has an energy $h\nu$ (h is Planck's constant), and by the relation $E = mc^2$, this quantum has a mass $m = h\nu/c^2$. To lift a mass m a height H requires expenditure of the energy mgH. Therefore, a photon emitted at the surface of the earth arrives at the height H with the energy

$$h\nu - (h\nu/c^2)\, gH = h\nu \left(1 - \frac{gH}{c^2}\right) = h\nu'$$

At the surface of the earth, the frequency shift amounts to

$$\frac{\Delta\nu}{\nu} = 1.1 \times 10^{-16}\ H(H \text{ in meters})$$

This shift was measured by Pound and Rebka, using the Mössbauer effect, in good agreement with the prediction. As standard clocks are determined by atomic transitions in freely falling atoms, it follows that if the same photon were emitted at the height H, it would be measured to have the frequency ν not ν'. Therefore, an observer at H must conclude that clocks at H run fast compared with the identical clocks on the ground in the ratio (ν/ν') (Fig. 3).

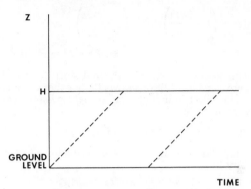

FIG. 3. Photons are emitted on the ground and are received at the height H. Between the two dotted lines representing the beginning and end of a pulse, the same number of oscillations, n, are received at H as are emitted at the ground level. Because of the red shift, the interval t' between oscillations at H is greater than the interval t between oscillations on the ground. Therefore, the time measured at H for the reception of the n oscillations is greater than the time required for their emission on the ground: $nt' > nt$. This result implies that clocks run faster at H than on the ground.

Einstein's Theory of Gravitation Albert Einstein assumed that gravitation is a physical effect produced by the curvature of a four-dimensional space-time. The generalization of Newton's gravitational potential is the metric tensor $g_{\mu\nu}$ in terms of which the four-dimensional distance, and hence the geometry of spacetime, is determined:

$$ds^2 = \sum_{\mu,\nu=1} g_{\mu\nu} dx^\mu dx^\nu$$

The curvature of space-time is defined in terms of a four-index tensor $R_{\nu\rho\sigma}{}^\mu$, the curvature tensor. The vanishing of the curvature tensor means that no real gravitational field is present. The field equations are ten linear combinations of the curvature components which are of the second order in the derivatives of the metric tensor and are a generalization of Poisson's equation [Eq. (2)]. Symbolically these equations are written

$$G^{\mu\nu} = 8\pi\kappa\, T^{\mu\nu}$$

where $T^{\mu\nu}$ is a symmetric tensor which describes the distribution of matter and energy throughout space-time and $\kappa = G/c^2$. In a weak-field static approximation, these equations contain Newton's theory of gravitation with the Newtonian gravitational potential given by $2\phi/c^2 = 1 - g_{44}$.

The metric tensor outside a static spherically symmetric mass distribution is given by the Schwarzschild solution:

$$ds^2 = \left(1 - \frac{2\kappa m}{r}\right) dt^2 - \left(1 - \frac{2\kappa m}{r}\right)^{-1} dr^2$$
$$- r^2 d\theta^2 - r^2 \sin^2\theta d\varphi^2$$

This geometry exhibits the red shift described above and in addition shows three other effects:

(1) The bending of a ray of light passing near the sun's edge by

$$\delta\theta = 1.75''.$$

(2) The precession of the perihelion of Mercury by

$$\delta\phi = 43''.03/\text{century}.$$

(3) The retardation of signals passing near the sun. For a radar pulse reflected from Mercury, this amounts to a maximum time delay

$$\Delta t = 1.6 \times 10^{-4} \text{ sec.}$$

Observations and experiments to check these predictions are still in progress.

Since one can see stars near the sun's edge only during an eclipse, the optical data on the bending of light have been slow and difficult to obtain and such measurements have poor reliability—about 10 to 25 per cent. A group under H. Hill has set up equipment using photo-multiplier tubes sensitive to a narrow spectral range so that the solar background can be filtered out. As a result, measurements at a fixed site can be made continuously as the sun moves into and out of a selected field of stars. Therefore, much improved accuracy is expected, but no results are yet available. However, using radio frequency measurements, I. I. Shapiro has observed the angular positions of two sources, 3C279 and 3C273 which have an angular separation of about $10°$. The latter source acts as the reference as 3C279 is occulted by the sun each year on October 8. Preliminary results give agreement with the predicted value within 20 per cent and the accuracy should improve in coming years.

Shapiro has also reevaluated the optical data with regard to the solar system and has also taken new data using radar ranging. In both cases he finds agreement with the predicted value for the perihelion precession of Mercury within 3 per cent. If he combines the data, he reduces the error to 1 per cent.

As a new test of Einstein's theory of general relativity, Shapiro suggested measuring the re-tardation of radar echo signals from Mercury when the planet moves into a position of superior conjunction. The gravitational field of the sun, as represented by the Schwarzschild solution, not only produces a bending of the ray, but also affects the time of flight of the signal. Therefore, the time delay between the transmission of a radar pulse to Mercury and the reception of the reflected signal will depend not only on the relative positions of the earth and Mercury in their respective orbits, but also on whether the radar signals pass near the sun (Fig. 4). Current measurements give agreement within 5 per cent.

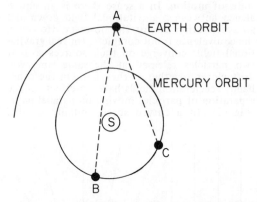

FIG. 4. There will be very little time delay, due to the sun's gravitational field, in the reception of the reflected radar signal when the earth-Mercury position is as in A-C compared to that when their position is as in A-B.

C. H. Brans and R. H. Dicke have proposed a "scalar-tensor" theory of gravitation in which the added scalar function determines the strength of the gravitational interaction. In this theory the gravitational constant G is no longer a universal constant, but depends on location and time. This effect has not been verified, but the theory also introduces small changes in the above predictions of the Einstein theory. Unfortunately, the experimental errors in the observations are such that one cannot distinguish between the Brans-Dicke and the Einstein theories. Nonetheless, the seeming arbitrariness of the scalar interaction makes the simpler Einstein theory preferable at the present time.

Gravitational Collapse The gravitational force between any two masses is attractive. Therefore, given a quantity of matter, under action of gravity alone it will become as compact as possible. In the planets the compaction process is stopped by the electrical forces which act between atoms and molecules in close range. The pressure in the sun, however, is much too great to be supported by such solid body forces. This tremendous pressure is balanced primarily by the counter pressure of electromagnetic radiation which is produced by the nuclear

processes at the sun's center. Stars in which the nuclear processes have ended undergo a further contraction which is stopped by the pressure of free electrons at the densities associated with white dwarfs. This pressure, which occurs because electrons obey the Pauli exclusion principle, is capable of supporting up to 1.4 solar masses within a volume of 10^{-4} to 10^{-8} of the solar volume. Objects which are more massive continue the crush. Neutrons become the most stable particles in the interior and the contraction is stopped by repulsive nuclear forces when a neutron occupies only about 10^{-39} cm^3, the nuclear volume. If the resulting neutron star is one solar mass, its radius is just 10 km and its volume 10^{-15} the sun's volume. Objects with more than about 1.2 solar masses cannot be stable as neutron stars. They continue to contract. Beyond this point the situation is confused by the abundance of exotic elementary particles, but there is no theoretical evidence that the contraction can be stopped.

One might have hoped that Einstein's theory of gravitation would contain a short-range repulsion which would stop this endless contraction. However, the opposite is the case. First of all, all forms of energy contribute to the attractive mass in general relativity, and secondly, the fact that matter determines the geometry means that there should be peculiarities in the space when an object is highly collapsed. There are several general theorems, particularly by R. Penrose and S. Hawking, whose general conclusion seems to be that as long as the energy density remains everywhere positive, collapse is inevitable. This does not mean that collapse actually occurs in nature. As a very massive star proceeds through the various stages indicated in the above paragraph, it may become unstable and throw off enough mass through an explosive process, such as a supernova, that it may settle down at a planetary size, or as a white dwarf, or as a neutron star. We have observational evidence for the existence of these objects. (A pulsar is thought to be a rapidly rotating neutron star.) So, not everything continues to collapse. But, there are many very massive stars and in the absence of more information it is unreasonable to rule out the possibility that some will indeed go through an indefinite collapse or that some may have already done so.

What physical effects result from the collapse? It was pointed out above, Eq. (4), that at the Schwarzschild radius the escape velocity from a point mass is the velocity of light. Thus, no signal can escape from a body which has collapsed below R_s. This result can in fact, be deduced from the Schwarzschild solution of the Einstein equations which is given above. As a result, our knowledge of events is limited at the Schwarzschild radius; the surface $r = R_s$ is an *absolute event horizon*. (Because we can receive no light or other signal from a source which has collapsed below its Schwarzschild radius, we call such objects *black holes*.)

Note that a neutron star of one solar mass has a radius of 10 km while $R_s = 3$ km; a neutron star of 10 solar masses will have a radius of 30 km and $R_s = 30$ km. Thus, we have observational evidence for the existence of objects which are very nearly black holes. There is at present an active search for peculiar stellar motions which might indicate the presence of a black hole. On the other hand, if there should be a collapsed object in the nucleus of a galaxy, the very high concentration of stars near the black hole would produce a cusp in the surface brightness. So far there is no positive evidence, but the existence of black holes in the center of galaxies or as collapsed individual stars has not been ruled out.

Gravitational Waves Einstein's field equations require that the gravitational field have a finite velocity of propagation—the same as that for light. Therefore, the gravitational field has independent dynamical degrees of freedom which permit gravitational waves to exist in two states of polarization. These states are wholly transverse. That is, the waves act on matter only in planes which are orthogonal to the direction of propagation. In passing through matter, one state produces oscillations such that there is a compression followed by elongation along one axis and a corresponding elongation followed by compression along the perpendicular axis (Fig. 5). For a periodic wave this process repeats at the frequency of the wave. The other state of polarization has the same effect along axes rotated by 45°. This character for the modes is caused by the tensor nature of the potentials $g_{\mu\nu}$ which limits the lowest order of gravitational waves to quadrupole radiation. A crude estimate of the energy radiated by the earth-sun system per year amounts to 10^{16} ergs (about 10^6 kWh). Radiating at this rate, the earth has lost about 10^{-15} of its available mechanical energy since its formation 5×10^9 years ago. Presumably there are stronger sources of gravitational waves available in the universe.

Experiments to detect gravitational radiation were begun in 1958 by J. Weber. For a detector he used an aluminum cylinder which is suspended in the earth's gravitational field. An in-

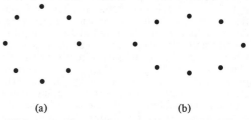

(a)　　　　　　　　　　　　　　　(b)

FIG. 5. (a) A circular arrangement of dust particles before a gravitational wave arrives. (b) The same particles after a passage of a wave consisting of one state of polarization. The second state of polarization would produce the same effect, rotated at 45°.

FIG. 6. One of the aluminum cylinders used by Professor Joseph Weber as a detector of gravitational waves. (Courtesy of Professor Weber.)

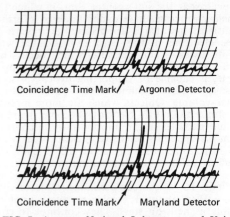

Coincidence Time Mark   Argonne Detector

Coincidence Time Mark   Maryland Detector

FIG. 7. Argonne National Laboratory and University of Maryland coincidence. (Courtesy of Professor Weber and *Physical Review Letters*.)

cident gravitational wave sets up transverse oscillations in the cylinder. These oscillations are transformed into electrical signals by piezoelectric crystals which are bonded to the surface of the cylinder (Fig. 6). However, the observations are made at room temperature and the thermal fluctuations produce displacement of the end faces of about 10^{-14} cm—an amount which, although only one-tenth the diameter of a nucleus, interferes with the expected gravitational effect. The gravity wave signal must be separated out from this background noise. To eliminate fluctuations due to earth tremors, trucks, or people dropping hammers, the whole apparatus is acoustically insulated from the ground.

The initial detection program used principally two identical cylinders, 153 cm long and 66 cm in diameter. One is located at the University of Maryland and the other at Argonne National Laboratory, 1000 km away. The electronic recording system is narrowly tuned to 1660 Hz which has an acoustic half-wavelength of 153 cm in aluminum. Thermal oscillations are randomly generated and one does not expect correlation between the outputs of two detectors, particularly if they are 1000 km apart. Therefore, Weber looks for coincidences in the output signals of the two detectors. The observation technique is to record each signal separately at its own location and at the same time to transmit the Argonne signal to Maryland where it can be compared directly with the Maryland signal. Coincidences of a certain pulse height are then marked (Fig. 7). A careful statistical analysis compares the coincidence rate due to random fluctuations with the observed rate. Weber concludes that there is a "significant coincidence rate of about one every two days."

Both cylinders are lined up in an east-west direction. Therefore, some directional information is available by studying the change in

coincidence rate as the earth rotates on its axis. The information is not very precise as the two-cylinder array is a broad-beam detector and there is twelve-hour symmetry in orientation because the earth does not absorb much energy. Nonetheless, there is a definite indication that a source of radiation lies in the direction of the center of the galaxy.

A very rough estimate of the total energy output of the source amounts to a yearly loss of about 200 $M_\odot$ from the center of the galaxy. This mass loss should produce a slow drifting apart of the stars in the vicinity of the sun. G. Field, M. Rees, and D. Sciama have pointed out that there is such an observable effect.

Construction of a satisfactory model for the source of the gravitational radiation has been hampered by the fact that known processes and already identified celestial objects do not radiate enough energy, particularly at 1660 Hz, to have an observable effect on Weber's cylinders. A major candidate as a source is a black hole into which fragments of one solar mass are falling. As such fragments fall into a black hole, presumably their radiation sweeps through 1660 Hz and a pulse would be recorded on Weber's equipment. So far this model is too complicated for a detailed analysis, but several groups are working on it.

Quantum Theory The gravitational interaction among the elementary particles is down by a factor of 10^{-40} from the electromagentic or strong nuclear interactions. Therefore, one cannot expect to observe quantum effects at the level of today's experiments. Nonetheless, because the gravitational field has two independent modes, the quantum field formalism requires that the gravitational field operators exist and satisfy appropriate commutation relations. However, the gravitational field equations are complicated by being nonlinear and by their covariance under arbitrary coordinate transformations. From its linear approximation,

one expects that the quantized field will be a spin 2 boson field. Furthermore, because of its connection with the geometry of space-time, the gravitational field will be a link among all particles and all interactions.

Cosmology One expects the gross structure of the universe to depend on global geometrical properties and the mean distribution of matter more than on the details of particle interactions. Among the various cosmological solutions of Einstein's equations are those models based on a homogeneous and isotropic matter distribution in which matter is streaming away from every point with a velocity dependent on its distance from that point. Such models agree with observations made by Hubble on the red shift in the spectra of distant galaxies. He interpreted this red shift as a Doppler effect due to a recessional velocity of the galaxy which is proportional to its distance:

$$v = Hr$$

with $H = 30$ km/sec/10^6 light-years and r measured in millions of light-years. This value of H leads to an age for the universe of about 10^{10} years.

The models based on Einstein's equations are evolutionary. This means that the rate of expansion of the universe, hence Hubble's constant H, depends on time. Bondi and his co-workers have suggested that the universe is in a steady state and that H is in fact independent of time. The steady-state theory says that the distribution of galaxies and the density of matter remain the same on the average. New matter is created in order to fill in the thinning density of matter as the universe maintains its expansion. One attempts to distinguish between the steady-state theories and the evolutionary models by counting the number of galaxies and the number of radio sources as a function of distance. These observations, though not definitive, suggest that the evolutionary models are correct.

There are two other observations which strengthen this conclusion. One of these is the recognition of the QSO (quasi-stellar objects) as extra-galactic objects. The QSO are very small, very luminous objects, and with very large red shifts. The simplest and most satisfactory interpretation of the observed red shifts is that it is the cosmological Doppler shift. With this interpretation, 3C273, the nearest, most luminous, and the first identified QSO, is at a distance of 1.6×10^9 light-years. This distance is so great that it is possible that an early state in the development of galaxies is being observed. On the other hand, the amount of energy being released is so great ($\sim 10^{49}$ ergs/sec) that a nuclear source for the energy is ruled out, and it is suggested that the energy comes from the gravitational contraction of 10^{10} $M_\odot$ down to its Schwarzschild radius of about 10^{10} km. However, it is equally possible that the QSO represent the opposite effect, the exploding of matter from a highly compacted state which is being thrust out. At present there is no understanding of the QSO. From the point of view of the steady-state cosmology, however, the QSO create serious problems. They are far away and there seems to be an overabundance of them at very large distances, hence a long time ago.

In 1949, George Gamow and his co-workers suggested that at an early stage in an evolutionary expanding universe, matter and radiation interacted very strongly and were in thermal equilibrium. As the universe expanded, the opportunity for interaction decreased, the radiation and matter were effectively decoupled. Matter cooled more rapidly and condensed into the galaxies and stars. The radiation maintained its thermal equilibrium distribution, its *blackbody* distribution, behaving like a gas which is undergoing an adiabatic expansion. Gamow estimated the temperature of this remnant of the primeval fireball at about 25°K. Fifteen years later, Dicke came to a comparable conclusion independently and set about to observe this radiation. In the meantime, Penzias and Wilson, while tracking down residual noise in a sensitive microwave radiometer, discovered an isotropic background radiation at a wavelength of 7.4 cm whose intensity corresponded to the

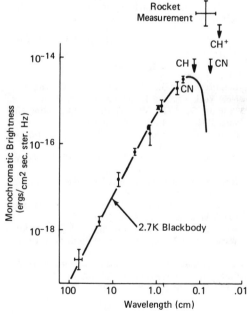

FIG. 8. This curve is a composite of all measurements through 1969. More recent measurements of the infrared indicate that the rocket measurement shown is much too high. At present there is no disagreement with the interpretation of the background radiation as corresponding to that from a blackbody at a temperature of 2.7 K. The points marked CN, CH, and CH$^+$ are discussed in the text. (Courtesy of R. B. Partridge and *American Scientist*.)

emission of a blackbody at a temperature of 3.5°K. Subsequent measurements by many observers have verified the existence of this background radiation, but have reduced the temperature to 2.7°K. The results are shown in Fig. 8. The points marked CN or CH are obtained by observing the intensities of absorption lines in dust clouds between us and certain bright stars. The relative intensities of the lines are an indication of the relative population of the energy levels of CN or CH and hence of the ambient temperature. Note that while the rise of the blackbody curve is well charted, the falloff after the peak is not. That is because of the absorption of infrared radiation in the earth's atmosphere. Initial measurements, using rockets to get above the atmosphere, gave readings which were too high, as shown in the figure. More recent measurements, however, do not disagree with the 2.7°K background radiation temperature.

The prediction and observation of the blackbody radiation and its interpretation as evidence of a primeval fireball give very strong support to the concept of an evolutionary universe, a universe which has expanded from a compact volume to its present size. However, it does not select a particular cosmological model from the many which are allowed by Einstein's gravitational theory, those permitted by the Brans-Dicke modification, or other possibilities which have not yet been constructed.

JOSHUA N. GOLDBERG

References

1. Bergmann, P. G., "The Riddle of Gravitation," New York, Charles Scribner and Sons, 1968.
2. Bonnor, W., "The Mystery of the Expanding Universe," New York, The Macmillan Co., 1964.
3. Gamow, G., "Gravity," Garden City, N.Y., Doubleday and Company, 1962.
4. Partridge, R. B., "The Primeval Fireball Today," American Scientist, 57, 37 (1969).
5. Rindler, W., "Essential Relativity," New York, Van Nostrand Reinhold, 1969.
6. Sciama, D., "Modern Cosmology," Cambridge, Cambridge University Press, 1971.
7. Weber, J., "General Relativity and Gravitational Waves," New York, Interscience Publishers, 1961.

Cross-references: ASTROMETRY, ASTROPHYSICS, COSMOLOGY, POTENTIAL, RADIO ASTRONOMY, RELATIVITY, SOLAR PHYSICS.

GYROSCOPE

The gyroscope consists of a flywheel or a sphere that is spinning (usually at high speed) about an axis. If this axis is free in space (such freedom may be provided by gimbals, by floating the spinning mass on a column of gas or fluid, or by suspension in a magnetic or an electrostatic field), the axis will remain parallel to its original position even though the gyroscope is mounted on a vehicle that translates and rotates in three dimensions. This property of the "free gyro" often referred to as "spatial memory" was used as an artificial horizon as early as 1744 by Serson. This permitted a ship's navigator to take readings with a sextant (measurement of the angular elevation of a star with respect to the horizon) when the horizon was obscured by darkness, fog, mist, etc. This early instrument has led to the modern vertical gyro.

In 1852, Leon Foucault built one of the first precise gyroscopes. Utilizing a flywheel only a few inches in diameter supported in near-frictionless gimbals, this instrument was sensitive enough to detect the rotation of the earth. This free gyro maintained a fixed orientation in space as the earth turned. The relative motion was observed through a microscope.

In 1896, the gyroscope saw its first application for guidance when Obry used it in a self-propelled torpedo. An unguided torpedo, under the influence of winds, currents, and ocean waves would not follow a prescribed course. The gyroscope, on the other hand, was pointed at the target before launching the torpedo, and by means of linkages connected to the spin axis support, it actuated the rudder of the torpedo, steering it along a straight course.

When the gyroscope is not free, that is, when the spin axis is forced to turn in space, the gyroscope develops a torque about an axis that is perpendicular to the plane containing the spin axis and the axis about which turning takes place. This property was utilized to find north by continually reorienting the spin axis until the gyroscope could not detect the rotation of the earth. This instrument, called the gyrocompass, was perfected in 1908 by Anschütz of Germany and by Elmer Sperry (1911) of the United States. This instrument used a wheel four to eight inches in diameter, and was suspended in such a way that it tended to remain vertical. Since the vertical turned with the earth, the gyroscope following it produced a torque. This torque, in turn, was used to provide self-turning of the spin axis in a direction that would reduce the torque. In the final equilibrium position, the instrument pointed north. The gyrocompass is still widely used today.

The gyroscopic torque is also used to stabilize ships. Due to the motion of waves, the unstabilized ship rolls considerably. It is impractical to shift huge masses fast enough to counteract the irregular motion. On the other hand, a gyroscope develops torque instantly and with much less effort. This led to the development of the gyroscopic ship stabilizer. Utilizing a wheel 10 to 20 feet in diameter, and a hydraulic turning mechanism, angular rates are applied to the spin axis support producing tremendous gyroscopic torques upon the ship. In moderately rough seas, the gyro stabilizer can eliminate 70 to 80 per cent of the roll motion. The control signal to the turning mechanism is provided by a small

"vertical gyro" which is very much like Serson's artificial horizon gyro. This essentially is a guidance system (like Obry's) using a small guidance gyro to provide the vertical and a large gyro to provide the action.

If the motion of the gyro is free, and if a torque is applied to the structure containing the spinning mass, it will turn or precess about an axis that is perpendicular to the plane containing the torque axis and the spin axis. This is the converse of the gyroscopic torque phenomenon. By adjusting the amount of torque, the gyroscope provides a controlled rate. This property is utilized in an autopilot during a constant rate of turn. The principle is also used for platform stabilization where the platform carries instruments which must bear specific orientations with respect to the earth. By carefully regulating the torque, the gyroscope and platform rotate with the earth without being in contact with the earth.

Inertial navigation is accomplished by a gyroscopic system combining all the phenomena previously mentioned. Inertial navigation is required whenever visual or radiation methods cannot be used as the link with the earth. In its simplest form, this system consists of a free gyro platform that can be torqued. Prior to making the journey, the platform is leveled. As the ship, submarine, or missile circles the earth, accelerometers mounted on the platform continuously measure vehicular acceleration. This is integrated twice to determine the distance trav-

eled. Dividing by the radius of the earth computes the angular position on earth (latitude and longitude). The gyroscope performs one of these integrations, and by appropriate scaling of the torque mechanism, it divides by the radius of the earth, tilting the platform through angles equal to the change in latitude and longitude. Thus, the system becomes an accurate analog of the motion of the vehicle on the earth.

In the more sophisticated inertial navigation systems, redundant measurements are made to minimize the growth of errors over long periods of time.

IRA COCHIN

References

Broxmeyer, Charles, "Inertial Navigation Systems," New York, McGraw-Hill Book Co., 1964.

Cochin, Ira, "Analysis and Design of the Gyroscope for Inertial Guidance," New York, John Wiley & Sons, 1963.

Macomber, George R., and Fernandes, Manuel, "Inertial Guidance Engineering," Englewood Cliffs, N.J., Prentice-Hall, 1962.

Savet, Paul H., "The Gyroscope," New York, McGraw-Hill Book Co., 1961.

Cross-references: ROTATION-CIRCULAR MOTION; INERTIAL GUIDANCE; MASS AND INERTIA; MECHANICS.

H

HALL EFFECT AND RELATED PHENOMENA

If a current of particles bearing charges of a single sign and constrained to move in a given direction is subjected to a transverse magnetic field, a potential gradient will exist in a direction perpendicular to both the current and the magnetic field. This phenomenon is called the Hall effect, after E. H. Hall who discovered it in a metal in 1879. Studies of the Hall effect provide extremely useful techniques for obtaining information about the electronic properties of solids. As will be discussed in more detail, Hall data can be used to obtain concentrations and numerous other properties of the charge carriers. The Hall effect is also the basis of a variety of specialized devices, in which the fundamental unit (often called a *Hall generator*) is made of a material in which the voltage or the power produced by the Hall effect is especially large. Finally, Hall phenomena play an important role in plasmas in magnetic fields and can be of importance in magnetohydrodynamics. In the latter case, Hall phenomena enter into the design of MHD electrical power generators.

Principles Involved The Hall effect is a manifestation of the force, usually known as the Lorentz force, which is exerted on a charged particle moving perpendicular to a magnetic field. The direction of the force is perpendicular to both the magnetic field and the velocity of the charge. If this sidewise thrust is not counteracted, the charged particle undergoes a deflection. The result of such motion is to create a charge unbalance and to produce a transverse electric field component, known as the *Hall field*. The force on the charged particle due to this Hall field tends to oppose the force resulting from the magnetic field. Mathematically, the forces and fields in question are represented by the following vector equation:

$$F = e\,[E + (1/c)\,v \times H] \qquad (1)$$

where F is the force, e the charge, and v the velocity of the particle, E is the electric field, and H is the magnetic field intensity. A permeability of unity is assumed, and for the Gaussian system of units, c is the speed of light. As the equation indicates, the total force on the particle of charge e is the vector sum of that due to the electric field E and that resulting from the magnetic field. The latter enters via the *vector cross product* $v \times H$, which represents a vector perpendicular to both v and H and in the direction indicated by the right hand rule as v is rotated into H. The magnitude of the vector $v \times H$ is equal to the product of the individual magnitudes of v and H times the sine of the angle between them. Hence, only the component of v perpendicular to H contributes to the sidewise force.

The physics involved in the Hall effect is conviently illustrated by considering a confined stream of free particles, each having a charge e and an initial velocity v_x. A magnetic field in the z direction produces initially a deflection of charges along the y direction. This charge unbalance creates an electric field E_y, and the process continues until the force on a moving charge due to the Hall field E_y counter-balances that due to the magnetic field so that further particles of the same velocity and charge* are no longer deflected. A pictorial representation of this is shown in Fig. 1. The magnitude of the Hall field follows at once from Eq. (1), with $F = 0$ at steady state, namely

$$E_y = (1/c)v_x H_z = J_x H_z / nec \ \text{(Gaussian}^\dagger \text{ units)} \qquad (2)$$

In obtaining the last equality, the electric current density J_x was expressed in terms of the density of charge carriers n by the product nev_x. For *electronic* (i.e., as opposed to *ionic*) conduction in solids, the magnitude of e is the electronic charge (1.6×10^{-19} coulomb, in practical units), and its sign is negative for transport by electrons and positive for transport by holes (deficit electrons). The *Hall coefficient* is

---

*If the particles have a *distribution* of velocities, then it is only those particles having a certain "average" velocity, which are undeflected. This point is expanded later.

†In the Gaussian system, mechanical quantities are in cgs units, electrical quantities in esu, and magnetic fields in gauss or oersteds. In the *practical* system, mechanical quantities are in cgs units, electrical quantities in volts and coulombs, and magnetic fields in gauss or oersteds. In all equations in this article, except for Eq. (1), conversion from the Gaussian system to the practical system is effected by replacing c by unity and replacing H by $H/10^8$, where these quantities explicitly occur. The practical units for R_H are $cm^3/coulomb$; those for mobility are $cm^2/volt\text{-}sec$.

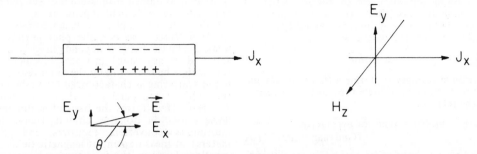

FIG. 1. Hall field due to action of magnetic field on positive charge carriers. For example shown, e, J_x, and H_z are positive and, therefore, v_x, E_x, and E_y are also. The resultant electric field and the Hall angle are shown at lower left. In the case of electrons, the Hall field is reversed for positive J_x, both v_x and e now being negative.

defined by the ratio E_y/J_xH_z, namely,

$$R_H \equiv E_y/J_xH_z = 1/nec \text{ (Gaussian units)} \quad (3)$$

Thus a very simple relation exists in the free-particle example between the Hall coefficient and the charge-carrier density. It is also seen that R_H is negative for conduction by electrons, positive for conduction by holes. Now the electric current density J_x exists by virtue of an applied electric field E_x. With the Hall field present, the *resultant* electric field in a solid* lies at some angle θ to the x axis. This angle is called the Hall angle, namely

$$\theta \equiv \tan^{-1} E_y/E_x \quad (4)$$

Thus the Hall effect may be described as a rotation of the electric field. At zero Hall field, the equipotential lines are perpendicular to **J**, but when the Hall field appears, they are oblique, so that a Hall voltage exists across the specimen in a direction normal to the current. The rotation aspect is also brought out by considering the components of the *conductivity tensor*, which relate electric current densities and fields. For the boundary condition that $J_z = 0$, we may write

$$J_x = \sigma_{xx}E_x + \sigma_{xy}E_y$$

$$J_z = 0, H = H_z \quad (5)$$

$$J_y = -\sigma_{xy}E_x + \sigma_{xx}E_y$$

Equations (5) hold for media of sufficient symmetry† that $\sigma_{xx} = \sigma_{yy}$ and that $\sigma_{xz} = \sigma_{yz} = \sigma_{zx} = \sigma_{zy} = 0$. The latter insures that E_z vanish when J_z is zero. Since the boundary conditions for Hall effect require that J_y vanish, Eqs. (4) and (5) yield the following result for the off-diagonal elements σ_{xy}:

$$\sigma_{xy} = \sigma_{xx} \tan\theta \quad (6)$$

The inverse of the conductivity tensor is the *resistivity* tensor, which relates **E** to **J**. A general definition of the Hall effect involves relating it to the antisymmetric‡ components of the resistivity tensor. This leads to the vector equation for the Hall field, namely

$$\mathbf{E}_H = R_H \mathbf{H} \times \mathbf{J} \text{ (Gaussian units)} \quad (7)$$

The identity in the first part of Eq. (3) is recognized as a special case of Eq. (7)

Application to Real Solids In a real solid the idealized free particle treatment no longer applies and must be replaced by a theory that takes into account the distribution of velocities and the interactions of the charge carriers with impurities, defects, and lattice thermal vibrations of the solid (i.e., the *scattering*), as well as the *band structure* of the solid. The latter consideration relates to the fact that the charge carriers in the solid are not free but exist in a potential energy field having the periodicity of the lattice. As a result of these constraints, only certain energy states, or *bands*, are allowed for the charge carriers. In addition, the relationship between the energy and velocity of the carriers is not the simple $\frac{1}{2}mv^2$ of the free electron, but is more complex. As an approximation, one frequently characterizes the charge carriers by an *effective* mass, $m^\star$. Taking into account most of the complexities mentioned above, one still obtains an expression similar to Eq. (3), namely

$$R_H = r/nec \text{ (Gaussian units)} \quad (8)$$

The *Hall coefficient factor*, r, actually depends on the nature of the scattering, the band structure, the magnetic field strength, and on the statistics characterizing the distribution of velocities of the carriers. Fortunately it depends weakly on these factors, and its value is usually within, say, 50 per cent of unity.

---

*Although the Hall effect can be discussed for any constrained electron gas, we shall, for simplicity, talk about a solid conductor.

†Isotropic media, e.g., or cubic systems with coordinate axes along cube axes.

‡These components are defined by the condition that $\rho_{ik} = -\rho_{ki}$, where the ρ_{ik} [cf. Eq. (5)] are defined by $E_i = \sum_{k=1}^{3} \rho_{ik}J_k$, $1 \equiv x$, $2 \equiv y$, $3 \equiv z$.

An important attribute of charge carriers is their mobility, i.e., their drift velocity per unit electric field. The conductivity mobility μ is related to the conductivity σ by

$$\mu = \sigma/ne \qquad (9)$$

It is also customary to define a *Hall mobility* μ_H for conduction by a single type of charge carrier by the relation

$$\mu_H H/c = \tan\theta, \text{ or } \mu_H = R_H \sigma c$$
$$\text{(Gaussian units)} \quad (10)$$

With the use of Eqs. (8) and (9), it can be seen that the ratio of Hall and conductivity mobilities is precisely the Hall coefficient factor. It follows that the Hall angle is proportional to μ and H.

When transport by two or more kinds of charge carriers occurs, Eq. (8) is not applicable, and one must return to the general relations of Eq. (5). For conduction by electrons and holes (of respective densities n, p), the *weak-field* Hall coefficient can be written in the form

$$R_0 = -(r_e\mu_e^2 n - r_h\mu_h^2 p)/$$
$$[\,|e|c(\mu_e n + \mu_h p)^2\,] \quad (11)$$

where $|e|$, μ_e, etc., are positive. We note that the charge-carrier densities are now weighted by the mobilities μ_e, μ_h. There are also Hall coefficient factors for each carrier. For arbitrary H, the terms involve field-dependent factors.

Analysis of Hall-effect data is one of the most widely used techniques for studying conduction mechanisms in solids, especially semiconductors. For the single-carrier case, one readily obtains carrier concentrations and mobilities, and it is usually of interest to study these as functions of temperature. This can supply information on the predominant charge-carrier scattering mechanisms and on activation energies, i.e., the energies necessary to excite carriers from impurity levels into the conduction band. Where two or more carriers are present, the analysis is more complicated [cf. Eq. (11)], but much information can be obtained from studies of the temperature and magnetic field dependencies.

Unlike, for example, the magnetoresistance, the Hall effect is a first-order phenomenon. At weak magnetic fields it depends linearly on H, and it does not vanish in isotropic solids if all the carriers have essentially the same velocity or if the scattering is characterized by a relaxation time which is independent of the carrier energy. The Hall effect forms the basis of a number of devices used in isolating circuits, transducers, multipliers, converters, rectifiers, and gaussmeters (for measurement of magnetic fields). As mentioned earlier, the fundamental component of such devices is a slab of material (often called a "Hall generator") possessing favorable Hall characteristics.

Experimental Determination A number of techniques are available, the most direct being to measure, by means of a potentiometer or other high-impedance device, the Hall voltage V_H across a parallelepiped in a direction normal to both **H** and **J**. The Hall coefficient follows from Equation (3) or (7):

$$R_H = 10^8 \, V_H t/IH, \text{(practical units)} \quad (12)$$

where t is the thickness of the specimen and I is the total current. The arrangement is shown in Fig. 2. Since V_H may be the order of microvolts, extreme care must be taken to avoid extraneous voltages. An example is the misalignment voltage, caused by probes 3 and 4 not being on an equipotential plane when $H = 0$. This may be eliminated by taking measurements for opposite directions of H and taking half the difference, inasmuch as $V_H(H)$ is odd in H. Alternatively, one can adjust the position of the Hall probes for a null reading with $H = 0$. Other techniques involve use of resistances with sliding contacts suitably attached to the specimen. Other spurious voltages can arise from temperature gradients and resulting thermoelectric or thermomagnetic emf's (see following section). Some of these can be eliminated by taking appropriate averages among measurements for reversed po-

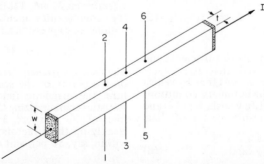

FIG. 2. Arrangement of contacts for measurement of Hall coefficient and related effects. Hall probes are 3 and 4. Probes 2 and 6 are for resistivity and magnetoresistance. Probes 1 and 5 allow a check of the uniformity of the specimen. For Hall effect and transverse magnetoresistance, the magnetic field is in the direction of the thickness t; for longitudinal magnetoresistance, it is along I. To avoid disturbances due to contact shorting, all probes should be at a distance of at least $2w$ from the end contacts.

larities of I and direction of H. It is usually desirable to maintain good thermal contact between all points of the specimen and a constant-temperature bath. Although it is possible to analyze *adiabatic* Hall data (no heat flow to or from the specimen during measurement), *isothermal* data are preferred because of the simplicity of the equations. All of the relations in this article are for isothermal conditions. Errors in measurement can also result from a shorting of the Hall voltage, especially by the end contacts. With regard to the latter, the error is essentially negligible if the length-to-width ratio of the specimen is about 4 or more, and the Hall probes are near the center.

Related Effects A widely-studied galvanomagnetic effect is *transverse magnetoresistance*, usually written $\Delta\rho/\rho_0$. This phenomenon can be illustrated by the pictorial scheme in Fig. 1. If a charge carrier is deflected by the Lorentz force so as to traverse a longer path, it will contribute less to the conductivity, and there will be a positive magnetoresistance. It was noted, however, that if all charge carriers have the same velocity, none will be deflected since the Hall field cancels the $\mathbf{v} \times \mathbf{H}$ force. This is the case in an isotropic metal, where the velocity of all the electrons is essentially the Fermi velocity. It is also true for electron scattering mechanisms described by a relaxation time which does not depend on energy. In these cases—assuming, of course, a single type of carrier—there is no magnetoresistance. If, however, there is a distribution of electron velocities—as in a semiconductor—then it is clear that only those electrons of a certain "average" velocity will be undeflected. The remaining carriers, having velocities either larger or smaller than the "average" will be deflected and will traverse longer paths, thus increasing the resistance of the conductor. A similar situation obtains if more than one type of carrier is present. It is also apparent that any mechanism which shorts out the Hall voltage—e.g., special geometry, shorting contacts, inhomogeneities in the specimen—will increase the magnetoresistance.

For the reasons discussed and the fact that $\Delta\rho/\rho_0$ varies as H^2 in weak fields, magnetoresistance is a second-order effect. It tends to saturate in strong magnetic fields, unless there is a disturbance of the Hall field as mentioned above. Magnetoresistance is even in H, and it is related to the *symmetric* components of the resistivity tensor, i.e., those for which $\rho_{ik} = \rho_{ki}$ [cf. footnote on p. 401]. It can be measured with the geometry shown in Fig. 2 by maintaining the current constant and determining the potential difference between probes 1 and 5 or 2 and 6 as a function of magnetic field. Magnetoresistance data can supply information on charge-carrier scattering and band structure. In the latter case, if anisotropy exists, it is useful to obtain data for different crystallographic directions. There is also a *longitudinal* magnetoresistance, measured when $\mathbf{H}$ is parallel to $\mathbf{J}$.

This effect vanishes in isotropic solids, and its presence indicates anisotropy in scattering or band structure, or inhomogeneities in the specimen.

By shorting the Hall field or by choosing a disk geometry so that such a field does not exist, one obtains a "magnetoresistance" (more strictly, a *magnetoconductivity*) which does not saturate. This is called the Corbino magnetoresistance or Corbino effect, after O. M. Corbino who studied circulating secondary currents in a "Corbino" disk carrying a primary radial electric current in a magnetic field.

There are a number of thermal effects in a magnetic field, which can produce transverse voltages or temperature gradients. These result from the velocity separation of charge carriers by the Lorentz force—the energetic ones going to one side, the slower ones going to the other. Temperature gradients are produced, and also electric fields. In the Righi-Leduc effect, a longitudinal temperature gradient produces a transverse temperature gradient (thermal analog of the Hall effect); in the Nernst effect, it produces a transverse electric field. In the Ettingshausen effect, a longitudinal electric current produces a transverse temperature gradient. This latter effect, if large, can disturb the Hall field since the potential probes and leads are seldom made of the same material as the specimen. Therefore the Ettingshausen temperature gradient can produce a thermoelectric voltage which adds to the Hall voltage.

ALBERT C. BEER

References

Alfvén, H., and Fälthammar, C.-G., "Cosmical Electrodynamics," esp. pp. 180–185, Oxford, Clarendon Press, 1963.

Baynham, A. C., and Boardman, A. D., "Plasma Effects in Semiconductors: Helicon and Alfvén Waves," esp. p. 30 ff., London, Taylor and Francis Ltd., 1971.

Beer, A. C., "Galvanomagnetic Effects in Semiconductors" (Supplement 4 to "Solid State Physics," F. Seitz and D. Turnbull, Eds.), New York, Academic Press, 1963.

Dunlap, W. Crawford, Jr., "An Introduction to Semiconductors," New York, John Wiley & Sons, Inc., 1957.

Fritzsche, Hellmut, "Galvanomagnetic and Thermomagnetic Effects," in "Methods of Experimental Physics" (L. Marton, Ed.), Vol. 6B, "Solid State Physics" (K. Lark-Horovitz and V. A. Johnson, Eds.), p. 145, New York, Academic Press, 1959.

Hall, E. H., *Amer. J. Math.*, **2**, 287 (1879); *Amer. J. Sci.*, **19**, 200 (1880).

Kuhrt, F., and Lippmann, H. J., "Hallgeneratoren" (in German), Berlin, Springer-Verlag, 1968.

Lindberg, O., *Proc. Inst. Radio Engrs.*, **40**, 1414 (1952).

Putley, E. H., "The Hall Effect and Related Phenomena" ("Semi-Conductor Monographs," C. A. Hogarth, Ed.), London, Butterworths, 1960.

Rosa, R. J., "Magnetohydrodynamic Energy Conversion," esp. p. 59 ff., New York, McGraw-Hill, 1968.

Seitz, Frederick, "The Modern Theory of Solids," New York, McGraw-Hill, 1940.

Shercliff, J. A., "A Textbook of Magnetohydrodynamics," esp. p. 18, Oxford, Pergamon Press, 1965.

Shockley, William, "Electrons and Holes in Semiconductors," New York, Van Nostrand Reinhold, 1950.

Swift-Hook, D. T., in "Direct Generation of Electricity" (K. H. Spring, Ed.), pp. 143–155, New York, Academic Press, 1965.

Cross-references: CONDUCTIVITY, ELECTRICAL; ELECTRIC POWER GENERATION; ELECTRICITY; MAGNETOMETRY; MAGNETO-FLUID-MECHANICS; POTENTIAL; SEMICONDUCTORS; THERMOELECTRICITY.

HEALTH PHYSICS

Health physics is the profession that is concerned solely with the protection of man from the damaging effects of ionizing* radiation. It attempts to understand the action of radiation on man and his environment, to establish appropriate limits for exposure to radiation, and to devise appropriate methods for detection, measurement and control of radiation exposure. Although this profession is relatively new, man's awareness and concern for the harmful effects of ionizing radiation are not of recent origin. Perhaps the earliest record of damage to man from ionizing radiation dates back to about 1500 when the high incidence of lung diseases was recognized among the Schneeberg miners of Saxony and the Joachimsthal miners of Bohemia. In 1879 Herting and Hess performed the first autopsies on these miners and reported malignant growths in the lungs; however, the cause of these malignancies was not understood until after 1896 when Roentgen first announced his discovery of x-rays and Becquerel reported the discovery of radiation due to uranium. Even during the first year following the discovery of x- and γ-radiation, many things were learned about both the harmful and useful characteristics of this new source of energy. Grubbé, a manufacturer of Crookes tubes in Chicago, Illinois, was using his equipment to study the fluorescence of chemicals even before the public press on January 4, 1896, heralded Roentgen's discovery of x-rays. During January, 1896, he first noticed an erythema on the back of his hand and later the formation of a blister with skin desquamation and epilation. His hand was sufficiently painful that he sought medical aid on January 27, 1896. Realizing from first-hand experience the destructive power of x-rays Grubbé on January 29, 1896, treated a patient for carcinoma of the breast with his Crookes tube. Not only was this treatment significant

*The Health Physics Society recently extended the scope of health physics to include also non-ionizing electromagnetic radiations.

because it was one of the earliest—if not the first—therapeutic uses of ionizing radiation, but it is noteworthy that he acted as one of the first health physicists when he used lead as a shield to protect the rest of the body of the patient. Even Becquerel and Madame Curie learned from first-hand experience the need for radiation protection when they received skin burns from the careless handling of radium (see RADIOACTIVITY).

S. Russ in 1915 made a comprehensive series of recommendations for radiation protection to the British Roentgen Society, and if these recommendations had been heeded, many of the early radiation fatalities might have been averted. It was not until 1928, when the International Commission on Radiological Protection was formed and published the first set of recommendations for radiation protection, that there began to be widespread interest and concern for this problem. In the following year the National Council on Radiation Protection was formed and it has set the standards in the United States.

Beginning at the time of the First World War and continuing until about 1930, there were many unfortunate exposures to radium. Some of these were the result of therapeutic injections of radium, the drinking of radium and radiothorium water, and occupational exposures of radium chemists. During this period, radium was considered to be a useful therapeutic agent, and as a result it was administered by physicians in the United States to hundreds of patients. In some cases it was taken as a general tonic, and in others it was given as a curative agent for hypertension, anemia, arthritis, and many other human ailments—even for insanity.

By far the most serious exposures were to young women engaged in the radium dial painting industry. Some of these women ingested relatively large quantities of radium as a consequence of tipping brushes with their lips as they applied radium paint on the dials of clocks and watches. The total number of radium dial painters and others who took radium by mouth or injection and, as a result, died with readily detectable symptoms of radiation damage is not known. The first recorded fatality due to radium-induced cancer, resulting from exposure in the radium dial industry, was in 1925, and since that time histories of over 1000 Ra cases have been recorded and studied in the United States.

In 1942–43 there was begun at the University of Chicago a program to explore the possibility of assembling a critical mass of natural uranium in such a way that a "pile" or NUCLEAR REACTOR could be operated for the production of the new element plutonium to be used in atomic weapons. A. H. Compton, the director, and his associates debated the wisdom of proceeding with this project because they realized that in a single large reactor there would be produced ionizing radiation equivalent to that from thousands of tons of radium. Yet all the radium that had been available to man throughout the world

only amounted to about two pounds, and these men were acutely aware of the extensive suffering and death that had resulted from its misuse. They decided to call together a rather unique group of scientists to evaluate these health problems, to develop new instruments, equipment, and techniques and to establish radiation standards for the protection of nuclear energy workers. The group assembled was concerned with the *health* of the workers and consisted mostly of *physicists*; hence, they were called *health physicists*. E. O. Wollan was the leader and the other senior members were H. M. Parker, C. C. Gamertsfelder, K. Z. Morgan, R. R. Coveyou, J. C. Hart, L. A. Pardue, and O. G. Landsverk. Thus in 1942–43 health physics had its beginning at the University of Chicago. Although prior to this time many early pioneers such as S. Russ (England), L. S. Taylor (United States), G. Failla (United States), A. Mutscheller (Germany) and R. Sievert (Sweden)—to name only a few—had devoted considerable attention to the radiation protection problem, it was not until the advent of health physics that a professional group was organized with this as its sole objective.

As the nuclear energy programs expanded, large laboratories were established to carry on the program at Oak Ridge, Los Alamos, Hanford, Berkeley, Brookhaven, Savannah River, etc., and as the need for health physicists was recognized beyond nuclear energy programs and in private industry, hospitals, military organizations, utility power companies, state and federal agencies of public health, and colleges and universities, the profession of health physics grew and expanded very rapidly so that today (1973) it is estimated there are about 9000 health physicists in the world. In 1956 the Health Physics Society was organized which now has a membership of over 3000. This society publishes the journal, *Health Physics*. In 1959 the American Board of Health Physics was formed for the certification of persons whose technical competence and judgment qualify them to be responsible for handling major problems of radiation exposure and/or contamination control. The International Radiation Protection Association was organized at the First International Congress on Radiation Protection in Rome on September 7, 1966, with K. Z. Morgan as its first president. In 1973 it included 22 affiliated societies with 6000 members living in 60 countries.

There are three principal areas in which health physicists are employed—education and training, applied activities, and research—and these three areas will be discussed below.

In the early period, health physicists were scientists who had to develop their own competence during employment on the various atomic energy programs. In 1948 AEC Health Physics Fellowship programs were established at Oak Ridge National Laboratory in cooperation with Vanderbilt University and the University of Rochester and later with other national laboratories and universities. This program, over a twenty-five-year period in the U.S., became the principal source of senior health physicists. Unfortunately, during 1973 the programs, which had expanded into some twenty universities, are being phased out. Although most of the early health physicists began as physicists, there is today a need for health physicists with many different backgrounds, e.g., physics, biology, chemistry, mathematics, engineering. In the AEC Health Physics Fellowship program the student satisfied the usual Ph.D. requirements of courses, research, and thesis in one of these major departments, and at the same time, he met additional requirements such as special courses and summer work at one of the National Laboratories where he was given practical experience in health physics. Likewise, some of the graduate programs of the U.S. Public Health Service have been, in more recent years, providing training in health physics. In spite of the various opportunities for education and training in health physics, the supply has not kept pace with the demand because of the rapid growth of this new profession. The shortage is increasing.

In addition to the above-mentioned graduate programs in health physics, there are education and training programs at all operating levels. These programs are important because the success of health physics can be measured, to a considerable degree, in terms of how well plant managers, supervisors, scientists, engineers, technicians and operations personnel are made to realize their responsibility for protecting themselves and their associates from radiation damage. They must be ever aware that to some degree all radiation exposure is harmful and no unnecessary exposure may be permitted unless it can be balanced by benefits of equal value. At the same time they must be made to respect ionizing radiation—not fear it.

The duties of the health physicist in applied operations are very diverse and differ considerably from place to place, depending upon the size and nature of the operation. For example, the health physicist in a reactor operation would have duties quite different from those of the health physicist associated with an accelerator program or the health physicist connected with a state public health organization charged with the survey of medical x-ray equipment. A few typical applied health physics activities may be summarized as follows:

(1) Aid in the selection of suitable locations for buildings in which radioactive materials are to be produced or used, and conduct pre-operation background surveys.

(2) Offer advice in the design of laboratories, hoods, remote control equipment, radiation shields, etc.

(3) Provide personnel monitoring meters for radiation dosimetry to all persons subject to radiation exposure and read these meters frequently; make thyroid counts, breath measure-

ments, urine and feces analyses; check body with scanners and total body counters and conduct other tests to aid in estimating how much (if any) radioactive material is fixed in the body; and maintain accurate records of the accumulated dose from each type of ionizing radiation received by each individual for his protection and for the protection of the employer.

(4) Make frequent surveys of all accessible reactor areas, radioactive sources, x-ray equipment, high voltage accelerators, chemistry and physics laboratories, metallurgical shops, and other working areas where radiation exposure is possible.

(5) Advise scientists, supervisors and research directors of all radiation exposure hazards, of permissible working time in a given area, and of radiation protection measures and techniques (e.g., protective clothing, shields, remote control equipment) and aid supervision in the solution of new radiation problems as they develop.

(6) Make frequent surveys of all radioactive waste discharged beyond the area of immediate control, maintain accurate records of the level of this radioactivity in the air, water, soil, vegetation, milk, etc., and advise management of remedial measures as they are needed.

(7) Aid in all emergency operations where there are associated radiation hazards.

(8) Purchase and maintain in working order and in proper calibration suitable health physics survey and monitoring instruments which are used as aids in the protection of personnel from radiation damage.

(9) Prepare operations manuals on "Rules and Procedures Governing Radiation Exposure."

(10) Assist in radiation protection problems related to civil defense, weapons fallout, the use of nuclear devices for excavation of canals and harbors, space radiation, nuclear power plants, etc.

Health physics research ranges from the applied and engineering programs to very basic studies. It is a working together of scientists of many disciplines—physicists, chemists, biologists, engineers, geologists, mathematicians—all studying the effects of ionizing radiation on man and on his environment. In these studies, they are working at all levels—nuclear, atomic, molecular, plasma, gas, solid, liquid, cell, animal, and the ecosystem. In this research program, radiation ecologists are studying the effects of low levels of radiation exposure on the environment. Some essential organisms in the environment are known to concentrate radioactive waste by a factor of 10,000 or more, and the health physicist must determine the importance of the indirect damage of ionizing radiation to man's environment as well as its direct effects. Internal dose studies are under way by researchers in health physics, studies which have led to the publication of the official handbooks on maximum permissible concentration of the various radionuclides in food, water, and air. These handbooks are issued by the National Council on Radiation Protection and the International Commission on Radiological Protection. They are under constant revision by the health physicist as more reliable and detailed information becomes available. Biologists in health physics are studying the uptake distribution and elimination of radionuclides which are taken into animals and man by the several modes of intake —ingestion, inhalation and skin penetration. Engineers in health physics are exploring and demonstrating new methods for the disposal of radioactive waste in deep wells thousands of feet below the earth's surface and in salt mines. They are studying the seepage rates of radionuclides into various soil formations, its slow dissipation from packages of radioactive waste deposited on the ocean floor, and the dilution of airborne radioactive waste as it is discharged from stacks under varying meteorological conditions. The physicists in health physics are making basic studies of the various energy exchanges that take place in matter when it is exposed to ionizing radiation. This information aids in the development of better radiation detection systems and leads to an understanding of the true meaning and consequence of radiation exposure. When high energy radiation (in the MeV or keV region) strikes living matter, there are innumerable, complex energy exchanges that take place as the ENTROPY of the system increases. An understanding of the many low energy transitions is basic to a proper interpretation of the effects of ionizing radiation on man. Health physicists are working toward the ultimate goal of developing a coherent theory of radiation damage. Only when such a theory is available can they have complete understanding and confidence in the many extrapolations to man of the effects of ionizing radiation on animals. Such information is essential in developing reliable radiation protection standards and measures that are enforced by the applied health physicist. Many health physicists are working on programs to reduce unnecessary medical diagnostic exposure, which at present accounts for over 90 percent of exposure of the United States population.

Health physics continues to grow as a most interesting and challenging profession for scientists of many backgrounds. The success of these programs is attested by the fact that ionizing radiation with unparalleled potential for radiation hazards has expanded in its use and applications into almost every area of human endeavor and yet the nuclear energy industry has become one of the safest of all industries.

KARL Z. MORGAN

Cross-references: MEDICAL PHYSICS, NUCLEAR INSTRUMENTS, NUCLEAR RADIATION, NUCLEAR REACTORS, NUCLEONICS, RADIOACTIVITY, REACTOR SHIELDING.

HEARING

The role of the sense organ of hearing is to code acoustic disturbances into neural signals suitable for transmission to the brain. The study of this process necessarily involves anatomy and physiology of the ear, the nature of auditory pathways and central nervous system activity in hearing, properties of acoustic signals that elicit auditory responses, and observed phenomena of auditory behavior. These aspects serve to define and delineate areas for investigations of hearing and are the topics of discussion for this article.

In this approach to hearing, questions are asked about the structure of the system, how the system functions, and the relationships between inputs and outputs of the system. These three kinds of data—morphological, physiological, and psychological—need to be compared and correlated for a full understanding of hearing. It is important, however, that these three frames of reference be kept separate and not be confused. Although physiological functions may correspond in a general way to anatomical sequences, several physiological functions may occur in the same anatomical structure or a single function may require several anatomical units. In a similar manner, physchological functions cannot usually be identified with specific physiological functions, and it is recognized that the central nervous system, as well as the auditory system, is involved in any auditory response. The correlations between and knowledge about structure and functions are best developed for peripheral, rather than central, parts of the auditory system because the ear is more accessible for examination and study than are the more central parts of the auditory system.

Traditional theories of hearing have been largely concerned with pitch perception or loudness of pure tones. Recently, there has been an increased awareness that any comprehensive theory of hearing needs to encompass various experimental phenomena of hearing. In this regard, increased attention has been given to auditory processing of complex signals including speech, to the examination of binaural inputs to the system, and to the study of pathological hearing conditions.

When the structure of the ear is examined, it is convenient to consider the external, middle, and inner ear separately. A cutaway drawing of the ear is shown in Fig. 1. From a functional point of view, the ear may be divided into an outer and inner part. The outer is concerned with the transformation of acoustic energy into mechanical energy and the inner with the transduction of mechanical energy into neural impulses. The auricle and external auditory meatus constitute the external ear. The meatus is an irregularly shaped tube approximately 27 mm long with a diameter of about 7 mm, terminated by the tympanic membrane. The ear canal is an acoustic resonator, and frequencies in the range of 3000 to 4000 Hz are increased in pressure at the ear drum as compared to the pressure at the entrance

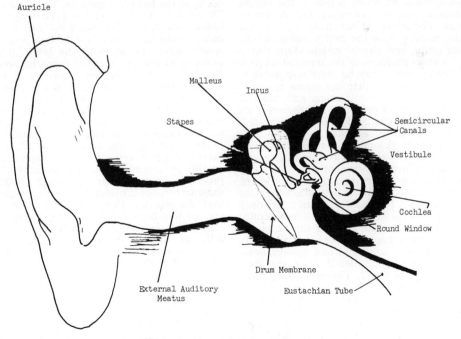

FIG. 1. A cutaway drawing of the ear.

to the canal. The ear drum is in a protected position at the end of the canal, and humidity and temperature conditions at the drum are relatively independent of those external to the ear.

The middle ear is an irregular, air-filled space in the petrous portion of the temporal bone. The three ossicles of the middle ear—the malleus, the incus, and the stapes—provide mechanical linkage between the tympanic membrane and the fenestra vestuli, an opening in the vestibule of the inner ear commonly known as the oval window. The handle of the malleus attaches to the tympanic membrane, and the footplate of the stapes attaches to the oval window. Two important functions are provided by the middle ear. The first is to amplify and deliver sound vibrations from the drum to the inner ear, and the second is that of protecting the inner ear from very loud sounds. The amplification of sound waves is accomplished by lever action of the ossicles that produces a greater force at the oval window than the force at the drum and because of the gain in force resulting from the relationship between the larger drum area and the smaller stapedial footplate area. The effective area of the drum is approximately 14 times that of the footplate of the stapes. The amplification gain of these two factors is approximately 25 dB. The effectiveness of the middle ear action in increasing hearing sensitivity is evidenced in middle ear pathologies where the ossicular chain is disrupted. A hearing loss of 25 dB or more occurs. The second function of the middle ear, that of protecting the inner ear from loud sounds, is accomplished by reflex action of the middle ear musculature, the stapedius, and the tensor tympani. The action of the muscles is to draw the stapes away from the oval window, retract the ear drum, and change ossicle vibrations in such a way as to decrease the transmitted pressure. The stapedius may be more responsive to accoustic stimulation than the tensor tympani. Latency of muscle contraction and possible muscle fatigue limit protection of the inner ear by these mechanisms. Middle ear air pressure is equalized by virtue of the eustachian tube which connects the middle ear and the nasopharynx. The pressure equalization is necessary for normal ear drum movement.

The inner ear is a system of cavities in the dense petrous portion of the temporal bone. One of the cavities is the cochlea, a bony labyrinth that is approximately 35 mm in length coiled around a central core for two and three-quarters turns. The spiral-shaped cochlea is divided into three ducts, two bony and one membranous. A cross section of cochlea showing the three ducts is shown in Fig. 2. The upper bony duct, the scala vestibuli and the lower bony duct, the scala tympani, are separated from each other by a membranous labyrinth, the cochlear duct. The cochlear duct is bound on top by Reissner's membrane and is bound below by the basilar membrane. The cochlear duct is filled with a viscous fluid called endolymph, and the duct is

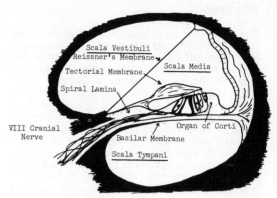

FIG. 2. Cross section of cochlea.

surrounded by a fluid called perilymph that has about twice the viscosity of water. The scala vestibuli and the scala tympani join at the apical end of the cochlea at a passage called the helicotrema. The scala tympani terminates at the basal end at the round window, a membrane-covered opening into the middle ear. The scala vestibuli is continuous with the vestibule; the oval window opens into the vestibule. Vibrations at the footplace of the stapes are transmitted into the fluid adjacent to the oval window. Vibration of the stapes and resultant disturbances in cochlear fluids results in movement of the basilar membrane. The cochlear duct contains the sensory receptors, specifically the organ of Corti, which lies upon the basilar membrane. There are about 25 000 hair cells; one end of each rests on the basilar membrane. The other ends of the hair cells are the cilia, very fine hairline processes, which make contact with the tectorial membrane, a membrane that overlaps the organ of Corti and that functionally behaves as if it were hinged at the cochlear wall. There are three rows of outer, and one row of inner, hair cells along most of the length of the basilar membrane. When vibrations are introduced into the inner ear and cause displacement of the basilar membrane, a shearing of the action of the cilia occurs that results in neural activity. It is assumed that amplification occurs in the inner ear in that small pressures on the basilar membrane result in a shearing force of considerably greater magnitude that distorts the hair cells. The result is increased sensitivity of the hearing system. Physical properties of the cochlea are such that different frequencies tend to localize at different points along the basilar membrane. The basilar membrane is narrowest and stiffest at the basal end, and most lax and widest at the apical end of the cochlea. High-frequency sounds result in the greatest disturbances near the basal end, and low-frequency sounds tend to localize near the apical end. When the role of the cochlea in pitch and loudness analyses is considered, it is now realized that more is involved in pitch perception than the

place of localization on the basilar membrane, although the particular neural fibers involved are probably relevant. Of particular interest in this regard is the phenomenon called periodicity pitch where the perceived pitch for a complex signal corresponds to the rate of the envelope change of the complex stimulus and where there is no energy at the frequency that corresponds to the perceived pitch. Our impression that we are hearing a fundamental pitch for a person talking over a telephone is a good example. Telephone circuits do not transmit frequencies in the fundamental pitch range so there is, in fact, no energy in this range yet an experience of pitch is experienced by the listener. Loudness is probably related to the total number of neural impulses per unit time.

The auditory pathways provide for the neural impulses from the ear to be transmitted to the cerebral centers of the auditory cortex. Processing of the neural signals probably occurs at synaptic connections as well as in the cortex. The cell bodies of the receptor neurons are located in the spiral ganglion. Neurons of the auditory nerve make synaptic connections with the hair cells of the cochlea. Nerve fibers typically innervate many hair cells, and more than one nerve fiber may make a connection with the same hair cell. There is recent evidence to indicate that there are also descending neural pathways as well as ascending ones. The central nervous system may thus be involved in auditory processing at the cochlea. Spiral ganglion axons make synaptic connections with cells of the central nervous system at the cochlear nucleus. At this point, there is interconnection between the pathways for the two ears. Other synaptic stations between this point and the auditory cortex include the inferior colliculus and the medial geniculate body. A schematic depicting the auditory pathways is shown in Fig. 3. It can be observed that the major projection is to the contralateral (opposite) cerebral hemisphere for each ear. That is, the right ear projects primarily to the left hemisphere and the left ear to the right hemisphere. Some evidence has been presented that for right-handed people, the left cerebral hemisphere processes speech and the right hemisphere processes non-speech signals. Evidence from pathological auditory systems is of particular interest with respect to the auditory pathways. In fact, one excellent way to understand the auditory system is to study the system when it is in a breakdown or pathological state. An imparied cochlea, for example, may result in a better than normal response to small amplitude changes in a sound. A lesion of the VIIIth Nerve is frequently manifested by a rapid decrease in the ability to respond under sustained stimulation. The ability to process speech is markedly affected when there is an involvement of the lower central nervous system. Cortical involvement does not affect usual speech or pure tone inputs.

The stimulus for hearing is sound. Sound

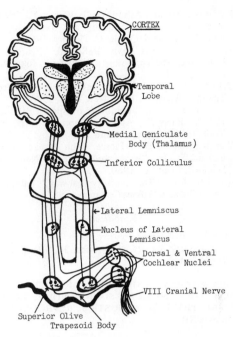

FIG. 3. Schematic depicting auditory pathways.

involves a disturbance in the air that is a forward and backward, rarefaction and compression, movement of air particles. The unit of force usually used in acoustics is the dyne. Sound pressure is frequently expressed in dynes per square centimeter. Intensities of sounds are usually measured on a decibel scale, a logarithmic ratio scale. The tremendous loudness range of the ear is exemplified by the fact that the most intense sound that can be tolerated is a million million times greater in intensity than a sound that is just audible. This is a range of approximately 120 dB. The frequency range of hearing is frequently given as 16 to 20 000 Hz. The ear is most sensitive in the middle frequency range of 1000 to 6000 Hz. In terms of discrimination of frequency and intensity, it is possible for about 1400 pitches and 280 intensity levels to be distinguished.

The truly phenomenal aspects of hearing can be observed in such behavior as localization of sounds, speech perception and particularly the understanding of one voice in the noisy environment of many, and the recognition of acoustic events that only last a few milliseconds. It is these and other behavioral phenomena that need to be accounted for in theories of hearing.

ROBERT W. PETERS

References

Books

Bekesy, Georg von, "Experiments in Hearing," New York, McGraw-Hill Book Co., 1960.

Rasmussen, Grant, Ed., and Windle, William F., "Neural Mechanisms of the Auditory and Vestibular Systems," Springfield, Charles C. Thomas, 1960.

Stevens, S. S., and Davis, Hallowell, "Hearing: Its Psychology and Physiology," New York, John Wiley & Sons, 1947.

Tobias, J. V. (Ed.), "Foundations of Modern Auditory Theory," Academic Press, New York, 1970.

Travis, L. E. (Ed.), "Handbook of Speech Pathology and Audiology," Appleton-Century-Crofts, New York, 1971 (Chapters 10 and 11).

Van Bergeijk, Willem, Pierce, John R., and David, Edward E., Jr., "Waves and the Ear," New York, Doubleday and Co., 1960.

Whitfield, I. C., "The Auditory Pathway," Baltimore, The Williams & Wilkins Company, 1967.

Periodicals

"The Bekesy Commemorative Issue," *The Journal of the Acoustic Society of America*, 34, 9 (September 1962) Part II.

Cross-references: ACOUSTICS; ARCHITECTURAL ACOUSTICS; MUSICAL SOUND; NOISE, ACOUSTICAL; PHYSICAL ACOUSTICS; REPRODUCTION OF SOUND.

HEAT

Heat vs Temperature   Heat is the imponderable but not intangible agency whose addition to or removal from a physical system is the cause of thermal changes of various types. These inlcude rise and fall of temperature, changes in length and volume, changes of physical states such as melting, evaporation and the like.

During the eighteenth century heat was assumed to be a subtle fluid called *caloric*, filling the interstices between the ultimate particles of matter and, under conditions of isolation from the surroundings, known to satisfy a conservation law. The production of heat by friction as well as its disappearance during the performance of external mechanical work established its essential physical nature as another form of *energy* and led to the overthrow of the caloric theory. Nevertheless, we still speak of the *flow* of heat as though it were a fluid and have retained the methods of measuring the *quantity of heat* originally devised by the upholders of the caloric view.

Our direct knowledge of heat is provided by the sensation of hotness and coldness when we come in contact with various physical bodies. It is possible to arrange a set of bodies in a sequence such that A feels hotter than B, B hotter than C, etc. We say that A has a higher *temperature* than B, B a higher one than C, and so on. Of course our sensations are qualitative and are considerably influenced by the thermal conductivity of the body we touch. Thus, on a frosty morning, the head of an ax, being metal, feels considerably colder than the wooden handle, though the two are presumably at the same temperature. To obtain a continuous and reproducible physical scale of temperature, various types of thermometers have been devised of which the mercury-in-glass or colored-alcohol-in-glass are familiar examples. The two temperature scales in common use are the Farenheit scale and the Celsius scale. The first assigns values of 32° and 212° to the normal freezing and boiling points of pure water, respectively, and divides this interval into 180 equal subintervals or degrees. The Celsius, formerly called Centigrade, scale assigns the respective values of 0° and 100° to the above fixed points; the standard interval is then divided into 100 equal degrees.

Temperature changes being produced by the addition or subtraction of heat from a body, temperature itself may be regarded as a measure of the concentration or *intensity* of heat. In general, the more heat we add to a given body the more its temperature rises.

Measurement of Heat   Since heat is imponderable and not directly observable, it is necessary to measure the size of a given quantity of heat by its effect on another body. If this effect is the production of a rise in temperature from some initial temperature, t_1, to a final temperature, t, then the rise $(t-t_1)$ is found to vary inversely with the mass of the test body. It is thus natural therefore, following the calorists, to regard the quantity of heat, say Q, as determined by the product of m and $(t-t_1)$. Thus we say

$$Q \text{ is proportional to } m \times (t-t_1)$$

To make this statement into an equation we write

$$Q = \text{constant} \times m \times (t-t_1) \qquad (1)$$

where the constant of proportionality depends on the substance, being large for some materials and small for others. This constant for water, for example, is about 33 times as great as for lead; water is said therefore to have a greater *heat capacity* than lead. Notice that the constant in Eq. (1) actually gives the numerical value of Q which is required to warm a unit mass of the substance through a temperature interval of exactly 1°. This constant is accordingly called the *specific heat capacity* (usually abbreviated to *specific heat*) and is indicated by c. Since it is found that the value of the specific heat, particularly for gases, but in principle for all materials, depends on the conditions under which the heat is absorbed, this must be indicated. We thus have c_p and c_v, for example, for the two important cases of absorption at constant pressure and constant volume respectively. Since the former characterizes the common laboratory case of working under atmospheric pressure, we accord-

ingly rewrite Eq. (1) as

$$Q_p = c_p m(t - t_1) \qquad (2)$$

Q_p now measures the heat absorbed under constant pressure, and c_p is the constant pressure specific heat. Since the right side of Eq. (2) contains *three* quantities, a mere choice of a mass unit and a degree unit is insufficient to establish a unit of heat. It is necessary to select some substance as a standard reference body and assign an arbitrary value of, say c_p equal to unity for it. Water is the universal choice for this standard body due not only to its cheapness and ease of purification but also to its large heat capacity.

With the selection of water as the standard with $c_p = 1$, the left side of Eq. (2) clearly becomes of unit value when m and $(t - t_1)$ are each of unit value. In the English system we accordingly have the *British thermal unit* (or Btu) as the heat required to warm 1 pound of pure water through an interval of 1°F. In the metric system, the corresponding unit is the *calorie*, the heat required to warm 1 gram of water 1°C. A large or *kilocalorie* corresponding to 1000 ordinary calories is also frequently used in scientific work.

Specific Heats Use of Eq. (2) reveals that the values of c_p obtained experimentally depend on the temperature interval used, indicating a dependence of c_p on temperature. Thus if c_p for water were actually unity throughout the 0 to 100°C range, a mass of water at 100°C mixed with an equal mass at 0°C would give a final mixture at exactly 50°C. The actual value is near 50.05°; this difference, although small, indicates the need to specify the calorie at some particular temperature. For this purpose, we suppose a system of mass m is warmed from t to $t + \Delta t$ by the addition at constant pressure of an increment of heat ΔQ_p. Then Eq. (2) becomes

$$\Delta Q_p = m \bar{c}_p \Delta t \qquad (3)$$

where now $\bar{c}_p$ is an average value of c_p over this interval. Then we define the *instantaneous* heat capacity, c_p, at t by the following relation:

$$c_p = \frac{1}{m} \lim_{\Delta t \to 0} \frac{\Delta Q_p}{\Delta t} = \frac{1}{m} \frac{dQ_p}{dt}$$

i.e., the heat absorbed per unit mass per degree as the interval becomes smaller and smaller without limit. This leads to the differential form of Eg. (3)

$$dQ_p = m c_p dt \qquad (4)$$

where dQ_p is the differential heat absorption which produces a differential temperature rise dt in a body of mass m and specific heat c_p.

The standard or 15° calorie is now defined as the rate of absorption of heat per gram per degree at 15°C and in practice is essentially the same as the average calorie over the 1° interval from 14.5 to 15.5°C.

If a mass m of water is warmed from t_1 to t, the integral of Eq. (4) gives for the total heat absorbed in 15° calories.

$$Q_p = \int_{t_1}^{t} dQ_p = m \int_{t_1}^{t} c_p dt =$$

$$= m \left[\int_{0°}^{t} c_p dt - \int_{0°}^{t_1} c_p dt \right] \qquad (5)$$

where the integral of c_p over the range t_1 to t has been written as the difference of two integrals from a common lower limit of 0°C. If, therefore, we evaluate an integral of the type

$$\int_{0°}^{t} c_p dt \text{ with } t \text{ varying in 1° steps and arrange}$$

these in a table, the right side of Eq. (5) may be evaluated by merely subtracting appropriate entries.

In Fig. 1, the value of c_p in 15° calories per gram per degree is plotted graphically from 0 to 100°C, and the integrals on the right of Eq. (5) are represented by appropriate areas under the c_p curve. Thus the integral from 0° to t is hatched with lines sloping up to the right, while that from 0° to t_1 has the lines sloping up to the left. The value of Q_p is then the singly hatched area.

With heat quantities measured in 15° calories, from the observed rise or fall of temperature in known masses of water, the specific heats of various substances, the heats absorbed on melting solids to liquids (heats of fusion), the heats absorbed on passage from the liquid to the vapor state (heats of vaporization), the heats evolved on combination of various substances, and the heats absorbed or evolved in chemical changes are at once determinable (see CALORIMETRY). For the present purpose, Table 1 gives the values of the constant pressure heat capacities of a few typical substances, variations with temperature being disregarded. Notice that c_p, although expressed in terms of calories per gram per degree, is in fact independent of the system of units,

TABLE 1

Substance	State	c_p(cal/g deg)
Water	Vapor	0.48
Water	Liquid	1.00
Water	Solid	0.50
Ethyl alcohol	Liquid	.54
Hydrogen	Gas	3.44
Air	Gas	.24
Aluminum	Solid	.22
Iron	Solid	.11
Lead	Solid	.03

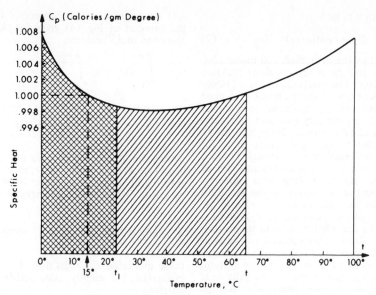

FIG. 1. Specific heat of water vs temperature.

since water is the reference body in all systems. Thus the specific heat of water in the English system would be 1 Btu per pound per degree Farenheit.

The Mechanical Nature of Heat The conservation of heat *per se* is observed only for systems involving the performance of no mechanical or electrical work. Count Rumford (ca. 1800) was the first to establish this fact in his famous cannon-boring experiments carried out in the arsenal of the Dutchy of Bavaria in Munich. He observed that when his drills became dull, heat was produced in great quantities limited only by the amount of work done against friction. He concluded that the large scale mechanical energy used in overcoming friction could only be converted into the motions of the ultimate particles of matter, a motion not directly observable but detected by our senses as heat. His results were confirmed and extended by the later work of Joule and Helmholtz, in particular, and also provided a more reliable value for the so-called *mechanical equivalent of heat*. This is taken as the amount of mechanical (or electrical) energy which when converted into heat is equivalent to exactly 1 calorie. The presently accepted value for this important constant is 4.185 joules per 15° calorie. Here the joule is the work performed when power is expended at the rate of 1 watt for 1 second. Thus an ordinary 100-watt lamp bulb converts 100 joules of electrical energy to thermal each second; this amounts to 100/4.185 or about 24 calories.

As a result of experiments such as these and a host of others, we are forced to recognize that heat is merely another form of the universal quantity *energy*. Its transformation always occurs at the rate of 4.185 joules per calorie

whether heat goes into external work or work is dissipated through friction into heat.

For details of the mechanical interpretations of heat in the case of ideal gases and simple solids see KINETIC THEORY.

FRANZO H. CRAWFORD

Reference

Crawford, Franzo H., "Heat, Thermodynamics and Statistical Physics," New York, Harcourt, Brace and World, 1963.

Cross-references: CALORIMETRY, HEAT CAPACITY, KINETIC THEORY, TEMPERATURE AND THERMOMETRY.

HEAT CAPACITY

The heat capacity of any thermodynamic system is

$$C = \frac{\delta q}{dT}, \qquad (1)$$

where δq is the quantity of heat* required to produce the temperature increment dT. If the system consists of a single substance with definite chemical composition and physical state, C is proportional to the total quantity of matter in the system. The heat capacity of 1 gram is the specific heat, and the heat capacity of one

*The symbol δ indicates a differential that is not exact, i.e., one for which a line integral is not determined by the initial and final points alone, but also depends on the path.

mole is sometimes called the molar heat capacity. Commonly used units of heat capacity include cal mole^{-1} deg^{-1}, cal g^{-1} deg^{-1}, and J mole^{-1} deg^{-1}.

The heat capacity of a substance depends on the variables that determine its thermodynamic state—e.g., temperature, pressure, electric and magnetic field—and also on the constraints imposed during the absorption of heat. Here we limit consideration to a substance subject to a hydrostatic pressure P and to no other forces. In this case, the thermodynamic state is determined by two variables, usually taken to be temperature and either pressure or molar volume V. The usual conditions for which C is of interest are constant volume and constant pressure, and the symbols C_V and C_P are used for the heat capacities measured under these conditions.

The difference between C_P and C_V is related to other thermodynamic properties by the first law of thermodynamics, which, for processes of interest here, may be written

$$\delta q = dU + P\,dV = dH - V\,dP, \qquad (2)$$

where U is the energy and $H = U + PV$ is the enthalpy. (We write this and all subsequent expressions involving thermodynamic properties for one mole.) From Eqs. (1) and (2), we have

$$C_V = \left(\frac{\partial U}{\partial T}\right)_P \qquad (3)$$

and

$$C_P = \left(\frac{\partial U}{\partial T}\right)_P + P\left(\frac{\partial V}{\partial T}\right)_P = \left(\frac{\partial H}{\partial T}\right)_P. \qquad (4)$$

Subtraction of Eq. (3) from Eq. (4) and substitution of the mathematical relation

$$\left(\frac{\partial U}{\partial T}\right)_P = \left(\frac{\partial U}{\partial T}\right)_V + \left(\frac{\partial U}{\partial V}\right)_T\left(\frac{\partial V}{\partial T}\right)_P \qquad (5)$$

gives

$$C_P - C_V = \left\{\left(\frac{\partial U}{\partial V}\right)_T + P\right\}\left(\frac{\partial V}{\partial T}\right)_P. \qquad (6)$$

The quantity of heat required to produce a certain temperature increase dT is greater at constant pressure than at constant volume by the sum of the work of expansion in the constant pressure process, $P(\partial V/\partial T)_P\,dT$, and the increase in internal energy accompanying the expansion, $(\partial U/\partial V)_T(\partial V/\partial T)_P\,dT$.

An expression for $C_P - C_V$ that is more useful than Eq. (6) is

$$C_P - C_V = TV\alpha^2/\kappa, \qquad (7)$$

which can be obtained from Eq. (6) by introducing a relation based on the second law of thermodynamics.

$$\left(\frac{\partial U}{\partial V}\right)_T + P = T\left(\frac{\partial P}{\partial T}\right)_V,$$

the mathematical relation

$$\left(\frac{\partial P}{\partial T}\right)_V = -\left(\frac{\partial V}{\partial T}\right)_P \bigg/ \left(\frac{\partial V}{\partial P}\right)_T,$$

and the definition of the coefficients of thermal expansion α and isothermal compressibility κ,

$$\alpha = \frac{1}{V}\left(\frac{\partial V}{\partial T}\right)_P, \qquad (8)$$

and

$$\kappa = -\frac{1}{V}\left(\frac{\partial V}{\partial P}\right)_T. \qquad (9)$$

The subject of the following sections is the relationship of the heat capacities of ideal gases and solids to the energies associated with different degrees of freedom of the constituent particles. The heat capacity of a liquid is more complicated and is not considered here.

Ideal Gases An ideal gas obeys the equation of state, $PV = RT = NkT$. The gas constant R is 8.314 J mole^{-1} K^{-1}, N is Avogadro's number, and $k = R/N$ is Boltzmann's constant. By Eqs. (7), (8) and (9), $C_P - C_V = R$.

In the application of statistical mechanics to the calculation of C_P or C_V it is convenient to consider first the predictions based on classical principles. The pertinent result of classical statistical mechanics is the principle of equipartition of energy: any term in the energy of a particle proportional to the square of either a coordinate or a momentum contributes an average of $\frac{1}{2}kT$ to U. Since the molecules of an ideal gas have three translational degrees of freedom, each with an associated kinetic energy proportional to the square of a momentum, the expected translational contributions to the energy and heat capacity are $U = \frac{3}{2}NkT = \frac{3}{2}RT$ and, by Eq. (3), $C_V = \frac{3}{2}R$. For monatomic gases this is the only contribution to C_V and this value is in excellent agreement with experiment.

Diatomic molecules can rotate about each of two independent axes perpendicular to the internuclear axis, and the two atoms can vibrate with respect to each other along the internuclear axis. Each of the two rotational degrees of freedom has a kinetic energy proportional to the square of a momentum, and the vibrational degree of freedom has both a kinetic energy proportional to the square of a momentum and a potential energy proportional to the square of a coordinate (the vibration is approximately harmonic). In classical statistical mechanics, C_V is therefore expected to be $\frac{7}{2}R$, but for most diatomic gases at room temperature C_V is close to $\frac{5}{2}R$. This discrepancy, one of the historically important failures of classical theory, is resolved by proper consideration of quantum effects as

suggested by Einstein. The allowed energy levels of a harmonic oscillator are not continuous as in classical mechanics, but are given by

$$\epsilon_n = nh\nu, \text{ with } n = 0, 1, 2, 3, \cdots ,$$

where h is Planck's constant, ν is the natural frequency of the oscillator, and the energies ϵ_n are measured from the lowest level. For the average energy of a single oscillator, quantum statistical mechanics gives

$$\bar{\epsilon} = \frac{h\nu}{e^{h\nu/kT} - 1} .$$

Instead of the classical value k, the contribution to C_V is

$$\frac{d\bar{\epsilon}}{dT} = k \frac{\left(\frac{h\nu}{kT}\right)^2 e^{k\nu/kT}}{(e^{h\nu/kT} - 1)^2}. \tag{10}$$

This contribution to C_V is negligible for $T \leqslant 0.1\ h\nu/k$ because most of the oscillators remain in the $n = 0$ level, but it increases rapidly near $T \approx \frac{1}{4}h\nu/k$ and approaches the classical value for $T \geqslant h\nu/k$. For many diatomic molecules, $h\nu/k$ is a few thousand degrees Kelvin or more, and a room-temperature C_V of $\frac{5}{2}R$ can be understood as the sum of the translational and rotational contributions. The details of the temperature dependence predicted by Eq. (10), including the approach of C_V to $\frac{7}{2}R$ at sufficiently high temperatures, have been verified experimentally for a number of gases.

In a few cases (H_2, HD and D_2), diatomic gases exist at temperatures for which kT is comparable to the spacing of the rotational energy levels, and quantum effects can be observed in the rotational contribution to C_V. For H_2, C_V drops below $\frac{5}{2}R$ as the temperature is reduced below about 300 K, and below 50 K it becomes equal to the $\frac{3}{2}R$ that is characteristic of translation. The translational energy levels of ordinary gases are so closely spaced that quantum effects are never important in the translational heat capacity.

The heat capacity of polyatomic gases can be treated by a straightforward generalization of the foregoing discussion. A molecule with n atoms has three translational degrees of freedom and, if it is nonlinear, three rotational and $3n - 6$ vibrational degrees of freedom. If it is linear, it has two rotational and $3n - 5$ vibrational degrees of freedom.

Solids For every solid there is a lattice heat capacity associated with vibrations of the atoms. If the interatomic forces are harmonic, the N atoms in one mole of a monatomic solid have $3N$ independent vibrational modes, and the lattice heat capacity is the sum of $3N$ terms given by Eq. (10). Since the spectrum of the $3N$ frequencies of a real solid is complicated and difficult to calculate, an approximation introduced by Debye is widely used. In the Debye model, the vibrational modes are sound waves in an elastic continuum; the boundaries of the solid determine the allowed wavelengths and the sound velocities then determine the frequencies. To limit the number of frequencies to $3N$, the spectrum is cut off at a maximum frequency $k\Theta_D/h$ where Θ_D, the Debye temperature, is determined by the sound velocities and is typically a few hundred degrees Kelvin. The cutoff corresponds to the fact that in a real crystal, the vibrations have a minimum wavelength comparable to the interatomic distance. The heat capacity is

$$C_V = \frac{12}{5}\pi^4 R\left(\frac{T}{\Theta_D}\right)^3 \tag{11}$$

for $T \leqslant \Theta_D/20$, but it increases less rapidly at higher temperatures and approaches the classical limit 3R for $T > \Theta_D$. The predicted high-temperature limit is in agreement with the empirical rule of Dulong and Petit: for most monatomic solids C_V is approximately $3R$ at room temperature. However, this value is often exceeded at very high temperatures, partly as a consequence of anharmonicity in the interatomic forces. At low temperatures, Eq. (11) is in good agreement with experiment; C_V is found to be proportional to T^3, although often only at temperatures below $\Theta_D/100$, and Θ_D is given accurately by the sound velocities. This agreement is to be expected because at low temperatures only low-frequency vibrations contribute, and these are treated accurately in the Debye model. At intermediate temperatures, the agreement with experiment is only approximate.

Occasionally the lattice heat capacity of a molecular crystal is represented by the sum of a Debye heat capacity for the vibrations of the N molecules as units and the appropriate number of terms given by Eq. (10) for the intermolecular vibrations.

In metals, there is an electronic heat capacity related to the translational motion of the conduction electrons. The small mass and high density of the electrons make quantum effects important, and Sommerfeld showed that their heat capacity should be proportional to temperature for temperatures below about 10^4 K. This contribution is usually significant below a few degrees Kelvin, where the lattice heat capacity is small, and also at high temperatures, where it contributes to deviations from the rule of Dulong and Petit.

The heat capacities of a number of solids have bumps or peaks superimposed on the smoothly varying lattice and electronic heat capacities. These are usually called anomalies and two distinct types can be recognized. A Schottky anomaly is a smooth bump that arises from a set of energy levels for a single particle. The splitting of the rotational states of magnetic

ions by electric fields, and of nuclei by electric or magnetic fields, are examples for which the associated anomalies occur in the ranges 10^{-1} to 10^3 K and 10^{-3} to 10^{-1} K, respectively. Lambda anomalies are sharp peaks produced by cooperative processes involving many particles in a transition from a low-temperature ordered state to a high-temperature disordered state. Examples are: the momentum ordering of ^{4}He atoms in liquid ^{4}He at 2.18 K and of electrons in superconductors at temperatures ranging from 10^{-1} to 10 K; the magnetic ordering of ferromagnets and antiferromagnets at temperatures from 10^{-3} to 10^3 K; the spatial ordering of different atoms of an alloy on a superlattice, e.g., β-brass at 750 K; and the rotational disorder in certain molecular crystals e.g., H_2 at 1.5 K.

NORMAN E. PHILLIPS

Cross-references: CALORIMETRY, GAS LAWS, HEAT, TEMPERATURE AND THERMOMETRY, THERMODYNAMICS.

HEAT TRANSFER

Establishment of thermodynamic equilibrium for a system consisting of a number of media requires that the temperature be locally uniform and time-wise constant. A departure from this condition causes a transfer of energy in the form of heat from locations with high temperature to locations with low temperature. Such an energy transfer occurs very frequently and is encountered in our everyday life as well as in many engineering applications or in scientific experiments. It has, therefore, been known for a long time. The fact that quantitative predictions have become possible in the recent past only is due to the situation that several mechanisms are usually involved and interrelated in such an energy transfer process. They are generally classified as conduction, convection and radiation.

Heat transfer by conduction is that process which transports heat in a medium from one location to another without involvement of any visible movement. It is generally the only or the dominating mode of heat transfer in a solid medium; however, it occurs also in liquids and gases. In such fluids, this energy transport is often augmented when parts of the fluid are in movement and carry energy along. This mechanism of heat transfer is classified as transfer by convection. All media can also release energy in the form of photons (electromagnetic waves). This energy travels in space essentially with the velocity of light until the photons are recaptured by some other atoms, causing in this way heat transfer by radiation. An example of this energy transport is the transfer of heat from the sun to the earth. The three modes of energy transfer mentioned above will be discussed consecutively in the following sections. However, it must be realized that they often occur simultaneously, so that in some cases the total energy transport will be the sum of the contributions of the individual mechanisms. In other cases, such a summation will not lead to the correct result when the individual transport mechanisms mutually interfere.

Conduction From a microscopic standpoint, thermal conduction refers to energy being handed down from one atom or molecule to the next one. In a liquid or gas, these particles change their position continuously even without visible movement and they transport energy also in this way. From a macroscopic or continuum viewpoint, thermal conduction is quantitatively described by Fourier's equation which states that the heat flux q per unit time and unit area through an area element arbitrarily located in the medium is proportional to the drop in temperature, $-\operatorname{grad} T$, per unit length in the direction normal to the area and to a transport property k characteristic of the medium and called thermal conductivity.

$$q = -k \operatorname{grad} T \qquad (1)$$

Predictions for the value of the thermal conductivity k can be made from considerations of the atomic structure. Accurate values, however, require experimentation in which the heat flux q and the temperature gradient, grad T, are measured and these values are inserted into Fourier's equation. Figure 1 presents thermal conductivity values for a number of media in a large temperature range. It can be recognized that metals have the largest conductivities and, among those, pure metals have larger values than alloys. Gases, on the other hand, have very low heat conductivity values. Electrically nonconducting solids and liquids are arranged in between. The low thermal conductivity of air is utilized in the development of thermally insulating materials. Such materials, like cork or glass fiber, consist of a solid substance with a very large number of small spaces filled by air. The thermal transport occurs then essentially through the air spaces, and the solid structure only supplies the framework which prevents convective currents. The range of thermal conductivities in Fig. 1 at ambient temperature extends through 5 powers of 10. This range is still small compared with the range for the electric conductivity of various substances where electric conductors have values which are larger by 25 powers of 10 than electric insulators. As a consequence of this fact, it is much easier to channel electricity along a desired path than to do so with heat, a fact which accounts for the difficulty in accurate experimentation in the field of heat transfer.

Fourier's equation can be used together with a statement on energy conservation to derive a differential equation describing the temperature field in a medium. Fourier was the first one to develop this equation and to devise means for its solution. In vector notation, this equation is

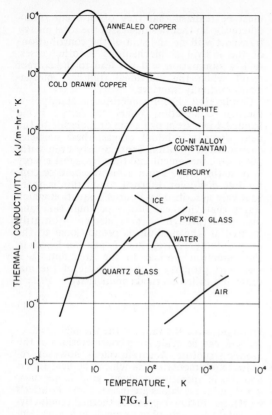

FIG. 1.

$$\rho c \frac{\partial T}{\partial t} = \nabla (k \nabla T) \qquad (2)$$

where ρ is the density, c is the specific heat, t is time, ∇ is the Nabla operator. The temperature field in a substance can either change in time (unsteady state) or it can be independent of time (steady state $\partial T/\partial t = 0$). For a steady-state situation, the temperature field depends primarily on the geometry of the body involved and on the boundary conditions. The simplest case of a steady state temperature field is the one in a plane wall with temperatures which are uniform on each surface, however different at the two surfaces. The temperature in the wall then changes linearly in the direction of the surface normal as long as the variation of the thermal conductivity in the temperature range involved can be neglected. For an unsteady process, the capacity of the medium to store energy enters the energy conservation equation; correspondingly, the specific heat of the material and its density become factors for the conduction process, as well as the thermal conductivity. A combination of these properties, defined as the ratio of the thermal conductivity to the product of specific heat and density, called thermal diffusivity $(k/\rho c)$, then determines how fast existing temperature differences in a medium equalize in time. It is found that

metals and gases have thermal diffusivity values which are approximately equal in magnitude and considerably higher than thermal diffusivities of liquid and solid nonconductors. This means that temperature differences equalize much faster in metals and gases than in other substances.

Various other physical processes lead in their mathematical description to equations of the same form as Eq. (2), especially in its steady-state form. Such processes are, for instance, the conduction of electricity in a conductor or the shape of a thin membrane stretched over a curved boundary. This situation has led to the development of analogies (electric analogy, soap film analogy) to heat conduction processes which are useful because they often offer the advantage of simpler experimentation.

Convection It has been mentioned before that in fluids, energy is often transported by convection. In such a situation, conduction takes care of the transport of heat from one stream tube to another and is the dominating mode of transfer near solid walls. Convection transports heat along the stream lines and is dominating in the main body of the fluid where the velocities are large. In many situations, the flow is turbulent; this means that unsteady mixing motions are superimposed on the mean flow. These mixing motions contribute also to a transport of heat between stream tubes, a process which can be thought of as being described by an "effective" conductivity which often has values by several powers of ten larger than the actual conductivity of the fluid.

The movement of the fluid may be generated by means external to the heat transfer process, as by fans, blowers, or pumps. It may also be created by density differences connected with the heat transfer process itself. The first mode is called *forced convection*, the second one *natural* or *free convection*. Convective heat transfer may also be classified as heat transfer in duct flow or in external flow (over cylinders, spheres, air foils, or similar objects). In the second case, the heat transfer process is essentially concentrated in a thin fluid layer surrounding the object (boundary layer).

Of special interest in such heat transfer processes is the knowledge of the heat flux from the surface of a solid object exposed to the flow. This heat flux q_w per unit area and time is conventionally described by Newton's equation

$$q_w = h(T_w - T_f) \qquad (3)$$

where T_w is the surface temperature and T_f is a characteristic temperature in the fluid. This equation defining the heat transfer coefficient h is convenient because in many situations the heat flux is at least approximately proportional to the temperature difference $T_w - T_f$. Information on the heat transfer coefficients can be obtained by a solution of the Navier-Stokes equations describing the flow of a viscous fluid and the related energy equation, or they are found

by experimentation. The availability of electronic computers has tremendously increased our ability to study heat transfer analytically at least for laminar flow, whereas in turbulent flow the bulk of our information is based on experiments. Such experimentation is made difficult by the large number of parameters involved. Dimensional analysis has therefore been applied to reduce the number of influencing parameters, and relations for convective heat transfer are correspondingly presented in modern handbooks as relations between dimensionless parameters. Such an analysis demonstrates, for instance, that heat transfer in forced flow can be described by a relation of the form

$$Nu = f(Re, Pr) \qquad (4)$$

in which the Nusselt number Nu is a dimensionless parameter hL/k, containing the heat transfer coefficient h; the Reynolds number $Re = \rho(VL/\mu)$ describes essentially the nature of the flow; and the Prandtl number $Pr = c_p\mu/k$ can be considered as a dimensionless transport property characterizing the fluid involved. L and V are an arbitrarily selected characteristic length and velocity, respectively, ρ denotes the density, μ the viscosity, and c_p the specific heat of the fluid at constant pressure. Occasionally the Stanton number, $St = Nu/Re\,Pr$, is used instead of the Nusselt number as a dimensionless expression of the heat transfer coefficient. Equation (4) is based on the assumption that the thermodynamic and transport properties involved in the heat transfer process can be considered as constant. Larger variations of such properties are usually accounted for by additional terms in Eq. (4) expressing the ratio of the varying transport properties or of parameters (temperature, pressure) on which they depend. Fluids occurring in nature cover a very large range of Prandtl numbers. Liquid metals, for instance, have values of order 0.001 to 0.01. Gases have values between 0.6 and 1, and oils have values up to 10 000 and more. Some heat transfer relations for forced convection are presented in Table 1. Relations for other situations can be found in the various texts mentioned at the end of this section or in corresponding handbooks. With regard to the relations in Table 1 and other similar equations, it has to be kept in mind that they are valid over a restricted range of the independent parameters only.

Heat transfer by free convection is described by relations of the form

$$Nu = f(Gr, Pr) \qquad (5)$$

In this equation, the Grashof number

$$Gr = \frac{\rho^2 g\beta(T_w - T_f)L^3}{\mu^2}$$

(where g is the gravitational constant, β is the thermal expansion coefficient, T_f is the fluid temperature at a distance where it is not influ-

TABLE 1   RELATIONS FOR CONVECTIVE HEAT TRANSFER

Forced Convection

Channel Flow
Flow through a tube:
  laminar ($Re < 3000$)

$$Nu = 3.65$$

  turbulent ($Re > 3000, Pr > 0.6$)

$$Nu = 0.116\,(Re^{2/3} - 125)\,Pr^{1/3}$$

$$\left(Nu = \frac{hD}{k}, Re = \frac{\overline{V}D}{\nu}, \right.$$

$$\left. D = \text{diameter}, \overline{V} = \text{mean velocity} \right)$$

External Flow
Flat plate parallel to flow:
  laminar ($1000 < Re < 500000, Pr > 0.6$)

$$Nu = 0.332\sqrt{Re}\,\sqrt[3]{Pr}$$

  turbulent ($Re > 500000, Pr > 0.6$)

$$Nu = \frac{0.0297\,Re^{4/5}\,Pr}{1 + 1.3Re^{-1/10}\,Pr^{-1/6}\,(Pr - 1)}$$

$$\left(Nu = \frac{hx}{k}, Re = \frac{\rho V_s x}{\mu}, x = \text{distance from leading edge}, \right.$$

$$\left. V_s = \text{velocity outside boundary layer} \right)$$

Cylinder normal to flow: $1 < Re < 4000$

$$Nu = 0.43 + 0.48\sqrt{Re}$$

$$\left(Nu = \frac{hD}{k}, Re = \frac{\rho V_0 D}{\mu}, D = \text{diameter}, \right.$$

$$\left. V_0 = \text{upstream velocity} \right)$$

Natural Convection

Vertical flat plate:
  laminar ($10^4 < Gr < 10^8$)

$$Nu = 0.508\,Gr^{1/4}\,Pr^{1/2}\,(0.952 + Pr)^{-1/4}$$

  turbulent ($Gr > 10^8$)

$$Nu = 0.0295\,Gr^{2/5}\,Pr^{7/5}\,(1 + 0.494\,Pr^{2/3})^{-2/5}$$

$$\left(Nu = \frac{hx}{k}, Gr = \frac{\rho^2 g\beta(T_w - T_f)x^3}{\mu^2}, x = \text{distance} \right.$$

from leading edge, T_w = wall temperature, T_f = fluid temperature at some distance from plate)
(All surfaces are assumed to have uniform temperature)

enced by the heated or cooled object with surface temperature T_w) replaces the Reynolds number. Sometimes a dimensionless parameter called Rayleigh number ($Ra = Gr\,Pr$) is used instead of the Grashof number. Equation (5) assumes again that the fluid properties involved are nearly constant. Examples for such relations are also contained in Table 1. Examples for free convection situations are the heat transfer from

a heating register in the room. Free convection is also an important factor in the establishment of the temperature in the atmosphere. In the free convection relations of Table 1 and in Eq. (5), it has been assumed that the convection flows are generated by the gravitational field. Natural convection can also be created by other body forces, like centrifugal and Coriolis forces or electromagnetic forces.

Space does not permit the discussion of other heat transfer processes, although such processes have found increasing attention in recent years. Especially large heat transfer coefficients are created by a boiling or condensation process. Boiling heat transfer is therefore used in applications which have to deal with very large heat fluxes like chambers and nozzles of rockets or the anodes in electric arc devices. Heat transfer is also often combined with mass transfer processes. This is, for instance, the case in evaporation devices. Heat transfer may also occur combined with chemical reactions as in processes involving gases at very high temperature where combustion, dissociation, or ionization occur.

Radiation Energy can also be transferred from one location to another within a medium or from one medium to another in the form of photons (electromagnetic waves). Usually a multiplicity of wavelengths λ is involved in such energy transfer. In vacuum, all waves regardless of their wavelength move with the same speed 2.9977×10^8 m/sec. In various substances, the wave velocity c changes somewhat with wavelength, and the ratio of the wave velocity in vacuum to the velocity in a substance is equal to the optical refraction index. Air and generally all gases have refraction indices which differ from one only in the fourth decimal. Their wave velocity is, therefore, practically equal to that in vacuum.

Prévost's principle states that the amount of energy emitted by a volume element within a radiating substance is completely independent of its surroundings. Whether the volume element increases or decreases its temperature by the process of radiation depends on whether it absorbs more foreign radiation than it emits or vice versa. One talks about thermal radiation when the emission of photons is thermally excited, i.e., when the substance within the volume element is nearly in thermodynamic equilibrium. The discussion in this section will be restricted to thermal radiation. For such radiation, Kirchhoff was able to derive a number of relations by consideration of a system of media in thermodynamic equilibrium. If j_ν indicates the co-efficient of emission, i.e., the radiative flux at the frequency ν^* emitted per unit volume into a unit solid angle, and n is the co-efficient of absorption at the same frequency, that is, the fraction of the intensity of a radiant beam which is absorbed per unit path length, then one of these relations states

$$c^2 \frac{j_\nu}{n_\nu} = f(T, \nu) \tag{6}$$

with c denoting the wave velocity. According to this relation, the combination of parameters on the left-hand side of the equation is a function of temperature T and frequency ν of the radiation only, but does not depend on the substance under consideration. Kirchhoff's law can also be expressed in parameters which refer to the interface of two media 1 and 2. It then takes the form

$$c^2 \frac{i_\nu}{\alpha_\nu} = f(T, \nu) \tag{7}$$

in which i_ν is the monochromatic intensity of the radiative flux at frequency ν originating in medium 2 and traveling through the interface into medium 1 per unit solid angle and area normal to the direction of the radiant beam. α_ν is the monochromatic absorptance or absorptivity, i.e., that fraction of a radiant beam approaching the interface in the medium 1 in the opposite direction that is absorbed in medium 2. c is the wave velocity in medium 1. Kirchhoff's law states that the combination of the parameters on the left-hand side of Eq. (7) is again a function of temperature and frequency only, but does not depend on the nature of the medium. A medium which absorbs all the radiation traveling into it through an interface ($\alpha_\nu = 1$) is called a blackbody. The intensity of radiation emitted by an arbitrary medium is, according to Eq. (7), in the following way related to the intensity of radiation $i_{b\nu}$ emitted by a blackbody at the same temperature and frequency

$$\frac{i_\nu}{\alpha_\nu} = i_{b\nu} \tag{8}$$

From the consideration of a system in thermodynamic equilibrium, it is also easily shown that $i_{b\nu}$ is independent of direction and that the total monochromatic radiant flux emitted by a blackbody per unit interface area and unit time is equal $\pi i_{b\nu}$.

The law describing the monochromatic intensity of radiation of a blackbody is given by Planck's equation

$$i_{b\nu} = \frac{2h\nu^3}{c^2(e^{h\nu/kT} - 1)} \tag{9}$$

(where h is Planck's quantum constant and k is Boltzmann's constant). Experimentalists prefer to use the intensity $i_{b\lambda}$ per unit wavelength ($i_{b\lambda}d\lambda = i_{b\nu}d\nu$). Figure 2 presents the wavelength dependence of the intensity of blackbody monochromatic radiation for a number of temperatures. It may be observed that for each temperature, the intensity has a maximum at a certain wavelength and that this maximum shifts toward short wavelengths with increasing temperature (Wien's law). The wavelength λ is plotted on the abscissa in microns $\mu(1000\mu =$

*Frequency and wavelength are used interchangeably. They are connected by the relation $\lambda\nu = c$.

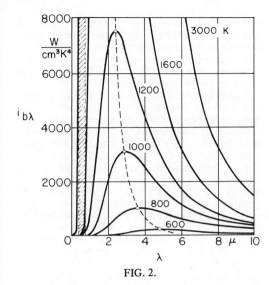

FIG. 2.

1 mm). Our eye is sensitive to radiation in the range 0.4 to 0.7μ (the dashed range). It may be observed that for temperatures with which we have largely to deal, the bulk of blackbody radiation is contained in the range of wavelengths larger than the visible ones (infrared range). This statement also holds for other media because Eq. (8) shows that no medium can have a monochromatic intensity which is higher than that of a blackbody. Only radiation coming from the sun has a major portion of the energy in the visible wavelength range (corresponding to a temperature of 6500 K).

The total energy flux q emitted per unit area and time from a blackbody can be obtained by integration of Eq. (9) over all frequencies and by multiplication of the result by π. For blackbody radiation into a vacuum (or with good approximation into a gas), the result is

$$q = \sigma T^4 \qquad (10)$$

The Stefan-Boltzmann constant σ has the value $5.67 \times 10^{-8}\,\mathrm{W/m^3 K^4}$

The following additional relation exists at an interface between two substances.

$$\rho_v + \alpha_v + \tau_v = 1 \qquad (11)$$

This equation describes that the radiant energy in a beam approaching in a medium 1 the interface with a medium 2 is found again either as radiation reflected back into the medium 1 or absorbed in the medium 2 or transmitted through the medium 2 into other media or back into medium 1. The monochromatic reflectance or reflectivity ρ_v is the ratio of reflected to incident radiant energy, α_v is the corresponding ratio for the absorbed, and τ_v for the transmitted energy. The vast majority of solids and liquids absorb radiant energy over most wavelengths in the infrared range within a very thin layer adjacent to the interface (of order 1μ to 1 mm). In heat transfer calculations, it can therefore usu-

ally be assumed that the transmissivity of such substances is equal to zero and that reflectivity and absorptivity are connected to the temperature of the interface. One talks then often in a simplified manner about radiative interchange between surfaces. Kirchhoff's law, Eq. (8), additionally connects the intensity of a beam emitted through the interface with the absorptivity and the intensity of a beam leaving a blackbody at the same temperature. Electromagnetic theory shows that electric nonconducting materials have in the infrared range generally high values of the absorptivity and correspondingly low values of the reflectivity. Metals (electric conductors), on the other hand, behave in the opposite way, having low absorptivity and high reflectivity values. This fact is utilized in aluminum-insulations and in vacuum thermos bottles. In the visible range, the appearance of surfaces of various materials to the eye already supplies information on approximate values of the reflectivity and absorptivity. A white surface, for instance, has a very low absorptivity. Gases behave differently with respect to radiation. They need fairly large layers in order to absorb the major part of incident radiation and radiate only in restricted wavelength ranges whereas solids and liquids have a more continuous spectrum.

Values for the radiation properties $(\rho_v, \alpha_v, \tau_v)$ together with the relations for blackbody radiation are the basis of calculations to determine heat exchange by radiation in a system with locally varying temperature. Calculations of such interchange are in general very involved, especially when substances with small absorption coefficients are involved. The formulation of such interchange leads to integral differential equations. The reader has in this connection to be referred to the books listed at the end of this section, and only a few relations for simple geometries will be presented here. Consider two area elements, dA_1 and dA_2, belonging to two blackbodies with the temperatures T_1 and T_2. The distance between the two area elements is s, and β_1 and β_2 are the angles between the two surface normals and the interconnecting line. The following equation then describes the net heat transfer dQ from area element dA_1 to area element dA_2 per unit time assuming that no radiation is absorbed or emitted in the space between the two surfaces.

$$dQ = \frac{\cos\beta_1 \cos\beta_2}{\pi s^2}\,dA_1\,dA_2\,\sigma(T_1{}^4 - T_2{}^4)$$

$$(12)$$

If non-black surfaces are involved, then the process of radiant interchange is much more involved, since part of the incident radiation is now reflected from the surfaces and travels in this way back and forth until it is finally absorbed. Simple relations exist in this case for the radiative interchange between the surfaces of two concentric spheres or cylinders with areas

A_1 and A_2 and temperatures T_1 and T_2. It is further assumed that both surfaces are emitting and reflecting in a perfectly diffuse way and that they are separated by a medium which does neither emit nor absorb radiation. The net monochromatic interchange $d\Phi_\nu$ between the two surfaces is then described by the equation

$$d\Phi_\nu = \frac{\pi}{\dfrac{1}{\alpha_{\nu 1}} + \dfrac{A_1}{A_2}\left(\dfrac{1}{\alpha_{\nu 2}} - 1\right)} dA_1 (i_{b\nu 1} - i_{b\nu 2})$$

(13)

The monochromatic intensities $i_{b\nu 1}$ and $i_{b\nu 2}$ are calculated with Eq. (9). The relation changes when the outer cylinder reflects radiation mirror-like (specularly) to

$$d\Phi_\nu = \frac{\pi}{\dfrac{1}{\alpha_{\nu 1}} + \left(\dfrac{1}{\alpha_{\nu 2}} - 1\right)} dA_1 (i_{b\nu 1} - i_{b\nu 2})$$

(14)

Both equations merge asymptotically into the same relation when the differences between the two radii become small. The corresponding relation then also holds for two parallel infinite planes. Equations (13) and (14) have to be integrated over all frequencies to obtain the net heat transfer between the two surfaces. The result is simple when the absorptances $\alpha_{\nu 1}$ and $\alpha_{\nu 2}$ are independent of frequency (gray surfaces). Equations (13) and (14) describe then the net heat transfer, when $i_{b\nu 1}$ and $i_{b\nu 2}$ are replaced by $(\sigma/\pi)T_1^4$ and $(\sigma/\pi)T_2^4$, respectively.

E. R. G. ECKERT

References

Eckert, E. R. G., and Drake, R. M., Jr., "Analysis of Heat and Mass Transfer," New York, McGraw-Hill, Inc., 1972.

Arpaci, V., "Conduction Heat Transfer," Reading, Mass., Addison–Wesley Publishing Co., 1966.

Kays, W. M., "Convective Heat and Mass Transfer," New York, McGraw-Hill Book Co., 1966.

Hottel, H. C., and Sarofim, A. F., "Radiative Transfer," New York, McGraw-Hill Book Co., 1967.

Cross-references: HEAT, HEAT CAPACITY, INFRARED RADIATION, REFLECTION.

HEISENBERG UNCERTAINTY PRINCIPLE

Classical physics is based on two assumptions that have been found experimentally to be untenable. The first of these is the existence of signals that can travel with infinite speed; the second is that the magnitude of the interaction between two systems can be reduced to arbitrarily small values. The realization that the speed of propagation of signals has a finite upper limit led to the development of relativity theory. The recognition of the existence of a finite quantum of action has been incorporated in quantum (wave) mechanics.

Quantum mechanics assigns a physical reality only to those variables whose value can, in principle, be experimentally determined. About the existence of phenomena or systems that cannot be experimentally observed, quantum mechanics is noncommittal. Questions regarding an isolated system are meaningless in quantum mechanics, for any observation made on such a system necessarily disturbs its isolation by at least one quantum of action. Heisenberg[5] observed that any measurement made on a system destroys some of the knowledge gained about that system through previous measurements. Any prediction about the future course of a system must be contingent on a knowledge about the measurements that will be made on that system, and is subject to uncertainties introduced by the measurements. Whereas one might speculate with some reliability about the future course of a system under the restriction that no more measurements will be performed on it, such speculations would be physically meaningless, as they could not be experimentally confirmed or denied.

In the broadest sense, then, the Heisenberg Uncertainty Principle states that the partitioning of the universe into observer (either a human observer, or a recording device such as a photographic plate) and observed is subject to a finite inaccuracy; one might say that the "knife" or "pencil" that makes the partition has a finite "thickness," h.

The concept of a monochromatic beam of radiation is not a difficult one to accept. Yet the experimental determination of the frequency of such a beam requires an infinite time interval; any finite portion chopped from the beam is shown by Fourier analysis to have a spectrum of finite width, hence not a single frequency at all. Quantum mechanics does not deny the existence of a monochromatic beam, but it does render the assignment of a definite frequency in a given time interval meaningless.

Fourier analysis shows that the specifications of the time interval, Δt, and of the spectral width, $\Delta \nu$, are reciprocally related:

$$\Delta \nu \, \Delta t \geqslant 1$$

(1)

This equation represents the uncertainty relation for classical waves: any attempt to specify the frequency at an instant of time results in a broadening of the frequency spectrum. This uncertainty relation applies to any wave, whether electromagnetic, acoustic, or otherwise.

Interference patterns observed when electron beams are reflected from crystalline surfaces[3] or transmitted through thin metallic films[7] indicate that these beams possess some wave character-

istics. DeBroglie[2], by independent theoretical considerations (see WAVE MECHANICS), postulated the following relations between the dynamic variables, energy (E) and linear momentum (p) of the beam, on the one hand, and the wave variables, frequency (ν) and wavelength (λ), on the other:

$$E = h\nu \qquad (2)$$

$$p = h/\lambda \qquad (3)$$

Substitution of Eq. (2) in Eq. (1) gives the uncertainty relation between energy and time:

$$\Delta E \cdot \Delta t \geqslant h \qquad (4)$$

For a beam of free electrons of mass m, traveling in the x direction, $\Delta t = m\,\Delta x/p_x$, where p_x is the linear momentum and Δx is the distance traveled in the time interval Δt. Since $E = p_x{}^2/2m$, $\Delta E \cong p_x\,\Delta p_x/m$, so that $\Delta E \cdot \Delta t = \Delta p_x \cdot \Delta x$, and

$$\Delta p_x \cdot \Delta x \geqslant h \qquad (5)$$

The pairs of variables (E, t) and (p_x, x) are called canonically conjugate pairs of variables. In quantum mechanics, the operators corresponding to canonically conjugate variables do not commute (see QUANTUM THEORY). Heisenberg originally stated his uncertainty principle in the following form: the values of canonically conjugate variables of a given system can only be determined with a finite lower limit of accuracy.

Among the many important experimental phenomena illustrating the uncertainty principle in the COMPTON EFFECT. Here, a photon is scattered by an electron; the momentum of the photon is rendered uncertain as a result of its scattering by the electron and the electron is moved from its original position by the impact received from the photon. If we consider the photon and the electron as separate systems, then their interaction (the collision) introduces uncertainties for each system, given by Equation (5).

A general uncertainty relation follows from the postulates of WAVE MECHANICS. Consider two variables, a and b, of a system, whose operators are $\mathfrak{A}$ and $\mathfrak{B}$. The expectation values of a and b are called $\bar{a}$ and $\bar{b}$ respectively. The uncertainties in a and b can then be defined quantitatively as their respective rms deviations from their expectation values; it follows from the postulates that

$$(\Delta a)^2 \equiv \oint \Psi^*(\mathfrak{A} - \bar{a})^2\,\Psi\,dq$$

where Ψ is the normalized wave function of the system under observation, and $\oint \ldots dq$ indicates integration over all values of all coordinates. Similarly,

$$(\Delta b)^2 \equiv \oint \Psi^*(\mathfrak{B} - \bar{b})^2\,\Psi\,dq$$

If $\mathfrak{A}$ and $\mathfrak{B}$ are Hermitian,[‡] $(\mathfrak{A} - \bar{a})^2$ and $(\mathfrak{B} - \bar{b})^2$ are also Hermitian. Therefore:

$$(\Delta a)^2 \cdot (\Delta b)^2 =$$

$$= \oint \Psi^*(\mathfrak{A} - \bar{a})^2\,\Psi\,dq \cdot \oint \Psi^*(\mathfrak{B} - \bar{b})^2\,\Psi\,dq$$

$$= \oint (\mathfrak{A} - \bar{a})\Psi(\mathfrak{A} - \bar{a})^*\,\Psi^*\,dq$$

$$\cdot \oint (\mathfrak{B} - \bar{b})\Psi(\mathfrak{B} - \bar{b})^*\,\Psi^*\,dq$$

$$= \oint |(\mathfrak{A} - \bar{a})\Psi|^2\,dq \cdot \oint |(\mathfrak{B} - \bar{b})\Psi|^2\,dq.$$

To put this product of two definite integrals in a more useful form, consider the function

$$f(q) = \lambda(\mathfrak{A} - \bar{a})\,\Psi + i(\mathfrak{B} - \bar{b})\,\Psi$$

where λ is real, and independent of coordinates, and $i \equiv \sqrt{-1}$. The function $|f(q)|^2$ must be non-negative:

$$\lambda^2|(\mathfrak{A} - \bar{a})\Psi|^2 + i\lambda[(\mathfrak{A}^* - \bar{a})\Psi^*(\mathfrak{B} - \bar{b})\Psi +$$

$$- (\mathfrak{A} - \bar{a})\Psi(\mathfrak{B}^* - \bar{b})\Psi^*] + |(\mathfrak{B} - \bar{b})\Psi|^2 \geqslant 0$$

When the left-hand side of this inequality is integrated over all values of all coordinates:

$$\lambda^2(\Delta a)^2 + (\Delta b)^2 + i\lambda\left[\oint (\mathfrak{A}^* - \bar{a})\Psi^*(\mathfrak{B} - \bar{b})\Psi\,dq + \right.$$

$$\left. - \oint (\mathfrak{A} - \bar{a})\Psi(\mathfrak{B}^* - \bar{b})\Psi^*\,dq\right] \geqslant 0$$

Since λ is real, the left-hand side of this inequality becomes negative unless the discriminant becomes zero or negative:

$$4(\Delta a)^2(\Delta b)^2 \geqslant -\left[\oint (\mathfrak{A}^* - \bar{a})\Psi^*(\mathfrak{B} - \bar{b})\Psi\,dq + \right.$$

$$\left. - \oint (\mathfrak{A} - \bar{a})\Psi(\mathfrak{B}^* - \bar{b})\Psi^*\,dq\right]^2$$

The right-hand side of this inequality is reduced as follows (remember that Ψ is normalized):

[‡]An operator $\mathfrak{F}$ is Hermitian, if for any properly behaved functions u and v: $\oint u\mathfrak{F}v\,dq = \oint v\mathfrak{F}^*u\,dq$, where * indicates complex conjugation. Quantum mechanical operators usually are, or can be made to be, Hermitian.

$$\oint (\mathfrak{A}^* - \bar{a})\Psi^*(\mathfrak{B} - \bar{b})\Psi \, dq = \oint (\mathfrak{A}\Psi)^*\mathfrak{B}\Psi \, dq +$$

$$- \bar{a}\oint \Psi^*\mathfrak{B}\Psi \, dq - \bar{b}\oint \Psi(\mathfrak{A}\Psi)^* \, dq + \bar{a}\bar{b}$$

$$\oint (\mathfrak{A} - \bar{a})\Psi(\mathfrak{B}^* - \bar{b})\Psi^* \, dq = \oint (\mathfrak{A}\Psi)(\mathfrak{B}\Psi)^* \, dq +$$

$$- \bar{a}\oint \Psi(\mathfrak{B}\Psi)^* \, dq - \bar{b}\oint \Psi^*(\mathfrak{A}\Psi) \, dq + \bar{a}\bar{b}$$

Since $\bar{b} = \oint \Psi^*\mathfrak{B}\Psi \, dq = \oint \Psi(\mathfrak{B}\Psi)^* \, dq$, and

$$\bar{a} = \oint \Psi^*\mathfrak{A}\Psi \, dq = \oint \Psi(\mathfrak{A}\Psi)^* \, dq,$$

$$4(\Delta a)^2 (\Delta b)^2 \geqslant - \left[\oint (\mathfrak{A}\Psi)^* (\mathfrak{B}\Psi) \, dq + \right.$$
$$\left. - \oint (\mathfrak{A}\Psi)(\mathfrak{B}\Psi)^* \, dq \right]^2$$

Since $\mathfrak{A}$ and $\mathfrak{B}$ are Hermitian

$$\oint (\mathfrak{A}\Psi)^* (\mathfrak{B}\Psi) \, dq \equiv \oint (\mathfrak{B}\Psi)(\mathfrak{A}\Psi)^* \, dq =$$

$$= \oint \Psi^*\mathfrak{A}\mathfrak{B}\Psi \, dq,$$

$$\oint (\mathfrak{A}\Psi)(\mathfrak{B}\Psi)^* \, dq = \oint \Psi^*\mathfrak{B}\mathfrak{A}\Psi \, dq \quad (6)$$

$$\therefore \; 4(\Delta a)^2 (\Delta b)^2 \geqslant - \left[\oint \Psi^*(\mathfrak{A}\mathfrak{B} - \mathfrak{B}\mathfrak{A})\Psi \, dq \right]^2$$

and $|\Delta a| \cdot |\Delta b| \geqslant \frac{1}{2} i \oint \Psi^*(\mathfrak{A}\mathfrak{B} - \mathfrak{B}\mathfrak{A})\Psi \, dq$

According to the postulates of wave mechanics, the operators for momentum and position are given respectively by: $\mathfrak{P} = -i\hbar\nabla$, where $\hbar = h/2\pi$, and $\mathfrak{Q} = q$ (multiplication by q).

For linear motion in the x direction, $\mathfrak{P}_x = -i\hbar\partial/\partial x$, $\mathfrak{Q} = x$. Hence $(\mathfrak{P}\mathfrak{Q} - \mathfrak{Q}\mathfrak{P})\Psi = -i\hbar(\partial/\partial x)(x\Psi) + i\hbar x(\partial\Psi/\partial x) = -i\hbar\Psi$. When this expression is substituted into Eq. (6), it follows that:

$$|\Delta p_x| \, |\Delta x| \geqslant h/4\pi$$

which is in agreement with Eq. (5). Equation (4) can be similarly derived from the postulates of wave mechanics by setting $\mathfrak{E} = (ih/2\pi)(\partial/\partial t)$, $\mathfrak{T} = t$.

A. L. LOEB

References

1. Bohm, David, "Quantum Theory," Englewood Cliffs, N.J., Prentice-Hall, 1951.
2. De Broglie, L., *J. Phys. Ser.* 6, 7, 1 "Introduction to Wave Mechanics," London, Methuen, (1926).
3. Davisson, C. J., and Germer, L. H., *Phys. Rev.*, **30**, 705 (1927); *Proc. Natl. Acad. Sci. U.S.*, **14**, 317 (1928).
4. Harris, L., and Loeb, A. L., "Introduction to Wave Mechanics," New York, McGraw-Hill Book Co., 1963.
5. Heisenberg, W., *Z. Physik*, **43**, 172; "The Physical Principles of the Quantum Theory," Chicago, University of Chicago Press, (1927).
6. Margenau, H., and Murphy, G. M., "The Mathematics of Physics and Chemistry," New York, Van Nostrand Reinhold, 1943.
7. Thomson, G. P., *Proc. Roy. Soc. London Ser. A*, **117**, 600 (1928); **119**, 651 (1928).

Cross-references: COMPTON EFFECT, MATRIX MECHANICS, QUANTUM THEORY, WAVE MECHANICS.

HIGH-VOLTAGE RESEARCH

High-voltage research deals with phenomena evoked by high voltages and intense electric fields, with the behavior of dielectrics and electrical components under such electrical stress, and with the utilization of electrostatic fields and forces for various purposes of science and industry. In the laboratory, this electrical stress is produced by the presence of electric charge on the opposing surfaces of two electrodes between which a voltage is applied. Pulsed, alternating and constant voltages ranging from a few kilovolts to 20 MV have been used in such studies. In nature, air currents and water precipitation cause electric charge to become separated between cloud and earth or between clouds; the stressed region may reach electrical pressure differences in excess of 1000 MV. Lightning, a rapid high-current discharge, completes the breakdown of the over-stressed air and dissipates the accumulated electrical energy. Many aspects of this natural high-voltage phenomena have been the subject of investigation because of their scientific interest and the danger of lightning to life and to susceptible structures such as electric power systems.

In the industrial high-voltage laboratory, the direct and induced effects of lightning discharges on electrical apparatus are often simulated by high-voltage impulse generators. These use the Marx method of first slowly charging a number of condensers in parallel and then suddenly connecting them in series by spark-gap switches which at the same instant impress the multiplied voltage upon the test circuit. A typical voltage wave produced by such impulse generators rises to its peak value of several million volts in 1 μsec and then diminishes exponentially reaching half-voltage in 10 μsec.

Electric Field between High-voltage Electrodes The region between and around electrodes which have been charged by the application of a voltage V between them is occupied by the electric field of that charge. In an isolated system, the positive

electrode has a deficiency of electrons exactly equal to the excess electrons on the negative electrode. The amount of electric charge Q on either electrode surface at any instant is given by $Q = CV$ where Q is in coulombs and C is the capacitance of the electrode system in farads. Energy is stored in the electrically stressed space between the electrodes; the amount of this electrical energy W can be expressed in terms of applied voltage or separated charge by $W = CV^2/2 = Q^2/2C$ joules.

The electric field intensity at any point is defined by the magnitude and direction of the force which would be experienced by a unit positive charge placed in the field at that point. Following Faraday, if we define a line of electric flux as a line drawn so that its direction is everywhere the direction of the force on a positive particle, and require that one line must originate on each unit positive charge and terminate on each unit negative charge, then the lines of flux will map out the electric field and the lines per unit area will be directly related to the electrical field intensity E. The electrostatic force acting on a particle with charge q placed in an electric field of intensity E volts per meter is given by $f = qE$ newtons. The electric field distribution depends upon the geometry of the electrodes but is affected by the presence of dielectric materials or of charged particles; a quantitative picture of the static or changing field picture is usually essential to high-voltage research.

Objectives of High-Voltage Research From antiquity to the present, the history of high-voltage research sparkles with many names well-known in electrical science—Thales of Miletus, von Guericke, Newton, Franklin whose kite experiment established the identity of natural lightning and electricity, Cavendish, Faraday, and Roentgen whose discovery of x-rays in 1895 marked the beginning of the atomic age. During the 60 years centered on the turn of the twentieth century, physicists studied the passage of electricity through gases at normal and reduced pressure, sought an understanding of long sparks and corona in atmospheric air, measured the conductivity and breakdown strength of liquid dielectrics, and examined the flashover of solid insulators in these media.

More recent research has been directed at the performance under high electrical stress of a wide range of solid, liquid, and gaseous dielectrics as well as vacuum-insulated systems. The solid materials vary from porcelains and glasses to hydrocarbon polymers and loaded epoxies. Superior gaseous insulation is now obtained by the combined use of such electronegative gas molecules as sulfur hexafluoride (SF_6) and Freon ($C_2Cl_2F_2$) with elevated pressures sometimes exceeding 5 or 10 atmospheres. Solid insulator supports are indispensable in gas, liquid, and vacuum insulated systems and are studied in combination with these media.

Research in the high-voltage field may also be directed at testing and increasing the insulation strength of power equipment subject to lightning or switching surges. The increasing trend toward higher voltages for the transmission of electric power over long distances has directed research toward reduction of radio interference and power loss by corona and surface leakage from high-voltage transmission line conductors and their suspension insulators. The need to bring such power into urban areas has produced the requirement for ac power cables in which the center conductor is reliably insulated for hundreds of kilovolts above earth. The inherent efficiency and stability of dc power transmission have led to the development of more adequate high-voltage rectification and conversion apparatus. For these purposes, the low-pressure metallic vapor tube has reached the highest power levels though solid state devices offer much promise for high-voltage, high-power switching.

In the field of science and medicine, high-voltage research seeks improved methods of producing high constant voltages, of measuring and stabilizing such voltages, and of applying them to the acceleration of atomic ions and electrons to high energies. Such particle accelerators are needed for nuclear structure research; for the study of the properties of energetic atoms, electrons, x-rays, and neutrons; for the treatment of deep-seated tumors with energetic particles and radiation, and for the radiation processing of materials.

Industrial objectives of high-voltage research include the development of high-power, high-frequency tubes and their power supplies for radar and long-range radio communication, the ionization of particulate matter by corona and its electrostatic collection as in smoke and chemical precipitators, and the elimination of electrostatic hazards which arise in processes such as the transfer or mixing of volatile hydrocarbons, dusts, and explosive gases.

JOHN G. TRUMP

References

Graggs, J. D., and Meek, J. M., "High Voltage Laboratory Technique," Butterworths Scientific Publications, London, 1954.

Trump, J. G., "Electrostatic Sources of Electric Power," *Elec. Eng.*, **66**, No. 6, 525–534 (June 1947).

Trump, J. G., "New Developments in High Voltage Technology," *IEEE Trans. on Nuclear Science* **NS-14** (3), 113–119 (June 1967).

Cross-references: ACCELERATOR, VAN DE GRAAFF; ELECTRICITY; POTENTIAL.

HISTORY OF PHYSICS

In the history of the genesis of man's ideas on the nature of the physical world, it is difficult to arrive at an absolute beginning. Regardless of how far we penetrate into the past which pre-

pared and suggested some scientific doctrine, we inevitably find opinions and ideas inspired, in their turn, by some forerunner, until the beginning is lost in the inscrutable past. As for physics, in this limited framework we can start only with the period when specific names are associated with the earliest development of scientific ideas. The Ionian period, that amazing flow of intellectual energy, paved the way for the fathers of Hellenic science. Physics, then closely linked with philosophy and astronomy, play an auxiliary role in man's ever paramount concern in cosmology and cosmogony.

Although physics as an independent field originated in the age of Renaissance and was associated with such giants as Galileo, Kepler, and Newton, even in this brief sketch it is indispensable to trace the fountainhead of this science, which is in the cornerstone of Western civilization. The port of Miletus in Ionia, on the eastern coast of the Aegean sea, can be singled out as among the most significant birthplaces of physical science. Located in a favorable geographic position, its flourishing commerce since the second millenium before our era provided an excellent clearing house between two river civilizations, Egypt and Mesopotamia. Exposing people to divergent ideas and traditions, it created an atmosphere of open-mindedness where new, unrestrained ideas could flourish. Consequently, several most unique rationalizing minds had their roots in this town alone.

Of the galaxy of great pioneers of Ionian science, Thales of Miletus (624-565 B.C.) stands out as a symbol of the era. Sir James Jeans maintains that most of the major achievements of physical science of our age can be traced back to the stream of knowledge started by this Ionian intellectual giant in Miletus. Pythagoras, Democritus, Anaxagoras, Aristarchos of Samos, to mention a few, represent as one historian exclaims, that "miracle of ancient Greece" that prepared and shaped the climax of Plato and Aristotle, who for two millenia were to inspire and guide, for better or worse, the evolution of physics.

Liberated from the mythology of pre-Socratic time, these ancient astounding thinkers represent every school of philosophy from the extreme idealism of illusion and nonexistence of the world of sense perception, in the Pythagorean-Platonic sense, to the atomism and materialism of Democritus and Anaxagoras with their doctrine of the primacy of matter in a universe manipulated by accidental mechanism. It has been said that everyone by nature is a disciple of either Plato or Aristotle, and Raphael in his famous painting of the School of Athens on the wall of the Vatican Palace appropriately illustrates Plato pointing upward and Aristotle downward to the ground. Thus, the Alexandrian School in Hellenistic Egypt with its lighthouse, Pharos, as a symbol irradiated the glory of Hellenic science for centuries, nourishing Western civilization with Euclides' *Stoicheia* and Ptolemy's *Almagest* which, outside the Bible,

were the most widespread literary sources in physical science relegated to antiquity.

With the rise of Christianity, followed by Islam half a millenium later, interest in the studies of natural science was temporarily paralyzed, to be later zealously renewed under the aegis of the theology of the new religion. A convert to Christianity, St. Augustine (A.D. 354–430), later Bishop of Hippo, was a pioneer in the realization that Plato's ideas on sense delusion conveniently responded to the devout Christian's search for the salvation of the soul. Like Socrates and Sophists about a millenium previously, so St. Augustine also turned his back on nature and advised, "Return to thyself. In the inner man dwells truth." Thus, for a thousand years the men who guided the thought of the Western world did not observe out-of-doors and learn from natural phenomena. Monasteries became leading establishments where sedentary monks pored over volumes of Plato and Aristotle. More than half a millenium after St. Augustine, St. Thomas Aquinas (A.D. 1227-1274) petrified Aristotelian peripatetic scholasticism into an authoritarian *Summa Theologica* that included all the answers man should know on the nature of the physical world.

This marked the climax of the Middle Ages, described unjustly as "dark ages." Although theology was the queen of sciences, this period was not devoid of scientific activity because speculations in physics were constantly being nourished by the mystery of the *Primum Mobile*, a sphere beyond the fixed stars. It was this Prime Mover to which Aristotelians ascribed the first supernatural impulses or "impetus." How else could motion first have started? With the rise of Humanism, the rediscovery of Greek literature of antiquity revealed vast subjects dealing with fields other than theology. Invigorating new studies spread through Western Europe invading universities, not by-passing some monasteries. Bold, unusual views on the nature of the physical world and methods of investigation aroused the suspicion of watchful scholasticians but the age of Renaissance could not be diverted. Even the prominent ecclesiastic Oresme (1332-1382), Bishop of Lisieux, sustained the main interest by challenging the Aristotelian doctrine of the fixity of the earth. Nearly a century later this was continued by Cardinal Nicolas of Cusa who, like the Franciscan monk, Roger Bacon, in the thirteenth century also advocated experimentation in order to learn how the laws of nature operate. Very penetrating studies on the mystery of "violent" motion and inertia were accomplished long before their actual fruition with the appearance of Galileo and Newton.

Signs of a new era in physics were imminent with ideas of the universal genius, Leonardo da Vinci, maintaining like Democritus and Anaximander that the whole universe conforms to unalterable mechanical laws. The coming dawn was evident when Nicolaus Copernicus (1473-1543) came to study in Bologna and

Padua. Being more an ancient Greek philosopher in his use of geometry in support of the heliocentric system, Copernicus at least prepared the way of Galileo (1564–1642), who finally mobilized all known physics with his inventive experimentalism that adumbrated the first full stream of scientific revolution. Symptomatically, Galileo's first work was on motion, *De motu*, a subject of great concern through the Middle Ages, and his was the final challenging blow to the Aristotelian doctrine, when he verified that force primarily produces acceleration instead of mere movement.

As a sign of continuity, Newton was born (1642–1727) the year Galileo passed away. The trend of mechanism of physical phenomena as a consequence of mathematical determinism reached its portentous finalization with the Galilean-Newtonian revolution. Newtonian classical physics, associated with the world view of the majestic Newtonian universe, eternal and infinite, was formulated in three laws of motion, climaxed by the universal law of gravitation. This physics continued in its progressive refinement until it was confirmed by the triumphant mathematical discovery of the planet Neptune by J. C. Adams and Leverrier in 1845. It was then considered the final shape of knowledge man was in position to realize. Previously, Laplace produced an overwhelming impression on the entire century when, in 1798, he used in his *Origin of the World System* his deterministic equations in the formulation of his hypothesis on the origin of the solar system.

With advancing crystallization, Newtonian physics radiated with a galaxy of great names, inspired builders of the classical view of the physical world. Only a few principal milestones can be indicated, each a giant of his own in a panoramic view of the glorious century of promise of a scientific paradise. From Laplace at the beginning of the nineteenth century, the epic unfolds from Avogadro to Faraday, from Carnot and Joule to Kelvin and Helmholtz, attaining its pre-Einsteinian peak in Maxwellian equations formulating the electromagnetic theory of light. These equations were impressively described by Boltzmann, himself at the cradle of thermodynamics, when he quoted from Goethe's *Faust*: "Who was the god who wrote these lines?" Yet, these equations so brilliantly describing natural processes, pointed inevitably to a deterministic and mechanistic universe. Although rigorous mechanicism had flourished in the past in varying degrees, Newton must be regarded as the founder of the mechanistic world view even though he had difficulty in harmonizing mechanistic natural philosophy with his belief in a God who not only created the world but also constantly preserves it. This mechanization of the world picture systematically led to the conception of God as a retired engineer, and it was only another step to His complete exclusion. Therefore, the universe was ultimately knowable and predictable. This *Weltanschauung* of triumphant physics encouraged

the rise of materialistic philosophy, that actually shaped the dialectic materialism of Marx and Engels, which became the official doctrine of the ruling communist state in the twentieth century.

Newtonian physics was not destined to remain the last form in the evolution of physics. When it appeared to reach its perfection, as some leading physicists advocated, the turn of the twentieth century again witnessed another tidal wave that changed the course of physics. By 1895, this second scientific revolution started with discoveries of the first magnitude, containing unfathomable consequences for the future. Becquerel's radioactivity, Roentgen's x-rays, J. J. Thomson's electron, Planck's quantum, Bohr's atom, Rutherford's nucleus, Einstein's relativity and equality of mass and energy, represent a revolution that will carry the exploring mind incomparably farther into the mysteries of the universe than Copernicus, Galileo, Kepler, or even Newton ever dreamed of. Heisenberg's principle of indeterminacy in the realm of microphysics not only shatters the once cherished corpuscular-kinetic determinism but points to a microcosmos much more complex than what Whitehead called "provincialism in time and space," and as valid in Newtonian mechanism. Combining this with the staggering discoveries in astrophysical macrocosmos, the Dopplerian red shift of external galaxies, quasars, neutron stars, and black holes, we confront a truly unprecedented era of future centuries that will bring about unimaginable amendments in the physics we know today and its subsequent world view.

In this new perspective, the last half-century along which physical science has moved since the beginning of the second scientific revolution is not only greater than the three centuries since Newton but surpasses the distance separating the world view of Newton from that of Aristotle. Indeed, the revolution initiated with the beginning of the present century is far more penetrating, and the intellectual distance between Aristotle and Newton far smaller than the distance separating Laplace from the wizards of the new physics of our present years. This conclusion is drawn because Newton as well as Aristotle built their world views from facts borrowed from our sensory perceptions, which allow easy construction in our minds of their mental image. We never have and never can perceive either an electron, nucleus, or quantum. We build their representation by a highly complex procedure which does not guarantee their actual reality. The great pioneer of new physics, Ernst Mach, once stated: "The senses do not lie, but they do not tell us truth."

KAREL HUJER

References

1. Sarton, George, "A History of Science," 2 Vols., Cambridge, Mass., Harvard University Press, 1952, 1959.

2. Munitz, Milton K., "Space, Time, and Creation," New York, Collier Books, 1961.
3. Singer, Charles, "A Short History of Scientific Ideas to 1900," London, Oxford University Press, 1959.
4. Jammer, Max, "Concepts of Space," New York, Harper Torchbooks, 1960.
5. Fermi, L., and Bernardini, G., "Galileo and the Scientific Revolution," Greenwich, Conn., Basic Books, Fawcett-World, 1961.
6. Manuel, F. E., "A Portrait of Isaac Newton," Cambridge, Mass., Harvard University Press, 1969.
7. Dijksterhuis, E. J., "The Mechanization of the World Picture," London, Oxford University Press, 1969.
8. Holton, Gerald, and Roller, Duane, "Foundation of Modern Physical Science," Reading, Mass., Addison-Wesley, 1958.
9. Schilpp, Paul A., "Albert Einstein, Philosopher Scientist," LaSalle, Ill., Open Court Publishing Co., 1949.
10. Einstein, Albert, and Infeld, Leopold, "The Evolution of Physics," New York, Simon and Schuster, 1942.
11. Heisenberg, Werner, "Physics and Philosophy," New York, Harper Torchbooks, 1958.
12. Bohm, David, "Causality, Chance in Modern Physics," New York, Harper Torchbooks, 1961.
13. Hoffman, B. H., "The Strange Story of Quantum," Second ed., New York, Dover Publications, 1959.
14. D'Abro, A., "The Rise of New Physics, Decline of Mechanism," New York, Dover Publications, 1951.
15. de Broglie, Louis, "The Revolution in Physics," New York, Noonday Press, 1958.
16. de Broglie, Louis, "Physics and Microphysics," New York, Harper Torchbooks, 1960.

HOLOGRAPHY

In 1948 a British scientist, Dennis Gabor, proposed a new two-step method of optical imagery. In the past few years the method that he proposed has become widely known and used, owing mainly to the general availability of the laser with the great temporal and spatial coherence of its light, and to the efforts in the early 1960s of two University of Michigan research workers, J. Upatnieks and E. N. Leith.

This method is known as *holography*. It is similar to photography in many respects, yet is fundamentally different. With photography, one generally records, by means of lens and film, the two-dimensional irradiance distribution in the image of an object. With holography, however, one records not the optically formed image of an object but the object wave itself. This wave is recorded (usually on photographic film) in such a way that a subsequent illumination of this record, called a *hologram*, reconstructs the original object wave. A visual observation of this reconstructed wavefront then yields a view of the object which is practically indiscernible from the original, including three-dimensional parallax effects.

Figure 1(a) shows schematically how a hologram is recorded. One starts with a single, monochromatic beam of light that has originated from a very small source. This single beam is split into two components, one of which is directed toward the object and the other to a suitable recording medium, most commonly a photographic emulsion. The component that is incident on the object is scattered by it, and this scattered radiation, now called the object wave, impinges on the recording medium. The wave that proceeds directly to the recording medium is called the *reference wave*. Since the object and reference waves originate from the same source, they are mutually coherent and form a stable interference pattern when they meet at the recording medium. The detailed record of this interference pattern constitutes the hologram.

When the hologram is illuminated with a beam similar to the original reference wave, it modulates the phase and/or amplitude of the illuminating wave in such a way that the transmitted wave divides into three separate components, *one of which exactly duplicates the original object wave*.

If the two interfering beams are traveling in substantially the same direction, the recording of the interference pattern is said to be a *Gabor hologram* or an *in-line* hologram. If the two interfering beams arrive at the recording medium from substantially different directions, the recording is a *Leith-Upatnieks* or *off-axis* hologram. If the two interfering beams are traveling in essentially opposite directions, the recorded hologram is said to be a *Lippmann* or *reflection* hologram, first invented by Y. N. Denisyuk.

Electromagnetic radiation is most commonly used, although acoustic radiation can be used. The most common electromagnetic radiation employed is light, but holograms have also been recorded successfully with electron beams, x-radiation, and microwaves.

Holograms can be classified by the way they diffract light. In an *amplitude hologram* the varying irradiance distribution of the interference pattern is recorded as a density variation of the recording medium. In this type of hologram the illuminating wave is always partially absorbed, i.e., the illuminating wave is *amplitude-modulated*. In a *phase hologram*, a *phase modulation* is imposed on the illuminating beam which in turn results in diffraction of the light. Phase modulation occurs when the optical path (thickness × index) varies with position. A phase hologram results from either relief-image or index variation, or both.

Either phase or amplitude holograms can be classified further as *Fresnel holograms* or as *Fraunhofer holograms*. Generally speaking, if the object is reasonably close to the recording medium, say just a few hologram or object diameters distant, the field at the hologram plane is the Fresnel diffraction pattern of the object. A hologram recorded in this manner is termed a *Fresnel hologram*.

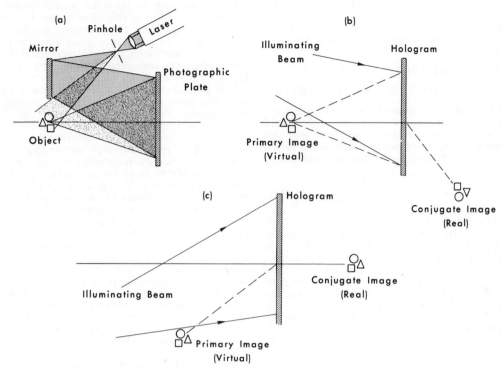

FIG. 1. A typical holographic arrangement. (a) Recording the hologram. (b) Reconstructing the primary object wave. (c) Reconstructing an undistorted conjugate wave.

If the object and hologram are separated by many object or hologram diameters, the field at the hologram due to the object alone is the Fraunhofer diffraction pattern of the object. A hologram recorded in this manner is termed a *Fraunhofer hologram*.

Any of these hologram types may be recorded as either a *thick* or a *thin* hologram. A *thin hologram* is one for which the thickness of the recording medium is thin compared to the spacing between the recorded interference fringes. A *thick* or *volume hologram* is one in which the thickness of the recording medium is of the order of or greater than the spacing of the recorded fringes.

Conceptually, the simplest form of an off-axis hologram is one for which the object is just a single, infinitely distant point so that the object wave at the recording medium is a plane wave. If the reference wave is also plane, and incident on the recording medium at an angle to the object wave, the hologram will consist of a series of Young's interference fringes. These recorded fringes are equally spaced straight lines running perpendicular to the plane of incidence. Since the hologram consists of a series of alternating clear and opaque strips, it is in the form of a diffraction grating. When the hologram is illuminated with a plane wave, the transmitted light consists of a zero-order wave traveling in the direction of the illuminating wave, plus two first-order waves. The higher diffracted orders are generally missing or very weak since the irradiance distribution of a two-beam interference pattern is sinusoidal. As long as the recording is essentially linear (irradiance proportional to final amplitude transmittance), the hologram will be a diffraction grating varying sinusoidally in amplitude transmittance, and only the first diffracted orders will be observed. One of these first-order waves will be traveling in the same direction as the object wave; this is the reconstructed wave.

To describe the recording of a hologram of a more complicated object, let O be a monochromatic wave from the object incident on the recording medium H, and let R be a wave coherent with O. The wave O contains information about the object, since the object has uniquely determined the amplitude and phase of O. The object can be thin and transmitting, such as a transparency, or it can be opaque and diffusely reflecting. Both the amplitude and phase of the wave O can be recorded with the aid of the reference beam R. The total field on H is $O + R$. A square-law recording medium, such as a photographic emulsion, will respond to the irradiance of the light $|O + R|^2$. Assume that after processing, the hologram possesses a certain complex amplitude transmittance $t(x)$ that can be expressed as a function of the exposure $E(x)$,

$$t(x) = f[E(x)]. \qquad (1)$$

The expansion of this function will yield a term linear in exposure, and by ignoring all terms except this one, one can write

$$t(x) = \beta E(x) = \beta \mid O + R \mid^2 \cdot T$$

$$= \beta T(\mid O \mid^2 + \mid R \mid^2 + OR^* + O^*R), \qquad (2)$$

where T is the exposure time, * indicates complex conjugate, and β is the constant coefficient of the linear term. When the hologram with this amplitude transmittance is illuminated with a wave C, the transmitted field at the hologram is

$$C \cdot t(x) = \beta T [C \mid O \mid^2 + C \mid R \mid^2$$

$$+ CR^*O + CRO^*]. \qquad (3)$$

If the illuminating wave C is sufficiently uniform so that CR^* is approximately constant across the hologram, the third term of Eq. (3) is $\beta TCR^*O = $ const. $\times O$. This term represents a wave identical with the object wave O. This wave has all of the properties of the original wave and can form an image of the object. The fact that this wave is separated from the rest can be seen most clearly by analogy with the diffraction-grating hologram described above. It can be shown that the other first-order diffracted wave corresponds to the conjugate image term $\beta TCRO^*$ of Eq. (3) and that the zero-order wave corresponds to the first two terms $\beta TC(\mid O \mid^2 + \mid R \mid^2)$. The object wave O is separated from the others and may be viewed independently.

Figure 1 illustrates the recording of a hologram and the subsequent reconstruction. In Fig. 1(a), the laser beam is first expanded and then divided by a mirror, which directs part of the beam directly onto the photographic plate; the rest of the light is reflected from the object. After processing, the hologram plate may be replaced in its original position [Fig. 1(b)] and the object removed. The light diffracted by the hologram forms, in part, the same wavefront that was originally scattered by the object. A viewer looking through the hologram will see an undistorted view of the object, just as if it were still present. Figure 2(a) shows a photomicrograph of an actual hologram, and 2(b), (c), and (d) photographs of three perspectives of the resulting image.

In addition to this virtual image, or *primary image,* a real, or *conjugate image* will be formed on the observer's side of the hologram. This image will appear unsharp and highly distorted, and it will also be inverted in depth, i.e., reversed front to back, as shown in Fig. 1(b). However, a distortion-free real image can be formed by changing the position of the illuminating beam so that all of the rays of the reference beam are reversed in direction. In this way, an undistorted, real, three-dimensional image of the object scene appears in front of the hologram as shown in Fig. 1(c).

Holograms may be recorded with diverging, parallel, or converging reference beams. If care is taken to maintain the recording geometry during reconstruction, it is even possible to form holograms with an arbitrary reference beam, the only requirement being that it be coherent with the object beam.

It is possible to produce color holograms by recording three separate holograms on a single photographic plate, each in a different color. Subsequent illumination with a three-color beam yields three separate wavefronts, one in each of the three colors representing the portion of the object corresponding to that color.

It is possible to make holograms that can be viewed in reflection. This is done by allowing the reference and object beams to enter the recording medium from opposite sides [Fig. 3(a)]. The fringes formed are planes lying approximately parallel to the plane of the hologram. When such a hologram is illuminated by a beam similar to the reference wave, a reflected wave is formed which exactly duplicates the object wave. The image is viewed in reflected light [Fig. 3(b)]. It is possible to illuminate this type of hologram with white light. The interference planes filter the light by acting as a $\lambda/2$ multilayer interference filter, in the same way as in Lippmann color photography.

Many applications have been proposed for holography. The most important of these are the ones that exploit the unique features of holography, rather than those that just do old tasks in a new way. The best example of this is holographic interferometry, whereby *arbitrary* wavefronts interfere with each other in such a way that interference bands are produced that depict only the *differences* between them. In practice the two wavefronts are nearly identical. There are several types of holographic interferometry.

For *single-exposure holographic interferometry,* a hologram of the object wave O is recorded in the usual way. The hologram is then placed in exactly the same position it occupied during exposure and it is illuminated with the reference wave and a slightly distorted object wave O'. The reference wave reconstructs the original object wave O, which interferes with the directly transmitted wave O'. This is a real-time technique, because when the wave O' changes, so do the interference bands. This technique can be used to measure surface deformations of all kinds, including thermal expansion and contraction, swelling caused by absorption, and any minute changes that might occur in an object.

Double-exposure holographic interferometry requires making two holograms on a single recording medium. One of the two holograms yields a primary image which constitutes the comparison wave, just as in the single-exposure case. The test wave is not the object itself, however, but a reconstructed wave from the changed object. Interference phenomena,

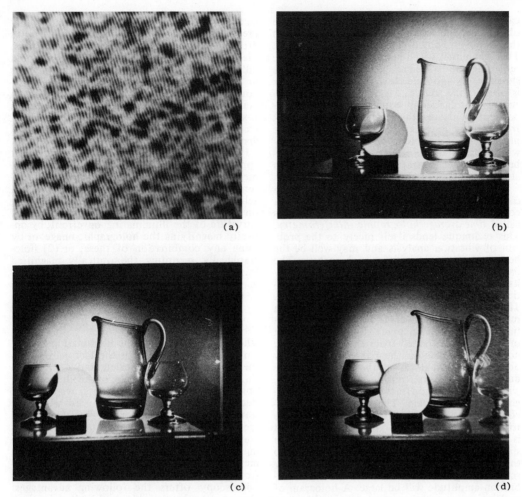

FIG. 2. A hologram of a diffusely illuminated object. (a) A highly magnified image of the hologram. (b), (c), (d) Three perspectives of the resulting image.

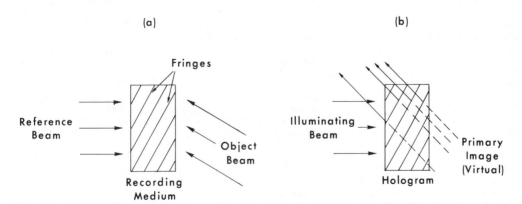

FIG. 3. Volume holograms that can be viewed in reflection. (a) Recording the hologram with object and reference waves incident in nearly opposite directions. (b) Reconstructing the primary wave in reflection.

caused by changes in optical path through the object between exposures, are produced when the doubly exposed hologram is illuminated. This technique is well suited to interferometric recording of transient phenomena, such as shock waves and fluid flow, when a pulsed laser is used as the source. All of the principles discussed thus far apply equally well to time-dependent events, and the very short pulse of light from a ruby laser can record the interference phenomena at a single instant of time. The very wide range of applicability of the method has been well demonstrated. This technique can also be extended to multiple exposures.

The idea of multiple-exposure interferometry can be extended to the limiting case of a continuum of exposures, resulting in what is called *time-average holographic interferometry*. This technique lends itself nicely to the problem of vibration analysis and may well be the best method yet devised for such analysis. The basis of the method is that since holography itself is an interferometric process, any instabilities of the interferometer cause fringe motion. Thus the hologram of a vibrating object is a record of the time-average irradiance distribution at the hologram plane. Since the amount of light flux diffracted from any region of the hologram depends on the fringe contrast, any object motion that causes the fringes to move during the exposure, causing a loss of contrast, will result in less diffracted flux from that region of the hologram. The strength of the reconstructed wave is therefore a function of the fringe motion during the exposure. If the object is vibrating in a normal mode, there will be standing waves of vibration on the surface, so that at the nodes the object motion will be very small or nonexistent. At the antinodes the vibration amplitude will be large. A hologram of such an object will then produce a bright image of the regions of the object for which little or no motion occurred during the exposure, whereas it will not produce images of antinodal points at all. This holographic method of vibration analysis has all of the advantages of all holographic interferometry. The method can be used regardless of the shape or complexity of the object; the vibration nodes can be examined in three dimensions, or at least from a variety of perspectives; and the method works regardless of whether the surface is optically smooth or diffusely reflecting.

One of the most striking aspects of the modern hologram is the three-dimensional image that it is capable of producing. This three-dimensional image indicates that there is a large amount of information contained in a single hologram—much more than is contained in a conventional photograph of the same size. Because of the many perspectives available, the hologram is well suited to display purposes. With a hologram, one can present all of the observable characteristics of a three-dimensional object clearly and concisely. Complicated molecular or anatomical structure can be simply presented with a single holographic image, with little chance of error or misinterpretation on the part of the viewer. Such a hologram could take the place of several conventional drawings or photographs. The use of holograms in textbooks would be a great aid to the student in many fields. Holograms made to be viewed with a small penlight and a colored filter have already been produced in large quantities and distributed in magazines and books.

Holographic microscopy is another important application. There are basically two distinct methods of holographic microscopy: (1) conventional holography with magnification achieved by changing the scale of the hologram, the illuminating wavelength, or the radius of curvature of the illuminating wavefront; by optically magnifying the holographic image; or by using any combination of these; or (2) holographically recording the optically magnified wavefront. For the first method, the lateral magnification is given by the formula

$$M = \frac{\mu m Z_c Z_R}{\mu Z_c (Z_R - Z_o) + m^2 Z_o Z_R},$$

where μ is the ratio of the illuminating and recording wavelengths, m is the factor by which the hologram has been scaled, and Z_c, Z_o, and Z_R are the radii of curvature of the illuminating, object, and reference wavefronts, respectively. Because aberrations are introduced when the wavelength is changed or the wavefront radii are changed, most of the current work in holographic microscopy involves optically magnifying the holographic image or using the second method, in which an optically magnified wavefront is recorded holographically. Holographic microscopy offers the following advantages: One can avoid the problems of limited depth of focus, off-axis observation, and the short working distance of the classical microscope. The hologram records a large volume of object space instantaneously. All of the usual image-processing techniques can be applied to the reconstructed wave, which may represent a large volume of space at an instant of time. No other method for doing this exists.

HOWARD M. SMITH

References

1. Smith, H. M., "Principles of Holography," New York, Wiley-Interscience, 1969.
2. DeVelis, J. B., and Reynolds, G. O., "Theory and Applications of Holography," Reading, Mass., Addison-Wesley, 1967.
3. Collier, R. J., Burckhardt, C. B., and Lin, L. H., "Optical Holography," New York, Academic Press, 1971.

Cross-references: DIFFRACTION; INTERFERENCE; OPTICS, GEOMETRICAL; OPTICS, PHYSICAL; WAVE MOTION.

I

IMPULSE AND MOMENTUM

The concept of impulse and momentum derives directly from Newton's law of motion.

Consider first the case of *linear* impulse and *linear* momentum. Newton's law states that in the proper frame of reference, force is equal to the (time) rate of change of momentum, where momentum is defined as the product of mass and velocity. Consider a force F acting for a time Δt on a particle of mass m, thereby changing its velocity from v_1 to v_2. The rate of change of momentum in this case is the change of momentum divided by the time interval during which the change occurs. Thus, Newton's law states

$$F = \frac{(mv)_2 - (mv)_1}{\Delta t}$$

Now if we multiply each side of this equation by Δt, we obtain

$$F \Delta t = (mv)_2 - (mv)_1$$

The left-hand side of this equation, $F \Delta t$, representing the product of a force and the time interval through which the force acts, is called "impulse." Thus, this equation states what is often known as the *Law of Impulse and Momentum*: Impulse is equal to the change of momentum.

It becomes apparent that a body will experience the same change of momentum irrespective of the separate values of F and Δt as long as their product $F \Delta t$ is the same. Thus, a large force acting briefly may have the same net effect as a smaller force acting longer, if the two impulses are the same. Going to the limit, we may consider an infinite force acting for an infinitesimal time such that their product remains a finite quantity. Under the action of such an impulse, a body will experience an instantaneous change of velocity. A common example is the change of velocity of a baseball as it is hit by a bat. For all practical purposes the change occurs instantaneously.

As a consequence of the Law of Impulse and Momentum described above, we find that if the total force is zero, so is the total impulse, and the momentum will remain unchanged. This is known as the *Conservation Law of Momentum*. It applies either to one particle or to a system of particles. Consider, for instance, the collision of two billiard balls, A and B. Taking each ball separately, the impulse on A by B is equal in magnitude but opposite in direction to the impulse on B by A. Thus, upon collision, the change of momentum of A is also equal and opposite to that of B. On the other hand, if we take *both* A and B as our system, then the two impulses are acting on the same system. Since the two are equal and opposite, they cancel out and the total impulse on this system is zero. The Conservation Law of Momentum then predicts that the total momentum of the system (which is the sum of momenta of all particles in the system) remains a constant no matter what goes on in the system.

The Conservation Law of Momentum forms one of the basic cornerstones in physics and engineering. Its application is all-pervading, from the motion of stars to the encounter and scattering of molecules, atoms and electrons.

We will now continue our discussion at a more precise level. First of all, in calculating the momentum mv, the mass m should be relativistic mass defined as

$$m = \frac{m_0}{\sqrt{1 - (v/c)^2}}$$

where m_0 is the rest mass, i.e., mass at zero velocity, and c is the velocity of light. It is seen that at velocities much less than the velocity of light, the relativistic mass and the rest mass are indistinguishable. Secondly, both force and velocity are vector quantities, i.e., they have a magnitude and a direction and obey the parallelogram law of addition, and we shall use letters **F** and **v** to represent them. Finally, as the time interval Δt approaches zero as a limit, the rate of change of momentum during Δt becomes a derivative and Newton's law becomes:

$$\mathbf{F} = \frac{d}{dt}(m\mathbf{v})$$

After integrating each side of this equation with respect to time t and taking the integration limits from $t = t_1$ to $t = t_2$, the result is:

$$\int_{t_1}^{t_2} \mathbf{F}\, dt = (m\mathbf{v})_2 - (m\mathbf{v})_1$$

The integral on the left-hand side is called "impulse," and we again reach the Law of

Impulse and Momentum given previously. In evaluating this integral, we must know the variation of $\mathbf{F}$ as a function of time, i.e., $\mathbf{F} = \mathbf{F}(t)$. Furthermore, in applying this law to a system of particles, we need only to count those impulses that are caused by *external* forces acting on the particles due to sources outside the system. As has been illustrated by the previous example on two billiard balls, the *internal* forces that any two particles exert on each other will generally cancel out if both particles are included in the system.

Up to this point we have discussed the laws of linear impulse and linear momentum. Entirely similar laws hold for *angular* impulse and *angular* momentum. The angular momentum of a particle about a point O is defined as

$$\mathbf{L} = \mathbf{r} \times m\mathbf{v}$$

where $\mathbf{r}$ is the radius vector from O to the particle. The moment of force or *torque* about O is defined as

$$\mathbf{T} = \mathbf{r} \times \mathbf{F}$$

If we take the cross product of $\mathbf{r}$ with each side of the expression for Newton's law as given before, we obtain

$$\mathbf{r} \times \mathbf{F} = \mathbf{T} = \mathbf{r} \times \frac{d}{dt}(m\mathbf{v})$$

The right-hand side can be identified to be just $d\mathbf{L}/dt$ on account of the vector identity:

$$\frac{d\mathbf{L}}{dt} = \frac{d}{dt}(\mathbf{r} \times m\mathbf{v}) = \mathbf{v} \times m\mathbf{v} + \mathbf{r} \times \frac{d}{dt}(m\mathbf{v})$$

where the first term on the right-hand side vanishes. Thus,

$$\mathbf{T} = \frac{d\mathbf{L}}{dt}$$

We now integrate this equation with respect to t and take the integration limits from $t = t_1$ to $t = t_2$. The result is

$$\int_{t_1}^{t_2} \mathbf{T}\, dt = \mathbf{L}_2 - \mathbf{L}_1$$

Analogous to the linear impulse, we may call the integral on the left-hand side of the above equation the angular impulse. Thus this equation states: Angular impulse is equal to the change of angular momentum. In particular, if the total torque is zero, so is the total angular impulse, and the angular momentum will remain unchanged. This is known as the *Conservation Law of Angular Momentum*.

HSUAN YEH

References

Yeh, Hsuan, and Abrams, Joel I., "Principles of Mechanics of Solids and Fluids," Vol. I, New York, McGraw-Hill Book Co., 1960.

Synge, John L., and Griffith, Byron A., "Principles of Mechanics," New York, McGraw-Hill Book Co., Third Edition, 1959.

Goldstein, Herbert, "Classical Mechanics," Reading, Mass., Addison-Wesley, 1950.

Cross-references: CONSERVATION LAWS AND SYMMETRY, DYNAMICS, MECHANICS, ROTATION–CIRCULAR MOTION, STATICS, VECTOR PHYSICS.

INDUCED ELECTROMOTIVE FORCE

Electromotive force and voltage drop are usually regarded as synonymous. When an electromotive force, or simply emf, is impressed on a closed metallic circuit, current results. The emf along a specified path C in space is defined as the work per unit charge W/q done by the electromagnetic fields on a small test charge moved along C. Since work is the line integral of force $\mathbf{F}$, the work per unit charge is the line integral of the force per unit charge. Letting $\mathbf{F}/q$ denote the vector electromagnetic force per unit charge in newtons per coulomb, we have

$$\text{emf} = \int_C \frac{\mathbf{F}}{q} \cdot d\mathbf{l} \text{ volts} \qquad (1)$$

The scalar product $(\mathbf{F}/q) \cdot d\mathbf{l}$ is the product $(F/q) \cos\theta\, dl$, with θ denoting the angle between the vectors $\mathbf{F}/q$ and $d\mathbf{l}$.

The electric force per unit charge is the electric field intensity $\mathbf{E}$ (volts per meter) and the magnetic force per unit charge is $\mathbf{v} \times \mathbf{B}$, with $\mathbf{v}$ denoting the velocity of the test charge in meters per second and $\mathbf{B}$ denoting the magnetic flux density in webers per square meter. In terms of the smaller angle θ between $\mathbf{v}$ and $\mathbf{B}$, the cross product $\mathbf{v} \times \mathbf{B}$ is a vector having magnitude $vB \sin\theta$; the direction of the vector $\mathbf{v} \times \mathbf{B}$ is normal to the plane of the vectors $\mathbf{v}$ and $\mathbf{B}$, with the sense of that of the extended thumb of the right hand oriented so that its fingers curl through the angle θ from $\mathbf{v}$ toward $\mathbf{B}$. As the total force per unit charge is $\mathbf{E} + \mathbf{v} \times \mathbf{B}$, the emf in terms of the fields is

$$\text{emf} = \int_C (\mathbf{E} + \mathbf{v} \times \mathbf{B}) \cdot d\mathbf{l} \qquad (2)$$

It might appear from Eq. (2) that the emf depends on the forward velocity with which the test charge is moved along the path C. However, this is not the case. If $\mathbf{v}$ and $d\mathbf{l}$ in Eq. (2) have the same direction, then the vectors $(\mathbf{v} \times \mathbf{B})$ and $d\mathbf{l}$ are normal, and their scalar product is zero. Consequently, only the component of $\mathbf{v}$ normal

to dl can contribute to the emf. This component has value only if the differential path length dl has sideways motion. *Thus* **v** *in Eq. (2) represents the sideways motion, if any, of* dl. The fields **E** and **B** of Eq. (2) may be functions of time as well as functions of the space coordinates. In addition, the velocity **v** of each differential path length dl may vary with time. However, Eq. (2) correctly expresses the emf, or voltage drop, along the path C as a function of time. That component of the emf consisting of the line integral of **v** × **B** is known as the *motional emf*, because it has value only when the path C is moving through a magnetic field, cutting lines of magnetic flux. For stationary paths there is no motional emf, and the voltage drop is simply the line integral of the electric field **E**.

For an emf to exist along a stationary path, it is necessary to have an electric field present. As electric charges are surrounded by electric fields, emfs are generated by devices that separate charge. A familiar example is the battery, which utilizes chemical forces to separate charge. Some other methods of separating charge are the heating of a thermocouple, the exposure of a photocell to incident light, and the rubbing together of different materials. Electric fields are also produced by time-changing magnetic fields, and this principle is extensively exploited, as is motional emf, to generate electric power. The remainder of this article is devoted to electromotive force induced by magnetic means.

A fundamental law of electromagnetism, often called the *Maxwell-Faraday law*, or the *first law of electromagnetic induction*, states that the line integral of the electric field intensity **E** around any closed path C equals $-\partial\phi/\partial t$, with ϕ representing the magnetic flux over any surface S having the closed path C as its contour. The positive side of the surface S and the direction of the line integral around the contour C are related by the right-hand rule; by this rule, the curled fingers are oriented so as to point around the loop in the direction of the integration and the extended thumb points out of the positive side of the surface S. The magnetic flux ϕ is the surface integral of the magnetic flux density **B**; that is,

$$\phi = \iint_S \mathbf{B} \cdot d\mathbf{S} \text{ webers} \tag{3}$$

In Eq. (3) the vector differential surface $d\mathbf{S}$ has area dS and is directed normal to the plane of dS out of the positive side. The partial time derivative of ϕ is defined as

$$\frac{\partial\phi}{\partial t} = \iint_S \frac{\partial\mathbf{B}}{\partial t} \cdot d\mathbf{S} \text{ volts} \tag{4}$$

and this is often referred to as the *magnetic current* through the surface S. For a moving surface

S the limits of the surface integral of Eq. (4) are functions of time, but Eq. (4) still applies. It is important to understand that in evaluating $\partial\phi/\partial t$ over a surface that is moving in a region containing a magnetic field, *we treat the surface at the instant under consideration as though it were stationary*. The partial time derivative of ϕ is the time rate of increase of the flux over the surface S due only to the changing magnetic field **B**; any increase in ϕ due to the motion of the surface in the **B**-field is *not* included. The Maxwell-Faraday law is

$$\oint_C \mathbf{E} \cdot d\mathbf{l} = -\frac{\partial\phi}{\partial t} \tag{5}$$

with ϕ being the magnetic flux in webers out of the positive side of *any* surface having the path C as its contour. The small circle on the integral sign indicates a closed path. We note from Eq. (5) that *an electric field must be present in any region containing a time-changing magnetic field*.

The application of Eq. (2) to a closed path C gives

$$\text{emf} = \oint_C \mathbf{E} \cdot d\mathbf{l} + \oint_C (\mathbf{v} \times \mathbf{B}) \cdot d\mathbf{l} \tag{6}$$

Utilizing Eq. (5) enables us to write Eq. (6) in the form

$$\text{emf} = -\frac{\partial\phi}{\partial t} + \oint_C (\mathbf{v} \times \mathbf{B}) \cdot d\mathbf{l} \tag{7}$$

Thus the emf around a closed path consists, in general, of two components. The component $-\partial\phi/\partial t$ is often referred to as the *variational emf* (or *transformer emf*), and the second component is, of course, the motional emf.

In Eq. (7) the relation $(\mathbf{v} \times \mathbf{B}) \cdot d\mathbf{l}$ can, by means of a common vector identity, be replaced with $-\mathbf{B} \cdot (\mathbf{v} \times d\mathbf{l}$ has magnitude $v\,dl$ and of $d\mathbf{l}$, the vector $\mathbf{v} \times d\mathbf{l}$ has magnitude $v\,dl$ and direction normal to the differential surface dS swept out by the moving length $d\mathbf{l}$ in the time dt. Letting B_n denote the component of **B** normal to this area, we note that $-\mathbf{B} \cdot (\mathbf{v} \times d\mathbf{l})$ becomes $-B_n v\,dl$, and Eq. (7) can be written

$$\text{emf} = -\left[\frac{\partial\phi}{\partial t} + \oint_C B_n v\,dl\right] \tag{8}$$

Clearly the integral of $B_n v$ around the closed contour C, with v denoting the magnitude of the sideways velocity of each $d\mathbf{l}$, is simply the time rate of increase of the magnetic flux over the surface bounded by C due to the path C cutting lines of magnetic flux. Hence, the complete expression in brackets is the time rate of increase of the magnetic flux ϕ, over any surface

S bounded by the closed path C, *due to the changing magnetic field and also due to the moving path cutting through the magnetic field.* Equation (8) is often written

$$\text{emf} = -\frac{d\phi}{dt} \qquad (9)$$

It is important to note carefully the distinction between Eqs. (5) and (9). Equation (5) is only the variational emf, and Eq. (9) is the sum of the variational and motional emfs. In Eq. (5), the partial time derivative of the magnetic flux ϕ is the rate of change of the flux due only to the time-changing magnetic field; in Eq. (9), the total time derivative is the rate of change of the flux due to the time-changing **B**-field and also to the path cutting through the magnetic field. Of course, if the closed path is not cutting lines of magnetic flux, then Eqs. (5) and (9) are equivalent. It is also important to note that $d\phi/dt$ in Eq. (9) does not necessarily mean the total time rate of change of the flux ϕ over the surface S. For example, the flux over a surface S bounded by the closed contour C of the left-hand electric circuit of Fig. 1 is changing when the coil is being unwound by the rotation of the cylinder. However, as **B** is static there is no variational emf, and since the conductors are not cutting flux lines, there is no motional emf.

Consequently, $d\phi/dt$ as used in Eq. (9) is zero even though the flux is changing with time. Note that $d\phi/dt$ in Eq. (9) was *defined* as representing the bracketed expression of Eq. (8), and $d\phi/dt$ must not be more broadly interpreted.

In the applications of the equations which have been presented, we must refer all flux densities and movements to a single specified coordinate system. In particular, the velocities are with respect to this system and are not relative velocities between conductors and moving lines of flux. Of course the coordinate system is arbitrarily selected, and *the relative magnitudes of the variational and motional emfs depend upon the selection.* Let us consider two examples.

Example 1 An electric generator is shown in Fig. 2. The parallel stationary conductors separated a distance l have a stationary voltmeter connected between them. The electric circuit is completed through a moving conductor that is connected electrically by means of sliding taps. This conductor is at $y = 0$ at time $t = 0$ and moves to the right with constant velocity $\mathbf{v} = v\mathbf{a}_y$. The applied flux density **B**, represented in Fig. 2 by dots, is $B_o \cos \beta y \cos \omega t\, \mathbf{a}_x$. Unit vectors in the directions of the respective coordinate axes are $\mathbf{a}_x$, $\mathbf{a}_y$, and $\mathbf{a}_z$. Find the instantaneous voltage across the voltmeter.

Solution. Let S denote the plane rectangular surface bounded by the closed electric circuit,

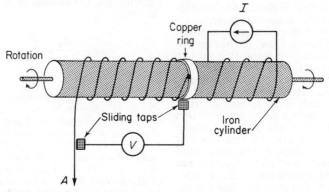

FIG. 1. The current generator produces a steady magnetic flux in the iron cylinder, which rotates as the wire is pulled at A.

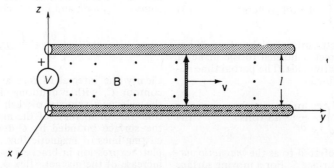

FIG. 2. Elementary electric generator.

with the positive side selected as the side facing the reader. The counterclockwise emf around the electric circuit is $-d\phi/dt$, with ϕ signifying the magnetic flux out of the positive side of S. As $d\mathbf{S} = l\,dy\,\mathbf{a}_x$, the scalar product $\mathbf{B} \cdot d\mathbf{S}$ is $B_o l \cos \beta y \cos \omega t\,dy$; integrating from $y = 0$ to $y = y_1$ gives

$$\phi = (B_o l/\beta) \sin \beta y_1 \cos \omega t \qquad (10)$$

with y_1 denoting the instantaneous y-position of the moving wire. The counterclockwise emf is found by replacing y_1 with vt and evaluating $-d\phi/dt$. The result is

emf $= \omega B_o l/\beta \sin \beta vt \sin \omega t$

$$- B_o l v \cos \beta vt \cos \omega t \qquad (11)$$

The variational (transformer) component is $-\partial\phi/\partial t$, which is determined with the aid of Eq. (10) to be $\omega B_o l/\beta \sin \beta y_1 \sin \omega t$, with $y_1 = vt$. This is the first component on the right side of Eq. (11). Note that y_1 was treated as constant when evaluating the partial time derivative of ϕ. The motional emf is the line integral of $\mathbf{v} \times \mathbf{B}$ along the path of the moving conductor. As $\mathbf{v} \times \mathbf{B}$ is $-B_o v \cos \beta y_1 \cos \omega t\,\mathbf{a}_z$ and as $d\mathbf{l}$ is $dz\,\mathbf{a}_z$, we evaluate the integral of $-B_o v \cos \beta y_1 \cos \omega t\,dz$ from $z = 0$ to $z = l$, obtaining a motional emf of $-B_o l v \cos \beta y_1 \cos \omega t$. This component results from the cutting of lines of magnetic flux by the moving conductor.

If the voltmeter draws no current, there can be no electromagnetic force on the free electrons of the wires. Therefore, *the emf along the path of the metal conductors, including the moving conductor, is zero*. The total voltage of Eq. (11) appears across the voltmeter.

Example 2 Suppose the conductor with sliding taps in Fig. 2 is stationary ($\mathbf{v} = 0$) and located at $y = y_1$. Also suppose that the magnetic field $\mathbf{B}$ is produced by a system of steady currents in conductors (not shown in Fig. 2) that are moving with constant velocity $\mathbf{v} = v\mathbf{a}_y$. At time $t = 0$ the magnetic field $\mathbf{B}$ is $B_o \sin \beta y\,\mathbf{a}_x$. Determine the voltage across the voltmeter.

Solution. There is no motional emf because the conductors of Fig. 2 are stationary with respect to our selected coordinate system. However, the magnetic field at points fixed with respect to the coordinate system is changing with time, and hence there is a variational emf. As the $\mathbf{B}$-field at $t = 0$ is $B_o \sin \beta y\,\mathbf{a}_x$ and moving with velocity $v\,\mathbf{a}_y$, the $\mathbf{B}$-field as a function of time is $B_o \sin [\beta(y - vt)]\,\mathbf{a}_x$. This is verified by noting that an observer at y_o at $t = 0$ moving in the y-direction with the velocity v of the moving current-carrying conductors, would have a y-coordinate of $y_o + vt$; hence according to the expression for $\mathbf{B}$, he would observe a constant field. The magnetic current density is

$$\partial\mathbf{B}/\partial t = -\beta v B_o \cos \beta(y - vt)\,\mathbf{a}_x$$

The negative of the integral of this over the rectangular surface bounded by the electric circuit,

with the positive side selected as the side facing the reader and with y limits of zero and y_1, gives the counter-clockwise emf. The result is

emf $= B_o l v [\sin \beta(y_1 - vt) + \sin \beta vt]$

This is the voltage across the meter.

CHARLES A. HOLT

References

Bewley, L. V., "Flux Linkages and Electromagnetic Induction," New York, Dover Publications, 1964.

Fano, R. M., Chu, L. J., and Adler, R. B. "Electromagnetic Fields, Energy, and Forces," New York, John Wiley and Sons, 1960.

Holt, C. A., "Introduction to Electromagnetic Fields and Waves, New York, John Wiley & Sons, 1963.

Moon, P., and Spencer, D. E., "Foundations of Electrodynamics," New York, Van Nostrand Reinhold, 1960.

Cross-references: ALTERNATING CURRENTS, CIRCUITRY, INDUCTANCE, INDUCTION HEATING, POTENTIAL.

INDUCTANCE

Inductance is a ratio of a magnetic flux Φ to an electric current i. The unit is the henry; 1 henry $\equiv 1$ weber/ampere. The *mutual inductance M* of two circuits is defined as the ratio of the magnetic flux, linking with one circuit, to the current in the other

$$M_{12} = \frac{\Phi_2}{i_1}, \; M_{21} = \frac{\Phi_1}{i_2}$$

The *self-inductance L* of a single circuit is defined as the ratio of the flux linking the circuit to the current flowing in the circuit.

$$L = \frac{\Phi}{i}$$

In the absence of any magnetic material, M and L depend only on the geometry of the circuits concerned. The mutual inductance of two circuits 1 and 2 can be calculated from the Neumann equation*

$$M_{12} = M_{21} = \frac{\mu_0}{4\pi} \oint_1 \oint_2 \frac{d\mathbf{l}_1 \cdot d\mathbf{l}_2}{r}$$

where $d\mathbf{l}_1$ and $d\mathbf{l}_2$ are vector elements of length in circuits 1 and 2, respectively, and $\mathbf{r}$ is the distance between these two elements. Note that this expression is completely symmetrical with respect to the two circuits. The self-inductance is calculated from the same equation, where the

_____
*μ_0 is the permeability of free space; $\mu_0 = 4\pi \times 10^{-7}$ henrys/m.

elements $\mathbf{dl}_1$ and $\mathbf{dl}_2$ are now situated on the same circuit. The double integral is evaluated by first keeping the position of $\mathbf{dl}_2$ fixed and integrating $\mathbf{dl}_1/r$ around the circuit. The process is then repeated for all other elements such as $\mathbf{dl}_2$, and the results are summed.

The *external inductance* of a circuit is the part of its self-inductance which is due to flux lying outside the surface of the conductor while the *internal inductance* is the contribution from the magnetic flux within the conductor itself.

If the current, and therefore the magnetic flux associated with it, varies with time, an electromotive force (emf) will be induced in any circuit linked by the flux. This provides an alternative method of defining inductance in terms of the emf induced by a given rate of change of current.

$$\mathcal{E}_2 = -M \frac{di_1}{dt}$$

$$\mathcal{E}_1 = -M \frac{di_2}{dt}$$

$$\mathcal{E} = -L \frac{di}{dt}$$

The negative signs are used to imply that the direction of the emf is always such as to tend to oppose the change of current (Lenz's law). Note, however, that although the self-inductance must always be positive, the mutual inductance of two circuits may be either positive or negative. An inductance of 1 henry corresponds to an induced emf of 1 volt for a rate of change of current of 1 ampere/sec.

In order to maintain a current i, the induced emf $-L di/dt$ must be balanced by an equal and opposite applied voltage so that the total applied voltage is

$$v = Ri + L \frac{di}{dt}$$

and the power supplied to the circuit is

$$vi = Ri^2 + \frac{d}{dt}\left(\frac{1}{2} Li^2\right)$$

where the resistance R is a measure of the power dissipated. This equation shows another way of interpreting inductance, namely as a measure of the amount of energy stored in the magnetic field when a given current flows. The stored energy is $\frac{1}{2}Li^2$ joules when L is measured in henrys and i in amperes.

Electric circuit theory is based on the use of sinusoidally varying currents and voltages. When the current varies sinusoidally with time, the rate of change of current has the same time waveform except for a phase shift of $\pi/2$ radians. This leads to the idea of a complex impedance, of which the real part is associated with the power lost from the circuit and the imaginary part is a reactance given by the ratio of the magnitude of the induced emf to that of the current. Since the phase of the applied voltage leads that of the current, the magnetically induced reactance is taken as being positive. We thus have

$$i = I \sin \omega t$$

$$v = Ri + L \frac{di}{dt}$$

The circuit impedance is Z where

$$Z = \frac{v}{i} = R + j\omega L$$

The self-inductance of a circuit can be regarded as a parameter which determines the inductive reactance presented to a sinusoidally varying current of given amplitude and frequency. In the same way, the mutual inductance determines the mutual reactance between two circuits.

Owing to magnetic hysteresis, the voltage and current time waveforms cannot both be sinusoidal if any magnetic material is present. Under these conditions, the reactance is defined as the ratio of the fundamental-frequency components of the voltage and current waveforms.

The sign of the mutual inductance can be specified in the following way. Suppose that the two circuits are connected in series. Then the total induced emf will be

$$-(L_1 + L_2 + 2M)\frac{di}{dt}$$

and the total reactance will therefore be

$$j\omega(L_1 + L_2 + 2M)$$

and will be greater than the sum of the reactances of the separate circuits when M is positive. A combination of two coils is said to be series aiding or series opposing, depending on whether they are connected so that M is positive or negative, respectively.

The *Q-factor* is used in describing the properties of an inductor. It is defined as

$$Q = \frac{\omega L}{R} = \tan \phi$$

where ϕ is the phase angle of the complex impedance Z. An alternative term is the *power-factor* $\cos \phi$, particularly when the emphasis is on power dissipated rather than on the damping of tuned circuits.

An impedance Z can be represented by an equivalent circuit consisting of a resistance R in series with an ideal *series inductance L*. An alternative is to start with the admittance $Y = 1/Z$ and to represent this by the parallel combination of a resistance R' and a *parallel inductance L'*.

$$R = \frac{R'}{1 + Q^2}$$

$$L = L\left(\frac{Q^2}{1 + Q^2}\right)$$

Note that, when Q is sufficiently large,

$$L' \simeq L$$

$$R' \simeq Q^2 R$$

Inductance Coil (Inductor). This is a device which is specially designed to possess inductance. The winding may have a ferromagnetic core composed of a dust-core material, metallic laminations or ferrite. An *air-cored* coil is one with no magnetic core.

Although it is the inductance which is of interest, the influence of the electric field often cannot be neglected and causes the effect known as self-capacitance. At relatively low frequencies, the inductor will behave as if an equivalent lumped capacitance were shunted across its terminals. This simple equivalent circuit fails as the frequency is approached at which the apparent lumped capacitance would resonate with the inductance of the coil. The problem then becomes one of electromagnetic wave propagation, and the concept of inductance is no longer relevant. The effect of a fixed parallel capacitance C is to reduce the Q-factor to Q_c, where

$$Q_c = Q\left[1 - \omega^2 LC\left(1 + \frac{1}{Q^2}\right)\right]$$

When Q is large, this becomes

$$Q_c \simeq Q(1 - \omega^2 LC)$$

The self-resonance effect is sometimes an advantage, e.g., in choke coils, where the object is to obtain a high impedance, irrespective of its phase angle. Generally however self-capacitance is an undesirable property, particularly in electrical networks in which the inductor forms part of a series resonant circuit.

The self-capacitance of a coil can be kept to a minimum by spacing the turns of the winding well apart and also, in the case of a multi-layer winding, by ensuring that wires which lie physically close together always belong to adjacent parts of the winding so that the potential difference between them is relatively small.

The inductance of some types of coil can be calculated directly, without recourse to the Neumann equation. An example is the *toroidal coil*, i.e., one consisting of a uniform winding around a ring-shaped former. In this case the magnetic flux exists in a well-defined magnetic circuit and the inductance is given, very nearly, by

$$L = \frac{\mu_0 N^2 A}{l}$$

where N is the number of turns in the winding and A and l are, respectively, the cross-sectional area and the length of the magnetic circuit. The same formula also holds for a long, thin *solenoidal coil*. Corrections must be applied unless both the diameter of each turn and the radial depth of the winding are small compared with the length of the magnetic circuit for the toroid or the length of the coil itself for the solenoid.

If the toroidal former is replaced by one made of a magnetic material having a relative permeability μ, the inductance will be increased by a factor μ. For coils of other geometrical shapes, where some of the flux linking the winding may lie partly or wholly outside the magnetic core, the presence of the latter will increase the inductance by a factor called the *effective permeability* μ_e. This can never exceed μ and may be considerably smaller than μ.

The relative permeability of a ferromagnetic material is not a constant but is a function of the instantaneous flux density. This increases power losses and causes distortion of the current and voltage time waveforms.

Power dissipation in a metallic core can be represented approximately by an equivalent series resistance R, where

$$\frac{R}{\mu_e f L} = c + h B_{\max} + ef$$

and $B_{\max}$ is the peak flux density. The parameters c and h depend on the hysteresis properties of the core material. The parameter e is a measure of eddy-current losses in the core.

Ferrite materials are practically insulators; therefore eddy-current losses are negligible. For a ferrite, however, the relative permeability must be regarded as a complex quantity

$$\mu = \mu'(1 - j \tan \delta)$$

Both μ' and the dissipation coefficients $\tan \delta$ are functions of frequency.

The useful frequency range of coils with laminated cores is often limited by magnetic skin effect. This causes both the inductance and the Q-factor to start to fall as the depth of penetration of the electromagnetic field becomes comparable with the thickness of the laminations. The depth of penetration d is given by

$$\frac{2}{d^2} = \omega \mu_0 \mu \sigma$$

where σ is the conductivity of the core material.

The inductance of a coil with a magnetic core is reduced if there is a superimposed unidirectional polarizing flux, caused for example by a dc current in the winding. This may be an unwanted effect or it may be used as a means of controlling the inductance.

Transverse air gaps are often introduced into the magnetic circuit. There are several reasons for this. An air gap reduces the flux density for

a given magnetizing force, thus reducing the inductance of a given coil. The power losses are, however, reduced at a greater rate than the inductance so that the power factor is improved. The performance of the inductor is made less dependent on the magnetic parameters of the core material. The waveform distortion due to hysteresis is also reduced. An air gap may be used to prevent saturation of the core by the polarizing flux when the coil is required to carry a dc current.

If the inductance of a coil, with a closed magnetic circuit of length l, is L, an air gap of length g will reduce the inductance to L_g where

$$L_g = L \cdot \left[\frac{\mu}{1 + \mu(g/l)} \right]$$

As the gap ratio g/l is increased, the inductance tends to become independent of μ, particularly when μ is large. Note however that the formula assumes that the presence of the air gap does not change the geometry of the flux distribution; an assumption which is generally only justified for relatively small gap ratios.

Dust-cored or ferrite-cored coils, for which the core eddy-current losses are small, are often wound with stranded wire. This is done to keep the eddy-current losses in the winding low by ensuring that the individual conductor strands have diameters which are small compared with the depth of penetration of the electromagnetic field into the material of which they are made. At very high frequencies, where this condition cannot be met, solid wire is often used and the diameter of the wire is increased to compensate for the fact that only part of its cross-sectional area is effective as a conductor.

V. G. WELSBY

References

Scott, W. T., "The Physics of Electricity and Magnetism," New York, John Wiley & Sons, 1959.
Plonsey, R., and Collins, R. E., "Principles and Applications of Electromagnetic Fields," New York, McGraw-Hill Book Co., 1961.
Welsby, V. G., "The Theory and Design of Inductance Coils," London, MacDonald & Co., 2nd Edition, 1960.

Cross-references: INDUCED ELECTROMOTIVE FORCE, INDUCTION HEATING, TRANSFORMER.

INDUCTION HEATING

Induction heating is a technique for generating heat in electrically conductive articles by causing current to circulate in them by induction from an adjacent coil carrying alternating current.

The frequency of the current exciting the coil ranges from supply frequency, 60 Hz, up to typically 450 kHz. Except for 60-Hz applica-

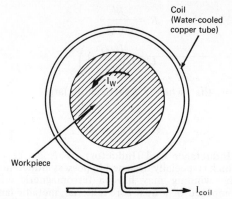

FIG. 1. Heating coil. I_w = current induced in material to be heated. I_{coil} = current through the water cooled coil.

tions, current may be obtained from rotary motor alternators, up to 10 kHz; magnetic multipliers using saturating cores, up to 540 Hz; valve oscillators, to over 1 MHz; and solid-state frequency changers up to 10 kHz. Coil-exciting voltages range from 400, 800, and 1 200 V in low-frequency systems (up to 10 kHz), to as much as 5 000 V for high-frequency valve oscillators.

Typical applications include general heating of metal parts, annealing, case and through hardening, melting in crucible-type furnaces, and heating of billets prior to forging.

In all cases of induction heating the fundamental principle is transformer action between the exciting coil and the workpiece which forms the secondary circuit. A typical arrangement is a solenoidal coil with a solid cylindrical workpiece. The currents induced in the charge flow in cylindrical paths centered on the longitudinal axis of the workpiece. Each of these paths has inductance and there is a consequent progressive decrease in current strength toward the center of the workpiece. This effect increases with increase in frequency, and as the current at any depth from the surface determines the rate of heat generation at that depth, the frequency can be chosen to control the heat pattern.

The effective depth of current penetration is a function not only of frequency, but also magnetic permeability and specific resistivity. It can

TABLE 1. EFFECTIVE DEPTH OF CURRENT
PENETRATION (in inches)

Frequency	50 Hz	1000 Hz	100 kHz
Copper	0.300	0.080	0.008
Aluminium	0.450	0.120	0.012
Brass	0.700	0.180	0.018
Steel	0.065	0.015	0.0015
Steel (above Curie)	3.200	0.750	0.075

be expressed by the relation:

$$D = 1.98 \sqrt{\frac{\rho}{\mu \times f}}$$

where D = depth in inches, ρ = resistivity in $\mu\Omega$, μ = permeability, and f = frequency in Hz.

The very marked change in current depth in ferromagnetic material (steel) as it passes from its high permeability state through Curie temperature to its low permeability, higher resistivity state should be noted.

The exciting coil together with the workpiece can be represented by an inductor in parallel with a resistor. To achieve efficient operation when used with the power sources described it is necessary to compensate for the reactive KVA taken by the inductance by adding capacitance in parallel to bring the power factor close to unity. Once this is achieved the effective load resistance must then be matched to the source resistance to achieve maximum power transfer to the workpiece.

Induction heating makes possible power densities (KW/in.² of workpiece area) up to 100 KW/in.² compared with the maximum equivalent power density from an oxyacetylene flame of about 10 KW/in.².

P. J. BILLING

Reference

Simpson, P. G., "Induction Heating," McGraw-Hill Book Co., 1960.

Cross-references: ALTERNATING CURRENTS; CONDUCTIVITY, ELECTRICAL; INDUCED ELECTROMOTIVE FORCE.

INERTIAL GUIDANCE*†

Many modern spacecraft, aircraft, ships, and submarines are being designed to navigate by inertial guidance systems which use only sensed acceleration and vehicle turning rates for input information. Early inertial guidance systems,

*Illustrations from Parvin's "Inertial Navigation" (Principles of Guided Missile Design Series), New York, Van Nostrand Reinhold, 1962.

†Editor was unable to locate author. Article is reprinted from first edition.

developed by the Germans during World War II, simply gyro-stabilized the airframe to the desired flight attitude, and used a single accelerometer to measure acceleration along the longitudinal (thrust) axis. When the integrated acceleration reached the desired injection velocity, the engines were cut off. Many unsophisticated systems still use this method.

Principles of Operation Conventional inertial systems today are designed to provide a gyro-stabilized platform which is gimbal-mounted to permit unlimited vehicle motion without disturbing the stable element. On the stable element are mounted linear accelerometers to measure the two or three components of the vehicle's acceleration vector.

These components of acceleration are inputs to the computer (Fig. 1), which solves the navigation equations—adding computed gravitation, integrating to find velocity, and integrating again to determine position:

$$\mathbf{R} = \int_0^t \int_0^t (\mathbf{A} + \mathbf{G})\, dt^2 + \mathbf{V}_0 t + \mathbf{R}_0$$

where

$\mathbf{R}$ = position vector
$\mathbf{A}$ = non-gravitational acceleration vector (sensed acceleration)
$\mathbf{G}$ = gravitational vector (calculated)
$\mathbf{V}_0$ = initial velocity vector (inserted)
t = time
$\mathbf{R}_0$ = initial radius vector (inserted).

This basic inertial navigation equation points up some of the basic characteristics of inertial systems:

(1) The inertial system must have initial position and initial velocity information (the two constants of integration).

(2) The accelerometer senses all non-gravitational forces (including thrust, drag, lift, and structural support).

(3) The gravitational field is not sensed; it must be calculated from known field equations.

Performance Characteristics Inertial systems have several distinct characteristics not common to other systems. They

(1) give continuous rather than discrete information on acceleration, velocity, position, and vehicle attitude;

(2) require no signals from outside the sys-

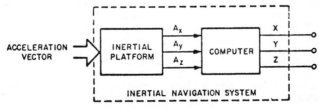

FIG. 1. Function of the basic inertial system.

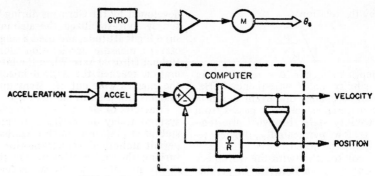

FIG. 2. Space-stabilized system block diagram.

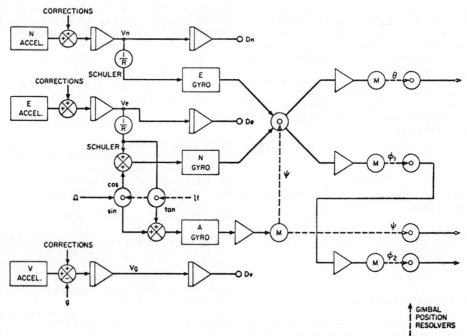

FIG. 3. Local vertical system (block diagram).

tem, so they are jamproof and can be used in vehicles launched in salvo;

(3) do not radiate signals, so they are difficult to detect in military applications;

(4) can be launched quickly but are most accurate when adequate prelaunch time is available for warmup, trim, and alignment;

(5) have errors that are a function of time rather than speed or distance;

(6) can provide by-product signals such as stabilization for flight control or radar antennas, velocity for mapping cameras, etc.

Error Characteristics Systematic errors in pure inertial systems based on error in the knowledge of the gravity vector have a characteristic Schuler oscillation corresponding to orbital period (84.5 minutes at the earth's surface) in the horizontal components of the navigation position vector and an unstable exponential error in the local vertical component.

Basic System Mechanization In the basic space-stabilized system (Fig. 2), the three accelerometer input axes are stabilized to any desired orientation in space by the GYROSCOPE stabilization control loops. A popular orientation for space vehicle launches is to have the Z axis vertical at time $t = 0$, the Z and X axes in the orbital or launch plane, and the Y axis orthogonal to Z and X. The gravitational force which starts out parallel to the Z axis is continuously computed as a function of the vehicle's position.

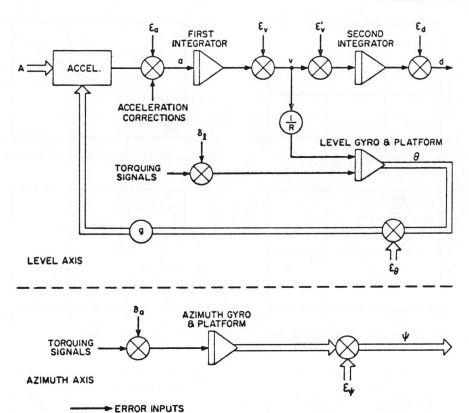

FIG. 4. Error inputs to local vertical system.

Local Vertical System Another commonly used system mechanization is the local vertical system that maintains the Z axis vertical and the X axis north throughout flight for convenience in surface and air navigation. This requires biasing each of the gyros with a turning rate which is a function of the earth's rotation rate plus the vehicle angular velocity around the curved earth's surface:

$$\omega_x = \Omega \cos lt + \frac{V_e}{R}$$

$$\omega_y = \frac{V_n}{R}$$

$$\omega_z = \Omega \sin lt + \frac{V_e}{R} \tan lt$$

where

$\omega_{x, y, z}$ = the computed bias signals to the x, y, z (north, east, and vertical) gyros
Ω = earth's sidereal rotation rate (15.041 deg/hr)
lt = local latitude of the vehicle
$V_{e, n}$ = vehicle east and north velocity
R = local earth's radius plus altitude.

In the local vertical system the accelerometers measure acceleration in a north, east, and vertical reference system which rotates in space and therefore requires CORIOLIS (q.v.) corrections. The explicit gravitational calculation is avoided in the two level axes, and the vertical axis is often unnecessary in two-dimensional surface navigation. This mechanization is shown in Fig. 3.

Errors in Local Vertical Systems The characteristic errors can be seen by analyzing the dynamic effect of errors entering the system at various points (Fig. 4). The position errors resulting from error inputs of assumed magnitude in each case are shown in Fig. 5. The total error in calculated position will be some combination of these.

Self-alignment During the navigation mode the gyros hold the stable element to the desired attitude, but this attitude must be assumed before the navigation mode begins. This can be done during a self-alignment mode. The stable element is placed in a local level attitude by using information from the two level accelerometers, whose outputs are null when their input axes are level. Azimuth orientation information is derived from the east gyro, which senses no component of the earth's rate of

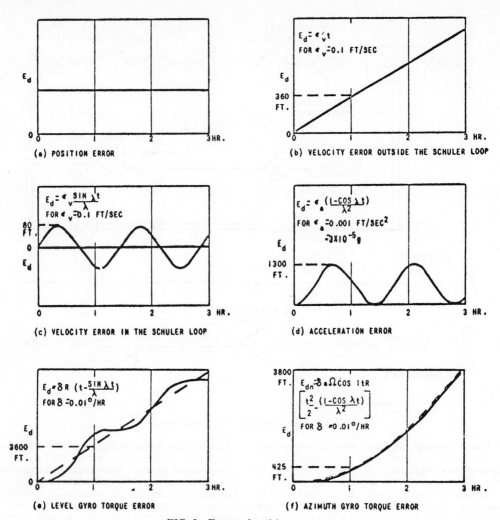

FIG. 5. Classes of position errors.

rotation when oriented east. The self-level and gyrocompass alignment mode is shown in Fig. 6.

Strapdown Systems In addition to the gimbaled gyro-stabilized systems, there are several gimballess or strapdown configurations. One is the relatively simple accelerometer, vehicle attitude control system first described. Another uses three accelerometers whose vehicle-referenced outputs pass through a dynamic coordinate transformation matrix in the computer. Three *rate* gyros provide the computer with vehicle attitude rate information necessary to compute the matrix. Although this approach eliminates gimbaling, it requires precision rate gyros and relatively large computer capacity to integrate attitude rate and provide a dynamic matrix.

A third gimballess system concept uses an inertial reference such as electrostatically suspended gyros to give vehicle *attitude* information to the computer for use in calculating the dynamic coordinate conversion matrix. Attitude rate integration is thereby avoided.

Steering Commands An inertial navigation system primarily provides vehicle velocity or position. Guidance can be provided by the inertial system by supplying target location information to the computer, which then compares vehicle position with target position and calculates steering and (in the case of space flight) engine shutoff commands.

RICHARD H. PARVIN

References

Parvin, Richard H., "How Coriolis Works," Electronic Industries, April, 1960.

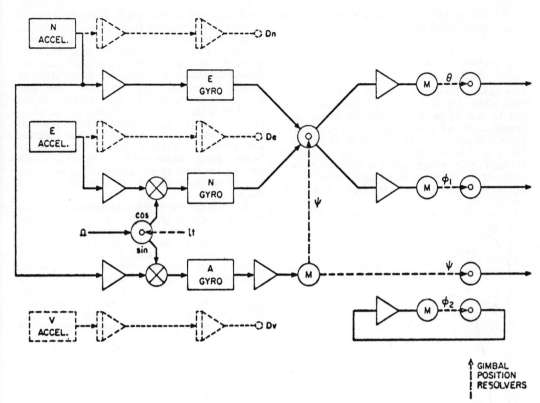

FIG. 6. Self-alignment mode.

Stearns, Edward V., "Navigation and Guidance in Space," Englewood Cliffs, N.J., Prentice-Hall, 1962.
Pitman, George R., "Inertial Guidance," New York, John Wiley & Sons, 1962.
Parvin, Richard H., "Inertial Navigation," New York, Van Nostrand Reinhold, 1962.

Cross-references: ASTRODYNAMICS, ASTRONAU-TICS, GYROSCOPE.

INFRARED RADIATION

The region of the electromagnetic spectrum between the wavelength limits 0.7 and 1000μm (7 × 10^{-5} and 1 × 10^{-1} cm) has become known as infrared radiation. The lower wavelength limit is set to coincide with the upper limit of the visible radiation region. Radiation of wavelength greater than 1000μm is generally thought of as the microwave spectrum. Both limits are arbitrary, and represent no change in characteristics as they are passed. Conventionally, the region between 0.7 and 1.5μm is called the *near infrared region*; that between 1.5 and 20μm, the *intermediate infrared region*; and that between 20 and 1000μm, the *far infrared region*.

For many applications, the location of infrared radiation in the spectrum is described by its wavelength in micrometers, μm, (1μm = 10^{-4} cm). In applications where the relative energy of the radiation is of interest, the *wave number*, σ, is used. The wave number is defined as the reciprocal of the wavelength, λ, in centimeters, and is expressed in units of cm^{-1} (called the kayser). This quantity is used more commonly than the frequency ν of the radiation, which is related to σ as follows:

$$\sigma = \nu/c \tag{1}$$

where c is the velocity of light.

Infrared radiation is produced principally by the emission of solid and liquid materials as a result of thermal excitation and by the emission of molecules of gases. Thermal emission from solids is contained in a continuous spectrum, whose wavelength distribution is described by the relation

$$M_\lambda \, d\lambda = \frac{2\pi \, c^2 \, h\epsilon_\lambda}{\lambda^5} \frac{1}{e^{ch/\lambda k T} - 1} \, d\lambda \tag{2}$$

where

M_λ = spectral radiant exitance of the solid into a hemisphere in the wavelength range from λ to $(\lambda + d\lambda)$

h = Planck's constant = 6.62×10^{-27} erg sec

ϵ_λ = spectral emittance

k = Boltzmann's constant = 1.38×10^{-16} erg/K

T = absolute temperature of the solid emitter, K.

The spectral emittance, ϵ_λ, is defined as the ratio of the emission at wavelength λ of the object to that of an ideal blackbody at the same temperature and wavelength. When ϵ_λ is unity, Eq. (2) becomes the Planck radiation equation for a blackbody. The distribution of radiant exitance with wavelength for blackbody radiators at different temperatures is shown in Fig. 1. It is apparent from the figure that black-

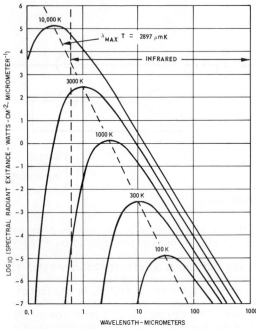

FIG. 1. Spectral radiant exitance of a blackbody at various temperatures.

body radiation from emitters at temperatures below about 2000 K falls predominantly in the infrared region. An emitter which exhibits a constant value less than unity of spectral emittance at all wavelengths is called a gray-body radiator. Most solid radiators show a general decrease in spectral emittance with increasing wavelength in the infrared; however, over limited spectral ranges, many materials are approximately gray-body radiators. Radiators which approach the characteristics of ideal blackbodies can be made in the form of uniformly heated cavities. A relatively small aperture, through which the cavity can be observed, serves as the source of blackbody radiation.

Infrared radiation is also observed as emitted from excited molecules of gases. Many of the energy transitions which take place in gases ex-

cited thermally or electrically result in radiation emission in the infrared region. Gaseous emission differs in character from solid emission in that the former consists of discrete spectrum lines or bands, with significant discontinuities, while the latter shows a continuous distribution of energy throughout the spectrum. The predominant source of molecular radiation in the infrared is the result of vibration of the molecules in characteristic modes. Energy transitions between various states of molecular rotation also produce infrared radiation. Complex molecular gases radiate intricate spectra, which may be analyzed to give information of the nature of the molecules or of the composition of the gas.

The propagation of infrared radiation through various media is, in general, subject to absorption which varies with the wavelength of the radiation. Molecular vibration and rotation in gases, which are related to the emission of radiation, are also responsible for resonance absorption of energy. The gases in the atmosphere, for example, exhibit pronounced absorption throughout the infrared spectrum. The principal gases of the atmosphere, nitrogen and oxygen, do not absorb significantly in the infrared region. However, the lesser constituents, water vapor (H_2O), carbon dioxide (CO_2), and ozone (O_3), are responsible for strong absorption in the infrared. The absorption of radiation is so prevalent that those spectral bands in which relatively little absorption occurs are identified as *atmospheric windows*.

Solid and liquid materials show, as a rule, strong absorption in the infrared. There are, however, many solids which transmit well in broad regions of the infrared spectrum. Many materials, such as water and silica glasses, which show little absorption in the visible, are opaque to infrared radiation at wavelengths greater than a few microns. Many of the electrically insulating crystals, such as the alkali halides and the alkaline-earth halides, which transmit well in the visible, also are transparent to much of the near and intermediate infrared spectrum. Several of the semiconductor materials absorb strongly in the visible, but become transparent in the infrared beyond certain wavelengths characteristic of the semiconductor.

Detection of the presence, distribution and/or quantity of infrared radiation requires techniques which are, in part, unique to this spectral region. The frequency of the radiation is such that essentially optical methods may be used to collect, direct, and filter the radiation. Transmitting optical elements, including lenses and windows, must be made of suitable materials, which may or may not be transparent in the visible spectrum. Table 1 gives characteristics of several transmitting materials suitable for use in infrared optical systems. To avoid chromatic aberration, reflecting mirrors are commonly used in infrared optical systems to focus and deviate the radiation when broad spectral bands are observed. Filters for the infrared are de-

TABLE 1. INFRARED TRANSMITTING MATERIALS

Material	Useful Transmission Region (μm)	Refractive Index Near Transmission Peak	Special Characteristics
Optical glasses	0.3–2.7	1.48–1.70	Best for near infrared
Fused silica	0.2–3.5–4.5	1.43	Some types show absorption near 2.7μm
Arsenic trisulfide	0.6–12.0	2.4	A glass; subject to striations
Calcium aluminate	0.3–5.5	1.8	A glass; subject to attack by water
Sapphire	0.17–6.0	1.7	Single crystal, hard, refractory
Silicon	1.1–>20	3.4	Low density; opaque to visible
Germanium	1.8–>20	4.0	Opaque to visible
NaCl	0.2–15	1.52	Water soluble
KBr	0.21–27	1.54	Water soluble
LiF	0.11–6	1.35	Low solubility in water
CaF$_2$	0.13–9	1.41	Insoluble
Thallium bromide-iodide (KRS-5)	0.5–40	2.38	Fairly soft; cold flows
AgCl	0.4–25	2.0	Soft; cold flows
Irtran 1	0.5–9	1.3	Polycrystalline MgF$_2$
Irtran 2	0.4–14.5	2.2	Polycrystalline ZnS
Irtran 3	<0.4–11.5	1.3	Polycrystalline CaF$_2$
Irtran 4	0.5–22	2.4	Polycrystalline ZnSe
Irtran 5	<0.4–9.5	1.7	Polycrystalline MgO
Irtran 6	0.9–31	2.7	Polycrystalline CdTe

signed and constructed like those for the visible, except for the choice of materials and, in the case of interference filters, the thickness of the layers.

The detector element for infrared represents the most unique component of the detection system. Photographic techniques can be used for the near infrared out to about 1.3μm. Photoemissive devices, comparable to the visible- and ultraviolet-sensitive photocells, are available with sensitivity also extending to about 1.3μm. The intermediate infrared region is most effectively detected by photoconductors. These elements, photosensitive semiconductors, are essentially photon detectors, which respond in proportion to the number of infrared photons in the spectral region of wavelength shorter than the cut-off wavelength. This cut-off wavelength corresponds to the minimum photon energy necessary to overcome the forbidden gap of the semiconductor. A number of sensitive photoconductors are available with spectral cutoff at various wavelengths in the infrared. Photoconductors are employed as resistive elements, as photovoltaic p-n diodes, or as photoelectromagnetic elements, according to the particular electrical advantage to be gained. All spectral regions from ultraviolet through visible, infrared, and microwaves, can be detected by an appropriately designed thermal element, which responds by being heated by the absorption of the incident radiation. In the infrared, thermal detectors take the forms of thermocouples, bolometers, and pneumatic devices. The thermal elements, in general, are not as sensitive or as rapidly responding as photoconductors in spectral regions where they both

respond. However, the broad spectral response and uniform energy sensitivity characteristics make them highly useful. Table 2 gives representative characteristics of several commonly used infrared detectors.

The most common application of infrared radiation is, of course, radiant heating. Solid radiators, such as hot tungsten filaments, alloy wires, and silicon carbide rods are employed extensively as sources of infrared to provide surface heating by radiation.

Infrared spectroscopy has become a powerful analytical tool in the chemistry laboratory. Organic molecules, in general, contain interatomic valence bonds which exhibit characteristic resonance frequencies which can be identified in the absorption spectrum of the material in gaseous form. Such information can be used to study the structure of complex molecules. It also serves in aiding the identification of the presence of known valence bonds in chemical analysis. Most absorption lines and bonds due to molecular vibrations fall in the frequency range 500 to 5000 cm^{-1} (wavelength range 2 to 20μm). A large quantity of data has been gathered on the detailed absorption spectra of many gaseous materials. The characteristic spectra of many organic molecules are such that identification of the presence of the molecules, as well as the presence of particular radicals within the molecules, can be readily observed. Petroleum chemistry, for example, has been greatly aided by the application of infrared spectroscopy to the identification of many of the complex constituents in petroleum products.

Observation of infrared absorption spectra is carried out by means of an infrared spectro-

TABLE 2. INFRARED DETECTORS

Detector (operating temperature)	Region (μm)	Specific Detectivity, D* at Peak $(cmHz^{1/2}w^{-1})$	Time Constant (sec)	Special Features
Si(295K)	Visible–1.0	2×10^{12}	5×10^{-6}	Photovoltaic crystal
PbS (295 K)	Visible–2.8	8×10^{10}	2×10^{-4}	Thin-film photoconductor
PbSe (195 K)	Visible–5.6	2×10^{10}	2×10^{-3}	Thin-film photoconductor
InSb (77 K)	1–5.6	10^{11}	$<2 \times 10^{-7}$	Photovoltaic crystal
(Hg · Cd)Te (77 K)	2–14	5×10^{9}	5×10^{-7}	Spectral cut-off varies with alloy composition
Ge (Hg doped) (25 K)	1–16	2×10^{10}	$<10^{-6}$	Photoconductor crystal
Ge (Cu doped (5 K)	1–29	3×10^{10}	$<10^{-6}$	Photoconductor crystal
Ge (Zn doped) (5 K)	1–40	3×10^{10}	10^{-8}	Photoconductor crystal
Thermistor bolometer (295 K)	All	2×10^{8}	10^{-3}–10^{-2}	Flake of mixed oxides
Golay cell (255 K)	All	2×10^{9}	1.5×10^{-2}	Pneumatic
Thermocouple (295 K)	All	2×10^{8}	1.5×10^{-2}	Used in spectrometers

photometer, in which the transmission of monochromatic radiation by a gaseous sample in a cell is compared with that of a blank cell, while the wavelength of the radiation is scanned through the spectral range of interest. Prism dispersing elements are usually used in the infrared, rather than gratings, because of the difficulty with the latter of separating the several orders in the wide spectral range covered. Far infrared spectroscopy is complicated by the omnipresence of background and scattered radiation of shorter wavelength emitted inside the instrument at room temperature. Special techniques of filtering must be employed to eliminate the effects of the short-wavelength radiation.

Optical-electronic devices of many varieties have been designed to determine the direction of weakly radiating remote objects by means of detection of their infrared emission. Military applications have been found which have been made possible uniquely by this technique. Missiles can be guided to their target by infrared detection of the self-emission of heated segments of the target. Detailed maps of the earth's surface can be made from aircraft at night by observing the varying infrared emission of the ground. Personnel can be detected in total darkness by the infrared radiation they emit as warm objects.

Such devices require the detection of low-level radiation in the intermediate infrared region. Optical lenses or mirrors are used to collect the observed radiation and concentrate it onto the sensitive infrared detector. High-gain, low-noise electronic amplifiers must be provided to increase the weak signal from the detector to a level which can be used to operate controls or displays, as demanded by the application. Optical filtering is applied in order to restrict the observed spectral region to one in which the target is effectively detected, with a minimum of interference from radiation from its background. The wavelength of detection is such that angular resolution capability, as set by diffraction, is much greater with infrared devices than that of radar devices. Detection of targets at great distances through intervening atmosphere is more effective in the infrared than in the visible because of the much lower atmospheric scattering in the infrared.

Detailed discussions of the characteristics, detection and applications of infrared radiation may be found in the references.

R. H. McFee

References

Jamieson, J. A., McFee, R. H., Plass, G. N., Grube, R. H., and Richards, R. G., "Infrared Physics and Engineering," New York, McGraw-Hill Book Co., 1963.

Smith, R. A., Jones, T. E., and Chasmar, R. P., "The Detection and Measurement of Infrared Radiation," Fair Lawn, N.J., Oxford University Press, 1957.

Herzberg, G., "Infrared and Raman Spectra of Polyatomic Molecules," New York, Van Nostrand Reinhold, 1945.

Szymanski, H. A., and Alperts, N. A., "IR: Theory and Practice of Infrared Spectroscopy," Plenum Press, 1964.

Kruse, P. W., McGlauchlin, L. D., and McQuistan, R. B., "Elements of Infrared Technology," New York, John Wiley & Sons, 1962.

Hudson, R. D., Jr., "Infrared System Engineering," New York, John Wiley & Sons, 1969.

Cross-references: ABSORPTION SPECTRA; LIGHT; RADIATION, THERMAL; SPECTROSCOPY.

INTERFERENCE AND INTERFEROMETRY

Interference is the term used to signify a large class of phenomena in light, and interferometry is the technique of high-precision measurement based on these phenomena. Ordinarily rays of

light crossing the same point in different directions do not interfere with each other; each ray is propagated as though it alone were present. However, there are certain interesting cases when these rays do interfere with each other; the interference may be destructive, as when they cancel each other's effect, or may be constructive, as when they reinforce each other. Interference is a consequence of light being propagated in the form of waves.

Young's Experiment The classic experiment in interference is the one performed by Thomas Young in 1802. A source of light SL (see Fig. 1) that is placed behind a narrow slit illuminates two other slits P and Q which are parallel and very close to each other. At some distance away is a screen which receives the light from the two slits. On the screen is seen a series of bright and dark fringes. If either of the two slits is covered, the fringes disappear, and the screen is almost uniformly illuminated. The combined effect due to the two slits is that at certain points there is no light at all, and at other points the brightness is four times that due to a single slit.

This puzzling phenomenon of light upon light producing darkness can be readily understood by considering the analogous case of ripples on the surface of water. Let a continuous series of ripples be produced by a vibrating metal strip dipping in and out of the surface of water. A light floating body, say a leaflet, wobbles up and down with the same frequency as the vibrator. The ripples spread out in widening circles. If now another vibrator of the same frequency is brought near the first, the appearance of the ripples is completely changed. Along certain radial lines starting from the two vibrators, the water surface seems undisturbed; the leaflet does not move if placed along these lines. In between these lines the ripples have a very large amplitude.

At points equidistant from the two vibrators, i.e., along the perpendicular bisector of the line joining the vibrators, the waves from both arrive in phase. Both systems of waves tend to move the water up or down at the same time. The amplitude of the waves along this line is double that due to either of the systems of waves. At some other point sufficiently away from the perpendicular bisector, the crest of one system arrives at the same time as the trough of another, and thus the two systems cancel each other. Destructive interference occurs if the distances of the two vibrators from the point differ by $(n + \frac{1}{2})\lambda$, where λ is the wavelength and n is zero or an integer. Constructive interference occurs if the path difference is $n\lambda$.

An important condition for interference is that the two systems of waves be coherent, i.e., that they always have the same phase relation to each other. If the two slits P and Q in Young's experiment were illuminated by waves from two different sources, interference effects would not be observed. The reason is that waves produced by two sources would have no phase relation to each other. When the two slits are illuminated by different parts of the same wave front, they always arrive at any point beyond the slit with a constant difference in phase.

Theory The mathematical expression for a progressive wave is

$$S = a \cos 2\pi v \left\{ \left(t - \frac{x}{v} \right) + \alpha \right\} \qquad (1)$$

where S is the magnitude of the electric or magnetic field, also called displacement, at time t and distance x, a is the amplitude, v the frequency, v the velocity, and α a term denoting the phase. Due to the superposition of two waves, denoted by subscripts 1 and 2.

$$S = S_1 + S_2 = a_1 \cos 2\pi v \left\{ \left(t - \frac{x}{v} \right) + \alpha_1 \right\}$$
$$+ a_2 \cos 2\pi v \left\{ \left(t - \frac{x}{v} \right) + \alpha_2 \right\} \qquad (2)$$

Both waves have the same frequency and velocity but different amplitudes and phases; x is measured from any arbitrary point. The displacement at $x = 0$ is given by

$$S = A \cos (2\pi vt + \alpha) \qquad (3)$$

where A is the amplitude and α the phase of the resulting wave. By expanding the right-hand sides of Eq. (2) with $x = 0$ and Eq. (3), equating coefficients of $\cos 2\pi vt$ and $\sin 2\pi vt$, squaring and adding, one can see that

$$A^2 = a_1{}^2 + a_2{}^2 + 2a_1 a_2 \cos(\alpha_1 - \alpha_2) \qquad (4)$$

As $\cos(\alpha_1 - \alpha_2)$ varies between $+1$ and -1, A varies between $(a_1 + a_2)$ and $(a_1 - a_2)$. If the amplitudes a_1 and a_2 are both equal to a, the

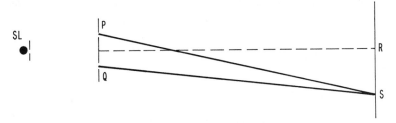

FIG. 1. Young's experiment.

minimum value of A is 0 and the maximum value is $2a$. Since the intensity is proportional to the square of the amplitude, the intensity at the maximum is 4 times that due to either wave. The condition for maximum brightness is: $\alpha_1 - \alpha_2 = 2n\pi$, which corresponds to a path difference of $n\lambda$.

Let R and S, Fig. 1, be the positions of the central fringe and the nth bright fringe below R. Let $PQ = s$, $RS = x$, and let D be the distance of the screen from the two slits.

$$PS^2 - QS^2 = \left\{ D^2 + \left(x + \frac{s}{2} \right)^2 \right\}$$
$$- \left\{ D^2 + \left(x - \frac{s}{2} \right)^2 \right\}$$
$$= 2xs$$

$$PS - QS = 2xs/(PS + QS) = 2xs/2D$$

since $PS + QS$ is very nearly equal to $2D$.

$$PS - QS = n\lambda, \text{ therefore } \lambda = \frac{1}{n} \frac{xs}{D} \quad (5)$$

Equation (5) formed the basis for the first experimental determination of the wavelength of light.

Young's experiment in its original form was difficult to perform and failed to carry conviction when the results were first published. If $s = 1$ mm, $D = 2$ meters, the distance between successive fringes for sodium yellow light ($\lambda = 5.89 \times 10^{-5}$ cm) is only 1.2 mm. The illumination is too poor, the fringes are too close, and two fine slits at 1 mm distance are difficult to produce. The controversy as to whether light is propagated as corpuscles or waves had existed for over a century and a half. Francesco M. Grimaldi, who is regarded as the founder of the wave theory of light, in his book *Physico-Mathesis de Lumine, Coloribus et Iride*, published in 1665, described several experiments on diffraction and interference of light, and presented the rudiments of a wave theory. Newton discussed several diffraction effects in his *Opticks*, published in 1708; he threw his weight heavily on the side of the corpuscular theory of light. Experiments more convincing than those of Young were needed to overthrow a theory based on Newton's authority. Between 1814 and 1816, Fresnel introduced two better methods of producing interference fringes, he also gave a more complete theory of the formation of the fringes, based on the hypothesis of secondary wavelets which was first developed in 1678 by Huygens. Huygens' hypothesis was that every point on a wave front acted as the source for a secondary train of waves and that the envelope of these secondary waves determined every successive position of the wavefront.

The two improved experimental arrangements introduced by Fresnel were the bimirror and the biprism. These solve the difficulty of obtaining two slits sufficiently narrow and close to each other. In the bimirror arrangement, light from a narrow slit is reflected by two plane mirrors inclined at a small angle to each other. Thus the two slits are replaced by the two images of a single slit, and the distance between these can be adjusted by changing the angle between the mirrors. In the biprism arrangement, two small angle prisms joined at their base each produce a small deflection of the light emerging from a single slit, and thus cause two sets of coherent waves to be superposed. A single mirror may also be used as devised by Lloyd to produce interference between wave trains produced by a slit and its image.

Applications of Interference Effects There are many interesting applications of the principle of interference. Refractometers based on interference effects are used to measure small changes in the refractive index of transparent media (see REFRACTION). In the Rayleigh refractometer (see Fig. 2), light from a linear source S, made parallel by a lens L_1, is split into two beams by two fairly wide slits, and then made to pass through two similar tubes T_1 and T_2. After transmission through the tubes, the two beams are brought to a common focus by another lens L_2. If the two tubes contain transparent media of the same refractive index, say the same liquid, the center of the fringe pattern is formed on the axis of the instrument. If the refractive index of the liquid in one of the two tubes is changed, as for example by introducing a solvent, the fringes shift across the focal plane of the viewing lens. By counting the number of fringes which cross a reference line, the equivalent path difference and hence the change in refractive index can be calculated. Compensator plates M_1 and M_2, which restore the fringe pattern to its original position, are convenient devices for counting the fringe shift.

Michelson's method of measuring stellar diameters is another application of interference. A beam mounted over the entrance aperture of

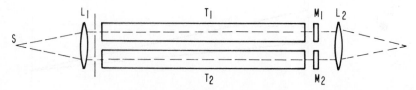

FIG. 2. Rayleigh refractometer.

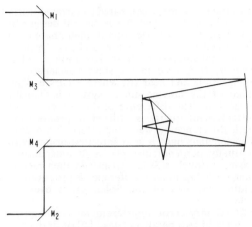

FIG. 3. Stellar interferometer.

divided into two or more beams by partial reflection and transmission, and these are recombined after they have traveled different path distances. Of the many different types of interferometers, only two which are widely used will be described here, the Michelson interferometer and the Fabry-Perot interferometer.

The Michelson interferometer is shown schematically in Fig. 4. Monochromatic light from

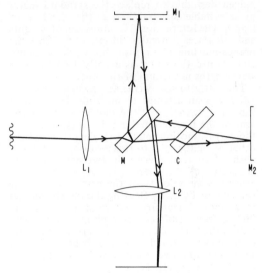

FIG. 4. Michelson interferometer.

a large telescope carries four mirrors as shown in Fig. 3. The arrangement is similar to that of Young's experiment, with the mirrors M_1 and M_2 as the slits and the star as the source. The diffraction image of the star is crossed by interference bands if M_1 and M_2 are relatively close to each other. As the distance between them is increased, the fringes become less distinct and finally disappear. This is due to the fringe pattern from one half of the star being completely canceled by that from the other. If the distance between M_1 and M_2 for disappearance of the fringes is s, r is the distance of the star, d its diameter, and λ the wavelength of light, $d/r = 1.22\lambda/s$. The first star to be measured by this method was Betelgeuse, for which the bands disappeared at $s = 306.5$ cm. Substituting values 5.75×10^{-5} cm for λ, and 1.712×10^{20} cm for r, as determined from the parallax of Betelgeuse, the diameter of the star is found to be 3.918×10^{13} cm, which is 31 per cent greater than the diameter of the earth's orbit around the sun. Several other near stars of large size have since been measured by the same method.

Thin films of transparent media produce striking interference effects, as for example, when a few drops of gasoline are spilled over a wet pavement. The two wave trains which interfere in this case are those reflected from the upper surface of the oil film and from the water-oil interface. The colors of butterflies' wings and sea shells have a similar origin. The so-called Newton's rings are produced by the air film between two partially reflecting, spherical surfaces. The optical quality of a glass surface can be tested by causing interference fringes between it and a standard test plate of high optical quality. The fringes are analogous to contour lines in geographical maps, each new fringe indicating deviation from true flatness by half a wavelength.

Interferometers Interferometers are instruments of high-precision measurement based on the principle of interference. A beam of light is

an extended source is collimated by a lens L_1 and falls on the beam splitter M of which the hind surface partially reflects half the intensity upward and transmits the other half. The two halves of the beam are returned by the mirrors M_1 and M_2, and the interference pattern is viewed in the focal plane of the lens L_2. C is a compensator plate similar to M, which gives the beam from M_2 an extra path equal to that traveled by the other beam in the beam splitter. The form of the fringes depends on the adjustment of the two mirrors M_1 and M_2. If they are not quite at right angles to each other, and the difference in path of the two beams is small, the image of M_2 in M forms a thin wedge with the front surface of M_1. The fringes are straight and parallel to the apex of the wedge. If the difference in path is large, the two mirrors should be adjusted so that the image of M_2 in M is exactly parallel to M_1. In this case, the fringes are circular. Each circle is due to pencils of light which have a constant inclination to the axis of the lens L_1.

Two of the applications of the Michelson interferometer are of historic importance: the standardization of the meter in terms of the wavelength of light and the Michelson-Morley experiment for the drift of ether. If one of the two mirrors is moved parallel to itself, the pattern of fringes shifts across the field of view.

The displacement of the mirror for each fringe shift is $\lambda/2$. This method was first used by Michelson and Benoit in 1892 for comparing the red line (6438Å) of cadmium with the International Prototype Meter which is kept in Paris, France. More precise measurements of the meter in terms of the wavelength of light have since been made by other observers. Since the wavelength of light is a more reliable standard and can be measured with greater accuracy, it was judged desirable to replace the standard meter by a suitable spectral line as the standard of length. The International Commission of Weights and Measures formally adopted in 1960 the orange-red line of krypton 86 as the standard and defined the meter as exactly 1 650 763.73 wavelengths in vacuum of this line.

The MICHELSON-MORLEY EXPERIMENT of 1887 was an attempt to measure the speed of the ether "wind" past the moving earth. If one arm of the interferometer is in the direction of the earth's motion relative to the ether and the other at right angles to this motion, the relative path difference between the two beams of light is nearly Lv^2/c^2, where L is the length of each arm, v is the velocity of the earth and c is the velocity of light. By floating the interferometer in a pool of mercury and rotating it through 90°, a fringe shift corresponding to twice this path difference should be observed. Accurate experiments showed that the fringes did not shift. This negative result served as the basis for the theory of relativity.

A recent application of the Michelson interferometer is for spectrophotometry of composite sources. The method is especially applicable for the infrared range. One of the two mirrors is moved parallel to itself at a very constant rate. The variation of intensity over a small area at the center of the ring system at P is measured by an infrared detector. If the source were strictly monochromatic, the output signal of the detector would vary sinusoidally with time. The displacement of the mirror between successive maxima is half a wavelength. With a composite source as input, the output is the sum of a large number of sine functions, each of them being due to the energy in a narrow wavelength band of the source. A Fourier transform of the output signal, as may well be obtained with the aid of a digital computer, gives the spectral energy distribution of the source. The compactness of the instrument

is a special advantage compared to infrared prism monochromators, and hence several designs of the interferometer spectrophotometer have been developed for use in satellites and space probes. Of special interest is the polarization interferometer. It is used in the short-wavelength region, visible and near IR, where accurate alignment of the moving mirror system is difficult to achieve. The difference in the two indices of refraction of quartz is utilized to produce the path difference between the interfering beams. The incident light is split into two beams with mutually perpendicular planes of polarization, passed through a Soleil prism and then recombined. Change in path difference is produced by sliding one half of the Soleil prism over the other.

The Fabry-Perot interferometer (see Fig. 5) consists of two parallel plates of glass or quartz. The inner surfaces are optically flat and semi-silvered. Light from an extended source is made parallel by a lens L_1, passes through the interferometer and is focused by another lens L_2. A system of circular fringes is observed in the focal plane of L_2. The path of an oblique ray of light in between the two plates is shown in Fig. 5. Interference takes place between the directly transmitted ray and the rays that undergo one or more reflections between the plates. A high degree of wavelength resolution is the main advantage of the Fabry-Perot interferometer. In a typical case of 1-cm separation of plates and 90 per cent reflectance, wavelength resolution is over a million; i.e., two wavelengths 0.005Å apart at 5000Å will give completely distinguishable ring systems. By increasing the reflectance of the plates or the separation between them, the wavelength resolution can be increased to any desired degree. Laser beams which give highly coherent single wavelengths permit plate separation of over a meter. Extensive use has been made of the Fabry-Perot interferometer for precision measurement of wavelengths of spectral lines.

M. P. THEKAEKARA

References

Born, M., and Wolf, E., "Principles of Optics," Chs. 7, 10, and 11, New York, Pergamon Press, 4th edn., 1970.

Cook, A. H., "Interference of Electromagnetic Waves," Oxford, Clarendon Press, 1971.

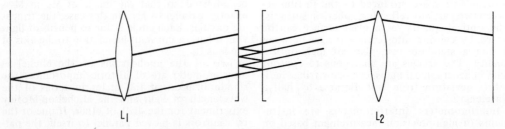

FIG. 5. Fabry-Perot interferometer.

Jenkins, F. A., and White, H. A., "Fundamentals of Optics," Chs. 12, 13, 14, and 17, New York, McGraw-Hill Book Co., 1957.

Klein, M. V., "Optics," Chs. 5 and 6, New York, John Wiley & Sons, Inc., 1970.

Mollet, P., Ed., "Optics in Metrology," Colloquia of the International Commission for Optics, New York, Pergamon Press, 1960. Several excellent articles on applications of interferometry.

Steel, W. H., "Interferometry," London, Cambridge University Press, 1967.

Strong, J., "Concepts of Classical Optics," Chs. 8, 11, 12, and Appendix F, San Francisco, W. H. Freeman and Co., 1958.

Cross-references: COHERENCE, DIFFRACTION BY MATTER AND DIFFRACTION GRATINGS, ELECTROMAGNETIC THEORY, LIGHT, MICHELSON-MORLEY EXPERIMENT, REFRACTION, RELATIVITY, WAVE MOTION.

INTERMOLECULAR FORCES

The terms "intermolecular forces" and "van der Waals forces" refer to the weak forces between molecules, and these forces are to be distinguished from the much stronger interatomic, intramolecular forces of chemical binding. The simplest example of an intermolecular force is provided by the interaction between two noble-gas atoms: The atoms are spherical and the force is central in this case.

Short-range Repulsion The volume of matter in the solid and liquid states is an extensive property, i.e., is proportional to the number of moles or molecules in the specimen, and this implies a molecular "size" or the existence of repulsive forces that prevent two molecules from occupying the same space at the same time. The very low compressibilities of solids and liquids indicate a very strong repulsion of two molecules when they begin to overlap each other. These self-evident conceptions were embodied in the nineteenth-century representation of molecules as little billiard balls. The origin of the "overlap forces" of repulsion was not explained until the advent of quantum mechanics and the Pauli exclusion principle. According to the latter, when two noble-gas atoms begin to overlap, the electrons tend to migrate from the crowded region in the middle to the far ends outside the nuclei, where they exert electrostatic forces that tend to pull the nuclei apart. This effect, which greatly exceeds the direct electrostatic repulsion of the partially shielded nuclei, cannot be represented by any simple analytic potential energy function. For reasons of mathematical convenience, however, an inverse-power law, especially r^{-12}, or a simple exponential function e^{-ar}, where r is the distance between the nuclei of the atoms, is often used to represent the potential energy of the overlap repulsion. The first calculation of an overlap repulsion (between H atoms) was made by Heitler and London in 1927.

Long-range Attraction When two noble-gas atoms are so far apart that there is negligible overlap of their charge clouds or wave packets, the atoms, although neutral and nonpolar, interact through a set of electrostatic multipole terms of which the most important is the lowest-order dipole-dipole term. An instantaneous electric dipole moment in one atom, which averages to zero, induces a dipole moment in the other atom which is proportional to the inducing moment and which interacts with it. It is readily seen that the interaction energy varies as r^{-6}, does not average to zero, and corresponds to an attraction between the atoms. Similarly an instantaneous electric quadrupole moment in one atom induces a dipole moment in the other which interacts with it to give an interaction energy, varying as r^{-8}, which is called the dipole-quadrupole term. These long-range multipole interactions, especially the dipole-dipole term, provide the explanation for the intermolecular attractive forces that are evidenced by imperfect-gas behavior, the Joule-Thomson effect, and the very existence of the liquid state. When the dipole-dipole term is calculated quantum-mechanically, the resulting attractive potential energy, varying as r^{-6}, is called the "dispersion potential." It was first treated by Wang (1927) and then by London (1930).

A Priori Calculations It has long been customary to assume that the intermolecular potential between two neutral, nonpolar molecules consists of a long-range dispersion attraction combined with a short-range overlap repulsion. The combined potential-energy curve for two noble-gas atoms then has a minimum at a distance r_m, and the potential vanishes at a distance σ which is referred to as the slow-collision diameter. However, it is questionable to decompose the interaction potential into parts, and in particular, to use the dispersion potential, which is an asymptotic expression, at distances as small as r_m. The coefficient of the dispersion potential for interactions between pairs of rare-gas atoms has been calculated with great accuracy in recent years, starting from the Schrödinger equation and using a small number of optical data. The a priori calculation of the complete potential energy curve, starting from Schrödinger's equation, is an extraordinarily difficult and laborious procedure even for the simplest atoms and even with the aid of modern electronic computers. Only within recent months (1972) has it been possible to achieve sufficient accuracy to obtain the He–He potential in the neighborhood of its minimum.

Nonadditivity Effects When three or more rare-gas atoms are in proximity, the mutual energy of interaction cannot be expressed as the sum of potential energies for all the interacting pairs, except to a first approximation. The deviations from additivity are associated with many-body forces, and in recent years the three-body interaction has received particular attention. The asymptotic form of the nonad-

ditive three-body interaction is called the triple-dipole potential; it arises from an instantaneous moment in one atom which induces moments in two other atoms, the induced moments then interacting to produce a three-body force. The quantum-mechanical calculation gives the result

$$u_{123} = \nu \, (r_{12} r_{23} r_{13})^{-3}$$

$$\cdot \, (1 + 3 \cos \theta_1 \cos \theta_2 \cos \theta_3)$$

for the triple-dipole potential, where r_{ij} are the sides and θ_i the interior angles of the triangular array and ν is a constant which can be calculated for rare-gas combinations. Little is known about three-body interactions in the region of overlap, and higher-order many-body forces have usually been neglected. Three-body forces appear to make a large contribution to the values of the third virial coefficients of the noble gases at temperatures close to the critical point.

Polar Molecules When the molecules possess permanent electric moments, additional electrostatic terms contribute to the intermolecular force. The dipole moments of simple polar molecules, such as LiH, can be calculated with considerable accuracy from the Schrödinger equation and compared with experimental values deduced from the temperature dependence of the dielectric constant. The potential energy of alignment of two polar molecules varies as r^{-6} and is usually smaller than the dispersion energy, but in the important case of H_2O at 20°C the alignment energy is four times as large as the dispersion energy. The nonspherical shape of polar molecules and the noncentral character of the electric force greatly complicate the mathematical analysis for most physical properties. Permanent electric quadrupole moments Q have also been calculated and measured, and their contributions to intermolecular forces through dipole-quadrupole and quadrupole-quadrupole interactions are important in special cases, e.g., for H_2O. Methods of measuring Q include molecular beam radiofrequency resonance, microwave pressure broadening, collision-induced absorption, nuclear magnetic resonance, and second dielectric virial coefficients.

Empirical Potential Functions Enough has been said to indicate that the nature of the intermolecular forces is qualitatively well understood but that accurate quantitative results cannot be obtained from wave mechanics except in a few special cases. The most detailed information about the actual magnitudes of intermolecular forces is obtained by the empirical procedure of (1) choosing an intermolecular force law, with two or more adjustable constants, on the grounds of physical plausibility and mathematical convenience, (2) selecting a macroscopic property that can be accurately measured and accurately calculated from the force law assumed, and (3) using the results of measurements over a wide range of experimental

conditions to fix the values of the adjustable parameters in the force law. The most popular of the empirical potential functions has been the Lennard-Jones (12, 6) potential

$$u(r) = 4\epsilon \, [(\sigma/r)^{12} - (\sigma/r)^6], \qquad \epsilon \equiv -u(r_m).$$

Here σ and ϵ are the adjustable parameters. The 6th-power term represents the dispersion forces and the 12th-power term, the repulsive forces. The parameter ϵ is the maximum energy of attraction, and σ is the value of r for which $u(r)$, the potential function, is zero. Although mathematically convenient and still widely used, this pair potential is now known to have serious defects (e.g., its behavior at small r and at large r are both greatly in error) which preclude its use in accurate, realistic investigations. Other simple two-parameter and three-parameter potentials have been proposed but they are insufficiently flexible to be able to account for the results of increasingly accurate measurements of numerous physical properties extended over wide ranges of the experimental variables. As an example of the multiparameter potential functions which are currently employed (1972), we mention the so-called Morse–spline–van der Waals function which uses a Morse potential for the short-range interaction, a combination of r^{-6} and r^{-8} for the long-range interaction, and a spline interpolation formula to join the two segments. Even more elaborate functions are in current use, some containing as many as 12 adjustable parameters.

Experimental Methods The types of experimental measurements that can be used to derive information about intermolecular forces include the following: (1) thermodynamic properties of gases, (2) transport properties of gases, (3) equilibrium properties of solids and liquids, (4) molecular beam scattering cross sections, and (5) spectroscopic and x-ray diffraction data. Although much used in the past, the calculation of lattice energies, lattice distances, compressibilities, and elastic constants of solids from assumed pair potentials cannot be regarded as an accurate method of determining intermolecular pair potentials because of uncertainty with regard to the contributions from many-body interactions, i.e., from nonadditivity effects. The use of the radial distribution function $g(r)$ of a liquid, determined from x-ray and neutron diffraction experiments, in conjunction with the vapor pressure near the triple point, provides information about the pair potential, and one may also use $g(r)$ in combination with the isotopic separation factor in liquid-vapor equilibrium to test the repulsive region of the potential. The x-ray diffraction results for dense gases and liquids can be analyzed in terms of theories of dense fluids (e.g., Percus-Yevick) to deduce a numerical intermolecular potential. All of these liquid-state methods are subject to uncertainties with respect to nonadditivity effects.

Although the latter may be small, it is safer to

deduce the pair potentials from phenomena that involve only binary interactions. In this category are the second virial coefficients $B(T)$, the viscosity coefficients $\eta(T)$, and other gas transport properties. The values of $B(T)$ extending from high to low temperatures do not provide a sensitive test for assumed forms of the pair potential; even the square-well and $(12, 6)$ potentials give a good representation of $B(T)$ data. It is also possible to fit viscosity data over a wide temperature range with simple potential functions; former disagreements at high temperatures have recently been shown to have resulted from experimental errors. However, the parameters of the simple potentials that give the best fit to $B(T)$ measurements differ from those needed to fit the viscosity data. Other transport properties which provide useful information about the pair potential are the isotopic thermal-diffusion coefficient, the isotopic mutual-diffusion coefficient, and the thermal conductivity (of monatomic gases) for like-molecule interactions and the mutual-diffusion coefficient for unlike-molecule interactions.

The most direct method of investigating the force between two molecules is to measure the elastic-scattering differential and total cross sections at different energies. Molecular beams formed from neutralized accelerated ions may be used with stationary gas targets to determine the repulsive wall of the potential at high energies. In order to investigate the region of the potential near its minimum, it is necessary to employ energies close to thermal, and the motion of the target molecules then precludes the use of a single beam. Two molecular beams passing through velocity selectors and intersecting at right angles have been used but much greater intensity is available from crossing two supersonic nozzle beams. Differential elastic-scattering cross sections measured by the latter method, showing well-resolved rainbow structure and symmetry oscillations, have recently provided accurate potential functions for pairs of rare-gas atoms (Lee et al., 1972).

Molecular spectroscopy furnishes a precision tool for investigating the potential energy curves for different electronic states of diatomic molecules, but these interatomic potentials refer to intramolecular rather than intermolecular interactions and will not be further discussed. The pressure broadening of spectral lines and the phenomenon of collision-induced absorption, measured in the microwave and infrared regions of the spectrum, provide additional methods for studying intermolecular forces. These methods are not accurate but they have yielded useful information about molecular quadrupole moments. A recent and important spectroscopic method of determining the intermolecular potential near its minimum, which has been applied to Ar and Ne, is to measure the ultraviolet absorption bands that correspond to electronic transitions out of the ground state of the dimer (Ar_2 and Ne_2). The spectroscopic constants derived from the vibrational levels of the ground state provide accurate information about the bowl of the potential curve including the well depth (ϵ), the curvature at the minimum, and the anharmonicity (Tanaka and Yoshino, 1970, 1972). The best-known intermolecular potential, for the interaction between two Ar atoms, currently has an accuracy of about ±4 per cent in the well depth.

R. D. PRESENT

References

Hirschfelder, J. O., Curtiss, C. F., and Bird, R. B., "Molecular Theory of Gases and Liquids," New York, John Wiley & Sons, 1954.
Hirschfelder, J. O., Ed., "Intermolecular Forces," *Adv. Chem. Phys.*, 12 (1967).
"Intermolecular Forces," *Disc. Faraday Soc.*, 40 (1965).
Margenau, H., and Kestner, N. R., "Theory of Intermolecular Forces," Oxford, Pergamon Press, 1971.
Schlier, C., in Eyring, H., Ed., *Ann. Rev. Phys. Chem.*, 20, 191–218 (1969).

Cross-references: CRITICAL PHENOMENA, GAS LAWS, LIQUID STATE, MOLECULAR SPECTROSCOPY, SOLID-STATE PHYSICS.

INTERNATIONAL GEOPHYSICAL YEAR AND INTERNATIONAL YEARS OF THE QUIET SUN

It has been recognized for some time that the sun, ultimate source of practically all of the energy utilized on earth (the only current exception being the relatively small amount of power produced by nuclear fuels), influences many earthly phenomena. Aside from the obvious solar control of the weather through visible and invisible light—electromagnetic radiation—continuously emitted by the sun, other less well-understood effects occur. For example, the so-called earth storm (not to be confused with a weather disturbance near the ground) results from the arrival not only of radiation but also of matter—streams of electrically charged particles—spewed out by the sun following violent eruptions or flares in the chromosphere, just above the sun's "surface" (photosphere).

A multitude of geophysical effects arises from the interactions of these radiation and particle fluxes with the upper reaches of the earth's atmosphere, manifesting themselves as phenomena such as magnetic storms, radio disturbances, and auroral displays. The frequency of occurrence of these transitory happenings in the upper atmosphere waxes and wanes as the level of solar activity changes during the well-known sunspot cycle.

Taken together, the International Geophysical Year (IGY) and the International Years of the Quiet Sun (IQSY) marked the beginning and

end points of a tremendously significant study of the extremes of the solar cycle. The first part, IGY (1957–1958), took place at the peak of sunspot activity (it was not only peak for the average eleven-year cycle—but, in intensity, has probably not been matched at least since Galileo first observed sunspots in the early seventeenth century). IQSY (1964–1965) was the follow-up aimed at catching the myriad inter-related phenomena of sun, space, and earth at the sun's nadir of activity. But the latter enterprise was not a small-scale repetition of its illustrious predecessor. On the contrary, in the fields that it embraced, the level of the effort far exceeded that which it was possible to attain even as recently as seven years earlier. In a sense, IGY really set the stage for IQSY.

Scientific Objectives The broad objective of IGY was to study every aspect of the earth as a planet, including its environment. Consequently, in addition to investigating the properties of the earth's interior (seismology, latitude and longitude, and gravimetry) and studying its surface characteristics (oceanography and glaciology), the program embraced observations in and beyond the earth's atmosphere, including investigations of sun-earth relationships (meteorology, nuclear radiations, geomagnetism, ionosphere, aurora and airglow, cosmic rays, and solar activity). And, to increase basic knowledge about the solar influences acting upon the earth, IGY was planned to cover a period at or near solar maximum (see also GEOPHYSICS and SOLAR PHYSICS).

IGY was *not* the first international effort, however. There had been similar undertakings before: The First International Polar Year, 1882–1883, and the Second International Polar Year, 1932–1933. The recent enterprises are distinctive for other reasons; they involved the first extensive *in situ* probing of the earth's envelope, thanks to the extensive development of rockets, and, most recently, of spacecraft.

One motivation for IQSY was to utilize to the fullest extent the remarkable new technology and facilities, spawned by IGY, that had matured to a previously undreamed of stage of development. Not only were vehicles available for conducting highly sophisticated experiments in space, but other new techniques added new dimensions greatly extending the possibilities which existed even as recently as seven years before. Furthermore, logistic capabilities had materialized that made it feasible to carry out large-scale programs in crucial but previously inaccessible regions of the globe.

Antarctica, as a locale for research, deserves special mention. Not only is it important for studying upper atmosphere phenomena on a global scale, but it is vital in the conduct of all studies of upper atmosphere phenomena. The key to the preeminent role of the polar regions in the upper atmospheric research is the terrestrial magnetic field. Electrically-charged particles approaching the earth can, unless they are endowed with higher energies, arrive only near the geomagnetic poles. Consequently, the lower energy protons and heavier atomic nuclei that are sometimes produced by the sun can be observed only in these regions. Similarly, auroral effects, as well as other phenomena relating to magnetic lines of force that extend to very great distances from the earth's surface can be observed only near the geomagnetic poles.

The purpose of IQSY was threefold. Some of the studies that were conducted are feasible, or are best undertaken, only at the time of solar minimum. Others were concerned with observing in detail isolated solar events, uncomplicated by the superposition in time of a number of concurrent outbursts. Finally, some investigations provided data characteristic of solar minimum conditions for comparison with those obtained previously during solar maximum.

Actually, at sunspot minimum, solar outbursts do not cease completely, but when they do occur, their effects can be observed under relatively "clean" conditions, free from confusing interferences. Hence, the entire sequence of events associated with a single outburst can be followed. Furthermore, smaller effects, previously lost in the high-level background of activity, are discernible. Thus, many IQSY projects took advantage of this period to make observations with greatly increased "amplification."

The IQSY Program The IQSY program was organized in eight disciplines, although in most cases there were overlapping interests, and no sharp boundary line was drawn. The disciplines involved were the following:

Meteorology. The upper 10 per cent of the atmosphere was emphasized. This is the region in which solar influences are propagated to the lower atmosphere. Every available technique, including the use of rockets and satellites, was utilized for determining the meteorological parameters that are relevant to atmospheric energy transfer (see METEOROLOGY).

Geomagnetism. A detailed study of the earth's main magnetic field was conducted. Magnetic disturbances, which are related to many geophysical phenomena, were observed by an extensive network of ground-based observatories. Rockets and satellites also provided important information extending through the magnetosphere, the magnetopause (termination of the earth's magnetic field), and the transition region between the interplanetary and terrestrial fields (see GEOPHYSICS).

Aurora. Instrumentation carried aloft by balloons, rockets, and satellites was employed to determine the characteristics of aurora-producing particles and the mechanisms of particle acceleration and precipitation, supplementing studies based upon observations from the ground (see AURORA AND AIRGLOW).

Airglow. Airglow emissions yielded important information about the structure and chemical composition of the upper atmosphere. The geo-

corona, a ring of hydrogen that girds the earth and is detectable through the Lyman-α light that it emits, was of special importance because of its response to the flow past the earth of the solar wind (see AURORA AND AIRGLOW).

Ionospheric Physics and Radioastronomy. The ionosphere, well known because of its association with radio transmission, was probed by a variety of means both from above and below. Observations at conjugate points (opposite ends of a magnetic line of force) on the earth's surface were also made. Advantage was taken of the decreased opacity of the ionosphere for extending radioastronomical observations of galactic and extragalactic sources to lower frequencies, and radio emissions from the planets were also studied (see IONOSPHERE and RADIOASTRONOMY).

The Sun and the Interplanetary Medium. Constant surveillance of the sun was maintained to detect disturbances over a broad spectrum of wavelengths. Solar structure was investigated with new techniques, and magnetic fields originating at the sun and carried into space by the corpuscular radiation which constitutes the solar wind were measured directly. The interplanetary medium was probed both by direct and indirect methods (see SOLAR PHYSICS and SPACE PHYSICS).

Cosmic Rays and Geomagnetically Trapped Radiation. The lower energy cosmic rays, shielded by clouds of magnetized plasma emitted by the sun, can be observed only at solar minimum. Various characteristics of both the galactic cosmic rays, and of solar-produced particles, were investigated by a variety of means (see COSMIC RAYS and RADIATION BELTS).

Aeronomy. In situ measurements with rocket and satellite vehicles are adding to our knowledge of the physics and chemistry of the upper atmosphere. By obtaining a complete description during quiet conditions, a base line was provided for comparison with events occuring in association with solar disturbances (see PLANETARY ATMOSPHERES).

In the United States, a Committee of the National Academy of Sciences, the U.S. Committee for IQSY, was responsible for development of the program. The members were: R. G. Athay (solar activity), J. W. Chamberlain (aurora and airglow), H. Friedman (aeronomy), J. Kaplan (member-at-large), W. W. Kellogg (meteorology), P. Meyer (cosmic rays), H. Odishaw (ex officio), M. A. Pomerantz (chairman), E. Dyer (executive secretary), M. A. Tuve (ex officio), E. H. Vestine (geomagnetism), and A. H. Waynick (ionospheric physics). Within the government, the National Science Foundation was designated by the president as the responsible agency for coordinating and implementing the program, and for correlating regular activities of the government that related to the program. Robert Fleischer, of the Office of Atmospheric Sciences, was NSF coordinator for IQSY.

The Special Committee for IQSY, established by the International Council of Scientific Unions (ICSU), with a Secretariat in London, formulated and executed the detailed plans of this great cooperative venture in which scientists of seventy-one nations participated. The Bureau was comprised of the following members: W. J. G. Beynon, president; M. A. Pomerantz, N. V. Pushkov, and G. Righini, vice presidents; and C. M. Minnis, secretary.

Perhaps one of the most significant achievements of IQSY was the solidification of earthsun research into a new scientific discipline—solar-terrestrial physics. This still burgeoning field of research is the study of the sun and its emissions, of the interplanetary medium, of the earth's environment, and of their interactions.

The modus operandi of IQSY has continued to be employed in carrying out imaginative, interdisciplinary, and international research projects. Thus, when in 1966 the IQSY program was drawing to an orderly conclusion and its international organization was closing down, a new and continuing body, the Inter-Union Commission on Solar-Terrestrial Physics (IUCSTP) was established by ICSU to plan and coordinate future programs in solar-terrestrial physics. The IUCSTP Bureau consists of: Herbert Friedman, president; W. J. G. Beynon, J. G. Roederer, Z. Švestka, S. N. Vernov, N. V. Pushkov, and E. R. Dyer, Jr., secretary.

The period 1969–1971 was designated by IUCSTP as the International Years of the Active Sun (IASY), and the program comprised a number of individual interdisciplinary projects.

MARTIN A. POMERANTZ

References

1. "Annals of the IGY," New York, Pergamon Press, 1959.
2. "Annals of the IQSY," Massachusetts, M.I.T. Press, 1969.
3. Pomerantz, Martin A., "The IQSY and Solar-Terrestrial Research," *Proc. Nat. Acad. Sci.*, **58** 2136 (1967).

Cross-references: AURORA AND AIR GLOW, COSMIC RAYS, GEOPHYSICS, IONIZATION, IONOSPHERE, PLANETARY ATMOSPHERES, RADIATION BELTS, RADIO ASTRONOMY.

IONIZATION

Ionization is the name given to any process by which a net electrical charge may be imparted to an atom or group of atoms. In the case of liquid solvents, molecules or ionic salts become dissociated to form positive and negative ions. This ionization process is known as *electrolysis*, and the name *electrolyte* is given to the solute or to

the conducting solution. The study of electrolysis is embodied in the subject of *electrochemistry*. Of great interest in recent years has been the study of ionized gases. Rockets, hypersonic flight, and space physics have spurred investigations of plasmas, shock waves and high-temperature chemical processes arising in a variety of terrestrial and celestial phenomena. Indeed, ionized gases make up a major portion of all matter in the universe. Our chronic need for new energy sources has transformed the speculation of a controlled thermonuclear fusion reaction into one of the greatest research efforts in history. These and other considerations have induced a vigorous growth in the study of ionization phenomena.

Electrolytes The degree of ionization found in electrolytes is highly variable and depends upon the solute, the solvent, and the interaction between them. *Weak* electrolytes, such as many organic compounds, are solutes which are barely dissociated into ions except in the limit of infinite dilution. *Strong* electrolytes are highly dissociated at any concentration. Ions formed in solution may bear one or several electronic charges. The *electrochemical equivalent weight* is the atomic weight divided by the number of charges carried by the ion. If electrodes are placed in an electrolyte and a current flows in the external circuit, the ions with positive charges, called *cations* (cathode + ions), will migrate toward the negative electrode (cathode). Those ions possessing a negative charge (*anions*) will migrate to the positive electrode (anode). The ions arriving at the cathode are neutralized by the acquisition of electrons; the atoms or molecules thus formed may then be evolved as a gas or retained as a deposit on the electrode. The cations are said to undergo *reduction*. Likewise, the anions experience a loss of electrons at the anode; this process is called *oxidation*. The quantity of electricity required to deposit one gram equivalent is called the faraday, in honor of Michael Faraday (1791–1867). Based on the physical scale of atomic weights, the faraday is numerically equal to 96 520 coulombs per equivalent.

As for any solid conductor of uniform cross sectional area A and length l, the electrical resistance R of an electrolyte is given by $l/\kappa A$. The conductivity κ is independent of geometrical shape and size, and bears the units $(\text{ohm cm})^{-1}$. Of greater importance in the study of electrolytes is the *equivalent conductivity*:

$$\Lambda = \kappa/C$$

where C is the concentration of the solute in equivalents per cubic centimeter. Plots of Λ as a function of concentration show very different behavior for weak and strong electrolytes. The latter exhibit a limiting value of Λ as C diminishes to zero, while the weak electrolytes do not. Such behavior provides insight into the nature of the ions, their mobilities and their interactions with the solvent material.

Formation of Gaseous Ions Studies in 1895 by J. J. Thomson of the effects of newly discovered x-rays on gases marked the beginning of a series of experiments which established the existence of the electron and clarified many questions on the nature of atomic structure.

Just as in electrolytes, both positive and negative ions may exist in an ionized gas. In addition to the ions, the presence of free electrons may profoundly influence the character of the gas. Negative ions may be formed by the attachment of free electrons to a neutral atom or molecule, by the dissociation of a neutral molecule into positive and negative fragments, or by electron transfer upon collision of two neutral atoms or molecules. Positive ions may be formed by dissociation, charge transfer, neutral-particle or electron collisions, or by photoabsorption (the absorption of electromagnetic radiation). Still another mechanism for the formation of ions is the emission of a nuclear particle, such as beta decay. Several of these processes are discussed below.

Photoionization Photoabsorption leading to excitation and ionization is of interest because of its significance in astrophysics and geophysics. The ionosphere is constituted of molecular and atomic ions which result from the absorption of solar ultraviolet and x-radiation. The frequency ν of the electromagnetic radiation giving rise to ionization must satisfy the relation $h\nu \geqslant V$, where h is Planck's constant and V is the *ionization potential*. The latter is defined as the energy required to remove completely an electron from an atom or molecule in the ground state, leaving the resulting ion in its lowest state. Photons having energy less than V may be absorbed by atoms or molecules, giving rise to excitation of internal states or perhaps molecular dissociation, or both.

Many laboratory investigations of photoabsorption have been performed. One type of experiment requires the measurement of the absorption coefficient, α, of a photon beam:

$$I = I_0\, e^{-ax}$$

in which I_0 is the initial intensity of the beam and I is the intensity after the beam has traversed a distance x in the absorbing gas. The absorption coefficient may then be studied as a function of photon energy (i.e., wavelength). It can be expressed in terms of a microscopic cross section for absorption or for ionization as a function of incident wavelength. This cross section curve for photoionization usually exhibits a sharp peak at the ionization threshold. Only a single, outermost electron is ejected from an atom which absorbs an ultraviolet photon. An x-ray photon generally will eject a more tightly bound electron from one of the atom's inner shells.

Other types of experiments utilize photoionization to study the deionization process for the ions thus formed. Of major importance are such processes as electron-ion recombination:

$$A^+ + e^- \rightarrow A$$

and ion-ion recombination if both charged species are ions.

Ionization by Heavy-particle Collisions By heavy particles is meant both atoms and molecules and their ions, ranging in mass from the hydrogen atomic ion (proton) to very heavy molecular systems of large atomic number. When two heavy particles collide with sufficient energy, one or more electrons may be ejected from either or both particles. In experimental work, the *target* molecules or atoms are in the form of a low-density gas having an energy corresponding to room temperature and usually negligible compared to the energy of the projectile particles. The latter are usually obtained through ionization of a selected gas in an ion source, and acceleration through a large electric potential difference E. Regardless of the mass of projectile particles, their kinetic energy will be equal numerically to E electron volts, if the potential difference E is in volts and if the particles carry but one elementary charge. One electron volt (eV) is equal to 1.6×10^{-12} erg.

If a beam thus formed with an intensity of B particles per second is incident on a target chamber of area A containing N target particles as a low-density gas, the electron ionization current i which is released is given by

$$i = BN\sigma_-/A \text{ electrons/ sec.}$$

This equation defines the effective ionization cross section σ_-. For energies at which multiple ionization is improbable, σ_- approaches the cross section for singly charged ions. Often the distinction is made between ionization of the target particle and the beam particle. Ionization of the latter is referred to as stripping.

In the quantitative description of heavy-particle collisions, one usually introduces the concepts of the (a) laboratory and (b) center-of-mass (CM) coordinate systems. The laboratory system is used to describe the motion of the particles as would be viewed by an observer standing at rest in the laboratory. The origin of the CM system moves with the center-of-mass of the two-particle system. If m and M are the masses of the projectile and target particles, the former moving with a velocity v much greater than the target velocity, the center-of-mass velocity V_c is

$$V_c = mv/(m + M) = \mu v/M$$

The latter relation defines μ, the reduced mass. The kinetic energy in the CM system is $\frac{1}{2}\mu v^2$, which is the projectile energy multiplied by $M/(M + m)$. For the case in which target and projectile are identical, the kinetic energy in the CM system is half that of the projectile. Using the law of conservation of linear momentum, one may show that the kinetic energy in the CM system is the maximum energy available for excitation and/or ionization.

Collisions in general are classified as (a) elastic in which no changes in internal states occur, and for which kinetic energy is conserved, and (b) inelastic, in which a part of the kinetic energy is converted to internal energy. A *superelastic* collision is one in which internal energy is transformed into kinetic energy. Because of the extreme complexity encountered in quantum-theoretical calculations of ionization cross sections for heavy-particle collisions, very little progress has been made in this important area of collision theory.

Ion-neutral collisions may give rise to free electrons, or simply *charge exchange* which, in its simplest form, is expressed by the equation.

$$A^+ + B \rightarrow A + B^+ + \Delta E$$

The neutral particle B has been ionized, but the electron has transferred to the incident ion, neutralizing it. The energy ΔE released in this process is the difference between the ionization potentials of the neutral particles A and B. For the case in which A and B are identical, $\Delta E = 0$ and the process is called *symmetric resonant* charge transfer. At low ion beam energies, this transfer proceeds with a large cross section.

Ionization by Electron Impact Of great importance in atomic physics is the ionization produced by collimated beams of electrons incident on heavy particles. Whether the target particles are atoms or molecules, the ionization is usually by the removal of single electrons from the outer most shell, as in photoionization. As a function of the incident electron energy, the ionization cross section rises rapidly from zero for energies just below the ionization potential and increases to a maximum value in the neighborhood of 50 to 100 eV; thereafter it decreases slowly and monotonically with increasing electron energy. Since an electron with a given energy travels at much higher speed than does a heavy projectile of the same energy, the electron collision induces a much more rapid perturbation on the target's orbital electrons. Thus, a larger ionization cross section at low energies is to be anticipated.

Much of the definitive work on electron impact ionization was performed in the 1930's by Tate, Smith, and Bleakney (cf. reference 4).

Collective Processes If, as in a glow discharge, a large number of charged particles are created, the collective interactions of these particles with each other and with external fields may permit the charged fluid to exhibit very unusual and distinct properties. An ionized gas possessing both positive and negative charges is called a *plasma* if the distance over which the gas can have an appreciable departure from charge neutrality is small compared to the dimensions of the gas. This distance is described by the *Debye-Hückel radius*, a quantity borrowed from the theory of strong electrolytes, which characterizes the decay of the shielded Coulomb potential surrounding the ionized particles of the fluid. If the charge neutrality in a plasma is

disturbed in some manner, the electrons will be forced to oscillate about their equilibrium positions in simple harmonic motion with a frequency characterized by the electron density. Longitudinal oscillation of the ions and electrons as a whole constitutes another type of motion called *ion-acoustical* waves. *Hydro-magnetic* waves, which appear in the presence of a magnetic field are still another form of motion not observed in a nonionized medium. The description of such phenomena goes beyond the scope of the ionization process.

ROBERT C. AMME

References

1. Condon, E. U., and Odishaw, H., "Handbook of Physics," second edition, New York, McGraw-Hill Book Co., 1967.
2. Spitzer, L., "Physics of Fully Ionized Gases," Interscience Tracts on Physics and Astronomy, New York, Interscience Publishers, 1956.
3. Loeb, L. B., "Basic Processes of Gaseous Electronics," Berkeley, University of California Press, 1955.
4. McDaniel, E. W., "Collision Phenomena in Ionized Gases," New York, John Wiley & Sons, 1964.
5. Hasted, J. B., "Physics of Atomic Collisions," Washington D.C., Butterworth, 1964.

Cross-references: COLLISIONS OF PARTICLES, CROSS SECTIONS AND STOPPING POWER, ELECTRICAL DISCHARGES IN GASES, ELECTROCHEMISTRY, IONOSPHERE, MAGNETO-FLUID-MECHANICS, PLASMAS.

IONOSPHERE

The ionosphere is the gas of thermal, charged particles that forms a fraction of the earth's atmosphere above about 50 km altitude. Above about 90 km the ionosphere behaves as a partially ionized PLASMA. The restriction to thermal particles in the definition of the ionosphere distinguishes it from the RADIATION BELTS, which consist of energetic, charged particles. The ionosphere is also sometimes defined as "the part of the earth's upper atmosphere where ions and electrons are present in quantities sufficient to affect the propagation of radio waves." Indeed, the ionosphere is studied largely by its effect on radio waves, although *in situ* measurements from rockets and satellites have come to play a crucial role. This definition also emphasizes the practical importance of the ionosphere: it refracts and reflects radio waves and so makes possible beyond-the-horizon radio propagation. Other planets have ionospheres too, although our knowledge of them is still rudimentary.

The ionosphere is usually divided into four regions or layers which are called, from bottom to top, the D, E, and F regions, and the protonosphere. The F region is subdivided into the F1 and F2 layers. These regions or layers are more or less identifiable on a graph of electron concentration vs. height, but they are properly defined in terms of the processes by which they are formed, and not by the height ranges in which they lie. Nevertheless, their typical heights are useful. The lower limit of the D region is conventionally 50 km. The boundary between the D and E regions is at about 90 km; between the E and F regions, at 120 to 140 km; and between the F1 and F2 layers, at about 200 km. The height of the boundary between the F2 layer and the protonosphere is quite variable, depending primarily on the atmospheric temperature. The lowest height is about 500 km, observed during night at solar minimum. The height is larger during daytime, and it increases with increasing solar activity up to a greatest height of perhaps 3000 km. The outer limit of the protonosphere and the ionosphere is variable and not well-defined.

In the D region the positive ions are overwhelmingly NO^+ and O_2^+ above about 80 km and mostly water cluster ions, $H_3O^+ (H_2O)_n$, with some NO^+ below that height. The negative charge is carried by electrons during daytime and partly by negative ions at night. In all of the higher regions, the negative charge is carried almost entirely by electrons. In the E and F1 regions, the positive ions are mostly O_2^+ and NO^+; in the F2 layer, O^+; and in the protonosphere, H^+ (protons). Throughout, the ionosphere is very nearly electrically neutral, i.e., the total positive and negative charge concentrations are very nearly equal.

Typical values of the electron concentration at noon are: D region, 10^2 to 10^3; E and F1 regions, 10^5; F2 layer, 10^6; protonosphere, 10^4 to 10^3. At night the concentrations in all of the regions tend to be smaller; in the D and E regions, by a factor of 10. In all of the regions, the electron concentration has complex dependences on the time of day, season, latitude, and solar and geomagnetic activity. The variations of the F2 layer are particularly large and well-observed: its concentration ranges from 10^4 to 10^7 electrons/cm^3 under different conditions.

Superimposed upon the rather smooth ionization concentration of the ionospheric regions are many kinds of spatial irregularities, which are loosely grouped into "Sporadic E" in the E region and "Spread F" in the F region. Sporadic E is usually found in thin horizontal sheets. One of the commonest types consists of a slab only a few hundred meters thick and tens of kilometers in horizontal extent in which the electron density may be as much as a factor of ten larger than in the ambient E region. In the F region, on the other hand, the irregularities are filaments aligned along the lines of force of the earth's magnetic field. They are from a few meters to a few kilometers across and they extend along the field lines from the lower F2 region indefinitely upwards, even to the opposite hemisphere. The individual filaments appear to

be arranged in east-west sheets. The electron concentration in the F-region irregularities is usually no more than a few per cent greater or less than that in the ambient ionosphere.

The observational and theoretical understanding of these irregularities has proceeded rapidly in recent years, but semiquantitative theories exist only for two or three kinds of Sporadic E.

The charged particles which constitute the ionosphere are formed by ionization of the atoms and molecules of the ambient un-ionized atmosphere. Under geomagnetically quiet conditions, all of the regions except the lower D region are caused by solar photons in the extreme ultraviolet and x-ray part of the spectrum.

The quiet D region is formed by the ionization of NO—a trace in the atmosphere—by the solar Lyman-α line at 1216Å. The quiet E and F regions are formed by the ionization of all of the atmospheric constituents there, i.e., N_2, O_2, and O (which is formed from O_2 by photodissociation), by solar photons in different bands between about 10 and 1027Å. The electrons released by photoionization, with energies up to about 60 eV, thermalize by inelastic (ionizing and exciting) collisions with neutral gas atoms and molecules and by elastic collisions with ambient electrons. Excitation of neutral particles leads to optical emissions, called "airglow" (see AURORA AND AIRGLOW). Elastic collisions with ambient electrons raise the temperature of the electron gas by $\sim 10^3$ K. Part of the original energy ends as kinetic energy of the neutral gas. This is the main source of heat for the neutral atmosphere in the F region in low and middle latitudes.

The rate of ionization is occasionally considerably increased by several kinds of disturbances. The lower D region in the polar regions is enhanced during Polar Cap Absorption events by protons emitted by very large solar flares. Enhancements of the D, E, and F regions by ionization by fast electrons (called Auroral Absorption events) are frequent in the polar regions but occur at lower latitudes only during geomagnetic disturbances. The D, E, and F regions are also enhanced by solar photons emitted during solar flares; these enhancements are called Sudden Ionospheric Disturbances. Enhancements of ionization in the D region cause increased absorption of radio waves, with deleterious effects on radio communication.

The positive and negative charges eventually recombine to form neutral particles. However, some of the species of ions—especially the atomic ions—are more likely to undergo reactions which form other species of ions than they are to recombine with electrons. Thus, the protons in the protonosphere are lost by transferring their charge to O atoms to form O^+ ions. Since the ionization potentials of H and O are almost equal, this reaction can also proceed in the other direction to form H^+ from O^+. This is the principal source of ionization in the proton-osphere. In the F2 layer and below, the O^+ ions are lost by chemical reactions with N_2 and O_2 which form NO^+ and O_2^+. These molecular ions can then recombine with electrons by a process (dissociative recombination) about 10^5 times faster than the recombination of atomic ions (by radiative recombination). Also, in the D region the electrons can attach themselves to neutral particles to form negative ions, which can then either recombine with positive ions or be detached. The recombination reactions excite some of the ions and atoms, leading to more airglow.

Above about 200 km, i.e., in the F2 layer and the protonosphere, plasma transport plays an important role in determining the spatial and temporal distribution of ionization. The forces which cause this transport are primarily gravity, concentration gradients, electric fields, and winds. Above the peak of the F2 layer, at about 300 km, the ionospheric plasma tends to be in diffusive equilibrium, and the electron concentration decreases exponentially with height, with a logarithmic decrement which is proportional to the mass of the ions divided by the plasma temperature.

The complex variations of the electron concentration in the ionospheric regions are the results of the interplay among the processes of ionization, recombination, and transport, each of which itself has a complex dependence on time of day, season, latitude, solar and geomagnetic activity, etc. The construction of theoretical models of the ionosphere requires the identification and quantification of each of the physical processes. Under some conditions, e.g., the E and F regions in low and middle latitude, the success of current models indicates that all of the important physical processes have been included in the models, with correct magnitudes. Under other conditions, e.g., the D region and the high-latitude ionosphere, the models are still only partially successful, showing either that some processes are still unidentified or that the magnitudes of the known processes are incorrect.

T. E. VAN ZANDT

References

VanZandt, T. E., Cohen, R., and Reid, G. C., in Campbell, W. H., and Matsushita, S., Eds., "Physics of Geomagnetic Phenomena," New York, Academic Press, 1965.

Rishbeth, H., and Garriott, O. K., "Introduction to Ionospheric Physics," New York, Academic Press, 1969.

Cross-references: AURORA AND AIRGLOW, INTERNATIONAL GEOPHYSICAL YEAR AND INTERNATIONAL YEARS OF THE QUIET SUN, IONIZATION, PLANETARY ATMOSPHERES, PLASMAS, RADIATION BELTS, SPACE PHYSICS.

IRRADIATION, DISPLACED ATOMS

High-energy particles interact with the atoms of a solid in several ways and thereby produce disturbances in the atomic and electronic structure of the solid. The practical importance of such interactions is that many physical properties are very sensitive to the disturbances produced by radiation. Drastic changes, often deleterious and therefore referred to as radiation damage, may occur in such properties of practical importance as dimensional stability, mechanical and electrical properties, thermal conductivity, etc. The scientific importance of the field arises from the fact that the study of radiation effects leads to new and valuable insight into the properties of imperfections in solids. Irradiation with energetic particles has become a powerful tool of solid-state research, since a large number of imperfections can be introduced into a solid in a reasonably well-controlled manner.

The most important basic processes arising from the interaction of high-energy particles with solids may be classified as follows: (1) production of displaced and excited electrons, i.e., ionization; (2) production of displaced atoms by direct collision; and (3) production of fission and thermal spikes. In some cases transmutation effects also have to be taken into account. Attention is focused here on the production and nature of displaced atoms. Neglect of ionization is realistic for metals whose electrical conductivity is high, because in such metals any ionization is so rapidly neutralized that ionization effects are not observable. In insulators, ionization effects are of primary importance, and in semiconductors, both ionization effects and displacement production are important. Ionization effects are discussed under such entries as COLOR CENTERS, RADIATION CHEMISTRY; RADIATION, IONIZING, BASIC INTERACTIONS. Fission and thermal spikes, rather complex disturbances, are important in materials of high atomic number irradiated with massive particles but will not be further discussed here (see references 3 and 4).

If a bombarding particle makes an elastic collision with an atom and transfers to it an amount of energy larger than the displacement threshold energy (typically about 25 eV), the atom will be displaced from its lattice position. In most cases the displaced atom, or knock-on, has enough recoil energy to travel a few atomic distances from its initial position, either directly through the lattice or via a series of replacement collisions (see below), before coming to rest in an interstitial position. Thus, the fundamental displacement pair is produced: the displaced atom or interstitial, and the lattice site which was left empty, the vacancy. A complete theory of defect production at all energies is not yet at hand, but a great deal of insight can be obtained from theoretical dynamic studies at rather low energies made with high-speed computers. In Fig. 1 three important processes that occur during displacement production are illustrated. Atom A, the primary knock-on, is assumed to have been struck by a bombarding particle and to have been given an initial energy of 40 eV in the direction indicated by the arrow at A. The lines in this Figure are the paths followed by the individual particles. By subsequent collisions, an interstitial has been produced at location D and a vacancy left behind at position A. Replacement collisions have occurred at locations B and C, where atom A replaced atom B and, in turn, atom B replaced atom C. Focusing collisions, preferential propagation of energy along rows of close-packed atoms, are also clearly seen in the figure. At higher energies the focusing collisions transport matter as well as energy and thus create interstitial atoms, after a series of replacement collisions, at some distance from the original point of impact. The picture becomes considerably more complex at still higher energies. Thus, results of experiments involving irradiations with electrons or gamma rays in the few-MeV range are much easier to interpret than the more complex damage resulting from irradiation with neutrons (in a reactor) or with heavy charged particles.

The displacement process is clearly quite complex, and no complete quantitative theory has been formulated. The average number of displaced atoms can be estimated by means of a simple model based on binary collisions. Comparison with experiment shows rather good agreement in the case of metals irradiated with electrons. Upon heavy particle or reactor irradiation, the experimentally observed concentration of displaced atoms is less than that predicted by theory by a factor of 5 to 10. A rather crude, but convenient, number to remember is that in most metals one atomic per cent vacancy-interstitial pairs are produced by 10^{20} neutrons/cm^2 in a reactor exposure to fast (epithermal) neutrons.

A convenient and accurate measure of defect concentration is the low-temperature electrical resistivity, or residual resistivity, of a metal. Much of the fundamental information available has been obtained by this technique. Other physical property changes, however, are far more important from a practical standpoint. For example, metals generally harden considerably upon reactor irradiation. The increase in critical shear stress is usually accompanied by a reduction in ductility leading to increased brittleness. Such changes are intricate since they involve the interaction of the radiation-induced defects with static and moving dislocations, and a full interpretation of the experiments is not at hand. As another example, graphite exhibits a large increase in volume upon reactor irradiation. It is quite clear in this case that the radiation-induced interstitials lodge between the graphite planes and push these planes apart.

A very important fundamental and practical property of the radiation-induced defects is their

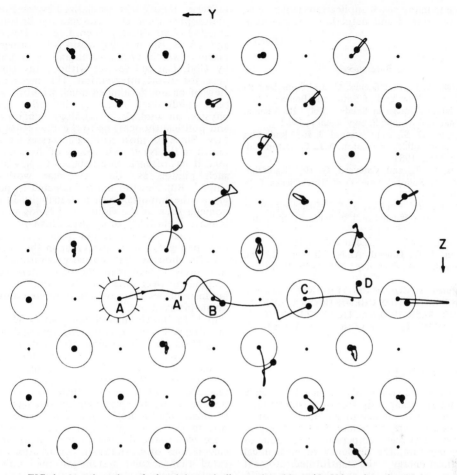

FIG. 1. Atomic paths, calculated dynamically, produced by a 40-eV knock-on in copper. The primary knock-on collision was at lattice position A (from reference 6).

mobility. The defects can migrate in the solid from one position to another by surmounting an energy barrier, i.e., their migration is characterized by an activation energy. Since an irradiated crystal is not in thermodynamic equilibrium, it will tend to revert to its stable unirradiated form at temperatures high enough for the defects to be mobile, i.e., the crystal can be annealed. The kinetics of the annealing process can be quite complex, since usually several competing processes are going on, such as vacancy-interstitial annihilation, defect migration to external and internal surfaces, defect aggregation, etc. From the fundamental standpoint, a great deal can be learned about the characteristics of the defects from detailed annealing experiments. The practical importance of annealing is that by raising the temperature undesirable radiation damage can be minimized. The situation is more complicated in alloys, since the migration of defects is equivalent to

diffusion, which may result in metallurgical changes. Indeed, radiation-enhanced diffusion, nucleation, precipitation, and phase transformation have been observed.

Ionic crystals are discussed elsewhere. In semiconductors, the fundamental displacement process is very similar to the one already described. However, the radiation-induced defects in semiconductors have localized energy states associated with them which alter the concentration and mobility of charge carriers and thereby lead to drastic and important changes in the electronic properties. Some of the defect energy states are occupied by electrons and are therefore donors, while others are vacant and act as acceptors. In some semiconducting crystals, the radiation-induced changes go very far indeed. For example, germanium and gallium antimonide are converted from n-type to p-type upon irradiation. The sensitivity of semiconductor devices to radiation is of great practical im-

portance in many space applications (solar cells, electronic control and detection devices, etc.).

G. J. DIENES

References

1. Damask, A. C., and Dienes, G. J., "Point Defects in Metals," New York, Gordon and Breach, 1963.
2. "Radiation Damage in Solids," Vol, I-III, Vienna, International Atomic Energy Agency, 1962.
3. Billington, D. S., and Crawford, J. H., "Radiation Damage in Solids," Princeton, N.J., Princeton University Press, 1961.
4. Dienes, G. J., and Vineyard, G. H., "Radiation Effects in Solids," New York, Interscience Publishers, 1957.
5. Seitz, F., and Koehler, J. S., "Displacement of Atoms During Irradiation", in Seitz, F., and Turnbull, D., Eds., "Solid State Physics", Vol. II, pp. 307–449, New York, Academic Press, 1956.
6. Gibson, J. B., Goland, A. N., Milgram, M., and Vineyard, G. H., *Phys. Rev.*, **120**, 1229 (1960).

Cross-references: COLOR CENTERS; NUCLEAR REACTIONS; RADIATION CHEMISTRY; RADIATION, IONIZING, BASIC INTERACTIONS; SEMICONDUCTORS; SOLID-STATE PHYSICS; SOLID-STATE THEORY.

IRREVERSIBILITY

Physical systems commonly display a tendency to change spontaneously from one state to another, but not to change in the opposite direction. Examples are the tendency of heat to pass from regions of high temperature to regions of low temperature, the tendency of mechanical or electrical energy to be transformed into heat by friction or resistance, and the mixing or diffusion of different substances. While irreversibility appears to be an obvious feature of macroscopic natural phenomena, so much so that violations of this tendency are scarcely conceivable, it is not yet established whether it should be considered a general law applicable on both the atomic and the cosmological scales. Most physicists accept the "statistical" explanation of irreversibility, according to which complex systems with many degrees of freedom tend to spread out among more and more diverse states in the "phase space" of possible configurations (see STATISTICAL MECHANICS). Scientific discussions of this question go back to the time of Newton and continue up to the present day. A brief review of these earlier discussions is necessary in order to illustrate how the problem of irreversibility is related to our general view of the world. We shall be concerned here mainly with the qualitative aspects of irreversibility as distinct from quantitative theories of particular processes (see, e.g., the articles on DIFFUSION, HEAT TRANSFER, THERMOELECTRICITY, and VISCOSITY).

In the seventeenth century, the "clockwork universe" theory was popularized by the French philosopher René Descartes and the British scientist Robert Boyle. According to Descartes and Boyle, the physical world is like a perfect machine which, once created and set in motion by God, can run forever without any further need for divine intervention. This mechanistic view of nature dominated much scientific work (and conditioned many of the influences of physics on biology, psychology, philosophy, and political thought) up to the nineteenth century. Since its most striking successes were attained in the Newtonian theory of the solar system, it has often been attributed to Newton in such phrases as "the Newtonian world-machine." But Newton himself rejected it, pointing to the importance of irreversibility in phenomena such as the viscosity of fluids and the imperfect elasticity of solids; in his *Opticks* he stated that "motion is much more apt to be lost than got, and is always upon the decay." He also thought that mutual gravitational perturbations of planets in the solar system would accumulate over long periods of time, producing instabilities that could be corrected only by divine intervention.

In 1715 the German philosopher G. W. Leibniz attacked Newton's opinion, arguing that the suggestion that "God almighty needs to wind up his watch from time to time; otherwise it would cease to move" (as Leibniz put it) was a slur on God's ability to make a perfect world-machine. Newton retorted that the clockwork metaphor was too materialistic, and was likely to encourage the notion that God has no active role in the world at all. Newton's suspicions were well-founded; later improvements on his calculations of gravitational perturbations indicated that a solar system governed only by Newton's laws is stable, so that all changes in planetary orbits merely oscillate between fixed limits. Thus when Napoleon asked the French mathematician P. S. de Laplace why he had not mentioned God in his treatise on celestial mechanics, Laplace could reply: "Sir, I have no need of that hypothesis."

When Newton asserted that motion tends to be lost in processes such as friction or inelastic collisions, he was refusing to accept the suggestion (already well-known at that time) that it is simply transformed into invisible molecular motion, perceptible only as heat. The modern concept of irreversibility is different from Newton's because it involves a *dissipation* but not a *destruction* of energy. One might therefore expect that the modern theory of irreversibility could be established only after the law of conservation of energy had been accepted (around 1850); in a sense this is true, but it is somewhat misleading historically, as we shall see.

In 1852 the British physicist William Thomson (later known as Lord Kelvin) published a short paper, "On a Universal Tendency in Nature to the Dissipation of Mechanical Energy." The immediate stimulus for this pronounce-

ment was Thomson's reflections on the consequences of Carnot's theory of steam engines, which he and the German physicist Rudolf Clausius had recently used as a basis for the second law of thermodynamics. In formulating the second law, Clausius and Thomson argued that it must be impossible to transfer heat from a cold body to a warm body without some kind of compensating process equivalent to the transfer of at least the same amount of heat in the opposite direction; or, as Thomson phrased it, it is impossible to obtain mechanical work by cooling a body below the temperature of its surroundings. But these "impossibility" or "impotency" statements of the second law were closely associated with the conviction that the forbidden processes were forbidden because they contravened a *natural tendency* for heat to flow from high temperatures to low. Thus, in the development of theories of energy dissipation, the simple flow of heat from hot to cold was the first irreversible process to be recognized; other processes were subsequently said to be irreversible, in part because they were equivalent or analogous to the equalization of temperature differences.

Although Thomson's explicit statement of the principle of dissipation of energy occurred in a thermodynamic context involving transformations of heat and mechanical work, it is evident from his own writings that he was equally concerned with an irreversible process that involved no change in the total quantity of heat: namely, the cooling of the earth from a hypothetical initial molten state to its present state (moderate surface temperature with residual internal heat), ultimately reaching the desolate cold of interplanetary space. This was the predicted "heat death" of the earth (and perhaps of the entire universe) that attracted the attention of popular science writers in the late nineteenth century, and was publicized further by the British astrophysicists J. H. Jeans and A. S. Eddington in the 1920s. But Thomson was not the first to discuss the cooling of the earth; indeed, this had been a favorite topic of debate among scientists in the eighteenth and early nineteenth centuries, and provided the occasion for several assertions that there is a natural tendency for heat to flow from hot to cold. Even the threat of a heat death as a fate common to all bodies in the universe had been hinted as early as 1777 by the French astronomer Jean-Sylvain Bailly. Fourier's theory of heat conduction (whose development was motivated in part by the problem of terrestrial temperatures) was the first major physical theory in modern times to incorporate irreversibility in its basic postulates.

With the advent of thermodynamics in the 1850s, the concept of irreversibility could be extended to processes involving transformations among different forms of energy. Thomson's use of the word "dissipation" introduced a moral connotation based on the observation that whenever heat flows through a finite temperature difference a certain amount of mechanical work *could* be obtained by appropriate use of a heat engine; the maximum work is obtained when each temperature difference in the cycle of operations is made infinitesimally small so that the direction of heat flow could be reversed by a slight alteration of the temperatures (see CARNOT CYCLES AND CARNOT ENGINES). Whenever that is not done, heat flows irreversibly and the chance of doing mechanical work has been missed, hence the energy involved has been "dissipated."

In 1854, Clausius formulated his thermodynamic theory in terms of the "equivalence-value of a transformation," defined as the amount of heat transferred at a certain temperature divided by that temperature. For a cyclic process the total equivalence-value would be determined by an integral over the path of this ratio,

$$\int \frac{dQ}{T}.$$

For a reversible process the value of this integral would be zero, according to Clausius's statement of the second law; whereas for an irreversible process it would be positive. Since this particular mathematical expression proved to be useful in developing his theory, Clausius finally gave it the name *entropy* in 1865; more precisely, the *change* in entropy in a process is defined as

$$dS = dQ/T.$$

Thus entropy provided an indicator of irreversibility, and Clausius could state the second law in the generalized form, "the entropy of the world tends toward a maximum." It is in this form, or simply the phrase "entropy tends to increase," that the principle of irreversibility or principle of dissipation of energy is now ordinarily stated. Eddington asserted that this principle "holds the supreme position among the laws of Nature" because it determines the direction of time itself—"time's arrow."

Although one could simply accept the principle of irreversible entropy increase as a fundamental law of physics without further explanation (as is sometimes done in texts on thermodynamics), there is widespread sentiment among scientists that it must be possible to reduce the law to a more basic postulate about atomic behavior (or about the universe as a whole). This reduction seemed an urgent necessity for those physicists in the nineteenth century who believed that all properties of matter and energy were ultimately explicable by mechanical models, using Newton's laws of motion. Since the kinetic theory of gases was being developed during the same period when entropy was being introduced into thermodynamics, that theory offered a natural starting point.

The following conclusions were reached as a result of analyses by Thomson, James Clerk Maxwell, and Ludwig Boltzmann (see KINETIC THEORY):

(1) It is reasonable to assume that the principle of irreversibility is *not* an absolute law of nature and that all processes involving individual atoms are perfectly reversible, since Newton's second law of motion is unchanged when $-t$ is substituted for t, and there is no direct evidence that interatomic forces are dissipative. In that case irreversibility can appear only when large numbers of atoms are involved, and is connected with the fact that observable macroscopic states (specified by parameters such as temperature and pressure) of a system correspond in general to enormously large collections of microscopic states, the latter being specified by values of the positions and velocities of all the atoms. In a typical irreversible process, a system passes from macroscopic state A corresponding to a small number of microscopic states, to another macroscopic state B corresponding to a much larger number of microscopic states. The process could be reversed only if there were some way to pick out the special microscopic states in B that had evolved from microscopic states in A, and then to reverse the directions of all atomic velocities.

(2) In this view irreversibility is a *statistical* property, which appears to be a general law of nature only because the probability of reversal (e.g., the probability that entropy will spontaneously decrease) is extremely small. There is some room for philosophical or methodological debate as to whether a statement that is always true in practice but *may* be wrong once in a billion years "in principle" (according to a theory of atomic behavior) should be considered a law of nature.

(3) The use of statistical terminology in explaining the principle of irreversibility nevertheless suggested that this principle may depend on *randomness at the atomic level*. In 1894, S. H. Burbury pointed out that the proof of Boltzmann's "H theorem" involved the assumption that two colliding molecules are uncorrelated *after* as well as *before* they collide, and argued that this assumption could be justified if the system were subjected to continuous random external disturbance. Boltzmann, and later Max Planck, agreed that such an assumption could be used to derive irreversibility. Yet it was not until the advent of quantum mechanics in the 1920s that most scientists were ready to accept the idea that atomic behavior may involve an inherent element of randomness or indeterminacy. While the late-nineteenth-century debates on irreversibility thus foreshadowed the breakdown of determinism in physics, it has not yet been established that irreversibility should be attributed to atomic randomness.

The statistical theory developed by Maxwell, Thomson, and Boltzmann achieved a substantial clarification by describing irreversible processes in terms of the *mixing* of atoms with different properties; the flow of heat, or the transformation of mechanical energy into heat, can be seen as special cases in which the relevant atomic property is velocity. Thus entropy increases whenever one goes from an ordered state to a disordered state, and entropy itself can be regarded as a measure of disorder. That terminology also suggests that entropy is a measure of the amount of *information* (or rather *lack* of information) which we have about the system (see ENTROPY). An extreme interpretation based on this idea is that irreversibility is not an inherent property of physical systems but is merely a necessary feature of any human description of them.

There have been numerous attempts to construct or imagine devices that would permit a violation of the second law of thermodynamics, i.e., to accomplish "perpetual motion of the second kind" by arranging for heat to flow from cold to hot regions, or by extracting mechanical work from an isothermal heat reservoir. Brownian movement has sometimes been considered an example of the latter kind. Nevertheless there are no generally accepted instances of violations of irreversibility. On the other hand, scientists hesitate to accept the view of Clausius that irreversible entropy increase leads to a final state in which "no further change could evermore take place, and the universe would be in a state of unchanging death."

In addition to the statistical explanation of irreversibility, there have been attempts to discover violations of "time-reversal invariance" in the interactions of elementary particles (see PARITY) and to associate the "direction of time" with the expansion of the universe (see the article by Gal-Or cited below). The biological significance of irreversibility is suggested by the title of Harold Blum's classic monograph, *Time's Arrow and Evolution*. The persistent philosophical interest in the nature of time ensures that debates about irreversibility will continue to enliven discussions of the foundations of physics for many years to come.

STEPHEN G. BRUSH

References

Brush, S. G., "Kinetic Theory," vol. 2, "Irreversible Processes," New York, Pergamon Press, 1966 (includes reprints and translations of papers by Maxwell, Boltzmann, Thomson, Poincaré, and Zermelo).

Brush, S. G., "Thermodynamics and History," *Graduate Journal*, 7, 477 (1967).

Brush, S. G., "The Development of the Kinetic Theory of Gases. VIII. Randomness and Irreversibility," *Archive for History of Exact Sciences* (in press).

Eddington, A. S., "The Nature of the Physical World," London, Cambridge University Press, 1928, Chapter IV.

Fraser, J. T., Haber, F. C., and Müller, G. H., eds., "The Study of Time," New York, Springer-Verlag, 1972.

Gal-Or, B., "The Crisis about the Origin of Irreversibility and Time Anisotropy," *Science*, **176**, 11 (1972). (This review includes references to many earlier works.)

Kubrin, D., "Newton and the Cyclical Cosmos: Providence and the Mechanical Philosophy," *Journal of the History of Ideas*, **28**, 325 (1967).

Reichenbach, H., "The Direction of Time," Berkeley, University of California Press, 1956.

Schlegel, R., "Time and the Physical World," New York, Dover Publications, 1968.

Cross-references: CARNOT CYCLES AND CARNOT ENGINES, DIFFUSION, ENTROPY, HEAT TRANSFER, KINETIC THEORY, PARITY, THERMODYNAMICS, THERMOELECTRICITY, VISCOSITY.

ISOSPIN*

Isospin (also called isobaric spin and isotopic spin) is an attribute ascribed to particles in a mathematical formalism introduced to simplify calculations involving the interactions among protons and neutrons through nuclear forces. In the isospin formalism, the neutron and proton are treated as though they were two different quantum-mechanical states of the same entity, the nucleon. A neutron, then, is distinguished from a proton by the value of its isospin projection quantum number, t_z: the value $t_z = \frac{1}{2}$ is assigned to the neutron and $t_z = -\frac{1}{2}$ to the proton. (This convention is common in nuclear structure literature, but the opposite assignments for t_z are sometimes found.)

The idea of using such a formalism for treating neutrons and protons was first suggested by Heisenberg,[1] who used the Pauli spin matrices to represent the property that we call isospin. Wigner[2] later named the concept "isotopic spin." Subsequent authors pointed out that the property, when extended to nuclei, is relevant not to isotopes but to nuclei with the same mass, hence the name isobaric spin replaced isotopic spin. In recent literature the name has been shortened to isospin. In spite of the name, the concept has nothing to do with mechanical angular momentum. (See MATHEMATICAL PRINCIPLES OF QUANTUM MECHANICS for a discussion of quantum-mechanical angular momentum).

The mathematical apparatus of the isospin formalism belongs to the general subject of group theory and is identical to that used for treating electron spin in atomic physics (see ELECTRON SPIN). Four quantum-mechanical operators, t_z, t^+, t^- and t^2, constitute the basic elements of the formalism. The number t_z that distinguishes neutrons from protons is the eigenvalue of the operator t_z, analogous to the operator s_z that gives the projection of the electron

*Research sponsored by the U.S. Atomic Energy Commission under contract with Union Carbide Corporation.

spin on the quantum axis. The operator t^+ operating on the representation of a proton changes it into the representation of a neutron, and t^- changes the representation of a neutron into that of a proton. The effects of these operators can be written symbolically as

$$t_z R(p) = -\tfrac{1}{2} R(p); \quad t_z R(n) = \tfrac{1}{2} R(n)$$

$$t^+ R(p) = R(n); \quad t^- R(n) = R(p)$$

$$t^+ R(n) = 0; \quad t^- R(p) = 0.$$

The letter R is used to indicate a representation of the entity specified in the parentheses. The representation can be a matrix, a wave function, a diagram, or any other representation appropriate to the method being employed in the calculation. The operator t^2 is related to the other operators by the equation $t^2 = \frac{1}{2}(t^+ t^- + t^- t^+) + t_z^2$. (Note that t^+ and t^- do not commute. Therefore $t^+ t^-$ does not equal $t^- t^+$.) For the case of the nucleon, where we have set up the defining equations to include only two states, t^2 has the eigenvalue $\frac{3}{4}$. More generally, if the formalism is applied to other kinds of particles, t^2 has eigenvalues of the form $t(t + 1)$, where t is either a half-integral or an integral number, and $2t + 1$ is the number of possible states. The value of t is called the isospin of the particle. Thus, it may be said that the nucleon is a particle of isospin $\frac{1}{2}$.

At the time Heisenberg introduced this method of manipulating neutron and proton representations it might well have looked like a contrived device of questionable utility. However, later in the 1930s, as evidence began to mount that the forces between nucleons were the same whether they were protons or neutrons except for the additional electrical repulsion between protons, the concept of isospin gained in apparent utility. Eventually the formalism evolved into something that could be applied to aggregate systems of neutrons and protons, i.e., to nuclei.

To gain insight into the rationale behind applying the concept of isospin to nuclei, one might note that part of the evidence for the charge independence of the nuclear force came from a study of the energy-level structure for mirror nuclei. Mirror nuclei are related to each other by an interchange of their neutron and proton numbers. For example, the nuclei ^{7}Li (3 protons and 4 neutrons) and ^{7}Be (4 protons and 3 neutrons) are a mirror pair and their energy levels accurately match each other except for an overall displacement. This correspondence suggests that it might be useful to view ^{7}Li and ^{7}Be, for example, as though one were related to the other as the neutron is related to the proton. The concept of total isospin in a many-nucleon system is defined in a way that is consistent with the single-nucleon formalism and gives meaning to statements of the type $T^+ R(^7Be) = R(^7Li)$. The concept of total isospin together with a structure model can provide the relationship between the isospin of the nucleus and the

arrangement of the constituent nucleons in the nucleus.

In the nuclear shell model, for example, one pictures the nucleus as though it contains a set of single-particle quantum states that result from the sum of the interactions among the nucleons. The different energy levels of the nucleus are then pictured as different combinations of occupancy by the nucleons of the available single-particle states. The similarity of level structure for mirror nuclei suggests that similar sets of single-particle states exist for protons and neutrons.

In an isospin formalism each single-particle state occurs twice, once with $t_z = \frac{1}{2}$ and once with $t_z = -\frac{1}{2}$, and the states are occupied by nucleons. We can define a set of total isospin operators for the aggregate system as follows: The total isospin projection operator $\mathbf{T}_z$ is the sum of the individual nucleon isospin projection operators, $\mathbf{T}_z = \Sigma_i t_z$. To find its eigenvalue we need only to sum the isospin projection quantum numbers for all the occupied states. We find that the eigenvalue of $\mathbf{T}_z$ is $T_z = \frac{1}{2}(N-Z)$, where N is the number of neutrons and Z the number of protons in the nucleus. We can also define total operators corresponding to the other single-nucleon operators that were discussed previously:

$$\mathbf{T}^+ = \Sigma t^+; \quad \mathbf{T}^- = \Sigma t^-;$$

$$\mathbf{T}^2 = \frac{1}{2}(\mathbf{T}^+\mathbf{T}^- + \mathbf{T}^-\mathbf{T}^+) + \mathbf{T}_z{}^2 .$$

The operator $\mathbf{T}^+$ when applied to a representation of a many-nucleon system changes it to a representation with $T_z + 1$, if T_z is the original value. Similarly $\mathbf{T}^-$ changes the representation to a new one with T_z-1. (Certain numerical factors have been omitted for simplicity. Refer to a textbook on quantum mechanics for a more complete treatment of raising and lowering operators.) The operator $\mathbf{T}^2$ has eigenvalues of the form $T(T+1)$, where T is a number that is referred to as the total isospin of the system. (For a definition of eigenvalue see MATHEMATICAL PRINCIPLES OF QUANTUM MECHANICS). T is always greater than or equal to the absolute value of T_z and is an integer for nuclei with an even number of nucleons and a half-integer for nuclei with an odd number of nucleons. An arbitrary representation of a many-nucleon system is not necessarily an eigenfunction of $\mathbf{T}^2$, but it can be reexpressed as a linear combination of representations that are eignefunctions of $\mathbf{T}^2$.

Before the 1960s the concept of total isospin was used in formal classifications of shell model states, but it was not generally believed that the simple eigenfunctions of $\mathbf{T}^2$ would provide useful descriptions of real nuclear states except with respect to mirror nuclei and very light nuclei. It was thought that in a nucleus with a large number of protons the Coulomb force would be strong enough to destroy the approximate symmetry between the proton and neutron states and isospin would not be a useful concept.

The discovery of isobaric analog states [3] gave isospin a new importance in nuclear structure physics. Analog states are energy levels of one nucleus that have a special relationship to energy levels in the neighboring nucleus with the same number of nucleons. If we compare the energy levels of a nucleus A(N,Z) with N neutrons and Z protons, to the energy levels of a nucleus B($N-1, Z+1$), we find in B a set of levels at high excitation energies that match one for one the lowest few levels of A with respect to energy spacing and other properties.

In terms of isospin, analog states can be understood as states that differ only in their isospin projection, T_z. That is, all quantum numbers except T_z of the state in nucleus A are the same as those of its analog in B. The ground state of a stable nucleus with more neutrons than protons is always characterized by $T = T_z = (N-Z)/2$. Its analog is characterized by the same value of T, but T_z is one unit lower; i.e., $T_z = T-1$. That state may in turn have an analog in its neighboring isobar with $T_z = T-2$, and so on until $T_z = -T$. States in mirror nuclei are simply analog states with T_z (for nucleus A) $= -T_z$ (for nucleus B).

The binding energy of an analog state differs from that of its parent state, and the energy difference is called the Coulomb displacement energy. The approximate value of this energy can be calculated in a rather simple way, if one assumes that the nuclear volume is filled with a uniform charge density. Since both parent and analog nuclei have the same number of nucleons, the volumes are the same. For the parent nucleus, the fraction $Z/(N+Z)$ of the nucleons are charged, while for the analog, $(Z+1)/(N+Z)$ of the nucleons are charged. The value of the Coulomb displacement energy is approximately the difference in the electrostatic energy for spherical volumes of charge densities implied by those two charge fractions. This has the value of about 12 MeV for nuclei of about 100 atomic mass units, for example. In spite of large differences in absolute binding energies, the analog level spacings match those of the parent accurately for nuclei of all masses that have been studied. It thus appears that the similarity between neutron and proton single-particle states persists even when the Coulomb force produces a large change in the absolute binding energies of the states.

Isospin considerations can be a guide to certain features of nuclear reactions. For example, a rule of conservation of isospin may be formulated in analogy with the principle of conservation of angular momentum. The rule states that if the initial system—the projectile plus the target—can be characterized by total isospin quantum numbers T and T_z, then the final system will also be characterized by the same values of T and T_z. The conservation of T_z is equivalent to the statement that the total number of protons and the total number of neutrons does not change in a nuclear reaction. The conservation of T implies restrictions on

the rearrangements of the nucleons within the nuclei but is not a very strict rule, since it is based on neglect of the Coulomb force between protons. It has been shown, however, that processes that violate the rule are severely inhibited compared to processes that follow the rule. Some broader implications of isospin conservation have been pointed out by Adair.[4]

Elementary particles other than nucleons also occur in groups with members that are very nearly identical except for their electrical charges. The concept of isospin is used also in the classification of those particles. (See ELEMENTARY PARTICLES.)

C. D. GOODMAN

References

1. Heisenberg, W., *Z. Physik*, 77, 1–11 (1932).
2. Wigner, E., *Phys. Rev.*, 51, 106–119 (1937).
3. Anderson, J. D., Wong, C., and McClure, J. W., *Phys. Rev.*, 126, 2170–2173 (1962).
4. Adair, R. K., *Phys. Rev.*, 87, 1041–1043 (1952).

For additional reading see:
   "Isospin in Nuclear Physics," Wilkinson, D. H., ed., Amsterdam, North-Holland Publishing Co., 1969.

Cross-references: ELECTRON SPIN, ELEMENTARY PARTICLES, MANY-BODY PROBLEM, MATHEMATICAL PRINCIPLES OF QUANTUM MECHANICS, MATRIX MECHANICS, NEUTRON, NUCLEAR STRUCTURE, PROTON, STRONG INTERACTIONS.

ISOTOPES*

The word "isotopes," stemming from the Greek words *isos* (same) and *topos* (place), refers to atoms of an element which have differing masses. The term was first proposed by Soddy in 1913 to designate substances having different atomic weights and yet having chemical properties which were so closely allied that no chemical method was effective in producing a separation. Hence, Soddy suggested that they were chemically identical; i.e., they occupied the same place in the periodic table. In 1905, Boldwood noted the presence of lead in uranium minerals and suggested that this might be the end product of the uranium series. As a result of the study of the relation of lead to uranium in a large number of minerals, this view was generally adopted. Soddy concluded that the end products of the uranium and thorium series should be lead with isotopic weights of 206 and 208, respectively, whereas ordinary lead has an atomic weight of 207.2. Soddy and Hyman reported in 1914 that the atomic weight of lead as found in thorite (consisting mainly of thorium, 1 to 2 per cent uranium, and 0.4

*Research sponsored by U.S. Atomic Energy Commission under contract with Union Carbide Corporation.

per cent lead) indeed had a slightly greater atomic weight than that of ordinary lead.

Some elements, such as sodium and cobalt, are mononuclidic; i.e., all of the natural stable atoms have the same mass. Others have many natural stable isotopes, as for example, tin, which is made up of atoms of ten different masses as it occurs in nature. Since the atoms in multinuclidic elements are chemically identical and have the same number of protons in the nucleus, the varying masses are accounted for by the variable number of neutrons in the nucleus. Table 1 lists in order of increasing atomic number Z (the charge or number of protons associated with the nucleus) the 105 known elements and, where available, the relative atomic weights.

Isotopes are divided into two groups: stable and radioactive (unstable). The total known isotopes number about 1850, of which 280 are stable and the balance are radioactive, having a transient existence ranging from millionths of a second to millions of years. Radioisotopes undergo transformation, or decay, emitting alpha, beta, gamma, or x-radiations during their return to a stable condition. Elements beyond bismuth ($Z = 83$) are radioactive (see RADIOACTIVITY).

Isotopes, both stable and radioactive, have grown in importance to science and technology in the last 40 years. Since atoms can be marked by their radioactivity, or in some cases by an atypical isotopic composition, the elements can be traced, a procedure of great value in physical and biological science, technology, and medical diagnosis. Further, radioisotopes emit corpuscular and/or electromagnetic radiations that can be used to probe into and through matter, affect it chemically and physically, produce heat and light, kill micro-organisms, and perform many other tasks of benefit in today's complex industrial society.

Stable Isotopes By 1900, physicists had found that positively charged particles formed by the passage of an electric discharge through an evacuated tube consisted of molecular ions of the gas present in the tube. Deflection of these positive rays by electric and magnetic fields offered a sensitive tool for the study of gaseous elements. By allowing the rays from a given element to fall on a photographic plate, a series of parabolic streaks was observed, each corresponding to a definite value of mass-to-charge ratio (m/e). Positive-ray photographs of neon (atomic weight 20.2) obtained by Thomson exhibited a heavy neon line at mass 20 and a faint line at 22. In an effort to elucidate the situation, Thomson's assistant, Aston, passed neon gas through a porous pipe-clay tube repeatedly and was able to show a significant alteration in the atomic weight of the two extreme fractions. This alteration was reflected in changes in the relative brightness of the two lines in subsequent positive-ray analyses.

Aston proceeded to redesign the positive-ray apparatus so that the particles having the same mass were brought to a focus to produce a

TABLE 1. TABLE OF RELATIVE ATOMIC WEIGHTS (1969) BASED ON THE ATOMIC MASS OF ^{12}C-12 ORDER OF ATOMIC NUMBER

Atomic Number	Name	Symbol	Atomic Weight	Atomic Number	Name	Symbol	Atomic Weight
1	Hydrogen	H	1.008	54	Xenon	Xe	131.30
2	Helium	He	4.00260	55	Cesium	Cs	132.9055
3	Lithium	Li	6.941	56	Barium	Ba	137.3
4	Beryllium	Be	9.01218	57	Lanthanum	La	138.905
5	Boron	B	10.81	58	Cerium	Ce	140.12
6	Carbon	C	12.011	59	Praseodymium	Pr	140.9077
7	Nitrogen	N	14.0067	60	Neodymium	Nd	144.2
8	Oxygen	O	15.999	61	Promethium	Pm	–
9	Fluorine	F	18.9984	62	Samarium	Sm	150.4
10	Neon	Ne	20.17	63	Europium	Eu	151.96
11	Sodium	Na	22.9898	64	Gadolinium	Gd	157.2
12	Magnesium	Mg	24.305	65	Terbium	Tb	158.9254
13	Aluminum	Al	26.9815	66	Dysprosium	Dy	162.5
14	Silicon	Si	28.08	67	Holmium	Ho	164.9303
15	Phosphorus	P	30.9738	68	Erbium	Er	167.2
16	Sulfur	S	32.06	69	Thulium	Tm	168.9342
17	Chlorine	Cl	35.453	70	Ytterbium	Yb	173.0
18	Argon	Ar	39.94	71	Lutetium	Lu	174.97
19	Potassium	K	39.10	72	Hafnium	Hf	178.4
20	Calcium	Ca	40.08	73	Tantalum	Ta	180.947
21	Scandium	Sc	44.9559	74	Wolfram (Tungsten)	W	183.8
22	Titanium	Ti	47.9				
23	Vanadium	V	50.941	75	Rhenium	Re	186.2
24	Chromium	Cr	51.996	76	Osmium	Os	190.2
25	Manganese	Mn	54.9380	77	Iridium	Ir	192.2
26	Iron	Fe	55.84	78	Platinum	Pt	195.0
27	Cobalt	Co	58.9332	79	Gold	Au	196.9665
28	Nickel	Ni	58.7	80	Mercury	Hg	200.5
29	Copper	Cu	63.54	81	Thallium	Tl	204.3
30	Zinc	Zn	65.3	82	Lead	Pb	207.2
31	Gallium	Ga	69.72	83	Bismuth	Bi	208.9806
32	Germanium	Ge	72.5	84	Polonium	Po	–
33	Arsenic	As	74.9216	85	Astatine	At	–
34	Selenium	Se	78.9	86	Radon	Rn	–
35	Bromine	Br	79.904	87	Francium	Fr	–
36	Krypton	Kr	83.80	88	Radium	Ra	226.0254
37	Rubidium	Rb	85.467	89	Actinium	Ac	–
38	Strontium	Sr	87.62	90	Thorium	Th	232.0381
39	Yttrium	Y	88.9059	91	Protactinium	Pa	231.0359
40	Zirconium	Zr	91.22	92	Uranium	U	238.029
41	Niobium	Nb	92.9064	93	Neptunium	Np	237.0482
42	Molybdenum	Mo	95.9	94	Plutonium	Pu	–
43	Technetium	Tc	98.9062	95	Americium	Am	–
44	Ruthenium	Ru	101.0	96	Curium	Cm	–
45	Rhodium	Rh	102.9055	97	Berkellium	Bk	–
46	Palladium	Pd	106.4	98	Californium	Cf	–
47	Silver	Ag	107.868	99	Einsteinium	Es	–
48	Cadmium	Cd	112.40	100	Fermium	Fm	–
49	Indium	In	114.82	101	Mendelevium	Md	–
50	Tin	Sn	118.6	102	Nobelium	No	–
51	Antimony	Sb	121.7	103	Lawrencium	Lw	–
52	Tellurium	Te	127.6	104	Rutherfordium[a]	Rf	–
53	Iodine	I	126.9045	105	Kurchatovium[a]	Ku	–

[a]Because of conflicting Soviet and United States claims to the discovery of elements 104 and 105, the International Union of Pure and Applied Chemistry has postponed naming them until its 1973 biennial conference.

sharp line rather than a parabola; the resulting instrument was called a mass spectrograph. With this instrument, Aston was able to confirm the finding that neon exists in at least two forms (atomic weights of 20 and 22) and that the proportions appeared to be 10:1, giving an average atomic weight of 20.2 to neon. Aston next analyzed chlorine and found that this also gave two lines, corresponding to 35 and 37.

The pioneering work of Aston and Dempster in 1918–19 with the electromagnetic mass spectrometer is the historical starting point for separation and study of the isotopes of the elements. The electromagnetic separation of isotopes is relatively simple in principle (see MASS SPECTROMETRY).

Separation of Stable Isotopes. There are a number of possible ways of separating isotopes using *electromagnetic* principles. However, the large-scale mass spectrometer known as a *calutron* is the device of that type now used almost exclusively. Within a tank maintained at high vacuum, ions of an element are produced by vaporization at high temperature, sometimes assisted by a chemical agent such as carbon tetrachloride (chlorination). The ions are accelerated by an electric potential and projected as a beam across a magnetic field. The trajectories of these ions are dependent on their masses; hence the path of the lighter ion has a greater curvature than that of the heavier ion. After traversing a circular path of $180°$ to $300°$, the divergent particle paths are interrupted by catcher pockets, usually made of slots in graphite or copper, water-cooled "receivers." The isotopes are then chemically recovered from the receiver pockets.

Only relatively small amounts of material can be separated in the calutron, since it separates the isotopes literally atom-by-atom. Nevertheless, ion currents up to one ampere can be maintained, allowing kilograms of material to be separated in a machine operating over a year's time. Virtually all of the isotopes of the elements have been separated in relatively high purity at Oak Ridge National Laboratory. The details on separated isotopes available and the procedures to be used in obtaining them are given in the ORNL Isotopes Catalog.

A number of gaseous elements, such as krypton, neon, and argon, are separated by thermal diffusion. Chemical exchange is used with such isotopes as hydrogen and nitrogen. Large-scale separation of ^{235}U is accomplished by diffusing uranium hexafluoride (UF_6) gas through porous barriers. The electrolytic method is used for deuterium separation, and distillation has been used for the enrichment of mercury isotopes. More recently large high-speed centrifuges are being investigated for large-scale isotopic separations. Other than the well-known uses of ^{235}U and ^3H in large-scale nuclear work, the separated isotopes have been used primarily for fundamental scientific work, such as measure-

ment of nuclear reaction cross sections, but there is a growing utilization of isotopic materials in all fields of fundamental research and as target materials for radioisotope production.

Radioisotopes Some radioisotopes occur in nature—e.g., uranium, radium, and thorium—ordinarily accompanied by their radioactive daughters (decay products). Radioisotopes that occur in nature have half-lives* greater than about 10^8 years or are the decay products of parent radioisotopes of such long-lived radioisotopes. These primordial radioisotopes were produced when the earth was formed and have not yet decayed away in the ensuing several billion years. Of the naturally occurring isotopes of the elements, roughly 280 are stable, and about 25 may be considered naturally radioactive. Some shorter-lived radioisotopes such as 5570-year ^{14}C and 12.46-year ^3H are normally formed by cosmic ray interactions with atmospheric nitrogen and hydrogen. Irene Curie-Joliot observed and identified the first artificially induced radioactivity in 1934 by irradiating targets of aluminum, magnesium, and boron with alpha particles from a 100-mCi† polonium source and noting that the targets continued to emit radiation after the alpha source was removed. This discovery offered the first chemical proof of artificial transmutation. After the introduction of the cyclotron and other particle accelerators, many elements were bombarded with deuterons and protons to produce hundreds of new radioisotopes, including the well-known ^{131}I, ^{32}P, and ^{14}C. Large-scale production of radioisotopes, however, did not come about until nuclear reactors were available after World War II to supply enormous amounts of neutrons. The number of artificially produced isotopes had reached 200 in 1937, and with the nuclear reactor as a source of neutrons in World War II, about 450 artificially radioactive isotopes were identified by 1944, and over 1850 by 1972. Each element has at least one radioactive isotope, and some have as many as 30.

The discovery of the first transuranic element, neptunium ($Z = 93$) in 1940 was followed by the identification of the other members of the actinide series ($Z = 89$–103), which are analogous to the lanthanide series or rare earths ($Z = 57$–71), thus completing the series. It is expected that rutherfordium ($Z = 104$) and kurchatovium ($Z = 105$) should demonstrate periodic characteristics of hafnium and tantalum, respectively. Indeed, predictions on both the chemical and nuclear bases have been made on the properties of other "super-heavy" elements. For example, islands of stability of the elements appear around $Z = 114$, and elements

---

*A half-life ($T_{1/2}$) is defined as the time required for one-half of an initially large number of radioactive atoms of a given species to decay.

†A curie (Ci) is defined as 3.70×10^{10} disintegrations/second.

117 to 120 lend themselves to reasonably detailed predictions of their macroscopic properties.

Radioisotopes are produced by disturbing a preferred neutron-proton ratio in the nuclei of elements. This is done by adding or removing charged particles such as protons, or by a combination of both. Usually, a nuclear reactor is used as the source of neutrons; a cyclotron or other particle accelerator is used as the source of charged particles. The radionuclides formed by increasing the neutron-proton ratio generally decay (or transform) back to a stable configuration by having a neutron transform to a proton, with the emission of a negative electron (beta particles, β^-) and a neutrino (ν)—an almost undetectable uncharged particle of negligible mass (see NUCLEAR REACTIONS).

$$n \rightarrow p + \beta^- + \nu$$

For those radionuclides resulting from a decrease in the neutron-proton ratio (i.e., neutron-deficient nuclei), the transformation again tends to reverse the cause for instability, and where energetically possible, a proton in the nucleus is transformed into a neutron, with the emission of a positive electron (positron, β^+).

$$p \rightarrow n + \beta^+ + \nu$$

In a competing process, neutron-deficient nuclei will regain stability by the capture of an orbital electron (EC). Indeed, it is the only beta-decay mode possible for such nuclei when the decay energy (the mass difference between the decaying and product atoms) is less than $2 \, mc^2$.

$$p + e^- \rightarrow n + \nu$$

The electronic vacancy produced in the K (or L, etc.) shell is filled by an electron from a less tightly bound state with the simultaneous emission of an x-ray (characteristic of the product element) or an electron produced by an internal photoelectric process (Auger electrons). These atomic rearrangements following electron capture, particularly in a heavy atom, may involve many x-ray emissions and Auger processes in successively higher shells. The adjustment can be quite extensive and includes such effects as Coster-Kronig transitions (Auger effect in the subshells). The fluorescence yield is defined as the fraction of vacancies filled by the emission of x-rays. The Auger yield is, in a similar fashion, defined as the fraction of vacancies filled by the emission of Auger electrons.

Many radioactive nuclei decay by two or more modes so that β^-, β^+, and EC decay with associated emissions and x-radiation are not uncommon. The branching ratio defines the relative amount of each mode of decay.

For heavy nuclei ($Z > 82$), the transformation to a more stable configuration usually takes place by the emission of an alpha particle (α or ^{4}He). As the nuclei become progressively heavier, the half-lives become shorter and the fission process becomes more dominant.

In alpha or beta decay processes the product nucleus may be left in either the ground state or, more frequently, in an excited state. A nucleus in an excited state may de-excite by the emission of electromagnetic radiation or photons (γ-radiation). Frequently the gamma transition does not proceed directly to the ground state, but rather may go in several steps involving intermediate excited states. The angular correlation between successive gamma rays depends on the multipole character of the radiations and on the spins of the intermediate states. An alternative to gamma-ray emission is the internal conversion process, an electromagnetic interaction between the nucleus and the orbital electrons. Thus, the transition between the two energy states of the nucleus is not evidenced by the emission of a photon. Instead the energy is imparted to an orbital electron which is ejected from the atom. The ratio of the internal conversion process to the rate of gamma emission is known as the internal conversion coefficient, α. The internal conversion process leaves the atom with a vacancy in one of the shells. The subsequent atomic rearrangement process is essentially identical to that following electron capture.

For some nuclei, only gamma radiation is emitted for the de-excitation from a metastable or isomeric state. Such decay is termed isomeric transition (IT) and is characterized by no change in mass number or atomic number. Here, too, the internal conversion process is a competing process.

Knowledge of the energies and intensities of the particulate radiation (α, β^-, β^+, and e^-) and the electromagnetic radiation (γ-rays and x-rays) serves to characterize a particular nucleus and as such is the principal means, along with the half-life, of identifying the radioisotope. Indeed, transuranic workers, using Moseley's law, have used the coincidence between the alpha particles of the parent and the K x-rays of the daughter to simultaneously establish the parent-daughter genetic relationship and the atomic number independently of other nuclear or chemical information.

Production of Radioisotopes. The bulk of the artificially produced radioisotopes are made by neutron reactions in the high-volume neutron fluxes available in NUCLEAR REACTORS. Neutrons, having no charge, can easily penetrate the coulombic barriers of the nucleus. The atomic nuclei of the elements vary in their ability to capture thermal neutrons (i.e., neutrons slowed down to 2200 m/sec or ~0.025 eV, or less) according to their cross sections, a term which expresses the probability of interaction of a neutron of a certain energy or velocity (see CROSS SECTIONS AND STOPPING POWER). When target materials are placed in the reactor and subjected to a flux of neutrons ϕ (number of neutrons traversing a unit area

per unit time), neutrons are captured in proportion to cross sections of the target element atoms present. Cross sections are expressed in *barns* (1 barn = 10^{-24} cm², which is approximately equal to the actual cross-sectional area of medium-weight nuclei). Certain materials, such as aluminum and graphite, have such small neutron capture cross sections that few neutrons are captured; others, such as cadmium, have such large cross sections that a thin foil will absorb almost all the thermal neutrons impinging upon it.

Radioisotopes are produced in a nuclear reactor by several different processes. Those processes that produce appreciable quantities of radioisotopes are described below.

(1) (n, γ) Process. In the (n, γ) process, which is most common, a neutron is captured by a target and simultaneously a photon is emitted. Since no change of atomic number Z occurs, the element remains the same as the target material. The (n, γ) reaction is primarily a thermal neutron reaction; cross sections for (n, γ) reactions vary from a few millibarns to many thousands of barns.

For example:

$$^{23}\text{Na}\,(n, \gamma)\,^{24}\text{Na} \qquad (T_{1/2} = 15.00 \text{ h})$$

The radioelement cannot be separated chemically unless a recoil collection is used. In the *Szilard-Chalmers process*, the recoil energy of the residual nucleus, resulting from the emission of the photon, is greater than the chemical binding energy of the nucleus in a compound.

Radioisotopes produced sometimes decay by beta emission (β^- or β^+) or electron capture to a radioactive daughter with a higher or lower atomic number. For example:

$$^{144}\text{Sm}\,(n, \gamma)\,^{145}\text{Sm}$$

$$^{145}\text{Sm}\xrightarrow[(340 \text{ d})]{EC}\,^{145}\text{Pm} \qquad (T_{1/2} = 18 \text{ y})$$

The daughter can be chemically separated to obtain high-specific-activity* material.

With the availability of thermal neutron fluxes well in excess of 2×10^{15} n/cm² sec, the preparation of millicurie amounts of radioisotopes by successive (n, γ) reactions has become feasible. For example:

$$^{64}\text{Ni}\,(n, \gamma)\,^{65}\text{Ni} \qquad (T_{1/2} = 2.56 \text{ h})$$

$$^{65}\text{Ni}\,(n, \gamma)\,^{66}\text{Ni} \qquad (T_{1/2} = 55. \text{ h})$$

(2) (n, p) Process. In the (n, p) process, which requires neutrons of higher-than-thermal energies,† a neutron enters a target nucleus with

---

*Specific activity is the amount of radioisotope per unit weight of the total element and is usually expressed as curies or millicuries/gram.

†A few exceptions are found among reactions with the light nuclei in cases where binding energy of a proton or particle is appreciably lower than that of a

sufficient energy to cause a proton to be released. The atomic number is reduced by 1, and the affected atom is transmuted into a different element, which can be separated chemically from the target material. Through chemical separation, high-specific-activity material can be obtained. For example:

$$^{32}\text{S}\,(n, p)\,^{32}\text{P} \qquad (T_{1/2} = 14.31 \text{ d})$$

Cross sections for such reactions, typically a few millibarns, are orders of magnitude less than those for (n, γ) reactions.

(3) (n, α) Process. The (n, α) process, like the (n, p) process, requires high-energy neutrons and typically has a cross section of a few millibarns. In the (n, α) process, a neutron of high energy enters a target atom and causes an alpha particle to be emitted. The atomic number of the target atom is reduced by 2, and a chemical separation yielding high-specific-activity material is possible. For example:

$$^{36}\text{Cl}\,(n, \alpha)\,^{33}\text{P} \qquad (T_{1/2} = 25.2 \text{ d})$$

(4) Fission. Under normal operating conditions, research reactors have 20 to 50 per cent burnup of the fissile material. The asymmetric fission process yields fission products of mass ranging between $A = 72$ and $A = 162$. The maximum fission yields of 6.5 per cent occur at $A = 95$ and $A = 138$. Since several isotopes of any one element are often produced, the isotopic purity will not be as high as that of radioisotopes produced by (n, p) and (n, α) reactions. This isotopic purity will depend somewhat upon the length of time that the uranium was exposed to neutrons and upon the elapsed time between removal from the reactor and the chemical separation. Fission products are routinely chemically separated and purified from high-level waste streams of AEC production facilities and represent an important source of such radioisotopes as ^{90}Sr (thermoelectric generator systems for terrestrial and underwater applications), ^{137}Cs (radiography, teletherapy, and large irradiation units), and ^{147}Pm (thermoelectric power generators).

The basic equation for radioisotope production is

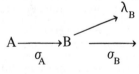

The target atom (A) captures neutrons to produce the product nuclide (B), which in turn is transformed by decay or further neutron capture. The effective cross sections (σ_A, σ_B) and the decay rate constant (λ_B) enable the rate and equilibrium values for the transformation

---

neutron: the reactions $^{10}\text{B}\,(n, p)\,^{10}\text{Be}$, $^{14}\text{N}\,(n, p)\,^{14}\text{C}$, $^{35}\text{Cl}\,(n, p)\,^{35}\text{S}$, $^{10}\text{B}\,(n, \alpha)\,^7\text{Li}$, and $^6\text{Li}\,(n, \alpha)\,^3\text{H}$ occur with thermal neutrons.

to be calculated for any particular irradiation conditions. The exact solution for the differential equation describing these rate processes for the number of atoms (N) of the product formed at time (t) in neutron flux ϕ is,

$$\lambda_B N_B = \frac{\lambda_B \phi \sigma_A N_A}{\lambda_B + \phi [\sigma_B - \sigma_A]}$$

$$\cdot [e^{-\phi \sigma_A t} - e^{-(\phi \sigma_B + \lambda_B)t}]$$

In most cases, one can neglect the "burnup" of the target atoms and the product radioisotope. In such cases, the above equation then reduces to:

$$\lambda_B N_B = N_{A_0} \phi \sigma_A (1 - e^{-\lambda_B t})$$

Here N_{A_0} refers to the number of original target atoms at time zero.

For irradiations of sufficient length ($t \gg T_{1/2}$), and again neglecting burnup, the saturation factor $(1 - e^{-\lambda_B t})$ approaches 1 and the equation further reduces to

$$\lambda_B N_B = N_{A_0} \phi \sigma_A$$

With the introduction of the *cyclotron* in the early 1930s, charged-particle reactions started to play a significant role in the preparation of a large variety of neutron-deficient radioisotopes. Indeed, until the advent of nuclear reactors in the mid-forties, proton-, deuteron-, and alpha-particle accelerators played the major role in supplying radioisotopes for medical, biological, and scientific research. During the period 1950 to 1970, the ORNL 86-Inch Cyclotron, exploiting a 2.6-mA (2×10^{16} particles/sec) beam of 23-MeV protons, supplied the major portion of neutron-deficient radioisotopes. With the development of *compact cyclotrons* the production and use of short-lived radioisotopes for medical purposes has gained impetus. *Heavy-ion accelerators*, developing beams of carbon, nitrogen, oxygen, neon, and argon, have opened additional areas for research. These devices, in conjunction with on-line mass separators, should make possible the production and identification of more of the 5000 or so theoretically possible nuclei. The Brookhaven Linac Isotope Producer (*BLIP*) and the Los Alamos Scientific Laboratory High Flux Meson Facility (*LAMPF*) offer the possibility of producing large amounts of neutron-deficient radioisotopes by high-energy proton-induced spallation reactions using 200-MeV and 750-MeV protons, respectively.

A method for preparing short-lived radioisotopes off-site has found widespread use in nuclear medicine. The radioisotope generator employs a relatively long-lived parent which is sorbed onto an ion exchanger; the short-lived daughter may be eluted, as required, with a suitable agent. The most common such system, the ^{99}Mo-^{99m}Tc generator, yielding 6.007-h ^{99m}Tc pertechnetate, has gained in popularity for use in diagnostic scanning and is rapidly supplanting the use of ^{131}I. Other systems are ^{87}Y-^{87m}Sr (2.83 h) and ^{113}Sn-^{113m}In (1.66 h).

Recent advances in *transuranic* isotope technology have made available substantial quantities of radioisotopes possessing properties uniquely suited for particular applications: ^{238}Pu, decaying by alpha emission with almost no concommitant gamma radiation, has been implanted in humans as "pacemakers" in cardiac support; larger units of ^{238}Pu thermoelectric energy sources have been left on the moon by Apollo crews as power sources for instruments; and 10 mg of ^{252}Cf as a fission source of neutrons presents a peak thermal neutron flux at moderator center of 1.1×10^8 n/cm^2 sec (compared to 1×10^5 n/cm^2 sec for a 1-g radium source mixed with beryllium). (See TRANSURANIUM ELEMENTS.)

Isotope Processing The techniques used for the processing of ultrahigh-purity chemicals are required for isotope work in recovering stable isotopes, preparing target materials, and separating and purifying radioisotopes. Practically every technique from traditional wet chemistry to ion exchange and chromatography is utilized, often with high-purity radioisotopes, at very low concentration levels (e.g., micrograms per liter). Sophisticated analytical methods (e.g., mass and radiation spectral analysis) are also required and make up a significant portion of the cost of isotope preparations.

The radioisotope industry includes about 100 private firms that produce radioisotopes, sealed sources, radiopharmaceuticals, and equipment for medical, industrial, and scientific uses of radioisotopes. The estimated sales for 1970 are >\$50 million: \$10 million in basic radioisotopes, \$12 million in radiochemicals, \$32 million in radiopharmaceuticals, and \$5 million in sealed sources. The present market for cyclotron-produced radioisotopes is estimated to be \$3–4 million per year. The total sales of isotopically enriched stable isotopes exceeded \$1 million in 1970.

A. F. RUPP
J. J. PINAJIAN

References

Nuclear and Radiochemistry

Barbier, Marcel, "Induced Radioactivity," Amsterdam, North-Holland Publishing Company, 1969.

Evans, R. D., "The Atomic Nucleus," New York, McGraw-Hill Book Co., Inc., 1955.

Friedlander, G., Kennedy, J. W., and Miller, J. M., "Nuclear and Radiochemistry," second edition, New York, John Wiley & Sons, Inc., 1964.

Oak Ridge National Laboratory, Research Materials: Separated Isotopes, Radioisotopes, Special Preparations,* sixth revision, April 1973.

*Available from Isotopes Development Center, Oak Ridge National Laboratory, Oak Ridge, Tennessee 37830.

Stable Isotopes

"National Uses and Needs for Separated Stable Isotopes," *Isotop. Radiat. Technol.*, **7**, 363–77 (1970).

Baker, P. S., "A Fifteen-Year Summary of Publications Involving the Uses of Electromagnetically Enriched Stable Isotopes," Oak Ridge National Laboratory Report, ORNL-3266,† March 1963.

Baker, P. S., "Stable Isotopes–Aid to Research," Chem. Eng. News, **37**, 60–7 (1959).

Davis, W. C., et al., "Chemical Recovery and Refinement Procedures in the Electromagnetic Separation of Isotopes," Oak Ridge National Laboratory Report, ORNL-4583† August 1970.

Underwood, J. N., Love, L. O., Prater, W. K., and Scheitlin, F. M., "Calutron Experiments with Milligram Quantities of Charge Material," *Nucl. Instrum. Methods*, **57**, 17–21 (1967).

Wagner, H., and Walcher, W., "Proceedings of the International Conference on Electromagnetic Isotope Separators and the Techniques of Their Applications, Marburg, Sept. 7 to Sept. 10, 1970," Bundesministerium für Bildung und Wissenschaft Research Report, BMBW-FB K 70-28, December 1970.

Rupp, A. F., "Separated Isotopes For Radioisotope Production," IAEA Symposium on New Developments in Radio-Pharmaceuticals and Labelled Compounds, Symp. No. 171, Paper No. 35, Copenhagen, March 26–30, 1973.

Reactor Production of Radioisotopes

Aebersold, P. C., and Rupp, A. F., "Production of Short-lived Radioisotopes," in "Production and Use of Short-lived Radioisotopes from Reactors," Vol. 1, pp. 31–47, International Atomic Energy Vienna, 1962.

Binford, F. T., Cole, T. E., and Cramer, E. N., "The High Flux Isotope Reactor," Oak Ridge National Laboratory Report, ORNL-3572 (Rev. 2),† May 1968.

Brookhaven National Laboratory, "Manual of Isotope Production Processes in Use at Brookhaven National Laboratory," BNL-864,† August 1964.

Brookhaven National Laboraotry, "Neutron Cross Sections," Vols. I, IIA, IIB, IIC, and III (1964–1965), BNL-325,† second edition, Supplement No. 2.

Crandall, J. L., "The Savannah River High Flux Demonstration," Savannah River Laboratory Report, DP-999, June 1965.

Friend, C. W., and Jenkins, A. R., "Isotopes–A Program for Neutron Product Yield and Decay Calculations Using a Control Data 1604-A Computer," Oak Ridge National Laboratory Report, ORNL-3673,† January 1965.

Knoll, Peter, "The Technology of Isotope Production," Part I. "Irradiation Technology," (Zentralinstitut fur Kernphysik Dresden) ZfK-RCH-1,‡ December 1961 (in German); for English translation see Pinajian, J. J., Oak Ridge National Laboratory Report, ORNL-tr-2400,† November 1970.

Oak Ridge National Laboratory, "ORNL Radioisotope Procedures Manual," ORNL-3633,† June 1964.

Pinajian, J. J., "Oak Ridge Research Reactor for Isotope Production," *Isotop. Radiat. Technol.*, **1**, 130–36 (Winter 1963–64).

Roy, J. C., and Hawton, J. M., "Table of Estimated Cross Sections for (*n*, *p*), (*n*, α), and (*n*, 2*n*) Reactions in a Fission Neutron Spectrum," Atomic Energy of Canada, Limited, Report, AECL-1181, December 1960.

Rupp, A. F., "Production of Radioisotopes with Very High Specific Activity," *Proc. Fifth Japan Conf. on Radioisotopes, Tokyo* (May 21–23, 1963).

Rupp, A. F., and Binford, F. T., "Production of Radioisotopes," in "Nuclear Engineering Handbook," ed. by H. Etherington, Section 14, pp. 26–37, New York, McGraw-Hill Book Co., 1958.

Rupp, A. F., and Binford, F. T., "Production of Radioisotopes," *J. Appl. Phys.*, **24**, 1069–81 (1953).

Accelerator Production of Radioisotopes

Lange, J., and Münzel, H., "Estimation of Unknown Excitation Functions for (α, *xn*), (α, *pxn*), (*d*, *xn*), (*d*, *pxn*), and (*p*, *xn*) Reactions," Karlsruhe Nuclear Research Center Report, KFK-767, May 1968 (in German); for English translation see Pinajian, J. J. and Kern, L. H., Oak Ridge National Laboratory Report, ORNL-tr-3020,† October 1970.

Laughlin, J. S., Tilbury, R. S., and Dahl, J. R., "The Cyclotron: Source of Short-lived Radionuclides and Positron Emitters for Medicine" in "Progress in Atomic Medicine, Volume 3: Recent Advances in Nuclear Medicine," ed. by J. H. Lawrence, New York, Grune & Stratton, 1971.

Pinajian, J. J., "ORNL 86-Inch Cyclotron," in "Radioactive Pharmaceuticals," ed. by G. A. Andrews, R. M. Kniseley, and H. N. Wagner, Chapter 9, pp. 143–54, U.S. Atomic Energy Commission, 1966.

Rosen, L., Schillaci, M. E., Dropesky, B. J., and O'Brien, H. A., "Use of LAMPF for Isotope Production, Briefing to the AEC Division of Isotopes Development, December 15, 1970," Los Alamos Scientific Laboratory Report, LA-4587-Ms,† February 1972.

Stang, L. G., Jr., Hillman, M., and Lebowitz, E., "The Production of Radioisotopes by Spallation," Brookhaven National Laboratory Report, BNL-50195,† August 1969.

General

Keller, O. L., Jr., Burnett, J. L., Carlson, T. A., and Nestor, C. W., Jr., "Predicted Properties of the Super Heavy Elements. I. Elements 113 and 114, Eka-Thallium and Eka-Lead," *J. Phys. Chem.*, **74**, 1127–34 (1970).

Ramayya, A. V., Hamilton, J. H., Little, P. E., Collins, E., and Pinajian, J. J., "Graphs for the Analysis of (1–3) Gamma-Gamma Directional Correlations," Oak Ridge National Laboratory Report, ORNL-4619,† April 1971.

† Available from Clearinghouse for Federal Scientific and Technical Information, National Bureau of Standards, U.S. Department of Commerce, Springfield, Va. 22151.

‡ Available from International Atomic Energy Agency Library, Vienna, Austria.

Seaborg, G. T., "Elements Beyond 100, Present Status and Future Prospects," *Ann. Rev. Nuclear Sci.*, **18**, 53–152 (1968).

U.S. Atomic Energy Commission, "Californium-252 Progress," Savannah River Operations Office Report, No. 9, October 1971.

Cross-references: ATOMIC PHYSICS, CROSS SECTIONS AND STOPPING POWER, ELECTRON, NUCLEAR REACTIONS, NUCLEAR REACTORS, NUCLEAR STRUCTURE, PERIODIC LAW AND PERIODIC TABLE, PROTON, RADIOACTIVITY, TRANSURANIUM ELEMENTS.

K

KEPLER'S LAWS OF PLANETARY MOTION*

The German astronomer and mathematician, Johannes Kepler (1571–1630), worked in the late 1500's with the Danish astronomer, Tycho Brahe, one of the most careful observers of astronomical motions of the pre-telescopic centuries. When Tycho Brahe died in 1601, Kepler inherited his data books to which he devoted several years of intensive work in an effort to bring orderly relations to light. Kepler was successful in deriving three experimental laws of planetary motion that led the way to the presently understood dynamics of the solar system. The first two laws were published in Prague in 1609, about the time when Galileo was first using his telescope to make significant discoveries about the planets and their moons; the third law did not appear until 1619.

Stated briefly, these laws are (see Fig. 1).

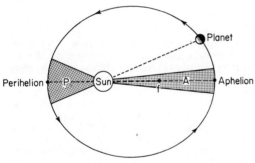

FIG. 1. Elliptic orbit of planet with sun at one focus. Areas A and P are described in equal lengths of time.

(1) Each planet moves in an elliptical orbit with the sun at one focus of the ellipse.
(2) The line from sun to any planet sweeps out equal areas of space in equal lengths of time.
(3) The squares of the sidereal periods of the several planets are proportional to the cubes of their mean distances from the sun.

An explanation of each of these laws follows, but first they should be seen against the background of the cosmology of Kepler's time, as

*Author deceased. Article is reprinted from first edition.

they signify a distinct break with ancient cosmology and they were a marked extension of Copernican ideas. Until Kepler's time, it had been supposed that the planets moved in circular orbits, that being the most perfect of curves and hence the path of the "perfect" celestial matter of which they were presumably composed. As observational accuracy increased, it became necessary to develop complex orbit by epicycles to preserve this idea of circular motion. The spectroscope would not show until after 1860 that heavenly matter and earthly matter were both composed of the same chemical elements. It is greatly to Kepler's credit that he established these three laws on such precise data and with such care, even though he himself did not know what they meant. In the ten years intervening between announcing laws (1) and (2) and publishing law (3), Kepler made innumerable attempts to find a relation between periods and distances in the solar system: some of these bordered on pure numerology and mysticism. Kepler had no adequate notion of force and hence he was prevented from continuing with his laws to their consequences, as Sir Isaac Newton did some five or six decades later.

Newton employed Kepler's laws to the full. The fact that planets move in ellipses with the sun at one focus he showed to be possible only if a force prevailed between sun and planet exactly proportional to the inverse square of the distance between them. This gave him confidence in the "inverse square law" (see GRAVITATION). The second law, Newton showed, was evidence of the great principle of conservation of angular momentum which Newton himself did so much to establish. Any object moving under a "central force," or a force directed toward a fixed point, will qualify for Kepler's second law, namely of sweeping out equal areas in equal times. However, although this law is not limited to inverse square forces, it shows, when coupled with the first law, that a planet such as the earth will move more rapidly about the sun at perihelion (closest to sun) than at aphelion (farthest from sun), as is observed. Finally, the third law falls into line as a necessary consequence if an inverse square law of force holds. One by-product of this law is the fact that the same force field is present from the primary body for each of the planets, diminishing with distance, but indicating that

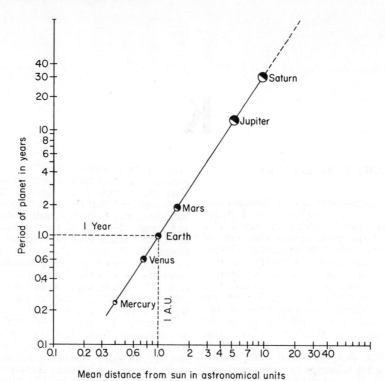

FIG. 2. Graph on log–log paper of relative mean distances of planets from sun, in astronomical units (where sun–earth distance is 1 A.U.), vs. period of planets about the sun in years. Straight-line graph with slope 3/2 means constant ratio of R^3 to T^2, which Kepler found in 1619. Planets beyond Saturn, unknown to Kepler, can be added.

the force depends upon the *product* of the masses of sun and planet.

It is interesting to see how easily the third law of Kepler's may be "discovered" by the use of techniques not available to Kepler. Kepler knew from Tycho's observations the *relative* distances from sun to any of the planets (out as far as Saturn); such relative distances can be found without knowing actual distances which were not found for another century. If one plots these relative distances against the planetary periods, using log-log graph paper, there results a fine straight line graph of points, one point for each planet, for which the slope is 3/2 (Fig. 2). This shows at once that there is a constant ratio of R^3/T^2; or the ratio of the cube of R, mean distance from the sun, to the square of the sidereal period T, is the same ratio for all planets. Thus, in a few minutes, one may discover what it took Kepler ten years to find!

It was probably fortunate that Kepler made his most intensive study on the orbit of the planet Mars, inasmuch as that planet has the greatest eccentricity of orbit of any of the planets known in his time. Thus he could cast out circular orbits in favor of ellipses. (Only Pluto, discovered 300 years later, has greater eccentricity.) One may, by relatively simple garden observation (non-telescopic), discover

the eccentricity of the earth's own orbit by introducing a useful point of view. Ordinarily, astronomers talk about the place of the sun among the stars in its annual apparent pilgrimage along the ecliptic, or the plane of the earth's orbit. However, it is not possible to see the stars when the sun is among them in the daytime, and it is therefore meaningful to ask "Where is the earth among the stars as seen from the sun?" This reversal of the point of view then means "What star (or position among the stars) is on the local meridian at true midnight, when the sun is on the anti-meridian beneath the observer's feet?" A vector drawn from sun to earth and thence to the stars would then be found to move eastward among the stars just as the earth proceeds eastward day by day around the sun. However, the rate of advance of this vector is not constant, although its *average* rate is only slightly less than one degree per day. Consequently, one would observe, by taking into account the equation of time (which reflects the variable apparent motion of the sun among the stars), that this "midnight vector" (see Fig. 3) does not progress uniformly: its rate of eastward motion is greatest near January 1 when it projects into the midst of the winter stars between Betelgeuse and Procyon; and it progresses least rapidly around

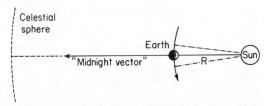

FIG. 3. The "place of the earth among the stars" is given by vector from sun to earth to celestial sphere (at midnight); the eastward sweep of this vector varies as R (the distance between sun and earth) varies, according to Kepler's second law; the angular speed of the vector multiplied by R^2 is constant.

July 1 when it projects into the region of the sky between Vega and Altair.

According to Kepler's second law, the product of angular velocity of the earth and the *square* of its radius vector from the sun should be constant, which means that in January when the earth is nearest to the sun, its angular velocity as measured by this technique, should be greater by about 7 per cent than in July when the earth is some 3 per cent farther from the sun. Despite the fact that star days are all the

same length, from the meridian crossing of any given star until its return to the meridian, the rate of progress of the true midnight meridian through the stars is not constant, but variable. It requires careful observation to measure the ratio of perihelion to aphelion distances in the manner suggested, but it can be done.

More simply, one may observe the application of Kepler's laws to the motion of the moon, for in one month one may discover that at certain times of the month when the moon is near perigee, or nearest the earth, it advances eastward among the stars at a greater rate than it advances about 13.5 days later when it is at apogee. Likewise, if one has any means for observing the apparent diameter of the moon from one end of its crescent to the other, one can also find that at perigee it subtends a greater angle by 11 per cent than at apogee. The variation in angular speed is quite pronounced inasmuch as the ratio of maximum to minimum distance is about 252/228 (in thousand miles) or 1.11. Conservation of momentum says that the product of angular speed and the *square* of the radius vector is constant, consistent with the constancy of areal velocity which depends on the square of the radius

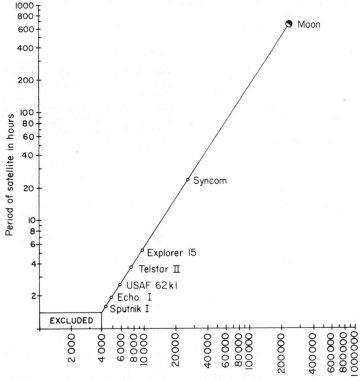

FIG. 4. Satellites of the earth—log–log graph of mean distance from center of earth vs. period of satellite, from Sputnik I (1957) to moon. This figure is similar to Fig. 2 except that the earth rather than the sun controls the satellite periods. Again, the R^3/T^2 constant ratio shows up in the 3/2 slope of the straight-line graph. Several representative satellites are listed.

vector. Hence, the maximum angular speed divided by the minimum angular speed would be $(1.11)^2$ or about 1.24. The maximum speed exceeds the minimum by some 24 per cent, a quantity rather easily observed if one takes a little care and patience.

Kepler's laws are, of course, applicable to the motion of artificial or man-launched satellites circling the earth. One may draw a graph similar to that drawn for the planets, except that now the earth rather than the sun is the controlling body. Just as no satellite could possibly continue to orbit the sun if its mean distance were less than the radius of the sun, no satellite can continue to orbit the earth if its orbit intersects the earth. (In fact, close-by satellites are captured by the atmosphere and such satellites are likely to be burned up in the upper atmosphere as their kinetic energy is rapidly turned into heat). It is interesting, however, to draw a straight line on our log-log graph from the point representing Sputnik I, the first artificial satellite launched in 1957 with its period of 96 minutes, to the moon with its period of 27.32 days. It will be found that other satellites lie as points on this line. The semi-major axis (or mean distance) of each satellite's orbit may be found from the addition of the earth's diameter to the usually published perigee and apogee distances, most commonly offered as minimum and maximum distances of the satellite above the earth's surface. Thus, for a satellite with minimum distance 1730 miles and maximum 2120 miles from the earth's surface, we add 7950 miles (for the earth's diameter) to the sum of these figures and divide by 2 to obtain 5900 miles as the mean distance of the satellite from the center of the earth, the point toward which the gravitational forces are effectively directed. Armed with this 5900-mile mean distance, we may read the period of the satellite directly from the graph, namely about 153 minutes (2.55 hours). (This happens to correspond with USAF satellite 1962 K 1, launched on April 9, 1962 at such elevation that it is likely to continue to orbit for many years.)

It may be remarked in conclusion that Kepler's law of areas is applicable also to repulsive forces. The path of an atomic particle, such as a proton, in the field of an atomic nucleus is a hyperbola because of the strong repulsion between the two. In this case, the repulsive center is situated at the far focus of the hyperbola (see Fig. 5). Rutherford made full use of this idea in his brilliant discovery of the atomic nucleus (1911).

RICHARD M. SUTTON

Cross-references: ASTRODYNAMICS, ASTROMETRY, DYNAMICS, ROTATION–CIRCULAR MOTION, MECHANICS.

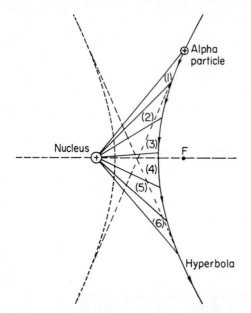

FIG. 5. Kepler's law of areas holds also for "central force" of repulsion between alpha particle and atomic nucleus; path of alpha particle is a hyperbola with nucleus in far focus. Areas 1, 2, 3, 4, 5, 6, etc., are equal and are described in equal lengths of time. A high-speed comet injected from outer space might, under gravity, describe the same kind of path, but with the sun at the near focus F.

KERR EFFECTS

The change in the refractive index of a medium due to an applied electric field is called the electro-optic effect. The Kerr (pronounced "car") effect is the quadratic electro-optic effect. In solids the index of refraction can be described by an index ellipsoid (or indicatrix). The equation for this surface is

$$\frac{x_1^2}{n_1^2} + \frac{x_2^2}{n_2^2} + \frac{x_3^2}{n_3^2} = 1$$

where the coordinates are parallel to the axis of the ellipsoid and the n_i are the principal refractive indices.

If an electric field is applied to a material, the general equation for the indicatrix can be written

$$\sum_{i,j,k\ell} \left(\frac{1}{n_{ij}^2} + z_{ijk}E_k + R_{ijk\ell}E_k E_\ell \right) x_i x_j = 1$$

where the indices run from 1 to 3. The coefficients $z_{(ij)k} \leftrightarrow r_{mk}$ and $R_{(ij)(k\ell)} \leftrightarrow R_{mn}$ in reduced notation are the linear electro-optic coefficient and quadratic electro-optic coefficient.[1] The linear electro-optic effect is called the Pockels effect and occurs in asymmetric crystals. The quadratic electro-optic effect or Kerr effect occurs both in crystals and liquids.[2] It is becoming increasingly common to refer to the quadratic electro-optic effect in solids and

to the Kerr effect in liquids, although the convention is not universal.

In solids, the quadratic electro-optic effect is usually written in terms of the polarization $g_{mn}P_kP_\ell$. Since $P_k = \epsilon_o(\epsilon_{ki} - 1)E_k$ where ϵ_{ki} is the permittivity, the definitions are interchangeable. Values for the linear and quadratic electro-optic coefficients are found in Ref. 1.

The Kerr effect for liquids is usually written in the form[3]

$$\varphi = 2\pi\Delta n\ell/\lambda = 2\pi KE^2\ell,$$

where φ is the phase retardation, Δn the induced birefringence, and K the Kerr constant. Values for the Kerr constant for liquids of interest are found in Ref. 4. Nitrobenzene with

$$K\lambda = 1.43 \times 10^{-18} \left(\frac{M}{V}\right)^2$$

has a Kerr effect that is an order of magnitude larger than other liquids.

The Kerr constant is related to the polarizability of individual anisotropic molecules. In general, K is proportional to an optical polarizability, a static polarizability, and a permanent dipole moment. The static polarizability and dipole moment interact with the applied field and tend to align individual molecules. This leads to induced anisotropy in the liquid with a resultant induced birefringence $n_\parallel - n_\perp$. In addition, the Kerr constant is inversely proportional to the wavelength of light and to temperature. A study of the Kerr effect can lead to an understanding of molecular structure and reorientation effects in liquids.

The *Kerr cell* has been used as a fast light shutter and as a laser Q-switch.[5] In this capacity the cell is usually pulsed and heating is not a problem. However, high-power laser radiation incident on a Kerr cell Q-switch may induce nonlinear scattering such as Raman scattering. The threshold for stimulated scattering is considerably reduced by beam-trapping effects which are related to the Kerr-induced index change.[6] In recent years Kerr cells have been replaced by Pockel's cells using high-quality electro-optic crystals such as KDP.

Kerr cell modulators have been constructed which operate with a dc bias field at low ac frequencies[7] and at microwave frequencies.[8] In the latter case a traveling wave configuration must be used to offset spatial dispersion.

Recently a novel extension of the Kerr effect has been demonstrated which selects and displays picosecond light pulses.[9] The Kerr shutter is optically switched by a high-power 10 psec laser pulse, exposing for that time the scene in the camera field. This device demonstrates the extremely rapid response of the Kerr effect in liquids as well as the continued use of the Kerr effect in applications.

ROBERT L. BYER

References

1. Kaminov, I. P., and Turner, E. H., "Electro-optic Light Modulator," *Appl. Optics*, **5**, 1612 (1966).
2. Kerr, J., *Phil. Mag.*, **50**, 337, 446 (1875); **8**, 85, 229 (1879). Beams, J. W., *Revs. Mod. Physics*, **4**, 133 (1932).
3. Zarem, A. M., Marshall, F. R., and Poole, F. L., *Trans. AIEE*, **68**, 84 (1949).
4. Condon, E. V., and Odishaw, H., "Handbook of Physics," second edition, New York, McGraw-Hill Book Co., 1967 (6–120).
5. McClung, F. J., and Hellworth, R. W., *Appl. Optics*, Suppl. **1**, 103 (1962).
6. Minck, R. W., Terhune, R. W., and Wang, C. C., "Nonlinear Optics," *Appl. Optics*, **5**, 1595 (1966).
7. Stone, Julian, Lynch, G., and Pontinen, R., "A dc-Biased Kerr Cell Light Modulator," *Appl. Optics*, **5**, 653 (1966).
8. Chenoweth, A. J., Gaddy, O. L., and Halshouser, D. F., "Carbon Disulfide Traveling-Wave Kerr Cells," *Appl. Optics*, **5**, 1652 (1966).
9. Duguay, M. A., and Mattick, A. T., "Ultrahigh Speed Photography of Picosecond Light Pulses and Echoes," *Appl. Optics*, **10**, 2162 (1971).

KINETIC THEORY

The kinetic theory is a branch of THEORETICAL PHYSICS developed in the nineteenth century to explain and calculate the properties of fluids. It is most useful for studying the physical properties of gases, but it can also be applied to liquids, electrons in metals, and neutrons passing through solids. The word "kinetic" means "pertaining to motion," in this case the motion of molecules or subatomic particles.

Historical Development The first attempt to develop a kinetic theory of gasses was made in 1738 by the Swiss mathematician Daniel Bernoulli. Bernoulli began with the idea that matter consists of tiny atoms moving about rapidly in all directions, which the Greek philosopher Democritus had presented, but was unable to prove. Bernoulli showed that the collisions of atoms against the walls of a container would produce a pressure which would be inversely proportional to the total volume of the container; he assumed that the space occupied by the atoms themselves is negligible compared to the total volume of the container and that the rest of the space is empty. He also found that the pressure would be directly proportional to the kinetic energy of motion of the atoms if the velocities of the atoms are changed while the volume is kept fixed. (The kinetic energy of an atom is half its mass multiplied by the square of its velocity.)

The British scientist Robert Boyle had already shown in 1662 that the pressure of air varies inversely as its volume if the temperature is held constant (see GAS LAWS). Thus Bernoulli's theory was able to explain a well-known fundamental property of air and other gasses. It was also known that the pressure of a gas

confined in a fixed volume increases with temperature. However, it was not until about 1800 that there was enough experimental evidence, and an accurate enough temperature scale, for Gay-Lussac (French) and others to establish a quantitative relation between pressure and temperature. This relation can be expressed by saying that pressure is proportional to the temperature measured from "absolute zero" (though it was not until later in the nineteenth century that the idea of absolute zero temperature was generally accepted). According to the kinetic theory, the absolute temperature is proportional to the kinetic energy of motion of molecules in a gas.

The kinetic theory was proposed again in the first half of the nineteenth century by two British scientists, John Herapath and J. J. Waterston. Neither of them was familiar with Bernoulli's theory, which had not made much impression on the world of science. Waterston obtained one important new result, which is now known as the "equipartition theorem": in a mixture of two or more different gases at the same temperature, the average kinetic energy of each kind of molecule will be the same. This means that heavy molecules will tend to move more slowly than light molecules, since when the mass of a molecule is greater, its velocity must be less in order to keep the kinetic energy the same.

In 1858, the German physicist Rudolf Clausius showed how the kinetic theory could be used to explain the rate of mixing of two gases and the rate of heat conduction. His work was extended by James Clerk Maxwell (British), who calculated the viscosity coefficient by the kinetic theory. He found that theoretically the VISCOSITY of a gas should be the same at different pressures, and should increase with temperature. This seemed to go against common sense, but later experiments by Maxwell himself and other physicists showed that the theory is correct. Soon afterward several scientists, starting with Josef Loschmidt (Austrian) in 1865, used the kinetic theory to calculate the diameter of an atom. At this time it began to appear that the atom is something that really exists in nature, since it can be measured, weighed, and counted, and is not merely a philosophical speculation. By then the atomic theory had already been accepted in chemistry as a basis for explaining chemical reactions, but it was the kinetic theory of gases that established the place of atoms in physics.

Starting from the foundations laid by Clausius and Maxwell, Ludwig Boltzmann (Austrian) and J. Willard Gibbs (American) worked out systematic methods for calculating all the properties of gases from kinetic theory (see STATISTICAL MECHANICS). Sydney Chapman (British) and David Enskog (Swedish) completed the theory, insofar as it pertains to the transport properties (diffusion, viscosity, and heat conduction) of gases at ordinary densities, although there are still some unsolved problems in the area of high-density gases and liquids, on the one hand, and rarefied (very low density) gases on the other. In the course of working out this theory, Chapman and Enskog discovered that it should be possible to separate the components of a mixture of a gas by making one side of the container hotter than the other. This effect—known as "thermal diffusion"—was soon afterwards established experimentally by Chapman and Dootson (British), thus confirming the prediction based on kinetic theory. (Thermal diffusion was used as one of the methods of separating isotopes of uranium during the development of the atomic bomb in World War II).

Although the kinetic theory was founded on the principles of classical Newtonian mechanics and led to some incorrect results because those principles are not valid on the molecular level, it is now generally agreed that the kinetic theory is valid for calculating the statistical properties of large numbers of molecules, provided that the properties of the individual molecules themselves are determined experimentally, or from the quantum theory. It is only when one tries to apply the kinetic theory to matter in extreme conditions (very low temperatures or very high densities) that he must take account of quantum-mechanical modifications of the statistical method itself (see QUANTUM THEORY and STATISTICAL MECHANICS).

Main Features of the Theory By assuming that the major part of the heat energy of a gas consists of kinetic energy of motion of the molecules, one finds that the average velocity of a molecule is several hundred meters per second under ordinary conditions. However, it is a fact of common observation that gases do not actually move as a whole at such speeds; a gas will eventually spread throughout any container in which it is placed, but it may be several seconds or minutes, for example, before chlorine gas generated at one end of a large laboratory is noticed at the other end. According to the kinetic theory, the reason for the relative slowness of gaseous diffusion, in contrast to the high average velocities of individual molecules, is that a molecule can travel on the average only a very short distance (its "mean free path") before it collides with another molecule and changes its direction of motion. In particular, at atmospheric pressure, if the molecular diameter is assumed to be about 0.00000001 cm (which is approximately true for most molecules), the mean free path would be approximately 0.00001 cm. At the same time, the average distance between neighboring molecules would be somewhat more than 0.0000001 cm, so that the fraction of the total volume occupied by the molecules themselves is less than 1 part in 1000. The average molecular velocity in air at 15°C is about 460 m/sec, so that a molecule will have about 4 600 000 000 collisions per second.

To simplify their calculations, Maxwell and Boltzmann made the following assumptions:

(1) Instead of trying to compute the exact path followed by every molecule, they assumed

that, because of the enormous frequency of collisions, the velocities and postions of molecules in a gas are distributed at random over all possible values consistent with the known physical state of the gas. For example, it is assumed that the average total velocity is known, as is the temperature (which fixes the mean square velocity). If variations of temperature and density from one place to another can be ignored, then the molecular velocities can be described by a statistical distribution—the "Maxwell distribution"—which is similar to the normal "bell-shaped curve" or law of errors in statistics.

It should be noted that the effect of a large number of collisions is *not* to make all the velocities equal, but rather to produce a wide range of velocities from zero up to very large values—though the probability of large deviations from the average is quite small. The existance of this "spread" of molecular velocities has been verified directly by various experiments.

(2) The diameter of a molecule is so small, compared to the average distance between molecules, that simultaneous collisions of three or more molecules may be ignored. The validity of this assumption for low-density gases makes it possible to develop a very accurate theory of gas properties, since these properties can be related to the interactions of molecules taken two at a time, and the mathematical description of such two-particle interactions is relatively simple. The corresponding kinetic theory of dense gases and liquids, on the other hand, involves the solution of difficult many-particle problems, and reliable results have been obtained only within the last few years.

(3) In treating the collision of two molecules, one supposes that there is no correlation between their velocities before the collision. In the elementary kinetic theory, one assumes that each molecule has the average velocity characteristic of the region of the gas in which it has most recently undergone a collision. It thus "forgets" its past history every time it collides with another molecule. This is obviously not strictly true for each individual molecule, but it is a useful approximation for dealing with average properties of large number of molecules.

In modern physics research, it is usual to distinguish between "equilibrium theory" and "transport theory," both of which grew out of the elementary kinetic theory. Equilibrium theory is described in the article on STATISTICAL MECHANICS (see also EQUILIBRIUM); it is used to study such properties as the heat capacity (amount of heat needed to raise the temperature by a certain amount) and the compressibility (change in volume produced by a small change in pressure). Equilibrium theory also tries to explain the existence of phase transitions, such as the condensation of gases to liquids, or the appearance of magnetic ordering in solids. From the theoretical viewpoint, the calculation of equilibrium properties is simpler than that of transport properties such as viscosity, because one merely averages over all the possible states

of the system (i.e., over all possible combinations of velocities and positions of the molecules) without having to worry about how one state follows another in time. TRANSPORT THEORY involves a detailed analysis of molecular collisions in order to determine how changes in the state of the system are related to external forces or nonuniform conditions imposed on it.

One of the most fruitful techniques in transport theory is the use of "Boltzmann's equation." This equation describes how the velocity distribution changes as a result of external forces and collisions between molecules. Unfortunately the equation is rather difficult to solve, because the term that expresses the effect of collisions on the velocity distribution is an integral over the values of the (unknown) velocity distribution itself for two colliding molecules. In order to calculate the transport properties it is necessary to resort to tedious computations with infinite series, except for certain artificial force laws (such as repulsive forces inversely proportional to the fifth power of the distance between two molecules) for which the integral can be simplified. In most cases, the results (as worked out by Chapman and Enskog) do not differ greatly from the ones obtained from the approximate elementary theory. However, the important phenomenon of thermal diffusion was discovered only because of a theoretical prediction by Enskog and Chapman; since the existence of this effect had not even been suggested by the earlier theories, this discovery must be regarded as one of the triumphs of mathematical analysis.

Irreversibility As indicated above, the kinetic theory assumes that the velocity of a molecule may depend on the conditions in the region where it has just suffered a collision, but is otherwise random—in other words, independent of its previous history. This assumption permits one to use the methods of probability theory even though, in classical mechanics, the actual motions of the molecules are regarded as completely determined by their initial configurations. As long as one uses the theory only to calculate properties of a gas that can actually be measured during a relatively short time, the assumption of randomness leads to no serious errors. However, it introduces an element of irreversibility which is inconsistent with the reversibility of the laws of classical mechanics. (A reversible process is one that can go equally well forwards or backwards, in contrast to an irreversible process, like scrambling an egg, which cannot be undone without a great expenditure of energy. The British physicist William Thomson, later Lord Kelvin, had pointed out the importance of irreversible processes in his "Principle of the Dissipation of Energy," in 1852.) The irreversible aspect of the kinetic theory is shown most clearly by Boltzmann's "*H*-theorem," which has led to a considerable amount of controversy about the foundations of kinetic theory. Boltzmann showed in 1872 that a certain quantity, later called *H*, which

depends on the velocity distribution, must always decrease with time, unless the velocity distribution is Maxwell's distribution, in which case H remains constant. In the latter case, which corresponds to the equilibrium state, H is proportional to the negative of the entropy (see article on THERMODYNAMICS). Thus the H-theorem provides a molecular interpretation of the second law of thermodynamics or, in particular, the principle that the entropy of an isolated system must always increase or remain constant. Irreversible processes are those in which entropy increases. The entropy itself can be regarded as a measure of the degree of randomness or disorder of the gas, although it must be recognized that disorder really means just our own lack of knowledge about the details of molecular configurations. The equilibrium state represents the maximum possible disorder; the H-theorem implies that a gas which is initially in a nonequilibrium (partly ordered) state will eventually reach equilibrium and then stay there forever if it is not disturbed.

If the long-term consequences of the H-theorem were applicable to all matter in the universe, one might expect that the universe would eventually "run down"; although the total energy might always remain the same, no useful work could be done with this energy because all matter would be at the same temperature (see THERMODYNAMICS). This final state has been called the "heat death" of the universe.

The contradiction between the H-theorem and the laws of classical mechanics is shown by two famous criticisms of the kinetic theory, the "reversibility paradox" and the "recurrence paradox." The first paradox is based on the fact that Newton's laws of motion are unchanged if one reverses the time direction, so that it would seem to be impossible to deduce from these equations a theorem that predicts irreversible behavior. Kelvin discussed this paradox in 1874, and concluded that while any single sequence of molecular motions could be reversed, leading to an ordered state, the number of disordered states is so much greater than the number of ordered states that it is virtually impossible to stay in an ordered state for any period of time. Thus irreversibility is a statistical but not an absolute consequence of kinetic theory. Boltzmann gave a similar answer when the problem was pointed out to him by Loschmidt a few years later. The second paradox is based on a theorem of Henri Poincaré (French): if a mechanical system is enclosed in a finite volume, then after a sufficiently long time it will return as closely as one likes to its initial state. Hence H must return to its original value; if it has decreased during some period of time, it must increase during some other period. The time between successive recurrences of the same state for the molecules in 1 cc of air is much longer than the present age of the universe, so one does not have to worry about recurrences in any actual experiment. In his attempt to resolve the recurrence paradox, Boltzmann was finally led to a remarkable psycho-cosmological speculation: he suggested that the "direction of time" as perceived by an animate being is *determined* by the direction of irreversible processes in his environment and in his body. Thus when the time comes for a recurrence, entropy will decrease but subjective time will flow in the opposite direction; thus the law "entropy increases with time" is a tautology! This idea of alternating time-directions in cosmic history was further explored by H. Reichenbach (*The Direction of Time*, Berkeley, 1956) and has been proposed again in recent theories of the expanding (and contracting) universe.

Some other aspects of this problem and its connection with atomic randomness are discussed in the article on IRREVERSIBILITY.

Recent Developments Since World War II there has been a revival of interest in the "classical" kinetic theory of gases, based on the assumptions of Clausius, Maxwell and Boltzmann and ignoring quantum effects except insofar as these may determine the intermolecular force law. In part this interest is due to applications involving high-speed aerodynamics and plasma physics, in part to renewed attempts to construct reliable theories of liquids as well as dense gases. New methods for obtaining accurate solutions of the Boltzmann equation have been developed by H. Grad, C. L. Pekeris, E. Ikenberry and C. Truesdell, and many others. These solutions have been used to describe the behavior of gases in many circumstances more complicated than those treated in the nineteenth century (including the interactions of charged particles and magnetic fields). Problems such as the propagation and dispersion of sound waves have also been treated by G. E. Uhlenbeck and his collaborators.

In 1946, three general formulations of kinetic theory were published, by M. Born and H. S. Green, by J. G. Kirkwood, and by N. N. Bogoliubov. In each case the goal was to derive a generalized Boltzmann equation in a form that would be valid when simultaneous interactions among more than two molecules have to be taken into account, and thence to obtain solutions of the equation from which transport properties of dense gases and liquids could be calculated. In each formulation certain approximations had to be made in order to obtain practical results; because of the difficulty in estimating the error involved in these approximations, and the great complexity of the equations involved, there was no clear evidence that the results for properties such as the viscosity coefficient would be significantly more accurate than those obtained by Enskog from his modified kinetic theory for dense gases published in 1922. Eventually, in the early 1960s, attention was centered on the systematic derivation of series expansions for the transport coefficients in ascending powers of the density, together with attempts to calculate the first few terms in such series for special molecular models such

as elastic spheres. In the meantime, an alternative and apparently more rigorous method for deriving theoretical expressions for transport coefficients, based on the "fluctuation-dissipation theorem" introduced in 1928 by H. Nyquist in electrical engineering problems, was developed by M. S. Green, H. Mori, and R. Kubo. This method had the heuristic advantage of bringing out clearly the connection between transport theory and the description of fluctuations in equilibrium statistical mechanics. Later it was proved that the Green-Mori-Kubo method gives results precisely equivalent to those that would be obtained from the Born-Green, Kirkwood, and Bogoliubov methods, and also those of yet another method developed by I. Prigogine, if in each case the calculations are done without approximation. Thus, just as in the case of quantum mechanics, several alternative approaches are equally valid in modern kinetic theory.

After intensive efforts to calculate terms in the density expansion of transport coefficients, it was finally discovered in 1965 that such a density expansion does not actually exist, for mathematical reasons associated with the persistence of weak correlations between colliding particles over very long times. The divergence of the expansion (and thus the inadequacy of the approximations on which most earlier theories had been based) was established almost simultaneously by J. R. Dorfman and E. G. D. Cohen, J. Weinstock, and R. Goldman and E. Frieman. The result has been a flurry of activity in kinetic theory, in which many of the intuitively plausible ideas about "relaxation" of initial states to steady nonequilibrium states, and destruction of correlations by intermolecular collisions, have been revised.

Other applications of the kinetic theory are discussed in the articles on AERODYNAMICS, BOLTZMANN'S DISTRIBUTION LAW, ELECTRICAL CONDUCTIVITY, LIQUID STATE, NUCLEAR REACTORS and PLASMA. See especially IRREVERSIBILITY.

STEPHEN G. BRUSH

References

For an elementary introduction, see Cowling, T. G., "Molecules in Motion," London, Hutchinson, 1950; reprinted by Harper Torchbooks, New York, 1960.

Diffusion and thermal diffusion: Furry, W. H., "On the Elementary Explanation of Diffusion Phenomena in Gases," Am. J. Physics, 16, 63 (1948).

Comprehensive treatments of the elementary theory and many applications: Loeb, L. B., "Kinetic Theory of Gases," New York, McGraw-Hill Book Co., 1934; Kennard, E. H., "Kinetic Theory of Gases, with an Introduction to Statistical Mechanics," New York, McGraw-Hill Book Co., 1938.

Theory of the Boltzmann equation: Chapman, S., and Cowling, T. G., "The Mathematical Theory of Non-Uniform Gases," Cambridge, Cambridge University Press, 1952; Grad, H., "Principles of the Kinetic Theory of Gases," in "Handbuch der Physik," Vol. 12, p. 205, Berlin, Springer, 1958.

Calculations of properties of fluids: Hirschfelder, J. O., Curtiss, C. F., and Bird, R. B., "Molecular Theory of Gases and Liquids," New York, John Wiley & Sons, 1954.

Reprints of original papers, with historical introduction: Brush, S. G., Ed., "Kinetic Theory," 3 vols., New York, Pergamon Press, 1965–72. (A survey of recent developments may be found in Part I of volume 3.)

L

LAPLACE TRANSFORM

Introduction The Laplace transform $\bar{f}(s)$ of a function $f(t)$ is defined to be the integral

$$\bar{f}(s) = \int_0^\infty e^{-st} f(t)\, dt$$

if the integral exists. It will certainly exist if $f(t)$ is itself integrable between zero and an arbitrary upper limit, and if, for a large enough real value of k, $e^{-kt} f(t) \to 0$ as $t \to \infty$. Then if it exists for one complex value of s it exists also for all complex s of greater real part, and so the integral "transforms" the function $f(t)$ into a function $\bar{f}(s)$ defined on a half-plane of the complex Argand plane.[10,6]

Operational Methods The Laplace transform is perhaps the best known and most useful of a number of integral transforms, whose application is that province of applied mathematics usually called operational methods.

The essential idea is to exploit the analogy between certain differential and algebraic operators. Historically, the idea goes back to Leibnitz, and has been employed by a number of mathematicians including Laplace, Lagrange and Riemann.[2] It was treated extensively by Boole, and Oliver Heaviside developed it to the point where he could apply it, particularly to circuit theory in electricity. In his D-notation, given the ordinary differential equation with constant coefficients

$$a_0 \frac{d^n y}{dt^n} + a_1 \frac{d^{n-1} y}{dt^{n-1}} + \cdots + a_{n-1} \frac{dy}{dt} + a_n y = F(t),$$

we introduce the operator $P(D) = \sum_{k=0}^{n} a_k D^{n-k}$ and so write the equation as

$$P(D)y = F(t).$$

Then it is formally solved as

$$y = \frac{1}{P(D)} F(t),$$

and one is left to interpret this result. The key to this interpretation lies in the three operational relations

$$D \equiv \frac{d}{dt}, \qquad D^{-1} = \int^t dt,$$

and

$$(1 - D)^{-1} = \sum_{k=0}^{\infty} D^k = \sum_{k=0}^{\infty} D^{-k-1}.$$

In these, D^{-1} is an indefinite integral and hence one of the major faults was that D and D^{-1} were not commutative, as $D^{-1}D - DD^{-1}$ would in general be a constant. Heaviside does not seem to have been clear which interpretation of $(1 - D)^{-1}$ to take, preferring the first but recognizing the difficulties of convergence implied. The method also fails to take account of the initial values under which the equation is to be solved.

Now it follows by successive integrations by parts that if $d^k y/dt^k$ has a Laplace transform it is

$$s^k \bar{y}(s) - \sum_{j=0}^{k-1} y_{k-j-1} s^j$$

where $\bar{y}$ is the Laplace transform of y, and $y_r = \lim_{t \to 0} d^r y/dt^r$. Thus the Laplace transform has the algebraic property of the D-operator, but the initial values are now included in the operation. If this is then applied to the differential equation above, the term to be interpreted becomes

$$\bar{y}(s) = \{\bar{F}(s) + Q(s)\}/P(s),$$

where $\bar{F}(s)$ is the Laplace transform of $F(t)$, and $Q(t)$ is a polynomial of degree $n - 1$ with coefficients depending on the constants y_r.

It can easily be verified that the Laplace transforms of $t^n e^{at}$, $e^{at} \cos bt$ and $e^{at} \sin bt$ are respectively $n!(s - a)^{-1-n}$, $(s - a)/\{(s - a)^2 + b^2\}$ and $b/\{(s - a)^2 + b^2\}$. If, then, the forcing function $F(t)$ is a finite sum of terms which are products of powers of t, exponentials, and trigonometric functions, the equation can be solved by resolving $\bar{y}(s)$ into partial fractions and interpreting separately the individual terms.

The Inversion Integral The justification for the procedure above involves the assumption that the relation between a function and its Laplace transform is unique. This follows from the Fourier integral theorem, and the relation between the Laplace and Fourier transforms.[8] This theorem establishes for a restricted class of functions, which vanish sufficiently strongly for large values of t, a unique reciprocal relation between a function $F(t)$ and its Fourier transform $\widehat{F}(p)$,

$$(2\pi)^{1/2}\widehat{F}(p) = \int_{-\infty}^{\infty} e^{ipt}F(t)dt,$$

$$(2\pi)^{1/2}F(t) = \lim_{X\to\infty} \int_{-X+ic}^{X+ic} e^{-ipt}\widehat{F}(p)dp,$$

where c is chosen so that the integral is meaningful.

If we introduce the unit function $H(t)$, which is one for positive t, and zero for negative t, a function often associated with the name of Heaviside, and we also write $p = is$, $F(t) = (2\pi)^{1/2}f(t)H(t)$, then $\widehat{F}$ (is) is the Laplace transform $\bar{f}(s)$. We therefore obtain the uniqueness theorem we desire, and in addition obtain an inversion formula for the Laplace transform, often known as the Bromwich integral

$$2\pi i f(t)H(t) = \lim_{X\to\infty} \int_{c-iX}^{c+iX} e^{st}\bar{f}(s)ds,$$

where c must be greater than the real part of any singularity of $\bar{f}(s)$.

We may use the method of residues to evaluate the inversion integral for a wide class of transforms,[6] and so with its use we can relax the restriction we had to place on the forcing function above.

An alternative form of the inversion formula can be given by[11]

$$f(t) = \lim_{n\to\infty} \frac{(-1)^n}{n!} \left(\frac{n}{t}\right)^{n+1} \bar{f}^{(n)}\left(\frac{n}{t}\right)$$

where $\bar{f}^{(n)}(s)$ is the nth derivative of $\bar{f}(s)$.

The Convolution Theorem We may also show that, for a suitably restricted class of functions, the Fourier transform has a convolution or Faltung theorem associated with it. This takes the form that if $\widehat{F}(p)$ and $\widehat{G}(p)$ are respectively the Fourier transforms of $F(t)$ and $G(t)$, then $(2\pi)^{1/2}\widehat{F}(p)\widehat{G}(p)$ is the Fourier transform of

$$\int_{-\infty}^{\infty} F(u)G(t-u)du.$$

If we interpret this as a theorem for the Laplace transform we obtain the result that if $\bar{f}(s)$ and $\bar{g}(s)$ are respectively the Laplace transforms of $f(t)$ and $g(t)$, then $\bar{f}(s)\bar{g}(s)$ is the Laplace transform of the function

$$\int_{0}^{t} f(u)g(t-u)du.$$

This theorem has an immediate application to the solution of the differential equation we have introduced above, for we can assert that if $Y(t)$ is the function whose Laplace transform is $1/P(s)$, then $\bar{F}(s)/P(s)$ is the Laplace transform of

$$\int_{0}^{t} F(u)Y(t-u)du.$$

Now $P(s)$ is a polynomial in s, and so we can write

$$P(s) = a_0 \prod_{k=1}^{m} (s - \alpha_k)^{N_R}$$

where the α_k are in general complex, and $\sum_{k=1}^{m} N_k = n$. We can then resolve $1/P(s)$ into partial fractions

$$\sum_{k=1}^{m} \sum_{j=1}^{N_k} \frac{A_{kj}}{(s - \alpha_k)^j}$$

(see Refs. 5 and 6) and so

$$Y(t) = \sum_{k=1}^{m} \sum_{j=1}^{N_k} \frac{A_{kj}}{(j-1)!} t^{j-1} e^{\alpha_k t}.$$

This is equivalent to solving the differential equation by the method of variation of parameters.

The convolution theorem is also of great assistance in the solution of integral equations with difference kernels, i.e., with kernels of the form $K(t, u) = K(t - u)$. In particular we see that the Volterra equation

$$f(t) = g(t) + \lambda \int_{0}^{t} K(t-u)f(u)du$$

leads directly to

$$\bar{f}(s) = \bar{g}(s)/\{1 - \lambda\bar{K}(s)\}.$$

The corresponding Fredholm integral equation with a difference kernel may also be solved using a transform. In this case, however, another integral equation is obtained which may be solved by the Wiener-Hopf technique.[6]

Other Properties of the Laplace Transform It can be proved quite easily[6] that within the half-plane in which it converges, $\bar{f}(s)$ is an analytic function of s, and so has derivatives of

all orders with respect to s. It then follows that

$$\frac{d^k \bar{f}(s)}{ds^k} = (-1)^k \int_0^\infty e^{-st} t^k f(t) dt.$$

We may apply this relation to ordinary differential equations whose coefficients are polynomials in t. If we combine this formula with the relation for the transform of a derivative we have used before, the equation

$$\sum_{k=0}^n \sum_{j=0}^{mk} a_{kj} t^j \frac{d^{n-k}y}{dt^{n-k}} = F(t)$$

is transformed into

$$\sum_{k=0}^n \sum_{j=0}^{mk} (-1)^j a_{kj} \left\{ \frac{d^j}{ds^j} (s^{n-k} \bar{y}) \right.$$

$$\left. - \sum_{i=j}^{n-k-1} \frac{i! y_{n-k-i-1}}{(i-j)!} s^{i-j} \right\} = \bar{F}(s).$$

Hence an ordinary linear differential equation of order n whose coefficients are polynomials in t of maximum degree m, becomes an ordinary linear differential equation for the transform which is of order m and whose coefficients are polynomials of degree n. This is exactly the same situation as arises if we attempt to solve the original equation by a contour integral of Laplace type.[7]

In fact the Laplace transform is only a special case of this more general technique, which is in consequence rather more useful.

One advantage does, however, remain for the use of the Laplace transform in this context. It has asymptotic properties which can allow the deduction of certain properties of a function from its transform without explicitly inverting it. It is an immediate deduction from Watson's lemma[7] that if, for small t,

$$f(t) = t^\nu \sum_{n=0}^\infty a_n t^n, \qquad \nu > -1,$$

then for $|s|$ large

$$\bar{f}(s) \sim s^{-1-\nu} \sum_{n=0}^\infty \Gamma(n + \nu + 1) a_n s^{-n}.$$

To deduce an expression for $f(t)$ for small t from the transform, a converse theorem is required and the conditions under which this is valid may be found in Ref. 4. The same text establishes conditions for the validity of another useful relation, which is that if a is the singularity of $\bar{f}(s)$ of greatest real part, and near it $\bar{f}(s)$ has an expansion

$$\bar{f}(s) = (s - a)^{-\nu-1} \sum_{n=0}^\infty A_n (s - a)^n,$$

then for large positive values of t

$$f(t) \sim t^\nu e^{at} \sum_{n=0}^\infty \frac{A_n}{\Gamma(\nu + 1 - n) t^n}.$$

Partial Differential Equations and Other Transforms Possibly the most useful application is to the solution of initial value problems for some of the linear partial differential equations of mathematical physics. This is exploited to the full in Ref. 1 and to a lesser extent in Refs. 5 and 6. In a number of these equations time derivatives appear with constant coefficients, so the use of the transform effectively reduces by one the number of independent variables. In particular, if there is only one other independent variable than the time, it produces an ordinary differential equation. The method has great flexibility since the asymptotic properties can often be used to extract information which conventional solutions in eigenvalue expansions conceal. It can be shown that if the Laplace transform of $f(t)H(t)$ is $\bar{f}(s)$, then the Laplace transform of $f(t - a)H(t - a)$ is $e^{-sa}\bar{f}(s)$. In problems involving wave propagation this can be exploited to analyze the solution into the components arising from multiple reflections.

It is clear from the way that the initial conditions appear in the Laplace transform of a derivative, that it can be used primarily for the solution of initial value problems, and hence for partial differential equations of hyperbolic or parabolic type only. In treating the solution of equations of elliptic type on infinite domains, in which the boundary conditions are given at both ends of the range, we require other integral transforms, the conditions at infinity being usually of a form which will ensure the convergence of the defining integral. The question of which transform to use is usually decided by the equation, the coordinate system, and the form in which the boundary conditions are given. It is convenient to illustrate some of the most commonly used transforms by reference to the Laplace equation $\nabla^2 \phi = 0$.

In Cartesian coordinates this has the form

$$\frac{\partial^2 \phi}{\partial x^2} + \frac{\partial^2 \phi}{\partial y^2} + \frac{\partial^2 \phi}{\partial z^2} = 0.$$

If the region in which a solution is sought extends over $(-\infty, \infty)$ in one coordinate, say x, and the boundary conditions are that $\phi \to 0$ as $|x| \to \infty$, we would use a Fourier transform, whose inversion formula and convolution integral have already been given. Like the Laplace transform, an asymptotic expansion of the transform is equivalent to the expansion of the function near the origin. The expansion of the transform near the singularity of least negative imaginary part gives the asymptotic expansion of the function near $x = \infty$, and of least positive imaginary part near $x = -\infty$.

If the range in x is only semi-infinite, we may use either a Fourier cosine transform, with the reciprocal relations

$$\bar{f}(s) = \left(\frac{2}{\pi}\right)^{1/2} \int_0^\infty f(x) \cos sx \, dx;$$

$$f(x) = \left(\frac{2}{\pi}\right)^{1/2} \int_0^\infty f(s) \cos sx \, dx$$

or the Fourier sine transform with the reciprocal relations

$$\bar{f}(s) = \left(\frac{2}{\pi}\right)^{1/2} \int_0^\infty f(x) \sin sx \, dx;$$

$$f(x) = \left(\frac{2}{\pi}\right)^{1/2} \int_0^\infty \bar{f}(s) \sin sx \, dx.$$

Both transforms require the boundary condition $\phi(x) \to 0$ as $x \to \infty$, but the choice between them is decided by whether ϕ or $\partial\phi/\partial x$ is given on $x = 0$, for if $\phi(x) \to 0$ as $x \to \infty$, and the integrals exist,

$$\int_0^\infty \frac{\partial^2 \phi}{\partial x^2} \cos sx \, dx$$

$$= -\left(\frac{\partial\phi}{\partial x}\right)_{x=0} - s^2 \int_0^\infty \phi(x) \cos sx \, dx,$$

while

$$\int_0^\infty \frac{\partial^2 \phi}{\partial x^2} \sin sx \, dx$$

$$= s\phi_{x=0} - s^2 \int_0^\infty \phi(x) \sin sx \, dx.$$

Convolution theorems and the asymptotic properties can be deduced by noting that if ϕ is continued for $x < 0$ as an even function, the cosine transform is the Fourier transform of the continued function, and if ϕ is continued as an odd function we relate the sine transform to the Fourier.

In spherical polar coordinates the Laplace equation has solutions like $R^\nu S_\nu$ where S_ν is a spherical harmonic of degree ν. This suggests that to solve problems in conical regions of infinite extent we use the Mellin transform and its inverse

$$\bar{f}(s) = \int_0^\infty R^{s-1} f(R) \, dR;$$

$$f(R) = \lim_{X \to \infty} \frac{1}{2\pi i} \int_{c-iX}^{c+iX} R^{-s} \bar{f}(s) \, ds.$$

This can be derived from the Fourier transform by substituting $R = e^x$, which also gives the convolution theorem that $\bar{f}(s)\bar{g}(s)$ is the transform of

$$\int_0^\infty f(\rho) g\left(\frac{R}{\rho}\right) \frac{d\rho}{\rho}.$$

To apply this transform to the equation, $R^s \phi$ must vanish at infinity and at $R = 0$. These conditions will also dictate what choice of c in the inversion integral will be needed for convergence. The singularity of $\bar{f}(s)$ whose real part is less than c but nearest to it will dominate the behavior of $f(R)$ for small R, and the singularity with real part greater than c but closest to it will dominate the behavior of $f(R)$ for large R.

If the Laplace equation is expressed in terms of cylindrical polar coordinates (r, θ, z) it has solutions of the form $\Phi_\nu(r, z)e^{i\nu\theta}$, and to determine the form of Φ_ν we may use a Hankel transform of order ν, defined by

$$\bar{f}_\nu(s) = \int_0^\infty r f(r) J_\nu(sr) \, dr,$$

$$f(r) = \int_0^\infty s \bar{f}_\nu(s) J_\nu(sr) \, dr$$

where $J_\nu(sr)$ is the Bessel function of first kind and of order $\nu \geqslant 0$.

For integer order this can be derived from applying simultaneous Fourier transforms to the x and y variables and then converting to polar coordinates by $x = r \cos\theta$, $y = r \sin\theta$. For noninteger order it is better to derive the result directly using a modified version of the method needed for the Fourier theorem and exploiting the analogy between the Bessel and circular functions. There is no convenient convolution theorem, though convolution theorems can be deduced. Once again the behavior of $f(r)$ for small r is deducible from the values of $\bar{f}_\nu(s)$ for large s, and the properties of $f(r)$ for large values of r follow essentially from the singularity of $\bar{f}_\nu(s)$ nearest the real axis. Any of these transforms can be applied simultaneously with other ones.

All these transforms and also the Hilbert transform

$$\bar{f}(s) = \frac{P}{\pi} \int_{-\infty}^\infty \frac{f(t)dt}{t - s}, \quad f(t) = \frac{1}{\pi} P \int_{-\infty}^\infty \frac{\bar{f}(s)ds}{s - t}$$

where $P\int$ is a Cauchy principal value, are treated rigorously in Ref. 8.

An alternative to the Fourier transform, provided $f(t)$ vanishes strongly enough at $t = \pm\infty$, is the so-called two-sided Laplace transform

$$\int_{-\infty}^{\infty} e^{-st} f(t)\,dt,$$

which is really a complex Fourier transform. An extended account of this and its application can be found in Ref. 9. Very many other integral transforms have appeared in the literature, and tables of them with some theory can be found in Ref. 3. A more general transform which embraces a number of those above is described in Ref. 11.

More Recent Work The introduction of the concept of generalized functions has considerably increased the class of functions whose transforms can be utilized. Thus, for example, the Fourier transform of t^k exists as a generalized function and is $(-i)^k (2\pi)^{1/2} \delta^{(k)}(s)$, where $\delta^{(k)}(s)$ is the kth distribution derivative of the Dirac delta function. In particular the growth condition for a generalized Laplace transform is relaxed to become one that is bounded above by a polynomial in $|s|$.

A treatment of a number of these generalized integral transforms can be found in Ref. 12.

M. G. SMITH

References

1. Carslaw, H. S., and Jaeger, J. C., "Conduction of Heat in Solids," Oxford, Clarendon Press, 1959.
2. Davis, H. T., "The Theory of Linear Operators," Bloomington, The Principia Press, 1936.
3. Ditkin, V. A., and Prudnikov, A. P., "Integral Transforms and Operational Calculus," Oxford, Pergamon Press, 1965.
4. Doetsch, G., "Theorie und Anwendung der Laplace-transformation," Berlin, Springer, 1937.
5. Jeffreys, H., and Jeffreys, B. S., "Methods of Mathematical Physics," London, Cambridge University Press, 1956.
6. Smith, M. G., "Laplace Transform Theory," London, Van Nostrand Reinhold, 1966.
7. Spain, B., and Smith, M. G., "Functions of Mathematical Physics," London, Van Nostrand Reinhold, 1970.
8. Titchmarsh, E. C., "Introduction to the Theory of Fourier Integrals," London, Clarendon Press, 1948.
9. Van der Pol, B., and Bremmer, H., "Operational Calculus Based on the Two-sided Laplace Transform," London, Cambridge University Press, 1955.
10. Widder, D. V., "The Laplace Transform," Princeton, Princeton University Press, 1941.
11. Widder, D. V., and Hirschman, I. I., "The Convolution Transform," Princeton, Princeton University Press, 1955.
12. Zemanian, A. H., "Generalized Integral Transformations," New York, Interscience, 1968.

Cross-references: CALCULUS OF PHYSICS, FOURIER ANALYSIS, MATHEMATICAL PRINCIPLES OF QUANTUM MECHANICS.

LASER

"Laser" is an acronym for l(ight) a(mplification by) s(timulated) e(mission of) r(adiation). This device is identical in theory of operation to the MASER except that it operates at frequencies in the optical region of the electromagnetic spectrum, rather than in the microwave. Laser operation has been demonstrated at wavelengths from 2000 to over 1 000 000Å or from 0.3 to 100μm. By common usage, these devices are all called lasers, although more descriptive terminology utilizes ultraviolet maser, optical maser, infrared maser, etc. Although the original microwave maser offers an extremely stable frequency source, its main use is as an amplifier with extremely low noise output. In contrast, the main significance of the laser is its ability to produce a single frequency at high intensity in the optical region, a feat heretofore impossible at these frequencies. Not only may the output be a single monochromatic wave, but the wave may be coherent, or in phase, over the whole surface of the radiator. In this mode of operation, the laser is actually an oscillator whose output depends upon the selective amplification of one of the single frequency modes of the resonant cavity containing the active laser medium.

Following the development of the microwave maser, Schawlow and Townes in 1958 proposed that optical maser action could be obtained by placing an active medium in an optical cavity. The medium would be a gas or solid which was excited electrically or by light in such a manner that any optical wave present would be amplified as it moved through the material. The cavity was proposed to be a Fabry-Perot resonator—two plane, parallel reflecting plates with a small transmission through which the radiation might escape. Upon excitation of the material, light will be emitted with a band of frequencies determined by the particular material. In addition, the direction of emission will be nominally random. In the presence of the cavity, some of the waves will escape after several back and forth reflections from the parallel plates, "walking off" the edge of the reflectors. Those waves which travel normal to the walls will remain in the cavity and be amplified provided they reinforce each other after each round-trip reflection at the two surfaces. This reinforcement or resonance is only satisfied if the spacing of the plates is an integral multiple of one-half the wavelength in the medium. Thus, after a short time, only that frequency which satisfies the resonant condition and those waves traveling normal to the reflector will build up to an appreciable intensity. The resultant light which is partially transmitted through one of the reflectors will thus be a single frequency or several discrete frequencies if there is more than one cavity resonance within the band of frequencies emitted by the laser material. In addition, the wave front will be in phase across the surface of the reflec-

tor since waves striking the surface at normal incidence are amplified most strongly. The resultant beam will then be diffraction limited, i.e., the beam will spread by an angle in radians given approximately by the ratio of the wavelength to the diameter of the beam. In actual practice, single-mode operation is obtained only under special conditions. Generally, several frequency modes are present due to the multiple resonances of the cavity and numerous "off-axis" modes are found which correspond to resonant waves which travel at small angles from the normal to reflectors. These waves "walk off" so slowly that they still are amplified appreciably. Refinements of the simple cavity proposed by Schawlow and Townes consist of concave reflectors which decrease the diffraction losses, or several parallel reflectors which limit the oscillation to a frequency common to each pair in the set.

The key to successful laser operation is of course the active medium which amplifies the wave. Qualitatively, a material which fluoresces or exhibits luminescence is an obvious candidate. In fluorescence, electrons are excited to an upper-energy state by short-wavelength light such as ultraviolet, while luminescence is produced by passing an electron current through the medium, such as in a gaseous discharge. In either process, stimulated emission can occur only if more electrons are produced in the upper-energy state than in the lower or terminal state for the radiating transition. In this case, an incident photon will stimulate further transitions and amplification will result. If the final state were more heavily populated, then the photon would cause more upward or absorbing transitions and the net effect would be absorption.

The first optical maser was demonstrated by Maiman of Hughes Research Laboratories in 1960 using ruby, which is single-crystal aluminum oxide "doped" with chromium impurities. By applying semitransparent reflective coatings on the ends of a rod about 2 inches long, he made the cavity and the crystal an integral unit. Then, exposure to an intense exciting light from a xenon flashtube was found to invert the population between the red-emitting level and the ground or lowest-energy state of the electrons. The result was a burst of intense red light emanating in a beam through the end reflectors. This was the first and is still one of the most powerful lasers. Advances in the art since that time have resulted in energies per pulse of the order of 1000 joules or watt-seconds. Peak powers are as high as 500 000 kW in short pulses of the order of 10^{-8} sec. Because of "off-axis" modes and multiple resonances, the output is not a single-frequency, single plane-wave mode, but generally consists of the order of 100 separate modes. The beam is still quite narrow, being the order of 1 milliradian or 0.05 degrees. As a comparison with conventional light sources, the energy radiated from 1 cm^2 of the brightest flash lamp is less than 10 kW and is distributed over the entire visible spectrum. In addition, the radiation is incoherent and is spread out uniformly in all angles from the source. Thus, the directivity and spectral purity of the laser source are many orders of magnitude superior to that of an incandescent source. The ruby laser suffers from a low efficiency, about 1 per cent, and except with elaborate cooling systems, only operates on a pulsed basis. Other crystalline or glass systems with impurity ions have been developed, which yield wavelengths from the ultraviolet to approximately $3\mu m$ wavelength in the infrared. Some, such as neodymium-doped yttrium aluminum garnet (YAG), operate in a continuous mode at the one-watt level while peak powers have reached values as high as 10^{14} W in pulses of the order of 10^{-12} sec. These ultrahigh powers are obtained in neodymium-doped glass systems using several stages of amplification and novel pulse-forming techniques.

Historically, the next development came in 1961 when Javan, Bennett and Herriott demonstrated laser action in a gaseous discharge of helium and neon. Again, the parallel-plate reflector cavity was used but this time with a spacing of several feet. Later, concave mirrors were used to decrease the loss of energy out the sides of the cavity. This device operates continuously and delivers power at levels up to one watt. Pulsing the gas discharge yields peak powers as high as 100 W. The first laser radiated at $1.15\mu m$ in the infrared, while further development with different gases has yielded outputs from the ultraviolet to $330\mu m$ or 0.33mm in the far infrared. In contrast to the ruby laser, the gaseous laser beam may be diffraction limited and the frequency is pure, i.e., oscillation may be limited to one mode. By careful design, the frequency may be stabilized to a few thousand cycles per second or approximately one part in 10^{13}. Although the original gas laser utilized electrical excitation of electronic transitions, later versions use vibrational transitions in molecules such as carbon dioxide, and the excitation mechanism may be electrical, chemical, or thermal. In the chemical laser, atomic species such as hydrogen and fluorine can be reacted to produce molecules in an excited vibrational state which in turn yields amplification or oscillation. Recent electrically excited lasers, particularly those using carbon dioxide at $10\mu m$, have been operated at atmospheric pressure using spark discharges or pre-ionization by voltages in the 100-kV range. The high pressure and the powerful electrical excitation result in peak powers in the 10 to 100-MW region. For continuous laser operation, the gas may be circulated rapidly to avoid excessive heating, and using an electrical discharge, powers from 1 to 10 kW have been obtained. An entirely new excitation process, essentially thermal, was announced by Gerry in 1970. In this, the gas dynamic laser, an appropriate fuel is burned to produce carbon dioxide and nitrogen at high temperature and pressure. When released through

a nozzle into the optical resonator region, the gas cools rapidly in terms of its kinetic or translational energy, but the population of the vibrational energy levels of the carbon dioxide molecules becomes inverted since the lower level of the laser transition relaxes much more rapidly. In addition, the vibrationally excited nitrogen molecules are in near resonance with the upper laser state of the carbon dioxide and transfer energy with high efficiency to maintain the inversion. This type of laser has produced continuous powers as high as 60 kW.

The third main type of laser utilizes a solid material, in this case a semiconductor. Here the electron current flowing across a junction between p- and n-type material produces extra electrons in the conduction band. These radiate upon making a transition back to the valence band or lower-energy states. If the junction current is large enough, there will be more electrons near the edge of the conduction band than there are at the edge of the valence band and a population inversion may occur. To utilize this effect, the semiconductor crystal is polished with two parallel faces perpendicular to the junction plane. The amplified waves may then propagate along the plane of the junction and are reflected back and forth at the surfaces. The gain in the material is high enough so that the reflection at the semiconductor-air interface is sufficient to produce oscillation without special reflective coatings. The first such device used gallium arsenide and radiated at 8400Å or just beyond the visible region in the infrared. This laser was developed by groups at General Electric, International Business Machines, and Lincoln Laboratory in 1962. The efficiency is high, about 40 per cent, and the power source is low-voltage direct current. One shortcoming is the requirement of liquid nitrogen cooling (77 K) to maintain power output and efficiency. Powers as high as 3 W continuous have been produced. The cavity in this case is extremely small, the reflector spacing being less than a millimeter. As a result, it is fairly easy to limit the oscillation to one frequency mode although small irregularities in the junction prevent coherence over the full width of the narrow radiating junction strip. The compactness and efficiency of the semiconductor laser make it particularly attractive for systems use. Wavelengths as long as $30\mu m$ and as short as 6300Å have been generated using different semiconductors such as indium arsenide, indium phosphide, indium antimonide, or alloys such as gallium arsenide-phosphide. In addition, these lasers may be tuned over several percent of their nominal frequency of operation by varying the current flow through the device. The tuning results from the variation in temperature with current which in turn changes the index of refraction and the resultant resonant frequency of the cavity. Since the linewidth of the radiation is only about 100 kHz the tunable semiconductor laser is an excellent tool for high resolution spectroscopy.

Laser action may also be obtained in liquids using either a flash tube or another laser as the pump. Early versions used rare earths in an organic liquid, while more recently organic dyes have been found to be more efficient but require a separate laser for the exciting radiation. The dye laser has the special attraction that one laser may be tuned over a significant fraction of the visible spectrum by using a reflection grating as one of the cavity mirrors. Another type of liquid laser utilizes a different principle than those above, depending upon stimulated Raman scattering. Raman laser action was discovered by Woodbury in 1962 using a ruby laser and nitrobenzene. Here the laser excites the nitrobenzene, which in turn shows amplification at a frequency displaced from the ruby line by the vibrational frequency of the molecule. There is no true inverted population in this case. The incident photon is scattered by the molecule which absorbs an amount of energy determined by its vibrational energy. The molecule is left in an excited state and the scattered photon is frequency shifted by the energy loss. This process may be stimulated, since the rate at which the scattered photons are produced is proportional to the number of photons already present in the cavity at the scattering wavelength. As in the normal stimulated emission case, the frequency and phase of the output wave are identical with the wave which stimulates the scattering. The Raman laser normally operates using the Stokes line, or the wavelength corresponding to the loss of one vibrational quantum. Other modes of operation utilize the second or third Stokes lines corresponding to double or triple vibrational absorptions. Similarly, higher-order effects in the medium may produce a series of anti-Stokes lines which correspond to vibrational energy being added to the initial energy of the photons from the driving laser. The wavelength range of Raman lasers using different liquids is from the visible to the near infrared.

The high instantaneous powers quoted for ruby are obtained by using the "Q-switched" mode of laser operation. This technique, due to Hellwarth and McClung, uses a cavity resonator whose reflectivity or "Q" may be controlled externally. The laser, usually ruby, is first excited by the flash lamp while the cavity is in a state of low reflectivity and thus low feedback. As a result, the inverted population reaches an extreme value before oscillation occurs. At the peak of inversion, the reflectivity is "switched on," and the resultant high reflectivity produces an intense burst of energy which almost completely depopulates the high-energy states in a time of the order of 10^{-8} sec. The switching is accomplished either by a Kerr electro-optic shutter in the cavity or by rotating one of the mirrors so that it is lined up parallel with the opposite reflector at the optimum time during the flash lamp pulse.

An alternative method for generating ex-

tremely short pulses utilizes the technique of mode-locking. Since a laser resonator has frequency modes equally spaced at a separation of $c/2L$, where L is the cavity length, oscillation can occur in any mode as long as it is within the natural emission linewidth of the laser transition. Many lasers oscillate in only one mode, since that with the highest gain takes over from any modes away from the line center. Now, if the cavity is modulated internally at a frequency equal to the mode spacing, all modes within the natural linewidth become coherently coupled and the result is a train of pulses at the modulation frequency with a pulse width roughly the inverse of the natural linewidth. An alternative way of looking at the process is to assume random noise pulses propagating back and forth between the cavity mirrors. Since the round-trip time is the same as the modulation period, a noise pulse which passes through the modulator at its maximum transmission will receive the most net gain in a round trip. Although the differential gain among differentially phased pulses is small, the cumulative effect after many round trips singles out the in-phase pulse train. The width of the pulse is determined by the amplifier bandwidth, which is the natural linewidth as mentioned above. After demonstration of this technique of pulse generation, it was discovered that a laser could be mode-locked by a saturable filter in the cavity, i.e., a material whose transmission loss decreased with increasing light intensity. In this case, a random pulse increases the transmission in the filter on each passage and produces its own transmission modulation. This so-called self-mode locking was soon discovered to exist in some lasers without the addition of a special saturable filter material. The measurement and discovery of these effects depends upon newly developed techniques of measuring short pulse lengths. In particular, the pulse train may be passed into a reflecting cell containing a material whose fluorescence is proportional to the square of the light intensity. Upon reflection back through the fluorescent material, the light output increases where one returning pulse passes an incoming pulse. In this manner, the physical width of the light pattern measures the pulse length. Using a laser material with a broad emission band has yielded pulse trains with widths of the order of 10^{-12} sec or a picosecond. This corresponds to physical lengths of the order of one millimeter.

R. H. KINGSTON

References

1. Lengyel, B. A., "Lasers," 2nd Edition, New York, Wiley-Interscience, 1971.
2. Levine and DeMaria, Eds., "Lasers: A Series of Advances," Vols. 1–3, New York, Marcel Dekker, Inc., 1970–71.
3. Special Conference Issue, *IEEE J. Quantum Electronics*, QE-8 (February 1972, Part II).
4. Special Conference Issue, *Applied Optics*, 11 (February 1972).

Cross-references: COHERENCE, LIGHT, MASER, OPTICAL PUMPING, RAMAN EFFECT AND RAMAN SPECTROSCOPY.

LATTICE DEFECTS

The crystal consists of a regular array of atoms (or molecules) (see CRYSTALLOGRAPHY). But the perfect crystal, in which all atoms are on precisely defined lattice points, is nonexistent. Real crystals contain more or less *lattice defects* or *lattice imperfections*. Even a small amount of lattice defects can affect properties of crystals remarkably, so that the understanding of the behavior of lattice defects is very important in modern solid-state physics.

Lattice defects are classified into three classes from the point of view of the dimensional extension. These are the *point defect*, the *line defect*, and the *plane defect*. Vacancies (atomic or ionic) and interstitials (atoms or ions) are the most elementary point defects. A dislocation is a line defect. Twin boundaries and extended dislocations are some examples of plane defects.

Dislocations Dislocations are lattice defects quite unique in that their movement produces the plastic deformation of crystals, and that mechanical properties of crystals are largely determined by the behavior of dislocations in crystals. The presence of dislocations, however, affects also various physical properties of crystals other than plastic and mechanical properties.

Figure 1 shows an edge dislocation in a simple cubic crystal, the dislocation line being perpendicular to the plane of the paper. The same atomic arrangement is repeated in the direction of the dislocation line. The edge dislocation is formed at the edge A of the inserted extra atomic half-plane AB. The edge dislocation A can also

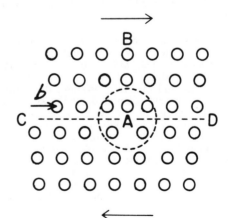

FIG. 1. An edge dislocation in a simple cubic crystal. A: center of a dislocation; AB: extra half-plane; CAD: slip plane; *b:* Burgers vector.

be formed by a partial slip of the crystal along a slip plane CAD by a shear stress shown by arrows in Fig. 1. The part CA of the slip plane has already slipped, but the part AD has not yet slipped. Therefore, the dislocation line A, which penetrates the plane of the paper perpendicularly at A, is defined as the boundary between the slipped and unslipped parts of the slip plane. When a dislocation sweeps the whole slip plane from C to D, the upper and lower half-crystals are sheared along the slip plane by an amount and in a direction shown in Fig. 1 by a vector b, which is called the Burgers vector. The slip produced by the movement of a dislocation is the elementary process of plastic deformation of crystals.

The Burgers vector of an edge dislocation is perpendicular to the line of dislocation as can be seen from Fig. 1. This is not the case in dislocations other than the edge dislocation. In the case of screw dislocation the Burgers vector is parallel to the line of dislocation. Atomic planes perpendicular to a screw dislocation form a continuous helicoid around the screw dislocation (AD) as shown in Fig. 2. In the case of a mixed

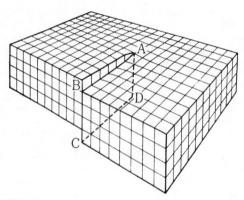

FIG. 2. A screw dislocation AD in a simple cubic crystal.

dislocation, which consists of the edge component and the screw component, the Burgers vector and the dislocation line make an angle between 0° and 90°.

The stress and the strain around a dislocation can be accurately calculated by the theory of elasticity except in the region called the dislocation core which is within a few atomic distances of the center of a dislocation (broken circle in Fig. 1), as the crystal regions outside the core can be treated as an elastic continuum, because the strain there is sufficiently small. The following are some of the important results of the elasticity theory of dislocations. The stress around a dislocation decreases inversely proportionally to the distance from the dislocation axis. The total strain energy integrated over the entire crystal outside the core is proportional to the square of the magnitude of the Burgers vector, and is of the order of magnitude of μb^2 for a unit length of a dislocation, where μ is the shear modulus and b is the magnitude of the Burgers vector. Two or more dislocations interact with one another through the stress field. Two parallel screw dislocations attract each other if their helicoidal windings are in opposite directions (i.e., a left-handed screw and a right-handed screw), and repel each other if their windings are in the same direction. Two parallel edge dislocations with parallel Burgers vectors attract or repel in a somewhat complicated way (for details, see any textbook of dislocation theory, e.g., Refs. 1, 2, and 3).

The stress, the strain, and the energy in a dislocation core can be computed if the discrete structure of the crystal is considered. The core energy of a dislocation in copper, for example, is of the order of 1 eV per dislocation length of an atomic spacing. This is considerably smaller than the elastic strain energy outside the core.

Another important property of dislocations which can be understood by considering the discrete and periodic structure of the crystal is the so-called Peierls potential. When an edge dislocation is located, e.g., at position A in Fig. 1, the atomic arrangement around the dislocation has a mirror symmetry so that the energy of the dislocation is at a minimum. When the dislocation has moved a distance b, the atomic arrangement around the dislocation resumes the same configuration as before and the energy is again at a minimum. Between these two positions with minimum energy the atomic configuration of the dislocation is not necessarily mirror symmetrical and the dislocation energy increases. Thus the potential energy of the dislocation changes periodically with the period b, when the dislocation moves along the slip plane. This potential barrier is called the Peierls potential. The Peierls potential is the intrinsic resistance to the movement of dislocations in crystals. It is relatively small in most metals, and is relatively large in such crystals as diamond, refractory oxides, and so on.

Incidentally, there are many extrinsic origins of resistance to the movement of dislocations, i.e., impurity atoms, point defects, plane defects, other dislocations, etc. These impurities and defects interact with the moving dislocations concerned, and act as obstacles to the movement of these dislocations. A larger resistance to the movement of dislocations means a larger resistance to the plastic deformation and accordingly a higher mechanical strength of crystals.

Properties of dislocations discussed so far are general ones and are not restricted to any specific crystal. But there are some properties which directly reflect specific crystal structures (e.g., extended dislocations) or specific physical characteristics of crystals (e.g., a space charge around a dislocation in semiconductors).

Now in discussing an extended dislocation, it would be more convenient to refer to a specific crystal structure, in which a dislocation is known

to extend. The face-centered cubic (fcc) lattice gives a good example. In fcc metals a total dislocation, whose Burgers vector is a lattice vector $(a/2)\{110\}$, dissociates into two partial dislocations, whose Burgers vectors are of the type $(a/6)\{112\}$ and are smaller in magnitude than a lattice vector. An example of dissociative reaction is:

$$(a/2)[10\bar{1}] \rightarrow (a/6)[11\bar{2}] + (a/6)[2\bar{1}\bar{1}],$$

where a is the lattice constant. The passage of the first partial dislocation $(a/6)[11\bar{2}]$ along a (111) slip plane in a perfect fcc lattice leaves behind it a fault of stacking of (111) atomic layers, which is a plane defect called a stacking fault. By the passage of the second partial dislocation $(a/6)[2\bar{1}\bar{1}]$ along the same slip plane, the faulted plane resumes its original perfect lattice. Thus between the two partial dislocation lines there is a strip of stacking fault. This dislocation configuration as a whole is called an extended dislocation. The width of the extended dislocation is determined by the balance of two forces, namely the repulsive force between two partial dislocations and the contractive force of the stacking fault. In copper and copper alloys, for example, the width is fairly large and is from 10 to 100 Å, while in aluminum, which has a large stacking-fault energy, the total dislocation practically does not extend. The extension of dislocations greatly affects the plastic and mechanical behaviors of crystals.

In elemental semiconductors with the diamond lattice, an edge dislocation has unpaired valence bonds or dangling bonds along the edge of the extra half-plane. In n-type germanium, for example, a dangling bond, which acts as an acceptor, traps an electron, so that an edge dislocation line is negatively charged. This negative line charge is shielded by a surrounding cylindrical positive space charge. This electrical structure of dislocations affects the electrical and other properties of semiconductors.

Dislocations are introduced into crystals by plastic deformation, and by precipitation of point defects such as vacancies or interstitials. They are also introduced during crystal growth to relax various internal stresses.

Point Defects Atomic or ionic vacancies and interstitial atoms or ions are the most elementary point defects. Di-vacancies, tri-vacancies, and higher clusters of vacancies, and di-interstitials, tri-interstitials, and higher clusters of interstitials can exist. Complexes of these point defects with impurity atoms are formed according to circumstances.

The most fundamental physical properties of point defects are the formation energy, the migration energy, the binding energy, and the atomic configuration around the point defect. These properties are widely different in different crystal structures and in different types of crystalline solids. In most metals and elemental semiconductors the formation energy of a single vacancy E_{fV} is smaller than the formation energy of a single interstitial E_{fI}, while the migration energy of a single vacancy E_{mV} is larger than the migration energy of a single interstitial E_{mI}. Typical examples of energy values are: $E_{fV} \approx 1$ eV and $E_{mV} \approx 1$ eV for copper; $E_{mV} \approx 0.2$ eV for p-type silicon and $E_{mV} \approx 0.3$ eV for n-type silicon; the binding energies between two single vacancies to form a di-vacancy are a few tenths of an eV in noble metals.

The relaxation of atoms around a single vacancy in most metals has a simple symmetry which is related to the symmetry of the crystal structure. But the atomic configuration around a single vacancy in covalent semiconductors is somewhat distorted because of the quantum-mechanical Jahn-Teller distortion. The atomic configuration of a single interstitial is rather complicated, because two different configurations for an interstitial are possible in some cases, and because the configuration often shows a lower symmetry than the host crystal. In cubic metals, for example, the so-called split-interstitial and crowdion-interstitial are possible, both of which have lower symmetries than the cubic symmetry (for details, see any textbook of point defects, e.g., Refs. 1 and 4).

In ionic crystals one or more of the following point defects are considered according to respective circumstances, i.e., vacancies of positive ions and of negative ions, and interstitials of positive ions and of negative ions. Some of them form complexes with impurity ions. Point defects in alkali halides and similar ionic crystals have been extensively investigated in connection with their optical properties, and many color centers are well analyzed in terms of point defects (see COLOR CENTER; for details, see, e.g., Ref. 5). In alkali halides, for example, the F center is a negative ion vacancy with a trapped electron, the M center is a pair of negative ion vacancies with two trapped electrons, and the H center is an interstitial negative ion with a considerably distorted configuration, having captured a positive hole.

The migration of point defects results in the transport of materials in crystals, i.e., self-diffusion, mutual diffusion, ionic conduction, etc. In most metals and covalent semiconductors the self-diffusion and the substitutional impurity diffusion occur by means of the migration of vacancies. The diffusion and the ionic conduction in ionic crystals take place by means of the migration of ionic vacancies and/or ionic interstitials.

Point defects are produced in crystals in thermal equilibrium, their concentration being approximately equal to $\exp(-E_f/kT)$ at the absolute temperature T, if the formation energy is E_f. Here k is Boltzmann's constant. Point defects are also introduced into crystals in excess of thermal equilibrium by irradiation of energetic radiation or by plastic deformation.

Excess point defects are annihilated by annealing, the kinetics of which is well investigated under various conditions (Ref. 4).

RYUKITI R. HASIGUTI

References

1. Hasiguti, R. R., "Crystal Lattice Defects," in "Solid State Physics," Ed. Kubo, R., and Nagamiya, T., New York, McGraw-Hill Book Co., Inc., 1969 (p. 719).
2. Friedel, J., "Dislocations," Oxford, Pergamon Press, 1964.
3. Nabarro, F. R. N., "Theory of Crystal Dislocations," Oxford, Oxford University Press, 1967.
4. Damask, A. C., and Dienes, G. J., "Point Defects in Metals," New York, Gordon and Breach, Science Publishers, 1963.
5. Schulman, J. H., and Compton, W. D., "Color Centers in Solids," Oxford, Pergamon Press, 1962.

Cross-references: COLOR CENTERS, CRYSTALLIZATION, CRYSTALLOGRAPHY, METALLURGY, SOLID-STATE PHYSICS, SOLID-STATE THEORY.

LENS

A lens is any element that focuses light to form images. Many lenses are found in nature. Ice crystals, waves on the surface of water, and all the eyes of humans and animals are examples of lenses. These lenses have one or more curved surfaces and are made of a transparent material. Manufactured lenses are usually made out of glass, plastic or crystal material. The simplest lens consists of two ground and polished spherical surfaces. A line connecting the centers of the two spheres is called the optical axis of the lens. The lens is edged to form a cylindrical surface centered on the optical axis. The spherical surfaces may be convex or concave, resulting in lenses which are positive refracting or negative refracting. A positive lens collects the light from a distant object and focuses it to a real image. The negative lens disperses the light and causes it to diverge from a virtual image. Positive and negative elements are used in combinations to form optical lens systems. The optical axes of each of the lens elements usually coincide to form centered optical systems. Most optical systems are designed to be centered optical systems, but in manufacture the centering is seldom perfect, so the system will have various degrees of defective performance.

Spherical surfaces are usually used in optical systems because of stringent requirements on the manufacture of optical elements. In order to perform properly, a given surface in an optical system often has to coincide with the prescribed surface to within a few millionths of an inch. Such extreme tolerances can be achieved on spherical surfaces because spheres may be ground and polished with self-correcting techniques.

A few lenses have been made using non-spherical surfaces, but they usually have rotational symmetry around the optical axis. These surfaces are called rotationally symmetric aspheric surfaces. Aspheric surfaces of this type are difficult to generate so they are used infrequently.

Some lenses are made with cylindrical and toric surfaces. Spectacle lenses often have surfaces of this type. It is practical to use aspherics in spectacle lenses because the beam of light entering a person's eye is small in diameter. The performance requirements are therefore not great. Cylindrical or toric surfaces are seldom used in telescopes, or microscopes of high performance.

There are many types of glass used in optical lenses. Some glasses are more dispersive (see REFRACTION) than others. By combining positive and negative lenses of different glass it is possible to correct for chromatic aberrations.

Theory of the Lens Most of the performance of a lens or lens system may be understood by considering that light travels as rays in straight lines until it encounters a change of index of refraction. The light is then refracted according to Snell's law (see REFRACTION). Light is emitted from a point source of light in the object as a diverging beam of rays. A lens is able to collect these rays and refocus them to an image point (see Fig. 1).

With analytical geometry, one may derive equations for calculating the path of any ray as it passes through the optical system. The procedure is called ray tracing. The mathematical equations used to trace rays are long and complicated, and have to be computed with many significant figures. Prior to the use of modern digital computers, the design and analysis of lens systems was a long tedious job. An average lens design required many months of calculation. Today most of these calculations are done on large computers, and few people need to be concerned about being able to ray trace.

Paraxial Rays Paraxial rays pass through the center portion of the lens and the assumption is made that the object points are close to the optical axis. The ray-tracing equations for paraxial rays are simple, and by using the paraxial approximation, many useful theorems for lens performance may be worked out.

In the paraxial region, any optical system may be described by locating six cardinal points along the optical axis. Once these cardinal points are known, the position and size of the image of any object may be computed from the following formulas (see Fig. 2).

$$m = \frac{\overline{y}_k}{\overline{y}_0} = -\frac{z'}{f} = -\frac{f'}{z} \qquad (1)$$

$$zz' = ff' \text{ and } \frac{f}{s} + \frac{f'}{s'} = 1 \qquad (2)$$

$$f/n_0 = f'/n_k \qquad (3)$$

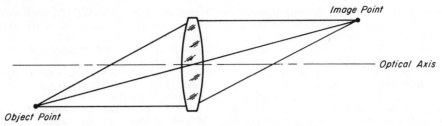

FIG. 1. A diagram showing how a lens collects diverging rays and focuses them at an image point.

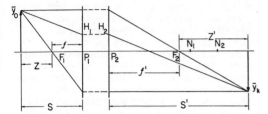

FIG. 2. Diagram showing the location of the six cardinal points in a lens system.

$$P_1 N_1 = P_2 N_2 \qquad (4)$$

$$P_1 P_2 = N_1 N_2 \qquad (5)$$

$$F_1 N_1 = f' \qquad (6)$$

$$N_2 F_2 = f \qquad (7)$$

P_1 and P_2 are called the first and second principal points. N_1 and N_2 are called the first and second nodal points. F_1 and F_2 are the first and second focal points. f and f' are the front and back focal lengths. n_0 and n_k are the indices of refraction in the object and image space.

The following terms are commonly used in connection with lenses:

Field of View. The field of view usually refers to the half angle subtended by the object as seen from the first principal point P_1. For example, it would be $\tan^{-1}(\bar{y}_0/S)$ in Fig. 2. When specified for a lens, it usually refers to the maximum size of object which may be imaged by the lens. Optical designers tend to describe the field of view by its half angle, as shown in Fig. 2. Marketing firms often refer to the full field which is twice the half angle. If not clearly stated, confusion over this term may result.

Relative Aperture. This refers to the half angle of the cone of rays converging to the axial image point. The sine of this angle is often called the numerical aperture and is written NA. If NA is large, the lens collects a large cone of light and focuses it on the image. Another way to describe this NA is to use the term f-number. The f-number of a lens and the NA of a lens are related by the following equation

$$f\text{-number} = \frac{0.5}{NA}$$

Aperture Stop. The aperture stop in a lens system is a diaphragm which determines the NA of the lens.

Lens Aberrations Lens designers attempt to combine elements and glass types to reduce the lens aberrations. All points in the object should be imaged as points in the image and should be located at or very near the position predicted by the paraxial rays. In lenses of large relative aperture and field of view, there are usually several residual aberrations that designers are unable to eliminate. There are the following types of aberrations:

(1) Spherical
(2) Coma
(3) Astigmatic
(4) Field curvature
(5) Distortion
(6) Axial chromatic aberrations
(7) Lateral chromatic aberrations.

These aberrations are corrected by using combinations of positive and negative elements. There are two general principles one may use as guide lines in correcting optical systems. (1) A closely spaced positive and negative lens with the aperture stop in contact may be corrected for spherical aberration, coma, axial and lateral chromatic aberration and distortion. (2) It is necessary to use positive and negative lenses with appreciable air space between them to correct field curvature and astigmatism.

There are many conflicting requirements in lens systems. Lenses of large relative aperture usually are designed to cover small fields of view. A large field of view normally dictates a small relative aperture. Wide fields and large aperture may be realized by using many elements or by compromising some of the image quality. For example, lenses of 140° total field working at $f/2$ are available, but they are complex and have large amounts of distortion. Periscopes allow one to look through a long pipe and see a wide field at high magnification, but there is always some residual chromatic aberration and field curvature left in the design.

Lenses are usually designed for specific applications, and the designer has made a careful balance between conflicting requirements. It is

seldom that a lens designed for one application will perform optically in another. In the past there was a tendency to misuse lenses, because it was difficult to design a new system. Today it is easy to obtain a new design. It is still expensive to build a new prototype design. Optical shop practice has not yet been appreciably affected by our modern technology. This is partly because there has not been sufficient economic pressure to stimulate the investment in equipment, but it is also because the tolerances are still beyond the capabilities of modern automated machine tools. The next few years should see many changes in the optical industry, and it is expected that new systems will be much more readily attainable. With this improvement in optical shop capability, we shall see many improvements in optical system capabilities because optical systems will be designed for specific tasks instead of for general use.

Lens Testing A designer specifies a set of curvatures, thicknesses and optical glasses for a nominal design. The work shop makes the lens to these specifications within certain tolerances. The final lens must then be tested to make sure that the over-all performance is as expected. It is rare indeed that a lens performs exactly as computed. It is then necessary to determine if the difference is negligible and, if not, what to do about it. First, one tests the complete assembled lens and attempts to predict the performance. By studying the defective image, it may be possible to locate the sources of error. The tests consist of studying the light distribution in the image of a point source. This is done on a lens bench or testing interferometer. Sometimes it is possible to locate the source of error by testing the over-all system, but usually the lens system is disassembled and all the lens surfaces, spaces and centering are checked separately.

Lens Types There are several optical systems which may be classified as types. There is considerable overlap between the types, but there is some value in the following classification.

Microscope Objectives. Microscope objectives are used to magnify small objects. They are usually used with a microscope eyepiece. Microscope objectives range in focal lengths from 2 to 48 mm and are used at magnifications ranging from 1000 to 5 ×. The high-power objectives are made up of many small elements. Some of the lenses are only a few millimeters in diameter. The lens making and mounting procedures for such small lenses are quite different from larger elements.

Telescope Objectives. Telescope objectives are used to view distant objects. Telescope objectives have a wide variety of focal lengths and diameters. They are usually corrected precisely for spherical aberration, coma and axial chromatic aberration. Since telescope objectives cover small fields of view, astigmatism and field curvature usually are not corrected. Telescope lenses of large diameter (20 inches or more) become afflicted with chromatic aberration which cannot be corrected, so many of the large telescopes used by astronomers are mirrors instead of lenses.

Telescope objectives are used in binoculars, opera glasses, surveying instruments, gunsights, and many laboratory instruments.

Periscopes. Periscopes are used to enable one to look through a long tube. The submarine periscope is one well-known example, but there are many other types used in industrial and medical instruments. Gastroscopes and cystoscopes are examples of periscopes used in medical instruments. Periscopes are made up of a train of telescope objectives and eyepieces.

Camera Objectives. By far the largest class of optical lens systems would be classified as camera lenses. They are used to record images on films as in common landscape cameras, but today they are also used with many other types of image recording systems such as television image tubes, electrostatic plates, etc. The distinguishing features of camera lenses are wide field and large aperture. Usually the image is located on a flat image plane. Camera lenses range in complexity from a single meniscus lens to systems with more than ten elements. Camera lenses cover such a wide range of uses that one could claim all lenses to be a form of camera lens. For example, a long focal length lens used on a 35-mm camera may actually be very similar to a telescope objective.

Eyepieces. Eyepieces are quite clearly a distinctive class of optical lens system. Eyepieces are designed to match the sensitivity and physical requirements of the human eye. For example, the eye is sensitive in the visual part of the spectrum so eyepieces are designed for this range of wavelengths. An eyepiece must also be located with its aperture stop in an external position so that the observer's eye may be located within it. This requirement imposes serious limitations on eyepieces, and they are seldom useful in any other applications.

Magnifiers are essentially eyepieces except they are designed to view opaque material while an eyepiece is designed to view an aerial image formed by an objective.

Condensers. Condensers are used to collect and focus large amounts of light. They are found in projectors and substages of microscopes. A searchlight mirror is a form of a condenser. The numerical aperture of a condenser is usually very large, and for many applications, the image-forming properties are not important. Condensers are often made, therefore, with low-quality surfaces. Some condenser lenses are molded. Condensers are usually placed close to an intense light source which heats and cracks the lenses if made of glass. Condensers are often made out of quartz because of its ability to withstand heat. Aspheric condenser lenses are common in condensers.

With some of the modern high-intensity light sources, it is necessary to correct for the image errors in order to obtain uniform illumination.

ROBERT E. HOPKINS

References

Hardy, A. C., and Perrin, F. H., "Principles of Optics," New York, McGraw-Hill Book Co., 1932.
Greenleaf, Allen, "Photographic Optics," New York, The Macmillan Co., 1950.
Conrady, A. E., "Applied Optics," London, Oxford University Press, 1929.

Cross-references: ABERRATIONS; MICROSCOPE; OPTICAL INSTRUMENTS; OPTICS, GEOMETRICAL; REFRACTION.

LIGHT

Light is a form of electromagnetic energy. It has a physical character similar to that of radiowaves. In order that the human eye may get the sensory perception of light, the electromagnetic waves entering the pupil should have a wavelength λ between 4000 and 7000Å ($1Å = 10^{-8}$ cm). The wavelength of a wave is inversely proportional to its frequency ν. The product of the two quantities equals the velocity of propagation. For light in vacuum one has $c = \nu\lambda = 3 \times 10^{10}$ cm/sec. The frequency of light waves is therefore almost a billion times higher, their wavelength a billion times shorter, than the waves of standard radio broadcast bands. The perception of color depends on the distribution of the electromagnetic energy over the visible wavelengths. White light is a superposition of waves at many frequencies. It can be decomposed into its monochromatic spectral components by a prism or other spectral apparatus. The violet end of the spectrum is near 4000Å, the red end near 7000Å. Whereas light in its narrow definition should be confined to this relatively narrow portion of the electromagnetic spectrum, it is customary to extend the definition to the ultraviolet and infrared portion of the spectrum. One sometimes speaks loosely of ultraviolet and infrared "light," although electromagnetic waves at these frequencies are not detected by the eye. The human mind and hands have, however, devised a large variety of instruments by which such invisible radiation can be detected and measured. Photographic plates can be made sensitive to x-rays, with a wavelength shorter than the ultraviolet, or to the much longer wavelengths of the infrared. Geiger counters can detect electromagnetic radiation of very short wavelength (λ-rays and x-rays). Photoelectric cells are sensitive in the ultra-violet and visible portion of the spectrum. Photoconductivity can be used to detect infrared radiation. At still longer wavelengths, the micro-

waves and radiowaves are detected by diode detectors in appropriately arranged microwave and radioreceivers. All these types of radiation can also be converted into heat by absorption in a blackbody, i.e., a material that can absorb radiation at all wavelengths. The radiation can be felt as heat, if it is absorbed by the human skin.

The study of the human eye as a detector of light is the task of *physiological optics*. The impression of light is not necessarily always connected with the simultaneous presence of electromagnetic energy at the retina. We see "stars" from a heavy mechanical blow in the dark. The impression of light is retained for about 0.1 second after the light source is shut off. This fact is made use of in the movies to create the impression of motion by a series of still images. The eye is a detector with a relatively long response time. Photoelectric cells can react more than a million times faster. Color vision is also subject to physiological peculiarities which are quite complex (see COLOR and VISION AND THE EYE).

The property of light which is most immediately accessible to observation is its propagation along straight lines (shadows). If light rays pass from one medium to another, their direction is changed according to the law of REFRACTION. If the light in medium 1 propagates with a velocity v_1 and makes an angle ϑ_1 with the normal to the boundary between media 1 and 2, the direction ϑ_2 in medium 2, with a velocity of propagation v_2 is given by Snell's law, $\sin \vartheta_1 / \sin \vartheta_2 = v_1/v_2 = n$. The constant n is called the relative index of refraction of medium 2 with respect to medium 1. These three laws are the basis of *geometrical optics*. This branch of the science of light describes the paths of light rays, the formation of images by mirrors and lenses, the action of telescopes, microscopes, prisms and other optical instruments.

The wave character of light becomes apparent by more refined observations. The phenomena of diffraction, interference and polarization are the subjects of *physical optics*. Diffraction describes how waves are bent around obstacles. They represent corrections to and deviations from the laws of geometrical optics. These effects become pronounced only when the material has a characteristic dimension comparable to the wavelength of the wave. When light waves reach the same point along different paths, the resulting intensity may be smaller than that produced by each individual wave separately. The relative phases of the waves may be such that they interfere destructively, when the arrival of one wave with maximum positive deflection coincides with that of another wave with maximum negative deflection. Observations of light in crystals of calcite (iceland spar) first showed that there are two different modes of vibrations for each direction of propagation.

These are called the two transverse modes of polarization.

All phenomena of geometrical and physical optics are described consistently by Maxwell's equations of electromagnetic theory. Optical phenomena are, therefore, closely related to other electric and magnetic phenomena. Around 1900 the prevailing opinion was that the wave character of light was unambigously established and the nature of light well understood.

There was, however, a mathematical difficulty with the intensity of radiation of ultraviolet and higher frequencies. The photoelectric effect could also be interpreted only by considering light to have a quality of particles. The number of electrons emitted from a photosensitive surface is proportional to the intensity of the light. The energy of the individual electrons is, however, determined by the light frequency. This led to the postulate of light quanta with energy $h\nu$, where h is Planck's constant. This duality in nature, in which "wave-like" and "particle-like" properties are combined, is described without internal contradiction by quantum mechanics. The combined "particle and wave" character of light is revealed by the combination of properties of the light sources, the electromagnetic field describing the light waves, and the detectors.

The study of the interaction of light waves with matter in the sources and in the detectors is the subject of SPECTROSCOPY. This is a wide field which encompases atomic and molecular spectroscopy, parts of solid-state physics and photochemistry. The quantum theory was largely developed on the basis of spectroscopic data. A light quantum is emitted by an excited atom, molecule or other material system, when an electron in such a particle makes a transition or "quantum jump" from a state with higher energy to a state with lower energy. The energy difference between these states is equal to the quantum energy $h\nu$. Similarly, the absorption of light quanta is accompanied by an electronic transition from a state with a lower energy to a state with an energy higher by an amount $h\nu$. In this manner, the frequencies of spectral lines are characteristic for the electronic energy levels in each material. The frequency of the light may be said to correspond to the frequencies of the vibrating charges or oscillators, which are represented by the electrons.

Light sources are thus bodies with a sizeable population of electrons in excited states. This may be accomplished by raising the temperature of the material. The most important source of light is the sun. The moon and other planets are visible only because they reflect sunlight, just as all other objects on the earth which we can see by daylight, but not at night. The sun is a star. In stars, the temperature is maintained at a very high temperature by nuclear reactions.

Man-made light sources range from the primitive fire, candles, and oil and kerosene lamps to the electric light bulb, fluorescent gas-discharge tubes, arcs, etc. In early sources, the material

particles of smoke or wick were heated by the chemical reaction of oxidation or burning; in the incandescent electric lamps, a wire is heated to a very high temperature by an electric current. There are so many energy levels in these luminous solid materials or gases at high pressures that the emitted light is white and contains essentially all frequencies. The higher the temperature, the more radiation is emitted and the higher the average frequency of radiation. It should be realized that most of the energy is emitted as invisible (infrared) radiation, even in the best incandescent lamps. Hot gases in flames may also emit sharp spectral lines characteristic of the atoms occurring in the flame. The yellow color which arises when kitchen salt is sprinkled in a flame is due to the characteristic yellow spectral line of sodium atoms.

In gas discharge tubes, atoms or molecules are excited by collisions with electrons in the ionized gas. The energy is provided by the generator which provides the voltage necessary to maintain the discharge current. An arc is a discharge in air or in a high-pressure vapor. Mercury and sodium discharges are used for street lighting. Fluorescent tubes for office and home lighting use a gas discharge with a substantial amount of ultraviolet components. This ultraviolet light excites electrons in fluorescent centers on the walls of the tube. The electrons drop immediately from the highly excited state to an intermediate state with a lower energy. From this state they finally drop down to the original ground energy level with the emission of visible light. Gas discharges at relatively low pressure may serve as spectroscopic sources to study the emission spectra of atoms, ions and molecules. From the relationship between the energy levels and the frequency of radiation, it follows that a material, when heated, can emit precisely those frequencies which it absorbs when it is in the lower energy level at low temperature.

All these light sources are incoherent in the sense that there is no phase relationship between the light waves emitted by the different atoms in the source. This is quite different from the property of the usual sources of electromagnetic radiation at lower frequencies. In the oscillator tubes of radio- or microwave transmitters, all electrons move and vibrate in step with each other. The analogy between light and low-frequency electromagnetic radiation raises the question, "Can coherent light sources be constructed?" Recently such coherent light sources have been developed. They are characterized by the emission of a highly directional, highly monochromatic light beam of high intensity. They are called LASERS because they are based on *l*ight *a*mplification by *s*timulated *e*mission of *r*adiation. In the conventional sources, all light is emitted spontaneously. In lasers, the original spontaneously emitted light forces the other excited atoms to emit their radiation in step, or coherently. If stimulated emission thus dominates the spontaneous emission, a laser results. This requires a high concentration of

excited atoms and a sufficient feedback mechanism of light by mirrors. In its simplest form a laser consists of a gas discharge in a tube of suitably chosen dimensions and gas pressure between a set of parallel mirrors. Because the atoms in the laser source all act constructively in step, these sources provide a more efficient means to transmit light energy.

The high light intensities available in focused laser beams have led to the development of the branch of nonlinear optics. The optical properties of materials are different at high intensities, because the electronic oscillators are driven so hard that anharmonic properties become evident. A typical effect is the harmonic generation of light in which red laser light is converted into ultraviolet light at exactly twice the frequency, when the high-intensity beam traverses a suitable crystal such as quartz. It should be possible to duplicate at light frequencies all nonlinear effects known from the field of radio communications, such as modulation, demodulation, frequency mixing, etc. It is no longer correct to say that the propagation of a light wave is independent of the presence of other light waves. At high intensities, there is a noticeable interaction between light waves of different frequencies.

The combination of the laws of quantum mechanics and electromagnetic theory gives a consistent description of the generation, propagation and detection of light. Since these same laws also describe many other properties of matter such as electronic structure, chemical binding, electricity and magnetism, etc., it may be said that the nature of light is well understood. In this context, it is not necessary and not even desirable to pose the question, "What is it, precisely, that vibrates in a light wave in vacuum?" The electromagnetic fields acquire meaning only through their relationships with detectors and sources. Human knowledge or understanding is here used in the operational sense that a relatively simple framework of physical concepts and mathematical relationships exists, which gives an accurate description of the wide variety of optical phenomena at present accessible to observation or verification in experimental situations. The following references will introduce the reader to the vast literature of optics and spectroscopy.

N. BLOEMBERGEN

References

Whittaker, E. T., "A History of the Theories of Aether and Electricity," Vols. I and II, London, Nelson & Sons, 1952.

Born, M., and Wolf, E., "Principles of Optics," London and New York, Pergamon Press, 1959.

"Lasers and Light," in "Readings from Scientific American," San Francisco, Freeman, 1969.

Ditchburn, M., "Light," New York, Interscience Publishers, 1963.

Minnaert, M. G. J., "Light and Color in the Open Air," Ann Arbor, Mich., Dover Publications, 1953.

Cross-references: ELECTROMAGNETIC THEORY; INFRARED RADIATION; INTERFERENCE AND INTERFEROMETRY; LASER; OPTICS, GEOMETRICAL; OPTICS, PHYSICAL; PHOTOCONDUCTIVITY; PHOTOELECTRICITY; QUANTUM THEORY; REFLECTION; REFRACTION; SPECTROSCOPY; ULTRAVIOLET RADIATION; VISION AND THE EYE.

LIGHT SCATTERING

When a beam of light falls on a particle, part of this incident beam is diverted from its original path; that part which is diverted and not absorbed is *scattered*.

Light scattering is a familiar phenomenon. The colors of visible objects (other than light sources) are determined by the wavelengths which they scatter most effectively. Scattering by small particles was first studied experimentally in great detail by Tyndall (1869) in connection with the blue of the sky (*Tyndall scattering*).

Classical physics is appropriate for the description of most light-scattering phenomena. Thus, light scattering is explained in terms of the forces exerted by the electromagnetic field on the electronic charges which all matter contains. The oscillating electromagnetic field of the incident light exerts a periodic force on each electronic charge, causing it to execute harmonic motion at the light-wave frequency. It is the fact that an oscillating charge radiates in all directions (except along the line of its motion) which accounts for the scattering. The intensity of the radiation scattered from a particle will be large in directions for which the radiation from the individual elements of the particle interferes constructively, and small in directions in which it interferes destructively.

For particles comparable in size to the light wavelength, the amount of energy scattered as well as the angular distribution of the intensity and polarization of the scattered light are influenced by the distribution of induced oscillating charge within each scatterer. Any correlation which may exist between the positions of the scatterers also affects the extent to which the radiation interferes constructively or destructively to make up the resultant scattered field. Thus, in principle, light scattering provides a tool for the investigation of the number, size, structure, and orientation of particles and their interactions.

The problem of relating the light scattering to these properties and vice versa has proved too difficult for solution in general, because it would be necessary to solve Maxwell's equations with the proper boundary conditions for each particle. Many important cases have been solved, however, subject to certain approximations. Widest success has been achieved for *single scattering*, i.e., for particles sufficiently dispersed that radiation scattered by any one particle can be considered to escape from the medium without being further scattered by other particles. Multiple scattering is relatively difficult to treat and is usually avoided when possible.

In many cases, light scattering is related to the composition and structure of the medium in a way similar to x-ray scattering. The criterion which must be satisfied is that the electromagnetic field within the scatterers should be closely approximated by the unperturbed incident field, just as in the x-ray case. Light scattering under this approximation is widely known as *Rayleigh-Gans*, or *Rayleigh-Debye*, scattering. It is applicable if the phase shift for radiation passing through a particle is not too different from the phase shift which would occur for radiation passing through the same distance in the surrounding medium. When this approximation is valid, the angular distribution of the scattered light is related, as in x-ray scattering, to a "form factor" which describes structure of the individual scatterers and to a "radial density function" or correlation function which describes the order in their spatial arrangement.

If the particles are less than about 1/10th of the light wavelength, and if their index of refraction is near to that of their surroundings, only the induced electric dipole radiation is important. Lord Rayleigh (1871) explained Tyndall's principal results in terms of the intensity and polarization of the induced electric dipole radiation. This type of scattering has since become known as *Rayleigh scattering*.

Rayleigh scattering is of particular importance. If the particles are dispersed at random (molecules of an ideal gas or widely dispersed macromolecules in an essentially homogeneous solution), the individual particles may be regarded as independent sources. In this event, the total scattered intensity is merely the sum of the intensities scattered by the individual particles. The special case of isotropic particles and unpolarized light is both simple and illuminating. The Rayleigh formula is

$$\frac{\text{Intensity of scattered light}}{\text{Intensity of incident light}} = \frac{8\pi^4 N\alpha^2 (1 + \cos^2 \theta)}{\lambda^4 r^2}$$

where N is the number of particles, α is their polarizability, θ is the angle of scattering, λ is the wavelength, and r is the distance from the scattering system to the point of observation (where $r \gg$ any relevant dimension of the scattering system). Thus, Rayleigh scattering from independent particles is proportional to the number of particles and is quite insensitive to their shapes. When the total mass of scatterers is known, it provides a tool for the measurement of molecular weight.[1]

As we consider larger particles which begin to violate the criterion that their dimensions be very small compared with the wavelength, the Rayleigh formula breaks down. This breakdown first appears at large scattering angles, where the destructive interference is first significant, and quickly spreads to moderate and small angles. Nevertheless, for scattering angles sufficiently near zero, the Rayleigh formula retains validity since for zero scattering angle the radiation from all volume elements within a particle is "in phase" regardless of the particle size. Thus, the Rayleigh formula is useful, when properly applied, over an extremely wide range of molecular weights (10^2 to 10^7).

For scattering from dense media such as liquids, the individual molecules can not ordinarily be treated as independent scatterers. Perhaps the most direct formulation of the problem is in terms of the radial density function mentioned earlier. Often, however, one would prefer to relate the light scattering directly to the thermodynamic properties of the medium. For liquids this may often be accomplished through an ingenious approach due to Smoluchowski (1908) and Einstein (1910). This approach takes advantage of the fact that for molecules small compared with the wavelength and for intermolecular forces extending over distances small compared with the wavelength, the scattered field may be regarded as made up of radiation from elements of volume small enough that each element may be considered an electric dipole source and yet large enough that the elements can be considered to be independent of each other. If the index of refraction of every element were identical, the solution would be homogeneous and no scattering would result. But the index of refraction of an element will fluctuate according to the number of molecules it contains. The total scattering is found to be proportional to the mean square fluctuation in index of refraction which is related to the thermodynamic properties of the solution through free energy[1]. For crystalline solids and other media in which correlation extends over distances comparable to the wavelength, it is necessary to use more specialized techniques.[2,3]

To this point, the frequency of the scattered light has been regarded as identical to that of the incident light. Actually, as predicted first by Brillouin (1914), a slight line broadening occurs due to motion of the scatterers (e.g., via the DOPPLER EFFECT), and also due to variations in the directions or magnitudes of their polarizability tensors (e.g., due to chemical reaction). Highly monochromatic laser light and techniques of light-beating spectroscopy extend the use of light scattering to the study of these kinetic phenomena,[2,3] e.g., to measurement of velocities and properties of particles which influence their motion, such as diffusion constants.

The scattered light also has a RAMAN SPECTRUM of relatively weak lines (or bands) first studied in detail by Raman (1928), originating from the light analog of the Cómpton effect, and explained by quantum theory.

R. W. HART

References

1. Kerker, M., "The Scattering of Light," New York, Academic Press, 1969.
2. Wright, G. B., Ed., "Light Scattering Spectra of Solids," New York, Springer-Verlag Co., 1969.

3. Wolf, E., Ed., "Progress in Optics," New York, American Elsevier Publishing Co., Vol. VIII, 1970, Vol. IX, 1971.

Cross-references: DOPPLER EFFECT; LIGHT; OPTICS, PHYSICAL; RAMAN EFFECT AND RAMAN SPECTROSCOPY.

LIQUEFACTION OF GASES

The liquefaction of all readily available gases has become a routine operation in industrial technology. Prominent among the reasons for converting a gas to a liquid are the net saving in cost of storing or of transporting a normally gaseous material in liquid form, the convenience and flexibility of providing very low temperature refrigeration to a multiplicity of sites of modest or intermittent consumption in the form of a low-boiling liquid, and the efficiency attainable in the separation of the components of a gaseous mixture by the partial liquefaction of the mixture, or its total liquefaction followed by rectification.

The transoceanic shipment of liquefied natural gas, the commercial distribution of liquid helium to scientific laboratories, and the production of pure oxygen and pure nitrogen from air are representative examples of the first, second and third reasons, respectively. The first and last examples currently operate on scales such that thousands of tons of liquid are produced daily.

To produce a cold liquid product from gaseous raw material at ambient temperature requires a heat pumping operation. Thermodynamic analysis gives the (unattainable) irreducible minimum work which must be expended in the heat pump, operating in an environment at temperature T_0, to convert a unit mass of warm gas to liquid to be

$$W_{min} = (H_{liquid} - H_{gas}) - T_0(S_{liquid} - S_{gas})$$

where H_{liquid} and H_{gas} are the enthalpies and S_{liquid} and S_{gas} are the entropies per unit mass of liquid product and gaseous raw material, respectively. These thermodynamically reversible works of liquefaction are listed for various of the "permanent" gases in Table 1, which assumes that the starting material is gas at one atmosphere pressure and 300 K. In large-scale

TABLE 1 MINIMUM WORK OF
LIQUEFACTION OF VARIOUS GASES

Substance	Boiling Point (K)	Work Required (kW-hr/kg)
Methane	111.7	.320
Oxygen	90.2	.176
Nitrogen	77.3	.212
Hydrogen	20.4	3.26
Helium	4.22	1.90

practical operations, the actual work requirement will range from ~3 times the minimum for a gas such as methane to ~15 times the minimum for helium.

To achieve the minimum thermodynamic work requirement for cooling and liquefying a stream of gas, an infinite sequence of perfectly efficient refrigerators operating at successively lower temperatures ranging from ambient to the boiling point of the material would be required. Various approximations to this theoretical ideal have been developed.

Cascade Process If the critical temperature of the gas which is to be liquefied lies well *above* the boiling point of some second fluid, whose critical temperature in turn lies above the boiling point of yet another fluid, and so on to some fluid which is condensable at ambient temperatures, then one can replace the infinite sequence of refrigerators of the thermodynamic ideal with this discrete series of liquid cooling baths.

The raw material is compressed to the pressure necessary to condense it at the temperature of the final refrigerant bath. The resulting liquid is expanded through a throttle valve, and the vapor which boils off in the throttling is recycled to conserve the refrigeration it represents. Such an arrangement is shown schematically in Fig. 1. The penalty in increased work over the thermodynamic minimum arises from the small number of steps in the sequence, with the attendant irreversible exchange of heat between the process gas and the much colder baths; from the throttling losses for the product liquid; and from the imperfect efficiency of *any* real refrigerator or compressor. In the simple liquefaction of any gas for which a cascade of refrigerants can be found, the economic performance of a cascade compares very favorably with any other process for truly large-scale operations.

For small-scale systems, the operational complexity and the equipment cost of a cascade are prohibitive.

Linde and Claude Processes A stream of cold gas, flowing countercurrent to the process stream in a heat exchanger which establishes perfect thermal equilibrium between the two streams at every point along their path can substitute perfectly for the infinite sequence of refrigerators in the theoretical ideal system. The problem is just to produce the stream of cold gas (let alone to produce it with perfect efficiency) and to produce a refrigerator to extract the heat of vaporization from the product material at its boiling point.

Application of the first law of thermodynamics to the system shown in Fig. 2, consisting of a constant high-pressure source of fluid at P_1 which flows at constant rate through an insulated heat exchanger B, then through a throttling device C and back through exchanger B, leaving the exchanger against some constant low pressure, P_2, at the *same* temperature at which high-pressure fluid enters, gives

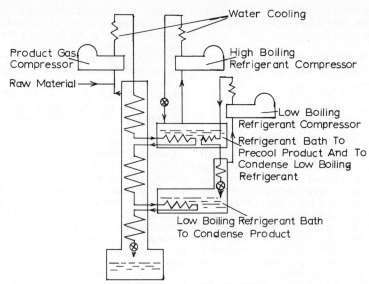

FIG. 1. Schematic arrangement for two-stage cascade.

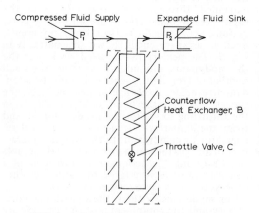

FIG. 2. Adiabatic throttling flow system.

$$H_1 + Q = H_2$$

H_1 and H_2 are the enthalpies per unit mass of fluid entering and leaving the system, respectively, and Q is the amount of heat *absorbed* by a unit mass of fluid in passing through the system. The initial and final kinetic and gravitational potential energies are assumed equal. H_1 will be smaller than H_2 for most gases at absolute temperatures less than 8 to 10 times their normal boiling point and for initial pressures of several hundred to a few thousand pounds per square inch. At higher temperatures, H_1 will be larger than H_2 so that Q is negative—heat is *liberated* within the exchanger-throttle valve system. If the thermal insulation of the exchanger-throttle valve system is *perfect*, then for $H_1 < H_2$, the exchanger-throttle valve system and the circulating gas itself will be continually cooled until some of the circulating

gas accumulates within the system as liquid and a new energy balance $H_1 = fH_\text{liquid} + (1 - f)H_2$ is attained. The fraction, f, of the entering gas accumulates within the system as liquid product with enthalpy H_liquid, and the fraction $(1 - f)$ returns through the exchanger as its refrigerant.

Carl von Linde, in 1885, was the first to couple the relatively feeble ($40°C$ maximum for air expanded from 4000 psi to one atmosphere room temperature) Joule-Thomson cooling, produced by throttling a high-pressure gas and a regenerative heat exchanger, to give the very simple system which is capable of liquefying any gas except helium, hydrogen and neon, starting from room temperature—albeit with poor efficiency. For helium, hydrogen and neon, throttling at room temperature produces heating ($H_2 < H_1$). Sir James Dewar used a bath of liquid oxygen to precool compressed hydrogen to ~90 K where $H_2 > H_1$. The cooled hydrogen was then fed into a simple Linde liquefier, and Dewar first liquefied hydrogen in this way in 1898.

Kamerlingh Onnes used a bath of liquid hydrogen boiling under vacuum near its freezing point to precool compressed helium to ~14 K (where $H_2 > H_1$ for helium). The helium was then fed into a simple Linde liquefier, and Onnes first liquefied helium in 1908.

For any real system, whose thermal insulation leaks q units of heat per unit mass of entering gas and whose exchanger permits gas to leave the system at $T_2' < T_1$, the energy balance becomes

$$H_1 + q = fH_\text{liquid} + (1 - f)[H_2 - C_p(T_2' - T_1)]$$

Poor insulation (large q) and an inefficient ex-

changer (large $T'_2 - T_1$) can easily reduce f to zero.

As the temperature of the gas entering the exchanger of a Linde liquefier approaches its critical temperature, the thermodynamic efficiency of the system as a refrigerator rises sharply. A simple Linde liquefier (commonly but improperly called a Joule-Thomson liquefier) is combined with any of several types of efficient auxiliary preliminary refrigerators and forms the final stage of almost every large scale liquefier in common use. Linde, himself, quickly modified the simple system to what in essence is a pair of simple liquefiers operating in cascade. The first (precooling) unit operates between a common initial high pressure and some intermediate pressure for optimum efficiency, rather than between the high pressure and one atmosphere. He also added a conventional ammonia refrigerator for precooling to further enhance efficiency.

It is possible to produce a cold stream of gas with relatively good efficiency by allowing compressed gas to expand in a reciprocating expansion engine, or in an expansion turbine. If the expansion engine is preceded by an efficient regenerative heat exchanger, relatively modest ratios of inlet pressure to exhaust pressure at the expansion engine will produce gas near its boiling point. The thermodynamic efficiency of such expanders commonly approaches or exceeds 80 per cent. A fraction of this cold exhaust gas can be used to refrigerate the feed stream to a simple Linde liquefier. Georges Claude in 1905 combined a reciprocating expansion engine with a simple Linde liquefier as shown schematically in Fig. 3 to produce an air liquefier of improved efficiency which became known as the Claude cycle.

Peter Kapitza combined a precooling bath of liquid nitrogen in sequence with a reciprocating expansion engine to precool compressed helium feed for a final Linde stage in 1934 and produced a Claude cycle liquefier which liquefied helium without the use of any auxiliary liquid

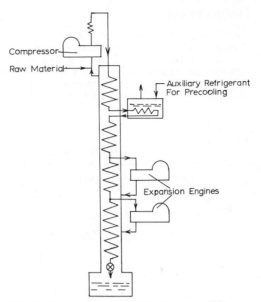

FIG. 4. Composite system for helium liquefaction.

hydrogen. Collins developed a similar machine which has been produced commercially in relatively large numbers. It uses a cascade of two expansion engines in a Claude cycle liquefier capable, when combined with liquid-nitrogen precooling, of producing ~8 liters of liquid helium per hour. The schematic arrangement is shown in Fig. 4. The same schematic arrangement of liquid precooling bath or baths followed by expansion engines all precooling the feed to a final Linde liquefier, could be used to describe in essence the large plants currently used for the liquefaction of hydrogen or helium.

DAVID N. LYON

References

Haselden, G. G., "Cryogenic Fundamentals," Ch. 2, New York, Academic Press 1971.

Barron, Randall, "Cryogenic Systems," Ch. 3, New York, McGraw-Hill Book Co., 1966.

Vance, R. W., "Cryogenic Technology," Ch. 2, New York, John Wiley & Sons, 1964.

Scott, R. B., "Cryogenic Engineering," Ch. 2, New York, Van Nostrand Reinhold, 1959.

Zemansky, M. W., "Heat and Thermodynamics," Third Edition, Ch. 14, New York, McGraw-Hill Book Co., 1951.

Dodge, B. F., "Chemical Engineering Thermodynamics," Ch. 10, New York, McGraw-Hill Book Co., 1944.

Collins, S. C., *Science*, **116**, 289 (1952).

Cross-references: CRYOGENICS, ENTROPY, GAS LAWS, REFRIGERATION, STATES OF MATTER, THERMODYNAMICS.

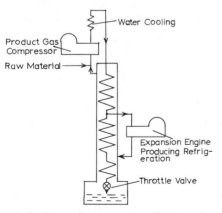

FIG. 3. Schematic arrangement Claude cycle.

LIQUID STATE

Liquid is the term used for a state of matter characterized by that of a pure substance above the temperature of melting and below the vaporization temperature, at any pressure between the triple point pressure and the critical pressure (see Fig. 1). The liquid state resembles

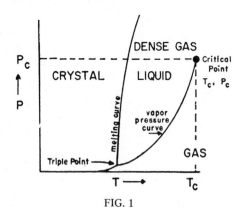

FIG. 1

the crystalline in the relatively low dependence of density on P and T, and resembles the gas state in the inability to support shear stresses (see reference to glasses below). Structurally the molecules are relatively close together but they lack long-range crystalline order. The mutual solubility of different liquids is also intermediate between the complete mutual solubility of most gases, and the relatively rare appreciable mutual solubility of pure crystalline compounds. Two liquids of similar molecules are usually soluble in all proportions, but very low solubility is sufficiently common to permit the demonstration of as many as seven separate liquid phases in equilibrium at one temperature and pressure (mercury, gallium, phosphorus, perfluoro-kerosene, water, aniline, and heptane at 50°C, 1 atm.

Stability Limits With the exception of helium and certain apparent exceptions discussed below, Fig. 1 gives a universal phase diagram for all pure compounds. The triple point of one P and one T is the single point at which all three phases, crystal, liquid, and gas, are in equilibrium. The triple point pressure is normally below atmospheric. Those substances, i.e., CO_2, $P_t = 3885$ mm, $T_t = -56.6°C$, for which it lies above, sublime without melting at atmospheric pressure.

From the triple point, the melting curve defines the equilibrium between crystal and liquid, usually rising with small but positive dT/dP, and presumably always with positive dT/dP at sufficiently high P values. The line is believed to extend infinitely without a critical point (it has been followed to $T \cong 16T_c$ for He, and calculations indicate that hard spheres would show a gas-crystal phase change). The

gas-liquid equilibrium line, the vapor pressure curve, has dT/dP always positive and greater than the melting curve. The vapor pressure curve always ends at a critical point, $P = P_c$, $T = T_c$, above which the liquid and gas phase are no longer distinguishable. Since the liquid can be continuously converted into the gas phase without discontinuous change of properties by any path in the P-T diagram passing above the critical point, there is no definite boundary between liquid and gas.

The term *liquid* is commonly reserved for $T < T_c$, and "dense gas" is used for $T > T_c$. However, certain properties, such as the ability to dissolve solids, change rather abruptly at the critical density. In many respects, the dense gas resembles the low-temperature liquid of the same density more closely than it does the dilute gas.

The slope, dT/dP, of all phase equilibrium lines obeys the thermodynamic Clapeyron equation:

$$dT/dP = \Delta V/\Delta S = T\Delta V/\Delta H \qquad (1)$$

with ΔV, ΔS, and ΔH the differences, for the two phases, of volume, entropy, and heat content or enthalpy, respectively. The quantity ΔH is the heat absorbed in the phase change at constant P. Since always $S_{cr.} < S_{liq.} < S_{gas}$ and usually $V_{cr.} < V_{liq.} < V_{gas}$, one usually has $dT/dP > 0$; the relatively rare cases, including water, for which $V_{liq.} < V_{cr.}$ at low pressures leads to $dT/dP < 0$ for the melting curve near the triple point.

Figure 1 gives the P-T boundaries of the stable liquid phase. Clean liquids can readily be superheated or supercooled, and in vessels having walls to which the liquid adheres, they can be made to support negative pressures of several tens of atmospheres. Thus the properties of the metastable liquid can be investigated outside the limits shown in the diagram.

Two apparent exceptions to the universality of the phase diagram of Fig. 1 deserve mention. First, many of the more complicated molecules decompose at temperatures below melting or boiling, and the diagram is unobservable. Secondly, some liquids, notably glycerine and SiO_2 and many multicomponent solutions, supercool so readily that crystallization is difficult to observe. In these cases, there is a continuous transition on cooling to a glass, which has the elastic properties of an isotropic solid. The structure of the glass is qualitatively that of the high-temperature liquid, lacking long-range order. Since glass and liquid are not sharply differentiated, the term *liquid* is sometimes used to include glasses, although common parlance reserves liquid for the state in which flow is relatively rapid.

Quantum Liquids The one real exception to the phase diagram of Fig. 1 is that of helium, Fig. 2. Both isotopes, ^{4}He and ^{3}He, have no triple point, the liquid is stable to 0 K below

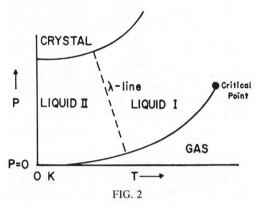

FIG. 2

about 20 atm for ^{4}He and below about 30 atm for ^{3}He. The liquids have zero entropy at 0 K in both cases. This is also the only case in which isotopic mixtures form two liquid phases at equilibrium, the isotopic solution separating below 1 K. The isotope ^{4}He has itself two phases, He I above the dotted λ-line of the diagram, and He II with remarkable properties of superfluidity, second sound, etc., below the λ-line. The phase transition along the λ-line is second order; that is, whereas S and V are continuous, heat capacity and compressibility change discontinuously across the λ-line.

Although no completely satisfactory single theory of liquid helium has yet been formulated, one can say that most of the remarkable properties are qualitatively understood and are due to the predominance of quantum effects, including the difference in the statistics of the even and odd isotopes. Thus helium is the one example in nature of a quantum liquid, all other liquids showing only minor deviations from classical behavior.

Structure Considerable confusion in the description of liquid structure exists, due primarily to difficulties of precise formulation of verbal concepts. The geometric arrangement of any small number (say 10 to 12) of close lying molecules resembles the arrangement in the crystal, but the order rapidly disappears as larger groups are considered. Long-range order is lacking. The fact that numerical theories based on a lattice or cell structure have some success is evidence only that most properties depend on the configuration of near neighbors alone. Insofar as the arrangement of nearest neighbors is describable in terms of that of the crystal, the structure of the normal liquid is probably characterized best by a somewhat closer spacing than the crystal of the same molecules, the reduced density arising from a considerable number of vacancies in the lattice; the coordination number or number of nearest neighbors is lower than in the crystal. The exception is water, in which the low coordination number, 4, of the crystal, is increased by interstitial molecules in the liquid, leading to a higher density of the liquid.

Structural descriptions of this nature usually lack the possibility of precise formulation. It is, however, possible to define for any disordered array of molecules in three-dimensional space an arrangement of contiguous cells, each containing one and only one molecule, the faces of the cells being the loci of the midpoints of neighboring molecules. The statistics of the fraction of cells with n faces and of the distances of the faces from the molecules would give the fraction of molecules having a given number of nearest neighbors and the distance distribution of these in a precisely defined manner. Neither present experimental information nor present theories lend themselves to analysis in such terms.

The only clearly defined manner of describing liquid structure in use at present involves the concept of a set of probability density functions, ρ_n, for ascending numbers, n, of molecules. The function ρ_n depends on the vector coordinates $r_1, r_2, \cdots, r_n$ of n molecules, and

$$\rho_n(r_1, r_2, \cdots, r_n) dr_1, \cdots, dr_n$$

is defined as being the probability that in the liquid of definite P and T, there will be at any instant of time, one molecule at each position, r_i, within the volume element, dr_i. For a fluid, unlike a perfect single crystal, $\rho_i(r)$ is a constant independent of r and equal to the number density: the number, ρ, of molecules per unit volume. The first significant member of the set is then the pair density function, $\rho_2(r_1, r_2)$, which depends only on the distance, $r = |r_1 - r_2|$, between the two molecules. At large distances $\rho_2(r \rightarrow \infty) = \rho^2$. This function can be found experimentally from the x-ray scattering intensities of the liquid (it is the three-dimensional Fourier transform of the scattering intensity at angle θ vs $(4\pi/\lambda)/\sin(\theta/2)$). A typical plot is shown in Fig. 3. The area under the ill-defined first peak integrated over $4\pi r^2 dr$ is the average number of nearest neighbors, and is of order 10 to 11 for normal liquids.

The quantity of dimensions of energy,

$$W_n(r_1, \cdots, r_n) = -kT \ln [\rho^{-n} \rho_n(r_1, \cdots, r_n)]$$

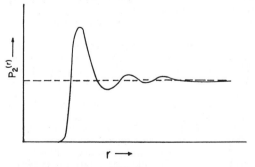

FIG. 3

can be shown to be the potential of average force of n molecules located at the positions $r_1, \cdots, r_n$. That is, if there are n molecules at these positions there will be some average force, $\bar{f}_{xi}$, along the x-coordinate of molecule i. This average is the sum of the direct force due to the other $n - 1$ plus the average of a fluctuating force due to the others, whose average position is affected by that of the n specified ones. This average force is

$$f_{xi} = -(\partial/\partial x_i) W_n(r_1, \cdots, r_n)$$

One frequently assumes that W_n is a sum of pair forces only,

$$W_n(r_1, \cdots, r_n) = \sum_{n \geqslant i > j \geqslant 1} \sum{}' W_2(r_{ij})$$

although this assumption is known to be only approximate. With this assumption, the pair average force potential, $W_2(r_{ij})$, can be computed as the solution of an integral equation, and the solutions agree quite well with the experimental curves.

The knowledge of the complete set of functions ρ_n plus that of the intermolecular forces would permit the computation of all equilibrium properties of the liquid, and indeed if the intermolecular forces are the sum of pair forces, only a knowledge of ρ_2 at all P, T values is necessary. An adequate, although numerically difficult, theory of the transport properties also exists, using the equilibrium functions, ρ_n. At present, only qualitative success is obtained in the completely a *priori* use of the equations.

Associated Liquids The description given above is adequate only for liquids composed of spherically symmetric molecules or molecules that are nearly so. These constitute the so-called normal liquids, which obey reasonably well the law of corresponding states, for which the entropy of vaporization at the boiling point has the Trouton's rule value of approximately 21 cal/deg. For molecules containing large dipole moments, or those forming mutual hydrogen bonds, the concept of the probability density functions must be extended to include angles or other internal degrees of freedom in the coordinates. Such inclusion is conceptually easy, but incredibly complicates the already difficult numerical evaluation of any equations. However, certain qualitative statements may be made.

Liquids composed of molecules with large dipole moments are frequently referred to as associated. Although in some instances relatively stable dimer or definite polymer units of relatively fixed orientation may exist, in many cases, notably water, it is extremely doubtful if an exact knowledge of the structure would reveal any distinguishable entities of associated molecules other than that of the whole liquid. In such cases, one would, however, expect that certain mutual angular orientations between neighboring molecules will be highly preferred,

whereas in the dilute gas this will not be the case. The effect of this restriction on the internal coordinates will be to decrease the entropy of the liquid markedly compared to the gas. This effect is qualitatively the same as in association, and the properties of these liquids, particularly the high entropy of vaporization, will simulate those of a liquid composed of definite associated complexes.

JOSEPH E. MAYER

Cross-references: CRYSTALLOGRAPHY, DIPOLE MOMENTS, ENTROPY, SUPERFLUIDITY, SURFACE TENSION, THERMODYNAMICS, TRANSPORT THEORY, VAPOR PRESSURE AND EVAPORATION.

LUMINANCE

Light has been defined[1] as "the aspect of radiant energy of which a human observer is aware through the visual sensations which arise from the stimulation of the retina of the eye."

One can specify the *radiant intensity* of a point source in a given direction quite simply as so many ergs/second/steradian (cgs system), or as watts/steradian (mks system). Similarly one can specify the *radiance* of an extended source, i.e., the areal density of point sources of unit radiant intensity to which the extended source is equivalent, as so many ergs/second/steradian/square centimeter, or as watts/steradian/square meter.

The problem, however, is that the visual effect is not simply related to the amount of radiation expressed in physical terms. It is evident from observation of the spectrum of a source radiating equal amounts of energy per unit wavelength interval throughout the visible spectrum, that equal energy per unit wavelength interval does not produce visual sensations having equal brightness. The problem is further compounded by the fact that the visual effect is also dependent upon the size of the field viewed, the duration of stimulation to some extent, the part of the retina stimulated, the adaptation state, and the characteristics of the individual observer.

For given conditions of observation, however, and a sufficiently large number of observers, one can determine the average *relative luminous efficiency* of a monochromatic radiation, i.e., the ratio of the luminous efficiency of that radiation to the maximum luminous efficiency, by a variety of indirect methods. The work of Gibson and Tyndall[2] is particularly relevant here as being the basis for the standards adopted by the International Commission on Illumination at Geneva in 1924.

Luminous flux can now be defined as "*that quantity characteristic of radiant flux which expresses its capacity to produce visual sensation, evaluated according to the values of relative luminous efficiency adopted by the Interna-*

TABLE 1. CONVERSION FACTORS FOR UNITS OF LUMINANCE[a]

	cd/m^2	cd/cm^2	$cd/in.^2$	cd/ft^2	L	mL	$apostilb$	$ft\text{-}L$
cd/m² (nit)	1	1×10^{-4}	6.452×10^{-4}	9.290×10^{-2}	3.142×10^{-4}	3.142×10^{-1}	3.142	2.919×10^{-1}
cd/cm² (stilb)	1×10^4	1	6.452	9.290×10^2	3.142	3.142×10^3	3.142×10^4	2.919×10^3
cd/in.²	1.550×10^3	1.550×10^{-1}	1	1.44×10^2	4.869×10^{-1}	4.869×10^2	4.869×10^3	4.524×10^2
cd/ft²	1.076×10	1.076×10^{-3}	6.944×10^{-3}	1	3.382×10^{-3}	3.382	3.382×10	3.142
lambert	3.183×10^3	3.183×10^{-1}	2.054	2.957×10^2	1	1×10^3	1×10^4	9.290×10^2
millilambert	3.183	3.183×10^{-4}	2.054×10^{-3}	2.957×10^{-1}	1×10^{-3}	1	1×10	9.290×10^{-1}
apostilb	3.183×10^{-1}	3.183×10^{-5}	2.054×10^{-4}	2.957×10^{-2}	1×10^{-4}	1×10^{-1}	1	9.290×10^{-2}
foot-lambert	3.426	3.426×10^{-4}	2.210×10^{-3}	3.183×10^{-1}	1.076×10^{-3}	1.076	1.076×10	1

[a]Value in units in left column multiplied by the conversion factor equals value in units in upper row.

tional Commission."[3] The luminous equivalents of radiant intensity and radiance now become *luminous intensity* and *luminance*. The former is defined, in any direction, as *the ratio of the luminous flux emitted by a source or by an element of a source, in an infinitesimal cone containing this direction, to the solid angle of this cone.*[3] The latter is defined, at a point of a surface and in any direction, as *the ratio of the luminous intensity in that direction of an infinitesimal element of, the surface containing the point under consideration, to the orthogonally projected area of this element on a plane perpendicular to that direction.*[3]

The unit of luminous intensity is the *candela*, which is of such a value that the luminous intensity of a full radiator at the freezing point of platinum is 60 units of luminous intensity per square centimeter. The unit of luminous flux is the *lumen*, the flux emitted in a solid angle of one steradian by a uniform point source having an intensity of one candela.

Since luminance is expressed in terms of luminous intensity per unit projected area, the unit of luminance is the candela per unit area. The unit recognized internationally is the *nit*, the candela per square meter. The other unit in the metric system is the *stilb*, or candela per square centimeter. In the British system, the units used are the candela per square inch and the candela per square foot.

Luminance can also be assessed in terms of reflected or emitted luminous flux per unit area, and this is the rationale for the system of units based on the lumen per unit area. The primary unit in the metric system is the *lambert*, the unit of a perfectly diffusing surface, emitting or reflecting light at the rate of one lumen per square centimeter. Commonly used derivatives of the lambert are the *millilambert* (10^{-3} lambert), and the *microlambert* (10^{-6} lambert). Sometimes encountered is the *apostilb* (10^{-4} lambert), which is the luminance of an ideal diffuser emitting or reflecting one lumen per square meter. The *foot-lambert* is the luminance of an ideal diffuser emitting or reflecting one lumen per square foot.

Since an ideal diffuser with a luminance of one candela per unit area in all directions, emits π (3.1416) lumens per unit area, one candela per square centimeter will be equal to π lamberts; one candela per square foot will be equal to π foot-lamberts; and one nit will be equal to π apostilbs.

This multiplicity of units is unfortunate, but should not be confusing if the above relationships are remembered. The obvious solution is to use the most convenient system and convert when necessary. Table 1 should prove helpful.

P. J. FOLEY

References

1. Committee on Colorimetry, Optical Society of America, *J. Opt. Soc. Am.* **34,** No. 5 (1944).

2. Gibson, K. S., and Tyndall, E. P. T., "Visibility of Radiant Energy," *Natl. Bur. St., Sci. Papers*, **19** (1923).

3. I.C.I. Definitions, Committee 1b, *J. Opt. Soc. Am.*, **41**, No. 10 (1951).

Recommended, in addition to the above references:

Wright, W. D., "Photometry and the Eye," London, Hatton Press Ltd., 1949.

Walsh, J. W. T., "Photometry," London, Constable and Co. Ltd., 1953.

Committee on Colorimetry, Optical Society of America, "The Science of Color," New York, Thomas Y. Crowell Co., 1954.

Cross-references: LIGHT; OPTICS, GEOMETRICAL; OPTICS, PHYSICAL; VISION AND THE EYE.

LUMINESCENCE

Introduction Luminescence is the phenomenon of light emission in excess of thermal radiation. Excitation of the luminescent substance is prerequisite to the luminescent emission. Photoluminescence depends upon excitation by photons; cathodoluminescence, by cathode rays; electroluminescence, by an applied voltage; chemiluminescence, by utilization of the energy of a chemical reaction. Luminescent emission involves optical transitions between electronic states characteristic of the radiating substance. The phenomenon is essentially the emission spectroscopy of gases, liquids, and solids. The same basic processes may yield infrared or ultraviolet radiation in substances with suitable electronic energy states; therefore, such emission in excess of thermal radiation is also described as luminescence.

Luminescence can be distinguished from the Raman effect, Compton and Raleigh scattering and Čerenkov emission on the basis of the time delay between excitation and luminescent emission being long compared to the period of the radiation, λ/c, where λ is the wavelength and c is the velocity of light. The radiative lifetimes of the excited states vary from 10^{-10} to 10^{-1} sec depending on the identity of the luminescent substances whereas λ/c is approximately 10^{-14} sec for visible radiation. At ordinary densities of excitation, the spontaneous transition probability predominates so that the luminescent radiation is incoherent; under conditions of high densities of excitation in suitable luminescent substances, the induced transition probability may predominate, the emitted radiation is coherent, and laser action is attained.

The initial persistence of luminescent emission following the removal of excitation depends on the lifetime of the excited state. This emission decays exponentially and is often called fluorescence. In many substances, there is an additional component to the afterglow which decays more slowly and with more complex kinetics. This is called phosphorescence.

For many inorganic crystals, the emission spectra for fluorescence and phosphorescence are the same; the difference in afterglow arises from electron traps from which thermal activation is prerequisite to emission. For organic molecules, the emission spectra for fluorescence and phosphorescence are often different: the former occurs from an excited singlet; the latter, from a triplet state.

Luminescence of Gases The simplest luminescent substances are monatomic gases. The electronic states are characteristic of the isolated atoms; therefore, the excitation and emission spectra depend only on the differences in energy of the stationary electronic states of the many-electron atom, and the spectral lines are broadened only by the lifetimes of the excited states or at higher pressures, by collisions. The transitions are to a good approximation one-electron transitions. Resonance fluorescence is photoluminescence in which the exciting radiation is the exact frequency or wavelength for the transition from the ground to the excited state and emission occurs with the same frequency. Resonance fluorescence is shown diagrammatically in Fig. 1 for low pressure alkali

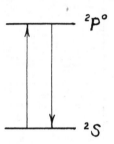

FIG. 1. Resonance fluorescence of atoms, e.g., Na.

metal vapor. The well-known 2537Å line of mercury vapor is another example of resonance fluorescence. This emission can also be excited by electrons accelerated by 5 or more volts. The simplest case of sensitized fluorescence (photoluminescence in which absorption of the exciting radiation is by one substance and the excitation is transferred to another which emits radiation) occurs with mixtures of monatomic gases. For example, the characteristic fluorescence of thallium is observed when mixtures of Tl and Hg vapors are illuminated with the 2537Å radiation of Hg.

For diatomic and polyatomic gases, the energies of the electronic states are dependent on the interatomic distances of the molecule. This dependence is shown in Fig. 2 for the ground and excited states. For a diatomic molecule the coordinate R is the distance between the two atoms. For each electronic state, there is a series of vibrational levels which are also shown in Fig. 2. Optical transitions occur between individual vibrational levels of one electronic state and individual vibrational levels of another electronic state. These transitions occur in ac-

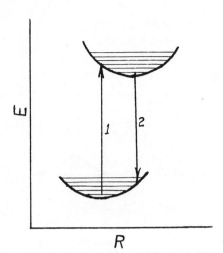

FIG. 2. Configuration coordinate model.

cordance with the Franck-Condon principle, i.e., with fixed nuclear coordinates, vertically as shown in transitions 1 and 2 of Fig. 2. In most cases the emission will involve a smaller transition energy and occur at longer wavelength than the photo-excitation. This is referred to as Stokes' emission. In some cases, for example at high temperatures when the higher vibrational levels of the ground electronic state are populated thermally, anti-Stokes' emission is also observed. Additional structure in the photoexcitation and emission spectra arises from rotational states of the molecule. Iodine is a typical diatomic luminescent molecule excited by green light with visible emission at slightly longer wavelengths. Benzene and aniline are typical polyatomic molecules which are luminescent as vapors.

Luminescence of Organic Materials The electronic states of most organic luminescent materials in the liquid or solid phase, either as pure materials or as solutes in dilute concentration in inert solvents, are to a good approximation describable in terms of the electronic states of the free molecule in the gaseous phase. In other words, the intermolecular forces are weak compared to the intramolecular forces. The photoexcitation and luminescent emission spectra of these substances in condensed phases are similar to the spectra of the vapors. The intermolecular forces are, however, great enough to bring about broadening of absorption and emission lines and in some cases to bring about electronic energy transfer between molecules before intramolecular, vibrational relaxation with the accompanying Stokes' shift can occur. On the other hand, in a viscous or rigid medium collisional, nonradiative de-excitation is reduced.

Many of the organic luminescent materials are aromatic molecules related to dyes. The sodium salt of fluorescein in dilute aqueous solution is well known as an efficient fluorescent material. Other organic substances luminesce efficiently

when dissolved in organic solvents. Terphenyl in xylene is a liquid β- and γ-ray scintillator with emission in the near ultraviolet. Some organic molecules luminesce most efficiently in a rigid medium. A solid solution of 1 per cent anthracene in napthalene is a scintillator with blue emission. For these solutions, energy is absorbed by the solvent molecules and transferred to the solute where the luminescent emission occurs. Crystals of some pure organic substances luminesce, particularly at low temperatures.

The fluorescent emission and the long-wavelength absorption of organic materials are often simply related as mirror images of each other. This is shown in Fig. 3 for rhodamine in etha-

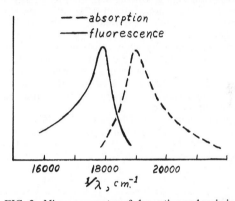

FIG. 3. Mirror symmetry of absorption and emission.

nol and can be explained on the basis of the configuration coordinate model in Fig. 2. with the force constants for the two electronic states approximately equal. For organic molecules, the configuration coordinate R is interpreted as representing, schematically, all the intramolecular nuclear coordinates. In addition to the fluorescent emission, many organic substances exhibit phosphorescent emission. This arises from nonradiative relaxation from the excited singlet to the triplet state followed by radiative decay from the triplet to the ground singlet state, as illustrated in Fig. 4. Because

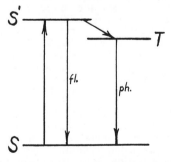

FIG. 4. Fluorescence and phosphorescence of organic molecules.

of the spin selection rule governing radiative transitions, the triplet has a long lifetime and the oscillator strength for direct excitation to the triplet is negligible. In suitable systems, polarized excitation and emission arising from the anisotropy of the organic molecules can be observed.

Chelates involving organic molecules as ligands bound to a metal atom or ion are a class of substances with members which luminesce. The fluorescence and phosphorescence of chlorophyll both *in vivo* and *in vitro* have been investigated for many years. On the other hand, rare earth chelates with organic ligands have been intensively investigated quite recently as lasers. The photoexcitation occurs in the broad absorption bands of the ligand; the energy is transferred to the localized $4f$ shell of the rare earth by a mechanism related to the transfer process occurring in the scintillators; luminescent line emission characteristic of the rare earth occurs as coherent radiation with high excitation intensities. More recently, a fluorinated Eu-acetonate dissolved in acetonitrile has been announced as a liquid laser operating near room temperature.

Luminescence of Inorganic Crystals Inorganic crystals which luminesce are often called phosphors. Their luminescence in most cases originates from impurities or imperfections. Exceptions include the luminescence of alkaline earth tungstates which is characteristic of the $WO_4{}^{2-}$ group perturbed by the crystal field, the luminescence of some rare earth salts, and radiative recombination of conduction electrons with valence band holes in semiconductors. The impurities and imperfections responsible for luminescence in inorganic crystals are of diverse atomic and molecular types whose characteristics depend on the structure of the defect and on the electronic structure of the pure crystal. In some cases, the electronic states involved in the luminescence can be described in terms of energy levels of the impurity ion perturbed by the crystal field; in other cases, in terms of the crystal band structure perturbed by the impurity. The existence of conduction bands in inorganic crystals, particularly in semiconducting crystals, introduces additional mechanisms for the excitation of luminescence and for phosphorescence. For example, suitable impurities can be excited by alternate capture of injected conduction electrons and valence band holes, thus providing one mechanism for electroluminescence; on the other hand, an excited luminescent impurity may lose an electron to another defect via the conduction band, and the thermal activation necessary for return to the luminescent impurity is responsible for phosphorescence.

The alkali halides are simple ionic crystals which become luminescent when doped with suitable impurities. Thallium substituted in dilute concentration at cation sites in potassium chloride has the absorption and emission shown

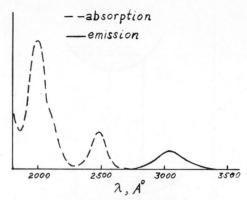

FIG. 5. Spectra of KCL:Tl.

in Fig. 5. The absorption bands involve the $^1S \rightarrow {}^3P^0$, $^1P^0$ transitions of the free ion perturbed by crystal interactions; the principal emission band, $^3P^0 \rightarrow {}^1S$, is similarly perturbed. The spectra can be understood qualitatively with the aid of Fig. 2, modified with a second excited state and with the configuration coordinate interpreted as symmetric displacement of the six nearest-neighbour Cl^- from the Tl^+. It is this interaction which is most dependent on the electronic state of the Tl^+ and is, therefore, largely responsible for the band widths and Stokes' shift.

Many inorganic crystals become luminescent when certain transition metal ions are dissolved in them. The luminescence involves intercombination transitions within the $3d$ shell; therefore, crystal field theory can be used to interpret the absorption and emission spectra. Divalent manganese is a common activator ion. Zn_2SiO_4, ZnS and $3Ca_3(PO_4)_2 \cdot CaF_2$ are important phosphors activated with Mn^{2+}. The last, activated also with Sb^{3+}, is the principal fluorescent lamp phosphor. The excitation at $2537Å$ from the Hg discharge occurs at the Sb^{3+}, whose energy level structure is similar to that of Tl^+; part of the energy is radiated in a blue band due to Sb^{3+} and part is transferred to the Mn^{2+} which is responsible for an orange emission band. It has recently been shown that the Sb^{3+} at a Ca^{2+} site is locally charge-compensated by an O^{2-} at a halide site and that the blue emission is in part an electron transfer transition. The ruby laser involves the luminescence of Cr^{3+} in Al_2O_3. Excitation occurs in a broad absorption band, and the system relaxes to another excited state from which emission occurs in a narrow band.

Rare earth ions, particularly trivalent, in solid solution in inorganic crystals and in glasses exhibit the emission characteristic of transitions in the $4f$ shell. For examples, samarium, europium, and terbium give visible emission; neodymium, infrared; and gadolinium, ultraviolet. Because of their narrow emission bands, the rare earth activated phosphors are of interest

as lasers and photon counters, and as phosphors for color television. Crystal field theory can be used to explain the optical absorption and luminescent emission of the $4f$ transitions of rare earth ions in crystals and glasses. Phosphors doubly activated with rare earths, e.g., YF_3: Yb, Tm, have been found to be capable of large anti-Stokes' emission. This occurs by multiphoton infrared excitation and with visible emission.

The zinc sulfide phosphors, which are widely used as cathodoluminescent phosphors and well-known for their electroluminescence, are now recognized as large band gap, compound semiconductors. Two impurities or imperfections are essential to the luminescence of many of these phosphors: an activator which determines the emission spectrum and a coactivator which is essential for the emission but in most cases has no effect on the spectrum. Activator atoms such as Cu, Ag and Au substitute at Zn sites and perturb a series of electronic states upward from the valence band edge. In a neutral crystal containing only these activator impurities, the highest state is empty, i.e., it contains a positive hole and can accept an electron from the valence band; therefore, in semiconductor notation, the activator is an acceptor. In a similar way, coactivators such as Ga or In at Zn sites or Cl at S sites are donors in ZnS. The simultaneous introduction of both types of impurities results in electron transfer from donor to acceptor lowering the energy of the crystal and leaving both impurities charged. The coulomb attraction of the donor and acceptor leads to a departure from a random distribuover lattice sites and to pairing. The electronic states and some of the transitions of acceptors, donors and donor-acceptor pairs are shown in Fig. 6. The spectrum of ZnS:Cu, Ga is shown

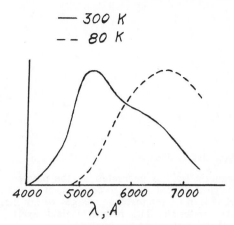

FIG. 7. Spectra of ZnS: Cu, Ga.

acceptors and their pairs, emission bands due to transition metals are well known for zinc sulfide as noted earlier. In zinc sulfide crystals, the donors which are unassociated with acceptors serve as electron traps and are responsible for long-persistent, temperature-dependent phosphorescence. Uncharged or isoelectronic dopants, such as N at phosphorous sites in GaP, have been shown to be efficient radiative recombination centers, particularly in indirect band gap semiconductors. The III-IV semiconductors with isoelectronic dopants or with donor-acceptor pairs are currently the principal electroluminescent light-emitting diodes.

FERD WILLIAMS

Reference

Pringsheim, P., "Fluorescence and Phosphorescence," New York, Interscience, 1949.
Curie, D., "Luminescence in Crystals" New York, J. Wiley & Sons, 1963 (translated by G. F. J. Garlick).
Goldberg, P., Ed., "Luminescence of Inorganic Solids," New York, Academic Press, 1966.
Crosswhite, H. M., and Moos, H. J., Eds., "Optical Properties in Crystals," New York, Wiley-Interscience, 1967.
Lim, E. C., Ed., "Molecular Luminescence," New York, Benjamin, 1969.
Williams, F., Ed., "Proceedings of International Conference on Luminescence," Amsterdam, North Holland, 1970.
Birks, J. B., "Photophysics of Aromatic Molecules," New York, Wiley-Interscience, 1970.
Williams, F., Ed., "Luminescence of Crystals, Molecules, and Solutions," New York, Plenum, 1973.

Cross-references: COLOR CENTERS; CRYSTALLOGRAPHY; ENERGY LEVELS; LASERS; PHOTOCONDUCTIVITY; RADIATION, THERMAL; RESONANCE; SEMICONDUCTORS; SOLID-STATE PHYSICS; SOLID-STATE THEORY; SPECTROSCOPY.

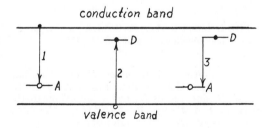

FIG. 6. Band model for acceptor, donor, and pair transitions.

in Fig. 7. The longer-wavelength emission band involves the transition from the lowest donor state to highest acceptor state (transition 3) in approximately fifth nearest-neighbor pairs; the shorter-wavelength emission corresponds more nearly to transition 1 of Fig. 6. Luminescent emission from donor-acceptor pairs has been more clearly seen with gallium phosphide crystals. In addition to luminescence due to donors,

M

MAGNETIC FIELD

Magnetic field is generated by the passage of electrical currents through conductors or by the circulation of microscopic charges within magnetic materials. The magnetic field exerts a mechanical stress on its sources.

Basic Equations To separate electromagnetic theory from the theory of the solid state, Maxwell's equations can be written in terms of the magnetic induction or flux-density **B** and the total current density **J**:

$$\nabla \cdot \mathbf{B} = 0 \tag{1}$$

$$\nabla \times \mathbf{B} = 4\pi \mathbf{J} \tag{2}$$

where, for purposes of the present article, the displacement current $(1/c^2)\partial\mathbf{E}/\partial t$ is neglected relative to $4\pi\mathbf{J}$ (see ELECTROMAGNETIC THEORY and MAGNETISM).

The solution of Eqs. (1) and (2) is

$$\mathbf{B}(\mathbf{r}) = \int d^3r_1 \frac{\mathbf{J}(\mathbf{r}_1) \times (\mathbf{r} - \mathbf{r}_1)}{|\mathbf{r} - \mathbf{r}_1|^3} \tag{3}$$

where the integral includes all current-carriers, and **B** vanishes at infinity.

From Eq. (3) it follows, for example, that an infinite straight conductor [Fig. 1(a)] carrying a total axial current I_c gives rise to an azimuthally directed external magnetic induction of strength $\mathbf{B} = 2I_c/r$, where r is the distance from the conductor axis. The same is true for an axial current in any axisymmetric conductor, e.g., the toroidal conductor of Fig. 1(b). An infinitely long circular cylindrical conductor [Fig. 2(a)] carrying an azimuthal current density I_c' per unit length contains an axially directed magnetic induction of strength $\mathbf{B} = 4\pi I_c'$. The same expression holds for a straight cylindrical conductor of arbitrary cross section [Fig. 2(b)],

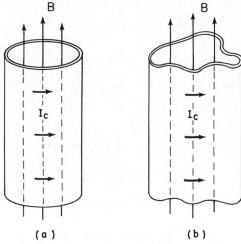

FIG. 2. Infinitely long cylindrical configurations with axially directed magnetic induction **B**.

or for an infinite plane current sheet. A circular cylinder like that of Fig. 2(a), but of finite length L and radius R, has a central magnetic induction of strength $\mathbf{B} = 4\pi I_c' L(L^2 + 4R^2)^{-1/2}$.

In terms of the vector potential **A**,

$$\mathbf{B} = \nabla \times \mathbf{A} \tag{4}$$

and the gauge $\nabla \cdot \mathbf{A} = 0$, one has

$$\nabla^2 \mathbf{A} = -4\pi \mathbf{J} \tag{5}$$

and

$$\mathbf{A}(\mathbf{r}) = \int d^3r_1 \frac{\mathbf{J}(\mathbf{r}_1)}{|\mathbf{r} - \mathbf{r}_1|} \tag{6}$$

for **A** vanishing at infinity.

Magnetic lines of force are defined by $d\mathbf{r} \propto \mathbf{B}$

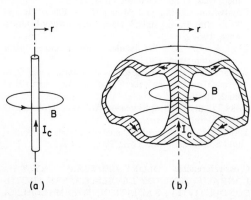

FIG. 1. Axisymmetric configurations with axially directed current I_c.

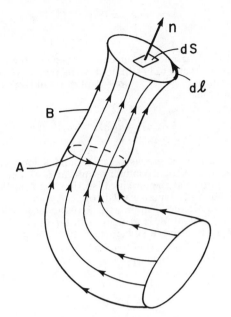

FIG. 3. Magnetic flux tube.

and are endless, by virtue of Eq. (1). The magnetic flux Φ through a surface S, bounded by a closed curve ℓ (Fig. 3), is given by

$$\Phi = \int dS\mathbf{B} \cdot \mathbf{n} = \oint d\ell \cdot \mathbf{A} \qquad (7)$$

where $\mathbf{n}$ is the normal to S. The flux tube defined by the field lines passing through ℓ contains constant flux, independent of S.

At a large distance from a localized current distribution at $\mathbf{r} = 0$, Eq. (6) gives the dipole potential

$$\mathbf{A} = \frac{\mathbf{m} \times \mathbf{r}}{r^3} \qquad (8)$$

where

$$\mathbf{m} = \frac{1}{2} \int d^3 r_1 \mathbf{r}_1 \times \mathbf{J}(\mathbf{r}_1) \qquad (9)$$

Equations in the Presence of Magnetic Materials A macroscopic current density $\mathbf{J}_M$ can be defined by local averaging of the microscopic current density $\mathbf{J}_m$ within magnetic materials

$$\mathbf{J}_M = \langle \mathbf{J}_m \rangle_{\text{av}} \qquad (10)$$

More conveniently, a magnetization vector $\mathbf{M}$ can be introduced, where

$$\mathbf{J}_M = \nabla \times \mathbf{M} \qquad (11)$$

In experiments, only $\mathbf{J}_M$ can be measured directly (via measurements on $\mathbf{B}$), and $\mathbf{M}$ is then uniquely derivable from Eq. (11) only with the added condition that it is to be a local state

variable of the magnetic material (i.e., it is constant in uniform samples and constant fields). This condition follows automatically from the interpretation of $\mathbf{M}$ as a magnetic-moment density per unit volume:

$$\mathbf{M} = N\mathbf{m}_0 \qquad (12)$$

The theoretical molecular magnetic moment $\mathbf{m}_0$ (with number density N) is derived from $\mathbf{J}_m$ by evaluation of Eq. (9) over the molecular volume.

For macroscopic purposes, the total current density $\mathbf{J}$ of the preceding section is now specified by

$$\mathbf{J} = \mathbf{J}_c + \mathbf{J}_M \qquad (13)$$

The component $\mathbf{J}_c$ flows in conductors of resistivity η in accordance with Ohm's law:

$$\eta\mathbf{J}_c = \mathbf{E} \qquad (14)$$

The component $\mathbf{J}_M$ is derived from $\mathbf{M}$.

In the analysis of configurations involving magnetic materials, the magnetic field $\mathbf{H}$ is a convenient vector

$$\mathbf{H} = \mathbf{B} - 4\pi\mathbf{M} \qquad (15)$$

Then Eqs. (1) and (2) take the form

$$\nabla \cdot \mathbf{H} = -4\pi\nabla \cdot \mathbf{M} \qquad (16)$$

$$\nabla \times \mathbf{H} = 4\pi\mathbf{J}_c \qquad (17)$$

At the interface between two magnetic materials, Eqs. (1) and (17) imply continuity of the normal component of $\mathbf{B}$ and of the tangential component of $\mathbf{H}$.

Across a sheet-current of density I'_c per unit length, the tangential component transverse to $\mathbf{J}_c$ of both $\mathbf{H}$ and $\mathbf{B}$ undergoes an increment $4\pi I'_c$. The other components of $\mathbf{H}$ and $\mathbf{B}$ are unaffected.

The field patterns set up by a magnetized sphere are illustrated in Fig. 4. The magnetic induction (a) and magnetic field (b) are identical outside the sphere, but differ inside it, because of the magnetization (c). The same pattern of magnetic induction could be generated in the absence of magnetization by a surface current (d). The source of the magnetic field in Eq. (16), that is to say the quantity $\nabla \cdot \mathbf{M}$, is also referred to as the magnetic pole density. The north and south polar regions are indicated in (c).

For weakly magnetic materials, Eq. (15) can generally be written in terms of a scalar magnetic permeability μ

$$\mu\mathbf{H} = \mathbf{B} \qquad (18)$$

For ferromagnetic materials, one can still write

$$\mu\mathbf{H} = \mathbf{B} - 4\pi\mathbf{M}_0 \qquad (19)$$

where $\mathbf{M}_0$ is a permanent magnetization, but μ now depends on the time history as well as the

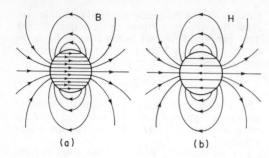

(a)   (b)

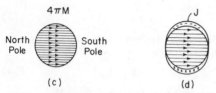

(c)   (d)

FIG. 4. Magnetic induction (a) and magnetic field (b) arising from sphere with magnetization pattern shown in (c) or with surface current pattern shown in (d).

magnitude of **H**. The typical relation between **B** and **H** for ferromagnetic materials is illustrated in Fig. 5.

When J_c is zero everywhere, one can define a scalar potential Ω, such that

$$\mathbf{H} = -\nabla\Omega \tag{20}$$

$$\nabla^2\Omega = 4\pi\nabla \cdot \mathbf{M} \tag{21}$$

If the boundary condition on Ω is simply that it vanish at infinity, the solution is

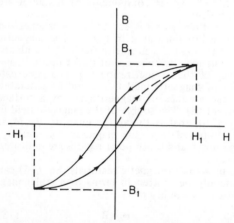

FIG. 5. As magnetic field **H** is initially raised to H_1, magnetic induction **B** rises to B_1. Cyclical pattern shown is typical of ferromagnetic materials: B saturates as H becomes large; B remains finite as H returns to null; B goes to $-B_1$ as H goes to $-H_1$. Double-valuedness of B(H) is known as hysteresis.

$$\Omega(\mathbf{r}) = -\int d^3r_1 \, \frac{\nabla_1 \cdot \mathbf{M}(\mathbf{r}_1)}{|\mathbf{r} - \mathbf{r}_1|} \tag{22}$$

In the presence of current-carrying conductors Eqs. (20) and (21) still hold in the region where $J_c = 0$, but Eq. (17) now implies a multivalued potential

$$\oint d\boldsymbol{\ell} \cdot \mathbf{H} = \oint d\Omega = 4\pi I_c \tag{23}$$

where the integral is taken around a loop enclosing the total conductor current I_c. To keep the potential single-valued, so that the solution of Eq. (22) remains valid, one may adopt the "magnetic-shell" approach: J_c is replaced with an equivalent **M**, in analogy with Eq. (11).

Magnetic Force and Energy From Maxwell's stress tensor, we find the volume force

$$\mathbf{f} = -\nabla\left(\frac{B^2}{8\pi}\right) + \frac{1}{4\pi}(\mathbf{B} \cdot \nabla)\mathbf{B} \tag{24}$$

$$= \mathbf{J} \times \mathbf{B}$$

which agrees with the summation of the Lorentz forces on the moving charges composing **J**. The "magnetic pressure" against a current sheet bounding a region of finite **B** (as in the Meissner effect or ordinary skin effect) is thus $B^2/8\pi$, evaluated at the surface. The force and torque on a body localized in a nearly uniform field are

$$\mathbf{F} = (\mathbf{m} \cdot \nabla)\mathbf{B} \tag{26}$$

$$\mathbf{N} = \mathbf{m} \times \mathbf{B} \tag{27}$$

From the microscopic point of view underlying Eq. (2), the magnetic energy density is

$$w = \frac{B^2}{8\pi} \tag{28}$$

In the presence of magnetic materials, one is more interested in the electrical input energy required to go from $\mathbf{B}_0$ to **B**, and this is given by

$$\Delta w = \frac{1}{4\pi}\int_{B_0}^{B} \mathbf{H} \cdot d\mathbf{B} \tag{29}$$

For $\mathbf{H} = \mu\mathbf{B}$, with constant μ, this becomes

$$\Delta w = \frac{1}{8\pi\mu}(B^2 - B_0^2) \tag{30}$$

The derivation of Eqs. (28) and (29) depends on the complete set of Maxwell's equations.

Units and Magnitudes The equations used here are based on the emu system. If the currents are expressed in amperes, they must be divided by 10 to give magnetic inductions in gauss or fields in oersteds. A magnetic induction of 10 kilogauss (one weber per square meter) can exert a maximum stress $B^2/8\pi$ of

about 4 atm, and contains an energy density of 0.4 joules/cm^{-3}.

The strength of the earth's magnetic induction is about 0.2 gauss. For typical ferromagnetic materials, the maximum value of $4\pi M$ is 20 kilogauss; at this point of saturation, the permeability μ approaches unity. At magnetic fields below one gauss, permeabilities of 1000 or more can be reached. The strength of materials limits the magnetic induction obtainable nondestructively with laboratory electromagnets to peak values well below a million gauss.

HAROLD P. FURTH

References

Stratton, J. A., "Electromagnetic Theory," New York, McGraw-Hill Book Co., 1941.
Jackson, J. D., "Classical Electrodynamics," New York, John Wiley & Sons, 1962.

Cross-references: ELECTROMAGNETIC THEORY, FERROMAGNETISM, MAGNETISM.

MAGNETIC RESONANCE

Electrons revolve about the nucleus of an atom and spin around their axes; in addition, the nucleus has a spin of its own. All of these moving charges have associated magnetic fields (magnetic moments), and *magnetic resonance* is concerned with the interactions of some of these fields with each other and with at least two external magnetic fields applied to the atom.

To facilitate understanding, consider an electron circulating about the nucleus. The electron has angular motion and it is a charged particle held in orbit by the oppositely charged nucleus.

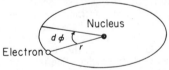

Assume KEPLER'S LAW of areas applies (radius vector of the particle sweeps out equal areas in equal times) and that angular momentum, P_ϕ, is conserved and quantized ($P_\phi = L\hbar = mr^2\dot{\phi}$); $L \equiv$ orbital quantum number, and $\hbar \equiv$ Planck's constant/2π. The area swept out in one period, t, is:

$$A = \int_0^t \tfrac{1}{2}(r^2\dot{\phi})\,dt = L\hbar\,t/2m.$$

From Ampère's Law, one can find the equivalent magnetic dipole moment, μ, produced by a closed current loop, I, to be: $\mu = I \cdot A$. Since current is e/t it follows that

$$\mu = L(e\hbar/2m) \qquad (1)$$

and $e\hbar/2m$ is defined as a Bohr magneton, μ_B.

Next, consider the ELECTRON SPIN about its own axis. A classical derivation of the spin moment similar to the above produces an electron spin moment of two Bohr magnetons. Dirac's relativistic quantum theory of the electron and many experiments give the correct value of one Bohr magneton; this means the spin quantum number of the electron is 1/2.

The total angular momentum, $\mathbf{P}_J$, is found by adding vectorially the orbital and spin angular momentum of the electron, $\mathbf{P}_J = \mathbf{P}_L + \mathbf{P}_S = \hbar(\mathbf{L} + \mathbf{S})$ and the total magnetic moment becomes: $\mu = \mu_B(\mathbf{L} + 2\mathbf{S})$. P_L and P_S can be thought of as precessing about P_J and only their components in the direction of P_J contribute to the average magnetic moment. Vectorially adding the moments gives:

$$\mu_J = \mu_B[L\cos(\mathbf{LJ}) + 2S\cos(\mathbf{SJ})]$$

$$= \mu_B J\left(1 + \frac{S^2 + J^2 - L^2}{2J^2}\right)$$

or using a more rigorous wave mechanics approach S^2 is replaced by $S(S + 1)$, etc., to give:

$$\mu_J = \mu_B g J \qquad (2)$$

where

$$g \equiv 1 + \frac{S(S + 1) + J(J + 1) - L(L + 1)}{2J(J + 1)}$$

The quantity g is called the Landé g-factor and for an atom in the ground state $L = 0$, $S = J$, and g becomes equal to 2. We could add the nuclear spin and its magnetic moment to this and the vector problem would become complex indeed! This will be done later in an easier way.

For simplicity, we will now add the external magnetic field, $\mathbf{H}$. Just as a spinning top will precess in the earth's gravitational field, so will the magnetic moment vector of the electron precess in the magnetic field, the torque in the electron case being produced by the interactions of the dipole and the external field. Equating the time rate of change of angular momentum to the torque on the dipole, one can derive the precessional frequency in complete analogy to the top problem.

This precessional frequency, called the Larmor frequency, can also be derived from an energy standpoint and will give us more insight. The potential energy of a magnetic dipole in a magnetic field is $W = -\mu H = \mu_B g J H$. If we confine ourselves to an atom in the ground state then $\mathbf{J} = \mathbf{S}$ and $S = \pm 1/2$, the spin being either parallel or antiparallel with the external field. The magnetic moment is defined as positive or negative according to the condition of parallelism or antiparallelism, respectively.

Thus the energy difference between the two possible electron spin states can be equated to $\hbar\omega_L$ where ω_L is the Larmor frequency of precession

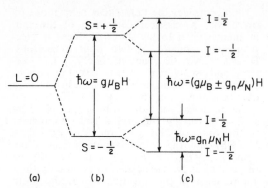

FIG. 1. Magnetic resonance energy levels. (a) orbital electron energy level; (b) electron spin moment in a magnetic field; (c) nuclear spin magnetic moments in a magnetic field.

$$\hbar\omega_L = W(S = -\tfrac{1}{2}) - W(S = \tfrac{1}{2})$$

$$= g\mu_B H = \lambda H \quad (3)$$

Electromagnetic radiation at the Larmor frequency and with the correct polarization will be absorbed by dipoles in the lower state, making transitions to the higher state. This is shown in Fig. 1(b). *Electron spin resonance* is the technique for measuring this splitting using radio-frequency technology.

Since the nucleus is known to carry a charge, its angular spin should and does produce a nuclear magnetic moment. A nuclear magneton, μ_n, is defined in the same manner as the Bohr magneton, except the mass of the electron is replaced by the mass of the proton. A nuclear g-factor ($g_n \equiv gI$) is also defined where I is the spin of the nucleus.

The proton's magnetic moment is 2.7935 nuclear magnetons while the neutron's moment is $-1.9135\,\mu_n$. The positive or negative sign refers to the condition of whether the angular momentum vector has the same or opposite direction as the magnetic moment. A nucleus with a spin, I, will have $2I + 1$ possible orientations in a magnetic field and corresponding $2I + 1$ energy levels. These give rise to a hyperfine structure.

For simplicity, consider a hydrogen atom in a molecule. The nucleus is a proton with a spin of 1/2 and, consequently, its magnetic moment is either parallel or antiparallel to the field. This produces energy levels as shown in Fig. 1(c).

Nuclear magnetic resonance is concerned with the use of radio-frequency techniques to study the transitions between nuclear spin states; in the case shown $\hbar\omega = g_p\mu_n H$ for the transition.

Consider a system of free magnetic dipoles in an external magnetic field. The magnetic dipoles would seek a position of minimum potential energy and consequently turn parallel with the field. In the world of nuclei and atoms we do not have such a closed system. The thermal agitation of the molecules and atoms coupled with

the nuclear spin through magnetic and electric field interactions produces a disorienting effect which tends to fill all energy states equally.

The energy for each degree of freedom of a molecule is $(\tfrac{1}{2})kT$ and at room temperatures is roughly 10^{-14} ergs while the difference in energy between the two states of a proton (hydrogen nucleus) in a magnetic field of 10 000 oersteds is about 10^{-20} ergs ($W = g\mu_n H$).

For some solids and for liquids near absolute zero, more sophisticated distributions must be used, but for liquids and gasses at room temperature, a simple Boltzmann distribution will be adequate, $N \propto \epsilon^{-W/kT}$. Thus, the ratio of the populations of the two states used for an example would be $N(\tfrac{1}{2})/N(-\tfrac{1}{2}) \simeq \epsilon^{(g\mu_n H/kT)}$ and for these protons at room temperature, one would find about seven more in the lower energy state out of every million.

As in electron resonance experiments, when an rf field is applied to the sample at right angles to the external field, an in-phase component of the rf field will cause the protons in the lower energy state to "flop" into the higher and the protons in the higher energy state into the lower.

In practice, only a certain percentage of each population is "flopped." However, a simple calculation will show that the population in both states will soon be practically the same; this condition is called saturation. The spin-lattice relaxation time, T_1, is defined as the time during which all but $1/\epsilon$ of the excess spins will have reached the final equilibrium state of lowest energy.

Let A_0 be the magnitude of the energy absorbed to reach saturation; then A_0 is proportional to $g_n\mu_n H/kT_0$ where T_0 is the absolute temperature of the sample. If resonance absorption is permitted to take place before equilibrium of the excess occurs, then the energy absorbed is defined by a new T. This leads to the concept that resonance elevates the spin temperature, or heats up the spins; and after resonance stops, the spins cool to the temperature of the lattice. The lattice is defined as everything in the sample but the spin in question. T_1 for nuclear moments varies from hours to milliseconds, and for oxygen-free water at room temperature, it is about 3.6 seconds.

Another relaxation effect is that associated with the spin-spin interaction. Imagine an effective inhomogeniety in the external field of magnitude ΔH to exist over the region of a sample of the nuclear moments being studied. There will be variations in the external field at different nuclei, and we obtain in effect a spread in the Larmor frequencies throughout the sample, $|\Delta\omega| = |\gamma|\,|\Delta H|$. Spin-spin interactions are concerned with the effect of each precessing moment on the neighboring spins through their magnetic fields. Thus, the total field at each nucleus consists of the external field value and the resultant of the local fields produced by the components of the neighboring magnetic dipoles.

T_2* (*transverse*, spin-spin, or phase relaxation time) is defined as the time characteristic of the spread in Larmor frequencies. T_2 is the time during which all but $(1/\epsilon)$ of a system of spins whose phase has been established return to a state of random phase.

If the external field is quite homogeneous, the fields produced by neighboring dipoles are sufficient to actually separate the resonance absorption spectrum of the molecule into patterns which identify the molecule. A very simple example of this is shown in Fig. 2 where the

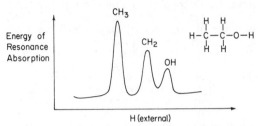

FIG. 2. Nuclear magnetic spectra of ethyl alcohol. Experimentally, the rf radiation on the atoms is usually held constant while the external magnetic field is varied. Absorption takes place when the Larmour frequency coincides with the radio frequency.

magnetic resonance spectrum of ethyl alcohol is shown. In each of the three peaks, the proton of the hydrogen atoms is causing the resonance absorption.

A little thought and the use of symmetry arguments will show that the largest peak belongs to CH_3, the next largest to CH_2, and the smallest absorption to OH. Nuclear magnetic resonance (NMR) has become a very powerful tool for organic chemists. Magnetic resonance is also used to study free radicals, crystalline orientation, and many other things concerning the structure of matter.

JAMES T. SMITH

Cross-references: ELECTRON SPIN, MAGNETISM, RESONANCE.

MAGNETISM

Magnetization Magnetic fields are produced both by macroscopic electric currents and by magnetized bodies. The first observed manifestations of magnetism were the forces between naturally occurring permanent magnets, and between these and the earth's field. North- and south-seeking poles could be identified. Poles were observed to be localized near the ends of long rods magnetized by contact with natural magnets or by a current-carrying coil. From the observed attraction and repulsion of unlike and like poles with an inverse square law came the

concept of pole strength and the definition of the unit pole, that which acts on another in vacuum with a force of one dyne at a distance of one centimeter. The unit magnetic field, the oersted, could then be defined as that in which a unit pole experiences a force of one dyne. The magnetic moment of a long, uniformly magnetized rod of length l with a pole strength of m unit poles at each end is defined as ml, the largest couple that the sample can experience in a field of one oersted. The magnetization, M, is defined as the magnetic moment per unit volume, ml/al, where a is the cross-sectional area, and is thus also equal to the pole strength per unit area, m/a.

Magnetic Induction The induction, or flux density, B, is numerically equal to the field H in free space and is described as one line of flux per square centimeter for a field of one oersted. Its direction is that of the force on a unit north pole. If magnetic material is present, the flux density is equal to $H + 4\pi M$, since 4π lines of force emanate from the unit pole at each end of a dipole equivalent to a specimen of unit magnetization. Magnetic poles are observed to occur in pairs. Lines of B are continuous, i.e., div $B = 0$. If a material becomes strongly magnetized in a small field, the lines of flux can be considered to crowd into the material, leaving their original locations and reducing the field there. This is how magnetic shielding is accomplished. Changes of B within a coil induce voltages which can be measured and form the basis of galvanometer and fluxmeter measurement methods. For a coil of N turns of cross-sectional area a, in which the flux is changing at dB/dt gauss/sec, E in volts is given by

$$E = -10^{-8} Na \frac{dB}{dt}$$

Forces on magnetic bodies in field gradients are proportional to M.

Types of Magnetic Behavior In general a field H will produce a magnetization M in any material. If M is in the same direction as H, a sample will be attracted to regions of stronger field in a field gradient. It will be repelled if M is in the opposite sense. This experiment, as first performed by Faraday, is the basis for the broad classification of materials into paramagnetic, diamagnetic, and ferromagnetic. The susceptibility κ is defined as M/H. The force F_x on a small specimen of volume v in a field H_y and a field gradient dH_y/dx is

$$F_x = (\kappa_2 - \kappa_1) v H_y \frac{dH_y}{dx}$$

where κ_2 and κ_1 are the volume susceptibilities of the specimen and the surrounding medium, usually air.

For paramagnetic materials, κ is small and positive, usually between 1 and 1.001 at ordinary temperatures. These substances contain atoms

or ions with at least one incomplete electron shell, giving them a non-zero atomic or ionic magnetic moment μ_a. Many salts of the iron-group and rare-earth metals are paramagnetic, as are the alkali metals, the platinum and palladium metals, carbon, oxygen, and various other elements. Antiferromagnetic substances also have small positive κ, as do ferromagnetics above their Curie temperatures. In the classical theory of paramagnetism, the orientations of the moments are considered to be initially thermally randomized in space. An applied field produces a net magnetic moment in its direction, as described by the classical Langevin function

$$\frac{M}{M_s} = \coth\left(\frac{\mu_a H}{kT}\right) - \frac{kT}{\mu_a H}$$

where k is the Boltzmann constant. M_s is the value of M attained for very large H/T. Under most conditions, only the initial portion of this curve is observed, with the corresponding constant κ. The conduction electrons at the top of the Fermi distribution in a metal can also give rise to a temperature-independent Pauli paramagnetism. The quantum-mechanical analogue of the Langevin function is called the Brillouin function (see PARAMAGNETISM).

For diamagnetic materials, κ is small and negative. Diamagnetism is a universal phenomenon but is often masked by paramagnetic or ferromagnetic effects. Net diamagnetic behavior is observed in a number of salts and metals, and in the rare gases, in which there is no net moment. The effect can be regarded as the operation of Lenz's law on an atomic scale (see DIAMAGNETISM).

Ferromagnetic materials show a value of M which may be of the order of 10^3 in small fields. Thus κ can be very large. It is common to describe their properties in terms of the permeability $\mu = B/H$. Since M saturates in ordinary fields, κ and μ are not constant. M is not necessarily in the same direction as H, so κ and μ are, in general, tensors. Furthermore, ferromagnetics generally exhibit hysteresis in the dependence of M on H, and the details are very structure-sensitive. Still another distinction is the rather abrupt disappearance of ferromagnetism at a characteristic temperature, the Curie temperature, T_c.

Atomic Magnetic Moments There are two possible sources for the moments of individual atoms. They are electron orbital motion and electron spin (see ELECTRON SPIN). In most ferromagnetic materials, most of the moment comes from spin rather than orbital motion, a fact that is revealed experimentally by gyromagnetic measurements (see FERROMAGNETISM) and by magnetic resonance experiments (see MAGNETIC RESONANCE). Orbital motions are quenched by the electric fields of the neighboring atoms in the crystal lattice. In the rare earth metals the unfilled shell is deep within the atom, orbital motion is not quenched, and the orbital contribution to the magnetic moment is observed. The unit of atomic moment is the Bohr magneton, μ_B, which is the moment associated with one electron spin, numerically equal to 0.9274×10^{-20} erg/oersted. The spin quantum number, S, is one-half the number of unpaired electrons. The moment per atom is $Sg\mu_B$ where g is the gyromagnetic ratio, close to 2 for most materials. The moment in Bohr magnetons of an isolated atom or ion of the first transition series is equal to the number of unpaired d electrons, considering the first five electron spins to have one orientation and the next five the opposite (Hund's rule). The Ni^{++} ion, with eight d electrons, has the expected moment of $2\mu_B$ in ferrites, in which the ionic spacing is great enough so that the d levels are not disturbed (see FERRITES). In metallic nickel, however, the d levels overlap considerably, and the moment corresponds to only 0.6 μ_B per atom. Similarly the Bohr magneton numbers for metallic iron and cobalt are 2.2 and 1.7 respectively.

Ferromagnetism Ferromagnetism can only occur in a material containing atoms with net moments. Also, quantum-mechanical electrostatic "exchange" forces must be present, holding neighboring atomic moments parallel below the Curie temperature. These are much greater than the Lorentz force due to the average magnetization and are, in fact, equivalent to an effective field on the order of 10^6 oersteds. Such an effective "molecular field" was postulated in 1907 by Weiss in extending the Langevin theory of paramagnetism to include ferromagnetic behavior. The Langevin function predicts a temperature dependence of magnetization, for small M, of

$$M = \frac{CH}{T}$$

where C is a constant. The susceptibility is then C/T, which is Curie's law. Weiss pointed out that if the field H were augmented by an additional field NM proportional to the magnetization, the temperature dependence became

$$M = \frac{CH}{T - T_c}$$

where $T_c = NC$. This is the Curie-Weiss law, approximately obeyed by ferromagnetic substances above their Curie points. Below T_c, the presence of the molecular field produces an alignment of the atomic moments corresponding to the spontaneous magnetization M_s even when no external field is present. However, ferromagnetic samples can have any net externally measured value of magnetization, including zero, which seems to contradict this result. Weiss therefore postulated the existence of domains separated by boundaries. In each domain the atomic moments are parallel, the

domain magnetizations having different orientations. The net external magnetization is then the vector sum of the domain magnetizations and can be varied by a rearrangement of the domain structure, which may happen in very small applied fields. This prediction has been completely verified by experiment. The motion of domain boundaries as observed under the microscope has been directly correlated with external changes in magnetization. Domain boundaries in iron are on the order of 1000 Å thick. Within a boundary, neighboring magnetic moments are not quite parallel. The change in orientation of the magnetization from one domain to another is distributed through the thickness of the boundary.

Within a domain, the magnetization will in general preferentially lie along some particular crystallographic direction. The energy difference between magnetization in the easiest and hardest direction may exceed 10^8 erg/cm^3. This anisotropy is described in an appropriate trigonometric series with coefficients K_i. Usually only a few terms are necessary. Often a material is described by a single K; this implies a uniaxial anisotropy energy of the form $K \sin^2 \theta$. The K_i may pass through zero and change sign with changing composition or temperature. Although such details cannot in general be predicted, the magnetocrystalline anisotropy will have the same over-all symmetry as the crystal structure. Anisotropy is best investigated in single crystals, by analysis of magnetization curves in various directions or from the relationship between the measured torque and the direction of the applied field (see FERROMAGNETISM). Dimensional changes are also associated with the position of the magnetization vector relative to the lattice (see MAGNETOSTRICTION).

There are two mechanisms available for changing the externally measured magnetization of a ferromagnetic material: domain boundary motion, and domain magnetization rotation. Broadly speaking, in magnetically soft materials, boundary motion accounts for most of the changes in low applied fields, leaving the magnetization in each domain in the easy direction nearest the applied field. Then rotation against anisotropy produces the remaining change in higher fields. In very low fields, boundary motion is practically reversible, but when boundaries move considerable distances, they experience a net drag from impurities and irregularities in the material, causing hysteresis in the dependence of B on H. There will in general be a remanence B_r, the flux density remaining after saturation when the field is reduced to zero, and a coercive force H_c, the reverse field required to reduce the flux density to zero. A loss associated with the irreversibility of magnetization changes also occurs in rotating fields. This loss becomes zero in very large fields, except in a few special cases.

Even in very slowly changing fields, a wall characteristically moves in jumps, each giving a sudden change in B. This irregularity has been known for a long time as the Barkhausen effect, and its physical origin is the irregularity of wall motion through various inhomogeneities in the material. Usually a very large number of these small jumps takes place. In special circumstances, however, the material may remain at B_r, until, in a sufficiently large field, a single wall will be nucleated and sweep all the way across the specimen, leaving it at B_r in the other direction. Such a material has only two stable states, $+B_r$ and $-B_r$, a useful behavior in some applications.

Direct microscopic observation of domains, e.g., by the Faraday effect or the magnetic Kerr effect, is an important research tool. Understanding and control of domain structures has progressed to the point that under appropriate conditions large numbers of tiny cylindrical domains can be deliberately produced and controllably moved in certain single-crystal materials, enabling the development of memory devices utilizing this ability.

It is also necessary to consider the behavior in rapidly varying fields, discussed below.

Antiferromagnetism Exchange forces can operate to hold neighboring moments antiparallel, rather than parallel. Materials whose magnetic moments are arranged in this way show no external permanent moment and are called antiferromagnetic. The sign of the exchange force may depend, among other things, on the atomic spacing. Metallic manganese, for example, is antiferromagnetic, while many alloys of manganese, in which the average Mn-Mn distance is greater, are ferromagnetic. In some antiferromagnetic compounds, the exchange interaction appears to be of a next-nearest-neighbor type, taking place through an intervening atom such as oxygen. This type of interaction is termed superexchange. Antiferromagnetic materials, having no net external moment, show small positive susceptibilities that reach a maximum at the temperature above which the exchange forces can no longer hold the moments aligned against thermal agitation. This temperature, T_N, the Néel temperature, corresponds to the Curie temperature of a ferromagnet. Magnetocrystalline anisotropy exists for antiferromagnets just as for ferromagnets (see ANTIFERROMAGNETISM).

Ferrimagnetism With more than one type of magnetic ion present, in certain compounds, antiferromagnetic coupling may lead to a net external moment corresponding to a Bohr magneton number equal to the difference in ionic moments. Other more complicated cases occur. Ferrites, insulating oxides with the spinel structure, are important examples of this class of material, called ferrimagnetics (see FERRIMAGNETISM).

Exchange Anisotropy A ferromagnetic phase may be in exchange coupling with an antiferromagnetic phase, as in a cobalt particle covered with CoO. This leads to new phenomena, in-

cluding non-vanishing high-field rotational hysteresis. Such a material cooled in a field through the Néel temperature, if $T_c > T_N$, may exhibit a hysteresis loop that is permanently displaced from the origin. This is equivalent to a unidirectional (not uniaxial) anisotropy and will appear in a torque curve as a $\sin \theta$ term. Ferromagnetic and antiferromagnetic regions in a single-phase alloy may also lead to these effects.

Other Configurations Atomic moments need not necessarily be either parallel or antiparallel. In a few materials they may be arranged in a triangular or spiral configuration. In some circumstances, an antiferromagnetic material may shift to a configuration having a large ferromagnetic moment in the appropriate combination of fields and temperatures (metamagnetism).

Permanent Magnets A useful permanent magnet material should have as large a hysteresis loop as possible. In the early magnet steels, wall motion was made difficult by a heterogeneous alloy structure. A different approach is based on the theory that sufficiently small particles should find it energetically unfavorable to contain domain boundaries. The critical size is proportional to $K^{1/2}/M_s$. Reversal must then proceed by the difficult process of rotation against shape, strain-magnetostriction, or crystal anisotropy. Fine-particle ($\sim$1000Å) iron and iron-cobalt materials utilizing shape anisotropy have been developed. The Alnico permanent magnet alloys have very fine precipitate structures and are probably also best regarded as fine-particle materials. A magnetic oxide, $BaO \cdot 6Fe_2O_3$, utilizes magnetocrystalline anisotropy in fine-particle ($\sim$1 μm) form. A new class of permanent magnet materials based on Co_5-(rare earth)$_2$ intermetallic compounds shows by far the highest permanent magnet properties of any material. These originate in the extremely high magnetocrystalline anisotropy of these materials.

Thin Films Since a surface atom's surroundings are different from those in the interior, the magnetization and Curie temperature of thin films should yield important information about the range of ferromagnetic interactions. Experimental difficulties, primarily with purity, have beclouded the subject to some extent, but it now appears that any surface layer on nickel having substantially different magnetic properties from the bulk cannot be more than a few Angstroms thick.

There have been many investigations of flux reversal in films, usually vapor-deposited on glass, which have been motivated by computer technology needs. Such films show a uniaxial anisotropy associated with fields present during deposition or sometimes with geometric effects such as the angle of incidence of the vapor beam.

Dynamic Behavior of Ferromagnetic Materials Changes in flux in a conductor induce emf's resulting in current flows whose fields tend to oppose the change in flux. For various time rates and geometries these can be calculated, leading to expressions for phase relationships and skin depth in conductors (see ELECTROMAGNETIC THEORY). These expressions have often been applied to magnetic materials at power frequencies by simply replacing H by B. This is in general not a good approximation and leads to erroneous results. It is more nearly correct to recognize that highly localized eddy currents around moving domain boundaries are the entire source of loss under these conditions. For a given dB/dt, the loss calculated in this way is much greater, decreasing to the classical value as the density of domain boundaries increases.

In bulk metals, domain wall velocities are usually determined by the damping associated with local eddy currents. In ferrites and thin films, other types of damping may predominate. These and many other aspects of the dynamic behavior of magnetic materials of all types have been investigated through resonance methods (see MAGNETIC RESONANCE).

Superparamagnetism For particles whose volume v is on the order of 10^{-18} cm^3 or less, the direction of the entire particle moment $M_s v$ may fluctuate thermally. An assembly of such particles will exhibit the Langevin function magnetization curve of a paramagnetic with the extremely large moment $M_s v$; thus it may be easily saturated with ordinary fields and temperatures. Such magnetization curves can be used to study particle sizes and size distributions.

JOSEPH J. BECKER

References

Bozorth, R. M., "Ferromagnetism," New York, Van Nostrand Reinhold, 1951.

Kneller, E., "Ferromagnetismus," Berlin, Springer, 1962.

Rado, G. T., and Suhl, H., Eds., "Magnetism," New York, Academic Press. Vol. I, 1963. Vol. IIA, 1965. Vol. IIB, 1966, Vol. III, 1963. Vol. IV, 1966.

Chikazumi, S., "Physics of Magnetism," New York, John Wiley & Sons, Inc., 1964.

Morrish, A. H., "The Physical Principles of Magnetism," New York, John Wiley & Sons, Inc., 1965.

Berkowitz, A. E., and Kneller, E., Eds., "Magnetism and Metallurgy," New York, Academic Press, 1969.

Becker, J. J., "Rare-Earth-Compound Permanent Magnets," *J. Appl. Phys.*, **41**, 1055–1064 (1970).

Bobeck, A. H., Fischer, R. F., Perneski, A. J., Remeika, J. P., and van Uitert, L. G., "Application of Orthoferrites to Domain-Wall Devices," *IEEE Trans. Magnetics*, **MAG-5**, 544–553 (1969).

Cross-references: ANTIFERROMAGNETISM, DIAMAGNETISM, FERRIMAGNETISM, FERROMAGNETISM, MAGNETIC FIELDS, MAGNETIC RESONANCE, THIN FILMS.

MAGNETO-FLUID-MECHANICS

Magneto-fluid-mechanics is the subject that deals with the mechanics of electrically conducting fluids (such as ionized gases and liquid metals) in the presence of electric and magnetic fields. Magneto-hydrodynamics is another name used extensively, but it suffers from the less general meaning of the words "hydro" and "dynamics." Other names used are: magneto-hydro-mechanics, magneto-gas-dynamics, magneto-plasma-dynamics, hydromagnetics, etc.

The fundamental assumptions underlying magneto-fluid-mechanics are those of continuous media. In this respect, magneto-fluid-mechanics is related to plasma physics (see PLASMAS) in the same way that ordinary fluid mechanics is related to the kinetic theory of gases. More specifically, such phenomenological coefficients as viscosity, thermal and electrical conductivities, mass diffusivities, dielectric constant, etc., are assumed to be known functions of the thermodynamic state, as derived from microscopic considerations or experiments.

From electromagnetic theory, we know that the "Maxwell stresses" give rise to a body force made. up of the following components: electrostatic (applied on a free electric space charge); ponderomotive (the macroscopic summation of the elementary Lorentz forces applied on charged particles); electrostrictive (present when the dielectric constant is a function of mass density); a force due to an inhomogeneous electric field and its magnetic counterpart; and the magnetostrictive force. For any fluid the last two forces are negligibly small at normal temperatures, whereas the ones associated with the behavior of the dielectric constant, although normally small, are of the same order of magnitude as the buoyant forces under certain conditions. On the assumption that we deal with electrically neutral but ionized fluids, the only substantial force that remains is the ponderomotive force. Indeed, what is today called magneto-fluid-mechanics deals almost exclusively with this force.

Fundamental Equations The equations that govern magneto-fluid-mechanics are the following:

(1) Equation of conservation of mass, which is the same as in ordinary fluid mechanics.

(2) Equation of conservation of momentum, which is altered by the forces enumerated above. In particular, the ponderomotive force per unit volume is given by $J \times B$ where J is the vector current density and B the magnetic induction, both measured in the laboratory.

(3) Equation of energy conservation; the same as in ordinary fluid mechanics with the addition of the Joulean dissipation $E' \cdot J'$. The primes indicate that the electric field and current density are measured in a frame of reference moving with the fluid. In the nonrelativistic case and for zero space charge, we have $E' = E + q \times B$ and $J' = J$. The barycentric stream velocity is indicated by q.

(4) Equation describing the thermodynamic state.

(5) Conservation of electric charge.

(6) Ampère's law.

(7) Faraday's law.

(8) Statement that the magnetic poles exist in pairs only.

(9) Ohm's phenomenological law.

(10) Constitutive equations linking the electric field with the displacement vector and the magnetic intensity field with the magnetic induction. Equations (1) to (3) are the conservation equations. Equations (5) to (8) are Maxwell's equations. For a large number of problems, the phenomenological coefficients of electrical and thermal conductivity, viscosity and the like are assumed to remain unaffected by the magnetic field. This implies that the collision frequencies among the particles are much higher than the cyclotron frequency associated with the property a charged particle has to rotate around a magnetic line under the influence of the Lorentz force. This means that the transfer of electric charge, mass, momentum, and energy is not realized in a preferential direction.

Physically, the magneto-fluid-mechanic system of the above equations is coupled in the following sense: A velocity field q cutting magnetic lines of flux B gives rise to an induced current whose magnitude is given by $J = \sigma(q \times B)$. At the same time the fluid feels an induced body force equal to $J \times B$. On the other hand, the electric currents induced by the motion create, according to Ampère's law, a magnetic field which distorts the original applied magnetic field. The basic mechanism of this distortion is the one created by the irreversibility introduced by the finite electrical conductivity, the same way that the distortion of the inviscid streamlines in ordinary fluid mechanics takes place by the action of viscosity.

Nondimensional Parameters and Some Important Theorems In order to study the nature of the solutions as they emerge from different problems, we shall form a number of nondimensional parameters that can be extracted from the different equations. The order of magnitude of the inertia force per unit volume is given by $\rho V^2/L$ where ρ is the mass density, V the velocity, and L a characteristic length; the order of magnitude of the ponderomotive force $J \times B$, after using Ohm's law, is equal to $\sigma B^2 V$. Also, the order of magnitude of the viscous force is: $\mu V/L^2$. The ratio of the typical inertia force over the viscous force is called the Reynolds number (Re) and, from the above, is found to be: $Re = \rho VL/\mu$. The ratio of the ponderomotive force over the inertia force is given by $\zeta = \sigma B^2 L/\rho V$. The ratio of the ponderomotive force over the viscous force is equal to $(Re) \cdot \zeta$ and is defined in the literature as the square of the "Hartmann number," denoted by M. We have $M = BL\sqrt{\sigma}/\sqrt{\mu}$.

The distortion of the magnetic field due to the hydrodynamic field can be studied best with the help of the following two equations:

$$\frac{d\Omega}{dt} = (\Omega \cdot \nabla)q + \frac{\mu}{\rho} \nabla^2 \Omega$$

$$\frac{d\mathbf{H}}{dt} = (\mathbf{H} \cdot \nabla)q + \frac{1}{\sigma\mu_e} \nabla^2 \mathbf{H}$$

In the above μ_e is the magnetic permeability and $\mathbf{H}$ the magnetic field intensity. The first equation describes the diffusion of vorticity $\Omega = \nabla \times q$, whereas the second can be obtained by a combination of Ampère's and Ohm's laws after elimination of the electric field by using Faraday's law. In the ordinary fluid mechanic case, the streamlines obtained after solving the inviscid problem are distorted in regions of high vorticity through the mechanism of viscosity (last term in first equation). Similarly the magnetic field calculated in the case of ideal, non-dissipative flow with $\sigma = \infty$ is distorted by the finite electrical conductivity (last term in second equation). The nondimensional number describing the influence of viscosity is the Reynolds number, and in perfect analogy as indicated by the above two equations, the magnetic field distortion is described by the number, $(Re)_m = \mu_e \sigma V L$ and is called the magnetic Reynolds number. When $(Re)_m$ is zero, the magnetic lines remain undisturbed, whereas in the limit $(Re)_m \to \infty$, the magnetic lines are frozen into the fluid in exactly the same way that vorticity is frozen according to Helmholtz's theorem. Mathematical similarities apart, the freezing of the magnetic lines with the motion is evident in the case of $\sigma \to \infty$ from the following physical considerations: An observer moving with the barycentric (stream) velocity in a medium of infinite electrical conductivity can measure only a zero electric field and hence he does not cut magnetic lines, which means that the magnetic lines must move along with his speed. From this argument it also follows that the total change in the magnetic flux through a given surface moving with the stream must be zero for an infinitely conducting medium. Finally, the remark should be made that except for stellar and interspace applications where the velocities and (especially) characteristic lengths are high, $(Re)_m$ is a small number. On the other hand, the assumption $(Re)_m = 0$ is a rather drastic one since it permits the uncoupling of Maxwell's equations from the conservation equations.

For the calculation of the ponderomotive force we can use Ampère's law $(\nabla \times \mathbf{H} = \mathbf{J})$ to find that $\mathbf{J} \times \mathbf{B} = (\nabla \times \mathbf{H}) \times \mathbf{B}$. Through regular vector operations, we can show that $(\nabla \times \mathbf{H}) \times \mathbf{B} = - \text{grad} \ (B^2/2\mu_e) + \text{div} \ (\mathbf{BB}/\mu_e)$. One can identify the last term as representing a tension equal to $B^2/2\mu_e$ acting along the lines of force, whereas the first one corresponds to an equivalent hydrostatic pressure equal to $B^2/2\mu_e$. This term is frequently called "magnetic pressure" and in different problems is found to behave precisely as the static pressure does. Fur-

thermore, one can show that if the magnetic lines are lengthened, the magnetic field intensity is increased.

Consider now the propagation of small disturbances in the form of acoustic waves for which the speed of sound for an ideal gas is proportional to $\sqrt{p/\rho}$. Now one can show through a linearization of the equations of conservation, assuming the presence of the magnetic pressure alone, that a small disturbance (for a gas of infinite electrical conductivity) will be propagated, in perfect analogy, with a speed equal to $\sqrt{B^2/\rho\mu_e}$. This is the so-called Alfven speed, and these waves are called magneto-fluid mechanic waves. Of interest also are combinations of several mechanisms of propagation which might include sound and gravitational waves.

Because of the property of the magnetic lines to increase their tension when lengthened, along with the additional ones of distortion and propagation of disturbances, their properties are presented in loose terms as resembling very much those of rubber bands.

Applications There are both astrophysical and terrestrial applications of magneto-fluid-mechanics. One of the earliest ones was perhaps suggested by Faraday, who thought to harness the river Thames with electrodes on its banks that would collect the induced electric current resulting from the flow of the river as it cuts the earth's magnetic field perpendicularly. Because of the small electrical conductivity of water, the small magnetic field of the earth and the small velocities, the interaction is too weak to be useful. However, in the laboratory, with a mutually perpendicular magnetic field, flow, and induced current density fields, a large interaction is possible when hot ionized gases are used in conjunction with strong magnetic fields. This area of research is called magneto-hydro-dynamic power generation, and its popularity emerges from the fact that mechanical energy can be converted to electrical without thermally stressed rotating parts. As a consequence, higher temperatures can be imparted to the working medium with better thermal efficiencies. This scheme, under development now, seems to be limited by losses due to heat transferred from the hot gas to the outside, corrosion of the electrodes, and Hall current losses. (When the gyrofrequency of the ionized particles is high compared to their collisional frequency, the particles drift in a direction parallel to the flow, and as a result, the current to be collected by the electrodes in the direction perpendicular to the flow, diminishes. The Hall effect can be turned to some advantage if it is designed to be substantial and if the current in the direction of flow is the one to be collected.)

One of the earliest astrophysical applications of magneto-fluid-mechanics lies in the area of solar physics and in particular the sunspots. Sunspots were seen and studied for the first time with the help of a telescope by Galileo

about 1610. Three hundred years later, Hale discovered, through the Zeeman effect, that the magnetic field in the sunspots is very high (of the order of several thousand gauss). It was, however, only in the middle 1930s and in particular after the last world war that an explanation was sought in which the magnetic field was involved. At the writing of this article, there is no complete sunspot theory. However, the majority of workers in this area agree on the following rough picture. Because of mechanical equilibrium considerations, the pressure is the same at a given distance from the center of the sun in the sunspot proper or in the photosphere which is free of a magnetic field. This means that the magnetic pressure plus the static pressure in the sunspot region must balance the static pressure in the photosphere, a fact that implies that the static pressure in the sunspot region is smaller. If we picture the sunspot magnetic lines to be radial, the pressure gradient in this direction is independent of the magnetic field and balances exactly the gravitational force per unit volume ρg. Hence ρ is constant inside and outside the sunspot. Since the static pressure is proportional to density and temperature, the above arguments force us to accept a lower temperature inside the spot with a resulting darkening. The only question that rises is whether the order of magnitude of the magnetic pressure is enough for the effect to be significant. This seems to be so. If we assume a magnetic field of 1500 gauss (typical in a sunspot), the magnetic pressure is about 0.1 of an atmosphere which is the typical pressure in the photosphere.

An explanation for the bipolar nature of sunspots and the difference in the sign of their polarity has been offered. The differential rotation of the sun is invoked. The toroidal magnetic lines of the sun's field lying on its surface are twisted, since for very high electrical conductivity, they are frozen with the motion. As a result, the magnetic intensity is amplified and so is the magnetic pressure. Simple considerations based on the observed kinematics of the differential rotation establish the location in latitude with time where the intensities will be high enough to give rise to sunspot activity. The result compares favorably with observations. In fact, it can be shown that the sunspot activity migrates, time-wise, from the higher latitudes towards the equator as observations show. Because the twisted field is symmetric with respect to the equatorial plane, this model describes correctly the symmetry of the activity in the north and south hemispheres along with the fact that the polarity between two symmetric sunspot pairs is opposite in sign.

Efforts have been made to discover the mechanism for the generation and maintenance of cosmic magnetic fields, such as fields in stars, the earth, and galaxies. The most promising direction seems to lie in the so called "dynamo theories." Here, some general magnetic field is assumed (not necessarily strong), which upon interaction with the motion of a conducting medium (convective, or motion due to Coriolis forces), induces currents which reinforce the original magnetic field. As the magnetic field is reinforced, the ponderomotive force suppresses the motion until some kind of a steady state for both the motion and the magnetic field is reached.

Magneto-fluid-mechanics also studies problems related to magnetic confinement of plasmas and their stability to small disturbances. Consider for instance the so-called "pinch effect." Here, a strong current is passed through a cylindrical column made up of a plasma. The axial current filaments create an azimuthal magnetic field (the magnetic lines are then rings with the cylinder axis as the locus of their centers,) and as a result, a ponderomotive force is induced which compresses the plasma radially*. Through this confinement, it is hoped that temperatures of the order of 10^6 to 10^7 K will be created so that thermonuclear FUSION can take place. Such configurations are normally subject to instabilities. Consider, for instance, the case in which a small distortion in the form of a "kink" is formed in a cylindrical plasma column, such that the rings in the concave side are pressed together, whereas the rings in the convex side are separated. As a result, the magnetic flux (and hence the magnetic pressure) will be higher on the concave side resulting in a force tending to increase the concavity. We say that this configuration is unstable, since the force induced by the imposed disturbance acts in a destabilizing direction. Note that in this configuration, the center of curvature of the undistorted plasma boundary cross section falls inside the plasma. One can now create another example in which the curvature of the confining undistorted boundary of the plasma is opposite (the center of curvature falls in the vacuum) and show that the configuration will be stable. We can then state that a sufficient condition for stability is met when the magnetic lines are everywhere convex towards the plasma. If the magnetic lines induced by the currents going through the plasma are in an unstable configuration, externally imposed magnetic fields can be used in order to "stiffen" the configuration.

The "aurora borealis" can be explained in terms of the interaction of the solar wind (due to the continuous expansion of the solar corona with a velocity of about 500 km/sec) with the geomagnetic field. The inertia associated with this "wind" will penetrate the magnetic lines of the earth, only up to the point where the induced magnetic pressure is smaller than these inertial forces. The earth's magnetic field falls off with the inverse third power from the center

---

*Pinch-effect devices are also useful in metallurgy where molten metals can be confined away from solid boundaries in order to remain pure.

of the earth. Knowing the mass density and the velocity of the solar wind, we can locate the remotest magnetic line from the earth that is strong enough to stop the penetration of the solar corpuscles. When this happens, these particles will glide along this magnetic line and eventually will come to the foot of this line at the surface of the earth. An elementary computation shows that the latitude of this line is the one where the "aurora borealis" is observed. (see AURORA AND AIRGLOW).

Convective motions can be effectively subdued by the presence of a magnetic field. Consider, for instance, the convection in a thin horizontal layer due to heating from below. Convective cells will be formed when the buoyant force is enough to counterbalance the viscous force of the motion. (These were formerly called Bénard cells because it was believed that Bénard had observed them. However, the name *convective cells* is preferred.) At the same time, balance of energy dictates that the heat convected upwards be equal to the heat conducted from the hot source at the bottom. The ratio of these two energies is called the "Rayleigh number," and for a given geometry, it must be higher than a critical value for the convective cells to appear. However, when a magnetic field is present, the ponderomotive force in general inhibits the motion and at the same time changes the geometry of the cell. The extent of this inhibition is given by the Hartmann number (defined earlier) so that the critical Rayleigh number is higher for higher Hartmann numbers. Available laboratory experimental results reconfirm the findings of this theory. On a cosmic scale, it has been hypothesized that the roll-like granulation in the sunspot penumbra is the result of the magneto-fluid-mechanic inhibition of the motion inside regular photospheric convective cells.

Magnetic fields are also known to inhibit the onset of turbulence. For instance, consider the flow of mercury in a channel. Experiments have shown that the flow can be laminar well above the critical Reynolds number of 2000 or so, if a coil is wrapped around the pipe thus creating an axial magnetic field. The small disturbances perpendicular to the direction of the main stream will be damped out through the action of the induced retarding ponderomotive force.

Many other cosmic scale phenomena seem to be explainable through magneto-fluid-mechanics. To list but a few, there are the solar flares and filaments, the spiral structure of some galaxies, the heating of the solar corona, explosion of magnetic stars and many others. Although order-of-magnitude analyses have been suggested to explain some of these phenomena, there are no complete self-consistent theories. Such theories seem to demand a simultaneous satisfaction of all the conservation and electromagnetic equations—a formidable, if ever possible, task. On the terrestial scale, many applications have been undertaken, and some of them are dependent upon technological development rather than fundamental physical understanding. To give a few more examples, in addition to those already mentioned, we list magneto-fluid-mechanic liquid metal pumps and flow meters, propulsion devices based on the acceleration of a neutral plasma through which a current and a normal magnetic field from the outside are supplied (an area called "plasma propulsion"), or a device in which positive ions (such as the ones easily produced by alkali metals) are accelerated with an electric field (ionic propulsion). Other examples are devices to reduce the heat transfer in reentry objects by using the decelerating action of a magnetic field carried by the vehicle or to use the ponderomotive force as a control force when needed for the navigation of space crafts.

PAUL S. LYKOUDIS

References

Ferraro, V. C. A., and Plumpton, C., "An Introduction to Magneto-Fluid-Dynamics," London, Oxford University Press, Second Edition, 1966.

Alfvén, H., and Fälthammar, C. G., "Cosmical Electro-Dynamics," Oxford, The Clarendon Press, 1963.

Chandrasekhar, S., "Hydrodynamic and Hydromagnetic Stability," Oxford, The Clarendon Press, 1961.

Cross-references: ASTROPHYSICS, AURORA AND AIRGLOW, CONSERVATION LAWS AND SYMMETRY, FLUID DYNAMICS, FLUID STATICS, HALL EFFECT AND RELATED PHENOMENA, IONIZATION, PLASMAS, SOLAR PHYSICS.

MAGNETOMETRY

The term "magnetometry" designates the scientific approaches for measuring the magnetization of materials and static magnetic fields. Magnetometers are scientific instruments used for the following purposes: (1) to measure the magnetic moment of the specimen and to determine the magnetization of materials; (2) to calibrate electromagnets and permanent magnets used in the production of magnetic fields in the laboratory, and (3) to measure the strength of magnetic fields and their components on or near the surface of the earth, as well as in space.

Four distinct principles are basic to the design of magnetometers: magnetostatic action, electromagnetic induction, deflection of carriers in semiconductors, and precession of nuclear and electronic spins. This article selects the basic features of some representative instruments from among the many available types.

The Classical Astatic Magnetometer This is used to determine the magnetic moment of rod-shaped samples. The specimen can be exposed to the controllable homogeneous magnetic field produced in the center region of a solenoid which is appreciably longer than the specimen.

Its magnetic moment is characterized by strength and direction of the field at a known distance from the sample. Two equivalent, permanent magnet needles horizontally placed and rigidly linked by a nonmagnetic rod in a vertical position comprise the measuring system. Arranged in antiparallel alignment, the needles have a wide distance between them, as compared to length. This astatic system, unaffected by the earth field, is suspended on a calibrated torsion wire. The axis of the test specimen is placed perpendicular to the axis of the lower needle and in its plane of rotation. It is possible to cancel the field of the magnetizing solenoid at the location of the sensing needle by means of a magnetically opposing solenoid located in the same plane. The magnetic moment of the specimen can be derived from the angular deviation of the needle occurring from the action of the static field. However, in order to determine the magnetization in this manner, there must be provision for homogeneous magnetic field throughout the sample volume. Therefore, the sample should be machined into a rotation ellipsoid with its long axis pointing in the direction of the needle. Calibration is by means of the well-defined moment of a coil.

With a modified astatic magnetometer, the magnetic properties of extremely small specimens in the form of fine wires or films have been measured. The specimen is arranged parallel to the axis of the astatic system and a short distance from the closely spaced short needles, in order that each needle will sense the pole of the neighboring sample. Under this method, films as thin as 10^{-5} cm, weighing less than 1 mg, have been investigated.

Concurrently, with the evolution of microwave techniques in the last two and one-half decades new magnetic materials suitable for these high frequencies have been discovered. Single crystals of ferrite, garnet, and related substances have become significant, both technically and scientifically. As a result, new types of magnetometers have been invented to determine the magnetization of extremely small samples. The new instruments are based on the relative periodic displacement of the dipole field of the specimen against pickup coils and subsequent amplification of the small induced ac voltages.

The Vibrating Sample Magnetometer This makes use of a mechanical oscillator that can be either a loudspeaker or a motor. The sample, attached to the lower end of a nonmagnetic shaft, moves up and down, between and parallel to the pole faces of an electromagnet. Amplitude of the oscillation is approximately 2 mm, the frequency approximately 80 Hz with loudspeaker drive. The sample stays within the homogeneous region of the magnetizing field. Two series opposing signal coils with approximately 20 000 turns each are located on each side of the sample, with axes parallel to its motion and perpendicular to the exciting field.

For small samples, only dipolar field lines are linked with the signal coils. The magnetic moment can be derived directly by comparison with the voltage excited by a standard sample of known magnetization (nickel). The vibrating sample magnetometer can be operated over a wide range of temperature with a maximum sensitivity (defined as the sample magnetic size needed for a 1 to 1 signal-to-noise ratio) of 10^{-6} to 10^{-5} emu.

The Vibrating Coil Magnetometer In this instrument, the sample is kept in a fixed position in the homogeneous region of the magnetic field between the pole faces. The signal coil oscillates at approximately 40 Hz, its axis and velocity vector being collinear with the dipole axis of the specimen. The distance between coil and sample is large enough to allow for installation of temperature- and pressure-generating apparatus to include the sample. Special precautions have to be taken to eliminate the signal produced by the curvature of the magnetizing field. The measurement, which can be recorded, is continuous. The sensitivity as reported is about 10^{-2} emu.

The Pendulum Magnetometer This is a rather simple apparatus which utilizes the pondero-motive force which a sample experiences in an inhomogeneous magnetic field. The device is based on the perception that this force is (for small deviations from the position of maximum field strength) proportional to the displacement perpendicular to the field lines between the hemispherical pole pieces of an electromagnet. This condition causes a simple harmonic motion. The specimen is fastened to a light bar whose movement is constrained only in the direction of its length and without rotation by a quinque-filar suspension. The magnetization is determined from measurements of the periods of oscillation with and without magnetic field.

The Vibrating Reed Magnetometer This has been developed as a result of the above-described principle for obtaining a harmonic oscillation between appropriately shaped pole faces. The pendulum is replaced by a metallic reed of nonmagnetic material, and the sample is attached to one end. The vibration of this spring is excited by a piezoelectric transducer driven from an oscillator; the resonance frequency of the reed is observed with and without field. The magnetization can be calculated by comparison with a reference sample. Accuracies of about 1 per cent can be obtained on specimens with magnetic moments of 50 emu. The vibrating reed magnetometer can also be used for measurements at elevated temperatures.

The term "magnetometer" was first applied to instruments that measured static magnetic fields. The magnetometric principle was originally developed for the study of the earth's magnetic field and its peculiarities. There is a basic identity in present-day methods used for measuring fields produced in the laboratory and the field pattern on and above the surface of the earth. Specific design of instruments and their

accessories are tailored to meet particular requirements; the magnitudes of the fields to be analyzed range from approximately 10^{-5} to 10^{+6} oersted.

The "Gaussmeter" or "Fluxmeter" This is a laboratory instrument widely used for the calibration of electromagnets. It comprises a small dc generator. A small generator coil is wound on a nonmagnetic core, placed at the end of a 3 to 4 foot long axis, and driven by an ac motor with constant speed of revolution. The induced sinusoidal voltage is rectified by a commutator and read on a voltmeter calibrated in magnetic field units. The device is inherently linear; a commercial version allows full-scale readings from 2.5 to 120 000 gauss with different coils (1 per cent accuracy). The instrument also yields an approximate determination of the direction of the field vector.

The Earth Inductor This geomagnetic survey instrument is used for measurement of the inclination (or magnetic dip) of the earth field. A coil, connected through commutater and brushes to a sensitive galvanometer, is rotated about its diameter by a hand-powered flexible shaft. When the rotation axis of the coil is brought in line with the earth field, the galvanometer will read zero; the inclination of the axis against the horizontal plane can be read with an accuracy of approximately one-tenth of a minute of arc.

The Classical Magnetometer of Gauss This instrument determines the horizontal field intensity of the earth field in stationary observatories. Two measurements are required: (1) the measurement of the period of a permanent magnet, which is vertically suspended on a torsion fiber, when it oscillates in the horizontal plane about the magnetic meridian; (2) the measurement of the deflection angle, which a magnetic needle experiences attached to the same suspension, when the permanent magnet acts at a preset distance in a preferred position together with the earth field upon the needle. This method is an absolute one.

The Sine Galvanometer This is an absolute instrument for the determination of horizontal intensity. With it, the suspended detector magnet is acted upon by a field produced by a calibrated coil and the horizontal field component. Accurate measurements of the coil current and deflection angle of the needle are required.

The Flux-gate Magnetometer This magnetometer, which lends itself to aircraft application, has been used successfully for detecting magnetic anomalies and for exploring the earth's surface in search of mineral deposits. It has also been used for submarine detection. The operation of this instrument is based on the change of permeability of a highly sensitive material in weak fields. A device known as the flux gate exploits this effect. It contains two permalloy cores in parallel position. A coil is wound on each of the cores; the two windings are opposed in their polarities and connected in an impedance bridge circuit in such a manner that an ac voltage supplying the bridge will not produce a diagonal voltage. The bridge is balanced in the absence of an external field. If a component of the earth's field parallels the axis of the core, the bridge becomes unbalanced due to the opposing magnetic biases. The voltage produced then acts upon servomechanisms. Measurement of the field is as follows: Three mutually perpendicular flux gates are mounted on a platform that can be rotated by servomotors in two perpendicular planes. Activated by the diagonal voltage from one flux gate, each servomotor rotates its twin core, decreasing the unbalance and holding the cores in zero position. The combined action of two gates then brings the cores of the third gate into the direction of the field. An additional field winding encloses both cores of the third gate; a servomechanism controlled by the diagonal voltage of this gate provides a current through the field winding, in order to annul the earth's field. The magnitude of this current determines the strength of the earth's field. The flux gate magnetometer is sensitive to variations of about 1 gamma ($=10^{-5}$ oersted).

Hall-effect Device In recent years, investigations on semiconductivity led to the Hall-effect device for measurement of magnetic fields. Hall voltage occurs in a current-carrying sample of semiconducting material perpendicular to the current and perpendicular to an applied static magnetic field. The magnitude of the voltage is proportional to the field. Low noise level is inherent in this device; dimensions of the sensing element can be kept rather small. The Hall voltage amounts to approximately 10 mV at 10 000 gauss, with 10 mA current. The operating temperature range is between -40 and $+85°C$ for a commercial device. The use of the Hall-effect device is mainly restricted to the laboratory.

The Nuclear Precession Magnetometer This device uses the phenomenon of nuclear magnetic resonance. This method covers a wide field range with high accuracy in determining field strengths. Nuclear probes are extensively used for determination of fields and field gradients of laboratory magnets. The technique lends itself to telemetering the information; it is capable of operating at small fields. Therefore, the proton-precession magnetometer is employed in space probes and satellites.

The nuclear resonance method is characterized by an outstanding feature: the sharp line width for absorption of rf power by the appropriate types of nuclei when exposed to a magnetic field. The resonance frequency for ^{1}H is 4257.8 Hz/gauss and 1654.6 Hz/gauss for ^{7}Li. The probes used for calibrating magnets are a few millimeters in size. The resonance frequency can be determined precisely by counting procedure.

For geomagnetic measurements, a larger probe (water) is required to obtain a sufficiently strong response at small fields. First, the probe is exposed for a few minutes to a strong field (100 gauss) perpendicular to the earth's field, in order

to obtain sufficient polarization. On sudden removal of this field, the spinning protons precess about the earth's field inducing a voltage in a coil suitably placed. The signal duration is approximately one second, at which time it relaxes toward zero. Nevertheless, accurate frequency measurements can be made within this time. This total-intensity nuclear magnetometer has been improved for the determination of vector field measurement.

ERNST R. CZERLINSKY

References

Kohlrausch, F., *Praktische Physik* 2, 80 (1943).

Foner, S., "Vibrating Sample Magnetometer," *Rev. Sci. Instr.* 27, 548 (1956).

Smith, D. O., "Development of a Vibrating-Coil Magnetometer," *Rev. Sci. Instr.*, 27, 261 (1956).

Nelson, J. H., *et al.*, "Magnetism of the Earth," *U.S. Dept. Comm. Publs.*, 40-1 (1962).

Jensen, Homer, "The Airborne Magnetometer," *Sci. Am.*, 204, 151 (1961).

Ingram, D. J. E., "Spectroscopy at Radio and Microwave Frequencies," pp. 102, 289, London, Butterworth, 1955. ·

Cross-references: GEOPHYSICS; HALL EFFECT AND RELATED PHENOMENA; MAGNETISM; MEASUREMENTS, PRINCIPLES OF.

MAGNETOSTRICTION

When a polycrystalline nickel sample is placed in a magnetic field, it contracts along the field direction by about 30 parts per million and elongates in the transverse direction by about half that amount. There is also a small volume change. Such changes in dimension of magnetic materials with variation of magnetic field strength or direction, are termed *magnetostriction*. They are measured by strain gages, optical dilatometers, capacitance variation, and x-ray analysis.

Below the Curie temperature, magnetostriction in weak fields is caused by domain rotation, becoming appreciable at fields near the knee of the *B-H* curve.

In saturating fields there is still a small linear dependence of magnetostriction on magnetic field strength, and above the magnetic ordering temperature magnetostriction is, except in rare instances, quadratic in magnetic field strength. Field strength dependent distortions in the saturated and paramagnetic regions, designated *forced magnetostriction*, are due to the paraprocess, the induction of a moment by the field.

The saturation magnetostriction of single crystals depends upon the direction of the (sublattice) magnetization, α, and the direction of measurement, β, with respect to the crystal axes. In a cubic crystal (with collinear sublattices), to lowest order,

$$\frac{\delta l}{l} = \lambda_0 + \frac{3}{2}\lambda_{100}\left[\alpha_1^2\beta_1^2 + \alpha_2^2\beta_2^2 + \alpha_3^2\beta_3^2 - \frac{1}{3}\right] + 3\lambda_{111}\left[\alpha_1\alpha_2\beta_1\beta_2 + \alpha_2\alpha_3\beta_2\beta_3 + \alpha_3\alpha_1\beta_3\beta_1\right] \quad (1)$$

Birss[1] gives higher order expressions for cubic and hexagonal symmetry and references for other symmetries. The distortion of an unmagnetized polycrystalline material placed in a saturating magnetic field can be calculated by averaging over directions in Eq. (1). For cubic polycrystals the change in length parallel to the field accompanying magnetization is given by

$$\bar{\lambda}_\| = \frac{2\lambda_{100} + 3\lambda_{111}}{5} \quad (2)$$

Birss[1] emphasizes the unreliability of the assumption of initially random domain distribution implicit in Eq. (2)

Magnetostriction coefficients vary greatly, depending upon the material, temperature, and magnetization state. For pure iron at room temperature, the saturation magnetostriction constants are $\lambda_{100} \sim 20 \times 10^{-6}$; $\lambda_{111} \sim -20 \times 10^{-6}$, while for alloys near 80Ni-20Fe (weight per cent) these constants are almost zero. The cobalt ion causes a large magnetostriction; for cobalt ferrite $\lambda_{100} \sim -500 \times 10^{-6}$ while for nickel ferrite $\lambda_{100} \sim -30 \times 10^{-6}$. The largest known magnetostriction is that of dysprosium metal.[2] As a magnetic field is rotated in the basal plane of this hexagonal crystal, there is a basal plane distortion of almost one per cent, at liquid nitrogen temperatures and below. At room temperature, $TbFe_2$ shows a magnetostriction 10 times larger than does any other material[3]; ($\lambda \sim 10^{-3}$).

The source of magnetostriction is the dependence of magnetic energy on strain. Because the elastic energy is quadratic in strain while the magnetoelastic energy is linear in strain, the minimum free energy occurs at nonzero strain. For example, in a cubic crystal the equilibrium shear strain ϵ_{xy} is given by

$$\epsilon_{xy} = \frac{B_2(T, H)}{c_{44}}\alpha_x\alpha_y \quad (3)$$

Here c_{44} is the elastic constant, the α's are magnetization direction cosines, and $B_2(T, H)$ is a magnetoelastic coefficient representing the variation of magnetic energy (magnetic anisotropy, dipolar, anisotropic exchange) with strain.

Quantum mechanical calculations of the magnetoelastic coefficients are in a somewhat more satisfactory state in the case of nonconductors than for metals. Extensive calculations by Tsuya of the B coefficients of the spinels are reviewed by Kanamori.[4]

The temperature dependence (and "forced" field dependence) of the magnetostriction coefficients is due to statistical averaging as the individual spins fluctuate around the average mag-

netization direction α. For some materials this temperature dependence can be expressed entirely in terms of a known function of the (sublattice) magnetization. For ferrimagnets[5]

$$\lambda_i(T, H) = \sum_n \lambda_i{}^n(0) \, f_i[m_n(T, H)] \quad (4)$$

That is, the magnetostriction coefficient $\lambda_i(T, H)$ is the sum over sublattices of temperature independent sublattice magnetostriction coefficients $[\lambda_{111}{}^n (0) = B_2{}^n(0)/c_{44}]$ times a function f_i of the sublattice magnetization $M_n(T, H)/M_n(0)$. At sufficiently low temperatures this function reduces to

$$f[m_n(T, H)] = \left[\frac{M_n(T, H)}{M_n(0)} \right]^3 ; \quad T \ll T_c \quad (5)$$

for both λ_{100} and λ_{111}.

Bozorth,[6] Carr,[7] and Callen[8] give references.

EARL CALLEN

References

1. Birss, R. R., *Advan. Phys.*, 8, 252 (1959).
2. Legvold, S., Alstad, J., Rhyne, J., *Phys. Rev. Letters* 10, 509 (1963); Clark, A. E., Bozorth, R. M., and DeSavage, B., *Physics Letters*, 5, 100 (1963).
3. Clark, A. E., Belson, H. S., AIP Conf. Proc. 5, 1498 (1972); Clark, A. E., Belson, H. S., Tomagawa, N., and Callen, E., Proc. Internat. Conf. on Magnetism, Moscow, August 1973.
4. Kanamori, J., "Magnetism" (Rado, G. T., and Suhl, H., Eds.), Vol. I, p. 127, New York, Academic Press, 1963.
5. Callen, E., Clark, A. E., DeSavage, B., Coleman, W., and Callen, H. B., *Phys. Rev.*, 130, 1735 (1963).
6. Bozorth, R. M., *Ferromagnetism*, New York, Van Nostrand Reinhold, 1951.
7. Carr, W. J., Jr., "Magnetic Properties of Metals and Alloys," Cleveland, Ohio, American Society for Metals, 1959.
8. Callen, E., *J. Appl. Phys.*, 39, 519 (1968).

Cross-references: FERRIMAGNETISM, FERROMAGNETISM, MAGNETIC FIELD, MAGNETISM.

MANY-BODY PROBLEM

Scope and Definition A large part of the experimental data of physics is concerned with natural objects which may be looked upon as being made up from smaller bodies. For example, we may think of the solar system as an object composed of the planets and the sun; ordinary matter, in solid, liquid or gaseous form, as composed of molecules and atoms; atoms and molecules themselves as made up from nuclei and electrons; and finally, the nuclei as composed from neutrons and protons. We shall call the composite object the system, and its constituents, the particles; and note that it seems most reasonable to suppose that the properties of the

system can be explained on the basis of the law of interaction between the particles and the laws of dynamics. The latter may be classical or quantum mechanical according to the demands of the situation. At each level of refinement we refrain from asking about the internal structure of the particles. This is to achieve a natural simplicity of description; but still, at each such level, we have a rich variety of natural phenomena to explain.

The many-body theory is not concerned with any fundamental or complete explanation of nature. Its chief aim is to formulate schemes according to which calculations of certain physical quantities can be performed theoretically and the results can be compared with experimental measurements. It is inherent in its methods that the number of particles is considered as being large, and no attempt is made to find all the details of motions of the particles —a characteristic which distinguishes it from the so-called one-, two- or three-body problems.

The main approaches to the theory of quantum-mechanical many-body systems, such as nuclei, solids, and fluids, were worked out in a period of approximately ten years starting in the early 1950s. This led to a great deal of activity and attracted much attention. As a result, the term many-body problem has come to mean, almost exclusively, the theory of such systems at or near the absolute zero of temperature. The latter qualification serves to distinguish the many-body problem as such from the closely related field of STATISTICAL MECHANICS. The new developments were based on the observation that when the number of particles is so large that it may be considered effectively infinite, then the system becomes very similar to that of interacting fields—except for the nature of interactions considered—and the general formal methods of quantum field theory and quantum electrodynamics may be used with advantage.

There is only one general theorem in many-body theory; it is known as Poincare's theorem. Roughly speaking, it states that any given initial state of a finite many-body system will be repeated provided one waits long enough. The quantum mechanical form of this theorem states that all observables in a finite system are almost periodic functions of time. This theorem has not had much practical use but has played an important role in discussions concerning the foundations of statistical mechanics.

The so-called many-body theory is mainly a collection of special approximate methods developed for particular problems. The chief common features of some of the methods, especially the ones connected with modern developments, will now be described.

Reduction to an Equivalent System of Noninteracting Particles The very fact that we can recognize the constituent particles leads us to believe that in the lowest approximation we may neglect their interactions. This approximation

is already quite successful in derivation of perfect gas laws and electron theory of metals. A slightly different form of this assumption occurs in the case of atoms, which are treated as systems of non-interacting electrons moving in the field of force of the nucleus. For planetary systems a similar approximation is used.

The normal mode analysis of a lattice provides an example where a transformation of coordinates is used to achieve such a reduction. Instead of considering the coordinates of individual particles which interact with each other through harmonic forces, one considers certain linear combinations of displacements, the modes. In terms of the new variables there are no interactions and the solution is immediately obtained. This is an example of a *transformation* which introduces a *collective* description of the system.

Another type of situation occurs in nuclear theory, where it is found that a shell-model of the nucleus, built in analogy with the atomic shell-model, is very successful. The non-interacting particles of this model are called neutrons and protons, but interaction between them which must be used in this model is vastly different from that observed in two-body scattering experiments. As a first approximation one can completely ignore the mutual interaction and assume that the particles move in a common one-body potential. This circumstance suggests that what are called neutrons and protons in this model are not the same as the free ones but are only some *quasi-particles* which are appropriate to the model and happen to have many properties in common with actual particles. An analogous situation occurs in some solids where the electrons are observed, by means of cyclotron resonance experiments, to possess an effective mass different from the mass of free electrons.

Effective Field Method This is one of the methods of taking into account the mutual interactions of the particles. One starts with a given motion of particles, e.g., from an approximation of the type described in the last paragraph, and calculates the field of force experienced by one of the particles under the influence of all the others. As a further refinement the field may be made *self-consistent*, that being the situation when the motion produced under the influence of the field is the same as that which generated it. But for the approximations made in the course of calculation, such as omission of the effects of correlations among the particles, a fully self-consistent theory would be a complete theory.

Examples are: Hartree-Fock theory, Fermi-Thomas approximations, Brueckner theory of nuclei, Wigner-Seitz cell model in solid state theory, and several others.

Collective Motion Theory In some phenomena, such as propagation of sound and plasma oscillations, it is clear that many particles are performing coordinated movements. To study such cases, one introduces some collective variables in addition to the usual ones, and the Hamiltonian is re-expressed in terms of these mixed variables. *Subsidiary conditions* have to be imposed upon this extended system of variables to preserve the original number of degrees of freedom. The collective variables should be such that there is no appreciable interaction between these and other degrees of freedom. When quantum mechanics is applicable, the collective motions are also excited in quanta which for all practical purposes may be treated as new (quasi) particles. The stability of collective motions is then expressed in terms of the lifetime of quasiparticles. Solid-state physics is particularly rich in exhibiting collective motions. Quasiparticles associated with some of them are: the phonons (sound, lattice vibration); the polarons (electron and its polarization field in dielectric); and the excitons (electron-hole excitations in insulators). Collective motions in nuclei can also be interpreted in a similar manner. Superconductivity and superfluidity are also examples of collective motion. The quasiparticles responsible for superconductivity are electron pairs with equal and opposite momenta.

Use of Techniques of Field Theory With these techniques it is possible to obtain formal expressions which represent the effect of interparticle interactions to any order in perturbation theory. By carrying out rearrangements and partial summations of terms in perturbation series it is possible to see that, as far as the motion inside the system is concerned, the relationship between the coordinates and momenta and the potential and kinetic energies is changed in such a way that it has to be described in terms of an effective mass and an effective interaction, which differ from the original quantities in a known way. In certain cases these effects can be calculated and are finite.

Brueckner's theory of nuclear matter is an example of this type. The effective mass is found to depend on the momentum of the particle inside the system, and the effective interaction, the so-called t- or K-matrix, is given by an integral equation involving the original interaction. A self-consistent calculation of the properties of the system (nuclei or atoms) can be based on this understanding.

Similar techniques can be used for studying collective motions. An example is the treatment of electron gas by Gell-Mann and Brueckner.

Perhaps the greatest advance has been made in the theory of superconductivity, where variational and canonical transformation methods have been used.

A combination of all these methods is needed to study the difficult problem of relationship between various excitations, i.e., the interaction between various quasiparticles of a many-body system. One of the most useful tools in these calculations is the representation of matrix elements by means of diagrams, first introduced by Feynman. Many of these methods were first developed in connection with the theory of

interacting fields and they are usually employed in many-body problems for the limiting case of an infinite number of particles, but these restrictions are not essential; in fact, they are quite general methods for treating arbitrary quantum mechanical systems.

KAILASH KUMAR

References

ter Haar, D., "Introduction to the Physics of Many-Body Systems," New York, Interscience Publishers, 1958.

De Witt, B., "The Many-Body Problem," London, Methuen, 1959.

Thouless, D. J., "The Quantum Mechanics of Many-Body Systems," New York, Academic Press, 1961.

Fetters, A. L., and Walecka, J. D., "Quantum Theory of Many Particle Systems," New York, McGraw-Hill, 1971.

Kumar, K., "Perturbation Theory and the Nuclear Many-Body Problem," Amsterdam, North-Holland Publishing Co., 1962.

Khilmi, G. F., "Qualitative Methods in Many-Body Problem," New York, Gordon and Breach, 1961 (for classical mechanics).

March, N. H., Young, W. H., Sampanthar, S., "The Many Body Problem in Quantum Mechanics," Cambridge, Cambridge University Press, 1967.

Ziman, J. M., "Elements of Advanced Quantum Theory," Cambridge, Cambridge University Press, 1969.

Collections of reprints of original articles and lecture notes on many-body problem have been published by various firms, e.g., Pines, D., "The Many-Body Problem," and Van Hove, L., Hugenholtz, N. M., and Howland, L. P., "Quantum Theory of Many-Particle Systems," New York, W. A. Benjamin, 1961.

Cross-references: EXCITON, FIELD THEORY, KINETIC THEORY, MATRIX MECHANICS, NUCLEAR STRUCTURE, PHONON, PLASMAS, QUANTUM ELECTRODYNAMICS, QUANTUM THEORY, SOLID-STATE THEORY, STATISTICAL MECHANICS, SUPERCONDUCTIVITY, SUPERFLUIDITY.

MASER

The term "maser," coined by Townes and co-workers who pioneered this field, stands for m(icrowave) a(mplification by) s(timulated) e(mission of) r(adiation). "Microwave" has proved restrictive; stimulated emission amplifiers have operated in the UHF (~300 MHz), and at infrared, visible, and ultraviolet frequencies (see LASER). The principal advantage of the maser amplifier is its small intrinsic internal noise: the equivalent *noise input temperature* is but a few degrees Kelvin. The theoretical minimum noise input temperature is hf_s/k, where h is Planck's constant, k is Boltzmann's constant, and f_s is the signal frequency. This is 0.48 K at $f_s = 10$ Ghz (Giga Hertz) or 10×10^9 Hz. Maser oscillators can generate exceedingly monochromatic radiation, e.g., the ammonia maser has a short-term frequency stability of ~5 parts in 10^{12}, and the atomic hydrogen maser has a short-term stability of better than 1 part in 10^{13}.

Because "quasi-optical" techniques are being employed increasingly in the millimeter and submillimeter regions, the distinction between LASER and maser in these regions is becoming eroded. Historically, maser oscillators used resonant systems of dimensions comparable to a cubic wavelength, (λ^3); laser oscillators used resonators with dimensions exceeding λ^3 by many orders of magnitude.

Stimulated Emission of Radiation Because its energy is quantized, a molecule (here a generic term) can exchange energy with the electromagnetic radiation field only in discrete amounts (quanta). The emission or absorption of a quantum (photon) is associated with a transition between molecular energy states. For two states, $|m>, |n>$ of energies W_m, W_n, $(W_m > W_n)$, the frequency f_{mn} of the radiation accompanying the (permitted) transition between them satisfies the Bohr condition

$$hf_{mn} = W_m - W_n. \tag{1}$$

A molecule in state $|n>$, exposed to radiation of frequency f_{mn} and energy density u, has a probability per unit time $u \times B_{nm}$ (B_{nm} is a constant) of absorbing a photon hf_{mn} and reaching state $|m>$. There is also a probability $u \times B_{mn}$ that a molecule in the upper state $|m>$ will *emit* a photon hf_{mn} and return to the lower state $|n>$. The upper state molecule is *stimulated* to emit radiation of frequency f_{mn} by the radiation field at this frequency. Stimulated emission, like absorption, is a process which is *phase coherent* with the incident radiation. Thermodynamical arguments by Einstein (1917) showed that

$$B_{nm} = B_{mn}. \tag{2}$$

A molecule in the upper energy state $|m>$ may also revert to the lower state $|n>$ by *spontaneously* emitting radiation of frequency f_{mn}. This spontaneous emission is a random process, which is phase incoherent with any incident radiation, and is therefore a source of noise in a maser.

The spontaneous emission probability A_{mn} is given by

$$A_{mn} = B_{mn} \times hf_{mn} \times \rho_f \tag{3}$$

where ρ_f is the number of wave modes per unit volume per unit frequency range open to radiation of frequency f_{mn}. Table 1 shows values of ρ_f under various conditions; c is the velocity of light, v_g is the group velocity of radiation.

In the microwave region (say, 1 to 100 GHz), $A_{mn} \ll B_{mn}$; spontaneous emission is therefore negligible except as a source of noise. However, maser spontaneous emission noise is usually

TABLE 1

Environment	ρ_f
Enclosure large compared with the wavelength c/f_{mn}	$8\pi f_{mn}^2/c^3$
Single mode resonant cavity, volume V, width of half-power response Δf	$2/(\Delta f \cdot \pi V)$
Waveguide, cross section A	$1/A v_g$

exceeded by noise arising from losses in ancillary microwave circuit elements.

Molecular transitions are excited by either the electric or magnetic component of the radiation field, depending upon whether the change in molecular energy is primarily electric or magnetic in character. Each radiative transition has associated with it an effective oscillating electric or magnetic moment, usually dipolar. The probability B_{mn} given above depends directly on this dipole moment and inversely on the frequency spread (line width) δ of the transition.

Conditions for Amplification Suppose radiation of frequency f_{mn} is incident on an assembly of molecules with an allowed transition at this frequency [Eq. (1)]. Let the number of molecules in the upper state $|m>$ be N_m, and in the lower state $|n>$ be N_n. If the incident radiation energy density is u, the power absorbed by the molecules will be

$$P_A = N_n u B_{mn} h f_{mn} \qquad (4)$$

and the power emitted will be (see equation 2)

$$P_E = N_m u B_{mn} h f_{mn}. \qquad (5)$$

Since at microwave frequencies spontaneous emission is negligible, the condition for amplification is

$$P_E > P_A; \text{ i.e., } N_m > N_n. \qquad (6)$$

There must be an excess of molecules in the *upper* energy state of the transition associated with the signal frequency.

For thermal equilibrium at temperature T, Boltzmann statistics give

$$(N_m/N_n) = \exp(-(W_m - W_n)/kT]$$

$$= \exp(-hf_{mn}/kT) \simeq 1 - (hf_{mn}/kT) \quad (7)$$

at microwave frequencies, where $hf \ll kT$. Clearly a molecular system in thermal equilibrium is thus always absorptive. Equation (7) allows the definition of an "effective temperature" T_m for an emissive system; Eq. (6) and (7) show that T_m will be a "negative" temperature, and that $|T_m| \to 0$ for $(N_m/N_n) \to \infty$. Obtaining an emissive condition, obtaining a "negative temperature," and obtaining "population inversion" are thus synonymous. The excitation of a molecular assembly to an emissive condition is perhaps the crux of the maser problem. The schemes used depend on the conditions and on the

molecular system. Discontinuous methods (pulse inversion, adiabatic fast passage) can be used, but the account here is confined to the principles of continuous methods. In a gas, actual separation of the upper-state molecules may be possible. For example, the upper-state molecules for the 23.87 GHz ammonia maser transition tend to increase their energy in a static electric field, while the lower-state molecules tend to decrease their energy (Quadratic Stark effect). In an inhomogeneous electric field, the wanted upper-state molecules will therefore drift to the low-field regions. An electrode system (with geometrical axial symmetry) which gives a low-field region along the symmetry axis will therefore confine the upper-state molecules in a beam along this axis while rejecting the lower-state ones.

Most masers operate on the multilevel excitation scheme, requiring an input of energy ("pumping") at some frequency other than the transition frequency; forms of energy other than electromagnetic may also be used. The principles of the scheme will be illustrated by reference to a molecule having 3 levels with energies $W_1 < W_2 < W_3$, such that all transitions between levels are allowed. (The transitions other than the signal transition need not radiate electromagnetically). In thermal equilibrium the number densities $(n_i)_e$ of the particles in the different states (i) will satisfy

$$(n_1)_e > (n_2)_e > (n_3)_e.$$

The frequencies f_{32}, f_{21}, f_{31} are defined from

$$f_{mn} = (W_m - W_n)/h.$$

Suppose now by some means, that the transition $1 \to 3$ is *saturated*, i.e., $n_1 \simeq n_3$. (This might be achieved by a sufficiently strong electromagnetic field at frequency f_{31} —known as the "pump" frequency). Under these conditions, it may happen either that $n_2 > n_1$, or that $n_3 > n_2$. In the first case, amplification will be possible at f_{21}; in the second case, at f_{32}, provided that the appropriate transition is electromagnetically radiative.

There are many variants of the simple scheme just described. The frequency f_{31} may lie in the optical region (OPTICAL PUMPING); the excitation may be by collision processes in a gas discharge; or more than three levels may be involved, and pump frequencies lower than the signal frequency can sometimes be used.

Maser Materials Maser action has been achieved in gases (e.g., ammonia, formaldehyde, hydrogen, rubidium vapor) and liquids (e.g., protons in water) but the most important maser materials are the solid-state ones, since these have a high concentration of active centers in a small space. Present emphasis is on the use of certain paramagnetic ions diluted in a host crystal lattice. Three-level excitation, or some variant, is usually employed.

PARAMAGNETISM is associated with ELECTRON SPIN. The directional quantization of

angular momentum leads to the quantization of the energy of the ionic magnetic moments in a steady magnetic field. In general, the ground-state multiplet of these ions is split by the crystal field of the host lattice (Stark effect), and the levels are completely separated by steady magnetic field (Zeeman effect). When the steady magnetic field is applied at an angle to the major symmetry axis of the crystal field, and the resultant Zeeman splitting is comparable with the initial Stark splitting of the levels, the usually forbidden "leap-frog" transitions necessary for 3- or multiple-level excitation become allowed. In crystal fields of low symmetry, "leap-frog" transitions may be allowed at very low or even zero magnetic fields. Clearly, ions having three or more energy levels are wanted, and any processes competing with radiative processes—e.g., the interaction of the "spins" with the lattice—are usually required to be small. Spin-lattice interaction can usually be reduced by cooling the lattice to a low absolute temperature; and indeed most solid-state paramagnetic masers operate at liquid nitrogen (77 K) or liquid helium (4.2 K) temperatures. Some ions and host lattices with which maser action has been achieved are listed in Table 2.

TABLE 2

Ion	Effective Spin	Host Lattice
Cr^{3+}	3/2	Al_2O_3, alumina (ruby)
Cr^{3+}	3/2	TiO_2, rutile
Fe^{3+}	5/2	Al_2O_3, alumina
Fe^{3+}	5/2	TiO_2, rutile
Gd^{3+}	7/2	$La(C_2H_3-SO_4)_3 \cdot 9H_2O$ (lanthanum ethylsulfate)

A "spin-spin" interaction process, known as *cross-relaxation* must also be taken into account, since it may either aid or inhibit maser action. Cross relaxation is dependent on spin concentration, but not on temperature. Consequently, maser action may be achieved at comparatively high temperature (77 K) but not at low temperature (4.2 K) where the considerably longer spin-lattice relaxation time might be expected to give better maser action. Rearrangement of the level populations occurs because of single or multiple quantum transitions between the levels, in which energy is "almost" conserved on the microscopic scale, any differential being exchanged with the energy of the macroscopic spin system (total magnetic moment).

Amplifier Systems Maser amplifiers may be of either traveling-wave or resonant circuit (cavity) form. Their performances are expressed in terms of a molecular Q-factor, Q_m, defined over unit length for the traveling-wave maser and over the resonator volume for a cavity maser. At the signal frequency f_s,

$$Q_m = -2\pi f_s \times \frac{\text{Energy stored in the structure}}{\text{Power emitted by the molecules}} \quad (8)$$

since the Q's similarly defined for losses are positive.

For a magnetic dipole transition,

$$|Q_m| \propto \delta(N^* p_m^2 \eta)^{-1} \quad (9)$$

where δ is the frequency width of the transition at half-intensity, N^* is the *excess* upper level population, p_m is the effective dipole moment for the transition, and η is the ratio of the magnetic energy coupled to the molecules to that stored in the microwave circuit.

Traveling-wave Maser The active maser material is placed in a waveguide carrying a pure traveling wave. The gain coefficient α_m is defined such that the power gain G for a length l of amplifier is given by

$$G = \exp(2\alpha_m l). \quad (10)$$

It can be shown that

$$\alpha_m = (2\pi f_s)/(|Q_m| v_g^{-1}) \quad (11)$$

where v_g is the group velocity of radiation in the guide. Because p_m is typically of the order of a Bohr magneton, and the active centers are diluted, it is necessary to use *slow-wave structures* ($v_g \simeq c/100$) in order to keep l to a reasonable value (a few centimeters). Suitable values of v_g are readily achieved by the resonant slowing obtained in periodic structures. Systems such as the Karp structure, comb structure, and meander line are favored, since these support waves with the magnetic field circularly polarized in a plane containing the direction of propagation and perpendicular to the plane of the periodic elements. A comb-structure traveling-wave maser is illustrated schematically in Fig. 1.

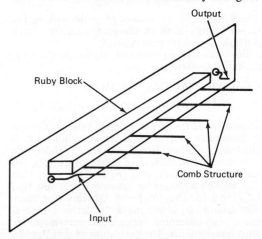

FIG. 1. A magnetic field is applied parallel to the "teeth" of the comb.

The sense of circular polarization is reversed on crossing this plane and is opposite in any reflected wave to that in the forward wave. The nonreciprocal gyromagnetic properties of para- and ferrimagnetic materials may then be employed to obtain forward gain and reverse attenuation with these slow waveguides.

The noise input temperature T_{in} of a traveling wave maser is given approximately by

$$T_{in} \simeq |T_m| + T_1 (|Q_m|/Q_e) \qquad (12)$$

where T_m is the effective negative temperature of the maser material, Q_m is the molecular Q (negative), Q_e is the similarly defined ohmic loss factor, and T_1 is the actual temperature of the waveguide (and contents). In this approximation, $|Q_m| \ll Q_e$. The bandwidth b_m of the amplifier is approximately equal to, but less than, δ.

The *Resonant circuit Maser* may be of either transmission (two-port) or reflection (one-port) type: only the reflection type is considered here, since it is superior in performance to the transmission type. A reflection cavity maser and necessary ancillary equipment are illustrated schematically in Fig. 2. Assuming that the unloaded resonant circuit (cavity) losses are negligible, the coupling to the external circuits will give rise to a Q-factor Q_e, say. The power gain G of the reflection cavity maser is then given by

$$G = (Q_e + |Q_m|)^2 (Q_e - |Q_m|)^{-2} \qquad (13)$$

The bandwidth b_c depends on the gain in such

a way that

$$G^{1/2} b_c \simeq 2|Q_m|/f_s (\text{for } G > 10, \text{ say})$$

The noise input temperature is given by Eq. (12) above, where now

$$Q_e^{-1} = Q_e^{-1} - |Q_m|^{-1}$$

It is necessary to have some nonreciprocal device to separate the reflected amplified output from the input signal; the ferrite circulator is most commonly used. The bandwidth and gain stability of the cavity maser are inferior to that of the traveling-wave maser, but the cavity maser is more easily constructed. If three-level excitation is used, it is clear that any maser system must support both "pump" and signal frequencies.

Maser Oscillators Equation (13) indicates that if $|Q_m|$ is small enough, G becomes infinite; i.e., oscillation occurs when the stimulated emission is large enough to overcome all losses. The width of the signal emitted by a maser oscillator is very much less than δ, so that for narrow δ an extremely pure oscillation signal results, and a molecular transition which is relatively insensitive to external influences will thus give oscillations of high stability in frequency. The ammonia maser and the atomic hydrogen masers are two examples.

Applications Maser amplifiers are now in use wherever the requirement for a very low noise amplifier outweighs the technological problems of cooling to low temperatures. They have been used in passive and active radioastronomical work, in satellite communications ("Project Echo") and as preamplifiers for microwave spectrometry. The "deep-space tracking" stations around the world use ruby maser preamplifiers for the reception of signals from planetary probes. The ammonia and the atomic hydrogen masers are being studied as frequency standards and have been used in a new accurate test of special relativity. Sources and amplifiers in the submillimeter, micron, and optical wavelength regions are being studied and developed (see LASER).

G. J. TROUP

References

Review Articles

Weber, J., *Rev. Mod. Phys.*, **31**, 681 (1959).
Wittke, J. P., *Proc. Inst. Radio Engrs.* (*N.Y.*) **45**, 291 (1957).

Books

Brotherton, M., "Masers and Lasers," New York, McGraw-Hill Book Co., 1964.
Fain, V. M., and Khanin, Ya. J., "Maser Amplifiers and Oscillators," in "Quantum Electronics," Vol. 2, Oxford, Pergamon Press, 1969.
Thorp, J. S., "Masers and Lasers," London, Macmillan & Co., 1967.

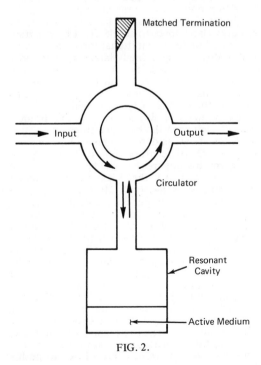

FIG. 2.

Siegman, A. E., "Microwave Solid State Masers," New York, McGraw-Hill Book Co., 1964.

Singer, J., "Masers," New York, John Wiley & Sons, 1959.

Troup, G., "Masers and Lasers," Second edition, London, Methuen and Co., 1963.

Vuylsteke, A. A., "Elementary Maser Theory," New York, Van Nostrand Reinhold, 1960.

Cross-references: ELECTRON SPIN, FERRIMAGNE-TISM, LASER, LIGHT, OPTICAL PUMPING, PARA-MAGNETISM, ZEEMAN AND STARK EFFECTS.

MASS AND INERTIA

One of the most fundamental and earliest known of physical phenomena is the simple fact that it takes some effort to push any object. To set some objects into motion by pushing is easier than to do the same for others. This property by virtue of which every body, however small, requires some force to push it is called "inertia."

As can easily be seen, the property of inertia is more general. Not only does it take some force to set a body in motion or to speed it up, but also to slow it down or stop it. The fact that a ball rolled on the ground soon stops is only because external forces, such as the friction on the ground, work on it to stop it. In these space days, it is not hard to believe that if a body were moving in empty space with no friction or air resistance, it would continue to move at the same speed without stopping. We also know that it takes force even to change the direction of motion of an object without any change of speed. One can feel this force while taking a car around a curve even when there is no accompanying change of speed.

All these are different manifestations of the property of inertia. This was neatly summed up by Sir Isaac Newton in the first of his laws of motion, which essentially says that a body will continue in its state of rest or of uniform motion along a straight line unless acted upon by an external force.

Given that it takes some force to change the state of motion of a body, the next question is—how much? Or, in other words, how do we quantitatively measure the inertia of a body? Experience tells us that "heavier" or "more massive" bodies have more inertia. The exact technical measure of inertia is "mass," which is closely related to "heaviness" or "weight." The larger the mass of an object, the more the force it takes to change its motion by a given amount, i.e., to give it a certain acceleration. Newton's second law of motion tells us that the force required is just the product of the mass of the body times the acceleration given to it.

$$\text{Force} = \text{mass} \times \text{acceleration}$$

During the early stages of the development of the concepts of mass, attempts were made to define it, not primarily as an index of inertia but as the "quantity of matter" in the body. Inertia was then considered to be a consequence of, and proportional to, this mass. However, it is not so easy to define precisely what one means by the "amount of matter" in an object. Clearly, one cannot use the size or volume of an object as an index of the quantity of matter or mass since a ball of wool and a ball of steel of the same size do not have the same mass. The "weight" of a body is quite often used to measure the mass, but this again is unsatisfactory since the weight of the same object can vary from place to place, even on different parts of our earth. Thus, it is best to understand mass as primarily an index of inertia, to which such properties as weight, size, etc., are closely related.

The fact that weight is such a good index of mass and has so successfully been used as a measure of mass is the key to some very important advances and speculations in physics. No discussion of inertia is complete without referring to this aspect of the story.

As we mentioned before (Newton's second law), under the action of a given force, e.g., a certain push of the hand, a body of larger mass M accelerates less than one of smaller mass m. This is evident repeatedly in daily life. However, there is one particular type of force, i.e., the gravitational force, under which all bodies react the same way. A "heavy" body and a "light" body, when dropped from a height reach the ground at the same time (except for small air viscosity corrections). The reason for this, well known to Newton himself, is that the gravitational force on a body, unlike any other type of force, is proportional to the mass or "inertia" of the body. Thus, a steel ball has large inertia and requires a large force to accelerate it by a certain amount. But the gravitational force on the steel ball is also correspondingly larger, so that under the influence of gravity alone, it would move exactly the same way a ball of cotton would. The fact that weight, which is essentially a name for the force of gravity, has been used as an index of mass is also a result of this proportionality between the two quantities.

All this, as we said, has been well known since the seventeenth century, but the deep significance of this apparent coincidence lay hidden until the time of the Viennese philosopher Ernst Mach (1838–1916). Mach's views, developed, modified and put on a firm mathematical footing by Einstein, form one of the cornerstones of the latter's brilliant general theory of relativity. Giving a wide berth to the complexities of the general theory, we will only mention here that according to general relativists, the inertia possessed by a body is a consequence of the gravitational force acting upon it from all the stars and galaxies in the universe. When we attempt to push an object, we are accelerating it relative to all the distant massive fixed stars. This produces a resultant gravitational force, resisting the acceleration we are trying to give. This is why we have to exert a force to push a body.

Much of this is speculative and is truly meaningful only in the mathematical framework of the theory. However, interested readers may find a very lucid and simple discussion in the book "The Unity of the Universe" by D. W. Sciama.*

R. RAJARAMAN

Cross-references: DYNAMICS, FRICTION, MECHANICS, RELATIVITY, STATICS.

MASS SPECTROMETRY

Mass spectrometry is based on observations of the behavior of positive rays by Thomson and Wien. In 1919, Aston demonstrated the existence of isotopes by introducing neon gas into a mass spectrograph. Prior to 1940, mass spectrographs and spectrometers were used primarily for isotopic studies in university laboratories. Analytical spectrometers became commercially available during the early years of World War II when their use for the rapid analysis of hydrocarbon mixtures was recognized.

Mass spectrometry provides information concerning the mass-to-charge ratio and the abundance of positive ions produced from gaseous species. There are several techniques for the production and measurement of the ions, and the design of an instrument is determined by its proposed application. The mass spectrograph, using a photographic plate for ion detection, was used primarily for isotopic studies but is now finding wide application for the analysis of trace constituents in solids. The mass spectrometer uses an electrical detection and recording system giving a metered output which provides a more accurate measure of the abundance of the ions than the photographic plate. The mass spectrometer is used primarily for the quantitative analysis of gases, liquids, and a limited number of solids.

The five basic components of the instrument are the sample introduction system, the ion source, the mass analyzer, the ion detector, and the recorder. A sample pressure of approximately 5×10^{-5} torr is generally required for a satisfactory analysis. An elevated temperature inlet system or other means of converting the sample into a gaseous state is required for less volatile species. Direct insertion probes for introducing samples directly into the region of ionization are available on many instruments.

The most common methods of producing positive ions are electron impact, thermal ionization, spark and arc sources, field emission, and chemical ionization. The electron impact source is the most widely used. Positive ions are produced by removing one or more electrons from the molecules. Thermal ionization produces positive ions by vaporizing material directly into the ion source from a filament coated with the sample. With a spark source, the material under

*Doubleday and Co., Garden City, N.Y.

investigation must be a conductor or else suitable means must be provided for initiating and maintaining a spark. Ions produced in the spark are taken directly into the mass analyzer. In the field emission source, a high potential is applied between the sample—generally deposited on the tip of a tungsten wire—and another electrode commonly in the form of a ring. Ionic species representative of the sample are removed by a high-intensity electric field. Chemical ionization involves the reaction, directly in the ion source, of ions from a reactant gas such as methane with molecules of the sample.

The four most widely used types of mass spectrometers are (1) the single-focusing, magnetic deflection, (2) the double-focusing, (3) the time-of-flight (T.O.F.), and (4) the quadrupole. These four types of instruments differ primarily in the method used for mass separation. The single-focusing analyzer with magnetic deflection is the most common design. The single-focusing analyzer achieves direction but not velocity focusing of the ions. Ions of the same mass-to-charge ratio, having slightly different velocities resulting from different kinetic energies imparted in the ionization process, will not be focused simultaneously, thus producing a broadening of the peak. The resolution of commercially available instruments of this type is generally limited to about one part in 500. That, is, mass 499 can be separated from mass 500 with about a 10 percent valley. With double-focusing instruments, an electric sector and a magnetic analyzer are placed in tandem to produce both velocity and direction focusing of the ions. Several commercial models of the double-focusing design are available having resolutions in excess of one part in 10000 with an electron impact source, and greater than one part in 3000 with a spark source. The double-focusing geometry is necessary with spark source operation because of the wide energy spread of ions produced in the spark. With both single- and double-focusing, the resolution varies directly with the radius of the analyzer tube and inversely with the width of the slits located in the ion source and ion collector regions. Sensitivity, the abundance of the ions collected per unit sample charge, varies inversely with slit width, and a compromise must be made between resolution and sensitivity. In the T.O.F. design, all ions produced in the source are accelerated through a given electric field and achieve velocities inversely proportional to their masses. Mass separation results from the different times required for various mass ions to traverse the distance to the collector through a linear drift tube. Resolution on the order of 1 part in 300 to 500 can be obtained with this type of mass analyzer. The major advantage of the T.O.F. instrument is its rapid production and recording of spectra. Over 10000 mass spectra can be produced each second extending through a mass range from 1 to 5000. Other types of mass resolving systems include cycloidal, and omegatron designs.

The two types of ion detection and recording systems are the photographic plate and the electrical detector. The photographic method is commonly used with double-focusing instruments such as the Mattauch-Herzog design which focuses all ions simultaneously in one plane. The photographic plate records a complete spectrum (mass range ~ 36:1) in a time interval of a few seconds to 10 minutes. However, the response of the plate to the ion intensity is nonlinear and quantitative results are more difficult to obtain than by electrical detection. Electrical detection systems use an ion collector, amplifier (commonly an electron multiplier), and recorder.

Positive and negative ions and neutral species are produced by the electron bombardment of molecules. The mass spectrum of a compound is a record of the positive ions collected. Positive ions are produced by the removal of one or more electrons from the molecule and by the rupture of one or more bonds, fragmenting the molecule. While the majority of the positive ions are singly charged, doubly and triply charged ions are observed in many instances. Certain mass ions produced from organic molecules must be attributed to the rearrangement of hydrogen atoms during the ionization and fragmentation processes. Metastable ions, formed when ions decompose while traversing the path to the collector, are also frequently observed. Metastable ions generally appear at non-integral mass units and produce broad, low-intensity peaks.

In the electron impact source, the electron energy is usually adjusted to 50 to 70 eV which is considerably above the appearance potential for molecular and fragment ions. For simplification of a complex spectrum, the bombarding energy can be reduced to provide sufficient energy to ionize the molecule but not enough to rupture bonds, thus achieving a spectrum consisting primarily of molecular ions. Mass ions appearing in the normal mass spectrum correspond to the various atoms and combinations of atoms in the original molecule. The pattern of mass-ion intensities observed is independent of pressure. Differences in the patterns obtained for various compounds can be used as the basis for the analysis of complex mixtures. Quantitative analysis is based on the ion current varying linearly with the partial pressure of the gas.

Some of the common uses for mass spectrometry include analysis of petroleum products, identification of drugs, determination of the structure of organic molecules, determination of trace impurities in gases, residual vacuum studies and leak detection in high-vacuum systems, geological age determinations, tracer techniques with stable isotopes, determination of unstable ionic species in flames, identification of compounds separated by gas chromatography (combined gas chromatography–mass spectrometry), trace element analysis in metals and other solids, microprobe studies of surfaces and of surface composition of various materials.

A. G. SHARKEY, JR.

References

1. Duckworth, Henry E., "Mass Spectroscopy," Cambridge, Cambridge University Press, 1958.
2. Beynon, J. H., "Mass Spectrometry and its Applications to Organic Chemistry," Amsterdam, Elsevier Publishing Co., 1960.
3. Biemann, K., "Mass Spectrometry: Organic Chemical Applications," New York, McGraw-Hill Book Co., 1962.
4. McLafferty, F. W., Ed., "Mass Spectrometry of Organic Ions," New York, Academic Press, 1963.
5. Hill, H. C., "Introduction to Mass Spectrometry," second edition, London, Heyden and Son, Ltd., 1973.
6. Hamming, Mynard C. and Norman G. Foster, "Interpretation of Mass Spectra," New York, Academic Press, 1972.

Cross-references: IONIZATION, SPECTROSCOPY.

MATHEMATICAL BIOPHYSICS*

The term was coined in 1934 by N. Rashevsky to denote a science which applies methods of mathematical physics to biology, just as "biophysics" applies methods of general and experimental physics to biology. Lately a more general term, *mathematical biology*, has been introduced. Mathematical biology stands in the same relation to experimental biology as mathematical physics to experimental physics. This means that mathematical biology develops mathematical theories of various biological phenomena, with the aim of better understanding their nature and of suggesting new avenues for experimental approach. Contrary to mathematical biophysics, however, mathematical biology does not necessarily introduce definite physical models. Some work on mathematical biology may be considered as the construction of purely formal mathematical models of biological phenomena. On the other hand, mathematical biophysics does specifically deal with physical models. Thus mathematical biology includes mathematical biophysics. It is not advantageous to attach specific labels to any particular scientific endeavor, especially in these days of increasing interdisciplinary research. Attaching such labels in science may be just as unwise as attaching definite labels to social and political situations. At best, it may be meaningless. Therefore, in a particular instance it may be difficult, if not impossible, to decide whether a given research belongs to mathematical biophysics or to mathematical biology.

The classical works of Alfred J. Lotka and of Vito Volterra, as well as the similar work by V. A. Kostitzin, on the interaction of species, as well as the wealth of mathematical work on genetics (Sewall Wright, J. B. S. Haldane) should be classed as mathematical biology. In this work no specific physical mechanisms are discussed.

*Author deceased. Article reprinted from first edition.

It is more formal or phenomenological. On the other hand, the mathematical work on the models of cardiovascular systems, which dates back to Leonard Euler in 1775, and which formed the subject of numerous papers by O. Frank between 1899 and 1928 (*Zeitschrift f. Biologie*), as well as the more recent work of S. Roston and Freeman Cope, J. Womersley, and Allen King on the elasticity of blood vessels, must definitely be considered as mathematical biophysics, even though much of that work was done before the term was coined. Similarly, the work of Braune and Fisher, at the turn of the century, on the dynamics of human locomotion is mathematical biophysics.

Mathematical biology is now frequently referred to as *biomathematics*. The latter term has the advantage of being shorter, but it suffers from a serious etymological shortcoming. One never uses the word *physicomathematics* or *physical mathematics*, instead of mathematical physics. The noun which denotes the principal field of study is *physics*. The word *mathematical* is used as an adjective to denote the type of tools used. Mathematics remains the same, whether it is applied in physics, in engineering or in biology. But mathematical physics and mathematical biology are different in the approaches to their problems from experimental physics or experimental biology.

From the point of view of the definition of mathematical biophysics given here, it is not quite as young a science as it appears to be. In fact, biological literature has been for quite some time sporadically sprinkled with studies which are essentially mathematical biophysics.

After coining this word in 1934, N. Rashevsky and his associates at the University of Chicago began a concerted effort of developing mathematical biophysics in a systematic way. For a while this concentrated effort was largely limited to the University of Chicago. Gradually, however, partly due to the migrations of individuals of the group, partly quite independently, work in mathematical biophysics began to spread very widely. The work of the Chicago group became gradually more general, and the many aspects of it are now better described by the more general term *mathematical biology*. There is no entirely comprehensive treatise that encompasses *all* the work done in mathematical biophysics. The references at the end of this article give a limited list of books and journals, some of which deal both with mathematical biophysics as well as more generally with the broader aspects of mathematical biology. The interested reader will find in these references a lead for further study.

In 1939 a special journal was founded by N. Rashevsky, *The Bulletin of Mathematical Biophysics*. It is now in its thirty-third year of existence. The *Journal of Theoretical Biology*, founded in 1961 by J. F. Danielli, is devoted to essentially the same subject. A number of important papers on mathematical biophysics has been published in the relatively new *Biophysical Journal* which is devoted to both experimental and theoretical work in biophysics. A great

deal of important work in mathematical biophysics is scattered throughout numerous classical journals in physiology and general biology. Hundreds of papers have been published in the *Bulletin* of *Mathematical Biophysics* alone. The aim of this article is therefore not to give a detailed mathematical discussion of any particular problems of mathematical biophysics, but rather to mention only *some* of the important work. The work that is not mentioned is omitted only because of lack of space, and not because it is considered as less important.

We have already mentioned the work on cardiovascular phenomena and on the dynamics of human locomotion. The work of Rashevsky began with an unsuccessful attempt at developing a theory of cell division on the basis of so-called diffusion drag forces. Those forces appear in any diffusion field and are due to the interaction between the molecules of the diffusing solute and those of the solvent. Since diffusion phenomena are known to be widespread in cells, the idea was investigated mathematically, as to whether the diffusion drag forces may not be the cause of cell division. Mathematically the problem divided into three parts: the calculation of diffusion fields, the calculation of diffusion drag forces, and the calculation of their possible mechanical effects. It was possible to show that under certain conditions those forces will produce a fission of a cell as a whole. Not only did the theory lead to correct order of magnitude for the average size of cells, but also to a correct quantitative representation of the over-all phenomena of original elongation and eventual construction of such cells as demembrated *Arbacia* eggs. Yet the theory failed completely in accounting for the all-important phenomena in the mitotic apparatus. The theory was developed at the time when little was known of the fine phenomena of replication of the smallest parts of the cell. It was based on the physics of "matter in bulk," whereas it is now clear that the whole problem must be attacked on a molecular level.

Nevertheless a number of side problems turned out to be of use. Thus the theoretical study of the limitation of cellular biochemical reactions by the diffusion processes led to a theory of the dependence of the rate of cell respiration on the amount of available oxygen. The theory was found to be in agreement with available data (H. D. Landahl).

An elaboration of the theory of diffusion drag forces led to a theory of self-regulating cell polarity and to a representation of some embryological phenomena.

Another example of the work of the Chicago group is H. D. Landahl's study of the retention of particulate material contained in the air inhaled through the respiratory tracts. This retention is due to a number of physical factors, such as impaction against nasal hairs, impaction against the mucus covered walls of the passages, Brownian movement and sedimentation. The results of this theoretical work are of great practical importance.

One of the most important fields of mathematical biophysics is the theory of biological membrane potentials, and the theory of transport across biological membranes. The classical work of J. F. Danielli on the structure of membranes must be mentioned here. Theoretical problems of transport across the membrane have been studied by H. H. Ussing, J. Frank and J. E. Mayer, C. Patlak, D. E. Goldman, and many others. The problems deal largely with the phenomenon of the transport of sodium and potassium ions from the side of the membrane where the concentration is lower, to the side where it is higher. Torsten Teorell has studied mathematically transport phenomena in membranes which involve not only the movements of ions but also the movement of water. He has shown, both mathematically and experimentally that periodic fluctuations of the membrane potential do arise under certain conditions. Those potential changes look remarkably similar to potential changes in repetitive nervous discharges, and thus give a possible clue for the understanding of phenomena of nervous excitation.

Kenneth Cole and his associates have contributed important experimental studies of the electrical properties of biological membranes, especially of their impedance. Their work is largely studded with interesting mathematical interpretations, which must be considered as falling into the domain of mathematical biophysics. Interesting physical models, which offer an explanation of the formal equivalence of some biological membranes with what is known as "equivalent electric circuits," have been recently studied by A. Mauro.

Somewhat in a class by itself stands the very important work of A. L. Hodgkin and A. F. Huxley on the mathematical description of nerve excitation. From a series of experiments, they came to the conclusion that the appearance of the action potential is due to the movement of sodium ions inward, into the nerve fiber, which makes the outside negative. The decrease of the action potential is interpreted as due to an outward movement of potassium ions. Empirical relations governing these movements are determined from experiments. The validity of the arguments which lead to those empirical relations is not yet generally recognized. Hodgkin and Huxley then show that from those empirical relations, obtained physiologically under somewhat artificial conditions of a "voltage clamp" which maintains a constant voltage in spite of redistribution of ions, the general shapes of the action potential curves can be calculated. Strictly speaking, the work of Hodgkin and Huxley does not represent a theory in the usual sense of the word. The authors themselves feel that they cannot go back to "first principles." Thus their work, in a sense, represents an empirical mathematical description of some important phenomena by means of a series of very complicated empirical equations. This, in spirit, is rather different from the deductive approach of a mathematical biophysicist. Yet some definite physical pictures are assumed, and their work therefore may be considered as falling at least partly into the domain of mathematical biophysics.

A great deal of mathematical work has been done in biochemistry. It covers, for example, such phenomena as biochemical reaction rates, enzyme activity, etc. To the extent that chemistry itself has now, through quantum mechanics, become a branch of physics, the above-mentioned studies do fall also into the domain of mathematical biophysics. This is enhanced by the fact mentioned in connection with Rashevsky's studies, that purely physical phenomena, such as diffusion, do impose limitations upon, and thus affect, the purely biochemical processes (J. Z. Hearon). This interaction of biophysics and biochemistry is brought to light particularly in the theory of distribution of different metabolites between the different "compartments" of an organism, between which there may be transport of material either by diffusion, convection, or some other mechanisms. This theoretical work is of particular importance for biological studies of movements of metabolites by means of radioactive tracers. In this connection the important work of C. W. Sheppard, J. S. Stevenson, A. Rescigno and G. Segré, and others should be mentioned.

A special application of this type of study has been made to the effects of drugs which are carried to various places in an organism. Here we must mention the beautiful recent work of R. Bellman, R. Kalaba and J. A. Jacquez. More elementary studies of this type date back some 35 years, to W. Gehlen and E. Beccari.

A great deal of mathematical work has been done on the central nervous system. Most of it, however, is of the broader nature of mathematical biology, rather than mathematical biophysics. Nevertheless, the work of W. Rall on the transmission at synapses must be considered as belonging to mathematical biophysics.

The mathematical theory of the regulation of the functions of the lung (J. Defares) should also be mentioned, as well as the work of L. Danziger and G. Elmergreen, and the quite recent work of N. Rashevsky, on oscillatory phenomena in the endocrine system. The size of this article, however, does not permit us to give justice to all the important work that has been done in mathematical biophysics. Instead, we have merely tried to give a general idea of what kind of problems have been studied. The reader will find much more in the references.

N. RASHEVSKY

References

Rashevsky, N., "Mathematical Biophysics: Physico-mathematical Foundations of Biology," Third edition, 2 volumes, New York, Dover, 1960.

Rashevsky, N., "Some Medical Aspects of Mathematical Biology," Springfield, Ill., Charles Thomas, 1964.

Rashevsky, N., Ed., "Physicomathematical Aspects of Biology," in "Proceedings, of the International School of Physics 'Enrico Fermi'," Varenna, Italy, New York and London, Academic Press, 1962.

Rashevsky, N., Ed., "Mathematical Theories of Biological Phenomena," a symposium, *Ann. N.Y. Acad. Sci.*, **96**, 895–1116 (1962).

Sheppard, C. W., "Basic Principles of the Tracer Method," New York and London, John Wiley & Sons, 1962.

Rescigno, A., and Segré, G., "La Cinetica dei Farmaci e dei Traccianti Radioattivi," Torino, Boringhieri, 1961.

Riggs, D. S., "The Mathematical Approach to Physiological Phenomena," Baltimore, Williams and Wilkins, 1963.

Grodins, F. S., "Control Theory and Biological Systems," New York, Columbia University Press, 1963.

Rashevsky, N., Ed., *The Bulletin of Mathematical Biophysics*, published since 1939.

Danielli, J. F., Ed., *Journal of Theoretical Biology*, published since 1961.

Oncley, J. L., Ed., *Biophysical Journal*, published since 1960.

Cross-references: BIOPHYSICS, MATHEMATICAL PHYSICS.

MATHEMATICAL PHYSICS

The term "mathematical physics" is almost synonymous with "THEORETICAL PHYSICS," but their difference is significant. It is like the difference between the descriptions of the electromagnetic field by Maxwell and by Faraday respectively. The theoretical (nonmathematical) description draws on analogies between elements of the field and familiar mechanical models—stretched strings, compressed fluids, vortex motion, etc.; the mathematical description made use of the abstract analytical properties of the elements of the field to set up a purely symbolic description without mechanical models. Classical theoretical physics was largely mathematical in content, but was nevertheless based on mechanical models in the spirit of Faraday's theory of the electromagnetic field. The atom and interactions between atoms were regarded as the "real," "external" objects in terms of which all physical phenomena could be explained. The mathematical formalism was merely a handy tool or language in terms of which to set up the explanation. The atoms themselves were not explained, but regarded as the fundamental "building blocks" of the physical world.

Einstein's theory of RELATIVITY is a magnificent historical example of mathematical physics we may cite to contrast with the classical atomic theory. Here mathematical abstractions, Minkowski space 4-vectors, Riemannian tensors, etc. were invented or adopted from the stock-in-trade of pure mathematicians, with analytical properties that were seen to match those of the data of experimental physics—velocities, forces, field variables, etc. Then the logical (i.e., mathematical) consequences of relations among these abstractions predicted new and unexpected relations among either already known or as yet undiscovered data of experimental physics. The construction of a self-consistent mathematical *description* of all physical phenomena, without the use of hypothetical building blocks of any kind, is the aim of mathematical physics as distinct from theoretical physics.

As a more recent example of this same concept, one may cite the deduction of conservation laws from generalized symmetry principles. The classically familiar conservation laws: energy, momentum, angular momentum, have for some time now been recognized as logical consequences of the homogeneity and isotropy of time and space. Interpreting these homogeneities and isotropy as meaning the invariance of physical laws under translation and rotation, one is led naturally to the theorem that each invariance principle corresponds to an appropriate conservation law. This theorem has yielded very significant discoveries in the study of elementary particles and nuclear structure where the most cunningly devised classical models have been not only fruitless but actually misleading. A non-technical account of this subject appears in Chapter 27 of R. K. Adair's text "Concepts in Physics," New York, Academic Press, 1969.

The activities of mathematical physicists have resulted in the invention of new mathematical abstractions some of which were at first rejected by pure mathematicians as illogical, only later to be granted a respectable status in the vocabulary of pure mathematics. Examples include Oliver Heaviside's operational calculus, J. Willard Gibbs' vector analysis, and P. A. M. Dirac's delta-function techniques. On the other hand, many branches of pure mathematics which initially had been regarded as so abstract as to be entirely "useless," have been found by mathematical physicists to serve as remarkably useful tools in describing physical phenomena. Examples include non-Euclidean geometry in the problems of COSMOLOGY; function space in modern QUANTUM MECHANICS; spinor analysis, or the theory of binary forms, in quantum FIELD THEORY. Again collaboration between mathematical physicists and mathematicians has in recent years resulted in the construction of new disciplines of great value, examples being group theory, operations analysis, the theory of random functions, information theory and CYBERNETICS. The names of many contemporary scientists are involved here, including Eugene P. Wigner, John von Neumann, C. E. Shannon, Norbert Wiener and many others.

On closer examination it becomes difficult to distinguish clearly between mathematical physics and applied mathematics; very frequently the same individual may be responsible for discoveries in both areas. Classical examples of this may be cited: Isaac Newton, Laplace, Carl Friedrich Gauss, Henri Poincaré, David Hilbert,

Ernst Mach, A. N. Whitehead. Evidently our attempt to define mathematical physics is degenerating into a simple catalog of items with only a vague hint of general characteristics common to all particulars. Physics has sometimes been defined as what physicists do, and one is expected to recognize the physicist without need for further definition than his own affirmation. Mathematical physics may then be defined as what physicists do with mathematics, or what mathematicians do with physics, or some superposition of the two. As the history of mathematical physics unfolds it becomes apparent that activity tends to cluster in a few fruitful directions at any one time. Current interests can be judged from the contents of the leading journals devoted to the subject; among these the reader should consult the *Journal of Mathematical Physics*, and the *Physical Review*, published by the American Institute of Physics; *The Proceedings of the Cambridge Philosophical Society; Comptes Rendus* (French Academy of Sciences); *Progress of Theoretical Physics* (Japan); *Nuovo Cimento* (Italy); *Indian Journal of Theoretical Physics; Zhurnal Eksperimental' noy i Teoreticheskoy Fiziki* (USSR) (in English Translation "JETP"); and other translations published by the American Institute of Physics. Probably the most popular fields in recent years have been in the wide application to solid-state physics and statistical mechanics of quantum field theoretical techniques introduced initially to deal with the phenomena of high energy physics—nuclear interactions, creation and destruction of particles, etc.

A philosophy of mathematical physics has gradually evolved with all this creative activity. For current thinking in this area, the reader is referred to two pertinent journals that have appeared in the past few years: *"Foundations of Physics,* and *International Journal of Theoretical Physics,* both from Plenum Press. Semipopular expositions are available in a number of recent texts in addition to the one by Adair, cited above: Kenneth W. Ford, "The World of Elementary Particles, 1967; F. A. Kaempffer, "The Elements of Physics," 1967; and Kenneth W. Ford, "Basic Physics," 1968; all from Blaisdell Publishing Co.

As for college level texts on mathematical physics, there are very few that are organized around physical concepts. We may refer to the classic series of volumes by Arnold Sommerfeld, and those by Slater and Frank, as prototypes. The standard modern work is the two-volume set by Morse and Feshbach, "Methods of Theoretical Physics," New York, McGraw-Hill, 1953. A less ambitious volume, William Band, "An Introduction to Mathematical Physics," New York, Van Nostrand Reinhold, 1959, served as an overall survey for advanced undergraduates. There is now a multitude of excellent texts whose major emphasis is the various mathematical techniques employed in theoretical physics, and we cite only three: Margenau and Murphy,

"The Mathematics of Physics and Chemistry," New York, Van Nostrand Reinhold, 2 volumes, 1956 and 1964; George Arfken, "Mathematical Methods for Physicists," New York, Academic Press, 1966; and Mary L. Boas, "Mathematical Methods for Physical Science," New York, Wiley, 1966.

WILLIAM BAND

Cross-references: COSMOLOGY, CYBERNETICS, FIELD THEORY, QUANTUM THEORY, RELATIVITY, THEORETICAL PHYSICS.

MATHEMATICAL PRINCIPLES OF QUANTUM MECHANICS

Classical Newtonian mechanics assumes that a physical system can be kept under continuous observation without thereby disturbing it. This is reasonable when the system is a planet or even a spinning top, but is unacceptable for microscopic systems such as an atom. To observe the motion of an electron, it is necessary to illuminate it with light of ultrashort wavelength (e.g., γ-rays); momentum is transferred from the radiation to the electron and the particle's velocity is therefore continually disturbed. The effect upon a system of observing it can never be determined exactly, and this means that the state of a system at any time can never be known with complete precision; this is *Heisenberg's uncertainty principle.* As a consequence, predictions regarding the behavior of microscopic systems have to be made on a probability basis and complete certainty can rarely be achieved. This limitation is accepted and is made one of the foundation stones upon which the theory of quantum mechanics is constructed.

Any physical quantity whose value is measured to determine the state of a physical system is called an *observable.* Thus, the coordinates of a particle, its velocity components, its energy, or its angular momentum components are all observables for the particle. A pair of observables of a system are *compatible* if the act of measuring either does not disturb the value of the other. The cartesian coordinates (x, y, z) of a particle are mutually compatible, but the x-component of its momentum p_x is incompatible with x (similarly, y, p_y are incompatible, etc.). $(p, q, \cdots w)$ constitute a *maximal set of compatible observables* if they are compatible in pairs and no observable is known which is compatible with every one of them. In quantum mechanics, the state of a system at an instant is fully specified by observing the values of a maximal set of compatible observables. Such a state is called a *pure state.* The act of observing a system in a pure state disturbs the system in a characteristic manner; the system is accordingly said to be *prepared* in the pure state by the observation. The cartesian coordinates (x, y, z) of a spinless (see below) particle

form a maximal set, and if the position of the particle is known, it is in a pure state; similarly, the momentum components (p_x, p_y, p_z) form a maximal set and a particle whose momentum is known is also in a (different) pure state.

A pure state in which the observables of a maximal set S have known values is termed an *eigenstate* of S and the observable values are called their *eigenvalues* in the eigenstate. If $(p_0, q_0, \cdots, w_0)$ are the eigenvalues, the eigenstate is sometimes denoted by the symbol $|p_0, q_0, \cdots, w_0 >$; in this article, pure states will be denoted more concisely by Greek letters. The eigenstates of S are represented by mutually orthogonal vectors, called the *base vectors*, defining a frame of rectangular axes F in an abstract *representation space*. The number n of such eigenstates is usually infinite, but for simplicity, it will first be assumed that each observable has only a finite number of eigenvalues and hence that the number n is finite; the representation space is then a straightforward generalization of ordinary space to n dimensions, with the additional requirement that the components of a vector will be permitted to take complex values. Any pure state of the system (not necessarily an eigenstate of S) is represented by a vector α in the representation space. If $(\alpha_1, \alpha_2, \cdots, \alpha_n)$ are the components of α with respect to F, and these components are arranged as a column matrix, this matrix is said to provide an S-representation of the state. The state, vector, and column matrix are all denoted by α.

The *scalar product* of two vectors α, β is denoted by (α, β) and is defined in terms of their components in F to be $\sum_{i=1}^{n} \alpha_i^* \beta_i$, where α_i^* is the complex conjugate of α_i. $\sqrt{(\alpha, \alpha)}$ is called the *norm* of α and corresponds to the length of an ordinary vector. All vectors representing pure states are taken to have unit norms and the S-eigenstates are accordingly represented in the S-representation by the columns $(1, 0, \cdots, 0)$, $(0, 1, \cdots, 0)$, etc.

Suppose a system is prepared in the state α at time t. The probability that the system can be observed in the state β at an instant immediately subsequent to t is taken to be $|(\alpha, \beta)|^2$. This event is termed a *transition* of the system from α to β. If β is identical with α, the probability of the transition is unity, as we expect. The probability of a transition from α into the eigenstate $(1, 0, \cdots, 0)$ is found to be $|\alpha_1|^2$. This provides a physical significance for the components of α in the frame F.

If the system is prepared in a state α on a number of occasions and an observable a is measured immediately after the preparation on each occasion, the values obtained will usually differ. If α is an eigenstate of a with eigenvalue a_1, then a will take this value with complete certainty. If, however, this is not the case, a will take all its possible eigenvalues a_i with associated probabilities p_i, and its *mean* or *expected value* $\bar{a}$ in the state α is given by $\bar{a} = \sum_i p_i a_i$. In the S-representation, an $n \times n$ matrix is associated with every observable a. This is said to represent a and is also denoted by a. Then, $\bar{a} = \alpha^\dagger a \alpha$, where α is the column matrix specifying the state and $\alpha^\dagger$ is its conjugate transpose. If a is a real observable, the matrix a is Hermitian (i.e., $a^\dagger = a$); this ensures that $\bar{a}$ is real. If a is one of the observables belonging to S, its matrix is diagonal, and the ith element in the principal diagonal is the eigenvalue a_i of a in the ith S-eigenstate; in this case, $\bar{a} = \sum_i \alpha_i^* \alpha_i a_i = \sum_i |\alpha_i|^2 a_i$, which is clearly correct, since $|\alpha_i|^2$ is the probability the system will be observed in the ith S-eigenstate.

A necessary and sufficient condition that the state α should be an eigenstate of a in which a takes the eigenvalue a_0 is that α should satisfy the matrix equation $a\alpha = a_0 \alpha$. a is said to be *sharp* in the state α.

Observables are often introduced as functions of other observables, e.g., the kinetic energy T of a particle of mass m is defined in terms of its momentum by $T = (p_x^2 + p_y^2 + p_z^2)/2m$. If a is defined in terms of $u, v, \cdots$ by the equation $a = \phi(u, v, \cdots)$, then this equation also defines the matrix representing a in terms of the matrices representing u, v, etc. There is, however, a proviso: wherever a product uv occurs in ϕ, this must be replaced by $\frac{1}{2}(uv + vu)$ before matrices are substituted, whenever the matrices u, v are such that $uv \neq vu$; this is called *symmetrization*. If $uv \neq vu$, we say that u, v do not *commute* and it is then found that the observables u, v are incompatible.

Thus far, the evolution of a system with time has not been considered. Suppose a system is prepared in a state $\alpha(0)$ at $t = 0$ and is not thereafter interfered with by further observation. Its state $\alpha(t)$ at a later time t is then determined by the *Schrödinger equation*,

$$H\alpha = \iota\hbar \frac{d\alpha}{dt}, \quad \iota = \sqrt{(-1)}$$

where $\hbar = h/2\pi$ (h is Planck's constant). Using the S-representation, α is the column matrix $(\alpha_1, \alpha_2, \cdots, \alpha_n)$ and H is an $n \times n$ matrix, characteristic of the system, called its *Hamiltonian*. H is Hermitian, and in the case of an isolated system, represents the *energy observable* of the system. An important property of H is that, if a is the matrix representing some observable and a and H commute, then a is a *constant* of the system; this means that, if a has a sharp value at one instant, it keeps this sharp value for all t, and otherwise, its probability distribution over its eigenvalues never changes.

If S' is a maximal set of compatible observables different from S, an alternative S'-

representation of the states and observables of a system can be developed. If α, α' are column matrices representing the same state in the two representations and a, a' are square matrices representing the same observable, the transformation equations relating the two representations take the forms

$$\alpha' = u\alpha, \quad a' = uau^{-1},$$

where u is a unitary $n \times n$ matrix (i.e., $u^{-1} = u\dagger$) characteristic of the two representations. In particular, the Hamiltonian H transforms as an observable.

The type of representation we have been describing is called a *Schrödinger representation*. It is also possible, by rotating the frame in the representation space appropriately, to keep α constant as t increases. If this is done, the matrices a, b, $\cdots$ representing the observables of the system necessarily become functions of t and are not constants as assumed previously. This type of representation is called a *Heisenberg representation*. The Schrödinger equation above ceases to be valid and is replaced by equations of motion for the observable matrices a, b, $\cdots$ taking the form

$$\frac{da}{dt} = \frac{\iota}{\hbar}\,[H, a],$$

where $[H, a] = Ha - aH$ is called the *commutator* of H and a. If H and a commute, $[H, a] = 0$ and a is a constant of the system as already stated.

If the number of basic eigenstates of a representation is infinite but enumerable (i.e., they can be placed in a sequence e_1, e_2, e_3, $\cdots$), the matrices appearing in the theory will have an infinite number of rows. This creates convergence difficulties in most formulae (e.g., that for $\bar{a}$), but otherwise, the form of the theory is not affected. If, however, some of the observables upon which the representation is based have eigenvalues which are spread continuously over real intervals, the basic eigenstates will not be enumerable and the matrix-type representation must be abandoned. Such an observable is said to have a *continuous spectrum* of eigenvalues; examples are provided by the coordinates (x, y, z) of a particle. In these circumstances, the discrete sequence α_n of vector components is replaced by a function $\psi(p, q, \cdots)$ of the continuous eigenvalues p, q, $\cdots$ of the observables of the representation set S. ψ is called a *wave function*. If the system is in the state specified by ψ, the probability that if p, q, etc. are measured they will be found to have values lying in the intervals $(p, p + dp)$, $(q, q + dq)$, etc., respectively is $\psi^*\psi dp dq \cdots$. The representation space is now a function space called a *Hilbert space* in which each vector corresponds to a wave function and the scalar product of the vectors corresponding to the wave functions $\psi(p, q, \cdots)$, $\phi(p, q, \cdots)$ is

defined by

$$(\psi, \phi) = \int \psi^*\phi dp dq \cdots,$$

the integration being over all possible eigenvalues of p, q, etc.

In this type of representation, observables are represented by *linear operators* which can operate upon the functions of the Hilbert space, transforming them into other functions belonging to the space. For example, if the system comprises a single particle and the representation being used is based on the particle's coordinates (x, y, z), its state is specified by a wave function $\psi(x, y, z)$ and its momentum components are represented by operators $p_x = (\hbar/\iota)(\partial/\partial x)$, $p_y = (\hbar/\iota)(\partial/\partial y)$, $p_z = (\hbar/\iota)(\partial/\partial z)$. This representation permits the immediate derivation of the important *commutation rules* for the coordinates and momenta, namely $[p_x, x] = \hbar/\iota$, $[p_x, y] = 0$, etc. Counterparts of all the results given earlier for a matrix representation can now be written down. Thus, if a is the operator representing some observable of a system which is in the state $\psi(p, q, \cdots)$, the expected value of a is given by

$$\bar{a} = \int \psi^*a\psi dp dq \cdots,$$

where a operates on the wave function ψ on its right. The necessary and sufficient condition for ψ to be an eigenstate of a with eigenvalue a_0 is $a\psi = a_0\psi$. Finally, the Schrödinger equation remains valid, but H is now an operator and α is replaced by the wave function ψ; for a single particle moving in a conservative field in which its potential energy is $V(x, y, z)$, employing the coordinate representation, the total energy $H = V + (p_x^2 + p_y^2 + p_z^2)/2m$, Schrödinger's equation becomes

$$-\frac{\hbar^2}{2m}\nabla^2\psi + V\psi = \iota\hbar\,\frac{\partial\psi}{\partial t}.$$

The simplest example of an observable with a discrete spectrum of eigenvalues is the *angular momentum* of a system about a point O. If (M_x, M_y, M_z) are the three components of angular momentum and $M^2 = M_x^2 + M_y^2 + M_z^2$ is the square of its magnitude, the following relations hold between the matrices or operators representing these observables

$$[M_y, M_z] = \iota\hbar M_x, \quad [M_z, M_x] = \iota\hbar M_y,$$

$$[M_x, M_y] = \iota\hbar M_z.$$

These are the angular momentum *commutation rules*. M^2 commutes with each of the components. It follows that the components are mutually incompatible, but each is compatible with M^2. Simultaneous eigenstates of M^2 and M_z exist in which the eigenvalues of M^2 are

$\ell(\ell + 1)\hbar^2$, where $\ell = 0, \frac{1}{2}, 1, \frac{3}{2}, \cdots$, and of M_z are $m\hbar$, where $m = -\ell, -\ell + 1, -\ell + 2, \cdots, \ell - 1, \ell$.

Part of the angular momentum of a system is due to the orbital motion of its particles about O and the remainder is contributed by the intrinsic angular momentum or *spin* of the particles. Let (s_x, s_y, s_z) be the components of spin of a particle and s^2 the square of its magnitude; then, if the particle is a fundamental one (e.g., an electron, proton, or vector meson), s^2 will have only one eigenvalue $\ell(\ell + 1)\hbar^2$ and the particle is then said to have spin $\ell\hbar$. For an electron or a proton, $\ell = \frac{1}{2}$ and for a vector meson $\ell = 1$. The eigenvalues of a spin component are then $-\ell\hbar, (-\ell + 1)\hbar, \cdots, \ell\hbar$. Thus, any spin component of an electron has but two eigenvalues, $-\frac{1}{2}\hbar, \frac{1}{2}\hbar$; a spin component of a vector meson has three eigenvalues $-\hbar, 0, \hbar$.

If all aspects of the state of a fundamental particle except its spin are ignored, (s^2, s_z) constitute a maximal set of compatible observables. Employing a representation based on this set, the number of basic eigenstates for a particle of spin $\ell\hbar$ will be $(2\ell + 1)$ and the general spin state of the particle will be represented by a column matrix $(\alpha_\ell, \alpha_{\ell-1}, \alpha_{\ell-2}, \cdots, \alpha_{-\ell})$, for a particle in this state, $|\alpha_k|^2$ is the probability of measuring s_z to take the value $k\hbar$. In the special case of an electron or a proton, $\ell = \frac{1}{2}$ and its spin state is specified by a column $(\alpha_{1/2}, \alpha_{-1/2})$ called a *spinor*; in this representation, the three components of spin are represented by 2×2 matrices, thus:

$$s_x = \frac{1}{2}\hbar \begin{pmatrix} 0 & 1 \\ 1 & 0 \end{pmatrix}, \; s_y = \frac{1}{2}\hbar \begin{pmatrix} 0 & -\iota \\ \iota & 0 \end{pmatrix}, \; s_z = \frac{1}{2}\hbar \begin{pmatrix} 1 & 0 \\ 0 & -1 \end{pmatrix}.$$

The three 2×2 matrices appearing in these formulae are called the *Pauli matrices* and are denoted by $\sigma_x, \sigma_y, \sigma_z$.

In recent years, much thought has been given to the problem of constructing Schrödinger equations for the fundamental particles, which remain unchanged in form when subjected to the group of Lorentz transformations of special relativity theory. Dirac's equation for the electron is one such equation. The fields governed by these equations have themselves been treated as physical systems and quantized, thus leading to a quantum theory of fields. The symmetry of these fields under rotations and other transformations has been fully exploited by the application of group theory and the properties of Lie algebras. Details will be found in Ref. 8 of the bibliography below.

D. F. LAWDEN

References

1. Cassels, J. M., "Basic Quantum Mechanics," New York, McGraw-Hill, 1970.
2. Dirac, P. A. M., "The Principles of Quantum Mechanics," London, Oxford University Press, 1958.
3. Landau, L. D., and Lifshitz, E. M., "Quantum Mechanics," London, Pergamon, 1965.
4. Landé, A., "New Foundation of Quantum Mechanics," Cambridge, Cambridge University Press, 1965.
5. Lawden, D. F., "Mathematical Principles of Quantum Mechanics," London, Methuen, 1967.
6. Mandl, F., "Quantum Mechanics," London, Butterworths, 1957.
7. Messiah, A., "Quantum Mechanics," Vols. I and II, Amsterdam, North-Holland, 1961.
8. Schweber, S. S., "Relativistic Quantum Field Theory," New York, Harper, 1961.

Cross-references: MATHEMATICAL PHYSICS, MATRIX MECHANICS, QUANTUM THEORY, SCHRÖDINGER EQUATION, THEORETICAL PHYSICS, WAVE MECHANICS.

MATRICES

Matrix notation and operations are introduced into theoretical physics so that algebraic equations and expressions in terms of rectangular arrays of numbers can be systematically handled.

An $n \times m$ matrix $\mathbf{A} = (a_{ij})$ possesses n columns and m rows, having in double suffix notation the form

$$\mathbf{A} = \begin{pmatrix} a_{11} & a_{12} & \cdots & a_{1n} \\ \cdot & \cdot & \cdots & \cdot \\ a_{m1} & a_{m2} & \cdots & a_{mn} \end{pmatrix}$$

The general element a_{ij} may be a complex number. If all elements are zero, $\mathbf{A}$ is the null matrix $\mathbf{O}$ or 0. When $n = 1$, the matrix is a column vector $\mathbf{v}$. If $m = n$, $\mathbf{A}$ is square of order n; if all elements not on the leading diagonal a_{11}, $a_{22}, \cdots, a_{nn}$ are zero, the matrix is a diagonal matrix $\mathbf{D}$, while $\mathbf{D}$ is the unit matrix $\mathbf{I}$ if $a_{11} = a_{22} = \cdots = a_{nn} = 1$.

The sum or difference of two $n \times m$ matrices $\mathbf{A}$ and $\mathbf{B}$ is an $n \times m$ matrix $\mathbf{C} = \mathbf{A} \pm \mathbf{B}$, where $c_{ij} = a_{ij} \pm b_{ij}$. The elements of $\alpha\mathbf{A}$ are αa_{ij}.

The transpose of $\mathbf{A}$ is denoted by $\mathbf{A}'$; this is an $m \times n$ matrix whose ith row and jth column are identical respectively with the ith column and jth row of $\mathbf{A}$. Hence $\mathbf{v}'$ is a row matrix with m elements. For convenience, the column $\mathbf{v}$ is often printed as a row with braces, $\{v_1 v_2 \cdots v_m\}$.

The product $\mathbf{C} = \mathbf{AB}$ is only defined when the number of columns of $\mathbf{A}$ equals the number of rows of $\mathbf{B}$; $\mathbf{A}$ and $\mathbf{B}$ are then conformable for multiplication. If $\mathbf{A}$ is $n \times m$ and $\mathbf{B}$ is $p \times n$, then $\mathbf{C}$ is $p \times m$, with

$$c_{ij} = \sum_{k=1}^{n} a_{ik} b_{kj}$$

Generally, multiplication is not commutative, but it is always associative. The transpose of a product is given by $(\mathbf{ABC})' = \mathbf{C}'\mathbf{B}'\mathbf{A}'$.

If $\mathbf{A}$ is square, then $\mathbf{A}$ is symmetric if $\mathbf{A} = \mathbf{A}'$, while if $\mathbf{A} = - \mathbf{A}'$ it is skew-symmetric. A quadratic form S_A in the n variables contained in the column $\mathbf{x} = \{x_1 x_2 \cdots x_n\}$ may be written as $S_A = \mathbf{x}'\mathbf{A}\mathbf{x}$, where $\mathbf{A}$ is symmetric.

Let det $\mathbf{A} \equiv |\mathbf{A}|$ denote the determinant of the square matrix $\mathbf{A}$. If det $\mathbf{A} \neq 0$, $\mathbf{A}$ is nonsingular. Then the definition of matrix multiplication ensures that

$$\det(\mathbf{AB}) = \det \mathbf{A} \det \mathbf{B}$$

where $\mathbf{A}$ and $\mathbf{B}$ are square matrices of the same order.

The cofactor of a_{ij} in the square matrix $\mathbf{A}$ equals $(-1)^{i+j}$ times the determinant formed by crossing out the ith row and jth column in $\mathbf{A}$. The adjoint of $\mathbf{A}$, denoted by adj $\mathbf{A}$, is the transpose of the matrix formed when each element of $\mathbf{A}$ is replaced by its cofactor. We have

$$\mathbf{A} \text{ adj } \mathbf{A} = (\text{adj } \mathbf{A})\mathbf{A} = (\det \mathbf{A})\mathbf{I}$$

and $\det(\text{adj } \mathbf{A}) = |\mathbf{A}|^{n-1}$. The unique reciprocal or inverse of a non-singular matrix $\mathbf{A}$ is given by

$$\mathbf{A}^{-1} = (\text{adj } \mathbf{A})/\det \mathbf{A}$$

This has the property that $\mathbf{AA}^{-1} = \mathbf{A}^{-1}\mathbf{A} = \mathbf{I}$. It follows that

$$(\mathbf{AB})^{-1} = \mathbf{B}^{-1}\mathbf{A}^{-1}$$

Linear equations relating n variables x_i to n variables y_i may be expressed as $\mathbf{x} = \mathbf{A}\mathbf{y}$; if det $\mathbf{A} \neq 0$, the unique solution for the y_i in terms of the x_i is $\mathbf{y} = \mathbf{A}^{-1}\mathbf{x}$.

The rank of an $n \times m$ matrix $\mathbf{A}$ is the order of the largest non-vanishing minor within $\mathbf{A}$; of the m linear expressions $\mathbf{Ax}$, the rank gives the number that are linearly independent. The m linear equations in n unknowns $\mathbf{Ax} = \mathbf{d}$, where $\mathbf{d}$ is a column with m elements, are consistent if the rank of $\mathbf{A}$ equals the rank of the augmented matrix $(\mathbf{A} \ \mathbf{d})$.

If the m linear equations $\mathbf{Ax} = \mathbf{d}$ are inconsistent, the "best" solution in the least squares sense for $x_1, x_2, \cdots x_n$ is given by the normal equations

$$\mathbf{A}'\mathbf{Ax} = \mathbf{A}'\mathbf{d}$$

An $n \times n$ matrix Λ is orthogonal if $\Lambda'\Lambda = \mathbf{I}$, that is, if $\Lambda^{-1} = \Lambda'$. Clearly, $|\Lambda| = \pm 1$. If $\mathbf{c}_i$ denotes the ith column of Λ, then $\mathbf{c}_i'\mathbf{c}_i = 1$ and $\mathbf{c}_i'\mathbf{c}_j = 0$ if $i \neq j$; similar results hold for the rows. The transformation $\mathbf{x}_1 = \Lambda\mathbf{x}$ represents a rotation of rectangular Cartesian axes in three dimensions; $|\Lambda| = +1$ if the right-handed character is preserved. The element λ_{ij} equals the cosine of the angle between the $(x_1)_i$ and x_j axes. If $\mathbf{N}$ is skew-symmetric, then $(\mathbf{I} + \mathbf{N})^{-1}(\mathbf{I} - \mathbf{N})$ is orthogonal.

Matrices with complex elements are manipulated according to the same rules. A square matrix $\mathbf{H}$ is Hermitian if $\mathbf{H}^{*'} = \mathbf{H}$, and skew-Hermitian if $\mathbf{H}^{*'} = -\mathbf{H}$, a star denoting the complex conjugate. A unitary matrix $\mathbf{U}$ satisfies $\mathbf{U}^{*'} = \mathbf{U}^{-1}$, the columns (and rows) enjoying the properties $\mathbf{c}_i^{*'}\mathbf{c}_j = 1$ if $i = j$ and 0 if $i \neq j$.

First- and second-order tensors, arising in many physical problems, may be expressed in matrix notation. If $\mathbf{x}_1 = \Lambda\mathbf{x}$ denotes a rotation of rectangular Cartesian axes, Λ being orthogonal, then $\mathbf{f}_1 = \Lambda\mathbf{f}$ and $\mathbf{F}_1 = \Lambda\mathbf{F}\Lambda'$ define Cartesian tensors of orders 1 and 2 respectively. Evidently, if $\mathbf{u}$ and $\mathbf{v}$ are vectors or tensors of order 1, then $\mathbf{u}'\mathbf{v}$ is an invariant, $\mathbf{Fu}$ is a tensor of order 1 and $\mathbf{uv}'$ is a tensor of order 2. For example, the vector product $\mathbf{u} \times \mathbf{v}$ may be written as $\mathbf{Uv}$, where

$$\mathbf{U} = \begin{pmatrix} 0 & -u_3 & u_2 \\ u_3 & 0 & -u_1 \\ -u_2 & u_1 & 0 \end{pmatrix}$$

$\mathbf{U}$ is a tensor of order 2 if $\mathbf{u}$ is a vector; $\mathbf{U}'$ is the dual of $\mathbf{u}$.

But if $\mathbf{x}_1 = \mathbf{Ax}$, where $\mathbf{A}$ is not orthogonal, $\mathbf{f}_1 = \mathbf{Af}$ defines a contravariant vector, but $\mathbf{g}_1 = \mathbf{A}'^{-1}\mathbf{g}$ defines a covariant vector. The product $\mathbf{g}'\mathbf{f}$ is now an invariant.

If $\mathbf{A}$ is square of order n, then the n homogeneous equations $\mathbf{Ak} = \lambda\mathbf{k}$ require $\det(\mathbf{A} - \lambda\mathbf{I}) = 0$ for non-trivial solutions. This characteristic equation possesses n characteristic or latent roots; if they are all distinct, n corresponding characteristic or latent vectors exist. The vector $\mathbf{k}_i$ corresponding to the root λ_i may consist of the n cofactors of any row of $\mathbf{A} - \lambda_i\mathbf{I}$; at least one non-trivial row exists.

The following properties are important. If $\mathbf{A}$ is real and symmetric, and if λ_i and λ_j are distinct, then $\mathbf{k}_i'\mathbf{k}_j = 0$; these two vectors are orthogonal. Again, if $\mathbf{A}$ is real and symmetric, the n values of λ are real, but if $\mathbf{A}$ is real and skew-symmetric, these n values are pure imaginary. For a real orthogonal matrix Λ, $|\lambda_i| = 1$ for all i. The characteristic roots of $\mathbf{A}^{-1}$ are $1/\lambda_i$, $\mathbf{k}_i$ still being the corresponding vectors. If $|\lambda_1|$ is the largest of the moduli of the n roots, then as $r \to \infty$, $\mathbf{A}^r\mathbf{x} \to \mathbf{k}_1$, where $\mathbf{x}$ is an arbitrary column.

If $\mathbf{A}$ is symmetric, n mutually orthogonal characteristic vectors may be found even if the roots are not all distinct. If each vector $\mathbf{k}_i$ is normalized, i.e., divided by $\sqrt{(\mathbf{k}_i'\mathbf{k}_i)}$, then the matrix

$$\Lambda = (\mathbf{k}_1 \ \mathbf{k}_2 \cdots \mathbf{k}_n)$$

is orthogonal, and the product $\Lambda'\mathbf{A}\Lambda$ equals $\mathbf{D}$, the diagonal matrix consisting of the n roots arranged down its leading diagonal in order. The matrix $\mathbf{A}$ is said to be diagonalized.

More generally, if $\mathbf{A}$ is a general square matrix of order n, then n independent vectors $\mathbf{k}_i$ may be found corresponding to the n roots if the

latter are distinct. Then

$$T = (k_1 \; k_2 \; \cdots \; k_n)$$

transforms A into diagonal form thus: $T^{-1}AT = D$. If the n roots are not all distinct, this reduction may or may not be possible; it is always possible if A is symmetric. Note $A^n = TD^nT^{-1}$.

Similar remarks apply to Hermitian matrices H. If $Hk = \lambda k$, all the n values of λ are real, and n vectors can always be found such that $k_i^{*'}k_j = \delta_{ij}$. The unitary matrix $U = (k_1 \; k_2 \; \cdots \; k_n)$ transforms H into diagonal form.

Two quadratic forms $S_A = x'Ax$, $S_B = x'Bx$, where A and B are symmetric and of the same order, may be reduced simultaneously to sums of squares. The equations $Ak = \lambda Bk$ demand $\det(A - \lambda B) = 0$; this possesses n roots λ_i and n corresponding vectors k_i. If

$$T = (k_1 \; k_2 \; \cdots \; k_n)$$

then $T'AT$ and $T'BT$ are both diagonal. The transformation $x = Ty$ yields the two sums of squares $S_A = y'(T'AT)y$ and $S_B = y'(T'BT)y$. In particular, if S_A is positive definite, $T'AT$ will equal I if new columns $\bar{k}_i$ are used in T, where $\bar{k}_i = k_i/\sqrt{(k_i' \, Ak_i)}$.

Necessary and sufficient conditions for the real quadratic form S_A to be positive definite for all real $x \neq 0$ are that the n determinants

$$a_{11}, \quad \begin{vmatrix} a_{11} & a_{12} \\ a_{21} & a_{22} \end{vmatrix}, \quad \begin{vmatrix} a_{11} & a_{12} & a_{13} \\ a_{21} & a_{22} & a_{23} \\ a_{31} & a_{32} & a_{33} \end{vmatrix}, \ldots, \det A$$

should be positive. This ensures that the n characteristic roots of A are all positive.

Finally, matrices may often usefully be partitioned employing matrices within matrices. Multiplication may still be performed provided each individual matrix product is permissible. For example,

$$\begin{pmatrix} a & b' \\ c & D \end{pmatrix} \begin{pmatrix} e & f' \\ g & H \end{pmatrix} = \begin{pmatrix} ae + b'g & af' + b'H \\ ce + Dg & cf' + DH \end{pmatrix}$$

where a, e are scalars, b, c, f, g are 1×3 columns and D, H are 3×3.

Applications *Differential Equations* If $dx/dt + Ax = f$, A being constant and $f = \{f_1(t), f_2(t), \ldots, f_n(t)\}$, then if T diagonalizes A, $x = Ty$ yields n non-simultaneous equations $dy/dt + Dy = T^{-1}f$. If $y_0(t)$ is a particular integral,

$$x(t) = T \begin{pmatrix} e^{-\lambda_1 t} \cdots & & 0 \\ & \cdots & \\ 0 & \cdots & e^{-\lambda_n t} \end{pmatrix}$$

$$\times \; [T^{-1}x(0) - y_0(0)] + Ty_0(t)$$

Geometry. In three-dimensional Cartesian coordinates,

$$a'x + d = 0$$

represents a plane, the perpendicular distance from x_1 being

$$(a'x_1 + d)/\sqrt{(a'a)}$$

The equation $x'Ax = d$ represents a central quadric. If Λ diagonalizes A, the rotation $x = \Lambda x_1$ yields $x'_1 Dx_1 = d$. The vectors k_1, k_2, k_3 specify the three principal axes, of semi-lengths $\sqrt{(d/\lambda_i)}$ when $d/\lambda_i > 0$.

Dynamics. The rotational equations of motion of a rigid body with respect to moving axes fixed in the body and with the origin fixed in space or at the centre of mass are

$$g = J\dot{\omega} + \Omega J\omega$$

where g = couple, ω = angular velocity, Ω' = dual ω. J denotes the inertia tensor $-\Sigma m XX$, where X' = dual x. Explicitly,

$$J = \begin{pmatrix} A & -H & -G \\ -H & B & -F \\ -G & -F & C \end{pmatrix}$$

The rotational kinetic energy is $\frac{1}{2}\omega'J\omega$. When principal axes of inertia are chosen, J is diagonal, yielding Euler's equations.

Small oscillations about a position of equilibrium are investigated by considering the second order approximations

$$K.E. = \dot{q}'A\dot{q}, \quad P.E. = q'Bq$$

q containing n generalized coordinates measured from their equilibrium values. A and B are constant symmetric matrices. If the n roots of $\det(A + \lambda B) = 0$ are considered, and if $q = Tx$, where $T = (k_1 \; k_2 \; \cdots \; k_n)$ reduces A to the unit matrix I, the equations of motion are

$$\ddot{x}_i + (1/\lambda_i)x_i = 0$$

The elements of x are the *normal coordinates*; each individual solution x_i in terms of the q's is a *normal mode* of period $2\pi\sqrt{\lambda_i}$.

Electromagnetic Theory. Maxwell's 3×3 stress tensor in matrix notation is

$$T = \frac{1}{2}[2\epsilon ee' + 2\mu hh' - \epsilon(e'e)I - \mu(h'h)I]$$

in mks rationalized units. The field exerts a force across an area element $n \, \delta S$ equal to $Tn \, \delta S$.

When electromagnetic waves are propagated in an ionized medium the equation

$$\text{curl curl } e = k^2(I + M)e$$

arises, where

$$M = -X(Y^2 nn' + iYN - I)/(Y^2 - 1)$$

in the usual notation with collisions neglected; here, n = unit vector directed along the external magnetic field, N' = dual n. These equations

may be rearranged in terms of the matrix

$$\mathbf{f} = \{E_x, -E_y, Z_0 H_x, Z_0 H_y\}$$

giving $d\mathbf{f}/dz = -ik\mathbf{Tf}$, where $\mathbf{T}$ is a 4×4 matrix. If the characteristic roots $\lambda_i(z)$ of $\mathbf{T}$ are found, and if $\mathbf{R}$ diagonalizes $\mathbf{T}$, then the transformation $\mathbf{f} = \mathbf{Rg}$ yields

$$\frac{d\mathbf{g}}{dz} = -ik\mathbf{Dg} - \mathbf{R}^{-1}\frac{d\mathbf{R}}{dz}\mathbf{g}$$

The solutions of the approximate equations $d\mathbf{g}/dz = -ik\mathbf{Dg}$ are related to the characteristic waves propagated in the medium.

Special Relativity. If $\mathbf{x} = \{ict, x, y, z\}$ refers to an inertial frame S, and if a second parallel frame S_1 has uniform relative velocity U along Ox, the Lorentz transformation is $\mathbf{x}_1 = \Lambda_U\mathbf{x}$, where

$$\Lambda_U = \begin{pmatrix} \beta & -iU\beta/c & 0 & 0 \\ iU\beta/c & \beta & 0 & 0 \\ 0 & 0 & 1 & 0 \\ 0 & 0 & 0 & 1 \end{pmatrix}$$

Λ is orthogonal, and $\beta = 1/\sqrt{(1 - U^2/c^2)}$. We have $\Lambda_V \Lambda_U = \Lambda_W$, where

$$W = (U + V)/(1 + UV/c^2).$$

For the general velocity $\mathbf{v}$ relating parallel frames,

$$\Lambda = \begin{pmatrix} \beta & -i\beta\mathbf{v}'/c \\ i\beta\mathbf{v}/c & \mathbf{I} + (\beta - 1)\mathbf{vv}'/v^2 \end{pmatrix}$$

The operator $\square = \{\partial/ic\partial t, \partial/\partial x, \partial/\partial y, \partial/\partial z\}$ is a four vector satisfying $\square_1 = \Lambda\square$; so are the four-current $\mathbf{i}$ and the four-potential $\mathbf{b}$,

$$\mathbf{i} = \begin{pmatrix} ic\rho \\ \mathbf{j} \end{pmatrix}, \quad \mathbf{b} = \begin{pmatrix} i\phi/c \\ \mathbf{a} \end{pmatrix}$$

where $\mathbf{a}$ is the vector potential. They satisfy $\square'\mathbf{i} = 0$ (conservation of charge), $\square'\mathbf{b} = 0$ (the Lorentz relation). Maxwell's equations in mks units in free space take the form

$$\square'\mathbf{F} = -\mathbf{i}'/\epsilon_0 c^2$$

$$\square'\mathbf{G} = 0$$

where

$$\mathbf{F} = \square\mathbf{b}' - (\square\mathbf{b}')' = \begin{pmatrix} 0 & i\mathbf{e}'/c \\ -i\mathbf{e}/c & -\mu_0\mathbf{H} \end{pmatrix}$$

and

$$\mathbf{G} = \begin{pmatrix} 0 & \mu_0\mathbf{h}' \\ -\mu_0\mathbf{h} & -i\mathbf{E}/c \end{pmatrix}$$

are tensors of order 2 under a Lorentz transformation. $\mathbf{E}'$ and $\mathbf{H}'$ are the respective 3×3

duals of $\mathbf{e}$ and $\mathbf{h}$. All tensor equations are invariant in form in all frames of reference.

The tensor

$$\mathbf{T} = \tfrac{1}{2}\epsilon_0 c^2 \mathbf{F}\,\mathbf{F} - \tfrac{1}{2}\mu_0^{-1}\mathbf{G}\,\mathbf{G}$$

$$= \tfrac{1}{2}\begin{pmatrix} \epsilon_0\mathbf{e}'\mathbf{e} + \mu_0\mathbf{h}'\mathbf{h} & -2i\mathbf{e}'\mathbf{H}/c \\ -2i\mathbf{E}\mathbf{h}/c & \epsilon_0\mathbf{e}\mathbf{e}' + \epsilon_0\mathbf{E}\mathbf{E} + \mu_0\mathbf{h}\mathbf{h}' + \\ & \mu_0\mathbf{H}\mathbf{H} \end{pmatrix}$$

contains the energy density, Poynting's vector, the momentum density and Maxwell's stress tensor in partitioned form.

Applications may likewise be made to circuit theory, to elasticity where 3×3 stress and strain tensors are defined, and to quantum mechanics, embracing, for example, matrix mechanics and the Dirac wave equation of the electron.

JOHN HEADING

References

Heading, J., "Matrix Theory for Physicists," London, Longmans, Green & Co.
Heading, J., "Electromagnetic Theory and Special Relativity," Cambridge, University Tutorial Press.
Jeffreys, H., and Jeffreys, B., "Methods of Mathematical Physics," Cambridge, The University Press.
Perlis, S., "Theory of Matrices," Reading, Mass., Addison-Wesley.

Cross-references: MATHEMATICAL PRINCIPLES OF QUANTUM MECHANICS, MATRIX MECHANICS, TENSORS.

MATRIX MECHANICS*

Introduction This article is a sequel to the article WAVE MECHANICS which appears in this Encyclopedia. We assume that the reader is familiar with the content of that article, which will be referred to here as WM.

The point of view adopted in WM is that nonrelativistic quantum mechanics can be formulated entirely in terms of the time-dependent Schrödinger wave equation. While this is true, there are, as remarked in the introduction of WM, situations in which the matrix approach, or a combination of matrix and wave methods, is useful. In the present article, we first discuss some properties of matrices and show how they appear in quantum mechanics. Purely matrix methods are then used to calculate the energy levels and some other properties of the linear harmonic oscillator (WM, p. 1007).

*Author deceased. Article is reprinted from first edition. Dr. Behram Kurşunoğlu very kindly reviewed this article to ensure that it was still valid and up-to-date.

Matrices in Quantum Mechanics A matrix is a square or rectangular array of numbers. Two or more matrices may be added or multiplied in accordance with certain rules. As a simple example, consider the matrix A, which has three rows and four columns; we write it:

$$A = \begin{pmatrix} (1|A|1) & (1|A|2) & (1|A|3) & (1|A|4) \\ (2|A|1) & (2|A|2) & (2|A|3) & (2|A|4) \\ (3|A|1) & (3|A|2) & (3|A|3) & (3|A|4) \end{pmatrix} \quad (1)$$

The twelve parenthetical symbols on the right side of Eq. (1) are the *matrix elements*, and in general are complex numbers which may be functions of some variable such as the time. Two matrices can be added only if they have the same number of rows and the same number of columns; addition then consists in forming the matrix whose elements are the sums of the corresponding elements of the original matrices:

$$C = A + B \text{ implies } (n|C|m) = (n|A|m) + (n|B|m)$$
$$(2)$$

Two matrices can be multiplied only if the number of columns of the left member of the product is equal to the number of rows of the right member:

$$C = AB \text{ implies } (n|C|m) = \sum_k (n|A|k)(k|B|m)$$
$$(3)$$

It is apparent from Eqs. (2) and (3) that addition is commutative, but multiplication in general is not.

A *unit matrix* is one which can multiply another matrix and leave it unchanged. It follows from Eq. (3) that it is a square matrix (equal number of rows and columns) that has unity along its principal diagonal (upper left to lower right) and zero elsewhere:

$$(n|1|m) = \delta_{nm} = 1 \text{ if } n = m \text{ and } 0 \text{ if } n \neq m \quad (4)$$

δ_{nm} is the Kronecker δ-symbol. A *constant matrix* $C = c1$ has the number c along the principal diagonal and zero elsewhere. A *diagonal matrix* D has the form:

$$(n|D|m) = D_n \delta_{nm} \quad (5)$$

The numbers D_n are called the eigenvalues of the matrix D.

A matrix A may or may not possess an inverse A^{-1}, which must satisfy both of the relations:

$$AA^{-1} = 1, \quad A^{-1}A = 1$$

The Hermitian adjoint $A^\dagger$ of a matrix A is the matrix formed by interchanging rows and columns and taking the complex conjugate of each element:

$$B = A^\dagger \text{ implies } (n|B|m) = (m|A|n)^* \quad (6)$$

A matrix is *Hermitian* or self-adjoint if it is equal to its Hermitian adjoint: $A = A^\dagger$. It follows from Eq. (6) that only square matrices can be Hermitian. A matrix is *unitary* if its Hermitian adjoint is equal to its inverse:

$$A^\dagger = A^{-1}, \text{ or } AA^\dagger = 1 \text{ and } A^\dagger A = 1 \quad (7)$$

The transformation of a square matrix A into a square matrix A' by means of the transformation matrix S is defined by:

$$SAS^{-1} = A' \quad (8)$$

It is evident that S^{-1} must exist, and that it transforms A' back into A. The form of a matrix equation is unaffected by transformation. Thus the equation

$$AB + CDE = F$$

may be transformed into

$$SABS^{-1} + SCDES^{-1} = SFS^{-1}$$

which is equivalent to

$$A'B' + C'D'E' = F'$$

where the primed and unprimed matrices are related by Eq. (8). This invariance of matrix equations with respect to transformations makes it possible to work with any convenient transformation of a set of matrices without affecting the validity of any results obtained.

It can be shown[a] that any Hermitian matrix can be transformed into diagonal form by means of a suitable unitary transformation matrix. The diagonal elements of the resulting diagonal matrix are called the eigenvalues of the original Hermitian matrix, as well as of the transformed matrix [see Eq. (5)]. These eigenvalues are easily seen to be real numbers. Since the eigenvalues are the measurable values of quantities represented by matrices, we shall require that physical quantities such as x, p, and H, which must have real eigenvalues, correspond to Hermitian matrices. It can also be shown that the necessary and sufficient condition that two Hermitian matrices A and B can be diagonalized by the same unitary transformation is that they commute, i.e., that $AB = BA$.

Suppose now that the Schrödinger equation [WM, Eq. (14)] is written in the form:

$$H\psi_m = E_m \psi_m \quad (9)$$

where E_m are the energy levels or eigenvalues and the ψ_m are the corresponding *eigenfunctions*. The eigenfunctions can not only be chosen to be normalized [WM, Eq. (19)], so

[a]The phrase "it can be shown," which appears occasionally in this article, means that the necessary proofs are too long to be given here. They may be found in the books listed as references at the end of the article.

that $\int \psi_m^* \psi_m d\tau = 1$, but also orthogonal to each other: $\int \psi_n^* \psi_m d\tau = 0$ if $n \neq m$. Thus if Eq. (9) is multiplied through by ψ_n^* and integrated over all coordinates, we obtain

$$\int \psi_n^* H \psi_m d\tau = E_m \delta_{nm} \qquad (10)$$

We define the matrix element of the Hamiltonian H in the representation specified by the functions ψ_m as:

$$(n|H|m) = \int \psi_n^* H \psi_m d\tau \qquad (11)$$

Equation (10) then shows that when the eigenfunctions ψ_m are used to define the representation, the matrix of H is diagonal, and the diagonal elements are the energy levels of the system.

If some other set of functions ϕ_k, also normalized and orthogonal so that $\int \phi_k^* \phi_l d\tau = \delta_{kl}$, is chosen to specify the representation, the matrix for H would not be in diagonal form. That is, the matrix element

$$(k|H|l) = \int \phi_k^* H \phi_l d\tau \qquad (12)$$

would not vanish when $k \neq l$. Now it can be shown that the transformation matrix S, defined by

$$(n|S|k) = \int \psi_n^* \phi_k d\tau \qquad (13)$$

is unitary, and transforms the nondiagonal matrix of Eq. (12) into the diagonal matrix of Eq. (11). That is, the transformation equation [Eq. (8)], with the substitution of Eq. (7), may be written:

$$SHS^\dagger = H'$$

or in matrix element form:

$$\sum_k \sum_l (n|S|k)(k|H|l)(l|S^\dagger|m)$$

$$= (n|H|m) = E_m \delta_{nm}$$

We see then that there are two general methods for finding the energy levels of a system. One is to solve the Schrödinger equation, as in WM, and determine the energy eigenvalues. The other is to choose a convenient set of functions ϕ_k, use them to calculate a matrix representation [Eq. (12)] for the Hamiltonian, and transform the resulting matrix into diagonal form. The eigenvalues of the diagonal form of H are then the energy levels. It may happen that H can be put in diagonal form directly, without explicit reference to a set of functions ϕ_k or the transformation matrix [Eq. (13)]. An example of this is given in the next section.

Linear Harmonic Oscillator The linear or one-dimensional harmonic oscillator is described by the Hamiltonian [WM, Eq. (21)]:

$$H = (1/2m)(p^2 + m^2 \omega^2 x^2) \qquad (14)$$

where $\omega/2\pi$ is the classical frequency of the oscillator. We also know that [WM, Eq. (15)]:

$$px - xp = \hbar/i \qquad (15)$$

We then see from the algebra of Eqs. (14) and (15) that

$$(p + im\omega x)(p - im\omega x) = p^2 + m^2 \omega^2 x^2$$
$$+ im\omega(xp - px) = 2mH - m\hbar\omega \quad (16)$$

and that

$$(p - im\omega x)(p + im\omega x) = 2mH + m\hbar\omega \quad (17)$$

If now we multiply Eq. (16) through on the right and Eq. (17) through on the left by $(p + im\omega x)$, we obtain

$$(2mH - m\hbar\omega)(p + im\omega x) = (p + im\omega x)$$
$$(p - im\omega x)(p + im\omega x)$$
$$= (p + im\omega x)(2mH + m\hbar\omega) \quad (18)$$

We choose a representation in which H is diagonal, so that, from Eqs. (10) and (11),[a]

$$(n|H|n') = E_n \delta_{nn'}$$

In this representation, a non-operator number, such as the right side of Eq. (15) or the term $m\hbar\omega$ that is added to or subtracted from $2mH$ in Eq. (18), must be thought of as a constant matrix [defined under Eq. (4)]. Thus if we write the left side of Eq. (18) out in terms of matrix elements, we encounter the term

$$(n|2mH - m\hbar\omega|n') = (n|2mH|n') - (n|m\hbar\omega 1|n')$$
$$= (2mE_n - m\hbar\omega)\delta_{nn'}$$

It follows that the left side of Eq. (18) is

$$(2mE_n - m\hbar\omega)(n|p + im\omega x|n')$$

and the right side is

$$(n|p + im\omega x|n')(2mE_{n'} + m\hbar\omega)$$

On equating these two expressions, rearranging terms, and cancelling a common factor $2m$, we obtain:

$$(E_n - E_{n'} - \hbar\omega)(n|p + im\omega x|n') = 0 \quad (19)$$

Equation (19) tells us that either $(E_n - E_{n'} - \hbar\omega)$ is zero, or $(n|p + im\omega x|n')$ is zero, or both. To make use of this result, we write the nth diagonal matrix element of Eq. (16):

$$\sum_{n'} (n|p + im\omega x|n')(n'|p - im\omega x|n)$$
$$= 2m(E_n - \tfrac{1}{2}\hbar\omega) \quad (20)$$

Now p and x are physical quantities, and so correspond to Hermitian matrices. Thus $p = p^\dagger$, $x = x^\dagger$, and $(p - im\omega x) = (p + im\omega x)^\dagger$, so that

---

[a]We use the matrix-index n' instead of m, in order to avoid confusion with the oscillator mass.

from Eq. (6):

$$(n'|p - im\omega x|n) = (n|p + im\omega x|n')^* \quad (21)$$

Substitution of Eq. (21) on the left side of Eq. (20) shows that each term in the sum is non-negative, so that the right side is also non-negative. From Eq. (19), not more than one term in the sum can fail to vanish; this is the term for which $E_{n'} = E_n - \hbar\omega$, if there is such a term. If there is no such term, or in other words if E_n is the lowest energy eigenvalue, then the left side of Eq. (20) is zero, and $E_n = \frac{1}{2}\hbar\omega$. If there is such a term, then $E_n \neq \frac{1}{2}\hbar\omega$, and $E_n - \hbar\omega$ is another eigenvalue.

We conclude that the energy levels of the linear harmonic oscillator form the infinite sequence:

$$\tfrac{1}{2}\hbar\omega, \quad \tfrac{3}{2}\hbar\omega, \quad \tfrac{5}{2}\hbar\omega, \cdots$$

or

$$E_n = (n + \tfrac{1}{2})\hbar\omega, n = 0, 1, 2, \cdots \quad (22)$$

This is in agreement with the lowest energy level obtained in WM, Eq. (23).

The diagonal matrix elements of a physical quantity are the *expectation values* of that quantity [see WM, Eq. (20)]. From the preceding discussion, we see that

$$(n|p + im\omega x|n) = 0 \text{ and } (n|p - im\omega x|n) = 0$$

so that, by addition and subtraction of these equations,

$$(n|p|n) = 0 \quad \text{and} \quad (n|x|n) = 0$$

Thus the expectation value of x and of $p = (\hbar/i)(d/dx)$ is zero for each oscillator eigenfunction. This is easily verified explicitly for the ground state wave function [WM, Eq. (22)]. However, the expectation values of p^2 and of x^2 are not zero, as we now show.

We know from Eq. (19) that $(n - 1|p + im\omega x|n) = 0$, and hence from Eq. (21) that

$$(n|p - im\omega x|n - 1) = 0 \quad (23)$$

We also know from the derivation of Eq. (22) that $(n|p + im\omega x|n - 1)$ is not in general zero, and we set it equal to $2A_n$:

$$(n|p + im\omega x|n - 1) = 2A_n \quad (24)$$

Adding and subtracting Eqs. (23) and (24) we obtain

$$(n|p|n - 1) = A_n \quad \text{and} \quad (n|x|n - 1) = -iA_n/m\omega$$

Since p and x are Hermitian, we have from Eq. (6) that

$$(n - 1|p|n) = A_n{}^* \quad \text{or} \quad (n|p|n + 1) = A_{n+1}{}^*,$$

and that

$$(n - 1|x|n) = iA_n{}^*/m\omega \text{ or}$$

$$(n|x|n + 1) = iA_{n+1}{}^*/m\omega$$

From Eq. (3):

$$(n|p^2|n) = \sum_{n'} (n|p|n')(n'|p|n)$$

$$= (n|p|n - 1)(n - 1|p|n) + (n|p|n + 1)$$
$$\cdot (n + 1|p|n)$$

since all other matrix elements in the sum are zero. Thus

$$(n|p^2|n) = |A_n|^2 + |A_{n+1}|^2 \quad (25)$$

and in similar fashion

$$(n|x^2|n) = (|A_n|^2 + |A_{n+1}|^2)/m^2\omega^2 \quad (26)$$

Substitution of Eq. (24) into Eq. (20), with the help of Eq. (22), gives:

$$4|A_n|^2 = 2m(E_n - \tfrac{1}{2}\hbar\omega) = 2nm\hbar\omega$$

so that Eqs. (25) and (26) yield:

$$(n|p^2|n) = (n + \tfrac{1}{2}) m\hbar\omega,$$

$$(n|x^2|n) = (n + \tfrac{1}{2})(\hbar/m\omega) \quad (27)$$

Comparison with Eq. (14) shows that the expectation values of the kinetic and potential parts of the energy are equal, and that each is half the energy eigenvalue. The results of Eq. (27) for the lowest state ($n = 0$) can be verified by using Eqs. (20) and (22) of WM, normalizing ψ_0, and performing the integrations.

Conclusion These two articles, WM and the present one, show in some detail how the Schrödinger wave equation and the matrix theory are related in a particular, relatively simple case. In more complicated situations it may be most convenient to use one or the other of these approaches, or, most often, a combination of the two. The reference books listed below give many examples of the applications of the theory described thus far, and also of its extension to relativistic motion.

LEONARD I. SCHIFF

References

Dirac, P. A. M., "The Principles of Quantum Mechanics," Fourth edition, London, Oxford Press, 1958.

Schiff, L. I., "Quantum Mechanics," Second edition, New York, McGraw-Hill Book Co., 1955.

Bohm, D., "Quantum Theory," Englewood Cliffs, N.J., Prentice-Hall, 1951.

Landau, L., and Lifshitz, E., "Quantum Mechanics, Non-Relativistic Theory," Reading, Mass., Addison-Wesley, 1958.

Messiah, A., "Quantum Mechanics," New York Interscience Publishers, 1961.

Cross-references: MATHEMATICAL PRINCIPLES OF QUANTUM MECHANICS, MATRICES, QUANTUM THEORY, SCHRÖDINGER EQUATION, WAVE MECHANICS.

MEASUREMENTS, PRINCIPLES OF*

Physics in its most fundamental aspect is an experimental science in the sense that speculation is guided by experience; its development depends on frequent comparison between observation and what is deduced from a hypothesis, itself formed to coordinate previous observations. A scientific experiment is a set of events deliberately arranged to reveal as clearly as possible, some regularity in the behavior of physical objects. Compared with other sciences, fundamental physics deals with simple systems, ranging from elementary particles to relatively simple arrangements of atoms. Its experiments are in principle simpler than those of biological science, where the experimenter interferes at his peril with the complicated systems which he studies, or those of cosmology, where the astronomer cannot interfere experimentally and is confined to pure observation of his enormous and remote fields of study. In fact, of course, the theoretical methods of the physicist are sophisticated and the experimental methods are often more elaborate than those employed in other sciences. This elaboration arises from two features of contemporary experimentation, the need to produce extraordinary circumstances, for example, streams of particles having unusually high velocities, and the need to isolate the phenomenon under investigation from all interference. For example, some of the phenomena of the solid state can only be profitably studied in crystalline matter of extreme purity: in many experiments in physics a good vacuum allows particles to travel a long distance without collision or a better vacuum allows a prepared surface to remain for an appreciable time free from contamination by foreign atoms.

Besides fundamental physics, there is a very large field of applied physics, passing imperceptibly into fundamental physics and into engineering; in this field, the systems studied are often man-made devices, and the object of experiments is to obtain data required for design purposes and to examine the performance of finished devices with a view to employing or improving them.

In both fundamental and applied fields, the results of an experiment usually take the form of a set of numerical data which are to be compared with a theoretical calculation, or with another set of experimental data. The value of an experiment may often be judged by the trustworthiness of a numerical result, which in turn depends on the probability of a certain difference (error) between the result and the result of an ideal experiment in which the required quantity is measured to the exclusion of all disturbance.

The easiest kind of experimental error to estimate and to eliminate is the kind called random;

*Editor was unable to locate author. Article is reprinted from first edition.

this may be caused by external disturbances or by inherent fluctuations of the kind we shall call noise. It is distinguished by the property that if the experiment is repeated, a different result is obtained, and if it is repeated many times, the difference between the means of groups of repetitions decreases with the number of results in each group. It is clear that the reduction of such errors depends essentially on averaging. There are well-defined experimental and mathematical methods for estimating these errors and reducing them in the most economical way. The accumulation of data for averaging is time-consuming, and since the averaging process necessarily smooths out short-term phenomena, it attenuates the high-frequency sensitivity of the experiment.

A much more serious difficulty arises in determining how far the conditions of an experiment agree with those assumed theoretically to exist. The distinctive skill of an experimental physicist lies in eliminating by design or calculation the systematic error which arises when some unwanted external or internal factor interacts in a consistent way with the system which is being studied. Effects of this kind are not necessarily detected or eliminated by simple repetition of the experiment, and there are no comprehensive rules for designing an experiment free from systematic error. It is sometimes possible to conduct an experiment in such a way that a potentially systematic error appears as a random error which can more easily be detected and eliminated. For example, in photographic photometry, a number of spectra are recorded on a photographic plate, and if the spatial order of the records on the plate coincides with the regular change of some variable in the experiment, a regular variation of plate sensitivity will give rise to an apparently systematic error, which could be avoided by arranging the spectra in random order. Effective techniques for randomizing have been worked out for more complicated situations than this and especially in connection with field trials in agriculture and product control in industry. They are available in books on the design of experiments. As a further application of this principle, if the characteristics of an experiment are liable to change with time, it is undesirable to change a variable of the experiment in a monotonic way since the drift then appears as an undetectable systematic error. It would have been apparent if variations had been made in random order. Apart from this possibility, external disturbances may sometimes be eliminated by means of isolation as discussed below; external conditions may be varied over as wide a range as practicable in order to detect unsuspected interactions, and conditions may then be held as nearly constant as possible during the important observations. Of course, the experiment must be carefully and repeatedly reviewed theoretically to search for possible disturbing effects, and subsidiary experiments or deliberate variations of the main

experiment may be required to detect them. In the final resort, it may be possible to invent a radically different experiment to measure a required quantity or substantiate a theoretical conclusion, the hope being that quite different systematic errors will then be encountered. It is true that most of the fundamental ideas of physics and most of the important numerical quantities used in it rest upon broad experimental foundations rather than single experiments. From time to time, single experiments assume a crucial status, decisive between two theories, as the Bothe-Geiger coincidence experiment of the thirties decided between the electromagnetic and the charged-particle views of penetrating cosmic rays, or the experiments of Wu, Ambler and others, settled the nonconservation of parity. However, such experiments have always appeared, in retrospect at least, as fitting into the broader background of experimental fact.

Every event in an experiment is in principle coupled with events in the outside world, and this coupling may lead to systematic or to random error. The coupling may be mechanical, thermal, or electromagnetic, or it may involve the incursion of radiation or of nuclear particles. Time variations of these disturbances are more important than the steady components, which can be eliminated by proper measurement techniques. The time variations are sometimes produced by the spontaneous variations (fundamental noise) associated with the disturbance. For example, the effective sensitivity of thermal detectors of radiation may be limited by the fluctuations in the (parasitic) exchange of radiation between detector and its immediate surroundings, and the fluctuations can be reduced by operating at a low temperature. Not all time variations are of this fundamental type, and it may be necessary to stabilize the environment (e.g., temperature, pressure, electrical supplies) by the established feedback techniques.

We now review some of the techniques for isolating an experiment from the disturbances considered above.

(a) Attenuation of *mechanical vibrations:* traditionally this is achieved by special building construction, placing mechanically critical experiments on ground or subterranean floors, providing special foundations not closely coupled to the rest of the building; these measures are applicable to astronomical telescopes, but their importance in the physical laboratory is probably decreasing. Mechanically vulnerable assemblies can be isolated by systems of masses, springs and dampers designed as mechanical filters, but there are practical difficulties in securing high attenuation at low frequencies. Sometimes attenuation is required in a particular direction, and vibrations in other directions are relatively unimportant; the design of an antivibration support may then be simplified, as where an antivibration mounting is provided for a rotational instrument like a galvanometer.

Finally, rotational disturbances of a suspended system can be produced by sideways accelerations if the rotating system does not satisfy the conditions for dynamic balance, and these conditions must be satisfied to improve steadiness.

(b) *Thermal effects* on measuring equipment may involve the actual temperature of a particular element, in which case thermostatic devices are required, and one of the most precise is the use of a phase-equilibrium bath, i.e., ice or some other solid in equilibrium with its liquid. But thermal effects may be produced by the appearance of temperature *differences* producing mechanical deformation, thermoelectric voltages, or changes in relative values of resistances. The reduction of these differences demands good thermal transfer among the parts themselves and poor thermal transfer between the parts and the external disturbances, so that insulation must be combined with good conducting layers, or even more effective, stirred liquid baths.

(c) *Magnetic systems* are protected from disturbances in two different ways: by shielding and by astatic design. The former involves layers of soft magnetic material, but it must be remembered that the materials of highest permeability (e.g., the permalloys) saturate in quite weak fields and then produce little or no attenuation of disturbances. They must generally be used within outer shields of substances like soft iron. The second method depends on constructing the measuring system (which may consist of suspended magnets or wound coils) in such a way that the effects of a disturbing field, uniform in space, neutralize one another while the effects to be measured do not. It is clear that the sensitivity to the gradient of a disturbing field depends on detailed design, e.g., the nearness of two coils, and that more complicated systems could be used to remove derivatives of higher order.

(d) *Electrostatic and electromagnetic disturbances* are often easy to eliminate by metallic shielding, but the effect of very small holes in the shielding may be appreciable. The effects are worst in electronic devices of high impedance, particularly electron tubes used as electrometers, which can rectify and detect high-frequency disturbances. Such sensitive equipment may require metallic shielding of nearly gastight quality or, indeed, complete double shielding. Furthermore, if the sensitive circuit forms a loop coupled with a varying magnetic flux, disturbances will be induced in it in spite of metal shielding of finite conductivity, and such loops must be avoided.

When the experiment has been protected from disturbances, the next step in measurement technique is to eliminate the steady or slowly varying effects which are still present; the simplest example is that of taking the zero of an instrument before and after a reading. If these readings are taken in a regular time sequence, a linear drift can be completely eliminated. It is important to arrange the apparatus so that "on"

and "off" readings, more generally "condition A" and "condition B," may be alternated *rapidly* and with *minimal disturbance* of conditions. This is often a distinctive feature of a well-designed measurement technique. A fundamentally similar but more sophisticated procedure is obtained by automatic alternation of conditions A and B, followed by automatic separation and subtraction of the results of the two conditions. The simplest example is the use of a "chopper" amplifier to measure quasi-steady voltages; a vibrating switch or its equivalent interrupts the input to an amplifier which is required only to amplify the alternating component and which can be free from long-period drift. The output of the amplifier is measured by a rectifying instrument or, more advantageously, by an instrument which is sensitive only to components properly related in phase to the alternations of the input.

Developments of this technique are far reaching, and there are two important extensions of it. The output obtained can be used to control condition A or condition B until they are equal; this is an application of the feedback principle. Furthermore, since the final output is a zero-frequency measure of the difference between A and B, it can be integrated over a long time by electrical, electronic or electromechanical methods (condenser charging, feedback integrator or integrating motor), and noise-type fluctuations, alternating disturbances outside an extremely small frequency band, and disturbances common to A and B—can be eliminated to a spectacular degree. The accuracy of every measurement is limited by fundamental or fluctuation phenomena which it is convenient to call *noise*, though often it is not practically necessary or technically possible to take the elimination of other disturbances to the point where this noise becomes limiting. If we are concerned with the measurement of a quasi-steady quantity, noise can always be removed by time-averaging, though this process will attenuate small, nonrecurring transitory events, and these must remain permanently masked by the noise.

The most fundamental limitations of this kind arise from the "uncertainty" limitations of quantum mechanics, since it is not possible to define simultaneously and accurately the variables belonging to certain canonical pairs such as energy and time, momentum and position. A practical example of this limitation is the finite width, in terms of quantum energy or spectral frequency, of a spectrum line, arising from an excited state of finite life. This limit ($\sim 10^{-7}$ in many cases) is reached in the determination of a wavelength as a standard of length, but there is no reason why the length should not be defined to greater accuracy by the mean wavelength emitted from a great many atoms. In fact, the present experimental limit lies in finding a light source in which the systematic disturbing effect of fields external to the atoms is sufficiently reproducible.

Many measurements in practice are affected by fluctuations coarser than the quantum limit, and important examples are thermal fluctuations and the effect of the discrete (particulate) nature of matter and electricity.

Every degree of freedom determining the configuration of a system is associated with some energy, which appears as fluctuations of the appropriate coordinate. In principle, the statistics of these fluctuations must be calculated from quantum theory, but in many cases of practical importance, the average kinetic energy associated with a particular coordinate has the equipartition value $\frac{1}{2}kT$, and an approximate value of the uncertainty in amplitude can be calculated from this result. In practice, thermal fluctuations are most often encountered in electrical circuits because electronic devices have a high sensitivity extending over a wide frequency band. The fluctuation noise can now be put in the form of an alternating voltage in series with each resistor, distributed over all frequencies in accordance with the formula $E^2 d\nu = 4kTRd\nu$ (non-quantum approximation for frequencies such that $h\nu \ll kT$). Here E^2 denotes the distribution function for the squared voltage at frequency ν, T is the temperature and R the resistance. The effect on any circuit can be calculated from this result. It is apparent that the total noise voltage increases with the frequency bandwidth to which the system responds, so that it can be reduced in a system which has a long time of response, either because it responds only to low frequencies or because its response is narrowly-selective. The phase-sensitive rectifier technique discussed above is a method of securing such a narrow response. Rapidly transient phenomena are, of course, excluded by any such system. It can be shown that if we can average our observations for a time τ, the relative accuracy varies as $\tau^{1/2}$. Thermal noise can be reduced in appropriate circumstances by reducing the temperature of the resistances involved, but the noise voltage distribution is then appreciably modified by quantum effects and does not disappear at absolute zero. It will be noted that thermal noise is explicitly connected with the resistive elements of a circuit. It can be reduced by using systems of amplification (parametric amplification) which do not in principle require resistive elements or by reducing the dissipative (resistive) element of a system by a properly phased feedback device.

In addition to the thermal noise, fluctuations can arise statistically from the passage of discrete electrons in a circuit, the full calculated value being observed in a saturated diode or in a photocell. The fluctuations are suppressed by the conduction mechanism of a metallic conductor or in part by the space charge of a triode or pentode, though in the pentode there is a new source of noise in the distribution of electrons between anode and screen. Noise of this kind (shot noise) is a major limitation in practical

high-frequency measurements, but it is to some extent amenable to reduction by circuit techniques. The corresponding effect in a photocell is due to the finite rate of reception of quanta (N per second) and the corresponding rate of emission of electrons ($N\epsilon$ where ϵ is the cathode quantum efficiency), and it is inescapable. Furthermore, it is overlaid by the fluctuations of the "dark current" which may flow in the absence of incident quanta. This dark current can be reduced by technical measures, and this must be done if the accuracy of the measurement of weak light is to be maximized. A further type of fluctuation, additional to thermal noise and shot noise, occurs in semiconductors and in the emission from most technical cathodes. It is not yet completely explained in theoretical terms: the squared distribution function is not uniform and increases rapidly at low frequencies; when this "excess noise" is present, it is desirable to "put the signal where the noise is not," i.e., to reduce the response of the measuring system at low frequencies and to make the signal appear at higher frequencies if the signal frequency can be chosen arbitrarily as in the case of a "chopper" detector or amplifier.

H. J. J. BRADDICK

Cross-references: ASTROMETRY; COSMIC RAYS; ELECTRICAL MEASUREMENTS; MAGNETOMETRY; NOISE, ACOUSTICAL; NUCLEAR INSTRUMENTS; OPTICAL INSTRUMENTS; PHOTOGRAPHY; PHOTOMETRY; THEORETICAL PHYSICS.

MECHANICAL PROPERTIES OF SOLIDS

When a material is in the solid phase, its constituent particles, which may be atoms, ions, or chemical molecules, vibrate about fixed equilibrium positions in which the interparticle force is zero. In most solids composed of small constituent particles, e.g., metals and ionic solids, these interparticle interactions produce an internal atomic or molecular arrangement which is regular and periodic in three dimensions over intervals which are large compared with the unit of periodicity. Such solids are called crystals.

Solids composed of larger units, e.g., polymers, can be crystalline, though the crystallinity is usually rather imperfect, or they can be amorphous.

When a solid is deformed by external forces, the constituent particles have their separations changed from the equilibrium values. The resultant of the interparticle forces acting on a particular particle is then no longer zero, but acts to restore the particle to its original position relative to its neighbors. When the solid is in equilibrium under the action of external forces, the interparticle (or internal) forces must be in equilibrium to give continuity of the material and must also be equal to the external forces, i.e., any element of the body must be in equilibrium. These internal forces are maintained as long as the external forces are applied. When the external forces are removed the internal forces restore to the constituent particles their original separations.

If, after unloading, the body returns exactly to its former size and shape its behavior is called perfectly elastic. If it retains completely its altered size and shape it is a perfectly plastic body. In general, the behavior of real bodies lies between these two extremes.

Stress and Strain Two types of forces may act on any element of a body: (a) surface forces, exerted by the surrounding material, which are proportional to the surface area of the element and (b) body forces, which are proportional to the volume of the element, e.g., gravitational forces. The effects of body forces are usually negligible compared with those resulting from surface forces.

For a body to be deformed and not merely accelerated when forces are applied to it the body must be in statical equilibrium under the action of the applied forces. The conditions of equilibrium are (a) there must be no unbalanced applied forces and (b) there must be no unbalanced applied couples. Further, the internal and external force equilibrium can be equated.

The effect produced in a given material by forces of given magnitudes depends on the size of the body to which they are applied, and hence, to enable a comparison to be made of the reaction to external loading of bodies of different size, the concept of *stress* is introduced.

The stress in an element is defined as force divided by area over which the force acts. It is described as a homogeneous stress if, for an element of fixed shape and orientation, the value is independent of the position of the element in the body. Usually the term stress is taken to mean stress at a point, and is the limiting value of force divided by area over which the force acts as the area tends to zero. If a force δF acts over a surface of area δA and makes an angle ϕ with the normal to the surface, the normal stress σ is

$$\sigma = \lim_{\delta A \to 0} \left(\frac{\delta F \cos \phi}{\delta A} \right)$$

and the tangential or shearing stress τ is

$$\tau = \lim_{\delta A \to 0} \left(\frac{\delta F \sin \phi}{\delta A} \right)$$

The stress is, of course transmitted through the solid.

The change in the separation of the constituent particles of the solid produced by the applied forces is seen on the macroscopic scale as a change in the size and shape of the body. Since the deformation of different bodies of a given material subjected to a particular load is a function of the size of body, comparisons are

made using the relative deformation, or strain, defined as

$$\text{strain} = \frac{\text{change in dimension}}{\text{original dimension}}.$$

A strain is homogeneous if, after deformation, lines of the body that were originally straight remain straight and lines that were originally parallel remain parallel.

The following strains are found to be convenient in describing the behavior of a body in various states of stress.

When a rod of unstretched length ℓ_0 has its length increased to ℓ by the application of external forces, the conventional, engineering, or nominal tensile strain ϵ is defined as

$$\epsilon = \frac{\ell - \ell_0}{\ell_0}.$$

Sometimes it is more convenient to use the true, natural, or logarithmic strain ϵ^*, defined as

$$\epsilon^* = \sum \frac{\delta\ell}{\ell} = \log_e \left(\frac{\ell}{\ell_0}\right).$$

Clearly

$$\epsilon^* = \log_e (1 + \epsilon)$$

If, as the result of the application of a uniform hydrostatic force, the volume of a solid changes from V_0 to V, the bulk strain θ is defined as

$$\theta = \frac{V - V_0}{V_0}.$$

When a solid is sheared by the application of couples, the angle of shear is taken as a measure of the strain, in this instance a shear strain.

Elastic Behavior For very small strains ($< \sim 0.1$ per cent) the behavior of many solid materials is almost perfectly elastic. In this strain range a specimen will exhibit a linear relationship between the magnitude of the applied forces and the deformation produced. This relationship is known as the Hooke law and in terms of stress and strain it may be stated in the form

$$\text{stress} = \text{constant} \times \text{strain}.$$

The constant in this equation is called a modulus of elasticity. Each strain has a corresponding modulus of elasticity. These moduli are temperature-dependent, and in general, depend on the direction of measurement, but if elastically isotropic solids are considered, the value of a particular modulus is independent of the direction in which it is measured. A solid is effectively isotropic if it is composed of grains whose size is small compared with the smallest dimension of the solid and if the orientations of the grains are randomly distributed.

Consider a bar of uniform area of cross-section A and unstretched length ℓ_0 acted upon by forces F applied uniformly at the ends. If ℓ is the length when this load is applied, the stress σ is given by $\sigma = F/A$ and the strain ϵ is $\epsilon = (\ell - \ell_0)/\ell_0$. (Tensile stresses are counted positive.) When the Hooke law is obeyed, $F/A = E(\ell - \ell_0)/\ell_0$ where E is a constant for a given material at a given temperature and is known as the Young modulus of the material.

When a solid has a hydrostatic stress σ applied to it, the volume changes from V_0 to V so that if the Hooke law is obeyed

$$\sigma = \frac{K(V - V_0)}{V_0}$$

where K is a constant at a given temperature and is known as the bulk modulus of the material.

When a solid is deformed by couples producing a shear stress τ, the angle of shear γ is taken as a measure of the strain so that, if the Hooke law is obeyed,

$$\tau = G\gamma$$

where G is a constant at a given temperature and is known as the rigidity modulus for the material.

The axial deformation of a prismatic bar with unloaded prismatic surfaces is accompanied by a change in the cross-sectional area. Experiment shows that the ratio

lateral strain/axial strain

is a constant known as the Poisson ratio ν. For the small strains encountered in pure elastic behavior the change in cross-sectional area is very small, so the difference in the stress calculated using the original area of cross-section and using that when the load is applied is negligible.

The elastic moduli are not independent and it can be shown that, for an isotropic solid,

$$E = 3K(1 - 2\nu)$$

and

$$G = \frac{E}{2(1 + \nu)}.$$

Plastic Behavior When a solid is deformed under an increasing stress, a stage is reached when the further deformation produced by a slight increase in stress, though still elastic, does not obey the Hooke law. The stress at which the departure from linearity of the stress-strain curve first occurs is called the proportional limit or elastic limit. If the stress is increased beyond the elastic limit, a value is reached at which permanent deformation occurs, i.e., the specimen does not recover completely its original size and shape on unloading. The stress at which permanent deformation is first detected has, for very many materials, a value characteristic

of the material at that temperature and is called the yield stress. The corresponding point on the stress-strain curve is the yield point. For many materials the elastic limit and yield stress have almost the same value and are not readily distinguished. The deformation not recovered on unloading is called the permanent set and the specimen is said to have suffered plastic deformation.

Plastic Deformation of Simple Crystalline Solids, e.g., Metals and Ionic Solids. The simplest mechanical test that can be performed on a solid is the tension test, and measurements made during such tests are often used to characterize particular materials.

Many simple crystalline solids are ductile at temperatures greater than about 0.3 to 0.4 of the melting temperature in kelvins. The plastic deformation of such materials takes place at approximately constant volume, and hence, for a specimen tested in tension, the cross-sectional area decreases as extension proceeds. This change in cross-sectional area with strain necessitates a more careful definition of stress. Two definitions are in common use, namely, conventional stress σ_c, sometimes called the nominal or engineering stress, defined by

$$\sigma_c = \frac{\text{load}}{\text{original area of cross section}}$$

and true stress σ_t, defined by

$$\sigma_t = \frac{\text{load}}{\text{area of cross section under that load}}$$

When a tensile test is carried out on a fine-grained sample of a ductile material the conventional stress σ_c vs engineering strain ϵ graph has the form shown by the solid line in Fig. 1. The actual shape of the curve depends on many variables, e.g., purity of the material, temperature of testing, and rate of straining.

Over the region OA the graph is a straight line passing through the origin, the behavior is perfectly elastic, and the Hooke law is obeyed. When the stress exceeds that at A macroscopic permanent deformation occurs and the curve bends towards the strain axis; the stress at A is the yield stress σ_y and A is the yield point. However, the stress needed to produce further plastic deformation increases with strain and the material is said to work-harden or strain-harden. If the specimen is unloaded when B is reached, the unloading path is BC, which has almost the same slope as OA; the elastic properties of the material are little affected by plastic deformation. The elastic strain FC is recovered, but the material retains the plastic strain OC, which is the permanent set. The plastic strain becomes an increasing fraction of the total

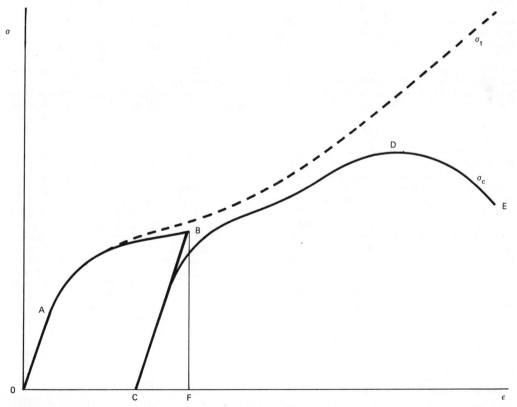

FIG. 1

TABLE 1

Material	E (Nm^{-2})	K (Nm^{-2})	G (Nm^{-2})	ν	σ_y (Nm^{-2})	σ_u (Nm^{-2})
Al	71×10^9	75×10^9	26×10^9	0.33	26×10^6	60×10^6
Cu	130×10^9	138×10^9	46×10^9	0.34	40×10^6	160×10^6
Steel	210×10^9	168×10^9	83×10^9	0.28	0.4×10^9 (σ_{UYS}) 0.3×10^9 (σ_{LYS})	460×10^6

strain as the latter increases. When the test is continued the stress rises along CB (ignoring a small amount of hysteresis which is sometimes observed), but before B is reached the curve bends towards the strain axis and then continues to rise as if unloading had not taken place. σ_c continues to rise until D is reached and then starts to fall. The load corresponding to D on the σ_c vs ϵ curve is the maximum load that the specimen can withstand in tension, and the value of σ_c corresponding to this load is called the ultimate stress or ultimate tensile strength σ_u.

For deformations represented by OD on the σ_c vs ϵ graph the extension is homogeneous, i.e., on the macroscopic scale the deformation is the same for all cross sections. At D, however, a neck forms in the specimen, all subsequent plastic deformation is restricted to this neck, and the load needed to produce further extension falls. The neck gets progressively narrower until fracture occurs at a strain corresponding to E.

When σ_t is plotted instead of σ_c, the curve has the form shown by the dotted line in Fig. 1. If, when the neck forms, σ_t is measured in the neck, σ_t continues to increase with strain up to fracture.

Mild steel and some other materials show a different behavior. The elastic range is terminated when the stress reaches a value known as the upper yield stress σ_{UYS}. There is an abrupt partial unloading and macroscopic plastic deformation occurs locally in regions called Lüders bands. These bands spread along the specimen and the value of σ_c oscillates about a relatively constant value known as the lower yield stress σ_{LYS}. When the Lüders bands cover the whole specimen, further deformation is macroscopically homogeneous and σ_c rises as the material work-hardens.

The stress-strain curves usually plotted use the engineering strain, but it should be noted that if true stress is plotted against true strain the resulting curve is the same for both compression and tension tests.

Some typical values of elastic moduli and yield stresses are given in Table 1. These values refer to measurements on fine-grained wires at room temperature.

The Deformation of Solid Polymers Polymer molecules consist of very long chains of atoms, often containing short side groups at regular intervals. In many of the most common polymers the linking between neighboring chains is weak. This type of polymer is rigid at low temperatures and soft and rubbery at higher temperatures, the transition being reversible. Such long-chain polymers whose mechanical properties depend strongly on the temperature of the measurement are called thermo-plastics.

At low temperatures a typical thermo-plastic has a Young modulus of 10^9 to 10^{10} Nm^{-2}, breaks or flows at strains greater than about 5 per cent, and is referred to as glass-like. When tested at high temperatures the Young modulus is typically 10^6 to 10^7 Nm^{-2}, the material can withstand large extensions (~ 100 per cent) without permanent deformation, and is termed rubber-like.

There is an intermediate temperature range, commonly called the glass-transition range, in which the behavior is neither glass-like nor rubber-like.

One manifestation of the glass transition is an abrupt change in the volume expansivity, and this can be used to define a glass-transition temperature T_g.

In the glass-transition range the polymer shows an intermediate value for the modulus and the stress-strain relationship is strongly time-dependent. This behavior is termed viscoelastic.

At comparatively low strains (~ 1 percent) all deformations are, to a first approximation, recoverable, though the stress-strain curve may show a hysteresis loop. For larger strains irreversible deformation may occur.

Polymers in which there are frequent strong links between neighboring molecules are said to be cross-linked. Cross-linked linear polymers have mechanical properties that are rubber-like.

Cross-linking is also found in the so-called thermosetting plastics in which nonlinear structures are formed. When these materials polymerize, a process accelerated by raising the temperature, the monomers group themselves into a rigid framework structure that is not softened when the temperature is raised again.

M. T. SPRACKLING

References

Benham, P. P., "Elementary Mechanics of Solids," New York, Pergamon Press, 1965.

Billmeyer, F. W., "Textbook of Polymer Science," New York, Interscience, 1962.

Calladine, C. R., "Engineering Plasticity," New York, Pergamon Press, 1969.

Gillam, E., "Materials Under Stress," London, Newnes, Butterworths, 1969.

Sprackling, M. T., "The Mechanical Properties of Matter," London, English Universities Press, 1970.

Cross-references: ELASTICITY, POLYMER PHYSICS, SOLID-STATE PHYSICS, VISCOELASTICITY.

MECHANICS

The beginning of the science of mechanics goes back to the Greeks inasmuch as they had derived some fundamental ideas on levers, vibrations of strings and on hydrostatics. However, not until the sixteenth century did mechanics make a real beginning whose progress has continued to the present day. Two great names are associated with the mechanics of the sixteenth and seventeenth centuries, namely Galileo Galilei in Italy and Sir Isaac Newton in England. Galileo (1564-1642) was essentially the one who insisted on the importance of observations of nature, of combining experiments and observations with careful thought, as opposed to the Aristotelians who at that time insisted that all knowledge came by thought alone. Many of the experiments that Galileo performed and the conclusions drawn from them are given in a book entitled "Two New Sciences," which, though written in a dialogue form, is still worthy of being read.

Following Galileo came another "natural philosopher," Sir Isaac Newton (1642-1727), who was one of the greatest of all time. It is interesting that the word "scientist" did not come into use until the middle of the nineteenth century, though the term "natural philosopher" is still used in some of the older universities. Newton's contributions in mathematics and physics were unique, for he invented the calculus and discovered the law of gravitation and the laws of motion. It is somewhat difficult to appreciate all that Newton did for the world. More than anyone else he ushered in the modern scientific era. The heavens were a region with its own particular laws, a region where speculation had relatively free reign. Newton changed all this. He applied to the planets the laws of motion, which were applicable to bodies on the earth, and he found he could account for the motion of the planets with remarkable accuracy.

So strong was the faith in the Newtonian principles that when the planet Uranus appeared to be deviating from its predicted orbit the assumption was made that there must be another planet as yet unknown. The position of this unknown planet was calculated and thus Neptune was found in 1846. Such was the success of the Newtonian conception of the universe.

Newton left the world a mechanical universe. Forces produced changes in motion between the sun and the planets just as they did between objects on the earth. It was the Newtonian idea that forces produced changes in motion in contradiction to the then current Aristotelean idea that force was required to keep motion going. Newton tried to be most careful in denying any "cause" in these laws of motion. He was trying to give a description of motion in terms of the laws. In his famous book "The Mathematical Principles of Natural Philosophy," usually referred to as "The Principia," Newton presents the scope of his work in mechanics, and what a grand scope it is. He not only discusses the motions of objects on the earth but the motion of the planets as well; the precession of the equinoxes, the tides and other problems in fluid motion.

Newton's "Principia" starts with a series of definitions the first of which states: "The quantity of matter is the measure of the same arising from its density and bulk conjointly." Quantity of matter is now most generally called mass, and here Newton takes density as fundamental and mass as a derived quantity, whereas nowadays mass is taken as fundamental and density is given as mass per unit volume. The mass of an object is generally defined in terms of the inertia of the object which is expressed in the third definition in the "Principia" namely: "The vis insita, or innate force of matter, is a power of resisting, by which every body, as much as in it lies, continues in its present state, whether it be at rest, or of moving uniformly forward in a straight line."

By inertia of an object is meant the property of opposing any change in motion of the object. To change the motion for an object, i.e., to accelerate or decelerate the object, a force, a push or pull, is required. A comparison of the masses of two objects can be made by placing the two objects on a frictionless horizontal surface with a compressed spring between them. When the masses are released they are accelerated in opposite directions and the larger acceleration occurs with the smaller inertia or mass of the object. Newton's second law is given as: The net applied force F on an object of inertia or mass m gives it an acceleration a, or $F = ma$. A freely falling object has a constant acceleration near the surface of the earth called the acceleration of gravity g, and this is equal to about 32 ft/sec every second or 9.8m/sec every second. The force producing this acceleration is called the weight of the object, i.e., the weight w equals the product of the mass m and the acceleration of gravity g, or $w = mg$.

From Newton's second law, $F = ma$, the unit of force, the Newton, is defined as that force which acting on a mass of one kilogram gives it an acceleration of one meter per second every second. Thus the weight of one kilogram near the surface of the earth where the acceleration of gravity is 9.8 m/sec every sec, is 9.8 Newtons. Since the acceleration of gravity is constant, at any location, the weight of an object is proportional to its mass. Thus the common method of

comparing masses is by comparing their weights with an equal arm balance. While weight and mass are proportional to one another it should be noted that they are different entities. Weight is a force, the vertical force of gravity, while mass is an inertial property.

The scientific caution which Newton showed in the Principia is illustrated by the following quotation: "For I here design only to give mathematical notion of those forces without considering their physical causes and seats." In another context he says: "You sometimes speak of GRAVITY as essential and inherent to matter. Pray do not ascribe that notion to me; for the cause of gravity is what I do not pretend to know."

Despite Newton's caution about the cause of gravity it soon became the custom to call the inverse square relationship between objects the *law of gravitation*. This law may be stated in the following manner: Every particle in the universe attracts every other particle with a force which is proportional to the product of their masses and inversely proportional to the square of their distance apart. The force of attraction F between two particles of masses m_1 and m_2 a distance d apart is given as F = constant $(m_1 \times m_2)/d^2$. In this equation the constant has to be determined experimentally and is found to be 6.673×10^{-11} Newtons $(m)^2/(k)^2$, so that two equal small masses each of mass one kilogram placed one meter apart would attract each other with a force of 6.673×10^{-11} Newtons. This is an extremely small force, for the force of one Newton is equal to the weight of about one-tenth of a kilogram.

The mass of an object referred to in the law of gravitation is called its gravitational mass and should be contrasted with the inertial mass. One and the same object has both properties, sometimes called the passive and active properties of the object. The question arises whether the gravitational and inertial masses are equal. Newton concluded from some simple experiments with pendulums that the two kinds of masses are equal to one part in 300; about the beginning of this century R. von Eötvös showed the equality to one part in a million (10^6), and more recently Professor R. H. Dicke of Princeton University showed the equality to one part in a hundred thousand million (10^{11}). Einstein used the equality of the inertial and gravitational mass as a basis for the general theory of relativity.

When two objects A and B collide or interact, then according to Newton's third law of motion the force of A on B is equal and opposite to the force of B on A. From Newton's second law, forces produce accelerations, or $F = ma = m \, \delta v/\delta t$ where δv is the change in the velocity of the mass m in the time change δt. Now the product of mass and velocity mv was called by Newton the quantity of motion and is now called momentum. This is a new and important concept as is seen in the following argument for interacting objects. When objects A and B collide the

force of A on B and the time rate of change of momentum of B are equal and opposite to the force of B on A and the time rate of change of momentum of A. Since δt, the time which the forces act during the collision, must be the same for A and B, it follows that the momentum change of A is equal and opposite to the momentum change of B. Thus the total momentum change at the collision is zero, or the momentum of A and B before the collision is equal to that after the collision. This result is known as the law of conservation of momentum for interacting objects and is assumed to apply to atoms and stars, and all other objects or particles.

Though there were no new physical principles, associated with mechanics, developed during the eighteenth and nineteenth centuries, there was much mathematical development. The Lagrange equations of motion are an elegant and different expression of the Newtonian equations of motion. Where Newton was concerned with forces, Lagrange was concerned with energy. In his "Mecanique Analytique" (1788), Lagrange showed how a mechanical problem could be solved on the basis of pure calculation without appealing to physical or geometrical considerations provided the kinetic and potential energies of the system were given in the appropriate form. Lagrange says in the preface "The reader will find no figures in the work. The methods which I set forth do not require either constructions or geometrical or mechanical reasonings; but only algebraic operations, subject to a regular and uniform rule of procedure." Considerable contributions to theoretical mechanics were also made by Sir William Rowan Hamilton (1805-1865) and C. G. J. Jacobi (1804-1851) together with a number of others: Gauss, Poisson, Poincaré and Mach.

An important concept in physics is that of energy. The energy of an object is measured in terms of the work which the object can do by virtue of the energy. In mechanics work is done whenever a force moves an object; the direction of motion being in the same or opposite direction as the force. When a car is accelerated work is done by the accelerating force and the car acquires energy of motion called *kinetic energy*. This kinetic energy is equal to the product of one-half the mass and the square of the velocity or $\frac{1}{2}mv^2$, and this is equal to the work done by the accelerating force Fd where F is the value of the force and d is the distance through which the object moves in the direction of the force. A practical application of this relationship of kinetic energy and work is in the stopping of a car by the brakes. Notice it is the brakes that stop the wheels but it is the friction between the tires and the road which stops the car. Assuming the mass m of the car is constant and the braking force F is also constant, it follows that the stopping distance is proportional to the square of the speed v. The stopping distance at 60 mph is four times that at 30 mph assuming the same braking force in the two cases.

Another form of energy is potential energy or energy due to position, such as an object lifted above a table or a wound-up spring in an alarm clock. If there are no frictional forces present, it may easily be shown that the motion of the system is such that the sum of the kinetic and potential energies is constant. An approximate example of such a system is an oscillating pendulum. To a first approximation the mechanical energy of the pendulum, the sum of the kinetic and potential energies, is a constant or is conserved during the oscillations.

When frictional forces are present, as for example when a moving car is brought to rest, the kinetic energy of the car is transformed into heat through the agency of the frictional force. It was about the middle of the last century when the English physicist James Prescott Joule (1818-1889) performed some very accurate experiments on the transformation of various forms of energy into heat. The unit of energy in science is the Joule and is the work done by a force of 1 Newton moved through a distance of 1 meter in the direction of the force. The corresponding unit of heat is the kilocalorie which is the quantity of heat required to raise the temperature of 1 kilogram of water 1° Centigrade. From his experiments Joule found that 1 kilocalorie is equivalent in energy to about 4187 Joules.

Just as an object moving along a straight line has translational kinetic energy, so an object rotating about some axis has rotational kinetic energy. To give an object rotational kinetic energy it is necessary to have a force acting so as to produce a torque or moment of force about the axis of rotation. The torque or moment of force about an axis is defined as the product of the force and the perpendicular distance between the axis of rotation and the line of action of the force. This distance is often called the lever arm of the force. With no frictional forces present the work done by the applied force is equal to the increase in rotational kinetic energy.

Towards the middle of the last century, the principle of conservation of energy was firmly established on experimental grounds. This has been of enormous importance, for as different forms of energy have been recognized they have been seen to fit into a much wider perspective. In the present century there has been the development of the theory of RELATIVITY by A. Einstein (1879-1955), important in the region of velocities close to the velocity of light, and of the QUANTUM MECHANICS applicable to the phenomena on the very small scale found in atoms.

It is obvious that motion is movement of some object relative to some other object. Newton recognized this in the "Principia," and on the considerations of linear and rotational motion, he found it necessary to postulate absolute space and absolute time. For motion at constant speed in a straight line it readily follows from Newton's laws that it is impossible to perform any physical experiment which can detect this motion. However, when the motion is accelerated, forces are required and the presence of the acceleration is readily determined. If a horizontal circular platform is turning with constant angular speed about a vertical axis through its center, then an observer on the moving platform experiences a centrifugal acceleration (see ROTATION—CIRCULAR MOTION). Also if he moves along a radius he experiences a sidewise acceleration called the CORIOLIS ACCELERATION. These accelerations are easily accounted for in terms of a rotating reference system. The earth is such a system and the centrifugal acceleration is shown in the systematic variation of the acceleration of gravity with latitude. For recognizable aspects of the Coriolis acceleration on the earth one has to examine large scale motions. The fact that the winds do not go directly from high pressure regions to low pressure ones in cyclones and anticyclones is readily explained by the Coriolis acceleration and force.

A major revision of thought came in mechanics in the present century when Einstein applied the theory of RELATIVITY to reference systems moving with constant velocity relative to one another. TIME and distance were not the same in the different systems though the speed of light was assumed to be constant in all the systems. This brought changes in mechanics which become appreciable when the speeds approach that of light, about 186 000 miles/sec. It is only in the realm of atomic and nuclear physics that speeds approaching this are encountered. In the macroscopic world of automobiles and airplanes the Newtonian mechanics is still applicable with considerable accuracy.

Mechanics has influenced many of the theories in other branches. It was a natural tendency to account for phemonena in mechanical terms whenever possible. Forces were experienced in electrical phenomena, and it was from the forces that entities such as electric charges were postulated. Vibratory motion, such as that undergone by an object hanging on a vertical spring, is used in explaining the scattering of light and x-rays.

There are two very important CONSERVATION LAWS in mechanics, namely conservation of momentum and conservation of energy. The expressions for these conservation laws, but not the principle of the laws, changes when the speeds of the objects approach that of light. Then the Einstein relativistic expressions must be used. For angular motion there is a corresponding law of conservation of angular momentum. Then there is the law of conservation of energy, a law which, when it includes mass m, as a form of energy E, by the relationship, $E = mc^2$, brings together two former conservation laws, namely the laws of conservation of mass and energy. The letter c indicates the velocity of light.

When forces are applied to a real object, the object changes its shape resulting in a change in length, or volume, or twist. No real object is

absolutely rigid though much of mechanics assumes rigid objects and ignores any change in shape resulting from the applied forces. It is the theory of elasticity which is primarily concerned with the effects of forces in changing the shape of objects. The applied force or forces produce a stress on the object, where the stress is defined as the force divided by the area over which it acts. The units of stress are Newtons per square meter or pounds per square foot, etc. The stress produces a strain in the object or an internal adjustment to the stress. By definition, a strain is dimensionless; it is a change in length (or volume) divided by the original length (or volume), or it is an angle of twist. For a homogeneous isotropic substance there are three moduli of elasticity corresponding to the changes in length, volume, or twist. In an anisotropic substance these moduli depend on the particular direction chosen in the crystal, and the theory for such substances is relatively complicated.

Thus we see that mechanics has a great theoretical structure and is also of great importance in the everyday world of machines and bridges. It has influenced all the sciences and today is as important as it ever was.

R. J. STEPHENSON

References

Elementary: Stephenson, R. J., "Mechanics and Properties of Matter," New York, John Wiley & Sons, Inc., 1960.
Intermediate: Fowles, G. R., "Analytical Mechanics," New York, Holt, Rinehart and Winston, 1962.
Advanced: Goldstein, H., "Classical Mechanics," Reading, Mass. Addison-Wesley Co., 1950.

Cross-references: DYNAMICS, ELASTICITY, GRAVITATION, MASS AND INERTIA, MECHANICAL PROPERTIES OF SOLIDS, STATICS.

MEDICAL PHYSICS

That physics has an important place in medicine can scarcely be denied. A physician's first move in examining a patient is to measure his temperature, count his pulse, listen to his heart sounds and take his blood pressure. Only much later does the physician get around to chemical and laboratory tests. Yet every hospital of any stature has a laboratory or a department of clinical chemistry. Laboratories of clinical physics are virtually nonexistent. While physics plays a large role in medical diagnosis and treatment, physicists have largely neglected the field.

Some of the earliest applications of the principles of physics to problems in medicine were in the fields of optics and sound. An early contributor was H. L. F. von Helmholtz, a physician as well as a physicist. His work in physiological optics and that on the sensations of tone are considered classics. Even earlier, J. L. M. Poiseuille,

a French physician and physicist, seeking a better understanding of the flow of blood, studied the flow of water in rigid tubes. His work not only contributed to physiology but also established an important relation in the physics of viscous fluids.

With the intensive development of the sciences of physics and medicine in the latter part of the nineteenth century, the two drew further apart. This period also saw rapid development in the science of physiology which is concerned not only with body chemistry but also with physical processes in the body. Clinical physiology abounds with such concepts as the pressure-velocity relationships in the flow of blood, the mechanics of the cardiac cycle, the work of breathing, gas exchange in the lungs, voltage gradient in cellular membranes, and cable properties of nerves, to name but a few. These concepts have, of necessity, been worked out by scientists with training and experience in the basic biological and clinical procedures. Physicists have been inactive in the field and have made very little contribution to its development. But there is a growing awareness among physiologists of the importance of physical principles and the need for precise statement of physical law. An example of this conviction is the 19th edition of Howell's Textbook of Physiology which carries the title, "Physiology and Biophysics."[1]

A phenomenon of the mid-twentieth century has been the development of interdisciplinary fields of science. BIOPHYSICS combines the most fundamental of the biological and physical sciences. It has had an extremely rapid growth, with something like 30 to 40 university Departments of Biophysics in America alone. Its emphasis has been on the application of physical principles to all aspects of biology—cellular, botanical, zoological as well as clinical.

An even more recent phenomenon has been the development of biomedical engineering. Its basis has been the application of the tremendous developments in electronics to medical measurements and instrumentation. In fact, the field is frequently referred to as biomedical electronics. Such recent developments as vector electrocardiography, implantable pacemakers for the heart, and intensive-care physiological monitors and recorders are examples of the impact of electronics on medicine. While these fields border on medical physics, none are concerned primarily with the application of physical principles to clinical problems. Yet they compete so effectively with medical physics that it is difficult to delineate the boundaries of the latter.

The discovery of X-RAYS by Roentgen in 1895 had an immediate impact upon medicine. Within a few months, the new rays were used both diagnostically and therapeutically. Indirectly, their application set the stage for the development of medical physics. Therapeutic application of x-rays raised questions concerning their quality and quantity—both of which are im-

portant in accurate dosimetry. Evaluation of early successes and failures indicated the importance of the proper distribution of dose between neoplasm and normal tissue. The physician turned to the physicist for assistance. The late Otto Glasser was one of the early radiological physicists; he and Fricke in 1924 constructed an air wall ionization chamber for the measurement of radiation dose.[2] Their construction eliminated some of the nonlinear effects due to quality, i.e., photon energy distribution, in the evaluation of biological response. Other early workers in America were Edith Quimby and the late G. Failla. In England, L. H. Gray and W. V. Mayneord were active. In 1936, Gray proposed the Bragg-Gray formula for determining the absolute amount of energy delivered to a medium from ionization measurements.[3] The work of Fricke, Glasser, and Failla along with that of L. S. Taylor[4] and others contributed to the establishment in 1928 by the Second International Congress of Radiology of the roentgen as a unit of radiation dose based on the amount of ionization generated in a standard volume of air. The use of higher energies and ionizing radiations other than x-rays led during the 1950's to the abandonment of the roentgen as a unit of absorbed dose. Dissatisfaction with the roentgen was also due to a growing realization that biological response was more nearly related to the energy absorbed in a medium. The Bragg-Gray formula permitted the calculation of absorbed dose in a medium, and the work of J. S. Laughlin[5] established the dosimetry of high-energy radiations in energy units by calorimetric methods. The International Commission on Radiological Units in 1956 adopted the *rad* as the unit of absorbed dose defining it as being equal to an absorption of 100 ergs per gram of material. The roentgen was retained as a unit of exposure dose for x-rays below 3 MeV, i.e., a measure of the intensity of a beam of x-rays to which a material might be exposed.

While radiological physics is clearly a part of the broader discipline of medical physics, it included in the early days practically all that was organized of the later subject. In 1943, the late Otto Glasser was persuaded to edit an encyclopedia on medical physics. It treated the physical aspects of the principal medically oriented subjects, including anatomy, dermatology, hematology, neurology, orthopedics, pathology, radiology and surgery, to name but a few, and still provides a good survey of the scope of the field.

Until recently there has been no organization of workers in the field of medical physics. Radiological physicists were associate members of the North American Radiological Society, naturally dominated by radiologists. First in Britain, (the Hospital Physicists' Association) and later in America, specialty groups have been organized. The American Association of Physicists in Medicine brings together those physicists working in hospitals and medical schools and interested in an understanding of the physical side of medical problems. The membership has been largely drawn from those working in the area of radiological physics, but a growing interest in the broader area pertaining to all of medicine can be discerned. The organization cooperates with its British counterpart in the publication of a journal— *Physics in Medicine and Biology*. A further indication of the developing awareness of this field is the organization of the First International Conference on Medical Physics which was held at Harrogate, England in 1965. The proceedings of the 2nd Conference are now available.[7]

One last word about a related field: Radiation protection was in the early days a part of radiological physics. In America, L. S. Taylor was active for many years at the Bureau of Standards in setting up guidelines for protection from radiation. During World War II, the Manhattan Project required large numbers of workers in the field of protection, and the term HEALTH PHYSICS was introduced. Since the war, the field has grown with the growth of the area of atomic energy. The Health Physics Society is a large and growing group with many local chapters and an international organization. The field seems, though, to be becoming more closely aligned with the area of public health than with clinical medicine.

That physics will play an increasingly important role in medicine cannot be challenged. But whether physicists will truly create a discipline of medical physics or whether that role will be played by physiologists, biophysicists, biomedical engineers or others remains to be seen.

LESTER S. SKAGGS

References

1. Ruch, T. C., and Patton, H. D., Eds., "Physiology and Biophysics," 19th edition, Philadelphia, W. B. Sauders, 1965.
2. Fricke, H., and Glasser, O., "Standardization of the Roentgen Ray Dose by Means of the Small Ionization Chambers," *Am. J. Roentgenol.* 13, 462 (1925).
3. Gray, L. H., "An Ionization Method for the Absolute Measurement of X-Ray Energy," *Proc. Roy. Soc., London Ser. A,* 156, 578 (1936).
4. Taylor, L. S., and Singer, G., "An Improved Form of Standard Ionization Chamber," *J. Res., Natl. Bur. Std.* 5, 507 (1930).
5. Genna, S., and Laughlin, J. S., "Absolute Calibration of Cobalt-60 Gamma Ray Beam," *Radiology* 65, 394 (1955).
6. Glasser, O., Ed., "Medical Physics," Chicago, Year book Publishers, 1960, 3 vols., cxxii, 3725 pp.
7. Laughlin, J. S., and Webster, E. W., Eds., "Advances in Medical Physics," Washington, Mc Gregor and Werner, Inc., 1971, xii, 360pp. (Obtainable from: The Second International Conference on Medical Physics, Inc. Secretary, Dr. E. W. Webster, Department of Radiology, Massachusetts General Hospital, Boston, Massachusetts, USA 02114.)

Cross-references. BIOPHYSICS, HEALTH PHYSICS, RADIOACTIVITY, X-RAYS.

METALLURGY

The metallurgical industry is one of the oldest of the arts, but one of the youngest of the subjects to be investigated systematically and considered analytically in the tradition of the pure sciences. It is only in comparatively recent times that any fundamental work has been carried out on metals and alloys, but there are now well-established and rapidly growing branches of science which are related to the metallurgical industry.

Extraction Metallurgy Extraction metallurgy, or the science of extracting metals from their ores, is broadly divided into two groups.

Ferrous. This branch is concerned with the production of *iron* (normally from iron ore, with coke and limestone in a blast furnace) and its subsequent refining into *steel*, by oxidizing the impurities either in an electric arc furnace by means of an appropriate slag on the surface or in a "converter," by blowing oxidizing gas through the molten iron. The most striking recent developments in this field have been the increasing use of pure gaseous oxygen in steel-making, and the increasing size of furnaces, with a resultant improvement in efficiency, rate of production, and quality of product.

Nonferrous. This is concerned with the production of the remaining metals. Those manufactured in greatest quantity include aluminum, copper, nickel, zinc, magnesium, lead, and tin, with titanium being an important newcomer in view of its low density, high melting point (1943 K) and resistance to corrosion. The precious metals, and the "refractory metals" of very high melting point (e.g., tungsten and molybdenum) are other important families.

Shaping of Metals This may be carried out in three main ways.

Casting. Although most metals are initially cast into *ingots*, which may be subsequently forged to shape, many alloys are designed to be cast into their final shape by pouring the molten alloy into an appropriate mold. These may be sand molds if only a small number of objects are required, and very massive castings (e.g., over 10^6 Kg in mass) may also be produced in this way. A permanent mold, or die casting, is employed if large numbers of the object are required (particularly in alloys of low melting point, such as zinc-based alloys), and high dimensional accuracy can be achieved by these means.

Forging. This entails shaping of the metal by rolling, pressing, hammering, etc., and may be carried out at high temperatures, when the metal is soft (hot-working), or at lower temperatures (cold-working) where deformation leads to progressive hardening of the metal (work-hardening). In contrast with casting, forgings usually exhibit differing physical and mechanical properties in different directions, due to the directional nature of the shaping operation.

Much modern research in physical metallurgy is concerned with investigating the plastic flow and work-hardening behavior of metals and alloys. Metal crystals yield plastically at stresses several orders of magnitude lower than the theoretical value for the deformation of perfect crystals. This discrepancy is accounted for by the presence of linear imperfections known as "dislocation lines" within the crystals. Plastic flow takes place in metal crystals by "slip" or "glide" in definite crystallographic directions on certain crystal planes, due to the movement of dislocation lines under the applied stress. Dislocations multiply and entangle as deformation proceeds, thus making further flow increasingly difficult (work-hardening)—the density of dislocations rising from about 10^5 mm^{-2} in soft (annealed) metal to about 10^{10} mm^{-2} in work-hardened material. These and other types of crystal defect (such as *stacking faults*, which are planar in geometry) can be studied by x-ray diffraction and also by means of the electron microscope and the field-ion microscope (q.v.).

Powder Metallurgy. This is a method of shaping by pressing finely powdered metal into an appropriately shaped die. The "green compact" thereby produced is of low strength and is subsequently heated in an inert atmosphere ("sintered"); the pressing and sintering may be repeated until strong, dense products are obtained. The technology was first developed for metals which were of too high a melting point for conventional casting and forging methods, and tungsten lamp filaments were first produced by this means. Other refractory metals and hard metal-cutting alloys may thus be shaped, and some magnetic and other special alloys are prepared in this way by suitable blending of powders, which avoids any contamination that may be associated with the melting process. The pressing and sintering conditions may be arranged to leave some residual porosity in the structure of, for example, bronze bearing alloys. The pores are filled with oil, thus producing the so-called oil-less bearings which can operate without further lubrication.

Joining. Riveting, soldering and brazing (in which metal components are joined by means of a layer of low-melting alloy), and welding are the important methods of joining metals. *Weldability* is often the critical factor in the selection of an alloy for a given purpose, since the metallurgical changes produced by localized heating are often associated with the development of deleterious properties at, or adjacent to, the weld.

Alloy Constitution Phase equilibria in alloy systems are represented on *phase diagrams*, which represent the temperature ranges of phase stability as a function of composition. An example of such a diagram is given in Fig. 1; they are experimentally established by, e.g., thermal analysis, dilatometry, microscopical, and x-ray diffraction methods. Phase diagrams are invaluable in the interpretation of the structures of alloys observed under the microscope.

The microstructure of an alloy (and hence its properties) will be determined not only by its

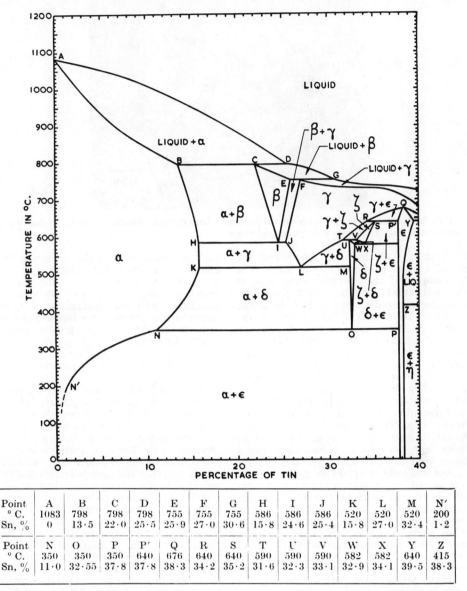

Point °C.	A	B	C	D	E	F	G	H	I	J	K	L	M	N'
°C.	1083	798	798	798	755	755	755	586	586	586	520	520	520	200
Sn, %	0	13·5	22·0	25·5	25·9	27·0	30·6	15·8	24·6	25·4	15·8	27·0	32·4	1·2

Point	N	O	P	P'	Q	R	S	T	U	V	W	X	Y	Z
°C.	350	350	350	640	676	640	640	590	590	590	582	582	640	415
Sn, %	11·0	32·55	37·8	37·8	38·3	34·2	35·2	31·6	32·3	33·1	32·9	34·1	39·5	38·3

FIG. 1. The copper-tin phase diagram. (G. V. Raynor, "Institute of Metals Annotated Equilibrium Diagram," Series No. 2, 1944.)

composition, but also by its thermal and mechanical history. Of particular importance is the metallurgical control of the mechanical properties of an alloy by *heat-treatment*, which affects the distribution of the phases present. Hardness, for example, will depend upon the state of deformation (i.e., the density of dislocations) and upon the composition of the alloy. Pure metal crystals can be hardened by other atoms in solid solution (solute hardening) as well as by finely dispersed particles of a hard second phase (precipitation, or dispersion hardening) which are effective in impeding the

motion of dislocations when the crystal is stressed. Fig. 2 is an electron micrograph showing dislocations on the slip plane of a copper alloy crystal, and it illustrates how the presence of hard particles has caused local entanglement of the dislocations. The relationship between the microstructure and properties of metals and alloys is of fundamental importance and is a field of intense scientific activity.

Although many common alloys were not developed scientifically, a considerable theory of alloys is developing, springing from empirical rules and principles (notably those due to W.

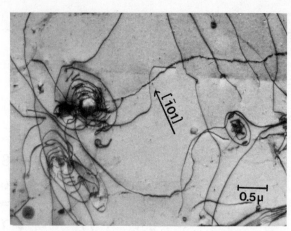

FIG. 2. A deformed copper alloy crystal containing hard particles. Electron micrograph showing interaction of dislocation lines with the second phase.

Hume-Rothery) which have generalized the facts and enabled predictions to be made. The early theories of the metallic state, due to Drude and Lorentz, and later to Sommerfeld, were developed and discussed by N. F. Mott and H. Jones in their book "The Theory of the Properties of Metals and Alloys." A great increase in our knowledge of transition metals and alloys has recently taken place, and some signs of general principles have begun to appear, although there is yet little theoretical knowledge enabling one to calculate properties or structures of alloys from fundamental principles.

The Effect of Environment Upon the Behavior of Metals *Low Temperature*. Some metals and alloys exhibit a spectacular change in mechanical behavior with decrease in temperature. Many metals of body-centered cubic crystal symmetry (e.g., iron and mild steel) which are tough and ductile at ordinary temperatures become completely brittle at subzero temperatures, the actual transition temperature depending upon the metallurgical condition of the alloy, the state of stress, and the rate of deformation. Some metals of hexagonal symmetry (e.g., zinc) exhibit this effect, but metals of face-centered cubic symmetry (e.g., copper) remain ductile to the lowest temperatures. This transition in behavior is clearly of critical importance in the selection of materials for low-temperature application.

High Temperature. Apart from problems of oxidation (discussed below), metals tend to deform under constant stress at elevated temperatures (the deformation is known as "creep"), and creep-resistant alloys are designed to provide strength at high temperatures. These are essentially alloys in a state of high thermodynamic stability, usually containing finely dispersed particles of a hard second phase which impede the movement of dislocations.

Fatigue. Metals break under oscillating stresses whose maximum value is smaller than that required to cause rupture in a static test, although many ferrous alloys show a "fatigue limit," or stress below which such fracture never occurs, however great the number of cycles of application. The phenomenon is associated with the nucleation of submicroscopic surface cracks in the fatigued component early in its life, which initially grow very slowly. Eventually a crack grows until the effective cross section of the piece is reduced to such a value that the applied stress cannot be supported, and rapid failure occurs.

Oxidation and Corrosion. With the exception of the "noble metals," which are intrinsically resistant to attack by the environment, metals in general owe their oxidation resistance, when they are heated in air, to the presence of impervious oxide films on their surfaces. Those which develop porous oxides (e.g., the refractory metals tungsten and molybdenum) oxidize very rapidly at high temperatures. Oxidation resistant alloys are designed to maintain a protective film under these conditions.

Corrosion occurs under conditions of high humidity or immersion in aqueous media. The phenomenon can be interpreted electrochemically—local anodes form at the region of metal dissolution, and local cathodes form where the electrons are discharged. "Galvanic corrosion" is encountered where dissimilar metals are in electrical contact under these conditions. Of particular importance is the *conjoint* action of stress and corrosion, where "stress corrosion" or (under fluctuating stresses) "corrosion fatigue" cracking may be encountered, in situations where no failure would occur under the action of the stress or the corrosive environment applied separately. Electrochemical principles are applied in the protection against corrosion.

Materials Technology The scientific principles which govern the behavior of metals are, of course, applicable to a wide range of other technologically important materials, such as polymers, ceramics, and glasses. In recent years many centers of metallurgical research both in

industry and in universities have broadened their approach in this way and are often described as Departments of Materials Technology.

JOHN W. MARTIN

References

Metallurgical Data

The series of "Metals Handbooks," published by the American Society for Metals, Cleveland, Ohio.

Smithells, C. J., "Metals Reference Book," London, Thornton Butterworth Ltd., 1967.

Hansen, M., "Constitution of Binary Alloys," New York, McGraw-Hill Book Co., 1958.

General Reading

Street, A., and Alexander, W. O., "Metals in the Service of Man," London, Pelican, 1973.

Martin, J. W., "Elementary Science of Metals," London, Wykeham Publications, 1969.

Hume-Rothery, W., "Electrons, Atoms, Metals and Alloys," New York, Dover, 1963.

Evans, U. R., "An Introduction to Metallic Corrosion," London, Edward Arnold, 1963.

Cross-references: CRYSTALLOGRAPHY, CRYSTAL STRUCTURE ANALYSIS, ELECTROCHEMISTRY, LATTICE DEFECTS, SOLID-STATE PHYSICS.

METEOROLOGY

The theme of meteorology over the past two decades has been expansion; expansion in all its aspects; expansion at accelerating pace. Meteorology has moved into an era of quantization and specialization. The reasons for this growth are not hard to find. The world has been making greater use of its atmosphere and must know more about its nature. At the same time, the modern electronic tools for probing the atmosphere in depth have become available. As a result there are more data, more interest, more research, and more services than ever before. Most recently the trend has changed again with the realization that the atmosphere is not only a resource to be used but an environment to be protected. Priorities in research and practice have altered accordingly.

Traditionally meteorological data were gathered by surface observers. Thirty-five years ago regular observations of the upper atmosphere began on a regular basis by means of balloon soundings using radio telemetry to transmit the data to the ground station. This proved to be the beginning of a veritable explosion in the sampling of the atmosphere. Instrumentation and balloon quality have steadily improved, but the network stations are now approaching the altitude limit of 32 km. Beyond this level, the rocket has replaced the balloon as the vehicle for sampling to about 60 km. Density, temperature and wind are being measured by a small but growing network. Beyond 60 km, rocket data

are limited by lack of instruments capable of measuring under these conditions. This will soon be overcome.

At a still higher level, the satellite operates as an observing platform. Sensors on this platform measure various types of radiation. From radiations in the visible bands come the familiar and impressive pictures of clouds and terrain. High-resolution infrared radiation is providing pictures on the dark side of the world as well as measurements of the temperature on the earth, clouds, and atmosphere. Other bands tell how much radiation is being removed by water vapor and other absorbers and, hence, provide a measure of the quantities and distributions of these constituents. The satellite samples equally well over difficult terrain and populated areas, and it promises to provide answers to one of the scientists' great problems—that of obtaining adequate data on a global scale. The point has been reached where satellites can provide real-time vertical temperature profiles of sufficient accuracy for operational analysis and prediction. It also provides a direct method of obtaining the radiational balance of the earth and atmosphere, a factor of fundamental importance in the energy budget of the earth-atmosphere system and a vital parameter in the general circulation and in long-range forecasting.

Meteorology requires data over wide areas as well as to great heights and here again progress has been great. Observational instructions have been standardized on a global basis and data are freely exchanged. Advances in speed of transmission have increased the volume of data exchanged, and the evidence is that the speed will increase further by many orders of magnitude. Processed data are being exchanged also in numerical, pictorial, and digital forms. In addition to the original radio and teletype, there is the facsimile for visual presentations and the communications satellite which will be important in future global networks. To meet the needs for speed, volume, and selectivity, highly sophisticated computer-controlled systems have now been developed.

The tools of measurement have undergone equally impressive development. The radiosonde is no longer restricted to measurement of the traditional pressure, temperature, humidity, and wind. It may also measure radiational flux, ozone distribution, and other factors in the upper air. Radar has come of age as a tool of great power in probing the secrets of cloud and precipitation physics. Micrometeorological systems consisting of thermometers and anemometers measure the parameters important for analysis of turbulent flow and diffusion. A new development of considerable promise here is the "sonic radar" which can probe the depths of the heat island over a city. They also exemplify the growing tendency to create systems which feed out processed rather than raw data, in this case in the form of statistical data in digitized form.

With the vastly increased capacity for obtaining data has come an increased capacity for digesting it. Data which may have future value are stored, often in the form of punched cards. However with increasing masses of data even the storage of punched cards is a problem, and even more concise forms are being developed. Data, particularly analyzed data, are being stored in digitized form on magnetic tapes. This makes them readily available for analysis on an electronic computer. With this sort of capability, the whole approach to research is undergoing change. In many areas, the analysis by electronic computer has become the normal approach. Synoptic analysis and prediction is rapidly moving into that class.

As one might expect with the avalanche of new data, research into the structure and behavior of the atmosphere has been experiencing a corresponding development. This is exemplified by the growth of institutions for research and teaching in meteorology. Thirty-five years ago, there were in the world only a few universities active in meteorology. Today there are 20 to 30 in the United States alone, and there are many more in certain specialized areas of the science. This period has seen the manyfold increase in direct participation by the governmental agencies in meteorological research. Journals to publish the resulting research have matured and multiplied. The private meteorological consultant has come into his own. Many have built medium-sized firms providing a large amount of specialized service including research under contract to private companies as well as to the government.

Thirty-five years ago, meteorology largely consisted of a semiqualitative science concerned with the synoptic scale motions of the atmosphere, those of importance to forecasting for the next 48 hours, and certain basic physical principles. This picture has changed completely in the intervening years. Gone is the simple flow concept of the atmosphere, and in its place is an atmosphere of almost unbelievable complexity. In place of the synoptic scale pattern of wave motion in the atmosphere, we have a hierarchy of scales. These include the hemispheric long waves, or Rossby waves, in the westerly flow having wavelengths of the order of 5000 km, and the synoptic scale of wavelength of the order of 1500 km. Then follows the mesoscale, phenomena of the order of 10 to 50 km, and the microscale which involves motions of the order of a few meters. According to Kolmogoroff, the driving energy of the atmosphere is transferred from one scale of motion to another of lower scale. Large-scale motions break down into smaller motions which themselves break down into still smaller motions. Thus energy cascades down the scale, the limit being reached when energy is absorbed into motions of the molecules, showing up as heat.

The middle-latitude westerly stream of air, formerly thought to be a broad steady flow, is organized into two or more jet streams; narrow streams of air concentrated at tropopause level and extending around the world with speeds up to 100 m/sec. The jet streams generally meander northward and southward outlining a more or less regular wave pattern of the order of 90° longitude wavelength. These Rossby waves move only slowly. Ridges in the system correspond to warmer than average air and troughs to colder. Thus these systems are the key to extended range forecasting, forecasting of the order of 5 days in advance.

The equations of motion of the atmosphere have been known since the early days of the science. However, these equations are nonlinear. A functional solution is not possible. A numerical solution is possible under simplifying assumptions but only if facilities are available for extensive calculation. The electronic computer has made this possible. Research over the past 20 years has shown which assumptions are necessary to produce representative mathematical models of the atmosphere amenable to solution. As it turns out, quite useful results can be obtained by a very rigid restriction, the assumption of a barotropic atmosphere. In such an atmosphere, all levels behave in exactly the same manner so that this model can only approximate the real atmosphere at one level. This level is approximately 4.5 km altitude. It was many years before baroclinic models, models without this restriction, produced as good results. This point has now been reached and present models are able to predict the effect of various influences on the development of cyclones and Rossby waves.

Insofar as these scales of motion are concerned, the computer has become the laboratory of the meteorologist in the truest sense. By altering the parameters in his models, the meteorologist can test the effects of various influences on the atmosphere. The newer models incorporate the effects of solar heating, radiational cooling, formation of clouds and precipitation, as well as the peculiarities of the earth's surface. Much work has been done, but this phase of the science is poised for great advance.

Spectacular changes, based on this work, are taking place in weather forecasting. Large-scale motions are being predicted through the use of electronic computers. Data from the teletype circuits are fed directly to computers which check them for consistency, analyze them for values of the variables at fixed grid points, predict the flow patterns, and draw the synoptic weather map. Having almost solved the problem of large-scale prediction at all levels, research has moved towards the development of cascading or telescoping models. In these a computer in a regional office would solve a prediction problem of smaller scale based on a finer grid within the context and boundary conditions provided from a world office from its solution of the large-scale problem.

The mesoscale studies deal with phenomena

such as thunderstorms and other small scale circulation systems. This scale of phenomena is also related to very short-range forecasting which is important for certain activities. An example is the forecasting for landing of supersonic aircraft in critical conditions. Such aircraft cannot fly long at low altitudes, and it is essential that the pilot have an accurate forecast for the next twenty to thirty minutes before descending. In the forecasting business, specialists in meso-scale predictions are being developed to work as a team with the specialists in the hemispheric and synoptic scales. This permits a better all-around use of the data. At all levels, the use of the computer will increase as research points the way toward more quantitative methods.

The significant emphasis now being placed on the atmosphere as a part of the environment is leading to important changes. Hydrometeorology, biometeorology, air-water interactions, etc., are becoming increasingly important. These are the areas where the atmospheric environment fringes on other physical and biological environments and the meteorological problems are in fact only parts of problems of the total environment. The practical importance of such studies are immense for they provide the basic information needed for environmental management. In the immediate decision-making process they may and should influence decisions on great economic projects such as dams and pipelines where the impact of man's activity runs through the total environment including the atmosphere.

For much the same reasons the measurement and study of air quality has led to recent changes. Both data and understanding are needed if man is to have an atmosphere of adequate quality. Quality is based on the chemical and particulate composition of the atmosphere, whether produced by man or nature. The measurement of the state and trends of air quality on all time and space scales is a new and major objective of the meteorologist; so is its prediction. On such information air pollution control decisions are made, and from such information new problem areas for the researcher are pinpointed. As a result, several meteorological subdisciplines have received a lease on life. The most obvious of these is atmospheric chemistry, which has enough problems to provide fascinating careers for many.

One of the great new fields of meteorological research is that of CLOUD PHYSICS. The major tool is the radar, but data are also gathered by other means such as instrumented aircraft and conventional ground instrumentation forming a very fine network. Clouds form when moist air rises, expands and cools. While condensation nuclei are necessary before droplets will form, the atmosphere always has an ample supply of these so that clouds always form when saturation is reached. It has been found also that there is no fixed freezing point for water in the atmosphere and indeed condensation takes place in the liquid state at temperatures substantially

below 0°C. The small droplets so formed have proved to be exceedingly stable, and one of the major problems of meteorology has been to learn more of the mechanisms which permit these droplets to grow into large ones. It has long been known that if some droplets freeze, there is the possibility of a distillation from the small droplets to the ice crystals causing the latter to grow. In middle latitudes, this is believed to be the major cause of growth of droplets to raindrop size. There are always a few nuclei in the atmosphere suitable for use as crystallization nuclei, but there are insufficient to cause a large percentage of the droplets to crystallize. Much research has been done to try to improve the richness of the atmosphere with respect to ice nuclei. Silver iodide has proved to be useful, because of its similar structure to that of the ice crystal, and is active at temperatures of about −5°C. Many experiments have been made using silver iodide as a seeding agent to supply additional nuclei to the atmosphere and to increase rainfall. Because of the natural variability of rainfall, it requires a very carefully designed experiment to permit meaningful statistical evaluation of such experiments. Even now it is uncertain that rainfall is actually increased significantly by such techniques except in regions where there is forced uplift of the air as in mountainous areas. Nevertheless, because of the great value that can be attached to even a modest increase in some instances, the commercial cloud-seeding operator has been able to find much business. The other major mechanism for growth of droplets is that of coalescence. This mechanism depends on the production of a few large drops, generally by giant condensation nuclei of hygroscopic salt, which then sweep out swaths of smaller droplets due to differential motion and momentum. This mechanism, important in the tropics, seems to be less amenable to adjustment by man.

Some of the more exciting areas of new knowledge lie in the higher atmosphere. The atmosphere seems to divide naturally into various layers. The lowest of these is the troposphere where convection rules. The temperature drops off steadily to about 9 to 10 km. The top of this layer is known as the tropopause. The temperature in the lower stratosphere is approximately constant with height but soon begins to increase until it reaches a peak at about 50 km with temperatures comparable to those at the earth's surface. This level is known as the stratopause. The temperature then drops off with height through the mesosphere to about 90 km, a level known as the mesopause.

With increasing amounts of data, what originally seemed to be a rather tranquil picture of the upper atmosphere has undergone some change. We find that the arctic stratosphere generates a rather strong westerly jet stream at about 25 km altitude in wintertime. The winter arctic stratosphere is subject to more or less sharp warmings of substantial magnitude each

year in the period between about January and March. This sudden warming marks the end of the stratospheric winter which then changes over to a summer regime. There is also a noticeable 26-month cycle in the tropical stratospheric wind, the direction changing from easterly to westerly about every 26 months. A similar tendency, but much more subdued, has been found at higher latitudes. There is evidence that this cycle affects the stratospheric warmings causing them to develop in Europe first one year and North America the next.

The whole field of services has grown as more knowledge is gained. It is possible here to give only some instances, but it should be realized that this development of widely diversified services based on meteorology is one of the great developments of the last 20 years.

D. P. McINTYRE

References

Byers, Horace, R., "Elements of Cloud Physics," Chicago, The University of Chicago Press, 1965 (191 p.).

Craig, Richard, "The Upper Atmosphere, Meteorology and Physics," New York, Academic Press, 1965 (509 p.).

Haltiner, George J., and Martin, Frank L., "Dynamical and Physical Meteorology," New York, McGraw-Hill 1957 (407 p.).

Palmén, E., and Newton, C. W., "Atmospheric Circulation Systems: Their Structure and Physical Interpretations," New York, Academic Press, 1969 (603 p.).

Scorer, Richard, "Air Pollution," New York, Pergamon Press, 1968 (151 p.).

Cross-references: CLOUD PHYSICS, COMPUTERS, HEAT, PLANETARY ATMOSPHERES, TELEMETRY, TEMPERATURE AND THERMOMETRY.

MICHELSON-MORLEY EXPERIMENT

Introduction The revival and development of the wave theory of light at the beginning of the nineteenth century, principally through the contributions of Young and Fresnel, posed a problem which proved to be of major interest for physics throughout the entire century. The question concerned the nature of the medium in which light is propagated. This medium was called the "aether" and an enormous amount of experimental and theoretical work was expended in efforts to determine its properties. On the experimental side, a long series of electrical and optical investigations were carried out attempting to measure the motion of the earth through the ether medium. For many years, the experimental precision permitted measurements only to the first power of the ratio of the speed of the earth in its orbit to the speed of light ($v/c \simeq 10^{-4}$), and these "first-order experi-

ments" uniformly gave null results. It became the accepted view that the earth's motion through the ether could not be detected by laboratory experiments of this sensitivity. With the development of Maxwell's electromagnetic theory of light, and especially with its extensions by Lorentz in his electron theory, theoretical explanations for the null results obtained in the early ether drift experiments were provided. These results were in harmony with the Galilean-Newtonian principle of relativity in mechanics, which explains why the essential features of all uniform motions are independent of the frame of reference in which they are observed. In Maxwell's electromagnetic theory, however, the situation was altered when quantities of the second order in (v/c) were considered. According to the Maxwell theory, effects depending on (v/c)^2 should have been detectable in optical and electrical experiments. The presence of these "second-order effects" would indicate a preferred reference frame for the phenomena in which the ether would be at rest. At first, this feature of Maxwell's theory implying observable ether drift effects of the second order in (v/c) raised a purely hypothetical question, since the accuracy needed for such experiments was a part in a hundred million, and no experimental techniques then known could attain this sensitivity.

Michelson pondered this problem and it led him to invent the Michelson interferometer, which was capable of measurements of the required sensitivity, and to plan the ether drift experiment which he carried to completion in collaboration with Edward W. Morley at Cleveland in 1887. This famous optical interference experiment was devised to measure the motion of the earth through the ether medium by means of an extremely sensitive comparison of the velocity of light traveling in two mutually perpendicular directions. The experiment, when completed in 1887, gave a most convincing null result and proved to be the culmination of the long nineteenth century search for the ether. At that time, the definitive null result of the Michelson-Morley experiment was a most disconcerting finding for theoretical physics, and indeed for many years repetitions of this experiment and related ones were performed with the hope of finding positive experimental evidence for the earth's motion through the ether. These later experiments, however, have all been shown to be consistent with the original null result obtained by Michelson and Morley. In the years following 1887, their experiment led to extensive and revolutionary developments in theoretical physics, and proved to be a major incentive for the work of FitzGerald, Lorentz, Larmor, Poincaré, and others, leading finally in 1905 to the special theory of relativity of Albert Einstein.

The optical paths in the Michelson-Morley interferometer are shown in plan in Fig. 1. Light from a is divided into two coherent beams at the half-reflecting, half-transmitting

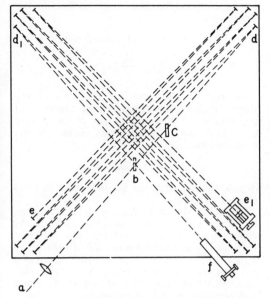

FIG. 1. Optical paths in the Michelson-Morley interferometer.

are exactly equal, a condition produced by moving the mirror at e_1 by a micrometer. c is an optical compensating plate. The effective optical path length of each arm of the apparatus was increased to 1100 cm by the repeated reflections from the mirror system.

Figure 2 is a perspective drawing of the Michelson-Morley interferometer showing the optical system mounted on a 5 foot square sandstone slab. The slab is supported on the annular wooden float, which in turn fitted into the annular cast-iron trough containing mercury which floated the apparatus. On the outside of this tank can be seen some of the numbers 1 to 16 used to locate the position of the interferometer in azimuth. The trough was mounted on a brick pier which in turn was supported by a special concrete base. The height of the apparatus was such that the telescope was at eye level to permit convenient observation of the fringes when the instrument was rotating in the mercury. While observations were being made, the optical parts were covered with a wooden box to reduce air currents and temperature fluctuations.

This arrangement permitted the interferometer to be continuously rotated in the horizontal plane so that observations of the interference fringes could be made at all azimuths with respect to the earth's orbital velocity through space. When set in motion, the interferometer would rotate slowly (about once in 6 minutes) for hours at a time. No starting and stopping was necessary, and the motion was so slow that accurate readings of fringe positions could easily be made while the apparatus rotated.

The experiment to observe "the relative mo-

rear surface of the optical flat b. These two beams travel at 90° to each other and are multiply reflected by two systems of mirrors d - e and d_1 - e_1. On returning to b part of the light from e - d is reflected into the telescope at f, and light from e_1 - d_1 is also transmitted to f. These two coherent beams of light produce interference fringes. These are formed in white only when the optical paths in the two arms

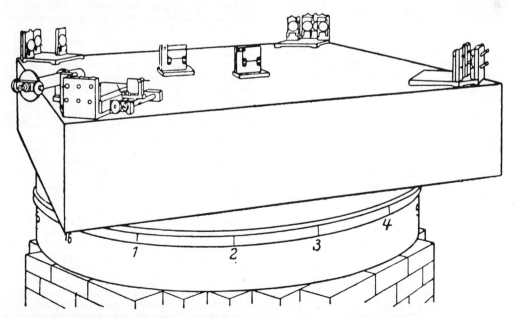

FIG. 2. Michelson-Morley interferometer used at Cleveland in 1887.

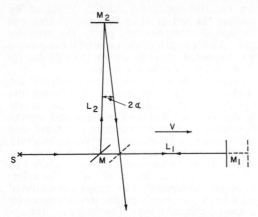

FIG. 3. The Michelson-Morley experiment.

tion of the earth and the luminiferous ether" for which this instrument was devised, was planned by Michelson and Morley as follows. When the interferometer is oriented as in Fig. 3 with the arm L_1 parallel to the direction of the earth's velocity v in space, the time required for light to travel from M to M_1 and return to M in its new position is,

$$t_{\parallel}(1) = \frac{L_1}{c-v} + \frac{L_1}{c+v} = \frac{2L_1}{c} \frac{1}{1-\beta^2} \quad \left(\beta = \frac{v}{c}\right)$$

The time for light to make the journey to and from the mirror M_2 in the other interferometer arm L_2 is,

$$t_{\perp}(1) = [2L_2(1 + \tan^2\alpha)^{1/2}/c]$$

and since $\tan^2\alpha = v^2/(c^2 - v^2)$

$$t_{\perp}(1) = \frac{2L_2}{c} \frac{1}{(1-\beta^2)^{1/2}}.$$

When the interferometer is rotated through 90° in the horizontal plane so that the arm L_2 is parallel to v, the corresponding times are,

$$t_{\parallel}(2) = \frac{2L_2}{c} \frac{1}{1-\beta^2}$$

$$t_{\perp}(2) = \frac{2L_1}{c} \frac{1}{(1-\beta^2)^{1/2}}$$

Thus, the total phase shift (in time) between the two light beams expected on the ether theory for a rotation of the interferometer through 90° is,

$$\Delta t = \frac{2L_1}{c} \left[\frac{1}{1-\beta^2} - \frac{1}{(1-\beta^2)^{1/2}} \right]$$

$$+ \frac{2L_2}{c} \left[\frac{1}{1-\beta^2} - \frac{1}{(1-\beta^2)^{1/2}} \right]$$

$$= \frac{2(L_1 + L_2)}{c} \left[\frac{1}{1-\beta^2} - \frac{1}{(1-\beta^2)^{1/2}} \right]$$

For equal interferometer arms, as used in this experiment,

$$L_1 = L_2 = L, \text{ and, since } \beta \ll 1,$$

$$\Delta t \simeq \frac{2L}{c} \beta^2$$

The observations give the positions of the fringes, rather than times, so the quantity of importance for the experiment is the change in optical path in the two arms of the interferometer.

$$A = c \Delta t = 2L(v/c)^2$$

This is the quantity of second order in (v/c) referred to above.

With the Michelson-Morley interferometer, the magnitude of the expected shift of the white-light interference pattern was 0.4 of a fringe as the instrument was rotated through an angle of 90° in the horizontal plane. Michelson and Morley felt completely confident that fringe shifts of this order of magnitude could be determined with high precision.

In July of 1887, Michelson and Morley were able to make their definitive observations. The experiments which gave their final measurements were conducted at noon and during the evening of the days of July 8, 9, 11, 12 of 1887. Instead of the expected shift of 0.4 of a fringe they found "that if there is any displacement due to the relative motion of the earth and the luminiferous ether, this cannot be much greater than 0.01 of the distance between the fringes."

The result of the Michelson-Morley experiment has always been accepted as definitive and formed an essential base for the long train of theoretical developments that finally culminated in the special theory of relativity. The first important suggestion advanced to explain the null result of Michelson and Morley was G. F. Fitz-Gerald's hypothesis that the length of the interferometer is contracted in the direction of its motion through the ether by the exact amount necessary to compensate for the increased time needed by the light signal in its to-and-fro path. This contraction hypothesis was made quantitative by H. A. Lorentz in further development of his electron theory in which he introduced the formalism which has since been known as the "Lorentz transformation" for the analysis of relative motions.

H. Poincaré also contributed greatly to both the philosophical and mathematical developments of the theory. As early as 1899, he asserted that the result of Michelson and Morley should be generalized to a doctrine that absolute motion is in principle not detectable by laboratory experiments of any kind. Poincaré further elaborated his ideas in 1900 and in 1904 and gave to his generalization the name "the principle of relativity." He also completed the theory of Lorentz and it was he who named the essential transformation "the Lorentz transformation."

In 1905 Einstein published his famous paper on the "Electrodynamics of Moving Bodies" in which he developed the special theory of relativity from two postulates: (1) the principle of relativity was accepted as the impossibility of detecting uniform motion by laboratory experiments, and (2) the constancy of the speed of light was generalized to a postulate that light is always propagated in empty space with a velocity independent of the motion of the source. Both postulates have a close relationship to the Michelson-Morley experiment, which Einstein knew through his study of the work of Lorentz. Einstein's paper is generally considered as the definitive exposition of the special relativity principle, and the climax of the century-long developments which had begun with Young and Fresnel to explain the electrical and optical properties of moving bodies. It has since become a major factor in the modern development of both classical and quantum physics.

R. S. SHANKLAND

References

Shankland, R. S., "Conversations with Albert Einstein," *Amer. J. Phys.*, **31**, 47 (1963); **41**, 895 (1973).
Shankland, R. S., "Michelson-Morley Experiment," *Amer. J. Phys.*, **32**, 16 (1964).
Shankland, R. S., "Michelson-Morley Experiment," *Sci. Amer.*, Nov. 1964, p. 107–114.
Cross-references: INTERFERENCE AND INTERFEROMETRY; LIGHT; OPTICS, GEOMETRICAL; OPTICS, PHYSICAL; RELATIVITY.

MICROSCOPE*

The word "microscope" comes from a Greek word that means "to view small." Before the microscope could come into existence, the LENS had to be developed. Early knowledge of lenses is very obscure, but we do know that the Chinese porcelain vases had figures on them wearing glasses. These vases date back to 1000 B.C. The Assyrian lens of 700 B.C. was found to be double convex. Sir Austen Henry Layard discovered a plano-convex lens of rock crystal at the Nineveh excavation. The Greeks and Romans wrote about the burning properties of glass lenses as well as the use of glass globules filled with water to aid in seeing small objects. Roger Bacon wrote about the magnification power of lenses to aid elderly persons in reading. After his book "Opus Majus" was published in 1266 A.D., nearly two hundred years passed before anything was written discussing advancements in optics. In 1542, the first references about telescopes appeared, and these were written by Nicholaus Copernicus of Poland, who discovered that the sun is the center of our universe and that other universes exist.

---

*Editor was unable to locate author. Article is reprinted from first Edition.

In Middleburg, Holland, about 1590, the story of the compound microscope begins. Zacharias Janssen developed, by accident, a microscope which was 1 inch in diameter and 6 feet long. This discovery started the parade of inventors and improvers of the microscope, too numerous to mention in their entirety in this article.

Galileo in 1610 introduced a microscope similar to Janssen's but with one major improvement. The Galileo microscope could be focused by means of screw threads on the body and mount, Fontana, Drebbel and Kepler also made microscopes in this early period.

The early microscope lenses had been formed on the ends of glass rods by heating and pressing into a given shape. Campani was the first to design and grind lenses which had curves that could be reproduced. Anton van Leeuwenhoek studied all types of specimens under a simple microscope with ground lenses of his own design. He made in excess of 100 microscopes with single lenses, some of which were $\frac{1}{8}$ inch in diameter and had very strong curvature. With these instruments, he discovered bacteria and the existence of corpuscles in the blood.

Robert Hooke, in the last quarter of the 1600's, made a compound microscope that was easy to use. Hooke used a doublet eyepiece from Christian Huyghens to make up the telescope portion (eyepiece) of his compound microscope. The Royal Microscopical Society published Robert Hooke's "Micrographia" in which he describes tissues, blood vessels, textiles, papers, sugar and salt crystals. In about 1750, another Englishman, by the name of John Dollond, improved lenses by devising an achromatic system compounded from both hard and soft glass. In 1759, Dollond succeeded in making an achromatic lens. However, this type of lens was not used in a microscope until 1825. In 1854, the first steps toward standardization of the microscope took place with the "X" designation for magnification based on 250 mm. In 1873, Ernst Abbe from the University of Jena wrote "Theory of Microscope Image Formation" and "Sub-Stage Illumination Apparatus." If the theories discussed in Abbe's book had not been followed, today's microscopes would form very poor, inferior images.

Objective Lenses   The use of simple lenses with high curves for high magnification presents problems that make their use impractical. As the curve of the lens increases, the focal length becomes shorter and more difficult to use. An example of this is the Leeuwenhoek microscope in which one's eye had to be placed on top of the lens in order to see the magnified specimen. A microscope is nothing more than an objective lens magnifying a specimen, the image of which is being viewed by a simple telescope at some convenient distance from the objective lens (Fig. 1).

The aberration of lenses is always a problem to the designers of objectives. The two most common problems are color aberration (chromatic) and distortion of   shape aberration

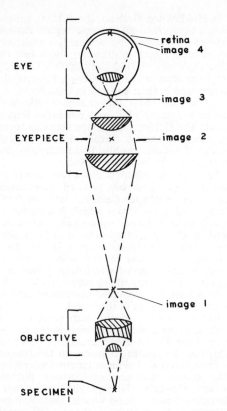

FIG. 1. Compound microscope showing optics and image position.

(spheric). If a beam of white light passes from a medium of one density into a medium of another density such as air to glass, the beam is bent. As white light is made up of different colors, each wavelength refracts a different amount, and thus we have a spread of the colors called dispersion (Fig. 2). The higher the index of refraction the greater the dispersion. Figures 3 and 4 show the reasons that aberrations appear in lenses. A simple, and many times the most economical, practical way to correct spherical aberration is to place a diaphragm in front of the lens so as to cut off the thin edges which bend the light more (Fig. 4 and 5). To correct chromatic aberrations various types of glass

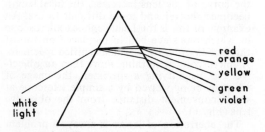

FIG. 2. Bending illustrates refraction; spreading illustrates dispersion.

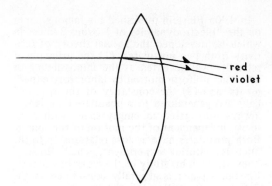

FIG. 3. Chromatic aberration.

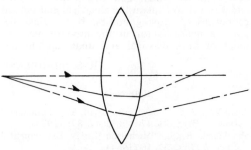

FIG. 4. Spherical aberration.

must be selected for index of refraction and dispersion; they should then be combined to have as many colors as possible come to focus at the same point.

The objective is the most important single factor of the microscope, for through its power to resolve minute structure, we see small objects crisp and clear. Magnification, although it is of secondary importance to the resolving power of the objective, is absolutely essential. In order to have high resolution, a lens must be the best possible compromise on the correction of the various aberrations such as spherical, coma, and chromatic. The matter of resolution in actual practice is based not only on the correction of the lenses, but on the ability of the user to use

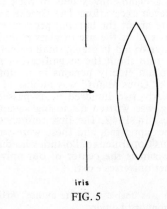

iris
FIG. 5

the proper objective, ocular, condenser, and illumination, and on controlling the aperture diaphragm and field diaphragms to their optimum settings for the system being used. It is not always possible to achieve the resolutions of a given lens even after proper manipulation because the detail is obscured by the background and the surrounding parts of the specimen. Technique in preparing the material being studied is of the utmost importance. Proper staining, thickness and mounting also determine how much we will resolve.

Resolution, angular aperture and wavelength of light being used are related. The angle of the cone of light is dependent on the refractive index of the medium between the objective front lens and the glass cover slip over the specimen (Fig. 6). Present-day objectives have clearly

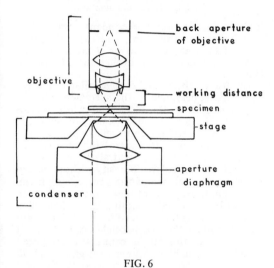

FIG. 6

marked on their mounts the relationship between the angular cone and refracture index of the working medium, expressed in terms of numerical aperture (N.A.)

$$N.A. = i \sin \theta$$

where θ is one-half the angle of the cone of light entering the objective and i is the refractive index of the medium in which the objective is working. From this formula theoretically one can see that the N.A. in air can never be greater than 1 because i would represent air with a refractive index of 1.

The relationship of N.A. and resolving power is as follows:

$$R = N.A./\lambda$$

where λ is wavelength of light and R is the number of lines being separated by the lens.

There are three main classes of objectives: achromatic, fluorite, and aphochromatic; the achromatics are corrected for two colors (red

and green) chromatically and one color spherically. To obtain more correction, substitution of the sandless glasses such as fluorite gives a little better correction than the achromats. The aphochromatic objectives produce the best images, those finest in color correction and clarity. Aphochromatic objectives are corrected for three colors chromatically and two spherically. To achieve the added value in the aphochromatic objectives, they must utilize compensating eyepieces to correct for the color spread and a corrected condenser of a numerical aperture equal to or greater than the objective numerical aperture.

When using the microscope, it is very important to consider the working distance, depth of field and coverglass thickness. The working distance is the amount of free space from the front of the objective to the coverglass, and as the power and the N.A. increase, the working distance becomes shorter, Therefore, when a counting chamber with its normal coverglass is used, magnifications up to about 45X and N.A.'s up to about .66 can be used to view specimens. Objectives of higher magnification and larger N.A.'s reduce the working distance sufficiently to cause breakage of cover slips or inability to focus sharply on the specimen.

Depth of focus is the amount of thickness of the specimen that is in focus at one time. This amount decreases as magnification and N.A. increase. In photomicrography this is very important and the specimen must be thin enough or parts of the specimen will be out of focus, obscuring detail of the portion that is in sharp focus. High-power dry objectives with correction collars to compensate for coverglass thickness should be used with cover glasses other than .18 mm to have optimum correction for spherical aberration. Objectives without the coverglass correction collar are designed and optically corrected for the use of coverglasses of .18 mm thickness. Coverglasses of other thickness increase the aberration, especially when using high dry objectives.

Eyepieces The eyepiece acts as the telescope of the system merely to remagnify the primary image of the objective; thus eyepiece magnification adds nothing to the resolution of the system. The practical rule is that one should not normally magnify more than 1000X the N.A. of the objective. More magnification is normally called empty magnification. However, in some instances to aid in counting, measuring, or drawing, ease of use can be achieved by using a higher-power eyepiece. Many companies are now making eyepieces with high eye relief so that persons requiring the additional distance between the eye lens and the ramsden circle of the eyepiece can continue to wear their glasses while using the microscope.

There are many types of eyepieces. Four of the most common are Huygenian, periplane, widefield and compensating. The Huygenian is by far the simplest in design having 2 elements

and being the least corrected, but most commonly, used eyepiece. Periplane eyepieces have greater correction thus producing better images as to color and flatness, while having about the same field of view as the Huygenian. Compensating eyepieces were designed for use with the aphochromatic objectives to compensate for the objective deficiencies. In recent years the need to view more has brought about the development of eyepieces which cover greater fields of view.

Condensers The condenser is commonly the most misused part of the microscope. A condenser has one optimum setting as to height and aperture diaphragm setting which controls the *N.A.* for each objective. The condenser height and aperture diaphragm should not be used to control the intensity of the illumination. If the aperture diaphragm is opened too far, the specimen is flooded with light and detail is washed out. If closed too far, the *N.A.* and detail are lost and diffraction becomes quite apparent.

Illuminators The illuminator is a very essential part of the microscope. If one is to achieve the maximum from the microscope in terms of resolution, clarity and ease on the eyes of the user, a good illuminator must be employed. An illuminator must have a condensing system large enough to accomodate the apertures of the microscope and an iris diaphragm, sometimes referred to as a field stop. The condensing system and field stop must be focusable. To achieve the ultimate in illumination, filters and adjustable mirrors in the illuminator help to adjust for maximum light through the system.

In the early days of microscopy, critical illumination was used by most microscopists. The source of light was broad such as the sun, reflection of the sun on white clouds or oil wick lamps. The source was focused so it would appear in the field of view (Fig. 7). Of course, the disadvantages of this system were size of the source and unevenness of illumination. The introduction of the concentrated coil filament lamps made use of critical illumination impractical due to the fact that the coil source was small and did not fill the aperture. Kohler solved this problem and the system is named after him. In Kohler illumination, the filament of the

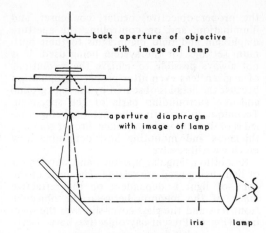

FIG. 8. Kohler illumination.

lamp is focused on the condenser iris (often called the aperture stop), and the field iris is focused so it will be in focus at the same plane as the specimen viewed through the microscope (Fig. 8).

The use of filters makes it possible to change the visual appearance of the specimen. The use of a green filter for black and white photomicrography will, in many cases, increase the contrast and produce an excellent photograph.

The proper way to control the intensity of illumination is to use neutral density filters. These filters control the intensity without changing the color balance of the source, e.g., if the source emits 20 per cent blue, 50 per cent green and 30 per cent red without a filter, then when a 50 per cent filter is placed in the system, only 50 per cent of the original light comes through the filter, but this 50 per cent is still composed of 20 per cent blue, 50 per cent green and 30 per cent red. We have cut down only the total intensity, not the balance.

Types of Microscope There are many types of microscopes. Basically they are all similar, i.e., they have one or more objectives, eyepieces, condensers and some mechanical means to focus and manipulate the specimens. Often, in order to change from one type of microscope to another, only accessories have to be added.

The phase contrast method of microscopy was introduced in 1935 by Professor F. Zernike. Phase contrast is most useful in research and industry where an approach, other than the normal one, is necessary. The main advantage lies in the fact that contrast can be greatly enhanced in living and/or unstained material, where, normally, little or no contrast exists with a bright field microscope. Direct observation of living material, such as yeast, bacteria and fungi, has made possible rapid, positive identification of specific organisms as well as observation of phenomena within the cells that have gone unnoticed for many years. Phase contrast relies on the combining of light waves and is dependent on amplitude and phase of these waves.

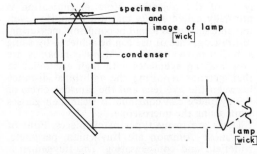

FIG. 7. Critical illumination.

Dark field microscopy consists of a condenser with an opaque central stop which will not allow any direct light to enter the objectives. The circular cone of light is focused on the specimen which becomes very bright on a black background. Dark field shows objects that are too small to be seen by the bright field microscope; it is often used in the identification of spirochaetes, colloidal materials and chemical bonding.

Polarizing microscopes, in addition to having the normal components, have a polarizer and an analyzer. The light enters the polarizer where it is forced to vibrate in one direction. The light then passes through the condenser and objective to the analyzer which is set with the direction of vibration $90°$ to the polarizer; consequently no light is allowed to pass to the eyepiece. When material is placed in the system at the specimen plane, the material, in many cases, rotates the plane of polarization. Now that the polarized light has been rotated, a portion will pass through the eyepiece and be observed. Crystals that rotate the plane of polarization become either colored or white on a dark background. Crystals are classified by the way that they look under polarized light and by the amount of rotation which differs for each crystal. Other properties of crystals that can be studied by the polarizing microscopes are optical sign, extinction angle, birefringence, refractive index and pleochroism (see POLARIZED LIGHT).

The stereoscopic microscope is basically two microscopes, one for each eye. These two microscopes are mounted conveniently in a single housing for easy use. Each eye views the same specimen from a different angle producing a stereoscopic, three-dimensional view. The view through this type of microscope gives the user greater depth, erect image and larger fields than with the compound microscope. These instruments are used in dissection, genetic studies, and the assembly of small parts.

There are many universities, companies and individuals that have advanced the microscope to its present form. It is certainly one of the most important factors in our knowledge of bacteriology and other medical sciences. Industry, in its quest for quality today, is investigating more closely the minute workings of its products, and with the advent of space exploration, the need for miniaturization has emphasized the part the microscope can play in studying, understanding and manipulating specimens.

DONALD A. BURGH

References

Spitta, E. J., "Microscopy," Third edition, London, John Murray, 1920.

Belling, J., "The Use of the Microscope," New York, McGraw-Hill Book Co., 1930.

Gage, S. H., "The Microscope," Seventeenth edition, Ithaca, Comstock, 1943.

Gray, P., "Handbook of Basic Microtechnique," Second edition, New York, McGraw-Hill Book Co., 1958.

Allen, R. M., "Photomicrography," Second edition, New York, Van Nostrand/Reinhold, 1959.

Bennett, Osterberg, Jupnik, and Richard, "Phase Microscopy," New York, John Wiley & Sons, 1951.

Cross-references: ABERRATION, DIFFRACTION THEORY OF; DIFFRACTION BY MATTER AND DIFFRACTION GRATINGS; ELECTRON MICROSCOPE; LENS; OPTICAL INSTRUMENTS; REFRACTION.

MICROWAVE SPECTROSCOPY

Microwaves are electromagnetic waves which range in length from about 30 cm to a fraction of a millimeter or in frequency from 10^9 to 0.5×10^{12} cps. This corresponds to the rotational frequency range of a large class of molecules. Thus, microwave radiation passing through a gas can be absorbed when the rotating electric dipole moment of the molecule interacts with the electric vector of the radiation. Likewise, absorption can take place if the rotating magnetic moment of the molecule interacts with the magnetic vector of the radiation.

Most microwave spectroscopy is based on a study of transitions induced by interaction of the molecular electric diode with the incident radiation.

A microwave spectrometer than consists basically of a monochromatic microwave source (klystron), an absorption cell, and a detector. The absorption cell must transmit the microwave of interest and in the centimeter region may have cross-sectional dimensions of 1×4 cm and may be a few meters in length. Normally a metal strip is inserted along the length of the cell and is insulated from the cell. In this way, an auxiliary, spatially uniform electric field may be established in the absorption cell without affecting the microwaves. The Stark effect thereby produced splits the molecular energy levels into a series of levels and enables one to identify the transition.

The Hamiltonian for a rotating rigid asymmetric molecule including possible fine and hyperfine structure terms is given in Eq. (1). It is assumed, as is most commonly so, that the molecule is in a $^1\Sigma$ state, i.e., that there is no net electronic angular momentum and no net electron spin (singlet state). The Hamiltonian written is quite general and in many cases not all of the terms shown in Eq. (1) need be included to account for spectra observed under normal resolution.

A brief description will be given of each term in order that one may most simply understand the kinds of interactions which may occur and which may be pertinent to an understanding of the spectra of rotating molecules.

$$H = H_R + H_{dist.} + H_S + H_{ze} + H_Q$$
$$+ H_{zi} + H_D \quad (1)$$

1. H_R is the framework rotational kinetic energy and may be written

$$H_R = \frac{\hbar^2}{8\pi^2}\left[\frac{J_a{}^2}{I_a} + \frac{J_b{}^2}{I_b} + \frac{J_c{}^2}{I_c}\right]$$

where J_a, J_b, and J_c are the components of the total angular momentum in units of $\hbar$ referred to body-fixed principal axes. I_a, I_b, and I_c are the moments of inertia about the respective principal axes. The Hamiltonian may be written

$$H_R = AJ_a{}^2 + BJ_b{}^2 + CJ_c{}^2$$

or displaying the total angular momentum J

$$H_R = AJ^2 + (B - A)J_b{}^2 + (C - A)J_c{}^2$$

A, B and C are rotational constants with $A > B > C$. In this form, units can be chosen so as to give energy levels directly in megacycles per second. H_R describes a rigid symmetric top if I_a is equal to I_b. For a diatomic molecule, $I_a = I_b$ and $I_c \cong 0$. ($1/I_c$ becomes very large, and the rotational levels about the c axis are too far apart to become excited by microwaves). For the spherical rotor, $I_a = I_b = I_c$, but this implies no dipole moment and therefore no observable rotational spectrum.

Energy levels for the symmetric top may be determined by analytical methods,[1] by factorization methods[2], or by using the commutation properties of the angular momenta.[3] In Eulerian coordinates, the wave equation separates, and the wave function has the form

$$\psi_J = N(JKM)e^{iK\phi}e^{iM\psi}\Theta_{JKM}(\theta)$$

Where Θ_{JKM} is the solution to the differential equation in the polar angle θ which results after separation of the simple terms in the azimuthal angle ϕ and the angle ψ which defines the direction of the line of nodes. The equation for Θ_{JKM} with appropriate change of variable becomes the equation for the Jacobi polynomials.

The solution ψ is characterized by three quantum numbers: J, the total angular momentum; K the component of angular momentum along the symmetry axis of the molecule; and M, the magnetic quantum number or projection of J along an arbitrary space axis. The energy does not depend on M in the absence of external electric or magnetic fields. The energy levels for the symmetric top have the form

$$E_{J,K} = BJ(J + 1) + (C - B)K^2$$

The rotational constants $A = B$ and C may typically range from 2000 to 300 000 MHz for presently observable spectra. A hertz is one cycle per second. A megahertz (MHz) is one million cycles per second.

Selection Rules In all but the accidentally symmetric top, the permanent dipole will be along the symmetry axis. In this case, the selection rules for absorption of radiation through rotation are:[4]

$$J \to J \pm 1, K \to K$$

For a component of the dipole moment perpendicular to the symmetry axis, the selection rules are

$$\Delta J = \pm 1, 0 \text{ and } \Delta K = \pm 1$$

In both cases, $\Delta M = \pm 1, 0$.

The wave functions of the asymmetric top are expressed as linear combinations of symmetric top functions. The energy remains diagonal in J but not in K. One must, therefore, arbitrarily label the energy levels and determine the selection rules. This will not be done here. In order to do this, however, one needs to know only the nonvanishing matrix elements of the three components of the dipole moment for the symmetric top given above.

The selection rule for diatomic molecules is simply $J \to J \pm 1, M \to M, M \pm 1$.

2. $H_{dist.}$ describes centrifugal stretching corrections to the energy levels which for an asymmetric molecule can be quite complicated. Corrections for a symmetric top molecule are easily derived, and the framework energy in this case including centrifugal stretching is given by

$$E_{J,K} = BJ(J + 1) + (C - B)K^2 - D_J J^2(J + 1)^2$$
$$- D_{JK}J(J + 1)K^2 - D_K K^{\cdot}$$

For a non-rigid diatomic molecule or linear polyatomic molecule, $K = 0$, and the energy is given by:

$$E_J = B_v J(J + 1) - D_v J^2(J + 1)^2$$

and since $J \to J + 1$, for absorption the line frequencies are:

$$\nu_r = 2B_v(J + 1) - 4D_v(J + 1)^3$$

where B_v is the "effective" spectral constant, $h(8\pi^2 I_v)$, for the particular vibrational state for which the rotational spectrum is observed, and where D_v is the centrifugal stretching constant for that state.

In terms of the constants B_e and D_e for the hypothetical vibrationless state, B_v and D_v for diatomic molecules are:

$$B_v = B_e - \alpha(v + \tfrac{1}{2})$$
$$D_v = D_e + \beta(v + \tfrac{1}{2})$$

where α and β are interaction constants which are very small in comparison with B and D, respectively, and where v is the vibrational quantum number. For linear polyatomic molecules, there is more than one vibrational mode, and the above equations must be written in the more general form

$$B_v = B_e + \sum_i \alpha_i \left(v_i + \frac{d_i}{2}\right)$$

$$D_v = D_e + \sum_i \beta_i \left(v_i + \frac{d_i}{2}\right)$$

where the summation is taken over all the fundamental modes of vibrations. The subscript i refers to the ith mode, and d_i represents the degeneracy of that mode.

In analysis of spectra, the variations of the stretching constants D_J and D_{JK} with vibrational state are customarily neglected. It is seldom possible to obtain sufficient data for the evaluation of these effects upon B and for determination of B_e even for the simpler symmetric tops.

Centrifugal stretching constants may typically range from 8.5 to 0.002 MHz or less.[6]

3. The third term H_S is the contribution to the Hamiltonian arising from the Stark effect and may be written as

$$H_S = \mu_e \cdot \mathcal{E}$$

where μ_e is the vector dipole moment and $\mathcal{E}$ is the external electric field.

If the dipole moment lies along the "c" body-fixed principal axis, H_S has the form

$$H_S = \mu_e(A_x{}^c\mathcal{E}_x + A_y{}^c\mathcal{E}_y + A_z{}^c\mathcal{E}_z)$$

where $A_x{}^c$, $A_y{}^c$, $A_z{}^c$ are the direction cosines of the c principal axis with space-fixed axes xyz. $\mathcal{E}_x$, $\mathcal{E}_y$, and $\mathcal{E}_z$ are the components of the electric field along the space-fixed axes. Additional terms will be added to this expression if the dipole moment has components along the remaining two principal axes. In order to obtain the contribution to the energy from this part of the Hamiltonian, one must evaluate matrix elements of the direction cosines with respect to symmetric top wave functions. Methods described in reference 5 enable one to do this.

In the case of a symmetric top, the dipole moment will have a component only along the c axis so that H_S consists of the single term $A_z{}^c\mathcal{E}_z$ when $\mathcal{E}_x = \mathcal{E}_y = 0$.

In this case, the energy associated with H_S is diagonal in all three quantum numbers JKM and has the form

$$E_S = -\mathcal{E}_z\mu_e\frac{MK}{J(J+1)}$$

where M, the "magnetic quantum number," measures the component of J along $\mathcal{E}_z$ and can take the values $M = J, J-1, \cdots, -J$. The selection rules for M are $M \rightarrow M$; $M \rightarrow M \pm 1$, depending on the polarization of the microwaves.

For asymmetric molecules, μ_e will in general have components along the A and B axes as well as C. The A and B components give rise to matrix elements off diagonal in J, K and M. For a dipole moment of 1 debye and an electric field of 1 volt/cm, $\mu_e\mathcal{E}$ is 0.5 MHz.

4. H_{ze} is the contribution to the Hamiltonian

due to the interaction of the external magnetic field with the magnetic moment which is created by rotation of the molecule.

We also include the interaction of the external magnetic field with the dipole moment of individual nuclei. For a molecule with two nuclear spins, I_1 and I_2, this may be written

$$H_{ze} = \sum_{j,\,k} \mu_n(J)_{jk}J_jH_k + \mu_ng_1(I_1 \cdot H)$$

$$+ \mu_ng_2(I_2 \cdot H)$$

where $g(J)$ is in general a tensor, J_j are components of J along axes to which H is referred, H_k are the components of the field H usually referred to the space-fixed axes, and g_1 and g_2 are called the nuclear magnetic g factors. The interaction between J and H is the same order as that between the nuclear spin and H. Therefore, we introduce the term μ_n so that g coefficients are of the order of unity. Thus for a field of one gauss, the quantity μ_ngH is 0.7 kHz.

For molecules with electronic angular momentum, μ_n in the first term is replaced by μ_0, the Bohr magneton which is 1836 times larger than μ_n. Thus, in this case μ_ngH is ~ 1.4 MHz for a field of one gauss. For a discussion of the problem of determining molecular g values, as well as magnetic susceptibility anisotropies and molecular quadrupole moments, see Ref. 5.

5. H_Q is the energy of interaction of the nuclear electric quadrupole with the gradient of the electric field produced by the electrons in the molecule at nucleus with spin I. For a nucleus on the axis of a symmetric top, the quadrupole operator is ordinarily considered to be of the form:

$$H_Q = \frac{-eQq}{2I(2I-1)(2J-1)(2J+3)}\left\{1 - \frac{3K^2}{J(J+1)}\right\}$$

$$\left[3(J+1)^2 + \frac{3}{2}(J \cdot I) - J^2I^2\right]$$

This operator yields only those matrix elements of the quadrupole interaction which are diagonal in J. The diagonal contributions are sufficient for most cases.

In the expression above, eQ is defined by

$$eQ = (I, I|\int \rho_n[3z_n{}^2 - r_n{}^2]d\tau_n|I, I)$$

where ρ_n is the nuclear charge density at a distance r_n from the center of charge of the nucleus and $d\tau$ is the differential volume element for the nuclear volume. z_n is the position coordinate along the direction of the nuclear spin I. The matrix element considered is that for which $M_I = I$.

The quantity q is defined as

$$q = \left[\frac{\partial^2 V}{\partial c^2}\right]_{(r_n = 0)}$$

where V is the electrostatic potential due to the electronic cloud and other nuclei surrounding the nucleus and c is the axis in the body-fixed system which is parallel to the symmetry axis of the molecule. The quantity eqQ varies from -1000 to 1000 MHz although the intermediate values are more common.[6] A tabulation of matrix elements for quadrupole interaction is given in Ref. 7. For a general discussion, see the book, Ref. 8.

6. H_{zi} represents the interaction between the magnetic field caused by rotation of the charged particles which make up the molecule and the nuclear magnetic moments of the nuclei. For the case of 2 nuclei, this takes the form

$$H_{zi} = \sum_{j,k} C(1)_{jk} J_j I_{1k} + \sum_{j,k} C(2)_{jk} J_j I_{2k}$$

$C(1)$ and $C(2)$ represent the internal magnetic moment tensors for the two nuclei. The C coefficients are of the order of 10^{-2} MHz.[9] J and I are pure numbers. This correction will therefore be unimportant for the large majority of molecules. For values of the coefficients as determined by molecular beam work, see Ref. 7 and 10.

7. H_D is the dipole interaction between the two nuclei which may be written in the form

$$H_D = \frac{g_1 g_2 \mu_n{}^2}{R^3} \left[I_1 \cdot I_2 - \frac{3(I_1 \cdot R)(I_2 \cdot R)}{R^2} \right]$$

where g_1 and g_2 are the nuclear gyromagnetic ratios of the nuclei, μ_n is the nuclear magneton and R is the distance between the two nuclei.

The operator which is usually used to represent this interaction is

$$H_D = \frac{g_1 g_2 \mu_n{}^2}{R^3} \cdot$$

$$\frac{[3(I_1 \cdot J)(I_2 \cdot J) + 3(I_2 \cdot J)(I_1 \cdot J) - 2I_1 \cdot I_2 J^2]}{(2J-1)(2J+3)}$$

This operator, like that given for the quadrupole interaction above, and usually quoted in the literature, will yield only those matrix elements which are diagonal in the quantum number J. The coefficient $g_1 g_2 \mu_n{}^2 / R^3$ may be of the order of a kilocycle. This correction is observed only in very rare cases.[9]

Matrix elements for all of the above-mentioned components of the Hamiltonian may be evaluated by the methods in references 11. The matrix elements themselves are too lengthy to be tabulated here.

There is an additional interaction which, for completeness, should be mentioned. The nuclear spins may interact with one another through mutual coupling with the surrounding electron cloud. This gives a correction of the form $CI_1 \cdot I_2$. The coefficient C may be larger than that in the dipole-dipole interaction term. In TlI, C has the value of 6.57 kHz.[7]

The preceding discussion emphasizes the interpretation of microwave absorption spectra. One is thereby led to a knowledge of the structure of the molecule, the value of nuclear spins, and various coupling constants. For a short review which emphasizes the experimental aspects of microwave spectroscopy see Ref. 12.

Microwave spectroscopy is also an effective technique for determination of barrier heights associated with internal rotation.[13,14,15]

A discussion of line shapes and intensities has been omitted. We have not discussed electron spin resonance (ESR), also called electron paramagnetic resonance.[16] (See RESONANCE and MAGNETIC RESONANCE.) In this case transitions occur between energy levels created by unpaired electron spins in the presence of an external magnetic field. Absorptions of this type are observed in molecules, free atoms, radicals, and solids.

For a review of properties of high-temperature species as studied by microwave absorption spectroscopy see Ref. 17.

For further details and discussion of topics omitted, the reader is referred to the book[13] by W. Gordy and R. L. Cooke. For other books see Ref. 6 and 18. For a current review of microwave spectroscopy see the article by D. R. Lide, Ref. 19.

The Hamiltonian required to explain the results of molecular beam electric resonance (MBER) experiments involving radio frequency transitions contains the same kind of interaction terms listed above. Therefore the literature on MBER may be referred to for further theoretical discussion. See, for example, English and Zorn, Ref. 19.

For a review of beam maser spectroscopy see Ref. 20.

For a comprehensive computation of microwave spectra including measured frequencies, assigned molecular species, assigned quantum number, and molecular constants determined from such data, the reader is referred to the five-volume work "Microwave Spectral Tables" prepared by personnel of the National Bureau of Standards.[21] These tables provide a detailed reference to the literature up to the early 1960s.

DONALD G. BURKHARD

References

1. Dennison, D. M., *Phys. Rev.*, **28**, 318 (1926); Reiche, F., and Rademacher, H., *Z. Physik*, **39**, 444 (1926), and **41**, 453 (1927).
2. Burkhard, D. G., *J. Mol. Spectry.*, **2**, 187 (1958); Shaffer, W. H., and Louck, J. D., *J. Mol. Spectry.*, **3**, 123 (1959).
3. Klein, O., *Z. Physik*, **58**, 730 (1929).
4. Dennison, D. M., *Rev. Mod. Phys.*, **3**, 280 (1931).
5. Flygare, W. H., and Benson, R. C., *Mol. Phys.*, **20**, 225 (1971).
6. Townes, C. H., and Schawlow, A. L., "Microwave Spectroscopy," New York, McGraw-Hill, 1955.
7. Stephenson, D. A., Dickinson, J. T., and Zorn, J. C., *J. Chem. Phys.*, **53**(4), 1529 (1970).

8. Lucken, E. A. C., "Nuclear Quadrupole Coupling Constants," New York, Academic Press, 1969.

9. Thaddeus, P., Krisher, L. C., and Loubser, J. M. N., *J. Chem. Phys.*, **40**, 257 (1964).

10. English, T. C., and Zorn, J. C., *J. Chem. Phys.*, **47**(10), 3896 (1967).

11. Condon, E. U., and Shortley, G. H., "Theory of Atomic Spectra," Cambridge University Press, 1953; Landau, L. D., and Lifshitz, E. M., "Quantum Mechanics," Reading, Mass., Addison-Wesley, 1958.

12. Strandberg, M. W. P., "Microwave Spectroscopy," McGraw-Hill Encyclopedia of Science and Technology, New York, McGraw-Hill, 1971.

13. Gordy, W., and Cooke, R. L., "Microwave Molecular Spectroscopy," New York, Wiley, 1966.

14. Lin, C. C., and Swalen, J. D., *Rev. Mod. Phys.*, **31**, 841 (1959).

15. Burkhard, D. G., *J. Opt. Soc. Am.*, **50**, 1214 (1960).

16. Squires, T. L., "An Introduction to Electron Spin Resonance," New York, Academic Press, 1963; Alger, R. S., "Electron Paramagnetic Resonance: Techniques and Applications," New York, Interscience, 1968; Carrington, A., Levy, D. H., and Miller, T. A., "Electron Resonance of Gaseous Diatomic Molecules," in "Advances in Chemical Physics," Vol. XVIII, New York, Interscience, 1970.

17. Lovas, F., and Lide, D. R., *Adv. High Temp. Chem.* 3 (1972).

18. Sugden, T. M., and Kenney, C. N., "Microwave Spectroscopy of Gases," New York, Van Nostrand Reinhold, 1965; Ingram, D. J. E., "Spectroscopy at Radio and Microwave Frequencies," 2nd Ed., New York, Plenum, 1967; Hedvig, P., and Zentai, G., "Microwave Study of Chemical Structures and Reactions," CRC Press, 1969; Svidzinskii, K. V., "Soviet Maser Research," Consultants Bureau, New York, Plenum Press, 1964.

19. English, T., and Zorn, J. C., "Molecular Beam Spectroscopy"; Lide, D. R., "Microwave Spectroscopy," in "Methods of Experimental Physics," Vol. 3, 2nd Ed., New York, Academic Press, 1972.

20. Laine, D. C., *Repts. Prog. Phys.* **33**, 1001 (1970).

21. "Microwave Spectral Tables," Superintendent of Documents, Gov. Printing Office, Washington, D.C. 20402.

Cross-references: ATOMIC AND MOLECULAR BEAMS, MAGNETIC RESONANCE, RESONANCE, SPECTROSCOPY, ZEEMAN AND STARK EFFECTS.

MICROWAVE TRANSMISSION

That portion of the electromagnetic spectrum which lies adjacent to the far-infrared region is commonly identified by the term microwaves. The shortest and longest practical microwave wavelengths are in the vicinity of 1 millimeter (mm) (3×10^{11} cycles per sec or 3×10^5 megacycles per sec, abbreviated 300 000 megahertz or 300 kilomegahertz or 300 gigahertz or 300 GHz), and 10 centimeter (cm) (3×10^9 cycles per sec, abbreviated 3000 megahertz or 3000 MHz or 3 GHz), respectively.

The development of microwave transmission on a large scale began in 1940 with the advent of the magnetron, an electronic generator of high-power microwaves. The magnetron made possible wartime radar at approximately 3 GHz and led to the utilization of waveguides for the efficient transmission of microwaves from the generator to the transmitting antenna and from the receiving antenna to the detector.

In essence, a waveguide is a hollow metal tube capable of propagating electromagnetic waves within its interior from its sending end to its receiving end. Unlike waves in space which propagate outward in all directions, waves in waveguides are fully confined while they propagate.

Propagation in a waveguide is limited by the cross-section dimensions of the guide. In a rectangular guide, the highest wavelength that can be propagated is equivalent to twice its width. For example, to transmit a 3 GHz signal in a rectangular waveguide, the width of the guide must be at least 5 cm. At 300 MHz, this width becomes 50 cm. Thus, for the transmission of microwaves, waveguides are reasonable in size. Furthermore, when used with ferrites and magnets, waveguide components can be designed to function as isolators, circulators, modulators, discriminators, or attenuators.

The propagation of radio signals in space between transmitting and receiving antennas can be described in terms of ground waves, sky waves and space waves. At microwave frequencies, ground waves attenuate completely within a few feet of travel, sky waves are influenced by the ionosphere and can penetrate through into outer space, and space waves behave like light waves as they travel through the atmosphere immediately above the surface of the earth. Microwave space waves travel in a direct line of sight, can be reflected from smooth conducting surfaces, and can be focused by reflectors or lenses. Their behavior is similar to light waves and they follow many of the rules of optics.

If a space wave is radiated from a point antenna, the radiated energy spreads out like an ever-expanding sphere, and the amount of energy per square foot of wave front decreases inversely with the square of the distance from the antenna. The power that can be extracted from a wave front by a similar point antenna varies inversely with the square of the frequency. Thus, a point antenna receives power which is inversely proportional to both the square of the distance from the source and the square of the frequency. The ratio of the power received to the total power radiated is known as path attenuation.

When the receiving antenna is a parabola-shaped dish, the power extracted from the wave front is greatly increased. The ratio of the power received by such an antenna to the power received by a theoretical point antenna is defined as antenna gain. The gain of a parabolic antenna increases with the antenna area and the operating frequency. Thus, for a given microwave path with fixed-size antennas, the path

attenuation increases with frequency, the antenna gain increases with frequency, and the over-all result is that one tends to offset the other.

In broadcast radio, signal power radiates equally in all directions and a receiving antenna picks up only a tiny fraction of the signal power. To overcome this low efficiency, the broadcast station must transmit a large amount of power. By contrast, a point-to-point microwave system radiates only a small amount of power, but it uses a directional transmitting antenna to concentrate power into a narrow beam directed toward the receiving antenna. Consequently, such systems are characterized by high efficiencies.

Because microwave transmission follows essentially a straight line, reflectors are often used to redirect a beam over or around an obstruction. The simplest and most common reflector system consists of a parabolic antenna mounted at ground level which focuses a beam on a reflector mounted at the top of a tower. This reflector inclined at 45° redirects the beam horizontally to a distant site where a similar "periscope" reflector system may be used to reflect the beam down to another ground level. If two sites are separated by a mountain, it may be necessary to use a large, flat surface reflector referred to as a "billboard" reflector. In a typical system, a "billboard" reflector might be located at a turn in a valley, effectively bending the beam to follow the valley. Many arrangements are possible which, in effect, resemble huge mirror systems.

Microwaves are ideally suited for communication systems where a broad frequency bandwidth of the order of several megacycles is required for the rapid transmission of signals which contain a large amount of information, such as in television. Most of the major cities of the United States are serviced by microwave television links so that they can receive television programs which originate from other cities. These systems can also accommodate thousands of telephone channels.

In 1960, experiments were initiated which aimed toward communicating over transoceanic distances via microwaves by utilizing balloons as reflectors. Echo I and Echo II were attempts in this direction as passive satellites. The first active repeater satellite (Telstar) was launched in 1962. Currently, dozens of communication satellites are employed globally involving voice, data, and television channels. The commonly utilized microwave frequencies are below 10 GHz.

Microwaves are broadly used for radar, navigation, and for the launching, guidance, and fusing of missiles. A typical defense project which uses microwave techniques is the DEW radar line which protects the United States from external enemy attacks.

The HAYSTACK facility which has been in operation since 1966 at Millstone Hill in Massachusetts is the first western radar built for spacecraft tracking, space communications, and radar astronomy. Through radar astronomical techniques, the multipurpose HAYSTACK 120-foot paraboloid antenna reflector has greatly enhanced our knowledge of the galaxy and solar system. Another famous facility is the 210-foot GOLDSTONE antenna at the NASA Deep Space Institute (California).

In recent years, radar astronomers have detected pulsars, celestial objects that emit intense bursts of energy principally, but not exclusively, at radio frequencies.

ANTHONY B. GIORDANO

References

Nichols, E. J., and Tear, J. D., "Joining the Infrared and Electric Wave Spectra," *Astrophys. J.*, **61**, 17–37 (1923).

Carter, S. P., and Solomon, L., "Modern Microwaves," *Electronics* (June 24, 1960).

Southworth, G. C., "Survey and History of the Progress of the Microwave Art," *Proc. IRE* (May 1962).

Evans, J. V., and Hagfors, T., Eds., "Radio Astronomy," New York, McGraw-Hill, 1968.

Cross-references: ANTENNAS, ELECTROMAGNETIC THEORY, MICROWAVE SPECTROSCOPY, PROPAGATION OF ELECTROMAGNETIC WAVES, RADAR, WAVEGUIDES.

MODULATION

Modulation is defined as the process, or the result of the process, whereby some characteristic of one wave is varied in accordance with some characteristic of another wave (ASA). Usually one of these waves is considered to be a carrier wave while the other is a modulating signal. The various types of modulation, such as amplitude, frequency, phase, pulse width, pulse time, and so on are designated in accordance with the parameter of the carrier which is being varied.

Amplitude modulation (AM) is easily accomplished and widely used. Inspection of Fig. 1 shows that the voltage of the amplitude modulated wave may be expressed by the following equation

$$v = V_c(1 + M \sin \omega_m t) \sin \omega_c t,$$

where V_c is the peak carrier voltage, ω_c and ω_m are the radian frequencies of the carrier and modulating signals, respectively, and t is time in seconds. The modulation index M may have values from zero to one. When the trigonometric identity $\sin a \sin b = \frac{1}{2} \cos (a - b) - \frac{1}{2} \cos (a + b)$ is used in the equation above, this equation becomes

$$v = V_c \sin \omega_c t + \frac{MV_c}{2} \cos (\omega_c - \omega_m)t$$

$$- \frac{MV_c}{2} \cos (\omega_c + \omega_m)t$$

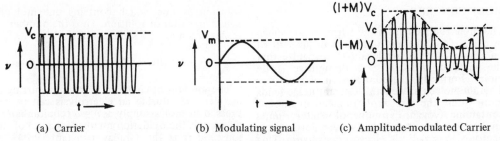

| (a) Carrier | (b) Modulating signal | (c) Amplitude-modulated Carrier |

FIG. 1. Amplitude modulation.

This equation shows that new frequencies, called side frequencies or side bands, are generated by the amplitude modulation process. These new frequencies are the sum and difference of the carrier and modulating frequencies.

Amplitude modulation is accomplished by mixing the carrier and modulating signals in a nonlinear device such as a vacuum tube or transistor amplifier operated in a nonlinear region of its characteristics. The nonlinear characteristic produces the new side-band frequencies. Frequency converters or translators and AM detectors are basically modulators. The various types of pulse modulation are actually special types of amplitude modulation.

Frequency modulation (FM) is illustrated by Fig. 2. The frequency variation, or deviation, is proportional to the amplitude of the modulating signal. The voltage equation for a frequency modulated wave follows.

$$v = V_c \sin (\omega_c t + M_f \sin \omega_m t)$$

The modulation index M_f is the ratio of maximum carrier frequency deviation to the modulating frequency. This ratio is known as the deviation ratio and may vary from zero to values of the order of 1000. FM requires a broader transmission bandwidth than AM but may have superior noise and interference rejection capabilities. A large value of modulation index provides excellent interference rejection capability but requires a comparatively large bandwidth. The approximate bandwidth requirement for a frequency modulated wave may be obtained from the following relationship

Bandwidth = 2 (Modulating frequency) $(M_f + 1)$

The noise and interference characteristics of FM transmission are normally considered satis-

factory when the modulation index or deviation ratio is five or greater.

Phase modulation is accomplished when the relative phase of the carrier is varied in accordance with the amplitude of the modulating signal. Since frequency is the time rate of change of phase, frequency modulation occurs when the phase modulating technique is used and vice versa. In fact, the equation given for a frequency-modulated wave is equally applicable for a phase-modulated wave. However, the phase-modulating technique results in a deviation ratio, or modulation index, which is independent of the modulating frequency, while the frequency modulating technique results in a deviation ratio which is inversely proportional to the modulating frequency, assuming invarient modulating voltage amplitude in each case.

The phase-modulating techniques can be used to produce frequency-modulated waves, providing the amplitude of the modulating voltage is inversely proportional to the modulating frequency. This inverse relationship can be obtained by including, in the modulator, a circuit which has a voltage transfer ratio inversely proportional to the frequency.

CHARLES L. ALLEY

References

Alley, C. L., and Atwood, K. W., "Electronic Engineering," 3rd Ed., New York, John Wiley & Sons, 1973.

Terman, F. E., "Radio Engineers Handbook," New York, McGraw-Hill Book Co., 1943.

Hund, August, "Frequency Modulation," New York, McGraw-Hill Book Co., 1942.

Lurch, E. N., "Fundamentals of Electronics," New York, John Wiley & Sons, 1960.

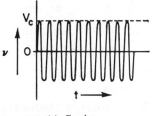 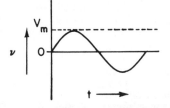 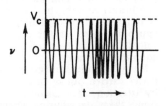

| (a) Carrier | (b) Modulating signal | (c) Frequency-modulated Carrier |

FIG. 2. Frequency modulation.

MOLE CONCEPT

The mole (derived from the Latin *moles* = heap or pile) is the chemist's measure of amount of pure substance. It is relevant to recognize that the familiar *molecule* is a diminutive (little mole). Formerly, the connotation of *mole* was a "gram molecular weight." Current usage tends more to use the term *mole* to mean an amount containing Avogadro's number of whatever units are being considered. Thus, we can have a mole of atoms, ions, radicals, electrons or quanta. This usage makes unnecessary such terms as "gram-atom," "gram-formula weight," etc.

A definition of the term is: *The mole is the amount of (pure) substance containing the same number of chemical units as there are atoms in exactly twelve grams of* ^{12}C. This definition involves the acceptance of two dictates—the scale of atomic masses and the magnitude of the gram. Both have been established by international agreement. Usage sometimes indicates a different mass unit, e.g., a "pound mole" or even a "ton mole"; substitution of "pound" or "ton" for "gram" in the above definition is implied.

solution is one which contains one mole of solute per liter of solution. Thus the number of moles of solute in a sample will be

$$n = \text{Volume (liters)} \times \text{Molarity (moles/liter)}$$

The amount of chemical reaction occurring at an electrode during an electrolysis can be expressed in moles simply as $n = q$ (coulombs)$/z\,\mathcal{F}$ where z is the oxidation number (charge) of the ion and $\mathcal{F}$ is the faraday constant, 96 487.0 coulombs/mole. Thus the *faraday* can be considered to be the charge on a mole of electrons. This affords one of the most accurate methods of evaluating the Avogadro number (6.0220×10^{23}), since the value of the elementary charge is known with high precision.

Modern chemistry increasingly uses data at the atomic level for calculation at the molar level. Since the former often are expressed as quanta, appropriate conversion factors must involve the Avogadro number. Thus the *einstein* of energy is that associated with a mole of photons, or $E = Nh\nu$. Thus light of 2537Å wavelength will represent energy of

$$E = \frac{6.02 \times 10^{23}(\text{photons/mole}) \times 6.62 \times 10^{-27}(\text{erg-sec}) \times 3.000 \times 10^{10}(\text{sec/cm})}{2.537 \times 10^{-5}(\text{cm}) \times 4.184 \times 10^{7}(\text{erg/cal}) \times 10^{3}(\text{cal/kcal})}$$

$$E = 113 \text{ kcal/mole}$$

If the SI system of units is used

$$E = \frac{6.022 \times 10^{23}(\text{mol}^{-1}) \times 6.626 \times 10^{-34}(\text{J} \cdot \text{s}) \times 3.000 \times 10^{8}(\text{ms}^{-1})}{2.537 \times 10^{-7}(\text{m})}$$

$$= 4.740 \times 10^{5}(\text{J mol}^{-1})$$

All stoichiometry essentially is based on the evaluation of the number of moles of substance. The most common involves the measurement of mass. Thus 25.000 grams of H_2O will contain 25.000/18.015 moles of H_2O; 25.000 grams of sodium will contain 25.000/22.990 moles of Na (atomic and formula masses used to five significant figures). The convenient measurements on gases are pressure, volume and temperature. Use of the ideal gas law constant R allows direct calculation of the number of moles $n = (P \times V)/(R \times T)$. T is the absolute temperature; R must be chosen in units appropriate for P, V and T (e.g., $R = 0.0820$ liter atm mole^{-1} deg K^{-1}). It may be noted that acceptance of Avogadro's principle (equal volumes of gases under identical conditions contain equal numbers of molecules) is inherent in this calculation. So too are the approximations of the ideal gas law. Refined calculations can be made by using more correct equations of state.

Many chemical reactions are most conveniently carried out or measured in solution (e.g., by titration). The usual concentration convention is the *molar* solution. (Some chemists prefer to use the equivalent term *formal*). A 1.0 molar

Another convenient conversion factor is 1 eV/particle = 23.05 kcal/mole.

The chemist's use of formulas and equations always implies reactions of moles of material, thus HCl(g) stands for one mole of hydrogen chloride in the gaseous state. Thermodynamic quantities are symbolized by capital letters standing for molar quantities, e.g., C_v (heat capacity at constant volume in cal mole^{-1} deg^{-1}), G (Gibbs function in cal/mole), etc. At times it is more convenient to convert an extensive property into an intensive expression. This is especially true in dealing with multicomponent systems. These are referred to as "partial molal quantities" and are given a symbol employing a bar over the letter. Thus the partial molal volume, $\overline{V}_1 = (\partial V/\partial n_1)$ is the rate of change of the total volume of a solution with the amount (number of moles) of component 1.

WILLIAM F. KIEFFER

References

Kieffer, W. F., "The Mole Concept in Chemistry," Ed. 2, New York, Van Nostrand Reinhold, 1973.

Lewis, G. N., and Randall, M., "Thermodynamics," Second edition, revised by Pitzer, K. S., and Brewer, L., New York, McGraw-Hill Book Co., 1961.

Cross-references: CHEMISTRY, ELECTROCHEMISTRY, GAS LAWS, MOLECULAR WEIGHT.

MOLECULAR SPECTROSCOPY

Theory, Instrumentation, Interpretation, and Applications A molecular spectrum is one that originates either by emission or absorption in the molecules of a chemical compound. As such it is to be distinguished from a line spectrum originating in the atoms of a chemical element. Molecular spectrum and band spectrum are essentially equivalent designations. The latter is to be considered mainly of historical significance originating at a time when low-dispersion instruments were generally used for observation, which imparted an appearance of unresolved bands to many of these spectra. Actually, if an exception is made of pure rotational spectra in the far infrared region, all band spectra are highly complex when observed under high resolution. The optical radiant energy identified with molecular spectra is distributed over a very wide range of frequencies extending from the ultraviolet to the far infrared, in effect joining the microwave region at wavelengths of the order of 1 mm. The dynamic conditions accounting for this distribution will be examined briefly.

The essential differences between atomic and molecular spectra are accounted for by the fact that the former are completely explained by quantized changes in the energy associated with the outer electronic structure, whereas the latter include not only this energy, but also contributions of energy resulting from the vibration of the component atoms relative to each other and from rotation of the molecule as a whole about an axis through the center of gravity. The actual energy pattern may be represented by a summation of these three contributions; that is, we may write $E = E_e + E_v + E_r$, or following the usual notation when the energy is expressed in wave number units or term values, $T = T_e + G + F$. All three forms of energy are quantized, but it may be shown that in some cases vibrational frequencies are the same as those predicted by classical mechanics. It is not necessary that all three forms of energy be present. There are instances of pure rotational energy. Since this energy is relatively small, such band spectra are found only in the far infrared beyond $20\mu m$.

Probably the outstanding example of a completely described rotational spectrum is to be found in the paper dealing with water vapor by Randall, Dennison, Ginsberg, and Weber.[1] Vibrational spectra with rotational structure are also of frequent occurrence. Owing to the magnitudes of interatomic forces, these are found in general between 3 and $15\mu m$.

Beginning with the observation of rotational fine structure of H_2O vapor by Eva von Bahr in 1913, and the subsequent observation of the same spectrum and those of the halogen acids by Sleator and Imes[2,3] a short time later, the quantum interpretation of band spectra developed rapidly. The body of information on this subject is remarkably complete. It may be stated safely that all observable features of well-resolved spectra of molecules in the vapor state may be completely accounted for within both the framework of classical quantum theory and that of wave mechanics.

The most complete discussion is to be found in two books by Herzberg.[4,5] The notation introduced in the following sections follows for the most part that employed by Herzberg. A fairly detailed treatment has been given by Ruark and Urey.[6] Attention is also called to review articles by R. S. Mulliken[7] and by D. M. Dennison.[8] As the development of the subject is lengthy and detailed, only a few basic concepts are included here. In general, the theory is built up by extensions of these ideas.

In the development of the quantum theoretical explanation of the detailed features of molecular spectra, it is customary to begin with the spectra of diatomic molecules. This introduces a relatively greater degree of simplicity because one is dealing essentially with a two-body problem. Furthermore, the full details of diatomic spectra are frequently completely observable, whereas the complexity of the spectra of polyatomic molecules is in general so formidable that the details may be resolved in relatively few instances, usually where considerations of symmetry permit a simplification of the model. The general features of polyatomic molecules may be explained by extending the concepts developed for diatomic molecules.

A physical model may be conceived for the diatomic molecule which closely represents its actual features and properties. It is thought of as a dumbbell structure. First we think of it as a rigid rotator with an axis through the center of mass perpendicular to the line joining the nuclei of the constituent atoms. A wave-mechanical treatment of this rotator leads to the following expression for the quantized energy:

$$E_{rot} = J(J + 1) \frac{h^2}{8\pi^2 I}$$

where h is Planck's constant, I is the moment of inertia and J is the rotational quantum number which can take a series of integral values 0, 1, 2, $\cdots$. This formula is generally written $F(J) = BJ(J + 1)$ where the constant

$$B = \frac{h}{8\pi^2 cI}$$

Each rotational energy state is characterized by one of these J values. The quantum mechanics also leads to a requirement for a selection rule

for transitions between energy states $\Delta J = \pm 1$. Since such transitions account for the emission or absorption of spectral lines the frequency of such lines is given by

$$\nu = F(J + 1) - F(J)$$

or

$$\nu = 2B(J + 1); \quad J = 0, 1, 2, \cdots$$

This leads to a series of equidistant lines. Such spectra are actually observed in the far infrared. The actual frequency of rotation of the rigid rotator may also be derived and turns out to be

$$\nu_{\text{rot}} = c2B\sqrt{J(J + 1)} \approx c2BJ$$

That is, for any state characterized by J, the rotational frequency is approximately equal to the frequency of the spectral line that has this state as its upper state. Actually, the molecule is not strictly rigid. A correction of the simple formula is necessary to account for modification of the observed spectral features resulting from centrifugal stretching. The effect is tied in with the vibrational frequency of the molecule and leads to a modified expression for the rotation energy $F(J) = BJ(J + 1) - DJ^2(J + 1)^2$, where $D = (4B^3/\omega^2)$, ω being the vibrational frequency. This extra term is always small.

The dumbbell model is next considered as a harmonic oscillator, characterized by a simple harmonic motion of the constituent atoms along the line joining them under Hooke's law forces. Since the observed spectral frequency is in some instances equal to the classical vibrational frequency of a molecule of the described configuration, it is of interest to recall the formula for simple harmonic motion

$$\nu_{\text{osc}} = \frac{1}{2\pi}\sqrt{\frac{k}{m}}$$

where k is the force constant, or force required to produce unit displacement, and m is the mass of the point moving with simple harmonic motion. For the model under consideration consisting of mass points, m_1 and m_2, m is replaced by the reduced mass μ, equal to $m_2 m_1/m_1 + m_2$. On the classical theory, only one vibration frequency is possible. The solution of the Schrödinger wave equation for the harmonic oscillation leads to the following equation specifying the vibrational energy states:

$$E(v) = h\nu_{\text{osc}}(v + \tfrac{1}{2})$$

where v is the vibrational quantum number that takes integral values $0, 1, 2, \cdots$. Transforming to term values the equation becomes

$$G(v) = \frac{\nu_{\text{osc}}}{c}(v + \tfrac{1}{2})$$

or

$$G(v) = \omega(v + \tfrac{1}{2})$$

where ω is the vibrational frequency in cm^{-1}. We thus obtain a series of equally spaced energy levels. The quantized emitted or absorbed energy in cm^{-1} takes place, respectively, by a transition from a higher to a lower or a lower to a higher vibrational state. The wave number characterizing such a transition is given by

$$\nu = G(v') - G(v'')$$

where v' and v'' are the vibrational quantum numbers of the upper and lower states, respectively. The selection rule that governs such transitions and which also has been accounted for by quantum mechanics is

$$\Delta v = v' - v'' = \pm 1$$

It may be noted immediately that

$$\nu = G(v + 1) - G = \omega$$

indicating that the quantum mechanically derived frequency is equal to the classical frequency for all transitions. Thus we are led to expect a single vibrational absorption or emission band. Actually, weak harmonics of approximately integral multiples of the fundamental frequency are sometimes observed, corresponding to transitions with Δj greater than 1. The reason for the appearance of harmonics is that there is an anharmonicity introduced into the oscillating system owing to the fact that the interatomic forces depart somewhat from Hooke's law both on close approach and extreme separation approaching dissociation. This leads to a breakdown of the selection rule. The correction for anharmonicity is in general relatively small.

The complete expression for the vibrational energy expressed as a term value is a power series including a quadratic and for extremely precise representation of wave numbers a cubic term in powers of $(v + \tfrac{1}{2})$. Thus we have

$$G(v) = \omega_e(v + \tfrac{1}{2}) - \omega_e x_e(v + \tfrac{1}{2})^2$$
$$+ \omega_e y_e(v + \tfrac{1}{2})^3 \cdots$$

where the subscript e refers to the equilibrium position. Neglecting the cubic term we obtain

$$\Delta g_{v+1/2} = \omega_e - 2\omega_e x_e - 2\omega_e x_e v$$

It is convenient to measure the levels from the zero point energy obtained setting $v = 0$. In this case, $\Delta g = \omega_0 - \omega_0 x_0 - 2\omega_0 x_0 v$.

It is prerequisite to the emission or absorption of energy that the fundamental vibration cause a change in the electric dipole moment of the molecule; otherwise it is "infrared inactive." Illustrative of such inactive vibrations are those of diatomic molecules containing identical atoms such as O_2 or N_2. In certain instances, inactive vibrations are observable as Raman effect displacements. Infrared and Raman effect observations therefore supplement each other advantageously.

The simultaneous occurrence of vibrational and rotational transitions accounts for the observed features of infrared spectra illustrated by those of the halogen acids.

The formulation may be summarized by combining the equations already given. The term value of the vibrating rotator becomes

$$T = G(v) + F_v(J) = \omega_e(v + \tfrac{1}{2}) - \omega_e x_e(v + \tfrac{1}{2})^2$$
$$+ \cdots + B_v J(J + 1) - D_v J^2 (J + 1)^2 + \cdots$$

From this we obtain the abbreviated form of the expression for the wave numbers neglecting the correction for centrifugal stretching:

$$\nu = \nu_0 + B_v'J'(J' + 1) - B_v''J''(J'' + 1)$$

where the values of B are appropriate to the respective vibrational states and take into account the interaction between rotation and vibration. If we set $\Delta J = + 1$ and $\Delta J = - 1$, respectively, and replace J'' by J, the above equation reduces to the following two:

$$\nu_R = \nu_0 + 2B_v' + (3B_v' - B_v'')J + (B_v' - B_v'')J^2$$
$$J = 0, 1, \cdots$$

$$\nu_P = \nu_0 - (B_v' + B_v'')J + (B_v' - B_v'')J^2$$
$$J = 1, 2, \cdots$$

These formulas represent two series of lines which are called the P and R branches. If the vibrations were strictly harmonic and if there were no centrifugal stretching accompanying the rotation or interaction between vibrations, the branches of the band would consist of equally spaced lines extending each direction from the zero energy position of the vibration band. Actually taking these effects into account the P branch shows a gradual increase in the separation of components and the R branch a decrease.

Up to this point, only cases have been considered where the electronic state of the molecule remains constant during the occurrence of vibrational and/or rotational transitions. A large class of bands, mostly in the visible and ultraviolet regions, is accounted for by a change in electronic energy, similar to that responsible for line emission spectra, accompanied by vibrational and rotational transitions. The electronic energy represents the largest contribution and accounts for the spectral location. These bands are characterized by recurrent regularities known as progressions. A rotational fine structure is superposed on the regularities. A good example is the CN bands which occur in emission with great intensity in the carbon arc. The electronic levels are characterized by vibrational structures which in turn have rotational fine structure. There is no strict selection rule for the vibrational transitions, i.e., a transition can occur between any vibrational level of one electronic state and all the vibrational levels of the other. The set of bands arising from such a group of transitions forms a progression. Similarly each of these vibrational transitions is accompanied by rotational transitions yielding the usual P and R branches and in addition a Q branch resulting from $J'' - J' = 0$. This new selection rule is accounted for by theory, based on the fact that there is a difference in the angular momentum associated with the upper and lower electronic states.

The explanation of the features of the spectra of polyatomic molecules is developed naturally from the principles outlined for diatomic molecules. Instead of a single mode of vibration, a polyatomic molecule possesses several determined by point group theory. For a molecule of N atoms there are $3N - 6$ possible modes of vibration; $3N - 5$ for a linear molecule. A fundamental radiation frequency would be expected for each of these modes. Some however are inactive, as for instance the totally symmetric vibration of a linear symmetric molecule such as CO_2. Except for what is described as a spherical top molecule, there are always several moments of inertia corresponding to various possible axes of rotation. In general, there is always a possibility of angular momentum about an axis of symmetry. This results in an extension of the selection rule for rotational quantum numbers to $\Delta J = 0$ in addition to $\Delta J = \pm 1$. There is a Q branch in these instances. An exception is the linear molecule. For example a CO_2 band shows no Q branch. As in the case of diatomic molecules, a change in dipole moment is required for emission or absorption of energy.

Even moderately complex molecules show large numbers of vibration bands, either fundamentals or in general less intense overtone or combination bands. The rotational structure is resolved only in a few instances of relatively simple molecules where the available optical resolution can be brought to bear advantageously. Examples are CO_2, CH_4, and NH_3. The observed absorption bands are generally envelopes that include the rotational energy accompanying the vibrations. Most of them occur in the "rock-salt region" between 2 and 15μm. As may be expected, some modifications in the structure of a spectrum occur when the material is in the liquid or solid state.

Molecular Spectra The spectrum of a molecule or an atom has been described as its most definitive characteristic. The fact that the spectrum is unique leads, of course, to applications in identification and analysis that are extremely useful and important. The term "fingerprinting" of molecules is of course familiar to all analysts. The spectrum not only establishes the identification of compounds but distinguishes between various types of stereoisomerism including *cis* and *trans* forms. In order to make the best use of spectra for identification, extensive libraries of spectral absorption curves have been assembled and are being extended. Among the first to attract widespread attention was the compilation by Barnes, Gore, Liddel, and Williams.[9] An ex-

tensive set of spectra of hydrocarbons now numbered in the thousands represents a continuing effort by the American Petroleum Institute.[10] A more recent program covering a wider range of chemical compounds is that sponsored by the Coblentz Society. The material collected by the organization is published and distributed by Sadtler.[11]

The utilization of infrared analytical methods has become an important tool for industrial research, particularly in support of those industries dealing with petroleum products, plastics, and organic chemicals. The manufacture of spectrophotometric equipment is of itself an important industry. The developments in this field have been covered by biennial survey articles in *Analytical Chemistry*. The survey articles in the infrared field, including extensive compilations of references, were initiated by Barnes and Gore[12] and continued by Gore.[13] This series provides an essentially complete index to current literature.

It was suggested by Coblentz[14], more than half a century ago, that the various radicals or structural elements of a molecule should contribute characteristic features to the absorption spectrum and that it might be possible to identify compounds on the basis of a synthesis of such features. The argument has considerable validity but is not entirely conclusive. Several correlations of atomic groups and absorption frequencies in the form of charts are available.

The first was that of Barnes, Gore, Stafford and Williams[15], published in 1948. The well-known Colthup[16] Chart was published in 1950. "Infrared Determination of Organic Structures," by Randall, Fowler, Fuson, and Dangl,[17] is largely devoted to a correlation of spectral features with various types of bonding. It also contains a compilation of spectra in chart form. The use of spectral data has made possible the identification and determination of properties of many short-lived molecules or free radicals. Examples are C_2, CH, and NH.

Many physical and chemical properties of molecules can be inferred from spectral data. The representation of a vibration frequency by a Hooke's law formula is recalled. Knowing the masses of the constituent atoms and the frequency, it is simple to derive the force constant associated with a given type of bonding and, from this, the heat of dissociation. Conversely, from a knowledge of bond strengths, the location of the fundamental frequencies may be predicted. The rotational structure permits calculation of the moments of inertia and derivation of interatomic distances. Interesting features of geometry or spatial configuration may be established. For instance, the regular spacing of the rotational components of the CO_2 bands proves that it is a linear molecule. Similarly it has, in the instance of the water molecule, been possible to compute the angle at the O atom between the bonds connecting it to the two hydrogens.

Band spectra are important for the identification of isotopes and, hence, are useful in the detection of rare products from reactors. The isotope effect, due to the presence of ^{37}Cl along with ^{35}Cl, was first observed by Imes[3] and later demonstrated under high resolution by Meyer and Levin.[18] The isotope effect is very large in the instance of deuterium substitution for hydrogen because of the large effect on the reduced mass of doubling the mass of one of the component atoms. It is of interest to compare the positions of the ν_2 and ν_3 fundamentals of H_2O and D_2O. The wave numbers are as follows:

	H_2O	D_2O
ν_2	1595	1179
ν_3	3756	2789

This has interesting possibilities for analytical procedures where a region of interest might be obscured by the presence of water or in certain instances its use as a solvent.

A final statement concerns the astrophysical significance of band spectra. The subject is a timely one because of the large-scale effort currently devoted to space programs, including the utilization of rocket-borne instrumentation and balloon-supported observing platforms. Since only optical radiant energy is a requirement without the necessary possession of the emitting sample, spectra may be used for a study of the atmospheres of planets or envelopes of stars. It is in this way that the presence of ammonia and methane in the atmosphere of Jupiter has been demonstrated. A detailed presentation covering the atmospheres of planets is to be found in a compilation edited by Kuiper.[19]

An outstanding recent achievement has been the utilization of high-resolution optical techniques, brought to a remarkable state of perfection by P. and J. Connes, in the observation and analysis of the spectrum of Venus.[20]

CURTIS J. HUMPHREYS

References

1. Randall, H. M., Dennison, D. M., Ginsburg, N., and Weber, L. R., "The Far Infared Spectrum of Water Vapor," *Phys. Rev.*, **52**, 160 (1937).
2. Sleator, W. W., "Absorption of Infra-red Radiation by Water-Vapour," *Astrophys. J.*, **48**, 125 (1918).
3. Imes, E. S., "Absorption Spectra of Some Diatomic Gases in the Near Infrared," *Astrophys. J.*, **50**, 251 (1919).
4. Herzberg, Gerhard F., "Molecular Spectra and Molecular Structure. I. Spectra of Diatomic Molecules," New York, Van Nostrand Reinhold, 1950.
5. Herzberg, Gerhard F., "Molecular Spectra and Molecular Structure. II. Infrared and Raman Spectra of Polyatomic Molecules," New York, Van Nostrand Reinhold, 1949.
6. Ruark, A. E., and Urey, H. C., "Atoms, Molecules, and Quanta," New York, McGraw-Hill Book Co., 1929.

7. Mulliken, R. S., "Interpretation of Band Spectra," *Rev. Mod. Phys.*, Parts I, IIa, IIb, **2**, 60, 506 (1930); IIc, **3**, 89 (1931); III, **4**, 1 (1932).

8. Dennison, D. M., "The Infrared Spectra of Polyatomic Molecules," *Rev. Mod. Phys.*, Part I, **3**, 280 (1931); Part II, **12**, 175 (1940).

9. Barnes, R. Bowling, Liddel, Urner, and Williams, Van Zandt, "Infrared Spectroscopy, Industrial Applications," *Ind. Eng. Chem., Anal. Ed.,* **15**, 659 (1959).

10. American Petroleum Institute Project 44, Petroleum Research Laboratory, Carnegie Institute of Technology, Pittsburgh, Pa.

11. Sadtler Research Laboratories, 1517 Vine Street, Philadelphia 2, Pa.

12. Barnes, R. B., and Gore, R. C., "Review of Fundamental Developments in Analysis—Infrared Spectroscopy," *Anal. Chem.*, **21**, 7 (1949).

13. Gore, R. C., *Anal. Chem.*, **22**, 7 (1950); **23**, 7 (1951); **24**, 8 (1952); **26**, 11 (1954); **28**, 577 (1956); **30**, 570 (1958).

14. Coblentz, W. W., "Investigations of Infrared Spectra," *Carnegie Inst. Wash. Publ.*, **35** (1905). Reprinted by the Coblentz Society and the Perkin-Elmer Corporation, 1962.

15. Barnes, R. Bowling, Gore, R. C., Stafford, R. W., and Williams, V. Z., "Qualitative Organic Analysis and Infrared Spectrometry," *Anal. Chem.*, **20**, 402 (1948).

16. Colthup, N. B., "Spectra-Structure Correlations in the Infrared Region," *J. Opt. Soc. Am.*, **40**, 397 (1950).

17. Randall, H. M., Fowler, R. G., Fuson, Nelson, and Dangl, J. R., "Infrared Determination of Organic Structures," New York, Van Nostrand Reinhold, 1949.

18. Meyer, C. F., and Levin, A. A., "Absorption Spectrum of Hydrogen Chloride," *Phys. Rev.*, **34**, 44 (1929).

19. Kuiper, G. P., "The Atmospheres of the Earth and Planets," Second edition, Chicago, The University of Chicago Press, 1952.

20. Connes, P., Connes, J., Kaplan, L. D., and Benedict, W. S., "Carbon Monoxide in the Venus Atmosphere," *Astrophys. J.*, **152**(3) Pt. 1, 731 (1968).

Cross-references: ABSORPTION SPECTRA, ATOMIC SPECTRA, SPECTROSCOPY.

MOLECULAR WEIGHT

The molecular weight of a chemical compound is the sum of the atomic weights of its constituent atoms. The molecule is the smallest weight of a substance which still retains all of its chemical properties. By convention, each atomic weight, and therefore molecular weights, are expressed relative to an arbitrary standard (see below). For example, the molecule of acetic acid, CH_3COOH, contains two atoms of carbon, four of hydrogen, and two of oxygen, so that its molecular weight is the sum of $2(12.01) + 4(1.01) + 2(16.00)$, which totals 60.06. This molecular weight value is clearly in arbitrary units, but a related quantity, the gram-molecular weight or mole, is the molecular weight expressed in grams. One mole of any compound has been found to contain 6.022×10^{23} molecules, and this number is called the Avogadro constant.

For many years, the standard used for atomic weights was the exact value 16 for the naturally occurring mixture of isotopes of oxygen. Another system of atomic weights, based on the value of 16 for the most abundant (99.8 per cent) oxygen isotope, came into use for comparisons involving single atoms or molecules where isotopic differences were important. A conference of the International Commission on Atomic Weights in 1961 adopted as the standard a value of exactly 12 for the carbon-12 isotope, and since then all atomic weights in use have been based on this standard.

The weights of molecules range from a value of about two for the hydrogen molecule to several millions for some virus molecules and certain polymeric compounds. Molecular dimensions accordingly range from a diameter of about 4Å for the hydrogen molecule to several thousand angstroms—which has permitted viewing single large molecules in the electron microscope. Molecular sizes are generally much smaller and are not measured directly, but are deduced from x-ray diffraction studies of ordered groups of molecules in the crystalline state or from the physical properties such as hydrodynamic behavior of molecules in the gaseous or liquid state.

Many methods for determining molecular weights which are described below depend fundamentally on counting the number of molecules present in a given weight of sample. However, any usable sample contains a very large number of molecules: at least ten trillion of the largest known molecules are present in the smallest weight measurable on a sensitive balance. Therefore, an indirect count is made by measuring physical properties which are proportional to the large number of molecules present. A consequence of the large number of molecules sampled is the averaging of any variations in content of atomic isotopes in individual molecules, so that normal isotopic fluctuations lead to no measurable deviation of molecular weight values. Abnormally high concentrations of isotopes in radiation products may, however, produce altered molecular weights.

The term molecular weight is properly applied to compounds in which chemical bonding of all atoms holds the molecule together under normal conditions (see BOND, CHEMICAL). Thus, covalent compounds, as represented by many organic substances, usually are found to have the same molecular weight in the solid, liquid, and gaseous states. However, substances in which some bonds are highly polar may exist as un-ionized or even associated molecules in the gaseous state and in nonpolar solvents, but they

may be ionized when dissolved in polar solvents. For example, ferric chloride exists in the gaseous state as $FeCl_3$ at high temperatures, as Fe_2Cl_6 at lower temperatures as well as in nonpolar solvents, but reverts to $FeCl_3$ in solvents of moderate polarity, and becomes ionic in water solutions—as chloride ions and hydrated ferric ions. Similarly, acetic acid and some other carboxylic acids associate as dimers in the vapor state and in solvents of low polarity, but exist as monomers with progressive ionization as the solvent polarity increases.

Truly ionic compounds, such as most salts, exist only as ions in the solid and dissolved states, so that the term molecule is not applicable and is not commonly used. Instead, the term, formula weight, is used; this denotes the sum of the atomic weights in the simplest formula representation of the compound. If a broad definition of a molecule as an aggregate of atoms held together by primary valence bonds is adopted, then salts in the crystalline state would appear to have a molecular weight which is essentially infinite and limited only by the size of the crystal, since each ion is surrounded by several ions of opposite polarity to which it is attached by ionic bonds of equal magnitude.

A further complication in the definition of molecular weights occurs with inorganic polymers whose polymeric nature is clearly evident in both their crystal structure and their highly viscous behavior in the molten state. However, the magnitude of their molecular weights often cannot be found by conventional methods because they are either insoluble or react with solvents, with consequent degradation. These examples indicate that the molecular weight often depends on the conditions used for measurement and must be specified where compounds subject to association, dissociation or reaction are studied.

The history of the clarification of molecular weight concepts is of considerable interest, since this was so intimately related to other developments in chemical knowledge. Although Dalton had published a table of atomic weights in 1808, and by 1825 molecular formulas, derived from combining weights, were in use, many misconceptions of these formulas remained until about 1860. Then evidence from chemical reactions and from measurements of vapor densities firmly established the formulas of many inorganic and simple organic compounds as they are represented today. The vapor density method, based on Avogadro's hypothesis, was thus the first molecular weight method and continues to be useful for compounds that can be easily volatilized. It was not until 1881 that Raoult showed that the depression of freezing points was proportional to the molar concentration of solute. In 1884, van't Hoff related the osmotic pressure of solutions to the vapor pressure, boiling point, and freezing point behavior, and these methods were quickly put into use for determining molecular weights. The abnormal physical properties of salt solutions were explained in 1887 by the ionization theory of Arrhenius, and the very careful measurements of many of these properties furnished the strongest confirmation of the theory. While these measurements provided the most precise determinations of the extent of dissociation of weak electrolytes, they also contributed to the development of the Debye-Hückel theory for strong electrolytes.

Molecular Weight Distributions There are many systems, particularly among the polymers and proteins, which consist of molecules of various chain lengths, and thus of various molecular weights—so-called polydisperse systems. In such cases, molecular weight values have an ambiguous meaning, and no single such value will completely represent a sample. Various techniques for measuring molecular weights, when applied to one of these materials, will produce values which often disagree by a factor of two or more. This disagreement arises from the different bases of the methods—for example, some methods yield so-called number-average molecular weights by determining the number-concentration of molecules in a sample, while other methods produce weight-average molecular weights which are related to the weight-concentrations of each species. Another common value is the viscosity-average molecular weight, which is related to the viscosity contribution of each species. Other bases are of importance for certain methods of study, and some of these are complex functions involving several averages. For some purposes, the determination of a single average molecular weight is sufficient for establishing relations between molecular weight and the behavior of polymers, but the type of molecular weight average must be so chosen as to have a close relation to the behavior property of interest. A more detailed knowledge of the constitution of a sample is sometimes required, particularly if several properties are to be considered, or if unusual forms of molecular weight distribution curve are present.

The problem of completely defining the molecular weight nature of polydisperse materials is most accurately solved by determining the frequency of occurrence of each molecular species and representing the results as a frequency distribution curve. Such a study is generally quite tedious, though there are a few methods which provide much of the required information in one experiment. The methods currently most used for determining molecular weight distributions of polymers are gel permeation chromatography and the related technique of gel filtration. These involve measurement of the differences in extent of permeation of polymer molecules of different sizes into porous gel structures. The distribution of molecular sizes found is converted into a distribution of molecular weights by calibration with standard polymer samples. The method is rapid and applicable to many polymer types. Alternatively, polymers can be separated by fractional

precipitation or fractional solution into a series of fractions each of which contains a fairly narrow distribution of molecular weights. Each fraction can then be characterized by one of the methods described below to yield an average molecular weight. Finally, the molecular weight distribution curve can be constructed by summation of these results. While the curve derived is somewhat inexact, it is the best approach to samples which are not susceptible to analysis by the gel permeation methods. The ultracentrifuge is less commonly used for determining molecular weight distributions in a single experiment, partly because of high instrumentation costs and partly because of the complexity of methods needed to analyze the data.

Uses. Molecular weight measurements, in conjunction with the law of combining proportions, have enabled the atomic weights of elements in compounds to be determined. When the atomic weights are known, molecular weight measurements permit the assignment of molecular formulas. Other applications to compounds of low molecular weight allow determination of the extent of ionization of weak electrolytes, and the extent of association of some uncharged compounds which aggregate. The study of molecular weights is becoming increasingly valuable in assessing the effects which various molecular species of a polymer sample have on the physical properties of the product. Through such knowledge, the synthetic process may be modified to improve the properties of polymers.

Methods of Measurement Many physical and certain chemical properties vary substantially with the molecular weight of compounds, and these properties are the bases of all molecular weight methods. The summary given in this section includes principally the methods which are most frequently used or have general applicability. The choice of the most suitable method for a given sample depends on its state (gas, liquid, or solid), the magnitude of the molecular weight and the accuracy required in its determination, as well as on the stability of the compound to physical or chemical treatment. Some mention of the applicability of the methods in these regards is given wherever possible.

Gases and Liquids Avogadro's hypothesis (1811) that equal volumes of different gases contain the same number of molecules under the same conditions made it possible to find how many times heavier a single molecule of one gas is than that of another. Thus, relative molecular weights of all gases could be established by comparing the weights of equal volumes of gases. The significance of the idea and utilization of this method were first clearly demonstrated by Cannizzaro in 1858, and this represents the first available method for determining molecular weights. With the additional information from chemical experiments on the number of atoms of each kind present in each molecule, the relative weights of each atom were obtained. The assumption of the integral value,

16, for the atomic weight of oxygen (to give a value close to unity for the lightest element, hydrogen) then enabled molecular weights of all gaseous compounds to be determined. The method obviously can be applied to other molecules which normally occur in the liquid state but can be volatilized by heating. The Dumas and Victor Meyer methods are most used for molecular weight determinations with liquids in this way. These methods have been refined so that gas densities can now be determined with an accuracy of 0.02 per cent, and extremely small weights of material (about 1 μg) can be similarly studied with somewhat less accuracy. High temperatures up to 2000°C have been used to study substances which are volatilized only with difficulty, provided decomposition can be avoided.

Solids Measured by Colligative Methods It has been shown that nonvolatile molecules dissolved in a solvent affect several physical properties of the solvent in proportion to the number of solute molecules present per unit volume. Among these properties are a decrease of the vapor pressure of the solvent, a rise in its boiling point, a decrease in its freezing point, and the development of osmotic pressure when the solution is separated from the solvent by a semipermeable membrane. Properties such as these which are related to the number of molecules in a sample rather than to the type of molecule are called colligative properties. They are the basis for some of the most useful techniques for molecular weight determination. The magnitude of the effects and the ease of measurement differ greatly, so that certain of the colligative properties are preferred for this purpose. For example, an aqueous solution containing 0.2 gram of sucrose (molecular weight 342) in 100 ml has a vapor pressure 0.01 per cent less than that of the solvent, a boiling point 0.003°C greater, and a freezing point 0.011°C lower than the solvent, but will develop an osmotic pressure of 150 cm of water. Since the effects are related to the number-concentration of solute molecules, each method leads to a number average molecular weight if the sample consists of a mixture of molecules of different sizes. Accurate results with any of the techniques are obtained only when measurements at a series of concentrations are extrapolated to infinite dilution where the system becomes ideal, i.e. is not affected by interactions between molecules.

Direct vapor pressure measurements with a differential manometer are generally limited to the larger depressions produced by low molecular weight solutes, while refined techniques such as isothermal distillation require the most exact control of conditions. Isopiestic methods allow the comparison of the vapor pressure of solutions of an unknown with those containing a known substance, and several modifications have been used more than other vapor pressure methods. Ebulliometric techniques which depend on the elevation of the boiling point of a solvent are often used for solutes of low molecu-

lar weight and find some use for large molecules. Since boiling points are highly sensitive to the atmospheric pressure, it is either necessary to control pressure very precisely, or more commonly to measure the boiling points of both the solvent and solution simultaneously. Often a differential thermometer is employed to determine only the difference of the two temperatures, and these devices have been made so sensitive that molecular weights as large as 30 000 have sometimes been studied. Techniques involving the lowering of the freezing point of a solvent (cryoscopic methods) are much used for rapid approximate determinations of molecular weights in the identification of organic compounds. For this purpose a substance such as camphor, which is a good solvent for many organic compounds and has a large molar depression constant, is often chosen to magnify the difference in freezing point of the solvent and the solution of the unknown. Since freezing-point depressions are not sensitive to atmospheric pressure, they are easier to measure accurately than the methods described above, and much use has been made of them for precise studies of solutes having low molecular weights. The possibility of association or ionization of the solute must be considered with any of these methods, since these effects will greatly influence the result.

Osmotic pressures are so much larger than any other colligative property that they are most widely used for molecular weight measurements, particularly for long-chain polymers where the high sensitivity of the method is required. For accurate measurements, a membrane is required which permits the flow of solvent through its pores but completely holds back solute molecules. This condition is best satisfied where there are large differences in size of the solute and solvent molecules or of their affinity for the membrane. Membranes made from cellulose compounds are often successfully used for polymers which contain little material with molecular weights below about 10 000. Below this molecular weight the pore size of the satisfactory membranes is so small that solvent flow is very slow, and thus a very long time is required to reach constant osmotic pressure. In spite of this handicap, some of the most precise osmotic pressure measurements have been obtained with aqueous solutions of sucrose and similar small solutes by the use of membranes prepared by precipitating such materials as copper ferrocyanide in the pores of a solid support. The upper limit of molecular weights satisfactorily measured by osmometry is usually about 500 000, which is fixed by the lowest pressures that can be measured precisely and by the maximum concentrations of material which still give satisfactory extrapolations to infinite dilution. In comparing various colligative properties for the characterization of polymers, osmometry has the advantage that it is unaffected by the presence of impurities of very low molecular weight which will diffuse through membranes able to retain the polymer, whereas the other properties are greatly affected by the same impurities.

Modern instrumentation has provided commercial instruments utilizing several of these colligative properties for routine, accurate measurements in very short time and with small samples. This is true for boiling point, vapor pressure, and freezing point measurements of molecular weights up to several thousand, and for membrane osmotic pressure measurements of high molecular weight samples.

X-ray Diffraction X-ray diffraction analysis is a powerful method for determining exact molecular weight and structural characteristics of compounds in their crystalline state. However the method is complicated and slower than many techniques which provide molecular weights of accuracy sufficient for many purposes and so is usually employed only when the additional structural information is needed. The sample to be examined must have a high degree of crystalline order and is preferably a single crystal at least 0.1 mm in size; such samples are prepared fairly readily from many inorganic and non-polymeric organic compounds. Alternatively, crystalline powders of certain crystal types may provide suitable results. Diffraction patterns are then obtained by one of several methods, and the angular positions of the reflections are used to calculate the lattice spacings, and thus the size of the unit cell. This unit cell is the smallest volume unit which retains all geometrical features of the crystalline class, and it contains a small integral number of molecules. A rough estimate of the molecular weight of the compound is needed from a determination by an independent method in order to obtain this integral number. Finally, the resultant molecular volume is multiplied by the exact bulk density of the crystal and by the Avogadro number to yield the molecular weight (see X-RAY DIFFRACTION).

Light Scattering Measurements of the intensity of light scattered by dissolved molecules allow the determination of molecular weights. Most commonly the method is used for polymers above 10 000 units, though under optimum conditions molecular weights as low as 1000 have been determined. Since the intensity scattered by a given weight of dissolved material is directly proportional to the mass of each molecule, a weight-average value of the molecular weight is obtained for a polydisperse system. An average dimension of the molecule can also be obtained by a study of the angular variation of scattered light intensity, provided some dimension of the molecules exceeds a few hundred angstroms. The interaction between dissolved molecules substantially affects the intensity of scattered light so that extrapolation to infinite dilution of data collected at several polymer concentrations is required. The method has been so well developed in the last decade that it is now probably the most used method for deter-

mining absolute molecular weights of polymers. In addition, it provides information on sizes which is furnished by few other methods. The greatest problem encountered is in the removal of suspended large particles which otherwise would distort the angular scattering pattern of the solutions. This is rather easily accomplished by filtration in some cases, but it may be a formidable difficulty for particles which are highly solvated or are peptized by the molecules to be studied. Auxiliary information is required on the refractive index increment of the sample, i.e., the change in refractive index of the solvent produced by unit concentration of the sample. This information is supplied by a differential refractometer using the same wavelength of light as that employed in measurements of the intensity of scatter.

The Ultracentrifuge. The sedimentation of large molecules in a strong centrifugal field enables the determination of both average molecular weights and the distribution of molecular weights in certain systems. When a solution containing polymer or other large molecules is centrifuged at forces up to 250 000 times gravity, the molecules begin to settle, leaving pure solvent above a boundary which progressively moves toward the bottom of the cell. This boundary is a rather sharp gradient of concentrations for molecules of uniform size, such as globular proteins, but for polydisperse systems, the boundary is diffuse, the lowest molecular weights lagging behind the larger molecules. An optical system is provided for viewing this boundary, and a study as a function of the time of centrifuging yields the rate of sedimentation for the single component or for each of many components of a polydisperse system. These sedimentation rates may then be related to the corresponding molecular weights of the species present after the diffusion coefficients for each species are determined by independent experiments. Both the sedimentation and the diffusion rates are affected by interactions between molecules, so that each must be studied as a function of concentration and extrapolated to infinite dilution as is done for the colligative properties. The result of this detailed work is the distribution of molecular weights in the sample which is available by few other methods. At present, this method is only partly satisfactory for molecular weight determinations with linear polymers because of the large concentration dependence of the diffusion coefficients. Difficulties have been found in reliably extrapolating diffusion coefficients beyond the lowest polymer concentrations which are experimentally attainable at present.

A modification of the sedimentation method which avoids the study of diffusion constants is the sedimentation equilibrium method in which molecules are allowed to sediment in a much weaker field. Under these conditions, the sedimenting force is balanced by the force of diffusion, so that after times from a day to two weeks molecules of each size reach different equilibrium positions, and the optical measurement of the concentration of polymer at each point gives the molecular weight distribution directly. However, again extrapolation to infinite dilution must be used to overcome interaction effects. The chief difficulty here is the long time of centrifuging required, and the necessary stability of the apparatus during the period. A newer and somewhat faster technique, the Archibald method, permits the determination of weight-average molecular weights of polymers by analysis of the concentration gradient near boundaries soon after sedimentation begins.

Chemical Analysis When reactive groups in a compound may be determined exactly and easily, this analysis may be used to determine the gram equivalent weight of the substance. This is the weight in grams which combines with or is equivalent to one gram-atomic weight of hydrogen. This equivalent weight may then be converted to the molecular weight by multiplying by the number of groups per molecule which reacted (provided they each are also equivalent to one hydrogen). If the number of reactive groups in the molecule is not known, then one of the physical methods for determining molecular weight must be used instead. The chemical method is convenient and often used for the identification of organic substances containing free carboxyl or amino groups which can readily be titrated, and for esters which can be saponified and determinations made of the amount of alkali consumed in this process. The equivalent weights of ionic substances containing, for example, halide or sulfate groups may also be determined by titration or by gravimetric analysis of insoluble compounds formed with reagents which act in a stoichiometric fashion. In the titration of acids, the "neutral equivalent" is the weight of material which combines with one equivalent of alkali, and a similar definition applies to the "saponification equivalent" of esters. If only one carboxyl or ester group is present in the molecule, these values equal the molecular weight of the compound.

In a similar way, if the terminal groups on polymer chains can be determined by a chemical reaction without affecting other groups in the molecule, the equivalent weight or molecular weight of the polymer may be obtained in certain cases. For polydisperse systems, a number-average value of the molecular weight is obtained because the process essentially counts the total number of groups per unit weight of sample. Since the method depends on the effect of a single group in a long chain, its sensitivity decreases as the molecular weight rises, and so is seldom applicable above molecular weights of 20 000. Particularly at high molecular weights, the method is very sensitive to small amounts of impurities which can react with the testing reagent, so that careful purification of samples is desired.

It is also important to know that impurities or

competing mechanisms of polymerization do not lead to branching or other processes which may provide greater or fewer reactive groups per molecule. The analysis for end groups must be carried out under mild conditions which do not degrade the polymer, since this would also lead to lower molecular weight values than expected. Labeling of end groups either with radioactive isotopes or with heavy isotopes which can be analyzed with the mass spectrometer provides a rapid and convenient analysis for end groups. This labeling can be accomplished with a labeled initiator if this remains at the chain ends, or after polymerization is complete, by exchange of weakly bonded groups with similar groups in a labeled compound. Molecular weight determinations by end group analysis are often used for condensation polymers of lower molecular weights and are especially valuable in studying degradation processes in polymers.

GEORGE L. BEYER

References

Daniels, F., Williams, J.W., Bender, P., Alberty, R. A., and Cornwell, C. D., "Experimental Physical Chemistry," Sixth edition, New York, McGraw-Hill Book Co., 1962.

Bonnar, R. U., Dimbat, M., Stross, F. H., "Number-Average Molecular Weights," New York, Interscience Publishers, 1958.

Allen, P. W., "Techniques of Polymer Characterization," London, Butterworths, 1959.

Stacey, K. A., "Light-Scattering in Physical Chemistry," New York, Academic Press, 1956.

Wells, A. F., "Structural Inorganic Chemistry," Oxford University Press, 1945.

Cross-references: ATOMIC PHYSICS; BOND, CHEMICAL; CENTRIFUGE; LIGHT SCATTERING; MOLECULES AND MOLECULAR STRUCTURE; OSMOSIS; POLYMER PHYSICS; VAPOR PRESSURE AND EVAPORATION; X-RAY DIFFRACTION.

MOLECULES AND MOLECULAR STRUCTURE

A molecule is a local assembly of atomic nuclei and electrons in a state of dynamic stability. The cohesive forces are electrostatic, but, in addition, relatively small electromagnetic interactions may occur between the spin and orbital motions of the electrons, especially in the neighborhood of heavy nuclei. The internuclear separations are of the order of 1 to 2×10^{-10} metres, and the energies required to dissociate a stable molecule into smaller fragments fall into the 1 to 5 eV range. The simplest diatomic species is the hydrogen molecule-ion H_2^+ with two nuclei and one electron. At the other extreme, the protein ribonuclease contains 1876 nuclei and 7396 electrons per molecule.

Historically, molecules were regarded as being formed by the association of individual atoms. This led to the concept of *valency*, i.e., the number of individual chemical bonds or linkages with which a particular atom can attach itself to other atoms. When the electronic theory of the atom was developed, these bonds were interpreted in terms of the behavior of the valence, or outer shell, electrons of the combining atoms. Each atom with a partly filled valence shell attempts to acquire a completed octet of outer electrons, either by electron transfer, as in (a), to give an electrovalent bond, resulting from Coulombic attraction between the oppositely charged ions

$$Na^+ \begin{bmatrix} :\!\overset{\cdot\cdot}{\underset{\cdot\cdot}{Cl}}\!: \end{bmatrix}^- \qquad :\!\overset{\cdot\cdot}{\underset{\cdot\cdot}{Cl}}\!:\!\overset{\cdot\cdot}{\underset{\cdot\cdot}{Cl}}\!: \qquad R:\!\overset{\overset{\textstyle R}{\cdot\cdot}}{\underset{\cdot\cdot}{N}}\!\overset{+}{:}\overset{\cdot\cdot}{\underset{\cdot\cdot}{O}}\!\overset{-}{:} $$

(a)   (b)   (c)   (R = CH₃)

(W. Kossel, 1916); or by electron sharing, as in (b) and (c), to give a covalent bond (G. N. Lewis, 1916). In (b), each chlorine atom donates one electron to form a homopolar bond, which is written Cl—Cl where the bar denotes on this theory one single bond, or shared electron pair. In (c), the nitrogen-oxygen bond is formed by two electrons donated by only the nitrogen atom, giving a *semipolar*, or *coordinate-covalent* bond, which is written $R_3N \rightarrow O$, and which is electrically polarized. Double or triple bonds result from the sharing of four or six electrons between adjacent atoms, as in ethylene (d) and acetylene (e) respectively.

$$\begin{array}{ccc} H & & H \\ & C\!=\!C & \\ H & & H \end{array} \qquad\qquad H\!-\!C\!\equiv\!C\!-\!H$$

(d)   (e)

However, difficulties arise in describing the structures of many molecules in this fashion. For example, in benzene (C_6H_6), a typical aromatic compound, the carbon nuclei form a plane regular hexagon, but the electrons can only be conventionally written as forming alternate single and double bonds between them. Furthermore, an electron cannot be identified as coming specifically from any of these bonds upon ionization. Such difficulties disappear in the quantum-mechanical theory of a polyatomic molecule, whose electronic wave function can be constructed from nonlocalized electron orbitals extending over all of the nuclei. The concept of valency is not basic to this theory, but is simply a convenient approximation by which the electron density distribution is partitioned in different regions in the molecule.

Molecular compounds consist of two or more stable species held together by weak forces. In *clathrates*, a gaseous substance such as SO_2, HCl, CO_2 or a rare gas is held in the crystal

lattice of a solid, such as β-quinol, by van der Waals-London dispersion forces. The *gas hydrates*, e.g., $Cl_2 \cdot 6H_2O$, contain halogen molecules similarly trapped in ice-like structures. The hydrogen bond, with energy ~ 0.25 eV, is responsible not only for the high degree of molecular association in liquids such as water $(O—H———O—H———)$ but also for such molecules as the formic acid dimer

which contains two hydrogen bonds indicated by dashed lines. *Molecular complexes* vary greatly in their stability; in donor-acceptor complexes, electronic charge is transferred from the donor (e.g., NH_3) to the acceptor (e.g., BF_3), as in a semipolar bond. The $BF_3 \cdot NH_3$ complex has a binding energy with respect to dissociation into NH_3 and BF_3 of 1.8 eV. The bond here is relatively strong; the electron transfer can occur between the components in their electronic ground states. On the other hand, in weaker complexes such as $C_6H_6 - I_2$, with binding energy of about 0.06 eV, there is only a fractional transfer of charge from benzene to iodine. The actual ionic charge-transfer state lies at much higher energy than the ground state of the complex.

The discovery of $XePtF_6$ by Bartlett (1962) has been followed by the synthesis of many other rare gas compounds whose existence was not predicted by classical valency theories. Compounds such as XeF_2, XeF_4, XeF_6 and $XeOF_4$ are quite stable, the average $Xe-F$ bond energy in the square planar molecule XeF_4 being 1.4 eV.

A molecule X is characterized by:

(1) A *stoichiometric formula* $A_a B_b C_c \cdots$ where $a,b,c, \cdots$ are the numbers of atoms of elements A,B,C, $\cdots$ that it contains. The ratio $a : b : c : \cdots$ is found by chemical analysis for these elements. The absolute values of a, b, c, $\cdots$ are then fixed by determination of the *molecular weight* of X. For a volatile substance, the gas density of X and of a gas of known molecular weight are compared at the same temperature and pressure. The molecular weights are in the ratio of the gas densities, since *Avogadro's principle* states that equal volumes of gases at the same temperature and pressure contain the same numbers of molecules. For a nonvolatile substance, a known weight can be dissolved in a solvent, and the resultant lowering of vapor pressure, elevation of the boiling point, or depression of the freezing point of the solvent can be measured. Each of these properties depends upon the number of molecules of solute present, so the number of molecules per unit weight of X is found and, hence, the molecular weight. For substances of high molecular weight such as proteins (molecular weight $\sim 34\,000-200-$ 000) or polymers, the molecular weight is found from osmotic pressure measurements or the rate of sedimentation in a centrifuge. The molecular weight of a molecule in crystalline form is determined when the density of the crystal and the dimensions of the unit cell from x-ray analysis are both known. Finally, for stable volatile compounds, it is often possible to form the ion X^+ and pass this through a mass spectrograph to determine the molecular weight.

(2) The spatial distribution of the nuclei in their mean equilibrium or "rest" positions. At an elementary level, this is described in geometrical language. For example, in carbon tetrachloride, CCl_4, the four chlorine nuclei are disposed at the corners of a regular tetrahedron, and the carbon nucleus is at the center. In the $[CoCl_4]^{2-}$ ion, the arrangement of the chlorine nuclei about the central metal nucleus is also tetrahedral, whereas in $[PdCl_4]^{2-}$ it is planar.

At a more sophisticated level, each molecule is classified under a *symmetry point group*. Most nonlinear molecules possess only 1, 2, 3, 4 or 6-fold rotation axes, and belong to one of the 32 crystallographic point groups. For example, the pyramidal ammonia molecule NH_3 has a threefold rotation axis C_3 through the nitrogen nucleus and three reflection planes σ_v intersecting at this axis, and belongs to the $C_{3v}(3m)$ point group. Tetrahedral molecules CX_4 belong to the $Td(\bar{4}3m)$ point group. Linear diatomic and polyatomic molecules belong to either of the continuous point groups $D_{\infty h}$ or $C_{\infty v}$ according to whether a center of symmetry is present or not.

The symmetry classification does not define the geometry of a molecule completely. The values of certain *bond lengths or angles* must also be specified. In carbon tetrachloride, it is sufficient to give the $C-Cl$ distance $(1.77 \times 10^{-10}$ meters$)$ since classification under the T_d point group implies that all four of these bonds have equal length and the angle between them is $109°\,28'$. In ammonia, both the $N-H$ distance $(1.015 \times 10^{-10}$ meters$)$ and the angle HNH $(107°)$ must be specified. In general, the lower the molecular symmetry, the greater is the number of such independent parameters required to characterize the geometry. Information about the symmetry and internal dimensions of a molecule is obtained experimentally by SPECTROSCOPY, ELECTRON DIFFRACTION, NEUTRON DIFFRACTION and X-RAY DIFFRACTION. (See these topics for details.)

(3) The *dynamical state* is defined by the values of certain observables associated with orbital and spin motions of the electrons and with vibration and rotation of the nuclei, and also by symmetry properties of the corresponding stationary-state wave functions. Except for cases when heavy nuclei are present, the total electron spin angular momentum of a molecule is separately conserved with magnitude $S\hbar$, and molecular states are classified as singlet, doublet, triplet, $\cdots$ according to the value of the multi-

plicity $(2S + 1)$. This is shown by a prefix superscript to the term symbol, as in atoms.

The Born-Oppenheimer approximation permits the molecular Hamiltonian H to be separated into a component H_e that depends only on the coordinates of the electrons relative to the nuclei plus a component depending upon the nuclear coordinates, which in turn can be written as a sum $H_v + H_r$ of terms for vibrational and rotational motion of the nuclei (we may ignore translation here). The eigenfunctions Ψ of H may correspondingly be factorized as the product $\Psi_e\Psi_v\Psi_r$ of eigenfunctions of these three operators, and the eigenvalues E decomposed as the sum $E_e + E_v + E_r$. In general, we find $E_e > E_v > E_r$.

Electronic states of molecules are classified according to the symmetry properties of Ψ_e (which forms a basis for an irreducible representation of the molecular point group). Thus $^3B_{1u}$ is a term symbol for benzene (D_{6h} point group) that denotes a triplet electronic state whose wave function transforms like the B_{1u} representation of the group. In the case of diatomic and linear polyatomic molecules, the term symbol shows the magnitude of the conserved component of orbital electronic angular momentum $\Lambda\hbar$ about the axis, states being classified as Σ, Π, Δ, $\cdots$ according to $\Lambda = 0, 1, 2, \cdots$. The superscript $+$ or $-$ shows the behavior of Ψ_e for a linear molecule upon reflection in a plane containing the molecular axis; for centrosymmetric linear molecules ($D_{\infty h}$ point group) the subscript g or u shows the parity $+1$ or -1 respectively for Ψ_e with respect to inversion at the center.

The vibrational wavefunction Ψ_v can be approximated by a product of $3N - 6$ harmonic oscillator wave functions ψ_i, each a function of a normal displacement coordinate Q_i,

$$\Psi_v = \prod_{i=1}^{3N-6} \psi_i(Q_i)$$

The product is $(3N-5)$, for a linear molecule; N is the number of nuclei. Each oscillatory mode can be excited with quanta $v_i = 0, 1, 2, \cdots$. When $v_i = 0$, ψ_i transforms like the totally symmetric representation of the molecular point group; when $v_i = 1$, ψ_i transforms like Q_i. The symmetry of Ψ_v under the molecular point group is found from the direct product for all the ψ_i. The vibrationless ground state with $v_1 = v_2 = \cdots = 0$ is always totally symmetrical.

Each rotational state is characterized by a value for the quantum number J, where $J(J + 1)\hbar^2$ is the squared angular momentum for rotation of the nuclei (apart from spin). If I_a, I_b and I_c denote the moments about the principal axes of inertia of the molecule, then a spherical top has $I_a = I_b = I_c$; a molecule with two principal moments equal is either a prolate ($I_c = I_b > I_a$) or an oblate ($I_c > I_b = I_a$) symmetric top; if $I_c > I_b > I_a$, the top is asymmetric. Symmetric

top molecules have C_n symmetry axes with $n \geqslant 3$ and belong to point groups with degenerate representations. The component $K\hbar$ of rotational angular momentum about the top axis is conserved and the rotational levels are also characterized by the value of the quantum number $K = 0, 1, 2, \cdots J$. A symmetry classification is made for Ψ_r under the rotational subgroup of the molecular point group. Finally, each eigenstate is described as $+$ or $-$ according to the parity of Ψ under inversion in a space-fixed coordinate system.

(4) In order to distinguish between different electronic states Ψ_e of the same symmetry and spin multiplicity, a further classification is obtained by expanding Ψ_e as a product of n single-electron wave functions ϕ_i, each a function of the coordinates of one of the n electrons in the molecule.

$$\Psi_e = (n!)^{-1/2} \det|\phi_1(1)\phi_2(2)\phi_3(3) \cdots \phi_n(n)|$$

where $(n!)^{-1/2}$ is a normalization factor. Each of the molecular orbitals (MO's) ϕ_i is constructed to transform like an irreducible representation of the molecular point group and is usually formed by linear combination of atomic orbitals (LCAO) χ_i centered upon the individual nuclei

$$\phi_i = \sum_p C_{ip}\chi_p$$

The MO's are written in order of decreasing energy necessary to ionize the electrons which occupy them, and electrons are assigned to the MO's in accordance with the Pauli principle. For example, the electronic ground state of ammonia (C_{3v} point group) is written

$$(1a_1)^2(2a_1)^2(1e)^4(3a_1)^2 \qquad {}^1A_1$$

where the superscripts show the distribution of the ten electrons among three MO's of a_1 symmetry and one of e symmetry, the electrons in the $(3a_1)$ orbital being most readily ionized. The symmetry of the resultant molecular wavefunction Ψ_e is found by taking direct products for each orbital occupied by an electron. Here Ψ_e belongs to the totally symmetrical representation (and is also singlet). Excited electronic states are obtained by promoting electrons into orbitals with higher energies, but the molecular symmetry in such states often differs from that in the ground state, as a result of changes in geometry.

In calculations of molecular properties, the MO's ϕ_i can be improved by variational methods which make them satisfy the *Hartree-Fock* equations. This gives *self-consistent field* (SCF) MO's, yielding a better wavefunction Ψ_e. However the latter is still, in practice, constructed from an incomplete set of basic functions. Further improvement is achieved by *configuration interaction* (CI), in which Ψ_e's of the

same symmetry are allowed to mix in linear combination.

G. W. KING

References

Coulson, C. A., "Valence," Second edition, London, Oxford University Press, 1961.

Eyring H., Walter, J., and Kimball, G. E., "Quantum Chemistry," New York, John Wiley & Sons, 1944.

King, G. W., "Spectroscopy and Molecular Structure," New York, Holt, Rinehart and Winston, Inc., 1964.

Levine, I. N., "Quantum Chemistry," Vols. I and II, Boston, Allyn and Bacon, Inc., 1970.

Pauling, L. C., "The Nature of the Chemical Bond," Third edition, Ithica, N.Y., Cornell University Press, 1960.

Cross-references: BOND, CHEMICAL; ELECTRON DIFFRACTION; INTERMOLECULAR FORCES; MOLECULAR WEIGHT; NEUTRON DIFFRACTION; QUANTUM THEORY; SPECTROSCOPY; X-RAY DIFFRACTION.

MÖSSBAUER EFFECT

The Mössbauer effect is the phenomenon of recoilless resonance fluorescence of gamma rays from nuclei bound in solids. It was first discovered in 1958 and brought its discoverer, Rudolf L. Mössbauer, the Nobel prize for physics in 1961. The extreme sharpness of the recoilless gamma transitions and the relative ease and accuracy in observing small energy differences make the Mössbauer effect an important tool in nuclear physics, solid-state physics, chemistry, biophysics, and metallurgy.

Resonance fluorescence involves the excitation of a quantized system (the absorber) from its ground state (0) to an excited state (1) by absorption of a photon emitted from an identical system (the source) decaying from state (1) to (0). Not every nucleus has a suitable gamma transition; however, the Mössbauer effect has been observed in more than 40 different isotopes. The parameters characterizing the nuclear resonance process for some typical isotopes are illustrated in Fig. 1.

To conserve energy and momentum in the emission and absorption processes, each system, the source and absorber, must acquire a recoil energy R equal to $E^2/2Mc^2$, where E is the photon energy, M is the mass of the recoiling system and c is the speed of light. The energy available for the excitation of the absorber is thus reduced by $2R$, and resonance fluorescence can be achieved only if the missing energy $2R$ is not larger than the widths of the levels involved. Before 1958, it was thought that for all gamma transitions the width required to get overlap between the emission and the absorption line was much larger than the natural width Γ, where Γ is related to the half-life $T_{1/2}$ of the excited

nuclear level by the expression $\Gamma T_{1/2} = 4.55 \times 10^{-16} \, eV$ sec. In fact, techniques had been developed to compensate for the recoil energy loss by applying large Doppler shifts with an ultracentrifuge or through thermal motion. These methods necessarily broaden the intrinsically narrow lines thereby reducing the absorption cross section.

Modifying a theory of W. E. Lamb, Mössbauer demonstrated that in some cases these difficulties may be removed by embedding the source and absorber nuclei in a crystal. Being part of a quantized vibrational system, these nuclei interact with the lattice by exchange of vibrational quanta or phonons only. If the characteristic phonon energy is large compared to the recoil energy R for a free nucleus, the probability for the emission of a gamma ray without a change in the vibrational state of the lattice is large. For such a zero phonon transition, the lattice as a whole absorbs the recoil momentum and the recoil energy loss is negligibly small. At the same time, the emission and absorption lines achieve the natural width Γ.

For an atom bound by harmonic forces, the fraction f of events without recoil energy loss is given by $f = \exp(-4\pi^2 \langle x^2 \rangle / \lambda^2)$. Here $\langle x^2 \rangle$ is the mean square displacement of the radiating atom taken along the direction of the photon with wavelength λ. In an environment of lower than cubic symmetry, $\langle x^2 \rangle$, and therefore f, may be anisotropic. A large recoilless fraction may be obtained when $\langle x^2 \rangle$ is small and λ large. The former condition implies small vibrational amplitude and thus low temperature, high vibrational frequency and large mass M, while the latter implies low photon energy, E. Both conditions imply small recoil energy R.

Recoilless transitions can also occur in amorphous substances like glasses and high-viscosity liquids. For the latter, the diffusive motion superimposed on the thermal vibration results in a broadening of the Mössbauer line.

For all Mössbauer isotopes, the nuclear half-life $T_{1/2}$, typically 10^{-8} second, is very long compared to the period of the lattice vibrations, typically 10^{-13} second. A conceivable first-order Doppler shift of the Mössbauer line due to the thermal motion will therefore average out to zero. The second-order Doppler effect, however, leads to an observable shift, sometimes called the temperature shift. The photons emitted by a source nucleus moving with a mean square velocity $\langle v_s^2 \rangle$ are lower in energy by a fraction $\langle v_s^2 \rangle / 2c^2$ as compared to the photons emitted at rest. Similarly the transition energy of a vibrating absorber nucleus appears lower to the incident photon by a fraction $\langle v_a^2 \rangle / 2c^2$. In principle, the two shifts may be different whenever the source and absorber are of different composition and/or temperature.

Mössbauer performed his original experiment with ^{191}Ir at 88 K, obtaining a recoilless fraction of 1 per cent. Since the natural line width in ^{191}Ir, as in most other Mössbauer nuclides, is

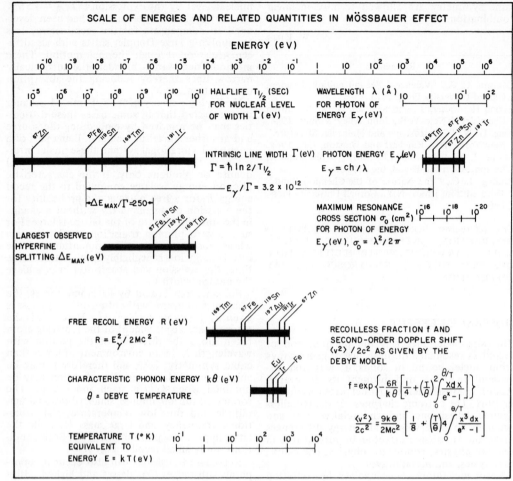

FIG. 1

extremely narrow, Mössbauer was able to alter the degree of overlap between the emission and absorption lines by simply moving the source relative to the absorber at speeds v of the order of 1 mm/sec. Thus the gamma rays were slightly shifted in energy via the first-order Doppler effect by an amount $\Delta E = Ev/c$. By plotting the transmission through the absorber as a function of the relative source-absorber velocity, one thus obtains the characteristic Mössbauer velocity spectrum which exhibits the shape of the resonance curve. From such a plot, one can determine the recoilless fraction, the lifetime of the excited state and any possible energy differences between the emission and the absorption line.

With extreme care, it is possible to determine energy differences of the order of 1/1000 of the line width Γ. The latter typically varies with isotope from 10^{-10} to 10^{-15} times the actual gamma ray energy E. The Mössbauer effect therefore enables one to detect extremely small changes in this energy. One of the earliest applications of this great precision was the laboratory

verification of the gravitational red shift by Pound and Rebka. According to Einstein's theory, photons have an apparent mass $m = E/c^2$. Thus if they fall toward the earth through a distance H, their energy increases by $\Delta E = mgH$, so that $\Delta E/E = gH/c^2 \cong 10^{-16}$ per meter. Using ^{57}Fe, which has a large recoilless fraction, and for which $\Gamma/E = 3 \times 10^{-13}$, the desired effect was observed when the photons were sent down the 22-meter tower at Harvard University.

It is well known from optical and high-frequency spectroscopy that a nucleus interacting with its environment through its charge distribution and magnetic moment can give rise to hyperfine shifts and splittings of the order of 10^{-9} eV to 10^{-5} eV. In Mössbauer experiments, such energy differences can readily be measured since the line width of the recoilless transitions is of the same order of magnitude. Perhaps, therefore, the most useful feature of the Mössbauer effect is that it may be used to obtain nuclear properties if the fields acting on the nucleus are known, and conversely, it is a

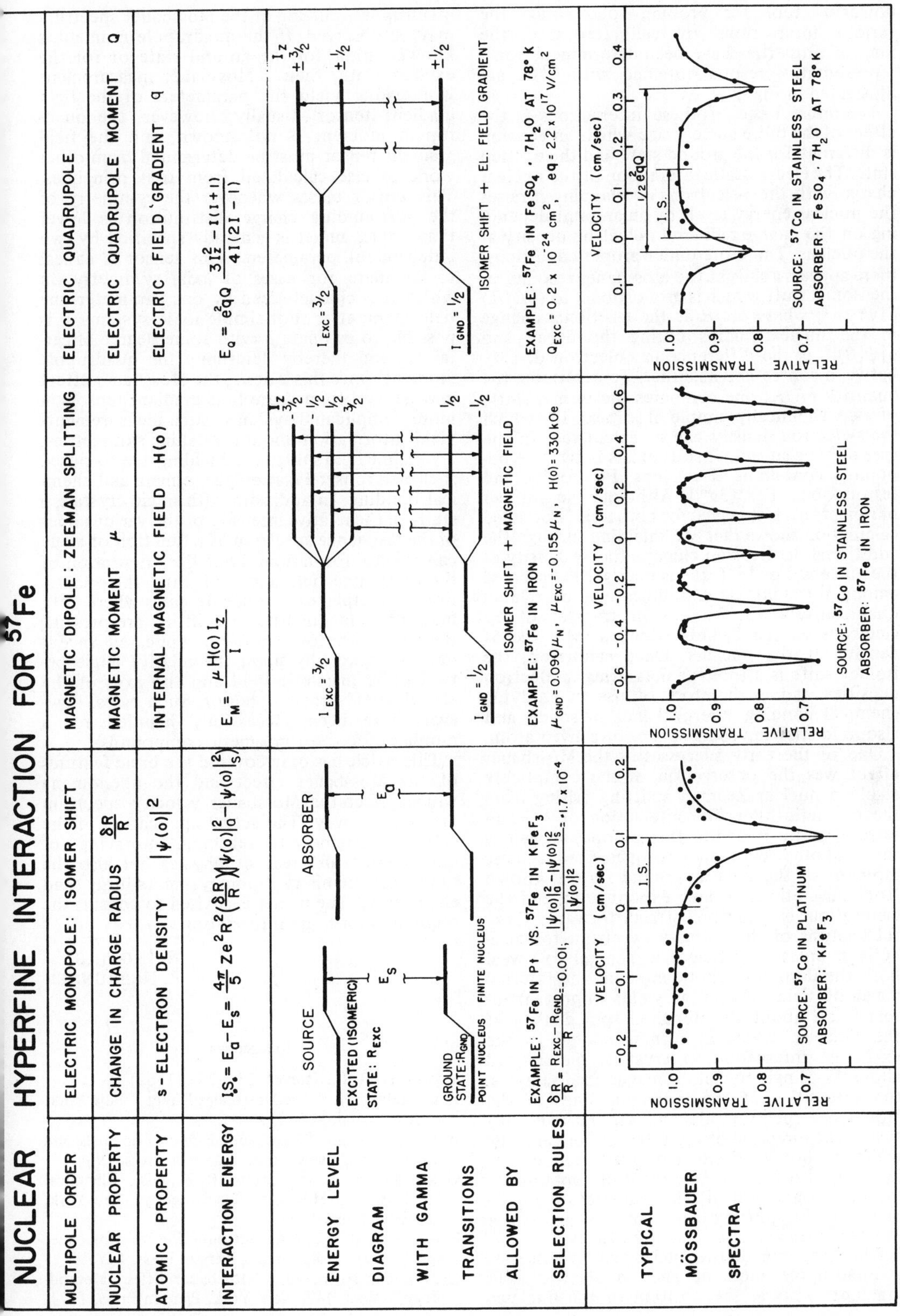
NUCLEAR HYPERFINE INTERACTION FOR ⁵⁷Fe
MULTIPOLE ORDER
NUCLEAR PROPERTY
ATOMIC PROPERTY
INTERACTION ENERGY
ENERGY LEVEL DIAGRAM WITH GAMMA TRANSITIONS ALLOWED BY SELECTION RULES
TYPICAL MÖSSBAUER SPECTRA
ELECTRIC MONOPOLE: ISOMER SHIFT
CHANGE IN CHARGE RADIUS δR/R
s-ELECTRON DENSITY |ψ(o)|²
I.S. = Eₐ − Eₛ = 4π/5 Ze²R²(δR/R)(|ψ(o)|ₐ² − |ψ(o)|ₛ²)
SOURCE
ABSORBER
EXCITED (ISOMERIC) STATE: R_EXC
GROUND STATE: R_GND
POINT NUCLEUS
FINITE NUCLEUS
Eₛ
Eₐ
EXAMPLE: ⁵⁷Fe IN Pt VS. ⁵⁷Fe IN KFeF₃
δR/R = (R_EXC − R_GND)/R = −0.001; (|ψ(o)|ₐ² − |ψ(o)|ₛ²)/|ψ(o)|² = +1.7 x 10⁻⁴
VELOCITY (cm/sec)
RELATIVE TRANSMISSION
I.S.
SOURCE: ⁵⁷Co IN PLATINUM
ABSORBER: KFeF₃
MAGNETIC DIPOLE: ZEEMAN SPLITTING
MAGNETIC MOMENT μ
INTERNAL MAGNETIC FIELD H(o)
E_M = μH(o)I_Z / I
I_EXC = 3/2
I_GND = 1/2
I_Z
3/2
1/2
−1/2
−3/2
ISOMER SHIFT + MAGNETIC FIELD
EXAMPLE: ⁵⁷Fe IN IRON
μ_GND = 0.090 μ_N, μ_EXC = −0.155 μ_N, H(o) = 330 kOe
SOURCE: ⁵⁷Co IN STAINLESS STEEL
ABSORBER: ⁵⁷Fe IN IRON
ELECTRIC QUADRUPOLE
ELECTRIC QUADRUPOLE MOMENT Q
ELECTRIC FIELD GRADIENT q
E_Q = e²qQ (3I_z² − I(I+1)) / (4I(2I − 1))
±3/2
±1/2
ISOMER SHIFT + EL. FIELD GRADIENT
EXAMPLE: ⁵⁷Fe IN FeSO₄ · 7H₂O AT 78° K
Q_EXC = 0.2 x 10⁻²⁴ cm², eq = 2.2 x 10¹⁷ V/cm²
1/2 e²qQ
SOURCE: ⁵⁷Co IN STAINLESS STEEL
ABSORBER: FeSO₄ · 7H₂O AT 78° K

FIG. 2

powerful tool for probing solids once the various interactions are calibrated, i.e., the nuclear properties have been determined. Some representative results obtained with ^{57}Fe are illustrated in Fig. 2.

The most basic of these interactions is the effect of the finite nuclear size which, in general, is different for the ground state and the excited state. The electrostatic interaction of the nuclear charge with the s-electrons overlapping it raises the nuclear energy levels by an amount depending on the charge radii and s-electron density at the nucleus. Therefore under proper conditions, there appears a shift in the Mössbauer resonance, the isomer shift, which is proportional to $(\delta R/R)$ $\delta|\psi(0)|^2$, where $\delta R/R$ is the fractional change in the nuclear radius during the decay and $\delta|\psi(0)|^2$ is the difference in s-electron density between source and absorber. To determine the quantity $\delta R/R$, one compares the isomer shifts of two chemically simple absorbers, for which the s-electron density can be calculated. In the case of ^{57}Fe an isomer shift exists between compounds containing ferric ions, $Fe^{3+}(3d^5)$, and ferrous ions, $Fe^{2+}(3d^6)$. Although the number of s-electrons is the same for both ions, a detailed calculation shows that the shielding through the additional $3d$ electron changes the $3s$ density at the nucleus. For ^{129}I, the isomer shifts observed among different alkali iodides can be related quantitatively to the known transfer of $5p$ electrons to the ligands which affects the $5s$ density at the nucleus. Once calibrated, the isomer shift is a tool for measuring s-electron densities and is therefore of use in studying chemical bonding, energy bands in solids, and also in identifying charge states of a given atom.

One of the early successes of the Mössbauer effect was the observation of the completely resolved nuclear Zeeman splitting arising from the magnetic hyperfine interaction of ^{57}Fe in ferromagnetic iron. For this isotope, as well as for most other Mössbauer isotopes, the magnetic moment of the nuclear ground state is known from magnetic resonance experiments, and the calibration is therefore straightforward. Careful analysis of the velocity spectrum for magnetic samples is sufficient in general to reveal both the desired magnetic moment and internal magnetic field. The latter yields important information about the unpaired spin density at the nucleus, which in turn is related to the exchange interaction in crystals, metals and alloys. For single crystals or magnetized samples, the intensities of the individual lines of the Mössbauer spectrum depend on the angle between the direction of the internal field and the emitted photon. From a measurement of the intensity distribution, one therefore obtains the internal magnetic field. The temperature dependence of the splitting can yield Néel and Curie temperatures and also relaxation times.

Whenever one of the nuclear levels possesses a quadrupole moment and an electric field gradient exists at the position of the nucleus, quadrupole splitting of the Mössbauer spectrum may be observed. If the quadrupole moment is known either for the ground state or for the excited state, then a Mössbauer measurement will readily yield the parameters of the field gradient tensor. Usually, however, the quadrupole moment is not known, and the field gradient tensor must be determined from other work or else calculated from first principles. This tensor exists whenever the symmetry of the surrounding charge distribution is lower than cubic, and it is generally specified by two independent parameters. This tensor is easiest to calculate for cases of axial symmetry, in which it is characterized by one parameter, the field gradient, q. For simple ionic systems, it is possible to estimate q with some degree of certainty, and thereby determine the quadrupole moment. Once this is done, the Mössbauer effect may be used to measure field gradient tensors in more complicated systems. Such measurements yield information about crystalline symmetries, crystalline field splittings, shielding due to closed shell electrons, relaxation phenomena and chemical bonding. In addition, with single crystals, a study of the relative intensity of the various lines of the resonance spectrum as a function of angle can yield information about the orientation of the crystalline field axes and, thus, the orientation of complexes in solids. In cases where both magnetic and quadrupole splitting are present, the analysis becomes more complicated since it depends markedly upon the relative angle between the magnetic field and the axes of the electric field gradient tensor. Such cases, however, have been successfully handled for a number of antiferromagnetic compounds.

This article has only covered the basic features of the Mössbauer effect and the phenomena which affect the Mössbauer velocity spectrum in a general way. The actual application of the effect is extremely far reaching, embracing not only almost all areas of physics but also the fields of chemistry, biology, metallurgy and engineering. The reader is advised to consult the references for more information.

R. INGALLS
P. DEBRUNNER

References

Mössbauer, R. L., *Science*, **137**, 731 (1962).

Frauenfelder, H., "The Mössbauer Effect," New York, W. A. Benjamin, 1962.

Wertheim, G. K., "Mössbauer Effect: Principles and Applications," New York, Academic Press, 1964.

Goldanskii, V. I., and Herber, R. H., eds., "Chemical Applications to Mössbauer Spectroscopy," New York, Academic Press, 1968.

May, Leopold, ed., "An Introduction to Mössbauer Spectroscopy," New York, Plenum Press, 1971.

Gruverman, Irwin, ed., "Mössbauer Effect Methodology," Vols. 1–7, New York, Plenum Press, 1971.

Cross-references: CONSERVATION LAWS AND SYMMETRY, DOPPLER EFFECT, ISOTOPES, LUMINESCENCE, PHONONS, RADIOACTIVITY, ZEEMAN AND STARK EFFECTS.

MOTORS, ELECTRIC

History Power conversion was discovered by M. Faraday in 1831; the commutator, by J. Henry, Pixii, and C. Wheatstone (1841); the electromagnetic field, by J. Brett (1840), Wheatstone and Cooke (1845), and W. von Siemens (1867); drum armatures, by Siemens, Pacinotti, and von Alteneck; ring armatures, by Gramme (1870); and disc armatures, by Desroziers (1885) and Fritsche (1890). Ring and disk types are now seldom used. Revolving magnetic fields (1885) and ac theory were discovered by G. Ferraris; polyphase motors and systems, by N. Tesla (1888); the squirrel-cage rotor, by C. S. Bradley (1889); and ac commutator motors, by R. Eickmeyer, E. Thomson, L. Atkinson, and others.

Principles These are the laws of Ohm, Kirchhoff, Lenz, and Maxwell; more specifically:

(1) Moving a conductor of length l across a magnetic field of flux of density B with a velocity v generates in it an electromotive force (emf) $e = vBl$ volts. In motors, e opposes the current i and decreases with increase in load.

(2) The force on such a conductor equals $F = Bil$ newtons. Fig. 1 shows the directions of current and force.

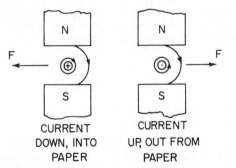

FIG. 1. Direction of force due to current in a magnetic field.

(3) Magnetic structures tend to move to the position of minimum reluctance with a force $F = dW/dx$ where W is stored magnetic energy and x is distance.

(4) The force between two coupled circuits equals

$$F = \frac{i_1{}^2}{2} \frac{dL_1}{dx} + i_1 i_2 \frac{dM}{dx} + \frac{i_2{}^2}{2} \frac{dL_2}{dx}$$

Frequently L_1 and L_2 are constant and then F

$= i_1 i_2 \, dM/dx$. Here i_1 and i_2 are currents; L_1 and L_2 are total self-inductances; M is mutual inductance.

Symbols

B = flux density in webers/m^2.
F = force in direction x in newtons.
$i, i_1, i_2,$ = instantaneous currents in amperes.
I_a, I_2 = dc and effective currents in amperes.
L_1, L_2, M = inductances in henrys.
s = slip = (Syn. rpm − rpm)/Syn. rpm.
v = velocity in meters per second.
W = energy in joules.
l, x = length, distance, in meters.
ϕ_a = useful flux per pole in webers.
ϕ_m = maximum flux per pole in webers.

Motor Types Of many hundreds, the most used are:

(1) *Direct-Current* (a) Series: The field coils are of heavy wire in series with the armature. The torque and current are high at low speeds and low at high speeds. These motors will run away at light loads, unless a speed-limiting device is used.

(b) Shunt: The field coils of fine wire are in parallel with the armature. The speed drops slightly and current and torque increase with load. In very small-size motors (and sometimes in fractional and integral horsepower sizes up to $7\frac{1}{2}$ hp), permanent magnet fields are used.

(c) Compound: Both shunt and series coils are used on the same motor. Behavior is intermediate between (a) and (b).

The current in all dc motors satisfies the relation $I_a = (V_a - E_a)/R_a$, where $E_a = p\phi_a Z_a S/(m_a \times 60)$; V_a = terminal emf; E_a = the counter electromotive force (cemf); R_a = resistance; m_a = number of paths; and Z_a = number of conductors, all for the armature; p = number of poles, S = rpm, ϕ_a = useful flux per pole. ϕ_a may be nearly constant or it may be a function of I_a.

Speed control is achieved by adjusting field current and/or armature terminal emf, tapped series coils, or (more rarely) field reluctance or double commutator. To avoid damage in starting, either starting resistances or voltage controls are needed, except for very small-size motors.

(2) *Alternating Current* (a) Polyphase Induction: These are usually 3-phase, with phase windings spaced equally in slots around the periphery to produce alternate N and S poles. When fed with polyphase current, there is set up a revolving field which turns with the speed $S = 120f/p$ rpm and induces the cemf $E = 2.22f\phi_m Zk_w$ volts per phase, where ϕ_m is the flux per pole and k_w is the winding factor.

With rotor open or running at synchronous speed S, each phase behaves as an inductance and draws an exciting current lagging nearly $\frac{1}{4}$ cycle behind the emf. Shaft load reduces the speed from S to $S(1 - s)$, where s is slip. When referred to primary, s generates in each rotor phase the emf sE (in volts) and current (in amperes)

$$I_2 = \frac{sE}{\sqrt{r_2{}^2 + (sx_2)^2}} = \frac{E}{\sqrt{\left(\dfrac{r_2}{s}\right)^2 + x_2{}^2}}$$

where r_2 is the resistance and x_2 is the leakage reactance of rotor in ohms per phase.

The current I_2 produces the needed torque. It introduces a new magnetomotive force (mmf) which turns at synchronous speed S in the same direction as that of the stator and lags behind it in space by the electrical angle $90° + \tan^{-1}$ (x_2/r_2). To balance this mmf, the stator draws an additional component of current sufficient to carry the load. Performance can be found (as for a transformer) if r_2/s is taken as the independent variable. Three-phase motors require less material than one- or two-phase motors.

(b) Single-phase Induction: With the rotor at rest, there is no revolving field; the motor will start in either direction only if given a push. Rotation sets up an elliptical revolving field which turns synchronously at nonuniform speed in the same direction as the rotor and pulsates between the limits ϕ_m and $\phi_m(1-s)$. The stator current is the resultant of (stator + cross-axis) magnetizing + load + loss currents. Analysis of this type of motor is less simple than that for a polyphase motor.

Starting is with a line switch, reduced voltage (auto-transformer or "compensator," wye-delta, series resistors or chokes), wound rotors and resistors, part-windings, or more elaborate schemes. For single-phase motors, auxiliary start windings (split-phase or capacitor), or repulsion-start, are used and are cut out at about $\frac{2}{3}$ speed. For sizes 0 to $\frac{1}{10}$ hp, and sometimes for sizes up to $\frac{1}{4}$ hp, shaded poles are used. *Speed Control* is by reduced voltage, wound rotor, or any one of a great number of possible techniques. Induction motors are "constant speed" machines and control apparatus is more expensive than that for direct current.

(c) Synchronous: Commonly these have a stationary phase-wound armature and revolving dc field structure. When up to speed and synchronized, the revolving mmf set up by the armature stands still relative to the dc field. When the angle $(I_a, E_a) = 0$, the armature mmf poles stand midway between the field poles. When I_a lags behind E_a, the armature mmf assists the dc field coils; it opposes them when I_a leads E_a. Armature current I_a takes a value and time phase position such that the cemf E_a and current I_a are correct to carry the existing load. Important relations are $I_a = (V - E_a)/Z_a$, power converted = $mI_aE_a \cos(I_a, E_a)$, input = $mI_aV \cos(I_a, V)$, and armature copper loss = $mI_a{}^2r_a$, where E_a is a function of I_a, I_f, and angle (I_a, E_a). In general, V and E_a are prevailingly in opposition and I_a increases with load. Here, m = number of phases.

Synchronous motors are used where the rpm must be fixed: for power factor correction, regulating transmission line voltages, or speeds too low for good induction motor performance.

They are not self-starting unless special means are provided, usually squirrel-cage or phase windings in the pole faces or part windings in combination with clutches (shaft or band brake on revolving stator). Precautions against high ac voltages in the dc field coils are needed when starting. The motors will carry some load with the dc field winding open. Small sizes (reluctance types) operate without field windings. Single-phase motors are less satisfactory because of lower efficiency, tendency to severe hunting, and problems in starting.

(d) ac Commutator: These are mostly single-phase series, repulsion, or combinations of these types. However, polyphase series, shunt, and compound; repulsion; and adjustable-speed induction motors have been built. Single-phase series motors are used in large quantities for portable tools, vacuum sweepers, household appliances, etc., and electric railways; though for this last, repulsion and combination types are also used. Rectifiers and dc motors are partly replacing ac types because they are lighter, simpler, cheaper, and can use power of all frequencies. But with rectifiers there is a tendency toward poorer commutation, increased heating, and reduced efficiency.

The ac series motor is similar to the dc motor, except for a laminated field, compensating winding (larger sizes), and precautions against low power factor and poor commutation. The runaway speed is high.

In the repulsion motor, the stator is like that of the single-phase induction motor. The rotor is similar to a dc armature. The brushes are short-circuited and set at a small angle so that stator and rotor axes differ by some 10 to 25 electrical degrees. Once this type was frequently used as a starting arrangement for single-phase induction motors. A centrifugal arrangement short-circuited the commutator and sometimes lifted the brushes at about $\frac{2}{3}$ speed. Now they are mostly superseded by capacitor motors. There is no electrical connection between stator or line and rotor.

The stator mmf has a component (field axis) which sets up the field flux, and another at right angles to it in the armature (or transformer) axis. The latter sets up the armature torque current by transformer action. When the armature turns, its conductors cut the field axis flux and generate an armature speed emf which sets up a second magnetizing component of armature current which induces the machine cemf in the transformer axis of the stator. It has an elliptical revolving field which tends to become circular at synchronism. Runaway speed is low, often not greatly above synchronism. Speed control is accomplished by adjusting voltage or series resistor or by shifting brushes. This last also permits reversing the direction of rotation. Combination series and repulsion motors are used for electric railways.

Probable Future Trends These include better magnetic materials, conducting materials with

lower resistivity and/or lower cost, insulating materials suitable for higher temperatures, and new discoveries.

A. F. PUCHSTEIN

References

dc Machinery

Gray, Alexander, and Wallace, G. A., "Principles and Practices of Electrical Engineering," 8th Ed., New York, McGraw-Hill Book Co., 1962.

Arnold, E., and Lacour, J. L., "Die Gleichstrom-maschine," Vol. I, "Theorie und Untersuchung," Third Ed., 1927; Vol. II, "Konstruktion, Berechnung und Arbeitsweise," Third Ed., 1927; Berlin, J. Springer.

ac Machinery

Arnold, E., and Lacour, J. L., "Die Wechselstromtech-nik," Vol. I, "Theorie der Wechselstrome," First Ed., 1923; Vol. II, "Die Transformatoren," Second Ed., 1923; Vol. III, "Die Wicklungen der Wechselstrom-maschinen," Second Ed., 1923; Vol. IV, "Die Synchronen Wechselstrommaschinen," Second Ed., 1923; Vol. V, Part 1, "Die Induktionsmaschinen," 1909 (1923), First Ed., Berlin, J. Springer.

Langsdorf, Alexander S., "Theory of Alternating Current Machinery," Second Ed., New York, McGraw-Hill Book Co., 1955.

Lawrence, Ralph R., "Principles of Alternating Current Machinery," Fourth Ed., New York and London, McGraw-Hill Book Co., 1953.

Tarboux, Joseph G., "Alternating-Current Machinery," Scranton, Pa., International Textbook Co., 1947.

ac and dc Machinery

Carr, C. C., "Electric Machinery—A Coordinated Presentation of A-C and D-C Machines," First Ed., New York, John Wiley & Sons, 1953.

Fitzgerald, A. E., and Kingsley, C., "Electric Machinery," Second Ed., 1961, Third Ed., 1971 (the Third Ed., is more elementary than the Second), New York, McGraw-Hill Book Co.

ac Commutator Motor

Oliver, C. W., "The A-C Commutator Motor," New York, Van Nostrand Reinhold, 1928.

Arnold, E., and Lacour, J. L., "Die Wechselstromkom-mutator-Maschine," Vol. V, Part 2 (see under ac Machinery), Berlin, J. Springer, 1912 (1923).

Cross-references: ALTERNATING CURRENTS, ELECTRICITY, INDUCED ELECTROMOTIVE FORCE, INDUCTANCE, MAGNETISM, TRANSFORMER.

MUSICAL SOUND

Musical sound may be characterized as an aural sensation caused by the rapid periodic motion of a sonorous body while noise is that due to non-periodic motions. The above statement, originally made by Helmholtz, may be modified slightly so that the frequencies of vibration of the body fall into the limits of hearing: 20 to 20 000 Hz. This definition is not clear cut; there are some noises in the note of a harp (the twang) as well as a recognizable note in the squeak of a shoe. In other cases it is even more difficult to make a distinction between music and noise. In some modern "electronic music" hisses and thumps are considered a part of the music. White noise is a complex sound whose frequency components are so closely spaced and so numerous that the sound ceases to have pitch. The loudness of these components is approximately the same over the whole audible range, and the noise has a hissing sound. Pink noise has its lower frequency components relatively louder than the high frequency components.

The attributes of musical sound and their subjective correlates are described briefly. The number of cycles per second, frequency, is a physical entity and may be measured objectively. Pitch, however, is a psychological phenomenon and needs a human subject to perceive it. In general, as the frequency of a sonorous body is raised, the pitch is higher. However, pitch and frequency do not bear a simple linear relationship. To show the relationship, a pitch scale can be constructed so that one note can be judged to be two times the pitch of another and so on. The unit of pitch is called the mel, and a pitch of 1000 mels is arbitrarily assigned to a frequency of 1000 Hz. In general, it is observed that the pitch is slightly less than the frequency at frequencies higher than 1000 Hz, and slightly more than the frequency at frequencies less than 1000 Hz. Pitch also depends on loudness. For a 200 Hz tone if the loudness is increased the pitch decreases, and the same happens for frequencies up to 1000 Hz. Between 1000 and 3000 Hz pitch is relatively independent of loudness, while above 4000 Hz, increasing the loudness raises the pitch. A rapid variation in pitch when the variation occurs at the rate of from two to five times per second is called vibrato. The pitch variations in mels may be large or small but the rate at which the pitch is varied is rarely greater than five times per second. Violinists produce vibrato by sliding their fingers back and forth a minute distance on a stopped string. A variation in loudness occurring at the rate of two to five times a second is called tremolo. Singers often produce a combination of tremolo and vibrato to give added color to their renditions.

Like frequency, intensity is a physical entity defined as the amount of sound energy passing through unit area per second in a direction perpendicular to the area. It is proportional to the square of the sound pressure, the latter being the rms pressure over and above the constant mean atmospheric pressure. Since sound pressure is proportional to the amplitude of a

longitudinal sound wave (see WAVE MOTION) and to the frequency of the wave, intensity is proportional to the square of the amplitude and the square of the frequency. Sound intensity is measured in watts per second per square centimeter and, since the ear is so sensitive to sound, a more usual unit is microwatts per second per square centimeter. By way of example, a soft speaking voice produces an intensity of .1 micromicrowatt/cm^2 sec, while fifteen hundred bass voices singing fortissimo at a distance 1 cm away produce 40 watt/cm^2 sec. Because of such large ranges of intensities, the decibel scale of intensity is normally used to designate intensity levels. An arbitrary level of 10^{-16} watts/cm^2 sec is taken as a standard for comparison at 1000 Hz. This is very close to the threshold of audibility. At this frequency, other sound levels are compared by forming the logarithm of the ratio of the desired sound to this arbitrary one. Thus $\log I/10^{-16}$ is the number of bels a sound of intensity I has, compared to this level. Since this unit is inconveniently large, it has been subdivided into the decibel one-tenth its size, $10 \log I/10^{-16}$ equals the number of decibels (dB) the sound has. A few intensity decibel levels are listed.

	db
Quiet whisper	10
Ordinary conversation	60
Noisy factory	90
Thunder (loud)	110
Pain threshold	120

While intensity levels can be measured physically, loudness levels are subjective and need human subjects for their evaluation. The unit of loudness is the phon, and an arbitrary level of zero phons is the loudness of a 1000 Hz note which has an intensity level of 0 dB. Sounds of equal loudness, however, do not have the same intensity levels for different frequencies. From a series of experiments involving human subjects, Fletcher and Munson in 1933 constructed a set of equal loudness contours for different frequencies of pure tones. These show that for quiet sounds (a level of 5 phons) the intensity level at 1000 Hz is about 5 dB lower than an equally loud sound at 2000 Hz, for 30 Hz about 70 dB lower, and at 10 000 Hz about 20 dB lower. In general, as the intensity level increases, loudness levels tend to be more alike at all frequencies. This means that as a sound gets less intense at all frequencies, the ear tends to hear the higher and lower portions of sound less loudly than the middle portions. Some high fidelity systems incorporate circuitry that automatically boosts the high and low frequencies as the intensity level of the sound is decreased. This control is usually designated a loudness control.

That entity which enables a person to recognize the difference between equally loud tones of the same pitch coming from different musical instruments is called timbre, quality, or tone color. A simple fundamental law in acoustics states that the ear recognizes only those sounds due to simple harmonic motions (see VIBRATION) as pure tones. A tuning fork of frequency f, when struck, causes the air to vibrate in a manner which is very nearly simple harmonic. The sound that is heard does, in fact, give the impression that it is simple and produces a pure tone of a single pitch. If one now strikes simultaneously a series of tuning forks having frequencies f (the fundamental), $2f$, $3f$, $4f$, $5f$, etc. (overtones), the pitch heard is the same as that of the single fork of frequency f except that the sound has a different quality. The quality of the sound of the series can be changed by altering the loudness of the individual forks from zero loudness to any given loudness. Another way to alter the tone quality is to vary the time it takes for a composite sound to grow and to decay. A slow growth of an envelope even though it contains the same frequencies makes for a different tone quality than one which has a rapid growth. The difference in quality between a b-flat saxophone and an oboe is almost entirely due to the difference in growth or decay time.

A fundamental theorem discovered by the mathematician Fourier states that any complicated periodic vibration may be analyzed into a set of components which has simple harmonic vibrations of single frequencies. If this method of analysis is applied to the composite tones of musical instruments, it is seen that these tones consist of a fundamental plus a series of overtones, the intensity of the overtones being different for instruments of differing timbre. Rise and decay times will also differ. The reverse of analysis is the synthesis of a musical sound. Helmholtz was able to synthesize sound by combining sets of oscillating tuning forks of various loudness to produce a single composite steady tone of a definite timbre. Modern synthesizers are more sophisticated. Electrical oscillators of the simple harmonic variety are combined electrically and then these electrical composite envelopes are electronically modified to produce differing rise and decay times. A transducer changes the electrical composite envelope into an acoustical one so that a sound of any desired timbre or rise and decay time can be produced. An alternate way to produce similar effects is to use an oscillation known as the square wave. When this is analyzed by the method of Fourier, it is shown to consist of a fundamental plus the odd harmonics or overtones. Another kind of oscillator, a sawtooth wave, when analyzed, is shown to consist of the fundamental and all harmonics—even and odd. A square wave or a sawtooth wave produced by an appropriate electrical oscillator can be passed through an electrical filter which can attenuate any range of frequencies of the original wave. This altered wave can later be transformed into the corresponding

sound wave. In this way sounds having a desired rise and decay time, plus the required fundamental and overtone structure, can be made as desired.

JESS J. JOSEPHS

References

Helmholtz, H., "On the Sensations of Tone," New York, Dover Publications, 1954.

Rayleigh, J. W. S., "The Theory of Sound," New York, Dover Publications, 1945.

Josephs, J. J., "The Physics of Musical Sound," New York, Van Nostrand Reinhold, 1967.

Cross-references: ACOUSTICS, NOISE, VIBRATION, WAVE MOTION.

N

NEUTRINO

The neutrino is an elementary particle postulated by W. Pauli[1] in 1930 to explain the apparent non-conservation of energy and momentum in that class of nuclear radioactivity known as beta decay. A quantitative theory of beta decay incorporating the neutrino hypothesis was formulated by E. Fermi[2] in 1933 in analogy with the quantum theory of radiation and served to predict the nature of the neutrino and its extremely weak interaction with matter. According to the Pauli-Fermi ideas, the neutrino (in Italian, "little neutral one") is a particle of vanishingly small and possibly zero rest mass, no electrical charge, with spin 1/2, and the ability to carry energy and linear and angular momentum. Its interaction with matter is so weak that a 3-MeV antineutrino is predicted to be capable of penetrating an astronomical thickness of matter, e.g., 100 light-years of liquid hydrogen. In 1956, a group of Los Alamos physicists[3] succeeded in making a direct observation of the neutrino, $\tilde{\nu}_e$, emitted from beta-decaying fission fragments produced in a powerful reactor at the Savannah River Plant operated by the du Pont Company for the U.S. Atomic Energy Commission. These investigators used giant liquid scintillation detectors to observe the inverse beta decay reaction

$$\tilde{\nu}_e + p \rightarrow e^+ + n$$

where p is the target proton and e^+ and n are the product positron and neutron. The experiment consisted of observing the distinctive delayed coincidence between the prompt annihilation of the positron and the capture of the neutron by a cadmium isotope dissolved in the scintillator. In 1957, following the "overthrow" of parity conservation in weak interactions as a result of the work of Lee and Yang[4], the character of the neutrino was further elucidated. Two kinds of neutrinos were accepted: the neutrino, ν_e, produced in beta decay in association with positrons, and the antineutrino, $\tilde{\nu}_e$, produced in beta decay in association with negative electrons. The neutrino emerged as completely polarized with the spin angular momentum parallel (antiparallel) to the linear momentum for the antineutrino (neutrino). A theory of weak interactions encompassing the neutrino, in which the relativistically invariant forms, vector and axial

vector, were found to be sufficient to account for most of the known characteristics of the weak interactions, was then formulated by Marshak and Sudarshan[5], and Feynman and Gell-Mann[6].

In 1962, an experiment at the Brookhaven National Laboratory by a Columbia-Brookhaven group[7], using a heavily shielded 10-ton spark chamber array, showed that the neutrino most frequently associated with the decay of the Π meson differed from the neutrino produced in nuclear beta decay, thus enlarging the class of neutrinos to four: ν_e, $\tilde{\nu}_e$, $\tilde{\nu}_\mu$, ν_μ. It now appears that any decay or inverse process involving an electron has associated with it an electron type neutrino while any such process involving a mu meson occurs in association with a mu-type neutrino.

A search with high-energy machines,[8,13] for a particle which may be responsible for the weak interaction and which decays into a muon associated neutrino and a muon, or an electron associated neutrino and an electron, shows that, if it exists, it is more massive than 5 protons.

A search for ν_e from the sun[9] using a 400-ton perchloroethylene ($C_2 Cl_4$) target located $\sim$ 1 mile below the earth's surface to diminish the background due to cosmic rays has, thus far, yielded unexpectedly negative results. In this experiment the ^{37}A produced by solar neutrinos via the reaction $\nu_e + {}^{37}Cl \rightarrow {}^{37}A + e^-$ was sought by collecting the ^{37}A from the $C_2 Cl_4$ container and counted in a tiny low background proportional counter. The limits set, a factor of $\sim$ 3 below expectation, are difficult to reconcile with the current solar model.[10]

Two groups, one 2 miles underground in a South African gold mine,[11] and the other in the Kolar gold fields[12] at a slightly lesser depth, have detected high-energy muon neutrinos produced in the atmosphere by the interaction of cosmic ray primaries. A measure of the meager flux and weakness of the interaction is indicated by the small number of neutrino-induced events collected: the Indian, Japanese, British Kolar group recorded $\sim$ 17 in two years of operation; the American, South African group detected $\sim$ 100 with somewhat larger equipment and four years of operation.

It is seen that neutrino physics encompasses low-energy reactions using fission reactors, work in the structure of the weak interaction using giant electronuclear machines, and the begin-

nings of various studies of natural neutrino sources such as the sun and high-energy cosmic rays.[13]

F. REINES

References

1. Pauli, W., Jr., "Rapports Septiems Conseil Physique, Solvay, Bruxelles, 1933," Paris, Gautier-Villars, 1934.
2. Fermi, E., *Z. Physik*, 88, 161 (1934).
3. Reines, F., and Cowan, C. L., Jr., *Phys. Rev.*, 92, 830 (1953); Cowan, C. L., Jr., Reines, F., Harrison, F. B., Kruse, H. W., and McGuire, A. D., *Science*, 124, 103 (1956); *Phys. Rev.*, 117, 159 (1960).
4. Lee, T. D., and Yang, C. N., *Phys. Rev.*, 105, 1671 (1957).
5. Marshak, R. E., and Sudarshan, E. C. G., *Phys. Rev.*, 109. 1860 (1958); proceedings of Padua-Venice Conference on Mesons and Newly Discovered Particles, Italy, September 1957.
6. Feynman, R. P., and Gell-Mann, M., *Phys. Rev.*, 109, 193 (1958).
7. Danby, G., Gaillard, J. M., Goulianos, K., Lederman, L. M., Mistry, N., Schwartz, M., and Steinberger, J., *Phys. Rev. Letters*, 9, 36 (1962).
8. Reported by the CERN Laboratory Group at the 1964 International High Energy Conference at Dubna, U.S.S.R.
9. Davis, R., Jr., Rogers, L. C., and Radeka, V., *Bull. Am. Phys. Soc.*, 16, 631 (1971).
10. Bahcall, J. N., and Sears, R. L., *Ann. Rev. Astron. Astrophys.* (1972).
11. Reines, F., Kropp, W. R., Sobel, H. W., Gurr, H. S., Lathrop, J., Crouch, M. F., Sellschop, J. P. F., and Meyer B. S. *Phys. Rev.*, D 4, 80 (1971).
12. Krishnaswamy, M. R., Menon, J. G. K., Narasimhan, F. S., Hinotani, K., Ito, N., Miyake, S., Osborne, J. L., Parsons, A. J., and Wolfendale, A. W., *Proc. Roy. Soc. London* A 323 (1971)
13. Further references and a more extensive discussion of the neutrino are given in Cowan, C. L., and Reines, F., contribution to "Cosmology, Fusion, and Other Matters," a Memorial to George Gamow, ed. Reines, F., Boulder: The Associated Colorado Press, 1972.
14. Barish, B., *Scientific American* (Aug., 1973).

Cross-references: CONSERVATION LAWS AND SYMMETRY, ELEMENTARY PARTICLES, RADIOACTIVITY, WEAK INTERACTIONS.

NEUTRON

Discovery The discovery of the neutron by Chadwick[1] in 1932 represented a great step forward in the investigation of nuclei of atoms. Chadwick found that a radiation emitted when α-rays from polonium reacted with beryllium could project protons from a thin sheet of paraffin wax. Although the radiation itself produced no observable ionization when passing through a gas, the protons released from the paraffin were detected in an ionization chamber. Inability to produce ionization was interpreted as a lack of electric charge. From measurements of the ionization from the protons, Chadwick deduced that the so-called beryllium radiation must consist of neutral particles with a mass very nearly equal to that of the proton. He announced the discovery of the neutron, a previously unknown particle. It has been confirmed that the neutron has no charge and a mass of 1.008665 atomic mass units. Thus it is heavier than the proton by 0.00139 mass unit. The introduction of the neutron into nuclear structure produced a sharp change in the previously held ideas. Lacking knowledge of the neutron, masses of atomic nuclei had been attributed solely to protons. The number of protons required on this basis for most nuclei greatly exceeded the known charge number. In an attempt to solve this dilemma, a number of electrons were assigned to each nucleus to adjust the charge number to the proper value. This compromise created an even greater problem, that of accommodating so many electrons in the small space occupied by a nucleus. Bringing the neutron into the picture, it is now only necessary that a nucleus contain protons to equal the charge number with the rest of the mass contributed by neutrons. No electrons are required.

Detection Because it is a neutral particle the neutron can be detected only by means of a secondary charged particle which it releases in passing through matter or by means of the radioactivity which the neutron can induce in stable elements. Protons may be projected by collisions with neutrons in hydrogenous material and the ionization from the protons can be measured in an ionization chamber, as in the original experiment with neutrons. Secondary charged particles may be the direct result of nuclear disintegration produced by neutrons, as in the case of the reaction $^{10}B + {}^{1}n \rightarrow {}^{7}Li + \alpha$. Commonly, the radioactivity induced in stable elements by neutron capture serves to detect neutrons, and this technique is known as the activated foil method. Also, fission may be utilized for detection of neutrons by placing fissionable material inside an ionization chamber and observing the ionization generated by the fission fragments.

Decay The neutron in the free state undergoes radioactive decay. Elaborate experiments by Robson[2] were required to identify the products of the decay and to measure the half-life of the neutron. He showed that the neutron emits a β-particle and becomes a proton. The half-life was found to be 12.8 minutes. In stable nuclei, neutrons are stable. In radioactive nuclei, decaying by β-emission, the neutrons decay with a half-life characteristic of the nuclei of which they are a part.

Energies The kinetic energy of neutrons has an important bearing on the behavior of neutrons when interacting with nuclei. These kinetic energies may range from near zero to as much

as 50 MeV. It is, therefore, natural to classify neutrons in terms of energy according to their properties in each range of energy. For example, energies from zero to about 1000 eV are usually called slow neutrons. Because they are more readily captured by nuclei than faster neutrons, slow neutrons are responsible for a large number of nuclear transformations. When slow neutrons have velocities in equilibrium with the velocities of thermal agitation of the molecules of the medium in which they are situated, they are called thermal neutrons. The distribution of these velocities approaches the Maxwell distribution

$$dn(v) = A v^2 e^{-(Mv^2/2kT)} \, dv$$

where v is the neutron velocity, M its mass, k is Boltzmann's constant and T the absolute temperature. In the slow neutron range of energies, various atomic nuclei show strong absorption (capture) of neutrons at fairly well-defined energies. Neutrons having energies corresponding to those of the absorption bands are called resonance neutrons. Frequently, neutrons with energies greater than 1000 eV and less than 0.5 MeV are termed intermediate neutrons. In more general terms, all neutrons with energies greater than 0.5 MeV are called fast neutrons. The practical upper limit of neutron energy is set by the devices so far developed for accelerating charged particles to extremely high energies.

Magnetic Moment and Spin Alvarez and Bloch[3] succeeded in measuring the moment of the magnetic dipole associated with the known spin of 1/2 possessed by the neutron. More refined measurements by Cohen, Corngold, and Ramsey[4] of the magnetic moment μ_n yielded a value of

$$\mu_n = -1.913148 \text{ nuclear magnetons}$$

Interactions with Nuclei Neutrons may be scattered or captured by heavy nuclei. Scattering may be elastic, resulting only in the change of direction of the neutrons, or inelastic in which the neutron loses part of its energy to the scattering nucleus. Collisions with light nuclei, in absence of capture, result in communicating considerable fractions of the neutron energy to the target nucleus. A neutron colliding head-on with a proton will give practically all its kinetic energy to the proton. As the mass of the target nucleus increases, the transfer of energy decreases, in accordance with the laws of conservation of energy and momentum. The loss of energy by mechanical impact is utilized in slowing down fast neutrons, a process known as moderation. Slow neutrons are most useful, for example, in the production of radioelements from stable elements by neutron capture. A good moderator should have low mass and a small capture cross section. The rate r of capture of neutrons from a neutron flux F (neutrons $cm^{-2} \ sec^{-1}$) incident on a layer of matter having N nuclei per square centimeter is given by

$$r = F \sigma N$$

where σ is the complete probability of capture. Replacing r by dN/dt and writing the flux as nv, where n is the number and v is the velocity of the neutrons, we have

$$\frac{dN}{dt} = -nv\sigma N$$

which integrated gives

$$N = N_0 e^{-nv\sigma t}$$

where N is the number of unchanged nuclei in the target area at time t and N_0 is the number at time $t = 0$. The cross section σ is so named because it has the dimensions of an area. The unit for the cross section is the barn equal to $10^{-24} cm^2$. When, as is often the case, σ is proportional to $1/v$, the advantage of slow neutrons in capture interactions becomes apparent. When the value of σ departs sharply from that predicted by the $1/v$ law, it usually increases over a narrow range of energies, and we have what is called a RESONANCE. Slow neutron cross sections are customarily quoted for thermal neutrons at 20°C, corresponding to a value of v of 2200 m/sec. In Table 1 values of σ are given for a few representative stable elements.

TABLE 1. THERMAL NEUTRON CAPTURE CROSS SECTIONS[a]
$v = 2200$ m/sec

Element	σ (barns)
Boron	759
Cobalt	38
Cadmium	2 450
Gadolinium	46 000
Gold	99.8
Helium	0
Lead	0.170
Oxygen	<0.0002

[a]See reference 5 for data for other elements.

Additional interactions of neutrons with nuclei include the release of charged particles by neutron-induced nuclear disintegration. Commonly known reactions are $n-p$, $n-d$, and $n-\alpha$. In these cases, the incident neutrons may contribute part of their kinetic energy to the target nucleus to effect the disintegration. Hence, more than mere neutron capture is involved. Then there is usually a lower threshold for the neutron energy below which the reaction fails to occur. Another important reaction involving neutrons is fission, which may occur under different conditions for either slow or or fast neutrons with appropriate fissionable material.

Sources of Neutrons Any nuclear reaction in which neutrons are released might serve as a

source of neutrons. In the initial experiments on neutrons, an α—n reaction was used. Because of the charge on the α-particle, it must have a high kinetic energy to penetrate a nucleus. Thus polonium α-particles could release neutrons from beryllium. Such a natural source produces relatively few neutrons. The yield of neutrons from charged particle reactions can be increased manyfold by the use of particle accelerators. Here large numbers of charged particles of high energy can be used in the bombardment of the target to release numerous neutrons. Frequently deuterons or protons are used for the bombardment. A far more prolific source is the nuclear reactor. Fission of uranium is usually the source of the neutrons in this case. A nuclear reactor, as usually constructed, generates neutrons of different energies in various parts of its structure. Neutrons of suitable energy for a given experiment may be brought outside the reactor through channels into appropriate sections of the reactor.

Structure of the Neutron Ordinarily the neutron is regarded simply as a particle which is a component of nuclei and which can exist only briefly in the free state. For many purposes this view is sufficient. However, it has become obvious from experiments, for example, in very high-energy accelerators, that the neutron must have a complex structure. This view is reinforced by the nature of the decay of the neutron. A β-particle is ejected from the neutron on decay, but it is quite certain that the electron did not exist within the neutron prior to the decay. Rearrangements of an internal structure of the neutron must provide the energy for the formation and ejection of the β-particle. One theory would have the neutron consist of a proton and a π^- meson bound together so that they oscillate between a completely bound state and a more loosely bound state. Such a theory might also explain the feeble interaction which has been observed between electrons and neutrons at very short range. At present, it may be sufficient to say that the neutron must have a complex internal structure of a nature at present not very clearly understood.

Additional information on the neutron may be obtained from the books listed below.[6,7]

L. F. CURTISS

References

1. Chadwick, J., *Proc. Roy. Soc. London Ser. A*, **136**, 692 (1932).
2. Robson, J. M., *Phys. Rev.*, **83**, 349 (1951).
3. Alvarez, L. W., and Bloch, F., *Phys. Rev.*, **57**, 111 (1940).
4. Cohen, V. W., Corngold, N. R., and Ramsey, N. F., *Phys. Rev.*, **104**, 283 (1956).
5. "American Institute of Physics Handbook," Second edition, Section 8, New York, McGraw-Hill Book Co., 1963.
6. Curtiss, L. F., "Introduction to Neutron Physics," New York, Van Nostrand Reinhold, 1958.
7. Evans, Robley D., "The Atomic Nucleus," New York, McGraw-Hill Book Co., 1955.

Cross-references: COLLISIONS OF PARTICLES, CROSS SECTIONS AND STOPPING POWER, ELECTRON, FISSION, NUCLEAR REACTIONS, NUCLEAR REACTORS, NEUTRON DIFFRACTION, PROTON, RADIOACTIVITY, RESONANCE.

NEUTRON ACTIVATION ANALYSIS

Neutron activation analysis is a method of elemental analysis based upon the quantitative detection of radioactive species produced in samples via nuclear reactions resulting from neutron bombardment of the samples.

Types of Neutron Reactions The neutron-induced reactions are of two main types: (1) those induced by very slow (thermal) neutrons, having energies of about 0.025 eV, and (2) those induced by fast neutrons, those having energies in the range of MeV.

All stable nuclides are capable of capturing thermal neutrons, but with characteristic reaction cross sections which vary widely from nuclide to nuclide, even of the same element. Promptly following the capture of a thermal neutron by a stable nucleus, the compound nucleus de-excites itself by the emission of one or more "prompt" gamma-ray photons. If the resulting product nucleus is a radionuclide, its later decay can be detected and can be of use in the activation analysis detection of that element. Thermal-neutron capture reactions are therefore referred to as "(n,γ)" reactions. For example, in the determination of vanadium, with thermal neutrons, some of the ^{51}V stable nuclei present in the sample to be analyzed undergo the ^{51}V$(n,\gamma)^{52}$V reaction. Vanadium-52 is radioactive, decaying with a half-life of 3.75 minutes, emitting a β^- particle and a 1.434-MeV gamma-ray photon.

Fast neutrons predominantly interact with nuclei by means of (n, p), (n, α), $(n, 2n)$, and (n,n') reactions. Whereas the thermal-neutron capture reaction forms a nuclide of the original element, but now one mass unit higher, the $(n, 2n)$ fast-neutron reaction forms a nuclide of the same element one mass unit lower. An example of this type of reaction is the ^{14}N$(n, 2n)$ ^{13}N reaction. Nitrogen-14 is the abundant stable nuclide of nitrogen, whereas ^{13}N is radioactive, decaying with a half-life of 9.96 minutes by positron emission. The (n, n') fast-neutron type of reaction, termed a "neutron inelastic scattering" reaction, forms an excited state (nuclear isomer) of the original nucleus, with unchanged mass number (A), but a measurable half-life. The ^{77}Se$(n, n')^{77m}$Se reaction is a good example of this type of reaction. Selenium-77 is one of the stable nuclides of selenium, whereas ^{77m}Se is a radioactive isomer of ^{77}Se that decays with a half-life of 17.5 seconds, emitting an isomeric-transition 0.161 MeV gamma-ray photon. In

(*n, p*) reactions, the product nucleus has the same mass number as the original nucleus, but is a different element, namely, lower by one unit in atomic number (Z). A widely utilized reaction of this type is the $^{16}O(n, p)^{16}N$ reaction. Oxygen-16 is the principal stable nuclide of oxygen; ^{16}N is a radioactive isotope of nitrogen, decaying with a half-life of 7.14 seconds, emitting exceptionally high-energy beta particles and gamma-ray photons. In (*n, α*) reactions, the product nucleus has a mass number 3 units lower than the original nucleus, and a Z that is 2 units lower than originally. For example, in the fast-neutron detection of phosphorus, the $^{31}P(n, α)^{28}Al$ reaction is often utilized. Normal phosphorus consists entirely of ^{31}P; ^{28}Al is a radioactive nuclide of aluminum, decaying with a half-life of 2.31 minutes, emitting a $β^-$ particle and a 1.780-MeV gamma-ray photon in each disintegration.

Theory of the Method When a sample containing N nuclei of a given type (a particular Z and A) is exposed to a flux ϕ of neutrons, resulting in a particular nuclear reaction having a cross section σ, the rate of formation of product nuclei by this reaction, in nuclei per second, is simply $N\phi\sigma$. The units of ϕ and σ are neutrons per square centimeter per second and square centimeters per nucleus, respectively. If the product nucleus is a radioactive species, some of these nuclei will be decaying while the irradiation is going on. If the irradiation of the sample with neutrons is continued for a long time, compared with the half-life of the radionuclide formed, a steady state, or "saturation" condition will be reached, in which previously formed nuclei are decaying at the same rate that new ones are being formed, thus with no further increase in the disintegration rate of this particular product with continued irradiation at that flux. Therefore, the saturation activity of a given species, at zero decay time (i.e., just at the conclusion of the irradiation), is $A_0(\text{satn}) = N\phi\sigma$.

At intermediate irradiation times (t_i), the activity of a particular induced species (A_o, expressed in disintegrations per second, i.e., dps) is equal to $N\phi\sigma S$, where S is a "saturation" term that is equal to $1 - \exp(-0.693t_i/t_{0.5})$, where $t_{0.5}$ is the half-life of the radioactive species. The saturation term is dimensionless and ranges only from 0 (at $t_i = 0$) to 1 (at $t_i = \infty$). It rapidly approaches a value of one, asymptotically, acquiring values of 1/2, 3/4, 7/8, 15/16, $\cdots$ at $t_i/t_{0.5}$ values of 1, 2, 3, 4, $\cdots$. Because of this rapid approach of S to its maximum value, it is pointless to activate a sample for a period of time longer than a few half-lives of the radioactive species of interest. Longer irradiation merely generates more interfering activities of longer half-lives.

In the basic activation equation, σ is the isotopic cross section for the particular type of nuclear reaction, for neutrons of a specified energy. It assumes that the neutron flux, and energy, are constant throughout the sample. The N term is itself equal to $wfaN_A/AW$, in which w is the weight of the sample (in grams), f is the weight fraction of the element in the sample, a is the fractional abundance of the target stable nuclide among all the stable nuclides of the element, N_A is Avogadro's number, and AW is the ordinary chemical atomic weight of the element. In actual analyses, of course, either f or the product wf is the unknown quantity.

Neutron Sources In neutron activation analysis work, the most widely used neutron sources are (1) research-type nuclear reactors, and (2) small accelerators. Modern research reactors are mostly of the pool type and operate at power levels of 10 to 10 000 kW, providing thermal-neutron fluxes of 10^{11} to 10^{14} n cm^{-2} sec^{-1} and fission spectrum fast-neutron fluxes of about the same magnitude. The small accelerators used in neutron activation analysis work are largely low-voltage (100 to 200 kV) Cockcroft-Walton deuteron accelerators, capable of producing up to about 10^{11} 14-MeV neutrons/sec from a tritium target (with a 1-mA deuteron beam current), via the $^3H(d, n)^4He$ reaction. Samples of typical size (~ 1 cm^3) can thus be exposed to a 14-MeV neutron flux of about 10^9 n cm^{-2} sec^{-1}. In a moderator, these can produce a thermal-neutron flux of the order of 10^8 n cm^{-2} sec^{-1}. Unfortunately, at full-power operation, the lifetime of the tritium target is only of the order of an hour to a few hours. Some work is carried out also with lower-energy neutrons generated by the $^9Be(d, n)^{10}B$ reaction with a 2-MeV positive-ion Van de Graaff accelerator, or by the $^9Be(x, n)^8Be$ reaction with bremsstrahlung produced by a 3MeV electron Van de Graaff accelerator. These produce thermal-neutron fluxes in the range of 10^8 to 10^9 n cm^{-2} sec^{-1}. Isotopic sources, such as $^{210}Po -$ Be, $^{239}Pu -$ Be, and $^{241}Am -$ Be, also generate neutrons, but the maximum thermal-neutron flux attainable with such sources is only about 10^5 n cm^{-2} sec^{-1}. They are useful for teaching purposes, but not for real analytical work. Californium-252 spontaneous-fission neutron sources generate 2.34×10^9 neutrons sec^{-1} per mg of ^{252}Cf.

Sensitivities for Various Elements As the available neutron flux increases, the level of induced activity per unit mass of an element also increases; hence, the sensitivity of detection is higher, i.e., the limit of detection is lower. With a nuclear-reactor thermal-neutron flux of 10^{13} n cm^{-2} sec^{-1}, a maximum t_i of one hour, and reasonable counting efficiencies, it is found that the median limit of detection for some 75 elements is about 10^{-3} μg. A few of these elements can be detected down as low as $10^{-7}\mu$g; a few only to about 10 μg. The method, with such high neutron fluxes, is the most sensitive known method for over half the elements of the periodic system. With 1-gram samples, the μg absolute sensitivities correspond to parts-per-million

(ppm) concentration sensitivities. Samples ranging from minute samples up to 10 grams or somewhat more can be irradiated and analyzed. With longer irradiation periods, the detection limits for about half of the 75 elements (those forming longer-lived induced activities) can be reduced further. The most sensitively detected elements (limits $\leqslant 10^{-3}$ μg) are the following: Ag, As, Au, Br, Co, Cu, Dy, Er, Eu, Ga, Ge, Ho, I, In, Ir, La, Lu, Mn, Na, Nb, Pd, Pr, Re, Rh, Sb, Sm, Sr, U, V, W, and Yb. A few elements are more sensitively determined by activation with fast neutrons than with thermal neutrons.

At the lower (10^8 to 10^9) thermal-neutron fluxes attainable with the small accelerators, the limits of detection are, of course, 10^4 to 10^5 times higher than for the reactor 10^{13} flux. At a 10^9 thermal-neutron flux, the sensitivities for the same 75 elements thus range from 10^{-3} μg to 0.1 gram, with a median of 10 μg. With a 14-MeV neutron flux of 10^9 n cm^{-2} sec^{-1}, a number of additional elements can be detected fairly sensitively, down to levels of 0.1 to 10 μg, e.g., N, O, F, Si, P, Cr, and Fe.

Forms of the Method In practical analytical work, one does not employ the basic activation analysis equation ($A_o = N\phi\sigma S$), per se, but instead uses a comparator technique. When samples are to be analyzed for one or more elements, standard samples of these elements are activated at the same time as the unknowns and then are counted in an identical manner (counting efficiency ϵ). When the counting data are corrected to the same decay time, then, A (unknown)/A(standard) = grams element in unknown/grams element in standard, since ϵ, f, AW, ϕ, σ, and S are the same for both unknown and standard. In the equation, A refers to the counting rate (rather than disintegration rate) of the radionuclide formed by the element in question—in unknown and standard, respectively. Not only is the comparison technique simpler, but it removes any dependence upon literature values of σ, and experimental values of ϵ and ϕ, which often are not accurately known. At levels well above the limits of detection, careful application of this comparison technique results in precisions and absolute accuracies in the range of ± 1 to 3 per cent of the value.

The method is employed in two different forms: the purely instrumental form and the radiochemical separation form. The instrumental form is fast and nondestructive, and is based upon the quantitative detection of induced gamma-ray emitters by means of multichannel gamma-ray spectrometry. It is the preferred method where it applies. Induced activities are identified by the energies of their gamma-ray photopeaks observed in the NaI(Tl) scintillation counter or Ge(Li) semiconductor detector pulse-height spectrum of the activated sample. The amount of the element present in a sample is usually computed from the photopeak (total absorption peak) height or area of its gamma ray, or one of its principal gamma rays, compared with that of the standard.

Where interferences from other induced activities are very serious, and cannot be removed adequately by decay, spectrum subtraction, or computer solution, one must turn to the radiochemical separation form of the method. Here the activated sample is put into solution and equilibrated chemically with measured amounts (typically 10 mg) of added carrier of each of the elements of interest, before chemical separations are carried out. The element to be detected needs then to be recovered in chemically, and radiochemically, pure form, but it need not be quantitatively recovered, since the carrier recovery is measured and the counting data are then normalized to 100 per cent recovery. This form of the method is slower, but it applies to pure beta emitters, as well as to gamma emitters, and it does eliminate interfering activities. It is free of the usual complications of microconcentration analysis: high blanks from reagent impurity, and losses by adsorption and coprecipitation.

Neutron activation analysis is now a well-established method of elemental analysis, carried out in many laboratories and utilized by many more through available commercial activation analysis services. It is now widely applied in almost every branch of science, engineering, and medicine, where either its great sensitivity (at high fluxes) or its speed (with the instrumental form of the method), or both, are used to advantage.

VINCENT P. GUINN

References

Bowen, H., and Gibbons, D., "Radioactivation Analysis," London, Oxford University Press, 1963.

DeVoe, J. R., ed., "Modern Trends in Activation Analysis," Nat'l. Bur. of Standards Special Publication 312, Washington, D.C., 1969.

Guinn, V. P., ed., "Proceedings of the First International Conference on Forensic Activation Analysis," Report GA-8171, San Diego, Calif., Gulf General Atomic, 1967.

Guinn, V. P., "Activation Analysis," chpater in Kolthoff, I. M., and Elving, P. J., eds., "Treatise on Analytical Chemistry," Part 1, Vol. 9, New York, John Wiley & Sons, 1971.

Int'l. Atomic Energy Agency, eds., "Radiochemical Methods of Analysis," Vienna, Int'l. Atomic Energy Agency, 1965.

Int'l. Atomic Energy Agency, eds., "Nuclear Activation Techniques in the Life Sciences," Vienna, Int'l. Atomic Energy Agency, 1967.

Int'l Atomic Energy Agency, eds., "Nuclear Techniques in Environmental Pollution," Vienna, Int'l. Atomic Energy Agency, 1971.

Kruger, P., "Principles of Activation Analysis," New York, Wiley Interscience, 1971.

Lenihan, J. M. A., and Thomson, S. J., eds., "Advances in Activation Analysis," Vol. 1, London, Academic Press, 1969 (and Vol. 2, 1972).

Lutz, G. J., Boreni, R. J., Maddock, R. S., and Meinke,

W. W., "Activation Analysis: A Bibliography," Nat'l. Bur. of Standards Technical Note 467, Washington, D. C., 1971.

Lyon, W. S., ed., "Guide to Activation Analysis," New York, Van Nostrand Reinhold, 1964.

Cross-references: ACCELERATORS, PARTICLE; ISOTOPES; NEUTRON; NUCLEAR REACTIONS; NUCLEAR REACTORS; RADIOACTIVITY.

NEUTRON DIFFRACTION

An experiment by Laue, Friedrich, and Knipping in 1912 demonstrated that x-rays were a form of electromagnetic radiation, with a wavelength of the same order of magnitude as the distance apart (10^{-8} cm) of atoms in crystals. This meant that beams of x-rays could be diffracted by crystals in a rather similar way to that in which an optical diffraction grating, in which the elements are separated by about 10^{-5} cm, will produce a spectrum for visible light. As a result of Laue's discovery, a technique for studying the underlying structure of solids by "x-ray diffraction" has grown up. For any given solid, the end product of this technique is a specification of the shape and content of the building block, or "unit cell," out of which the solid is built. The content is specified in terms of "electron density," and it follows that the various atoms or ions which make up the molecule of the substance can be identified.

A rather similar, but in some respects a much more powerful, technique has grown up using beams of neutrons instead of x-rays. A neutron is often thought of simply as a particle, with a mass approximately equal to that of a hydrogen atom, but in terms of wave mechanics a beam of neutrons can be regarded as a wave motion. If the neutrons are moving with velocity v, then they can be considered to have a wavelength equal to h/mv, where m is the mass of the neutron and h is Planck's constant. If such a neutron beam is scattered by a solid, it will be distributed in space as if it were radiation of this wavelength. It so happens that for neutrons having energies equivalent to a temperature of a few hundred degrees centigrade, which are readily obtainable from nuclear reactors, the wavelength is about 10^{-8} cm, i.e., 1Å, which, as we have seen above, is about equal to the interatomic distance in solids. It was shown in 1936 that neutrons, then obtainable only from a radium-beryllium source, could indeed by diffracted by solids. However, it is only since nuclear reactors have produced *intense* beams of suitable neutrons that the application of diffraction techniques to the study of solids has proved worthwhile.

Since high-intensity neutron beams are only available at a limited number of research institutions throughout the world, we shall be concerned only with their application to problems which cannot be solved by any other method. In particular, we shall enquire what can be achieved with neutrons which cannot be found out by using a beam of x-rays, and we shall see the answers to this question by making a comparison of the ways in which atoms and solids scatter x-rays and neutrons. *X-rays* are scattered by the outer, extranuclear, electrons in an atom, and it is for this reason that x-ray diffraction studies produce a picture of electron density. It follows that heavy atoms, such as lead and uranium which contain many electrons, will predominate in these pictures and that a one-electron atom, i.e., hydrogen, can be located and detailed with much less accuracy. On the other hand, *neutrons* are scattered not by electrons but by the neucleus of an atom, and the way in which the scattering power increases with the mass of the atom is very far from being a steadily increasing function. The scattering power or, more precisely, what we call the "scattering length" arises from the summation of two quite separate effects. The first of these depends on the size of the nucleus, which has a radius proportional to the cube-root of the atomic weight, so that this effect does indeed increase with atomic weight, but nevertheless fairly slowly. Superimposed on this scattering, however, is resonance scattering, which depends in a complicated way on the actual structure of the nucleus and on its energy levels. This additional scattering often varies quite considerably from atom to atom, and sometimes from isotope to isotope, as we advance up the periodic table. When we combine together the two effects, and thus assess the resultant scattering by a nucleus, we find that it varies quite irregularly from atom to atom and this is illustrated for elements at the lower end of the periodic system in Fig. 1. It will, however, be noted that there is a relatively small spread of values among these scattering lengths. The mean value for all the nuclei which have so far been measured is 0.62×10^{-12} cm, and practically all elements have values which lie between a half and twice this average. As a result of this we find that most elements are roughly equally "visible" to neutrons, though there are a few very interesting exceptions. The practical outcome of this is that hydrogen atoms can be located quite accurately in whatever environment they are found, and this has meant important advances in our knowledge of the role of hydrogen bonds and molecules of water of crystallization in building up the structures of both inorganic and organic crystals. At the same time, we have often been able to get much improved information on the thermal motion of molecules, particularly in those common cases where hydrogen atoms are found on the outside of molecules and which, therefore, provide a very good index of the molecular movement. The technique of detection becomes much more powerful if we can use *deuterated* material, instead of ordinary hydrogen. Deuterium has a neutron scattering length of 0.65×10^{-12} cm and is, therefore, a "good average" atom,

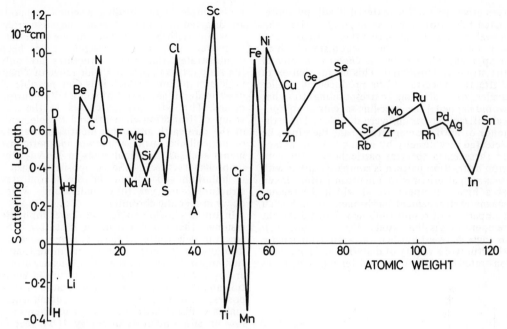

FIG. 1. The variation of the nuclear scattering amplitude of elements for neutrons, shown as a function of atomic weight, in units of 10^{-12} cm.

whereas ordinary hydrogen, at 0.38×10^{-12} cm, is somewhat below average. This comparison provides a very good example of a difference between the scattering behavior of two different isotopes of an element, arising from differences in the nuclear structures.

Another important field of chemistry to which neutron diffraction has contributed some useful results is in the study of the compounds of uranium, and post-uranic elements, with nitrogen and oxygen. In the case of x-ray studies, the 92 electrons of a uranium atom completely overshadow the seven and eight of nitrogen and oxygen respectively. For neutrons, however, the value of the scattering length for uranium $(0.85 \times 10^{-12}$ cm$)$ is actually less than the value for nitrogen $(0.94 \times 10^{-12}$ cm$)$ and is only fractionally greater than that of oxygen $(0.58 \times 10^{-12}$ cm$)$.

Of intrinsic interest, and having particular significance in the growing field of study of chemicals of biological importance is the so-called "anomalous scattering" of neutrons by a few elements, such as cadmium and samarium, for which the nuclear scattering amplitude is a complex quantity, with real and imaginary components. This can provide crucial information for determining the structure of large molecules such as insulin if one of these anomalous scatterers can be incorporated in the molecule.

So far we have been considering the process whereby the neutron is scattered by the atomic *nucleus*, and this is a process which occurs for all atoms. There is, however, an additional scattering which takes place for *magnetic* atoms,

i.e., for atoms which have a resultant magnetic moment on account of the fact that the atoms contain unpaired electrons. Examples of this are an atom of iron in metallic iron, which appears to contain 2.2 unpaired electrons, and the doubly-charged manganese ion Mn^{++}, which contains 5 unpaired electrons, in manganese salts. Such atoms or ions scatter additional neutrons, making an additional contribution to the scattering length by an amount which is proportional to the magnetic moment. If the magnetic moments in such a material are not arranged in any regular single direction, but point haphazardly as in a *paramagnetic* material, then there will not be any well-defined diffracted beams but there will be a broadly distributed contribution to the scattered background. This contribution may be a little difficult to identify but, nevertheless, the identification can be achieved and the phenomenon can be confirmed. In other magnetic materials, however, all the magnetic moments in a single domain lie parallel to a single direction, and in the particular case of a *ferromagnetic* material they all point *algebraically* in the same sense. In this circumstance the magnetically scattered neutrons contribute specifically to the diffracted beams and the intensity of these is observed to vary with increase of temperature, falling to a minimum at the approach of the Curie temperature, above which no ferromagnetic alignment takes place. In the case of antiferromagnetic materials, in which the moments lie parallel to a single direction but alternately up and down with opposite algebraic sense, the neutron data are extremely in-

formative. In such a material it will be appreciated that, from a *magnetic* point of view, the repeat distance (considering the alternate + and − moments) is twice the repeat distance which is apparent when only the *chemical* nature of the atoms is considered. This means that extra diffraction spectra will be produced at smaller angles of scattering, corresponding to what would happen if the inter-line spacing of an optical diffraction grating were doubled. The existence of antiferromagnetism can, therefore, be detected very directly by noting the appearance of these extra spectra, particularly if the neutron diffraction pattern is compared either with an x-ray pattern or with a neutron pattern taken at a higher temperature at which the regular magnetic arrangement has broken down. Such a comparison of results obtained at two different temperatures is illustrated in Fig. 2. Results such as these have established the antiferromagnetic structures of a variety of materials and have demonstrated the true nature of ferrimagnetism, as

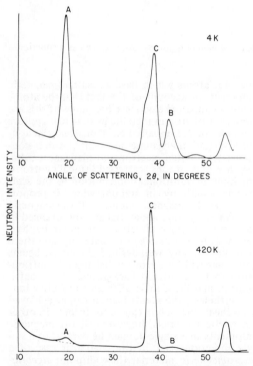

FIG. 2. A comparison of neutron diffraction patterns taken at 4 and 420 K for an antiferromagnetic alloy, $Au_2Mn_{1.7}Al_{0.3}$. At the lower temperature, intense magnetic lines A and B appear, but at the higher temperature, where very little magnetic order remains, these extra lines have practically disappeared. The patterns also show the composite nature of the nuclear scattering line C at low temperature, which occurs because the crystal symmetry changes from cubic to tetragonal when the magnetic order becomes established.

for example in the ferrites in which moments are directed in both positive and negative directions but with a net balance in one direction. Moreover, with further research, it has been demonstrated that these structures are only the simplest examples of a wide range of "magnetic architecture" which it is now possible to draw in detail as a result of study with neutron beams. This later work, devoted to the iron group of transition elements and the elements of the rare earth group, has identified a variety of noncollinear arrangements of magnetic moments such as the spiral spins in $MnAu_2$, the umbrella structure in CrSe, composite structures in holmium and erbium and the complicated structures, not yet fully understood, which occur in metallic chromium.

In our discussion so far, we have implicitly assumed that when a neutron is scattered by an atom it is scattered *elastically* and does not lose any of its energy. This is no more than a first approximation to the truth, because atoms are by no means rigidly fixed but are in vibration about their mean positions because of their possession of thermal energy. A neutron which makes collision with an atom may, therefore, lose or gain a quantity of energy. If we keep in mind the fact that atoms in a solid are not isolated, and that the movement of one atom will invariably affect to some degree the motion of its neighbors, it becomes fruitful to regard the interchange of energy as occurring between the neutron and the lattice vibrations of the solid. Indeed we speak of "phonons" which are the embodiment in *particle* form, from the point of view of wave mechanics, of the quanta of energy among the crystal vibrations. If we could measure accurately the interchanges of energy, then we could learn about, and indeed study in detail, the phonon spectra and the dispersion law for the solid. In fact, for *neutron* scattering, but not for x-rays, such a measurement can be made and this gives a quite unique value to the use of inelastic neutron scattering for studying solids. The particular supremacy of neutrons becomes clear if we consider the actual energies of a neutron and x-ray quantum which possess the same wavelength. We find in fact that the latter is roughly 10^5 times larger. Thus, whereas the energy of a neutron of wavelength 1Å is about equal to that of a quantum of crystal energy, yet the energy of 1Å x-ray is 10^5 times greater. It follows, therefore, that if a neutron gains or loses such a quantum, then its own energy will be greatly changed; for example, it could easily be roughly doubled or halved. On the other hand such an interchange for an x-ray would be quite insignificant and the resulting change of wavelength could not be detected. It is in fact possible, therefore, to measure both momentum and energy changes in neutron-phonon interchanges, and this information leads directly to the details of the dispersion law in the solid. The full power of these methods can be achieved only by detailed and extensive ob-

servations with single crystals. Nevertheless a relatively simple technique of neutron spectroscopy is available for powdered and polycrystalline samples, which has rather similar aims to conventional infrared and Raman spectroscopy, but with some distinctive advantages. In particular, any vibrations in which hydrogen atoms are involved are greatly enhanced, and moreover, the selection rules which limit the observation of transitions in optical spectra do not generally apply to the neutron spectra of inelastic scattering.

As the intensity of the beams of neutrons available from research reactors steadily increases, with roughly a ten fold increase each ten years, these techniques become progressively more powerful and determinative, leading to a steadily widening view of solids and liquids in the several unique respects which we have discussed. The limitations in the use of these techniques are those set by the limited availability of suitable nuclear reactors, and it may be fairly said that many promising applications have not yet been tested.

G. E. BACON

Reference

Bacon, G. E., "Neutron Diffraction," Second Edition, London, Oxford University Press, 1962.

Egelstaff, P. A. Ed. "Thermal Neutron Scattering," London, Academic Press Inc., 1965.

Izyumov, Yu. A, and Ozerov, R. P., "Magnetic Neutron Diffraction," New York, Plenum Press, 1970.

Marshall, W., and Lovesey, S. W., "Theory of Thermal Neutron Scattering," London, Oxford University Press, 1971.

Cross-references: DIFFRACTION BY MATTER AND DIFFRACTION GRATINGS, MAGNETISM, NEUTRON, PARAMAGNETISM, X-RAYS.

NOISE, ACOUSTICAL

Strictly defined, noise is any unwanted sound, whether pleasant or unpleasant. More commonly, however, sounds that are unpleasant and disturbing, or that mask desired sound, are termed noise. Thus, noise, in a general sense, may be thought of as any sonic disturbance. Depending upon the degree of pitch distribution, intensity, and persistance, noise can range from being merely annoying, to hazardous or injurious. In our highly industrialized society, with its rapid growth of energy-producing and converting systems, noise has become a major problem. Some of its harmful effects are interference with mental and skilled work, impairment of sleep, creation of emotional disturbances, damage to hearing and a deterioration of health and well-being. Consequently, the control and reduction of noise has become an important science.

Adequate measuring means are a prime requirement in the scientific control and reduction of noise. Even then, the problem of establishing a true relationship between the subjective and objective properties of noise is difficult because of the many different aspects of human reaction to noise. The first relationship between the subjective and objective measurement of sound is the simplified rule relating *loudness in sones* to the *loudness level in phons*. The loudness scale in sones is proportional to the average person's estimate of the loudness. Also, the loudness level, P, of a given sound, in phons, is numerically equal to the median sound pressure level, p_L, of a free progressive wave at a frequency of 1000 Hz presented to listeners facing the source, which is judged by the listeners to be equally loud. The sound pressure level, p_L, is defined as

$$p_L = 20 \log_{10} \frac{p}{p_0} \text{ (decibels)} \qquad (1)$$

where p is measured sound pressure, in microbars, and $p_0 = 2 \times 10^{-4}$ microbars.

The relation between sones, S, and phons, P, is given by

$$S = 2^{(P-40)/10} \qquad (2)$$

Referring to Eq. (2), a loudness level of 40 phons produces a loudness of one sone, and a loudness level of 80 phons produces a loudness level of sixteen sones, etc.

The simplest means for the measurement of noise is the sound level meter, an instrument comprising a microphone, an amplifier, frequency weighting networks, and an output meter. The characteristics of the frequency weighting networks in the meter are based upon the equal loudness contours of hearing for different levels.

More sophisticated means for measuring noise include octave band and one-third octave band sound analyzers that supply information on the sound level in various frequency ranges. These analyzers are used for research on the reduction of machine noise, transmission and other areas where information on the sound levels in specific frequency bands is required. Narrow-band analyzers may be used to obtain the spectrum of a noise. The sound-pressure spectrum level is that level within a frequency band of 1 Hz. This level is plotted against frequency to obtain the spectrum frequency characteristic of the noise. If the spectrum level of a noise is known, sophisticated means may be used to relate the objective to the subjective qualities of the noise.

As noted earlier, noise abatement has become an important science. For instance intensive research on the quieting of automobiles has been in progress for three decades, with outstanding results; some of the major problems remaining to be solved involve wind- and road-induced noise. Similarly, research has been carried out on the reduction of noise of all

types of household appliances employing motors, fans, compressors, pumps, gears, and other moving parts. Another phase of acoustical engineering involves methods for reducing the transmission of sound through the walls, floors, ceiling and partitions in all manner of buildings or enclosure by the use of construction and materials based on fundamental acoustical principles.

The noise in typical environments and noise produced by various sources are given in Table 1.

TABLE I. NOISE LEVELS FOR VARIOUS SOURCES AND LOCATIONS[a]

Source or Description of Noise		Noise Level (dB)
Threshold of pain		130
Hammer blows on steel plate	2 ft	114
Riveter	35 ft	97
Factory		78
Busy street traffic		68
Large office		65
Ordinary conversation	3 ft	65
Large store		63
Factory office		63
Medium store		62
Restaurant		60
Residential street		58
Medium office		58
Garage		55
Small store		52
Theatre		42
Hotel		42
Apartment		42
House, large city		40
House, country		30
Average whisper	4 ft	20
Quiet whisper	5 ft	10
Rustle of leaves in gentle breeze		10
Threshold of hearing		0

[a]Olson, Harry F., "Acoustical Engineering," p. 256, New York, Van Nostrand Reinhold, 1957.

The masking effect produced by noise reduces the intelligibility of speech. For example, if the speaker and listener are separated by 5 feet, the levels of noise that will barely permit reliable word intelligibility are 51 dB for normal conversation, 57 dB for raised speech, 63 dB for very loud speech, and 69 dB for shouting.

A person subjected to high noise levels for long periods of time may suffer considerable impairment of hearing. The use of ear protectors may provide sufficient insulation under such conditions.

There are now federal regulations on permissible noise in industry as given in the reference below. Examples of the permissible noise exposures are as follows: for 8 hours per day the permissible sound level is 90 dBA, for 4 hours per day 95 dBA, for 1 hour per day 105 dBA, etc.

HARRY F. OLSON

References

Federal Register, Saturday, May 29, 1971, Vol. **36**, No. 105, Part II, Department of Labor, "Occupational Safety and Health Administration." Article 1910.95, "Occupational Noise Exposure."

Goodfriend, Lewis S., "Noise Pollution," CRC Scientific Publications, Cleveland, Ohio, 1972.

Harris, G. M., "Handbook of Noise Control," New York McGraw-Hill Book Company, 1957.

Cross-references: ACOUSTICS; ARCHITECTURAL ACOUSTICS; HEARING; MEASUREMENTS, PRINCIPLES OF; MUSICAL SOUND.

NUCLEAR INSTRUMENTS

Nuclear instruments are those devices which are used to make the group of measurements which is commonly described as nuclear radiation detection. These measurements are understood to encompass not only the indication of the presence of nuclear radiation but also the determination of the amount, energy, and related properties. The nuclear instrument may be considered to consist of two parts, a detector and a measuring apparatus. The interaction of the radiation with the instrument takes place in the detector, while the measuring apparatus takes the output of the detector and performs the required analysis to accomplish the measurement.

Nuclear instruments are either pulse type or non-pulse type. In the pulse-type instrument, the output of the detector is a series of signals separated or resolved in time, each signal representing the interaction of a nuclear particle with the detector. If the pulse feature of the detector output is used, e.g., in counting particles or in measurement of the distribution in energy of particles, the nuclear instrument is said to be pulse type.

In the non-pulse type of operation of a nuclear system, no attempt is made to resolve the signals of individual particles. Instead, the average effect due to many interactions of the radiation with the detector is measured directly. This type of instrument, which can be described as a mean-level type detection system, is typified by the current-type ionization system. The current output is proportional to the number of particles incident upon the detector per unit time.

For the study of the physics of the interaction of NUCLEAR RADIATION with the detectors, it is convenient to divide the numerous forms of radiation into classes, based on the mode of interaction with matter as in a detector, and to discuss the properties of a prototype of each class. The radiations which are convenient as prototypes are protons, electrons, fission fragments, gamma rays, and neutrons.

The prototype protons, fission products, electrons, and all other radiations consisting of charged particles each interact with matter pri-

marily by the production of excitation and ionization of the matter through which it is passing, with ionization playing the major role. The nuclear particles lose energy at a rate w per ion pair formed. Values of w for particles passing through gases range from 25 to 50 eV per ion pair. The three types of particles differ primarily in their penetrating ability; for example, a 0.03 MeV electron will pass through 2.2 mg/cm^2 of air, while a proton would need 0.9 MeV of energy and a fission product 64 MeV to penetrate the same thickness.

Gamma rays and neutrons, being uncharged radiations, differ in their primary mode of interaction from the types discussed above. However, both gamma rays and neutrons undergo primary interactions with matter which produce secondary charged particles that interact with the detector, thereby producing effects which make possible the detection as in the case of the radiation types which consist of charged particles. The interaction of gamma rays with matter produces secondary electrons through the principal mechanisms of photoelectric effect (see PHOTOELECTRICITY), Compton scattering and pair production, as well as through several other secondary mechanisms.

In the case of neutrons, there are also several mechanisms by which the interaction with matter takes place, each of which is the basis for a potential method of detection. The most useful ones are: (1) neutron-induced transmutations in which the product particles make detection possible; examples are (n, α), (n, p), (n, γ), and $(n, \text{fission})$ reactions; (2) neutron-induced transmutations, leading to radioactive nuclei, the subsequent decay of which makes the detection possible; (3) elastic scattering of neutrons (for example, by a proton) in which the recoil proton can be detected.

Several nuclear radiation detectors depend for their operation on the IONIZATION that is produced in them by the passage of charged particles. This group of detectors includes ionization chambers, proportional counters, Geiger-Müller counters, semiconductor radiation detectors, cloud chambers, and spark chambers. For the uncharged particles, such as neutrons and gamma rays, the charged particles which are required for the production of ionization originate by the secondary processes referred to above.

In other detectors, excitation and sometimes molecular dissociation also play important roles. These phenomena, in combination with ionization, bring about the LUMINESCENCE in scintillation detectors and the latent images in photographic emulsions. Also, molecular dissociaiton is important in chemical detection systems, i.e., those devices that function through the occurrence of certain chemical reactions.

One of the oldest, but still most widely used, types of detector employs a gas-filled chamber. Depending on the mode of operation of this chamber, the detector type is known either as

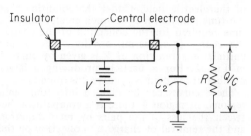

FIG. 1. Schematic diagram for pulse operation of gas-filled chamber. (Reprinted from Price, W. J., "Nuclear Radiation Detection." p. 42, New York, McGraw-Hill Cook Company, Inc., 1964)

an ionization chamber, a proportional counter, or a Geiger-Müller (G-M) tube. The principles of operation and the differences in the three modes of operation can be explained by the use of Fig. 1 and 2. The system shown in Fig. 1 consists of a gas-filled chamber containing a central electrode that is well insulated from the chamber wall. A potential V is applied between the central electrode and the chamber wall through the high resistance R shunted by the capacitor C_2.

Assume that the passage of a nuclear particle releases N_1 ion pairs within the chamber. The positive and negative charges within the chamber move toward the chamber wall and central electrode, respectively, because of the direction

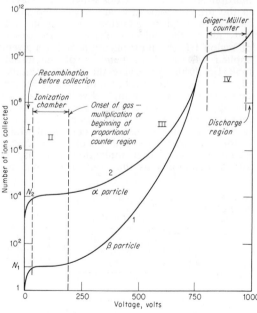

FIG. 2. Pulse-height vs applied-voltage curves to illustrate ionization, proportional, and Geiger-Müller regions of operation. [Reprinted from Montgomery, C. G., and Montgomery, D. C., *J. Franklin Inst.*, **231**, 449 (1941)]

of the electric field. Under the condition that the time constant RC_2 is much greater than the time required for the collection of the charge, the charge Q appearing on the capacitor per particle as a function of V is given by curve 1 in Fig. 2. For a particle producing a larger number of ion pairs N_2, curve 2 is obtained.

These curves can be divided into four main regions. In region 1 there is a competition between the loss of ion pairs by recombination and the removal of charge by collection on the electrodes. With increasing field, the drift velocity of the ions increases; therefore the time available for recombination decreases, and the fraction of the charge which is collected becomes larger.

In region II the recombination loss is negligible, and the charge collected is

$$Q_1 = N_1 e \quad \text{and} \quad Q_2 = N_2 e$$

The change in voltage across the capacitor C_2 is

$$\Delta V_1 = \frac{N_1 e}{C} \quad \text{and} \quad \Delta V_2 = \frac{N_2 e}{C}$$

where C is the sum of the ionization-chamber capacity and C_2. This region is referred to as the saturation region or the ionization-chamber region.

In region III the collected charge is increased by a factor M through the phenomenon of gas multiplication. The electrons which are released in the primary ionization are accelerated sufficiently to produce additional ionization and thus add to the collected charge. At the onset of region III, the multiplication M for a given applied voltage is independent of the initial ionization, thus preserving the proportionality of pulse sizes. This strict proportionality breaks down with increase in applied voltage until, at the upper limit of region III, the pulse size is independent of the initial ionization. This region, in which gas multiplication is employed while at the same time a dependence of the collected charge on the initial ionization remains, is known commonly as the proportional region.

The upper end of it is designated as the region of limited proportionality.

In region IV the charge collected is independent of the ionization initiating it. Rather, gas multiplication increases the charge to a value that is limited by the characteristics of the chamber and the external circuit. This region is known as the G-M region.

Ionization chambers find wide-scale use in non-pulse-type applications, for example, in monitoring of radiation for personnel protection. Pulse-type operation is not attractive in the ionization chamber region because of the relatively small-size pulse released by an individual nuclear particle. On the other hand, in the proportional region, gas multiplication increases the size of pulses while at the same time information concerning the size of the initial ionization is maintained. Therefore, proportional counters are useful as counting devices (with the ability to discriminate between particles making different amounts of ionization) and for energy measurements. Geiger-Müller counters are widely used for counting electrons between particles and gamma rays inasmuch as the large discharge pulse is triggered by the very small ionization which these particles produce. However, they have no capability for differentiating between radiation types or for measuring the energy of the particles which trigger the discharge.

Inasmuch as Lord Rutherford utilized light scintillations in his famous alpha-scattering experiments, the scintillation detector is one of the oldest methods of nuclear radiation detection. However, the modern scintillation detector, a device of great utility, only evolved after the development of special photomultiplier tubes for the purpose. Figure 3 shows the schematic of a modern scintillation detector for counting. When charged particles pass through certain substances, ionized and/or excited states are produced, which, during their return to the normal states, produce light flashes, or scintillations. By coupling the scintillators with a photomultiplier tube, a pulse of charge can be passed to an electronic system, as shown in Fig. 3, thus making counting possible. Also, if

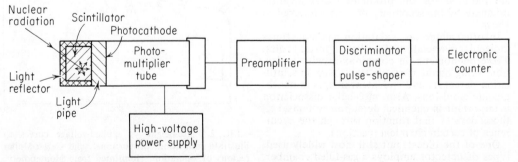

FIG. 3. Schematic diagram of a scintillation detector. (Reprinted from Price, W. J., "Nuclear Radiation Detection, p. 160, New York, McGraw-Hill Book Company, Inc., 1964)

the electronic counter is replaced by electronic equipment for measuring the pulse size, the scintillation detector is very useful for energy measurements.

Various scintillators are available, including crystals of inorganic and organic materials, liquids, powders, plastics, glasses, and gases. Therefore, the designer has available a wide range of sizes, shapes, and compositions, and consequently can optimize conditions for a wide variety of measurement problems including a wide range of radiation types and energies. In addition, the time duration of the pulse produced can be much shorter than those in the gas-filled chambers, and the density of the detection medium is usually much higher. As a result of these several advantages, there is a large group of applications in which the scintillation detectors have superiority over gas-filled chambers as well as over other detectors. Gamma-ray spectroscopy is an outstanding example of an important class of measurement made possible by the scintillation detectors.

The newest of the important nuclear radiation detectors is commonly referred to as the semiconductor radiation detector, after the fact that it is the properties of semiconductor materials that make these detectors possible. In this detector an electric field is set up across a semiconducting medium of low electrical conductivity. Usually the low conductivity region is the charge-depletion region in a semiconductor diode operated at reverse bias. When a charged particle passes through the semiconductor, electron-hole pairs are produced in it. The charges are caused to separate by the electric field, and the resulting electrical signal can be transmitted to the electronic measuring system to give important information concerning the particle detected.

The semiconductor radiation detector has several key properties, the combination of which accounts for the rapid rise of importance of this detector type. These properties include linearity of pulse height vs energy, very rapid response time, high resolution, convenient dimensions, thin windows, insensitivity to magnetic fields, variable sensitivity with respect to particle energy, relative insensitivity to gammas and neutrons, and relatively low cost. For example, the availability of semiconductor radiation detectors has revolutionized the spectrometry of charged particles.

Several other types of detectors are in use and are quite important in specialized measurements. These other detectors include nuclear-track plates, cloud chambers, spark chambers, Čerenkov counters, chemical detectors, calorimetric methods and various special types of neutron detectors. For details on the principles of operations and the characteristics of these detectors, as well as more information on the three detector types described above, the reader is referred to the textbook "Nuclear Radiation Detection", by W. J. Price (New York, McGraw-Hill Book Co., Inc., 1964) and the references included in that book.

WILLIAM J. PRICE

Cross-references: IONIZATION; LUMINESCENCE; MEASUREMENTS, PRINCIPLES OF; NUCLEAR RADIATION; RADIATION, IONIZING, BASIC INTERACTIONS; RADIOACTIVITY; SPARK AND BUBBLE CHAMBER.

NUCLEAR RADIATION

Nuclear radiation results from the transitions of atomic nuclei. The two chief types of transition in natural radioactivity are those in which the number of constituent particles of a given nucleus (nuclide) are changed by the emission of one or more particles, and those in which there is a rearrangement of the particles of a given nuclide, without change in number, such that the nuclide passes from a state of higher energy to a state of lower energy with the emission of radiant energy.

Soon after the discovery of radioactivity in 1896, it was found that naturally radioactive substances emit three kinds of radiation; alpha (α), beta (β) and gamma (γ) rays. The first two consist of high-speed charged particles, alpha and beta particles respectively. They are called *particle* rays to distinguish them from the gamma rays discovered by Villard in 1900. The latter were shown by a series of experiments to be a form of high-frequency electromagnetic radiation traveling with the speed of light. However, in discussing the nature of these rays, it must be remembered that later experiments clearly showed that the so-called *particles* may exhibit distinctly *wavelike* characteristics, and conversely the higher the frequency of the gamma radiation the more pronounced becomes the *particle-like* character of its individual quanta or photons. From such considerations came the concept of wave-particle duality and present-day quantum mechanical theory.

Two of the most important differences between alpha rays and beta rays are: (1) they are deflected in opposite directions by a magnetic field indicating that they are oppositely charged, and (2) the alpha particle is far more massive than the beta particle. Early measurements indicated that alpha particles may be emitted with speeds up to 1/15 the speed c of light, and beta rays with speeds up to $0.96c$. The rest masses of the two particles and their energy equivalents in millions of electron volts (MeV) are

$$M_0(\text{alpha particle}) = 6.645 \times 10^{-27}\text{kg}$$

$$= 3727.2 \text{ MeV}$$

$$m_0(\text{beta particle}) = 9.109 \times 10^{-31}\text{kg}$$

$$= 0.511 \text{ MeV}$$

Thus the alpha particle is nearly 7300 times more massive than the beta particle. The reason for such a difference in the masses was found early in this century. In experiments begun in 1903, Rutherford showed that an alpha particle is the doubly charged (positive) nucleus of a helium atom. Experiments of Becquerel and others identified the beta particle as the then recently discovered, negatively charged electron.

With the discovery of what has been called "artificial" or induced radioactivity by Irene Curie-Joliot and her husband Frederick Joliot in 1933, it was found that positive electron (positron) emission may occur in nuclides whose instability results from the nucleus possessing "too much charge for its mass." This is, of course, only another form of beta emission represented as β^+, whereas ordinary electron emission is represented as β^-.

Certain characteristics of nuclear radiation such as their great penetrating power, their capacity to ionize gas, affect a photographic plate, or produce serious or fatal burns, and the ability of alpha rays to produce scintillations in a fluorescent screen were early recognized. The exact penetrating power of a particular ray depends upon the energy with which it is emitted by the parent nucleus, but in general it may be said that alpha rays may usually be stopped by a few sheets of paper and beta rays by a few millimeters of aluminum. Alpha and beta rays, because of their particle character, have a more sharply defined range than gamma rays, and a significant fraction of the gamma radiation may pass through a number of centimeters of metal shield. This is because particles lose speed and kinetic energy in both ionizing and non-ionizing collisions with other particles, whereas a gamma-ray-photon always travels at the same speed, and the beam of photons is usually weakened by some process such as scattering or absorption of photons. The frequencies of photons may also be reduced by the so-called *Compton collisions* (see COMPTON EFFECT).

One of the most important characteristics of alpha and beta rays is their capacity to produce ions in a gas and render it conducting. In normal air, an alpha ray will produce between 20 000 and 70 000 ion pairs per centimeter of path, depending on the speed of the ray, with maximum ionization being reached near the end of the path. A beta ray on the other hand may only produce 200 ion pairs or less per centimeter. Thus such rays lose energy rapidly in passing through a gas, and rays of a particular type of energy have a rather sharply defined range (see IONIZATION).

The range of alpha particles in air at 76 cm mercury pressure (15°C) varies from 2.7 cm for alpha particles from uranium to 8.62 cm for alpha particles from thorium C' (Po^{212}). The former are emitted with energies of 4.2 MeV while the latter, the most energetic of any from a naturally radioactive substance, are emitted with energies of 8.6 MeV.

In 1929, Rosenblum discovered the fine structure of alpha rays. That is, alpha rays from a single type of nuclide may not all have exactly the same energy and range but often consist of two or more groups with slightly different but sharply defined ranges and consequently different initial energies. This led to the ultimate recognition of the existence of different energy levels in the nucleus and is one of the most important properties of alpha rays in sharp contrast with the nature and behavior of beta rays. Along with the discovery of nuclear energy levels came recognition of the origin of gamma radiation. After the emission of an alpha (or a beta) particle, if the nucleus is left in an excited state of higher energy than the lowest or ground state, gamma radiation occurs as the result of a transition to a lower-energy state.

Beta rays have ranges in air at 76 cm mercury pressure (15°C) varying from a fraction of a centimeter for those of a few thousand volts energy to more than 400 cm for those of energies of 1 MeV. However, the beta rays from a single type of nuclide have a wide distribution of ranges and energies, the distribution being approximately continuous up to a certain maximum for the particular type of nuclide. The lack of a characteristic disintegration energy and range for the various beta particles from a given type of nuclide results from the nature of the emission process as first explained by Fermi in 1934. When a beta particle is emitted, it is necessary that at least one other particle (a NEUTRINO) also be emitted in order to conserve angular momentum of spin. Conservation of energy then demands that any energy this neutrino possesses must subtract from the energy that might have been carried off by the beta particle in the process of emission from some sharply defined energy level in the nucleus. Only the maximum possible or "endpoint" energy of a given beta-ray emission curve is therefore significant for that particular nuclide. On the other hand, gamma rays result from the return of a nuclide from a higher-energy state of excitation to a lower state, or to the ground state, and have sharply defined values characteristic of the states of that nuclide. Different groups of beta rays having different end-point energies may originate from the same type of nuclide and represent different nuclear energy levels.

The experimental detection of the neutrino (and antineutrino) in the years following 1956 confirmed the main aspects of the Fermi theory and added another particle and antiparticle, albeit of zero mass and zero charge, to those types which may be ejected from the atomic nucleus. *Nuclear radiation* may involve all of these types of rays and also the neutrons and other particles resulting from occasional spontaneous fission of a nucleus or from the intense fission in a nuclear reactor.

In addition to natural and induced radioactivity, and nuclear fission, many types of nuclear transformation or disintegration may oc-

cur in bombardment of nuclei by cosmic rays or by high-energy particles from man-made accelerators. Most of the particles produced in such occurrences are themselves unstable and decay by the emission of other particles. For instance, a neutron decays to a proton by the emission of a negative electron and an antineutrino. A pion (pi meson) may decay to a muon (mu meson) and a neutrino, and the muon may decay to an electron and two neutrinos. To complicate matters, the neutrinos and antineutrinos in the two decay processes seem to be slightly different. In a wider sense, all the nuclear particles and antiparticles emitted by any nuclear process must be included in the forms of nuclear radiation.

The experimental study of nuclear radiations has given us our most direct knowledge of the nature of the atomic nucleus. On the more practical side it is involved in the design and operation of nuclear reactors. The physiological effects of various nuclear radiations form most of the field of health physics and relate also to the hazards of space travel.

Since the advent of rockets and space travel, radiation measurements have been made outside the earth's atmosphere. Actually, streams of nuclear radiations from stellar objects pervade all space, and x-ray and gamma-ray astronomies along with cosmic rays have led astrophysicists to many new ideas about nuclear processes in stellar objects and in stellar evolution. In the newer field of neutrino astronomy, despite the inherent difficulties in detecting so elusive a particle, some measurements have been made of the neutrino emission from our sun in order more accurately to determine the nuclear process occurring inside that body.

ROGERS D. RUSK

Reference

Evans, R. D., *The Atomic Nucleus,* New York, McGraw-Hill Book Co., 1955.

Lapp, R. E., and Andrews, H. L., "Nuclear Radiation Physics," Fourth edition, Englewood Cliffs, N.J., Prentice-Hall, 1972.

Rusk, R. D., "Introduction to Atomic and Nuclear Physics," Second edition, New York, Appleton-Century-Crofts, 1964.

Weekes, T. C., "High Energy Astrophysics," London, Chapman and Hall, 1969.

Early Work

Rutherford, E., Chadwick, J., and Ellis, C. D., "Radiations from Radioactive Substances," New York, The Macmillan Co., 1930.

Cross-references: ELECTRON; ELEMENTARY PARTICLES; FISSION; NEUTRON; NUCLEAR REACTIONS; NUCLEAR RADIATION SHIELDING; NUCLEAR STRUCTURE; POSITRON; PROTON; RADIATION, IONIZING, BASIC INTERACTIONS; RADIOACTIVITY.

NUCLEAR RADIATION SHIELDING

Nuclear reactors, based upon the fission of heavy nuclei, have become an important power source for the generation of electricity. The great intensity of nuclear radiations produced in the reactors requires radiation shielding. Fast neutrons and gamma rays are by far the most penetrating of the radiations produced; therefore, most shield design is concerned with reducing their levels by factors of as much as 10^{15}.

A variety of other systems gives rise to shielding problems which are related more or less closely to those of the fission reactor and these are treated with many of the same methods which are used in reactor shielding. After discussing these various areas of application, the problem of calculating and confirming the design or performance of a radiation shield is outlined.

Areas of Application *Fission Reactors.* In the United States and much of the rest of the world, the fission power plants now being installed for electricity generation (or ship propulsion) are based upon the use of water as the reactor moderator and coolant. As a shield, water has no cracks and it offers simplifications following from the fact that it tends to produce an equilibrium neutron energy distribution due to the inverse dependence upon energy of the hydrogen neutron cross section. This equilibrium fast-neutron spectrum has allowed the use of simple attenuation methods with empirically derived constants to solve many design problems which do not require much detail in the answer.

Current interest in the development of advanced reactor types centers upon the breeders, especially the liquid-metal-cooled fast breeder reactor (LMFBR) using the ^{238}U to ^{239}Pu breeding cycle. Breeders are essential if nuclear fission is to make a long-term contribution to our energy needs. The LMFBR operates at high temperatures ($\sim$500 to 600°C) and with neutrons of high energy ($\sim$100 keV average energy for neutrons producing fission). Both conditions tend to exclude hydrogenous materials from the vicinity of the reactor, and sodium, the liquid-metal coolant usually considered, is the dominant medium near the core. The fast-neutron spectrum does not attain an equilibrium after attenuation in any thickness of sodium (to 15 ft) so far as is presently known, and much more detail in the neutron spectra must be predicted for LMFBR shield design.

Fast-neutron streaming through clearance gaps and sodium-filled pipes, which necessarily surround or penetrate the LMFBR shields, must be calculated for geometries which become quite complex in actual practice. For the coolant pipes, both the sodium and the insulation required by the high temperatures are of low density and constitute significant gaps in the shield. For gas-cooled reactors, the coolant

pipes become even larger and these radiation-streaming problems are exacerbated.

Finally, for fission reactors used to propel or to provide auxiliary power for space vehicles, the weight of the power plant becomes crucial to the feasibility of the mission. Since the radiation shield may account for as much as two-thirds of the total power-plant weight, the radiation shield design must be made with the highest attainable accuracy. Efforts are centered upon methods of optimizing the shield design with respect to weight. This can now be done directly and accurately insofar as the power plant can be considered one-dimensional. Two-dimensional optimization methods are now under development.

Fusion Reactors. Potential advantages of safety and unlimited fuel supply justify current efforts to develop controlled thermonuclear reactors (CTR) based upon the fusion of light nuclei. The most commonly considered reaction of deuterium and tritium produces 14-MeV neutrons which must be absorbed to prevent radiation damage, to breed more tritium as a fuel, and to gain the energy (heat) which the fast neutrons carry from the reaction. A major requirement of the radiation-transport calculations for CTR systems is to insure radiation levels that will not destroy components of the system; e.g., the cyrogenic magnet used to contain the fusion reaction. Similar problems of radiation damage to system components are important for fission reactors as well.

Nuclear Weapons Radiations. Nuclear explosives may produce radiations by both the fission and fusion processes and there are substantial overlaps in the radiation-shielding problems with the reactors considered above. For the protection of military or civilian systems against radiations from nuclear weapons, initial attention must be given to the radiation transport through air from the source to the system. As a result of many years of study of this basic problem, air-transport methods and results are now available in detail with accuracies (except for problems with the cross sections for the production of secondary gamma rays by fast neutrons) of the order of 10 to 20 percent[1].

An overview of the problem of shielding military systems against weapons radiations is given in the multivolume DNA Handbook.[2]

Accelerators. Radiation of virtually all types (including neutrons and gamma rays) and energies can be produced by the many types of charged-particle accelerators. Over the energy range to ~20 MeV there may be quite direct overlap in the radiation-shielding problems with reactors or weapons radiations. For higher-energy accelerators additional reactions and new particle types such as mesons may be involved. High-energy particles which are slowed down (reduced in energy) in the shield eventually pass through or give rise to additional particles in the lower energy range applicable to fission and fusion reactors. Thus methods developed at low energy may be incorporated as part of the solution of accelerator shielding problems. In any case, the methods of solution tend to be closely related.

Space Vehicles. The space environment includes charged particles ranging from the electrons (trapped by the magnetic field of the earth) through protons and alpha particles (helium nuclei) to heavier nuclei. The protons tend to be the most numerous and their interactions the best understood. Nuclear interactions of heavy nuclei are little understood and will likely constitute a major problem for future manned interplanetary space travel.

All of the charged particles lose energy dominantly by ionization which creates essentially no transport or shielding problems. Nuclear reactions do occur, however, at energies above a few MeV and ignoring these may lead to dosimetry estimates in error by 25 per cent or much more depending upon the incident-particle energy spectrum and system geometry.

The methods employed for space radiation shielding are largely those also used for accelerator shield design. However, in general, the requirements in space radiation shielding are for highly accurate calculations for thin shields. For accelerators, less accuracy is usually required but much thicker shields (approaching or surpassing the attenuations of reactor shields) may be required. Space radiation shielding is treated in a recent handbook.[3]

Nature of the Problem Stated generally, the problem of radiation shielding is to solve the Boltzmann transport equation which describes the radiation transport. It is possible in principle, of course, to make direct measurements of the necessary radiation attenuations, but in practice this is seldom practical. Thus, given the necessary nuclear data, radiation-shielding analysis reduces largely to (1) developing necessarily approximate methods of solving the Boltzmann equation, (2) testing their validity, usually against measurements in simplified geometries, and (3) applying these methods to design problems.

The Boltzmann equation may be considered simply as a balance equation tabulating the sources and disappearances of particles. In this sense, and ignoring time dependence, it may be written as:

$$\nabla \cdot \overline{\Omega} \phi(\bar{r}, E, \overline{\Omega}) + \Sigma_t(\bar{r}, E) \phi(\bar{r}, E, \overline{\Omega})$$

$$= S(\bar{r}, E, \overline{\Omega}) + \iint \Sigma_s(\bar{r}, \overline{\Omega}' \to \overline{\Omega}, E' \to E) \times$$

$$\phi(\bar{r}, E', \overline{\Omega}') \, dE' \, d\overline{\Omega}'$$

where ϕ is the number flux of particles of energy E, at position $\bar{r}$, with angular direction $\overline{\Omega}$. The left side of the equation represents all losses including leakage out of the region of interest and disappearance by reactions of all types with probability $\Sigma_t \phi$. On the right

side, S represents all neutron sources such as fission and the integral includes in-scattering into the spatial and energy region of interest of particles scattered from elsewhere. This "scattering" process may in the most general sense include the production of gamma rays upon the interaction of neutrons.

Solving this integro-differential equation requires input for the radiation sources S and interaction probabilities Σ including details about secondary particles which may be produced. The allowable radiation levels corresponding to $\phi(E)$ are generally provided as constraints determined by the radiosensitivity of man, materials, or systems which may be exposed to the radiations. Then one solves for the minimum shield thickness (or weight or cost) consistent with the constraints.

Nuclear Data *Sources of Radiation.* Fission produces neutron and gamma-ray sources important for shield design. The characteristic and much-studied distribution in energy of neutrons (~ 5 MeV/fission total energy release with $\bar{E} \sim 2$ MeV) varies with the isotope undergoing fission and slowly with the energy of the neutron producing fission. Delayed neutrons, which follow β-decay of fission fragments, have an intensity relative to the "prompt" neutrons of the order of 1 to 2 per cent and become important largely for fluid fuel reactors where they may be emitted beyond part of the primary shield and thus enhanced in importance. Gamma rays are emitted at essentially all times after fission but a major share (~ 8 MeV/fission) appear within a few nanoseconds. Gamma rays following isomeric transitions in fission-fragment nuclei (important for times after fission $\lesssim 1$ sec) and following β-decay (for $t > 1$ sec) together amount to another ~ 7 MeV/fission.

The 14-MeV neutrons produced in fusion of light nuclei constitute the dominant radiation for a fusion source. For high-energy accelerators or space vehicles, the sources of penetrating radiations are dominantly due to nuclear interactions of the primary charged particles. μ-mesons, formed from the decay of other particles, are extremely penetrating due to their small interaction cross sections, and they tend to dominate parts of the shield for accelerators with energies > 10 GeV.

A broad review of radiation sources is given in the *"Engineering Compendium of Radiation Shielding."*[4]

Cross Sections. The probability of interaction or cross section must be treated in great detail in radiation-shielding problems, especially for neutrons. The cross sections are strongly energy-dependent, in part with rapid variations or fluctuations with neutron energy. Neutrons may (1) disappear, giving rise only to charged particles of no consequence for the radiation transport; (2) produce fission or fusion with the sources these reactions imply; (3) scatter, changing energy and direction, thus introducing "new" particles into the transport equation; (4) scatter as in (3) with the additional production of deexcitation gamma rays; or (5) be "captured" with the emission of capture gamma rays. For shielding, one requires the sum of gamma rays produced in fission, capture, and inelastic scattering.

The vast amount of cross-section information required for accurate shielding calculations constitutes a central problem, and perhaps more effort is applied altogether in cross-section preparation than in transport calculations. Neutron cross sections are measured at many "points" in energy. These detailed point sets are then commonly reduced to a limited number of energy groups (~ 30 to ~ 300 groups) with the energy variation in cross section within each group represented by a weighted average. Weighting schemes approximate the proper but unavailable weighting by $\phi(E)$ for the problem being considered. Since $\phi(E)$ is a function of position, no single set of weights can be exact. The group structure must be especially selected for difficult problems. The validity of sets of group cross sections must be established by comparing the results of calculations using them with values obtained from calculations with point cross-section sets or from benchmark experiments.

The use of group cross sections allows treating scattering by introducing group-to-group transfer matrices with a large reduction in necessary information storage. Similarly, group cross sections can be readily generated to handle secondary gamma-ray production.

As for neutrons, gamma-ray cross sections can be considered as point or group-averaged functions of energy. Gamma-ray cross sections tend to be known more accurately than those for neutrons, and the production of other particle types (e.g., neutrons) by gamma rays can usually be ignored for low-energy transport problems.

Nuclear Data Stores. The wealth of cross-section detail demands computer-based handling and efficient storage. A National Nuclear Cross Section Center (NNCSC) has been established at the Brookhaven National Laboratory for storing neutron and gamma-ray cross sections, and this is the appropriate primary source of information in the United States.[5] Very important is the fact that a cooperative group (The Cross Section Evaluation Working Group or CSEWG) has been set up to identify the "best" set of data for each reaction type and nuclei. This choice may require choosing among sets of experimental measurements with different values for the same quantities, or may require filling gaps covered by no measurements, on the basis of nuclear-model calculations or systematics. This Evaluated Nuclear Data File (ENDF), which changes with time as new data become available, is also available from NNCSC.[5] Similar, but more preliminary, data and sets of groups of cross sections derived from them are available from the Radiation Shielding Informa-

tion Center (RSIC) at the Oak Ridge National Laboratory.[6]

Methods of Solution Exact analytic solutions of the transport equation are not possible for practical shielding problems, but numerous approximate, basically numerical methods are available. Two of these have assumed the greatest importance today, the discrete ordinates and Monte Carlo methods. Applied in their most highly developed forms, the residual approximations become unimportant. The effort and cost required for such applications may be substantial, however. Other methods which are easier to use offer approximations to the desired solution which have more or less vailidity depending upon the complexity of the problem and its similarity to those from which the approximate method has been derived. Perhaps the best recent review of transport methods is available in the revised Chapter 3 of the "Weapons Radiation Shielding Handbook."[2]

Virtually all solutions of problems of practical interest depend upon use of a digital computer, and the type of computer available and its cost of operation may constrain the choice of methods. The availability of computer codes developed by others is very important. Codes of shielding interest are collected and made available by the Radiation Shielding Information Center,[6] which also assists new users in making them operable.

Discrete Ordinates. The nature of the Boltzmann transport equation as a balance of particle flow is closely matched by the discrete ordinates formulation as a finite difference equation, and the equivalence has been demonstrated for one-dimensional geometries. Thus, few approximations are necessarily required in the application of this method, which obtains the desired flux $\phi(\bar{r}, E, \bar{\Omega})$ by successive iterations over the difference cells. A derivation and a method of solution of the finite-difference equations which are required for a one-space dimension time-independent problem are given in Ref. 2.

The adaptation of the discrete ordinates method, which was originally developed for other purposes, to radiation shielding required special attention to several features of the method. In particular, the steep flux gradients characteristic of good shields have required modified schemes for iteration within the difference cells. For deep penetration in a shield, the angular distributions of scattered particles become very important since the forward-scattered radiation can penetrate most readily. To handle the anisotropic scattering in a practical manner, the angular distributions after scattering from energy group to energy group are approximated by a Legendre series. A low order of expansion, P_3, usually suffices.

The discrete ordinates methods have been expanded to two dimensions and widely applied to practical design problems. Demands upon computer time have provided incentives for developing improved forced-convergence techniques including those which concentrate upon the spatial or energy region of interest. Flux aberrations have been frequently observed in two-dimensional problems for small radiation sources. These "ray effects" preserve indications of the finite angular directions in the flux solution, and various methods have been devised to eliminate or control them.

Practical computer codes are available[6] which incorporate the discrete ordinates method. One-dimensional calculations are very fast and have been used as the basis of iterative shield optimization procedures which perform a series of flux solutions in one pass on the computer. Two-dimensional calculations require fast computers with large memory stores. It should be noted that the division of neutron energies into groups allows a convenient method of handling the production of secondary gamma rays by neutron capture and inelastic scattering. Proper treatment of these secondary gamma rays is essential in almost all radiation-shielding problems which include fission or fusion sources.

Overall, discrete ordinates is the method of choice for most one- or two-dimensional radiation-shielding problems. The major complication which is encountered in its use is that there is no clear a priori approach to defining the best (or even certainly adequate) sets of directions, space meshes, and energy groups for a given problem. Experience is the best guide to these choices and it must be based upon detailed comparison of test calculations with benchmark experiments which are designed for for the purpose.

Monte Carlo. Under the pressure of necessity, many components of radiation shields may be approximated in one or two dimensions. There remain, however, complicated problems, such as the streaming of neutrons through holes, which require a three-dimensional treatment. At present, the Monte Carlo method is the only approach to such problems which is free of serious approximations.

The Monte Carlo method depends upon stochastic estimation or random sampling from the probabilities describing the stochastic processes that determine the solution of the transport equation. This mathematical analog for a problem of interest may be made as exact as desired, limited only by the investment of effort and computing time. The size of the sample of particles of interest (i.e., those penetrating the shield) determines the statistical accuracy achieved.

The major determinant of the success of the Monte Carlo method for problems whose important parameters depend on very unlikely events, such as penetration through thick shields, is the method of sampling. Through "importance sampling," larger numbers of particles can be chosen which contribute to the unlikely events of interest.[2] Thus the sampling is biased without, hopefully, biasing the result, since correction factors are applied. The most power-

ful biasing technique uses an importance or value function based upon an adjoint solution of the transport equation, using the best available method, which will usually be one- or two-dimensional discrete ordinates. Such biasing in energy and space is routine but angular biasing has usually been limited to one-dimensional problems. Estimates of the variance calculated upon the basis of a normal distribution may be grossly in error, since Monte Carlo distributions are frequently nonnormal, and unfortunately, error estimates are usually too low. This difficulty must be kept in mind in using the Monte Carlo method for shielding problems.

Several powerful and general Monte Carlo codes are available[6] for a variety of computer types. The inherent flexibility of the method, however, requires considerable effort on the part of the user for solving a given problem. Recent developments in Monte Carlo methods have tended toward systems, such as those using standard neutron energy groups, which ease the user's burdens. Using the same energy groups as those of the discrete ordinates method greatly facilitates comparisons of results. The ultimate verification of results from Monte Carlo calculations as for all other methods must rest upon comparisons with benchmark experiments.

Other Transport Methods. Many other methods have been considered and used to a limited extent for solving the transport equation. In one approach, the angle-dependent terms are represented by expansions in spherical harmonic polynomials, P_n. Development of the method has been restricted by the requirement to consider many terms in the scattering representation and the difficulty of treating multidimensional shielding problems. Limited use of the P_3 approximation has been made for one-dimensional problems, but no two-dimensional calculations are known. Diffusion theory, which corresponds to the P_1 approximation, is widely used for reactor criticality calculations because of its relative simplicity, and multidimensional versions are available. Its validity is limited to nearly isotropic fluxes, however, as opposed to the highly forward-directed fluxes characteristic of shields. Diffusion theory can sometimes be used for the inner portions of a reactor shield or to provide a source for transport shielding calculations, but the current trend is to use the transport calculation throughout the system.

Another approach to solving the transport equation consists of transforming the problem by constructing spatial moments of the flux and calculating in the transform space. This moments method has a number of computational advantages and it was used widely for gamma-ray transport. It is, however, greatly restricted in the geometries that can be considered, and has been applied largely to infinite homogenous media. Furthermore, for neutron transport, difficulties persist in reconstructing the flux from the moments.

The so-called invariant imbedding, or matrix, method does not solve the transport equation directly, but rather solves for reflection and transmission functions throughout the medium. A particular (shield) configuration is imbedded in a larger class of configurations, and solutions are obtained for all in one calculation, an obvious efficiency. Definition of reflection and transmission functions and their solution by numerical methods do not differ greatly from other approaches to the transport equation. Boundaries are precisely included in the formulation, it is well suited for heterogeneous shields, it is efficient for thick shields and inefficient for thin. The outstanding limitation is that applications have been made only for slab geometries.

Approximate Methods. Before large computers made transport solutions practical, the kernel technique for radiation transport based upon the use of a Green's function was widely used. The point kernel, $K(|\bar{r} - \bar{r}'|)$, relates the desired response of a detector at point $\bar{r}$ to a radiation source at point $\bar{r}'$. Integration over a source volume yields the solution to problems of arbitrary geometry. However, values for the kernels have been obtained from solutions by methods valid only for infinite homogeneous media, and these kernels give results which are in error when applied to finite media. Scattering may be approximated by adding one of a variety of build-up factors as a function of energy E and separation $|\bar{r} - \bar{r}'|$. For gamma rays, useful build-up factors were derived from moments-method calculations.

For neutron attenuation, many shields contain large regions of water following other materials. This water has the effect of filtering out scattered neutrons, making the material appear as an absorber. The absorption or removal cross section, as derived empirically from experiment, was used in defining a kernel applicable for shields with outer hydrogenous regions. Other kernel approaches have been used in order to parameterize the results of transport solutions.

A logical extension of the removal concept was to follow the deep penetration of neutrons as described by the removal process by moderation in energy using diffusion theory. This removal-diffusion method has been highly developed and widely applied, especially in Europe, in the design of shields for power reactors using fission induced by thermal neutrons. The basic assumptions upon which the method is based are not fulfilled for fast reactors. The removal process is considered for many energy groups (to 18) from which neutrons can be transferred to other energy groups used to describe the diffusion process. The key step then becomes derivation of the group-transfer matrices from experiments which determine the penetration of monoenergetic neutrons in various materials.

Validation of Calculations Mock-up experiments, which are universally used to validate reactor-core criticality calculations, are much

less common for shielding calculations. The penalty for error or overdesign tends to be less and the costs for meaningful mockups excessive. An obvious exception would be the space reactors for which the shield design is crucial. Measurements on reactors as built can in principle be used to validate calculation methods. In practice, however, access to interesting portions of reactor or accelerator shields is limited and down time required for performing meaningful measurements is very expensive. The test is also rather late for judging methods for anything other than serial production of power plants.

The most useful tests of transport methods follow from comparisons with experiments specifically designed for the purpose. Such experiments attempt to reproduce in the simplest arrangement attainable the essential features of the system of interest (e.g., a fast-neutron spectrum for applications to fast reactors or large attenuations in the pertinent materials for thick shields). The experimental results must be accurate, reliable, and unambiguously interpretable above all else. Measurements include the neutron energy distributions penetrating the shield, using one or more of the various neutron spectrometers which have been developed for the purpose. An example of the test of a two-dimensional discrete-ordinates code against measurements of neutron spectra serves to illustrate the process.[7]

For Further Information The development of radiation-shielding technology has been quite rapid over the past decade following the development of high-speed digital computers. The dependence of reliable solutions to transport problems upon computer codes with masses of nuclear data required as input precludes the handbook approach to practical design problems. Therefore, an information center has been established to assist in providing the necessary tools for solving shielding problems and in providing means of retrieving the pertinent literature. The center does not attempt to solve problems directly. It does attempt to provide coverage of the literature for all of the indicated areas of application with support from the AEC, DOD, and NASA. It may be contacted at the address given.[6]

FRED C. MAIENSCHEIN

References

1. Straker, E. A., "The Effect of the Ground on the Steady-State and Time-Dependent Transport of Neutrons and Secondary Gamma Rays in the Atmosphere," *Nucl. Sci. Eng.*, **46**, 334 (1971).
2. "Weapons Radiation Shielding Handbook," Eds. Abbott, L. S., Claiborne, H. C., and Clifford, C. E., DNA-1892 (formerly DASA 1892). Chapter 3 has been issued in revised form as DNA-1892-3, Rev. 1 (March 1972). Available from National Technical Information Service, Springfield, Virginia 22151.
3. "Shielding of Manned Space Vehicles Against Protons and Alpha Particles," Alsmiller, R. G., Jr., et al., ORNL-RSIC-35 (Nov. 1972).
4. "Engineering Compendium on Radiation Shielding," Eds. Jaeger, R. G., et al., Vol I., "Shielding Fundamentals and Methods," New York-Berlin, Springer-Verlag, 1970.
5. National Neutron Cross Section Center, Brookhaven National Laboratory, Upton, L. I., N.Y. 11973.
6. Radiation Shielding Information Center, Oak Ridge National Laboratory, Post Office Box X, Oak Ridge, Tennessee 37830.
7. Mynatt, F. R., Muckenthaler, F. J., and Stevens, P. N., "Development of Two-Dimensional Discrete Ordinates Transport Theory for Radiation Shielding," CTC-INF-952 (Aug. 11, 1969). Available from National Technical Information Service, Springfield, Virginia, 22151, as AD-692168.

Cross-references: FISSION, FUSION, NUCLEAR RADIATION, NUCLEAR REACTIONS, NUCLEAR REACTORS, NUCLEAR STRUCTURE, NUCLEONICS.

NUCLEAR REACTIONS

Several years after the discovery of the nucleus by scattering α-particles from gold, Rutherford and his collaborators noticed that if air were exposed to the flux of α-particles, occasionally a very penetrating particle was observed. After some nuclear detective work, this phenomenon was explained in the following way: the nitrogen nucleus and the α-particle react to produce an isotope of oxygen and an energetic proton. In the chemical notation, such a reaction may be written as $^{14}N + \alpha \rightarrow {}^{17}O + p$, where the superscripts are the atomic mass numbers of the elements in question.

Nuclear reactions may take place only when a target nucleus and a projectile come close enough together for the nuclear forces to take effect. The range of nuclear forces is very short, about 1.5 fermis (1 fermi = 10^{-13} cm). Since nuclei and all the massive projectiles except neutrons are charged positively, they repel each other, and if they are to be brought into sufficiently intimate contact to interact, the energy of the projectile must equal or surpass the repulsive electrostatic force. Typically, for protons on light nuclei, the energy required is 1 or 2 MeV, rising to 15 MeV for protons on very heavy, highly charged nuclei. Thus to produce nuclear reactions by the collision of charged particles, we must first accelerate one of them to an energy sufficient to overcome the electrostatic repulsive force. In all nuclear reactions, energies are usually given in million electron volts and masses in atomic mass units (amu). One MeV is the energy acquired by a particle of one electronic charge as it is accelerated by an electrical potential of one million volts. An atomic mass unit is currently defined

as one-twelfth the mass of a neutral carbon-12 atom.

A nuclear reaction just as its chemical counterpart, may be exoergic (kinetic energy is liberated) or endoergic (kinetic energy is absorbed). For example, Rutherford's original reaction is endoergic, consuming 1.19 MeV which is converted into mass of the product particles according to Einstein's $E=mc^2$. In the case of endoergic reactions, energy must be supplied in the form of projectile kinetic energy to make the reaction possible.

In the course of a nuclear reaction, the projectile and the target may fuse completely, or parts of nuclear matter, neutrons, protons, or clusters of these, may be transferred from the target to the projectile or vice versa. The most common projectiles are ISOTOPES of hydrogen, protons or deuterons, and α-particles which are nuclei of helium atoms. Because of their low charge, these feel the lowest electrostatic repulsion from the target. Heavier projectiles are, however, frequently used, and these include lithium, carbon, nitrogen, and oxygen ions; a few experiments have been done with projectiles as heavy as ^{40}Ar. Neutrons form a special class of projectile, since they are not charged and need not possess any large amount of energy to overcome a repulsive barrier. In fact, the slower the neutrons are, the more likely they are to interact with the target simply because they spend more time in the vicinity of each target nucleus. Nuclear reactions may also be initiated by PHOTONS (electromagnetic radiation quanta) of very high energy, greater than 5 to 10 MeV. The photons are produced as x-rays when high-energy electrons from a betatron, synchrotron, or linear accelerator impinge on a target. Since photons are not charged electrically, there is no barrier, but all photonuclear reactions are endoergic, that is they require several-million-electron-volt x-rays to take place.

Rutherford's original reaction would now be commonly written thus: ^{14}N$(\alpha, p)^{17}$O. The target nucleus comes first, the projectile and the emitted particle or particles appear in that order inside the parentheses, and the residual nucleus is last. The superscript gives the atomic mass of the isotope. Some common abbreviations are p for proton, n for neutron, d for deuteron (^{2}H), t for triton (^{3}H), γ for γ-ray.

The projectile energy range over which nuclear reactions are important varies from a fraction of an electron volt for neutrons to several hundred million electron volts per atomic mass unit for charged particles. At very high energies, the projectiles appear to interact with the individual neutrons and protons of the target rather than with the nucleus as a whole, and we leave the domain of nuclear reactions to enter the field of ELEMENTARY PARTICLE interactions.

Nuclear reactions are literally the foundation on which our world is built. The energy of the sun is nuclear in origin, deriving principally from the fusion of four protons into a helium nucleus, in the course of which 22.7 MeV are released in each fusion. The fusion is not a direct four-body reaction, but rather proceeds by stages through many two-body reactions (see SOLAR ENERGY SOURCES). Not only is our chief source of energy of nuclear origin, but the constituents of the earth are also the result of long-gone nuclear reactions, principally a series of (n, γ) processes which served to build up the elements in the earth as we now find them. One particularly pleasing success of nuclear reaction theory and experiment is the fact that the abundance of the elements and their isotopic ratios as they occur in nature can be calculated simply on the basis of the probability with which neutrons are captured by various nuclei, these probabilities having been measured in nuclear research centers.

Not only nature's energy source is of nuclear origin. The two mightiest sources of man-made energy, nuclear FISSION and nuclear FUSION, derive from nuclear reactions.

In fission, a neutron is captured by a uranium nucleus which splits (fissions) into, say, a Ba and Zr nucleus, in the process releasing about 200 MeV of energy and some neutrons which in turn split other U nuclei in the vicinity. This leads to the familiar chain reaction which, if controlled, is used to produce power by converting the fission energy (heat) into either motive power or electricity. If the chain reaction is allowed to proceed without control, a violent explosion results, i.e., an atomic bomb. We note parenthetically that what is commonly known as atomic energy should really be called nuclear energy since its source is not the entire atom, but only its nucleus. Burning of coal, on the other hand, is atomic energy, since heat is derived from the combination of a carbon atom with two oxygen atoms to form CO_2.

Fusion as a source of energy derives from a reaction such as ^{2}H$(d, n)^3$He in which 3.3 MeV are released. This process is similar to the source of solar energy, in that hydrogen nuclei fuse to produce helium. It has not proved possible yet to control the nuclear fusion reaction in such a way that it will proceed slowly. Many laboratories are currently working on this. An uncontrolled fusion reaction has, however, been achieved—it constitutes the energy source of the hydrogen bomb.

It is clear that reserves of coal and oil must someday be exhausted. When this happens, man will necessarily turn to nuclear reactions, fission, or fusion for his sources of power. In 1965, nuclear fission power plants accounted for only 0.6 per cent of the electricity generated in the U.S., however, it is expected that 7 per cent of the power will be of nuclear origin by 1980, and 45 per cent by the year 2000.

The terrors of war and the blessings of

abundant power both come from nuclear reactions. But that is not all. Perhaps the most significant contribution to all sciences has been the use of radioactive elements produced in nuclear reactions. Let us take a typical example. Consider the reaction $^{13}C(n,\gamma)^{14}C$. This reaction produces radioactive ^{14}C which has a half-life of 5700 years. The radioactive carbon decays with the emission of an electron which can be counted with a suitable detector. Thus we are able to locate individual atoms of carbon and separate them from all others which are not radioactive. Such radioactive atoms are called tracers, and by using a variety of them, ^{13}C, ^{18}F, ^{32}P, ^{35}S, ^{131}I, ^{198}Au, all produced by some sort of nuclear reaction, unprecedented advances have been made in biology, chemistry, metallurgy, physiology, and medicine. Furthermore, radioactive isotopes in large amounts can be used instead of x-rays for treatment of cancer, for metallography, and for food preservation.

By means of nuclear reactions such as ^{241}Am $(^{11}B, 4n)^{248}Fm$, scientists have been able to make new elements not found in nature. Some of these, for example plutonium and californium, have found important uses as reactor fuels or portable power sources. The preparation of new elements has played a decisive role in our understanding of the chemistry of heavy elements.

We turn now to a description of nuclear reactions themselves. These may be regarded as proceeding in two principal ways. First, the colliding particles may fuse, their components get thoroughly mixed in a very "hot" compound nucleus. This compound nucleus may exist in a heated state for a period varying between 10^{-16} and 10^{-20} second, a time we normally consider imponderably short, but which is nevertheless long on the nuclear time scale when compared with the transit time of a nucleon across the nucleus (10^{-22} second). The compound nucleus boils off fragments, mainly neutrons, protons, and α-particles, and in this way cools down to a normal energy content. In its final state, it is called a residual nucleus, and it may be radioactive or stable depending on the details of the reaction. If the target, the projectile, and the energy of the projectile are known, it is possible to predict what the residual nucleus will be and thus, if certain isotopes are wanted, one can tailor the reaction accordingly. We note here, however, that the exact mechanism of these reactions is very complicated and is not really understood in a fundamental way.

In the other kind of reaction, the nuclei do not fuse, but only part of the nuclear matter is transferred from one nucleus to the other. This is often called a direct reaction, and includes stripping reactions, pickup reactions, and transfer reactions. A typical example is $^{27}Al(d, p)^{28}Al$, where a neutron is stripped from the deuteron and caught by the Al nucleus, while the remaining proton stays relatively undisturbed on its original course. The nuclei in such reactions do not come into intimate contact, and the reaction is fast, on the time scale of 10^{-22} second.

We recall now that there is at present little fundamental understanding of the nucleus, i.e., we do not know precisely how it is built up from its constituent neutrons and protons, and what the properties of the nuclear force are which holds it together (see NUCLEAR STRUCTURE). An important use of nuclear reactions is to throw light on this problem. By a careful study of nuclear reactions where all the details such as the precise energy of the projectile, the nature, energy, and angle of emission of the reaction products are measured, much insight has been gained concerning the nucleus itself. The problem is really twofold; we have to understand and be able to express mathematically the mechanism of a nuclear reaction, and then we must proceed to extract information about the participating nuclei from it. At present both aspects are only promising, so that our deeper understanding seems to await either a clear breakthrough or a painstaking development of more detailed experiments and ever more complicated theoretical calculations. The prize, however, is worth reaching for: its promise is to reveal the nature of nuclei, the smallest stable constituents of matter, and the laws which govern their interactions to give man immense power for war or for peace.

A. ZUCKER

References

Two advanced books which deal with nuclear reactions are:

Endt, P. M., and Demeur, M., "Nuclear Reactions," Vol. I, Amsterdam, North-Holland Publishing Company, 1959.

Eisenbud, L., and Wigner, E. P., "Nuclear Structure," Princeton, N.J., Princeton University Press, 1958.

Cross-references: ELEMENTARY PARTICLES, FISSION, FUSION, ISOTOPES, NEUTRON, NUCLEAR STRUCTURE, PHOTON, PROTON, RADIOACTIVITY, SOLAR ENERGY SOURCES, TRANSURANIUM ELEMENTS.

NUCLEAR REACTORS

A nuclear reactor is a facility in which nuclear fuel is assembled for the purpose of supporting a sustained, controlled, neutron-fission chain reaction.

The controlled fissioning of atoms of nuclear fuel, resulting from interaction with neutrons, is the crucial event in a nuclear reactor. All of the manifold applications of "atomic energy," from nuclear power to atomic bombs, to radioactive isotopes, depend directly on the fissioning of fuel atoms or on the by-products there-

from. Basically, all these applications of atomic energy derive from just three consequences or by-products of fission: (1) release of heat energy, (2) release of direct radiation including neutrons, and (3) generation of "fission products," the fragments of the fissioned atoms, which themselves are highly radioactive isotopic species.

Role of Neutrons Within an assemblage of nuclear fuel, neutrons are initially obtained from spontaneous fission or from an inserted neutron source.* Some of these neutrons cause fission of fuel atoms. Each fission releases, among other radiations, more than two additional neutrons on the average, which, in turn, may either collide with other fuel atoms and cause them to fission, or may suffer a variety of other fates. Whether a neutron causes fission or ends its life some other way depends on the quantity and geometrical distribution of fuel, the moderating or poisoning effects of other materials present, and many other factors. When the fuel and other components are so arranged that a given instantaneous population of neutrons can cause sufficient fissioning to produce at least an equivalent average population of neutrons at later times, the neutron-fission chain reaction is said to be "sustained." The physical facility of which such fuel arrangement is a component part is a nuclear reactor. (In earlier days, the word "pile" instead of "reactor" was frequently used. This originated from the very first nuclear reactor which consisted of a huge "pile" of graphite and uranium appropriately intermixed.)

Thus, neutrons are the lifeblood of a reactor, just as oxygen is the essential ingredient and controller of chemical combustion of coal in an ordinary furnace. By neutron interactions, the vital process of successive generations of fission in atoms of the fuel, with their attendant release of energy, is carried on. In any given assembly, at any given moment, the rate of fissioning is proportional to the average population of neutrons. When the neutron population is constant, the rate of fissioning is steady, and the power level, i.e., the rate of energy release, is also constant. If conditions are altered so the neutron population and the rate of fissioning increase or decrease, the power level or the rate of energy release of the reactor is correspondingly increased or decreased.

Purposes for which Reactors Are Built Reactors are usually designed to make maximum use of one or another of the products of fission: heat, radiation, or fission products.

(*a*) *Utilization of Heat Energy*. Fissioning of 1 pound of uranium releases 3.6×10^{10} Btu of heat; or the heat equivalent of 2 000 000 pounds

*A neutron source, for example, would be a small capsule containing a mixture of polonium and beryllium. Alphas from the radioactively decaying polonium would interact with the beryllium to yield neutrons: $_2{}^4d + _4{}^9\text{Be} \rightarrow _6{}^{12}\text{C} + _0{}^1\text{n}$.

of oil; 1 gram of fissioned uranium yields the heat equivalent of 1 megawatt-day of electricity.

When an atom fissions, most of the heat energy is released instantaneously and essentially at the point of fission. However, most of the energy of the gammas, betas and neutrons which radiate out in all directions is also transformed into heat energy in surrounding materials. Further, the delayed radiation given off by the radioactive fission products is likewise converted into heat energy. Thus, a mixture of fission products continues to generate heat for a long time after occurrence of the fission events which produced them.

As a source of heat energy for generation of electric power, for desalting of ocean water, for propulsion of mobile vehicles, for the driving force in endothermic chemical processes of industry, and for other similar uses, the heat from nuclear fission has countless potential applications of major dimensions. In such applications, radiation may be at best an incidental by-product or a nuisance.

(*b*) *Utilization of Radiation*. Gammas, neutrons, betas and some alphas comprise the radiation given off when an atom is fissioned. The composition of the average radiation is different from one fuel isotope to another. For example, 2.5 neutrons, on the average, are released from each ^{235}U fission, while fission from each ^{239}Pu releases 3.0 neutrons.

The excess neutrons, beyond those needed for sustaining the chain reaction (which is just 1 per fission for maintaining a status quo fissioning rate) and the gamma radiation from fission have many and diverse uses. Some reactors are built for generation and utilization of this radiation, in which applications heat may be at best an incidental by-product or a nuisance.

As examples, radiation may be used for:

(1) Radioisotope production: Many very useful radioisotopes are produced when excess neutrons from a reactor are captured by ordinary, nonradioactive isotopic species.

(2) Nuclear fuel production: Excess neutrons may also be used to convert certain "fertile" isotopic species, which are not useful as nuclear fuels, into readily fissionable nuclear fuels. For example, thorium 232, useless as a nuclear fuel, is transformed by neutron capture and subsequent radioactive decay, into uranium 233, a valuable fissionable fuel. The abundant uranium 238 is transformed by neutron capture from its natural worthless (fuel) value into plutonium 239, an extremely valuable fissionable fuel.

Breeder Reactors. Since, as explained above, each fission event produces, on the average, more than two neutrons, and since only one is needed to maintain a sustained reaction, it is clearly conceivable in principle that more than one excess neutron from each fission could result in conversion of more than one atom of fertile fuel into atoms of fissionable fuel. That is, fissioning to fuel atoms in a reactor can produce power from the heat released and,

simultaneously, if atoms of fertile fuel are appropriately intermixed among the fuel atoms, the excess neutrons can convert a larger amount of fertile material into fissionable fuel than the amount of fuel consumed. A reactor in which more fuel is generated than the amount consumed is called a breeder reactor.

Actually, in the currently prevalent water-type reactors using fuels of low enrichments of ^{235}U intermixed with ^{238}U, some conversion of ^{238}U to ^{239}Pu occurs, but the conversion ratio (of Pu generated to ^{235}U fissioned) is less than 1. Such reactors are called "converters," whereas in breeders the conversion ratio is greater than one.

The possibilities of breeding and the combinations of most promising materials for breeding have been extensively studied. Breeding has been demonstrated in experimental and developmental reactors, and in many technically advanced countries extensive efforts are being addressed to the development of large commercially feasible breeder reactors.

What is needed is (a) a fissionable fuel that produces a relatively high yield of neutrons per fission (it must be more than 2); (b) a fertile material that will yield a relatively high conversion rate into fissionable fuel per neutron absorbed; and (c) minimization of other materials (poisons, etc.) or arrangements (leakage, etc.) which cause unproductive neutron loss.

In principle, breeding can be achieved with appropriate combinations of ingredients in thermal or in fast reactors. However, in thermal reactors it is difficult to achieve a conversion ratio greater than one because of unproductive neutron losses by absorption in moderator and structural materials. Conversion ratios of about 0.7 can be obtained in graphite-moderated gas-cooled thermal reactors, and a ratio slightly greater than one has been achieved in a graphite-moderated reactor with ^{235}U fuel and ^{232}Th fertile material dispersed in a molten-salt coolant.

In fast reactors neutron losses by absorption in nonfertile materials are sharply reduced and conversion ratios in the range of 1.3 can readily be achieved. A promising fast reactor concept uses sodium as coolant, ^{235}U or ^{239}Pu as fuel, and ^{238}U as the fertile ingredient. The use of ^{233}U as fuel with ^{232}Th as the fertile material also holds promise.

Thus, by using excess neutrons from nuclear reactors, the potential nuclear fuel supply of the world may be increased many times. ^{235}U is the principal naturally occurring nuclear fuel. ^{238}U is 140 times more plentiful. Thorium is 7 times as abundant as all the uranium.

(3) Sterilization of food; chemical catalysts: The vast gamma and neutron fluxes generated in fission reactors are capable of causing various changes in the physical characteristics of materials, some detrimental and some beneficial, and profound effects in living organisms, including alteration of genetic characteristics. Foods can be sterilized, and bacteriological processes inhibited; chemical reactions can be catalyzed, and certain types of organic materials can be polymerized by exposure to radiation. The gammas rather than neutrons are principally used in such applications because neutrons may cause undesirable radioactivity in some of the materials.

(c) *Utilization of Fission Products.* Fission products removed from the spent fuel elements of reactors can be used for many purposes. For examples:

(1) Gamma radiation from fission products in bulk has been used for sterilization of food and polymerization of chemicals.

(2) Iodine 132, and various other particular species, have been isolated and used extensively in medical diagnosis and therapy.

(3) Separated, high specific activity isotopes in the multi-megacurie range have been used for radiation therapy sources, for radiography in place of x-rays, and for concentrated sources of heat. For example, ^{90}Sr has been used as a concentrated source of heat for direct thermoelectric generation of electricity to be used for instruments in satellites and in remote weather stations.

On the whole, however, to date there are practical uses for only a small fraction of the fission products now being generated, and the chief present concern is for safe and economical storage or disposal of these by-products of fission.

Components of Reactors: Types of Reactors For controlled neutron-fission chain reaction in nuclear fuel to proceed, there must be: (1) an assemblage of fuel of appropriate quantity, dimensions and arrangements; (2) a ready means of adjusting the fissioning rate (power level) to any desired level, i.e., a control system; (3) a means of sensing and measuring the processes in progress, i.e., an instrumentation-intelligence system; (4) a means of removing heat from the fuel and disposing of or using it, i.e., a cooling system; (5) a means of protecting the environment from the direct radiation flux of escaping gammas and neutrons, i.e., shielding; (6) a confinement system for retention of the fission products; and (7) other auxiliary components.

In the following sections, some of the basic principles applicable to the functioning of these systems are briefly sketched.

(a) *The Reactor Core.* A reactor core consists of the fuel assembly, of whatever quantity, composition, physical form, dimensions and configuration are required to enable the neutron chain reaction to proceed under the conditions and for the purposes desired in any particular case. In addition, the core includes all other intermixed components, supporting members and immediately adjacent structures and materials.

Reactor fuels are metallic in elemental form but may be readily processed into various compound forms. They may be used in reactors in any of a wide variety of chemical and physical

forms. No physical or chemical circumstance affects the fissioning or other nuclear characteristics of any materials.

(b) *Coolant.* When a reactor is to be operated at power levels high enough to generate substantial quantities of heat within the fuel, means must be provided for removal of this heat. Thus, in high-power reactors, fuel is customarily in the solid forms of rods, tubes or plates, having large surface area-to-mass ratios to facilitate escape of heat. Flow channels between adjacent fuel elements accommodate circulation of a fluid heat-removal coolant. In a power reactor, the coolant becomes sufficiently hot to be converted into steam (where water is the coolant) or hot enough to generate steam in the heat exchangers outside the core. The steam then drives turbines to produce electricity in the usual way. Coolants which have been used include air, CO_2, He, N_2, water, organic liquids, sodium, and sodium potassium mixtures. In present power reactors, water is the coolant most prevalently used.

(c) *Fuel Cladding.* During reactor operation as fissioning proceeds, fission products generated in the fuel tend in many instances to migrate to the surface where, by escape into the circulating coolant, they may be carried to external parts of the system and there give rise to radiation hazards. In most cases, therefore, the fuel itself is clad in a thin impervious metallic sheath which prevents escape of the fission products. Cladding materials include aluminum, stainless steel, ceramic coatings, and various alloys of aluminum or zirconium.

(d) *Moderator.* When fission occurs, the neutrons released are of very high energy, 2 MeV or so, on the average. It so happens that such high-energy neutrons are inefficient in causing fission in commonly used fuel atoms. Slow neutrons,* however, with energies below 1 eV, have much higher fission efficiencies per collision. Therefore, for most large reactors presently being built, arrangements are made for the fission neutrons to be quickly degraded in energy to slow, thermal energies, and the fission process proceeds mainly by thermal neutron fission. Reactors in which this is the case are called thermal reactors. It is possible and, to achieve certain objectives, it is desirable for the fissioning process to be carried on by the inefficient fast neutron process. Reactors where this applies are called fast reactors.

Neutrons lose energy only, by elastic (i.e., "mechanical," non-nuclear interaction) collision with other atoms. They lose least energy per collision with heavy (e.g., uranium) atoms and most energy per collision with low mass atoms.

In thermal reactors, appropriate quantities of low-mass elements such as hydrogen, deuterium, lithium, beryllium, and carbon are intermixed with the fuel to insure that the energetic fission neutrons are promptly degraded in energy, i.e., are moderated in velocity, to the thermal range. Such low mass materials are called moderators. In some cases coolants also serve as moderators.

In fast reactors, all moderating materials are carefully excluded, so the fission neutrons are forced to collide only with heavy mass atoms and hence lose energy slowly. They eventually do cause fission or may be captured in nonfissionable atoms.

(e) *Reactor Control.* Materials which capture neutrons without subsequently undergoing nuclear fission are called poisons. All materials, even "good" nuclear fuels, are to some extent poisons. Some materials have a much higher non-fission cross section,† i.e., poisoning effect per unit quantity, than do others. Poison materials serve a very useful purpose. They provide the one most frequently used mechanism, though there are also others, for controlling the fissioning rate or power level of the reactor. In an operating reactor, the judicious insertion or withdrawal of an appropriate quantity of poison can control the rise or fall of the neutron population, and hence the rate of fissioning can be adjusted at will.

In practice, boron or cadmium, in rod form or other suitable shape, attached to drive motors or other suitable remotely manipulated devices, is so arranged that the operator can remove or insert at will just the appropriate amount of poison to cause the neutron population originating from a fixed source to grow rapidly or slowly, remain constant or decrease slowly or rapidly. A reactor is "shut down" when sufficient poison is inserted (or other means are used) to essentially terminate the fission chain reaction. Upon termination of the chain reaction, fissioning ceases. However, this has no effect on the radioactivity from the accumulated fission products; this continues, unabated, at the respective decay rates of the radionuclides involved.

(f) *Auxiliary Systems.* In addition to the essential components of reactors mentioned above, fuel, coolant, controls and moderator, many other components and systems are necessary for the protection of people and the utilization of the reactor. Appropriate instrumentation is needed to enable the operator to know the status of various processes, neutron flux, radiation levels, temperatures, coolant flow rates, etc. Shielding against radiation fluxes and containment mechanisms to prevent escape of

---

*Neutrons in thermal, Brownian equilibrium with surrounding atoms at nominal room temperatures have energies of about 0.25 eV. Such neutrons are called thermal neutrons.

†The "cross-section" of some given nuclear event is the probability per collision that that particular event will occur. For example, an atom of a fuel which possesses a high neutron fission cross section has a high probability of fissioning when a neutron collision occurs.

radioactivity are needed for the protection of people. Machinery for collection and utilization of the heat, or to provide access to the radiation fluxes, is necessary to the intended uses of reactors.

A large nuclear reactor facility employed for the generation of electricity or for the propulsion of an oceangoing vessel is exceedingly complicated and expensive.

(g) *Reactors in Use*. At the end of 1971, almost 700 reactors, in 48 countries, were listed as "operable"; many older ones had been decommissioned and a vary larger number were "being built" or "planned." Statistics listed here are excerpted from two documents:

(1) "Nuclear Reactors Built, Being Built, or Planned in the U.S. as of December 31, 1971."

(2) "Foreign Reactors Operating, Being Built, or Planned as of November 1971," USAEC Technical Information Center.

It is almost impossible to know the precise number in existence at any given time and the assorted purposes for which they are used.

Appropriate electricity capacity from nuclear reactors was listed as follows:

U.K., 6000 MW; U.S., 10,000 MW; U.S.- S.R., 3000 MW; France, 2000 MW; Canada, 1500 MW; Japan, 1300 MW; Germany, 1000 MW; Italy 620 MW; all others, 2500 MW.

As an illustration of the variety and distribution of reactor types in use, Table 1 below lists the reactors built to operable status by the United States up to the end of 1971.

CLIFFORD K. BECK

Cross-references: ATOMIC ENERGY, FISSION, FUSION, ISOTOPES, NEUTRON, NUCLEAR REACTIONS, NUCLEONICS, RADIOACTIVITY, NUCLEAR REACTOR SHIELDING.

TABLE 1. REACTORS BUILT IN THE UNITED STATES 1942[a] THROUGH 1971

Power Reactors	22
Experimental Power	5
Test Research and Training	100
Production and Process Development	8
Military Reactors for Propulsion and Other Uses	132
Reactors for Export	71
Total	338

[a]The first sustained, controlled nuclear chain reaction was achieved in a graphite natural uranium assembly in Chicago in December, 1942.

TABLE 2. REACTORS LISTED AS "OPERABLE" IN COUNTRIES OTHER THAN THE UNITED STATES TO END OF 1971

Country	No.
Canada	13
France	34
West Germany	36
Italy	17
Japan	15
Netherlands	6
Sweden	7
United Kingdom	37
U.S.S.R.	34
All others recorded	74
Total	273

NUCLEAR STRUCTURE

The basic problem of nuclear structure was first sharply defined in 1932 when Chadwick discovered the neutron. The nucleus was then recognized to be a system of A particles (nucleons) of nearly equal mass (Z protons and $N = A - Z$ neutrons). The forces binding the "nucleons" together must be quite distinct from the well-known electromagnetic interactions which will evidently operate to push the nucleons apart, as well as gravitational forces which appear to be too weak to have any influence in the nucleus at all.

The nuclear forces are found to be of short range ($\sim 10^{-13}$ cm). Within their short radius of interaction, they become strongly attractive (depths near 100 MeV), but at very small distances the interaction becomes so powerfully repulsive that nucleons seldom come closer than about 0.4×10^{-13} cm from one another. This character of the nuclear force produces "saturation." The binding energy per nucleon is nearly constant ($\sim 8.0 \pm 1$ MeV) throughout the periodic table, while each nucleon occupies a volume which may be approximated by a sphere of radius 10^{-13} cm.

The forces described above are assumed to operate between each pair of nucleons. Their exact nature is rather complicated and depends upon the motion, and even the orientation of the nucleons. We do not as yet have a completely trustworthy expression for this force, but rapid progress is being made in this field.

Even if the nuclear force were precisely known, the structure of the nucleus would not be immediately understood in its entirety. Methods are not at present available for solving the three-body problem in closed form for simple interactions, and for more than three bodies, drastic approximations must be used to make the problems tractable. For this reason, considerable attention in physics is devoted to constructing simplified models of the nucleus. The purpose of these models is to isolate the salient characteristics of the nucleus, and thereby obtain some understanding of its behavior.

Two very general classes of nuclear models have received considerable attention. The simplest may be described as "powder models." Here it is assumed that the motion of nucleons within the nucleus is so complicated that statistical mechanics may be employed. In one version of this model, the nucleus is treated in analogy to a drop of liquid (the nuclear forces described above are qualitatively quite similar to forces between the molecules of a liquid). Such a chaotic state seems to ensue if the nucleus is highly excited, so that the nucleons have a great deal of kinetic energy. For this reason, powder models have found their greatest usefulness in describing the nucleus during a nuclear reaction, and especially in describing nuclear fission.

In the shell model (sometimes called the independent particle model), the motion of the individual nucleons is assumed to be much more simple. Each nucleon is, in fact, assigned a definite orbit within the nucleus. The resultant motion is then reminiscent of our usual picture of electrons within the atom, all revolving nearly independently of each other about the nucleus. The motivation for introducing this model into nuclear physics came from the early (1934) observation that nuclei that contained certain numbers of protons or neutrons were unusually stable and abundant. These numbers are generally referred to as magic numbers. The set we recognize today as magic are

N or $Z = 2, 6, 8, 14, 20, 28, 50, 82$, and 126

The major details which focus attention on these numbers may be summarized as follows:

(1) *Stability and abundance*. Nuclei with N or Z magic are unusually tightly bound and correspondingly very abundant. If both N and Z are magic ($_2\text{He}_2$, $_6\text{C}_6$, $_8\text{O}_8$, $_{14}\text{Si}_{14}$, $_{20}\text{Ca}_{20}$, $_{20}\text{Ca}_{28}$, and $_{82}\text{Pb}_{126}$), then the nucleus is even more tightly bound (here, the left subscript is the number of protons; the right is the number of neutrons). The last nucleon to complete a magic number has sometimes nearly twice the binding energy of an average nucleon. Furthermore, nuclei with Z magic possess an unusually large number of stable isotopes, and nuclei with N magic have an unusually large number of stable isotones.

(2) *Neutron capture cross sections*. Nuclei with neutron number one short of a magic number have a large neutron capture cross section, while nuclei with a magic number of neutrons exhibit a small neutron capture cross section.

(3) *Islands of isomerism*. Long lived γ-active nuclear states (half-life~1 second) appear just prior to the completion of a magic number.

(4) *Electric quadrupole moments*. Nuclear quadrupole moments tend to be small near magic numbers and large far from magic numbers. A nucleus with N or Z magic appears, therefore, to prefer a spherical shape.

(5) *Delayed neutron emission*. Delayed neutron emitters (e.g., $_{36}\text{Kr}_{51}$, $_{54}\text{Xe}_{83}$, and $_8\text{O}_9$) appear when N is one greater than a magic number.

The data clearly point to an interpretation of the magic numbers in terms of shell closures, analogous to the atomic structure of noble gases. Thus it appears that the nucleon-nucleon interaction somehow averages out within the nucleus so that each nucleon, to a reasonable first approximation, sees a fairly smooth potential. Such a potential should be flat near the origin (like an harmonic oscillator), and should go rapidly to zero outside the nucleus (like a square well). A suitable form which has undergone much study is the Fermi function.

$$V(r) = V_0 [1 + \exp \alpha(r - a)]^{-1} \qquad (1)$$

In order to reproduce the magic numbers one must add a spin-orbit term:

$$f(r)\mathbf{l}\cdot\mathbf{s} \qquad (2)$$

to this central potential. Here $\mathbf{l}$ is the orbital angular momentum of a nucleon, and $\mathbf{s}$ its spin. The effect of this $\mathbf{l}\cdot\mathbf{s}$ interaction is to couple the orbital and spin angular momenta so that the states with total angular momentum $j = l + \frac{1}{2}$ will be lower in energy than states with $j = l + \frac{1}{2}$. Shell closures obtained with such a potential are found to reproduce the observed magic numbers in a simple and striking manner.

The fact that the shell model works at all in nuclei is somewhat surprising since the theoretical motivation that enhances its success in atomic structure is lacking. One has no strong central field originally in nuclei, and furthermore the nucleons are much more closely packed. Consequently, collisions, which should tend to scatter a nucleon out of its orbit, should be more frequent. It is found that the Pauli exclusion principle plays a vital role here. When such a collision occurs, the orbit into which a nucleon would tend to be scattered is actually occupied by another nucleon. This fact makes the shell model a far better first approximation than one would originally suspect.

The main effect of the nucleon-nucleon interaction is to produce the average shell model (single-particle) potential. This, of course, is not the sole effect. Many refinements are required before an adequate description of nuclei may be attained.

Consider, for example, a nucleus with just two nucleons beyond a double closed shell. One of the nucleons will go into an orbit j, and the other into an orbit j'. These two orbits may orient themselves such that the nucleus may have total angular momentum J anywhere within the range

$$|j - j'| \leqslant J \leqslant j + j' \qquad (3)$$

so long as one is consistent with the Pauli exclusion principle. If one only had single-particle potentials all states of this configuration would

have the same energy independent of J. To determine the level order actually observed, one must recognize that not all of the original nucleon-nucleon interaction is used up in constructing the single-particle potential. Some "residual interaction" is left over. This residual interaction will still be of the two-body type, and it will remove the degeneracy between states of the same configuration.

The most important feature of the residual interaction is that it produces a pairing force for like orbitals (i.e., $j = j'$). If $j = j'$, and we have like nucleons, the interaction is by far the strongest if $J = 0$. This has the important consequence that for nuclei with both an even number of protons and an even number of neutrons, one must have net angular momentum equal to zero. This rule is never violated. If one adds one nucleon to this even-even nucleus, the result will be a J equal to the j of the odd nucleon. This rule is violated in only a very few cases.

There are a few nuclear phenomena which the shell model cannot describe at all. The sign of the static, nuclear, electric quadrupole moments are generally given correctly by a single-particle model, but the magnitude is frequently found to be larger than that predicted by more than a factor of ten. Similarly, electric quadrupole transition rates are frequently much faster than those given by the shell model. It seems that even in low-lying nuclear levels it is not possible to attribute all of the properties of the nucleus to the nucleons in unfilled orbits. One must take into account possible distortions of the orbits of nucleons in the closed shells.

This line of thought gives rise to the "collective model," in which the nucleons in the core (closed shells) are treated as an incompressible, irrotational fluid capable of surface oscillations. Nucleons in unfilled shells will exert a centrifugal force on this fluid and tend to deform it into a nonspherical shape. In regions of the periodic table where several shell model orbitals are nearly degenerate in energy ($90 \leqslant N \leqslant 114$ and $Z > 88$), the nuclear core takes on a rather large spheroidal deformation. The formalism of the theory is reminiscent of that for diatomic molecules. Low-lying excited states are generated through a rotation of the entire system about an axis perpendicular to the axis of symmetry. This gives rise to a band of energy levels:

$$E_J = E_0 + (\hbar^2/2I)J(J+1) \qquad (4)$$

where I is a moment of inertia. The identification of spectra in nuclei which could be empirically fitted to Eq. (4) was a great truimph of the collective model.

It should be noted that I is not the moment of inertia of the entire nucleus. It is only the moment of inertia of the part of the nucleus which participates in the rotation, and this is, of course, always less than the "rigid body" value.

We note that the shell model and collective model appear to be quite different in their basic assumptions. The collective model presumes that the nucleon motions are so closely correlated that we can treat a rotation of the nucleus on the whole, while the shell model begins with independent orbitals. It is very important to remember, in this regard, that the shell-model orbitals must be properly coupled together in the nucleus. The Pauli exclusion principle must be satisfied, angular momentum must be a good quantum number, and so on. These orbitals are, therefore not so independent as it might seem. They may very well give rise to collective effects depending upon the exact way in which they are coupled together to obtain the final nuclear wave function.

Various coupling schemes have recently been examined to investigate this, but these are beyond the scope of this article. We present here a simple illustrative example. Consider a set of identical particles attracted by means of identical springs to a common origin. At time $t = 0$ each particle is at the origin and is given some arbitrary velocity. Even though each particle has a different initial velocity, and moves independently of every other particle, the system will undergo a periodic dilation and contraction due to the fact that the frequency of vibration is the same for each particle. Thus we have a collective motion exhibited by a set of independently moving particles.

The next step in the investigation must be to attain a quantitative interpretation of the individual particle motion itself. This must come directly from a full treatment of the many-body nuclear problem using realistic nucleon-nucleon interactions. This problem is complicated by the fact that nuclear forces become sharply repulsive at very short nucleon-nucleon separations. Thus the nuclear wave function exhibits strong correlations between nucleons which must be accounted for in any final theory. The two-body correlations seem well accounted for by a formalism devised by Bruechner, Bethe, and Goldstone, but the effects attained when three or more nucleons all come into close proximity are yet to be completely evaluated in finite nuclei.

PAUL GOLDHAMMER

References

Baranger, M., "Recent Progress in the Understanding of Finite Nuclei from the Two-Nucleon Interaction," *Proceedings of the International School of Physics,* Course 40, p. 511 (Academic Press, 1969).

Eisenbud, L., and Wigner, E. P., "Nuclear Structure," Princeton, N.J., Princeton University Press, 1958.

Elliott, J. P., and Lane, A. M., "Handbuch der Physik, Vol. 39, p. 241, Berlin, Springer-Verlag, 1957.

Feenberg, E., "Shell Theory of the Nucleus," Princeton, N.J., Princeton University Press, 1955.

Goldhammer, P., *Rev. Mod. Phys.,* **35,** 40 (1963).

Inglis, D. R., *Rev. Mod. Phys.,* **25,** 390 (1953).

Mayer, M. G., and Jensen, J. H. D., "Elementary Theory of Nuclear Shell Structure," New York, John Wiley & Sons, 1955.

Rajaraman, R., and Bethe, H. A., *Revs. Modern Phys.*, 39, 745 (1967).

Cross-references: ATOMIC PHYSICS; NUCLEAR REACTIONS; NEUTRON; NUCLEONICS; PROTON; STRONG INTERACTIONS; WEAK INTERACTIONS.

NUCLEONICS

Nucleonics (nü'kli-on'iks) is a name proposed by Z. Jeffries of the Manhattan District in 1944 to describe the general field of nuclear science and technology. As popularly used, it encompasses not only the study of the atomic nucleus, but also related physical techniques, instrumentation, radiochemistry, and the applications of radioisotopes. In its strict technical sense, it refers only to the first of these and is so used here.

Prior to 1900 atoms were considered to be unalterable and indivisible entities of which the elements were composed. With the discovery of the nuclear transmutations resulting from the radioactive decay process, however, it became apparent that atoms themselves possessed internal structure.

Upon observing that in passing through matter, alpha particles were scattered through larger angles than the then current concepts of the atom would predict, Rutherford suggested that the atom actually consisted of a small, heavy, positively charged nucleus surrounded by negative charges of the same magnitude. Further observations and theoretical refinements have led to the now generally accepted concept that the nucleus also contains elementary particles, i.e., neutrons, which are electrically neutral and have a mass of 1.008665, and protons, which are positively charged and have a mass of 1.0072765.* Stated in simple form, then, the atom consists of a positively charged nucleus, containing neutrons and protons, surrounded by a number of negatively charged electrons sufficient to provide electrical neutrality. Although this concept of the atom has not been in serious question for almost 50 years, complete understanding of the forces which hold the neutrons and protons together has not yet been achieved.

In 1927, Aston found that experimentally measured isotopic weights differed slightly from whole numbers. From this he was led to the concept of the packing fraction, which is defined as the algebraic difference between the isotopic weight and the mass number, divided by the mass number. Although the theoretical significance of the packing fraction is difficult to assess, it does lead to some interesting conclusions with respect to nuclear stability. A negative packing fraction derives from a situation where the isotopic weight is less than the mass number, inferring that in the formation of the

*Using the standard scale of atomic weights.

nucleus from its constituent particles, some mass is converted into energy. Since an equivalent amount of energy would be necessary to break up the nucleus into its constituent particles again, a negative packing fraction suggests a high order of nuclear stability. By the same reasoning, a positive packing fraction indicates nuclear instability. Stable elements with mass numbers above about 175 and below about 25 have positive packing fractions. It is interesting to note that the packing fractions of both hydrogen and uranium are positive.

Actually, a comparison of the isotopic weight with the mass number (as is done in determining the packing fraction) is somewhat artificial. A rigorous determination of the mass-energy interconversion in the formation of an atom would seem to require a calculation of the difference between the sum of the masses of the constituent particles of the atom and the experimentally measured isotopic weight. The value of the mass difference thus obtained is the mass defect. The energy equivalent of this mass difference as derived from the Einstein equation yields a measure of the binding energy of the nucleus. Division of the binding energy of a nucleus by the number of nucleons (the total number of protons and neutrons) therein yields the binding energy per nucleon. In stable isotopes, the binding energy per nucleon decreases with increasing mass number, a fact which is important in nuclear fission. Secondly, the binding energy per nucleon derived in the manner described above is an average value, whereas each additional nucleon added to the nucleus has a binding energy less than those which preceded it. Thus, the most recently added nucleons are bound less tightly than those already present.

Additional considerations regarding nuclear stability may be gleaned from a consideration of the odd or even nature of the numbers of protons and neutrons in the nucleus. According to the Pauli exclusion principle, no two extranuclear electrons having an identical set of quantum numbers can occupy the same electron energy state. The application of this principle to the nucleus leads to conclusions which at least are not at variance with observations of nuclear stability. Thus, it is inferred that no two nucleons possessing an identical set of quantum numbers may occupy the same nuclear energy state. It would appear, then, that both protons and neutrons which differ only in their angular momenta or spins may exist in a nuclear state. The exclusion principle requires, therefore, that only protons having opposite spins can exist in the same state. The same consideration applies to neutrons. Accordingly, two protons and two neutrons might occupy the same nuclear energy state provided the nucleons in each pair have opposite spins. Such two-proton-two-neutron groupings are termed "closed shells," and by virtue of their proton-neutron interaction, they confer exceptional stability to nuclei which are made up

of them. The nuclear forces, in closed shells are said to be "saturated," which means that the nucleons therein interact strongly with each other, but weakly with those in other states. Since like particles tend to complete an energy state by pairing of opposite spins, two neutrons of opposite spin or a single neutron or proton also might exist in a particular energy state.

Any of the above conditions may be achieved when the nucleus contains an even number of both protons and neutrons, or an even number of one and an odd number of the other. Since there is an excess of neutrons over protons for all but the lowest atomic number elements, in the odd-odd situation there is a deficiency of protons necessary to complete the two-proton–two-neutron quartets. It might be expected that these could be provided by the production of protons via beta decay. As a matter of fact, there exist only four stable nuclei of odd-odd composition, whereas there are 108 such nuclei in the even-odd form and 162 in the even-even series. It will be seen that the order of stability, and presumably the binding energy per nucleon, from greatest to smallest, seems to be even-even, even-odd, odd-odd.

Although the existence of binding energies holding the nucleus together has been demonstrated, the problem of defining the nature of these forces presents itself. Clearly, repulsive electrostatic forces must exist between protons. These are "long range" in effect. To achieve nuclear stability then, compensating attractive forces also must exist. It has been concluded that "short-range" attractive forces exist between protons, neutrons, and protons and neutrons. The $(p - n)$ attractive forces are considered to be of the greatest magnitude while the $(n - n)$ and $(p - p)$ forces are of lesser intensity, with the latter decreased by virtue of electrostatic repulsion. When the number of protons in a nucleus is greater than twenty, it is found that the ratio of neutrons to protons exceeds unity. The additional short-range attractive forces provided by the excess neutrons, therefore, may be considered as compensating for the long-range electrostatic repulsive forces between the protons. Nevertheless, when the number of protons exceeds about 50, the short-range forces are insufficient to counteract the electrostatic forces completely, with the result that the binding energy per each additional nucleon decreases.

Unfortunately, the nature of the short-range attractive forces between nucleons remains essentially unresolved. An interpretation of them has been presented by Heisenberg, however, in terms of wave-mechanical exchange forces. Thus, if the basic difference between the proton and neutron in a system composed of these two particles is considered to be that the former is electrically charged while the latter is not, then the transfer of the electric charge from the proton to the neutron results in an exchange of individual identity but not a change in the system. That is to say, the system still is composed of a proton and neutron, despite the fact that the particles have exchanged their identities. Since the system itself has the same composition, it must possess the same energy after the exchange as it did before. One of the principles of wave mechanics is that if a system may be represented by two states, each of which has the same energy, then the actual state of the system is a result of the combination, i.e., resonance, of the two separate states and is more stable than either. In the proton-neutron system under discussion, the energy difference between the "combined" state and the individual states may be considered as the "exchange energy" or "attractive force" between the particles. In an extension of Heisenberg's proposal, Yukawa has postulated that the exchange energy is carried by a new particle which has been given the name meson. Particles having the properties attributed by Yukawa to mesons have been identified in cosmic rays.

With these concepts of nuclear structure and stability, however imperfect, the process of nuclear fission of uranium can now be considered. Although fast neutrons (greater than 0.1 MeV) can cause fission in both uranium 235 and uranium 238, thermal neutrons (about 0.03 eV) are effective only with uranium 235. Uranium 238 is unsatisfactory as a fissionable material for most purposes, however, since it has a high probability for "resonance capture" of fast neutrons, which is a nonfission process. It is instructive to ponder why uranium 235 fissions with thermal neutrons and uranium 238 does not. It will be recalled that the binding energy for an even-even nucleus exceeds that for an even-odd. Consequently, the addition of a neutron to uranium 235, which yields an even-even compound nucleus, will contribute a greater binding energy than in the case of uranium 238 where an even-odd compound nucleus would be produced. Calculations yield a value of 6.81 MeV for the additional neutron in the former case, and 5.31 MeV in the latter. Using Bohr and Wheeler's calculations, it is found that the activation energy for fission is 5.2 MeV for uranium 235 and 5.9 MeV for uranium 238. Thus, the binding energy for an additional neutron in uranium 235 exceeds its fission activation energy, whereas it is less in the case of uranium 238. It can be seen then that uranium-235 fission is energetically feasible with thermal neutrons while the fissioning of uranium 238 is not.

In considering the physical forces acting in fission, use may be made of the Bohr liquid drop model of the nucleus. Here it is assumed that in its normal energy state a nucleus is spherical and has a homogeneously distributed electrical charge. Under the influence of the activation energy furnished by the incident neutron, however, oscillations are set up which tend to deform the nucleus. In the ellipsoid form, the distribution of the protons is such that they are concentrated in the areas of the two foci. The electrostatic forces of repulsion between the protons

at the opposite ends of the ellipse may then further deform the nucleus into a dumbbell shape. From this condition there can be no recovery, and fission results.

It will be recalled that the binding energy per nucleon decreases with increasing mass number. To state it differently, a greater amount of energy is released in the formation of nuclei of intermediate mass number from their constituent nucleons than is the case in nuclei of high mass number. Thus, energy is released in fission because the binding energy of the high mass number uranium-236 compound nucleus is less than that of the intermediate mass number fission products which are produced. The total energy thus liberated in fission is about 200 MeV. Of this the kinetic energy of the fission products accounts for 160 MeV. These fragments, being of significantly lower atomic number, require fewer neutrons for stability than they actually contain immediately after fission. These excess neutrons, therefore, are "boiled off" the fission fragments, the process occurring in two distinct phases. In the first phase, "prompt" neutrons of about 2-MeV energy are released within 10^{-12} seconds after fission occurs and take up about 7 per cent of the fission energy. Subsequently, after several seconds, additional "delayed" neutrons with about 0.5-MeV energy are boiled off the fission products. These play an extremely important role in the control of the chain reaction in nuclear reactors.

Measurements made by Zinn and Szilard indicate that an average of 2.3 neutrons are released per fission. If in each fission, therefore, at least one of the released neutrons caused the fissioning of another uranium nucleus, there would result a series of fissions, i.e., a self-sustaining chain reaction. The establishment of this condition basically is dependent upon two related factors: (1) the number of neutrons which are lost by escape from the geometrical confines of the system and (2) the number which are used up in nonfission processes, such as capture by uranium 238. Loss by escape is proportional to the surface area of the system. A sphere, for example, would provide a maximum volume of fissionable material for a minimum surface area. Loss by capture may be controlled by the use of uranium suitably enriched in the 235 isotope. Thus, the quantity, quality and geometry of the system may be varied until a "critical" mass is obtained. Under these conditions, there is a constant number of neutrons in the system, that is to say, the "reproduction factor" is unity.

In order that the chain reaction might proceed under controlled conditions, certain additional features must be built into the system. Thus, the neutrons must be slowed down so that the thermal neutron uranium-235 fission process will be maximized and fast neutron uranium-238 nonfission capture will be minimized. This may be accomplished by causing the fast neutrons to undergo a series of collisions, say with carbon atoms, until their energy has been reduced below the excitation energy for the fast fission process and the threshold energy for nonfission capture. In addition, some means must be had to control the reproduction factor. The introduction of variable amounts of a strongly neutron-absorbing materials, such as boron, will serve this purpose. Lastly, protection must be afforded against the lethal radiations accompanying the chain reaction.

All of the above features are incorporated in the nuclear reactor. In the typical graphite reactor, a "pile" of graphite blocks are stacked atop each other in the form of a cube. Through each block, a hole is bored, into which the uranium fuel rods are placed. Interlaced between the graphite blocks are boron control rods whose depth of penetration into the pile may be varied. Around the whole structure a several foot thick concrete shield is poured. In operation then, the fast neutrons produced by fissioning of the uranium are thermalized in the graphite blocks. The number of thermal neutrons in the system, and hence the reproduction factor, is controlled by varying the depth of the strongly neutron-absorbing boron control rods. The radiations are absorbed in the concrete shield.

It will be recalled that the prompt neutrons are released within 10^{-12} second. Manipulation of the control rods to prevent an excessive buildup in the power level would be difficult in view of the small latitude permitted by this time interval. The delayed neutrons are emitted only after several seconds, however, and thus provide the required time for the operation of the control rod mechanism.

The graphite reactor is an example of the "heterogeneous" type reactor. In this system the fuel and the moderator (graphite) are fabricated separately in rods and blocks and stacked in a lattice form. With "homogeneous" reactors, on the other hand, the fuel and moderator are intimately mixed, as in a solution or slurry.

In the operation of a nuclear reactor, both heat and radioactive isotopes are produced. The latter may be obtained as byproducts from the processing of fuel elements to remove the fission products or by insertion of a target material in the reactor for neutron irradiation. Where the radioactive product is isotopic with the target, it usually is not possible or practical (and for most purposes not necessary) to separate the two species. If the product is not isotopic with the target, of course, chemical separation is feasible. Radioactive materials find wide use in basic and applied research, industrial applications, agricultural studies, and medical research, diagnosis, and therapy.

The large amount of heat produced in the nuclear reactor immediately suggested the possibility of using the reactor for the production of electric power. The basic change over conventional power stations involved only the replacement of the coal furnace by the reactor as a source of heat. The turbines, transmission lines, etc., remain basically, unaffected. The design of a reactor power station must incorporate features

which will minimize the danger to surrounding communities in the event of an accident. Provision also must be made for safe disposal of the radioactive waste products (see NUCLEAR REACTORS).

In 1932, Cockcroft and Walton, using an accelerator, bombarded lithium 7 with protons and obtained helium 4. The reaction was accompanied by an energy release of 17.3 MeV

$$_1^1H + {}_3^7Li \rightarrow 2{}_2^4He + 17.3 \text{ MeV}$$

This was the first demonstration of nuclear fusion, i.e., the production of elements of higher atomic number (e.g., He) from elements of lower atomic number (e.g., H). As in the case of the fission reaction, energy is released because the binding energy of the proton is less than that of the alpha particle produced.

Unlike the fission reaction, in which there is no electrostatic repulsion to the approach of the uncharged neutron to the target nucleus, the fusion reaction requires the coalescence of two positively charged nuclei. It is clear that at least one of the reacting particles must possess exceedingly high energy to overcome this potential barrier. A temperature of about 20 million degrees centigrade is necessary to effect the reaction:

$$_1^3H + {}_1^2H \rightarrow {}_2^4He + {}_0n^1 + E \qquad (1)$$

while even higher energy is required in the case of

$$_1^2H + {}_3^6Li \rightarrow 2{}_2^4He + E \qquad (2)$$

Although the Atomic Energy Commission has not released full information concerning "thermonuclear devices," discussions of them available in the open literature are of interest. Several writers have postulated that a conventional fission bomb provides the energy necessary to initiate reaction (1) and this in turn furnishes sufficient energy to trigger reaction (2). These authors believe it would not be feasible to employ a sufficiently large initial charge of tritium to make a practical device and therefore conclude that the neutron produced in reaction (1) reacts with the lithium 6 employed in reaction (2) to yield further quantities of tritium:

$$_3^6Li + {}_0^1n \rightarrow {}_2^4He + {}_1^3H \qquad (3)$$

Assuming this to be the case, only a small initial charge of tritium would be necessary since the additional quantities produced in reaction (3) would be available to react with deuterium as per reaction (1). Thus, they envisage a type of "chain reaction" involving the sequence $1 \rightarrow 2 + 3 \rightarrow 1$. Extensive efforts are in progress in several countries on controlled thermonuclear reactions. See FUSION for more details on these reactors.

JOSEPH E. MACHUREK

Cross-references: ATOMIC PHYSICS, NUCLEAR RADIATION, NUCLEAR REACTIONS, NUCLEAR REACTORS, NUCLEAR STRUCTURE, RADIOACTIVITY, STRONG INTERACTIONS, WEAK INTERACTIONS.

O

OPTICAL INSTRUMENTS

Optical instruments are of two main types: those which project a real image, e.g., the slide projector lantern and the camera, and those in which the eye views a virtual image, e.g., the microscope and telescope.

The main features of optical instruments can be conveniently considered under the concepts which have been devised in their study.

Magnifying Power or Angular Magnification This is the ratio of the angle subtended at the eye by the image to the angle subtended at the eye by the object, when the latter is in the most favorable position for observation.

Microscopes For a normal eye, an object cannot be brought nearer than 25 cm for distinct and comfortable vision. A single converging lens, of focal length f cm, forming a virtual image at the least distance of distinct vision, has a magnifying power of $25/f + 1$. Thus a lens of focal length 2.5 cm has a magnifying power of 11 and this is about the maximum conveniently attainable with a single lens since aberrations increase considerably as the focal length becomes shorter and a short-focus lens has to be held very close to the object (see LENS).

In the (compound) microscope a converging lens, called the objective, produces a real inverted image with a magnification of v/u, where v and u are the distances of the image and object respectively from the lens (Fig. 1). An eyepiece, acting like a magnifying glass, further magnifies this image, giving a combined magnifying power of $v/u\,(25/f_2 + 1)$. The magnification produced by the objective could be made large by making v large and u small. However v is limited by the length of the microscope tube—usually 16 cm. The maximum useful magnifying power of a microscope is about 2000 because of the limited resolving power of the instrument. There is little point in increasing the size of the final image if no further detail in the object is thereby revealed (see MICROSCOPE).

Telescopes In the case of the telescope, the object cannot normally be brought closer to the eye, and the magnifying power is the ratio of the angle subtended at the eye by the image to the angle subtended at the eye by the object. When the telescope is in normal adjustment (with the final image at infinity), the magnifying power is f_1/f_2, where f_1 and f_2 are the focal lengths of the objective and eyepiece respectively.

If the objective of a simple astronomical telescope, consisting of two converging lenses, is illuminated with a ground glass screen and a lamp, the eye lens will form an image of the objective which can be focused on a sheet of paper. This image is known as the *exit pupil* (Fig. 2), and all rays leaving the instrument must

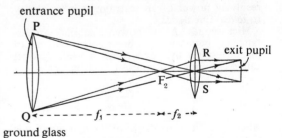

FIG. 2

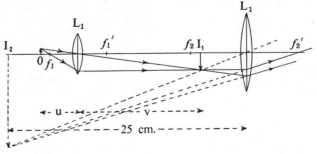

FIG. 1

pass through it. A metal cap with a circular hole is usually placed here in an actual instrument. The *entrance pupil* determines the amount of light which can enter the instrument and in this case it is the objective. When the telescope is in normal adjustment,

$$\text{Magnifying power} = \frac{\text{Diameter of entrance pupil}}{\text{Diameter of exit pupil}}$$

Astronomical telescopes are classified by the diameters of their objectives because this determines their resolving power. At night, the pupil of the eye has a diameter of about 8 mm or $\frac{1}{3}$ inch, and hence the diameter of the exit pupil of the telescope should be the same. In the case of a 6-inch telescope,

$$\text{Magnifying power} = \frac{6}{\frac{1}{3}} = 18$$

A lower power than this should not be used because the effective aperture of the objective would be reduced.

The ratio of the diameter of the objective to its focal length, known as the *relative aperture*, determines the amount of aberration in the image. If it is decided to use an $f/15$ objective, its focal length must be $6 \times 15 = 90$ inches. Hence the focal length of the eyepiece must be $90/18 = 5$ inches. Thus the focal lengths of the lenses in a telescope are controlled by the diameters of the objective and of the pupil of the eye and also by the relative aperture of the objective.

Resolving Power and Limit of Resolution The resolving power of an instrument is its ability to reveal fine detail.

Microscopes Abbe showed that the least distance, x, between two object points which can just be resolved by the objective of a microscope, called the limit of resolution, is given by

$$x = \frac{\lambda}{2\mu \sin \alpha}$$

where λ is the wavelength of the light used, μ is the refractive index of the medium between the object and objective, and 2α is the angle subtended by the diameter of the objective at the object points (Fig. 3); the term $\mu \sin \alpha$ is called

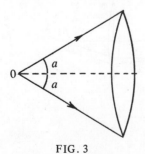

FIG. 3

the *numerical aperture*. When the object is in air and $\mu = 1$, since the maximum value of $\sin \alpha$ is 1, the maximum limit of resolution of the objective is $\lambda/2$. Thus two object points would just be resolvable if separated by at least half the wavelength of the light used.

For the highest resolving power, the angular aperture, 2α, of the objective of a microscope must be as large as possible. Hence the object must be brought as close as possible to the front surface of the objective. This is achieved by constructing objectives of very short focal length (2/3, 1/6 or 1/12 inch).

The resolving power can also be increased by increasing the value of μ in the above formula; cedar oil is placed between the cover slip and the objective, an arrangement known as the *oil immersion objective* (Fig. 4).

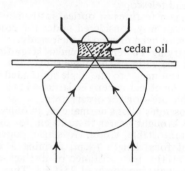

cedar oil

FIG. 4

Yet another way of increasing the resolving power is to reduce the value of λ, and this is done in the *ultraviolet microscope*, employing radiation of wavelength about half that of visible light. The resolving power is thereby doubled and the useful magnification is likewise doubled. This microscope must be combined with a camera to make the image visible.

The *reflecting microscope*, still in process of development, in which the objective is a concave mirror, also is used mainly with ultraviolet light. One of the chief advantages of the instrument is its long working distance, i.e., the distance between the object and the objective.

Electrons may be focused by electric or magnetic fields and hence may be used in a microscope instead of light. Electrons behave like waves, and the wavelength is shorter the greater their speed. When accelerated under a potential difference of 60 kV—one commonly used in *electron microscopes*—the electrons have a wavelength only 1/100 000th that of light, giving a resolving power 100,000 times greater (see ELECTRON MICROSCOPE).

Telescopes The angle, ϕ, subtended at the objective of a telescope by two points on an object which can just be resolved, called the limit of resolution, is given by

$$\phi = \frac{1.22\lambda}{a}$$

where λ is the wavelength of the light and a is the diameter of the objective. Hence, to obtain a high resolving power, the diameter of the objective must be made as large as possible. Furthermore, the full aperture of the objective must be utilized by ensuring that the exit pupil is not greater than that of the pupil of the eye.

The Yerkes telescope, the largest refractor in the world, has an objective of diameter 40 inches. Taking $\lambda = 6 \times 10^{-5}$ cm as the average wavelength of white light,

$$\phi = \frac{1.22 \times 6 \times 10^{-5}}{40 \times 2.54} \qquad (1 \text{ inch} = 2.54 \text{ cm})$$

$$= 0.15 \text{ second of arc}$$

The same expression for the limit of resolution applies to concave mirrors as well as to converging lenses. The largest concave mirror objective, at Mount Palomar, has a diameter of 200 inches, five times that of the Yerkes objective, and hence its limit of resolution is $0.15/5 = 0.03$ second of arc.

By comparison, the limit of resolution of the unaided eye is about 1 minute of arc.

Depth of Focus and Depth of Field The greatest distance the plate of a camera can be moved without spoiling the definition of the image is called the depth of focus. The corresponding distance between the positions of the object at which it is sufficiently in focus on the plate is called the depth of the field (also called depth of focus).

If a point object at a particular distance from a camera lens is exactly focused, so that its image on the plate is a point, then another point object at a different distance from the lens will give rise to an image consisting of a blurred circular patch. Since the visual acuity of the eye is about 1 minute of arc, the distance apart, x cm, of two points which are just distinguishable at the least distance of distinct vision, 25 cm, is given by

$$\frac{x}{25} = 1 \times \frac{\pi}{180 \times 60} \text{ radians}$$

$$x = 0.007 \text{ cm}.$$

Two circular patches, of diameters 0.007 cm, with their centers 0.007 cm apart, would, of course, just touch each other.

For contact prints, a circle of diameter 0.025 cm is taken instead of 0.007 cm, as a sufficiently small image of a point object, but this is clearly too big if the photograph is to be enlarged.

The depth of focus of a lens can be increased by reducing its aperture with a stop. In Fig. 5, the diameter of the patch of light on the plate is reduced by the stop and the image of O will be reasonably clearly focused if the diameter does not exceed 0.025 cm.

The depth of focus of a microscope is approximately inversely proportional to the square of

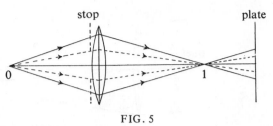

FIG. 5

the numerical aperture. An objective of numerical aperture 1.40 has, at a magnification of 1000X, a depth of focus of only 0.0005 mm.

Field of View The field of view of an instrument is the angle subtended at the eye by the largest object, the whole of which can just be seen. This angle in the case of a simple telescope consisting of two converging lenses, is $a_2/(f_1 + f_2)$, (Fig. 6), where a_2 is the aperture of the eye lens and f_1 and f_2 are the focal lengths of the objective and eye lens respectively. If f_1 is doubled, thereby doubling the magnifying power, the field of view is nearly halved (f_2 is small compared with f_1).

The falling off in brightness of the edge of the image, owing to some rays from the objective failing to strike the eye lens, is called *vignetting*, and it is avoided or kept to a reasonable value by placing a circular opening, called the *field stop*, of suitable size where the image formed by the objective is situated.

Illumination in Microscopes The final image in a microscope magnifying 1000X has an area one million times that of the object. It is therefore only one-millionth as bright, assuming no light loss in the instrument. Light is concentrated on the (transparent) object by means of a *substage condenser*.

Dark ground illumination is used for viewing tiny particles or very fine lines. The illumination is made too oblique for light to pass direct from the condenser into the objective. The objects are seen by scattered and diffracted light against a dark background.

Phase contrast illumination is a method of making the structure of transparent objects visible. The arrangement consists of an annular stop at the condenser and, beyond the objective, a phase plate consisting of a glass plate on which there is an annular layer of material to increase the optical path of the light by a quarter of a wavelength. Interference between direct and diffracted light augments the diffraction pattern of the image.

Interference microscopy is another method of making fine structure visible. The transparent object is placed between two-semi-silvered surfaces and the interference between light passing through the object and light passing by it is observed.

Polarized light, obtained by a suitable polarizer below the condenser, is used in microscopes designed for geological testing of constituents in rock specimens.

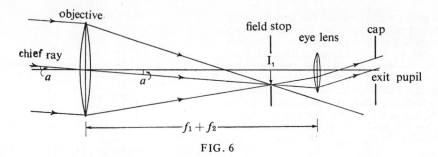

FIG. 6

Other Instruments The telescope and the microscope are the two classical instruments of science and the principles of these two underlie most modern optical instruments. However, the range of modern optical instruments is very large and each instrument involves many subtleties and refinements in its design. An outline of the fields covered by such instruments is all that can be presented here and the reader who wishes more detailed information should refer to the last of the cited references.

The area covered by photography alone is vast and ranges from special microfilming equipment, ever more important as the volume of printed matter increases, to the latest sophisticated cameras devised for use in satellites. It includes the techniques of motion-picture and high-speed photography. The design of each type of camera or projector involves many mechanical refinements and considerable progress has recently been made, as evidenced by the increasingly sophisticated still cameras available for the mass market.

The medical profession uses many specialized optical instruments, the main design feature being to enable the doctor to see inside the various openings and cavities of the body. These are essentially periscopes with very thin transmission tubes; optical fibers are often used in the design. There is also a range of ophthalmic instruments enabling the doctor to see into, and perform various measurements on, the human eye. The military profession employs telescopic gun sights, binoculars, periscopes, and range finders, and recently infrared devices for night-time use. Civil engineers use theodolites for surveying, and there is a variety of optical instruments used in the machine tool industry for angular measurements and aligning.

There is an important class of scientific instruments, whose principles have not been discussed here, based on the dispersive properties of prisms and diffraction gratings. These devices analyze a source of light by splitting the light into its constituent pure colors; called spectrometers, they are important in atomic physics, astronomy, and chemistry because many atoms and molecules have characteristic spectra when analyzed in this way and hence their presence can be detected in a source of light. Modern automatic devices called spectrophotometers split the light from a source into its constituent primary colors then measure the intensity of each constituent photoelectrically. Other related instruments working on similar principles are interferometers, used for fine distance measurement and instrument testing; refractometers, which measure the refractive index of a substance; and radiometers used for high-temperature measurement.

Finally, the field of laser physics should be mentioned. This is still an active research area with a fast-developing literature, so it would not be appropriate to discuss it in detail here. Many new and important instruments are likely to be invented using lasers. One already in use is the fine laser beam used to align tunnel digging equipment. Another which may come soon is three-dimensional cinema using the techniques of holography.

A. E. E. McKenzie*
N. C. McKenzie

References

Cooper, H. J., Ed., "Scientific Instruments," Vols. I and II, London, 1946 and 1948.
Martin, L. C., "Technical Optics," Second edition, Vols. 1 and II, London, 1961.
Kingslake, R., Ed., "Applied Optics and Optical Engineering," Vols. IV and V, London, Academic Press, 1967 and 1969.

Cross-references: ABERRATIONS; HOLOGRAPHY; INTERFERENCE AND INTERFEROMETRY; LASERS; LENS; MICROSCOPE; OPTICS, GEOMETRICAL; REFLECTION; REFRACTION; SPECTROSCOPY.

OPTICAL PUMPING

The term "pompage optique" was coined by A. Kastler (the 1966 Nobel Laureate, honored for this work) to describe the process of "pumping" atoms from one hyperfine quantum state to another by a process of resonant fluorescent scattering of light. The original purpose was to facilitate the detection and measurement of the radio-frequency (rf) fine and hyperfine structure, which otherwise is observable by magnetic

*Deceased.

resonance and atomic beam methods (see MAG-NETIC RESONANCE, also see ATOMIC MOLEC-ULAR BEAMS), yet which cannot be directly observed by optical spectroscopy, primarily because of the Doppler width of spectral lines. Optical pumping has now come to embrace any experimental work in which fine and hyperfine structure, rf spectroscopic measurements, polarization of electrons or nuclei, atomic cross sections, and oscillator strengths are measured or produced by means of polarized, filtered, or modulated light, and perhaps detected by the light as well. The distinction between measurements made in this way and those of conventional spectroscopy arises from the fact that the wavelength of the light is not used to measure energy splittings.

A description of the process may be given in schematic form. Consider a sample of atoms in gas or vapor phase, which have a $^2S_{1/2}$ ground state. Sodium is a good example, but we ignore the nuclear spin. If exposed to the resonance radiation coupling this ground state to the $P_{1/2}$ and $P_{3/2}$ states, the atom will absorb and reemit rapidly, and if the absorbed radiation is circularly polarized, the atoms will absorb one unit $(h/2\pi)$ of angular momentum with respect to a fixed axis of quantization (or lose one depending on the sign of the circular polarization) as shown in Fig. 1. If the atom is not disturbed during the time it is in the excited state, it will reemit any polarization, but on the average will return to the ground state with one higher (or lower) unit of angular momentum in the quantization direction. This polarization is that of the electron, but if the nucleus has a spin it is so tightly coupled to the electron spin at low fields and in the radiation process that the resulting polarization is that of the combined nucleus and electron according to the angular momentum coupling rules for $\vec{I} + \vec{J} = \vec{F}$. The polarization may be measured by disorienting the atoms by adiabatic field direction changes, or by in-ducing transitions between the various hyperfine or Zeeman levels and measuring the transmitted or scattered light.

If the sample vapor is mixed with a "buffer gas," usually a noble gas, which helps to prevent the diffusion of the sample vapor out of the light beam and reduces the Doppler width of the hyperfine lines, then the atoms may be disoriented in the excited state and the pumping is reduced. However, if filtering is used, it is possible to maintain orientation effects even at several atmospheres of the buffer gas. In the example mentioned, removal of the light which couples the $S_{1/2}$ to the $P_{3/2}$ state means that the absorption probability of one of the $S_{1/2}$ states is reduced to zero and so equilibrium is established with the least-absorbing state most populated.

Another example will show the use of the technique in excited states. A sample such as mercury (or other Group II element) is exposed to its resonance radiation which is linearly polarized parallel to axis of quantization. This light will cause transitions from the $^1S_0$ ground state to the $^3P_1$ $m = 0$ state. The scattered light will have the same polarization. However, if magnetic dipole transitions between the excited state levels of different m, as shown in Fig. 2, are induced by rf fields, circular polarization will also be emitted and may be readily detected by a polarization analyzer. If the mercury nucleus has a spin, the ground state will also be polarized in the manner described in the first example, and the measurements are equivalent to observation of nuclear magnetic resonance in a gas, but detected by light.

A typical experimental arrangement to observe optical pumping is shown in Fig. 3. A powerful and non-noisy resonance radiation lamp is focused through polarizers and filters onto the sample cell, which may be heated to get the required vapor pressure of sample. An

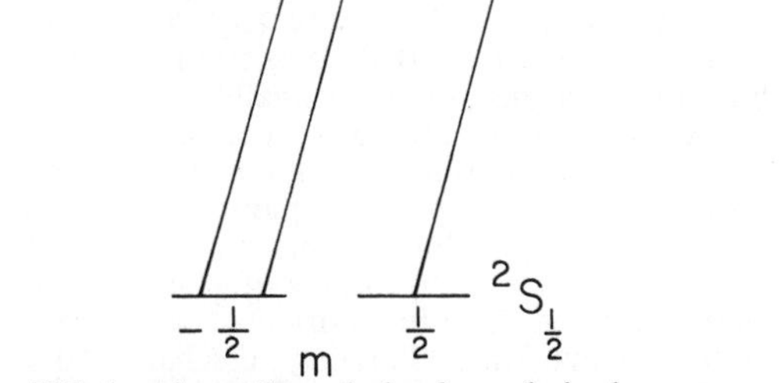

FIG. 1. Absorption of circular polarized resonance radiation by a typical alkali metal.

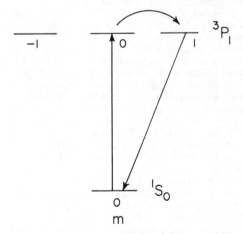

FIG. 2. Absorption and scattering of plane polarized resonance radiation by mercury vapor when excited-state transitions are made.

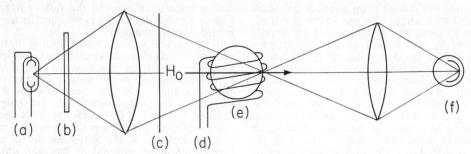

FIG. 3. Typical optical pumping apparatus: (a) resonance radiation lamp, (b) filter, (c) polarizer, (d) rf coils, (e) sample cell, (f) photodetector.

axis of quantization is established by a magnet, solenoid or Helmholtz coils. Transmitted or scattered light is collected and monitored by a photodetector. To facilitate detection it is often desirable to make use of modulation techniques, similar to those used in magnetic resonance experiments (see MODULATION and MAGNETIC RESONANCE), in which the magnetic field or radio frequency is modulated, and the resulting alternating current signal synchronously detected or amplified by a phase sensitive amplifier. Because of the high efficiency in the scattering and detection process with light quanta, optical pumping signals are usually much stronger than could be obtained by direct radiofrequency or microwave absorption experiments on comparable samples.

The optical pumping of many isotopes of the Group I and II elements has been studied. It is difficult to polarize atoms in gas cells which do not have an S ground state because collisions will rapidly disorient the orbital angular momentum of the electrons, but these atoms may be studied in a beam. The process cannot be used in most cases at sample pressures higher than 10^{-3} or 10^{-4} torr, because the light will not penetrate such dense samples.

It is not possible to describe briefly a general theory of optical pumping. Each system has its own spectroscopic splitting which must be analyzed. It is usually necessary to write a "master equation" to determine the equilibrium populations in the sublevels, taking into consideration the transition probabilities into and out of these levels, and the relaxation rates. Fortunately, in most cases, all that is needed is knowledge of the relative transition probabilities, and these will probably depend only on the angular momentum quantum numbers.

More detailed and recent theories have treated the light and the vapor as a coupled system and have considered the polarization and time dependence of the "state" of the light as well as the "state" of the atoms. On the basis of these "strong coupling" theories, more subtle dynamic and coherence effects may be predicted than can be described here.

One of the most effective means of extending optical orientation to other elements is by means of the spin exchange process. Outer electrons will overlap during the collision of atoms, and the spins will interchange as a consequence of a "beat" between symmetric and antisymmetric spin configurations. In the case of S-state wave functions, the coupled angular momentum is conserved and the polarization produced by optical pumping on one atom will be thermodynamically shared with all other atoms with which a spin exchange is possible. Since outer electrons may overlap at interatomic distances much greater than a collision impact parameter, the spin exchange cross section is usually much greater than the collision cross section. Atomic hydrogen and atomic nitrogen, as well as the alkali metals, have been studied by these methods. In fact, optical orientation and spin exchange may be expected to work on ions, and the first observation of spin exchange was made with the free electron. Polarized electrons were removed by ultraviolet or discharge ionization from an optically pumped sodium vapor sample. The electrons were disoriented by rf fields, and subsequently disoriented the sodium by exchange in an observable way.

Other methods of coupling optically produced orientation also exist. Metastable ($^3S_1$) helium atoms are long lived and may be optically pumped. The metastability is transferred with a reasonably large cross section to ground state ($^1S_0$) atoms, and if the helium is the isotope ^{3}He, the nuclear polarization is also efficiently transferred to the ground state, making it possible to produce, at pressures of several torr, samples of 40 per cent polarized ^{3}He with relaxation times of about one hour. The contact hyperfine interaction and dipolar interactions also can transfer the angular momentum of optically oriented atoms to other atoms, but cross sections are much smaller.

Recently it has been found possible to study the rf spectroscopy of ions and excited states of atoms by using optically pumped energetic metastable ($^3S_1$) helium atoms in a discharge to excite and ionize other kinds of atoms in collisions and leave them in an oriented or polarized state as well. Such "Penning" discharge polarization effects are one of the very few ways that the rf spectroscopy of ions may be studied.

Several interesting light modulation effects may be observed in pumping experiments. Light beat and modulation effects occur when an atom scatters light while it is simultaneously undergoing hyperfine transitions. If a sample is oriented in the Z direction, and a rf field excites a Zeeman resonance, the atoms will precess coherently. An additional polarized light beam passing through the sample will be modulated at the Larmor frequency. As an inverse effect, if the pumping light itself is modulated at the appropriate radio frequencies, transitions will be induced. In the example of mercury, if magnetic dipole transitions are induced in the sublevels of the $(^3P_1)$ states, the scattered light will show the beat frequency modulation of the sublevels. The varieties of these modulation effects are by no means yet exhausted.

A useful effect for studying hyperfine structure in cases where the system cannot easily be pumped is the "level-crossing" effect. Some of the levels of the fine and hyperfine structure of states of atoms more complicated than the examples described here cross one another at particular values of a perturbing magnetic field. At these points, the optical opacity of the sample to the appropriate light will be changed, and from the values of the magnetic field, and a knowledge of the general form of hyperfine splitting, magnetic moments and hyperfine energies may be determined.

Optical pumping in solids is becoming increasingly important and useful. One interesting example, to illustrate many, is given: Thulium ions in CaF_2 have a Kramers doublet ground state of spin 1/2, which absorbs circular polarized light in a differential spin dependent manner. At low temperatures this differential absorption causes spin polarization which can also be monitored by the polarization of the transmitted beam. Since the ground state spin polarization is relaxed by phonons in the crystal, the sample may be used as a "phonon" spectrometer, and it may be tuned to different phonon frequencies in a variable magnetic field, which changes the magnetic energy splitting of the ground state.

There are numerous practical applications of these methods. Optically pumped gas cell magnetometers have been made utilizing rubidium vapor or metastable helium (see MAGNETOMETRY). If modulated light is fed back to rf coils, a self-contained oscillator may be built. Rubidium and cesium gas cell ATOMIC CLOCKS have been built with stabilities of 1 part in 10^{11}. These may be made in a very simple manner, utilizing those hyperfine transitions which are not perturbed by magnetic fields. Using optically pumped helium, targets and ion sources of polarized ^3He may be made for use in nuclear physics, and polarized electron sources may also be made. Atomic gyroscopes may be constructed by using the optically pumped angular momentum and the light to detect precession. Perhaps the most important application has been

to produce population inversion required in the operation of masers and lasers, particularly potassium and rubidium vapor, and chromium in ruby (see LASER and MASER).

THOMAS R. CARVER

References

Bernheim, R. A., "Optical Pumping; an Introduction," New York, W. A. Benjamin, 1965.
Bloom, A. L., *Sci. Am.,* **203,** 72 (1960).
Carver, T. R., *Science,* **141,** 599 (1963).
De Zafra, R., *Am. J., Phys.,* **28,** 646 (1960).
Happer, W., "Progress in Quantum Electronics," Vol. 1, p.51, New York, Pergamon Press, 1970.
Happer, W., *Rev. Mod. Phys.,* **44,** 169 (1972).
Kastler, A., and Cohen-Tannoudji, C., "Progress in Optics," Vol. 5, p. 3, Amsterdam, North-Holland, 1966.
Kastler, A., *J. Opt. Soc. Am.,* **47,** 460 (1957).
Series, G. W., *Rept. Progr. Phys.,* **23,** 280 (1959).
Skrotskii, G. V., and Izyumova, T. G., *Soviet Phys.-Usp. (English transl.),* **4,** 177 (1961).

Cross-references: ATOMIC AND MOLECULAR BEAMS, ATOMIC CLOCKS, ELECTRON SPIN, LASER, MAGNETIC RESONANCE, MAGNETOMETRY, MASER, MODULATION, POLARIZED LIGHT, SPECTROSCOPY, ZEEMAN AND STARK EFFECTS.

OPTICS, GEOMETRICAL

The radiant energy emitted from a point of a luminous source situated in a homogeneous medium free from obstacles travels through the medium as a spherical wave front whose velocity of advance is a characteristic of the medium. A radius of this wave front is a light ray. If a ray experiences a change of medium or encounters an obstacle, it will, in general, deviate from the rectilinear path defined by the radius. The science of geometrical optics is concerned with controlled deviations.

The Law of Reflection (a) The directions of incidence and reflection and of the normal to the reflecting surface are coplanar.

(b) The angle of reflection is equal to the angle of incidence, both angles being taken with respect to the normal (see Fig. 1(a)).

The Law of Refraction (a) The directions of incidence and refraction and of the normal to the refracting surface are coplanar.

(b) The ratio of the sines of the angles of incidence and refraction, both angles being taken with respect to the normal, is a constant whose magnitude is a function of the properties of the two media on either side of the refracting surface (see Fig. 1(b)). The function is

$$\sin \theta_1 / \sin \theta_2 = \mu_{12}$$

The constant μ_{12} is the index of refraction for the two media when light travels from medium 1 to medium 2. If the direction of the ray is

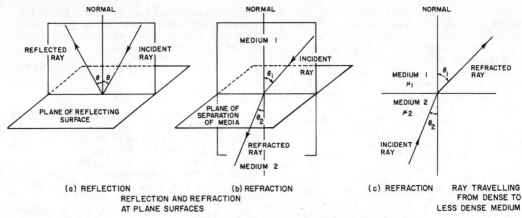

FIG. 1. Reflection and refraction at plane surfaces.

reversed, as in Fig. 1(c), it traverses exactly the same path so that

$$\sin \theta_2 / \sin \theta_1 = \mu_{21}, \quad \therefore \mu_{21} = 1/\mu_{12}$$

If the first medium is air, it is usual to drop the suffixes and to replace μ_{12} by n. If the first medium is a vacuum then μ_{12} is the absolute refractive index of the second. For air at NTP the value is 1.00028 so that, for most practical purposes the distinction between μ_{12} and n, with air as the first medium, is negligible for substances, such as glass, commonly used for light control. The value of n depends on the wavelength of the light. For sodium yellow of 5890.6Å, the values of n for a number of media are:

Crown glass	1.517
Flint glass	1.650
Quartz	1.544
Fused silica	1.459
Water at 20°C	1.333
Diamond	2.42

For a mathematically plane surface, the coefficient of reflection for normal incidence is

dependent on the value of μ_{12}. Fresnel's law gives for this coefficient

$$\rho = [(\mu_{12} - 1)/(\mu_{12} + 1)]^2$$

Clean polished surfaces give results largely in accord with Fresnel's law. Films of grease or slight roughness appreciably reduce the value of ρ.

Total Reflection Figure 2(a) shows a series of rays passing from air into a denser medium. Ray No. 1 experiences no deviation. The others experience progressively increasing deviations until, with the tangential ray, No. 4, the angle of refraction θ_c is the greatest possible for that particular medium. Since the angle of incidence is 90°

$$1/\sin \theta_c = n, \quad \therefore \sin \theta_c = 1/n$$

By reversing the directions of the rays, we see that an angle of incidence θ_c is the maximum possible angle for emergence into the air. For angles $> \theta_c$ there is internal reflection, as in Fig. 2(b), governed by the law of reflection. The angle θ_c is called the critical angle for the particular combination of media. Figure 3 shows

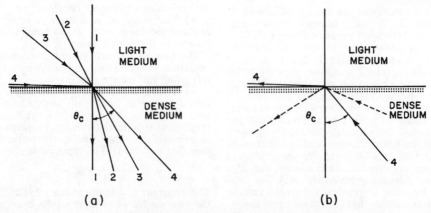

FIG. 2. Illustrating total reflections.

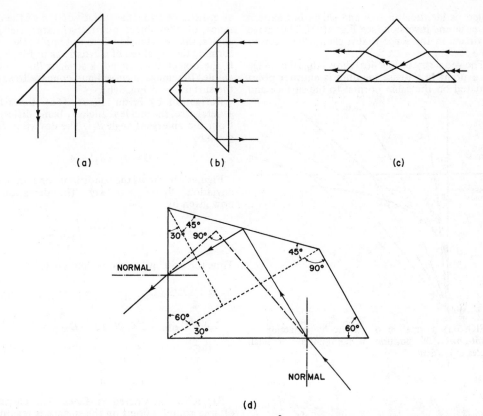

FIG. 3. (a), (b) and (c) show three methods of using the 45° prism. (d) is a constant deviation prism as used in spectrometers.

a number of practical applications of total reflection.

Image Formation The geometry of Fig. 4(a) shows that the image in a plane mirror of a point in front of it is another point which lies behind the mirror along the normal from the object point, and is as far behind the mirror as the object is in front. The image of an extended

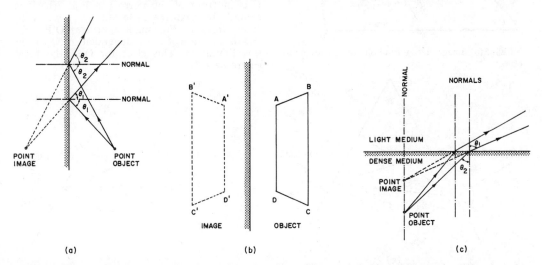

FIG. 4. Image formation by plane surfaces: (a) point object, (b) extended object, (c) image by diffraction of a point object.

object is identical in size and shape but experiences lateral inversion (see Fig. 4(b)). The image is virtual in the sense that it cannot be received on a screen.

The geometry of Fig. 4(c) shows that the image of a point in a dense medium is another point situated on the same normal to the surface and

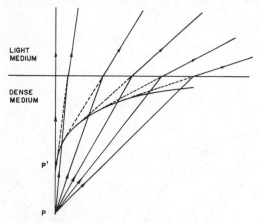

LIGHT
MEDIUM

DENSE
MEDIUM

FIG. 5(a). Formation of caustic by refraction. P, point-object. P', position of point-image for small angles of incidence.

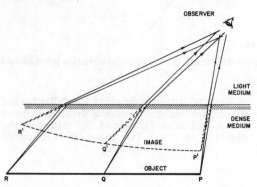

OBSERVER

LIGHT
MEDIUM

DENSE
MEDIUM

IMAGE

OBJECT

FIG. 5(b) Image by refraction of an extended object.

at a distance from the surface of $1/n$ of the distance of the object point. For large viewing angles, this relationship does not apply, the rays forming the envelope of a caustic as in Fig. 5(a). If the object is extended, a straight line for example, the image is curved and concave towards the surface as in Fig. 5(b).

Refraction by Prism Figure (6a) shows the general case, the incident angle θ_1 being different from the emergent angle θ_1'. The deviation D is given by

$$D = \theta_1 + \theta_1' - A$$

Figure 6(b) shows the conditions for minimum deviation. $\theta_1 = \theta_2 = \theta$, say. The deviation is now given by

$$n = \sin \frac{A + D_{min}}{2} \Big/ \sin \frac{A}{2}$$

Thus for a 60° prism for which $n = 1.517$

$$\sin \frac{A + D_{min}}{2} = n \sin A/2 = 1.517 \times 0.5 = 0.7585$$

$$\therefore A + D_{min} = 2 \times 49°20'; \quad D_{min} = 38°40'$$

A "thin" prism is one for which $A \not> 15°$, so that $\theta(\text{radians}) \simeq \sin \theta$. This gives

$$D_{min} \simeq (n - 1)A$$

Reflection at Curved Surfaces The element of area round a point on the surface is regarded as part of the tangent plane at that point. First consider a spherical surface, Figs. (7a) and (b), and let the aperture be small compared with the radius of curvature. In each Figure, O is the center of curvature, OP is a radius, and O' is the "pole" of the mirror. A ray parallel to the axis is reflected to a point F, the focus. In Fig. 7(a), F is in front of the mirror; in Fig. 7(b) it is behind, so that the reflected ray *appears* to come from F. For small apertures O'F ≈ PF and the position of F is independent of O within this limitation. This gives for O'F, the focal length $f = r/2$.

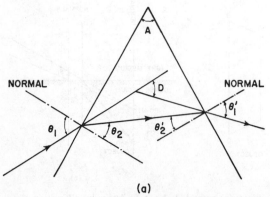

A

NORMAL

NORMAL

θ_1

θ_2

D

θ_2'

θ_1'

(a)

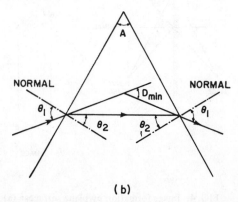

A

NORMAL

NORMAL

θ_1

θ_2

D_{min}

θ_2

θ_1

(b)

FIG. 6. Deviation by prism: (a) General case, (b) condition for minimum deviation.

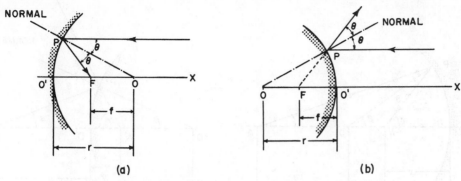

FIG. 7. Reflection at spherical mirrors. (a) Concave, (b) convex.

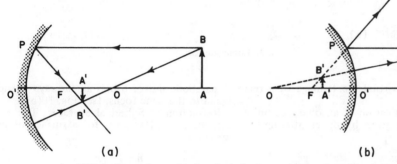

FIG. 8. Image formation in spherical mirrors. (a) Concave, (b) convex.

Concave Mirror	Convex Mirror
u and r negative	u negative and r positive
$u = -8, r = -6, f = -3$	$u = -8, r = +6, f = +3$
$\therefore \dfrac{1}{v} = -\dfrac{1}{3} - \left(-\dfrac{1}{8}\right) = -\dfrac{1}{4.8}$	$\therefore \dfrac{1}{v} = \dfrac{1}{3} - \left(-\dfrac{1}{8}\right) = \dfrac{11}{24}$
$v = -4.8$	$v = +2.18m$

Image Formation For an object of small dimensions, the image can be obtained by drawing two rays only: (a) a ray through O—this strikes the mirror normally and is returned along the same path; (b) a ray parallel to the axis—this is reflected through the focal point F.

In Fig. 8, AB is the object and A′B′ the image. In Fig. 8(a) the image is real, in Fig. 8(b) it is virtual. An image is real when the reflected rays actually pass through points in it; it is virtual if they have to be traced back, so that they only appear to come from the image.

Conjugate Foci In Fig. 9(a) a point object A produces a point image A′. If A and A′ are interchanged, the rays take identical paths but the arrows are reversed. A and A′ are called conjugate foci. In Fig. 9(b) the image A′ in the convex mirror is virtual. The relationship between the angles is as follows:—

$$\gamma = \theta + \beta, \ \beta = \theta + \alpha; \ \therefore \alpha + \gamma = 2\beta$$

For small apertures

$$\alpha = PO'/O'A, \ \beta = PO'/O'O, \ \gamma = PO'/O'A'$$

$$\therefore \frac{1}{v} + \frac{1}{u} = \frac{2}{r} = \frac{1}{f}$$

This is purely quantitative relationship. For general application it is necessary to adopt a convention regarding signs. Distances are always measured from the mirror, and the direction of the incident light is reckoned positive. As an example let $u = 8$ and $r = 6$. (See calculations under Fig. 8.)

The magnification

$$m = \frac{A'B'}{AB} = \frac{v}{u}$$

This is positive if v and u have the same sign as with the real inverted image of a real object, Fig. 8(a). It is negative if u and v are of opposite

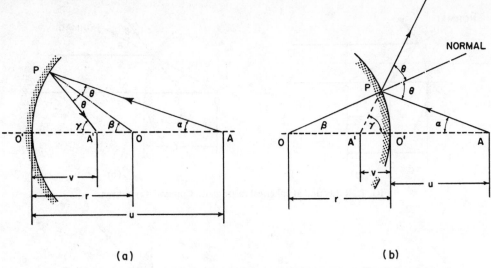

FIG. 9. Conjugate foci.

sign as with the virtual erect image of a real object, Fig. 8(b).

The axial magnification of an object of finite axial dimension is given by differentiating the above equation.

$$-\frac{dv}{v^2} - \frac{du}{u^2} = 0, \quad \therefore \frac{dv}{du} = -\frac{v^2}{u^2}$$

This shows that if an object is moved towards the mirror a distance du, the image will move $dv = -v^2 du/u^2$. Thus the image will move more rapidly when u is small.

Parabolic Mirror For large apertures for which the angle β is not small, the rays of a parallel axial beam are not all brought to a focus at F, but form the envelope of a cusp, as in Fig. 10(a).

A parabolic mirror brings all the rays of such a beam to the same focus. [see Fig. 10(b)].

Refraction at Spherical Surfaces The geometry of Fig. 11(a) gives for a surface of small aperture

$$\frac{n-1}{r} = \frac{n}{v} - \frac{1}{u}$$

If we put $v = \infty$, so that the rays are parallel after refraction and put f_1 for the corresponding value of u

$$\frac{n-1}{r} = -\frac{1}{f_1}$$

If we put $u = \infty$, so that the incident rays are

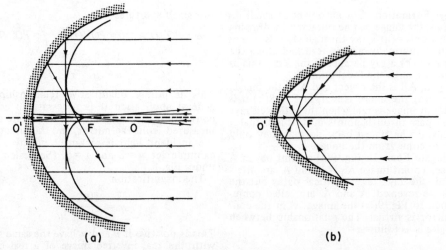

FIG. 10. Reflection by mirrors of wide aperture. (a) Spherical, (b) parabolic.

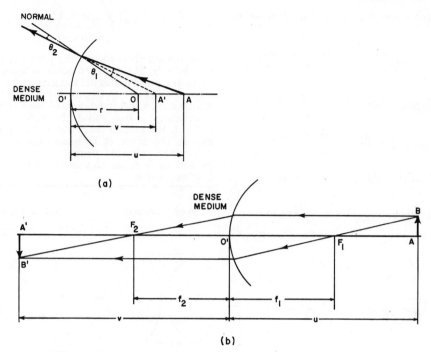

(a)

(b)

FIG. 11. Refraction at spherical surface of separation between two media.

parallel, the corresponding value of v (call it f_2) is given by

$$\frac{n-1}{r} = + \frac{n}{f_2}, \quad \therefore \frac{n}{f_2} + \frac{1}{f_1} = 0$$

For an object AB, Fig. 11(b), we obtain the position of the image by drawing two rays from B; the first parallel to the axis, thereby passing through F_2 after refraction; the second passing through F_1, thereby becoming parallel to the axis after refraction.

$$m = \frac{f_1}{u - f_1} \quad \text{or} \quad \frac{v - f_2}{f_2}$$

Lenses Figure 12 shows three media separated by spherical surfaces. Considering each surface

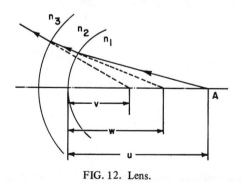

FIG. 12. Lens.

in turn

$$\frac{n_2}{n_1} \cdot \frac{1}{w} - \frac{1}{u} = \left(\frac{n_2}{n_1} - 1\right) / r_1$$

$$\therefore \frac{n_2}{w} - \frac{n_1}{u} = \frac{n_2 - n_1}{r_1}$$

Similarly

$$\frac{n_3}{v} - \frac{n_2}{w} = \frac{n_3 - n_2}{r_2}$$

adding,

$$\frac{n_3}{v} - \frac{n_1}{u} = \frac{n_3 - n_2}{r_2} + \frac{n_2 - n_1}{r_1}$$

In the case of a lens, $n_3 = n_1$, giving

$$\frac{1}{v} - \frac{1}{u} = \left(\frac{n_2}{n_1} - 1\right) \left(\frac{1}{r_1} - \frac{1}{r_2}\right)$$

with air on either side of the central section, $n_1 = n_3 = 1$, and we can put $n_2 = n$.

$$\therefore \frac{1}{v} - \frac{1}{u} = (n - 1) \left(\frac{1}{r_1} - \frac{1}{r_2}\right)$$

If we put $u = \infty$ then $v = f$, the focal length,

$$\therefore \frac{1}{f} = (u - 1)\left(\frac{1}{r_1} - \frac{1}{r_2}\right)^* ; \quad f = \frac{r_1 r_2}{(n - 1)(r_2 - r_1)}$$

Lateral magnification $m = \dfrac{v}{u}$ or $\dfrac{f}{u - f}$

Axial magnification $\dfrac{dv}{du} = -\dfrac{v^2}{u^2}$

Example $r_1 = 10$, $r_2 = 15$, $\mu = 1.6$

$$\frac{r}{2}\left(\frac{1}{\cos\theta} - 1\right)$$

Astigmatism results when the object is situated off the axis. The reflected pencil is brought to a focus at a point I, also off the axis, and is spread into an axial line $Q_1 Q_2$, as in Fig. 13(a). If the mirror is turned through a small angle, the point I describes a line called the first focal line. $Q_1 Q_2$ is the second focal line and is perpendicular to the other. In between there is a region where the reflected pencil is the nearest approach to a circle; this is called the circle of least confusion.

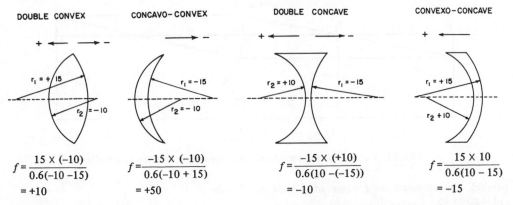

$$\begin{array}{cccc}
\textbf{DOUBLE CONVEX} & \textbf{CONCAVO - CONVEX} & \textbf{DOUBLE CONCAVE} & \textbf{CONVEXO - CONCAVE}
\end{array}$$

$$f = \frac{15 \times (-10)}{0.6(-10 - 15)} = +10 \qquad f = \frac{-15 \times (-10)}{0.6(-10 + 15)} = +50 \qquad f = \frac{-15 \times (+10)}{0.6(10 - (-15))} = -10 \qquad f = \frac{15 \times 10}{0.6(10 - 15)} = -15$$

With the convex lenses the focus is on the far side of the lens from the source; with the concave lenses it is on the same side as the source. With plano-convex and plano-concave lenses, $1/r$ for the plane surface is zero.

Defects in Mirrors and Lenses An aperture which is large compared with the focal length introduces errors in both mirrors and lenses. One of these is the axial spread of the focus as shown in Fig. 10(a). The amount of spread for a mirror of aperture 2θ is

*Some authors give this equation with a + sign in the second bracket. In such a case it is necessary to use different signs for convex and concave surfaces, a confusion which is avoided by the simple convention adopted in this article.

Figure 13(b) shows longitudinal spherical aberration in a lens; rays very close to the axis pass through the focal point as defined for a thin lens, while increasing divergence brings the focus nearer to the lens. Figure 13(c) shows chromatic aberration—the focal length, even for a thin lens, being a function of the wavelength. This is because n varies with the wavelength and increases as the wavelength decreases. Thus the focal length for violet is less than for red.

Curvature of the Field The image of a plane object lies, in general, on a slightly curved field (Fig. 14), and this combines with the effects of astigmatism. Pincushion distortion results when a lens is used as a magnifying glass; barrel distortion results when an object is viewed through a lens at some distance from the eye.

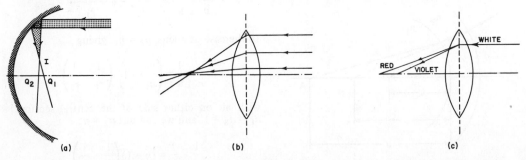

FIG. 13. Image defects. (a) Astigmatism, (b) longitudinal spherical aberration, (c) chromatic aberration.

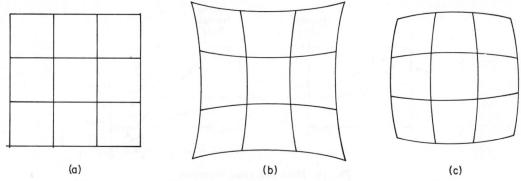

FIG. 14. Image distortion. (a) Object, (b) pincushion distortion, (c) barrel distortion.

Systems of Lenses The inverse of the focal length of a lens is called the power of the lens. If the unit of length is the centimeter, the unit of power is the diopter:

$$D = \frac{1}{f}$$

If a number of thin lenses are in contact, the power of the combination is the *algebraic sum* of the individual powers. As an example, consider two thin lenses for which $f_1 = 10$ and $f_2 = -15$ cm.

$$D_1 = \frac{1}{10} = 0.1 \text{ diopter};$$

$$D_2 = -\frac{1}{15} = -0.0667 \text{ diopter}$$

$$D = 0.1 - 0.0667 = +0.0333$$

$$\therefore f = +30 \text{ cm}$$

If two coaxial lenses are separated a distance d, then the focal length of the combination is given by

$$\frac{1}{f} = \frac{1}{f_1} + \frac{1}{f_2} - \frac{d}{f_1 f_2}$$

For a minimum longitudinal spherical aberra- tion, the distance d should be

$$d = f_1 - f_2$$

Thick Lens Figure 15(a) shows a thick converging lens receiving a parallel beam of light. The axial ray 1 passes through the lens without deviation. Any other ray, such as 2, on emerging intersects the axis at some point F'. If we extend the incident ray forward and the emergent ray backwards, as shown by dotted lines, they will intersect at some point P'. The point F' is called the *second focal point* and the plane through P' to which the axis is perpendicular is called the *second principal plane*.

Figure 15(b) shows a system of rays starting from a point F such that the emergent beam is parallel. Then point F is the *first focal point* and the plane through P, determined as before, the first principal plane.

The solution of the thick lens is therefore dependent on the following: The lens behaves as though the deviation of the rays leaving point F all takes place at the plane P; also the deviation of the emergent rays appears to take place at the plane P^1. Image formation is therefore in accordance with Fig. 16.

From the geometry of the figure we see that

$$ff' = xx' \quad \therefore m = -\frac{f}{x} = -\frac{x'}{f'}$$

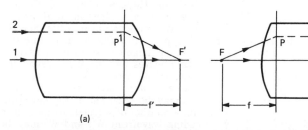

FIG. 15. Thick lens: principal focal points and principal planes.

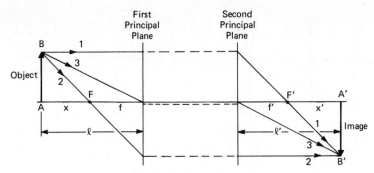

FIG. 16. Thick lens: image formation.

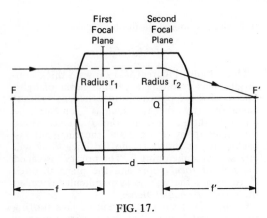

FIG. 17.

also

$$\frac{f'}{\ell'} + \frac{f}{\ell} = 1, \quad \therefore m - \frac{f\ell'}{f'\ell}$$

The focal length of a thick lens is reckoned from the second focal plane, namely, the distance OF' in Fig. 17. In terms of the radii it is given by

$$f' = (\mu - 1)\left(\frac{1}{r_1} - \frac{1}{r_2} + \frac{\mu - 1}{\mu}\frac{d}{r_1 r_2}\right).$$

It differs from the expression for the focal length of a thin lens by the term

$$\frac{\mu - 1}{\mu}\frac{d}{r_1 r_2},$$

and this, of course, is zero when $d = 0$.

For light traveling from right to left and for which a parallel beam is brought to a focus at F

$$f = (\mu - 1)\left(\frac{1}{r_2} - \frac{1}{r_1} + \frac{\mu - 1}{\mu}\frac{d}{r_1 r_2}\right)$$

$$f = -f'.$$

H. COTTON

References

Curry, G., "Geometrical Optics," London, Arnold, 1953.

Jenkins, F. A., and White, H. E., "Fundamentals of Optics," New York, McGraw-Hill Book Co., 1957.

Kingslake, R., Ed., "Applied Optics and Optical Engineering," Vol. 1, New York, Academic Press, 1965–1969.

Kline, M., and Kay, E. W., "Electromagnetic Theory and Geometrical Optics," New York, Interscience Publishers, 1965.

Longhurst, R. S., "Geometrical and Physical Optics," London, Longmans, 1967.

Smith, F. G., and Thomson, J. H., "Optics," London, John Wiley & Sons, 1971.

Welford, W. T., "Geometrical Optics: Optical Instrumentation," Amsterdam, North-Holland, 1962.

Cross-references: ABERRATION THEORY; LENS; LIGHT; OPTICAL INSTRUMENTS; OPTICS, PHYSICAL; REFLECTION; REFRACTION.

OPTICS, PHYSICAL

In this branch of the subject of optics, we deal with phenomena connected with the nature of light itself. We assume that it is a transverse wave motion and that the underlying principles are embodied in the electromagnetic theory conceived by James Clerk Maxwell (1831–1879). A very brief outline of the major phenomena will be all that can be attempted in this article.

An excellent prerequisite to an understanding of the progress of light is Huygens' principle. Christian Huygens (1629–1695), a contemporary of Sir Isaac Newton, doubtless got the idea of wave propagation by observing the progress of ripples on a Dutch canal. The famous principle, applicable to surface waves on a liquid, to sound waves and to light waves, is that *each point of a wave front may be regarded as a source of new waves.* In Fig. 1, the wavefront W'' may be regarded as the envelope of an infinite number of wavelets forming from the preceding wavefront W', and W' may be likewise formed from W.

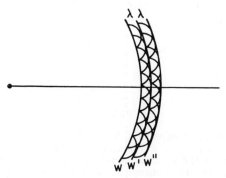

FIG. 1

Interference A very important special case of the superposition of waves occurs when two identical wave trains W_1 and W_2 of wavelength λ (Fig. 2), start out in phase from a source S and travel to a point of crossing S'—the one train

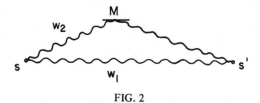

FIG. 2

going directly to S', the other train going by way of a reflecting (or refracting) device M, and thus traversing a greater distance. The "distance" in each case is known as the *optical path*. What will be the effect at S' due to the superposition of the two coherent wave trains? The path difference taken by W_2 and W_1 is arranged experimentally so that it is a whole number of half wavelengths, or

$$(SM + MS') - SS' = n\frac{\lambda}{2}$$

(i) when n is odd, there is *destructive* interference

(ii) when n is even, there is *constructive* interference.

In (i) the amplitudes of the two waves will cancel, since there is a phase difference of 180°, and light plus light will produce darkness at the point S'. In (ii) the amplitudes of the two waves will add, and there will be a maximum intensity at the point S'. It is assumed that the vibrations of the two wave trains are in the same *plane* in each instance. If they are not, a new effect is observed. For points near S' on either side, there will be gradations between zero and a maximum intensity. In the hands of outstanding experimenters such as Albert A. Michelson (1852–1931) the phenomena of interference have been put to great practical use in the measurement of extremely minute distances and angles (see INTERFERENCE AND INTERFEROMETRY).

It was the behavior of light during interference that enabled Thomas Young (1773–1829) to enunciate the wave theory of light and thus to upset the corpuscular theory which had been held by Newton. Material particles would not show interference, but wave trains—under the carefully specified conditions—would do so. As Young's crucial experiment is performed today, a train of plane waves W of wavelength λ is incident upon a screen C_1 (normal to the plane of the diagram, Fig. 3) which has cut in it a nar-

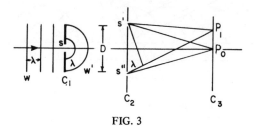

FIG. 3

row slit S that serves as a line source of an emerging train of semicylindrical waves W', in accord with Huygens' principle. Parallel to C_1 and relatively far away is a second screen C_2 which has cut in it two narrow slits S' and S'', separated by a distance D and equally disposed on the two sides of the normal to C_1 at S. By Huygens' principle, S' and S'', being parts of the same wave front, will send out wave trains that are coherent. If the normal through S cuts a third screen C_3, that is parallel to the other two, at P_0; then at this point there will be zero path difference between it and the two slits S' and S''. A bright line of light will be seen here, due to constructive interference. For two other points, P_1 and P_1', equidistant from P_0, the path difference $P_1 S'' - P_1 S'$ will be λ. Here again there will be constructive interference. Upon the screen C_3 there will be seen an interference pattern.

Diffraction In general, the term diffraction denotes the departure of a train of waves from a straight course. Thus, ocean waves, parallel to the shore outside of an inlet, are seen, when they enter the harbor, to run along the inner shores—diffracted by the passage from the inlet to the harbor. Sound waves in a concert hall are readily heard in the "shadow" of a column that supports a gallery. By the same principle, light waves bend into the geometrical shadow when passing a straight edge. If, in the discussion of interference from two slits (Fig. 3), the widths of the slits were increased so as to include a larger number of "points" on the incident wavefronts, then the effects on the third screen C_3 would be more complex (see DIFFRACTION BY MATTER AND DIFFRACTION GRATINGS).

Dispersion As used in optics, dispersion implies the separation of a light beam of more than one wavelength into its component parts. The operation can be effected by means of a

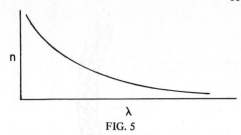

FIG. 5

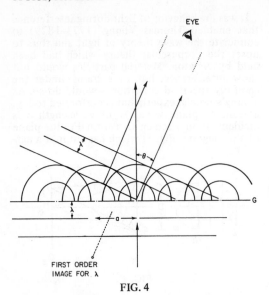

FIG. 4

diffraction grating or by a prism. In the simple case of dispersion by a grating G (Fig. 4), the wavelength λ, the angle of dispersion θ and the distance a between the centers of any two consecutive openings are related by $n\lambda = a \sin \theta$, where n, a positive integer, known as the *order* of the spectrum, is the number of whole wavelengths difference in path between the observer's eye and the centers of any two consecutive openings—assuming that parallel light is incident upon the grating. For dispersion by a prism, the angular spread of spectrum between the limits λ_1 (e.g., violet) and λ_2 (e.g., red) is given by $\alpha = A(n_1 - n_2)$ if the angle of the prism A is "small," say $15°$ or less, and the prism is very nearly at minimum deviation for the extreme wavelengths. Prismatic dispersion is observed with a spectrometer or a spectroscope. The most celebrated example of prismatic dispersion was Newton's experiment with a prism held in the path of sunlight. The measure of dispersion depends upon a definite prism of given material and refracting angle, together with the values of the wavelengths involved. The *dispersive power* of the prism material is defined by $p = (n_1 - n_2)/(n_3 - 1)$ between the limits 1 and 2, the center of the range being at some intermediate wavelength λ_3. The angular dispersion of a given prism, or rate of change of deviation D with wavelength, may be regarded as the product of the quantity dD/dn, calculable by geometrical optics, and the quantity $dn/d\lambda$ (a property of the material). The last may be found from the *normal dispersion curve* (Fig. 5) plotted from data taken with a spectrometer using a prism of the given material and employing light sources emitting known wavelengths. The angular dispersion is found from a consideration of the equation

$$\frac{dD}{d\lambda} = \frac{dD}{dn} \times \frac{dn}{d\lambda}$$

In normal dispersion, the index of refraction decreases with wavelength; i.e., the velocity of light in the material increases with wavelength, and the rate of change of index with wavelength decreases with greater wavelengths. The phenomenon of dispersion is of prime importance in the science of spectroscopy but is a decided liability in the design of lenses for optical instruments, since any one lens by itself will not focus all colors at the same point. Exceptions to the general trend of index variation with wavelength are very common for certain substances throughout particular wavelength bands. The topic of anomalous dispersion is to be treated under the subdivision absorption spectroscopy (see ABSORPTION SPECTRA).

Polarization Although the wave theory has been very satisfactory in "explaining" the phenomena of interference and diffraction, the crucial test for the necessity of that theory was not presented. What sort of waves are they? Are they longitudinal (as in sound), or circular (as in or on a water surface), or are they transverse (as along a violin string)? Strong experimental evidence, as well as the electromagnetic theory of light itself, points to the transverse type of wave form for light—as well as for radiant heat, radio waves, and the other regions of the so-called *electromagnetic spectrum*. In Fig. 6(a) imagine that a beam of natural light is emerging from the paper at O and that the "light vectors" can take in turn any possible direction making an angle with the x-axis. If, now, a very finely ruled grill PP' ("polarizer") is placed in the beam as in Fig. 6(b), only those vibrations, or components of vibrations, which are parallel to PP' will be transmitted. The light that emerges will be *plane polarized*. Now let a similar grill AA' ("analyzer") Fig. 6(c) be placed in this transmitted beam, with an angle θ between the directions PP' and AA'. Then only those vibrations, or components of vibrations, emerging from PP' which are parallel to AA' will be transmitted by the latter. The incident light (from PP') has

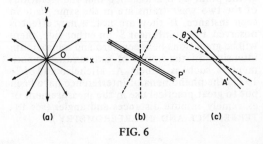

(a)   (b)   (c)

FIG. 6

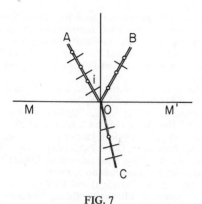

FIG. 7

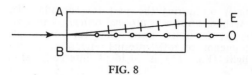

FIG. 8

therefore been "analyzed." An everyday example of plane polarization was first observed by Étienne Louis Malus (1775–1812) through a chance "analysis" of sunlight reflected from a distant window. The Malus effect may be understood from Fig. 7. AO is a beam of natural light in the plane of the paper, incident upon the surface MM′ at an angle i. The plane of the paper is the plane of incidence and MM′ is perpendicular to it. The beam of natural light has as many light vector components at right angles to the plane of incidence ($\cdots$) as there are in that plane ($/ / / /$). Malus found that the reflected beam (OB) is partially plane polarized, which means that there are in it more of the ($\cdots$) components than there are of the ($/ / / /$) components. The situation is reversed in the refracted beam (OC). Several years later, David Brewster showed that if the reflected and refracted beams are at right angles to each other, the polarization of the former is complete and that the tangent of the then angle of incidence is the index of refraction of the material (for that wavelength).

Optical Activity It is not always true that a beam of plane polarized light maintains its vibrational direction as it proceeds into a transparent substance. Many materials actually rotate the plane of vibration by an amount that depends directly upon the distance traversed. *Optical activity* is exhibited by quartz, sodium chlorate, turpentine, sugar crystals (even if dissolved in water), etc. In the case of a solution, the rotation is also proportional to the concentration, and it may be clockwise or counterclockwise. The wavelength of the light and the temperature are also factors in the total rotation observed. The apparatus used in the measurement of the angular displacement of the incident beam is a *polarimeter*.

Double Refraction Certain materials, such as quartz, mica, Iceland spar and tourmaline, are able to refract a beam of light into two portions which, in general, travel thereafter in different directions. The phenomenon of *double refraction* was first described in 1669 by Erasmus Batholinus. In Fig. 8 we imagine a beam of natural light of a given wavelength to fall upon

the face AB of a crystal of Iceland spar (a clear form of calcium carbonate). One part, after passing the interface, travels on through the crystal in accord with Snell's law, and is known as the *ordinary* beam. The other part of the incident beam, after passing the interface, goes off at an angle with the first part. This is the *extraordinary* beam. If the crystal faces are parallel, the two beams will emerge parallel. It was soon found that they are plane-polarized at right angles to each other. The symbols (○) and (/) serve to denote this fact. Each crystal has an optic axis along which optical properties remain constant. If the incident light is normal to, or parallel to the optic axis, there is no separation of the ordinary and extraordinary beams. Huygens explained double refraction of Iceland spar in terms of concentric spherical and ellipsoidal wavefronts (Fig. 9). The small doubleheaded arrows denote the vibrational directions of the transverse waves.

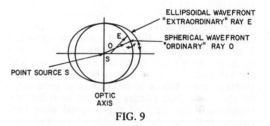

FIG. 9

Photoelasticity Many ordinary materials, such as plastics, can be made doubly refracting if they are placed under a stress. This new property will show up if the specimen is placed between two "crossed" polarizing sheets (Fig. 10).

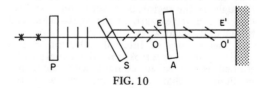

FIG. 10

Natural light is plane-polarized by the first sheet (polarizer) P and is then split by the specimen into ordinary and extraordinary beams, O and E. The second polarizing screen (analyzer) A suppresses one component of each beam so that the light vectors O′ and E′ that emerge from the analyzer are in the same plane and are in the condition to show interference at the screen.

Internal Reflection Spectroscopy A new method for studying optical spectra has been

built up during the past few decades. This method, known as *internal reflection spectroscopy*, is based upon the well-known phenomenon of total internal reflection. A ray of light (Fig. 11) is incident internally at an

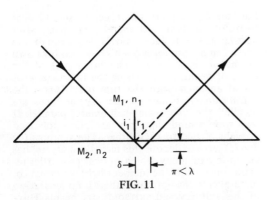

FIG. 11

angle i_1, greater than the critical angle for the denser medium M_1, on the interface between two transparent media M_1 and M_2 of different refractive indices $n_1 > n_2$. It is seen that the reflected ray travels out from the interface in the *direction* required by the first law of reflection, but there is a *lateral displacement* δ that can be explained by assuming that part of the incident wave enters the second medium and then reenters the first medium. Newton himself observed this effect, regarded the curved path in the second medium as parabolic, and showed that if an object were brought up to the interface from below to either a close proximity or else into final contact, the total reflection disappears! The part of the original wave that enters the less dense medium we call the *evanescent* wave, since it has a *fleeting* or *fading* aspect. Newton incorrectly explained the effect on the corpuscular theory, but we can invoke the electromagnetic theory. Research has shown that there is a standing wave in the dense medium at the point of incidence and that the electric vector decays exponentially throughout the region of *penetration* π—a fraction of the wavelength of the light—evidenced by the evanescent wave.

In making use of internal reflection in this special type of spectroscopy, the sample to be studied is placed in contact with the dense medium so that it can interact with the evanescent field. By this means spectra of monomolecular films and surfaces can be obtained. Liquids, powders, and fibers are amenable to this investigation.

C. HARRISON DWIGHT

References

Harrick, N. J., "Internal Reflection Spectroscopy," New York, Interscience Publishers, 1967.

Pierce, John R., and Levene, John R., "Visual Science," Proceedings of the 1968 International Symposium, Bloomington, Indiana University Press, 1968.

Sokolov, A. V., "Optical Properties of Metals," New York, American Elsevier Publishing Company, Inc., 1967.

Nudelman, S., and Mitra, S. S., Eds., "Optical Properties of Solids," New York, Plenum Press, 1969.

Haidemenakis, E. D., Ed., "Optical Properties of Solids," New York, Gordon & Breach, 1970.

Heavens, O. S., "Optical Properties of Thin Solid Films," New York, Dover Publications, Inc., 1965.

Wright, W. D., "The Measurement of Colour," New York, Van Nostrand Reinhold, 1969.

Henderson, S. T., "Daylight and Its Spectrum," New York, American Elsevier Publishing Company, Inc., 1970.

Wyszecki, Gunter, and Stiles, W. S., "Color Science: Concepts and Methods, Quantitative Data and Formulas," New York, John Wiley & Sons, Inc., 1967.

Yves, Le Grand, "Form and Space Vision," tr. by Michel Millidot and Gordon G. Heath, Bloomington, Indiana University Press, 1967.

Cross-references: DIFFRACTION BY MATTER AND DIFFRACTION GRATINGS; INTERFERENCE AND INTERFEROMETRY; OPTICS, GEOMETRICAL; POLARIZED LIGHT; REFRACTION.

OSCILLOSCOPES

The cathode-ray oscilloscope is an instrument that displays changing events in graphical form on the screen of a cathode-ray tube. The display is usually presented in terms of X-Y coordinates, with time represented horizontally from left to right, and the electrical analog of the event by a vertical displacement, up or down from some zero point (the abscissa and ordinate, respectively) (see ELECTRON OPTICS).

The first known use of the cathode-ray tube to display changing phenomena occurred in 1897, the same year that the tube was used to prove that cathode rays were electrified and would respond to a magnetic field. As the oscilloscope has come into greater use, it has been required to permit more and more accurate measurements of time and amplitude, directly from the display if possible. The engineering efforts to satisfy these requirements have influenced the basic philosophy of the instrument, have initiated developments in circuitry and components as well, and have resulted in sophisticated instruments that are actually small but complex "systems." For example, some "straightforward" oscilloscopes meant for broad general-purpose laboratory use contain more than 150 vacuum tubes and semiconductor devices, while a sampling oscilloscope will contain nearly 250. Other instruments, designed to measure and automatically print out several parameters of semiconductor devices at the rate of several per second, contain over 600 semiconductors and tubes. Actually, in this last ex-

ample, the cathode-ray tube has assumed the important but subsidiary function of a monitor for setting up and observing the desired performance of the testing equipment.

The events displayed by an oscilloscope are usually referred to as signals, and the parameters of the signal which it is desired to observe determine the characteristics the instrument must have. The design of an instrument, therefore, should reflect the desired range of signals it is expected to display. An instrument to deal with a narrow range of uniformly repetitive signals will be quite simple and will exhibit a different design philosophy than one expected to deal with arbitrary signals. These latter impose the most stringent design requirements, as there is no way of anticipating the time of signal occurrence, how soon it will occur again (if ever), duration, and its character or "form" (which determines its content).

An oscilloscope consists of three or four basic elements: cathode-ray tube, time-base generator, vertical deflection channel and power supply (which is quite important, as it sets the limits to both long-term and short-term stability of performance of the other elements). (Many would say that the signal pick-up is a basic element since it determines whether the instrument has a "good" signal to display.)

The case of a signal consisting of a single arbitrary event illustrates the relationship between these basic elements. Such a signal, or one whose duration is very short compared with the time until its next occurrence, presents a special problem whose solution permits viewing almost any other kind of signal. The problem can best be stated in the form of a question: How can all of such a signal be seen when the chain of complex events which permit it to be displayed must wait until its occurrence to be initiated?

The time relationships involved require that the signal not appear on the vertical deflection plates of the cathode-ray tube until the time base has been impressed on the horizontal deflection plates. Clearly, the signal must be "held up," stored, or somehow delayed until the sweep generator is well started and the electron beam in the cathode-ray tube is flowing. Normally this delay is performed in the vertical amplifier by a transmission line which requires a large amount of time for the signal to traverse compared to the onset of the signal and the starting time of the sweep.

Signal amplifiers in the cathode-ray oscilloscope are usually required to respond accurately to both the dc level at which a signal may occur and the signal itself, no matter how transient it may be. At the present time, signals between 10^{-11} and 10^{-12} second are of interest, and present-day vacuum tube amplifier techniques are simply incapable of handling such a range of signals.

This problem has been approached in several ways, using vacuum tubes, semiconductors and a combination of the two technologies.

The vacuum-tube approaches reflect the fact that electrical currents and fields take time to move from place to place—whether through the space in a vacuum tube or along a conductor from one component to another. This fact makes it possible to space electrical elements physically so that they will influence the same electron or signal at different times. Consequently, we can apply the same deflecting field to the same electron or amplify the same signal a number of times at successive intervals. Sizeable improvements in bandwidth at a given deflection sensitivity in a cathode ray tube, or in gain at a given bandwidth in an amplifier, are made possible by these techniques. Devices designed in this way are often referred to as "distributed deflection plate" cathode-ray tubes or "distributed" amplifiers. (Traveling wave amplifiers, cyclotrons, klystrons and magnetrons all employ the principle of using the same field to affect the same electron at successive instants of time.)

Semiconductor devices in the proper physical form are capable of responding in exceedingly short periods of time—a few picoseconds (10^{-12} second), in fact. This capability, coupled with the recently developed microcircuitry or deposited film technology, has made some interesting and useful devices possible.

Another way in which an apparent increase in bandwidth can be obtained is by the sampling method. It is possible to generate very short voltage pulses in a very precise manner, both as to time of occurrence and form. If such a pulse is combined with a repetitively recurring signal at successively later instants (in relation to some arbitrary "point" on the signal), a series of voltage pulses is developed whose amplitude varies in the same manner as that of the signal in question, but whose duration is expanded by as much as is desired. In other words a signal of very short duration can be expanded into one of long duration, which can be handled by conventional amplifier techniques. An effective increase in bandwidth of 100 times or more can be obtained by this method (see PULSE GENERATION).

The development of deposited film technology makes it possible to obtain extremely wide-range performance never before attainable with vaccum tube or even conventional transistor technology. These new techniques hold a great deal of promise for obtaining increased performance in the oscilloscope art.

In at least one respect, the oscilloscope differs from most other instruments; it is expected to display the change in some phenomenon without distortion in either time or magnitude. In contrast with most other instruments, it does not deal with only one aspect of a phenomenon, such as an average value, a peak value, the time between two events, the number of events, etc. In these cases, the attributes of no concern can be distorted if necessary to facilitate measuring the desired attribute. The oscilloscope, however, must display the "way" in which

something changes, and it should "process the information" between the receiving of it and the displaying of it in an essentially passive manner.

Consequently, the use of the oscilloscope implies that it "displays" precisely what is put into it (otherwise it would not be very useful!). This is not absolutely possible in the general case because certain signals whose characteristics fall near or outside the range of the oscilloscope amplifier are distorted to some degree. Such distortion is inevitable. The problem is to determine which kind of distortion is acceptable.

Ordinarily, bandwidth has been considered to be the principal criterion of performance of an amplifier. However, when an amplifier is handling arbitrary signals, it is nearly impossible to adjust it to give undistorted response over the whole range of performance by using conventional bandwidth-testing techniques. The most effective method that has been developed to adjust an amplifier for uniform undistorted response is by the use of step functions or square waves. A step function is a "no-time" transition from one dc voltage level to another. A square wave is simply a series of step functions "alternating" between two dc levels of voltage in a regular manner. The value of a square wave is that its quality can be evaluated by eye with a precision unmatched by most conventional, easily used bandwidth-testing techniques. Once the criteria of distortion have been agreed upon, evaluations can be made which are limited only by the skill and experience of the viewer.

Several kinds of distortion of a step function may occur in an amplifier. For example, it can be adjusted to give the shortest possible risetime, since the step function rises in "no time." Although such an adjustment gives the best possible reproduction of the actual transition, it also causes the signal to "overshoot," adding high frequencies to the display that were not present in the original signal. Conversely, the amplifier can be adjusted so that the dc levels between the transitions are completely undisturbed and the result is a gradual transition from one voltage level to the other which subtracts high frequencies from the signal. However, there is an optimum region of performance where the transition takes place as rapidly as is possible under the circuit conditions but with no overshoot and a minimum of detectable distortion in the stable voltage levels following the transition. In this situation, the circuit itself determines the response to a step function, the deteriorated portion of the step function can be computed from the observed risetime and the known amplifier risetime, and most important, there is never any question whether a particular element of the display is due to the amplifier or is actually present in the signal. If something appears in the display, it is present to at least that degree in the signal. It may be present in the signal to a greater degree

than the display indicates, in which case responses of about one-fifth of the risetime of the amplifier can be estimated to a reasonable accuracy.

The problem of determining fidelity of response is a never-ending one. The testing square wave must be "square" enough that it does not contribute any distortion to the ultimate display. However, only by having a measuring system with capabilities much beyond the characteristics of the testing square wave can we be reasonably confident of the quality of this signal. But we can only test this latter measuring system for fidelity of response by having another testing square wave of known fidelity so that any distortion in the amplifier will be apparent to the user. The solution of this problem takes on the character of attempting to lift oneself by one's own bootstraps and, of course, is never satisfactorily resolved.

JACK E. DAY

References

MacGregor-Morris, J. T., and Mines, R. J., *J. Inst. Elec. Engrs.*, **63**, 1056 (1925).

Kuehni, H. P., and Ramo, S., *Elec. Eng.*, 721 (1937).

Day, J. E., "Recent Developments in the Cathode-Ray Oscilloscope," *Advan. Electron. Electron Phys.*, **10** (1958).

Noel, D. R., and Susskind, C., *Elec. Ind.*, 92–98 (August 1961).

Kobbe, John, "The Sophisticated Oscilloscope," *Industrial Research* (March 1964).

Cross-references: ELECTRON OPTICS, PULSE GENERATION.

OSMOSIS

If, into the bottom of a jar containing water, a solution of cane sugar is introduced with care so as to avoid mixing, not only will the molecules of cane sugar diffuse into the water but the molecules of water will diffuse into the sugar solution. These processes will go on until the concentration of sugar, and of water, is the same throughout.

If the solution is placed in a container, whose walls are relatively impermeable to the sugar while being permeable to the water, and the container is placed in water, the water will pass from the outside into the container. The term osmosis is usually restricted to the passage of water. If the influx of the water results in an overflow of solution to somewhere other than the surrounding water this overflow will continue until all the sugar is removed from the container. If the container is closed, water will continue to enter until there is sufficient stress in the stretched walls to cause a pressure on the solution inside; this will eventually stop the influx. Of course, if the walls of the

container are not completely impermeable to sugar, then the sugar will be escaping into the water outside the container and this will go on until the concentration of sugar is the same outside and inside. If the walls of the container were impermeable to water but permeable to solute, the latter would escape. The cause of this osmosis, this "pushing," of water into the solution is that the tendency of the water molecules to escape from the pure water is greater than that of the water molecules in the solution. Consider water in contact with a limited volume of air. Of those molecules of water striking the surface some will have sufficient energy to escape into the air and this escape will result in net loss to the air which will continue until the concentration of water vapor molecules there is such that the rate of escape from the air (into the water) equals the rate of escape from the water (into the air). If the volume of the air space is fixed, the pressure will rise. Just as the temperature of all bodies is the same when they are in thermal equilibrium, although their heat content per unit volume varies with their specific heat, so the escaping tendency of the water is the same in all systems when they are in aqueous equilibrium, whether the system is pure water, solution, gas phase, wettable solid, etc. The same concept can be applied to any substance, say mercury in pure mercury, in air containing mercury vapor, and in an amalgam with another metal such as zinc. The term osmosis is usually restricted to the passage of water from a solution where the escaping tendency is higher to a solution where it is lower. Moreover it is usually restricted to the passage through a solid or liquid barrier which prevents the solutions from rapidly mixing. It is not used for the passage of water in the form of vapor through the air from a dilute solution to a stronger solution in the same confined space, although the process is fundamentally the same. It is sometimes restricted to the case where the barrier is semipermeable, that is, lets through water but not solute.

The escaping tendency of water is lowered by the addition of a solute. If the molecules of the solute have no other effect than to reduce the number of molecules of water in unit volume, then the escaping tendency of the water will be reduced proportionately to the reduction in the mole fraction of water, N_1, the ratio of the moles of water to the sum of the moles of water and solute. Such is a "perfect" solution. If, however, there is some attraction between the solute and water molecules, a smaller fraction of the latter will have energy sufficient to escape—a "nonperfect" solution. The escaping tendency is increased by pressure. Hence a solution in which the water has lower escaping tendency than it has in pure water at the same pressure, P^0, can be brought to water equilibrium by a sufficient increase in the pressure on the solution to a value P. This sufficient increase, $P - P^0$, is the osmotic pressure of the solution. In general we cannot state $P - P^0$, the osmotic pressure, knowing only N_2, the ratio of moles of solute to the sum of the moles of water plus solute, the mole fraction of solute. ($N_2 = 1 - N_1$).

What we can say is, that if in a solution with a mole fraction N_2 of solute under a pressure P the water has the same escaping tendency as it has in pure water at the same temperature and at a pressure P^0, then $dP/dN_2 = A/B$ where dP/dN_2 is the increase of P relative to increase of N_2 to keep the escaping tendency unchanged; A is the decrease of escaping tendency relative to increase of N_2 when P is unchanged; and B is the increase in escaping tendency relative to increase in P when N_2 is unchanged. For dilute solutions A/B approximates to RT/V_1 and so $P - P^0$ approximates to N_2RT/V_1 where V_1 is the volume of one mole of water, R is constant 82.07 cm^3 atm/deg, and T is the absolute temperature. For very dilute solutions N_2/V_1 approaches n_2/V, the number of moles of solute in a volume V of solution and $P - P^0 = n_2RT/V$ (van't Hoff's equation). This gives an osmotic pressure of 1 atm for one mole of solute in 22.4 liters at 0°C. There is a departure from both these equations for stronger solutions. The fact that one mole of a perfect gas in 22.4 liters at 0°C exerts a pressure of 1 atmos, coupled with the above, has led some to say that the osmotic pressure is the bombardment pressure of the solute molecules. It is correct to say that for very dilute solutions the osmotic pressure of a solution is equal in magnitude to the pressure the solute molecules would exert if they were alone in the same volume and behaved as a perfect gas, but that is another matter.

To measure the osmotic pressure, a semipermeable membrane must be prepared which itself can stand sufficient pressure, or it must be deposited in the walls of a porous pot so that the pressure can be sustained. With the solution being inside and water out, pressure is applied to the former until there is no net movement of water.

Observations by Berkeley and Hartley showed that for 3.393 gms of cane sugar per 100 gms H_2O, the osmotic pressure at 0°C is 2.23 atmos while the van't Hoff equation gives 2.17 atmos since $n_2/V = 9.27 \times 10^{-15}$. If N_2/V_1 is used instead of n_2/V, the value of 2.22 is obtained. With stronger solutions the measured osmotic pressure exceeds that calculated: with 33.945 gms of sugar, 24.55 atmos is the value measured, while van't Hoff's equation gives 18.41 and the other 21.8 atmos. The observed value is given if, in calculating N_2/N_1, it is assumed that each sugar molecule immobilizes five molecules of water.

The solutes in the vacuole of a plant cell are exposed to the inward pressure of the distended cell wall and that of the turgid surrounding cells. Water will pass into the cell vacuole from

water outside as long as the total inward pressure on the vacuole falls short of the osmotic pressure of the solution in the vacuole. Passage of water into the vacuole dilutes the contents and lowers the osmotic pressure and increases the inward pressure by distension. The amount by which the inward pressure falls short of the osmotic pressure is called by some the suction pressure.

A substance such as cellulose or gelatin tends to take up water, the tendency decreasing with increase in water content until the stress in the substance causes a sufficient rise in the escaping tendency of the water in the substance. This process, which like osmosis is a movement from higher to lower escaping tendency, is called imbibition, and the pressure on the substance sufficient to stop the uptake is the imbibitional pressure. Hence, if a plant cell with a cellulose wall, after coming to equilibrium with a solution, is transferred to water, the wall takes up water by imbibition and the vacuole by osmosis. The latter considers only the over-all movement from outside to vacuole and does not consider the movement from cellulose to vacuole, a process which is the reverse of imbibition. A plant cell in equilibrium with a solution having an osmotic pressure of 25 atmos would also be in equilibrium with air about 98 per cent saturated with water vapor. If the cell were transferred to a saturated atmosphere, it would take up water. We lack precise terms for the passage of water from air into the cellulose and into the vacuole. Condensation, which might be used, ranges more widely.

The escaping tendency of water is affected by factors other than concentration of solute and pressure. Increase of temperature increases escaping tendency. This is a complex problem involving not only transfer of water but also of heat. To a minor extent, the passage of water from pure water to a solution involves a heat transfer.

For many naturally occurring membranes which are not completely semipermeable, i.e., they let solute molecules through slowly, electro-osmosis is important. If the membrane tends to lose negative charges to, or take negative charges from, water or solutions, then the water molecules, in the pores of the membrane, will tend to take on an opposite charge to the membrane. If there is a gradient of electric potential across the membrane, the charged water will move in the appropriate direction. If the potential difference is established by the use of electrodes, this is electro-osmosis.

If, for any reason such as the greater solubility of the solute relative to that of water in the membrane, the volume flow of the solute from the side of higher concentration is greater than that of water in the opposite direction, then there is negative osmosis. This occurs with some plant cells with lipid-soluble substances of small molecular weight.

The rate of osmosis depends, not only on the excess of the escaping tendency of the water in the phase from which it moves, over that in the phase to which it moves, but also upon the area of surface of interchange and the over-all resistance experienced by the water. The rate of shrinkage of the vacuole of a plant cell when it is placed in a strong solution at first seems surprisingly high. When allowance is made for the fact that the ratio of surface to volume increases as the linear dimension is reduced then it is realized that when the vacuole of a spherical cell of radius $30\ \mu$ shrinks to half its volume in say 5 minutes the passage of water is only 1 ml per $10\ 000\ cm^2$ per minute although the thickness of the layer between vacuole and external solution is of the order of $1\ \mu$ in thickness. Under other circumstances, this layer might be said to be relatively impermeable to water. It seems probable that much of the resistance resides not in the cellulose wall or cytoplasm but in the tonoplast which separates the latter from the vacuole.

G. E. BRIGGS

P

PARACRYSTALS*

There are three states of aggregation: solid, liquid and gaseous. This categoric division, however, does not explain why there are, within the solids category, such different substances as metals, minerals, and glasses, or why liquids, when solidifying, convert partly into a crystalline and partly into a glassy state. At the same time substances exist which do not belong in any one of these groups. The word "paracrystal" was used for the first time by Stanley (1) in connection with biological substances and by Rinne (2) in connection with liquid crystals. It is the task of this contribution to find an atomistic definition of the paracrystal (3) and to demonstrate the fundamental importance of this idea relative to concept and application. In doing this one cannot neglect discussing at the same time the x-ray interferences of all these substances, because without the discovery by von Laue (4) that one can gain direct information on shape and ordering of atoms and molecules, everything would remain pure philosophy. One can understand the paracrystalline state only if one simultaneously has knowledge of the other existing modes of solids.

Gases The gaseous state is characterized by a maximum of disorder. The molecules are distributed in space completely irregularly according to purely statistical laws. Their distribution of velocity and proximity obeys, in the ideal case, the Boltzmann statistics. The more compressed the gas, the narrower become these distribution functions.

Liquids The mobility of molecules in liquids is considerably less than that in gases; opinions on their spatial order, however, are at present still divided. The school of Bernal (6) advocates the extreme of highest disorder; whereas the other extreme of quasicrystalline order is supported by Kaplow, Strong and Averbach (7).

Liquid Crystals Whereas liquids generally exhibit equal properties in all three dimensions, i.e., they are isotropic; so-called "crystalline liquids"† are also known, which in the vicinity of the interface with their container exhibit anisotropic optical and electrical properties. The explanation for this phenomenon is derived from the shape and the dipole moment of the molecules of the (mostly organic) liquids. They are oblong or platelet-shaped as in soap solutions.

Crystals Today we have much more knowledge of the crystalline state. The regular and plane-facets-limited shape of a polyether, which exhibits many single crystals, has inspired Haüy (8) to speak of "elementary building blocks" of equal size in the crystal, in the shape of cubes or parallelepipeds, which accumulate densely like a three-dimensional chessboard. In present terminology these are the "lattice-cells," and Seeber (9) recognized very early that they represent the space in which the basic unit of atoms, ions, or molecules of the crystal is housed. Since the distance between centers of gravity (CG) of the basic units is absolutely constant, i.e., 4 Å in certain lattice directions,* we can safely say that in a range of 1 μ† in these directions, exactly 2500 building blocks are situated, or that the distance from one CG to the 2501st neighbor is 10004 μ. Thus, because the building blocks are lined up in a countable fashion, one uses the expression "ideal remote order."

Amorphous Solids Almost all glasses, ceramics, and plastics have properties, which can be explained by the presence of "amorphous" components, in which the atoms are particularly disordered. How one visualizes the order of the atoms is open to discussion. It is generally agreed upon, however, that no lattice regions and no remote order exist here.

The Idea of Paracrystals The status today is that we have lattice structures with remote order on one hand and amorphous materials, liquids, and melts as structures without lattice and without remote order on the other hand opposing each other. On the basis of some fundamental work by J. J. Hermans (10) it was shown (3) that the idea of a statistical close-order for all building blocks, as it is advocated by Zernike (11) and Debye (12), definitely allows three-dimensional lattices of

---

*The editor is indebted to Mr. Walter Trapp of the Air Force Materials Laboratory for his careful translation of this article.

†See the essay by B. Böttcher and D. Gross in *Umschau in Wissenschaft und Technik*, **69**, 574 (1969).

*1 Å(named after the Swedish physicist Ångström) is equal to one ten-thousandth of a micron.

†1 μ(micron) is equal to one ten-thousandth of a centimeter.

the CG of the building blocks. These lattices consist of rows of countable building blocks (running number p), spaces (running number q), and columns (running number r); however, these are not straight lattice lines, but somehow curved in such a way that, for instance, along the rows of building blocks the distances between adjacent CGs (p, q, r) and $(p + 1, q, r)$ are not constant but adopt different values y with the frequency $H(y)$. This means also that this frequency distribution guarantees the same close-order ratios for all building blocks (p, q, r).

From the building block $(p + 1, q, r)$ to the adjacent CG $(p + 2, q, r)$, one finds a completely different distance vector z, which once more obeys the same probability level $H(z)$. According to the rules of probability the combination of the quantities y and z occurs with the frequency $H(y) \cdot H(z)$.

If one is interested in the statistics of the distance between nearest neighbors (p, q, r) and $(p + 2, q, r)$, one has to calculate the frequency $H_2(x)$ for the vector $y + z = x$, taking into consideration at the same time all possible

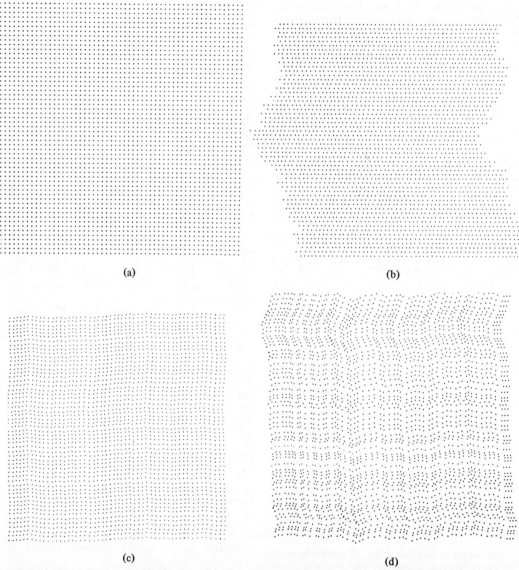

(a)

(b)

(c)

(d)

FIG. 1. Two-dimensional point-lattices; computer-drawn, with disturbances increasing from left to right. (a) Crystal. (b) Fibrous material (fiber axis vertical) in which, especially, the horizontal lines are not distorted and proceed equidistantly. (c) Metal melt with relative distance variations of 10 percent and without any partial crystalline residue. (d) Compressed gas, idealized by building blocks sorted in lines and columns.

combinations of y with z as long as they lead to the same x. This means that one has to ensure that $z = x - y$ and only y varies. This leads to the following "convolution integral"*

$$H_2(\mathbf{x}) = \int H(\mathbf{y}) H(\mathbf{x} - \mathbf{y}) \, d\mathbf{y}.$$

In order to derive the distance statistics between third neighbors one has to apply this folding process twice, etc. In this manner the statistics of the whole distorted lattice is derived from knowledge of the neighbor relationship. Since the scatter of distance increases with the distance of the building blocks from each other, the remote order is lost in the paracrystalline lattices. In Fig. 1 a few two-dimensional examples are given, which demonstrate that the paracrystal contains the gaseous as well as the crytalline state as degenerated exceptions.

Macroscopic Examples Nature, as it is directly visible to us, offers many more examples of paracrystalline structures than one would normally believe. Figure 2, for instance, shows a paracrystalline laminar lattice created by water running off of a sand beach. Repeatedly new waves are introduced, which correspond to step dislocations in solid-state physics. The statistical deviations in the direction and in the spacing of the waves obey the laws of paracrystals. The same holds for the two-dimensional lattices, which are exhibited by the grains

*In pure mathematics "convolution integrals" have been well known for a long time, particularly in the theory of the Laplace transformation. (compare, i.e., (15)). Their importance for mathematical physics has become obvious only in the last few years, specifically since more and more numerical problems have become solvable through the use of modern computers.

FIG. 2. Beach at the Tagliamento as an example of a paracrystalline laminate lattice, as it appears also in biological and synthetic fiber structures transverse to the fiber axis.

of the corncobs in Fig. 3. Since they are statistically of various sizes, only a paracrystalline lattice can originate. This is clearly evidenced in Fig. 4. by the experiment with steel balls of two different sizes located in the

FIG. 3. Two corn cobs, wrapped in cellophane, the grains of which build a multitude of two-dimensional paracrystals with disturbances.

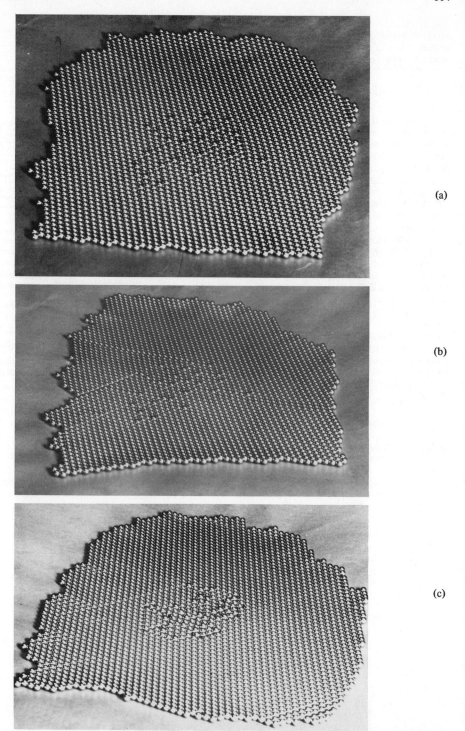

(a)

(b)

(c)

FIG. 4. Identical steel balls on a slightly sagging support. (a) In the middle section, a few balls are carefully re-placed with a pair of tweezers by slightly larger ones, without disturbing the surrounding area. (b) The same after shaking lightly. The large balls make space for themselves, which is done by way of step dislocations in the sur-rounding host-lattice. (Two can be seen in upper left corner.) (c) The large balls have reached the support and thus created a paracrystalline lattice in the center.

center of the structure. Outside all balls have the same diameter and they form the crytalline lattice in whose center the paracrystal is embedded.

Electron-microscopic Examples   Synthetic high polymers in colloidal dimensions (below 1 μ to $\overline{1}/100$ μ $\sim$100Å) supply us with excellent examples of paracrystalline laminar structures analogous to Fig. 2. As soon as one transforms them into fibers, for instance in a spin process, one recognizes in the electron microscope that they consist of subfibers ("ultrafibers") of 100

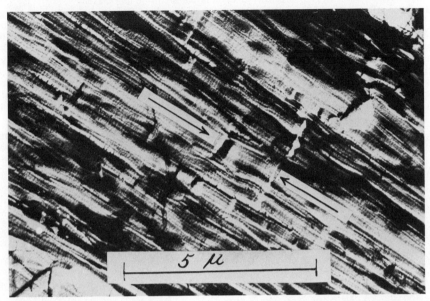

FIG. 5. Electron micrograph of a paracrystalline laminar structure, transverse to fiber, in Teflon (14). Chain molecules are located in direction of arrow. Fibrils are cross-striped. Interval of laminates is approximately 500 Å.

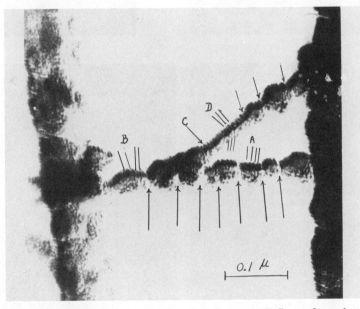

FIG. 6. Electron micrograph (light-field) of a small section of a scraped Teflon surface, where a few ultrafibrils have splintered off (14). The arrows, in an interval of approximately 500 Å, designate the boundaries of the individual blocks. These blocks each consist of about 8 disks that either are oriented vertically to the fiber (A) or are partly inclined due to paracrystalline disturbances (B) or bent (C) or buckled.

to 500Å. In these, crystalline and amorphous regions, with a paracrystalline period between 50 and 1000Å (depending on treatment), follow each other as in a string of pearls. By the assembling of ultrafibers into a microfiber the laminar structure originates (Fig. 5). But even in isotropic material (cast in the form of plates) one finds these ultrafibers (14) as is shown in Fig. 6. Here, the crystalline ranges, being approximately 500 Å thick and about equally high, consist of eight lamellae. These cross striations can be found in almost all biological fibers. However, here one reaches the limit of resolution of the electron microscope.

Interferences The only route to take from here is to investigate the interferences generated by the structures. As an example, Fig. 7 shows the Fraunhofer diffraction patterns of the greatly reduced, transparent negatives of the models in Fig. 1, which have been produced with monochromatic visible light. Through their study the static parameters of the paracrystalline lattices can be calculated.

X-ray Interferences In order to generate interference patterns of atomic structures, the wavelength used must be smaller than the length of the edges of the lattice cells. This, for instance, is the case for x-rays which emanate from a copper anode when it is irradiated with electrons. The larger the lattice cells the closer the interference points move together and they finally yield, as for instance

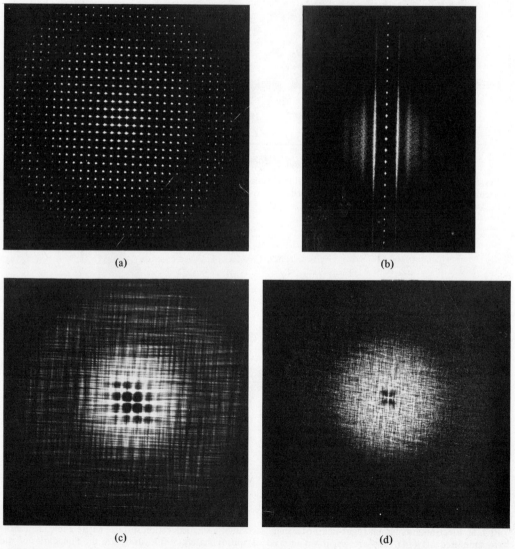

(a)

(b)

(c)

(d)

FIG. 7. Fraunhofer diffraction pattern made from the reduced transparent negatives of Fig. 1 with a He, Ne laser (13).

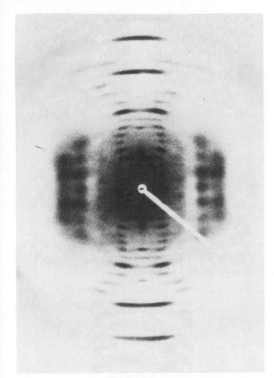

FIG. 8. X-ray small angle diagram of β-keratin of the quill of a seagull (23). Observe the similarity with Fig. 7(b). From the angle position of the interferences one can calculate that the bent lines parallel to the fiber have a distance from each other of about 12 Å, whereas the points along these lines, i.e., the centers of gravity of the basic building blocks of the protofibrils, have a distance of 183Å. This means that the basic building block is very long and thin.

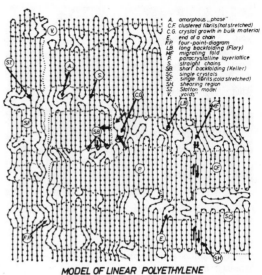

MODEL OF LINEAR POLYETHYLENE

FIG. 9. Principal figure of the structure of a synthetic material consisting of long molecules. The paracrystals consist of 100 to 500 Å thick bundles of parallel-oriented chain molecules. On the front planes, part of the molecules is folded back in larger or smaller loops; some of these run, stretched out, into the next paracrystallite and some are more or less bent. On cold drawing, chains of paracrystallites split into ultra-fibrils, separating from each other (left); whereas, with heat-treatment they join again close to each other, whereby the paracrystallites form a paracrystalline, laminate-super-lattice (center). When grown from solution, the portion of the chains which does not fold back decreases with the degree of dilution (right).

in Fig. 8, a so called x-ray angle diagram. The one shown here was the first with which it could be proven that in biological materials paracrystals exist in submicroscopic dimension (17). Their building blocks, being long, thin structures, have the characteristics of fibers, since they can deviate along the fiber only in direction and not in distance from each other.

Superstructures in Polyethylene Similarly, large lattice cells are exhibited also by the so-called "superstructures" which frequently occur in synthetic polymers. As an example, a few results from polyethylenes are given which are representative of many plastic products with long molecules and which have been obtained from the analysis of large and small angle x-ray interferences (18). The fundamental Fig. 9 shows that a lattice cell of the superstructure consists (in the fiber direction) of many basic chemical building blocks C_2H_4 (their CG marked by a dot) and is limited in the fiber direction by amorphous regions in which the chain-back-folding takes place. The lateral extension in the extreme left is particularly evident during cold

drawing, where the fibrils separate spatialy. In these lateral grain boundaries, as in the grain boundaries of a crystal, an increased disorder exists. This increased disorder is thought to be caused mainly by a high concentration of "kinks" as displayed in Fig. 10 [according to Pechhold (19)].

Influence of Mechanical Properties In the lateral grain boundaries an increased mobility of the chains relative to each other exists, because kinks can move along the chain by means of the simple flipping-over of some of the CH_2 groups, and the chain therefore creeps on like a caterpillar according to Renecker (20). If one clamps, for instance, both ends of a synthetic fiber and moves them parallel to each other as shown in Fig. 11, one can see in the small inserted diagram that the fibrils glide relative to each other. This explains why metal fibers are much less flexible, and glass fibers can only be bent elastically. In Fig. 12 the influence of heat treatment on the superstructure of stretched polyethylene is shown, by which the mechanical properties are changed. With increasing temperature the crystalline re-

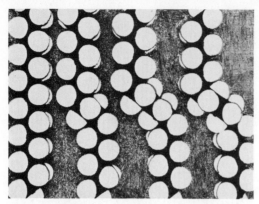

FIG. 10. Model for various kinds of "kinks" in linear polyethylene after Pechhold (19). The white half-spheres represent the hydrogen atoms. They mask the black-symbolized Carbon atoms to a great extent. In the crystalline state (extreme left) the CH_2-groups are arranged in zig-zag fashion.

FIG. 11. Bending of a hot-worked piece of poly-ethylene (schematic). From the x-ray small-angle dia-gram (at the top) one calculates the superstructures. On the left, before, and on the right, after, bending of both ends of the piece. The crystalline ranges are marked black.

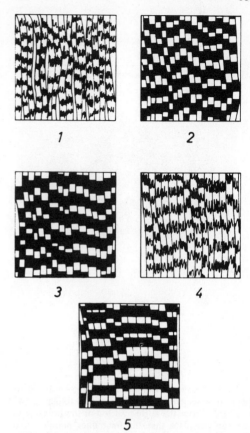

FIG. 12. Influence of heat treatment on the super-structures of polyethylene (18). 1, Cold-stretched. Splintering into ultrafibrils. 2, 500 hours tempered at 110°C. The empty spaces or vacancies have disap-peared; the front planes are more distinctly defined. No other changes have occurred. 3, 5 minutes at 120°C produces additionally an elongation in cross-section of the paracrystals. 4, 10 minutes at 120°C causes growth of the average value of the lengths at constant density, but gives a more diffuse front plane. 5, 500 hours at 120°C recrystallizes the adjacent ultrafibrils at the same time generating thicker paracrystallites with smaller disturbances. The density and the average laminate interval grow, and the front planes are again well defined.

regions grow and the fiber finally loses its desirable properties.

Paracrystalline Atomic Lattices As Fig. 7(c) shows, the widths of the reflexes increase with growing scatter angle the larger the paracrystal-line disturbances are.* These disturbances can qualitatively be determined by accurate mea-surements of line profiles of x-ray angle inter-

*Unlike the widening of reflexes through internal stresses, these vary not in a linear fashion, but with the square of the sine of the Bragg angle.

ferences. According to Fig. 4 they grow with the mixing ratio and the differences in size of the building blocks. Thus, one gets information on their shape when one knows their concen-tration. In this manner, the ammonia catalyst (enriched with 3 weight per cent aluminum) was investigated. It distinguished itself by the fact that its inner surfaces do not decline even with long service times, thus keeping the con-nected regions equally small. The result is shown in Fig. 13: A considerable part of the aluminum is built into the cubic-centered α-iron lattice in form of $FeAl_2O_4$ "motives" or units. One unit displaces seven iron atoms. It has the

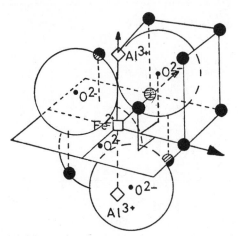

FIG. 13. Atom model of the ammonia catalyst, promoted with 3 weight per cent aluminum. $FeAl_2O_4$ units are built into the metallic iron atom lattice (●) under the substitution of seven atoms each, which fit into the lattice only in respect to their volume but not their shape. The unit consists therefore of one iron ion (□), two aluminum ions (◇), and four oxygen ions (○).

same volume, but not the same shape as these, a fact which explains the measured paracrystalline disturbances quantitatively (21). Similar measurements on polyethylenes demonstrated that the disturbances in the transverse direction of the paracrystalline microfibrils become smaller with their extension. In all the cases mentioned here, the distance variations are at the largest, 3 per cent, which is hardly reeognizable in models. Figure 1(c), in comparison, with 10 per cent relative paracrystalline disturbance variations, corresponds to those values which are found for the very small lattice ranges in metallic melts (22).

Outlook The sketched examples may demonstrate that the theory of paracrystals can be applied to a multitude of groups of substances, and that it furnishes quantitative criteria for the definition of these substances through a series of novel statistical structure parameters. One result, already of interest in colloid-chemistry, is that the lattice ranges are, and remain, smaller the larger their paracrystalline disturbances are. The large and stable inner surface of the ammonia catalyst and the remarkable similarity between many biological and synthetic super-structures, as well as the similarity of a metal structure above and below the melting point, indicate that new fundamentals have been found upon which one could build.

ROLF HOSEMANN

References

1. Stanley, W. M., *Science*, **81**, 644 (1935).
2. Rinne, F., *Trans. Farad. Soc.*, **29**, 1016 (1933),
   "*Investigations and Considerations concerning Paracrystallinity*."
3. Hosemann, R., *Zs. f. Phsy.*, **128**, 1 (1950).
4. Laue, M., F. Friedrich und P. Knipping (1912) *Sitzungs Ber. Bayer. Akad. Wiss. Math. Phys.* K1, **303**, 363.
5. Boltzmann, L. (1895) "Vorlesungen über Gastheorie," Johann Ambrosius, Leipzig.
6. Bernal, J. D., *Nature*, **185**, 68 (1960).
7. Kaplow, F., Strong, S. L., and Averbach, B. L., *Phys. Rev.*, **138** A, 1336 (1965).
8. Haüy, R. J., *Journ. de Phys. Paris* (1782).
9. Seeber, L. A., *Gilberts Annalen*, **76**, 349 (1824).
10. Hermans, J. J., *Rec. Trav. Chim. Pays.–Bas.*, **63**, 5 (1944).
11. Zernike, F., and Prins, J. A., *Zs. Phys.*, **41**, 184 (1927).
12. Debye, P. P., *Phys. Zs.*, **31**, 348 (1930).
13. Hosemann, R., and Müller, B., *Mol. Cryst. and Liqu. Cryst.*, **10**, 273 (1970).
14. O'Leary, K. J., "Dissertation," Case Institite, Cleveland, Ohio (1965).
15. Doetsch, G., "Theorie und Anwendung der Laplace-Transformation," Springer Verlag, Leipzig, 1937.
16. Hosemann, R., and Bagchi, S. N., "Direct Analysis of Diffraction by Matter," North. Holl. Publ. Comp., Amsterdam, 1962.
17. Hosemann, R., "Die Erforschung der Struktur hochmolekularer und Kolloider Stoffe mittels Kleinwinkelstreuung," *Erg, d, Ex. Nat. Wiss.*, **24**, 142–221, Springer Verlag, Berlin, 1951.
18. Loboda, J., Hosemann, R., and Wilke, W., *Koll. Zs. u. Zs. Polym.*, **235**, 1162 (1969).
19. Pechhold, W., and Blasenbrey, S., *Koll. Zs. u. Zs. Polym.*, **235**, 216 (1967).
20. Renecker, D. H., *J. Polym. Sci.*, **59**, 39 (1962).
21. Preisinger, A., Hosemann, R., and Vogel, W., *Ber. Buns. Ges. Phys. Chem.*, **70**, 796 (1966).
22. Lemm, K., *Mol. Cryst. and Liqu. Cryst.*, **10**, 259 (1970).

Cross-references: CRYSTALLIZATION, CRYSTALLOGRAPHY, DIFFRACTION BY MATTER AND DIFFRACTION GRATINGS, ELECTRON MICROSCOPE, INTERFERENCE AND INTERFEROMETRY, LIQUID STATE.

PARAMAGNETISM

A substance is said to be paramagnetic if it is attracted to a magnetic field in contradistinction to a diamagnetic substance which is repelled by a magnetic field. Excluding FERROMAGNETISM, which is an extremely strong type of paramagnetism, paramagnetic substances can be roughly divided into 3 categories—strong, weak, and very weak paramagnets.

Strong paramagnetism is exhibited by elements of the iron, platinum, palladium, rare earth, and uranium groups and (generally) compounds formed from elements of these groups. For such elements the paramagnetism arises from unpaired electron spins associated with the non-

valence electrons of the atoms, each unpaired electron behaving much as a particle having an intrinsic spin angular momentum and associated magnetic moment which is orbiting about the central nucleus. For compounds in which the paramagnetic ions are dispersed sufficiently so that there are only negligible interactions between the paramagnetic electrons, the magnetic susceptibility, which is the ratio of the induced magnetization of the sample, M, to the externally applied magnetic field strength, H, is given by $\chi = C/(T - \theta)$ for small values of H/T, T being the absolute temperature of the sample. In this equation, called the Curie-Weiss Law after P. Curie (1905) and P. Weiss (1907), who did much of the early work on paramagnetism, C is called the Curie constant and was shown by Langevin (1905), using classical arguments, to be equal to $N\mu^2/3k$, N being the number of paramagnetic ions per unit volume, μ the magnetic moment of each ion, and k Boltzmann's constant. θ is called the Curie or Curie-Weiss temperature and may be either positive, negative, or zero depending on the particular compound being studied. If $\theta = 0$ the Curie-Weiss Law reduces to the Curie Law $\chi = C/T$. For $T \lesssim \theta$, interactions among the ions can no longer be ignored and the Curie-Weiss Law is no longer valid. Later quantum mechanical calculations have shown that in the limit where $\mu H/kT \ll 1$, the Curie-Weiss Law is still valid providing that in the Curie constant C, μ is replaced by

$$\mu_{\text{eff}} = g\mu_B\sqrt{J(J + 1)}$$

where g is the Landé g factor, having a value of about 2, μ_B is the Bohr magneton $|e|h/2mc$, and J is the total angular momentum quantum number of the ion in question. For some ions, notably those of the iron group, the contribution of the orbital angular momentum is partially or totally quenched by the crystalline electric field, in which case μ_{eff} is better given by the equation

$$\mu_{\text{eff}} = g\mu_B\sqrt{S(S + 1)}$$

where S is the spin angular momentum quantum number of the paramagnetic ion. A more complete derivation of χ for arbitrary values of H/T and for negligible interactions gives for the classical derivation (Langevin, 1905)

$$\chi = \frac{N\mu}{H} L\left(\frac{\mu H}{kT}\right), \qquad L\left(\frac{\mu H}{kT}\right)$$

being the Langevin Function of the argument $\mu H/kT$. A quantum mechanical derivation gives

$$\chi = \frac{Ng\mu_B J}{H} B_J\left(\frac{g\mu_B JH}{kT}\right), \qquad B_J$$

being the Brillouin Function. The Langevin and Brillouin Functions are given by the formulas

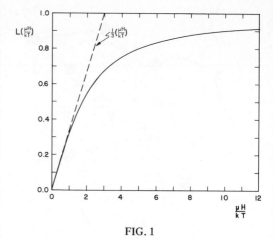

FIG. 1

$$L(x) = \operatorname{ctnh} x - \frac{1}{x} \quad \text{and} \quad B_J(x)$$

$$= \frac{2J + 1}{2J} \operatorname{ctnh}\left[\frac{(2J + 1)}{2J}x\right] - \frac{1}{2J}\operatorname{ctnh}\left[\frac{x}{2J}\right]$$

A plot of $L(\mu H/kT)$ vs $\mu H/kT$ is shown in Fig. 1. It is noticed that for small values of $\mu H/kT$ the Langevin Function reduces to $1/3(\mu H/kT)$ which gives the Curie Law, while for large values of $\mu H/kT$ the Langevin Function approaches an asymptotic limit, which results in the saturation of the magnetization of the sample. A plot of the Brillouin Function for a given ion has the same qualitative shape as that shown for the Langevin Function. At room temperature the strong paramagnetism of the electrons ranges from 10^{-3} to 10^2 cgs units.

Weak paramagnetism is a strictly quantum mechanical phenomenon exhibited primarily by metals and is associated with the conduction electrons near the top of the Fermi distribution. Only those electrons having an energy within approximately $2\mu H$ of the Fermi energy are able to reorient or align themselves in a magnetic field and change their energy state, since all energy states below the Fermi energy are filled. Thus only the fraction of the total number of electrons kT/kT_F, where kT_F is the Fermi energy and T is the absolute temperature of the sample, can contribute to the susceptibility. Ignoring interactions among the electrons the susceptibility is then given by

$$\chi = \frac{C}{T} \cdot \frac{kT}{kT_F} = \frac{C}{T_F}$$

which is independent of temperature. A more rigorous quantum mechanical derivation of the susceptibility for this case gives the result that

$$\chi = \frac{3}{2}\frac{N\mu_B^2}{kT_F} - \frac{1}{3}\left(\frac{3}{2}\frac{N\mu_B^2}{kT_F}\right) = \frac{N\mu_B^2}{kT_F}$$

where the first term is the paramagnetic contribution associated with the electrons assumed to be stationary (Pauli, 1927), while the second term is the diamagnetic contribution due to the spatial motion of the electrons (Landau, 1930). At room temperature the susceptibility of the conduction electrons in a metal ranges from about 10^{-4} to 10 cgs units.

The very weak paramagnetism associated with some nuclei is due to their intrinsic spin angular momentum and associated magnetic moment. The nuclear susceptibility is described by the Brillouin equation as given above with J replaced by the nuclear spin quantum number I. At room temperature the nuclear susceptibility is approximately 10^{-11} to 10^{-10} cgs units and so is generally swamped by the paramagnetism of the electrons if such is present.

Electron paramagnetism is often studied experimentally using the Faraday or Gouy methods or the indirect method of electron paramagnetic resonance. The only direct measurement of nuclear paramagnetism was performed by Lasarew and Shubnikow (1937) for protons in solid hydrogen, although the sensitive techniques of nuclear magnetic resonance have now been used to study most known paramagnetic nuclei.

RONALD A. LAING

References

Feynman, R. P., Leighton, R. B., and Sands, M., "The Feynman Lectures on Physics," Vol. 2, Reading, Mass., Addison-Wesley, 1964.

Stoner, E. C., "Magnetism," Fourth edition, London, Methuen, 1948.

Bates, L. F., "Modern Magnetism," Fourth edition, London, Cambridge, 1961.

Kittel, C., "Introduction to Solid State Physics," Fourth edition, New York, John Wiley & Sons, Inc., 1971.

Van Vleck, J. H., "Theory of Electric and Magnetic Susceptibilities," London, Oxford, 1932.

Cross-reference: MAGNETISM.

PARITY

The theoretical description of any physical process in the relativistic domain must be Lorentz-invariant. In a classical theory, where the interactions depend on the relative space-time coordinates and the relative four momenta of the interacting particles, the description must be independent of the coordinate frame in which the process is described. A proper Lorentz transformation from one frame S to another S' is given by

$$x_\mu' = a_{\mu\nu} x_\nu$$

where

$$x_\mu \equiv (x_1, x_2, x_3, x_4) = (x, y, z, ict).$$

A summation is to be made over repeated indices. Similarly

$$p_\mu' = a_{\mu\nu} p_\nu$$

where

$$p_\mu \equiv (p_1, p_2, p_3, p_4) = (p_x, p_y, p_z, iE/c).$$

The $a_{\mu\nu}$ are constants independent of the space-time coordinates such that the relativistic interval is to remain invariant:

$$x_\mu x_\mu = x_\mu' x_\mu' = a_{\mu\nu} x_\nu a_{\mu\tau} x_\tau$$
$$p_\mu p_\mu = p_\mu' p_\mu' = a_{\mu\nu} p_\nu a_{\mu\tau} p_\tau = -m^2 c^2.$$

This invariance requires that

$$a_{\mu\nu} a_{\mu\tau} = \delta_{\nu\tau}$$

and, in order to preserve the reality conditions of the space-time coordinates, $a_{\mu\nu}$ with $\mu, \nu = 1$, 2, 3 and a_{44} are real, while $a_{\mu 4}$ and $a_{4\mu}$ are imaginary.

These transformations are continuous, being obtained from a series of infinitesimal transformations from unity, and are characterized by $\det(a_{\mu\nu}) = 1$. They do not change the direction of the time axis.

Such a formalism can be used to describe proper rotations of the physical system and boosts to a different velocity of the physical system with respect to the space-time coordinate system. The requirement of equivalence between different Lorentz frames leads directly to the laws of conservation of four momentum and angular momentum.

In addition, there are the improper Lorentz transformations of space inversion and time inversion, which are discontinuous, unlike the proper Lorentz transformations. These improper transformations each have the property that $\det(a_{\mu\nu}) = -1$. The transformed system under space inversion is

$$x_i' = -x_i \quad \text{where } i = 1, 2, 3$$

and under time inversion is

$$x_4' = -x_4$$

Clearly, $x_\mu' x_\mu' = x_\mu x_\mu$ for either case or for both taken together. It should be noted that the reversal of the space coordinates changes a right-handed coordinate system to a left-handed system, or vice versa. This implies that if there is a physical system in nature that has a definite handedness it is also possible to have a system of the opposite handedness obeying the same physical laws. Classically, this invariance under reflections leads to no conservation law in the way that invariance under rotations leads to the conservation of angular momentum. This is not so in quantum mechanics.

In a relativistic theory time inversion is *not* equivalent to an operation where every velocity is replaced by the opposite velocity so that the

position of a particle at $+t$ becomes the same as it was, without time inversion, at $-t$. This latter operation may properly be called velocity reversal or motion reversal, but in quantum mechanics or quantum field theory it is usually, perhaps illogically, called time reversal or Wigner time reversal. The laws of classical physics, apart from statistical effects such as frictional forces and electrical resistance, are invariant under time reversal where one has the normal motion in reverse.

Time inversion is actually the product of time reversal and charge conjugation, an operation where all particles are changed into their antiparticles. Charge conjugation is a relativistic quantum-mechanical concept only, and like space and time inversion, is a discontinuous operation. In the limit where a nonrelativistic approximation if valid, the operation of charge conjugation is not meaningful, so only space inversion and time reversal have physical meaning there.

In quantum mechanics, the interacting objects such as elementary particles, atoms, and nuclei are described by a wave function $\psi(\mathbf{r}, t)$ which is itself a function of the space-time coordinates. Here a symmetry property called *parity* is introduced to express the equivalence between left and right. If we denote by $\psi(-\mathbf{r}, t)$ the wave function in the space-reflected system, then

$$\psi(\mathbf{r}, t) = \eta_P \psi(-\mathbf{r}, t)$$

The space inversion quantum number η_P is called parity and has two eigenvalues ± 1. When $\eta_P = 1$ the wave function is said to have even parity and when $\eta_P = -1$ the wave function is said to have odd parity.

The supposition that any nondegenerate stationary quantum-mechanical state of an object, such as an atom or nucleus, will have a definite parity has led to very powerful conservation laws in the description of physical processes involving interactions of atoms or nuclei. The principle that the total parity of the system was conserved was regarded until recently as a fundamental principle of physics.

Stated formally, if P is a unitary operator that inverts the space coordinates through the origin such that

$$P \psi(\mathbf{r}, t) = \psi'(\mathbf{r}', t) = \eta_P \psi(-\mathbf{r}, t)$$

then the wave equation

$$H \psi(\mathbf{r}, t) = E \psi(\mathbf{r}, t)$$

can be transformed into

$$PHP^{-1} \psi'(\mathbf{r}', t) = E \psi'(\mathbf{r}', t).$$

The wave equation in the transformed coordinate system is unchanged provided that $PHP^{-1} = H$ or $PH - HP = 0$. The Heisenberg relation for a time rate of change of an operator P is

$$\frac{dP}{dt} = \frac{\hbar}{i} (HP - PH).$$

Therefore P is a constant of motion provided it commutes with the Hamiltonian operator. Operating twice with P on any wave function gives the same wave function, i.e., $P^2 = 1$, so the only possible eigenvalues of P are $+1$ and -1.

It is now well established that the strong interactions between elementary particles and the electromagnetic interactions are invariant under space inversion, so any nondegenerate energy eigenstate of an atom or nucleus will be also an eigenstate of the parity operator P. Similar statements can be made for the time reversal operator T and the charge conjugation operator C.

A quantum-mechanical system such as an atom or nucleus is usually described by wave functions in the angular momentum representation. The one-particle wave functions of the individual constituents are a product of an intrinsic part that may be also an eigenfunction of the spin angular momentum operator and an orbital part that is an eigenfunction of the orbital angular momentum operator ℓ_z. The latter eigenfunction is a spherical harmonic $Y_\ell^m(\vartheta, \varphi)$ having an eigenvalue $(-1)^\ell$ of the space inversion operator P. The total parity of the system is then the product of the parities of the constituents. The intrinsic parity of any elementary particle cannot be determined theoretically, nor can the eigenvalues of the time-reversal operator T and the charge-conjugation operator C, often called "time parity" and "charge parity."

For a meaningful and satisfactory formulation of charge conjugation and time reversal it is essential to consider the field operators in a quantized theory taking into account the ordering of operators and their commutation relations appropriate to Bose statistics for integer spins and Fermi statistics for half-integer spins. The wave function for a particle is the one-particle expectation value of the field operator. In Table 1, the transformation properties of various kinds of field operators are listed for the linear transformations P and C and the antilinear transformation T. These transformation properties are obtained by considering the invariance of the free-field equations of motion.

In Table 2 the transformation properties of various physical observables are listed. The transformed observables are independent of the values of η_P, η_T and η_C of the fields.

The phases η_P, η_T, η_C, etc. for those particles that can be created or destroyed can be found experimentally from the properties of their mutual interactions, assuming conservation of P, T, or C in these interactions. For example, the π^0 neutral meson decays into two photons; an analysis shows that its intrinsic parity

TABLE I. TRANSFORMATION OF INTRINSIC FIELDS UNDER SPACE INVERSION, TIME REVERSAL, AND CHARGE CONJUGATION

Intrinsic Field		P	T	C
Scalar	$\varphi(\mathbf{r}, t)$	$\eta_{P'}\varphi(-\mathbf{r}, t)$	$\eta_{T'}\varphi(\mathbf{r}, t)$	$\eta_{C'}\varphi^+(\mathbf{r}, t)$
Dirac spinor	$\psi(\mathbf{r}, t)$	$\eta_P\gamma_4\psi(-\mathbf{r}, t)$	$\eta_T\gamma_3\gamma_1\psi^*(\mathbf{r}, -t)$	$\eta_C\gamma_2\psi^*(\mathbf{r}, t)$
Four vector	$A_\mu(\mathbf{r}, t)$	$\eta_{P''}(-1)^{\delta\mu4}A_\mu(-\mathbf{r}, t)$	$\eta_{T''}(-1)^{\delta\mu4}A^*(\mathbf{r}, -t)$	$\eta_{C''}A_\mu^*(\mathbf{r}, t)$
Pseudoscalar	$\pi(\mathbf{r}, t)$	$\eta_{P'''}\pi(-\mathbf{r}, t)$	$\eta_{T'''}\pi^*(\mathbf{r}, -t)$	$\eta_{C'''}\pi^*(\mathbf{r}, t)$
Electric field	$\mathcal{E}(\mathbf{r}, t)$	$\eta_P\mathcal{E}(-\mathbf{r}, t)$	$-\eta_{T''}\mathcal{E}(\mathbf{r}, -t)$	$\eta_{C''}\mathcal{E}(\mathbf{r}, t)$
Magnetic field	$\mathcal{B}(\mathbf{r}, t)$	$-\eta_P\mathcal{B}(-\mathbf{r}, t)$	$\eta_{T''}\mathcal{B}(\mathbf{r}, -t)$	$\eta_{C''}\mathcal{B}(\mathbf{r}, t)$
Two-component neutrino	$\psi_{(\nu)}(\mathbf{r}, t)$	does not exist	$\eta_T\gamma_3\gamma_1\psi_{(\nu)}(\mathbf{r}, -t)$	does not exist

TABLE 2. TRANSFORMATION OF OBSERVABLES UNDER SPACE INVERSION, TIME REVERSAL, CHARGE CONJUGATION, AND TIME INVERSION

Observable	P	T	C	P_4
Position	x	−x	x	x	x
Time	t	t	−t	t	−t
Velocity	v	−v	−v	v	−v
Momentum	p	−p	−p	p	−p
Energy	E	E	E	E	E
Mass	m	m	m	m	m
Orbital angular momentum	ℓ	ℓ	$-\ell$	ℓ	$-\ell$
Spin angular momentum	s	s	−s	s	−s
Charge	e	e	e	−e	−e
Force	f	−f	f	f	f
Acceleration	a	−a	a	a	a

$\eta_{P'} = -1$ independently of the η_{P}'' for the electromagnetic field. The π^0, having odd parity and zero spin, is therefore a pseudo-scalar particle as opposed to a scalar particle having even parity and zero spin. The charged mesons $\pi^\pm$ also have $\eta_P = -1$ but charge conservation prevents their decay into two photons so that an interaction where the $\pi^\pm$ are created or absorbed through interactions with nucleons must be considered. The number of nucleons is conserved, so only the product $|\eta_P|^2 = 1$ is determined for the nucleons. Similarly, the electromagnetic field interacting with an electron current determines $\eta_P'' = -1$ for the electromagnetic field and $|\eta_P|^2 = 1$ for the electrons. In analogous ways all the phases for those particles with integer spin (bosons) can be found by experiment while those with half-integer spin (fermions) cannot and, indeed, are indeterminate. Although the intrinsic parity is indeterminate for fermions, the intrinsic parity for an antiparticle is opposite to that for a particle, in contrast to the boson case; e.g., the intrinsic parity is odd for e^+e^- in an S state and even for $\pi^+\pi^-$ in an S state. Considering the conservation of C, P, and angular momentum, J, the only allowed modes of annihilation of an electron-positron system are a singlet-S system decaying into two photons and a triplet-S system decaying into three photons.

Conventional usage assigns $\eta_P = +1$, i.e., positive parity, for fermions. Any fermion state of total angular momentum j can be specified by $\psi_{j\ell s}$ where $j = \ell + s$ and has total parity $(-1)^\ell$ by convention. Similar arguments define a "time parity" and a "charge parity" for each quantum-mechanical state. Likewise, the electromagnetic field can be expanded into multipoles in an angular momentum representation; however, here the intrinsic parity is specified. A photon of angular momentum J can have two possible parities, characterized by electric multipole radiation, EJ, with parity $(-1)^J$ and magnetic multipole radiation, MJ, with parity $(-1)^{J\pm1}$. These different types result from possible vector products of the intrinsic spin and the orbital angular momentum to give the same J.

Several examples of the use of parity conservation follow. Consider the interaction of the electromagnetic field with a quantum-mechanical system, a transition from an initial state of definite angular momentum, I_i, and parity, π_i, to a final state of definite I_f and π_f with the emission or absorption of electromagnetic radiation of angular momentum, J, and parity, π. The conservation of angular momentum and parity requires that

$$|I_i - I_f| \leqslant J \leqslant I_i + I_f$$

$$\pi_i\pi_f\pi = 1.$$

The possible transitions are shown in Table 3.

TABLE 3. ELECTROMAGNETIC MULTIPOLE SELECTION RULES

$\Pi_i\Pi_f$	ΔI 0 $I \neq 0$	1	2	3	4	5
+	M1	M1	E2	M3	E4	M5
−	E1	E1	M2	E3	M4	E5

In atoms, the predominant electromagnetic transitions are of electric dipole type. The characteristic lifetimes of the other multipoles are long compared to the typical atomic collision times, an alternative method of deexcitation. The first concept of the use of parity in atomic physics resulted from the experiments of Laporte showing that the initial and final states were always of opposite parity. This result is predicted in Table 3.

In nuclei, collision plays little role, so all electromagnetic multipoles can contribute, but usually the lowest-order multipole compatible with the conservation of angular momentum and parity predominates. These restrictions are known as angular momentum and parity selection rules.

The parity of the probability density $\psi^+\psi$ is always even. The expectation value of an operator θ is $\psi^+\theta\psi$ and vanishes if θ is an odd function under the parity operation. From the properties of the multipole operators, all odd electric multipole moments and all even magnetic multipole moments vanish. The restriction to nondegeneracy is essential and is satisfied for all atomic and nuclear systems. In molecular systems there are many observed static electric dipole moments. These usually result from the accidental degeneracy of coulomb wave functions with different orbital angular momenta.

One of the best evidences for the conservation of parity and invariance under time reversal in electromagnetic interactions is the lack of an electric dipole moment in the neutron.

A plane wave of definite linear momentum can be decomposed into a sum of degenerate, even and odd, angular momentum states and is not an eigenstate of parity. Localized wave packets can be obtained by superimposing many plane waves. Any macroscopic classical body, so described, will be degenerate in states of opposite parities and thus can have such properties as electric dipole moments.

In 1956 T. D. Lee and C. N. Yang, after a careful examination of experimental evidence, concluded that there is abundant evidence for parity conservation in strong and electromagnetic interactions but could not find any evidence for conservation in weak interactions, including nuclear beta decay. They suggested several experiments to test parity conservation in weak interactions.

An experiment performed by C. S. Wu, E. Ambler, R. W. Hayward, D. D. Hoppes, and R. P. Hudson in 1956 at the National Bureau of Standards and published in 1957 demonstrated that parity conservation was violated in nuclear beta decay. The experiment measured the angular distribution of beta and gamma radiation from radioactive ^{60}Co nuclei that had been cryogenically oriented. The angular distribution for the beta radiation obeyed a relation

$$W(\vartheta) = 1 + a\,\frac{\langle j\rangle}{|j|}\cdot\frac{p}{|p|}$$

where j is the nuclear spin and p the momentum of the beta particle. The angular distribution of the gamma radiation is a known function that depends only on even powers of $j\cdot k$, where k is the momentum of the photon, and on numerical factors depending on the spin of the nuclear states involved in the gamma transition.

A measurement of the gamma ray anisotropy, in turn, determines the amount of nuclear polarization $\langle j\rangle/|j|$. Inspection of Table 2 indicates that momenta change sign under the parity operation while the spins do not. Neither the momenta nor spins change sign under the charge conjugation operation. The beta ray angular distribution will change under the operations P or CP but not C, while the gamma ray angular distribution is unaltered under C, P, or CP. The measured beta ray angular distribution from ^{60}Co gave a value for the coefficient $a = -v/c$, apart from some small coulomb corrections. A subsequent experiment measuring the angular distribution of positrons from polarized ^{58}Co gave similar results but with the opposite sign for the coefficient a. The nonzero value for the coefficient a indicates that space inversion invariance is violated. The opposite signs for the coefficient a, depending on whether electrons or positrons are emitted, indicate that charge conjugation invariance is violated. An analysis shows that both the P and C violations are maximal but that the product CP is conserved.

In the beta-decay process we have a proton making a transition to a neutron with the emission of an electron and an antineutrino. One of the most satisfactory explanations of the violation of C and P in the beta-decay process can be ascribed to the properties of the neutrino. Rather than being a particle which can be described by the Dirac equation with a four-component wave function, its zero mass permits a modification of the Dirac equation to one that has a two-component wave function. This two-component description, although invariant under proper Lorentz transformations, is not invariant under C or P.

Experiment shows that the antineutrino emitted in beta decay is right-handed, i.e., its intrinsic spin is parallel to its momentum. Noninvariance under P implies that there is no left-handed antineutrino, while noninvariance under C implies that there is no right-handed neutrino. Invariance under CP implies the existence of a left-handed neutrino as well as the right-handed antineutrino. The symmetry of right- and left-handedness in matter is broken and replaced by a symmetry where matter has a characteristic handedness and antimatter the opposite handedness.

A left-handed, massless neutrino appears as a left-handed neutrino in all Lorentz frames which can be continuously transformed into one another. The postulate of space inversion symmetry allows us to infer the existence of a right-handed massless neutrino; however, there

is no reflection symmetry, so the existence of both right- and left-handed neutrinos in nature would be coincidental. Only if the neutrino had mass could the existence of both helicity states follow from the existence of a single state and from the properties of proper Lorentz transformations.

In all the weak-interaction phenomena, which includes all decays of the elementary particles, except the electromagnetic decays $\pi^0 \to 2\gamma$ and $\Sigma^0 \to \Lambda + \gamma$ that were experimentally investigated prior to 1964, the violation of P and C invariance and conservation of CP and T invariance was fully established. In 1964, experiments at the Brookhaven National Laboratory showed that the K° meson, which should decay only into three π-mesons according to CP invariance, decayed a small fraction of the time into two π-mesons, a process violating CP invariance. Vigorous experimental research since that time has fully confirmed this CP violation result, but no other process has been observed where CP is violated. There have been many theoretical attempts to account for this small CP violation, but no fully satisfactory explanation has emerged.

Whether or not there is invariance under the operations C, P, T, or CP individually, any local field theory must be invariant under the product CPT. This invariance is known as the CPT theorem. The combined operation is equivalent to the product of space inversion and time inversion and is often referred to as "strong reflection." This transformation in which $x_\mu{}' = -x_\mu$, although discontinuous, is characterized by $\det(a_{\mu\nu}) = 1$, and an equivalent transformation can be achieved by a proper Lorentz transformation, i.e., continuous rotations in space-time. At present only the CPT invariance remains unbroken experimentally.

RAYMOND W. HAYWARD

References

Sakurai, J. J., "Invariance Principles and Elementary Particles," Princeton, Princeton University Press, 1964.

DeBenedetti, Sergio, "Nuclear Interactions," New York, John Wiley & Sons, 1964.

Lee, T. D., and Yang, C. N., "Question of Parity Conservation in Weak Interactions," *Phys. Rev.*, **104**, 254 (1956).

Wu, C. S., Ambler, E., Hayward, R. W., Hoppes, D. D., and Hudson, R. P., "Experimental Test of Parity Conservation in Beta Decay," *Phys. Rev.*, **105**, 1413 (1957).

Christenson, J. H., Cronin, J. W., Fitch, V. L., and Turlay, R., "Evidence for the 2π Decay of the K_2° Meson," *Phys. Rev. Lett.*, **13**, 138 (1964).

Cross-references: ANTIPARTICLES, CONSERVATION LAWS AND SYMMETRY, ELECTROMAGNETIC THEORY, NEUTRINO, RELATIVITY, STRONG INTERACTIONS, WEAK INTERACTIONS.

PERIODIC LAW AND PERIODIC TABLE

When the chemical elements are compared in order of increasing atomic number, many of their physical and chemical properties are observed to vary periodically rather than randomly or steadily. This relationship, recognized empirically a century ago by de Chancourtois in France, Newlands in England, Lothar Meyer in Germany, and Mendeleev in Russia, is now known to be the logical and inevitable consequence of the fundamental periodicity of atomic structure. The familiar statment of the periodic law is this: "The properties of the chemical elements vary periodically with their atomic number." A more informative statement of this same law is: *The atomic structures of the chemical elements vary periodically with their atomic number; all physical and chemical properties that depend on atomic structure therefore tend also to vary periodically with atomic number.*

The periodicity of atomic structure (see ATOMIC PHYSICS) is described by quantum theory as developed through modern wave mechanics. Each successive electron, beginning with the first, that comes within the field of an atomic nucleus, occupies the most stable position available to it. The number of possible positions is limited by quantum restrictions which describe each position in terms of four quantum numbers, and by the Pauli exclusion principle that no two electrons within the same atom may have the same four quantum numbers. These electron positions, or energy levels, are grouped with respect to their average distance from the nucleus as "principal quantum levels or shells," designated by the "principal quantum number" $n = 1, 2, 3, 4, \cdots$, successive integral values increasing in order of increasing average distance from the nucleus. The total capacity of each shell can be expressed as $2n^2$, being 2 for $n = 1$, 8 for $n = 2$, 18 for $n = 3$, and 32 for $n = 4$; no higher level actually contains more than 32 electrons.

These total capacities can easily be accounted for by the several quantum number restrictions and the Pauli principle. Within each principal energy level are differently shaped regions called "orbitals," that can be occupied by electrons. The shape of each orbital is designated by the "orbital quantum number" l, which may only have integral values from 0 up to $n - 1$. The number of orbitals of each shape that can exist within a principal quantum level depends on the fact that an electron in an orbital is a charge in motion and therefore has magnetic properties which influence the orientation of the orbital in an external magnetic field. The possible orientations are designated by the "orbital magnetic quantum number" m_l, which may have values from 0 to plus or minus the orbital quantum number l. Thus when $n = 1$, l can only have the value 0, which means that only one orbital is possible, having orbital magnetic quantum

number 0. When $n = 2$, l can have the values 0 and 1. For the value 0, one orbital is possible, but when $l = 1$, m_l can have values 0, +1, and −1, corresponding to three orbitals. Four orbitals are therefore possible in the principal quantum level $n = 2$. When $n = 3$, the same kinds of four orbitals are possible, and in addition, l can equal 2. This gives five possible values, for m_l: 0, +1, +2, −1, and −2, corresponding to five more orbitals for a total of 9. When $n = 4$, the same kinds of 9 orbitals are possible, and in addition l can equal 3. This gives seven possible values for m_l: 0, +1, +2, +3, −1, −2, and −3, corresponding to 7 more orbitals for a total of 16. No principal quantum level uses more than 16 orbitals even though more are theoretically possible when $n = 5$ or more.

One additional property of an electron in an atom needs to be considered. This is its property as a magnet, irrespective of its orbital motion. This is designated by the "spin magnetic quantum number," which can have only the values $+\frac{1}{2}$ and $-\frac{1}{2}$. Since each orbital is uniquely specified by the first three quantum numbers, n, l, and m_l, the capacity of each orbital is thus limited to 2 electrons, and these only if, according to the Pauli principle, they are of opposed spins (differ in the fourth quantum number). The total capacity of each principal quantum level is therefore twice the number of orbitals within it, because this represents the total number of permissible combinations of four quantum numbers within that level. For example, the capacity of the $n = 4$ level is limited to 32 electrons by the fact that only 32 different combinations of the four quantum numbers are possible within that level; these electrons will occupy 16 orbitals.

The differently shaped orbitals having orbital quantum numbers $l = 0$, 1, 2, and 3 are commonly called s, p, d, and f orbitals. From the above discussion, it should be clear that within any principal quantum shell, there can be only one s orbital, three p orbitals, five d orbitals, and seven f orbitals. The p orbitals do not appear until $n = 2$, the d until $n = 3$, and the f until $n = 4$. Within any given principal quantum shell, the order of decreasing stability, and therefore the order of filling with electrons, is always s-p-d-f.

The periodicity of atomic structure arises from the recurrent filling of new outermost principal quantum levels, but it is complicated by the fact that, although the principal quantum levels represent very roughly the general order of magnitude of energy, there is considerable overlapping. This overlapping is such that the outermost shell of an isolated atom can never contain more than 8 electrons. In the building up of successively higher atomic numbers, electrons always find more stable positions, once a set of p orbitals in a given principal quantum level is filled, in the s orbital of the *next higher* principal quantum level rather than the d or-

bitals of the same principal quantum level. When this s orbital is filled, electrons then go into the underlying d orbitals until these are filled, before continuing to fill the outermost shell by entering its p orbitals. The building-up of the atoms of successive atomic numbers may be represented by the following sequence: $1s$, $2s$, $2p$, $3s$, $3p$, $4s$, $3d$, $4p$, $5s$, $4d$, $5p$, $6s$, $5d$, $4f$, $6p$, $7s$, $6d$, $5f$. *The periodicity of atomic structure thus consists of the recurrent filling of the outermost shell with from one to 8 electrons that corresponds to the steady increase in nuclear charge.*

A *period* is considered to begin with the first electron in a new principal quantum shell and to end with the completion of the octet in this outermost shell, except, of course, for the very first period, in which the outermost shell is filled to capacity with only two electrons. From the order of orbital filling given above, it should be apparent that periods so defined cannot be alike in length. The first period, consisting of hydrogen and helium, has only two elements. The second period, beginning with lithium (3) and ending with neon (10), contains 8 elements, as does the third period, which begins with sodium (11) and ends with argon (18). The fourth period begins with potassium (19), but following calcium (20), the filling of the outermost (fourth) shell octet is interrupted by the filling of the d orbitals in the *third* shell. Thus 10 more elements enter this period before filling of the outermost shell is resumed, making the total number of elements in this period 18. In the fifth period, the first two outermost electrons are added in rubidium (37) and strontium (38), but then this outer shell filling is interrupted by the filling of penultimate shell d orbitals, which again adds 10 elements before filling of the outermost shell is resumed; this period also contains 18 elements. The sixth period begins as before with two electrons in the outermost shell, but then there is an interruption at lanthanum (57) to begin filling the $5d$ orbitals. Here, however, occurs an additional interruption, in which 14 elements are formed through filling of the $4f$ orbitals, before the remaining $5d$ orbitals can be filled, and in turn before the outermost shell receives any more electrons. Consequently here it takes 32 elements to bring the outermost shell to 8 electrons and thus end the period. The seventh period is similar but incomplete. In principle it would end with element 118, but artificial element 105 is the highest in atomic number known at the time of writing.

These elements which represent interruptions in the filling of the outermost s and p orbital octet are called "transitional elements" (where d orbitals are being filled), and "inner transitional elements" (where f orbitals are being filled). This is to distinguish them from the other, "major group," elements in which underlying d or f orbitals are either completely empty or completely filled.

Physical properties of the elements that depend only on the electronic structure of the individual atom, such as the ionization potential and atomic radius, vary periodically with atomic number simply because of the recurrent filling of the outermost shell. Increasing the atomic number by increasing the nuclear charge while adding to the outermost shell electrons increases the attractive interaction between nucleus and outermost electrons more than it increases the repulsive forces among the electrons, with the result that the electronic cloud tends to be held closer (smaller radius) and more tightly (higher ionization energy), the more outermost shell electrons there are. For example, carbon (6) with half-filled octet has radius and ionization energy intermediate between the larger lithium (3) atoms with low ionization energy and the smaller fluorine (9) atoms with high ionization energy. Similar but smaller effects are observable for the addition of d or f electrons to underlying shells.

The bonding properties of elements also depend on the electronic structure of the individual atom and therefore likewise vary periodically. For example, each period (except the first) begins with an alkali metal, lithium (3), sodium (11), potassium (19), rubidium (37),

MAJOR GROUPS

No.	M 1	M 2	M 2'	M 3	M 4	M 5	M 6	M 7	M 8
1				H 1					He 2
2	Li 3	Be 4		B 5	C 6	N 7	O 8	F 9	Ne 10
3	Na 11	Mg 12		Al 13	Si 14	P 15	S 16	Cl 17	Ar 18
4	K 19	Ca	Zn	Ga 31	Ge 32	As 33	Se 34	Br 35	Kr 36
5	Rb 37	Sr	Cd	In 49	Sn 50	Sb 51	Te 52	I 53	Xe 54
6	Cs 55	Ba	Hg	Tl 81	Pb 82	Bi 83	Po 84	At 85	Rn 86
7	Fr 87	Ra							

TRANSITION

	T 3	T 4	T 5	T 6	T 7	T 8	T 9	T 10	T 11
4	Sc 21	Ti 22	V 23	Cr 24	Mn 25	Fe 26	Co 27	Ni 28	Cu 29
5	Y 39	Zr 40	Nb 41	Mo 42	Tc 43	Ru 44	Rh 45	Pd 46	Ag 47
6	La 57 | Lu	Hf 72	Ta 73	W 74	Re 75	Os 76	Ir 77	Pt 78	Au 79
7	Ac 89 | Lr	104	105	106	107	108	109	110	111

INNER TRANSITION

6	Ce 58	Pr 59	Nd 60	Pm 61	Sm 62	Eu 63	Gd 64	Tb 65	Dy 66	Ho 67	Er 68	Tm 69	Yb 70
7	Th 90	Pa 91	U 92	Np 93	Pu 94	Am 95	Cm 96	Bk 97	Cf 98	Es 99	Fm 100	Md 101	No 102

COMPLETE LONG FORM

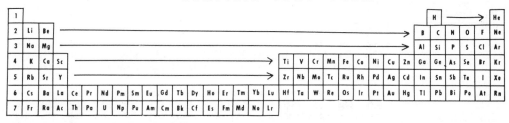

FIG. 1. Periodic chart of the chemical elements (reprinted from *J. Chem. Educ.*, 188 (1964); copyright 1964 by Division of Chemical Education, American Chemical Society, and reprinted by permission of the copyright owner, with modifications by the author).

cesium (55), and francium (87), all of which show similar metallic bonding, crystallizing in a body-centered cubic lattice. Each has but one outermost electron per atom and can therefore form but one covalent bond. Each is very low in electronegativity and thus tends to become highly positive when bonded to another element. Crossing each period the elements become less metallic, higher in electronegativity, and able to form a greater number of bonds until limited by the number of outer shell vacancies rather than the number of electrons. The halogens, fluorine (9), chlorine (17), bromine (35), iodine (53), and astatine (85), each of which is next to the end of its period, are all nonmetals, highest of their respective periods in electronegativity and thus tending to become highly negative when bonded to other elements. Having seven outermost electrons, each has but one vacancy, permitting but one covalent bond.

Physical properties of the elements that are of greatest interest are usually properties that depend indirectly on the atomic structure but directly on the nature of the aggregate of atoms which results from the atomic structure. Such properties are melting point, density, and volatility. They may tend to vary periodically, but the periodicity is not necessarily consistent or even evident, because of abrupt differences in the type of poly-atomic aggregate. For example, the identical atoms of carbon may form graph-

ite or diamond, depending on the kind of bonding, with entirely different properties resulting. Nitrogen follows carbon in atomic number, but because it forms N_2 molecules instead of giant three-dimensional structures like diamond or graphite, it is a gas with physical properties strikingly different from those of either form of carbon.

Among the most useful applications of the periodic law is to an understanding of the differences among compounds, whose properties also vary in a periodic manner. For example, oxides of elements at the beginnings of periods tend to be very stable, high-melting, nonvolatile solids of strongly basic character and practically no oxidizing power. Oxide properties change progressively across each period until toward the end the oxides tend to be unstable, low-melting, volatile compounds, acidic in nature and of high oxidizing power. Such periodicity is recognizable throughout a very large part of chemistry.

In order to erect a framework upon which the myriad facts that accord with the Periodic Law can be organized, the chemical elements can be arranged in an orderly manner called a "periodic table." Any such arrangement[1] can be satisfactory if it organizes the elements in some order of increasing atomic number, showing the separate periods and at the same time grouping elements of greatest similarity together.

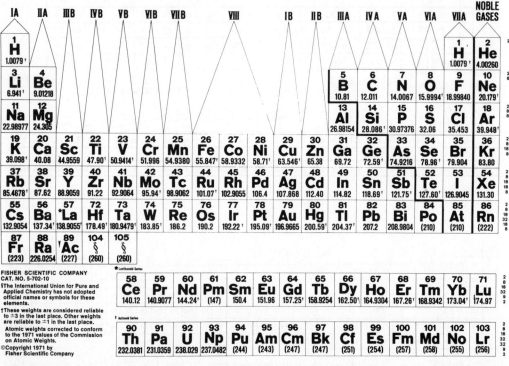

FIG. 2. Periodic chart of the elements (reproduced with permission of copyright owner, Fisher Scientific Company).

In Fig. 1 is shown a modern version of the periodic table[2], together with the "long form." Figure 2 shows the "long form" as currently most widely used. From left to right across the table are the "periods," representing the elements in order of successively increasing atomic number and therefore progressive change in atomic strucutre. Across the period, the properties of the elements and their compounds tend to change from one extreme to the opposite. From top to bottom the periods are placed so that the most similar elements are grouped together. A distinction (shown by a physical separation) is made between "major groups" and "transitional groups" because of the bonding dissimilarities originating in the availability in the transitional elements of underlying d orbitals that are not available in the major group elements. In older tables, major groups are usually, although inconsistently, designated as "A" and transitional groups as "B." In Fig. 1, the designations are consistently "M" (major) and "T" (transitional). But whether in the major group or the transitional group, the elements are arranged vertically on the basis of similarity in electronic configuration, which is then reflected in similarities in the physical and chemical properties of the elements and their compounds.

No amount of organization or correlation will ever alter the fact that each chemical element is an individual and unique, nor will the properties of any element be changed one iota by placing that element in any special position in a periodic table. Nevertheless, there is enough consistency to the structure and behavior of atoms to make any reasonable form of the periodic table an extremely useful framework upon which to organize and correlate an enormous quantity of chemical information[3]. The periodic law is truly one of the great generalizations of science.

R. T. SANDERSON

References

1. Mazurs, E., "Types of Graphic Representation of the Periodic System of Chemical Elements," published by the author, 6 S. Madison Ave., La Grange, Ill. 1957.
2. Sanderson, R. T., *J. Chem. Educ.*, **41**, 187 (1964).
3. Sanderson, R. T., "Inorganic Chemistry," New York, Van Nostrand Reinhold, 1967.

Cross-references: ATOMIC PHYSICS; ELECTRON; ELEMENTS, CHEMICAL; ISOTOPES; QUANTUM THEORY; TRANSURANIUM ELEMENTS.

PHASE RULE

The phase rule is a general equation $F = n - r - 2$, stating the conditions of thermodynamic equilibrium in a system of chemical reactants. The number of degrees of freedom or variance

(F) allowed in a given heterogeneous system may be examined by analysis or observation and plotted on a graph by proper choice of the components (n), the phases (r), and the independently variable factors of temperature and pressure.

Josiah Willard Gibbs propounded the rule about 1877, and H. W. B. Roozeboom about 1890 began pioneering in specific cases. This rule has been an important instrument in the study of stability and metastability in geology, physics, metallurgy, ceramics, mineralogy, and engineering (e.g., in the exploitation of the salt deposits at Stassfurt, Germany, and Searles Lake, California, in the development of alloys, solid-state devices, and large crystals). Its use in the sophistication of techniques continues to expand; as an example, the calculation of reactions from basic structural data by computer techniques.

A phase is a homogeneous, physically distinct and mechanically separable portion of a system. H_2O has the three phases: water, vapor and ice. Each crystal form present is a phase. The relative amounts of each phase do not affect the EQUILIBRIUM.

The one-component system, water-vapor-solid, is unary. The components of a system are the smallest number of independently variable constituents by means of which the composition of each phase taking part in the equilibrium can be expressed in the form of a chemical equation.

With the components fixed in a system, variance—the degrees of freedom (F)—depends on the number of phases present. If water vapor alone is present, the system is bivariant since both temperature and pressure can vary within limits without affecting the number of phases; but if a second phase, liquid water, is present, the system is univariant and if either the temperature or pressure of the system in equilibrium is set, the other is automatically fixed as long as a second phase is present. A third phase, ice, makes the system invariant (the triple point), and any change in temperature or pressure, if maintained, results in the disappearance of one phase. Addition of another component forms a binary system, one degree of freedom is added, and the system is univariant until a fourth phase appears and the system becomes invariant (the quadruple point).

Schematic phase equilibrium diagrams outline experimental observations of physical and chemical changes in the system as the conditions of temperature, pressure and composition are varied. For unary systems, the diagram has two dimensions, for binary systems, three, and for ternary systems, four, etc. Binary systems are easily plotted with pressure or temperature constant, while ternary systems may be treated similarly as condensed systems with both constant if the vapor pressure is less than atmospheric. This added restriction reduces the variance by one, and at constant temperature,

composition relationships may be plotted on a triangular diagram. Quarternary or quinary systems and ternary systems above atmospheric pressure may be treated by projections of surfaces of thermodynamic stability, but more complex systems require a mathematical approach.

The simple one-component system, water, plotted with rectangular coordinates, i.e., pressure and temperature, shows a variety of concepts which may be extended to more complex systems (see Fig. 1 in STATES OF MATTER). Each area in the diagram is a bivariant, one-phase state. Each curve separating the areas is a univariant, two-phase state showing the conditions under which a transition of the phase occurs. These are also called "indifferent phase reactions," where the amount of the phases may vary and are contrasted with "invariant equilibrium," where the degree of freedom is zero. The fusion curve for the equilibria between the solid phase and the liquid phase, the sublimation curve for solid and vapor, and the vaporization curve for liquid and vapor meet at the triple point. The three distinct phases differ in all properties except chemical potential. The end of the vaporization curve is a singular point, the critical point where liquid and vapor become identical, a restriction which reduces the variance by one so that F becomes zero.

In a binary (or higher) system, a liquidus is a curve representing the composition of the equilibrium liquid phase and a solidus represents the composition of the solid phase. The conjugate vapor phase is represented by a vaporous with tie-lines or conodes to the liquidus or solidus points in equilibrium. A minimum point for the existence of a liquid is the eutectic, sometimes (in an aqueous system) called the cryohydric point. In a ternary system the eutectics of three binary systems initiate curves leading to a ternary eutectic. If two liquids form a miscibility gap in the system, multiple quadruple points are possible. At a peritectic, a phase transition occurs at other than a minimum, i.e., one solid melts to another solid and a liquid. The solid may be a compound or a solid solution (mixed crystals) in which the composition of the solid varies with relative proportion of components and is shown by the solidus. A congruent melting point is a maximum in its curve, i.e., the solid melts to a liquid of the same composition. Where two phases become identical in composition, an indifferent or critical point exists. Where two conjugate phases become identical, the point may also be called a consolute point.

JOHN H. WILLS

References

Ricci, John E., "The Phase Rule and Heterogeneous Equilibrium," New York, Van Nostrand Reinhold, 1951.

Levin, E. M., McMurdie, H. F., and Hall, F. P.,

"Phase Diagrams for Ceramists," Columbus, Ohio, The American Ceramic Society, 1956, 1959.

Masing, G., "Ternary Systems," New York, Van Nostrand Reinhold, 1944.

Wetmore, F. E. W., and LeRoy, D. J., "Principles of Phase Equilibria," New York, McGraw-Hill Book Co., 1951.

Haase, R., and Schönert, H. (translated by E. S. Halberstadt), "Solid-Liquid Equilibrium," Topic 13, Vol. 1 of "International Encyclopedia of Physical Chemistry and Chemical Physics," New York, Pergamon Press, 1969.

Refractory Materials Series, J. L. Margrave, Editor, Volume 4, Kaufman, L. K., and Bernstein, H., "Computer Calculation of Phase Diagrams," New York, Academic Press, 1970. Volume 6, Alper, A.M., "Phase Diagrams: Materials, Science and Technology" (3 volumes), New York, Academic Press, 1970.

Cross-references: EQUILIBRIUM STATES OF MATTER, THERMODYNAMICS.

PHONONS

Many of the thermal and vibrational properties of solids can be explained by considering the material to be a volume made up of a gas of particles called phonons. This particle description is a method of taking into account the actual motion of the atoms and molecules in the solid. Since each atom possesses energy due to its thermal environment, and since there are forces between the atoms which keep the solid together, each atom tends to oscillate about its equilibrium position. The formal mathematical development, obtained through solving the equations of motion of the array of individual atoms and molecules, indicates that the thermal energy of the solid is contained in certain combinations of the particle vibrations which are equivalent to standing elastic waves in the sample and are called normal modes. Each normal mode contains a number of discreet quanta of energy $E = \hbar\omega$, where ω is the frequency of the mode (or wave) and $\hbar$ is Planck's constant divided by 2π. Each of these quanta is called a phonon (in analogy with the light quanta or photon whose energy-frequency relationship is identical). The remaining discussion can be best understood by considering the phonons only as particles, each having an energy $E = \hbar\omega$, a momentum q, and a velocity $v = \partial\omega/\partial q \sim \omega/q$ (see QUANTUM THEORY).

Analogous to the energy levels of electrons in a solid, phonons can have only certain allowed energies. A typical phonon spectrum, which relates the energy of the phonons to their momentum (or wave vector), is shown in Fig. 1. In this Figure, the phonon energy is $\hbar\omega$ and the momentum (or wave vector) is q. There are $3N$ discreet values of q associated with a lattice containing N particles, and the maximum value of q is of the order of $(\pi/a)(\sim 10^8 \mathrm{cm}^{-1})$ where

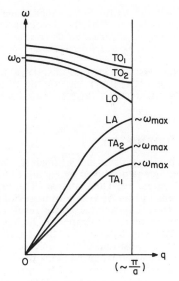

FIG. 1. Phonon spectrum.

a^3 is the volume of a unit cell. (A unit cell is the approximate volume taken up by each molecule of the crystal.) Typical values of the points marked ω_{max} are 10^{12} to 10^{13} radians/sec.

The two types of phonon branches shown in Fig. 1 (A and O), are the acoustical branch ($\omega = 0$ at $q = 0$) and the optical branch. The motion of the atoms which is represented by the acoustical branch is similar to that which is obtained when a sound wave is propagated in the crystal. The optical branch represents motion in which the center of mass of the different atoms in a unit cell (or a molecule) remains fixed, but the atoms in the molecule move relative to each other. This type of motion is often excited by an electric field or a light wave, hence the name optical phonon.

Each branch is further divided into longitudinal (L) and transverse (T) modes, again in analogy with propagation of sound waves. In the longitudinal branch, the atoms vibrate in the same direction that the phonon moves, while in the transverse branches, the atoms vibrate perpendicular to the phonon motion. It should be noted that there is a forbidden energy gap between LA and LO which indicates that phonons having these frequencies do not exist in the material.

Several equations which represent the energy content of the phonon modes complete the description. The total energy of each mode q is quantized according to

$$E_q = n_q \hbar \omega_q \qquad (1)$$

where n_q is the number of quanta excited at temperature T with frequency ω_q and is given by

$$n_q = [\exp (\hbar \omega_q / kT) - 1]^{-1} \qquad (2)$$

where k is Boltzmann's constant. By combining Eq. (1) and (2), we note that at any temperature T, most of the phonons have an energy of about kT, as long as $kT/\hbar < (\omega_q)_{max}$. The value of $T = (\hbar \omega_q)_{max}/k$ is approximately θ_D, the Debye temperature.

For completeness, a density term $p_j/(\omega)$ should be defined. This represents the fraction of phonons of the jth branch which have frequencies between ω and $\omega + d\omega$. However, the form of the distribution is complicated, depending on the symmetry of the lattice and the strength of the restoring forces between atoms. For low-frequency acoustical phonons, in a three-dimensional lattice,

$$p_j(\omega) \propto \omega^2 d\omega \qquad (3)$$

In any process in which phonons interact with any other particles (or excitations) in the solid, for example electrons, photons, or neutrons, the normal conservation laws must be satisfied. That is, total energy and total momentum must be unchanged. Thus if a phonon is destroyed in an interaction with an electron, the electron must gain an amount of energy $\hbar \omega$ and momentum q which the phonon originally had.

Phonon Interactions and Transport Many of the thermal properties of solids which are due to the lattice, as distinguished from the electrons, can be obtained using the energy of Eq. (1) in the normal thermodynamic relations. For example, the specific heat C_q due to all the phonons with momentum q is given by

$$C_q = \frac{\partial E_q}{\partial T} = k \left(\frac{\hbar \omega}{kT}\right)^2 \frac{e^{\hbar \omega / kT}}{(e^{\hbar \omega / kT} - 1)^2} \qquad (4)$$

To obtain the total specific heat, we simply add up the contributions from each mode q. This sum is most easily obtained if we know the distribution function $p_j(\omega)$ and the value of $(\omega_q)_{max}$. For example, the Debye theory uses approximate expressions for these quantities and obtains

$$C = 9Nk(T/\theta_D)^3 \int_0^{\theta_D/T} \frac{x^4 e^x dx}{(e^x - 1)^2} \qquad (5)$$

where N is the number of atoms per unit volume.

To obtain the heat conductivity in solids, the transport of energy by means of the phonons must be considered. Phonons can be very efficient heat carriers, as indicated by the fact that the maximum thermal conductivity due to electrons in copper is about 50 watts/cm deg as compared to about 200 watts/cm deg due to phonons in pure single crystal sapphire, in which all the heat is carried by phonons.

The heat conducted by the phonons of momentum q is given approximately by

$$\kappa_q \approx \frac{1}{3} C_q v_q l_q. \qquad (6)$$

The total thermal conductivity is obtained by summing the values of κ_q over all the possible values of q. The mean free path l_q is a measure of how far a phonon travels before it interacts, or is scattered. Phonons can be scattered by impurities and imperfections, by electrons, by other phonons and by the walls of the solid. The mean free path for any of these processes can be determined, to some extent, by examining the temperature dependence of the thermal conductivity.

Another method of investigating the scattering of phonons is through the investigation of the attenuation of very high-frequency sound waves in solids. It is possible to generate "ultrasonic" sound waves with frequencies in excess of 10^9 Hz. These correspond to the lowest values of ω shown in Fig. 1 and would be, for example, the majority of the phonons if the sample were held at 0.5 K. In the near future these ultrasonic frequencies will be increased, and more of the phonon spectrum will be investigated using this tool.

The Determination of the Phonon Spectra The actual values for the ω-vs-q curves which make up the phonon spectrum are obtained in a variety of ways. The value ω_0 of the $q = 0$ optical phonon is related to the infrared Reststrahl frequency. The low q values for the acoustic branches can be obtained by measuring the velocity of transverse and longitudinal sound waves in solids. The values of ω near the zone boundaries ($q \approx \pi/a$) can often be obtained from infrared absorption experiments. However, the most important tool for elucidating the details of the phonon spectrum has been slow neutron scattering. By examining the intensity and position of a scattered neutron beam, a large portion of the ω-vs-q curves can be mapped. Once the ω-vs-q curves have been obtained for a solid, it is possible by mathematical analysis to examine the nature and the magnitude of the forces between the atoms of that particular material. This has been done for a number of materials.

The phonon is of importance to a great many phenomena; electron mobility, optical absorption. electron spin resonance, electron tunneling, and superconductivity are a few. At the same time, the phonon spectrum represents a detailed picture of the forces which hold solids together. Thus it is clear why the phonon has been and will continue to be of fundamental importance in solid-state physics.

M. G. HOLLAND

References

Ziman, J., "Electrons and Phonons," Oxford, The Clarendon Press, 1960.

Kittel, C., "Introduction to Solid State Physics," New York, John Wiley & Sons, 1956.

Klemens, P. G., "Thermal Conductivity and Lattice Vibrational Modes," in Seitz, F., and Turnbull, D., Eds., "Solid State Physics," Vol. 7, p. 1, New York, Academic Press, 1958.

Shull, C. G., and Wollan, E. O., "Applications of Neutron Diffraction to Solid State Problems," in Seitz, F., and Turnbull, D., Eds., "Solid State Physics," Vol. 2, p. 137, New York, Academic Press, 1956.

Cross-references: CRYSTALLOGRAPHY, ELECTRON, HEAT CAPACITY, HEAT TRANSFER, NEUTRON, PHOTON, QUANTUM THEORY, ULTRASONICS.

PHOTOCHEMISTRY*

Photochemistry deals in its broadest sense with the phenomena produced by energy-rich photoexcited states.[1,2,3] These states, when produced by the absorption of visible or ultraviolet light, are electronically excited states resulting from the transfer of an electron to a higher energy level. The time required for this transfer is so short that the positions of the nuclei of the atoms involved remain unchanged. This primary act is followed by the movement of the nuclei to new equilibrium positions and by a great many different kinds of processes such as fluorescence, phosphorescence, degradation of the absorbed energy to heat, the intra- or intermolecular transfer of the electronic energy, or of electrons, protons or hydrogen atoms, or the breaking apart of the energy rich excited species, such as Cl_2 into Cl atoms, O_3 into O_2 and O, the production of a wide variety of ions, radicals, new molecules or chemical reactions. Such reactions are the natural photosynthetic process, photography, the electron transfer reaction in which gaseous hydrogen and oxygen are produced from water by light absorbed by cerium ions in water, photochromism as in the ortho-nitrotoluenes, *cis* to *trans* and *trans* to *cis* isomerization as in the case of the thioindigos, anils and azo compounds, shifting of the positions of double bonds as occurs when ergosterol is converted into Vitamin D and addition reactions to multiple bonds.

The unit of light energy most useful in photochemistry is the photon, $\epsilon = hc/\lambda$, where h is Planck's constant (6.5×10^{-27} erg sec), c is the velocity of light (3×10^{10} cm/sec) and λ is the wavelength of the light, e.g., 6700Å or 6700×10^{-8} cm for the most intense light reaching the earth from the sun. Another photochemical unit of light energy is the einstein which is the energy of 6×10^{23} or one mole, N, of light quanta. Thus one einstein of red light is $N\epsilon = Nhc/\lambda = 6 \times 10^{23} \times 6.5 \times 10^{-27} \times 3 \times 10^{10}/6700 \times 10^{-8} = 17.5 \times 10^{11}$ ergs or $17.5 \times 10^{11}/4.186 \times 10^7 = 42\ 000$ calories or $42\ 000/23\ 024 = 1.8$ eV. This amount of energy is greater than the energy of activation required to initiate most thermal reactions.

*This is a publication from a member of the Faculty of Chemistry of Emmanuel College, Boston, Massachusetts 02115 and the Massachusetts Institute of Technology, Cambridge, Massachusetts 02139.

In a narrower sense, photochemistry deals only with the chemical reactions brought about by the absorbed light. This includes studies of the kinetics and mechanisms of reactions such as the mechanism of the reaction between H_2 and Cl_2 to produce HCl. In this case only the Cl_2 molecules absorb visible light and the reaction proceeds mainly as follows:

$$Cl_2 + light = 2Cl, \text{ chain initiating reaction} \quad (1)$$

$$Cl + H_2 = HCl + H, \text{ chain propagating reaction} \quad (2)$$

$$H + Cl_2 = HCl + Cl, \text{ chain propagating reaction} \quad (3)$$

$$X + X + M = X_2 + M, \text{ chain terminating reaction} \quad (4)$$

where X is either H or Cl, and M is any third body. The net quantum yield for this chain reaction has been found under favorable conditions to be over one million moles of HCl produced per mole of visible light quanta absorbed by the chlorine molecules.

The natural photosynthetic process converts solar energy into energy available in storage for man's use. One part of the process is the oxidation of water to molecular oxygen by the over-all half reaction:

$$2H_2O(1) = O_2 + 4H^+ + 4e^- \quad (5)$$

The other part of the process is the reduction of carbon dioxide to carbohydrate by the over-all half reaction:

$$4e^- + 4H^+ + CO_2(g) = CH_2O + H_2O(1) \quad (6)$$

The sum of reactions (5) and (6) is the charge and energy transfer process:

$$H_2O(1) + CO_2(g) = CH_2O + O_2 \quad (7)$$

which is brought about by sunlight absorbed neither by the water nor the carbon dioxide but by the green substance, chlorophyll, in the proper watery environment.

The production of heat and light by the burning of wood in oxygen is the reverse of reaction (7). It thus becomes apparent that the energy produced in this way came originally from the sunlight which produced reaction (7) and thereby converted solar energy into energy available in storage for man's use.

The path of oxygen in the natural photosynthetic process has been followed by the use of the oxygen isotope of mass 18 and the path of carbon by the use of the radioactive isotope of mass 14. Very little is known, however, about the way the light absorbed by the chlorophyll brings about the reaction. Studies designed for this purpose would require the identification of all the light-absorbed species, including the transient intermediates, and their absorption spectra and absorbances.

Another photochemical process converting solar energy into chemical energy available in storage for man's use is the cerium-catalyzed conversion of water into gaseous hydrogen and oxygen by sunlight absorbed by certain selected cerous, CeIII, and ceric, CeIV, species in solution in the water. Here the energy storage step is the photochemical production of hydrogen accompanying the conversion of CeIII into CeIV. The key intermediate producing hydrogen is presumably the hydrated hydrogen molecule ions, H_2^+, which thermally abstracts an electron from CeIII to produce CeIV. The H_2^+ is formed by the hydrated CeIII species $CeOH_3^{+4}$.

The key intermediate producing oxygen is presumably H_2O_2, which is formed by the hydrated CeIV species, $Ce(OH)_2Ce^{+6}$, via the production of OH within the ceric dimer. The H_2O_2 produces O_2 thermally via HO_2 by the transfer of electrons to the remaining CeIV.

One key to the elucidation of photochemical reactions is the determination of net quantum yields based on the amount of the measured reaction produced by light of nearly uniform intensity absorbed by the species which thereby initiated the measured reaction in an adequately mixed system under nearly equilibrium conditions. Especially helpful is the study of the influence upon the net yields of such variables as light intensity, temperature and the absolute and relative concentrations of the components of the system.

Net quantum yields are usually calculated from gross quantum yields which are based on the amounts of the measured effect and light absorbed by the entire system and on the absorption spectra, absorbances and concentrations of the different light absorbing species. Net quantum yields are evaluated most easily when the light is monochromatic, i.e., when the light consists of a narrow band of wavelengths such as the light of 2537Å isolated from a low-pressure mercury vapor lamp.[4,8] This light, however, needs to be sufficiently intense to produce an appropriate amount of reaction in a convenient length of time.

Another key to the elucidation of photochemical reactions is the employment of flash photolysis made possible by apparatus consisting of a flash source and auxiliary apparatus for studying light absorbing intermediates of lifetimes as short as a few microseconds.[6,7]

LAWRENCE J. HEIDT

References

There are now several excellent text books on photochemical reactions:

1. Craig, R. A., "The Upper Atmosphere, Meteorology and Physics," New York, Academic Press, 1965.
2. Calvert, J. G., and Pitts, J. N., Jr., "Photochemistry," New York, John Wiley & Sons, Inc., 1967.

3. Brown, G. H., Ed., "Photochromism," New York, Wiley-Interscience, 1971.

See also:

4. Heidt and Boyles, *J. Am. Chem. Soc.* **73**, 5728 (1951).
5. Heidt and McMillan, *ibid*, **76**, 2135 (1954).
6. Heidt, "The Path of Oxygen from Water to O_2," *J. Chem. Ed.*, **43**, 623 (1966).
7. Landi, Heidt, "Flash Photolysis etc." *J. Phys. Chem.* **73**, 2361 (1969).
8. Tregay, Middleton, Jr., and Heidt, *J. Phys. Chem.*, **74**, 1876 (1970).
9. Napoli, Mahaney, and Heidt, *Phys. Chem. Div. Meeting*, *Am. Chem. Soc. Boston* (April 1972) and International Meeting Photochem. and Photobiology Congress, Bochum, Germany (Aug. 1972).

Cross-references: PHOTOSYNTHESIS, RADIATION CHEMISTRY.

PHOTOCONDUCTIVITY

Photoconductivity is the increase in electrical conductivity which occurs in a nonmetallic solid when it is exposed to electromagnetic radiation. The conductivity increase is due to the additional free carriers which are generated when photon energies are absorbed in electronic transitions. The rate at which free carriers are generated and the length of time they persist in conducting states (lifetime) determines the amount of conductivity change.

The absorption transitions and, therefore, the photoconductivity resulting from them are termed intrinsic or extrinsic according to the energy states involved. When the photon energy is at least equal to the forbidden energy gap $(hc/\lambda \geqslant E_g)$, electrons may be excited from the filled band to the conduction band. This intrinsic absorption transition produces an electron-hole pair, an electron in the conduction band and a hole in the valence band. Free carriers may be produced at lower photon energies when there are impurities or other crystal defects which give rise to energy states in the forbidden gap. Such a state is at an energy $E_c - E$ below the conduction band and $E - E_v$ above the valence band. Depending on whether the state is or is not occupied by an electron, a photon of appropriate energy may produce a transition from the state to the conduction band $(hc/\lambda \geqslant E_c - E)$ or from the valence band to the impurity state $(hc/\lambda \geqslant E - E_v)$. The former transition produces a free electron and the latter a free hole.

The carriers so generated are "excess" carriers, i.e., in excess of the number of carriers present in the solid in thermal equilibrium. In equilibrium, in the absence of light, the rate at which free carriers are generated by thermal processes and the rate at which they return to nonconducting ground states (recombination rate) are equal. The density of free carriers remains constant in time, aside from statistical fluctuations. The production of free carriers by absorption of

radiation amounts to an increase in the total generation rate of free carriers, unbalancing the equilibrium. The recombination rate is a function of free-carrier density, so it will also increase as the free-carrier density increases. Thus, under steady illumination, there will be a new equilibrium (steady-state) at a new carrier density $(n_0 + \Delta n)$, at which the rate of generation of carriers due to absorption (G) is equaled by the increase in the recombination rate (ΔU) due to the increased carrier density (Δn).

The rate of change of excess carrier concentration is described by the equation

$$\frac{d \Delta n}{dt} = G - \frac{\Delta n}{\tau} = G - \Delta U \qquad (1)$$

in which the parameter τ is the lifetime of excess carriers. In the steady state, $d \Delta n/dt = 0$ and $\tau = \Delta n/G$. τ may be thought of as the average length of time that an excess carrier remains in a conducting state between the time that it is generated and the time that it recombines. In general τ is not independent of Δn so ΔU is not always simply proportional to Δn. The dependence of τ on Δn is a property of the recombination mechanism. There are a variety of possible recombination mechanisms. Recombination may occur by a direct recombination of a free electron and a free hole or indirectly through a localized energy level (recombination center) which captures a hole and then an electron or vice-versa. In extrinsic photoconduction, the localized energy state from which the free carrier was excited is, in effect, an immobilized carrier of the opposite type. In this case the recombination kinetics are essentially the same as for direct recombination. Several recombination processes may operate simultaneously. However, in most cases one will have the highest recombination rate and will dominate.

Direct Recombination In direct recombination the recombination rate is the same for electrons and holes since they recombine in a single process. The total rate is given by

$$U = C(n_0 + \Delta n)(p_0 + \Delta p) \qquad (2)$$

where C is the capture probability, n_0 and p_0 are the equilibrium densities of electrons and holes, and Δn and Δp are the excess carrier densities. Δn is equal to Δp since electrons and holes are generated and recombine in pairs. The equilibrium recombination rate is Cn_0p_0 so the excess recombination rate is

$$\Delta U = C(n_0 + p_0 + \Delta n)\Delta n \qquad (3)$$

and the lifetime of excess carriers is

$$\tau = [C(n_0 + p_0 + \Delta n)]^{-1} \qquad (4)$$

For small signals τ is independent of Δn. However, when Δn is comparable with $(n_0 + p_0)$, this is no longer the case. In insulators (where $n_0 + p_0$ is very small) or for large signals, $\Delta n \gg n_0 + p_0$. This leads to the steady-state

relation

$$\Delta n = G\tau = \sqrt{G/C} \qquad (5)$$

Recombination Centers and Traps Indirect recombination through localized centers requires separate equations for electrons and holes, since the recombination rates for electrons and holes are not necessarily equal except in steady state. There are four transitions involved in the kinetics of localized centers: (1) A filled center may capture a hole from the valence band, or (2) the electron may be thermally excited to the conduction band; (3) an empty center may capture an electron from the conduction band, or (4) the trapped hole may be excited to the valence band. The rate of capture of electrons by localized centers is given by $C(1 - f)Nn$ where C is the capture probability of the empty centers for electrons, N is the density of centers, f is the fraction of centers already occupied by electrons, and n is the electron density. The product $(CN)^{-1} = \tau_{n0}$ is the characteristic lifetime due to capture by that center when n is the minority carrier in p-type material. The rate of thermal excitation from the centers is given by $CfNN_c \exp(- E/kT)$, where N_c is the effective density of states in the conduction band and E is the thermal ionization energy for the centers. With $N_c \exp(- E/kT) = n'$, the total capture rate for electrons may be written

$$U_n = \frac{(1 - f)n}{\tau_{n0}} - \frac{fn'}{\tau_{n0}} \qquad (6)$$

The expression for holes, with equivalent definitions, is

$$U_p = \frac{fp}{\tau_{p0}} - \frac{(1 - f)p'}{\tau_{p0}} . \qquad (7)$$

In thermal equilibrium, these net capture rates are each equal to zero. When n and p are increased (f remaining constant for the moment) the capture rates for electrons and holes increase by $[(1 - f)\Delta n]/\tau_{n0}$ and $(f \Delta p)/\tau_{p0}$, respectively. If f is not too nearly equal to unity and $\tau_{p0} \gg \tau_{n0}$, then $(1 - f)/\tau_{n0} \gg f/\tau_{p0}$. With Δn and Δp being generated in equal densities, the capture rate for excess holes does not balance that for excess electrons. As a consequence, f must increase; i.e., electrons are trapped. If N is large, then the density of trapped electrons, $N \Delta f$, may be large. On the other hand $(1 - f)/\tau_{n0}$ may be comparable to f/τ_{p0} in which case the center may function as an efficient recombination center. If N is not too large, a small amount of trapping may suffice to equilibrate the two capture rates.

The discussion of the basic photoconductive effect above has tacitly assumed uniform material, neutral contacts, and uniformly absorbed photon flux. Nonuniformity of material, either resistivity gradients or p-n junctions, gives rise to observable voltages due to diffusion of photoexcited carriers. This photovoltaic effect

is used in solar cells and exposure meters. Nonuniformly absorbed radiation, as will occur when strongly absorbed radiation is absorbed entirely in a thin surface layer on a bulk crystal, will produce a diffusion of photoexcited carriers into the bulk of the crystal. When mobilities are different or trapping is present, a voltage may be detected (the Dember voltage) or, in the presence of a magnetic field, the photoelectromagnetic effect. Even when a photoconductor is otherwise uniform in composition, its surfaces introduce a perturbing influence. For example, the surface may contain a set of very efficient recombination centers, so that lifetime near the surface is much smaller than in the bulk. This will cause a nonuniformity in excess carrier concentration which will not be constant in time (in general). This surface recombination may dominate lifetime in a thin sample, and in a thick sample it may cause a deviation from exponential decay even if the bulk lifetime is independent of Δn.

The phenomenon of photoconductivity is intimately related to semiconductor device phenomena since most devices, e.g., transistors, lasers, luminescent materials, operate by means of nonequilibrium densities of carriers which are subject to the same recombination and trapping kinetics as in photoconductivity.

JOSEPH F. WOODS

References

Bube, R. H., "Photoconductivity of Solids," New York, John Wiley & Sons, Inc., 1960.
Tauc, J., "Photo- and Thermoelectric Effects in Semiconductors," New York, Pergamon Press, 1962.
Levinstein, H., Ed., "Proceedings of the 1961 International Conference on Photoconductivity," *J. Phys. Chem. Solids*, **22** (1961).
Moss, T. S., "Photoconductivity in the Elements," London, Butterworths, 1952.
Kruse, P. W., McGlauchlin, L. D., and McQuistan, R. B., "Elements of Infrared Technology," New York, John Wiley & Sons, 1962.
Rose, A., "Concepts in Photoconductivity," New York, Interscience Publishers, 1963.
Pankove, J. I., "Optical Processes in Semiconductors," Englewood Cliffs, N.J., Prentice-Hall, Inc., 1971.

Cross-references: CONDUCTIVITY, ELECTRICAL; ENERGY LEVELS; PHOTOELECTRICITY; PHOTON; PHOTOVOLTAIC EFFECT; SEMICONDUCTORS.

PHOTOELASTICITY*

Photoelasticity is a method of determining stresses or strains in transparent materials by means of polarized light. It is widely used in engineering laboratories for the analysis of stress distributions in models of structures and

*Editor was unable to locate author. Article is reprinted from first edition.

machine parts. In the majority of problems, the results of such model tests are directly transferable to the metallic prototypes, as long as the materials of the models and prototypes both remain *elastic* (hence the origin of the term).

The *photoelastic effect* can be explained by assuming that an initially plane-polarized light beam, in passing through the stressed plane specimen, breaks up at every point into two components (*birefringence*), corresponding to the directions of the two principal stresses at that point (see POLARIZED LIGHT). The relative retardation between these two components will be proportional to the difference of principal stresses at each point. If the emergent light is passed through a second plane-polarizing unit (the *analyzer*), the principal plane of which is usually put at right angles to the first one, the two relatively retarded components are reduced into one plane and give rise to interference. In general, a number of such interference bands will appear in the model simultaneously, along each of which the principal stress difference (or maximum shear) will be of a constant value, that can be determined by calibration. If white light is used for the source, these bands will appear in the subsequent colors of the spectrum and are thus called *isochromatics*. At points where the incident plane-polarized light happens to coincide with the direction of one of the principal stresses, the light will merely pass through as a plane wave and, subsequently, will be cut out by the crossed analyzer. All such points in the piece will thus be connected with a dark band for any particular inclination of the crossed polarizer and analyzer. These bands are the *isoclinics*, which define the orientation of the principal stresses. They can be eliminated by the use of quarter-wave-plates, which produce circularly polarized light, devoid of the above directional property.

The isochromatics and isoclinics furnish two of the three independent parameters needed to define the state of stress at any point in a two-dimensional field. The third parameter may be obtained by a variety of supplementary means such as lateral extensometry, mechanical or electrical analogies, or by numerical integration.

The increased use of the photoelastic method was greatly aided by successive improvements in model materials, from glass and celluloids to the latest thermosetting resins, such as the epoxies.

An extension of the method to spatial problems (three-dimensional photoelasticity) provides the only known experimental means for the determination of the state of stress in the interior of solids. The method is also used in dynamic (transient stress) studies, and its scope is extended now into nonelastic fields (photoplasticity and photoviscoelasticity).

M. HETÉNYI

References

Coker, E. G., and Filon, L. N. G., "A Treatise on Photo-Elasticity," Cambridge, Cambridge University Press, 1931.

Hetényi, M., "The Fundamentals of Three-Dimensional Photoelasticity," *J. Appl. Mech.*, 5, No. 4 (1938).

Frocht, M. M., "Photoelasticity," Vol. I (1941), Vol. II (1948), New York, John Wiley & Sons.

Hetényi, M., Ed., "Handbook of Experimental Stress Analysis," New York, John Wiley & Sons, 1950.

Hetényi, M., "Photoelasticity and Photoplasticity," in Goodier, J. N., and Hoff, J., Eds., "Structural Mechanics," New York, Pergamon Press, 1960.

Cross-references: ELASTICITY, INTERFERENCE AND INTERFEROMETRY, POLARIZED LIGHT.

PHOTOELECTRICITY

For the purposes of this article, photoelectricity is defined as the emission of electrons resulting from the absorption of radiation in a material. This definition is purposely broad: by radiation, we understand electromagnetic radiation ranging from the shortest wavelength to the longest, from gamma-rays into infrared. The electrons can be released into vacuum or into a second material and the material itself can be either a solid, a liquid, or a gas.

Although there may have been some observations, which with hindsight could be called photoelectric observations, the real history of photoelectricity starts with the work of Hertz. It was in the course of his experiments on electrical resonance that he observed that the length of the spark which could be induced in an auxiliary circuit was greater if the spark gap was irradiated by the ultraviolet light generated by the spark of the primary circuit. He found also that the effect is most marked when the electrode, which is illuminated, is negative. Stimulated by the investigations of Hertz, Hallwachs made a more thorough investigation of the phenomenon, and his work, coupled with that of Elster and Geitel, Lenard, and J. J. Thomson, led to Einstein's fundamental concept. He pointed out that so far as the photoelectric effect is concerned, light can be regarded as being made up of individual particles, or light quanta, each containing an amount of energy equal to $h\nu$ where h is the constant of Planck and ν is the frequency of the light.

$$h(\nu - \nu_0) = \tfrac{1}{2}m v_{max}^2 = eV$$

$$h\nu_0 = e\phi$$

In this formulation of the Einstein photoelectric equation, the maximum kinetic energy of the electron ejected from the material is a function of the frequency of the exciting light minus the frequency of a threshold characteristic for the material. m, e and v are the mass, charge and velocity of the emitted electron, and V is the potential difference required to reduce the velocity of the emitted electron to zero. The quantity $h\nu_0$ is usually called the work function, whereby the work function ϕ is defined as the work necessary to remove to infinity an electron from the lowest free electron state in the metal,

W_0. If the electron is taken from the Fermi level, its work function $\phi = W_0 - W_f$.

Einstein's law predicts that the emission current should be directly proportional to the intensity of the incident light, a statement which underwent numerous critical investigations and was found to be correct. It is also consistent with a three-step model of the photoelectric emission from a solid. In the first step, the photon is absorbed. Absorption may be at any distance from the surface, governed by the light absorption constant of the material. As the emitted electron may be ejected at a finite depth, it has to diffuse through a crystal lattice to the surface and may lose energy in the diffusion process. The third step is the escape of the electron from the solid over a potential barrier.

While the above model is consistent with the Einstein equation, this latter does not predict the entire behavior of the photoemission from a solid. In particular, it does not say anything about the temperature coefficient. A theory was, therefore, necessary, and a quantum mechanical theory was provided by Fowler. On the basis of the initial assumption, that all electrons with normal components of energy greater than ϕ would escape, he established a relationship between the photoelectric current I and the temperature T

$$I = \alpha A T^2 \varphi(x)$$

where α and A are constants and x is defined by

$$x = \frac{h(\nu - \nu_0)}{kT}$$

The function φ is an exponential series, whose numerical values have been tabulated. The Fowler equation allows a very convenient plotting of photoelectric emission results, and the typical Fowler curve is a presentation of logarithm I/T^2 plus a constant vs x. Incidentally, this presentation allows a very convenient and fast determination of the wavelength threshold value, which is equivalent to the work function for the material.

The detailed remarks of the last two paragraphs are essentially limited to the photoelectric effect in pure metals and the ejection of the electron into vacuum. Most work functions are relatively high, with a resulting threshold in the ultraviolet region. ϕ ranges in metals from 1.9 eV (7000Å) for Cs to about 5.4 eV (2300Å) for Pt. Quite a bit of effort was made for many years to create photoemitters with low work functions for practical applications in the visible part of the spectrum or even in the infrared. One group of substances, offering considerably lower values than those of the metals, are semi-conductors. While in a metal the photoelectrons originate in the conduction band relatively close to the Fermi level, in semi-conductors they originate in the valence band or in impurity states. If the latter are more favorably placed than the Fermi level, a corresponding reduction of the work function may result. For instance, in Ag-O-Cs

ϕ equals 1.0 eV (12300Å). It was found that intermetallic compounds of the I-V or II-V type, such as Cs_3Sb or Na-K-Cs-Sb, offer great advantages.

The considerations outlined thus far apply to low-energy excitation of the photoelectron. At higher energies other effects appear and require different interpretations. At photon energies above the range of 10 eV, penetrating radiation can release photoelectrons from inner atomic shells. A vacancy produced in an inner shell is followed by the filling of this vacancy from a less tightly bound state, with the simultaneous emission of a second electron from another less tightly bound state. This effect was discovered by Pierre Auger in 1926.

In the collision between a high-energy photon ($h\nu_0 > 10$ keV) and an electron initially at rest, the laws of conservation of energy and of momentum require that the energy transferred to the electron be subtracted from the energy of the incident photon. The resulting new photon $h\nu'$ is represented by the equation:

$$h\nu_0 = h\nu' + mc^2\left(\frac{1}{(1 - \beta^2)^{1/2}} - 1\right)$$

where the second term represents the kinetic energy of the ejected electron ($\beta = v/c$; the velocity of the ejected electron divided by the speed of light). The effect is called the Compton effect in honor of its discoverer, Arthur H. Compton.

If the energy of the photon is sufficiently high for its wavelength to become comparable with nuclear dimensions, a variety of nuclear reactions may take place. These are called photonuclear reactions and become apparent at photon energies above 100 MeV (roughly).

Observations in the early days of photoelectric research have shown that surface conditions may modify considerably the photoemissive properties of surfaces. The most commonly occurring surface impurity is an oxide layer, and for practical applications it was found that oxidation often enhances the photoelectric current. Although the mechanism of the photoemission of such surfaces is sometimes very complicated, part of the reason can be found in the enhanced light absorption (reduced reflection) of the photoelectric surface.

Practical application of surface photoemission in the early days was largely limited by the very weak currents which can be obtained from substances with a low efficiency of photoelectric emission. This led to schemes of charge multiplication which produce higher currents. A first such scheme used collision-ionization in a gas. Within a reasonable limit, the so-called gas-filled photocells show a very linear behavior with intensity. In the last 20 years, gas-filled photocells have been almost entirely replaced by photomultipliers, i.e., combinations of photocathodes with secondary electron multipliers. In these latter devices, the multiplication factor may vary from 10^4 to 10^7.

With increasing attention to the far-ultraviolet range of the spectrum, a few metals with higher

work functions find favor as applied devices. In some modern applications, advantage is taken of the insensitivity of a high work function photocathode to visible light. Its response is limited to far-ultraviolet light alone, in the so-called solarblind type cell.

The second important group of phenomena, which has found many important practical applications, is that in which the ejected electron may travel through the emitting material, to enter a solid electrode in contact with the photo-emitter instead of going to the anode through a vacuum. There are two subgroups: one is photo-conductivity which is treated elsewhere in this volume, and the second is a group that bears the generic name of photovoltaic effects. This name is generally applied to the phenomena leading to the direct conversion of a part of the energy absorbed from the impinging photons into usable electrical energy. Most common examples are selenium cells, the barrier-layer-type copper oxide cells, and the so-called solar batteries or solar photovoltaic converter, consisting usually of a semiconductor crystal like silicon containing a composition gradient termed the p-n junction. These last devices have now reached a relatively high grade of efficiency where up to 15 per cent of the energy of the incident light may be converted into electric current. Theoretically, 50 per cent efficiency might be obtained in a three-semiconductor sandwich assembly.

Photoelectric effects in liquids and in gases are essentially of the photoconductive type.

L. MARTON

References

Weissler, G., "Photo Ionization in Gases and Photoelectric Emission from Solids," in Flügge, S., Ed., "Encyclopedia of Physics," Vol. XXI, pp. 304–382, Berlin, Springer, 1956.

Simon, H., and Suhrmann, R., "Der Lichtelektrische Effekt," Second edition, Berlin, Springer, 1958.

Sommer, A. H., and Spicer, W. E., "Photoelectric Emission," in "Photoelectronic Materials and Devices," Larach, S., Ed., pp. 175–221, New York, Van Nostrand Reinhold, 1965.

Derbenwick, G. F., Price, D. T., and Spicer, W. E., "Experimental Techniques for Visible and Ultraviolet Photoemission," in Vol. XI, 67–122 of "Methods of Experimental Physics," Coleman, R. V., Ed., Marton, L., Gen. Ed., New York, Academic Press, 1973.

Evans, R. D., "Compton Effect," in "Encyclopedia of Physics," Flügge, S., Ed., Vol. 34, Berlin, Springer, 1958.

Levinger, J. S., "Nuclear Photodisintegration," London, Oxford University Press, 1960.

Advances in Electronics and Electron Physics, **12** (1960), **16** (1963), **22** (1966), **28** (1969), and **33** (1973), New York, Academic Press.

Cross-references: AUGER EFFECT, COMPTON EFFECT, PHOTOCONDUCTIVITY, PHOTOMULTIPLIER TUBE, PHOTON, PHOTOVOLTAIC EFFECT.

PHOTOGRAPHY

The history of photography spans more than a century and embraces many techniques for producing photographic images. Within the past decade alone, important innovations have been made in photographic recording.

Every photographic technique includes an optical system, a photosensitive material, and a development process. Light from the subject passes through the optical system or camera, and impinges on the photosensitive material to form a latent or invisible image. The latent image is transformed by chemical or physical means into a visible negative or positive image.

Most photographic processes use mixtures of the silver halides, i.e., silver bromide, iodide, and chloride, as the photosensitive materials. (The "speed" of a material depends on the relative proportions, with "fast" materials having a large percentage of silver bromide and little or no silver chloride.) These processes include conventional black-and-white and color photography, Polaroid black-and-white photography, Polacolor, and lensless photography. A number of other processes are based on photochemical reactions of organic dyes, and of inorganic metal salts other than silver halides. Still other processes employ light-induced changes in the physical properties of materials such as photoconductors or thermoplastics.

In conventional silver halide photography, the camera consists of a light-proof box with a lens for admitting and focusing light, a diaphragm for controlling the size of the effective lens aperture, a shutter for regulating length of exposure, and the photosensitive film. There must also be film-holding and film-transporting devices, and a viewfinder. A simple box camera (Fig. 1) has only one lens aperture and one shutter speed. The distance from lens to film is fixed, and the lens has a short focal length so that all objects within the range of six feet to infinity are in focus on the film. Other types of cameras have systems for varying the lens-to-film distance, the effective aperture, and the shutter speed.

The two most common types of shutters (Fig. 2) are the leaf shutter consisting of three or five interleaved blades, each pivoted on the outer end, and the focal plane shutter consisting of a slit which traverses the film plane during exposure.

A recent development called holography,[1] or lensless photography, uses an unconventional image-forming system (Fig. 3a). Monochromatic light from a laser is split into two beams, one of which enters the lensless camera after reflection from a plane mirror, while the other enters after reflection from a three-dimensional object. The two beams combine to form a Fresnel diffraction pattern of the image, which is recorded on film. This recorded pattern is called a hologram. To reconstruct the image, a beam of laser light is transmitted through the hologram to generate a second diffraction pattern, a component of which is an exact duplicate of

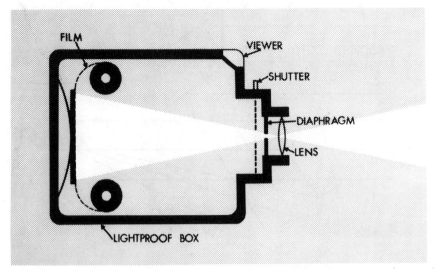

FIG. 1. Box camera. (Figures 1, 2, and 3 are redrawn from "The Encyclopedia Americana," International Edition, 1971.)

LEAF SHUTTER

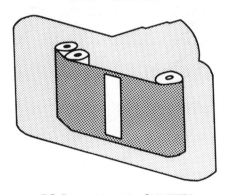

FOCAL PLANE SHUTTER

FIG. 2. Shutters.

the original wave reflected from the object. This wave appears to come from the object, i.e., it yields a three-dimensional virtual image which appears suspended in space behind the hologram (Fig. 3b). Another component of the diffraction pattern forms a three-dimensional real image which appears suspended in front of

the hologram. Holography has become an important scientific tool with many unique applications. (see HOLOGRAPHY.)

Another new process makes it possible to mass-produce a three-dimensional image known as a "parallax panoramogram" on a two-dimensional card.[2] The picture is coated with a plastic layer composed of vertical rows of cylindrical lenses which give the illusion of depth.

Ordinary photographic film is a suspension of microscopic silver halide crystals in gelatin coated on a supporting layer. Gelatin is a stable porous medium which permits the processing solutions to reach the dispersed crystals. Gelatin contains organic sulfide impurities which react with silver halides to form sensitivity centers. These are tiny silver sulfide centers of at least ten molecules each, which form on the surface of the crystals and catalyze the formation of the latent image by light.[3] When the film is exposed to light, the crystals absorb photons which generate mobile electrons. These electrons migrate to the sensitivity centers, where they are trapped. They attract and neutralize silver ions, forming specks of metallic silver on the silver halide crystals at the sites of the sensitivity centers. These specks constitute the latent image. The smallest latent image speck that can make an exposed crystal develop during processing has from four to ten atoms of silver. Not all absorbed photons contribute to the latent image. Assuming that a typical speck of ten atoms formed by absorbing one hundred photons can cause development of a crystal with 10^{10} ion pairs, the amplification factor is about 10^8, which is higher than that of any other photographic material.

The developer reduces all the silver ions in an exposed crystal to silver atoms, which deposit on the specks. The unexposed crystals are removed from the emulsion by a "fixing" solu-

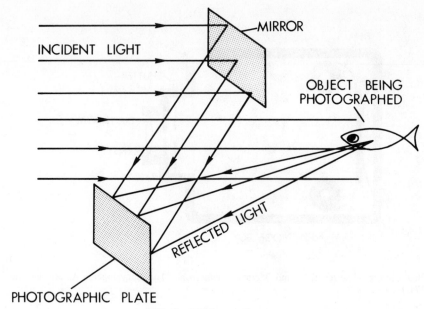

FIG. 3a. Making a hologram.

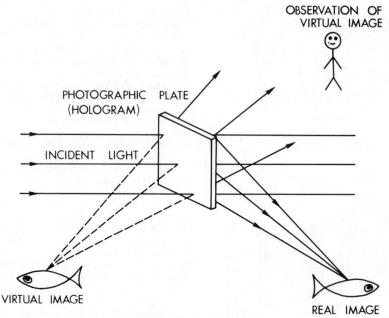

FIG. 3b. Viewing a hologram.

tion to form the negative. A positive print is obtained by exposing an emulsion-coated paper to light through the negative, and developing it.

In the Polaroid camera developed by E. H. Land, a positive print is obtained directly from the camera ten seconds after exposure. The negative emulsion layer is pressed against a non-sensitive layer of paper between metal rollers in the camera. Pods containing a viscous devel-

oper are ruptured as the two layers are pressed together, squeezing the developer uniformly between the layers. The developer develops the negative image, and then dissolves the unexposed crystals and transfers them to the paper layer which contains dry developer to develop the positive print.

Silver halide emulsions are sensitive to ultraviolet and visible light, with maximum response

in the blue at about 4200Å. Their range can be extended to any wavelength up to 13000Å in the near infrared by sensitizing dyes which absorb light in the desired spectral regions and transfer the energy to the crystals. A common emulsion is that used in panchromatic film, which is sensitized to the visible spectrum up to 6200Å.

In modern color photography, integral tripack films are usually used. An integral tripack is a film of three sensitive layers separated by gelatin. Each layer contains crystals sensitized to one of the primary colors for light mixing, i.e., red, green, or blue. After exposure, the three silver negatives in the nonseparable multi-layered film are developed.

The most common method of forming the dye image is the dye coupling process. During development of the silver negative, the developer is oxidized in proportion to the silver reduced. The oxidized developer reacts or "couples" with a chemical to form a dye which produces a negative color image. A cyan dye in the red-sensitized layer absorbs red light and reflects its complement (i.e., cyan), while the blue-sensitized emulsion acquires a yellow dye, and the green-sensitized emulsion a magenta dye. The superposition of the three color negatives then transmits the colors complementary to those of the original image.

To make color prints, the colors are reversed by exposing a three-layer emulsion coated on paper to white light through the color negative. To make positive transparencies, the color reversal is performed directly on the three emulsion layers by changing the development procedure.

Infrared false color photography[4] is a relatively new process, in which the film has three layers sensitized to green, red, and infrared (to 13000 Å), instead of to the normal blue, green, and red. A positive print or transparency then depicts the green, red, and infrared in the original scene as blue, green, and red, respectively. This process has important applications to aerial reconnaissance, medicine, and many other disciplines.

Many practical innovations have recently been made in amateur photography. Development trays have now been replaced by drums or tanks which permit development in full daylight. Kits are available for developing color slides, prints, or negatives under noncritical environmental conditions. Liquid concentrates with almost unlimited shelf life may be used to prepare small quantities of development solutions by simple methods. Miniature cameras, simplified film loading, cheap paper film, and high-speed films are now available.

The Polacolor process developed by Land produces a color print fifty seconds after exposure.[5] The camera and the mechanical operations are similar to those described above for Polaroid black-and-white photography. One innovation in this process is a new type of molecule with a preformed dye on one end and a developer on the other. The dye-developer linked molecules are placed inside the negative which is an integral tripack. After exposure, the viscous reagent liberated from the pods sets the linked molecules in motion. Those that hit an exposed crystal in the appropriately sensitized emulsion layer become fixed to the crystal site during development, and form a negative color image. Those linked molecules that do not hit a crystal in the appropriate emulsion layer traverse the negative emulsion, and enter the positive emulsion, which is pressed against the negative in the camera. The larger the exposure in a given color, the fewer the linked molecules with the appropriate dye that reach the positive. The positive is a silver halide integral tripack which is exposed together with the negative. The linked molecules containing the three types of dyes develop the exposed crystals to form the positive print.

In May 1972, Dr. Land announced a revolutionary new system of Polaroid photography, which features a miniature single-lens reflex camera measuring only 7 X 4 X 1 inches and weighing 26 ounces. All operations except composing and focusing the picture are controlled electronically. There are few moving parts, so essentially "only the electrons move." Within a minute of exposure, a hard, dry, scratch-resistant print emerges from the camera. It has a three-dimensional quality, "true" colors, and a luminous appearance as if internally lighted. Timing and waste disposal are eliminated. Pictures may be taken at the rate of one every 1.3 sec. Provision is made for time exposures, and for flash bulb lighting. Fresh batteries are included in each film pack. This system was developed by a large team of researchers over a 20-year period. It was marketed in 1972.

Photographic processes using photochemical systems other than silver halides have much lower sensitivity to light, but may be used to achieve special effects.[6]

A class of processes known as electrophotography uses materials which show an increase in electrical conductivity during light exposure. Electrophotography is widely used for office copying machines. In one type of electrophotography, charges are sprayed on a selenium or zinc oxide layer by a corona wire charged to five or ten thousand volts.[3] During exposure, the charges leak off image-wise through the photoconductive layer. The remaining charge pattern is the latent image, which is developed by applying an oppositely charged black resin powder which adheres to the charged areas. The image is fixed by slight heating to fuse the resin. "Electrofax" and "Xerography" are commercial adaptations of this process.

An image-forming system for wavelengths longer than 13000 Å, i.e., beyond the limit for sensitized photographic emulsions, is now used in remote sensing from aircraft or spacecraft. This system does not require any image-forming

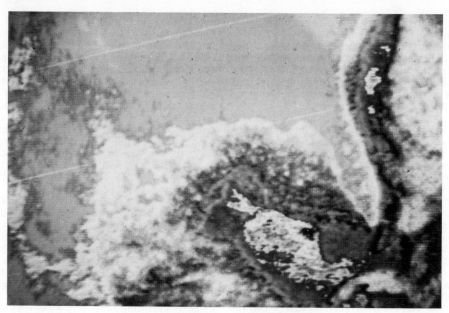

FIG. 4. Loop Current and Gulf Stream.

optics; hence it is not true photography. Instead, a detector sensitive to infrared or microwave radiation scans the field of view, and the received intensity from each point in the scene is electronically converted to a visible intensity at a corresponding point on a cathode ray tube. The visible image of the infrared or microwave scene is then recorded by conventional photography. This system has many applications to medicine, geology, agriculture, forestry, and oceanography.

Figure 4 was produced by scanning as described above, and represents an infrared photograph showing the warm Loop Current in the Gulf of Mexico, and the Gulf Stream. It has been processed so that bright areas in the center of the currents represent *very* warm water and dark areas represent *quite* warm water. Bright regions along the shore and outside of these currents represent very cold water. Thus bright areas depict both hot and cold water, while dark areas show the location of water at an intermediate temperature.[7]

The past decade has brought about these many innovations to photography. By extrapolation, the future promises even greater wonders.

MIRIAM SIDRAN

References

1. Pennington, K. S., "Advances in Holography," *Sci. Amer.* **218,** 2 (1968).
2. Lipton, L., "Color 3-D Printing Process Permits Mass Press Run, Glassless Viewing," *Popular Photography,* **92** (May 1964).
3. Neblette, C. B., "Photography, Its Materials and Processes," New York, Van Nostrand Reinhold, Sixth Edition, 1962.
4. "Applied Infrared Photography," Eastman Kodak Publication M-28, 1972.
5. "Background Information about Polaroid Land Color Film," Polaroid Corporation, 1962.
6. Hepher, M., "Not by Silver Alone," *Perspective,* **1,** 28 (1959).
7. Sidran, M. and Hebard, F., "Charting the Loop Current by Satellite," Proceedings of The Eighth International Symposium on Remote Sensing of Environment, Willow Run Laboratories, Ann Arbor, Michigan, October 2–6, 1972, pp. 1121–1126.

Cross-references: COLOR, HOLOGRAPHY, INFRARED RADIATION, LENS, LIGHT, OPTICAL INSTRUMENTS, PHOTOCONDUCTIVITY, ULTRAVIOLET RADIATION.

PHOTOMETRY

Photometry is concerned with the measurement of light, or much more frequently, of the time rate of flow of light. Light is the aspect of radiant energy to which the human eye responds, or more precisely it is Q_v in the equation:

$$Q_v = K_m \int V(\lambda) Q_{e\lambda} d\lambda$$

in which K_m is the maximum luminous efficacy of radiant energy (about 680 lumens/watt), $V(\lambda)$ is the CIE (International Commission on Illumination) spectral luminous efficiency function[1] which is curve 4 of the figure shown in the article on COLOR in this Encyclopedia, and $Q_{e\lambda}$ is the spectral distribution of radiant energy.

Reference 1 is highly recommended as a short discussion of the basic principles of photometry.

The quantities with which photometry is concerned are luminous intensity and flux, illuminance and LUMINANCE, and luminous reflectance and transmittance.

The devices that are used to measure these quantities are called photometers. They fall into two general categories, namely, visual and physical. The making of brightness matches is a requisite in the use of visual photometers, while in physical photometers, which are usually of the photoelectric or thermoelectric type, luminous energy incident on a receiver is transformed into electric energy and the latter is measured by means of sensitive electric meters or devices. In visual photometry, observers with so-called normal color vision are used, it being tacitly assumed that the average spectral response of the observers used to make the observations approximates the standard CIE luminous efficiency curve. In physical photometry, the receiver should be equipped with a filter, the spectral transmittance of which when multiplied by the relative spectral response of the receiver, wavelength by wavelength, closely approximates the CIE luminous efficiency curve. In all photometric measurements that involve differences between the spectral distribution of the standard source used to calibrate the photometer and that of the test source, the accuracy of the results obtained is dependent on the degree of approximation of the spectral response curve of the photometer to the CIE spectral luminous efficiency curve.

The unit of luminous intensity (often called candlepower) is the candela. Its magnitude is such that the luminous intensity of one-sixtieth of one square centimeter of projected area of a blackbody at the freezing point of platinum[2] is one candela. Such a blackbody has been the international standard of light since January 1, 1948. National standardizing laboratories, like the National Bureau of Standards in the United States, calibrate incandescent-lamp reference standards of luminous intensity in terms of the international standard. The calibration for luminous intensity of other incandescent lamps relative to these reference standards or to other standards of luminous intensity is usually done on a bar photometer, which consists of a horizontal bar equipped with movable carriages, on one of which the standards and lamps to be calibrated are mounted in turn, while the photometric measuring device is mounted on the other carriage. The calibration involves the use of the inverse-square law which states that the illuminance at a point on a surface varies directly with the luminous intensity I of the source and inversely as the square of the distance d between the source and the point on the surface. If the surface at the point is perpendicular to the direction of the incident light, the law may be expressed as follows: $E = I/d^2$. In the measurement of the intensity I_2 of a source relative to the intensity I_1 of a standard, the illumination at the photometer from the two sources is made equal by varying the distance d, so that $I_2 = I_1 d_2^2/d_1^2$ in which d_2 and d_1 are the distances for the unknown and standard, respectively. The important precautions that must be taken in calibrating and using standards of luminous intensity are (1) that the distance between the standard and photometric receiver is sufficiently large relative to the size of the source and of the receiver so that the source and receiver act approximately as points,[3] (2) that the standard is accurately oriented with respect to the receiver,[4] and (3) that by the use of baffles no flux is incident on the receiver other than that which comes directly from the standard.

Illuminance is incident luminous flux per unit area. In the measurement of illuminance, a photometer, in this application often called an illuminometer, is used. The illuminometer is calibrated at n points by the use of a standard of luminous intensity I placed at n distances d from the test plate of a visual photometer or the surface of the receiver, thus yielding n illuminances E computed from the inverse-square law $E = I/d^2$. It is important that the geometric characteristics of the receiver of the illuminometer be such as to enable it to evaluate, without bias, luminous flux that is incident on the receiver from all directions; special precautions are usually necessary if flux incident at large angles to the perpendiuclar to the receiver is to be properly evaluated.

The unit of luminous flux is the lumen which is defined as the luminous flux in a unit solid angle (steradian) from a point source having a directionally uniform intensity of one candela. Standards of luminous flux are calibrated in terms of standards of luminous intensity by the use of a two-step procedure. In one step, the luminous intensity in a specified direction of the lamp to be calibrated is determined, and in the other step, by the use of a distribution photometer, the relative luminous intensity of this lamp in a multiplicity of directions is determined. To enable one to see how each of these intensities is effective in contributing luminous flux, one notes that each direction intersects a hypothetical sphere circumscribed about the lamp and that around the point of intersection on the sphere surface an area can logically be assigned which defines the solid angle in which the luminous intensity in that direction is effective in supplying luminous flux. These solid angles in steradians, by which the luminous intensity values must be multiplied to obtain the lumens incident on the respective areas, are called zonal constants. Such constants for various patterns of distribution measurements have been published and are thus readily available.[5,6] Reference standards of luminous flux are calibrated by this procedure, but other standards are calibrated in terms of the reference standards or of other standards of luminous

flux by the use of an integrating sphere, sometimes called an Ulbricht sphere. It is a spherical hollow enclosure with a uniform, diffusely reflecting inner surface. In such an enclosure, the illuminance due to reflected flux is the same at every point on the surface and is directly proportional to the flux emitted by a source in the sphere, independent of its angular distribution. The ratio of the fluxes emitted by two sources is thus the ratio of the illuminances at any point on the sphere surface that is shielded from receiving flux directly from the sources. The principal precautions in the use of spheres are (1) that the inner surface be a good diffuser, uniform in reflectance from point to point, and (2) that the spectral selectivity of the sphere throughout the visible region of the spectrum (0.4 to 0.7μm) be compensated. This compensation is usually accomplished by the use of filters, but another procedure is to disperse the flux from the sphere wall by means of a prism and insert in the spectrum thus formed a template whose shape compensates for both the spectral selectivity of the sphere and the spectral response of the receiver.[7] It must be remembered that the effect of the spectral selectivity is greatly amplified because of the interreflections within the sphere so that the illuminance on the sphere wall by reflection only is $\rho/(1-\rho)$ times the average illuminance by directly incident flux, where ρ is the reflectance of the sphere wall; thus if the reflectances at two wavelengths are, for example, 0.80 and 0.72, the spectral irradiance by reflection only at the wavelength of lower reflectance will be only 64 per cent of that at the wavelength of higher reflectance.

There are two related systems of units of luminance that have been and are still being used. In one of these systems the luminance is expressed in terms of luminous intensity per unit projected area or in terms of luminous flux per unit solid angle and unit projected area. The other system is that in which luminance is expressed in terms of the flux per unit area that would leave a perfect diffuser having the same luminance; the lambert and footlambert are units of this system and their magnitudes are such that one lumen per square centimeter and per square foot, respectively, would leave a perfect diffuser of unit luminance. Standards of luminance are usually combinations of luminous intensity standards and surfaces of known transmittance factor or reflectance factor (see below). The product of the illuminance of a surface by the appropriate one of these factors gives its luminance; for example, for each lumen per square centimeter incident perpendicularly on a freshly prepared surface of MgO, the luminance at an angle of 45° from the perpendicular will be approximately one lambert because the reflectance factor of MgO for this geometry is approximately 1.00. In lieu of the MgO surface, use is more generally made of a highly diffusing glass or plastic plate of known transmittance factor for perpendicular incidence on one side of the plate and perpendicular viewing on the other side. The measurement of luminance relative to

a luminance standard by visual photometry introduces no serious problems other than those inherent in photometry generally, because the receptor, in this case the eye, intercepts flux in a very small solid angle which can, for all practical purposes, be considered to be infinitesimally small. In physical photometry, however, because of the need to collect flux in an amount that will result in adequate sensitivity, the solid angle of reception is relatively large and cannot in general be considered to be infinitesimally small, so that there is introduced into the measurements an inaccuracy whose magnitude is related to the magnitude of the variation of the flux per infinitesimal solid angle within the solid angle of reception.

In addition to the measurement of the dimensional quantities discussed above, photometry is concerned with the measurement of the dimensionless quantities transmittance, transmittance factor, reflectance, and reflectance factor. Transmittance and reflectance are the ratio of transmitted and reflected flux, respectively, to incident flux. For a nondiffusing specimen, the measurement of transmittance or reflectance usually poses no great problem. For a diffusing specimen, the measurement of totally diffuse transmittance or reflectance (reception over a solid angle of 2π steradians) for specified modes of illumination of the specimen is usually made with instruments that incorporate integrating spheres;[8] for solid angles of reception smaller than 2π steradians, the measurement of the ratio of transmitted or reflected flux to incident flux yields what is designated as fractional transmittance or fractional reflectance, respectively, quantities which generally are not of as much interest as are the transmittance factor and the reflectance factor (usually in the United States widely but inappropriately called directional transmittance and directional reflectance). These factors are defined[9] as the ratio of the flux transmitted (or reflected) in the solid angle of interest to that transmitted (or reflected) in the solid angle by the ideal perfect diffuse transmitter (or reflector) identically illuminated; the ideal perfect diffuse transmitter (or reflector) is one that transmits (or reflects) all of the luminous flux incident on it in accord with the Lambert cosine law, i.e., so that the flux per unit solid angle in any direction from it varies as the cosine of the angle between that direction and the perpendicular to the transmitter (or reflector). For a solid angle of reception of 2π steradians, the term transmittance (or reflectance) factor is synonymous with transmittance (or reflectance). For infinitesimal solid angles of reception and nonfluorescing specimens, the term transmittance (or reflectance) factor is synonymous with luminance factor which for any specimen is defined as the ratio of the luminance of the specimen to the luminance of a perfect diffuser identically illuminated.

The most commonly used photometric and related radiometric quantities, their defining equations and units, and symbols for them

Quantity[a]	Symbol[a]	Defining Equation	Unit	Symbol
Radiant energy	Q		Erg	
			Joule[e]	J
			Calorie	cal
			Kilowatt-hour	kWh
Radiant density	w	$w = dQ/dV$	Joule per cubic meter[e]	J/m^3
			Erg per cubic centimeter	erg/cm^3
Radiant flux	Φ	$\Phi = dQ/dt$	Erg per second	erg/s
			Watt[e]	W
Radiant flux density at a surface				
Radiant emittance[b] (Radiant exitance)	M	$M = d\Phi/dA$	Watt per square centimeter	W/cm^2
Irradiance	E	$E = d\Phi/dA$	Watt per square meter[e], etc.	W/m^2
Radiant intensity	I	$I = d\Phi/d\omega$ (ω = solid angle through which flux from point source is radiated)	Watt per steradian[e]	W/sr
Radiance	L	$L = d^2\Phi/d\omega(dA \cos\theta)$ $= dI/(dA \cos\theta)$ (θ = angle between line of sight and normal to surface considered)	Watt per steradian and square centimeter; Watt per steradian and square meter[e]	$W \cdot sr^{-1} cm^{-2}$; $W \cdot sr^{-1} m^{-2}$
Emissivity	ϵ	$\epsilon = M/M_{blackbody}$	None (dimensionless)	—
Absorptance	α	$\alpha = \Phi_a/\Phi_i$[d]	None (dimensionless)	—
Reflectance	ρ	$\rho = \Phi_r/\Phi_i$[d]	None (dimensionless)	—
Transmittance	τ	$\tau = \Phi_t/\Phi_i$[d]	None (dimensionless)	—

NOTE: The symbols for photometric quantities (see below) are the same as those for the corresponding radiometric quantities (see above). When it is necessary to differentiate them the subscripts v and e respectively should be used, e.g., Q_v and Q_e.

Quantity	Symbol	Defining Equation	Unit	Symbol
Luminous energy	Q	$Q_v = \int_{380}^{760} K(\lambda)Q_{e\lambda}d\lambda$	Lumen-hour	$lm \cdot h$
(quantity of light)			Lumen-second (talbot)[e]	$lm \cdot s$
Luminous density	w	$w = dQ/dV$	Lumen-second per cubic meter[e]	$lm \cdot s \cdot m^{-3}$
Luminous flux	Φ	$\Phi = dQ/dt$	Lumen[e]	lm
Luminous flux density at a surface				
Luminous emittance[c] (Luminous exitance)	M	$M = d\Phi/dA$	Lumen per square foot	lm/ft^2
Illumination (Illuminance)	E	$E = d\Phi/dA$	Footcandle (lumen per square foot)	fc
			Lux (lm/m^2)[e]	lx
			Phot (lm/cm^2)	ph
Luminous intensity (candlepower)	I	$I = d\Phi/d\omega$ (ω = solid angle through which flux from point source is radiated)	Candela (lumen per steradian)[e]	cd
Luminance (photometric brightness)	L	$L = d^2\Phi/d\omega(dA \cos\theta)$ $= dI/(dA \cos\theta)$ (θ = angle between line of sight and normal to surface considered)	Candela per unit area	cd/in^2, etc.
			Stilb (cd/cm^2)	sb
			Nit (cd^e/m^2)	nt
			Footlambert ($cd/\pi ft^2$)	fL
			Lambert ($cd/\pi cm^2$)	L
			Apostilb ($cd/\pi m^2$)	asb
Luminous efficiency	V	$V = K/K_{max}$	None (dimensionless)	—
Luminous efficacy	K	$K = \Phi_v/\Phi_e$	Lumen per watt[e]	lm/W

[a]Quantities may be restricted to a narrow wavelength band by adding the word spectral and indicating the wavelength. The corresponding symbols are changed by adding a subscript λ, e.g., $Q\lambda$, for a spectral concentration or a λ in parentheses, e.g., $K(\lambda)$, for a function of wavelength.
[b]Should be deprecated in favor of emitted radiant exitance.
[c]Should be deprecated in favor of emitted luminous exitance.
[d]Φ_i = incident flux; Φ_a = absorbed flux; Φ_r = reflected flux; Φ_t = transmitted flux.
[e]The International System (SI) unit.

which are consistent with those agreed upon to date by the International Commission on Illumination, the International Electrotechnical Commission, the International Organization for Standardization, and the Commission for Symbols, Units, and Nomenclature of the International Union of Pure and Applied Physics are listed in Table 1.

L. E. BARBROW

References

1. "Principles of Light Measurement," Bureau Central de la CIE, 4 Av. du Recteur Poincaré, 75 Paris 16e, France (1970).
2. Wensel, H. T., Roeser, W. F., Barbrow, L. E., and Caldwell, F. R., "The Waidner-Burgess Standard of Light," J. Res. *Natl Bur. Std.*, 6, 1103 (June 1931).
3. Walsh, J. W. T., "Photometry," 3rd Ed., New York, Dover Publications, 1958.
4. Barbrow, L. E., Wilson, S. W., "Vertical Distribution of Light from Gas-Filled Candlepower Standards," *Illum. Eng.*, 53, 645 (December 1958).
5. "IES Lighting Handbook," 5th Edition, Illuminating Engineering Society, New York, 1972.
6. Cotton, H., "Principles of Illumination," New York, John Wiley & Sons, 1961.
7. Winch, G. T., "Photometry and Colorimetry of Fluorescent and Other Electric Discharge Lamps," *Trans. Illum. Eng. Soc.* (London), 11, 107 (June 1946).
8. Taylor, A. H., "Errors in Reflectometry," *J. Opt. Soc. Am.*, 25, 51 (February 1935).
9. "International Lighting Vocabulary," Bureau Central de la CIE, 4 Av. du Recteur Poincaré, 75 Paris 16e, France (1970).

Cross-references: COLOR; LUMINANCE; MEASUREMENTS, PRINCIPLES OF; OPTICS, GEOMETRICAL, REFLECTION.

PHOTOMULTIPLIER*

Photomultipliers make use of the phenomena of photoemission and secondary-electron emission in order to detect very low light levels. The

*Author deceased; article reprinted from first edition.

electrons released from the photocathode by incident light are accelerated and focused onto a secondary-emission surface (called a dynode). Several electrons are emitted from the dynode for each incident primary electron. These secondary electrons are then directed onto a second dynode where more electrons are released. The whole process is repeated a number of times depending on the number of dynodes. In this manner, it is possible to amplify the initial photocurrent by a factor of 10^8 or more in practical photomultipliers. It is, therefore, evident that the photomultiplier represents an extremely sensitive detector of light.

The major characteristics of the photomultiplier with which the user is generally most concerned are as follows:

(a) sensitivity, spectral response, and thermal emission of photocathodes;

(b) amplification factor;

(c) noise characteristics and the signal-to-noise ratio.

Sensitivity, Spectral Response, and Thermal Emission of Photocathodes Many different types of photocathodes are being used in photomultipliers. With a selection of various cathodes, it is possible to cover the range of response from the soft x-ray region (approximately 5 to 500Å) to the near infrared (approximately 12 000Å). Photocathodes in common use are listed in Table 1. Typical spectral response curves are shown in Fig. 1. The thermal emission at 25°C of CuI and CsI is lower than that of the other cathodes listed.

Amplification Factor The amplification factor in a photomultiplier depends on the secondary emission characteristics of the dynode and to some extent on the design of the multiplier structure.

Most secondary-emission surfaces used in commercial photomultipliers fall into two classes:

(1) Alkali metal compounds, e.g., cesium antimony.

(2) Metal oxide layers, e.g., magnesium oxide on silver-magnesium alloy.

The alkali metal compounds have higher gain at low primary electron energy (of the order of 75 V). The metal oxide layers show less fatigue at high current density of emission (i.e., at sev-

TABLE 1   CHARACTERISTICS OF COMMON PHOTOCATHODES

Photocathode	Retma Code Number	λm, at max. (Å)	λ_0, 1% of max. (Å)	Quantum Efficiency, at λm	Average Thermionic Emission at 25°C (amp/cm^2)	Average μ A/lumen (2870 K tungsten source)
Cs—O—Ag	S-1	8000	12,000	0.005	10^{-11}	10–20
Cs—Sb(0) opaque	S-4	4000	7,000	0.25	10^{-14}	60–100
Cs—Sb(0)	S-11	4500	7,000	0.20	10^{-14}	40–80
Cs—Ag—Bi	S-10	4500	7,500	0.10	10^{-13}	40–60
Na—K—Sb		4000	6,200	0.20	10^{-16}	30–60
Na—K—Cs—Sb	S-20	4250	8,250	0.25	10^{-14}	150–180
CuI		1100	1,900	0.30		
CsI		1250	1,950	0.30		

eral microamperes per square centimeter or higher).

Table 2 lists some characteristics of the common dynode surfaces.

TABLE 2   CHARACTERISTICS OF COMMON DYNODE SURFACES

Surface	Maximum Secondary Emission Ratio	Primary Voltage for Maximum Ratio
Cs—Sb	8.0	500
Cs—Ag—O	5.8–9.5	500–1000
MgO (on AgMg)	9.8	500
BeO (on CuBe)	3.5–5.5	500–700
BeO (on NiBe)	12.3	700
Al_2O_3	1.5–4.8	350–1300

The multiplier structures may be divided into two main types, dynamic and static.

The dynamic multiplier in its simplest form consists of two parallel dynode surfaces with an alternating electric field applied between them. Electrons leaving one surface at the proper phase of the applied field are accelerated to the other surface where they knock out secondary electrons. These electrons in turn are accelerated back to the first plate when the field reverses, creating still more secondary electrons. Eventually the secondary electrons are collected by an anode placed in the tube; if they are not, a self-maintained discharge occurs. In practice, dynamic multipliers have been replaced by static ones mainly because the latter have better stability and are easier to operate.

The static multipliers may be either magnetically or electrostatically focused.

Figure 2(A) illustrates one type of multiplier structure using *magnetic* focusing. Primary elec-

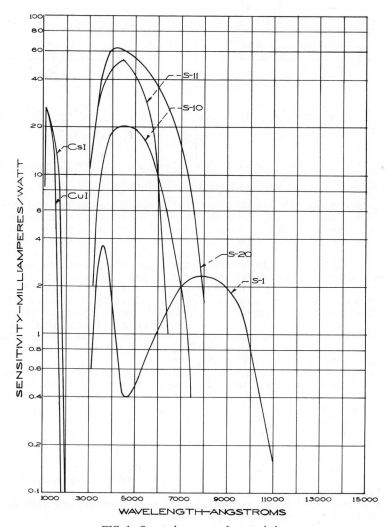

FIG. 1. Spectral response characteristics.

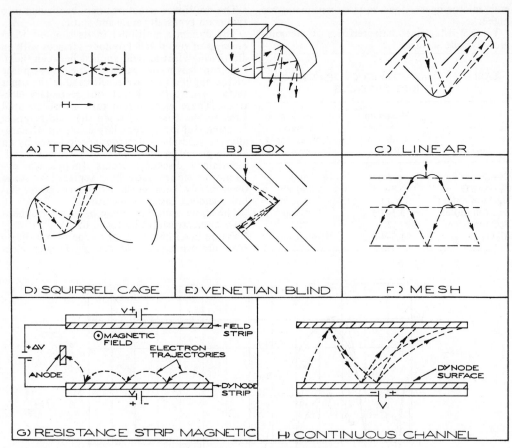

FIG. 2. Various multiplier structures.

trons impinging on one side of a dynode cause the emission of secondary electrons from the opposite side. These electrons are then focused onto the next dynode by means of the axial magnetic field.

Figures 2(B) through (F) illustrate the more common types of *electrostatic* multiplier structures. The structures shown in Fig. 2(B), (C), and (D) actually use focusing from one stage to the next. The structures in Fig. 2(E) and (F) are unfocused.

Advanced technology has made possible the deposition of thin semiconductor secondary emission surfaces onto insulating substrates. Such dynode strips have been used in designing rugged miniature multiplier structures. Two such structures are shown in Fig. 2(G) and (H). In both these structures the secondary electrons are accelerated along the length of the dynode strip by means of the potential applied across the strip. The structure in Fig. 2(H) can be made particularly small, the dimensions of a typical unit being 0.5 mm outside diameter and 10 mm long.

The unfocused electrostatic structures have less sensitivity to stray electric and magnetic fields. The focused structures, especially (C) and

(D) in Fig. 2, can be made to have very short transit-time spreads. Often special accelerating electrodes are placed between the dynodes to improve their transit-time spread and space-charge characteristics. At 200 to 300 V/stage, the transit-time spread may be less than 10^{-9} second, and peak pulse outputs of the order of 200 mA may be drawn before nonlinearity owing to space-charge saturation sets in.

In the normal operating range, the over-all amplification G of the multiplier is proportional to V^β, where V is the over-all voltage and β is a constant of the order of seven for a ten-stage structure.

Noise Characteristics and the Signal-to-noise Ratio It is necessary to distinguish between two types of noise in photomultipliers, dark and shot noise.

The *dark noise* in photomultipliers is caused mainly by the following:

(1) leakage current across insulating supports,

(2) field emission from electrodes,

(3) thermal emission from the photocathode and dynodes,

(4) positive ion feedback to the photocathode, and

(5) fluorescence from dynodes and insulator supports.

By careful design and construction of the photomultiplier it is possible to limit the dark noise principally to item (3).

Associated with the photocurrent from the photocathode is *shot noise*. There is also shot noise from secondary emission in the multiplier structure. The mean-square shot noise current $\overline{i_n^2}$ at the anode is given to a close approximation by

$$\overline{i_n^2} = 2ebG^2\overline{i_p}\Delta f$$

where e is the electronic charge, G is the amplification, $\overline{i_p}$ is the average photocurrent, Δf is the bandwidth of the system, and b is a factor equal to approximately 1.5 which accounts for the shot noise created in the multiplier. The signal-to-noise ratio S/N is then given by

$$S/N = \frac{G\overline{i_p}}{\sqrt{\overline{i_n^2}}} = \sqrt{\frac{\overline{i_p}}{2eb\,\Delta f}}$$

Uses of Photomultipliers One of the major uses of photomultipliers is in the scintillation counter where in combination with a fluorescent material it is used to detect nuclear radiation. The advent of the space program has led to applications in star and planet tracking for guidance systems as well as in star photometry and quantitative measurements of soft x-rays in outer space. Other applications include use in facsimile transmission, spectral analysis, automatic process control, and many other areas where extremely low light levels must be detected.

BERNARD R. LINDEN

References

Engstrom, R. W., "Multiplier Phototube Characteristics. Application to Low Light Levels," *J. Opt. Soc. Am.*, 37, 420–430 (1947).

Dunkelman, L., *et. al.*, "Spectrally Selective Photodetectors for the Middle and Vacuum Ultraviolet," *Appl. Opt.*, 1, 695–700 (1962).

Linden, B. R., "Five New Photomultipliers for Scintillation Counting," *Nucleonics*, 11, 30–33 (1953).

Rodman, H. P., and Smith, H. J., "Tests of Photomultipliers for Astronomical Pulse Counting Applications," *Appl. Opt.*, 2, 181–186 (1963).

See also the Proceedings of the Scintillation Counting Symposia in *IRE Trans. Nucl. Sci.*, 3, No. 4, 1956; 5, No. 3, 1958; 7, No. 2–3, 1960; 9, No. 3, 1962.

Cross-references: FIELD EMISSION, PHOTOCONDUCTIVITY; PHOTOELECTRICITY, THERMIONICS.

PHOTON

The existence of the photon was first suggested by Planck's famous research, about 1900, into the distribution in frequency of blackbody radiation. He arrived at agreement with the experimental distribution only by making the drastic (for those times) assumption that the radiation exists in discrete amounts with energy $E = hf$. Here f is the frequency of the radiation and h is Planck's constant, $6.626(10)^{-27}$ erg sec. Confirmation of the existence of these quanta of electromagnetic energy was provided by Einstein's interpretation of the photoelectric effect (1905); he made it clear that electrons in a solid absorb light energy in the discrete amounts hf. The full realization that the photon is a particle with energy and momentum was provided by the Compton effect (1922), an aspect of the scattering of light by free electrons. Compton showed that features of the scattering are understood by balancing energy and momentum in the collision in the usual way, the light considered as a beam of photons each with energy hf and momentum hf/c.

The modern point of view is that, for every particle that exists, there is a corresponding field with wave properties. In the development of this point of view the particle aspects of electrons and nuclei were evident at the beginning and the field or wave aspects were found later (this was the development of quantum mechanics). In contrast, the wave aspects of the photon were understood first (this was the classical electromagnetic theory of Maxwell) and its particle aspects only discovered later.

From this modern point of view the photon is the particle corresponding to the electromagnetic field. It is a particle with zero rest mass and spin one. For a photon moving in a specific direction, the energy E and the momentum q of the particle are related to the frequency f and wavelength λ of the field by the Planck equation $E = hf$ and the de Broglie equation $q = h/\lambda$. As for all massless particles, the energy and momentum are related by $E = cq$ and the photon can only exist moving at light speed c. Another property of all massless particles is this: given the momentum, the particle can exist in just two states of spin orientation. The spin can be parallel or antiparallel to the momentum but no other directions are possible. The photon state with the spin and momentum parallel (antiparallel) is said to be right- (left-) handed and is a right- (left-) hand circularly polarized wave. In analogy with the neutrino, one can say that the state has positive (negative) helicity and can call the right-handed particle the antiphoton, the left-handed particle the photon. There is an operation, *CP* conjugation, that converts a photon state into an antiphoton state and vice versa. It is possible to superpose photon and antiphoton states in such a way that the superposition is unchanged by *CP* conjugation and so gives a type of photon that is its own antiparticle. The photons produced by transitions between states of definite parities in atoms or nuclei are their own antiparticles in this sense. As for all particles with integer spin, the photon follows Bose-Einstein statistics. This means that a large number of photons may be accumulated into a

single state. Macroscopically observable electromagnetic waves, such as those resonating in a microwave cavity for example, are understood to be large numbers of photons all in the same state. The photon, among all the particles, is unique in having its states be macroscopically observable this way.

The electric and magnetic fields **E** and **B** describe the state of the photon and make up the wave function of the particle. Maxwell's equations give the time development of the fields and take the place, for the photon, that Schrödinger's equation takes for a material particle. Many of the remarks above follow as direct consequences of Maxwell's equations. In Gaussian units, where both **E** and **B** are measured in gauss or dynes per electrostatic unit of charge, the equations for the free fields are

$$\epsilon_{jkl}\partial E_l/\partial x_k + c^{-1}\partial B_j/\partial t = 0 \qquad (1)$$

$$\epsilon_{jkl}\partial B_l/\partial x_k - c^{-1}\partial E_j/\partial t = 0 \qquad (2)$$

$$\partial E_j/\partial x_j = \partial B_j/\partial x_j = 0 \qquad (3)$$

The particle aspect of the equations becomes evident when the equations are written in terms of the complex three-vector

$$\psi_j = E_j - iB_j \qquad (4)$$

in which case they become

$$\epsilon_{jkl}\partial \psi_l/\partial x_k + ic^{-1}\partial \psi_j/\partial t = 0 \qquad (5)$$

$$\partial \psi_j/\partial x_j = 0 \qquad (6)$$

Equation (6) is to be considered as an initial condition rather than as a equation of motion since it follows from Eq. (5) that

$$\partial(\partial \psi_j/\partial x_j)/\partial t = ic\epsilon_{jkl}\partial^2\psi_l/\partial x_j\partial x_k = 0$$

so if $\partial \psi_j/\partial x_j$ is zero at the start, it is zero forever. Equation (5) can be cast into Hamiltonian form. One writes the three components ψ_j as a column matrix ψ and introduces three, three-by-three, matrices by

$$(s_k)_{jl} = i\epsilon_{jkl} \qquad (7)$$

With this notation, Eq. (5) becomes

$$ic(s_k)_{jl}\partial \psi_l/\partial x_k = i\partial \psi_j/\partial t$$

or

$$H\psi = i\hbar\partial \psi/\partial t \qquad (8)$$

where

$$H = -\, c\mathbf{s} \cdot \mathbf{p} \qquad (9)$$

and **p** is $-i\hbar\nabla$. The Hamiltonian for the photon is thus $-cs \cdot \mathbf{p}$. In detail, the matrices that occur here are

$$s_1 = \begin{pmatrix} 0 & 0 & 0 \\ 0 & 0 & -i \\ 0 & i & 0 \end{pmatrix}, \qquad s_2 = \begin{pmatrix} 0 & 0 & i \\ 0 & 0 & 0 \\ -i & 0 & 0 \end{pmatrix},$$

$$s_3 = \begin{pmatrix} 0 & -i & 0 \\ i & 0 & 0 \\ 0 & 0 & 0 \end{pmatrix} \qquad (10)$$

They are Hermitian and, as is easily verified, they fulfill the commutation rules

$$[s_i, s_j] = i\epsilon_{ijk}s_k$$

and so are a set of angular momentum matrices. Evidently each has eigenvalues $0, \pm 1$ so they are a representation of spin one.

Next consider the plane wave solutions. Let them be propagating in the 3-direction; so substitute

$$\psi = u \exp[i\hbar^{-1}(p_3 z - Wt)]$$

into Eq. (8). Here the same symbol p_3 is used for the eigenvalue as for the operator. The system reduces to the matrix eigenvalue problem

$$-c\begin{pmatrix} 0 & -ip_3 & 0 \\ ip_3 & 0 & 0 \\ 0 & 0 & 0 \end{pmatrix}u = Wu$$

The eigenvalues are found to be $W = 0, \pm cp$, where p is $|p_3|$, and the corresponding eigenvectors are

$$u_0 = \begin{pmatrix} 0 \\ 0 \\ 1 \end{pmatrix}, u_\pm = \frac{1}{\sqrt{2}}\begin{pmatrix} \pm p_3/p \\ -i \\ 0 \end{pmatrix}$$

The $W = 0$ possibility does not satisfy the initial condition, Eq. (6), and so must be discarded. The solutions $u_\pm$ are valid for either sign of p_3; choose $p_3 = \pm p$ so both waves are propagating in the positive z direction. The two solutions of the problem are then

$$\psi_\pm = \frac{1}{\sqrt{2}}\begin{pmatrix} 1 \\ -i \\ 0 \end{pmatrix}\exp[\pm ip\hbar^{-1}(z - ct)] \qquad (11)$$

The subscript $+1(-1)$ denotes a particle (antiparticle) solution with positive (negative) frequency of $W/h = + cp/h$ ($- cp/h$). Also $\psi_\pm$ are evidently eigenstates of the helicity operator $\mathbf{s} \cdot \mathbf{p}/p$ with eigenvalues ∓ 1. The electric and magnetic fields are the real and imaginary parts:

$$E_{\pm,x} = 2^{-1/2}\cos[p\hbar^{-1}(z - ct)] \qquad (12a)$$

$$E_{\pm,y} = \pm\, 2^{-1/2}\sin[p\hbar^{-1}(z - ct)] \qquad (12b)$$

$$B_{\pm,x} = \mp\, 2^{-1/2}\sin[p\hbar^{-1}(z - ct)] \qquad (12c)$$

$$B_{\pm,y} = 2^{-1/2}\cos[p\hbar^{-1}(z - ct)] \qquad (12d)$$

$$E_{\pm z} = B_{\pm z} = 0 \qquad (12e)$$

Here it is seen that the $-1(+1)$ helicity solution

is left- (right-) hand circularly polarized with respect to the propagation direction.

The allowed states of the photon are eigenstates of the Hamiltonian H with eigenvalues $\pm cp$. Let $|H|$ be the operator which, applied to the same states, gives eigenvalue cp. The operators for the physical energy, momentum, and angular momentum of the photon are $|H|$, $(H/|H|)\mathbf{p}$, and $(H/|H|)(\mathbf{x} \times \mathbf{p} + \hbar\mathbf{s})$. One can understand these assignments for the energy and momentum by considering the plane wave states of Eq. (11). The states are eigenstates of the operators with energy eigenvalue cp and with momentum eigenvalue p in the positive z direction. As further justification for these operator assignments, the expectation values of the operators are directly related to the classical formulas for energy, momentum, and angular momemtum in the electromagnetic field:

$$(\psi, |H|\psi) = (8\pi)^{-1} \int d^3x (E^2 + B^2)$$
$$(13a)$$

$$\left(\psi, \frac{H}{|H|}\mathbf{p}\,\psi\right) = (4\pi c)^{-1} \int d^3x (\mathbf{E} \times \mathbf{B})$$
$$(13b)$$

$$\left(\psi, \frac{H}{|H|}(\mathbf{x} \times \mathbf{p} + \hbar\mathbf{s})\,\psi\right) =$$

$$(4\pi c)^{-1} \int d^3x\; \mathbf{x} \times (\mathbf{E} \times \mathbf{B}) \quad (13c)$$

where the rule for taking the inner product is

$$(\psi_1, \psi_2) = \frac{1}{8\pi c} \int d^3x\; \psi_1^\dagger \frac{1}{p} \psi_2 \quad (14)$$

These equalities apply for any solution ψ of Eqs. (6) and (8). The dagger denotes the Hermitian conjugate. The operation $(1/p)\psi$ in Eq. (14) is to be carried out by expanding ψ in the plane wave components like $\psi_\pm$ and replacing the operator $(1/p)$ by the number $(1/p)$ in each component. Proofs of Eqs. (13) will not be given here; they can be made by expressing each side of the equations in terms of the plane wave expansion coefficients. Accepting these operator assignments, one sees that the helicity operator $\mathbf{s} \cdot \mathbf{p}/p$ is the component of the spin of the photon $(H/|H|)\mathbf{s}$ in the direction of its momentum $(H/|H|)\mathbf{p}$.

The CP conjugation operation is related to the space reflection covariance of Maxwell's equations. Consider a primed and an unprimed coordinate system such that the coordinates of any point in space referred to the two axes are related by $\mathbf{x}' = -\mathbf{x}$. Suppose the electric field is axial and the magnetic field is polar so that the functions describing the fields are related by $\mathbf{E}'(\mathbf{x}', t) = \mathbf{E}(\mathbf{x}, t)$ and $\mathbf{B}'(\mathbf{x}', t) = -\mathbf{B}(\mathbf{x}, t)$. It is

evident that Maxwell's equations have the same form in both coordinate systems and that the transformation rule for ψ is $\psi'(\mathbf{x}', t) = \psi^*(\mathbf{x}, t)$ where the asterisk denotes the complex conjugate. The fact that the equations have the same form in both systems implies further that if $\psi(\mathbf{x}, t)$ is any solution then $\psi'(\mathbf{x}, t)$, or equivalently $\psi^*(-\mathbf{x}, t)$, is also a solution. The operation that carries $\psi(\mathbf{x}, t)$ into $\psi'(\mathbf{x}, t)$ is called CP conjugation and one writes

$$\psi^{CP} = KP\psi \quad (15)$$

where K is the operation "take complex conjugate" and the operator P changes $\mathbf{x}$ into $-\mathbf{x}$. If ψ is a solution of Maxwell's equations so also is ψ^{CP}. However KP anticommutes with $\mathbf{s} \cdot \mathbf{p}$ so if the solution ψ has $\mp$ helicity, then ψ^{CP} has $\pm$ helicity. The CP conjugation thus converts the particle into the antiparticle. The KP operator also anticommutes with the physical momentum operator $(H/|H|)\mathbf{p}$ so for a state $\psi\pm(\mathbf{q})$ with definite helicity $\mp$ and physical momentum $\mathbf{q}$ one has

$$KP\psi_\pm(\mathbf{q}) = \psi_\mp(-\mathbf{q}) \quad (16)$$

Instead of the two states ψ_+ and ψ_-, one may consider the superpositions

$$\psi_1(\mathbf{q}) = 2^{-1/2}[\psi_+(\mathbf{q}) + \psi_-(\mathbf{q})] \quad (17a)$$

$$\psi_2(\mathbf{q}) = 2^{-1/2}[\psi_+(\mathbf{q}) - \psi_-(\mathbf{q})] \quad (17b)$$

The reason for introducing them is the property

$$KP\psi_1(\mathbf{q}) = \psi_1(-\mathbf{q}) \quad (18a)$$

$$KP\psi_2(\mathbf{q}) = -\psi_2(-\mathbf{q}) \quad (18b)$$

Thus the KP operation applied to ψ_1 or ψ_2 reproduces the state, only traveling in the opposite direction and with a change of phase for ψ_2. The states ψ_1 and ψ_2 in this way are their own antiparticles. These self-antiparticle states are plane polarized in perpendicular directions. For the states with momenta in the positive z direction, as given by Eqs. (11) and (12), the fields are seen to be

$$E_{1x} = \cos[p\hbar^{-1}(z - ct)] \quad (19a)$$

$$B_{1y} = \cos[p\hbar^{-1}(z - ct)] \quad (19b)$$

$$E_{2y} = \sin[p\hbar^{-1}(z - ct)] \quad (19c)$$

$$B_{2x} = -\sin[p\hbar^{-1}(z - ct)] \quad (19d)$$

with all other components zero.

The final point to be demonstrated here is that only a self-antiparticle type of photon is emitted or absorbed when a system makes a transition between states of definite parity. Consider for simplicity a spinless charged particle described by a Schrödinger wave function $\psi_m(\mathbf{x}, t)$. [The subscripts m and γ are used for the material particle and the photon.] Suppose the particle

is bound in some system and makes a transition from an initial state i to a final state f, both eigenstates of parity P, with emission or absorption of a photon. As is well known, the transition probability is determined by the interaction integral

$$I = - (e/Mc) \int d^3x [\psi_{mf}*(\mathbf{x}, t)\mathbf{p}\psi_{mi}(\mathbf{x}, t)]$$
$$\cdot \mathbf{A}(\mathbf{x}, t) \quad (20)$$

where e and M are the charge and mass of the particle and $\mathbf{A}$ is the vector potential of the photon in the Coulomb gauge,

$$\nabla \cdot \mathbf{A} = 0 \quad (21)$$

Here and below, the integrals extend over all space. The fields are found from the potential by the relations

$$\mathbf{E} = - c^{-1}\partial\mathbf{A}/\partial t \quad (22)$$

$$\mathbf{B} = \nabla \times \mathbf{A} \quad (23)$$

To make the argument, one first expresses the interaction explicitly in terms of the fields. The potential is found from the fields by integrating this way:

$$\mathbf{A}(\mathbf{x}, t) = \frac{1}{4\pi} \nabla \times \int d^3y \frac{\mathbf{B}(\mathbf{y}, t)}{|\mathbf{x} - \mathbf{y}|} \quad (24)$$

It is easily verified that this expression for $\mathbf{A}$ satisfies Eqs. (21), (22), and (23) by using Eqs. (1), (3), and the fact that $\nabla^2|\mathbf{x} - \mathbf{y}|^{-1} = - 4\pi\delta(\mathbf{x} - \mathbf{y})$. In the verification it is assumed that fields of interest will be zero outside a finite region of space so that in making partial integrations there are no contributions from infinity. Then by using Eq. (24) and replacing $\mathbf{B}$ by $i(\psi_\gamma - \psi_\gamma*)/2$, one can rewrite the interaction integral as

$$I = \frac{- ie}{8\pi Mc} \int d^3x [\psi_{mf}*(\mathbf{x}, t)\mathbf{p}\psi_{mi}(\mathbf{x}, t)]$$
$$\cdot \nabla \times \int \frac{d^3y}{|\mathbf{x} - \mathbf{y}|} [\psi_\gamma(\mathbf{y}, t) - \psi_\gamma*(\mathbf{y}, t)]$$

However, if i and f are eigenstates of parity, then, by changing integration variables from $\mathbf{x}$ and $\mathbf{y}$ to $-\mathbf{x}$ and $-\mathbf{y}$ in the $\psi_\gamma*$ term, one sees that

$$I = \frac{- ie}{8\pi Mc} \int d^3x [\psi_{mf}*(\mathbf{x}, t)\mathbf{p}\,\psi_{mi}(\mathbf{x}, t)$$
$$\cdot \nabla \times \int \frac{d^3y}{|\mathbf{x} - \mathbf{y}|} (1 \mp KP)\psi_\gamma(\mathbf{y}, t)$$

where the factor is $(1 - KP)$ if i and f have the same parity, $(1 + KP)$ if i and f have opposite parity. Since

$$KP(1 \mp KP)\psi_\gamma = \mp (1 \mp KP)\psi_\gamma$$

only a type of photon that is its own antiparticle can be involved in the transition in either case. As examples, the electric dipole radiation field has $KP = +1$ and the magnetic dipole field has $KP = -1$.

R. H. GOOD, JR.

References

Heitler, W., "The Quantum Theory of Radiation," London, Oxford University Press, 1954. Heitler discusses the properties of photons from different points of view than used here and especially shows various techniques for the quantization of the electromagnetic field.

Good, R. H., Jr., *Am. J. Phys.*, **28**, 659 (1960). A nonmathematical pictorial discussion of the different types of photons is given.

Good, R. H., Jr., and Nelson, T. J., "Classical Theory of Electric and Magnetic Fields," New York, Academic Press, 1971, Chap. XI. A more complete treatment of the subject is given here.

Cross-references: BOSE-EINSTEIN STATISTICS AND BOSONS, ELECTROMAGNETIC THEORY, LIGHT, MATRICES.

PHOTOSYNTHESIS*

The light-driven synthetic reactions of plant chloroplasts, blue-green algae, and photosynthetic bacteria are briefly summarized and somewhat oversimplified by the van Niel equation:

$$2H_2A + CO_2 \xrightarrow{\text{light}} (CH_2O) + H_2O + 2A$$

where H_2A represents a hydrogen donor and (CH_2O) represents carbohydrate. For chloroplasts and blue-green algae H_2A is water and A is oxygen; for photosynthetic bacteria H_2A is often H_2S or other sulfur compounds, but is *never* water.

The primary action of light in photosynthetic systems is the excitation of pigment molecules. Singlet-state excitation is transferred from the light-harvesting pigment molecules to those few specialized molecule which participate in primary photochemistry at reaction centers. When excitation becomes localized at a reaction center, there is a charge separation in which an electron moves from an excited chlorophyll molecules to a primary acceptor molecule, thus leaving a chlorophyll cation radical which is easily detected by electron spin resonance techniques. The identities of various primary acceptor molecules are still uncertain, but an iron-sulfur protein is a likely candidate for one type of reaction center (photochemical system 1) in chloroplasts. The array of light-harvesting pigments which deliver excitation energy to a single reaction center is called a photosynthetic

*Support by the U.S. Atomic Energy Commission is acknowledged.

unit. The size of photosynthetic units varies from roughly 50 to 2000 pigment molecules per reaction center in various systems; for plant chloroplasts 200 is a typical figure. The physical description of excitation transfer depends upon the structure of the photosynthetic unit in question. In most photosynthetic systems, there appears to be a heterogeneous arrangement of pigments with weak exciton coupling between closely spaced molecules (10 to 15 Å) and Förster resonance transfer between more widely separated molecules (e.g., 50 Å). In all cases energy transfer is a nonradiative process.

The pigments universally associated with photosynthesis are the chlorophylls. Chlorophyll *a* is essential for oxygen-evolving systems, and its close relative, bacteriochlorophyll, is characteristic of bacterial systems. Other types of chlorophyll as well as phycobilins and carotenoids function as accessory pigments which harvest light and transfer excitation to either chlorophyll *a* or bacteriochlorophyll.

Reaction centers have been characterized most thoroughly in purple photosynthetic bacteria. As shown in Fig. 1, the primary photo-

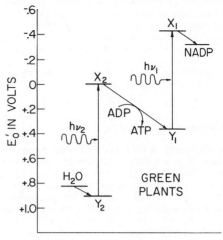

FIG. 2.

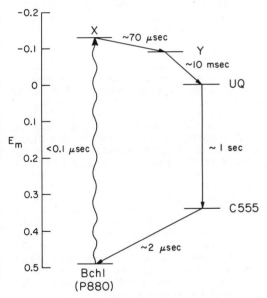

FIG. 1. *Chromatium vinosum*.

chemical electron transfer can be driven by a single 880-nm photon (1.4 eV), but the electrochemical free energy stored in the primary products is only about 0.6 eV. The return of the electron to bacteriochlorophyll via the intermediates (secondary acceptor Y, ubiquinone UQ, and cytochrome C555) in the cyclic transport chain is coupled to the formation of adenosine triphosphate (ATP) from adenosine diphosphate (ADP) and inorganic phosphate in which 0.3 eV per ATP is stored. Many bacteria also generate reducing power in the form of reduced nicotinamide-adenine dinucleotide

(NADH) from external hydrogen donors such as H_2S.

The formation of reduced organic compounds from CO_2 is driven by reducing power and ATP in a series of enzymic reactions. No light is required for these reactions.

In blue-green algae and plant chloroplasts two distinct photochemical reactions in physically separate reaction centers are required to generate reducing power (NADPH) from water. Photochemical system 2 generates an oxidant powerful enough to extract electrons from water and evolve oxygen. Photochemical system 1 generates the powerful reductant for CO_2 reduction. As shown in Fig. 2, the flow of electrons from the top of system 2 to the bottom of system 1 is coupled to the formation of ATP. In addition to the noncyclic electron transport pathway shown in Fig. 2, most oxygen-evolving systems also operate a cyclic pathway similar to that shown for bacteria in Fig. 1. However, in reaction centers containing chlorophyll *a*, the free energy stored in each photochemical charge separation is between 1.0 and 1.2 eV.

JOHN M. OLSON

References

1. Clayton, R. K., "Light and Living Matter," Volume 2: "The Biological Part," New York, McGraw-Hill, 1971 (243 pp.).
2. Rabinowitch, E., and Govindjee, "Photosynthesis," New York, John Wiley & Sons, 1969 (273 pp.).
3. Förster, Th., in "Modern Quantum Chemistry," Vol. 3, Sinanoglu, O., Ed., New York, Academic Press, 1965 (p. 93.).
4. Case, G. D., and Parson, W. W., "Thermodynamics of the Primary and Secondary Photochemical Reactions in *Chromatium*," *Biochim. Biophys. Acta*, 253, 187–202 (1971).
5. Knox, R. S., "Thermodynamics and the Primary Processes of Photosynthesis," *Biophys. J.*, 9, 1351–1362 (1969).

6. Ross, R. T., and Calvin, M., "Thermodynamics of Light Emission and Free-Energy Storage in Photosynthesis," *Biophys. J.*, 7, 595–614 (1967).

7. Pearlstein, R. M., Ed., "The Photosynthetic Unit," *Photochem. Photobiol.*, 14, 231–473 (1971).

Cross-references: LIGHT, PHOTOVOLTAIC EFFECT, SOLAR ENERGY UTILIZATION.

PHOTOVOLTAIC EFFECT

The photovoltaic effect (PVE) is the generation of an emf as a result of the absorption of light. Three phenomena are involved in the effect. The first of these is photoionization, i.e., the generation of equal numbers of positive and negative charges by light absorption. The second is the migration of one or both of the photo-liberated charges to a region where separation of the positive and negative charges can occur. The third is the presence of a charge-separation mechanism. The photovoltaic effect can occur in gases, liquids and solids, but it has been studied most intensively in solids and, therefore, this discussion will be limited to solids, especially semiconductors.

Photoionization Semiconductors and insulators are characterized by a threshold energy for photoionization equal to the energy difference between the bottom of the conduction band and the top of the valence band, i.e., the forbidden energy gap E_g. Only those photons whose energy exceeds E_g can cause photoionization. Values of E_g range from several electron volts, corresponding to an ultraviolet threshold, to small fractions of an electron volt corresponding to an infrared threshold.

The absorption of light follows Lambert's law which states that

$$N(x) = N(0)e^{-\alpha x}$$

where $N(0)$ and $N(x)$ are the numbers of photons crossing unit area per second at a reference point (0) and at a distance x from the reference point along the direction of propagation of the light beam, and α is the absorption constant. Figure 1 shows how α changes with photon energy in a number of semiconductors used in photovoltaic cells. This dependence of α on photon energy $h\nu$ is intimately related to the dependence of the photovoltaic effect parameters on $h\nu$.

Migration of the Photo-liberated Charges Because of Lambert's law, the photo-liberated charges are distributed along the path of the light beam. Normally, they would move about at random until they recombine with carriers of opposite sign. This recombination process is characterized by a mean free lifetime of a pair, which must be large enough to permit the carriers to move to a charge-separation region either by diffusion or under the action of a built-in electrostatic field.

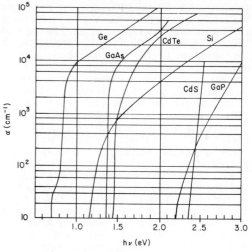

FIG. 1

Charge-separation Mechanism Charge separation requires a change in electrostatic potential between two regions of the solid, so that when a pair of opposite charges migrates to the region of the potential change, one of them can lower its potential by moving across this region. A large photovoltaic effect requires that the change in potential should be large and that it should occur over a distance which is short compared to the mean distance a free carrier can travel before recombination. These requirements imply the presence of a dipole layer which, in turn, implies an abrupt change in some property of the material. Such a dipole layer can occur either at the surface or in the interior of the material. A surface barrier usually involves a metal-semiconductor contact, a contact between the semiconductor and its oxide or, more generally, a contact with some other semiconductor. A barrier inside a material implies an abrupt change in the conductivity, which in the extreme case involves a change of conductivity type, as in a *p-n* junction. The strongest photovoltaic effects are those which arise at *p-n* junctions, and therefore, the remainder of this article will be devoted to the *p-n* junction photovoltaic effect.

Photovoltaic Effect at *p-n* Junctions A *p-n* junction is formed by arranging the chemical impurity distribution in a single crystal of a semiconductor so that electric current is carried primarily by electrons on one side of the junction (the *n*-side) and primarily by holes on the other side (the *p*-side). The resulting electrostatic potential profile is such that excess holes can lower their energy by moving from the *n*- to the *p*-side while excess electrons lower their energy by moving in the opposite direction. Light absorption in either region leads to an increase in the concentrations of both holes and electrons, which are separated at the *p-n* junc-

tion. If a resistive load is connected between ohmic contacts to the p- and n-regions of a p-n junction illuminated by photons with energy $h\nu > E_g$, the current through the load I_L is related to the voltage across the load by the relation

$$I_L = I_s - I_0 \left(e^{qV/kT} - 1\right)$$

where I_0 is the reverse saturation current of the p-n junction; q is the charge on the electron, k is Boltzmann's constant, T is the absolute temperature, and I_s is the photogenerated current which would flow if the load were a short circuit. The current I_s is a function of the absorption constant α; the spectral composition of the incident light, the pair lifetime and of the junction geometry.

Applications The photovoltaic effect can be used to convert sunlight to electricity, and indeed p-n junction silicon solar cells have been the principal power sources on artificial earth satellites. Silicon cells have a solar energy conversion efficiency of about 12 percent. Theoretical studies indicate that efficiencies in the vicinity of 20 percent should be possible. Studies of the feasibility of large-scale power generation to satisfy the ever-growing terrestrial demands for electric power are currently under way. The principal impediment to such large-scale utilization is the high cost of cells. However, it has been suggested that mass production of silicon cells could lead to the necessary cost reductions. Furthermore, it has been proposed that thin-film copper-cadmium sulfide solar cells, though less efficient than silicon cells, have an ultimately lower cost per watt. The photovoltaic effect can also be used to detect small intensities of light. Since the ionizing radiation need not be light, the effect can be used to detect x-rays, beta rays, protons, etc. Studies of the spectral response of the photovoltaic effect can yield information about basic material parameters such as α, τ, and E_g. It can be used to study surface effects, radiation damage, and other phenomena in semiconductors.

JOSEPH J. LOFERSKI

References

Wolf, M., "A New Look at Silicon Solar Cell Performance," *Energy Conversion*, **II**, 63 (1971).

van Aerschodt, A. E., et al., "The Photovoltaic Effect in the Cu-Cd-S System," *IEEE Trans. Electron Devices*, **ED-18**, 471 (1971).

Angrist, S. W., "Direct Energy Conversion," Boston, Allyn and Bacon, 1971.

Cross-references: ENERGY LEVELS, PHOTOCONDUCTIVITY, PHOTOELECTRICITY, SEMICONDUCTORS, SOLAR ENERGY SOURCES, SOLAR ENERGY UTILIZATION.

PHYSICAL ACOUSTICS

Sound waves in the ideal sense are mechanical disturbances propagating in a continuous medium. The basic fact of interest from a physical standpoint is that these waves carry momentum and energy without a net transport of mass. In addition there are two other facts worth mentioning which are that sound waves propagate in almost all substances and that sound waves can be used to study the physical properties of, or to cause physical changes in the substances through which they propagate.

In practice, the approximation that natural materials are continuous fails when the wavelength is short enough to be comparable to interatomic or intermolecular distances—in a gas, the mean-free-path of a molecule; in a solid, the distance between atoms. The region of validity of the approximation that the waves are of small amplitude is more difficult to circumscribe since it depends on more than one property of the medium. In most cases, the approximation is valid when the disturbance in the velocity of the medium as the wave passes is small compared to the speed of sound in the medium. In air under normal conditions, this will occur when the pressure disturbance becomes an appreciable fraction of atmospheric pressure. In liquids and solids, however, pressure disturbances of hundreds or thousands of atmospheres propagate as small-amplitude waves. The low compressibility, or high "stiffness," of these media increase the speed of sound and at the same time require a larger pressure fluctuation to produce a given velocity fluctuation. If the medium is in a critical state, however, the definition of what constitutes a small disturbance can depend on other factors. For example, cavitation in a liquid occurs at particular sites that are called cavitation nuclei. While the reasons for the existence of these sites in a fluid are not completely understood, it is clear that they are regions that are subject to fracture at pressures far below those that would fracture the pure liquid.

The energy transported by the wave per unit area normal to the direction of propagation is called the intensity and can be measured in watts per square meter (the mixed unit, watt per square centimeter, is also in common use). A sound wave in air of intensity comparable to that of sunlight would be just beyond the pain threshold of the ear, and acoustic waves within the range of human tolerance do not produce a noticeable warming, as does sunlight. The heat generated when sound is absorbed can be measured, however, and in the design of absorbers for very high intensity sound the effect of the resulting heat production on the absorber may have to be taken into account. The principle of conservation of energy applied to energy transport by wave motion is a very useful tool, just as it is in mechanics.

The momentum transport per second per unit area is the intensity divided by the wave speed.

Since this is also true for electromagnetic waves, it follows that a sound wave in air (speed 330 m/sec) of a given intensity transports about a million times more momentum than an electromagnetic wave of the same intensity. When the wave is absorbed or reflected, there is a radiation pressure on the absorber or reflector equal to the rate of change of momentum per unit area that is I/c on a perfect absorber and $2I/c$ on a perfect reflector, where I is the intensity and c the speed of sound. The measurement of this pressure is a fundamental method for measuring the amplitude of the wave.

The basic equations for a continuous medium are the continuity equation, which is an expression of the law of conservation of mass, and the Navier-Stokes equation, which relates the time rate of change of momentum in each volume element to the forces on the element. In differential form these equations are

$$\frac{\partial \rho}{\partial t} + \rho_0 \frac{\partial u}{\partial x} = 0 \quad \text{(continuity)}$$

$$\rho_0 \frac{\partial u}{\partial t} + \frac{\partial p}{\partial x} = 0 \quad \text{(conservation of momentum)}$$

The equations are presented here in one-dimensional form, and viscosity has been neglected. The inclusion of the two additional spatial dimensions and viscous effects is straightforward, and the complete equations can be found in most texts on acoustics. The dependent variables are p and ρ, the disturbances in pressure and density associated with the wave, and u, the disturbance in velocity. The parameter ρ_0 is the ambient density of the medium. In metric units (cgs) pressure is measured in dynes per square centimeter, density in grams per cubic centimeter, and velocity in centimeters per second. An additional equation is required that relates the scalar pressure to the other variables. While this third equation must be derived from the laws of thermodynamics, a relationship that is widely applicable is

$$\rho = \kappa \rho_0 p$$

where κ is the compressibility of the medium in units of inverse pressure. This relationship is useful as long as the wave does not change the value of κ appreciably. If there is no dissipation in the medium or if the dissipation is viscous, p and ρ will be in phase. In cases where dissipation exists due to irreversible heat flow, or the stress-strain relationship contains time derivatives, the equation can be retained by allowing κ to become complex. The three equations can be combined to give the wave equation

$$\left(\frac{\partial^2}{\partial x^2} - \frac{1}{c^2} \frac{\partial^2}{\partial t^2} \right) f = 0$$

where $c = 1\sqrt{\kappa \rho_0}$ is the speed of propagation of the wave, and f stands for any of the disturbances, p, ρ, or u.

The wave equation is a second-order partial differential equation and as such has a unique solution only if certain boundary conditions are applied. In the case of an unbounded medium, the boundary condition is that all sources of sound must radiate energy outward, and this is sufficient to produce a unique solution. In a bounded region, reflections must be taken into account. A sufficient boundary condition is that the impedance of the boundary, defined as the ratio of the pressure disturbance to the normal component of the velocity disturbance, be specified at each point on the boundary. In simple cases, the boundary conditions can be satisfied by a superposition of elementary solutions. The impedance tube is an example of a case where plane waves are used to measure the reflective and absorptive properties of a sample placed at one end of the tube in terms of the incident and reflected waves. The details of the distribution of sound in an auditorium, however, can be a complex problem. Another approach is to reformulate the equations as an integral equation containing the boundary conditions explicitly. This integral equation, a mathematical expression of Huygens' principle, is known in acoustics as Kirchhoff's formula. A third approach is to include the boundary conditions in the differential equations. An example of this procedure is the propagation of sound in a duct of varying cross section. If the change in width of the duct per wavelength is small compared to the wavelength of sound in the duct, the shape of the duct can be introduced into the continuity equation. This procedure leads to the "horn equation" which describes sound propagation in flared ducts. The subject of boundary conditions is further complicated by the fact that waves may propagate in the boundary itself. A boundary characterized by the fact that each point behaves independently is called a locally reacting boundary. If neighboring parts of a boundary interact to support wave motion, the boundary is non-locally interacting, and if the wave speed in such a boundary is higher than in the medium, energy can propagate along the boundary and leak back into the medium. In such a case, the wave may find a shorter time travel path through the boundary than through the medium itself.

Sound waves are generated in regions where time-varying forces act on the medium. While in some cases it may be convenient to think in terms of boundary conditions, this is not always convenient or even possible. A moving piston, such as the cone of a loudspeaker, can be thought of as a boundary condition in that the normal velocity, or pressure gradient, is specified. Sound generated by a region of turbulence, however, cannot be treated in this fashion because the source strength is distributed over the entire turbulent volume and not restricted to a surface. In fact, in the region of turbulence it is difficult to separate the motion of the medium into hydrodynamic and acoustical components. If the mechanism of sound generation is confined

to a definite region, it is natural to describe the sound field at a distance in terms of spherical harmonics, and the amplitudes of these harmonics can be related to integrals of moments of the motion of the medium taken over the source region. The most simple natural source, the monopole, can be described as a periodic injection and removal of mass at some point in the medium. In a stationary medium, the wave fronts are concentric spheres and the pressure disturbance is proportional to the time rate of change of mass flow. The next higher spherical harmonic, the dipole, is related to the net fluctuating force on the medium. For example, if an airfoil is subject to fluctuating lift and drag forces, there are equal and opposite forces exerted on the medium. These forces give rise to dipole sound radiation, and the sound pressure is proportional to the time rate of change of the forces. The sound fields generated by turbulence and by earthquakes are related to the integral of shear motions over the source volume and have a quadrupole distribution.

If the ambient properties of the medium are everywhere the same, the medium is said to be homogeneous. A uniform translational motion of the medium, however, deserves special attention. While a suitable coordinate transformation can remove a translational motion without changing the basic equations, such a transformation does not remove relative motion between the medium and any sources or receivers, and such motion causes the medium to be anisotropic. Although a receiver is never completely passive, the usual approximation is to assume that it is. In this case, the receiver has no physical effect on the medium and simply registers what it sees. A source, on the other hand, is contributing energy and momentum to the medium, and the distribution of these quantities is affected by the motion. Surfaces of constant phase are carried along by the medium in the same way as ripples from a pebble dropped in moving water, and for a monopole source at rest in a moving medium, they form spheres centered a distance RU/c downstream from the source, where R is the radius of the sphere, U the speed of the medium, and c the speed of sound in the medium at rest. The surfaces of constant pressure for such a source, on the other hand, are ellipsoids of revolution centered at the source with the minor axis in the flow direction. It follows that the pressure is greater to one side than it is at an equal distance either upstream or downstream. In general, the problem is complicated by the fact that the energy flow vector is not perpendicular to a surface of constant phase.

The dispersion relationship for acoustic plane waves relates the phase velocity and attenuation (or growth) of these waves to physical properties of the medium. Classically, the important parameters for a fluid are viscosity and heat conduction. While a general solution including these parameters leads to a sixth-order polynomial, in cases where they are small the problem can be solved to a good approximation by three pairs

of roots representing two plane waves, two viscous shear waves, and two thermal waves. The plane waves, traveling in opposite directions, are attenuated slightly by viscosity and heat conduction. The shear waves and thermal waves are not excited in the bulk of the medium. At boundaries, the shear and thermal waves will exist, however, to satisfy tangential velocity and thermal boundary conditions. While the viscous and thermal waves exist only in thin boundary layers (the real and imaginary parts of the propagation constant are equal), they may be responsible for a major part of the absorption. For example, in the case of plane waves propagating in the air in a pipe the ratio of boundary absorption coefficient to bulk absorption coefficient is about $10^8/Lf^{3/2}$ where L is the ratio of the area of the pipe to its perimeter and f is the frequency. For very narrow pipes, the ratio is larger.

In general, the measured value of attenuation of plane waves exceeds the classical predictions based on heat conductivity and viscosity. The discrepancy varies not only from one substance to another but also may depend on the past history of the substance. The additional attenuation is caused by (and reflects) interactions between particles on a small scale compared to a wavelength—in other words, between individual atoms, molecules, or groups of molecules. The problems are as various as the chemical properties of matter.

In solids, it has been shown that dissipation usually is related to departures from ideal crystalline structure on a relatively large scale. Annealing greatly reduces the attenuation of sound. In fluids, it has been shown, however, that attenuation can be related to interatomic binding forces as well as the forces binding clusters of molecules. The vibrational relaxation of O_2 in air and of magnesium salts in water, for example, can account for the excess attenuation of sound waves in the atmosphere and in seawater.

L. WALLACE DEAN, III

References

Morse, P. M., "Vibration and Sound," Second edition, New York, McGraw-Hill Book Co., 1948.

Rayleigh, "Theory of Sound," New York, Dover, 1945.

Blokhintzev, D., "Acoustics of an Inhomogeneous, Moving Medium," NACA TM1399 (1956).

Lighthill, M. J., "On Sound Generated Aerodynamically," Proc. Roy. Soc., A, 211, 564 (1952).

Mason, W. P., Ed., "Physical Acoustics," 7 Volumes, New York, Academic Press, 1964–1971.

Morse, P. M., and Ingard, K. U., "Theoretical Acoustics," New York, McGraw-Hill Book Co., 1968.

Cross-references: ACOUSTICS; ARCHITECTURAL ACOUSTICS; CAVITATION; ELECTROACOUSTICS; MUSICAL SOUND; RESONANCE; ULTRASONICS.

PHYSICAL CHEMISTRY

Physical chemistry emerged as a separate discipline in the second half of the nineteenth century; van't Hoff, Ostwald and Arrhenius contributed conspicuously in laying its foundation; van't Hoff is especially remembered for his explanation of osmotic pressure. According to him, a solute in a vessel separated from pure solvent by a membrane permeable only to the solvent exerts the same pressure which the same number of moles of gas would if confined in the same volume. In exerting this pressure, the solute draws solvent through the semipermeable membrane except as it is restrained by a pressure equal to the osmotic pressure. He also codified equilibrium theory in his celebrated "Études de Dynamique Chimique" published in 1884. It is interesting that van't Hoff received the first Nobel prize for chemistry in 1901.

Ostwald's dilution law and Arrhenius' theories of reaction rates and of the ionization of electrolytic solutions played key roles in getting physical chemistry off to an impressive beginning. Willard Gibbs' development of thermodynamics and statistical mechanics and van der Waals' equation of state are further milestones in the onward march of the new discipline.

Physical chemistry is the attempt to codify into laws the many qualitative observations made on all types of molecular systems. Such an ambitious goal can only be achieved by using the full spectrum of experimental and theoretical procedures. Atoms are known to consist of positive nuclei surrounded by electrons circulating in orbits about the nuclei. Since the electrostatic and magnetic laws of force are known for the atoms and since with wave mechanics we can express the laws of motion of particles in terms of the known potentials, it follows that the laws of chemistry are known. As a consequence of this, all properties of atoms and molecules can be calculated exactly, in principle. Nevertheless, such calculations are so difficult that only for the simplest systems can the calculations be carried out exactly. However, even for complicated systems, wave mechanics provides the framework into which all observations can be fitted.

Bohr's Model of the Atom It seems useful to trace quantum mechanics briefly from its beginnings. In 1913, Bohr working in Rutherford's laboratory, postulated that the angular momentum, $mr^2\omega$, of an electron moving in a circle about a nucleus, when multiplied by the number of radians, 2π, in the circular orbit, must equal some integer n times Planck's unit of action h. Accordingly he wrote

$$mr^2\omega 2\pi = nh \qquad (1)$$

He also equated the centrifugal force, $mr\omega^2$, to the coulomb force of attraction, e^2/r^2, to give

$$mr\omega^2 = \frac{e^2}{r^2} \qquad (2)$$

Finally the total energy E is the sum of the kinetic energy $\frac{1}{2}mr^2\omega^2$ and the potential energy $-e^2/r$, that is

$$E = \tfrac{1}{2}mr^2\omega^2 - \frac{e^2}{r} = -\tfrac{1}{2}\frac{e^2}{r} \qquad (3)$$

Here, m, r and ω are the reduced mass of the electron, the radius of the electron orbit, and the angular momentum, respectively. Solving these equations we find for the radius

$$r = \frac{n^2 h^2}{4\pi^2 m e^2} \qquad (4)$$

and for the energy

$$E = -\frac{2\pi^2 m e^4}{n^2 h^2} \qquad (5)$$

The number n is the principal quantum number. Equation (5) may be used to predict the spectra of hydrogen exactly, and thus constituted a great step forward in explaining atomic structure. The energy for a single electron circulating about a nucleus of charge ze is

$$E = -\frac{2\pi^2 m z^2 e^4}{n^2 h^2} \qquad (6)$$

If an electron is circulating about a nucleus whose charge is ze, but whose effective charge is reduced to $(z-s)e$ by a screening cloud of other electrons, there is a corresponding reduction of the electron's binding energy to

$$E = -\frac{2\pi^2 m e^4 (z-s)^2}{n^2 h^2} \qquad (7)$$

Here, s is called the screening constant. Equation (7) explains much of chemistry. In spite of this agreement, Bohr's theory is incomplete since it provides no procedure for calculating the screening constant.

The de Broglie Wavelength In the middle twenties, this complication was resolved by the advent of quantum mechanics. The matrix theory of Heisenberg was followed by de Broglie's interpretation of particle motion as wave motion. In the new theory, Bohr's quantization of orbits as formulated in Eq. (1) was replaced by the idea that the circumference of a circular orbit, $2\pi r$, must be an integral number of wavelengths, $n\lambda$. Thus,

$$n\lambda = 2\pi r = \frac{n^2 h^2}{2\pi m e^2} \qquad (8)$$

Substituting into Eq. (8) the value for the momentum, p, obtained from the kinetic energy equation $p^2/2m = \tfrac{1}{2}e^2/r$ leads to the famous de Broglie relation

$$\lambda = h/p \qquad (9)$$

This same result applies to photons, which have both a particle and a wave aspect. Thus, according to Einstein

$$E = h\nu = mc^2 = mc\lambda\nu \qquad (10)$$

Whence

$$\lambda = \frac{h}{mc} = h/p \qquad (11)$$

Confirmation of the De Broglie wavelength for electrons was soon provided by Davisson and Germer and by G. P. Thomson who demonstrated that electrons were in fact diffracted by crystalline materials much as x-rays are.

The Wave Equation Schrödinger took the the next step by substituting into the wave equation

$$\frac{1}{a^2}\frac{\partial^2\psi}{\partial t^2} = \frac{\partial^2\psi}{\partial x^2} + \frac{\partial^2\psi}{\partial y^2} + \frac{\partial^2\psi}{\partial z^2} \qquad (12)$$

values for a, the wave velocity. Thus

$$a = \lambda\nu = \frac{h}{p}\frac{E}{h} = \frac{E}{\sqrt{2m(E - V)}} \qquad (13)$$

Here ψ is the amplitude of the wave, while t is the time and x, y and z are the coordinates of position for the particle. For stationary waves, the amplitude may be expressed as

$$\psi = \phi(x,y,z)e^{-\frac{2\pi iEt}{h}} \qquad (14)$$

which when substituted along with Eq. (13) into Eq. (12) leads to Schrödinger's famous time-independent equation

$$\frac{\partial^2\phi}{\partial x^2} + \frac{\partial^2\phi}{\partial y^2} + \frac{\partial^2\phi}{\partial z^2} + \frac{8\pi^2 m}{h^2}(E - V)\phi = 0 \quad (15)$$

From Eq. (14), we note that

$$-\frac{h}{2\pi i}\frac{\partial}{\partial t}\psi = E\psi \qquad (16)$$

Using this result we see that Eq. (15) may be generalized to the time dependent form

$$\left[-\frac{h^2}{8\pi^2 m}\left(\frac{\partial^2}{\partial x^2} + \frac{\partial^2}{\partial y^2} + \frac{\partial^2}{\partial z^2}\right) + V\right]\psi = -\frac{h}{2\pi i}\frac{\partial\psi}{\partial t} \qquad (17)$$

Now since ϕ in Eq. (15) is the amplitude of the wave, the square of the amplitude $|\phi^2|$ is necessarily interpreted as proportional to the probability of a particle being at a point in space, just as the square of the amplitude of the wave expresses the density of radiation at a point in physical optics. Restricting the allowed solutions of Eq. (15) to those eigenfunctions ϕ which have acceptable values leads to the allowed values of the energy E which Bohr found for hydrogen.

It is important to note that we now have a theory that can be generalized to many particles. The operator in square brackets on the left of Eq. (17) is just the expression for the energy of a particle providing $(h/2\pi i)(\partial/\partial x)$, $(h/2\pi i)(\partial/\partial y)$ and $(h/2\pi i)(\partial/\partial z)$ are replaced by the corresponding momenta p_x, p_y and p_z respectively. Analogously $(-h/2\pi i)(\partial/\partial t)$ is the operator for the energy E or H as was noted in arriving at Schrödinger's time-dependent equation. It thus seems natural to generalize Eq. (17) to many particles by having V express the total potential energy for the system and taking as the operator for the kinetic energy, the sum over all particles

$$\sum_i\left[-\frac{h^2}{8\pi^2 m}\left(\frac{\partial^2}{\partial x^2} + \frac{\partial^2}{\partial y^2} + \frac{\partial^2}{\partial z^2}\right)\right]$$

This is not the place to elaborate quantum mechanics in detail, but clearly it completely transforms physical chemistry from an almost exclusively experimental discipline to one for which there is a fundamental theory as well.

Mean Values of Properties According to quantum mechanics, the mean value of any property, x, of a system in the state ψ_i having the energy ϵ_i is

$$\bar{x}_i = \int \psi_i{}^*\mathbf{x}\,\psi_i dT$$

Here $\mathbf{x}$ is the quantum mechanical operator for the property x, it is obtained from the latter by replacing each momentum p_i by $(h/2\pi i)(\partial/\partial q_i)$, where q_i is the corresponding positional coordinate, and keeping the q's and t unchanged. If there are ambiguities, $\mathbf{x}$ must be chosen to give real values for the calculated property. Now since the probability, p_i, of a system at equilibrium being in the state ψ_i is

$$P_i = \frac{e^{-\epsilon_i/kT}}{\sum_i e^{-\epsilon_i/kT}} \qquad (18)$$

the mean value of the property, x, for the system is

$$\langle x \rangle = \frac{\sum_i \bar{x}_i e^{\epsilon_i/kT}}{\sum_i e^{-\epsilon_i/kT}} \qquad (19)$$

Thus, in principle, the values of all properties can be calculated. Actually such calculations are quite difficult and are rarely carried through exactly. The sum $\sum_i e^{-\epsilon_i/kT}$ over all the states is called a partition function and is frequently represented by the symbol f.

Statistical Mechanics Statistical mechanics, whose beginnings go back to Maxwell and Boltzmann, was greatly developed and systematized by J. Willard Gibbs. It provides still another cornerstone of theoretical physical chemistry.

The probability, P_i, of a system being in the state i with energy ϵ_i is already given in Eq. (18). The average energy E is accordingly

$$E = \frac{\sum_i \epsilon_i e^{-\epsilon_i/kT}}{\sum_i e^{-\epsilon_i/kT}} \equiv kT^2 \frac{d \ln}{\partial T} \left(\sum_i e^{-\epsilon_i/kT} \right) \quad (20)$$

But, from thermodynamics, we have for the average energy of a system

$$E = - T^2 \frac{\partial (A/T)}{\partial T} \quad (21)$$

Here, A is the Helmholtz free energy and $A_1 - A_2$ is the maximum work a system can be made to perform at constant temperature in passing from state 1 to state 2. Equating the two values of E, given in Eqs. (20) and (21) and integrating gives

$$A = kT \ln \sum_i e^{-\epsilon_i/kT} + cT \quad (22)$$

Here c is an integration constant. Now the lowest state of the system must be nondegenerate and c must be zero in order that Eq. (22) will yield zero entropy for the system at the absolute zero of temperature as is required by the third law of thermodynamics. Thus, we can write the exciting result

$$A = - kT \ln \sum_i e^{-\epsilon_i/kT} \quad (23)$$

as the fundamental equation relating statistical mechanics and thermodynamics. If the energy levels ϵ_i are known as functions of the volume of the system, then A is known as a function of V and T, and all the thermodynamic properties of the system can be calculated.

Equilibrium Theory The probability, P_i, of a system which obeys Boltzmann statistics, being in the ith state is equal to n_i/N where n_i is the number of systems in the ith state and N is the total number of systems. Thus we can rewrite Eq. (19) in the form

$$\frac{n_i}{e^{-\epsilon_i/kT}} = \frac{N}{\sum_i e^{-\epsilon_i/kT}} = \lambda = e^{\mu/kT} \quad (24)$$

Here λ is called the absolute activity and μ is the chemical potential. For a system at equilibrium we can write

$$aA + bB + \cdots = dD + eE + \cdots \quad (25)$$

Here, a molecules of substance A react with b molecules of B to give d molecules of D plus e molecules of E, etc. According to thermodynamics, a system at equilibrium is incapable of doing work so that the reaction involves no change of chemical potential. Thus,

$$a\mu_A + b\mu_B + \cdots = d\mu_D + e\mu_E + \cdots \quad (26)$$

and

$$\lambda_A{}^a \lambda_B{}^b \cdots = \lambda_D{}^d \lambda_E{}^e \cdots \quad (27)$$

Whence

$$\frac{(n_A)^a}{f_A{}^a} \frac{(n_B)^b}{f_B{}^b} \cdots = \frac{(n_D)^d}{f_D{}^d} \frac{(n_E)^e}{f_E{}^e} \cdots \quad (28)$$

Here n_A is the number of molecules of the Ath kind distributed over the partition function f_A with analogous meanings for the other symbols. If we define c_A as the concentration of A then we have

$$n_A/V = c_A \quad (29)$$

and $f_A/V = F_A$. Here F_A is the partition function per unit volume. Equation (29) can now be rewritten in the form of an equilibrium constant K_c. Thus

$$K_c = \frac{(C_D)^d (C_E)^e \cdots}{(C_A)^a (C_B)^b \cdots} = \frac{F_D{}^d F_E{}^e \cdots}{F_A{}^a F_B{}^b \cdots} \quad (30)$$

Now even when systems do not obey Boltzmann statistics, we still have Eqs. (26) and (27) remaining true with the auxiliary equation

$$\left(\frac{\partial A}{\partial n_A} \right)_{V,T,n_B} = \mu_A \quad (31)$$

as well as the other analogous equations. Thus equilibria for systems obeying all types of statistics are readily formulated using statistical mechanics. We now turn to rates of reaction.

Reaction Rates A chemical reaction ordinarily proceeds slowly because it involves passage through a transition state, which is difficult to attain. The transition state lies at the saddle point of a landscape separating two valleys, one corresponding to reactants and the other to products. Such landscapes are ordinarily multidimensional. The path through the saddle point is called the reaction coordinate. A system at the saddle point is called the activated complex and is like other molecules except for its fleeting passage along the reaction coordinate. The reaction coordinate of the activated complex can be treated as a translational degree of freedom if due account is taken of reflection and barrier leakage. Since the transition state is the point of no return, it is the logical region for calculating the rate of reaction. If we rewrite Eq. (25) to include the activated complex $C\ddagger$, we have

$$aA + bB + \cdots \rightarrow C\ddagger \rightarrow dD + eE + \cdots \quad (32)$$

The rate of reaction in the forward direction, r_f, at equilibrium is

$$r_f = \mathcal{H} \frac{1}{2} C_\delta \ddagger \frac{\bar{u}}{\delta} \equiv \mathcal{H} \frac{1}{2} C\ddagger \frac{(2\pi mkT)^{\frac{1}{2}}}{h} \delta \left(\frac{2kT}{\pi m} \right)^{\frac{1}{2}} \frac{1}{\delta}$$

$$= \mathcal{H} C\ddagger \frac{kT}{h} = \mathcal{H} F\ddagger \frac{kT}{h} \lambda_f \ddagger \quad (33)$$

Here $\mathcal{H}$ is the transmission coefficient which corrects the rate for reflection, barrier leakage and non-equilibrium; $\bar{u}$, the average velocity across the barrier, has the value $(2kT/\pi m^{\ddagger})^{1/2}$; $C_{\delta}^{\ddagger}$ is the concentration of activated complex per length δ along the reaction coordinate while $C^{\ddagger}$ is the same quantity per single quantum state along the reaction coordinate. $F^{\ddagger}$ and $\lambda_f^{\ddagger}$ are the partition functions per unit volume and the absolute activity of the activated complexes moving in the forward direction, respectively. The net rate is thus

$$r = \mathcal{H} \frac{kT}{h} F^{\ddagger} (\lambda_f^{\ddagger} - \lambda_b^{\ddagger}) \qquad (34)$$

Here $\lambda_b^{\ddagger}$ is the absolute activity of reactants moving in the backward direction and may be replaced by the product of the absolute activities of the products of reaction while $\lambda_f^{\ddagger}$ may be replaced by the products of the absolute activities of the reactants; r is of course zero at equilibrium.

Experimental Methods In recent times, physical chemistry has added many new techniques to the standard procedures which were used earlier in such fields as solution chemistry and in gas kinetics. Analysis of the products of reaction by mass spectrography has solved many difficult kinetic problems. Computer techniques have greatly speeded up structure determination by x-rays and by other diffraction techniques using electrons and neutrons. The development of radar in wartime provided a basis for microwave spectroscopy. Microwaves with wave lengths around one centimeter can be used to study the inversion of ammonia and internal rotations around $C-C$ and other bonds. Microwave spectroscopy, because of the extremely long wavelengths involved, brings phenomenal precision into molecular structure measurements.

Nuclear magnetic resonance, measuring as it does the magnetic moments of atomic nuclei, reveals the different diamagnetic and paramagnetic environments surrounding atoms. For example, one can distinguish various environments of hydrogen and rates of migration between such environments. Electron spin resonance yields parallel information about the unpaired electrons. Thus free radicals are detected, and changes involving them are followed.

Chromatography makes use of the differential distribution of the components of a mixture between a stationary and a moving phase separating the components because of the different times that they require to traverse a column. At low temperatures, even *ortho-* and *para*-hydrogen can be separated by helium moving past carbon. Chromatographic separation is in fact one of the milestones in chemistry.

Valence and Molecular Structure The electron pair bond of G. N. Lewis is explained in terms of quantum mechanics and the Pauli Exclusion Principle. Thus quantum mechanics is used to find the best bonding orbitals and the

Exclusion Principle requires that only two electrons having unlike spins can occupy the orbital. The recent discovery of fluorides of the rare gases shows that novel findings are still possible in valence and molecular structure. Pauling has given us an interesting presentation of valence in his book with that title.

Thermodynamics The thermodynamics of solutions is developing along the lines of providing mechanistic models to explain activity coefficients at the higher concentrations not explained by Debye-Hückel theory. This gives added insight into the structure of solutions. Better models are being developed to explain simple liquids. The best of them yield very realistic calculations of the properties of liquids.

Concluding Remarks The boundaries between disciplines regularly grow more blurred with time. This is especially true of the border between chemistry and physics. Here physical chemistry or chemical physics continues to spread into new fields with no ends in sight. Physical chemistry's second century should be even more spectacular than the first has been.

HENRY EYRING

Cross-references: CHEMICAL KINETICS, CHEMICAL PHYSICS, CHEMISTRY, MICROWAVE SPECTROSCOPY, OSMOSIS, STATISTICAL MECHANICS, THERMODYNAMICS.

PHYSICS

Physics can be defined as the branch of natural science that treats those phenomena of material objects included in the subjects of mechanics, properties of matter, heat, sound, light, electricity and magnetism, and molecular and atomic processes. It describes and correlates energy and radiation, and has sometimes been defined as the study of matter and energy. While such definitions attempt to distinguish between physics and other sciences, it should be stressed that physics is not set off by itself, but is very closely related to other sciences, and there is a good deal of overlap with their spheres of interest. In some cases, the differences are partially matters of emphasis. Chemistry stresses the regrouping of atoms to form new compounds, while physics picks a particular substance and studies its behavior. Biology restricts its interest to living organisms, while physics largely omits them from its consideration. Geology confines its investigations to the earth itself and the inanimate material of which it is composed. Astronomy, on the other hand, finds its field of interest in the vast expanses of space which run on and on away from the earth.

The extent to which these sciences overlap is shown by the special branches of science dealing with borderline areas. Astrophysics treats physical phenomena as they occur in regions beyond the immediate vicinity of the earth. It includes studies of the physical processes in

stars and of the nature of the radiations they emit. Physical chemistry, as its name implies, covers phenomena common to both physics and chemistry. Energy relations in chemical reactions and the effects of changes in temperature or pressure on the reactions are samples of the topics included. Geophysics relates physics and geology, and involves studies of the earth's magnetism and the effects of high pressure in the earth's interior. Biophysics deals with the physical processes that are of specific interest to the study of living organisms. Each of these fields has grown to include a vast array of scientific knowledge, and each is discussed in a separate article in this book.

The field of engineering is closely related to physics and other sciences. In general, it can be said that as knowledge about some specific topic grows to the point where use can be made of it in every-day life or in industrial processes, the topic passes over to engineering, and engineers develop and improve things using the basic information. Scientists concern themselves with the basic phenomena themselves, while engineers direct their efforts toward the solution of problems dictated by specific applications.

Historical Background The word "physics" can be traced to the Greek word *physos,* meaning nature. All studies about nature were grouped together by the Greek philosophers, but in many cases theories suffered from a lack of experimental research, so that the name, "natural philosophy" was more descriptive of their efforts than a name such as "natural science" would have been.

A summary of the important features in the development of physics from its early beginnings to the present advanced state can be found in the article on HISTORY OF PHYSICS.

Major Divisions of Physics For purposes of study, physics can be reasonably well divided into major areas, which will be discussed briefly here and in greater detail in other articles in this book.

Mechanics is the science of the motions of material bodies, the forces which produce or change these motions, and the energy relations involved. Newton's three laws of motion and his law of gravitation form the foundation of this study. Work, momentum, vibration, wave motion, pressure, elasticity, and viscosity are other topics considered to be parts of mechanics.

Heat is the energy which an object possesses by virtue of the motions of the molecules of which it is composed plus the potential energy resulting from interatomic forces. The field is of great importance to other areas of learning, as well as to physics, and appears as a topic in chemistry and engineering. The term heat is also used in a different but related sense to indicate energy in the process of transfer between an object and its surroundings because a difference exists between their temperatures. Thermo-

dynamics is the name given to the study of the relationships between heat and mechanics.

Acoustics is the science of sound. Sometimes wave motion is studied under acoustics rather than under mechanics because sound provides good illustrations of wave motion. Objects which are in vibrating motion in a medium can set that medium in motion, and the disturbance can travel through the medium in the form of a wave. Energy is transferred without the transfer of particles of the medium. Sound is the type of wave motion which has such a frequency that, if it reaches a human ear, it can cause a stimulus to reach the brain and hearing results. Thus, to the physicist, sound is the wave motion itself. Sound can also be defined as the sensation produced when sound waves reach the ear. Because both definitions are in common use, care must be taken to avoid confusion.

Light is the particular part of the gamut of electromagnetic waves to which the eye responds. Here, varying electric and magnetic fields travel through a vacuum or a transparent medium. The energy travels in even multiples of specific small amounts called "quanta." Related to light are infrared radiations, those frequencies which are just too low to cause the sensation of light in the normal human eye, and ultraviolet rays, similar radiations whose frequencies are just too high for the human eye. Optics, which is the study of light, often includes infrared and ultraviolet radiation.

Electricity and magnetism are so closely related that neither topic can be studied in any depth without involving the other. Electricity deals with the forces which charged particles exert upon each other, the effects of such forces, and the phenomena caused by the motions of charged particles. Magnetism was first known in the form of the peculiar attraction which a mineral called lodestone exerted because of the particular electron orientations in the material. It was found that magnetic effects could be caused or altered by electric currents. Further, it is possible to use magnetic materials to advantage in producing electric currents, which are streams of charged particles. An important branch of electricity is electronics, and this area has attracted the attention of more physicists in this country than any other part of physics. This subject deals with the flow of electric currents in vacuum tubes, semiconductors, and associated circuits, and with the use of these circuits to form devices of many kinds.

Solid-state physics is a well established area cutting across some of the other areas mentioned above. It includes those phenomena which are exhibited by materials in the solid state, with emphasis on electronic properties and their relations to the composition of crystalline substances and to energy levels in these materials.

Modern physics is a title under which physi-

cists sometimes group many topics of comparatively recent development involving or relating to atoms and other submolecular particles or radiation resulting from atomic processes. Subjects which are considered here include radioactivity (both natural and artificially induced), x-rays, atomic and molecular structure, the quantum theory, wave mechanics and matrix mechanics, and nuclear fission and fusion.

Experimental physics and theoretical physics are two general categories into which the entire field of physics can be divided. The experimentalist attempts to discover new phenomena through the manipulation of apparatus and to make measurements of old or newly discovered properties. The theoretical physicist attempts to correlate measurements and to simplify theories. He tries to predict new phenomena and to relate one effect to another. Mathematical physics uses mathematics to describe physical phenomena, and extends or adapts mathematics to make it applicable to specific theories.

General discussions of major areas of physics can be found in the articles listed as cross-references at the end of this article.

Future Trends It is of course impossible to predict the flow of any science as it varies from quiet pools to violent rapids. Present trends lead one to expect that certain areas will receive emphasis, but a new discovery or even gradual progress in an old area can open up vast new vistas. Computers and computer techniques are speeding calculations on nuclear forces, and some of the riddles of their existence may yield to intensive research. Fundamental-particle physics is another region with many questions which have been posed but not answered. We have no really adequate theory for these particles, and current descriptions of them and of their interactions are very largely phenomenological. Which, if any, of the particles that we know now are truly fundamental? And what does "charged" imply when applied to particles? What will even more powerful accelerators reveal? The emission of coherent radiation and its behavior combine to form an area in which effort is being accelerated. The Fermi surfaces of metals, semiconductivity and superconductivity, and other cryogenic phenomena are fruitful, lively and interesting areas. Astrophysics is a very active area and many new experiments, discoveries, and theories may be expected from this field. Pulsars, quasars, neutron stars, and black holes are new concepts, and theories about them are still fairly nebulous, and mainly unproven. Undoubtedly more and more surprises are in store from exciting new research programs.

Physics Organizations Throughout the world there are many societies and other organizations that have the objectives of advancing physics and distributing knowledge of that science. In addition, other organizations deal with broader or related fields and include physics as part of their interests. As of October, 1973, eight societies were members of the American Institute of Physics: American Physical Society, American Association of Physics Teachers, Optical Society of America, Acoustical Society of America, Society of Rheology, American Crystallographic Association, American Astronomical Society, and American Association of Physicists in Medicine. The Institute was set up to assist the societies in their activities. Many other organizations are associated or affiliated with the Institute. It maintains an Information Center on International Physics Activities and publishes an "Information Booklet on Physics Organizations Abroad." Inquiries should be sent to the director of the Information Center, American Institute of Physics, 335 East 45th Street, New York, N. Y. 10017, U.S.A. In addition, scientific personnel attached to embassies in Washington, D.C. can provide information about activities in their respective countries.

ROBERT M. BESANÇON

Cross-references: ACOUSTICS; ASTROPHYSICS; ATOMIC PHYSICS; BIOPHYSICS; CHEMISTRY; ELECTRICITY; ELECTRONICS; GEOPHYSICS; GRAVITATION; HEAT; LIGHT; MAGNETISM; MATHEMATICAL PHYSICS; MEASUREMENTS, PRINCIPLES OF; MECHANICS; MOLECULES AND MOLECULAR STRUCTURE; PHYSICAL CHEMISTRY; RADIOACTIVITY; RELATIVITY; THEORETICAL PHYSICS.

PLANETARY ATMOSPHERES

Introduction The atmospheres of the planets within our solar system are very different from each other; in fact, no two planets have identical atmospheres. Nevertheless, the planets can be divided into two major categories within which some similar characteristics are present. These two categories are the "terrestrial" planets, earth, Venus, Mars, and Mercury, which are fairly high density solid planets with relatively thin atmospheres; and the "giant" planets, Jupiter, Saturn, Uranus, and Neptune, which have much lower densities and extensive atmospheres.

Within these categories a distinction can be made between those characteristics such as temperature and concentration of impinging radiant energy, which are determined primarily by the planet's distance from the sun; and others, such as escape velocity, which are determined by the mass of the planet itself. However, these distinctions are subject to variation due to interaction of various environmental factors and as a result each planet must be considered individually for best understanding.

Our own planet, naturally, is the one about which we have the most extensive information and thus is the one which is best understood. Conclusions about the nature of other planetary atmospheres must often be made from very inadequate data and consequently may some-

TABLE 1   PLANETARY DATA[a]

Planet or Satellite	Distance from Sun (Earth = 1)	Mass (Earth = 1)	Radius (Earth = 1)	Density	Period of Rev.	Period of Rot.	Escape Velocity (km/sec)
Mercury	0.3871	0.0543	0.39	5.05	87.96d	58.6d	4.3
Venus	0.7233	0.8136	0.973	4.88	224.69d	–243d	10.4
Earth	1	1	1	5.52	365.25d	23hr 56m	11.3
Mars	1.5237	0.1080	0.520	4.24	686.95d	24hr 37m	5.1
Jupiter	5.2028	318.35	10.97	1.33	11.86y	9hr 50m	61.0
Saturn	9.5388	95.3	9.03	0.714	29.56y	10hr 14m	36.7
Uranus	19.19	14.54	3.72	1.56	83.95y	10hr 49m	22.4
Neptune	30.07	17.26	3.50	2.22	163.9y	15hr 40m	25.5
Pluto	39.52	0.033(?)	0.45(?)	2.0(?)	247.3y	6d9hr 17m	3(?)
Titan	9.5388	0.0236	0.384	2.30			2.8

[a]Data in the first four columns are taken from Urey's[1] article, and the next two columns are from Inglis.[2] The values in the last column are those given by Kuiper.[3]

times be speculative. Our major sources of information about the composition of other planetary atmospheres are the spectroscopic studies made by astronomers for many years. In recent years our knowledge of Venus and Mars has been supplemented by the results of the Mariner and Venera instrument probes. Tables 1 and 2 list important data for the various planets.

Mercury is the closest planet to the sun, and as expected, has a relatively high temperature. At its median distance from the sun, the planet's maximum temperature has been measured as 613 K.[6] Recent observations indicate an average temperature of about 400 K for the sunlit side and 220 K for the dark side.[2] Because of its low mass and correspondingly low escape velocity, Mercury should have long since lost any significant atmosphere it might once have had. Urey has discussed the possibility that a very thin atmosphere of high molecular weight substances, mostly inert gases, may exist.[1] Spectroscopic studies have also indicated some likelihood of CO_2 in the atmosphere of Mercury with possible amounts ranging from 150 to 3500 cm-atm.[6]* N. A. Kozyrev has observed spectroscopic evidence of slight amounts of hydrogen on Mercury. Although this gas would continually escape into space, a stable concentration could be maintained if the planet captures hydrogen atoms expelled from the sun. These results are, however, based on highly sensitive measurements, and much more investigation is necessary before they can be finally accepted.

The atmosphere of *Venus* is still somewhat mysterious despite centuries of observation. The planet is covered with a dense cloud layer

Editor's note. One cm-atm is an amount of gas equivalent to a column 1 cm in height at normal atmosphere pressure and temperature on the earth. (NTP-earth) is sometimes added to indicate more clearly that the standard is Normal Temperature and Pressure on the earth.

that limits spectroscopic observation to the upper atmosphere. Carbon dioxide is the major constituent with current estimates given as 95 per cent CO_2 and 5 per cent N_2. In addition, observations show one part in 10^4 of H_2O^2 and CO, one part in 10^6 of HCl, and one part in 10^8 of HF.[4] Spectroscopic upper limits have been set for other gases but none have been positively identified.

The trace amount of CO probably results from the photodissociation of CO_2. If this is indeed the case, small amounts of O_2 should also be present. The absence of significant quantities of water is reasonable in light of the high CO_2 concentration. CO_2 is believed to have been removed from the earth's atmosphere by reaction with silicate rocks, a reaction which proceeds only in the presence of water. The composition of the cloud cover is still a subject of much speculation.

Due to the absence of visible markings on Venus, the Planet's rotation has been the subject of much controversy. Radar measurements now show it to be 243 days, but in reverse direction to the rest of the planets in the solar system. Strangely, at this rate of rotation, Venus presents the same side toward earth every time it passes between the earth and sun. Some have suggested that the earth is controlling its rotation, but no conclusive answer has been found.

Venera 7 yielded the only direct measurements at the planet's surface—a temperature of 747 K and a pressure of about 90 atm.[5] Microwave studies had previously indicated temperatures much higher than had been expected by radiative equilibrium calculations. This high temperature (greater than that of Mercury) is somewhat of an anomaly. It is not yet known whether the "greenhouse" effect can account for such high temperatures in a consistent model of the atmosphere.

The atmosphere of our own planet, *earth*, has been the subject of many extensive studies for years and a great deal of information has

TABLE 2   CONSTITUENTS OF PLANETARY ATMOSPHERES[a]

Planet or Satellite	Constituent	Amount cm-atm, (NTP-Earth)	Remarks
Venus	CO_2	100 000	Observed spectroscopically above the cloud layer
	N_2		Possible minor constituent
	CO	100	Observed spectroscopically above the cloud layer
	H_2O	100	Maximum uncertain
	HCl	1	Observed spectroscopically
	HF	0.01	Above the cloud layer[4]
Earth	N_2	625 000	
	O_2	168 000	
	Ar	7 400	
	CO_2	200	
	Ne	15	
	He	4	
	Kr	0.9	
	Xe	0.07	
	H_2	0.4	
	CH_4	1.2	
	N_2O	0.4	
	O_3	0.3	
	H_2O	variable	
Mars	CO_2	7 800	Observed spectroscopically[5]
	N_2		Possible minor constituent
	H_2O		Trace amounts observed
Jupiter	CH_4	15 000	Observed spectroscopically
	NH_3	700	Observed spectroscopically
	H_2	2.7×10^7	Calculated by Urey[1] from cosmic abundances; based on low density of planet
	He	5.6×10^6	
	N_2	4×10^3	
	Ne	1.7×10^4	
Saturn	CH_4	35 000	Observed spectroscopically
	NH_3	200	Observed spectroscopically
	H_2	6.3×10^7	Calculated by Urey[1] from cosmic abundances; based on low density of planet
	He	1.3×10^7	
	N_2	9.5×10^3	
	Ne	2.7×10^4	
Uranus	CH_4	220 000	Observed spectroscopically
	H_2	4.2×10^6	H_2 observed spectroscopically
	He	8.6×10^5	Abundances calculated by Urey[1]
	N_2	4.2×10^6	
Neptune	CH_4	370 000	Observed spectroscopically
	H_2		Detected spectroscopically at higher intensity than Uranus
	N_2		
	He		
Titan	CH_4	20 000	Observed spectroscopically[2]
	NH_3	<300	Spectroscopic upper limit

[a]No constituents are listed for Mercury since no conclusive observational evidence is available.

been gathered. The major atmospheric constituents are nitrogen and oxygen in a 4:1 ratio. Other minor constituents include CO_2, H_2O, and Ar, plus trace amounts of the other noble gases. Hydrogen and helium escape from the earth's atmosphere over geologic time spans. The variation of pressure with altitude follows the exponential equation

$$P = P_o e^{\frac{-\mu g h}{RT}}$$

where μ is the average molecular weight and g is the acceleration due to gravity. The quantity $RT/\mu g$ is called the scale height and is given the symbol H. This relationship is only approximately correct because neither μ nor T is constant throughout the atmosphere and even variations in g can be considered. The earth's atmosphere shows an interesting variation of temperature with altitude which arises from several factors. The earth's atmosphere is transparent to most solar radiation, which penetrates

to the earth's surface and heats it to a temperature of about 290 K. The earth radiates this energy back out to space, heating the atmosphere to an extent which decreases with increasing distance from the surface. The atmospheric temperature drops gradually to 217 K at 20 km. At about 20 km, the temperature of the atmosphere begins to show changes brought about by the basic photochemistry of the atmosphere. The temperature rises to a value of about 283 K at 50 km and then decreases gradually to 168 K at 80 km. Above this altitude the temperature rises steadily to about 1500 K at 400 km and above. This maximum changes with the sunspot activity and at sunspot minimum is 1000 K.[7]

The photochemical processes contributing to these variations include the following. Ultraviolet light from the sun is absorbed by O_2 molecules in the upper atmosphere, resulting in their dissociation into oxygen atoms. The atoms may then react with other O_2 molecules to form ozone

$$O + O_2 + M \longrightarrow O_3 + M$$

The ozone absorbs light of wavelengths below 3000 Å very strongly, and, in fact, protects the earth's inhabitants from this energetic radiation. The ozone is destroyed both by this absorption of light and by further reaction with atomic oxygen

$$O_3 + O \longrightarrow 2O_2$$

with a steady-state equilibrium being set up between formation and destruction. This occurs in a relatively narrow band at ~30 km altitude, known as the ozone layer. The energy absorbed in this narrow layer is responsible for the temperature rise. At the highest altitudes very high energy solar radiation is absorbed, producing ions of oxygen, nitrogen, and other gases. This region is known as the ionosphere. Detailed discussions of the physics and chemistry of the earth's atmosphere have been published by Kuiper[3], and Bates[8] as well as others. Very extensive studies of the earth's atmosphere have been carried out in recent years using rocket probes. Much of the information obtained in this way has been summarized by Johnson[7] in the "Satellite Environment Handbook."

The atmosphere of *Mars* is relatively thin, as might be expected from the low mass and consequent low escape velocity. Urey[1] notes that over geological ages even oxygen and nitrogen atoms may have escaped from Mars (in addition to hydrogen and helium) if the upper atmosphere is high enough. The major atmospheric constituent has been identified as CO_2, but it is possible that nitrogen is present in minor amounts. The total atmospheric surface pressure has been estimated as on the order of 1 per cent of that of the earth. Small amounts of CO and O atoms may be present in the upper atmosphere as the result of photodissociation of

the CO_2. Water vapor has been observed in trace amounts and there is some recent evidence of underground ice deposits. It seems improbable that oxides of nitrogen can be present in the Martian atmosphere. Kinetic studies on the fixation of nitrogen by ionizing radiation have shown that such compounds do not form in appreciable amounts at these pressures. Any small amounts actually formed would be destroyed by solar ultraviolet radiation.

Temperature measurements yield a range of about 155 K at the dark polar regions to 275 K on the sunlit equator.[2] The Martian surface has polar caps composed mainly of frozen CO_2 which disappear in summer and reappear as winter approaches. Dust storms which occasionally obscure vast portions of the surface have been observed both from earth-based studies and the recent Mariner 9 probe. Much of the surface material is, therefore, assumed to be finely divided sands.

Giant Planets Because of their high masses and consequent high escape velocities the atmospheres of the giant planets differ substantially from those of the terrestrial planets. Hydrogen and helium cannot escape from the giant planets, and on the basis of cosmic abundance, can be expected as the major atmospheric constituents. Supporting this expectation of a reducing atmosphere is the observed presence of a large amount of methane in the atmospheres of all these planets and the mean molecular weight of 2.35 calculated for Jupiter from the attenuation of the atmosphere.

The atmosphere of *Jupiter* contains appreciable amounts of ammonia (700 cm-atm) in addition to an observed 15 000 cm-atm of CH_4. Urey[1] has calculated that 2.7×10^7 cm-atm of hydrogen and 5.6×10^6 cm-atm of helium should also be present. Many colors are observed in the Jupiter atmosphere: blues, greens, yellows, and reds. Often distinct bands appear. Rice[9] has suggested that these colors may be caused by free radicals formed photochemically and stable at the low ambient temperatures. Depending upon the microwave region observed, the temperature of the planet has been found to lie in the range of 130 to 150 K.[6] The most notable feature of the Jupiter atmosphere is the great red spot. This unusual formation floats (in the atmosphere) and is not rigidly attached. No satisfactory explanation has been proposed for its nature or origin. The turbulence of the cloud bands indicates that very stormy conditions prevail in the atmosphere. Recent microwave radiometer data indicate that Jupiter is surrounded by an intense radiation belt similar to the van Allen belt.

The atmosphere of *Saturn* appears to be similar in nature to that of Jupiter, with 35 000 cm-atm of methane and 200 cm-atm of ammonia being observed spectroscopically. From cosmic abundances, 6.3×10^7 and 1.3×10^7 cm-atm of hydrogen and helium have been calculated by Urey.[1] Neon and nitrogen should also be

expected. The planet's temperature has been measured to be 125 K. Colors and bands are observed in the atmosphere but they are much less pronounced that those of Jupiter. The rings of Saturn, one of the most striking features of the solar system, are believed by Kuiper[3] to be ice particles.

Uranus and *Neptune*, because of their high densities, appear to have different compositions, specifically, containing smaller proportions of hydrogen and helium than do Jupiter and Saturn.[1] Ammonia has not been detected in either planet, but is probably present in the form of crystals because of the low temperature. Kuiper[3] reports 220 000 and 370 000 cm-atm of methane on Uranus and Neptune, respectively. The $(v^1, v^{11}) = (3, 0)$ pressure induced rotation-vibration band of H_2 has also been identified by Herzberg (see Refs. (1) and (3)). Several other spectroscopic bands have been observed which have not been positively identified to date. Radio observations of Uranus suggest a temperature of 100 K.

No observational data are available on Neptune but a radiative equilibrium temperature of 43 K has been calculated by Urey;[1] however, the actual temperature is probably higher, as evidenced by the significant amounts of CH_4 present.

Almost nothing is known about *Pluto* which because of its great distance from the sun, is very cold. No atmospheric constituents have been detected. Except for hydrogen, helium, and neon, all other substances have no appreciable vapor pressure at this low temperature of 42 K.

Jupiter, Saturn, and Neptune all have fairly large satellites, but of these only *Titan*, a satellite of Saturn, has a detectable atmosphere. Methane (20 000 cm-atm) is the only constituent observed.

P. HARTECK
B. THOMPSON COLEBERD

References

1. Urey, H. C., "The Atmospheres of Planets," pp. 363–418 in Vol. LII, "Handbuch der Physik," Berlin, Springer Verlag, 1959.
2. Inglis, S. J., "Planets, Stars, and Galaxies," New York, John Wiley & Sons, Inc., 1972.
3. Kuiper, G. P., Ed., "The Atmospheres of the Earth and Planets," Chicago, University of Chicago Press, 1952.
4. Lewis, J. S., "The Atmosphere, Clouds, and Surface of Venus," *Amer. Sci.*, **59** 5, 557 (1971).
5. "Aeronomy of CO_2 Atmospheres," *Atmospheric Sci.*, **28** (6) (September 1971) (articles by several authors).
6. Moroz, V. I., "Physics of Planets," NASA, National Technical Information Service, Springfield, Va., 1968 (N68-21802).
7. Johnson, F. S., Ed., "Satellite Environment Handbook," Stanford, Stanford University Press, 1961.
8. Bates, D. R., "The Earth and Its Atmosphere," New York, Basic Books, 1957.
9. Rice, F. O., *Sci., Amer.*, **194** (6), 119 (1956).

Cross-references: CLOUD PHYSICS, IONOSPHERE, RADIATION BELTS.

PLASMAS

When a gas is raised to sufficiently high temperatures, the atoms and molecules of the gas become ionized since electrons are stripped off by the more violent collisions ensuing from the increased thermal agitation of the particles. In the resultant highly ionized state, the dynamical behavior of the gas can be dominated by the electromagnetic forces acting on the now unbound electrons and ions, and the properties become sufficiently different from those of the normal un-ionized gas to warrant a new name, *plasma*, to describe the gas in this highly ionized state. This name arose from the expression "plasma oscillation" coined by Langmuir to describe the very high frequency (1 000 Mc/sec) longitudinal oscillations sustained by plasma in regimes where normal sound waves are characteristically strongly damped.

The modern studies of molecular, atomic, and nuclear physics had their origins in the study of the conduction of electricity through gases, and indeed, until quite recently, the (weakly) ionized gas has been used primarily to study atomic structure and the complex of collision processes—ionization, excitation, inelastic and resonant scattering, etc.—which occur when an electron strikes an atom, rather than the plasma properties (see COLLISIONS OF PARTICLES and IONIZATION). The highly ionized plasma, with its dominant collective behavior, can be produced and observed in the laboratory only with considerable difficulty, and it is not surprising that the study of ionized gases was largely the study of atomic collision processes.

Largely due to the astrophysicist, the interest in the plasma *per se* has been revived in recent years. It was realized that the plasma state was essentially the normal state of matter in this universe. Hydrogen, which is overwhelmingly the most abundant element in the stars and space, is mostly ionized and hence totally stripped. Helium, the next most abundant element is stripped of its two electrons inside the sun and in the solar corona. Nearer home, the properties of the solar wind, Van Allen belts, and the ionosphere, demand a plasma description.

Most recently, the technological possibilities of plasmas have attracted attention, most significantly in the research directed toward the controlled release of energy from the thermonuclear fusion of light elements, and it was with this stimulus that a considerable advance in the description and understanding of plasma phenomena took place. The possibilities of ionic propulsion for interplanetary flight and schemes

for direct thermionic conversion have also attracted considerable attention.

We thus see that the study of the ideal plasma, a gas composed entirely of electrons and bare ions in which the inelastic atomic processes of normal gaseous electronics are unimportant, is a subject worthy of investigation.

The problems encountered in analyzing a fully ionized plasma are of several types. Although the basic physical processes are simpler than in an ordinary gas, the motions are vastly more complicated because of the strong coupling to the electromagnetic field. From a macroscopic point of view, the plasma interacting with a strong magnetic field can often be considered, in a certain approximation, as a highly electrically conducting fluid, and thus described by a combination of hydrodynamic equations for the fluid and Maxwell's equation for the electromagnetic field. As expected, the resultant motions yield a vastly richer variety of flows than encountered in ordinary hydrodynamics and these analyses have developed into a separate discipline called *magnetohydrodynamics*, *hydromagnetics*, or MAGNETO-FLUID-MECHANICS.

Even in the absence of a magnetic field, the electrical properties of plasma permit complicated macroscopic motions, which involve electrostatic restoring forces and which have no parallel in ordinary gases.

From a microscopic point of view, the plasma consists of an assembly of charged particles interacting under simple inverse-square forces (and any external electromagnetic fields) and appears as an ideal subject for classical kinetic theory. However, because of the long-range character of the coulomb force, the simple picture of a diffuse gas in which the interaction can be represented as a scarce, catastrophic, binary encounter, is not valid. The microscopic dynamics of a plasma must be properly treated as a problem in many-body physics, and it is only quite recently that it has been learned how to do this in a systematic way.

The statistical many-body description of plasma may be characterized by the orders in an expansion in the parameter $\epsilon = 1/n\lambda_D{}^3$, where n is the average number density of particles, and λ_D, the Debye shielding distance, is given by

$$\lambda_D = [4\pi n e^2(1 + Z/\Theta)]^{-1/2}$$

Here, e is the absolute value of the electronic charge, Z is the atomic number, and $\Theta = kT$ where T is the absolute temperature and k is Boltzmann's constant.*

The parameter ϵ, the inverse of the number of particles in a Debye sphere, is small and ranges, typically, from 10^{-2} to 10^{-9}; indeed, the smallness of this parameter typifies the plasma state. The Debye length characterizes the distance

*Unrationalized gaussian (cgs) units are used throughout this article.

over which there can be considerable departure from average charge neutrality. It measures not only the thickness of the charged sheath which forms when plasma is in contact with a solid surface, but also the effective range of the potential due to a singled-out test charge at rest

$$\phi(r) = \frac{q}{r} e^{-r/\lambda_D}$$

where r is the distance from the charge q. The exponential decay factor represents the average collective many-body shielding effect.

There is an important interpretation of the smallness of the plasma number ϵ. If one computes the ratio of the potential energy of interaction of one particle with its neighbor and compares it with the mean kinetic energy per particle, one finds

$$PE/KE \sim \frac{e^2 n^{1/3}}{\Theta} \sim (n\lambda_D{}^3)^{-2/3} \ll 1$$

Thus the effect of any one particle on a given particle is small compared to the average collective many-body effect of all its neighbors within a Debye sphere.

The average collective behavior of plasma is described (to zero order in ϵ) by the so-called Vlasov or self-consistent approximation for the density, in the six-dimensional $\mathbf{r}$, $\mathbf{v}$ phase space. The density (or one-particle distribution function) $f_s(\mathbf{r}, \mathbf{v}, t)$ satisfies the equation for each species s

$$\frac{\partial f_s}{\partial t} + \mathbf{v} \cdot \frac{\partial f_s}{\partial \mathbf{x}} + \frac{e_s}{m_s}\left[\mathbf{E}(\mathbf{r}, t) + \frac{\mathbf{v}}{c} \times \mathbf{B}(\mathbf{r}, t)\right] \cdot \frac{\partial f_s}{\partial \mathbf{v}}$$
$$+ \frac{\mathbf{F}_{ext}}{m_s} \cdot \frac{\partial f_s}{\partial \mathbf{v}} = 0 \quad (1)$$

where $e_s = Ze$ = ionic charge of species s, m_s is the ionic mass of species s, and c is the velocity of light. $\mathbf{E}$ and $\mathbf{B}$ satisfy Maxwell's equations with sources

$$\sigma(\mathbf{r}, t) = \sum_s e_s \int d^3v f_s$$

and

$$\mathbf{j}(\mathbf{r}, t) = \sum_s e_s \int d^3v \, \mathbf{v}f_s$$

Here σ and $\mathbf{j}$ are the average charge and current density respectively. $\mathbf{F}_{ext}$ represents any external force field which may be present.

For undriven systems which are spatially homogeneous on the average $\mathbf{E} = \mathbf{B} = 0$, hence $\partial f/\partial t = 0$, and one must proceed to next order in the plasma number, where interaction (collisions) between pairs of *shielded* particles is considered, in order to discuss the time evolution of f.

It is observed that, in this lowest approximation, any f_0 which is a function of v alone satisfies this set of equaitons for the spatially homogeneous state. If one considers small departures from the spatially homogeneous situation with $f_0 = f_0(|v|)$ one finds the plasma capable of sustaining high-frequency, long-wavelength, plane-wave excitations of two types: longitudinal, $(k\|E)$, with

$$\omega^2 \cong \omega_p{}^2 + 3\frac{\Theta}{m} k^2$$

and transverse, $(k \perp E)$, with

$$\omega^2 \cong \omega_p{}^2 + c^2 k^2$$

Here $\omega_p = (4\pi n e^2/m)^{1/2}$ is the *electron plasma frequency* and m is the mass of the electron. The much more massive ions play no role in this high-frequency situation. The electrostatic (Langmuir) oscillations actually are found to be damped, even in this collisionless approximation, by the interaction of the wave with particles traveling near the phase velocity of the wave, "Landau Damping." If the ion temperature is small compared to the electron temperature, there also exist low-frequency ion excitations in which the electrons play a quasistatic role.

The presence of a uniform magnetic field greatly increases the variety of excitations possible, but these will not be discussed here.

If the distribution f_0 is sufficiently anisotropic in velocity space, it is possible under certain circumstances, to find growing excitations. The ultimate fate of these oscillations cannot be described by the linearized theory, and a nonlinear treatment must be invoked. If the growth rate of these excitations is small, however, a "quasi-linear" or adiabatic treatment is justified and such investigations are currently very much in vogue with plasma physicists. In the presence of an external magnetic field, even small average density and temperature gradients can lead to unstable situations.

In the next order in ϵ, the effects of particle discreteness (collisions) come into play, and here one meets the kinetic theory of plasma. The relaxation to thermal equilibrium is described by a modified *Fokker-Planck* collision term which is added to the lowest order description and which is characterized as a superposition of weak, statistically independent, but dynamically shielded, binary encounters. A novel addition to the usual type dissipative collisional mechanism is the emission of the forementioned longitudinal electrostatic oscillations by superthermal particles.

An interesting and important property of plasmas is their ability to radiate. At the Vlasov level of description, a spatially bounded plasma in a state of longitudinal excitation can emit transverse waves (very much like an antenna!). To first order in ϵ, and in the presence of a magnetic field, the acceleration of charged particles in their spiraling motion about the magnetic field lines gives rise to radiation at the gyro-frequency, $\omega_c = eB/mc$, and its harmonics. These lines are not sharp, however, due to the Doppler effect of motion along the field lines, and the change in frequency due to the relativistic mass correction.

To second order in ϵ, the radiation from the particle acceleration involved in binary collisions, *bremsstrahlung*, is described.

These radiative loss mechanisms represent serious competition for the energy gain in the efforts for the controlled release of energy through the fusion of light elements.

CARL OBERMAN

References

Spitzer, L., Jr., "Physics of Fully Ionized Gases," New York, Interscience Publishers, Inc., 1956.
Stix, T. H., "Theory of Plasma Waves," New York, McGraw-Hill Book Co., 1962.
Thompson, W. B., "Introduction to Plasma Physics," London, Pergamon Press, 1962.

Cross-references: ASTROPHYSICS, COLLISIONS OF PARTICLES, IONIZATION, IONOSPHERE, KINETIC THEORY, MAGNETO-FLUID-MECHANICS, RADIATION BELTS.

POLAR MOLECULES

The term "polar" is applied to molecules in which there exists a permanent spatial separation of the centroids of positive and negative charge, or dipole moment. Such a moment was first postulated by P. Debye for molecules having structural asymmetry in order to explain certain of the observed electrical properties. He chose for his model an electrical dipole contained in a spherical molecule, free to rotate into alignment with an applied electric field, but subject to disorientation by collisions with other molecules due to thermal motion. At ordinary temperatures and field strengths, the electrical energy involved in the orientation is much smaller than the thermal energy kT so that only a small fraction of the dipoles are aligned with the field (k is Boltzmann's constant and T is the temperature in degrees Kelvin). The net dipole moment per mole (*molar polarization*) is then calculated statistically to be

$$P = \frac{4\pi}{3} N \left(\alpha + \frac{\mu^2}{3kT} \right) \tag{1}$$

where μ is the permanent dipole moment per molecule, i.e., the charge multiplied by the distance of separation, and N is Avogadro's number. The polarizability α represents the induced moment per molecule resulting from the temporary distortion of the electron orbits by the applied field. For nonpolar molecules, it is the

only contribution; it corresponds to the optical polarizability as measured by the refractive index.

The molar polarization may be related to the dielectric constant ϵ by the approximate equation of Clausius and Mosotti

$$\frac{\epsilon - 1}{\epsilon + 2}\frac{M}{d} = P \tag{2}$$

where M is the molecular weight and d is the density. The permanent dipole moment of a molecule may therefore be determined by measuring the temperature coefficient of the dielectric constant as seen by combining Eqs. (1) and (2). Alternatively, a companion measurement of the optical refractive index may be made to determine α, and the dipole moment is then obtained as the difference between the total polarization and the optical contribution. The measurements are made in dilute vapor or solution phase, so that the individual dipoles are sufficiently far apart that they do not influence one another (see REFRACTION).

Equation (1) is valid in the low-frequency region where the dipoles are able to rotate in phase with the applied electric field. This rotation is subject to various restraints; in the simple case of a spherical molecule of radius a rotating in a fluid of viscosity η, this leads to a relaxation time

$$\tau = \frac{4\pi a^3 \eta}{kT} \tag{3}$$

corresponding to a frequency range of *anomalous dispersion* in which the molecules become unable to follow the oscillations of the applied field. This gives rise to an out-of-phase component of the dielectric constant representing a conductivity or *dielectric loss*, ϵ'', i.e., a dissipation of energy in the form of heat. Mathematically this is expressed as a complex dielectric constant.

$$\epsilon = \epsilon' - j\epsilon'' \tag{4}$$

$$\epsilon' - \epsilon_\infty' = \frac{\epsilon_0' - \epsilon_\infty'}{1 + \omega^2 \tau^2} \tag{5}$$

$$\epsilon'' = \frac{(\epsilon_0' - \epsilon_\infty')\omega\tau}{1 + \omega^2 \tau^2} \tag{6}$$

ω is $2\pi \times$ the frequency, and the subscripts 0 and ∞ refer to dielectric constant measured at very low and very high frequency, respectively. Cole and Cole showed for polar molecules having a unique relaxation time that a plot ϵ'' vs ϵ' is a semicircle centered on the ϵ'-axis. For more complicated molecules or high polymers, the center becomes depressed below the ϵ'-axis and the curve may be further distorted. This behavior is generally characterized by a distribution of relaxation times as a result of the orientation of molecular segments of various shapes and sizes. Information regarding the freedom of orientation within the molecules may thus be gained.

These simple relationships between dipole moment and dielectric constant fail for concentrated solutions or pure polar liquids because they do not take into account the interaction of the dipoles, both permanent and induced, with one another. The calculations have been extended by Onsager, Kirkwood, and others, to include these effects. It becomes necessary to include in the theory a correlation factor which is a measure of the extent of nonrandom orientation of the dipoles, i.e., the tendency of the dipoles to aggregate parallel or antiparallel to one another. Experimental determination of this quantity yields further insight into the structure of polar liquids.

In the solid state, most crystalline polar compounds exhibit low dielectric constants because the rotational freedom necessary for dipole orientation has been frozen out. A few compounds, however, do show a persistence of high dielectric constant to temperatures below the melting point, indicating rotational freedom in the solid. At some lower temperature the rotation ceases and the dielectric constant drops. This change in dielectric constant has frequently been used as a method of detecting second-order transitions in polar compounds.

Some success in the correlation of dipole moment with molecular structure has been achieved. A series of moments assigned to individual bonds was developed empirically by Smyth, Pauling, and others from measurements on simple molecules. They are intended for approximate calculation of dipole moments of complex molecules by vectorial addition along the bond directions as determined by other means. It is assumed that there is no interaction between bonds; this generally results in the calculated values being higher than the measured moment because of inductive effects, i.e., electrons being shared in a bond between two atoms are not wholly available to a neighboring bond, so that neither bond attains its full moment. An approximate correction for this effect has been made by Eyring and co-workers. Despite these inadequacies, the calculated moments are often helpful in determining molecular structures and have often applied in the case of various substituted benzene-ring compounds. Of special importance is the ability to decide between a polar or nonpolar, i.e., symmetrical, structure.

More detailed quantum mechanical calculations of dipole moments have been less successful. Rather the experimentally determined moments have been used to assign varying degrees of ionicity and covalency to the bonds in establishing the electronic hybridization structure. Quantum mechanics has also shown how it is possible to obtain extremely accurate measurements of the dipole moments from spectroscopic Stark splittings.

D. EDELSON

Cross-references: DIELECTRIC THEORY, DIPOLE MOMENTS, MOLECULES AND MOLECULAR STRUCTURE, POLYMER PHYSICS, QUANTUM THEORY, REFRACTION, ZEEMAN AND STARK EFFECTS.

POLARIZED LIGHT

Polarized light is an especially simple form of light and can be defined easily in terms of either of the two prevalent theories of light: the wave theory and the photon theory (see LIGHT). According to the former, light consists of trains of electromagnetic waves whose wavelengths lie in the range from about 4×10^{-7} to 7×10^{-7} meters. A noteworthy feature of the waves is that two kinds of displacements are involved: electric and magnetic. Another significant feature is that, when the waves are traveling in empty space (or in glass, water, or other isotropic medium), the electric and magnetic displacements are perpendicular to the direction of propagation of energy; i.e., they are transverse, not longitudinal. Since the electric and magnetic displacements are always perpendicular to one another and have equivalent magnitudes, it is sufficient to specify just one of these quantities; most authors choose to deal with the electric displacement.

Consider, now, a slender beam of light that is traveling east, i.e., from left to right in Fig. 1.

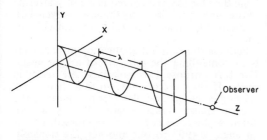

FIG. 1. Monochromatic beam of wavelength λ traveling horizontally to the right. Since, in this example, the electric displacement is vertical, the sectional pattern (indicated at right) consists of a vertical line and the beam is said to be vertically linearly polarized. The observer is situated far to the right, facing the light source.

If it happens that the direction of electric displacement is everywhere up or down, but not north or south, the beam is said to be linearly polarized in the vertical plane. If, alternatively, the displacements were north and south, the beam would be called *horizontally* linearly polarized. The displacement might, of course, lie in some tilted plane specified by an angle α; in such case, any given displacement may be regarded as the resultant of a vertical displacement and a horizontal displacement. The *sectional pattern* of any such beam is conventionally indicated

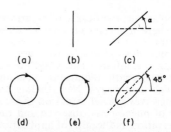

FIG. 2. Variety of sectional patterns of polarized light: (a) horizontally polarized; (b) vertically polarized; (c) linearly polarized at azimuth α; (d) right circularly polarized; (e) left circularly polarized; (f) right elliptically polarized at 45° azimuth and with ellipticity, or ratio of semi-axes, of approximately 3.

by a straight line segment at the appropriate azimuth α, as indicated in Fig. 2(c). Linearly polarized beams that have azimuths differing by 90° are said to have *orthogonal* polarization forms.

Circular and elliptical polarization forms exist also. Circularly polarized light may be regarded as the result of combining two linearly polarized beams that have the same wavelength and same intensity, are polarized in orthogonal directions (e.g., horizontal and vertical) and differ in phase by 1/4 cycle, or 90°. If the horizontally polarized component *lags* in phase by 90°, the sectional pattern of the combined beam is drawn as a circle executed clockwise, as judged by an observer facing towards the light source. If the horizontally polarized component *leads* by 90°, the circle has a counterclockwise sense and the light is called left circularly polarized. In the general case, the components may differ in magnitude and the phase difference may have any value; the general sectional pattern is an ellipse.

A different description of polarized light is required when the light is regarded as a stream of photons. This is the case when the photons are so infrequent and so energetic that they can be detected individually. In such case, it is the spin, i.e., the angular momentum, of the photon that constitutes the polarization. A right circularly polarized photon has a spin of +1 unit, and a left circularly polarized photon has a spin of –1 unit. Theory and experiment are in agreement that the magnitude of the unit in question is $h/2\pi$, where h is Planck's constant (see QUANTUM THEORY). Linearly and elliptically polarized photons may be regarded as combinations, in suitable proportions, of positive and negative spins.

Unpolarized light is more complex than polarized light, hence it is harder to describe. It consists of light in which the azimuth, ellipticity, and handedness of polarization vary rapidly and at random, so that no one type of polarization predominates. No simple diagram can depict the chaos and impartiality of the sectional pattern. If, in a given beam, one particular sectional pattern slightly outweighs all other patterns, the beam is said to be par-

tially polarized; the degree of polarization may lie anywhere in the range from 0 to 100 per cent.

Polarization is not confined to visible light, but applies also to longer-wavelength radiations including the infrared and radio ranges and to shorter-wavelength radiations including ultra-violet light and x-rays. Nevertheless, the visual range deserves special attention in view of the variety of phenomena observed and the nicety of observation and wealth of applications.

Polarization was discovered by the Dutch scientist Christian Huygens in 1690, but it was not well understood until the transverse nature of the vibration, suggested by the English Physicist Robert Hooke in 1757, was confirmed by Thomas Young in 1817. Further clarification came in 1873 when Maxwell showed that light waves belong to the family of electromagnetic waves.

Today many simple methods of producing polarized light are known. Usually, an investigator starts with a beam of unpolarized light and then polarizes it by inserting a suitable optical device—a polarizer. However, the invention of the LASER makes it feasible to generate light that is polarized from the outset; no polarizer is needed. Various natural sources of polarized light exist, e.g. rays of light from a portion of the blue sky that is viewed in direction at 90° to the direction of the sun, also light from certain distant galaxies, such as the Crab nebula.

Conceptually, the simplest polarizer is the *micro-wire grid*, which consists of an array of parallel metallic wires each of which is less than a wavelength in diameter and is separated from its neighbors by comparably small distances. When a beam of unpolarized light strikes the grid, the component of the electric vibration that is perpendicular to the wires passes through readily, while the component that is parallel to the wires induces electric currents along them and is reflected or absorbed. The transmission axis of the device, defined in terms of the electric vibration of the transmitted component, is perpendicular to the wires. A far more economical type of polarizer is one that employs long, thin absorbing molecules, rather than wires. The most popular of the commercially produced polarizers, called H-sheet, contains large numbers of long, thin polymeric molecules consisting mainly of iodine atoms. These molecules are embedded in a plastic film that has previously been stretched unidirectionally so as to have a pronounced "grain"; the long slender molecules of iodine conform to this grain. Polarizers containing small absorbing units (whether wires or molecules) that show markedly different extents of absorption for different directions of electric vibration in the incident beam are called *dichroic* polarizers.

The first highly efficient polarizer was of birefringent type: it was made of the crystal *calcite* ($CaO \cdot CO_2$) which has two refractive indices and thus divides any incident beam into two beams. Each of these is linearly polarized, and the sectional patterns are orthogonal. Usually the crystal is artificially shaped so that one of the polarized beams is transmitted straight ahead and the other is deviated and disposed of by total internal reflection. The calcite prism designed by the Scottish physicist Nicol in 1828 was a basic piece of equipment in optics laboratories for over a hundred years. Types devised subsequently by Wollaston, Ahrens, and Foucault have proven to be superior in several respects.

Polarizers of reflection type are also well known. A typical reflection polarizer consists of a plate of glass that is mounted obliquely in the given beam of unpolarized light. The component that is transmitted is found to be partially polarized, and the reflected component is even more highly polarized—with the orthogonal sectional pattern. If the obliquity of the incident beam (measured from the normal to the plate) corresponds to *Brewster's angle*, defined as the angle that has a tangent of n, where n is the refractive index of the plate, the reflected beam is 100 per cent polarized. For ordinary glass, n has the value 1.5 and Brewster's angle is about 56°. Polarization by reflection is of common occurrence; yet few persons are aware of it; they are unaware, for example, that light reflected obliquely from the surface of a pond, a wet road, or a glossy sheet of paper is partially linearly polarized.

Asymmetric scattering is another process that polarizes light. The polarization observed in light from the blue sky is a consequence of scattering of the sun's rays, especially the short-wavelength or blue component thereof, by the molecules of the air.

Perhaps the simplest application of polarizers is in controlling the intensity of a light beam. For this purpose two polarizers are used, in series. If they are oriented so that their transmission axes are parallel to one another, the over-all transmittance is large. If they are oriented so that the two axes are crossed, i.e., at an angle $\theta = 90°$ to one another, the transmittance is zero; the beam is said to be extinguished. For intermediate angles-of-crossing the transmission is easily calculated from Malus' law, which affirms that the transmittance is proportional to $(\cos \theta)^2$. If the incident beam is already polarized, a single polarizer suffices to reduce the intensity to any desired extent. Polarizing sunglasses are effective in this manner thanks to the fact that light reflected obliquely from roads and most other nearly horizontal surfaces is partially *horizontally* polarized; since the polarizer lenses of the sunglasses are oriented with their transmission axes *vertical*, much of this reflected "glare" light is blocked. A polarizer that is employed to block an already polarized beam is called an analyzer.

Much of the interest in polarized light stems from the surprising convertibility of polarization form. By interposing an appropriate retardation plate, or *retarder*, in a given polarized beam, an

experimenter can alter the polarization form at will, and with almost 100 per cent efficiency. A typical retarder consists of a thin flat crystal that exhibits birefringence, i.e., has two different refractive indices. Mica, being birefringent and being easily cleaved into thin plates, is often used. When a beam of polarized light enters a plate of mica, the beam is divided into two components and the phases of these are affected ("retarded") to different extents; thus when the components emerge from the plate and unite to form a single beam again, this latter is found to have a drastically altered sectional pattern. Especially versatile and accurate control of polarization form can be achieved with retarders of calcite or quartz. The effect of any given retarder on any given beam can be predicted accurately by various conventional means and, more recently, by a matrix algebra perfected by the American scientist, Hans Mueller; the procedure is to multiply the four-element vector representing the beam by the sixteen-element matrix representing the retarder. Since the vectors and matrices are tabulated in various books, the procedure entails little effort; indeed it is readily extended to cases in which there are several retarders arranged in series. In cases where high accuracy is not needed, predictions can be made especially rapidly with the aid of a kind of map, or spherical slide-rule, called the Poincaré sphere after its inventor Henri Poincaré.

When an object of glass or transparent plastic is subjected to a unidirectional stretching or compressing force, it becomes birefringent and thus acts like a retarder. Accordingly an engineer who wishes to evaluate the unidirectional strain within such an object can do so by directing a beam of polarized light through it and, with the aid of a calibrated retarder and an analyzer, measuring the change in the sectional pattern of the beam. Using conversion factors published in books on photoelastic analysis, he can interpret the change in terms of the direction and magnitude of the strain (see PHOTOELASTICITY).

Many microscopic biological objects, such as components of living cells, appear transparent and virtually invisible under a microscope. Yet such components often contain groups of aligned birefringent molecules and thus are capable of acting like miniature retarders. If the biologist illuminates a living cell with polarized light and examines it under a microscope that is equipped with an analyzer, he finds the birefringent components to be highly visible. Thus the use of polarizers renders visible a microscopic world that is normally invisible. Similarly, mineralogists find that the polarizing microscope greatly increases the visibility of small birefringent crystals.

There are many other applications of polarizers. Photographers use them to increase the contrast between white clouds and the (polarized) blue sky. Chemists use them to measure the extents to which various liquid solutions rotate the sectional pattern of a linearly polarized beam; the extent of rotation is a measure of the concentration of the solution. Electronics engineers use circular polarizers to trap and thus eliminate reflected flare from radar screens. Illumination engineers have devised systems of polarizing filters for automobile headlights and windshields that eliminate glare in night-time driving. Biologists have found that the direction of growth of certain algae can be controlled by illuminating the algae with polarized light of controlled sectional pattern. Bees and ants can detect linear polarization directly by eye, and they employ the polarization of blue sky light as a navigational aid. Even man can learn to detect the polarization of white light with the naked eye, and he can also distinguish right from left circularly polarized light.

Physicists use polarizers to study the emission of polarized light by atoms situated in regions of strong electric or magnetic field, to determine the strength of the sun's magnetic field by measuring the polarization of certain solar spectral lines, and to determine the pattern of magnetic fields within the Crab Nebula. They use polarizers to analyze the behavior of the remarkable light source *the laser* and to verify theoretical predictions as to the polarization inherent in the synchrotron radiation emitted by certain high-energy accelerators.

Because of light's puzzling dual character (waves and photons) and its central position in the growing field of physics, and because *polarized* light is a most elemental form of light, physicists are confident that polarized light will continue to be an outstandingly challenging enigma as well as a most versatile tool for many generations to come.

WILLIAM A. SHURCLIFF

References

Ditchburn, R. W., "Light," Second edition, New York, Interscience Publishers, 1963, 833 pp.

Jenkins, F. A., and White H. E., "Fundamentals of Optics," Third edition, New York, McGraw-Hill Book Co., 1957, 639 pp.

Land, E. H., "Some Aspects of the Development of Sheet Polarizers," *J. Opt. Soc. Am.*, **41**, 957 (1951).

Shurcliff, W. A., "Polarized Light: Production and Use," Cambridge, Mass., Harvard University Press, 1962, 207 pp.

Shurcliff, W. A., and Ballard, S. S., "Polarized Light," New York, Van Nostrand Reinhold, 1964.

Cross-references: ELECTROMAGNETIC THEORY, LASER, LIGHT, PHOTOELASTICITY, PHOTON, QUANTUM THEORY.

POLARON

An electron in the conduction band of an insulator (or a hole in the valence band) polarizes the medium in its neighborhood—this effect is

particularly important in ionic crystals, on account of their high polarizability. The name "polaron" is given to the electron together with its associated cloud of lattice polarization. The subject has been of interest since Landau[1] suggested that an electron could become self-trapped by the lattice polarization it induces; this would mean that its effective mass would be very large compared with its "bare" mass (as given by band theory).

Fröhlich, Pelzer and Zienau[2] have proposed a simple model Hamiltonian for the polaron. They assume that the ionic medium can be represented by a set of harmonic oscillators. Each oscillator is characterized by a wave vector q, but the frequency ω is simply related to the Reststrahl frequency ω_t, and does not depend on q. If p is the electron momentum and r its position, m the band mass, a_q^+ and a_q canonical creation and annihilation operators for oscillator quanta ("optical phonons"), and Ω is the normalization volume, then the Hamiltonian is

$$H = -\tfrac{1}{2}\nabla^2 + \sum_q a_q^+ a_q + i\left(\frac{2\sqrt{2\pi\alpha}}{\Omega}\right)^{1/2}$$

$$\sum_q (a_q^+ e^{-iq\cdot r} - a_q e^{iq\cdot r}), \quad (1)$$

in units such that the electron band mass $m = 1$, $\hbar = 1$, and $\omega = 1$. The parameter α is defined as

$$\alpha = \frac{e^2}{\hbar}\left(\frac{1}{\epsilon_\infty} - \frac{1}{\epsilon_0}\right)\sqrt{\frac{m}{2\hbar\omega}} \quad (2)$$

with ϵ_ω the frequency-dependent dielectric constant.

The theory, as so far formulated, is one of a particle interacting in a very simple way with a (nonrelativistic) field—the only parameter is the dimensionless coupling constant α. The problem is therefore of fundamental field-theoretical interest, as well as being interesting for its applications.

For very small α ($\alpha \lesssim 1$), a perturbation-theoretical and a Tamm-Dancoff type of variational calculation agree that Landau self-trapping does *not* occur.[2] For rather larger α ("intermediate coupling", $\alpha \lesssim 5$), the canonical transformation of Lee, Low and Pines,[3]

$$\left.\begin{aligned} a_q' &= (a_q + ic_q)\, e^{-iq\cdot r}, \\ a_q^{+\prime} &= (a_q^+ - ic_q)\, e^{iq\cdot r}; \\ p' &= p + \sum_q \hbar q a_q^+ a_q, \\ r' &= r, \end{aligned}\right\} \quad (3)$$

partially decouples the electrons from the phonons and extends the perturbation-theoretical results. The binding energy (in units of $\hbar\omega$) is

$$E_0 = -\alpha + O(\alpha^2) \quad (4)$$

and the effective mass

$$m^* = 1 + \tfrac{1}{6}\alpha \quad (5)$$

The result confirms the view of Fröhlich, Pelzer and Zienau[2] that self-trapping does not occur in, for example, the alkali halides ($\alpha \simeq 5$ for NaCl).

For very large α ("strong coupling", $\alpha \gtrsim 10$), a variational treatment by Pekar[4] *does* lead to very large effective masses; he finds

$$E_0 = -0.10\alpha^2 \quad (6)$$

$$m^* = 230(\alpha/10)^4 \quad (7)$$

However, for intermediate values of α, neither method is very good. A method due to Feynman[5] provides a "bridge" between the strong- and intermediate-coupling regimes. The electron propagator (for states with no free phonons) is expressed as an integral over all possible paths of the exponential of an action functional. The oscillator coordinates do not appear explicitly, but the action contains a term which represents an interaction of the electron *with itself at earlier times*, through a Coulomb potential:

$$\langle r_1 t' | r_2 t'' \rangle = \int \mathfrak{D}(r(t)) e^s \quad (8)$$

$$S = -\int_{t'}^{t''} \tfrac{1}{2}\dot{r}^2\, dt + \frac{\alpha}{2^{3/2}}\iint_{t'}^{t''} dt_1 dt_2$$

$$\frac{\exp - (t_1 - t_2)}{|r(t_1) - r(t_2)|} \quad (9)$$

[For convenience, we use an imaginary time variable.]

Feynman makes the variational ansatz for the action

$$S_0 = -\tfrac{1}{2}\int_{t'}^{t''} \dot{r}^2\, dt - C\iint_{t'}^{t''} dt_1 dt_2$$

$$(r(t_1) - r(t_2))^2 \exp - w(t_1 - t_2) \quad (10)$$

where C and w are parameters to be determined. This trial functional is the exact action for a model system in which the electron is coupled to a fictitious particle of mass $M = 4C/w^3$ through a spring constant $K = 4C/w$, after the coordinates of the fictitious particle have been eliminated. An upper bound for the energy can be derived:

$$E = \frac{3}{4}\frac{(v - w)^2}{v} - \frac{\alpha}{\sqrt{\pi}}\frac{v}{w}\int_0^\infty dt e^{-t}$$

$$\left\{ t\left(1 + \frac{v^2 - w^2}{vw^2}\left[\frac{1 - e^{-vt}}{t}\right]\right)\right\}^{-1/2} \quad (11)$$

where $v^2 = (4C/w) + w^2$. Equation (11) then has

to be minimized with respect to w and v. In the limits $\alpha \lesssim 3$, $\alpha \gtrsim 10$, it reduces to the Lee-Low-Pines[3] and Pekar[4] solutions respectively, but for intermediate values E has had to be evaluated numerically[5]. The effective mass and the mobility have also been calculated,[6] and vary smoothly with α. Higher-order corrections[7] are < 2 percent for all α.

By comparing the Hall mobility and the Ohmic mobility of alkali halides, F. C. Brown[8] and his collaborators have been able to disentangle the parameters, and to obtain explicit experimental estimates of m, m^*, and α. Their independent estimate of m^* from cyclotron resonance is in moderate agreement with the estimate from the mobilities.

When α is very large, the radius of the polaron becomes small. A measure of the radius, R, is the amplitude of zero-point oscillation of the two-particle model system,

$$R \sim \left(\frac{v^2 - w^2}{3v}\right)^{-\frac{1}{2}} \qquad (12)$$

For large α, R is found to be $\approx \alpha^{-1}$. Since the unit of length, $\sqrt{\hbar/m\omega} \sim 10\text{Å}$, R can become less than the lattice spacing; the continuum model must then break down. In this case (the "small" or "localized" polaron), Fröhlich and Sewell[9] showed that the appropriate model is a Bloch tight-binding one; the overlap integrals between polaron wave functions localized on adjacent lattice sites are assumed small. The polaron mass is then very large. Conduction at finite temperatures occurs largely by the electron "hopping" from one site to another—the jump frequency is related to the overlap integrals. Hopping conduction is characterized by a temperature-dependent mobility $\mu \propto T^{-1}$, which has been used as a "signature" of small-polaron formation.

Some transition-metal oxides (in particular NiO, CoO, MnO, and Fe_2O_3) exhibit very low electron mobilities, which have been ascribed to small polarons. It is thought[10] that the charge carriers in the pure oxides are probably non-localized polarons, but that small polarons are formed in the neighborhood of impurity centers.

C. G. KUPER

References

General reference: Kuper, C. G., and Whitfield, G. D. Eds., "Polarons and Excitons," Edinburgh, Oliver & Boyd, Ltd., 1963.
1. Landau, L. D., Phys. Z. Sowjetunion, 3, 644 (1933).
2. Fröhlich, H., Pelzer, H., and Zienau, S., Phil. Mag., 41, 221 (1950).
3. Lee, T.-D., Low, F., and Pines, D., Phys. Rev. 90, 297 (1953); Gurari, M., Phil. Mag., 44, 329 (1953).
4. Pekar, S. I., Zh. Eksperim. i Teor Fiz., 16, 335, 341 (1946); Allcock, G. R., "Polarons and Excitons," p. 45, 1963.
5. Feynman, R. P., Phys. Rev., 97, 660 (1955); Schultz, T. D., Phys. Rev., 116, 526, (1959).
6. Feynman, R. P., Hellwarth, R. W., Iddings, C. K. and Platzman, P. M., Phys. Rev., 127, 1004 (1962).
7. Marshall, J. T., and Mills, L. R., Phys. Rev., B 2, 3143 (1970); Marshall, J. T., and Chawla, M. S., Phys. Rev., B 2, 4209 (1970).
8. Brown, F. C., "Polarons and Excitons," p. 323, 1963. Ascarelli, G., "Polarons and Excitons," p. 357, 1963.
9. Fröhlich, H., and Sewell, G. L., Proc. Phys. Soc., 74, 643 (1959); Sewell, G. L., Phil. Mag., 3, 1361 (1958). Holstein, T., Ann. Phys., 8, 343, (1959).
10. Austin, I. G., and Mott, N. F., Adv. Phys., 18, 41 (1970); Bosman, A. J., and van Daal, H. J., Adv. Phys., 19, 1 (1971).

Cross-references: EXCITONS, POLAR MOLECULES.

POLYMER PHYSICS

Polymers are long-chain molecules with molecular weights of from thousands to many, millions (generally between 20 000 and 10^7 for materials of practical interest). The molecules may be linear, branched, or cross-linked to give a gel structure.

The size and shape of polymer molecules are generally determined from measurements in dilute solution. Molecular weights are obtained from osmotic pressure (number average molecular weight), light scattering (weight average molecular weight), and intrinsic viscosity measurements. Dissymmetry of light scattered by dilute solutions gives the size of molecules. Extent of chain branching can be estimated from light scattering or solution viscosity measurements by comparing the branched polymer with a linear polymer of the same molecular weight. The degree of cross-linking can be determined from the extent of swelling in a solvent or from the elastic modulus by using kinetic theory of rubber. Swelling decreases and modulus increases as cross-linking increases. Solution properties are not only sensitive to molecular weight but also to the interaction between the polymer and solvent molecules. Most polymers have a distribution of molecular weights. In addition to the results from fractionations, the width of the distribution can be estimated from the ratio of weight average to number average molecular weights. This ratio is 1.0 if all the molecules are the same; it is around 2 for most polymers, but may be much greater for some highly branched polymers.

The molecular structure of polymers is unusually complex since the molecules can assume many conformations; more than one type of monomeric unit can make up the chains to give an infinite variety of distribution of sequence lengths, or the monomeric units can be arranged in different types of stereoregularity—isotactic, syndiotactic, or atactic forms. Nuclear magnetic resonance and infrared spectroscopy

are especially powerful techniques for studying the structure of polymers. For polymers capable of crystallizing, x-ray diffraction is another useful tool.

The most important quantity determining the mechanical and many other physical properties of polymers is the glass transition temperature. If the glass transition temperature, T_g, is below ambient temperature, the molecules have extensive freedom of movement, so the material is either a viscous liquid or a rubbery material with a low elastic modulus. If T_g is above ambient temperature, the movement of the molecules is frozen-in, so that the polymer is a rigid solid with a high elastic modulus of the order of 10^{10} dynes/cm^2. The glass transition temperature is not sharply defined but depends to some extent on the time scale of the experiment—the faster the experiment, the higher is the apparent T_g. Glass transitions may be measured by many techniques such as where breaks occur in the slope of volume or refractive index vs temperature curves or by the rapid change in elastic modulus with temperature in the transition region. The position of T_g on the temperature scale is largely due to the stiffness of the polymer chains. Flexible molecules such as polybutadiene and silicone rubbers have low T_g, while stiff molecules such as polystyrene and polymethyl methacrylate have high transition temperatures. Cohesive energy density or polarity is another important factor in determining T_g. Symmetry plays a secondary role. Glass transitions can be regulated by copolymerization or by addition of a plasticizer which lowers T_g.

Many polymers including polyethylene and isotactic polypropylene are semicrystalline. In their bulk behavior such polymers behave as though they are a mixture of amorphous and crystalline materials, but the exact nature of the crystalline state is not yet clearly defined for such materials. In the crystal lattice, some types of polymer chains assume a zig-zag conformation while others crystallize in the form of helices. Single crystals of some polymers have been grown from dilute solutions. In these single crystals the chains are perpendicular to the faces making up the thin lamellar crystals, so that each polymer chain must fold back on itself several times. There is some morphological evidence, based on electron microscopy studies, that even in the bulk polymer cooled down from the melt there is extensive chain folding in the crystalline phase. In terms of a two-phase model, the degree of crystallinity may be determined by x-ray, density or heat capacity measurements. Different techniques generally give similar but not identical values for the degree of crystallinity; typical values vary from 40 per cent crystallinity for low-density polyethylene to 85 per cent for high-density polyethylene. Crystallinity is greatly affected by chain perfection. Copolymerization and branching greatly reduce crystallinity.

Highly stereoregular polymers such as isotactic polystyrene tend to be crystalline, while the random atactic polymers are noncrystalline. The melting point also depends upon chain perfection—the greater the degree of imperfection, the lower is the melting point.

Many polymers of commercial importance are not linear polymers consisting of a single type of monomeric unit. Copolymers contain two or more kinds of monomers. If one type of monomer makes up the backbone and another type side chains, the polymers are called graft polymers. If two polymers are mechanically mixed together, the mixture is called a polyblend. Most, but not all, polyblends are two-phase systems. Block polymers, consisting of long sequences of one kind of polymer chain attached to the end of another kind of polymer chain, are also generally two-phase systems in which parts of a single molecule can be in two phases simultaneously. Two-phase systems are important commercially because of their great toughness.

Even at high temperatures where linear polymers are liquid, they tend to be very viscous. The melt viscosity is especially high if the molecular weight is above a critical value where chain entanglements can occur. At molecular weights above which entanglements occur, the melt viscosity at low rates of shear depends approximately on molecular weight. These viscous polymer melts are also more or less elastic in nature and behave somewhat like rubber. If the molecules are cross-linked to one another, the elastic behavior becomes dominant and true vulcanized rubbers result. Polymer melts are generally non-Newtonian, and the properties are very dependent upon the rate of shear. Molecular theories have been developed by Rouse, Zimm, and Bueche which explain quite well many of the rheological properties of melts and solutions.

The usefulness of polymers depends primarily upon their mechanical properties. The elastic modulus of rubbers is explained quite satisfactorily by the kinetic theory of rubber elasticity. No satisfactory theory is yet available for rigid polymers. Dynamic mechanical measurements using oscillating stresses or strains have been especially useful in relating mechanical properties to molecular structure; such tests are generally made to measure the elastic modulus and mechanical damping over a wide range of frequencies and temperatures. Generally the effects of temperature and frequency (or time) can be made equivalent by a superposition treatment such as developed by Williams, Landel, and Ferry. The phenomenological theory of viscoelasticity has developed to the stage where it is possible to interconvert data from one type of test (say dynamic mechanical) to other types of tests such as creep, stress relaxation and, to a lesser extent, stress-strain data. On heating a rigid organic polymer, the modulus drops from about 10^{10} dynes/cm^2 to a low

value of about 10^7 dynes/cm^2 in a small temperature interval near the glass transition temperature, unless the polymer is highly cross-linked or crystalline. Both crystallinity and cross-linking can greatly increase the modulus about T_g, but they have little effect on the modulus below T_g. Polymers are unique in that some of them can be elongated over 1000 per cent before they break.

The dielectric constant and power factor or electrical loss depend upon the number and type of dipoles. At low temperatures (or high frequencies) where the dipoles are frozen-in, the dielectric constant and electrical loss are both low. At high temperatures (or low frequencies) where the molecules have high mobility, the dielectric constant is high while the electrical loss is often low. At intermediate temperatures or frequencies where the main relaxation times for dipolar motion are approximately the same as the applied electrical frequency, the electrical loss goes through a pronounced maximum, and the dielectric constant changes rapidly with either frequency or temperature. Since the mobility of the chain backbone is related to the ease with which dipoles can move, there is often a good correlation between electrical and mechanical properties. Impurities in polymers can be very detrimental to good electrical properties, especially at high temperatures where conductivity can be relatively high.

Most pure amorphous polymers are transparent. Crystallinity often makes a material milky or white in appearance. Long chain molecules can be oriented by stretching in the molten state or by cold-drawing in some cases. Such oriented materials are generally highly birefringent, since the polarizability along the chain is usually quite different from the polarizability perpendicular to the chain. The mechanical properties of oriented polymers such as fibers are also highly anisotropic. For instance, the modulus and tensile strength are generally much greater parallel to the chain axis than perpendicular to it.

Polymers have very high coefficients of thermal expansion compared to most rigid materials. The coefficient of expansion shows a distinct break at the glass transition temperature—the coefficient being greater above T_g. Most polymers would be classed as thermal insulators rather than as thermal conductors.

LAWRENCE E. NIELSEN

References

Bueche, F., "Physical Properties of Polymers," New York, Interscience Publishers, 1962

Nielsen, L., "Mechanical Properties of Polymers," New York, Van Nostrand Reinhold, 1962

Tobolsky, A. V., and Mark, H., "Polymer Science and Materials," New York, Wiley-Interscience, 1971.

Cross-references: DIELECTRIC THEORY, LIGHT SCATTERING, MOLECULAR WEIGHT, MOLECULES AND MOLECULAR STRUCTURE, OSMOSIS, VISCOELASTICITY, VISCOSITY.

POSITRON

The positron is one of many fundamental bits of matter. Its rest mass (9.109×10^{-31} kg) is the same as the mass of the electron, and its charge ($+1.602 \times 10^{-19}$ coulomb) is the same magnitude but opposite in sign to that of the electron. The positron and electron are antiparticles for each other. The positron has spin 1/2 and is described by Fermi-Dirac statistics as is the electron (see ELECTRON).

The positron was discovered in 1932 by C. D. Anderson at the California Institute of Technology while doing cloud chamber experiments on cosmic rays. The cloud chamber tracks of some particles were observed to curve in such a direction in a magnetic field that the charge had to be positive. In all other respects, the tracks resembled those of high-energy electrons. The discovery of the positron was in accord with the theoretical work of Dirac on the negative energy states of electrons. These negative energy states were interpreted as predicting the existence of a positively charged particle.

Positrons can be produced by either nuclear decay or the transformation of the energy of a gamma ray into an electron-positron pair. In nuclei which are proton-rich, a mode of decay which permits a reduction in the number of protons with a small expenditure of energy is positron emission. The reaction taking place during decay is

$$p^+ \to n^0 + e^+ + \nu$$

where p^+ represents the PROTON, n^0 the NEUTRON, e^+ the POSITRON, and ν a massless, chargeless entity called a NEUTRINO. The positron and neutrino are emitted from the nucleus while the neutron remains bound within the nucleus. Although none of the naturally occuring radioactive nuclides are positron emitters, many artificial radioisotopes which decay by positron emission have been produced. In fact the first observed case of positron decay of nuclei was also the first observed case of artificial radioactivity. An example of such a nuclear decay is

$$_{11}Na^{22} \to {}_{10}Ne^{22} + e^+ + \nu \text{ (half-life} \approx 2.6 \text{ years)}$$

This particular decay provides a practical, usable source of positrons for experimental purposes.

The process of pair production occurs when a high-energy gamma ray interacts in the electromagnetic field of a nucleus to create a pair of particles—a positron and an electron. Pair production is an excellent example of the fact that the rest mass of a particle represents a fixed amount of energy. Since the rest energy (E_{rest} =

$m_{rest}c^2$) of the positron plus electron is 1.022 MeV, this energy is the gamma energy threshold and no pair production can take place for lower-energy gammas. In general, the cross section for pair production increases with increasing gamma energy and also with increasing Z number of the nucleus in whose electromagnetic field the interaction takes place.

The positron is a stable particle (i.e., it does not decay itself), but when it is combined with its antiparticle, the electron, the two annihilate each other and the total energy of the particles appears in the form of gamma rays. Before annihilation with an electron, most positrons come to thermal equilibrium with their surroundings. In the process of losing energy and becoming thermalized, a high-energy positron interacts with its surroundings in almost the same way as does the electron. Thus for positrons, curves of distance traversed in a medium as a function of initial particle energy are almost identical with those of electrons.

It is energetically possible for a positron and an electron to form a bound system similar to the hydrogen atom, with the positron taking the place of the proton. This bound system has been given the name "positronium" and the chemical symbol Ps. Although the possibility of positronium formation was predicted as early as 1934, the first experimental demonstration of its existence came in 1951 during an investigation of positron annihilation rates in gases as a function of pressure. The energy levels of positronium are about one-half those of the hydrogen atom since the reduced mass of positronium is about one-half that of the hydrogen atom. This also causes the radius of the positronium system to be about twice that of the hydrogen atom. Thus positronium is a bound system with a radius of 1.06Å and a ground state binding energy of 6.8eV. As mentioned previously, the positron has an intrinsic magnetic moment and an intrinsic angular momentum, or spin. In positronium, the spins of the electron and positron can be oriented so they are either parallel or antiparallel. These two states, called ortho-positronium and para-positronium respectively, have very different annihilation characteristics. Most positrons entering a medium do not form positronium, but the general annihilation characteristics show the same dependence on orientation of the spins, regardless of whether the annihilation occurs in a collision or from the bound state.

In principle, positronium can be observed through the emission of its characteristic spectral lines, which should be similar to hydrogen's except that the wavelengths of all corresponding lines are doubled. All attempts to detect these lines have been unsuccessful. Positronium is also the ideal system in which the calculations of quantum electrodynamics can be compared with experimental results. In fact measurement of the fine-structure splitting of the positronium ground state has served as an important confirmation of the theory of quantum electrodynamics.

It is possible for a positron-electron system to annihilate with the emission of one, two, three, or more, gamma rays. However, not all processes are equally probable. One-gamma annihilation requires another particle to participate to conserve momentum. This process is a very infrequent type decay. The most probable decay is by the emission of two gamma rays, directed in opposite directions, with each possessing about one-half the energy of the system. The presence of these 0.511-MeV ($=m_ec^2$) gamma rays is always found when positrons are present. Whether annihilation is to be by the emission of one, two or three gammas depends on the orientation of the spins of the positron and electron. Conservation of angular momentum requires that the decay be by two-gamma emission if the spins are antiparallel, and by three-gamma (or one-gamma) emission if the spins are parallel.

If formed in free space, positronium exhibits two characteristic lifetimes against self-annihilation. These are $\tau_1 = 1.25 \times 10^{-10}$ second for the anti-parallel spin case (also called the singlet state) and $\tau_3 = 1.39 \times 10^{-7}$ second for the parallel spin case (called the triplet state). Another lifetime, characteristic of the physical surroundings of the positron, is found when positronium is formed in certain condensed materials. This lifetime (known as τ_2) is longer than the singlet free space lifetime τ_1, but is much shorter than the triplet free space lifetime τ_3. In general, this τ_2 lifetime is a measure of the rate of "pickoff" of atomic electrons with antiparallel spins by the positrons in triplet positronium. In this process, the positron enters the material and forms triplet positronium with an electron, but then annihilates with an electron belonging to one of the surrounding atoms, whose spin is oriented opposite to that of the positron. That the probability of "pickoff" and the subsequent two-gamma annihilation depend on the properties of the surroundings is to be expected. Indeed, the τ_2 lifetime is a function of the material, the temperature, the density, the degree of crystallinity, the phase, etc. It has been found in some cases that even in the same material not all positrons in triplet positronium have the same "pickoff" probability, a fact revealed by the presence of more than one τ_2 component. Positron lifetimes have been measured in a great variety of substances in an effort to correlate trends in the τ_2 lifetime values with chemical or physical properties.

The angular correlation of the annihilation gammas has been measured for both the two-gamma and three-gamma cases. In three-gamma annihilation, the gammas are coplanar as predicted, and azimuthally correlated such that their energies and directions are consistent with the conservation laws of energy and momentum. Two-gamma annihilation studies have been extensive, the results showing that the two gammas are emitted within a few milliradians of 180° from each other. The width of the two-gamma angular distributions is a measure of the linear

momentum of the positron-electron system when annihilation occurs. These measurements can be used to gain information on the momentum distribution of the electrons with which the positrons annihilate. Thus positron annihilation becomes a tool to learn more concerning the internal structure of materials.

B. CLARK GROSECLOSE
WILLIAM W. WALKER

References

1. Berko, S., and Hereford, F. L., *Rev. Mod. Phys.*, **28**, 299 (1956).
2. Ferrell, R. A., *Rev. Mod. Phys.*, **28**, 308 (1956).
3. Green J., and Lee, J., "Positronium Chemistry," New York, Academic Press, 1964.
4. Wallace, P. R., *Solid State Phys.*, **10**, 1 (1960).
5. Stewart, A. T., and Roellig, L. O., Eds., "Positron Annihilation, Proceedings of the International Conference," New York, Academic Press, 1967.
6. Goldanskii, V. I., *Atomic Energy Rev.*, **6**, 1 (1968).

Cross-references: ATOMIC PHYSICS, ELECTRON, ELEMENTARY PARTICLES, NEUTRINO, NEUTRON, NUCLEAR STRUCTURE, PROTON.

POTENTIAL

The concept of potential has developed in several fields in physical phenomena from either one or another of two viewpoints. One idea is that there can be the storage of some entity which results in energy storage in the system. This stored energy may be released for dynamic use. The energy so stored can thus be considered as potential energy.

The other idea from which the concept of potential has been developed is that it is some scalar function whose space rate of change yields a vector force which may be useful for mathematical analyses or for the development of other physical quantities. As will be shown, these two ideas are compatible.

From one, the other, or both of these general viewpoints has developed the concept of potential as an entity in the subjects of gravitation, electricity, magnetism, heat conduction, fluid flow, elastic stress, and others. The early analysis of entities in many of these subjects began through experimental observations and mathematical hypotheses of various sorts, but the concept of potential eventually became apparent if it was not in the original analysis.

The development of the concept of potential as a significant entity for the analysis of electric phenomena was developed by Simeon Poisson, George Green, and others in the period from about 1813 to 1827. It was realized that energy could be released from electrically charged bodies, and the concept of potential was developed as one characteristic of such a charged system that measured the ability of the system to release this energy. The energy stored in the system was and is called *potential energy* and is a scalar quantity.

The discussion of this article is phrased in electrical terminology, although many of the interrelationships among entities discussed here are applicable to the subjects of gravitation, heat conduction, fluid flow, and other subjects. The concepts of scalar magnetic potential and vector magnetic potential are included here so that the basic concepts in electromagnetism are complete.

Closely associated with the concept of electric potential was the concept of *charge* that had been formulated by Charles Augustin de Coulomb and others over about a 100-year period starting about 1737. The electric scalar potential of a macroscopic system is defined as the electric energy of the system divided by the electric charge. This simple definition presumes a basic two-conductor, statically charged system. The mathematical expression for the definition of the potential Φ is

$$\Phi = \frac{W}{Q}$$

where W is the energy of the system and Q is the charge (see list of units at end of article).

Modern electric systems employ the concept of potential for much more sophisticated forms through the use of summations of charge effects either in discrete or in distributed forms. The complete expression for electric potential caused by the accumulation of a number of concentrated charges Q_k, surface charge density σ over a surface S, and volume charge density ρ in a volume V, all being located in a dielectric medium of uniform permittivity ϵ, is

$$\Phi = \sum_{k=1}^{n} \frac{Q_k}{4\pi\epsilon r} + \frac{1}{4\pi\epsilon} \int_S \frac{\sigma ds}{r} + \frac{1}{4\pi\epsilon} \int_V \frac{\rho dv}{1}$$

where r measures the magnitude of the distance from the point at which the electric potential is evaluated to each charged particle or element of charge.

The difference in electric potential from one point a to another point b in a static electric field is related to a vector function called the electric field intensity $\mathcal{E}$ (a characteristic of the space related to the negative of the gradient of the electric potential) through the line integral relationship

$$\Phi_{ab} = -\int_a^b \mathcal{E} \cdot d\mathbf{l},$$

where $\mathbf{l}$ is a vector direction measured along the path in the direction from the point a to the point b, and the scalar product between $\mathcal{E}$ and $d\mathbf{l}$ is denoted by the dot or scalar product notation.

The inverse form of this integral expression is the gradient form for the static electric field

intensity, namely

$$\mathcal{E} = -\nabla\Phi$$

where the ∇ symbol is a vector differential space operator which, when applied to the scalar electric potential Φ, yields the electric potential gradient.

An extension of spatial derivative operations yields another function of the scalar electric potential Φ, known as the scalar Laplacian, as $\nabla^2\Phi$. This term, when equated to the negative of the volume space charge density ρ divided by the permittivity of the space, is known as Poisson's equation. Thus,

$$\nabla^2\Phi = -\rho/\epsilon$$

If the electric volume charge density is zero, the above relationship becomes

$$\nabla^2\Phi = 0$$

and is known as Laplace's equation.

Electric charges in motion produce magnetic effects, which result in a magnetic field intensity vector $\mathbf{H}$, somewhat analogous to the corresponding vector $\mathcal{E}$ in electric field phenomena. The line integral relationship between this vector $\mathbf{H}$ and the vector direction measured along a path in space from point a to b establishes an analogous scalar magnetic potential Ψ_{ab} as

$$\Psi_{ab} = -\int_a^b \mathbf{H} \cdot d\mathbf{l}$$

This function is useful in the evaluation of magnetic field geometric relations for locations in space where the electric current density is zero.

For regions in magnetic fields where current densities exist, a designation of a magnetic potential relation can only be made through a function called the *vector magnetic potential*. This vector is defined in a form similar to the expression for scalar electric potential caused by a volume distribution of electric charge density as given earlier. Thus, the vector magnetic potential $\mathbf{A}$ at a point in space, caused by a distribution of current density $\mathbf{J}$ over a volume V is

$$\mathbf{A} = \frac{\mu}{4\pi}\int_V \frac{\mathbf{J}\,dv}{r}$$

where μ is the permeability of space and r is the magnitude of the distance from the point at which $\mathbf{A}$ is evaluated to each element of current density of the system. The point under consideration can be a point within the region of current density.

The vector magnetic flux density $\mathbf{B}$ in such a space is related to the vector magnetic potential $\mathbf{A}$ through a spatial differential function called the curl and symbolized by the operational form as

$$\mathbf{B} = \nabla \times \mathbf{A}$$

An extension of spatial derivative operations upon the vector magnetic potential also yields another function of this potential known as the vector Laplacian, $\nabla^2\mathbf{A}$. This term is related to the current density $\mathbf{J}$ at a point in the field as

$$\nabla^2\mathbf{A} = -\mu\mathbf{J}$$

This expression is analogous to the similar scalar Laplacian of the electric potential which was related to the electric charge density at the point of evaluation.

For systems in which the charges are moving in such a manner that the vector magnetic potential is not constant with respect to time, the elementary form of the relationship between the electric field intensity $\mathcal{E}$ and the scalar electric potential Φ must be modified to include a function of the vector magnetic potential, namely

$$\mathcal{E} = -\nabla\Phi - \frac{\partial\mathbf{A}}{\partial t}$$

This is the general expression that is valid at a point in space for all conditions. As action at a distance is considered, the elementary forms for the evaluation of the scalar electric potential Φ and of the vector magnetic potential $\mathbf{A}$, however, must recognize the time delay in action with respect to the causes.

If the scalar electric potential at a point P is to be evaluated at some time t, the *retarded potential* must consider the finite velocity of propagation that occurs in the path length r between the point P and the location of the charge that causes the electric potential.

Depending upon the nature of the charge, the retarded potential expression can be expressed in terms of the retarded time $t - r/c$, where c is the velocity of the propagated effect in free space. For the case in which the charge is distributed over a volume, the expression becomes

$$\Phi_{P,t} = \frac{1}{4\pi\epsilon}\int_V \frac{[\rho]_{t-r/c}\,dv}{r}$$

The symbol $[\rho]_{t-r/c}$ indicates that the charge density at the source of the field is that evaluated at an earlier time $t - r/c$. If the charges are discrete or distributed over surfaces, the corresponding forms of the potential function for these geometries would be used.

In a similar manner, the retarded vector magnetic potential can be expressed for a volume distribution of current density as

$$\mathbf{A}_{P,t} = \frac{\mu}{4\pi}\int_V \frac{[\mathbf{J}]_{t-r/c}\,dv}{r}$$

All preceding relations are expressed in a form that results if a rationalized system of

units is used. The internationally accepted metric (SI) units that conform with these preceeding relationships are:

Entity	Symbol	Unit
Energy	W	joule
Potential (electric)	Φ	volt
Charge	Q	coulomb
Length	r, l	meter
Area	S	meter^2
Volume	V	meter^3
Surface charge density	σ	coulomb/meter^2
Volume charge density	ρ	coulomb/meter^3
Permittivity	ϵ	farad/meter
Electric field intensity	$\mathscr{E}$	volt/meter
Magnetic field intensity	H	ampere/meter
Scalar magnetic potential	Ψ	ampere
Vector magnetic potential	A	weber/meter
Permeability	μ	weber/meter-ampere
Magnetic flux density	B	tesla
Current density	J	ampere/meter^2
Time	t	second
Velocity	c	meter/second

WARREN B. BOAST

References

Boast, W. B., "Vector Fields," New York, Harper & Row, 1964.

Bradshaw, M. D., and Byatt, W. J., "Introductory Engineering Field Theory," Englewood Cliffs, N.J., Prentice-Hall, 1967.

Durney, C. H., and Johnson, C. C., "Introduction to Modern Electromagnetics," New York, McGraw-Hill, 1969.

Holt, C. A., "Introduction to Electromagnetic Fields and Waves," New York, Wiley, 1963.

Javid, M., and Brown, P. M., "Field Analysis and Electromagnetics," New York, McGraw-Hill, 1963.

Paris, D. T., and Hurd, F. K., "Basic Electromagnetic Theory," New York, McGraw-Hill, 1969.

Plonsey, R., and Colin, R. E., "Principles and Applications of Electromagnetic Fields," New York, McGraw-Hill, 1961.

Ramo, S., Whinnery, J. R., and Van Duzer, T., "Fields and Waves in Communication Electronics," New York, Wiley, 1965.

Rao, N. N., "Basic Electromagnetics with Applications," Englewood Cliffs, N.J., Prentice-Hall, 1972.

Silvester, P., "Modern Electromagnetics," Englewood Cliffs, N. J., Prentice-Hall, 1968.

Cross-references: ELECTRICITY, ELECTROMAGNETIC THEORY, STATIC ELECTRICITY.

PRESSURE, VERY HIGH

For the purposes of this article "very high pressure" is defined as the range above 50 kilobars. Discussion is confined to apparatus and experiments capable of performance in this range. Thus, no discussion of the vast array of sophisticated measurements in the 12 to 20 kilobar range is included.

The increasing interest in research at very high pressure has been stimulated in part by the synthesis of diamond at General Electric, in part by an expansion of experimental GEO-PHYSICS, and in large part by an increased appreciation of the importance of relatively large variations of interatomic distance in our understanding of the electronic structure of solids.

It is convenient to divide the available types of equipment into those capable of chemical synthesis on a reasonable scale and those primarily useful for physical measurements.

Among the former group, the most straightforward is the piston and cylinder device brought to its highest development by Kennedy and his colleagues at UCLA. With appropriate support it is capable of 70 kilobars. In this apparatus the pressure determination is more direct and probably more accurate than in the others.

The most generally useful apparatus for relatively large scale work at higher pressures is the General Electric "belt." As originally designed by Hall, pressures of perhaps 140 kilobars were possible. Later modifications by Bundy have extended this range by another 40 to 50 kilobars. The essential feature of the device is support for the pistons which increases with increasing pressure.

A third "large volume" apparatus in general use is the tetrahedral press first developed by Hall and modified by Hutton. In its smaller scale versions it appears capable of 100 kilobars or more, but the larger scale-ups are somewhat more limited.

All three of the above types of equipment can be operated at elevated temperatures, to 1000 C or beyond, although the accuracy of both pressure and temperature measurements is limited under these extreme conditions.

By far the most common "small scale" equipment used for physical measurements at high pressure is the tapered anvil design originated by P. W. Bridgman. It has the great advantage of relative cheapness of construction and ease of loading. While pressure gradients are a problem, they have not limited its broad application. Originally developed for electrical resistance measurements, it has since been applied to x-ray scattering, to Mössbauer studies, and (with diamond anvils) to optical absorption studies. While there have been a number of estimates of the pressure range of Bridgman anvils, the probable upper limit is near 150 kilobars.

A modification of the tapered anvil apparatus has given the highest pressures yet obtained statically. This involves very small flats, work hardened, sintered, tungsten carbide pistons, and support on the taper which increases with increasing pressure, so that the net effect is that measurements are made in a cell surrounded by rings of material at continuously decreasing pressure. With modifications of this apparatus, optical absorption measurements have been

made to 160 to 170 kilobars, electrical resistance and x-ray diffraction studies to over 500 kilobars, and Mössbauer studies to beyond 250 kilobars. The apparatus has been operated from 77 to 650 K, but increasing temperature above 300 K limits the pressure range rapidly.

Finally, mention should be made of shock velocity measurements. With this technique p-v measurements have been made at pressures of 2000 kilobars both at Los Alamos and by Russian workers. Measurements have largely been confined to p-v relations to date, but other types are apparently possible. The correction from adiabatic experiments to isothermal data limits the accuracy for very compressible materials.

The problem of calibration is a complex one, and only an outline can be given here. The most usual method has been to observe discontinuities in electrical resistance due to first-order phase changes in certain metals. A serious problem is that these materials exhibit varying degrees of metastability which are not independent of the apparatus. The calibration problem at elevated or reduced temperature is still more serious. Points most frequently used at 300 K are transitions in bismuth at 25 and 87 kilobars, in thallium at 37 kilobars, in barium at 59 and 140 kilobars, in iron at 130 kilobars, and in lead at approximately 160 kilobars. Beyond this point, the difficulties increase. By means of x-ray measurements on systems where shock wave data are available, consistency between shock and static measurements has been established to over 500 kilobars. Internal consistency among some shock measurements has also been shown by x-rays on mixed powders. One certain conclusion is that extensive extrapolation of linear calibrations established at low pressure invariably predicts pressures much higher than are obtainable.

In a brief article such as this it would be impractical to review in any detail the experimental results, but an outline of major features is feasible.

A great deal of careful effort has gone into the establishment of melting curves and phase boundaries between two solid phases. Items of particular interest in the first category include maxima in the melting points of cesium and barium discussed by Kennedy and co-workers. High pressure phase transitions to a metallic state have been discovered in silicon, germanium, gallium arsenide, gallium antimonide, aluminum antimonide, indium arsenide, indium phosphide, indium antimonide, zinc sulfide, zinc selenide, zinc telluride, and other III–V and III–IV compounds. Recent x-ray studies indicate that the high pressure phases of silicon and germanium have the white tin structure while a number of the III–V compounds have a closely related atomic arrangement. On the other hand, ZnSe and ZnTe appear to adopt the face-centered-cubic NaCl structure at high pressure. In the case of InSb and a few related compounds it has been possible to quench in the high pressure phase at

one atmosphere and to show that these are indeed SUPERCONDUCTORS below about 3 K. (See CRYSTALLIZATION, CRYSTALLOGRAPHY and SEMICONDUCTORS.)

The General Electric group has shown that after compression into the metallic phase and release of pressure, silicon and germanium retain a rather complex cubic or tetragonal arrangement which is neither white tin nor diamond. It has not yet been shown whether these intermediate phases have any definite range of true stability. Moderate heating at one atmosphere suffices to return these materials to the diamond structure.

The pressure-volume measurements by Swenson and his co-workers at Iowa State on alkali metals and solidified rare gases at liquid helium temperature have given an important impetus to our understanding of interatomic forces in relatively simple systems.

Shock wave studies have provided p-v data on nineteen metals to 2000 kilobars and a number of others to 500 kilobars, as well as compressibilities of a number of alkali halides to the 300 to 400 kilobar region.

A very interesting high-pressure phenomenon is the electronic transition. A cusp in the resistance of cesium at 41 kilobars is associated with a change in the conduction band from $6s$ to $5d$ character. A second maximum near 135 kilobars may involve the introduction of $4f$ and $5p$ character to the conduction band. Similar events occur at higher pressures in rubidium and possibly also potassium. Electronic transitions in the rare earth metals probably involve the promotion of a $4f$ electron into a $5d$ orbital or into the conduction band.

Recently it has been demonstrated that for a wide variety of materials there is sufficient shift of one type of orbital with respect to another to establish a new ground state for the system or to greatly modify the ground state characteristics by mixing of orbitals. These new ground states may have different chemical as well as physical characteristics. With increasing pressure, ferric iron reduces to ferrous iron and there may be increases or decreases in multiplicity (spin changes) which affect chemical and magnetic properties. These transformations, which occur over a range of pressures, are irreversible, although with some hysteresis. New ground states in aromatic hydrocarbons and their complexes greatly change their chemical characteristics.

A discontinuous insulator-metal transition in mixed transition metal oxides confirms many aspects of the theoretical analysis of Mott, who predicted such electronic transitions.

In insulators and SEMICONDUCTORS, one of the more significant studies involves the shift of the optical absorption edge (gap between the conduction and valence band) with pressure and the accompanying change in electrical resistance. A number of features concerning the band structure of silicon, germanium, and

related compounds have been revealed by these measurements.

The continuous approach to the metallic state is best illustrated by studies on iodine, where a very close agreement is shown between the activation energy for electrical conduction and half the optical energy gap. Between 130 and 170 kilobars the resistance is metallic in one direction but not in the other, much like graphite. At higher pressures the behavior is distinctly metallic.

High pressure optical studies on the alkali halides have been important in elucidating the electronic structure in the neighborhood of imperfections. The local compressibility of the F center is about twice the bulk compressibility at low pressure and decreases to perhaps 1.2 to 1.4 times the bulk compressibility above 100 kilobars. This is quite consistent with the picture of a vacancy containing a trapped electron.

Crystal field theory has been a very important first-order picture of the ENERGY LEVELS of transition metal ions in crystals and complexes. The effect of pressure on the transition energy shows very clearly the applicability and limitations of the theory. In most cases, it is clear that the point "charge" assumption of crystal field theory is inadequate for quantitative calculations, and increasing pressure results in spreading out of the electron cloud and decreased interelectronic repulsion among the $3d$ electrons.

It is not hard to see that there is scarcely an area of solid-state physics where high pressure measurements are not capable of providing a significant test of theory.

A number of good references are available. Bridgman's[1] monograph remains a classic. A book edited by Wentorf[2] and one by C. C. Bradley[3] give excellent discussions of technique. The two-volume review edited by R. S. Bradley[4] is still a useful general reference. Recent solid-state developments are found in conference proceedings edited by Tomizuka and Emrick[5] and by D. Bloch.[6] There is also a recent monograph on electronic transitions.[7]

H. G. DRICKAMER

References

1. Bridgman, P. W., "Physics of High Pressure," Second edition, New York, Bell and Company, 1949.
2. Wentorf, R. H., Ed., "Modern Very High Pressure Techniques," London, Butterworths, 1962.
3. Bradley, C. C., "High Pressure Methods in Solid State Research," New York, Plenum Press, 1969.
4. Bradley, R. S., Ed., "Physics and Chemistry of High Pressure," New York, Academic Press, 1963.
5. Tomizuka, C. C., and Emrick, R. M., "Physics of Solids at High Pressure," New York, Academic Press, 1965.
6. Bloch, D. Ed., "Propriétés Physiques des Solides Sous Pression" (in English) Paris, C.N.R.S., 1970.
7. Drickamer, H. G. and Frank, C. W., "Electronic Transitions and High Pressure Chemistry and Physics of Solids," London, Chapman and Hall, New York, Halsted Press, 1973.

Cross-references: FLUID STATICS: GAS LAWS; GASES, THERMODYNAMIC PROPERTIES.

PROPAGATION OF ELECTROMAGNETIC WAVES

The discussion of propagation phenomena in general media requires a rather elaborate and sophisticated mathematical formalism. For a detailed treatment of those disturbances that fall into a category of wave phenomena, an ELECTROMAGNETIC THEORY of characteristics whose origin lies in the subject of partial differential equations has long been available.

Two viewpoints are of interest for an understanding of the mechanism of propagation of an electromagnetic wave: the macroscopic phenomenological theory of Maxwell and the microscopic theory of Lorentz. The Maxwell theory avoids the explanation of what happens to the individual charged particles that constitute the medium in which the phenomena are taking place; the influence of the medium is accounted for by means of factors called constitutive parameters. The effect of the electric field of equal numbers of oppositely charged particles that make up the medium is accounted for by the permittivity ϵ. The effects of the motions of the charges comprising the medium on the fields are taken into account in the following manner: the motion of the unbound charges is subsumed under the conduction current by means of a conductivity σ; the translational motion of the bound charges is subsumed in the electric-displacement field by means of the permittivity ϵ; and the rotational motion of the constituent charges is subsumed in the magnetic-induction field by means of the permeability μ.

This representation of the dynamical behavior of the constituent charges by means of the parameters ϵ, μ, and σ has proved to be of great practical importance, since one can separate the study of the macroscopic behavior of the fields from that of the macroscopic behavior of the constituents of the medium in which the fields are present. In many media these constitutive parameters can be determined by empirical means much more easily than by theoretical considerations. For such media the macroscopic theory is clearly most suitable.

In an ionized gas (in contrast to media made up of neutral molecules), it is difficult to measure the constitutive parameters. The difficulty arises from the fact that the space charges present and the boundary condition imposed by the measuring apparatus affect each other significantly. To determine these parameters a knowledge of the dynamical behavior of the microscopic constituents is required, which leads us to the second point of view, the exhaustive

microscopic theory of Lorentz. This theory attempts to describe all electrical phenomena in terms of the elementary positive and negative charges comprising the medium. The theory dispenses with the concept of the material medium and considers only the ensemble of negative and positive charges (which actually constitute the medium) in free space. More specifically, the theory postulates that in all permeable bodies there exists a large number of charged particles of very small size, which are separated from each other by free space. Conducting bodies are imagined to be constituted of a large number of free particles capable of being moved through the body under the action of an electric force. Nonconducting or weakly conducting bodies are considered to be made up of particles bound to their positions of equilibrium by an elastic force. Even though they are displaced from their equilibrium positions, this displacement is not very large (small oscillations). It is also postulated that the medium has no net charge, so that the positive and negative charges balance exactly. When particles are displaced from their equilibrium positions, the medium becomes polarized.

The Lorentz theory further assumes that the free-space displacement current exists not only in the empty space between the particles but also within the particles themselves. The action of the material medium participates in this theory if we consider the motions of the charged particles under the influence of the electromagnetic forces as a fundamental concept. If each particle has a charge q and a mass m, then under the action of the electric force the particle is displaced from its equilibrium position, and at time t has a velocity of magnitude v. However, the moving charge produces a current qv, and if there are N such particles per unit volume, they give rise to a convection current density Nqv (by v we understand the *time-average* value of the charge velocity). The average convection current density can be written as $Nqv = \rho v = J$ regardless of whether the charges are free or bound.

For varying fields, it is not clear *a priori* whether this total current is a conduction current proportional to the electric intensity and in phase with it, or a displacement current proportional to $\dot{E}$ and out of phase with the electric intensity E by $\pi/2$. Consequently, the total current density must be written as the sum of the free-space displacement current and the material convection current.

Let us summarize the two views: the Maxwell theory describes the phenomena in terms of the equations

$$\nabla \times E + \dot{B} = 0 \tag{1}$$

$$\nabla \times H = J + \dot{D} \tag{2}$$

$$\nabla \cdot D = \rho \tag{3}$$

$$\nabla \cdot B = 0 \tag{4}$$

supplemented by the relations

$$B = \mu H \tag{5}$$

$$D = \epsilon E \tag{6}$$

$$J = \sigma E \tag{7}$$

The Lorentz microscopic theory describes the electromagnetic phenomena by the same set of Maxwell's equations as given above, but since there is no medium in this point of view, the relations (eqs. 5, 6, and 7) must be given in vacuo,

$$\mu = \mu_0 \quad \epsilon = \epsilon_0 \tag{8}$$

and the current density is given directly in terms of the moving charges:

$$J = \sum_k q_k v_k / \text{volume of region containing charges} \tag{9}$$

Maxwell's equations relate the fields to the charges and their motions, but since these motions are not known, it is necessary to supplement them with the dynamical equations of motion for the charges. These equations have the form, for each particle q_k,

$$\frac{d(m_k v_k)}{dt} = q_k(E + v_k \times B) \tag{10}$$

where B is the *total* magnetic induction field evaluated at the position r_k of the kth particle and E is the total electric field evaluated at r_k. These fields can consist in part of external fields and in part of fields due to the q_k's themselves.

Equations (1) through (10) must be solved simultaneously for the dynamical behavior of the charges, and from this behavior we can derive the constitutive parameters for the macroscopic model of the medium.

In the Lorentz theory, the motion of the electrical charges is described in terms of the polarization vector (dipole moment per unit volume) rather than in terms of the convection current. In this case the polarization vector $P = Nqr$, r being the average displacement of the charged particles. Consequently, $J = \dot{P}$.

In order to discuss propagation in PLASMAS, the relationship between the polarizations (or the current density) and the electric intensity must be added to Maxwell's equations; this completed set we call the Maxwell-Lorentz equations.

In the ionized gas, the electrons and ions are detached completely from their parent molecules; no elastic forces bind them as in the case of a solid body such as a crystal; the particles have no free period of oscillation of their own. But under the influence of an applied force, they are disturbed by collisions with the neutral molecules. In the collision process some of the energy

of motion of the electrons and ions is converted into energy of random motion of particles, i.e., heat energy. The charged particles are therefore losing energy continually, and this loss can be represented as a resistance to their motions. This simple model of a resistive mechanism is incorporated into the equations of motion of the charged particles as a damping force.

The electron theory of Lorentz gives some idea of the mechanism by which the charged particles alter the phase velocity of a propagating electromagnetic wave field. Consider a semi-infinite medium separated by a plane interface from the free space, and imagine an electromagnetic wave field propagating in free space impinging upon the medium. The electromagnetic wave traveling through the free space between the particles excites the charged particles and causes them to oscillate so that they essentially become small dipole oscillators, the wave field governing their phase of oscillation.

At each point either in or external to the region in which the particles are contained, the secondary waves radiated by the oscillators interfere with the original wave field and with the other radiated waves; the sum of all the waves is a resultant field at the point. Moreover, it is the resultant field that acts on the particles at the given point which causes them to vibrate. The total intensity at any point is the vector sum of the intensity of the original wave field and the resultant intensity due to all the oscillating particles. According to this picture, in general, the emerging wave has its phase velocity altered. Reflective waves are treated in a similar manner.

Plane Wave Fields: Dispersion Relations Consider the kind of waves that an unbounded homogeneous medium can support, in the presence of a uniform (in space-time) externally applied magnetic field. Although this is not the most general situation, a great many of the salient features may be culled from it. The Maxwell-Lorentz equations, together with the postulated magnetic field, permit us to examine the existence of simple plane wave fields, i.e., field quantities proportional to $\exp(-j\mathbf{k} \cdot \mathbf{r})$ where $\mathbf{k}$ is the wave vector whose components are in general, complex. For fields with harmonic time dependence, the above assumptions lead to the condition for propagation which takes the form

$$\Delta(\mathbf{n}, \omega, \cdots)\mathbf{E} = 0 \qquad (11)$$

The condition for propagation is thus seen to reduce to the question of the existence of nontrivial fields, i.e., $\mathbf{E} \not\equiv 0$. The necessary and sufficient condition for this is simply the vanishing of the determinant

$$\Delta(\mathbf{n}, \omega, \cdots) = 0 \qquad (12)$$

which expresses an algebraic relation between the wave normal direction $\mathbf{n}$ (defined through $\mathbf{k} = k\mathbf{n}$, k a complex scalar) and the impressed frequency ω of the wave field. The other factors

not specifically indicated are functions of the parameters of the medium itself. This algebraic relation is often called a "dispersion relation," since it is a relation for ω. It is only when this condition is fulfilled that a propagating plane wave field is possible. This condition also implies an equation for the refractive index of the medium. The same considerations that led to this relation also lead to a relation between the displacement field $\mathbf{D}$ and the electric field $\mathbf{E}$, in the form

$$\mathbf{D} = \epsilon_0 \epsilon' \mathbf{E} \qquad (13)$$

where ϵ' is a tensor whose structure for a particular choice of coordinate system (applied magnetic field co-directional with the x_3-axis) is

$$\epsilon' = \begin{pmatrix} \epsilon_1 & j\epsilon_2 & 0 \\ -j\epsilon_2 & \epsilon_1 & 0 \\ 0 & 0 & \epsilon_3 \end{pmatrix} \qquad (14)$$

Here, the $\epsilon_j (j = 1, 2, 3)$ are complex valued and are functions of the parameters of the medium. If the medium is magneto-ionic (ions, electrons, and neutral molecules) and if collisions take place only between the charged species and the neutrals comprising the medium, the ϵ_j's are rational functions of the medium parameters and the dispersion relation is also called the Appleton-Hartree equation, named after the two scientists who derived the relation independently.

The fact that the dispersion relation of such a medium depends upon the direction of the wave normal direction, and upon ω, makes the fourth-degree algebraic equation defining the refractive index complicated in practice. Theoretically, two indices are defined; the medium is doubly refracting in this case, analogous but certainly not identical with propagation in certain crystals, and this plasma crystal optics analogy can be advantageously exploited.[1] The propagating wave fields associated with each index are called, respectively, the *ordinary* mode, because it is least effected by the applied magnetic field, and the *extraordinary* mode. These two modes are linearly independent i.e., one of them cannot be expressed as a simple multiple of the remaining one. Both modes, in passing through the medium, undergo attenuation and rotation of their respective planes of polarization; the so-called FARADAY EFFECT is present here as in some crystals. This effect is used in electron-density determinations, since the density can be expressed in terms of the angle of rotation of these planes. The planes of polarization of each mode rotate opposite to each other.

Two important parameters (characteristic frequencies) are involved in discussing propagation: (1) the *plasma* frequencies of the constituents ω_j, defined by

$$\sqrt{N_j e^2 / \epsilon_0 m_j},$$

where subscript j stands for the type of species (electron, ion, etc.), N_j is the number density, m_j its mass, and e the electronic charge; and (2) the gyro or *Larmor* frequency defined by $\Omega_j = B_0 e/m_j\omega$, where B_0 is the magnitude of the applied magnetic field and ω is the impressed wave frequency. The plasma frequency is essentially a resonant frequency and is more closely tied to the concept of collective motion or plasma oscillations. The Larmor frequency is a well-known concept and is substantially the frequency with which a charged particle "winds" itself about the externally applied magnetic field in the absence of collisions. If $\omega > \omega_j$ for all j, propagation is possible; if the medium consists only of electrons, the above condition is well known in ionospheric radio wave propagation.

Plasma Waves For a more complicated description of the medium, other modes of propagation are possible. If the Lorentz force equation is extended so as to include pressure gradients (temperature effects are naturally included in the description by simple use of the gas laws), a hydrodynamic model of the gas results; and since this model is coupled to the electrodynamic equations through the Lorentz force term, we speak of magnetohydrodynamics or (to be more inclusive) magneto-fluid dynamics and its various synonyms (see MAGNETO-FLUID-MECHANICS). To see the effect of this coupling, we should recall that a completely incompressible perfect fluid with no magnetic field imposed cannot support any wave-like disturbances, as is obvious on physical grounds. This result is also clear on mathematical grounds in which the velocity potential satisfies Laplace's equation whose solutions are certainly not wave-like. If now the fluid is still incompressible but conducting and with a magnetic field imposed upon it, wave phenomena are now possible; the resulting waves are called magnetohydrodynamic and include both longitudinal and transverse types.

In the high-frequency limit, these waves yield the usual radio waves mentioned above; in the low-frequency limit, the resultant waves are no different in principle. However, because of the coupling of the more extensive hydrodynamic model with the electrodynamic field equations, the intermediate frequency region is naturally more complicated. The conditions for propagation (i.e., the dispersion relations) can no longer be readily discussed in general. The coupling, on the other hand, opens up a vast new area of investigation of wave phenomena, the existence of plasma waves, which was investigated initially by the astrophysicist Alfvén. In the case of an unbounded homogeneous medium, it is possible to treat, in a systematic way, the propagation of plane wave fields.

The conclusions drawn from the extensive hydrodynamical model in the low-frequency limit are also obtainable from a simpler point of view. For a magneto-ionic medium and $\omega \ll \omega_p$, Astrom and others deduced the properties of plane wave propagation by elementary consider-

ations and arrived at the same result as Alfvén. The energy associated with the extraordinary mode proves to be propagated along the magnetic field lines. This manner of propagation sheds light on whistlers, a low-frequency natural phenomenon that exhibits similar properties. It is also worthwhile noting that since the dielectric tensor is in general non-symmetric, the condition of reciprocity (interchange of transmitter and receiver) does not hold as in the isotropic case in which ϵ reduces to a single scalar quantity. Finally, in the homogeneous unbounded case, the mean Poynting vector is *not* co-directional with the wave normal direction of either mode.

Nonhomogeneous Media In nonhomogeneous, nonmagnetic media whose dielectric tensor varies in only one direction, the problem of calculating the wave fields can be reduced to the calculation of a Hertzian vector potential function, which satisfies an integral-equation relation. Here, one can employ variational techniques similar to those used by Schwinger, Levine, and others to find approximate solutions. Numerical techniques based on matrix theory have likewise been exploited. General reflection and transmission matrices are byproducts of this problem. Other attempts to deal with this kind of problem, particularly for a doubly refracting medium separated from free space by a horizontal plane, are based on the ideas of Booker *et al.* A plane wave penetrating the medium from free space below splits into an ordinary and extraordinary wave. Because of the inhomogeneity of the medium, the penetrating waves which start at the plane interface generate along their path two ascending and two descending waves, the latter because of postulated internal reflections. The four waves so produced have different wave normal and Poynting vector directions. Snell's law is valid for both the ordinary and extraordinary waves. The inhomogeneous character of the medium causes the four waves, each of different elliptical polarization, to be coupled to each other. K. Suchy has shown that in the general nonhomogeneous medium, with no assumptions of stratification, Maxwell's equations reduce to a pair of coupled equations which has its simplest structure for a certain class or curvilinear coordinates. He has also treated the propagation of electromagnetic waves in absorbing, anisotropic, inhomogeneous, and unbounded media and studied in some detail the transition from the full vector wave equation with arbitrary wavelength λ to small (but nonvanishing) values of λ.

Ray-theoretic Approach The study of propagation in anisotropic, inhomogeneous media becomes amenable to analysis by means of a ray theory. Under the assumption that the wavelength λ is very much smaller than some characteristic dimension of the medium, it becomes possible to replace the more complicated vector field equations defined through the Maxwell-Lorentz system by a much simpler structure. By analogy with the homogeneous case, **E** is taken

to be proportional to

$$A(\mathbf{r}) \exp\left[j\left(\omega t - \omega \int \mathbf{M} \cdot d\mathbf{r} \right) \right]$$

where $\mathbf{M}$ is in general a complex-valued vector. The $\mathbf{H}$ field is expressed similarly. If this expression is used in the vector wave equation for $\mathbf{E}$ we are led to a system with the following structure:

$$(\mathbf{L} - \boldsymbol{\varepsilon})\mathbf{E} = 0 \tag{15}$$

where $\mathbf{L}$ is a matrix whose elements contain the differential operators $\partial^2/\partial x_i \partial x_j$, and are complex. The condition for propagation is still the vanishing of the determinant $|\mathbf{L} - \boldsymbol{\varepsilon}|$, which is now a nonlinear partial differential equation of the second order for the three components of $\mathbf{M}$. The matrix $\mathbf{L}$ is known as the "Eikonal matrix," and the above dispersion equation constitutes a generalization of the usual Eikonal equation or equation of geometrical optics. To understand the significance of the Eikonal equation, we consider a scalar wave equation whose spatial dependence f is of the form,

$$\nabla^2 f + \left(\frac{\omega M}{c} \right)^2 f = 0 \tag{16}$$

By taking $f(\mathbf{r}) = A(\mathbf{r}) \exp [-2\pi j \psi(\mathbf{r})]$ and setting both the real and imaginary parts to zero, we obtain two nonlinear partial differential equations for the determination of both A and ψ. If both of these functions vary slowly within a distance of a wavelength, these equations simplify and one can find ψ without also having to find A. The resulting expression under these conditions for ψ is the Eikonal equation

$$4\pi^2 (\nabla \psi)^2 = \left(\frac{\omega M}{c} \right)^2 \tag{17}$$

whereas that for A takes the form

$$\nabla \cdot (A^2 \nabla \psi) = 0 \tag{18}$$

We can now easily relate ψ to $\mathbf{M}$; indeed we put

$$\psi = \psi_1 - j\psi_2, \quad \mathbf{M} = \boldsymbol{\mu} - j\boldsymbol{\chi} \tag{19}$$

and in general both ψ and $\mathbf{M}$ are functions also of frequency. The complex phase ψ is defined through

$$\psi = \int_{p_0}^{p} \nabla \psi \cdot d\mathbf{r} = \frac{\nu}{c} \int_{p_0}^{p} \mathbf{M} \cdot d\mathbf{r} \tag{20}$$

where $d\mathbf{r}$ is a real vector and ν the frequency. The vector $\boldsymbol{\mu}$ is normal to the family of surfaces $\psi_1 = $ constant, and $\boldsymbol{\chi}$ is normal to the family $\psi_2 = $ constant; these surfaces are in general distinct, and therefore we put

$$2\pi\psi_1 = \frac{\omega}{c} \int_{p_0}^{p} \boldsymbol{\mu} \cdot d\mathbf{r} \tag{21}$$

$$2\pi\psi_2 = \frac{\omega}{c} \int_{p_0}^{p} \boldsymbol{\chi} \cdot d\mathbf{r} \tag{22}$$

To find expressions for the magntiude of μ and χ we have

$$M^2 = (\mu - j\chi) = P - jQ \tag{23}$$

which is equivalent to

$$\mu^2 - \chi^2 = P; \quad 2\mu\chi \cos\theta = Q \tag{24}$$

where θ is the angle between $\boldsymbol{\mu}$ and $\boldsymbol{\chi}$. These two relations yield

$$\mu^2 = \tfrac{1}{2} \{ [P^2 + (Q/\cos\theta)^2]^{1/2} + P \}$$
$$\chi^2 = \tfrac{1}{2} \{ [P^2 + (Q/\cos\theta)^2]^{1/2} - P \} \tag{25}$$

the first expression defines a refractive index surface, and the second, an extinction index surface.

The equation defining A suggests a conservation law (equation of continuity) as applied to a fictitious fluid. By analogy we consider $A^2 \nabla \psi$ proportional to the current density of this fluid, and an application of the divergence theorem gives

$$0 = \int_V \nabla \cdot (A^2 \nabla) \, dV = \int_S A^2 \nabla \psi \cdot \mathbf{n} dS \tag{26}$$

where V is some volume containing the fluid and bounded by a surface S with outward drawn normal $\mathbf{n}$. If we consider this fluid to have (material) density proportional to A^2 and velocity proportional to grad ψ, then the above expression states that A^2 is conserved in time. If we assume that $|A|^2$ is a measure of the energy localized in the wave at each point, that grad ψ is proportional to the energy flux at each point and is directed along the ray associated with the wave, then it appears as if the energy is a fluid which is conserved as it flows along the rays. Thus, the rays appear as trajectories of energy, a thin pencil of rays being analogous to a tube through which the energy flows.

In a homogeneous, anisotropic, but nonabsorbing medium the concept of ray is defined as the trajectory whose direction is the same as that of the mean Poynting vector. This direction, as mentioned previously, is not the same as the wave normal direction. The task of defining the ray direction becomes more difficult for a nonhomogeneous, anisotropic, absorbing, and dispersive medium. It can be shown that starting with the concept of a pulse in such a medium, one can derive extensions or generalizations of the usual Fermat's principle. This principle states that in a nonabsorbing, isotropic medium characterized by an index μ_r, a function of position only, the path of a so-called light ray makes the integral of μ_r between two fixed points assume a stationary value. The pulse concept for the general case leads to the following stationary

principles:

$$\delta \int \mu_r \cdot d\mathbf{r} = 0$$

$$\delta \int \chi \cdot d\mathbf{r} = 0 \qquad (27)$$

$$\delta \int \frac{\partial}{\partial \omega} (\omega \mu) \cdot d\mathbf{r} = 0$$

where δ is the symbol of variation. In the non-absorbing case the first of Eqs. (27) gives the phase path, which is always normal to the surfaces of constant phase. Similarly, the trajectory of the amplitude surfaces is also normal to the surfaces of constant amplitude. For the absorbing case we retain these two definitions. This means that μ_r is always tangent to a path element of the phase trajectory and χ is tangent to a path element of the amplitude trajectory. These path elements are denoted, respectively, by $d\mathbf{r}_p$ and $d\mathbf{r}_a$. The pulse principle permits us to define, in addition to the above surfaces, the surfaces of constant group amplitude. These surfaces are distinguished from those of constant wave amplitude and constant wave phase. If $d\mathbf{r}_g$ denotes an element of the path along which the group amplitude propagates, then the stationary principle for this path takes the form

$$\delta \int \mu_r \cdot d\mathbf{r}_g = \delta \int \frac{\partial}{\partial \omega} \omega \mu_r \cdot d\mathbf{r}_g = 0 \quad (28)$$

and in general the direction of the vector $\partial / \partial \omega (\omega \mu_r)$ is not parallel to $d\mathbf{r}_g$. The vector $\partial / \partial \omega (\omega \mu_r)$ is the basis for the definition of the group velocity. By definition, the displacement of the center of the wave group in a time dt is

$$\mathbf{v}_g dt = d\mathbf{r}_g \qquad (29)$$

where $\mathbf{v}_g$ is the group velocity. If we define a vector $(\mathbf{v}_g)^{-1}$ (symbolic meaning only), such that

$$\mathbf{v}_g \cdot (\mathbf{v}_g)^{-1} = 1 \qquad (30)$$

it is not difficult to show that

$$(\mathbf{v}_g)^{-1} = \frac{1}{c} \frac{\partial}{\partial \omega} (\omega \mu_r) \qquad (31)$$

We take the path of energy propagation to be the path of group amplitude. This condition is certainly plausible when we consider that the energy of a field is usually proportional to the square of the amplitude of its oscillations.

In the case of an electromagnetic field, it is not so clear that the group path is also the energy path if this energy is measured by the mean Poynting vector, and the conditions under which this holds require careful analysis.

The question naturally arises as to how one actually calculates a ray path in the general case. The answer has been available for a long time.

Hamilton's work in optics actually provides a *modus operandi* for the practical calculation of the ray paths. Fermat's principle provides the starting point; we assume that the medium is characterized by an index function $m(\mathbf{r}, \alpha, \omega)$ called the ray refractive index. This function depends on position $\mathbf{r}$, direction α, and frequency ω, and is a homogeneous function of the first degree in α. The rays are defined as those curves such that

$$\delta \int_{p_0}^{p} m \, ds = 0 \qquad (32)$$

where s is the parameter of arc length. The anisotropy is defined through the direction α which is normalized so that

$$\alpha \cdot \alpha = \frac{d\mathbf{r}}{ds} \cdot \frac{d\mathbf{r}}{ds} = 1 \qquad (33)$$

that is, α defines the tangent to the ray. In the isotropic case this dependence is lacking and $m(\mathbf{r})$ is invariant with respect to proper rotations. Usually we do not know $m(\mathbf{r}, \alpha, \omega)$ but rather $\mu_r(\mathbf{r}, \mathbf{n}, \omega)$ where $\mathbf{n}$ is the wave normal direction, as in the Appleton-Hartree equation. Thus it is desirable to attempt to express the ray path through the phase refractive index μ_r. This is accomplished by constructing a Hamiltonian defined by

$$H(\mathbf{r}, \sigma, \omega) = \frac{|\sigma|}{\mu_r(\mathbf{r}, \mathbf{n}, \omega)} = 1 \qquad (34)$$

which is a homogeneous function of the first degree in σ, where $\sigma = \partial m / \partial \mathbf{r}$ is a vector in the direction of $\mathbf{n}$. It can be shown that the rays which satisfy Fermat's principle with m as index are identical with those satisfying

$$\delta \int_{p_0}^{p} \sigma \cdot d\mathbf{r} = 0 \qquad (35)$$

whose variations are subject to the constraint $H(\mathbf{r}, \sigma, \omega) = 1$.[1] The latter is Hamilton's principle and is fully equivalent to Fermat's principle. It follows from Hamilton's principle that the rays satisfy Hamilton's canonical equations

$$\frac{d\mathbf{r}}{dt} = \frac{\partial H}{\partial \sigma}, \frac{d\sigma}{dt} = -\frac{\partial H}{\partial \mathbf{r}} \qquad (36)$$

where t is a parameter along the path. Equations (36) are six simultaneous first-order nonlinear ordinary differential equations. Subject to initial conditions these equations have a unique solution. The advantage of defining the rays in terms of the first-order system as above are many, particularly from a computational point of view. The rays can be calculated for rather general media, and no assumptions of stratification are needed. The form of Hamilton's equations can easily be found for any coordinate system by

tensor methods. Finally, we mention that a systematic study of ray propagation is possible without alluding to wave concepts although the ray-wave duality is implicit.

J. J. BRANDSTATTER

References

1. Brandstatter, J. J., "An Introduction to Waves, Rays and Radiation in Plasma Media," New York, McGraw-Hill Book Co., 1963.
2. Kelso, J. M., "Radio Ray Propagation in the Ionosphere," New York, McGraw-Hill Book Co., 1964.
3. Brandstatter, J. J., "Stochastic Ray Tracing." (to be published).

Cross-references: ELECTROMAGNETIC THEORY, FARADAY EFFECT, MAGNETO-FLUID-MECHANICS, PLASMAS, REFRACTION.

PROTON*†

Protons in Atoms The proton is the atomic nucleus of the element hydrogen, the second most abundant element on earth. Positively charged hydrogen atoms or "protons" were identified by J. J. Thomson in a series of experiments initiated in 1906. Although the structure of the hydrogen atom was not correctly understood at that time, several properties of the proton were determined. The electric charge on the proton was found to be equal but opposite in sign to that of an electron, and the measured value for the mass was much greater than that of the electron. The currently accepted proton mass is 1836 times the electron rest mass, or 1.672×10^{-24} grams.

A correct estimate of the size of the proton and an understanding of the structure of the hydrogen atom resulted from two major developments in atomic physics: the Rutherford scattering experiment (1911) and the Bohr model of the atom (1913). Rutherford showed that the nucleus is vanishingly small compared to the size of an atom. The radius of a proton is on the order of 10^{-13} cm as compared with atomic radii of 10^{-8} cm. Thus, the size of a hydrogen atom is determined by the radius of the electron orbits, but the mass is essentially that of the proton.

In the Bohr model of the hydrogen atom, the proton is a massive positive point charge about which the electron moves. By placing quantum mechanical conditions upon an otherwise classical planetary motion of the electron, Bohr explained the lines observed in optical spectra as transitions between discrete quantum mechanical energy states. Except for hyperfine splitting,

*Supported in part by The U.S. Air Force Office of Scientific Research.
†Editor was unable to locate the author. Article is reprinted from first edition.

which is a minute decomposition of spectrum lines into a group of closely spaced lines, the proton plays a passive role in the mechanics of the hydrogen atom. It simply provides the attractive central force field for the electron.

The proton is the lightest nucleus with atomic number one. Other singly charged nuclei are the deuteron and the triton which are nearly two and three times heavier than the proton, respectively, and are the nuclei of the hydrogen isotopes deuterium (stable) and tritium (radioactive). The difference in the nuclear masses of the isotopes accounts for a part of the hyperfine structure called the "isotope shift."

In 1924, difficulties in explaining certain hyperfine structures prompted Pauli to suggest that a nucleus possesses an intrinsic angular momentum or "spin" and an associated magnetic moment. The proton spin quantum number (I) is $1/2$, and the angular momentum is given by $[I(I+1)h^2/(2\pi)^2]^{1/2}$ where h is Planck's constant. The intrinsic magnetic moment is 2.793 in units of nuclear magnetons (0.50504×10^{-23} erg/gauss) which is about a factor of 660 less than the magnetic moment of the electron.

Two types of hydrogen molecule result from the two possible couplings of the proton spins. At room temperature, hydrogen gas is made up of 75 per cent orthohydrogen (proton spins parallel) and 25 per cent parahydrogen (proton spins antiparallel). Several gross properties, such as specific heat, strongly depend on the ortho or para character of the gas.

Protons in Nuclei Protons and neutrons are regarded as "nucleons" or fundamental constituents of nuclei in most theories of nuclear structure and reactions. The nuclear forces operating between them are much stronger than the electrostatic forces which govern atomic and molecular systems but operate over very short ranges, the order of several times 10^{-13} cm. Of particular significance in the structure of nuclei is the apparent charge independence of the forces. That is, the nuclear force between two nucleons may be considered separately from the electrostatic forces due to electric charges the nucleons may carry. In addition to mass and charge, other properties such as spin and parity play important roles in determining the mechanics of nuclei.

The mass of a nucleus is the sum of the masses of the nucleons contained, plus a correction due to the total binding energy of the nucleons. This correction is an application of the Einstein mass-energy equivalence ($E = mc^2$). The atomic number or positive charge of a nucleus is given by the number of protons.

A detailed description of the motion of a proton in a nucleus is complicated by the many-body, quantum mechanical nature of the problem, but several simplified theories or models have been very successful in predicting many of the properties of nuclei. One of the best known nuclear structure models is the shell model in which a nucleon is assumed to move in a central

force field. This field represents the average interaction of the proton (or neutron) with all other nucleons. An essential additional assumption is a coupling of the orbital angular momentum of the independent nucleon with its spin.

The success of a theory in which a nucleon moves among its close-packed neighbors as if they were not present is due in part to quantum mechanical restrictions, in particular to the Pauli exclusion principle.

The optical model for the scattering of protons by nuclei also rests on the assumption that the interaction with many nucleons may be represented by an average potential well. An imaginary potential term is included which accounts for reactions other than elastic scattering.

Much of nuclear physics may be understood with a picture in which the proton exists as an independent particle in the nucleus. Refinements of an independent particle model to include collective effects and deformation involve a consideration of the residual interaction between nucleons and the details of the individual nucleon interaction with the average potential well.

Certain aspects of the very strong nuclear forces are understood. These forces involve π mesons in somewhat the same way that electrostatic forces responsible for atomic structure involve photons. Yukawa introduced the π meson as the field quantum for nuclear forces in 1935, and the interaction potential derived from this early theory is commonly used in nuclear physics.

Structure of the Proton A major objective of physics is to identify elementary particles and determine their properties. The proton is important in these investigations in several connections. It is itself an elementary particle. It is used as a projectile in the production and study of other elementary particles. It has been used as a target in the study of nucleon structure.

One view is to consider all fundamental particles as states of excitation of a limited number of particles. The resulting simplification correlates a large body of experimental data.

The internal structure of the proton is still being studied. In one of the experiments, the proton is a target which is probed by very short-wavelength electrons. Electrons produced by a high-energy linear accelerator are scattered from protons to study the electric charge distribution in a proton.

Questions concerning the structure of the proton or the neutron are difficult due to the ambiguity of experimental results. One cause of uncertainty is that the probe is not defined in sufficient detail. It appears desirable to use a strong interaction probe, that is, another nucleon or meson, but the structure of the probe may be no better understood than the structure of the target.

A mantel of mesons has been found about the proton. A current question is whether or not there is an internal or intrinsic core of a proton.

R. H. DAVIS

References

Shortley, George, and Williams, Dudley, "Elements of Physics," Englewood Cliffs, N.J., Prentice-Hall, 1961.
Born, Max, "Atomic Physics," Glasgow, Blackie & Son, Ltd., 1946.
Weidner, Richard T., and Sells, Robert L., "Elementary Modern Physics," Boston, Allyn and Bacon, 1960.
Richtmyer, F. K., Kennard, E. H., and Lauritsen, T., "Introduction to Modern Physics," New York, McGraw-Hill, 1955.

Cross-references: ACCELERATORS, PARTICLE; ATOMIC AND MOLECULAR BEAMS; ATOMIC PHYSICS; ELECTRON; ELEMENTARY PARTICLES; ISOTOPES; NEUTRON; NUCLEAR STRUCTURE; PARITY; QUANTUM THEORY; RADIOACTIVITY; RELATIVITY.

PULSARS

In November 1967 a group of radioastronomers at Cambridge, England, discovered a new type of star in our galaxy. The star emitted radio waves at frequencies ranging from 100 to 1000 MHz and the radiation was confined to short pulses a few hundredths of a second in duration which repeated at very regular intervals of about one second. Systematic searches soon led to the discovery of further pulsars, and 61 had been located at the end of 1971. Attempts to detect visible light from pulsars have been unsuccessful except in the case of the Crab Nebula which contains, near its center, a pulsar emitting simultaneous pulses of x-rays, light, and radio waves. This pulsar has given important clues regarding the origin of pulsars and it radiates at intervals of approximately 33 msec, the precise value being maintained to an accuracy in the region of 1 part in 10^{10}.

Pulsar distances can be estimated from the different arrival times of a given pulse when recorded at different radio frequencies. This pulse dispersion is caused by ionized gas in interstellar space, and the gas density must be known to calculate the distance. Estimates, accurate within a factor of 2 or 3, place the pulsars at distances typically between 0.1 and 5 kiloparsec; since the total extent of our galaxy is about 30 kiloparsec it follows that only a small fraction of the pulsars which it contains have so far been detected.

No satisfactory explanation of pulsars yet exists but it is generally believed that they are rapidly spinning neutron stars that emit a beam of radiation in some preferred direction so that a "lighthouse" effect accounts for the pulses. Only the intense gravitational force in neutron stars, which are predicted to have radii of about 10 km, would be sufficient to prevent stars' disrupting when they spin rapidly enough to explain the pulsars of shortest period. If this theory is correct pulsars provide the first evidence for the existence of neutron stars.

Neutron stars represent the end-point of stellar evolution and contain matter in which

thermonuclear processes have been completed. Sufficiently low-mass stars are stable, in this condition, as white dwarfs, but electron pressure in degenerate matter cannot balance gravity in stars heavier than 1.4 solar masses. Heavy stars must therefore collapse, when nuclear energy generation within them ceases, and such a catastrophic collapse has been suggested as the origin of stellar explosions visible as supernovae.

The fact that the Crab Nebula (perhaps the most famous supernova of all; the explosion was documented by Chinese astronomers in the year 1054) contains a pulsar provides strong circumstantial evidence of the correctness of the neutron star theory. One additional pulsar, with a period of 89 msec, is associated with an extended radio source Vela X in the southern sky which is also probably the remnant of an old supernova. Certainly the estimated occurrence rate of supernovae in the galaxy accounts reasonably well for the total number of pulsars which are found. Moreover the observation that pulsars lie close to the galactic plane is in agreement with the distribution of massive OB stars that are likely to develop into supernovae.

Extended timing measurements on many pulsars have revealed, without exception, a systematic increase of period entirely in accordance with the rotating-star theory. Typical pulsars, which have periods in the range 0.5 to 1.5 sec, are slowing down at such a rate that 10^6 to 10^7 years must elapse before the pulse interval is doubled. For the Crab pulsar, however, this time is only 2200 years. If a neutron star model is assumed, it is simple to compute, from the observed lengthening of the period, the rate at which the spinning star is losing energy. Rotational energy, and a small amount of residual heat, comprise the principal energy reserves of a neutron star. Hence the spin-down energy loss should be directly related to the energy radiated. Applying this argument to the Crab pulsar shows that the rotational energy loss is sufficient to explain not only the pulsar radiation, but also all the visible light from the remainder of the nebula. It has been known for many years that some source that provided a large output of high-speed electrons was necessary to maintain the luminosity of the nebula, but its origin was a mystery. The fact that a central neutron star can provide this source gives further evidence favoring the neutron star theory.

The mechanism by which a neutron star converts rotational energy into pulsed electromagnetic radiation is a topic of speculation at present. Virtually nothing is known about physical conditions at the surface, and in the environment, of a neutron star. It is probable that a neutron star is encased in a rigid shell of crystalline ^{56}Fe nuclei permeated by a Fermi sea of degenerate electrons. Somewhere beneath the surface, where the density rises above 10^{13} g/cm^3, the nuclei become unstable and matter is largely in the form of a neutron fluid. It is likely that magnetic flux is conserved during gravitational collapse, which leads to immense magnetic field strengths of 10^{12} to 10^{15} G, and that conservation of angular momentum gives initial rotation speeds up to 10^3 rotations per second.

The rapid motion of the collapsed star, in the presence of its large magnetic field, generates an intense electric field which causes electrons and protons to be torn off the surface and distributed in space about the star. The resulting atmosphere must rotate with the star, and at a critical distance—the velocity of light cylinder—its tangential speed will approach the velocity of light. Beyond this region the atmosphere must stream outwards as a stellar wind, and it is likely that the flow-lines connect with the star's surface near the magnetic poles. In addition to these processes other phenomena arise if the magnetic axis of the star is not aligned with the rotation axis. A misaligned magnetic axis causes the star to radiate electromagnetic waves at the rotation frequency since it then acts as a giant oscillating magnetic dipole. Such outgoing fields can accelerate charged particles to relativistic energies in a manner analogous to linear accelerators in the laboratory and this may, for example, account for the injection of energetic electrons into the Crab Nebula which subsequently emit visible light by synchrotron radiation.

An important feature of the radiation mechanism is that it must produce a directed beam to yield the lighthouse effect. The duration of the observed pulses is almost independent of the radio wavelength and one idea common to several theories is that the beaming is a phenomenon of relativity. One well-known consequence of Special Relativity concerns a moving source of radiation; if the source radiates equally in all directions when it is stationary, the emitted waves must be cast into a narrow beam along the line of motion when the velocity is near that of light. Applying this to pulsars, it has been suggested that radiation emitted by charged particles moving outwards from the (misaligned) magnetic poles might be relativistically beamed along the magnetic axis, or alternatively, that the large tangential speed of the stellar atmosphere near the velocity of light cylinder could produce beaming in directions perpendicular to the rotation axis. Another feature of the radiation is that it must be coherent, involving the collective motion of groups of similarly charged particles, since otherwise, ridiculously high temperatures would be involved. Various possibilities such as wave amplification induced by plasma instabilities, or "antenna" mechanisms in which radiation is generated by the acceleration of bunched charges, have been suggested.

Unfortunately, no theory has yet been worked out in sufficient detail to allow comparison with the wealth of observational evidence now available. The radiated pulses have complex shapes, which differ from one source to the next, and may change rapidly with time. Usually the radiation is found to be highly polarized and the sense of polarization may vary syste-

matically through the pulse; this shows that the radiation is emitted in a region containing a highly organized magnetic field, although different zones may be active from one instant to the next. In effect, during each pulse a "window" is opened through which complex time-dependent phenomena in the neutron star may be scrutinized.

Pulsars pose a challenge in many fields of physics including solid-state theory, relativistic plasma physics, and electrodynamics. They also provide astronomers with a new means of probing the galaxy and determining quantities such as the interstellar magnetic field strength and gas density.

ANTONY HEWISH

References

Hewish, A., *Ann. Rev. Astron. Astrophys.*, 8 (1970).

Ostriker, J. P., and Gunn, J. E., *Astrophys. J.*, 157, 1395 (1969).

Goldreich, P., and Julian, W. H., *Astrophys. J.*, 160, 971 (1970).

Davies, R. D., and Smith, F. G., "The Crab Nebula," Reidel, Dordrecht, 1971.

Goldreich, P., Pacini, F., and Rees, M. J., *Comments Astrophys. Space Phys.*, 3, 185 (1971).

Cross-references: ASTROMETRY, ASTROPHYSICS, QUASARS.

PULSE GENERATION

Pulse waveforms are distinguished by abrupt, often almost discontinuous features. Such features may serve as time markers: pulses can carry information in the time domain (e.g., in computers). Also, such waveforms can have a very low duty cycle (= fractional time the pulse is present); pulses can supply momentary large bursts of power to equipment whose average

rating is relatively low, e.g., high-power microwave pulse transmitters for radar.

The fundamental element in pulse generation is the switch. Opening or closing a switch generates a step-function pulse, e.g., in key telegraphy; one or more such steps, together with suitable wave-shaping operations, may yield the final desired waveform.

For low-level pulses, overdriven amplifiers using transistors or vacuum tubes are commonly used as switching elements. The simplest example is that of a *clipping amplifier*; when driven by a large sinusoid, this produces an approximately square-wave output whose abrupt level changes may serve as sources of pulse waveforms. The transition *risetime*, beyond its dependence on the driving signal, is limited by amplifier properties such as internal capacitances and charge storage in transistors. Low-power transistors may have risetimes of the order of nanoseconds; high-power units are typically an order of magnitude slower.

Two amplifiers can be cross-connected to drive each other alternately over the switching range. Depending on the coupling circuits, the pair can be bistable, monostable, or astable (Fig. 1). The *univibrator* rests in its quiescent state until driven into the other by the trigger pulse; it relapses into the rest state after a time determined by the R-C coupling, approximately given by $RC \ln(1 + V_{cc}/V_{bb})$. Thus the trigger produces an output of standardized amplitude and width. The *multivibrator*, with two R-C couplings, free-runs and thus serves as a pulse source or clock. Timing or frequency stabilities of order 1 per cent are typical.

The *blocking oscillator* is a single amplifier which drives itself over the switching range by means of transformer feedback. A monostable arrangement is shown in Fig. 2. The transistor is brought momentarily into conduction by the trigger pulse; thereafter it drives itself into saturation. The width of the output pulse is determined mostly by the transformer proper-

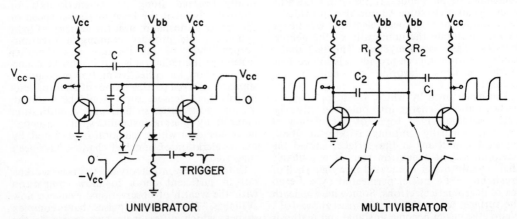

UNIVIBRATOR   MULTIVIBRATOR

FIG. 1. Univibrator (monostable) and multivibrator (astable). If both cross-couplings are resistive, a bistable binary results; this requires a trigger on either side to change state.

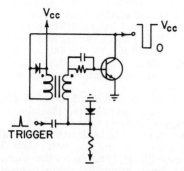

FIG. 2. Monostable blocking oscillator.

ties, above all by the magnetic saturation of the core. The regenerative self-drive permits the blocking oscillator to supply relatively large currents to the load.

Steps and rectangles can be shaped into other forms by many techniques.[1] Three classes, linear, nonlinear, and delay-line shaping are typified by the examples in Fig. 3. The delay-

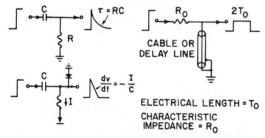

FIG. 3. Examples of shaping circuits to produce short pulses from a step.

line circuit produces a narrow rectangle from a step; the trailing edge is formed by the reflection of the leading edge in the unmatched delay line. The pulse falltime is thus as short as the risetime, within the limitations of the delay line response.

Whenever possible, switching and shaping are carried out directly at the output power level. In that case, the energy in the delivered pulse may come from that *stored* in the pulse-forming

network, the switch dissipation being negligible (current and voltage not present simultaneously); the power supply recharges the network slowly between pulses. For some shapes, the forming process is inefficient and must be carried out at low level; a linear output amplifier is then required. This, as well as the supply, must momentarily handle large power. Vacuum-tube amplifiers are common in this type of service, using voltages up to about 50 kV and currents to several tens of amperes.

Some other types of switching element are listed below:

(*a*) *Mechanical Switches*. These are usually reed relays with mercury-wetted contacts to eliminate bounce and may generate steps with sub-nanosecond risetime. The electromechanical drive limits the frequency to a few hundred cycles per second.

(*b*) *Unijunction Transistors*[2] (double-base diodes) switch regeneratively when the emitter becomes forward biased; the injected carriers increase the conductivity of the base material. Switching times of the order of 1 μsec are typical.

(*c*) *Thyratrons* are hot-cathode gas or vapor filled tubes. A discharge is initiated by a trigger signal applied to the grid. To extinguish the discharge, the anode must be reverse-biased; the deionization time, on the order of 100 μsec, limits the minimum pulse spacing. Extremely high power levels may be handled: up to about 50 kV, 5 kA. The risetime is as short as a few nanoseconds in hydrogen tubes. Figure 4 shows a pulse modulator for a microwave klystron. The power stored in the pulse-forming network is delivered to the load via a pulse transformer. Recharge takes place through a "ringing choke," avoiding the power loss associated with a charging resistor.

(*d*) *Ignitrons, Triggered Spark Gaps.* These are high-power gaseous discharge switches. Spark gaps are simple and produce extremely short risetimes, but electrode erosion may be a problem.

(*e*) *Controlled Rectifiers*[3] (*pnpn* devices) have operating characteristics in many ways similar to those of thyratrons. In most types, the load current must be interrupted to restore the nonconducting state; some low power devices

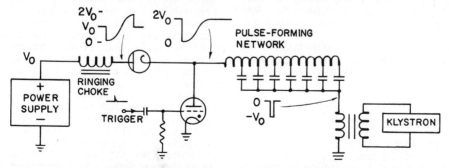

FIG. 4. High-power pulser using hydrogen thyratron.

(controlled switches) can be turned off by their control electrode. Risetimes are typically below 1 μsec.

(f) *Avalanche Transistors*[4]. Collector-to-emitter breakdown may occur regeneratively with sub-nanosecond risetime in certain transistors. This may be initiated by overvolting the collector or by suddenly changing the base potential. Avalanche transistors can generate fast, large pulses, e.g., 30 V, at high repetition rates (e.g., 5 Mc/sec).

(g) *Tunnel Diodes*[5]. Heavily doped diodes have extremely thin depletion layers through which quantum-mechanical tunneling of majority charge carriers can occur over a narrow voltage range (about 0.1 V). At higher voltage, after a sharp drop of this tunnel current, ordinary injection current sets in (about 0.5 V). The diode may switch from tunneling to injection voltage at sub-ns speed. Choice of loadline results in bistable, monostable, or astable operation; transitions may be provoked by suitable current signals. The voltage level of operation is very low (about 0.5 V).

(h) *Snap Diodes*[6]. Stored charge resulting from a period of forward conduction causes a diode to conduct freely when reverse bias is first applied. In special step-recovery diodes, this reverse current ceases abruptly, with sub-nanosecond falltime, and the resulting opening of the switch can generate fast pulses at high repetition rates (100 Mc/sec) and relatively high level (tens of volts).

R. M. Littauer

References

1. Strauss, L., "Wave Generation and Shaping," New York, McGraw-Hill Book Company, 1960.
2. "Transistor Manual," Sixth edition, Ch. 13, General Electric Company, Syracuse, N. Y., 1962.
3. "Silicon Controlled Rectifier Manual," Second edition, General Electric Company, Auburn, N.Y., 1961.
4. Henebry, W. M., "Avalanche Transistor Circuits," *Rev. Sci. Instr.*, **32**, 1198 (1961).
5. "RCA Tunnel Diode Manual," Radio Corporation of America, Somerville, N.J., 1963.
6. Moll, J. L., *et al.*, "P-N Junction Charge Diodes," *Proc. IRE*, **50**, 43 (1962); Giorgis, J., "Understanding Snap Diodes," *Application Note*, **90.17** (1963), General Electric Company, Syracuse, N.Y.

Cross-references: DIODE (SEMICONDUCTOR), ELECTRICITY, ELECTRON TUBES, FEEDBACK, RADAR, SEMICONDUCTOR DEVICES, TRANSISTOR, TUNNELING.

PYROMETRY, OPTICAL

Optical pyrometry is that branch of thermometry in which the temperature of a solid or liquid is determined by measuring the radiation emitted in a relatively narrow spectral region. The International Practical Temperature Scale of 1968 (IPTS) above the melting point of gold (1337.58 K or 1064.43°C) is defined in terms of such radiation, and an optical pyrometer is usually used to realize the IPTS above this temperature.

Figure 1 is a schematic diagram of a common type of optical pyrometer. The objective lens (B) images that part of the source (A) for which the temperature is to be determined in the plane of the filament of the pyrometer lamp (E). The microscope (G, H, I) magnifies the source image and the small pyrometer lamp filament by a factor of about fifteen. The red filter (F) and the spectral response of the eye limit the spectral band pass of the instrument to wavelengths from about 6200 to 7100Å with the effective value about 6500Å. The absorption filter (D) is inserted at source brightness temperatures above about 1300°C so that the pyrometer lamp need not be operated at higher temperatures where its stability is poor.

The optical pyrometer shown in Fig. 1 is

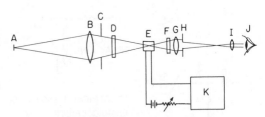

FIG. 1. Schematic diagram of a disappearing filament optical pyrometer. A. Source; B. Objective lens; C. Objective aperature; D. Absorption filter (used for temp. above 1300 C); E. Pyrometer lamp; F. Red filter; G. Microscope objective lens; H. Microscope aperture stop; I. Microscope ocular; J. Eye; K. Current measuring instrument.

operated by adjusting the current in the pyrometer lamp filament until the brightness of the filament equals the brightness of the image of the source. From this current and a previous calibration of the pyrometer, the brightness temperature of that part of the source or object sighted upon can be determined. The brightness temperature of an object is defined as the temperature of a blackbody which emits the same spectral radiance as the object. Spectral radiance is defined as the limit of the quotient of the radiant power emitted in a particular wavelength interval and in a particular direction by the product of the wavelength interval, the solid angle and the emitting area projected perpendicular to the direction of sighting as the latter three quantities tend to zero. If the object is a blackbody, the brightness temperature of the blackbody is its temperature. If the object is not a blackbody, the temperature of the object can be obtained from its brightness temperature

and the equation

$$\epsilon_\lambda = \frac{e^{c_2/\lambda T} - 1}{e^{c_2/\lambda T_B} - 1} \qquad (1)$$

where ϵ_λ is the spectral emissivity (also called spectral emittance), λ is the wavelength, in centimeters, at which the pyrometer is effectively operating (usually about 0.65×10^{-4} cm), c_2 is the second radiation constant (1.4388 centimeter degrees on the IPTS), T_B is the brightness temperature and T is the temperature, both in Kelvins. The spectral emissivity of a surface is the fraction of blackbody spectral radiance emitted by the surface when it has the same temperature as the blackbody. Spectral emissivities for a wavelength of 0.65×10^{-4} cm have been determined for a large number of materials. When $C_2/\lambda T$ is greater than about 5, Eq. (1) can be replaced, with negligible error, by the simpler equation

$$\frac{1}{T} = \frac{1}{T_B} + \frac{\lambda}{C_2} \ln \epsilon_\lambda \qquad (2)$$

where ln is the symbol for the natural logarithm.

The calibration of an optical pyrometer from basic principles is called a primary calibration and is usually performed in national standard laboratories such as the National Bureau of Standards. The first step of a primary calibration of an optical pyrometer is making a brightness match while sighting on a blackbody surrounded by freezing gold. The temperature of freezing gold is defined to be 1337.58 K or 1064.43°C on the International Practical Temperature Scale of 1968. Higher brightness temperature points are obtained by using the defining equation of the IPTS,

$$R = \frac{e^{c_2/\lambda T_B} - 1}{e^{c_2/\lambda T_{Au}} - 1} \qquad (3)$$

Experimentally, the brightness temperature of a stable source is adjusted until the source, as seen through a rotating sectored disk with transmittance R, has the same brightness as a gold blackbody. Independent measurement of R and λ then permit, from Eq. (3), a calculation of T_B. The pyrometer lamp current required for making a brightness match while sighting on the source without the sectored disk completes the calibration at this higher temperature. This process is repeated with a sufficient number of sectored disks and temperatures so that a smooth curve can be drawn relating current in the pyrometer lamp to the brightness temperature of the source. With a well-designed optical pyrometer of the type in Fig. 1, it is possible to realize the IPTS in a primary calibration with an estimated uncertainty of ±0.4 deg at 1337 K, ±2.0 deg at 2300 K and ±10.0 deg at 4300 K. The National Bureau of Standards also calibrates commercial

pyrometers of the type in Fig. 1 by comparison to a primary calibrated pyrometer. The uncertainty of this comparison calibration is estimated to be ±3 deg, ±6 deg, and ±40 deg respectively at the temperatures given above. These figures apply to brightness or blackbody temperatures. The accuracy with which an optical pyrometer can determine the temperature of a non-blackbody depends not only on the pyrometer calibration in terms of brightness temperature, but also on the uncertainty of the spectral emissivity required. This often produces an error greater than the calibration uncertainties given above.

By 1960, photoelectric pyrometers had been developed which replace the eye with a photomultiplier tube and use an interference filter or monochromator to limit the spectral band pass. With the increased sensitivity and smaller band pass in these instruments, the International Practical Temperature Scale above 1337.58 K can be realized with about one-third the uncertainty possible with the visual instrument in Fig. 1. The present limitation in realizing the IPTS with a photoelectric pyrometer appears to be the instability of the pyrometer lamps. To improve the accuracy further, lamps with greater stability will have to be developed or a different type optical pyrometer designed, possibly one using only the gold-point blackbody as a reference source. The gold-point blackbody is at least a factor of ten more stable then pyrometer lamps.

In addition to optical pyrometers, total radiation pyrometers and two color pyrometers are sometimes used for measuring temperatures. Usually, however, these instruments are less accurate than optical pyrometers and are primarily intended for controlling temperature rather than for measuring it.

H. J. KOSTKOWSKI

References

Kostkowski, H. J., and Burns, G. W., "Thermocouple and Radiation Thermometry Above 900°K, Measurement of Thermal Radiation Properties of Solids (1963)," Office of Scientific and Technical Information, National Aeronautics and Space Administration, U.S. Government Printing Office, Washington, D.C.

Kostkowski, H. J., and Lee, R. D., "Theory and Methods of Optical Pyrometry," *Natl. Bur. Std. Monograph*, 4 (1962).

Forsythe, W. E., "Optical Pyrometry," in Temperature, its Measurement and Control in Science and Industry," p. 115, New York, Van Nostrand Reinhold, 1941.

"Temperature, Its Measurement and Control in Science and Industry," Vol. III, Parts 1 and 2, New York, Van Nostrand Reinhold, 1962.

The International Practical Temperature Scale of 1968, *Metrologia*, 5, 35 (1960).

Comptes Rendues de la Treizième Conférence Générale

des Poids et Mesures, 1967–1968, Annexe 2. (In French.)

Kostkowski, H. J., Proceedings, IES Solar Simulation Committee Meeting. NASA Langley Research Center, November 21, 1969.

Willson, R. C., "Active Cavity Radiometric Scale, International Pyrheliometric Scale and Solar Constant, *J. Geophys. Research*, 76, 4325 (1971).

Cross-references: RADIATION, THERMAL; TEMPERATURE AND THERMOMETRY.

Q

QUANTUM ELECTRODYNAMICS*

Introduction Quantum electrodynamics is the fundamental theory of electromagnetic interactions. As far as we know, its equations provide a mathematically exact description of the interactions of electrons, muons, and photons (the quanta of the electromagnetic field). By extension, quantum electrodynamics (QED) is the underlying theory of all electromagnetic phenomena including atomic and chemical forces.

QED is without question the most successful dynamical theory in all of physics. Because of the pioneering theoretical efforts of Dirac, Feynman, Schwinger, and Tomonaga, and heroic labors by many others, QED possesses a systematic calculational scheme which has met with brilliant quantitative successes when faced with all experimental challenges. Its range of application has over the years been extended from atomic ($\sim 10^{-8}$ cm) to electron ($\sim 10^{-11}$ cm) to nuclear ($\sim 10^{-14}$ cm) dimensions. Adding in the classical aspects of electrodynamics, the total range of verification actually covers more than 23 decades out to 10^9 cm where satellite measurements have verified the predicted cubic power law fall-off of the earth's magnetic field. In several cases the predictions of the theory have been confirmed at the parts per million level.

Basic Features and Early History Quantum electrodynamics, the quantum theory of photons and electrons, has a simple conceptual basis. Shortly after the birth of quantum mechanics in 1926–27, P. A. M. Dirac, W. Heisenberg, and W. Pauli noted that the energy in the electromagnetic field amplitudes $\vec{E}(\vec{x}, t)$ and $\vec{B}(\vec{x}, t)$ described by Maxwell's equation must be quantized—as required by quantum mechanics for the energy of any physical system. The quanta of the radiation field could be identified exactly with Planck's photon, the fundamental carrier of light and electromagnetic radiation. The quantized form of Maxwell's equations require that the photon be a particle of zero mass, with velocity c and one unit of angular momentum $\hbar$ (Planck's constant divided by 2π)—directed either along or against its

*Supported in part by the U.S. Atomic Energy Commission.

direction of motion. Upon quantization, the classical field amplitudes $\vec{E}$ and $\vec{B}$ (and the four-vector potential $A^\mu(x)$) become quantum-mechanical operators which have nonzero matrix elements only between states which differ by exactly one photon. This was the foundation stone of quantum electrodynamics, which as developed by Dirac, successfully described the emission and absorption of radiation in atomic systems.

During this exciting period in which developments in quantum theory came at an incredible rate, Dirac also presented his famous equation

$$[i\gamma_\mu(\partial^\mu - eA^\mu) - m]\,\psi(x) = 0,$$

which described the motion and spin (internal angular momentum) of an electron or positron in an electromagnetic potential. The application of this equation to an electron bound in a Coulomb field led to a successful prediction of the fine structure of the energy-level separations in the hydrogen atom. Soon afterwards P. Jordan and E. Wigner applied the quantization procedure to the energy contained in the ψ amplitude just as had been done for Maxwell's equation. The quanta of the ψ field can, in fact, be exactly identified with the physical electrons and positrons—particles (and antiparticles) which have charge $\pm e$, mass m, and angular momentum $\frac{1}{2}\hbar$ directed along or against their motion, which must obey the Pauli principle. The Dirac ψ field thus became a quantum-mechanical operator which connects states that differ by one electron or one positron.

The Dirac theory also determines the basic interaction of electrons, positrons and photons and thus provides the fundamental dynamical assumptions of quantum electrodynamics. The form of the interaction density is

$$e\overline{\psi}(x)\gamma_\mu\,\psi(x)A^\mu(x)$$

which, in fact, is the simplest form consistent with the principles of quantum mechanics and relativity. Because of quantization of ψ and A, the interaction only has nonzero matrix elements for the basic electron-positron-photon vertex shown in Fig. 1. The vertex conserves charge and is "local," i.e., it describes the creation or absorption of a photon at the same point $x = (\vec{x}, t)$ in space and time where an electron (or positron) scatters or where an electron-positron

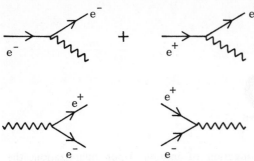

FIG. 1. The basic interaction vertex of quantum electrodynamics. The photon (denoted by a wavy line) is emitted or absorbed by a scattered electron or positron, or by the creation or annihilation of an electron-positron pair. The interaction conserves momentum and charge. The coupling strength is proportional to the electron charge e.

pair is created or destroyed. The amplitude for more complicated physical processes in QED can then be obtained from the iteration of the basic three-point interaction (i.e., a perturbation expansion in powers of e). The absolute square of the sum of all the possible amplitudes for the process gives the quantum mechanical probability, or in the case of a collision process, the cross section.

Rules for calculating the contributing amplitudes have been given in a very elegant and simple form by R. P. Feynman. The rules are explicitly covariant (i.e., independent of the choice of reference frame). For example, the contributing amplitudes (through order e^4) for electron-positron collisions are computed from the "Feynman diagrams" shown in Fig. 2. The lowest order contributing diagrams are of order e^2 since only the iteration of two basic three-point interactions is required. The amplitude for the first diagram in Fig. 2(a) is of the form

$$e^2 J_\mu(e^-) J^\mu(e^+) \frac{1}{q^2}$$

which contains factors from Dirac current of the electron $J_\mu(e^-) = \bar{u}(p')\gamma^\mu u(p)$, the Dirac current of the positron, and a factor $(q^2)^{-1} = [(E - E')^2 - (\vec{p} - \vec{p}')^2]^{-1}$ for the propagation of the photon carrying momentum $\vec{q} = \vec{p} - \vec{p}'$ and energy $E - E'$ from the electron to the positron. The last factor for the photon (the "Feynman propagator") automatically accounts for the process in which the photon is emitted by the positron

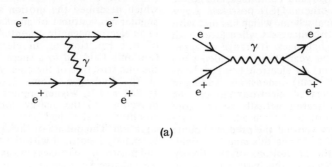

(a)

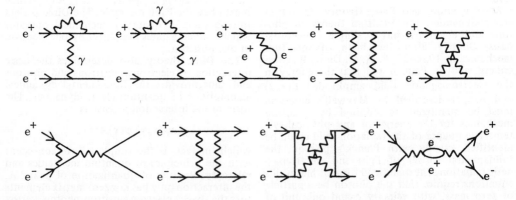

(b)

FIG. 2. Feynman diagrams for electron-positron scattering. Figure 2(a) represents the amplitudes of order e^2 obtained from the application of the basic interaction vertex of Fig. 1 to second order in perturbation theory. Figure 2(b) shows representative amplitude in order e^4 for electron-positron scattering.

and then absorbed by the electron as well. A similar propagator $(\gamma_\mu q^\mu - m)^{-1}$ occurs in diagrams such as Fig. 2(b) for the propagation of the internal electron or positron. The diagrams in Fig. 2(b) are of order e^4, and give contributions to the collision cross section which are smaller by a factor of

$$\alpha = e^2/4\pi\hbar c = 1/137.03608(26),$$

which is the fundamental dimensionless constant of QED. Because of the smallness of the fine-structure constant α (so named since its square determines the ratio of the fine structure separation to the Rydberg in the Dirac theory for the hydrogen atom), it is seldom necessary to retain terms in perturbation theory beyond the first few orders in order to compare with high-energy scattering experiments.

Recently, very high energy (short-distance) tests of the predictions of quantum electrodynamics for electron-positron scattering have been performed at colliding electron-positron beam facilities at Stanford, Orsay, Novosibirsk, and Frascati. The cross section is predicted to fall inversely with the square of the center of mass energy. The measurements have directly confirmed this prediction at center of mass energies as high as four billion electron volts. The measurements rule out any modification or breakdown of QED unless it occurs at distances smaller than 10^{-15} cm. Colliding-beam experiments in which a muon pair is produced from the annihilation of an electron pair (see Fig. 3)

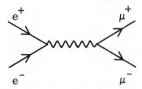

FIG. 3. The lowest-order Feynman diagram for the annihilation of an electron-positron pair into a muon pair. This process can be studied experimentally at electron-positron colliding-beam facilities with beam energies up to five billion electron volts. In these experiments, the electron and positron collide with equal and opposite momenta, producing an intermediate photon at rest in the laboratory, which then decays to the final muon pair.

have provided dramatic verification of the correctness of the application of QED to the electromagnetic interactions of the muon as well.

Other high-energy collision measurements including electron or muon pair production and other inelastic processes have shown complete agreement with theory and no sign of any fundamental length at small distances, or additional heavy leptons or photons.

Complementary to these high-energy tests are the precision atomic physics and magnetic moment measurements, which have confirmed the validity of quantum electrodynamics at the

level of billionths of an electron volt. For these tests, which are performed at the ppm level, an expansion through high orders in e is required, and the precise value of the fine-structure constant α is essential. The numerical value of α is obtained independently of QED from a combination of measurements from very diverse fields, expressed via the relation

$$\alpha^{-2} = \frac{1}{4\text{Ry}_\infty} \frac{1}{\gamma_{p'}} \frac{\mu_{p'}}{\mu_B} \frac{2e}{h} \frac{c\Omega_{\text{abs}}}{\Omega_{\text{NBS}}}$$

The Rydberg Ry_∞, the proton gyromagnetic ratio in water $\gamma_{p'}$, the magnetic moment $\mu_{p'}/\mu_B$ of the proton (in a water sample) in units of the electron Bohr magnetron, and $c\Omega_{\text{abs}}/\Omega_{\text{NBS}}$, the ratio of absolute to NBS ohm (required for standard voltage measurements), are known to one or two parts per million, and the ratio $2e/h$ has been determined recently to better than 1 ppm via the A. C. Josephson effect in superconductors by W. H. Parker, B. N. Taylor, D. N. Langenberg, and co-workers.

The Self-Energy Problem and the Lamb Shift Despite the apparent correctness of the basic structure of the interaction between the photon and the electron, and the elegance of its equations, there is a central problem in quantum electrodynamics, which reflects on its fundamental validity. This problem involves the "self-energy" corrections of the theory. For example, the calculation of the energy shift of a free electron due to its emission and subsequent reabsorption of a single photon, gives an infinite result! This divergence is a consequence of the point-like (local) nature of the basic three-point vertex of QED.

Progress on this problem only because of an extraordinary experiment performed by W. Lamb and his co-workers in 1948. The Dirac equation for an electron bound in a Coulomb field predicted that the energy levels with the same quantum number n and total angular momentum j should be degenerate; in particular, negligible energy separation between the $2P_{1/2}$ and $2S_{1/2}$ excited levels in atomic hydrogen was predicted. The Lamb experiment, however, conclusively demonstrated that the levels were in fact separated by ~ 1000 MHz, a full tenth of the fine-structure separation of the $n = 2$ levels (the Lamb shift). Then, in a historic paper, H. Bethe was able to show that not only could quantum electrodynamics explain the Lamb shift, but also that the divergence problem in the self-energy calculation could be circumvented.

In his 1947 paper, Bethe pointed out that when one calculates the self-energy correction to a bound electron from the emission and absorption of a photon, part of the energy shift—in fact, the divergent part—should be identified with the energy or "self-mass" of the electron itself. When the self-mass term is identified and canceled out, or alternately if the difference of energy shifts for two bound state levels is calculated, the result is a finite energy

shift. Bethe's calculations showed that the net energy shift due to the electron in the hydrogen atom emitting and absorbing one photon causes the $2S_{1/2}$ level to be displaced above the $2P_{1/2}$ level by about 1080 MHz. This can be understood physically by the fact that the emission and subsequent reabsorption of the photon causes the position of the electron charge to fluctuate over a distance of the Compton wavelength of the electron ($\hbar/m_e c$) a percentage α of the time. The degeneracy predicted by the Dirac equation is a strict consequence of the inverse r dependence of the electron-nucleus Coulomb potential, and this is destroyed by the effective spreading of the electron's position from QED. Another important effect is "vacuum polarization," which increases the binding of the electron and reduces the $2S_{1/2} - 2P_{1/2}$ separation by 27 MHz. This quantum-electrodynamical effect, which was discussed by R. Serber and E. A. Uehling in 1935, is due to the modification of the Coulomb potential due to the virtual electron-positron pairs. In fact, because two charged particles always see each other through a cloud of virtual particle-antiparticle pairs, the charge e_0 that appears as a parameter in the equations of quantum electrodynamics is not precisely the physical charge e of the electron (as defined classically for an electron scattering at large distances from a test electric field).

Over the years both the theory and measurements of the Lamb shift have been developed to extraordinary precision. The theory accounts for higher-order photon processes and the relativistic effects of a two-particle bound state system (relativistic recoil corrections) using a covariant equation developed by H. Bethe and E. Salpeter. The theoretical prediction is

$$\Delta E(2S_{1/2} - 2P_{1/2}) = 1057.912 \pm 0.011 \text{ MHz}.$$

The most recent measurement (by R. T. Robiscoe and T. W. Shyn) is

$$\Delta E(2S_{1/2} - 2P_{1/2}) = 1057.90 \pm 0.06 \text{ MHz}.$$

Other precision atomic physics tests of QED are described below.

Renormalization Theory Within a few years after Bethe's work, R. Feynman, J. Schwinger, S. Tomonaga, and F. Dyson demonstrated that all the divergences in quantum-electrodynamic calculations could be circumvented order by order in perturbation theory. This procedure, which is called the renormalization program, was shown to be covariant (independent of Lorentz frame), and despite the presence of infinite quantities in intermediate expressions, the calculations were shown always to lead to unambiguous finite results.

Briefly, one notes that the "bare charge" e_0 and "bare mass" m_0 which appear as parameters in the equations of quantum electrodynamics are not the physical charge and mass of the electron, but must be chosen correctly. Thus (to any given order in perturbation theory) one must adjust the values of m_0 and e_0 so that after calculation of all the contributing diagrams, electron-electron scattering at large distances will agree with classical Coulomb scattering for two particles of charge e, and that Compton scattering (elastic electron-photon scattering) at zero frequency will agree with the Thomson limit which defines the ratio e^2/m. After this adjustment is made, calculations of all *physical* quantities are finite, although the values in perturbation theory for the quantities e_0 and m_0 are mathematically divergent. In recent years, much theoretical work has been done in order to remove this last mathematical problem —either by attempts to demonstrate that e_0 and m_0 are actually finite and calculable when all orders in perturbation theory are taken into account, or by modifications of quantum electrodynamics at very small distances. As yet none of these approaches has been shown to be correct.

Other Precision Tests of QED The classic and most basic test of quantum electrodynamics is the measurement of the anomalous magnetic moment of the electron. Thus far it has been one of the most stunning triumphs of experimental and theoretical analysis. The measurements are based on the following facts: An electron in a uniform magnetic field obeys a helical orbit with a rotational frequency $\omega_L = e\hbar/2mc$. If the electron's magnetic interactions conformed to the simple Dirac equation, the direction of its internal spin would precess with exactly the same frequency. The first experimental determination of a deviation of the electron moment from the Dirac value was made by H. M. Foley and P. Kusch in 1947; their results for the electron's "anomalous moment" were in agreement with J. Schwinger's calculation of the quantum-electrodynamic effect on the electron's spin precession frequency due to the emission and absorption of a single photon. Small corrections to the normal Dirac value can in fact be measured to tremendous precision since the net angle between the momentum and spin vectors of the electron can be determined to a few parts per million, as was demonstrated by D. T. Wilkinson and H. R. Crane in 1963. The most recent result by A. Rich and J. C. Wesley (1971) is

$$a_e^{\exp} = 0.001\ 159\ 6567$$
$$\pm 0.000\ 000\ 0035$$

which is in rather incredible agreement with the theoretical value:

$$a_e^{\text{th}} = \frac{\alpha}{2\pi} - 0.328479 \left(\frac{\alpha}{\pi}\right)^2 + 1.21 \pm 0.07 \left(\frac{\alpha}{\pi}\right)^3$$
$$= 0.001\ 159\ 6519$$
$$\pm 0.000\ 000\ 0025.$$

The gyromagnetic ratio of the electron $g =$

$2(1 + a)$, the ratio of the spin and rotation frequencies, which is a fundamental constant of nature, is thus correctly predicted by QED to 11 significant figures!

The theoretical result for the anomalous moment includes contributions due to emission and absorption of up to three photons by the electron. One class of diagrams includes the effect of the electron emitting three photons which annihilate into an electron-positron pair which in turn interacts with the magnetic field. The calculations are carried out six orders in perturbation theory beyond the lowest order and are the most complex of any in theoretical physics. The application of computerized algebraic and numerical computation techniques has been required.

Measurements of the muon anomalous magnetic moment by F. J. M. Farley and his co-workers are also in agreement with quantum electrodynamics. In this and in other precision measurements, the muon has been found to have symmetrical properties to the electron but for its heavier mass:

$$m_\mu/m_e = 206.7683 \pm 0.0009.$$

Other precision tests of quantum electrodynamics which have confirmed the correctness of the theory, including the renormalization procedure, involve the hyperfine separation of the ground state of fundamental atoms such as hydrogen, muonium, and positronium. The hyperfine separation occurs because of the difference in energy which occurs when the electron and nuclear magnetic moments are parallel and antiparallel. Measurements (based on the properties of the hydrogen maser) by D. Kleppner, P. Crampton, and N. Ramsey have determined this separation to 13 significant figures in atomic hydrogen. The results agree with the theoretical predictions to six significant figures. Other measurements of hyperfine splittings in positronium (the positron-electron atom) by V. Hughes et al. and muonium (the positive muon-electron atom) by V. Hughes et al. and V. Telegdi et al. are in good agreement with the quantum electrodynamics predictions at nearly the same precision.

Other applications of quantum electrodynamics include high Z muonic atoms, coherent and incoherent electromagnetic processes, and general electromagnetic phenomena. The theory is often used as a model and guide to hadronic and weak interactions in elementary particle physics.

Conclusions As far as we know, quantum electrodynamics provides a mathematically exact description of the electromagnetic properties of the electron and muon. To the extent that the electromagnetic properties of the nucleus are known, the theory provides the fundamental dynamical theory of the relativistic atom, including its external electromagnetic interactions. At present there is no outstanding discrepancy with any of its predictions, despite our pursuing the limits of the theory to very high accuracy and very small distances.

Breakdown of the theory could still occur at short distances or at high precision if any of the following existed: (a) intrinsic lepton size or nonlocal currents, (b) heavy leptons, (c) heavy photons, (d) magnetic charge, (e) breakdown of perturbation theory or anomalous subtraction constants not given by the renormalization procedure. All of these modifications are ruled out to some extent by the various tests discussed in this article. In addition, the basic space-time symmetries of QED, conservation laws, the constancy in time of α, c, etc. have all been checked to various degrees.

All of the suggested modifications would mar the essential simplicity of Maxwell's equations and the Dirac form of the vertex interaction. Despite this simplicity, however, and despite its phenomenal success, the fundamental problems of renormalization in local field theory and the nature of the exact solutions of quantum electrodynamics are still to be resolved.

STANLEY J. BRODSKY

References

1. Schwinger, J., Ed., "Quantum Electrodynamics," New York, Dover Publications, 1958. (The historical development of QED can be traced through this literature collection.)
2. Brodsky, S. J., and Drell, S. D., "The Present Status of Quantum Electrodynamics," *Ann. Rev. Nucl. Sci.*, **20**, 177 (1970).
3. Bjorken, J. D., and Drell, S. D., "Relativistic Quantum Mechanics" and "Relativistic Quantum Fields," New York, McGraw-Hill, 1965.
4. Taylor, B. N., Parker, W. H., and Langenberg, D. N., "The Fundamental Constants and Quantum Electrodynamics," *Rev. Mod. Phys.*, **41** (1969).

Cross-references: ANTIPARTICLES, ELECTROMAGNETIC THEORY, ELEMENTARY PARTICLES, MANY-BODY PROBLEM, MATRIX MECHANICS, POSITRON, QUANTUM THEORY.

QUANTUM THEORY

Experiments on thermal radiation, with their gross disagreement with classical theories, gave birth to quantum theory. The equilibrium distribution of electromagnetic radiation (that is, emission and absorption of radiation at constant temperature) in a hollow cavity could not be explained on the basis of classical electrodynamics (Maxwell's equations plus the laws of motion of particles). Thermal radiation is a certain function of the temperature (T) of the emitting body. When dispersed by a prism, thermal radiation forms a continuous spectrum. It was found that the energy distribution of the radiation had a regular dependence on its wavelength. Furthermore the energy E_ν as a function of the temperature of the material did not depend upon the

structure of the cavity or its shape. On these bases it was shown that the energy E_ν ought to have a functional dependence upon frequency ν, at temperature T, in the form

$$E_\nu = \nu^3 F\left(\frac{cT}{\nu}\right)$$

All attempts to find the correct form of the function F on the basis of classical theory failed. The classical theory led to the now well-known "ultraviolet catastrophe," since the contribution of high frequencies caused the energy to assume infinite value. The difficulty was removed by a hypothesis of Planck, according to which the energy of a monochromatic wave with frequency ν can only assume those values which are integral multiples of energy $h\nu$; that is, $E_n = nh\nu$, where n is an integer referring to the number of "photons." Thus the energy of a single PHOTON of frequency ν is

$$E = h\nu \qquad (1)$$

The finiteness of Planck's constant h and its resulting implications laid the foundations of quantum theory. Quantum theory, like the special theory of relativity, was discovered through experiments on electromagnetic phenomena and their theoretical interpretations.

The fundamental equation of quantum mechanics [Eq. (1)] implies, on the one hand, that energy of radiation stays concentrated in limited regions of space in amounts of $h\nu$ and, therefore, behaves like the energy of particles; on the other hand, it establishes a definite relationship between the frequency ν and the energy E of an electromagnetic wave. This dual behavior of light corresponds, in one way, to experimental situations of the interference properties of radiation, for the description of which one uses the wave theory of light; in another way, it corresponds to the properties of exchange of energy and momentum between radiation and matter, which require for their explanation the particle picture of light. Thus the dual behavior of light has necessitated the quantum description (quantization) of the electromagnetic field. A unified point of view was formulated quantitatively by de Broglie, according to which all forms of energy and momentum related to matter will manifest a dual behavior of belonging to a wave or particle description of the physical system, depending on the type of experiment performed.

The most interesting example of a quantum mechanical object is the photon itself. By using the relativistic and quantum mechanical definition of the photon energy, we can obtain a quantitative formulation of the above ideas. The relativistic form of the total energy of a particle with rest mass m and momentum p is

$$E = c\sqrt{(p^2 + m^2 c^2)} \qquad (2)$$

We set $m = 0$ and obtain the relativistic definition of the energy of a photon:

$$E = cp \qquad (3)$$

Hence the first unification of relativity and quantum theory originated from the combination of Eqs. (1) and (3) in the form

$$cp = h\nu \qquad (4)$$

By using $\nu\lambda = c$ for the plane electromagnetic wave, we obtain the fundamental statement of quantum mechanics,

$$\lambdabar p = \hbar \qquad (5)$$

valid for all particles with or without mass, where

$$\lambdabar = \frac{\lambda}{2\pi}, \quad \hbar = \frac{h}{2\pi}$$

These assumptions of quantum theory have laid the foundations of new physical and philosophical concepts for the process of measurement in physics and the definition of physical reality.

We need to develop a dynamical theory to describe the wave character of material particles. We shall base our approach on the idea that the concept of the photon must play a fundamental role in building a quantum theory of matter. To this end, a preliminary understanding of free photons in a quantum theory will provide a first orientation, and it will set a clear path for further generalizations of the subject matter.

In the case of particles with mass, one has the possibility of comparing their kinetic energies with their rest masses. If the kinetic energy is small compared to rest energy then we can formulate a nonrelativistic theory. However, with the photon there exists no possibility for the formulation of a nonrelativistic theory. The theory of a free photon will have to be a relativistic one; it is a relativistic particle. There are important advantages in entering quantum mechanics via the photon:

(a) The energy of a photon is a quantum mechanical quantity, $E = h\nu$.

(b) It has provided a natural basis to postulate the wave-particle relation, $\lambda = h/p$.

(c) The wave aspects of the photon are completely described by charge-free Maxwell equations. Therefore, it is natural to try to reconcile Planck's hypothesis with the wave theory of light.

A reinterpretation of Maxwell's equations in conjunction with the quantum relations $E = h\nu$ and $\lambda = h/p$ will, in a natural way, lead us to a wave equation for the photon.

We begin with the free-field Maxwell equations

$$\frac{1}{c}\frac{\partial \mathcal{E}}{\partial t} - \nabla \times \mathcal{H} = 0, \frac{1}{c}\frac{\partial \mathcal{H}}{\partial t} + \nabla \times \mathcal{E} = 0 \qquad (6)$$

$$\nabla \cdot \mathcal{E} = 0, \quad \nabla \cdot \mathcal{H} = 0 \qquad (7)$$

Now consider the complex three-dimensional vector

$$\mathbf{X} = \mathcal{E} + i\mathcal{H} \qquad (8)$$

It has the following interesting properties.

(a) For a plane electromagnetic wave, whose electric and magnetic vectors are perpendicular and equal (in magnitude), the Lorentz-invariant square of X vanishes; i.e.,

$$(\mathcal{E} - i\mathcal{H})^2 = \mathcal{E}^2 - \mathcal{H}^2 - 2i\mathcal{E} \cdot \mathcal{H} = 0 \qquad (9)$$

or

$$|\mathcal{E}| = |\mathcal{H}|, \quad \mathcal{E} \cdot \mathcal{H} = 0$$

The latter two are the two Lorentz-invariant properties of a plane electromagnetic wave.

(b) The energy density of the field can be expressed in terms of the rotation-invariant square of X as

$$cP_4 = \frac{1}{8\pi} |X|^2 = \frac{1}{8\pi} \langle X|X \rangle = \frac{\mathcal{E}^2 + \mathcal{H}^2}{8\pi} \qquad (10)$$

where $|X\rangle$ is the column vector

$$|X\rangle = \begin{bmatrix} X_1 \\ X_2 \\ X_3 \end{bmatrix}$$

and $\langle X| = [X_1{}^*, X_2{}^*, X_3{}^*]$ is the Hermitian conjugate row vector of $|X\rangle$.

(c) The momentum density of the field has the form

$$P_i = \frac{1}{8\pi c} \langle X|K_i|X \rangle \qquad (11)$$

where the Hermitian 3×3 matrices K_i are defined by

$$K_j = \begin{bmatrix} 0 & -i\delta_{j3} & i\delta_{j2} \\ i\delta_{j3} & 0 & -i\delta_{j1} \\ -i\delta_{j2} & i\delta_{j1} & 0 \end{bmatrix} \qquad (12)$$

where δ_{ij} is the usual Kronecker tensor with $\delta_{ij} = 1$ if $i = j$ and $\delta_{ij} = 0$ if $i \neq j$.

The two expressions of Eqs. (10) and (11) for energy and momentum densities, respectively, can be combined into a single equation,

$$cP_\mu = \frac{1}{8\pi} \langle X|K_\mu|X \rangle \qquad (13)$$

where K_4, corresponding to $\mu = 4$, is the 3×3 unit matrix. In order to illustrate the meaning of Eq. (13) we shall, as an example, work out the third component of Eq. (13). It is given by

$$cP_3 = \frac{1}{8\pi} [X_1{}^*, X_2{}^*, X_3{}^*] \begin{bmatrix} 0 & -i & 0 \\ i & 0 & 0 \\ 0 & 0 & 0 \end{bmatrix} \begin{bmatrix} X_1 \\ X_2 \\ X_3 \end{bmatrix}$$

$$= \frac{i}{8\pi} (X_1 X_2{}^* - X_1{}^* X_2) = \frac{1}{4\pi} (\mathcal{E}_1 \mathcal{H}_2$$

$$- \mathcal{E}_2 \mathcal{H}_1) = \frac{1}{4\pi} (\mathcal{E} \times \mathcal{H})_3$$

which verifies the statement in (c) above.

(d) The momentum and energy densities of the field are conserved; i.e.,

$$c \frac{\partial P_\mu}{\partial x_\mu} = \frac{\partial P_4}{\partial t} + c\mathbf{\nabla} \cdot \mathbf{P} = 0 \qquad (14)$$

provided the complex vector $|X\rangle$ satisfies the equation

$$K_\mu \frac{\partial}{\partial x_\mu} |X\rangle = 0 \qquad (15)$$

Equation (15) can also be written as

$$i \frac{\partial}{\partial t} |X\rangle = -ic\mathbf{K} \cdot \mathbf{\nabla} |X\rangle \qquad (16)$$

whence it is easy to see,

$$i\mathbf{K} \cdot \mathbf{\nabla} |X\rangle = \mathbf{\nabla} \times \mathbf{X} \qquad (17)$$

Hence Eq. (16) is equivalent to Maxwell's equations [Eq. (6)]. Therefore, the conservation of energy and momentum density of the field is a consequence of Maxwell's equations or, conversely, if Maxwells' equations are satisfied, the vector P_μ is conserved.

We write Maxwells' equations in the form

$$ih \frac{\partial}{\partial t} |X\rangle = H|X\rangle \qquad (18)$$

where

$$\mathbf{\nabla} \cdot \mathbf{X} = 0 \qquad (19)$$

$$H = -ich\mathbf{K} \cdot \mathbf{\nabla} = c\mathbf{K} \cdot \mathbf{p} \qquad (20)$$

has the dimensions of energy. The momentum operator $\mathbf{p}$ is defined as

$$\mathbf{p} = -ih\mathbf{\nabla}$$

The complex vector $|X\rangle$ has the physical dimensions of the square root of energy density. It will be more convenient to work with a complex vector $|\eta\rangle$, having the dimensions of the square root of (volume)$^{-1}$, defined by

$$|X\rangle = \sqrt{(8\pi E)}|\eta\rangle \qquad (21)$$

and satisfying the condition of normalization,

$$\int \langle \eta|\eta \rangle \, d^3x = 1 \qquad (22)$$

where E is the energy of the photon. With these premises, the wave equation (or Schrödinger's equation) of the photon becomes

$$ih \frac{\partial}{\partial t} |\eta\rangle = H|\eta\rangle \qquad (23)$$

$$\mathbf{\nabla} \cdot \eta = 0 \qquad (24)$$

The formalism contained in Eqs. (23) and (24), with the definitions of H by Eq. (20), will be

shown to be consistent and compatible with the observed facts $E = h\nu$ and $\lambda = h/p$ of the photon.

The Fourier series expansion of the wave function can be given as

$$|\eta\rangle = \frac{1}{\sqrt{V}} \sum_k e^{i\mathbf{k}\cdot\mathbf{r}}|\phi_k\rangle \qquad (25)$$

where summation refers to all three components of the k vector and is, over all the k, defined according to

$$k_1 = \frac{2\pi}{L}n_1, \quad k_2 = \frac{2\pi}{L}n_2, \quad k_3 = \frac{2\pi}{L}n_3 \qquad (26)$$

The complex vectors $|\phi_k(t)\rangle$ are functions of the wave number and of time t. By substituting the function $|\eta\rangle$ given by Eq. (25), in Eqs. (23) and (24), we obtain

$$i\hbar \frac{\partial}{\partial t}|\phi_k\rangle = H|\phi_k\rangle \qquad (27)$$

$$\mathbf{k}\cdot\boldsymbol{\phi}_k = 0 \qquad (28)$$

where n_1, n_2, n_3 are integral numbers specifying wave number vector k in a plane wave exp $(i\mathbf{k}\cdot\mathbf{r})$, and

$$H = \hbar c \mathbf{k}\cdot\mathbf{K}$$

so the operator p acts on $|\phi_k\rangle$ according to

$$\mathbf{p}|\phi_k\rangle = \hbar\mathbf{k}|\phi_k\rangle \qquad (29)$$

Thus the vector $\hbar\mathbf{k}$ can be interpreted as the eigen-value of the operator p corresponding to the eigenvector $|\phi_k\rangle$.

In order to find the eigenvalues of the operator H, we may look for the stationary-state solutions of Eq. (27). We assume that the vector $|\phi_k(t)\rangle$ is periodic in time and that in accordance with the relation $E = h\nu$, we write

$$|\phi_k(t)\rangle = |a_k\rangle e^{-(i/\hbar)Et} \qquad (30)$$

This form of the wave refers to a stationary state. The first expression of Eq. (27) now becomes

$$E|a_k\rangle = H|a_k\rangle \qquad (31)$$

In matrix form, it can be written as

$$\begin{bmatrix} E & icp_3 & -icp_2 \\ -icp_3 & E & icp_1 \\ icp_2 & -icp_1 & E \end{bmatrix} \begin{bmatrix} a_{k1} \\ a_{k2} \\ a_{k3} \end{bmatrix} = 0 \qquad (32)$$

Solutions for Eq. (32) require the vanishing of the determinant of $(E - H)$. In Eq. (32) the vector a_k is, of course, subject to the condition

$$\mathbf{k}\cdot\mathbf{a}_k = 0$$

By taking the determinant of $(E - H)$ we obtain

$$E(E^2 - c^2 p^2) = 0$$

The eigenvalue $E = 0$ implies [as seen from Eq. (32)] that the vectors a_k and p are parallel, which is not consistent with $p\cdot a_k = 0$. Hence the solution $E = 0$ must be discarded by the condition of transversality of the wave. The remaining two solutions are

$$E = cp = c\hbar k = h\nu$$

$$E = -cp = -c\hbar k = -h\nu$$

The negative sign in the second case is not to be understood as referring to a negative energy state. It has to do with the spin degree of freedom of the photon. This can be seen from writing the wave equation for negative energy,

$$(c\mathbf{p}\cdot\mathbf{K})|\eta\rangle = -E|\eta\rangle$$

and taking complex conjugate of both sides in the form

$$c\mathbf{p}\cdot\mathbf{K}|\eta^*\rangle = E|\eta^*\rangle.$$

Thus both energy states are positive and they refer respectively to the energy of a right circularly or left circularly polarized photon, with spin parallel or antiparallel to $\mathbf{k}$. The two states can be represented by $|\eta\rangle$ and $|\eta^*\rangle$.

We have seen that at a given time, the value of the wave function can be obtained by a certain superposition of plane waves. In analogy to the classical definition of the intensity of a wave we shall look upon the real quantity

$$P = \langle\eta|\eta\rangle$$

as a probability density in the sense that EP is the energy density over a region that is large compared to the wavelength of the photon. The probability depends, of course, on the value of the wave function at the particular point. We can choose $|\eta\rangle$ in such a way that it differs from zero only over a region Ω of the dimensions of the wavelength of the photon. It shall be composed of monochromatic plane waves that interfere destructively outside the region Ω; the frequencies and wavenumbers of these waves differ very little from each other inside the region Ω. In this particular region, the waves interfere constructively and the wave function $|\eta\rangle$ assumes large values there. This is equivalent to a localization of the photon. If this localization process is described in accordance with uncertainty relations between the dynamical variables of the photon, then the region in question is a wave packet. These arguments are, of course, valid also for massive particles.

The amplitudes of the waves that constitute a packet are different from zero only in the packet. These wave amplitudes constitute a wave group and have a group velocity that differs from the velocity of a single plane wave ("phase velocity").

In classical mechanics, the specification of positions and velocities of a dynamical system at each time is sufficient for a complete determination of its state. The basic concepts of classical

theory (mechanics) consist of the material point, the force of interaction between material points (potential energy), and the inertial system (= the Cartesian coordinate system + the time coordinate f or all reference frames in uniform relative motion). When the electromagnetic field is included, classical physics gains the concept of field, a region of space at every point of which a material particle can experience a force. Thus a field has an energy and momentum content. Special relativity brings into the structure of the inertial system the constancy of the velocity of light. In this theory, one cannot preserve the concepts of action at a distance and potential energy and this in turn implies that the concept of the material point can be discarded and replaced by the field concept.

A more profound change in our concepts of space and time came with the discovery of general relativity (the principle of general covariance, invariance of the laws of nature with respect to all coordinate transformations, not necessarily in uniform relative motion). According to this theory, inertial systems need not be qualified as the only group of systems for the formulation of physical laws. The "space" represented by the inertial group (the Lorentz group), and considered as a part of the physical reality, can have only a limited meaning. The inertial group is used to determine the behavior of mass points in space and time, without itself being influenced by mass points. Therefore, according to special relativity, the inertial group occupies an absolute position in the description of physical phenomena.

In general relativity, however, the inertial group does not have this privileged position; in general relativity, it has been integrated into the field and has, therefore, been deprived of its "absoluteness." It is the field which has an independent meaning, and it depends on four parameters (the coordinates). The space aspect of matter itself is described by the field. The inertial character of real things must be derivable from a field; we do not try to fit a field to a given inertial group or to a mechanical system without considering that it will not change or influence the inertial system. In short, the mechanics of a system should be derivable from a field.

In quantum theory, we retain the inertial frame and the action-at-a-distance concepts, but it is no longer true that a state is completely defined by the initial conditions of the dynamical system.

According to quantum theory a "small system"—i.e., a system that can change its state (energy, momentum, position, angular momentum, and so on) by an act of observation—cannot be observed with the greatest conceivable amount of detail. The behavior of nature in the micro system is such that there exists a limitation or a lower limit to the power of observation. This limitation on the observability of a dynamical system implies a restriction on the data that can be assigned to the state of the physical system.

Both classical and relativisitic mechanics permit a definite distinction between observer and observed. This is essentially a complete fulfillment of the principle of causality in a deterministic sense. Accordingly, the interaction between observed and observer, arising in the act of observation, can be made infinitely small. For this reason it is meaningful, in classical mechanics, to say that the state of a dynamical system can be defined in its entirety with no limitation on the detail of the data. The continuous nature of things, for example the absorption of a wave by an electron, will allow enough time to measure its position and momentum rapidly before it absorbs sufficient energy from the incident wave to change its state abruptly.

The quantum mechanical point of view, at the expense of some loss of exact information on the dynamical system, recognized the impossibility of controlling the interaction between observer and observed. In the act of observation large changes in the state of the system being observed must be taking place. It is, therefore, not possible to assign simultaneous "initial values" to canonically conjugate variables referring to the same degree of freedom of the dynamical system, e.g., x and p_x the coordinate and the corresponding linear momentum. This proposal of quantum mechanics can only be reconciled with a statistical or probabilistic approach to the description of physical reality. The complete determinism of classical theory is replaced by an indeterministic description, the extent of nondeterminism being determined by the size of the universal constant h, Planck's constant. In classical mechanics, a cause produces another definite cause. In quantum mechanics, a cause can only produce a statistical trend to a given cause. This in turn can be regarded as a tendency towards some effect. The mode of the statistical tendency can be incorporated into a fundamental principle of nature, first enunciated by Heisenberg as the "principle of uncertainty" in the origination of physical events (see HEISENBERG UNCERTAINTY PRINCIPLE).

According to the principle of uncertainty, the position of an electron can be defined within a certain accuracy Δx at a time t, where Δx is a possible spread in the location of the electron; i.e., the electron can be seen within a region of the dimensions of Δx. The size of this region will depend on the spread of its momentum caused by the act of observation. In modern theory it is believed that the only description consistent with the principle of uncertainty is to represent the spread Δx as a "wave packet," the particle under observation being the wave itself. A wave packet has the properties of waves whose amplitudes are different from zero only in a limited region of space-time.

A dynamical system, having a well-defined single path in classical mechanics, is described in quantum mechanics by a wave packet containing coordinates and momenta with approximate numerical values that are restricted by the uncertainty principle. The size of the packet will

increase with time; i.e., a wave packet can spread out and decay. If we succeed in obtaining, during our act of observation, a wave packet that can be located in a region smaller than Δx, then the location of the electron is sharper than ever. The latter result can only be approached as a result of large interaction between the electron and observer, resulting in a spread of the momentum of the wave packet much larger than the spread in its position. This uncertainty must be regarded as a fundamental property of a small object (electron) and, indeed, as its definition. The mathematical statement of the principle of uncertainty is contained in the relation

$$\Delta x \, \Delta p_x \geqq \hbar \qquad (33)$$

The same kind of uncertainties will, of course, prevail for all other canonically conjugate dynamical variables of the wave packet. For example, the spread in its energy—and the corresponding spread in the time will satisfy the uncertainty relation

$$\Delta t \, \Delta E \geqq \hbar \qquad (34)$$

The question now arises: what is it that the act of observation does to a dynamical system? What kind of a statement is the observer going to make following the observation of the dynamical system? An observable in quantum mechanics—such as energy, momentum, etc.—is, first of all, represented by a linear Hermitian operator. Let α be such an operator, with eigenstates $|\alpha'\rangle$ corresponding to its eigenvalue α'. If the state of the dynamical system during the act of measurement happens to be the eigenstate of α, then the eigenvalue α' is the result of the measurement. Whatever the state of the system prior to measurement was, the act of observation has caused it to jump to its eigenstate $|\alpha'\rangle$. A second measurement carried out in the state represented by $|\alpha'\rangle$ must give the same result. Therefore, any result of a measurement of an observable is one of its eigenvalues. The eigenvalues of a dynamical variable come into existence as a result of acts of measurement. Without the act of observation, we cannot talk of any state and consequently there exists no wave function prior to the process of measurement. Quantum mechanics is not concerned with the state and the corresponding possible values of a dynamical variable prior to observation. Quantum mechanics predicts the future from the present data in accordance with the principle of uncertainty. In general, every experiment aimed at a determination of some numerical quantity causes a loss of information in some other quantity, related to the former by uncertainty relations. The uncontrollable perturbation of the observed systems alters the value of the previously determined quantities, except when the corresponding linear Hermitian operators commute with one another, i.e., the measurement of one is not affected by the measurement of the other.

BEHRAM KURŞUNOĞLU

References

Bethe, H. A., "Intermediate Quantum Mechanics," New York and Amsterdam, W. A. Benjamin, Inc., 1964.
Dirac, P. A. M., "The Principles of Quantum Mechanics," Fourth edition, Oxford, Clarendon Press, 1958.
Kurşunoğlu, B., "Modern Quantum Theory," San Francisco and London, Freeman and Co., 1962.

Cross-references: HEISENBERG UNCERTAINTY PRINCIPLE; MATHEMATICAL PRINCIPLES OF QUANTUM MECHANICS; MATRIX MECHANICS; PHOTON; RADIATION, THERMAL; SCHRÖDINGER EQUATION; WAVE MECHANICS.

QUARKS

Introduction It seems that protons and neutrons (in fact, the various hadrons) are not the fundamental constituents of nuclear matter. These particles, themselves, have a detailed, and possibly complicated, structure. Several theoretical physicists have suggested that they may be composed of various combinations of a few much more "fundamental" objects. These objects have been called "quarks" by Gell-Mann (1964); "aces" by Zweig (1964). In both these schemes the new "fundamental" particles have electric charges less than the charge on the electron. In other schemes, developed later, the charges are normal.

Chemical experiments in the late eighteenth and early nineteenth centuries led Dalton to revive the atomic hypothesis. Atoms, at first, were thought of as small impenetrable spheres. By the end of the nineteenth century it had become obvious that the atoms themselves had a detailed structure. Research, particularly on radioactivity, showed that they consist of a central, small ($\sim 10^{-12}$ cm diameter), massive, positively charged nucleus surrounded by a light, negative, and comparatively large ($\sim 10^{-8}$ cm diameter) electron cloud. The structure of the nucleus itself then came under investigation. By 1932 it was known that nuclei are made of comparatively small numbers of neutrons and protons. A new force was discovered (in addition to the electromagnetic and gravitational forces) that held the positive protons and electrically uncharged neutrons together in the nucleus. This nuclear force was very strong but of limited range. Its "quantum," the particle analogous to the photon in the electromagnetic field, was of nonzero rest mass. This particle, now called the π-meson, or pion, was predicted by Yukawa in 1936 and discovered in *Cosmic Radiation* by Lattes, Occhialini, and Powell in 1947. For a short time in that year it seemed that physicists had achieved a clear, simple, and correct theory of the fundamental constitution of matter. However, later in the same year two new and unpredicted particles were reported, again in *Cosmic Radiation*, by Rochester and Butler. The first of these was another meson, somewhat like the pion but more massive. The second was

probably a hyperon, i.e., a strongly interacting particle heavier than the neutron. Since then many more examples of both classes have been found.

To describe these particles one gives the values of various parameters, or quantum numbers. Some of these are familiar. For instance, the particles have different masses, and some relationships between these masses are now quite well understood. They have various electric charges which are integral multiples of the electronic charge. They possess intrinsic angular momentum or spin (sometimes this is zero). They have an analogous property called isotopic spin (or isospin). The mesons are distinguished from particles like the proton, neutron, and various hyperons (which are collectively called baryons) by a quantity, baryon number, which is an extension of the old atomic weight. The parity of the wave function describing the particle is an important property. There is also a quantum number called "strangeness." This has zero value for the "familiar" particles such as the proton, neutron, and pion, ±1 for the early strange particles discovered by Rochester and Butler, and as high as ±3 for some fairly recently discovered particles.

There are about one hundred of these "fundamental" particles now known. They interact with each other via various fields. Two of these have been known for some time, the gravitational and electromagnetic fields. Two others, the weak nuclear field and the strong nuclear field, were discovered in the 1930s. It seems likely from the results of experiments in high-energy cosmic radiation that there is at least one more, the superstrong field.

The large number of these particles has made physicists suspect that they are not "fundamental" but must themselves have structure, just as in the nineteenth century the large number of different types of atoms discovered suggested that atoms had structure. Also, many of the properties of these particles point to an internal structure. For instance, the neutron has a total electric charge which is indistinguishable from zero down to very fine limits, yet the neutron has a sizeable magnetic moment.

The Quark Hypothesis In 1964 M. Gell-Mann and G. Zweig independently pointed out that all the known hadrons (i.e., particles that interact via the strong nuclear force) could be constructed out of simple combinations of three particles (and their three antiparticles). These hypothetical particles had to have slightly peculiar properties (the most peculiar being a fractional electric charge). Gell-Mann called them quarks (referring to a sentence in James Joyce's work *Finnegan's Wake*, "Three quarks for Muster Mark"). The three quarks are designated p, n, and λ because they somewhat resemble the proton, neutron, and Λ° hyperon. Some of their quantum numbers are given in Table 1.

The theory supposes that three quarks bind together to form a baryon, while a quark and an antiquark bind together to form a meson. If one supposes that the binding is such that the internal motion of the quarks is nonrelativistic (which requires that the quarks be massive and sit in a broad potential well), then many quite detailed properties of the hadrons can be explained.

Predictions and Verification of the Nonrelativistic Quark Theory (1) *The Predicted and Observed Particles.* The particles which can interact via the strong nuclear force are called hadrons. Hadrons can be divided into two main classes, the mesons (with baryon number zero) and the baryons (with nonzero baryon number). Within each of the classes there are small subclasses. The subclass of baryons which has been known longest consists of those particles with spin $\frac{1}{2}$ and even parity. The members of this class are the proton, the neutron, the Λ° hyperon, the three Σ hyperons and the two Ξ hyperons. There are no other baryons with spin $\frac{1}{2}$ and even parity (or, to use the usual notation, $J^P = \frac{1}{2}^+$). The next "family" of baryons has ten members, each with $J^P = \frac{3}{2}^+$. The mesons can be grouped into similar families. One of the first successes of the quark model was to explain just why there should be eight baryons with $J^P = \frac{1}{2}^+$, 10 with $\frac{3}{2}^+$, and so on and why the various members of these families have the particular quantum numbers observed. The explanation is most easily understood if we start with the $\frac{3}{2}^+$ baryon family.

On the left-hand side of Fig. 1 the members of the family are arranged on a plot on which the ordinate is the value of their strangeness and the abscissa that of their electric charge. Most

TABLE 1. SOME OF THE SUGGESTED CHARACTERISTICS OF THE THREE QUARKS. M_p IS NOT DEFINED BY THE THEORY OTHER THAN THAT IT SHOULD BE CONSIDERABLE; THE UNITS OF MASS ARE MeV/c^2.

Particle	Charge	Spin	Baryon No.	Strangeness	Mass	Isospin	I_z
p	$\frac{2}{3}e$	$\frac{1}{2}$	$\frac{1}{3}$	0	M_p	$\frac{1}{2}$	$-\frac{1}{2}$
n	$-\frac{1}{3}e$	$\frac{1}{2}$	$\frac{1}{3}$	0	$\sim M_p$	$\frac{1}{2}$	$\frac{1}{2}$
λ	$-\frac{1}{3}e$	$\frac{1}{2}$	$\frac{1}{3}$	-1	$M_p + 146$	0	0

Charge Strangeness	+2	+1	0	-1	Mass in MeV/c²	Quark Scheme
-3				Ω^-	1672	$\lambda\lambda\lambda$
-2			$\Xi^{\circ *}$	Ξ^{-*}	1526	$p\lambda\lambda, n\lambda\lambda$
-1		Σ^{+*}	$\Sigma^{\circ *}$	Σ^{-*}	1380	$pp\lambda, pn\lambda, nn\lambda$
0	Δ^{++}	Δ^+	Δ°	Δ^-	1236	ppp, ppn, nnp, nnn

FIG. 1. The family of baryons with $J^P = \frac{3}{2}^+$ and their quark groupings that explain them.

Charge Strangeness	+1	0	-1	Quark Scheme			
-2		Ξ°	Ξ^-			$p\lambda\lambda$	$n\lambda\lambda$
-1	Σ^+	Σ°	Σ^-	$pp\lambda$	$pn\lambda$		
		Λ°			$pn\lambda$		$nn\lambda$
0	P	N		ppn	pnn		

FIG. 2. The baryon family with $J^P = \frac{1}{2}^+$.

Charge Strangeness	+1	0	-1	Quark Scheme			
-1		$\overline{K}^{\circ}$	K^-			$\lambda\overline{n}$	$\lambda\overline{p}$
0	π^+	$\pi^{\circ}, \eta^{\circ}, \chi^{\circ}$	π^-	$p\overline{n}$	$(p\overline{p}, n\overline{n}, \lambda\overline{\lambda})$		$n\overline{p}$
+1	K^+	K°		$p\overline{\lambda}$	$n\overline{\lambda}$		

FIG. 3. The meson family with $J^P = 0^-$.

of the particles have rather short lifetimes but otherwise are not very different from "ordinary" baryons like the neutron. On the right-hand side of the diagram we see the way in which quark theory suggests that the particles arise. For instance, the Ω^- hyperon is supposed to consist of three λ quarks. The spin of all these baryons is $\frac{3}{2}$, so all three quark spins must be aligned. One then has ten, and only ten, possible combinations of three quarks and all these combinations exist. Moreover the quark model gives just the right quantum numbers for all particles. If we assume, in addition, that λ is 146 MeV/c² more massive than p and n (which we take to be about equally massive) then we have at once an explanation of the mass differences. The "apex" particle, the Ω^-, had its existence and detailed properties predicted before its discovery.

The $J^P = \frac{1}{2}^+$ baryon family is similarly treated in Fig. 2. In this case, to get spin $\frac{1}{2}$ we must always have one quark with its spin antiparallel. This explains the absence of "corner" particles like $\lambda\lambda\lambda$ and also the occurrence of two different particles in the center position. For, if we

consider both groups, we must obviously have a particle with spin $\frac{3}{2}$ and spin projection on the z axis (s_z) equal to $\frac{3}{2}$. For the p quark, for instance, this is the particle $\Delta^{++} = p \uparrow p \uparrow p \uparrow$. This particle with $s = \frac{3}{2}$ must equally obviously have a state with spin projection $\frac{1}{2}$ (i.e., $s = \frac{3}{2}$, $s_z = \frac{1}{2}$). This is the case $p \uparrow p \downarrow p \uparrow$. But that is the only possibility, because $p \uparrow p \downarrow p \uparrow = p \downarrow p \uparrow p \uparrow = p \uparrow p \uparrow p \downarrow$, since the p's are indistinguishable. So no $s = \frac{1}{2}$ state is possible from three p's (or 3 n's or 3 λ's). However, for the combination of $p, n,$ and λ we can have either an $s = \frac{3}{2}$ state or an $s = \frac{1}{2}$ state with either the n and λ spins parallel, or p and λ parallel. So two different $s = \frac{1}{2}$, $s_z = \frac{1}{2}$ combinations of these three can occur, and indeed, are found (the Σ° and the singlet Λ° hyperons.)

The various mesons are constructed from pairs of quarks and antiquarks. The scheme for the pseudoscalar, $J^P = 0^-$, mesons is shown in Fig. 3. These include the pions and kaons.

The theory predicts all the known particles. Extensive searches have been made for particles *not* predicted by the theory (the so called "exotic" particles), so far without success.

TABLE 2. THE MASSES IN MeV/c^2 OF VARIOUS PARTICLES
PREDICTED BY THE QUARKS MODEL AND THEIR
EXPERIMENTALLY DETERMINED VALUES.

Particle	N	Λ	Σ	Δ	Ξ	Ω$^-$	π	K	ρ	ω	φ
Quark theory prediction	928	1108	1195	1238	1340	1675	133	490	753	753	1010
Experimental	939	1116	1193	1236	1318	1672	137	445	765	783	1020

TABLE 3. MASS DIFFERENCES OF VARIOUS PARTICLES

Particles	Mass Difference in MeV/c^2	
	Prediction of Quark Model	Experiment
Neutron-proton	1.3	1.3
Σ$^-$ − Σ^0	4.8	4.8
Σ$^-$ − Σ$^+$	7.9	7.9
Ξ$^-$ − Ξ^0	6.6	6.5
Δ$^-$ − Δ^{++}	3.9	7.9 ± 6.8
Δ^0 − Δ^{++}	0.89	5.8 ± 3.9

TABLE 4. THE CALCULATED AND OBSERVED MAGNETIC
MOMENTS (IN NUCLEAR MAGNETONS)
OF VARIOUS PARTICLES.[a]

	Particle	Proton	Neutron	Λ^0	Σ$^+$
Magnetic Moment	Calculated	+2.79	−1.86	−0.93	+2.79
	Observed	+2.79	−1.91	−0.73 ± 0.16	+2.5 ± 0.5

[a]Many other aspects of electromagnetic behavior also can be calculated with good accuracy using the quark model.

(2) *Particle Masses*. The masses of the various particles can be calculated using the nonrelativistic quark model. Some of these are given in Table 2. The model predicts the masses both of mesons and baryons with very fair accuracy. Note that this table gives the mean masses of various subfamilies. Thus proton and neutron are taken together and designated by N (for nucleon) and have a mean mass of 939 MeV/c^2.

The quark model also predicts the mass differences within these subgroups rather accurately. A few of the predicted and observed differences are given in Table 3.

(3) *The Electromagnetic Properties of Hadrons*. If the uncharged neutron were a "simple" elementary particle with no substructure, then it should not have a magnetic moment. On the other hand the quark model supposes that the neutron is composed of three charged particles (two with charge − $\frac{1}{3}e$ and the third with charge + $\frac{2}{3}e$). Thus, on this theory, we expect it to have a magnetic moment. The magnetic moments of various particles calculated using the quark model are given in Table 4 and compared with observation. The two are obviously in good agreement.

Many other aspects of electromagnetic behavior also can be calculated with good accuracy using the quark model.

(4) *Scattering of High-energy Hadrons*. The total cross sections for proton-proton and pion-proton scattering at high energies (> 20 GeV) are predicted by the quark model to be in the ratio 3:2 (crudely, because a proton is supposed to contain three quarks and a pion two quarks). The observed value is (1.58 ± 0.05):1. This result has not been predicted by any other model.

The nonrelativistic quark model has also had considerable success in explaining the scattering of positrons by negative electrons at high energies and the deep inelastic scattering of electrons by protons.

More complicated theories of quark interactions have also been published.

Defects of the Quark Model The chief drawback to the theory is our inability, so far, to produce a beam of individual quarks, as we can now produce beams of pions, kaons, negative protons, and so on.

Many searches have been made for individual quarks. The quarks suggested by Gell-Mann and

Zweig have three features which should make their detection easy. These are their fractional charge, their large mass, and the stability of at least one quark (heavier quarks could possibly decay to lighter quarks but once the lightest quark is reached there is no fractionally charged particle into which it can decay.) These properties lead to a large number of possible ways of finding quarks.

When a quark has been produced it will first be slowed to thermal energies by ionization loss. If it is negatively charged it will then be captured by an atomic nucleus. Because of the large mass of the quark, its K shell lies within the (positive) nucleus. Quarks cannot disappear then, because of their fractional charge, and could only be annihilated by a positive antiquark. This, however, would be repelled by the positive charge on the nucleus. So we should be left with a permanently fractionally charged atom. Many searches for such atoms have been made using the Millikan oil drop type of experiment, mass spectrographic experiments, searches for predicted quark spectral lines, and so on. The results are exasperating in that many experiments are negative, some are positive, and some find quark-like effects which could possibly be due to some experimental effect. Millikan himself wrote in 1910 (*Philosophical Magazine*, **19**, 209,): "I have discarded one uncertain and unduplicated observation apparently upon a singly charged drop which gave a value of the charge some 30 per cent lower than the final value of e', that is a charge of $\sim \frac{2}{3}e$."

Searches using accelerators have similar results. Quark-like events have been seen, but other explanations may account for them. This is generally stated to mean either that fractionally charged quarks do not exist, or that their mass is greater than the energy available, or, for some reason, their production cross section at these energies is very low.

Searches using low-energy (~ 100 GeV) cosmic radiation have not produced any certain candidates. Searches in the cores of air showers (whose primary energy is around 10^6 GeV) have in several cases, revealed apparently fractionally charged particles. These have been, in some cases, disputed by other experimentalists. In other cases they have not appeared in similar experiments. Various groups have apparently found massive particles in air shower cores, but whether or not these are fractionally charged is not yet known.

Several explanations of this peculiar state have been offered. One obvious one is that quarks exist and have already been seen in a dozen or so experiments. On the other hand, it has been suggested that they do not exist but that the hadrons behave as if they did. A somewhat similar belief was once held by some concerning the neutrino. Some physicists have produced quark-like models in which the "new quarks" are not fractionally charged. These models have considerable drawbacks. Others again have pointed to the long time lag (over 20 years) between the prediction and discovery of such now well-established particles as the antiproton. The situation is intriguing. Since very many experiments are in progress it may well be resolved in the time between the writing of this article and its publication.

C. B. A. McCusker

References

Chew, G., Gell-Mann, M., and Rosenfeld, A., "Strongly Interacting Particles," *Sci. Amer.* (February 1964).

Zel'dovich, Y. B., "The Classification of Elementary Particles and Quarks," *Soviet Physics USPEKHI*, **8**, 489 (1965).

Levin, E. M., and Frankfurt, L. L., "The Non-relativistic Quark Model," *Soviet Physics USPEKHI*, **11**, 106 (1968).

Panofsky, W. K. H., and Dalitz, R. H., "Particle Physics," in "Nuclear Energy Today and Tomorrow," Messel, H., and Butler, S. T., Eds., Sydney, Australia, Shakespeare Head Press, 1969.

Cross-references: ELEMENTARY PARTICLES, NUCLEAR STRUCTURE, STRONG INTERACTIONS.

R

RADAR

Radar is the name given to the use of electromagnetic energy for the detection and location of reflecting objects. It operates by transmitting an electromagnetic signal and comparing the echo reflected from the target with the transmitted signal.

The first demonstration of the basic radar effects was by Heinrich Hertz in his famous experiments in the late 1880's in which he verified Maxwell's electromagnetic theory. Hertz showed that short-wave radiation could be reflected from metallic and dielectric bodies. Although the basic principle of radar was embodied in Hertz's experiments, the practical development of radar had to wait more than 50 years for radio technology to advance sufficiently. It wasn't until the late 1930's that practical models of radars appeared. The rapid advance in radar technology during World War II was aided by the many significant contributions of physicists and other scientists pressed into the practical pursuit of a new technology important to the military. In addition to its military application, radar has been applied to the peace-time needs of air and ship navigation, air traffic control, rainfall observation, tornado detection, hurricane tracking, surveying, radar astronomy, and the familiar speed measuring meter of the highway police.

The measurement of distance, or range, is probably the most distinctive feature of radar. Range is determined from the time taken by the transmitted signal to travel out to the target and back. The distances involved might be as short as a few feet or as long as interplanetary distances.

If the target is in motion relative to the radar, the echo signal will be shifted in frequency by the DOPPLER EFFECT and may be used as a direct measurement of the relative target velocity. A more important application of the Doppler shift is to separate moving targets from stationary targets (clutter) by means of frequency filtering. This is the basis of MTI (moving target indication) radar.

Radar antennas are large compared to the wavelength so as to produce narrow, directive beams. The direction of the target may be inferred from the angle of arrival of the echo. Radar antenna technology has profited greatly from the theory and practice of optics. Both the lens and the parabolic mirror have their counterpart in radar, and the analysis of antenna radiation patterns follows from diffraction theory developed for optics. The greater versatility of materials in the radar frequency region of the electromagnetic spectrum, however, offers more flexibility in implementing many of the principles of optics not practical in the visual portion of the spectrum.

The external appearance of a radar is dominated by its ANTENNA. Most radars use some form of parabolic reflector. The radar antenna can also be a fixed array of many small radiating elements (perhaps several thousand or more) operating in unison to produce the desired radiation characteristics. Array antennas have the advantage of greater flexibility and more rapid beam steering than mechanically steered reflector antennas because the beam movement can be accomplished by electrically changing the relative phase at each antenna element. High power can be radiated since a separate transmitter can be applied at each element. The flexibility and speed of an array antenna make it necessary in many instances to control its functions and analyze its output by automatic data processing equipment rather than with an operator using a grease pencil to mark the face of a cathode ray tube.

Radars are generally found within the microwave portion of the electromagnetic spectrum, typically from about 200 MHz (1.5 meters wavelength) to about 35,000 MHz (8.5 mm wavelength). These are not firm bounds. Many radars operate outside these limits. The famous British CH radar system of World War II which provided warning of air attack, operated in the high-frequency region of the spectrum in the vicinity of 25 MHz. Experimental radars have also been demonstrated in the millimeter wavelength region where small physical apertures are capable of narrow beam widths and good angular resolution. The radar principle has also been applied at optical frequencies with LASERS for the measurement of range and detection of small motions (using the Doppler effect).

The detection performance of a radar system is specified by the *radar equation* which states

$$P_{\text{rec}} = \frac{P_t G}{4\pi R^2} \times \quad \sigma \quad \times \frac{1}{4\pi R^2} \times A$$

Received = Power × Target × Space × Antenna
power   density back-   atten-   collect-
           at a   scatter uation   ing
           distance cross   on   area
           R section return
                             path

where P_t is the transmitted power, G is the transmitting antenna gain, R is the range, σ is the target backscatter cross section, and A is the effective receiving aperture of the antenna. The wavelength λ of the radar signal does not appear explicitly in this expression, but it can be introduced by the relationship between the gain and effective receiving area of an antenna which states $G = 4\pi A/\lambda^2$.

The detection capability and the measurement accuracy of a radar are ultimately limited by noise. The noise may be generated within the radar receiver itself, or it may be external and enter the receiver via the antenna along with the desired signal. External noise is generally small at microwave frequencies, but it can be a significant part of the overall noise if low-noise receiving devices such as the MASER and the parametric amplifier are used (see MEASUREMENTS, PRINCIPLES OF).

Since the effects of noise must be considered in statistical terms, the analysis and understanding of the basic properties of radar have benefited from the application of the mathematical theory of statistics. The statistical theory of hypothesis testing has been applied to the radar detection problem where it is necessary to determine which of two hypotheses is correct: the output of a radar receiver is due to (1) noise alone or (2) signal plus noise. One of the results is the quantitative specification of the signal-to-noise ratio required at the receiver for reliable detection. Also derived from hypothesis testing based on the likelihood ratio or *a posteriori* probability are concepts for ideal detection methods with which to compare the performance of practical receivers. The statistical theory of parameter estimation has also been applied with success to analyze the accuracy and theoretical limits of radar measurements.

Reliable detection of targets requires signal-to-noise power ratios of the order of 10 to 100 at the receiver, depending on the degree of error that can be tolerated in making the decision as to the presence or absence of a target. Even larger values are generally needed for the accurate measurement of target parameters. (These values may seem surprisingly high but, for comparison, the minimum signal-to-noise ratio of quality television signals is usually of the order of 10 000.)

The rms error δT in measuring the time delay to the target and back (the range measurement) can be expressed as

$$\delta T = \frac{1}{\beta\sqrt{2E/N_0}}$$

where β is defined as the effective signal bandwidth, E is the total energy of the received signal, and N_0 is the noise power per unit cycle of bandwidth assuming the noise has a uniform spectrum over the bandwidth of the receiver. The square of β is equal to $(2\pi)^2$ times the second central moment of the power spectrum normalized with respect to the signal energy. For a simple rectangular pulse, E/N_0 is approximately equal to the signal-to-noise (power) ratio. To obtain an accurate range measurement, E/N_0 and the signal bandwidth must be large. A similar expression applies to the accuracy of the measurement of Doppler frequency if the rms time delay error is replaced by the rms frequency error and the effective bandwidth is replaced by the effective time duration of the signal. Thus, the longer the signal duration and the greater the ratio E/N_0, the more accurate is the Doppler frequency measurement. Likewise the angular measurement accuracy also depends on the ratio E/N_0 and the effective aperture size.

In addition to noise, radar can be limited by the presence of unwanted interfering echoes from large nearby objects such as the surface of the ground, trees, vegetation, sea waves, and weather. Although these "clutter" echoes may be troublesome in some applications, they are sometimes the echoes of interest as, for example, in ground mapping and meteorological applications.

Radar comes in many sizes and shapes. The smallest can be held in the hand and might radiate as little as a few milliwatts and be used to detect the movement of people at short range. The largest might radiate megawatts of average power and operate with antennas the size of a football field and would be used for the detection of space objects at ranges of many thousands of miles or more.

MERRILL I. SKOLNIK

References

Ridenour, L. N., "Radar System Engineering," MIT Radiation Laboratory Series, Vol. 1, New York, McGraw-Hill Book Co., 1947.

Skolnik, M. I., "Radar Handbook," New York, McGraw-Hill Book Co., 1970.

Nathanson, F., "Radar Signal Processing and the Environment," New York, McGraw-Hill Book Co., 1969.

Barton, D. K., "Radar System Analysis," Englewood Cliffs, N.J., Prentice-Hall, Inc., 1964.

Barton, D. K., and Ward, H. R., "Handbook of Radar Measurement," Englewood Cliffs, N.J., Prentice-Hall, Inc., 1969.

Skolnik, M. I., "Introduction to Radar Systems," New York, McGraw-Hill Book Co., 1962.

Cross-references: ANTENNAS; DOPPLER EFFECT; LASER; MASER; MEASUREMENTS, PRINCIPLES OF; MICROWAVE TRANSMISSION; PROPAGATION OF ELECTROMAGNETIC WAVES.

RADIATION BELTS

The first U.S. satellite Explorer I in 1958 carried Geiger counters designed by Van Allen of Iowa. This instrument discovered the high flux of energetic charged particles trapped in the magnetic field of the earth now called the Van Allen radiation belt. We now know that this belt is made up of high-energy protons and electrons put into the magnetic field from several different sources. The particles travel in helical paths along field lines bouncing back and forth from one hemisphere to the other. The fact that the field lines converge towards the earth produces a force on the particle of $F = evB_\perp$ where $B_\perp$ is the component of the magnetic field perpendicular to the field lines. This force pushes the particle out of the region of converging field and produces the bouncing motion. Without this bouncing motion, radiation belts would not exist. Other forces such as the centrifugal force on a particle moving along a curved field line make the particle drift in longitude around the earth. This combination of motions makes a roughly spherical belt of particles around the earth. The particles are not observed below about 500 km altitude. The fact that the earth's magnetic field is not symmetric but is weaker in the South Atlantic means the trapped particles are observed at lower altitudes there. The absence of trapped particles at low altitudes is clearly due to the presence of the atmosphere. The particles are lost very rapidly below this by coulomb scattering and energy loss to the thermal atmospheric atoms.

In 1959, Freden and White flew nuclear emulsions on an Atlas rocket, recovered them, and measured the tracks to show that the most energetic particles in the inner part of the radiation belt were protons with energies up to at least 700 MeV. This particle population stays constant for long periods of time with a maximum flux of about 10^4 cm^{-2} sec^{-1}. We understand well how these high-energy protons are made. Very high-energy cosmic rays from space bombard the earth's atmosphere, collide with nitrogen or oxygen nuclei, and produce neutrons. Some of these neutrons emerge from the top of the atmosphere and, being radioactive, decay in space, producing protons and electrons. A quantitative study of these neutron-decay protons shows they have all the right properties to be the source of the observed protons from 10 MeV up.

The radiation belt extends out to about 10 earth radii and then stops abruptly. This outer edge is caused by the action of the sun on the earth. The solar corona is very hot and is unstable. Because of this, the sun continuously blows a wind of protons and electrons at the earth with a velocity of about 400 km/sec. This plasma pushes in the geomagnetic field until the solar wind pressure is balanced by $B^2/8\pi$, the pressure of the distorted geomagnetic field pushing outwards. Thus a boundary, called the magnetopause, exists between the solar environment and the geomagnetic field. Only inside the cavity, called the magnetosphere, occupied by the earth's field can trapped particles exist. The low energy trapped electrons found inside the magnetosphere have similar energies and flux to those outside, suggesting that the boundary is leaky and the electrons somehow diffuse in across the boundary.

Upstream of the magnetopause is a shock wave. When the highspeed solar wind encounters the magnetosphere, it acts like an obstacle and forms a detached shock like that ahead of a supersonic jet aircraft. The solar wind is thermalized behind this shock, and electrons are energized in this region. These electrons are outside the magnetosphere and are not trapped.

The magnetic field of the earth is pulled out in the antisolar direction to form a tail somewhat like a comet reaching out several hundred earth radii behind the earth. Near the middle of this tail is a nearly neutral sheet where the magnetic field is very small. Below this sheet the field lines point away from the earth, and above the sheet they point toward the earth. Figure 1 shows a north-south slice through the magnetosphere, earth, and radiation belt.

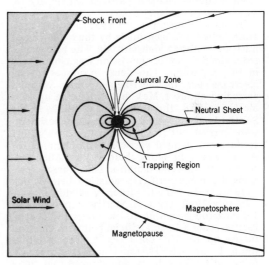

FIG. 1

We know that auroras are made mostly by energetic electrons striking the upper atmosphere. There is clearly a relationship between auroras and the trapped electrons found in the outer part of the radiation belt. They seem to be made by the same process (see AURORA AND AIRGLOW).

A large population of protons of about 10^8 cm^{-2} sec^{-1} is found in the outer part of the magnetosphere. They have energies of the order of 1 MeV. The protons have systematically

higher energies closer to the earth as would be expected if they were drifting inwards and being accelerated by the increasing magnetic field as th'ey go. A varying intensity solar wind can change the size of the magnetosphere, and as a result, a series of changes magnetically pump these particles inward to give the observed properties of the protons.

Magnetic storms occur at the earth usually a day or so after a disturbance at the sun. The solar wind, strengthened by the disturbance, pushes against the geomagnetic field and increases this field at the surface of the earth. Then, during the main phase of a magnetic storm, the magnetic field at the earth is decreased. This is due to a very large number of low-energy particles that have been introduced into the magnetosphere for a few days, and then lost probably by charge exchange. These particles have been observed by satellite detectors, and it is now known that they are mostly protons of a few keV energy.

Probably all of the important components of the radiation belt have been found now. However, we still have major uncertainties about some of the processes that accelerate particles or put them inside the radiation belt or cause them to be lost. A considerable amount has been learned about the natural Van Allen belt from studying charged particles artificially injected into the magnetosphere.

On seven occasions since 1958, artificial radiation belts have been made by the explosion of nuclear bombs at high altitude. The belt results from the β decay of the fission fragments made in the explosion. The decay produces several electrons per fission fragment with energies averaging about 1 MeV but extending up to 8 MeV. In 1958, three nuclear explosions in the South Atlantic, called the Argus experiment, were carried out to show that the earth's field could store charged particles. The planning for Argus was well along before Van Allen discovered the natural radiation belt. These explosions did make artificial radiation belts which were studied by the Explorer IV satellite.

In July 1962, the U.S. Starfish explosion of a 1.4-megaton bomb at 400 km over the central Pacific made a large artificial belt with electron fluxes up to 10^9 cm^{-2} sec^{-1}. The satellites Injun I and III, Telstar I and Explorer XV followed the belt decay and showed that there are two different processes acting to remove the electrons. Below about 3000 km altitude, the electrons are lost mostly by coulomb scattering on the nuclei of the air atoms present, changing their direction of motion and diffusing down magnetic field lines into the atmosphere. An electron at 2000 km lives roughly a year before being lost this way. At higher altitudes, the electrons are lost faster than this. Three Soviet high altitude explosions in the fall of 1962 produced artificial belts that decayed similarly to the Starfish belt. At 10 000 km altitude, the electron lifetime is just a few days. It seems probable that the electrons are lost here by interacting with electromagnetic waves, called whistlers. These waves are circularly polarized waves traveling along field lines. When the particle's gyration frequency resonates with the whistler wave frequency, the interaction can disturb the particle's motion and scatter it out of the trapping region.

We have some knowledge of radiation belts on other planets besides the earth. The Mariner space craft went within 40 000 km of Venus. It did not find a measurable planetary magnetic field or any trapped radiation belt. This does not necessarily mean that Venus does not have one at all. It does mean that if a magnetosphere filled with trapped particles exists on Venus, it must be quite small in size. Radio waves received from Jupiter, identified as synchrotron radiation from electrons gyrating around magnetic field lines, show that Jupiter has a trapped radiation belt. It must have considerably more high-energy trapped electrons than the earth's belt has because we haven't been able to observe synchrotron radiation from the natural Van Allen belt.

WILMOT N. HESS

Cross-references: ELECTRON, GEOPHYSICS, IONOSPHERE, PLANETARY ATMOSPHERES, PROTON, SPACE PHYSICS.

RADIATION CHEMISTRY

Radiation chemistry is the study of the chemical effects produced by the absorption of ionizing radiation. It includes chemical effects produced by the absorption of radiation from radioactive nuclei (α, β, and γ rays), of high-energy particles (electrons, protons, neutrons, recoil nuclei, etc.), and of electromagnetic radiation of short wavelength (x-rays with a wavelength less than about 100Å and an energy greater than about 100 eV, for example). Electromagnetic radiation of rather longer wavelength, in the ultraviolet and visible regions of the spectrum, may also initiate chemical reactions, though normally without producing ions as reactive intermediates; such reactions are the province of photochemistry. Reactions chemically similar to those caused by the absorption of ionizing radiation can be initiated by electric discharges; others, initiated in various ways, occur in the upper atmosphere.

Radiation chemistry originated with the observations by Röentgen (1895) and by Becquerel (1896) that led to the discovery of x-rays and of radioactivity, namely that photographic plates become fogged when placed near discharge tubes and uranium salts respectively. The subject was studied to only a limited extent until about 1942, when the advent of nuclear reactors and the increased interest in high-energy physics provided both the incentive and the means (in the form of relatively cheap artificial radioactive isotopes and of large particle accelerators) for

a more intensive study. In the following two decades, earlier work was consolidated and the basic mechanisms for radiation-induced action were established in outline, making possible an extremely rapid development of the subject since about 1960.

Absorption of any form of ionizing radiation by matter (A) produces positive ions (A^+), electrons (e^-), and electronically excited atoms or molecules (A^*) distributed along the tracks of charged particles. The charged particles may be those which comprise the radiation (e.g., electrons or helium nuclei with fast electron or α-irradiation) or secondary particles produced by interactions of the primary radiation (e.g., fast secondary electrons formed by the absorption

photochemistry, where excited molecules are produced with an essentially uniform distribution in any plane at right angles to the direction of the beam of light. The excited molecules involved in radiation chemistry include excited states similar to those formed by the absorption of ultraviolet or visible light and also other states, formed by optically forbidden transitions or with more intrinsic energy, that are not produced photochemically.

Chemical changes in the irradiated material are brought about by breakdown or reaction of the ions and excited molecules and via free radicals formed by these primary species. The sequence of events in many radiation-induced (radiolysis) reactions may be represented as:

$$A \xrightarrow{\text{irradiation}} \begin{Bmatrix} A^* \\ A^+ \\ e^- \end{Bmatrix} \longrightarrow \text{free radicals} \longrightarrow \text{chemical products}$$

A
(original molecules)

free radicals
(including e^-_{solv} in polar media)

chemical products

Approximate interval after passage of ionizing particle 10^{-15} 10^{-11} 10^{-3} sec

of x- or γ-rays, or fast protons produced by interaction of neutrons with hydrogenous materials). In addition, some of the electrons produced by ionization in the medium will have sufficient energy to produce further ionization and excitation, and will do so in slowing down to thermal energy (such electrons are known as δ-rays). Except in gases, where the ions and excited molecules can diffuse apart quite readily, these primary species are initially concentrated within about 10Å of the track of the ionizing particle. Heavy charged particles (protons and, particularly, helium nuclei and heavier particles) lose energy very rapidly in liquids and solids and leave a track densely populated with the primary species; radiations of this type are said to have a "high LET," where LET stands for linear energy transfer. In contrast, fast electrons and the secondary electrons produced by the absorption of x- and γ-rays lose energy relatively slowly and form the primary species (which are the same as those produced by the heavier particles) in small groups containing, on an average, two or three ion pairs and about the same number of excited molecules. These groups (called *spurs*), with an initial diameter of ~ 20Å, are separated by a relatively great distance (~ 10^3Å) from neighboring spurs along the same track, and the radiation responsible is said to have a "low LET." However, the spurs along an electron track become closer together as the electron loses energy, and eventually overlap each other. The initial localization of the ions and excited molecules in the track of a high-LET particle or in spurs produced by a low-LET particle causes spatial, or track, effects in radiation-induced reactions which are absent in

Electronically excited molecules and ions are produced by passage of an ionizing particle. The excited molecules may return to the ground state without producing chemical change, dissociate to free radicals, or dissociate directly to stable chemical products. Positive ions also give rise to free radicals or stable products by dissociation, reaction with the substrate (in ion-molecule reactions), or upon neutralization by an electron. In polar media the neutralization may be delayed by solvation (association of the ion with a group of solvent molecules held by electrostatic forces), and the solvated ions, particularly the solvated electron, may react in a similar manner to free radicals. The events outlined above are often considered to occur in three stages: a *physical stage* lasting about 10^{-14} sec corresponding with the initial dissipation of energy in the system; a *physiochemical stage* lasting from ~ 10^{-14} to ~ 10^{-10} sec during which thermal equilibrium is established, dissociation of excited molecules and positive ions occurs, and (in polar media) ions become solvated; and a *chemical stage* lasting about 10^{-3} sec during which radical reactions occur and give rise to chemically stable molecules. Processes occurring during the late physiochemical and the chemical stages can sometimes be observed directly by absorption spectroscopy following a brief radiation pulse. This technique, known as *pulse radiolysis*, is routinely used to investigate reactions occurring microseconds after the radiation pulse and is currently being extended into the nanosecond and picosecond regions.

Free radicals, which are formed when most materials except metals are irradiated, are atoms

or molecules which have unpaired valence electrons; the solvated electron behaves like, and is often described as, a free radical. Free radicals are generally chemically unstable species and react rapidly in such a manner that the unpaired electrons become paired, for example by combination of two free radicals (shown below with a · to represent the unpaired electron)

$$2 \cdot OH \longrightarrow HO-OH \text{ (or } H_2O_2)$$

or transfer of an atom (disproportionation)

$$CH_3CH_2 \cdot + \cdot CH_2CH_3 \longrightarrow$$
$$CH_3-CH_3 + CH_2=CH_2$$

or an electron

$$\cdot OH + Fe^{2+} \longrightarrow OH^- + Fe^{3+}.$$

Other common radical reactions are addition to oxygen and doubly bonded (unsaturated) compounds and abstraction of hydrogen or halogen atoms from compounds, e.g.,

$$e_{aq}^- + O_2 \longrightarrow O_2^-$$
$$\cdot CH_3 + CH_2=CH_2 \longrightarrow CH_3-CH_2-CH_2 \cdot$$
$$H \cdot + CCl_4 \longrightarrow HCl + \cdot CCl_3.$$

These reactions do not result in electron pairing but instead give rise to less reactive (more stable) radicals. Many free radicals have been identified in irradiated systems by pulse radiolysis, and in solid or frozen systems, by electron spin resonance.

Quantitative studies in radiation chemistry are based either on the number of ions (N) formed in the irradiated medium or on the energy absorbed from the radiation. Ionization measurements in irradiated gases allow N to be estimated, and radiation yields in gases are best expressed as the *ionic* (or *ion-pair*) *yield*, M/N, where M is the number of molecules of product formed by radiation which produces N ion pairs. Reliable estimates of N are, at present, only available for gaseous systems, and for condensed materials it is usual to express the radiolysis yield as a G value (the number of molecules of product formed, or of starting material changed, per 100 eV of energy absorbed). Ionic yields and G values are related by $G = M/N \times 100/W$, where W (electron volts) is the mean energy required to form an ion pair in the material being irradiated. The determination of N, or of the energy absorbed, is termed "dosimetry" and may involve ionization measurements, calorimetry, measurement of the charge carried by a beam of charged particles of known energy, or measurement of a chemical change produced by irradiation [the oxidation of ferrous iron to ferric iron in 0.4 M sulfuric acid solution is often used (Fricke dosimeter)]. However, chemical dosimeters must first be calibrated against some absolute physical measurement. The energy absorbed by an irradiated system is generally expressed in units of *rads* (1 rad is an energy absorption of 100 ergs g^{-1}) or of eV g^{-1} or eV ml^{-1}.

Radiation-induced reactions have been studied in the gas, liquid and solid phases and in inorganic, organic, and biological systems. They have also been studied over a wide range of temperatures.

Most thoroughly studied of all radiation-induced reactions is the radiolysis of water and aqueous solutions, where the following have been identified as the major products formed in the tracks or spurs: hydrogen (H_2), hydrogen peroxide (H_2O_2), hydrogen atoms ($H \cdot$), hydroxyl radicals ($\cdot OH$), and solvated, or hydrated, electrons (e_{aq}^-). These products are thought to be formed by the primary species, H_2O^+, e^-, and H_2O^*, and, in the case of hydrogen and hydrogen peroxide, by $H \cdot$, $\cdot OH$, and e_{aq}^-. Relatively more hydrogen and hydrogen peroxide are formed in the track of a high-LET α-particle [$G(H_2) \sim 1.57$, $G(H_2O_2) \sim 1.45$] than in the spurs associated with a high-energy, low-LET, electron [$G(H_2) \sim 0.40$, $G(H_2O_2) \sim 0.80$] since the concentration of the precursors is greater in the track than in the spurs. However, relatively more of the other products ($H \cdot$, $\cdot OH$, and e_{aq}^-) escape from the spurs [G(radical) ~ 6.5] than from the α-particle track [G(radical) ~ 1.2]. These three species are free radicals and react very readily with substances present in solution, the hydroxyl radical generally producing oxidation, and the hydrogen atom and the solvated electron producing reduction, of the solute if the solution is free of air. Both the hydrogen atom and the solvated electron react rapidly with oxygen to give oxidizing species, so that oxidation reactions predominate when aerated aqueous solutions are irradiated. In acid solutions, solvated electrons are rapidly converted to hydrogen atoms ($H \cdot$) by reaction with hydrogen ions (H^+).

Many organic materials have been irradiated and, making a very rough generalization, the products are those expected if the action of the radiation is to break the organic molecules randomly into two fragments (free radicals). The fragments then react together in pairs, again in a random fashion, either combining to form larger molecules or transferring an atom from one fragment to the other to give two stable molecules. The products from a hydrocarbon, for example, include hydrogen and hydrocarbons ranging in size from methane (CH_4) to compounds containing twice as many carbon atoms as the original compound; unsaturated materials, containing relatively less hydrogen than the original compound, will also be formed. Hexane, $CH_3-(CH_2)_4-CH_3$, forms at least 16 products upon irradiation, of which the two most abundant are hydrogen ($G = 5.0$) and dimeric C_{12} hydrocarbons ($G = 2.0$); the remaining products are formed with G values of 0.5 or less. More complex compounds may break preferentially (though generally not ex-

clusively) at a particular point in the molecule; thus the carbon-iodine bond breaks most frequently when methyl iodide CH_3I is irradiated. Some classes of compound can enter into chain reactions in which the reaction, once started, continues on its own. Typical of such substances are the unsaturated "monomers" which polymerize to produce polymers such as polymethyl methacrylate ("Lucite") and polyvinyl chloride (PVC). The chain reactions here are initiated by free radicals, and other means of producing free radicals besides irradiation bring about the same effect. G values for chain reactions may run from a few hundred to many thousands.

Aromatic compounds such as benzene are more resistant to radiation than most compounds lacking the "benzene" ring. Thus $G(H_2)$ from liquid benzene is only 0.036, and the total yield of radiolysis products does not exceed $G = 1$. In favorable instances, aromatic compounds can reduce the radiation damage in non-aromatic compounds mixed with them, energy absorbed by the second component being transferred in part to the "protecting" aromatic compound.

Apart from its intrinsic interest, the importance of radiation chemistry until the present time has rested largely upon its application to problems of reactor technology and its close relationship to radiation biology and radiation medicine. Recently, however, several industrial applications have been realized, e.g., the treatment of polyethylene to produce a higher-melting polymer and the synthesis of ethyl bromide via a radiation-induced chain reaction between ethylene and hydrogen bromide. Other commercial applications will undoubtedly follow, probably depending for their success on the special properties of high-energy radiation since it seems unlikely that high-energy radiation will ever be a very cheap means of introducing energy into a chemical system.

J. W. T. SPINKS
R. J. WOODS

References

Spinks, J. W. T., and Woods, R. J., "An Introduction to Radiation Chemistry," New York, John Wiley & Sons, 1964.

O'Donnell, J. H., and Sangster, D. F., "Principles of Radiation Chemistry," London, Edward Arnold Ltd., 1970.

Ausloos, P., Ed., "Fundamental Processes in Radiation Chemistry," New York, Interscience, 1968.

Matheson, M. S., and Dorfman, L. M., "Pulse Radiolysis," Cambridge, Mass., M.I.T. Press, 1969.

Attix, F. H., Roesch, W. C., and Tochilin, E., Eds., "Radiation Dosimetry," Second Edition, New York, Academic Press, 1966.

Ebert, M., Keene, J. P., Swallow, A. J., and Baxendale, J. H., Eds., "Pulse Radiolysis," New York, Academic Press, 1965.

Hart, E. J., and Anbar, M., "The Hydrated Electron," New York, Wiley-Interscience, 1970.

Lind, S. C., "Radiation Chemistry of Gases," New York, Van Nostrand Reinhold, 1961.

Allen, A. O., "The Radiation Chemistry of Water and Aqueous Solutions," New York, Van Nostrand Reinhold, 1961.

Swallow, A. J., "Radiation Chemistry of Organic Compounds," New York, Pergamon Press, 1960.

Charlesby, A., "Atomic Radiation and Polymers," New York, Pergamon Press, 1960.

Chapiro, A., "Radiation Chemistry of Polymeric Systems," New York, Interscience Publishers, 1962.

Haissinsku, M., Ed., "Actions Chimiques et Biologiques des Radiations," Vol. 1, Paris, Masson et Cie., 1955, and succeeding volumes.

Review articles in *Ann. Rev. Phys. Chem.*, **1** (1950) and succeeding volumes.

Burton, M., and Magee, J. L., Eds., "Advances in Radiation Chemistry," Vol. 1, New York, Wiley-Interscience, 1969 and succeeding volumes.

Cross-references: IONIZATION; MAGNETIC RESONANCE; PHOTOCHEMISTRY; RADIATION, IONIZING, BASIC INTERACTIONS; SECONDARY EMISSION.

RADIATION, IONIZING, BASIC INTERACTIONS*

Radiations of a large class, called ionizing, which interact with matter in its many forms and lead to a wide variety of "observed" or expressed effects have similar basic interaction pathways. Sources of ionizing radiations are varied and include radioactive isotopes, fission and fusion reactions, particle accelerators, and cosmic rays. Regardless of the source of any given radiation (applied to a given target), the basic interaction depends only upon the fundamental properties of the radiation itself.

Ionizing Radiations The principal ionizing radiations are summarized in Table 1. Although only the gamma or x-rays are electromagnetic in character and thus "radiations" in the classical sense, the distinction between "radiations" and ionizing "particles" is often not made (x-rays are distinguished from gamma rays only with respect to their origins; gamma rays result from nuclear interactions or decays; x-rays result from transitions of atomic or free electrons, produced artificially by bombarding metallic targets with energetic electrons). It is sometimes difficult to make a clear distinction between ionizing and nonionizing electromagnetic radiations, particularly in condensed phases. The ionization potential of *gaseous* elements i.e., the energy required for removal of the first electron, varies from 3.9 eV (Cs) to 24.6 eV (He). Comparable values are not well known for most complicated molecular systems or liquid- and solid-state systems,

---

*Editor was unable to locate author. Article is reprinted from first edition.

TABLE 1

Name	Symbol	Location in Atom	Relative Rest Mass	Charge
Proton (H^1)$^+$	p	Nucleus	1	+1
Neutron	n	Nucleus	1	0
Electron	e	Outer shells	0.00055	−1
Beta− (electron)	β	Emmitted during decay processes	0.00055	−1
Beta$^+$ (positron)	β^+		0.00055	+1
Alpha (He^4)$^{++}$	α		4	+2
Gamma^a (photon)	γ	Emitted during decay processes	0.0	0

^{a}X-rays of equal energy are identical, but of extranuclear origin.

but they are probably in or near this general range. Although ultraviolet and even visible light can in special cases cause ionizations, the general assumption is that more energetic x- or gamma radiation is required to insure ionization. Hence the name "ionizing radiation" is reserved for electromagnetic radiation at least as energetic as x-rays and for charged particles of similar energies. Neutrons also lead to ionization, but for other reasons, described below. *Ionization* is, of course, not the sole interaction of high-energy particles and radiations with matter. The *excitation* of atomic electrons into higher-energy states always accompanies ionization.

Basic Action The fundamental processes leading to ionization differ for charged particles, electromagnetic radiations, and neutrons.

Charged Particles. Fast charged particles are produced in radioactive decay processes, particle accelerators, nuclear reactions, and extraterrestrial sources. They undergo *coulombic* and *nuclear* interactions. The latter are far less probable and are discussed in other parts of this encyclopedia (see NUCLEAR REACTIONS). There are two principal means whereby charged particles can lose energy by coulomb interaction: radiative loss and direct ionization. The probability of radiative energy loss (BREMSSTRAHLUNG) is roughly proportional to

$$\frac{z^2 Z^2 T}{M_0{}^2}$$

where z is the particle charge in units of the electron charge e, Z is the atomic number of the target material, T is the particle kinetic energy, and M_0 is the rest mass of the particle. The ratio of energy lost by bremsstrahlung to that by ionization can be approximated by

$$\left(\frac{m_0}{M_0}\right)^2 \frac{ZT}{1600 \, m_0 c^2}$$

in which m_0 is the rest mass of the electron and c^2 is the speed of light squared, or 931 MeV per atomic mass unit. Electrons in the 10-MeV region lose about half of their energy by bremsstrahlung (in high-Z material), whereas heavier charged particles lose nearly all of their energy by ionization.

Loss of energy by ionization results when the particle undergoes coulomb collision with the *electrons* of the target. From the ratio of total energy lost to the number of ion pairs produced in cloud chambers (see Fig. 1), it has been estimated that approximately 100 eV are dissipated in each *primary ionization event* and that each event results in the production of, on the average, three ion pairs, each consisting of a free electron and a positive ion. If a resulting electron carries more than a certain amount (usually considered to be about 100 eV) of kinetic energy, it is called a *delta ray*, because it is capable of further ionizations. "Delta ray" and "track core" ionizations are depicted in Fig. 1. The experimentally determined energy required to produce each *observed* ion pair lies in the range of 20 to 40 eV per ion pair for gases. A figure in the neighborhood of 30 eV per ion pair is commonly assumed for condensed phases of matter. This value is called "W" and is generally slightly different for electrons and heavy particles in the same material.

On the basis of coulomb scattering theory, it is possible to calculate the energy loss per unit path length ($-dT/dx$) for charged particles. For electrons and positrons the theory is complicated by the quantum mechanical effects of spin, identity, and relativity. In general, the *total* expectation energy loss per unit path length (also termed *mass stopping power* when path length is expressed in grams per square centimeter) for electrons and positrons can be expressed by

$$-\frac{dT}{dx} = \frac{2\pi e^4}{m_0 V^2} NZ \left\{ \ln\left[\frac{m_0 V^2 T}{2I^2(1-\beta^2)}\right] - \beta^2 \right\}$$

IONIZATION BY DELTA RAYS

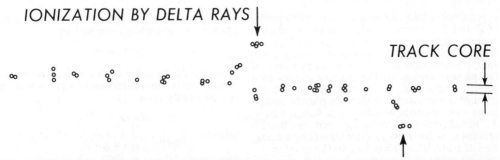

FIG. 1. Schematic drawing of a cloud-chamber photograph of the track of an ionizing particle, illustrating that ion pairs (illustrated by small circles) occur in clusters. Spurs indicated by arrows are ionizations due to *delta rays*. The arbitrary identification of the *track core* is also indicated.

in which V is the particle velocity, beta is V/c, N is the number of atoms per unit mass, and I is the geometric mean ionization and excitation energy of the atoms of the target material. Classical theory is more adequate in describing the loss of energy by heavy charged particles, and the mass stopping power is determined from

$$-\frac{dT}{dx} = \frac{4\pi e^4 z^2}{m_0 V^2} NB$$

where B is called the *stopping number* and assumes various forms, some examples of which are

$$B = Z \ln \frac{2m_0 V^2}{I}$$

for nonrelativistic particles in material of low Z;

$$B = Z \left[\ln \frac{2m_0 V^2}{I} - \ln(1 - \beta^2) - \beta^2 \right]$$

for relativistic particles in materials of low Z; and

$$B = Z \left[\ln \frac{2m_0 V^2}{I} - \ln(1 - \beta^2) - \beta^2 - \frac{C_K}{Z} \right]$$

for relativistic particles in material of high Z, in which C_K is a term which corrects for the relative unavailability of K electrons for coulomb interactions. Corrections for L and M electrons may be required for very high-Z material.

Instead of stopping power, the term *linear energy transfer* (LET) is frequently used. The two quantities are not strictly interconvertible, according to a recent decision by the international committee on radiation units (see *National Bureau of Standards* (*U.S.*) *Handbook* 84). Mass stopping power should be used only in the sense described above, whereas LET should be used only for energy lost by the particle within a specified distance of the track core. (Stopping power is usually expressed in units of million electron volts per gram per square centimeter, and LET in units of kiloelectron volts per micron.) These are both measures of linear *density of ionization* in the target material.

From the above equations, it is possible to derive range-energy relationships for charged particles by simple integration. Theoretical and experimental range-energy curves are now available in the literature for nearly all charged particles.

Electromagnetic Radiation (X, gamma). For fast, charged particles interacting with matter we had, above, relations of the form

$$-\frac{dT}{dx} \propto \frac{(\text{charge})^2}{(\text{velocity})^2}$$

If it were permissible to extend this idea to electromagnetic radiation, one might expect photons with no charge (and with the velocity of light) not to ionize at all. They indeed do ionize sparsely though for different reasons. The three principal mechanisms of interaction can be summarized as follows:

(1) Photoelectric effect. Low-energy photons can give up all their energy to a bound electron, forming an ion pair and disappearing in the process. (Generally unimportant above 1 MeV.)

(2) Compton scattering. For medium-energy photons (0.5 to 5 MeV), this elastic collision process predominates, leading to ejection of a recoil electron plus the partially degraded (longer-wavelength) photon.

(3) Pair production. Photons of highest energy most often interact by forming an electron-positron pair in the field of a nucleus and disappearing in the process. The absolute energy threshold for this process is the rest mass energy of the pair: 1.02 MeV.

The net result of all three processes is the formation of (charged) ion pairs and in particular of electrons having energies ranging up to the photon energy but on the average only a fraction of this maximum. The discussion on charged particles thus applies to x- or gamma-ray action also. Each of these processes will now be considered in more detail.

In the *photoelectric process*, the photon collides directly with an atomic electron, imparting kinetic energy

$$T = h\nu - B_e$$

where B_e is the atomic binding energy of the electron and $h\nu$ is the photon energy. For a considerable range of photon energies and target material Z's, the probability of this process is

approximately dependent upon the fourth power of Z and the inverse third power of the photon energy. There are, however, very specific energies at which photoelectric absorption is very probable ("absorption edges"), due to nearness of the photon energy to the binding energy of a specific electron (K, L, M, etc.). The probability per unit thickness of absorber of a photon undergoing photoelectric absorption is denoted by τ. An initial photon intensity I_0 is reduced by this process to an intensity I_x after traversing a thickness of material, x, according to the relation

$$I_x/I_0 = e^{-\tau x}$$

The *Compton process* differs from the photoelectric process in two important ways: the photon usually loses less than all of its energy to the electron with which it collides, giving rise to a lower-energy scattered photon, and the process may occur with a free or loosely bound electron. Momentum and energy are conserved according to the laws of classical mechanics, and the energetics can be described by

$$h\nu = h\nu' + (m - m_0)c^2$$

where $h\nu'$ is the energy of the secondary photon, and $(m - m_0)c^2$ is the kinetic energy of the recoil electron (expressed in terms of the relativistic mass increase). At high photon energies, the collision probabilities are governed by the laws of quantum mechanics. Photons are lost by the Compton process according to the relation

$$I_x/I_0 = e^{-\sigma x}$$

where σ is the absorption probability per unit thickness.

If the energy of the photon is greater than two electron masses (1.02 MeV), there is a finite probability that it will interact with the nuclear field giving rise to electron-positron *pair production*. In pair production, energy is conserved according to

$$h\nu - 2m_0c^2 = T_+ + T_-$$

where T_+ and T_- are the positron and electron kinetic energies, respectively. The positive electron is ultimately annihilated by a negative electron, and the masses of both are converted into photons with energies distributed about 0.51 MeV (one electron mass each). Very high-energy electron-positron pairs may, in turn, produce further photons by bremsstrahlung, initiating a sequence of photon-electron-photon, etc., interactions, known as a *cascade*. (If the photon energy is greater than four electron masses, pair production may occur in the field of an electron, under which condition the original electron is set in motion, and the process is called "triplet production.") The probability of pair production increases very rapidly with increasing photon energy above 1.02 MeV and increases as Z^2, the square of the atomic number of the target material. The absorption probability per unit

thickness is denoted by κ, so that high-energy photons are absorbed according to

$$I_x/I_0 = e^{-\kappa x}$$

It is usually desirable to know the *total* photon absorption per unit thickness of a given material, so one simply states

$$I_x/I_0 = e^{-\mu x}$$

where

$$\mu = \tau + \sigma + \kappa.$$

μ is called the "total linear absorption coefficient" and is expressed in units reciprocal to those in which x is measured.

Neutrons. Because of their lack of charge, neutrons do not interact electrostatically either with orbital electrons or with nuclei. They do interact with nuclei, however, in various other ways.

Fast neutrons (up to a few MeV) lose energy primarily by elastic collisions with other nuclei. From considerations of momentum transfer, this process is most efficient for target nuclei of about the same mass (i.e., protons in hydrogenous materials), though other light nuclei are also effective. On the *average*, about half the initial neutron kinetic energy is transferred to the protons, so that fast-neutron bombardment looks (to a hydrogenous material) like bombardment with fast protons of half the neutron energy. In addition to such simple collision processes, fast neutrons also induce nuclear reactions in certain elements, leading to emission of particles or photons with their previously described interactions.

After about 20 collisions, neutrons are no longer sufficiently energetic to eject recoil protons but have become "thermalized," i.e., they act (for a short time) like a gas in thermal equilibrium with its surroundings (energies of about 1/40 eV).

When a neutron has become thermalized and wanders into a nucleus, it is quite often captured, momentarily yielding an excited isotope of the original nucleus. Nuclei usually lose their excitation by emission of particles or characteristic gamma rays. Thus, even an uncharged slow neutron gives rise to the release of ionizing radiation inside a material being irradiated. In living tissue, slow neutrons commonly are captured by H^1 nuclei with emission of an energetic gamma ray, and by N^{14} nuclei with emission of an energetic proton.

Associated or Post-ionization Events Subsequent to the primary and secondary molecular ionizations (and excitations), a number of events can occur that depend rather strongly on the form of the target material, including

(1) dissociation of molecules and formation of free radicals (species with unpaired electrons, hence great chemical reactivity, e.g., in water, H, OH, HO_2);

(2) recombination of ions and radicals, leading to no net change;

(3) dispersion of energetic ions and radicals, and reaction with other species present or with each other;

(4) nondiffusion migration of electronic excitation to energy "sinks," e.g., in macro-molecules or crystals; and

(5) eventual degradation of the excess absorbed energy to heat (insignificant from the standpoint of effects).

For many systems the basic interactions must be considered only the initiators of a complex sequence of later events.

Comparison of the Radiations Diverse electromagnetic and particulate radiations thus have in common as their basic interaction (or closely following upon it) the production of molecular ionizations (and excitations, dissociations, free radicals) inside target matter. They differ in the *geometry* of these events (especially in LET), a difference that leads to wide variations in range or penetrating ability and, thus, in the subsequent reactions leading to the final expression of the radiation effect.

The slower, more highly charged, heavy particles (such as alphas) travel in straight-line tracks ionizing densely along the track and exhibiting discrete ranges characteristic of the particle energy. Lighter, less highly charged particles such as electrons have their tracks more easily deflected and therefore have less precisely specified ranges in matter (although they have a maximum range). With a lower ionization density, however, they travel much farther than heavy charged particles of the same energy. Gamma or x-rays interact causing release of electrons in matter but at widely spaced intervals and in a random fashion; they have a still lower ionization density (LET) and much longer "range." (Since the resultant of all their absorption processes is a roughly exponential attenuation in matter, their "range" must be described in terms of a parameter such as "half thickness," $x_{1/2}$, the thickness of material that reduces incident intensity to 50 per cent. The relation $x_{1/2} = 0.693/\mu$ is seen to follow from the above equation for total photon absorption.) X-ray interaction has been likened to a "shotgun" effect in contrast to the "rifle" effect from incident heavy charged particles. Neutrons, which only interact with nuclei, may have either high or low LET. Their penetration in matter is great though difficult to specify well except in terms of specific materials. For much of their path, *fast* neutrons also are attenuated roughly exponentially.

The approximate range r or half thickness $x_{1/2}$ is given in Table 2 for several 1-MeV radiations in water.

TABLE 2

$\alpha(r)$ (cm)	β^-(max r) (cm)	γ $(x_{1/2})$ (cm)	Neutrons $(x_{1/2})$ (cm)
0.0007	0.4	10	5–10

Finally, a variety of conventional particle and wave interactions (such as reflection, transmission, and refraction) are also experienced by the above radiations. Moreover, many other more-or-less-ionizing radiations have been omitted from this discussion, including mesons, hyperons, heavy cosmic particles, large fission and spallation products, and anti-particles. Their relative interactions can be quite well predicted from their composition, charge, and velocity, and the above considerations.

HOWARD C. MEL
PAUL W. TODD

Cross-references: ATOMIC PHYSICS, BREMSSTRAHLUNG, COMPTON EFFECT, ELECTRON, IONIZATION, NEUTRON, NUCLEAR REACTIONS, NUCLEAR STRUCTURE, PHOTOELECTRICITY, PHOTON, POSITRON, PROTON, RADIATION CHEMISTRY, RADIOACTIVITY, X-RAYS.

RADIATION, THERMAL

The term thermal radiation refers to the electromagnetic energy that all substances radiate, by transformation of their thermal energy. If a body lacks a source of replenishment for the thermal energy thus transformed, it will radiate away all of its available energy, and its temperature will approach absolute zero. As long as the temperature remains above approximately 500°C, some of the thermal radiation will lie in the visible spectrum. At lower temperatures, the energy lies at wavelengths too long to be seen.

The discovery that radiation existed outside the visible spectral region was made by Sir William Herschel in 1800. He formed a prismatic solar spectrum on a table top in a dark room and found that the temperature, as indicated by a sensitive thermometer, continued to increase beyond the red end of the spectrum.

Sources other than the sun were also studied. One that is of fundamental importance is an isothermal enclosure, or hohlraum, with a small hole for viewing the radiation escaping from the interior. Kirchhoff had proved, from the second law of thermodynamics, that the flux and the spectral distribution of the radiation are the same in all such enclosures at a given temperature, irrespective of the materials composing them. A related fact, known as Kirchhoff's law, is that the ratio of radiant emittance to absorptance is the same for all surfaces at the same temperature. (The radiant emittance of a surface is the integrated power radiated in all directions per unit area of surface. Definitions of other radiometric quantities, symbols and units will be found in the references.) In accordance with this law, metallic surfaces, having high reflectance and hence low absorptance, also have a low radiant emittance. Hence, the inner surfaces of the double walls of a Dewar flask are silvered, to minimize radiant heat loss.

At a given temperature, the surface having

maximum absorptance will also have maximum emittance of radiant energy. Since such a surface absorbs all incident energy, it appears black, and the radiation it emits is known as "blackbody radiation." Like the pupil of the eye, an opening in the surface of a hollow body appears to be perfectly black (as long as there is no reflection back out) and the opening acts as a blackbody radiator as well as absorber. No surface can have a larger radiant emittance than a blackbody, at a given temperature.

Toward the end of the nineteenth century, quantitative studies of the magnitude and spectral distribution of blackbody radiation were made (see INFRARED RADIATION for typical curves). Stefan had found experimentally in 1879 that the radiant emittance of a blackbody, integrated over all wavelengths, is proportional to the fourth power of the absolute temperature. And, in 1884, Boltzmann gave a theoretical derivation for what is now known as the Stefan-Boltzmann law: $W = \sigma T^4$. The value of the constant σ is 5.67×10^{-12} watts cm^{-2} deg^{-4}. In 1893, Wien derived a "displacement law," one of whose implications is that $\lambda_{\max} T = 2898$, where $\lambda_{\max}$ is the wavelength (in microns) at which maximum radiance occurs for a blackbody at absolute temperature T.

In 1896, Wien derived the following distribution law for the spectral radiant emittance W_λ of a blackbody: $W_\lambda = c_1 \lambda^{-5} \exp(-c_2/\lambda T)$. This fits the experimental observations within 1 per cent, provided λT is less than 3100, i.e., $\lambda \lesssim \lambda_{\max}$; but at larger values, the predicted values rapidly become too low (see Fig. 1). On the other hand, by applying the classical equipartition theorem of statistical mechanics to the radiation, Rayleigh and Jeans derived the following formula: $W_\lambda = (c_1/c_2)\lambda^{-4} T$. For $\lambda \gtrsim 250\lambda_{\max}$, the Rayleigh-Jeans equation matches the experimental data to 1 per cent, but it

diverges, leading to the "ultraviolet catastrophe," as $\lambda \to 0$. It remained for Max Planck in 1900 to find an expression that is valid at all wavelengths and temperatures, namely: $W_\lambda = c_1 \lambda^{-5}/[\exp(c_2/\lambda T) - 1]$. c_1 and c_2 are known as the first and second radiation constants, respectively, and have the values $c_1 = 3.74 \times 10^{-12}$ watt cm^2; $c_2 = 1.44$ cm degree. Planck's theory leads to the following expressions for the radiation constants in terms of fundamental physical quantities: $c_1 = 2\pi hc^2$; $c_2 = hc/k$, c being the velocity of light, and k Boltzmann's constant. The validity of these expressions has been experimentally justified.

Planck first developed this law empirically, and tried unsuccessfully to justify it on the basis of classical physics. He was forced to postulate that the elementary oscillators, of which a radiating body consists, did not have a continuous distribution of energy, but only quantized values. According to the "quantum hypothesis," the energy E that an oscillator may assume is given by $E = nh\nu$, where n is an integer, and the proportionality constant h (now known as Planck's constant) $= 6.63 \times 10^{-34}$ watt sec^2. Though forced to assume that the energies of the elementary oscillators, of which the radiator is composed, could take on only discrete values, Planck considered the emitted radiation to be propagated according to classical electromagnetic theory. The quantization of the radiant energy into photons was conceived by Einstein and used by him to explain the phenomena of photoelectricity. These quantum concepts were later extended by Bohr and Sommerfeld to explain atomic spectra and by Schrödinger, Heisenberg, Dirac, and others to develop quantum mechanics. Thus, they stand as one of the most important milestones in the history of theoretical physics.

Integration of Planck's equation leads to the

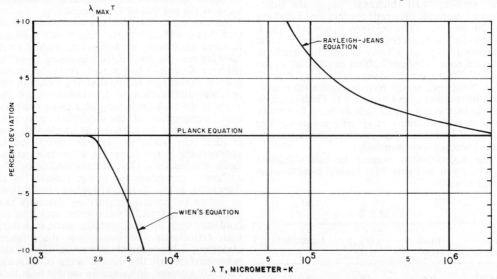

FIG. 1. Fractional deviation of classical radiation equations from the Planck equation.

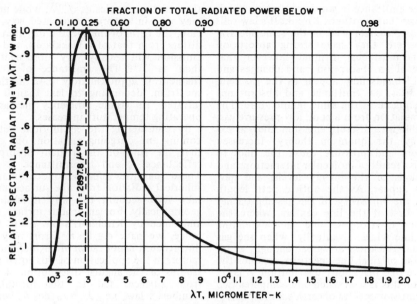

FIG. 2. General blackbody radiation curve.

Stefan-Boltzmann equation. Wien's laws and the Rayleigh-Jeans law may also be derived from Planck's law under appropriate conditions. For example, when dealing with photons whose energy $h\nu$ is sufficiently small compared to the thermal energy kT, the product λT is large enough so that the exponential in the denominator of Planck's law may be replaced by the first two terms of a series expansion. This leads to the Rayleigh-Jeans law.

High-speed computers have been used to compile tables of spectral radiance and related functions for a blackbody over a broad range of wavelengths and temperatures. There are also several radiation calculators, or slide rules, that are convenient for engineering use. Some of these make use of the fact that a log-log plot of blackbody radiation vs wavelength has the same shape at all temperatures. The radiance curve for a given temperature blackbody may then be obtained by sliding the universal curve in such a way that its peak falls on the line corresponding to the Wien displacement law (see Fig. 1 in INFRARED RADIATION). It is convenient to remember that the peak radiance varies as T^5; that a quarter of the total power radiated lies between $\lambda = 0$ and $\lambda = \lambda_{\max}$ (see Fig. 2); and that this power, on the short-wavelength side of the peak of the radiation curve varies as $T^{6.4}$. At wavelengths less than $\lambda_{\max}$, the monochromatic radiance changes as T^n, where $n \cong 15000/\lambda T$. For an object at 1500 K, for example, observed through an optical pyrometer with a filter transmitting at $0.6\mu m$, $n \cong 17$. This relatively high value of n is advantageous in reducing the temperature error resulting from uncertainty in the observed radiance or the emittance of a surface.

The ratio by which the surface radiation falls short of that of an ideal blackbody, is denoted as the surface's emissivity or emittance. Some authorities prefer to use "emissivity" as a material property characterizing an ideally pure and polished surface of the material, as distinguished from the properties of engineering samples. The emittance of some substances, though less than one, is essentially the same at all wavelengths. Such radiators are referred to as gray bodies. In most real substances, however, emittance varies as a function of wavelength as well as temperature.

If one can make a reasonable estimate of the emittance of a surface, a measurement of its thermal emission will give its temperature. This is the basis of contactless, radiometric temperature measurement. Should the emittance be unknown, but assumed to be relatively constant, a temperature may be inferred from the shape of the spectral distribution curve. Other schemes have also been used to determine the temperature of surfaces of undetermined characteristics.

The *color temperature* of a body is that temperature of a blackbody which has the same ratio of radiances as the selective radiator in two spectral intervals. In general, the value of the color temperature depends on the choice of the two spectral intervals. However, if these wavelengths are in the visible region, the color temperature is relatively insensitive to the specific values chosen. The color temperature of a gray body equals its true temperature. When dealing with semitransparent materials such as glass in the near infrared, one speaks of volume emissivity, which in turn is related to the optical constants of the material.

In some solids, and especially in gases and

flames, the emittance in some spectral regions is much larger than in others. Kirchhoff's law tells us that gases radiate well in the same spectral regions where they have strong absorption bands. One must bear in mind, however, that the shape of an absorption band changes and new "hot" bands may appear as the gas temperature rises, so emittance and absorptance must be equated at the same temperature. The thermal radiation from a cool, low-pressure gas, is resolvable into discrete emission lines, as explained by the quantum theory. Increased temperature and pressure cause the lines to broaden as a result of molecular interactions and perturbations of the energy levels, and new lines also appear. As the optical path length increases, the emissivity of the gas approaches unity, at first at the line centers, where the absorptance is strongest, and then extending into the line wings. Eventually, when the gas density and thickness are great enough, as on the sun, the original line spectrum assumes the appearance of a blackbody distribution. A good example of this is seen when one compares two infrared emission spectra of earth's atmosphere—first looking overhead from a mountain top, and then along the horizon at a humid seacoast. The latter spectrum's blackbody-like shape (from which, incidentally, the atmosphere's temperature may be inferred) contrasts strongly with the peaks and valleys of the former.

In strongly absorbing spectral regions, only a relatively thin layer of gas, nearest the viewer, contributes to the observed radiance, the radiation by the more distant molecules having been almost completely absorbed by the nearer molecules. For this reason, the Fraunhofer lines in the solar spectrum, occurring at strongly absorbing atomic wavelengths, originate in the cooler outer part of the sun and appear relatively dark.

In exceptional situations, it is possible to circumvent the consequences of Kirchhoff's law. The Doppler shift, due to the relative motion of the earth and Mars, prevents the narrow line radiation by planetary H_2O from being reabsorbed by terrestrial water vapor. As a result, it has been possible to estimate the water vapor concentration on Mars (see DOPPLER EFFECT and PLANETARY ATMOSPHERES).

The spectral emittance of gases is an important area of investigation, with respect to such topics as the heat budget of the earth; the composition of planetary atmospheres; and radiation by flames and rocket engines. The analysis of the gas radiation transfer in many of these applications is complicated by the fact that conditions are nonisothermal.

The Welsbach mantle (or the Coleman lantern) is an example of selective radiation in a solid; in this case, its efficiency as a source of visible light is enhanced by the high emittance in the visible, and low emittance in the near infrared, of the mixture of thoria and cerium oxide of which the source is composed. For some metals,

the emittance varies as $\sqrt{T/\lambda}$, while in others it may vary in a more complicated way. In either case, the form of the spectral distribution curve differs from that of a blackbody, and the total emission will usually vary more nearly as T^5 than as T^4. The emittance of a tungsten filament is approximately 0.45 in the visible spectrum, decreasing to less than 0.2 in the infrared. Its visible efficiency increases as its operating temperature increases.

By considering the equilibrium between incoming and outgoing radiation, one can show that the sum of the radiant absorptance a, reflectance r, and transmittance t, is unity. These quantities refer to monochromatic, hemispherical radiation from the surface and do not take into account the way it is distributed geometrically. For an opaque surface, $a + r = 1$, and since by Kirchhoff's law $a = e$, the emittance, we have $e = 1 - r$. Errors may result if due account is not taken of angular and spectral factors in the application of this equation. Early studies of the angular distribution of radiation from surfaces led to the formulation of Lambert's law, i.e., $J_\theta = J_n \cos \theta$, where J_θ is the source intensity or radiant power per unit solid angle in a direction making an angle θ with the normal to the surface, and J_n is the intensity along the normal. A surface that obeys Lambert's law is said to be perfectly diffuse, like a sheet of blotting paper in the visible. Its radiance, N (intensity per unit of projected area of source), is constant and independent of θ. Integration over the hemisphere leads to the relationship $W = \pi N$. A truly black surface obeys Lambert's law exactly. Although the law is a useful approximation for many radiators and reflectors, there are numerous exceptions. The emissivity of clean, smooth surfaces of some materials has been studied from a basic theoretical viewpoint and related to their optical constants. The analysis, whose results agree generally with experimental determinations, indicates that for electrical conductors, the normal emissivity is quite low and increases with θ; whereas insulators have relatively high normal emissivity, decreasing at large values of θ. Insulators, as well as metals covered with thick oxide films, behave approximately as diffuse radiators. In the case of many practical materials, however, the surfaces are either rough or chemically complex, and it is necessary to rely upon empirically determined emittances. Many substances, such as concrete, porcelain, and paper, have a higher absorptance for long- than for short-wave radiation. Many more data are needed on the spectral emittances of various materials under different conditions. In addition to their engineering uses in radiant heat transfer calculations, emittance and reflectance data have been used to deduce the chemical composition of the moon and planets.

Space vehicles absorb energy from the sun and lose it by radiation to space. By the application of coatings with suitable radiative characteristics,

the internal temperature of a vehicle may be controlled within desired limits. The quantity a/e is often used to characterize such coatings. It refers to the ratio of the absorptance of solar radiation (approximated by a 6000 K blackbody) to the emittance at the temperature of the vehicle's surface. High-temperature emittances of many materials are being studied in connection with the design of ablative nose cones, and reentry vehicles.

Although all objects are continuously emitting and absorbing thermal radiation, specially designed sources are available for particular applications. For industrial heating and drying, for example, there are numerous varieties of heaters and infrared lamps. The latter are similar to incandescent lamps used for lighting purposes, but designed for operation at lower temperatures, with reduced visible output. In recent years, high-temperature lamps with quartz envelopes have been used increasingly for both heating and illumination. The clarity of the envelope is maintained, and the filament life prolonged, by incorporating a small amount of iodine within the tube. Tungsten that has evaporated onto the tube walls combines with the iodine vapor to form tungsten iodide. This is a gas which decomposes thermally when it comes in contact with the hot filament, thus replenishing the latter and liberating the iodine for use again.

For scientific purposes, such as calibrating a radiometer or spectrometer, a reproducible source of known characteristics is essential. Sources with characteristics approaching those of an ideal blackbody, have been built for operation from cryogenic temperatures to about 3000 K. Most of the commercially available blackbodies, which come with a variety of aperture sizes and in many configurations, use a conical cavity (Fig. 3), the interior walls of

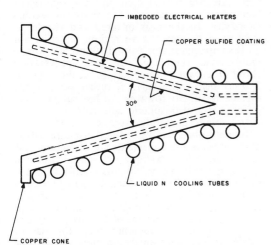

FIG. 3. Schematic representation of a conical blackbody that can be used at high or low temperature.

which are oxidized or blackened to decrease their reflectance. Electrical heating is most often used, in conjunction with a thermostatic controller. A number of authors have discussed the considerations involved in designing a blackbody, and it is possible to calculate how closely a given design approximates an ideal blackbody. It is sometimes necessary to have a black radiating surface whose area is impractical to obtain with a cavity-type body. Flat surfaces have been coated with "blacks" whose emittances are close to unity over a broad spectral range. These are generally not suitable for high-temperature use, however. Other methods that have been used to obtain high-emittance surfaces include: wedges or closely stacked razor blades viewed edge on, a telescoped cone pattern similar to that of a Fresnel lens impressed on a flat surface, a vortex in a liquid or molten metal, etc. The National Bureau of Standards has calibrated some special tungsten filament lamps for use as spectral irradiance standards from about 0.3 to 2.6μm. Beyond 2.6μm, strong, but variable, atmospheric absorption becomes troublesome. When using infrared sources for quantitative thermal radiation measurements, one must make due allowance for the absorption at different infrared wavelengths by the CO_2 and water vapor in the atmosphere between the source and the instrument being calibrated.

For reasons of compactness and convenience, it is sometimes desirable to use non-blackbody sources of thermal radiation. Among the most common of these are the Nernst glower, which is a hollow rod approximately 25 mm long and 2 mm in diameter, made of a mixture of oxides of zirconium, yttrium, and thorium and the globar, a rod of bonded silicon carbide. These are most useful at the shorter infrared wavelengths. In the far infrared, mercury discharge tubes and other sources have been used. At long wavelengths, the power output of a thermal radiator increases almost linearly with temperature, as indicated by the Rayleigh-Jeans law, and inordinately high temperatures would be required for a significant increase in power. Nonthermal sources, in particular lasers, or other coherent radiators can generate much greater power, and, though generally limited to a narrow spectral interval, lasers that can be tuned over a considerable spectral range are coming into increasing use.

In order to study the properties of materials at very high temperatures without contamination, it is convenient to heat them by thermal radiation rather than convection. Solar furnaces have been used for this purpose, as well as arc-imaging furnaces, in which a specially designed high-intensity carbon arc replaces the sun as the source.

Thermal radiation can be detected by eye when the source temperature is sufficiently high. Figure 4 shows the luminous efficiency of a blackbody as a function of temperature. And although its sensitivity is greatly reduced at

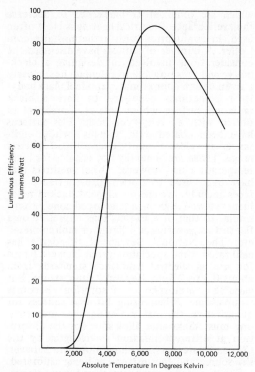

FIG. 4. Luminous efficiency of blackbody radiation (based on K_{max} = 683 lumens/watt). (This K_{max} corresponds to a choice of 2041 K for the freezing point of platinum.)

longer wavelengths, the human eye has some sensitivity to radiation at wavelengths as long as $1.2 \mu m$. Some insects, such as moths, respond to thermal radiation at even longer wavelengths, and some snakes can detect the heat of a warm-blooded animal at an appreciable distance.

Many types of detectors have been developed for thermal radiation. In some of these, known as quantum detectors, the energy of the incident photon must exceed some lower limit, but its effects are very rapid. An example is the lead sulfide detector, which responds to wavelengths less than $3 \mu m$, or HgCdTe, which is most sensitive to radiation around $10 \mu m$, where objects at ambient temperatures emit most copiously. In others, thermal radiation of any wavelength can be detected by virtue of its effect on some physical property of the detector. The response of the latter kind of detector is slower than that of the former. Among the thermal detectors are: metal and thermistor bolometers, in which the absorbed radiation causes a slight temperature rise and consequent change in the resistance of the detector; thermocouples and thermopiles in which the differential heating of two junctions of dissimilar materials generates an emf; pyroelectric crystals whose polarization changes with temperature; the Golay cell or pneumatic detector, where the absorbed

radiation heats a gas and distorts a reflecting optical element; the evaporograph in which the incident radiation causes differences in the rate of evaporation of a thin oil film and the resulting differences in thickness give rise to interferometric patterns. Numerous other physical mechanisms have been exploited for radiation detection. (The more usual infrared detectors are discussed under INFRARED RADIATION.)

For coverage of an extended field of view, mosaics of conventional detectors have been used, as well as electronic imaging tubes such as infrared vidicons and orthicons. Whether by such detectors or by raster-like scanning of a small elemental field of view, it is possible to study the temperature pattern of an extended source of thermal radiation. Thermography is such a process, in which the temperature gradients are displayed in visible form, e.g., on photographic film, or in real time, on a cathode ray tube. When properly interpreted, the thermograph can be a valuable diagnostic aid to the physician. Industrial thermography, as applied, for example, to the nondestructive testing of integrated electronic circuit boards is useful for design purposes or for quality assurance. In interpreting the observed patterns, one must bear in mind that radiance variations may result from differences in either or both surface emittance and surface temperature from point to point. This fact is less troublesome in medical thermography because the emittance of the body is close to unity. In a similar way, the radiometry of lakes, rivers, and oceans by an instrument looking vertically down from an aircraft, takes advantage of the near-unity emissivity of water within the range of wavelengths to which the radiometer is sensitive. Thermal pollution can thus be detected remotely. Oil films, due to pollution, or occurring naturally in association with schools of certain fish, can also be detected; but the significant factor here is the effect of the oil on the water's emissivity. In the near infrared and visible, as well as in the microwave region, water is not quite so opaque as it is around $10 \mu m$. Microwave radiometry, therefore, can give information about the water temperature slightly (1 or 2 mm) below the surface, rather than at the surface itself. Microwaves are less subject than infrared to atmospheric absorption and are better able to penetrate overcast and clouds.

Satellite observations of the thermal radiation of the oceans and continents are of meteorological value. For example, a special infrared spectrometer flown on Nimbus satellites records the radiation by atmospheric CO_2 in a series of narrow wavelength intervals centered around the strong absorption band at $15 \mu m$. Knowledge of the varying emittances of the atmosphere at these wavelengths, together with the use of mathematical inversion techniques, permit one to compute profiles of temperature vs height on a global scale, for a variety of atmospheric con-

ditions; these are generally in good agreement with data from radiosondes. Data from another infrared interferometric spectrometer have yielded distribution profiles for atmospheric water vapor and ozone.

LEONARD EISNER

References

Forsythe, W. E., "Measurement of Radiant Energy," New York, McGraw-Hill Book Co., 1937.

Worthing, A. G., and Halliday, D., "Heat," New York, John Wiley & Sons, 1948.

Richtmyer, F. K., and Kennard, E. H., "Introduction to Modern Physics," Fifth edition, New York, McGraw-Hill Book Co., 1955.

Klein, M. J., "Max Planck and the Beginnings of the Quantum Theory," in *Archive for History of Exact Sciences*, 1 (5), 459–479 (1962).

Pivovonsky, M., and Nagel, M. R., "Tables of Blackbody Radiation Functions," New York, The Macmillan Co., 1961.

Rutgers, G. A. W., "Temperature Radiation of Solids," Flugge, S., Ed., "Handbuch der Physik," Vol. 26, pp. 129–170, Berlin, Springer, 1958.

Harrison, W. N., *et al.*, National Bureau of Standards, "Standardization of Thermal Emittance Measurements," WADC Technical Report 59-510, in 4 parts 1960–64, Office of Technical Services, U.S. Dept. of Commerce.

Gubareff, G. G., Janssen, J. E., and Torborg, R. H., "Thermal Radiation Properties Survey," Second edition, Minneapolis-Honeywell Regulator Co., Honeywell Research Center, Minneapolis, Minn., 1960.

Richmond, J. C., Ed., "Measurement of Thermal Radiation Properties of Solids," A Symposium held at Dayton, Ohio, Sept. 5–7, 1962, NASA SP-31, for sale by U.S. Govt. Printing Office.

Katzoff, S., Ed., "Symposium on Thermal Radiation of Solids," University of California, San Francisco, California, March 4, 5, 6, 1964, NASA SP-55, 1965.

Penner, S. S., "Quantitative Molecular Spectroscopy and Gas Emissivities," Reading, Mass., Addison-Wesley Publishing Co., 1959.

Sobolev, V. V., "A Treatise on Radiative Transfer," New York, Van Nostrand Reinhold, 1963; translated by S. F. Gaposchkin.

Glaser, P. E., and Walker, R. F., Eds., "Thermal Imaging Techniques," New York, Plenum Press, 1964.

Baker, H. D., Ryder, E. A., and Baker, N. H., "Temperature Measurement in Engineering," 2 vols., New York, John Wiley & Sons, 1953 and 1961.

American Institute of Physics, "Temperature, Its Measurement and Control in Science and Industry," Vols. 1–3, New York, Van Nostrand Reinhold, 1941–1963.

Touloukian, Y. S., and Ho, C. Y., "Thermophysical Properties of Matter," New York, Plenum Press, Vols. 7 and 8, 1972; Vol. 9, 1973.

Svet, D. Ya, "Thermal Radiation," New York Consultants Bureau, 1965.

Hottel, H. C., and Sarofim, A. F., "Heat Transfer," New York, McGraw-Hill Book Co., 1968.

Goody, R. M., "Atmospheric Radiation. I. Theoretical Basis," Oxford, Oxford University Press, 1964.

Summer, W., "Ultraviolet and Infrared Engineering," New York, Interscience Publishers, 1962.

Kattawar, G. W., and Eisner, M., "Radiation from a Homogeneous Isothermal Sphere," *Applied Optics*, 9, 2685 (1970).

Proceedings of 8th Remote Sensing Symposium, Oct. 1972, Univ. of Michigan.

Sparrow, E. M., and Cess, R. D., "Radiation Heat Transfer," New York, Brooks-Cole, 1966.

Wiebelt, J. A., "Engineering Heat Transfer," New York, Holt, Rinehart, and Winston, 1966.

Harrison, T. R., "Radiation Pyrometry and Its Underlying Principles of Radiant Heat Transfer," New York, John Wiley & Sons, 1960.

Cross-references: DOPPLER EFFECT: HEAT TRANSFER; INFRARED RADIATION; KINETIC THEORY; LASER; LIGHT; OPTICS, GEOMETRICAL; OPTICS, PHYSICAL; PHOTON; PLANETARY ATMOSPHERES; QUANTUM THEORY; REFLECTION; SOLAR PHYSICS; SPECTROSCOPY; STATISTICAL MECHANICS; TEMPERATURE AND THERMOMETRY.

RADIO ASTRONOMY

Radio astronomy, the study of radio-frequency radiation emitted naturally by celestial objects, began in 1932 with the discovery of radio emission from the galaxy by K. G. Jansky at the Bell Telephone Laboratories. Fourteen years later, the U.S. Army Signal Corps and the Hungarian scientist Z. Bay, working independently, succeeded in obtaining radar echoes from the moon—thereby launching the related field of *radar astronomy*. More recently, *space radio astronomy* has allowed us to observe the low frequency radio waves that cannot penetrate the earth's ionosphere; a major achievement was the launch of the Radio Astronomy Explorer satellite in 1968.

Radio Telescopes A radio telescope consists basically of one or more aerials and a radiometer. The chief factor taken into account in the design of these components is the frequency range within which observations are to be made, and this in turn depends on the nature of the studies proposed for the telescope. Investigations at meter wavelengths are chiefly limited by confusion of adjacent radio sources, rather than by instrumental sensitivity. Therefore, the emphasis in designing telescopes for use at these frequencies has been on the attainment of high spatial resolution, and this requirement has generally led to the adoption of interferometers in preference to "single-dish" or filled-aperture antennae.

L. L. McCready, J. L. Pawsey, and R. Payne-Scott at Sydney introduced the technique of interferometry to radio astronomy in 1946. They used the Lloyd's mirror principle, with the ocean surface as reflector, to measure the an-

gular diameter and position of a localized source of solar radio emission.

Two-element interferometers were employed for sky survey work at the Mullard Radio Astronomy Observatory; others, notably those at Jodrell Bank, Owens Valley, and Nançay, yielded basic data on the brightness distributions of individual sources by means of variable-baseline interferometry. This technique has been generalized to the case where there are two or more antennae, located any distance apart, and not connected to each other in any sense. Instead, in this *very long baseline interferometry* (VLBI) a given source is observed simultaneously at each location, with the radiometer output being recorded on magnetic tape, along with an atomic clock signal. Then, the data are combined in an off-line computer, and a resolving power corresponding to the separation of the antennae is obtained. Thus, the earth's diameter is the limiting baseline.

The simple interferometer has a fan beam, i.e., its high resolution is limited to one coordinate. Symmetrical or pencil beams were first synthesized at meter wavelengths with two-dimensional arrays of interferometer elements such as the Mills Cross developed at Sydney. However, the need for better resolution led to the construction of such arrays with characteristic dimensions on the order of a mile. The VLA (Very Large Array), planned for construction near Socorro, New Mexico in the 1970s, would extend over more than 30 miles. Aperture synthesis, an approach introduced by M. Ryle and A. Hewish at Cambridge, involves the use of two or more aerials, at least one of which is movable, to simulate a larger array. Data must be taken with the aerials in each of many different relative orientations in order to obtain one "observation."

The 250-foot "dish" at Jodrell Bank was the largest fully steerable parabolic antenna until the construction of the 330-foot antenna near Bonn in 1972. In the Southern Hemisphere, the major dish antenna is the 210-foot telescope at Parkes, New South Wales, Australia.

Millimeter-wave radio astronomy requires highly precise reflecting surfaces. At present, the best available telescope is the 36-foot antenna at Kitt Peak, which is housed in a dome and is fully automated.

Several approaches to the problem of the mechanical support of large, steerable reflectors have been tried. Among these are the Ohio State University instrument, which consists of a fixed parabolic section and a tiltable flat reflector; the parabolic strip antenna of Pulkovo Observatory; and the cylindrical paraboloid of the University of Illinois. The homologous deflection technique proposed by S. von Hoerner is playing an important role in studies of the "largest feasible steerable reflector." The basic idea is to allow the antenna to sag in such a way that the deformed surface is always a paraboloid.

Gain stability, phase stability, and low receiver noise temperature are the prime desiderata in a radiometer. Compensation for gain variation by switching between the object signal and a reference standard was achieved by R. H. Dicke in 1946. Many refinements of this technique have since been developed. Traveling-wave tubes, masers, parametric amplifiers, and tunnel diodes have all been used to provide low-noise amplification, particularly in the microwave region where the average intensity of cosmic sources is low. New detection methods that show promise for high-frequency radio astronomy include the use of Josephson junction and other solid-state, cryogenically cooled devices. Multichannel receivers are used for spectral line studies.

Cosmic Radio Sources In the solar system, radio emission has been detected from the sun and from all of the planets except Pluto. Solar radio waves arise from all levels in the quiet atmosphere of the sun, and from transient phenomena such as active regions and flares. The corona has been probed also by radar. The radio emission from Mercury and Mars is thermal and originates at the surfaces of these planets. Venus is a much stronger source than expected for a blackbody in equilibrium with solar radiation; its radio emission arises in the atmosphere, which is heated by a greenhouse-type process. At microwave frequencies, Jupiter, Saturn, Uranus, and Neptune also are all stronger thermal sources than expected. This may indicate the presence of some self-luminosity in addition to the heat that they receive from the sun. At low frequencies Jupiter is also a variable, nonthermal source; in 1955, radio bursts from this planet were accidentally discovered by B. F. Burke and K. L. Franklin of the Carnegie Institution. Their report led C. A. Shain to identify over 50 previously unidentified Jovian bursts in prediscovery Australian radio observations; he also inferred the existence of a localized burst source on the planet from the fact that the frequency of burst occurrence depended on the longitude of the Jovian central meridian. At present, due chiefly to long series of observations made at Yale, Florida, and Colorado, it is known that the Jovian bursts occur predominantly in the frequency range below 45 MHz and that they are beamed from three discrete sites on the planet. The occurrence rate of the bursts is correlated with the position of the Jovian satellite, Io. Continuous radio emission, in both the spectral and temporal senses, is observed in the decimeter region. It has a nonthermal spectrum and originates in the Jovian magnetosphere; at 3000 MHz the most intense signals arise in the magnetic equatorial plane, at about two planetary radii from the center of Jupiter.

In 1973–74 Comet Kohoutek (1973F) was found to emit both microwave continuum and molecular line radiation.

Among stars in the galaxy, novae, flare stars, binary systems, and pulsars have been studied by radio astronomers. The nova emission originates in the gaseous envelope ejected by the stellar explosion. Flare stars are small, cool ($T = 2900$ K, typically) objects. Their radio outbursts are

of much greater absolute intensity than typical solar flare events. Binary stars observed at radio frequencies, notably by R. Hjellming and C. M. Wade (National Radio Astronomy Observatory) include Antares (the radio source is its faint blue companion), the famous eclipsing systems Algol and beta Lyrae, and several binaries associated with x-ray sources. Pulsars, discovered in 1967 by A. Hewish, S. J. Bell, and their colleagues at Cambridge University, are sources of discrete, periodic pulsed signals, with typical duty cycles of about 5 per cent. As of mid 1973, 105 pulsars had been found, and their pulse periods ranged from 0.033 to 3.75 sec. In general, these periods are slowly lengthening. It is believed that these objects do not actually emit pulses; rather the pulsar phenomenon is interpreted as beaming of nonthermal radiation from rotating, highly magnetized neutron stars. As a pulsar beam sweeps along the surface of the earth (at a rate, in the case of the Crab Nebula pulsar NP 0532, of 10^{24} cm/sec!) it is detected momentarily at a given observatory, and the effect is that of a "pulse" (see PULSARS).

Also in the Milky Way galaxy, the interstellar medium and clouds, the galactic cosmic ray gas, the H II regions, planetary nebulae, supernova remnants, and several large gaseous structures of uncertain origin—the galactic spurs or "giant loops"—are all radio emitters.

At a 1944 Leiden Observatory colloquim, H. C. van de Hulst predicted that a spectral line could be observed by radio astronomers, who previously had worked only in the continuum. He referred to the 1420-MHz hyperfine transition in the ground state of neutral hydrogen, the now-famous 21-cm line. Seven years later, H. I. Ewen and E. M. Purcell at Harvard made the first successful detection of this radiation. The importance of the 21-cm line is twofold: (1) it originates in the most abundant known constituent of interstellar matter; (2) Doppler shifts are readily measurable in line radiation but not in the continuum. As a result of many 21-cm investigations, notably those of the Harvard, Leiden, and Australian groups, it has been possible to map the distribution of interstellar hydrogen in the galaxy and to study the dynamics of the gas. In 1963, A. H. Barrett, M. L. Meeks, and S. Weinreb at M.I.T. succeeded in detecting the 18-cm lines of OH. Since then, the line radiation of a few dozen molecules, including some as complex as formaldehyde and methyl alcohol, has been discovered in radio studies of the galaxy. These observations pose considerable problems to theorists: How do the molecules survive dissociation by the interstellar ultraviolet radiation field? How is the remarkably intense emission of some molecules, such as H_2O, generated? What relation does the unexpected presence of the organic molecules bear to the origin of life? In addition, a number of recombination lines have been detected in the radio spectra of H II regions. These arise from upper levels with very high principal quantum numbers, e.g., $n = 109$ in hydrogen.

Beyond the Milky Way, the known radio sources are galaxies, quasars, and the microwave background radiation. Radio astronomers originally considered two categories of galaxies. A weak emitter, or *ordinary galaxy* (such as our own system, or M 31 in Andromeda) typically radiates 10^{38} erg/sec in radio waves, compared with 10^{44} erg/sec in the optical region. The strong emitters, or *radio galaxies*, each produce up to 10^{45} erg/sec in the radio range alone. In both types of galaxy, the radio continuum is accounted for on the synchrotron theory. D. S. Heeschen and C. M. Wade at Green Bank made a systematic study of bright galaxies; they concluded that all normal spiral and irregular galaxies are probably weak radio sources. On the other hand, the strong emitters tend to be elliptical galaxies, often distinguished by peculiar optical phenomena, and they probably constitute the bulk of the nearly 1300 discrete sources listed in the *General Catalogue* of W. E. Howard and S. P. Maran. Another, much rarer type of radio galaxy is the Seyfert galaxy. These objects are spiral galaxies characterized by strong, broad emission lines in the optical spectra of their central regions. The interferometric studies of A. T. Moffet and P. Maltby at the California Institute of Technology and of J. Lequeux at Nançay enabled them to divide the resolved extragalactic sources into three groups on the basis of brightness distribution: *simple*, *double*, and *core-halo* sources. C. Hazard and M. B. Mackey at Sydney used the method of lunar occultations to resolve detail as small as 0.5 second of arc and detected triple and even more complex structure in some sources. Moffet found that the emission in a given lobe of a double source tends to be concentrated at the end furthest from the other lobe, in accord with an expanding model. The VLBI technique has recently allowed us to detect extremely fine detail in radio galaxies and quasars; the observations of a few sources have been interpreted as evidence for expansion at velocities higher than c, although multiple source components (Christmas tree model) constitute a simpler explanation. Linear polarization measurements at several frequencies made it possible to study depolarization and the rotation of the electric vector. This led to model-dependent estimates of the electron density and magnetic field strength in interstellar and extragalactic space as well as in the sources themselves. Similar estimates for the sources are obtained from their radio spectra and angular diameters combined with distances obtained from application of the Hubble law to optically observed redshifts, according to the method of G. R. Burbidge (see COSMOLOGY). Since 1968, observations of the effect of the interstellar medium on the frequency dependence of the arrival times, intensities, and polarization of pulsar pulses have enabled us to map the distribution of magnetic field and electron density in some parts of our own galaxy.

The identification in 1963 of a new class of

radio source, the *quasistellar objects*, now called "quasars," had a profound impact on physics and astronomy. Originally thought to be peculiar stars within our galaxy, quasars are now believed to be among the most distant objects in the universe. Although their radio emission typically is similar to that of a strong radio galaxy and the optical emission rates are up to 100 times greater than those of any known galaxy, they occupy volumes that are extremely small compared to typical galactic dimensions. Radio observations show that the quasars are variable in their flux densities, spectral shapes, polarization characteristics, and brightness distributions. In some cases, the observations are consistent with transient, expanding radio sources within quasars. The source of quasar energy is a major problem. Among the possibilities that have been considered are the gravitational collapse of large masses, a high rate of supernova explosions due to collisions in dense star clusters, the mutual annihilation of matter and antimatter, and energy derived from the slow-down of rotating, magnetized stars.

Radio Astronomy and Cosmology Radio astronomy has provided the single most important observation available to cosmologists—the discovery of the microwave background radiation. Reported in 1965 by A. A. Penzias and R. W. Wilson of the Bell Telephone Laboratories, this radiation appears to arrive in equal amounts from all directions in space; it has a spectrum corresponding to that of a blackbody at 3 K and is almost certainly the red-shifted emission from the "Big Bang" that occurred at the origin of the universe. Precisely such radiation was predicted by G. Gamow. Surveys of extragalactic radio sources have also been analyzed for comparison with the predictions of various cosmological theories as to the number of sources that can be detected in each discrete range of flux density, the relation between the angular diameters and flux densities of sources, and similar tests. In this work, however, there is still no firmly established result.

STEPHEN P. MARAN

References

Pacholczyk, A. G., "Radio Astrophysics," San Francisco, W. H. Freeman and Co., 1970.
Christiansen, W. N., and Högbom, J. A., "Radiotelescopes," Cambridge, Cambridge University Press, 1969.

Cross-references: ANTENNAS, ASTROPHYSICS, COSMOLOGY, INTERFERENCE AND INTERFEROMETRY, PULSARS, SOLAR PHYSICS.

RADIOACTIVE TRACERS

The use of radioisotopes as tracers rests on the nearly indistinguishable physical and chemical properties of all the isotopes of a given element. Proper incorporation into a material of a radioisotope that can be measured with appropriate radiation detectors provides a means of studying the behavior of the material or a component thereof. Thus, a radioisotope may be used to study the chemistry or physics of an element, a chemical compound, or a mixture of substances. For example, ^{131}I, a radioisotope with an eight-day half-life, has been used to study the distribution of iodine in multiple phase systems, to study the biochemistry of ^{131}I-tagged diiodotyrosine, and to measure the flow rates of underground streams.

Shortly after the end of World War II, the U.S. Atomic Energy Commission made a variety of radioisotopes available from the Oak Ridge National Laboratory. Subsequently, additional suppliers have been established in the United States and in other countries. One may now purchase useful radioisotopes of 68 out of the 81 "stable" elements. Isotopes of very short half-life (minutes to an hour or so) exist for another 10 "stable" elements. Useful radiotracers are completely absent only for the elements, He, Li, and B. Most radioisotopes are produced in nuclear reactors by fission or other neutron-induced reactions; however, some are produced with accelerators. Available radioisotopes, their sources and their prices are catalogued in "The Isotope Index, 1963-1964," J. L. Sommerville, Editor, Scientific Equipment Co., Indianapolis, Indiana, 1963.

Facilities for the formation of radioactive tracers directly within a sample or test material have also become available. For example, it is possible to form radioactive iron 59 within a sample of steel by irradiating the sample in a nuclear reactor.

The wide choice of radioisotopic tracers and the availability of sensitive detection systems to fit most circumstances have made possible the use of radiotracer techniques in many branches of science, medicine, and industry. Radiotracers have a number of features that make their use generally attractive. Unlike other types of tracers, they provide unequivocal evidence of their presence by virtue of their own radiation. Most species of radioisotopes are inexpensive (although incorporation into a specific compound can be somewhat costly), and detection equipment can be obtained at moderate expense. Also, due to the excellent detection efficiency of available equipment, it is possible to carry out most experiments without undue health hazards. Investigators trained in the safe handling of radioisotopes can follow gas, liquid, solid, or mixed-state systems at the laboratory, pilot-plant or even full plant scale with complete safety.

The following examples of radiotracer applications comprise but a partial list of uses.

Absorption of gaseous or liquid-phase constituents can be readily studied with the aid of radiotracers. Either the deposition of tracer onto the substrate or the disappearance of tracer from its initial phase may be measured.

Analysis of chemical composition may be

accomplished either by utilizing the reaction of tagged reagents or by "isotope dilution." An example of the former method is the use of[110] Ag-tagged silver nitrate reagent in chloride determinations by the precipitation of AgCl from solution; a sharp rise in liquid-phase radioactivity indicates the point of essentially complete chloride precipitation. Isotope dilution utilizes an isotope of an element to measure the amount of the same element in a sample. It is based on the fact that the amount of radioactivity per unit weight of the element or compound (specific activity) in the tracer reagent will be decreased when the reagent is added to a solution containing the naturally-occurring element or compound. The change in specific activity is an analytical measure of the amount of the element or compound originally present in the sample.

Radiotracers may be used as analytical adjuncts, also. They provide a convenient means of checking the degree of completion of analytical steps, such as precipitation and extraction, and can provide a measure of chemical losses in analytical procedures. They may be used to mark compound locations in chromatographic separation procedures.

Many other aspects of chemistry have been elucidated with radiotracer techniques. Chemical reaction rates, equilibria, and mechanisms have been studied. Diffusion rates, exchange rates, solubility products, partition coefficients, dissociation constants, and vapor pressures have been measured. Processes due to the effects of high-energy radiation, photolysis, and catalysis have been unraveled. Many of the recent advances in biochemistry would not have been possible without the use of radioactive tracers, especially in the study of biological catalysis (enzyme reactions).

Many of the above subjects have been studied in connection with fields other than chemistry. Thus, while diffusion rates are of interest in elucidating rate-limiting chemical processes, they are also of considerable interest in electronics, metallurgy, and process industries. The self-diffusion of alloy components as a function of alloy composition and grain substructure has been investigated. Diffusion in other solid-state materials, such as semiconductors, has been measured. The specific sulfide surface area of metal sulfides supported on alumina has been determined by exchange of normal surface sulfur with ^{35}S-tagged H_2S. The rate of such exchange is of interest, and the final equilibrium state gives a measure of the surface sulfide area. These are examples of problems that are not amenable to solution with techniques other than the radiotracer method.

Industry has obtained marked economic benefits from radiotracer applications. Corrosion and wear studies can be carried out with rapidity and insight otherwise impossible. The corrosion of a steel pipe containing ^{59}Fe (produced by irradiating a section of pipe) can be followed in situ by measuring the appearance of radioactivity in the corrosive medium or by following the disappearance of radioactivity of the part. Similarly, wear of an irradiated part such as a piston ring, cylinder sleeve, or gear, can be measured in situ. Prior to the availability of radiotracers, such wear studies required frequent dismantling of machinery for weight measurements. Furthermore, it is now often possible to obtain detailed wear or corrosion patterns by autoradiography. The techniques used in wear studies have also been used to study the effectiveness of lubricants and the mechanism of wear prevention.

Radioactive tracers have been used to examine fluid processes. They are highly useful in detecting leaks and are used routinely to mark the interface between two different products moving consecutively through a pipe-line. The gamma rays from an isotope such as ^{140}Ba in soluble form at the interface can be discerned easily through the walls of the pipe. In a similar fashion, flow rates may be measured by quickly injecting a tracer into a stream and noting the time required for the radioactive pulse to travel the distance between two detectors or between the injection point and a single detector. Rapid injection and accurate timing may be avoided where the amount of radioactivity injected and the detection efficiency of a downstream detector are accurately calibrated. The total signal from the tracer is inversely proportional to the velocity with which it goes past the detector. The techniques have been used in pilot plants, refineries, chemical plants, and even to study the flow rates and patterns of rivers and ocean currents.

The disposition of materials in various process units has been evaluated. Stream splitting, recycling, residence times, entrainment in distillations, mixing, and unit inventories have been measured.

The techniques of use in industrial fluid processes also apply in other fields. Stream splitting in capillary gas chromatography sampling units has been studied. Blood flow rate, total blood volume, and heart function are examples of medical applications.

H. R. LUKENS

References

Broda, E., and Schonfeld, T., "The Technical Applications of Radioactivity," Vol. 1, Oxford, Pergamon Press, 1966. Contains 2500 literature references.

Overman, R. T., and Clark, H. M., "Radioisotope Techniques," New York, McGraw-Hill Book Co., 1960. Describes general laboratory radioisotope procedures.

Kohl, J., Zentner, R. D., and Lukens, H. R., "Radioisotopes Applications Engineering," New York, Van Nostrand, Reinhold, 1961. Tracer applications are treated in detail, including tracer selection, calculations, and measurement.

Seymour Rothchild, Ed., "Advances in Tracer Methodology," Vol. 1, New York, Plenum Press, 1963. Places particular emphasis on the uses of tritium (H^3) and carbon 14.

Cross-references: ACCELERATORS, PARTICLE; ISO-TOPES; NUCLEAR INSTRUMENTS; NUCLEAR RADIATION; NUCLEAR REACTORS; RADIATION CHEMISTRY; RADIATION, IONIZING, BASIC INTERACTIONS; RADIOACTIVITY.

RADIOACTIVITY*

Radioactivity is the term applied to the spontaneous disintegration of atomic nuclei. It was one of the first and most important phenomena which led to our present understanding of nuclear structure. Credit for the discovery of radioactivity is usually given to Henri Becquerel, who made the observation in 1896 that penetrating radiation was given off by certain compounds of heavy elements in the absence of any external stimulus. Many other scientists were working in the field of radiation, however, and the announcement by Becquerel led to a flood of discoveries about the nature of the radiations which were emitted. A number of workers determined that certain of the radiations from these radioactive substances could be deflected in a magnetic field, and by 1900 three separate types of rays were identified. They were given the names alpha, beta, and gamma rays.

Distinction is frequently made between natural radioactivity, which was observed by the early workers, and artificial radioactivity which was first produced by F. Joliot and I. Curie-Joliot in 1934. These workers bombarded ^{27}Al with alpha particles to produce ^{30}P. For purposes of our discussion, we shall not distinguish between the sources of the radioactive material.

A discussion of radioactivity requires that mention be made of the stability of nuclei. Stable nuclear species or nuclides exist for all elements having proton numbers in the range from 1 to 83 except for elements 43 and 61 (technetium and promethium). In general, elements having even atomic numbers have two or more stable isotopes, whereas odd-numbered nuclei never have more than two.

The assumption is usually made that all possible nuclides were formed in the original atomic production processes, and that those which remain at the present time do so because of some inherent stability. In general, this stability involves the neutron-proton ratio, and a number of theoretical studies have been undertaken to determine the conditions for the maximum stability for nuclei.

Stability may be considered from three different standpoints: relative to the size and the number of particles in the nucleus, the ratio of the neutrons and protons in the nucleus, and the ratio of the total mass-energy of the nucleus. A nucleus which is unstable with respect to its size will emit alpha particles whereas a nucleus unstable with respect to its neutron-proton ratio may emit a negative or positive electron or may

*Editor was unable to locate author. Article is reprinted from first edition.

capture an electron. If a nucleus is unstable with respect to its total energy, the excess energy may be given off as gamma radiation which is electromagnetic in nature. Let us consider these emissions in more detail.

Alpha Emission It is evident that there are two types of forces existing in the nucleus. The first is a disruptive force arising from the repulsion of similarly charged particles. In addition, however, there are very strong attractive forces arising from the interactions of the nucleons. These attractive forces are very strong within the nucleus, but drop off quite sharply beyond about 10^{-12} cm from the center of the nucleus. Alpha particles, consisting of two protons and two neutrons, are, with certain exceptions, observed to come only from the larger nuclei. The mechanism of the emission process, however, is not a simple force phenomenon.

If we make calculations involving only the energies of the nucleus and the ejected particle, we should find, for example, that an alpha particle should come from a ^{226}Ra nucleus with approximately 27 MeV of energy. Instead, the emerging particle is observed to have about 5.3 MeV. This difference in energy cannot be explained using classical energy computations. The explanation of the alpha emission is usually given in terms of a "tunneling" effect, which is a quantum mechanical description first developed by Gamow and by Gurney and Condon. There are two equivalent ways of looking at this effect. One is to consider the alpha particle as being in motion inside the nucleus. In this picture, we visualize the particles as striking the potential "wall" of the nucleus. According to the quantum mechanical treatment for a particle striking such a barrier, there is a finite probability of passing through the barrier and appearing on the outside. Calculations making use of this probability give correct values for the observed half life and energies of the alpha particles from radioactive nuclides.

The other description of this process considers the alpha particle as being a wave packet with a very high probability of being found within the nuclear radius, but also having a finite probability of being outside the nucleus. According to this notion, the probability of finding the alpha wave packet at a distance greater than the nuclear radius, likewise gives the proper lifetime and energy values. It can be shown that this type of radioactivity is more probable in elements of high atomic number, and present extrapolations for this type of instability suggest that the highest atomic number element which can exist may be in the region of 108 or 109. It appears that elements 105 and higher will not exist long enough to be identified chemically, since the alpha emission will be extremely probable, affording an extremely short half-life.

Beta Radiation There are over 800 nuclear species which have been artificially produced in the laboratory. Nearly all of these have been produced by the reactions which give rise to a net

gain or loss of neutrons from the stable nuclei. In such a case the residual nucleus is characterized by having a neutron-proton ratio higher or lower than stable nuclei of that element. Similarly, if one considers alpha-emitting nuclei as being the "stable" nuclides for elements above lead, certain nuclides may be formed after the alpha emission with neutron-proton ratios higher or lower than the original element. The general decay process for nuclides with differing n/p ratios involves the reorganization of the nucleus in a manner which will leave a nucleus having a neutron-proton ratio corresponding to that requisite for stability.

Let us first consider the case in which a nucleus has a neutron-proton ratio higher than a stable isotope of that element. For example, the nuclei of all stable phosphorous atoms contain 15 protons and 16 neutrons. If a nuclear reaction takes place which leaves a nucleus with 15 protons and 17 neutrons we have a nucleus of ^{32}P. Since only ^{31}P occurs in nature, we know that some adjustment will take place to bring about stability. In this case, one of the neutrons is transformed into a proton, a negative electron, and a neutrino (specifically an anti-neutrino) which is shown in the following reaction:

$$n \rightarrow p + e^- + \bar{\nu}$$

The negative electron cannot exist as part of the nucleus and is ejected from the nucleus along with the neutrino. When the electron is investigated, it is found to be identical to other negative electrons, but when it is formed in this process, it is given the name negatron or negative beta particle. The residual nucleus then contains 16 protons and 16 neutrons. The element possessing 16 protons is sulfur, so the nucleus resulting from this negative beta emission is ^{32}S. In general, then, nuclei with neutron-proton ratios higher than stable nuclei eject a negative electron from each nucleus and are thus transmuted into nuclei of the next higher atomic number.

There are also types of nuclear reactions which may leave a nucleus with a neutron-proton ratio lower than the corresponding stable nucleus. In this type of instability, there are two processes which may compete with one another for the production of a stable nucleus. In the first of these, an extranuclear electron may be captured by the nucleus and combined with one of the protons. The most likely electron taking part in this process is one from the K level. L or M level electrons may be "captured," however. This electron capture reaction may be shown as follows:

$$p + e^- \rightarrow n + \nu$$

A neutrino is also ejected in this process. When this reaction takes place, the nucleus then contains one less proton than before, and is thus a nucleus of one lower atomic number. For example, if ^{55}Fe "decays" by electron capture, the resulting nucleus of ^{55}Mn is stable. This process can take place whenever the neutron-proton ratio is too low for stability.

The reaction which competes with electron capture may occur if the neutron-proton ratio is low, and if there exists a certain minimum mass-energy difference between the unstable nucleus and a possible stable nucleus having one less proton. If there is at least 1.02 MeV mass-energy difference a proton may transform into a neutron, a positive electron (or positron), and a neutrino according to the following equation:

$$1.02 \text{ MeV} + p \rightarrow n + e^+ + \nu$$

The positron is then ejected from the nucleus. The characteristics of the positron are identical to those of the negatron except for its positive charge. A number of cases are known in which both electron capture and positron emission processes take place in the same nuclear species. A radioactive nuclide is characterized as having a certain "branching ratio" when more than one type of decay is possible.

Gamma Radiation The usual modes of decay which involve the reorganization of the nucleus are those described above. In many cases, however, another step is involved in attaining final stability. After one of the nuclear transformations described above takes place, the nucleus may still possess excess energy. In this case, the extra energy is given off directly as gamma radiation. These are electromagnetic radiations which have energies corresponding to the difference in energy levels in the nucleus from which they come. A particular nuclide thus exhibits a certain pattern or disintegration scheme by which it decays. For example, ^{32}P decays by negative beta emissions, which are not followed by gammas. On the other hand, ^{60}Co emits negative beta radiation which is followed in each case by two gamma rays in cascade. These gamma radiations have energy of 1.17 and 1.33 MeV respectively. In general, the gamma radiations are emitted in time periods less than 10^{-12} seconds following the first transmutation step. In some cases, however, excited energy states may exist for significantly longer periods. Experimental determinations of the lifetimes of these slower gamma ray transitions range from 10^{-8} second to several months. If such an excited state exists in a nuclide for a period long enough to be measured experimentally, the nuclide is called a nuclear isomer, and the transition process involving such gamma radiation is called an isomeric transition (I.T.).

It should be mentioned also that gamma radiation is given off following nuclear reactions. Such gamma rays called "capture" or "prompt" are discussed in conjunction with nuclear reactions, although isomeric states are often formed in this manner, and isomeric transitions may leave the nuclei in radioactive rather than stable states.

Decay Schemes and Units Information as to the radioactive transitions which take place in a given case is frequently presented in what is

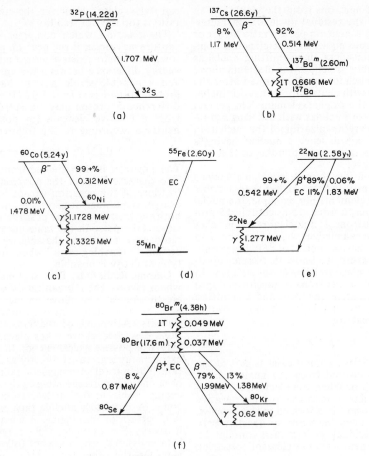

FIG. 1. Decay schemes.

called a decay scheme. A group of simple decay schemes is shown in Fig. 1. These indicate the type of radioactive process which the nucleus undergoes, the energies of the radiations given off, and the branching which may take place. Most nuclei have decay schemes which are much more complex than those represented in the Figure, but they involve only multiple occurrence of the processes which have been described.

Decay Rate It can be seen from the foregoing that a nucleus may change from an unstable to a stable form by one of several decay processes. We can thus speak of the decay rate of a sample of radioactive material in disintegrations per unit time—usually disintegrations per second. This refers specifically to the transformation of the nucleus, and does not give any indication of the kind or energy of the radiations emitted. The unit of activity is the "curie" and is defined to be 3.7000×10^{10} disintegrations per second. Submultiples or multiples of this unit in common use are micro-, milli-, kilo-, and megacurie. A sample containing one millicurie of radioactive material is a sample which decays at the rate of 3.7000×10^{7} disintegrations per second.

We have no way to determine when any given nucleus will decay, but some of the most important work in the early study of radioactivity involved the study of decay rates. It was shown very early that the rate of radioactive decay is proportional to the amount of the radioactive material present. This can be expressed in the following equation:

$$A = -\lambda N$$

in which A is the disintegration rate, N is the number of radioactive atoms present, and λ is a proportionality constant characteristic of each radioactive species. This relationship is sometimes important, but often a more useful relationship is the following:

$$N = N_0 e^{-\lambda t}$$

in which N_0 is the number of atoms present at some reference time, and N is the number of atoms present at some time t later, and e is the base of the natural logarithms. This exponential decay relationship is of fundamental concern in working with radioactive materials, even though

it is valid only for a statistically large number of atoms (i.e., all unstable nuclei will eventually decay).

The above equations are valid for any single radioactive species, and the exponential expression states that a given fraction of nuclei will decay in a given time period. In practice, we frequently refer to the time required for one-half of the atoms to decay. This is called the half-life of the radioactive material. It is related to the decay constant in the following way:

$$T_{1/2} = \frac{0.693}{\lambda}$$

It can also be shown that the average life, $\tau = 1.44$ times the half-life.

There are many cases in which a series of radioactive steps takes place. For example, ^{238}U undergoes 14 successive decays before arriving at the stable end product, ^{206}Pb. These steps involve the emission of successive alpha and beta rays along with gamma radiation in some cases. Although the calculations are somewhat more complex, it is possible to determine the disintegration rate of each of the daughter radioactive species formed in these processes. Details of this type of calculations are given in the references below.

RALPH T. OVERMAN

References

Evans, R., "The Atomic Nucleus," New York, McGraw-Hill Book Co., 1955.

Glasstone, S., "Sourcebook on Atomic Energy," Second edition, New York, Van Nostrand Reinhold, 1958.

Lapp and Andrews, "Nuclear Radiation Physics," Third edition, Englewood Cliffs, N.J., Prentice-Hall, 1963.

Overman, R. T. and Clark, "Radioisotope Techniques," New York, McGraw-Hill Book Co., 1960.

Cross-references: ELECTRON, NEUTRINO, NEUTRON, NUCLEAR RADIATION, NUCLEAR STRUCTURE, NUCLEONICS, POSITRON, PROTON, TUNNELING.

RAMAN EFFECT AND RAMAN SPECTROSCOPY

The Raman effect is the phenomenon of light scattering from a material medium, whereby the light undergoes a wavelength change in the scattering process. For a given medium, the Raman scattering per unit volume is of the order of one-thousandth of the intensity of the ordinary or Rayleigh scattering, in which there is no change of wavelength (see LIGHT SCATTERING). The Raman-scattered light bears no phase relationship with the incident light, whereas the Rayleigh light is a residual effect resulting from the departure of the incident and the scattered light from complete mutual coherence. The Raman intensity per molecule is thus independent of the state of the medium, apart from a certain small refractive index effect. The Rayleigh intensity per molecule, on the other hand, depends strongly on the degree of randomness of the spatial positions and orientations of the molecules of the medium; it is small for a crystal at absolute zero and greatest for a gas at low density.

Scattering of light with change of wavelength was predicted in 1923 by Smekal, inspired by the discovery of the Compton effect. The Raman effect was discovered experimentally in 1928 in India by Raman and Krishnan, who showed that the spectrum of the scattered light of liquids and solids, strongly illuminated with monochromatic light, contains frequencies which are not present in the exciting light and which are characteristic of the scattering medium. Independently, and almost simultaneously, Landsberg and Mandelstam in Russia discovered the effect in crystals. The phenomenon is called combination scattering of light in present-day Russian literature.

The method of observing the Raman spectrum is usually some modification of the arrangement introduced originally by R. W. Wood. The specimen, e.g., a liquid contained in a tube 1 cm in diameter and 10 cm long, is strongly illuminated along its length by mercury arcs, with filters interposed between the arcs and the tube to isolate monochromatic radiation if necessary. The scattered light is observed along the axis of the tube through a plane window at one end of the tube. The other end of the tube is usually drawn out in a cone which, when blackened, forms a dark background against which the scattered light is observed. The scattered light is analyzed by a spectrograph or recording spectrometer.[1]

The experimentally confirmed laws of Raman scattering are as follows:

(a) The pattern of Raman lines, expressed as *frequency* shifts from the exciting line, $\Delta\nu_i$ ($i = 1, 2, \cdots$), is independent of the exciting frequency.

(b) The pattern of Raman frequency shifts, $\Delta\nu_i$, is symmetrical about the exciting line. However, the lines on the low-frequency side of the exciting line (Stokes lines) are always more intense than the corresponding lines on the high-frequency side (anti-Stokes lines). The ratio of the intensities of corresponding anti-Stokes and Stokes lines is $I_a/I_s = \exp(-\Delta\nu_i hc/kT)$, where the Raman shift $\Delta\nu_i$ is expressed as usual in cm^{-1}. Thus anti-Stokes lines for $\Delta\nu_i > \sim 1000$ cm^{-1} are too weak to be observed at room temperature.

(c) A given Raman line shows a degree of polarization which depends on the origin of the line and on the experimental arrangement. For strictly transverse observation, i.e., observation at right angles to the incident light, the depolarization factor, ρ_n, has a value in the range 0 to 6/7 for unpolarized incident light.

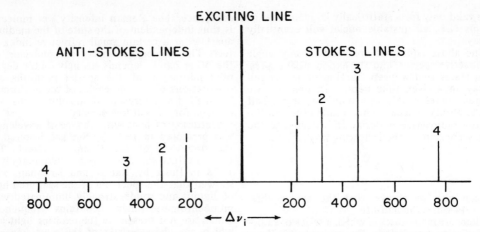

FIG. 1. Schematic diagram of the Raman spectrum of carbon tetrachloride. The heights of the Raman lines represent their relative intensities.

Figure 1 shows a schematic diagram of the Raman spectrum of carbon tetrachloride. The four Raman shifts, $\Delta\nu_i$ ($i = 1, 2, 3, 4$), are 218, 314, 459 and 775 cm^{-1}; the corresponding values of ρ_n are 6/7, 6/7, 0, and 6/7.

The Raman shifts, $\Delta\nu_i$, correspond to energy differences (in cm^{-1}) between discrete stationary states of the scattering system. Thus, in the quantum picture, the incident photons collide *elastically* with the molecules to give Rayleigh scattering, or *inelastically* to give Raman scattering, the latter process being much less probable than the former. For a Stokes Raman line, the photon furnishes energy to raise the molecule from a lower to a higher state; for an anti-Stokes line, the molecule must furnish energy to the scattered photon and move to a lower energy state. The anti-Stokes line thus originates in a less highly populated state and is weaker than the corresponding Stokes line. The Raman process can be described classically, but not as accurately, as the modulation of the scattered light wave by the internal motions of the scattering molecule, the Raman lines constituting "sidebands" of the Rayleigh "carrier" frequency.

A rigorous theory of the Raman effect, based on the quantum theory of dispersion, has been given by Placzek.[2] The process of light scattering can be visualized as the absorption of an incident photon of frequency, ν_e, by a molecule in a given initial state, thus raising the molecule to a "virtual" state from which it immediately returns to a final state emitting the scattered photon. Figure 2 illustrates the production of the Rayleigh line and Stokes and anti-Stokes Raman lines for a two-level system. If the exciting frequency ν_e is far away from any allowed electronic absorption of the molecule, the intensity of a Stokes line $\Delta\nu_i$ varies with ν_e according to the law, $I_i \propto (\nu_e - \Delta\nu_i)^4$. As ν_e approaches an electronic absorption the intensity increases more rapidly; this is the region of so-

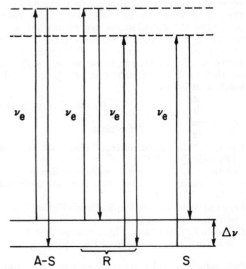

FIG. 2. Illustrating the production of Stokes (S) and anti-Stokes (A-S) Raman lines and the Rayleigh line (R) by an exciting frequency, ν_e, for a two-level system. The dashed lines represent virtual states of the system.

called *resonance* Raman scattering.[3] Finally, if ν_e is such that the virtual state coincides with a real energy state of the system, the Raman effect goes over into molecular fluorescence provided the states involved can combine with one another according to the selection rules.

In principle, the Raman shifts, $\Delta\nu_i$, can represent energy differences between electronic, vibrational or rotational energy states. In practice, Raman spectroscopy has been concerned chiefly with the determination of vibrational frequencies of polyatomic molecules from the scattered light spectrum and the correlation of the observed frequencies with possible modes of vibration of the molecules. In this role, Raman

spectroscopy forms an important complement to near-infrared spectroscopy which also furnishes precise information on molecular vibration frequencies.[4]

The so-called polarizability theory of Placzek[2] is an approximate theory which is particularly useful in relating observed vibrational Raman lines to the normal vibrations of the scattering molecule. In the equation, $\mathbf{m} = \alpha\mathbf{E}$, $\mathbf{m}$ is the electric dipole induced in the molecule by the oscillating light field $\mathbf{E}$. The constant of proportionality, α, is the molecular polarizability, which can be developed in a Taylor series in the vibrational coordinate q,

$$\alpha = \alpha_0 + (\partial\alpha/\partial q)_0 q + (1/2)(\partial^2\alpha/\partial q^2)_0 q^2 + \cdots$$

The intensity of the fundamental Raman band, corresponding to the $v = 0$ to $v = 1$ transition where v is the quantum number of the vibration, depends essentially on the *rate of change of polarizability*, $\alpha' \equiv (\partial\alpha/\partial q)_0$, with respect to the coordinate q. The vibration is active in Raman scattering if, because of the symmetry properties of the vibration, α' is not identically zero. Also the depolarization, ρ_n, of a Raman band can be related by the polarizability theory to the symmetry of the vibration. Thus, the single polarized ($\rho_n = 0$) line of carbon tetrachloride at 459 cm^{-1} (Fig. 1) can be identified immediately with the "breathing" vibration of the tetrahedral CCl_4 molecule, and the three depolarized ($\rho_n = 6/7$) lines with the three degenerate vibration forms of the molecule.

Since the infrared activity of a molecule depends on the molecular dipole, whereas the Raman activity depends on the molecular polarizability, the selection rules for two types of spectra can be very different. For example, all four fundamental vibrations of CCl_4 are active in Raman scattering (Fig. 1), whereas only two of these ($i = 2, 4$) are active in infrared absorption. An extreme case occurs for molecules with a center of symmetry: vibrations which are active in infrared absorption are not active in Raman effect and vice versa.

Although most investigations of the Raman effect have dealt with liquids and solids, i.e., high-density materials, systematic Raman studies of low-pressure gases have been made possible by the development of special equipment.[5] Since the molecules in gases are freely rotating, pure rotational Raman spectra and the rotational structure of vibrational bands can be observed. Here again, Raman studies supplement infrared investigations since the rotational selection rules are $\Delta J = 0, \pm 1, \pm 2$ for the former and $\Delta J = 0, \pm 1$ for the latter, where ΔJ is the allowed change in the rotational quantum number J.

In the past the 435.8, 404.7, and 253.7 nm lines of high-intensity mercury arcs were generally used to excite Raman spectra. However, mercury lamps have now been almost entirely superseded by gas lasers, particularly the He-Ne laser operating at 632.8 nm and the argon ion laser operating at 488.0 or 514.5 nm. The high flux density, monochromaticity, directionality, and polarization of the laser beam combine to make it an almost ideal source for the excitation of Raman spectra. As a result, there has been an extraordinary expansion of Raman studies in the last few years.

The directionality and polarization properties of the laser beam are particularly advantageous in Raman studies of crystals.[6] The direction of propagation of both the incident beam and the observed scattered beam, as well as the polarization vectors of these beams, can be set in various well-defined relationships with respect to the crystal axes of the specimen; the result is that much precise information can be obtained concerning the structure and the elementary excitations of the crystal. The usual components of the Raman spectrum of a crystal can be assigned to (a) *internal* vibrations (vibrons), i.e., the vibrations of the molecules or ions of the crystal coupled by the intermolecular forces; and (b) *external* vibrations (phonons), i.e., optically active vibrations of the crystal lattice. Other elementary excitations in particular crystals have also been detected recently by laser Raman spectra: spin waves (magnons) in ferromagnetic and antiferromagnetic crystals, coupled photon-electric dipole exciton modes (polaritons) in dipole crystals, and spin waves of angular momentum (librons) due to the almost free rotation of molecules in the ordered phase of ortho-enriched solid hydrogen. Phonon excitations in metals and electronic Raman transitions of ions in solids have also been studied.

In principle, laser excitation is well suited for studies of high-resolution Raman spectra of gases since, in single-mode operation, the exciting radiation has a half-width of < 0.02 cm^{-1}, as compared with ~ 0.2 cm^{-1} for mercury lamps. Although there have been promising recent attempts [7,8], the full potential of the method has not yet been realized, chiefly because of the difficulty of recording such faint spectra at high resolution.

In addition to its importance in studies of ordinary or *spontaneous* Raman scattering, the laser has led to the discovery of three essentially new spectroscopic phenomena, which will undoubtedly be of considerable significance in future Raman research; these are *stimulated* Raman scattering, the *inverse* Raman effect, and the *hyper* Raman effect. Each of these effects depends on the intense electric field produced in a material medium when it is illuminated by the focused beam of a giant-pulse (Q-switched) ruby laser.

In stimulated Raman scattering the giant laser pulse causes a coherent stimulated emission of a Stokes Raman frequency $\nu_e - \Delta\nu_i$, when the incident intensity exceeds a certain threshold value.[9] As a rule, only one Raman frequency is emitted and this corresponds to the line with the greatest peak intensity in the spontaneous

Raman spectrum. At higher incident intensities, harmonics (not overtones) of the first Stokes emission appear at $\nu_e - 2\Delta\nu_i$, $\nu_e - 3\Delta\nu_i$, $\cdots$ along with corresponding anti-Stokes frequencies.

When a substance is irradiated by the radiation ν_e of a giant-pulse laser and simultaneously by a continuum lying at frequencies higher than ν_e, the Raman shifts $\Delta\nu_i$ appear as absorption lines at frequencies $\nu_1 + \Delta\nu_i$; this is the so-called inverse Raman effect[10],[11]. In this case all the Raman-active molecular transitions can appear in the spectrum. Since the spectrum is generated in liquids and solids in a time of ~ 40 nsec, and since there are possibilities of reducing the time much further, the effect can perhaps furnish a high-speed spectroscopic method for studying short-lived molecular species and other transient phenomena. The use of laser excitation combined with recording by image-converter tubes also has attractive possibilities for high-speed Raman spectroscopy.[12]

The hyper Raman effect[13] occurs when the incident electric field E is so large that non-linear susceptibility terms are no longer negligible. Thus, the equation $m = \alpha E$ must be written

$$m_k = \alpha_{k\ell}E_\ell + \tfrac{1}{2}\beta_{k\ell m}E_\ell E_m + \tfrac{1}{6}\gamma_{k\ell mn}E_\ell E_m E_n$$
$$+ \cdots (k, \ell, m, n = x, y, z),$$

where the *hyperpolarizabilities* β, γ, $\cdots$ are tensors of the 3rd, 4th, $\cdots$ orders. The term in β gives rise to scattering at $2\nu_e$ and $2\nu_e \pm \Delta\nu_i$, and the further terms to higher harmonics. The selection rules for hyper Raman scattering are of course different from those for the ordinary case,[14] and when further developments in the recording of extremely low intensities have been made, the effect will constitute an important extension of ordinary Raman scattering.

H. L. WELSH

References

1. Harrison, G. R., and Lord, R. C., "Practical Spectroscopy," Second Edition, Englewood Cliffs, N.J., Prentice-Hall, 1965.
2. Placzek, G., "Rayleigh Scattering and the Raman Effect," in "Handbuch der Radiologie," Marx, E., Ed., Vol. 6, pt. 2, Leipzig, Akademische Verlagsgesellschaft, 1934; English translation by A. Werbin, Livermore, Lawrence Radiation Laboratory, University of California, 1959.
3. Szymanski, H. A., Ed., "Raman Scattering— Theory and Practice," New York, Plenum Press, Vol. 1, 1967, Vol. 2, 1970.
4. Herzberg, G., "Infrared and Raman Spectra of Polyatomic Molecules," New York, Van Nostrand Reinhold, 1945.
5. Stoicheff, B. P., in "Advances in Spectroscopy," Thompson, H. W., Ed., Vol. 1, New York, Interscience, 1959.
6. Wright, J. B., Ed., "Raman Scattering Spectra of Solids," New York, Springer-Verlag, 1969.
7. Butcher, R. J., Willetts, D. V., and Jones, W. V., *Proc. Roy. Soc. (London)*, A324, 231 (1971).
8. Weber, A., and Schlupf, J., *J. Opt. Soc. Amer.*, 62, 428 (1972).
9. Hellworth, R. W., *Phys. Rev.*, 130, 1850 (1963).
10. Jones, W. J., and Stoicheff, B. P., *Phys. Rev. Letters*, 13, 657 (1964).
11. McLaren, R. A., and Stoicheff, B. P., *App. Phys. Letters*, 16, 140 (1970).
12. Delhaye, M., and Migeon, M., *Compt. rendu.*, 261, 2613 (1965).
13. Terhune, R. W., Maker, P. D., and Savage, C. M., *Phys. Rev. Letters*, 14, 681 (1965).
14. Long, D. A., in "Essays in Structural Chemistry," Downs, A. J., Long, D. A., and Stavely, L. A. K., Eds., Chap. 2, London, Macmillan, 1971.

Cross-references: LASER, LIGHT SCATTERING, POLARIZED LIGHT.

RARE EARTHS

The rare-earth elements (also called "rare earths," "lanthanides," and "lanthanons") are a group of fifteen elements of similar properties in Group III of the periodic table. Their properties are somewhat similar to those of scandium, yttrium, and actinium in the same group. The rare earths have atomic numbers 57 to 71, inclusive, and are, in serial order: lanthanum (La), cerium (Ce), praseodymium (Pr), neodymium (Nd), promethium (Pm), samarium (Sm), europium (Eu), gadolinium (Gd), terbium (Tb), dysprosium (Dy), holmium (Ho), erbium (Er), thulium (Tm), ytterbium (Yb), and lutetium (Lu). The rare earths from lanthanum to samarium are called the "cerium earths"; those from europium to dysprosium are "terbium earths." Those from holmium to lutetium are called "yttrium earths" because of their resemblance to yttrium which is similar to and always occurs with the rare earths.

The rare earths are inner transition elements characterized by progressive filling up of the $4f$ electrons without changing the outer $5s^2 5p^6 5d^0$ or $6s^2$ levels, resulting in a concurrent decrease in atomic size. This reduction in atomic radii with increasing atomic number is known as the *lanthanide contraction*. In this respect, and also in chemical behavior, the rare earths resemble the actinides, the second rare-earth-like series beginning with actinium, which shows a similar *actinide contraction* (see TRANSURANIUM ELEMENTS).

Occurrence The only commercial minerals of importance are monazite and monazite sand, and bastnasite. Monazite is a rare-earth-thorium phosphate which occurs as small crystals in many acid granites and is recovered from placers resulting from the weathering of such rocks. It also occurs in some pegmatites, but commercial pegmatite deposits are rare. Bastnasite is a rare-earth fluocarbonate which occurs in hydrothermal deposits associated with barite, fluorite,

and calcite. Monazite sand is usually recovered as a by-product of ilmenite, zircon, and rutile recovery. Important beach placer deposits are in Florida and southeastern United States, Brazil, India, Australia, and Malaysia. In the United States, bastnasite from California is an important rare-earth source.

Other minerals, sometimes useful for the extraction of the heavier rare earths, are gadolinite, $Fe(RE)_2Be_2(Si_2O_{10})$; samarskite, a rare-earth-iron-calcium-magnesium niobotantalate; and xenotime, an yttrium-earth-rare-earth phosphate.

The cerium earths predominate in monazite and bastnasite. Cerium is the most abundant rare earth, being comparable to boron in occurrence in the earth's crust. Promethium is formed in the fission of ^{238}U; in some rare-earth minerals it is present to the extent of about 10^{-17} per cent from the decay of the short-lived ^{147}Nd isotope.

Properties The elements are tervalent in most compounds. Cerium, praseodymium, and terbium exist in the tetravalent state, and samarium, europium, and ytterbium form easily oxidized divalent compounds. Due to similarities in atomic structure, many chemical properties of the rare earths are quite similar and vary only slightly from one rare earth to the adjacent neighbor. Consequently, their separation is difficult unless use is made of oxidation states other than the tervalent. With increasing atomic number, the rare earths become less basic, the salts generally become more soluble, and the differences between adjacent members decrease.

Ordinary rare-earth similarities are usually based on conventional chemical observations. Thus, in aqueous systems, the relatively large degree of hydration of rare-earth ions tends to mask differences. In non-solvent systems where the masking effect is not present, differences between rare earths are more apparent. Rare-earth metals and simple compounds do indeed show more marked differences, and the more sophisticated research on rare earths since about 1950 shows that mutual similarity is not necessarily an inherent property of these elements.

With the exception of lanthanum and lutetium, rare earth compounds show characteristic sharp absorption bands in the ultraviolet and visible spectra. This absorption is responsible for the pastel colors of the colored rare earth salts (green Pr, pink Nd, yellow Sm and Ho, rose Er, and pale green Tm).

Transitions in the $4f$ electrons account for most unusual properties: sharp absorption spectra in the ultraviolet, visible, and infrared—useful in optical devices, in the study of spectra theories, and in lasers. Complete pairing or formation of complete inner electron shells, resulting in balancing of magnetic moments causes ions to be diamagnetic (as for La, Lu, and Y); unpaired electrons lead to paramagnetic ions (as for Dy, Tb, and Ho).

Rare-earth Metals The metals have a silver-gray luster which tarnishes quickly in air if the metals are easily oxidized (La, Ce, Sm, Eu). Hardness varies from that comparable to lead (Eu, Yb), to tin (Ce, La), to zinc (Nd, Pr), to mild steel (Gd, Y). Densities (grams per cubic centimeter) vary from 6.18 for La and 6.8 for Ce to 9.8 for Tm and 7.0 for Yb. Melting points vary from 804°C for Ce to about 1700°C for Lu, and the boiling points are in the range 1490 to 4200°C.

Being active reducing agents, the metals react slowly with water and are soluble in dilute acids. They are pyrophoric when finely divided, cerium igniting in air at 150 to 180°C. Above 200 C, they combine directly with halogens, and they form nitrides with nitrogen above 1000°C. Interstitial hydrides approximating RH_2 or RH_3 are formed by absorption of hydrogen.

The mixture of rare-earth metals made commercially without appreciable separation of rare earths is known as "misch" metal. It contains about 22 per cent La, 50 per cent Ce, 18 per cent Nd, 5 per cent Pr, 1 per cent Sm, and 2 per cent other rare-earth metals. It is often sold as "cerium" metal.

Rare-earth Compounds Common water-soluble salts are the acetates, chlorides, nitrates, and sulfates. The carbonates, oxalates, hydroxides, oxides, phosphates, and fluorides are insoluble. Cerous (Ce^{+3}) salts are similar to the other tervalent rare earth salts, while ceric (Ce^{+4}) salts are more like those of thorium. Tervalent acetates and sulfates show decreased solubility in hot solutions.

Acetates are made by treating the hydroxide, carbonate or oxide with acetic acid. Carbonates are precipitated by the addition of alkali carbonates to neutral rare-earth solutions; they are only slightly soluble in excess of alkali carbonate. Fluorides are precipitated in hydrated form on adding hydrofluoric acid or soluble fluorides to rare-earth solutions. The precipitates are insoluble in excess hydrofluoric acid and in mineral acids. Anhydrous fluorides are made by hydrofluorinating the oxides at elevated temperatures.

Chlorides, bromides and iodides are prepared by dissolution of the hydroxide, oxide, or carbonate in the halogen acid. The salts crystallize from water as hydrates. Anhydrous chlorides and bromides are made by heating oxides with the ammonium halide, followed by sublimation of the excess ammonium salts in vacuum. Nitrates are formed similarly to the other water-soluble salts. They form many double nitrates with alkali and alkaline earth nitrates. Oxalates are precipitated from slightly acid solution with oxalic acid or alkali oxalates. They are important in the analysis for rare earths, and in the separation of rare earths from other metals. Hydroxides are precipitated from solution by alkali and ammonium hydroxides. The sulfates are characterized by their formation of sparingly soluble double sulfates with alkali sulfates. The

most important double sulfate is the sodium salt, $RE_2(SO_4)_3 \cdot Na_2SO_4 \cdot 2H_2O$.

Extraction and Separation The extraction of rare earths from monazite is commercially important. The ore is opened by heating with sulfuric acid to form anhydrous rare-earth and thorium sulfates and phosphoric acid, or by heating with sodium hydroxide solutions to form rare-earth and thorium hydroxides and sodium phosphate. The reaction products are lixiviated in water, and if the alkaline method is used, the washed rare-earth-thorium hydroxides are dissolved with acid.

Thorium is separated from the rare earths by fractional basicity precipitation or by precipitation of compounds such as thorium pyrophosphate. Rare earths are usually recovered from the thorium filtrates by precipitation of the double rare-earth sodium sulfate. The double sulfate precipitate is converted to rare-earth hydroxide which serves as the starting material for making commercial rare-earth salts.

Cerium is separated from the rare earths by oxidation to the tetravalent ceric state, followed by basicity separations or crystallizations of insoluble ceric compounds. Ceric salts are generally much less soluble than those of the tervalent rare earths. Crystallization of ammonium hexanitratocerate or ammonium trisulfatocerate, precipitation of basic ceric nitrates or sulfates, and fractional basicity separations with the hydrous oxides are commonly used procedures to separate and purify cerium.

Separation of the cerium-free rare earth mixture (often called "didymium") formerly was done by long series of fractional crystallizations and fractional precipitations. Ion exchange and solvent extraction methods of separation have replaced tedious fractional crystallization, and are used commercially to produce both technical and ultrahigh-purity rare earths. Exclusive of nonrare earth impurities, the purity of commercially available individual rare-earth compounds is usually 99.9 per cent, and in some cases as high as 99.9999 per cent.

Uses Most uses are based on unseparated rare-earth mixtures, or on technical cerium and "didymium" materials. The largest single use for mixed rare earths is in molecular sieve catalysts for gasoline production by petroleum cracking. Rare-earth-cored carbons are indispensable to the motion picture industry and are also used in military searchlights.

Rare-earth metal (misch metal) and cerium metal are important in the manufacture of lighter flints and certain alloys. Rare-earth-zirconium-magnesium alloys have outstanding high-temperature properties. Certain types of ferrous and stainless alloys are improved by the addition of misch metal or rare-earth compounds.

Rare-earth salts have important uses in the coloring and decolorizing of glass. Specially prepared cerium oxide and rare-earth oxide are widely used in polishing spectacle and optical instrument lenses, as well as mirrors, glass products, and granite.

Miscellaneous uses of the rare earths are: lanthanum oxide in silica-free optical glass, neodymium oxide as a coloring material for novelty glassware, "didymium" salts in temperature-compensating ceramic capacitors, rare-earth oxalate as a nausea preventive, rare-earth compounds as activators in phosphors, and various rare-earth salts in catalyst manufacture. Cerium compounds are used as laboratory reagents and as scavengers in explosive manufacturing.

As nuclear poisons, Sm, Gd, Eu, and Dy materials are useful because of the very high neutron cross sections of some of their isotopes. Gadolinium oxide and nitrate are used as burnable poisons in nuclear reactor fuels, in reactor shut-down devices, and in the reprocessing of spent nuclear fuels.

Yttrium oxide is a component of microwave ferrites of the garnet type. Most of the individual rare earths are important as host materials or dopants in laser crystals.

Europium-activated yttrium vanadate, oxide, and oxysulfide phosphors are used as the red phosphor component of color television tubes. Yttrium aluminum garnet ("YAG") single crystals are used as imitation diamonds in jewelry. Yttrium oxide is a stabilizer for zirconium dioxide refractories.

Samarium-cobalt alloys of the composition $SmCo_5$ are used as hard permanent magnet materials, particularly in space-critical microwave traveling-wave amplifiers to replace platinum-cobalt alloys. The samarium-cobalt permanent magnets have relative coercive forces about six to seven times those of ferrites, and nearly twice those of Pt-Co alloys. The Ce, Pr, Y, La, and mixed rare earth metal alloys with cobalt are also of interest as permanent magnet materials.

HOWARD E. KREMERS

References

Eyring, L., "Progress in The Science and Technology of the Rare Earths," Vols. 1, 2, 3, New York, Pergamon Press Ltd., 1964, 1966, 1968.

Field, P. E., "Ninth Rare Earth Research Conference Proceedings," Springfield, Va., National Technical Information Service, 1971.

Gould, R. F., Ed., "Lanthanide–Actinide Chemistry," Washington D. C., American Chemical Society, 1967.

Gschneidner, K. A., Ed., *Rare Earth Information Center News*, Ames, Iowa, Institute for Atomic Research, Iowa State University, published quarterly.

Gschneidner, K. A., "Rare Earth Alloys," New York, Van Nostrand Reinhold, 1961.

Pascal, Paul, "Nouveau Traité de Chimie Minerale," Vol. VII, Paris, Masson et Cie., 1959.

Silvernail, W., and Goetzinger, N., "Encyclopedia of Chemical Technology," Vol. 17, New York, John F. Wiley & Sons Inc., 1968.

Spedding, F. H., and Daane, A. H., "The Rare Earths,"
New York, John Wiley & Sons, Inc., 1961.

Tipton, C. R., Ed., "Reactor Handbook," Second
edition, Vol. 1, New York, Interscience Publishers,
Inc., 1960.

Cross-references: ELEMENTS,   TRANSURANIUM
ELEMENTS.

RECTIFIERS*

Rectification (Electric) Energy is most conviently transmitted and distributed by means of
galvanic electric currents in metallic conductors
(see CONDUCTIVITY, ELECTRICAL). In this form
energy is easily transported with very low losses,
easily accessible, and easy to control (see
ELECTRIC POWER GENERATION). Transmission
by electric current may also communicate
intelligence, such as images, electroacoustic
signals or counting pulses. Most human activities
depend on some form of electric energy transport or distribution, such as power, telephone,
radio, television, and most control functions.

Generators of electric energy from other
physical forms normally utilize a mechanical
intermediary (involving rotation or harmonic
oscillation) followed by an electromagnetic
generator. The output current is then equally
alternating in both directions, it can thus be
transformed to any desired current and voltage
level. Alternating current is ideal for generating
and transporting energy alone because no net
electronic or electrolytic charge or material
transport is required. On the other hand, in
usage, whenever electrical energy is stored in
batteries, energizes vacuum tube amplifiers, or
is used for electrochemical separation or particle
acceleration, the permanent and irreversible
transport of charges is mandatory, hence a
direct current is needed.

Rectifiers provide the physical means which
achieve electric rectification, comprising all the
elements which connect a complete ac circuit to
a complete dc circuit, without being part of
either (see Fig. 3). One rectifier may consist of a
plurality of rectifier diodes; their mode of interconnection is called a *rectifier circuit*.

Rectifier Diodes These are unilaterally conducting component devices with two terminals,
similar to resistors because they are passive
(i.e., not generating electric energy) and non-
reactive (i.e., not able to store electric energy).
The difference is in their being essentially
nonlinear (whereas resistors are linear), their
differential resistance varying over a very wide
range, depending only on the direction and
magnitude of the current through the device,
i.e., they are not time-dependent (see Fig. 1).

Rectifier Switching Rectification implies the
concept of switching, i.e., introducing a circuit

*Editor was unable to locate author. Article is re-
printed from first edition.

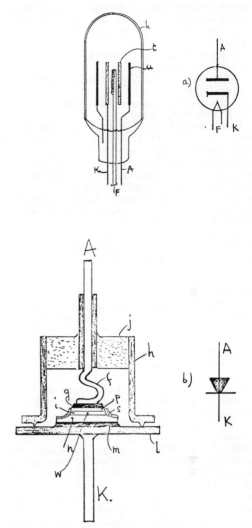

FIG. 1. Rectifier diode cross section and schematic
diagram: (a) vacuum tube, (b) semiconductor.

A = Anode. K = Cathode. F = Filament.
Current flow (forward) A to K.
Voltage blocking (reverse) K positive, A negative.
f = Metallic anode lead, hermetically sealed.
h = Metallic case, welded to l, gas filled.
i = Intrinsic silicon (not doped with impurities).
j = Ceramic insulator.
k = Glass tube, evacuated.
l = Metallic base plate.
m = Metallic bond to cathode.
n = Negatively doped silicon.
p = Positively doped silicon.
q = Metallic bond to anode.
s = Surface of water, insulated.
t = Tubular cathode insulator coated with metal
      oxide.
u = Tubular outer electrode.
w = Wafer of silicon.

element which has a resistance which varies instantaneously over such a wide range that it may (mathematically) be considered as a discontinuity.

Example: Semiconductor diode
Circuit impedance: 20 ohm
Diode forward resistance: 0.028 ohm = 1/700 of circuit
Diode reverse resistance hot: 500 000 ohm = 25 000 times circuit.

Controlled Rectifiers (Fig. 2) Controlled rectifiers are similar to rectifier diodes, except that they have two states of forward conductivity: forward blocking (same resistance characteristic as in the reverse direction, which is the same as in a diode) and forward conducting (same as in a diode). A control element (gate, grid) allows switching from the forward blocking to the forward conducting state. This control is very rapid and requires very little energy. Hence, the rectifier output can be controlled with a high amplification and with high speed. Gas tube controlled rectifiers are thyratrons. Semiconductor controlled rectifiers (SCR) are also known as thyristors.

Electronic Rectifier *Vacuum Tube* (*Diode, Triode, etc.*). Electronic rectifiers are based on the Edison effect (see ELECTRON TUBES, ELECTRONICS, THERMIONICS). Thermally emitted electrons from a hot metal oxide cathode are propelled across a short gap in high vacuum to a cold metallic anode. The high velocity of thermal electrons and the absence of a gas, generating positive ions, assure ideal conditions for electric rectification, i.e., a flow of pure electrons. Because of their high speed, the high-frequency response is very good. The potential field of the driving voltage accelerates the electrons, hence the rectifier is essentially a linear resistor in the forward direction and a good insulator in the reverse direction. The applications of the vacuum tube are far beyond the scope of simple rectification. All the grid- and beam-controlled tubes are also rectifier diodes, although generally not defined as such. This is because the resistance changes (see MODULATION) in the current-carrying direction are technically and economically much more important.

Thyratron. Rectifier tubes containing a low-pressure gas instead of a vacuum have the property that the resistance in the current-carrying stage is very low but not linear, as in a vacuum tube. This makes the device useless for variable resistance control (amplification), but much more efficient for rectification; a major resistance in the current flow direction is eliminated. This reduction of resistance is caused by impact ionization of the gas, hence the thyratron responds less rapidly than the vacuum tube. The ionized gas is usually a pure element (e.g., mercury, hydrogen, krypton) to avoid chemical reactions between ions and electrodes. Current is carried both as positive ions and negative

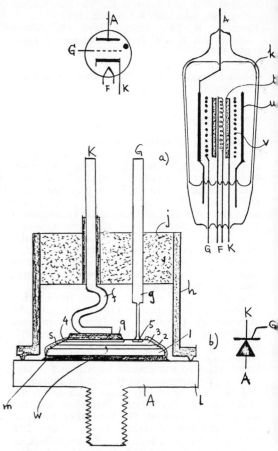

FIG. 2. Controlled rectifiers. Cross section and schematic diagrams: (a) thyratron, (b) semiconductor controlled rectifier (thyristor).

A = Anode. K = Cathode. G = Grid or Gate.
F = Filament.
Current flow (forward) A to K.
Reverse voltage blocking, K positive, A negative.
1 = *p*-type anode layer.
2 = *n*-type intermediary layer.
3 = *p*-type gate layer.
4 = *n*-type cathode layer.
5 = *p*-type contact for gate.
f = Metallic cathode lead, hermetically sealed.
g = Metallic gate lead.
h = Metallic case, welded to 1, gas-filled.
j = Ceramic insulator.
k = Glass tube, gas-filled.
l = Metallic base plate.
m = Metallic bond to anode.
q = Metallic bond to cathode.
s = Surface of wafer, insulated.
t = Tubular cathode insulator, coated with metal oxide.
u = Tubular outer electrode.
v = Helicoidal grid structure.
w = Wafer of silicon.

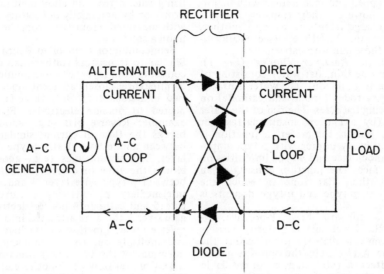

FIG. 3. Rectifier circuit: single-phase bridge. Four rectifier diodes are connected together to achieve full rectification of both (negative and positive) waves of a single phase alternating current. The alternating current flowing in the closed loop (ac circuit) on the left-hand side is converted into a direct current flowing in the closed loop (dc circuit) on the right-hand side.

electrons. Thus, reversing the voltage on the gap results in a definite period of current reversal (ion sweep-out). This severely limits the useful operating frequency. A control grid allows one to select the time at which the thyratron becomes conductive ("firing"). Once conduction is initiated, the grid field is neutralized by the ionized gas, hence grid control has no effect (see Controlled Rectifier above).

Excitron (Mercury-arc Rectifier). This is similar to the thyratron, except the cathode is a pool of liquid mercury. An arc is sustained between the cathode and an exciting anode; conduction to the main anode is controlled both by anode voltage and a control grid.

Ignitron. Replacing the heated solid cathode of a diode by a pool of liquid mercury gives an ignitron. To initiate conduction, a localized spot on the liquid surface (cathode spot) is forcibly overheated (ignited). Selecting the firing time (controlled rectifier) is achieved by energizing an ignitor which creates a cathode spot at a definite time. Ignitors are silicon carbide rods dipping into the mercury; subjected to a brief current pulse, a surface arc occurs at the mercury-silicon carbide interface. The liquid is locally driven to a very high temperature by forced electron emission and ion impact, resulting in violent evaporation and ionization of the mercury. Once conducting, the ignitron has the properties of a gas-filled tube (thyratron); it also requires the same deionization time and ion sweep-out current. Excess mercury vapor precipitates on the cold walls of the tube, flowing back into the liquid cathode. The ignitron is particularly applicable

to very high power. It presents the advantages of high efficiency, high reliability and small size.

Semiconductor Rectifier Crystallized semimetals (such as selenium, copper oxide, germanium or silicon) and some organic compositions can be used to make devices which rectify electric currents (see SEMICONDUCTORS and TRANSISTOR). Semiconductors carry current by excess electrons or electron vacancies (carriers) moving in the solid crystal lattice. The transfer of charges is very rapid and driven by very small potential differences. The polarity of a semiconductor is not determined by the material itself but by relatively few impurity nuclei ("doping") substituted in the crystal. Impurities (compared to the base material) have either an excess (n-type, negative, conducting by "electrons") or a deficiency (p-type, positive, conducting by "holes") of nuclear charges and hence electron shells. In the rigid lattice, the nuclei and normal electron shells are immobile. Excess or defect carriers are freely mobile. The density of these majority carriers is determined by the relative content of impurities in the crystal. The background of the lattice with its mutually neutralizing nuclei and electron shells does not contribute to the conduction or to the distribution of potentials.

Semiconductors conduct both by majority carriers (e.g., holes in p-type), and minority carriers (e.g., electrons in p-type) if such are injected by a junction with the opposite polarity material, e.g., majority carrier electrons coming from n-type material injected into p-type (see TRANSISTOR). Injected minority carriers are

ultimately trapped and recombined with majority carriers; however, they transfer a major quantity of charge from one zone to another, depending on the "lifetime" (see SEMICONDUCTOR) of these minority carriers.

Semiconductor Rectifier Diodes (Fig. 1). They contain one thin, flat wafer consisting of a single crystal (e.g., silicon). The wafer is brazed to metallic electrodes (anode and cathode) on its two opposing flat sides. The rim of the wafer is insulated (by oxidation, insulating resin or fused glass). Within the wafer, a junction is established by heavy doping with *p*-type impurities on its anode face and *n*-type impurities on the cathode face. The junction consists of an intermediate, thin, flat zone in which the density of both *p*-type and *n*-type dopants is very low.

Applying a forward bias (P-positive, N-negative) to the device injects majority carriers from both zones through the junction into the opposite zone. Attracted by the opposite potential, they effect a total transfer of available charges; i.e., a current flows with only a low driving potential difference. An unlimited number of carriers can flow across the small potential (energy level) barrier between the zones, carriers are replenished by metal-to-semiconductor brazed joints on both faces of the wafer.

Reversing the bias at the junction (N-positive, P-negative) reverses the flow of carriers. Majority carriers from both zones are displaced away from the junction, a potential wall is created by depleting the crystal of its mobile carriers. The immovable charges of the lattice-bound nuclei which are now uncompensated by the displaced mobile charges, create a high potential wall. A very small reverse current flows, sustained only by the thermally generated minority carriers of both zones which are swept across the junction. When applying a very high potential (e.g., 1000 volts), these highly accelerated carriers generate more carriers by avalanche multiplication due to impact with the lattice; above a certain voltage, so many carriers are generated that the reverse characteristic remains at a constant voltage at any current level. Semiconductor diodes have a very low forward voltage drop (e.g., 1 volt) and the forward resistance is not constant but decreases with increasing current. The reverse current is negligibly small, except at very high voltage where the reverse resistance is negligible.

Varying the semiconductor material (mainly germanium and silicon), the impurity content, the distribution of impurities across the junction, the area of the junction, and its peripheral configuration (planar, mesa, cut wafer) allows for a multitude of possible designs, each preferred for certain applications. Silicon wafers with diffused impurities (e.g., boron and phosphorus) are used for high-power, low-frequency rectifier diodes. Planar junctions on the surface of a solid wafer, in which the impurities are diffused under a layer of protective oxide, give diodes with good high-frequency and low-noise response. Junctions are also made by recrystal-lizing silicon from an alloy melt (alloyed junctions) or by epitaxially depositing pure silicon, with measured impurities, from the vapor phase upon a solid wafer.

Semiconductor Controlled Rectifiers (Fig. 2) Similar to transistors (rather than diodes) they consist of four layers of semiconductor material forming three closely adjacent junctions (against two in a transistor). Only three layers are connected to outside electrodes. Figure 2 is an example: Reverse bias (e.g., anode negative) blocks the flow of current similar to a diode between anode layer 1 and *n*-type intermediary layer 2. Forward bias (e.g., anode positive) blocks the flow of current similar to a diode between *p*-type gate layer 3 and *n*-type layer intermediary 2. Initiating a current between gate 5 and cathode 4 injects electrons into the gate layer 3; these are attracted into the adjacent reverse biased junction (3-2) where they attract and multiply due to (forward current) carrier injection by the two outer junctions (1-2 and 3-4). Counter-flow of opposite carriers through the same junction results in a very low voltage drop.

Reverse and forward blocking characteristics are similar to diode reverse characteristics. Forward conducting characteristics are similar to diode forward characteristics.

Mechanical Rectifier A coil of wire rotating in a magnetic field generates an alternating voltage; if the ends of many similar coils are connected to "commutator bars" (arranged on a cylindrical commutator), the output of two stationary brushes contacting the bars is a direct current. This dynamo is of historic and economic significance. Trial-and-error improvements have made this combination of rotating machine and mechanical rectifier an efficient and economic system. Mechanical rectifiers separated from the moving coils (i.e., a commutator driven by a synchronous motor) are workable but less reliable (because subject to wear) and less economical than other rectifiers.

Electrolytic Rectifier Some electrolytic batteries can serve as rectifiers because of the rapid and thorough polarization of one of the electrodes, whereas the other electrode may carry the current rather easily. The system is permanently changed by the flow of current; hence, it is not reliable or economical. Its speed of response is low, depending on the slow diffusion of ions in the electrolyte.

EDWARD J. DIEBOLD

Cross-references: CONDUCTIVITY, ELECTRICAL; ELECTRIC POWER GENERATION; ELECTRON TUBES; ELECTRONICS; MODULATION; SEMICONDUCTORS; THERMIONICS; TRANSISTOR.

REFLECTION

If a perfectly smooth and flat interface exists between two homogeneous media, the ratio of the reflected to the incident intensity of light

striking the interface is called the *reflectivity*. A real surface, however, is not ideally smooth and undistorted so that the situation is complicated by surface conditions such as films, roughness, and disorder in the crystal lattice at the surface introduced by the polishing process. The measured ratio is thus usually termed the *reflectance* to distinguish it from the former more- or less-idealized situation.

The reflectivity of a material is intimately connected with its band structure.[1] In a single atom, the electrons surrounding the nucleus can have only certain discrete energies. In a solid or liquid, neighboring atoms interact with each other changing these discrete energy levels into energy bands. The energy band structure depends not only on the type of atoms involved but also on the interatomic spacing, and hence in a crystalline material on the lattice structure. In a noncrystalline solid or in a liquid, the correlation function takes the place of the crystalline lattice. The highest occupied energy band may be completely filled with electrons, as in the case of a dielectric or semiconductor, or only partially filled, as for a metal. If the band is not completely full, electrons may absorb energy from the incident light beam and be raised to higher energies in the band, thus affecting the reflectivity of the material. These *intraband* transitions of the conduction electrons, or, in case of a nearly filled band, holes (the absence of electrons), largely determine the reflectivity of metals and some semiconductors in the infrared region of the spectrum. At shorter wavelengths, the light has sufficient energy to raise the electrons from one energy band to another, and the reflectivity is then also affected by these *interband* transitions.

In dielectric materials, where the occupied band having the highest energy is completely filled and the gap between allowed energy bands is large, the energy in the incident light beam cannot be absorbed either in intraband transitions or, except at very short wavelengths, in interband transitions. Such materials are therefore often transparent over an extended wavelength region in the ultraviolet, visible and near infrared, and have a nonzero reflectivity in this wavelength region only because of the difference in the speed of light in the material and in the surrounding medium. However various types of imperfections, termed F centers, M centers, etc., may exist in the lattices of crystalline materials, and electrons trapped in such centers can strongly absorb certain energies, thus affecting the reflectivity. In the intermediate and far infrared, dielectrics and many semiconductors absorb because the incident light excites vibrations in their crystal lattices. Since the frequencies of these lattice vibrations are quantized, this so-called phonon absorption results in maxima in the reflectivity spectra, termed restrahlen bands.

Other mechanisms also contribute to the reflectivity. Some which should be mentioned are transitions between a localized impurity level and an energy band, absorption by a bound hole-electron pair or exciton, and indirect or phonon-assisted interband transitions.

Electromagnetic Theory The reflectivity of any material can be calculated from electromagnetic theory[2,3] if the optical constants of the material are known. This theory, which is based entirely on Maxwell's equations, is phenomenological in that it does not attempt to explain why materials behave as they do, but rather sets forth relationships which exist between various properties of the material. In order to calculate the reflectance of a material from this theory, the two optical constants, n and k, must be known. The index of refraction n is equal to the ratio of the phase velocity of light in vacuum to the phase velocity in the material. The extinction coefficient k is equal to $\lambda/4\pi$ times the absorption coefficient of the material and is thus a measure of the fraction of light absorbed by a unit thickness of the material. These parameters, which are frequently combined into the complex refractive index $\bar{n} = n - jk$, arise in the solution to the wave equation and completely describe all the optical properties of the material.

The equation for the propagation of an electromagnetic wave can be obtained directly from Maxwell's equations, and in Gaussian units can be written

$$\nabla^2 \mathbf{E} = \frac{\epsilon}{c^2}\frac{\partial^2 \mathbf{E}}{\partial t^2} + \frac{4\pi\sigma}{c^2}\frac{\partial \mathbf{E}}{\partial t} \tag{1}$$

where ∇^2 is the Laplacian operator $\partial^2/\partial x^2 + \partial^2/\partial y^2 + \partial^2/\partial z^2$, $\mathbf{E}$ the electric field strength of the traveling wave, t the time, c the velocity of light and ϵ and σ the dielectric constant and conductivity of the material, respectively, at the frequency of the wave. The solution representing a plane wave traveling in the z direction is

$$E = E_0 e^{j\omega(t - \bar{n}z/c)} \tag{2}$$

where $\omega = 2\pi\nu$ is the angular frequency of the wave, E_0 the amplitude, and $\bar{n}$ the complex refractive index. By matching E_0 and its first derivative on either side of a smooth, plane interface between a transparent material of index n_0, the medium of incidence, and a second material of index $\bar{n}_1$, one can obtain r, the ratio of the reflected to the incident amplitude, called the *amplitude reflection coefficient*:

$$r = \frac{\eta_0 - \bar{\eta}_1}{\eta_0 + \bar{\eta}_1} \tag{3}$$

where η_0 and $\bar{\eta}_1$ are the effective indices. At normal incidence, $\eta_0 = n_0$ and $\bar{\eta}_1 = \bar{n}_1 = n_1 - jk_1$.

At non-normal incidence, Snell's law may be used to determine the angle of refraction ϕ_r corresponding to a given angle of incidence ϕ_i. For the case when both materials are nonabsorbing, Snell's law states

$$\frac{\sin \phi_i}{\sin \phi_r} = \frac{n_1}{n_0} \tag{4}$$

It is also necessary to specify the state of polarization of the incident light. Since **E** is a vector quantity, it is always possible to resolve it into two components, the so-called p and s components, polarized parallel to and perpendicular to the plane of incidence (the plane containing both the incident beam and the normal to the surface). There are then two effective indices, η_p and η_s, for each medium at a given angle of incidence. For nonabsorbing materials they are defined as

$$\eta_s = n \cos \phi \qquad (5)$$

$$\eta_p = \frac{n}{\cos \phi} \qquad (6)$$

where ϕ is the angle of incidence or refraction in the medium of index n. In the medium of incidence, ϕ becomes ϕ_i while in the second medium, ϕ becomes ϕ_r. If the second medium is absorbing ($k \neq 0$), $\cos \phi$ becomes complex, making η_s and η_p also complex. They may then be most easily calculated from the following expressions:[4]

$$\bar{\eta}_s = A - jB \qquad (7)$$

$$\bar{\eta}_p = C - jD \qquad (8)$$

where

$$A^2 - B^2 = n_1{}^2 - k_1{}^2 - n_0{}^2 \sin^2 \phi_i \qquad (9)$$

$$AB = n_1 k_1 \qquad (10)$$

$$C = A \left[1 + \frac{n_0{}^2 \sin^2 \phi_i}{A^2 + B^2} \right] \qquad (11)$$

$$D = B \left[1 - \frac{n_0{}^2 \sin^2 \phi_i}{A^2 + B^2} \right] \qquad (12)$$

The *intensity reflection coefficient* or *reflectivity* R, defined as the ratio of the intensities of the reflected and incident light, is obtained by multiplying the amplitude reflection coefficient of Eq. (3) by its complex conjugate. At normal incidence for an absorbing material

$$R = \frac{(n_1 - n_0)^2 + k_1{}^2}{(n_1 + n_0)^2 + k_1{}^2} \qquad (13)$$

At non-normal incidence, the expressions for R_s and R_p for absorbing materials become quite complicated. However, for nonabsorbing materials

$$R_s = \frac{\sin^2 (\phi_i - \phi_r)}{\sin^2 (\phi_i + \phi_r)} \qquad (14)$$

and

$$R_p = \frac{\tan^2 (\phi_i - \phi_r)}{\tan^2 (\phi_i + \phi_r)} \qquad (15)$$

Equations (14) and (15) are the intensity expressions for Fresnel's equations. From Eq. (15) it is seen that when $\phi_i + \phi_r = 90°$, $R_p = 0$ so that all of the reflected light is polarized in the s direction. The angle of incidence for this case is called the polarizing angle and is given by

$$\tan \phi_i = \frac{n_1}{n_0} \qquad (16)$$

A plot of the reflectivity R_p and R_s as a function of angle of incidence is shown in Fig. 1(a) for a transparent material in air and in Fig. 1(b) for an absorbing material. Note that the R_p curve for the transparent material goes to zero while the R_p curve for the absorbing material does not.

The phenomenon of total internal reflection is important for transparent materials. If light passes from a more optically dense (higher index) medium of index n_0 to a less optically dense (lower index) medium of index n_1, when $\sin \phi_i = n_1/n_0$, the angle of refraction in the less dense medium is $90°$, as can be seen from Eq. (4). At larger angles of incidence, the light is totally internally reflected in the more dense medium. This method of obtaining a surface whose reflectivity is 100 per cent is widely used in optical instruments such as binoculars and periscopes, which contain internally reflecting prisms.

Whenever light is reflected from a surface, a change in phase occurs in the electric vector. For the case of a normal incidence reflection in air from a dielectric, the phase change β is $180°$, while for a reflection in the more dense medium, β is $0°$. When the reflection is from an absorbing material, β depends on the optical constants of the material,[5] and $\tan \beta$ is given by the ratio of the imaginary to the real part of Eq. (3). If the medium of incidence is air,

$$\tan \beta = - \frac{2k}{n^2 + k^2 - 1} \qquad (17)$$

for a normal incidence reflection from an absorbing material with $\bar{n} = n - jk$. At non-normal incidence, the phase change on reflection is different for the p and s components. By a technique called ellipsometry,[6] this difference in phase can be measured and used, along with other data, to determine the optical constants of a material. If a surface film is present, the phase difference between the p and s components can also be used to measure its growth. Films as thin as a monolayer or less can be detected in this way.

As was indicated at the beginning of this section, Maxwell's equations by themselves do not give sufficient information to relate the optical constants of a material to basic atomic parameters. A fundamental problem in the theory of the optical properties of solids is thus to supplement electromagnetic theory in such a way as to relate the optical constants of a

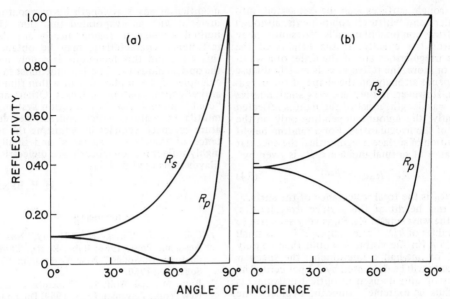

FIG. 1. Graph of the reflectivity R_p and R_s as a function of angle of incidence for (a) a transparent material ($n = 2$) in air, and (b) an absorbing material ($n = 2$ and $k = 2$) in air.

material to nonoptical quantities which can be experimentally determined. If Eq. (2) is substituted into Eq. (1), one obtains the basic equations relating the optical constants to the dielectric constant and conductivity measured at optical frequencies:

$$n^2 - k^2 = \epsilon \qquad (18)$$

$$nk = \sigma/\nu \qquad (19)$$

The problem is how to relate ϵ and σ to the dielectric constant and conductivity at zero frequency, ϵ_0 and σ_0, or to atomic parameters such as the effective mass m^*, number of free carriers per cubic centimeter N, oscillator strength f, etc. A classical simple harmonic oscillator theory first proposed by H. A. Lorentz in 1880 has been successfully used to solve this problem for materials in which the absorption is caused by forced vibrations, while a companion classical theory proposed by P. Drude in 1901 has had similar success for materials where the absorption is due to free electrons and holes. Quantum mechanical treatments give rise to equations having the same form as the classical ones, but containing parameters whose values can be calculated rather than having to be empirically determined. Although these theories will not be discussed here, it can be pointed out that, to a very good approximation, the reflectivity of good conductors in the infrared region is given by[7]

$$R = 1 - \left[\frac{2\omega}{\pi\sigma_0}\right]^{1/2} [(1 + \omega^2\tau^2)^{1/2} - \omega\tau]^{1/2} \qquad (20)$$

where the relaxation time τ is given by

$$\tau = \frac{m^*\sigma_0}{Ne^2} \qquad (21)$$

and e is the electronic charge. At sufficiently long wavelengths, $\omega\tau \ll 1$ and the reflectivity is then given by the Hagen-Rubens relation

$$R = 1 - \left[\frac{2\omega}{\pi\sigma_0}\right]^{1/2} \qquad (22)$$

which may also be obtained directly from Eqs. (13), (18) and (19). Both Eqs. (20) and (22) are in good agreement with experiment.

Reflectance of Real Surfaces In the preceding discussion, it has been assumed that there are two homogeneous media separated by a perfectly smooth and flat interface. In actual fact this situation does not occur, and it is necessary to consider how the deviation of real surfaces from this model affects the observed reflectance. Consider first the effect of surface roughness. For a perfectly smooth surface, all light is reflected at the specular angle, which is equal to the angle of incidence. At the other extreme, the angular dependence of light reflected from a perfectly diffuse reflector is independent of the angle of incidence, and Lambert's law then holds. This law may be stated

$$I_d(\theta) = I_0 \cos \theta \qquad (23)$$

where I_0 is the total amount of light reflected per unit area normal to a perfectly diffuse plane reflector, and $I_d(\theta)$ that reflected per unit area at an angle θ to the normal. The reflectance of

actual rough surfaces can be separated into "specular" and "diffuse" components, although the diffuse component usually does not obey Lambert's law exactly. If the heights of the surface irregularities are of the order of a wavelength or more, the reflectance is mostly diffuse and depends strongly on the shape of the irregularities. However, if they are very small relative to the wavelength, most of the light is reflected specularly, the amount depending only on the height of the irregularities. For a random height distribution of surface irregularities, the specular reflectance at normal incidence R_s is given by[8]

$$R_s = R_0 e^{-(4\pi h/\lambda)^2} \qquad (24)$$

where R_0 is the total reflectance of the surface, h the rms height of the surface irregularities, and λ the wavelength. R_s/R_0 is very sensitive to small values of h/λ. For example, if h is as small as 0.025λ (in the visible h would then be only 12 nm, or one-half a microinch), the specular reflectance will be decreased by 10 per cent. The surfaces of mirrors used in optical instruments must thus be extremely smooth. Typically the rms roughness of such mirrors is about 2.5 nm (0.1 microinch) rms and may be as small as 0.8 nm (0.03 microinch) rms. Roughness of 2.5 nm are large enough to reduce the reflectance of metals slightly in the infrared via the anomalous skin effect.[9] In addition, at wavelengths near the surface plasmon frequency for a metal the reflectance may be reduced significantly for 2.5 nm rms surfaces by optical excitation of surface plasmons.[10] This effect is of primary importance in the ultraviolet, but for metals such as silver it extends into the visible region. Since the excited plasmons may decay by incoherent reemission, scattered light may also increase where plasmon excitation occurs.

The reflectance may also be affected by distortion of the crystal lattice at the surface caused by the polishing process. The amplitude penetration depth δ of light into an absorbing medium, given by

$$\delta = \lambda/2\pi k \qquad (25)$$

is usually only a few tens of nanometers or roughly one microinch for metals or semiconductors in the intrinsic absorption region. On the other hand, lattice distortion introduced by optical polishing may extend for many hundreds of nanometers below the surface, so that the reflection takes place entirely in the disturbed surface layer. Fortunately, the lattice distortion on the surface can be nearly eliminated in many cases by using proper electropolishing techniques.[11] Optical polishing can also produce changes in the reflectance of dielectrics and noncrystalline materials such as optical glass.

Finally, surface films can have a large effect on the reflectance. Although naturally occurring oxide films are important mainly in the ultraviolet, the reflectance may be substantially modified at any wavelength by overcoating the material with an evaporated thin film. Over a limited wavelength region, nearly any desired reflectance characteristic may be obtained in this way, and this technique is widely used in the optical industry.[12] Perhaps the most familiar example of the application of a thin film is the antireflection coating on lenses. Others are the "cold" mirrors used in projection systems, the multilayer coatings which control the temperature of space vehicles by adjusting the reflectance of their outer surfaces, and finally the highly reflecting, low-absorbance dielectric multilayer films used with lasers.

H. E. BENNETT

References

1. Callaway, J., "Energy Band Theory," New York, Academic Press, 1964; Bube, R. H., "Photoconductivity of Solids," New York, John Wiley & Sons, Inc., 1960.
2. Born, M., and Wolf, E., "Principles of Optics," New York, Pergamon Press, 1959; Ditchburn, R. W., "Light," Second edition, London, Blackie and Son Ltd., 1963.
3. Stratton, J. A., "Electromagnetic Theory," New York, McGraw-Hill Book Co., 1941; Slater, J. C., and Frank, N. H., "Electromagnetism," New York, McGraw-Hill Book Co., 1947.
4. Abelès, F., "Progress in Optics," Vol. 2, Amsterdam, North-Holland Publishing Co., 1963.
5. Bennett, J. M., *J. Opt. Soc. Am.*, **54**, 612 (1964).
6. McCrackin, F. L., Passaglia, E., Stromberg, R. R., and Steinberg, H. L., *J. Res. Natl. Bur. St.*, **67A**, 363 (1963).
7. Seitz, F., "The Modern Theory of Solids," New York, McGraw-Hill Book Co., 1940; Bennett, H. E., Silver, M., and Ashley, E. J., *J. Opt. Soc. Am.*, **53**, 1089 (1963).
8. Bennett, H. E., and Porteus, J. O., *J. Opt. Soc. Am.*, **51**, 123 (1961); Porteus, J. O., *J. Opt. Soc. Am.*, **53**, 1394 (1963); Beckmann, P., and Spizzichino, A., "The Scattering of Electromagnetic Waves from Rough Surfaces," New York, The Macmillan Co., 1963.
9. Bennett, H. E., Bennett, J. M., Ashley, E. J., and Motyka, R. J., *Phys. Rev.*, **165**, 755 (1968).
10. Jasperson, S. N., and Schnatterly, S. E., *Phys. Rev.*, **188**, 759 (1969); Endriz, J. G., and Spicer, W. E., *Phys. Rev.*, **4B**, 4144 (1971); Elson, J. M., and Ritchie, R. H., *Phys. Rev.*, **4B**, 4129 (1971).
11. Donovan, T. M., Ashley, E. J., and Bennett, H. E., *J. Opt. Soc. Am.*, **53**, 1403 (1963); Holland, L., "The Properties of Glass Surfaces," London, Chapman and Hall, 1964.
12. Heavens, O. S., *Rep. Progr. Phys.*, **23**, 1 (1960); Heavens, O. S., "Optical Properties of Thin Solid Films," London, Butterworths Scientific Publications, 1955.

Cross-references: ENERGY LEVELS; OPTICS, GEOMETRICAL; OPTICS, PHYSICAL; POLARIZED LIGHT; REFRACTION; SEMICONDUCTORS.

REFRACTION

Refraction is the name given to the bending of a ray of light as it crosses the boundary separating two transparent media having differing propagation velocities.

In an attempt to discover a law connecting the directions of the light rays in the two media, W. Snell (1621) observed that there is a constant ratio between the lengths PB, PC of the two rays (Fig. 1) measured from the point of incidence P to any line such as DD' drawn parallel to the normal PN at the point of incidence. Later Descartes recognized that Snell's construction is equivalent to the mathematical expression

$$n \sin I = n' \sin I'$$

when I, I' are the angles of incidence between the two rays and the normal, and n, n' are the *refractive indices* of the two media respectively. The ratio of n' to n is called the "relative" refractive index of the two media.

Huygens' Wavelets C. Huygens (1690) attempted to explain how a wave front progresses through a transparent medium. He supposed that each point on the wave front acts as an independent source of wavelets which expand at the velocity of light, the new wave front being the common envelope of all the little wavelets. After an instant of time, each point in the new wave front becomes a source of new wavelets, and so on. In a homogeneous isotropic medium, the wavelets will be spheres, and the new wave front is a parallel curve to the original wave front. The light energy travels along *rays* which are everywhere perpendicular to the wave fronts. Malus (1808) showed that the rays and wave fronts remain always orthogonal as the beam of light from an object point traverses an optical system.

The absolute refractive index of a medium is defined as the ratio of the velocity of light in

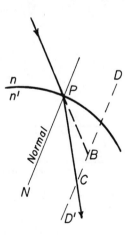

FIG. 1. Illustrates Snell's construction.

vacuum to its velocity in the medium. Because the presence of matter has the effect of making light travel more slowly, all absolute refractive indices are necessarily positive and greater than unity. Since the frequency of the light waves must remain constant, the wavelength in a dense medium will be less than the wavelength in vacuum in proportion to the refractive index of the medium. Refractive indices of liquids and crystals generally drop with increasing temperature; glasses are, however, often exceptional in this regard.[1]

Refractive indices range from as low as 1.3 for some liquids such as water, through 1.5 to 1.9 for various types of glass, 2.5 for diamond, up to as high as 4.0 for some materials (germanium) in the infrared. These exceptionally high indices are generally associated with complete opacity in the visible part of the spectrum.

Dispersion It is found that the refractive index of all common materials rises with increasing frequency of the light (shorter wavelengths) leading to the phenomenon of *dispersion*. Because of this, a glass prism bends blue light more than red, thus spreading a ray of white light into

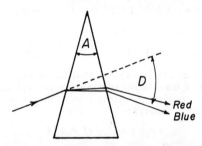

FIG. 2. The dispersion caused by a prism.

its component colors (Fig. 2). For a prism of very small angle A, the deviation angle D is given by

$$D = A(n - 1)$$

and the angular dispersion Δ between wavelengths a and b is given by

$$\Delta = A(n_b - n_a)$$

It has been customary to define the dispersive power w of a material as the ratio of the dispersion between the F and C Fraunhofer lines to the mean deviation, i.e., the deviation for the D Fraunhofer line. Thus

$$w = (n_F - n_C)/(n_D - 1)$$

The vacuum wavelengths of these lines are $C = 0.6563\mu$, $D = 0.5893\mu$, and $F = 0.4861\mu$. In the optical industry, the reciprocal of the dispersive power is, however, more generally used; i.e.,

$$V = 1/w = (n_D - 1)/(n_F - n_C)$$

This so-called "V-value" or "Abbe number" of optical glass ranges from about 25 for the densest

flints up to about 70 for the lightest fluor crowns. Liquids and crystals are known in which the *V*-numbers range from about 16 (methylene iodide) to 95 (calcium fluoride).

Many attempts have been made to develop a formula connecting the refractive index of a material with the wavelength of the light. The best known and most comprehensive is that proposed by Sellmeier,[2] namely,

$$n^2 = 1.0 + \sum \frac{b\lambda^2}{c^2 - \lambda^2}$$

Here *n* is the refractive index corresponding to wavelength λ, while *b* and *c* are constants. The constant *c* represents the center of an absorption band for which the refractive index becomes infinite; there are thus as many terms under the summation sign as there are absorption bands to be considered. For most transparent materials, it is sufficient to include one absorption band in the ultraviolet and one in the infrared.

This general formula may be reduced to a simpler form for a limited spectral range, some well-known simplifications being

$$n = a + b/\lambda^2 + c/\lambda^4 + \cdots \quad \text{(Cauchy)}$$

$$n = 1 + b/(c - \lambda) \quad \text{(Hartmann)}$$

$$n = a + b/\lambda + c/\lambda^{7/2} \quad \text{(Conrady)}$$

Herzberger[3] has shown that the refractive index of a transparent substance such as glass can be accurately represented by a four-constant formula of this type:

$$n = a + b\lambda^2 + cL + dL^2$$

where $L = 1/(\lambda^2 - 0.028)$.

Birefringence, or Double Refraction Glasses, liquids, and some (e.g., cubic) crystals are *isotropic*, meaning that the velocity of light in the medium is independent of direction and the Huygenian wavelets are spherical. However, there are other crystals which are *anisotropic*. These have the property that a beam of light on entering the crystal is split into two perpendicularly polarized beams, one of which (the ordinary") behaves normally, while the other (the "extraordinary") behaves abnormally in that the wave front is not perpendicular to the direction of propagation.

These two wave fronts can be explained by supposing that two Huygenian wavelets are formed at any point of incidence, the ordinary wavelet being spherical while the extraordinary wavelet is an ellipsoid, (Fig. 3).[4] The advancing wave front is the common tangent to a row of wavelets, and the ray, or direction of travel, is found by joining the point of origin of the wavelet to the point of contact between the wavelet and the advancing wave front. The spherical wavelets thus yield a ray which is perpendicular to the wave front, but the ellipsoidal wavelets do not.

All anisotropic crystals possess either one or two directions ("optic axes") along which a ray of light is not divided into two. These are represented by the axes of symmetry of the ellipsoidal wavelets. Evidently if parallel light is travelling along an optic axis, the two advancing wave fronts will be parallel to one another and the two rays will coincide (see POLARIZED LIGHT).

Refraction by an Inhomogeneous Medium Suppose we have a parallel plate of material of which the refractive index varies laterally across the plate. A ray entering such a plate perpendicularly to its surface will suffer no refraction itself since the incidence angle is zero, but because there is a gradient of refractive index at right angles to the ray, the ray inside the plate will be bent towards the high-index region and will follow a curved path. This is readily seen if we remember that the ray will be perpendicular to the wave front and that each point on the wave front travels at a rate which is inversely

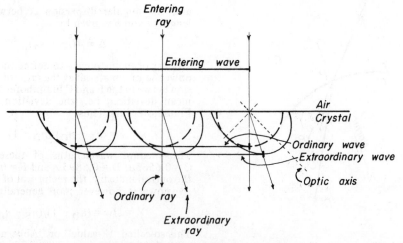

FIG. 3. Explanation of double refraction.

proportional to the refractive index at that point. To determine the curvature of the ray inside the medium, we may refer to Fig. 4 in which CC′ represents the surface of a nonhomogeneous

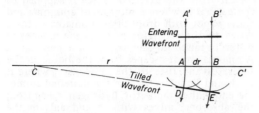

FIG. 4. Bending of a light ray in an inhomogeneous medium.

medium, and A′A, B′B represent two very close rays entering perpendicular to the surface. We shall suppose the velocity of light in the material to be v at A and $(v + dv)$ at B, the refractive indices being $(n + dn)$ and n respectively. Typical wavelets have been added at A and B, having radii AD and BE which are proportional to the velocities v and $(v + dv)$. Hence the refracted wave front is ED; this intersects the surface at C, which is therefore the instantaneous center of curvature of the rays within the medium.

If r is the radius of ray AD,

$$\frac{CA}{CB} = \frac{r}{r + dr} = \frac{AD}{BE} = \frac{v}{v + dv} = \frac{n + dn}{n}$$

Neglecting second-order infinitesimals this gives

$$\frac{1}{r} = -\frac{1}{n}\left(\frac{dn}{dr}\right)$$

The curvature of the ray is, therefore, proportional to the rate of change of refractive index in a direction perpendicular to the ray itself.

This property of inhomogeneous media provides the explanation of mirages and also the well-known atmospheric refraction which makes celestial objects appear to be raised up by as much as half a degree for objects situated near the horizon.

R. KINGSLAKE

References

1. Molby, F. A., *J. Opt. Soc. Am.*, **39**, 600–611 (1949)
2. Wood, R. W., "Physical Optics," page 470, New York, Dover, 1967.
3. Herzberger, M. J., *Optica Acta*, **6**, 197–215 (1959).
4. Wood, R. W., "Physical Optics," Third Edition, pp. 365–387, New York, Dover, 1967.

Cross-references: LIGHT; OPTICS, GEOMETRICAL; OPTICS, PHYSICAL; POLARIZED LIGHT; REFLECTION; WAVE MOTION.

REFRIGERATION

Refrigeration is the process of cooling or freezing a substance to a temperature well below that of the surroundings and maintaining it in the cold state. The simplest device for this purpose consists of a box or a cryostat immersed in a cooling agent such as cold running water, circulating air cooled by melting ice, liquid air, liquid helium, etc. Generally, the coolant must be replenished periodically, an inconvenient and often inefficient procedure. Since the invention of vapor-compression and vapor-absorption refrigeration methods, recirculating mechanical refrigerators have become commonplace. Other refrigeration methods exploit the thermoelectric properties of semiconductors, the magneto-thermoelectric effects in semi-metals, or the diffusion of ^{3}He atoms across the interface between distinct phases of liquid helium having high and low concentrations of ^{3}He in ^{4}He.

A refrigerator operating in a cyclic process may be considered a heat pump, for it continually extracts heat from a low-temperature region and delivers it to a high-temperature region. It is rated by its *coefficient of performance*, defined as the ratio of the heat removed from the cold region (room, box, cryostat) per unit time to the net input power for operating the device, in symbols $K = Q_t/P$. Vapor-absorption and thermoelectric refrigerators have lower coefficients of performance than vapor-compression refrigerators, but they have other characteristics that are superior, such as quietness of operation and compactness.

Vapor-compression Refrigerator This machine consists of a compressor, a condenser, a storage tank, a throttling valve, and an evapo-

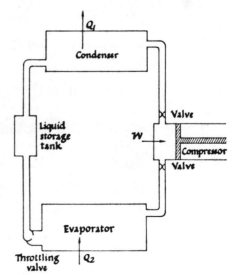

FIG. 1. Vapor-compression refrigerator (from "Thermophysics," by Allen L. King, San Francisco, W. H. Freeman and Co., 1962).

rator connected by suitable tubes with intake and outlet valves, as shown schematically in Fig. 1. The refrigerant is a liquid which partially vaporizes and cools as it passes through the throttling valve. Among the common refrigerants are ammonia, sulfur dioxide, and certain halide compounds of methane and ethane. Perhaps the most widely used of these in industry is ammonia and in the household dichlorodifluoromethane ("Freon-12"). Nearly constant pressures are maintained on either side of the throttling valve by means of the compressor. The mixed liquid and vapor entering the evaporator is colder than the near-surround; it absorbs heat from the interior of the refrigerator box or cold room and completely vaporizes. The vapor is then forced into the compressor where its temperature and pressure increase as it is compressed. The compressed vapor finally pours into the condenser where it cools down and liquefies as the heat is transferred to cold air, water, or other fluid flowing by the cooling coils.

Comparative tests have shown that the coefficient of performance of vapor-compression refrigerators depends very little on the nature of the refrigerant. Because of mechanical inefficiencies, its actual value may be well below the ideal value—ordinarily, between 2 and 3.

Vapor-absorption Refrigerator In this system there are no moving parts; the added energy comes from a gas or liquid fuel burner or from an electrical heater, as heat, rather than from a compressor, as work. A simplified diagram of it is shown in Fig. 2. The refrigerant is ammonia gas, which is liberated from a water solution and transported from one region to another by the aid of hydrogen. The total pressure throughout the system is constant and therefore no valves are needed.

Heat from the external source is supplied to the generator where a mixture of ammonia and water vapor with drops of ammoniated water is raised to the separator in the same manner as water is raised to the coffee in a percolator. Ammonia vapor escapes from the liquid in the separator and rises to the condenser, where it cools and liquefies. Before the liquefied ammonia enters the evaporator, hydrogen, rising from the absorber, mixes with it and aids in the evaporation process. Finally, the mixture of hydrogen and ammonia vapor enters the absorber, where water from the separator dissolves the ammonia. The ammonia water returns to the generator to complete the cycle. In this cycle heat enters the system not only at the generator but also at the evaporator, and heat leaves the system at both the condenser and the absorber to enter the atmosphere by means of radiating fins.

No external work is done, and the change in internal energy of the refrigerant during a complete cycle is zero. The total heat $Q_a + Q_c$ released to the atmosphere per unit time by the absorber and the condenser equals the total heat $Q_g + Q_c$ absorbed per unit time from the heater at the generator and from the cold box at the evaporator; so $Q_e = Q_a + Q_c - Q_g$, and therefore the coefficient of performance is $K = Q_e/Q_g = \{(Q_a + Q_c)/Q_g\} - 1$.

The vapor-absorption refrigerator is free from intermittent noises; but it requires a con-

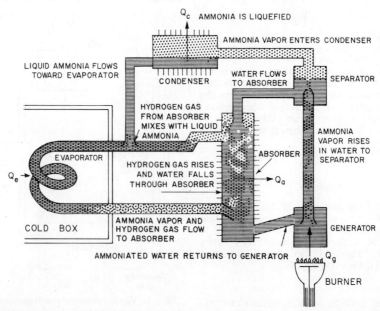

FIG. 2. Vapor-absorption refrigerator (from "Thermophysics," by Allen L. King, San Francisco, W. H. Freeman and Co., 1962).

tinuous supply of heat, as from bottled gas or electrical generators. Refrigerators of this type are found in camps and farm houses not supplied with commercial electric power and in apartment houses where unnecessary noise is prohibited.

Dilution Refrigerator Below a temperature of 0.87 K liquid mixtures of ^{3}He and ^{4}He at certain concentrations separate into two distinct phases, a concentrated (^{3}He-rich) phase floating on a denser (^{4}He-rich) phase with a visible surface between them. The concentrations of ^{3}He in the two phases are functions of temperature, approaching 100 per cent in the concentrated phase and about 6 per cent in the dilute phase at 0 K. The transfer of ^{3}He atoms from the concentrated to the dilute phase, like an evaporation process, entails a latent heat, an increase in entropy, and a lowering of temperature. This effect is utilized in the dilution refrigerator for obtaining temperatures of extremely low values.

The diagram in Fig. 3 shows the main components of a recirculating dilution refrigerator. The pump forces helium vapor (primarily ^{3}He) from the still into the condenser, where it is

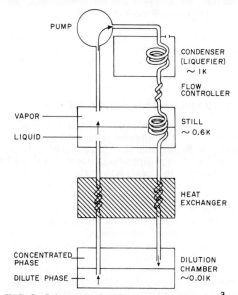

PUMP

CONDENSER
(LIQUEFIER)
~ 1K

FLOW
CONTROLLER

VAPOR

LIQUID

STILL
~ 0.6K

HEAT
EXCHANGER

CONCENTRATED
PHASE

DILUTE PHASE

DILUTION
CHAMBER
~0.01K

FIG. 3. Schematic showing components of a ^{3}He–^{4}He recirculating dilution refrigerator.

liquefied at a temperature near 1 K in a bath of rapidly evaporating ^{4}He, through a flow controller consisting of a narrow tube of suitable diameter to obtain an optimum rate of flow, and then through the still where its temperature is further reduced to about 0.6 K. The liquefied ^{3}He next passes through a heat exchanger (sintered copper) so as to reduce its temperature to nearly that of the dilution chamber, by giving up thermal energy to the counterflowing dilute phase, before entering the concentrated

phase therein. The diffusion of ^{3}He atoms from the concentrated into the dilute phase within this chamber can produce steady temperatures of very low values (0.01 K or less). Liquid ^{3}He from the dilute phase then passes through the heat exchanger to the still where it is warmed to transform the liquid to the vapor phase that goes to the pump thus completing the cycle. Modified versions of this system have been constructed, sometimes with an added single-cycle process for producing temporarily even lower temperatures. The low-temperature limit in any of these systems is determined largely by two important sources of inefficiency that cannot be completely eliminated; heat leakage, especially severe because of the extreme range of temperatures, and recirculation of some ^{4}He with ^{3}He.

Thermoelectric Refrigerator This device utilizes the thermoelectric effect, discovered by Peltier in 1834 (see THERMOELECTRICITY), wherein heat is either absorbed or generated at the junction of two different conductors, or semiconductors, depending on the direction of an electrical current through it. For satisfactory operation in refrigerating devices the thermojunctions should be made of materials having not only high thermoelectric coefficients but also high electrical conductivities, so as to reduce Joule heating, and low thermal conductivities, so as to minimize heat losses by conduction. These requirements are best met by semiconductors such as lead telluride and bismuth telluride.

A thermoelectric refrigerator unit consists of one or more stages of series-connected n-type and p-type semiconductors as illustrated in Fig. 4(a). The charge carriers are electrons in the n-type semiconductor and holes in the p-type semiconductor. When a difference of potential is maintained across AB with B at the higher potential, the negative electrons carry both kinetic and potential energy away from C as they move toward B in the n-type semiconductor; the positive holes do the same as they move away from C toward A in the p-type semiconductor. Since energy is carried away from C to AB in both arms of the thermocouple, junction C becomes cold and junctions AB become warm. Temperature differences as large as 75 C have been obtained in a single-stage unit. Larger temperature differences may be produced by arranging several stages in cascade as illustrated by the two-stage system in Fig. 4(b). In this way a temperature of $-118°C$ was reached in a small seven-stage thermoelectric refrigerator only 38 mm high, employing bismuth telluride alloys in the thermojunctions and water at 27°C as the heat sink.

The coefficient of performance of a multistage thermoelectric refrigerator is no greater than that of one of its units. Let the temperature difference between AB and C in Fig. 4(a) be ΔT. As a result of the Peltier effect, the cold junction cools down at the rate $\bar{\alpha}(T_m - \frac{1}{2}\Delta T)I$,

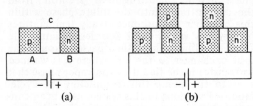

FIG. 4. Thermoelectric refrigerator: (a) single stage, (b) two stage cascade.

where $\bar{\alpha}$ is the mean value of the Seebeck coefficients for the n-type and p-type semiconductors, T_m is the mean temperature of the thermocouple, and I is the current through it. But due to Joule heating and thermal conduction from the warm to the cold junction, the rate of cooling at C is only $Q_t = \bar{\alpha}(T_m - \frac{1}{2}\Delta T)I - \frac{1}{2}I^2 R - \lambda \Delta T$, where the total resistance of the couple $R = (l_p/A_p\sigma_p) + (l_n/A_n\sigma_n)$ and its thermal conductance $\lambda = (A_p k_p/l_p) + (A_n k_n/l_n)$ in which A_p and A_n are the cross-sectional areas of the p-type and n-type semiconductors, l_p and l_n are their lengths, σ_p and σ_n are their electrical conductivities, and k_p and k_n are their thermal conductivities. The power supplied externally must just equal the total Seebeck and Joule terms, namely, $P = \bar{\alpha}I\,\Delta T + I^2 R$. The coefficient of performance, therefore, is

$$K = Q_t/P = \frac{\bar{\alpha}(T_m - \frac{1}{2}\Delta T)I - \frac{1}{2}I^2 R - \lambda \Delta T}{\bar{\alpha}I\,\Delta T + I^2 R}$$

It reaches a maximum value when the products of the thermal and electrical conductances for the two semiconductors have the same value and when the electrical resistance at the junctions is much smaller than R. The optimum current then is given by the equation $(IR)_{opt} = \bar{\alpha}\,\Delta T[\sqrt{1 + ZT_m} - 1]^{-1}$ where Z is the *figure of merit* of the thermocouple,

$$Z = \bar{\alpha}^2/[(k_p/\sigma_p)^{1/2} + (k_n/\sigma_n)^{1/2}]^2$$

The maximum value of K can now be written in the form

$$K_{max} = \frac{T_m(\sqrt{1 + ZT_m} - 1)}{\Delta T(\sqrt{1 + ZT_m} + 1)} - \frac{1}{2}$$

Thus K_{max} increases with an increase in the figure of merit, reaching the value $(T_m - \frac{1}{2}\Delta T)/\Delta T$ for very large Z. This is the coefficient of performance for an ideal thermodynamic machine.

The thermoelectric refrigerator is useful where space is at a premium or where, for other reasons, mechanical refrigerators are inconvenient.

Thermomagnetic and Magnetothermoelectric Refrigerators In 1958 O'Brien and Wallace suggested that by means of the Ettingshausen effect, one should be able to achieve cooling for refrigeration purposes (see HALL EFFECT AND

RELATED PHENOMENA). This suggestion has been followed up with some success at low temperatures and even with the heat sink near room temperature by a special "cascading" device. In 1962, Smith and Wolfe discovered that the thermoelectric figure of merit for bismuth-antimony alloys can be increased by means of a magnetic field and that this enhancement is especially pronounced at low temperatures. These effects may be applied advantageously to refrigeration at low ambient temperatures.

ALLEN L. KING

References

Betts, D. S., "Helium Isotope Refrigeration," *Contemporary Physics*, 9, 97–114 (1968).
Goldsmid, H. J., "Applications of Thermoelectricity," London, Methuen and Co., Ltd., 1960.
King, A. L., "Thermophysics," San Francisco, W. H. Freeman and Co., 1962.
Wolfe, R., "Magnetothermoelectricity," *Sci. Am.*, 210, 70 (1964).
Worthing, A. G., and Halliday, D., "Heat," New York, John Wiley & Sons, 1948.
Zemansky, M. W., "Heat and Thermodynamics," New York, McGraw-Hill Book Co., 1968.

Cross-references: CRYOGENICS, HALL EFFECT AND RELATED PHENOMENA, HEAT, HEAT TRANSFER, LIQUEFACTION OF GASES, SEMICONDUCTORS.

REGGE POLES AND REGGE THEORY

The study of scattering amplitudes as analytic functions of the angular momentum was initiated by T. Regge in his investigation of potential scattering. These amplitudes were found to be meromorphic in a certain domain of the angular momentum plane, and the poles that occur there bear the name of their discoverer.

Similar analytic properties and the existence of such poles have had an enormous utility in the discussion of phenomena of high-energy elementary particle reactions. There is no rigorous derivation of the existence of any analyticity or the occurrence of these poles that is valid for high-energy relativistic scattering. The most honest statement is that these properties are postulated. There are, however, heuristic arguments and models which do indicate results analogous to those of potential theory. We shall use one of these models due to Feynman and Van Hove which illuminates both the nature of these singularities and their applicability to the phenomenology of scattering processes.

We shall be interested in reactions involving two particles in the initial state and two particles or more generally resonances in the final state:

$$A + B \longrightarrow C + D. \qquad (1)$$

Such a reaction will be parameterized by two kinematic variables. For simplicity we shall take

all the masses entering into process (1) to be equal. One variable is the center of mass energy, energy $\sqrt{s}$, related to the center of mass momentum q by

$$s = 4(q^2 + \mu^2) \tag{2}$$

where μ is the common mass of the particles involved; the other variable is the momentum transfer t related to the scattering angle θ by

$$t = -2q^2(1 - \cos\theta). \tag{3}$$

The differential cross section may be obtained from the scattering amplitude $A(s, t)$, and the normalization is such that

$$\frac{d\sigma}{dt} = \frac{16\pi}{s^2} |A(s, t)|^2 \tag{4}$$

and in the case of elastic scattering the total cross section σ_T is obtained via the optional theorem

$$\sigma_T(A, B) = \frac{16\pi}{s} Im\ A(s, t = 0). \tag{5}$$

The physically accessible region of s and t is $s > 4\mu^2$ and $-4q^2 < t < 0$. The amplitude $A(s, t)$ is, however, assumed to be analytic and thus we may continue it to other regions of s and t. From crossing symmetry, a general concept derived from field theory, the same function $A(s, t)$, in the region $s < 0$ and $t > 4\mu^2$ represents the scattering amplitude for the reaction

$$A + \bar{C} \longrightarrow \bar{B} + D, \tag{6}$$

where $\bar{C}(\bar{B})$ denotes the antiparticle of C(B). For this reaction $\sqrt{t}$ represents the energy and s the momentum transfer.

As mentioned previously, our interest will be in reaction (1) for large s and small t. Thus it will prove convenient to investigate reaction (6) where small t implies low-energy, AC scattering, and we may use our intuition and experience for low-energy elementary particle scattering in order to obtain information on a related high-energy process.

Low-energy reactions are expected to be dominated by low-lying resonances. For a resonance of spin J and mass $m(J)$ the usual Breit-Wigner resonant scattering amplitude is [t close to $m^2(J)$ and s large]

$$A(s, t) \approx (2J + 1) g(J) \frac{s^J}{t - m^2(J)} \tag{7}$$

where $g(J)$ is the product of the coupling constants of the resonance in question to AC and $\bar{B}D$. For reaction (1) in the small t region we expect the state with the smallest $m(J)$ to dominate. This is the so-called peripheral model which has had some success in describing reactions for small t and moderate s. For $J > 1$ the energy dependence of Eq. (7) is too rapid and is in violation with certain fundamental notions

(Froisart's theorem) that limit the asymptotic growth of an amplitude to essentially linear behavior in s.

In general, we expect a sum of terms as in Eq. (7). Again for simplicity assume that for each angular momentum J there is only one resonance. This is not a crucial assumption and will be dropped subsequently. The scattering amplitude has the form

$$A(s, t) \approx \sum_J (2J + 1) g(J) \frac{s^J}{t - m^2(J)}. \tag{8}$$

As J increases, the aforementioned difficulty is expected to compound itself; it may, however, under certain conditions be turned into an advantage. These are:

(1) $g(J)$ and $m^2(J)$ are analytic functions of J in some domain including the half-plane, $Re J > 0$.

(2) $g^2(J) \to 0$ as $J \to \infty$.

(3) $m^2(J)$ is monotonically increasing in J.

For reasons having to do with the existence of exchange forces let us separately treat sums over even or odd J:

$$A(s, t) = A_+(s, t) + A_-(s, t)$$

$$A_\pm(s, t) = \sum (2j + 1) g(J) \frac{s^J \pm (-s)^J}{t - m^2(J)}. \tag{9}$$

By the use of the above assumptions the summation of Eq. (9) can be expressed as a Watson-Sommerfeld integral

$$A_\pm(s, t) \approx \frac{1}{2i} \int_{C_1} dj\ (2j + 1)$$

$$g(J) \frac{(-s)^J \pm s^j}{[t - m^2(J)] \sin \pi j} \tag{10}$$

where the contour C_1 is indicated in Fig. 1. We may now deform the contour C_1 to C_2, carefully retaining a possible pole when $m^2(J) = t$ at $J = \alpha(t)$. As long as the real part of $\alpha(t)$ is greater than the real part of the contour C_2, the asymptotic behavior of $A(s, t)$ in s will be given by

$$A_\pm(s, t) \approx \beta_\pm(t) s^{\alpha_\pm(t)} \frac{e^{i\pi\alpha_\pm(t)} \pm 1}{\sin \pi\alpha_\pm(t)} \tag{11}$$

with $\beta_\pm(t)$ proportional to $g[J = \alpha(t)]$ and containing all other factors in the residue of $1/[t - m^2(J)]$. Some concepts and terminology associated with the above expression are:

(1) $J = \alpha(t)$ is a pole of the scattering amplitude known as a Regge pole.

(2) The function $m^2(J)$ is the Regge trajectory associated with this pole.

(3) $\beta(t)$ is referred to as the residue function.

(4) Trajectories contributing to A_+ or A_- are known even or odd signature trajectories.

We may now remove the restriction to one family, $m^2(J)$, and consider several such trajec-

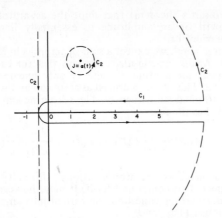

FIG. 1. The complex j-plane with the Watson-Sommerfeld contour, C_1, and the deformed contour C_2 and a Regge pole at $J = \alpha(t)$.

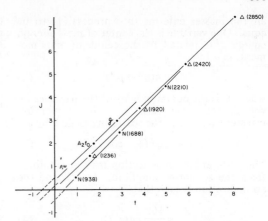

FIG. 2. Particles and resonances belonging to several Regge families. The dashed lines indicate phenomenological values of $\alpha(t)$ used in fitting high-energy scattering data.

tories, and a useful high-energy approximation to the scattering amplitude $A(s, t)$ is

$$A(s, t) = \sum_i \frac{\beta_i(t)s^{\alpha_i(t)}}{\sin \pi \alpha_i(t)} \left(e^{i\pi\alpha_i(t)} + \tau_i \right) \quad (12)$$

where $\tau_i = \pm 1$.

Let us now turn to the experimental consequences of Eq. (12). For $t > 0$ the function $\alpha(t)$ is related to particles and resonances that occur in $A\bar{C} \to \bar{B}D$ scattering. Namely, $\alpha[m^2(J)] = J$. It is a remarkable fact that most particles and resonances found in elementary particle spectroscopy may be grouped into simple families of increasing J as indicated in Fig. 2. A further remarkable observation is that $\alpha(t)$ as obtained from the mass spectrum is fairly linear in t

$$\alpha(t) = \alpha_0 + \alpha' t. \quad (13)$$

At present we have no theoretical justification for this simplicity. For $t < 0$ these trajectory functions are connected to the high-energy scattering process (1). In this region the $\alpha_i(t)$ may be determined by empirical data fitting to the energy variation of the cross section. The third remarkable fact is that a simple continuation of the spectroscopically determined $\alpha(t)$ coincides with the phenomenologically determined $\alpha(t)$. *In the absence of this simplicity and in lacking convincing theoretical models for the functional form of $\alpha(t)$ the physical content of the concept of Regge poles would be lacking*. It is fortunate that with the present lack of theoretical models most trajectories necessary to fit scattering data have such a simple connection with the position of particles that lie on them.

There is, however, one trajectory that has certain unique properties. An empirical fact is that total cross sections approach constants when the energy becomes sufficiently large. This behavior may be implemented within the Regge pole framework by postulating the existence of a Regge trajectory $\alpha(t)$ such that $\alpha(t = 0) = 1$. An elastic scattering amplitude would then be linear in s and the optical theorem, Eq. (5), would guarantee the constancy of the total cross section. A further empirical observation that the difference of cross section for a process initiated by a particle and its antiparticle or by particles belonging to the same symmetry multiplet (as isotopic spin) goes to zero as s increases, leads to the hypothesis that this trajectory has the quantum numbers of the vacuum. This ensures that it can occur in all elastic processes and thus all total cross sections will approach a constant. This trajectory is known as the Pomeranchuck trajectory. What distinguishes it from the others is that it is found to have a smaller variation in t; in fact it is consistent with being independent of t and having a fixed value of one. The other feature distinguishing it from other trajectories is that no particles have been found that can be associated with it. These peculiarities have lead people to speculate that this Pomeranchuck trajectory may be more intricate than a simple pole, which leads us to a discussion of possibly more complicated analytic structures in the complex plane.

For ordinary potential scattering, the structure of the scattering amplitude is fairly simple. As discussed earlier, the only singularities we encounter (at least in the domain $Rej > - |j_0|$ for some j_0) are simple poles. For high-energy relativistic scattering the situation is bound to be much more complicated. Assuming the existence

of Regge poles one can demonstrate fairly convincingly that cuts (appropriately called Regge cuts) must exist. Completely nonanalytic parts of the scattering amplitude are likewise not excluded. As these structures do not have such a simple connection with low-energy resonances, their positions, and in turn influence on high-energy scattering processes, are unknown. At best one appeals to fairly crude models to calculate their effects; at worst one ignores them with the hope that, whatever their effect, it is small. The singularity at $J = 1$ which we have called the Pomeranchuck pole may in fact be a much more complicated entity, e.g., a cut or an envelope of cuts.

To summarize, the concept of poles in the angular momentum plane has permitted a remarkable correlation between *low*-mass particles and resonances on one hand and certain gross features of *high*-energy scattering on the other hand. The existence of such a correlation, no matter how crude, must be considered a triumph. An attempt at a more detailed understanding of this situation leads to complications which we are at present unable to resolve. So it is with most theories of high-energy elementary particle processes.

MYRON BANDER

References

1. de Alfaro, V., and Regge, T., "Potential Scattering," Amsterdam, North Holland Publishing Company, 1965.
2. Barger, V., and Cline, D., "Phenomenological Theories of High Energy Scattering," New York, W. A. Benjamin, Inc., 1969.
3. Frautschi, S., "Regge Poles and S-Matrix Theory," New York, W. A. Benjamin, Inc., 1963.
4. Newton, R., "The Complex j-Plane," New York, W. A. Benjamin, Inc., 1966.
5. Eden, R., "High Energy Collisions of Elementary Particles," Cambridge, Cambridge University Press, 1967.

Cross-references: ANTIPARTICLES, COLLISIONS OF PARTICLES, CONSERVATION LAWS AND SYMMETRY, ELEMENTARY PARTICLES.

RELATIVITY

The basic ideas of modern relativity theory are largely due to one man: Albert Einstein (1879–1955). Both main branches of pre-Einstein physics had relied on an absolute space. To Newton this had served as the agent responsible for a particle's resistance to acceleration; to Maxwell—in the guise of an "aether"—it was the carrier of electromagnetic stresses and waves. Relativity may be defined briefly as the abolition of absolute space. Special relativity (1905) abolished it in its Maxwellian sense, and general relativity (1915) in its Newtonian sense as well.

Before looking at the theoretical background of relativity, we shall mention some of its more striking practical implications. According to special relativity, for example, a rod moving longitudinally at speed v through an inertial frame is shortened, relative to that frame, by a factor $\gamma = (1 - v^2/c^2)^{-\frac{1}{2}}$, where c is the speed of light. This factor increases with v; when v is as large as $\frac{1}{7} c$, γ is only 1.01, but at higher speeds it grows rapidly and becomes infinite when $v = c$. The rate of a clock moving at speed v is decreased by the same factor γ; this is one aspect of the revolutionary prediction that time is not absolute and that, for example, after journeying at high speed through space, one could, upon return, find the world aged very much more than oneself. In fact, time and space become merged in a four-dimensional continuum in which neither possesses more absoluteness than, e.g., the x-separation between points in a Cartesian plane, which depends on the choice of axes. According to special relativity, time- and space-separations between events similarly depend on the choice of motion of the observer. The mass of a body moving at speed v is also increased by the factor γ and thus becomes infinite at the speed of light. This illustrates another prediction of the theory—that no body or physical effect can travel faster than light. But the single most important result of special relativity, in Einstein's opinion, was the equivalence of mass m and energy E according to the formula $E = mc^2$. Although the original impact of special relativity was mainly theoretical and philosophical, technology since 1905 has made such vast strides (atomic power, particle accelerators, Mössbauer effect, etc.) that today special relativity is one of the most practical and, at the same time, best verified branches of all physics.

The same cannot yet be said for general relativity, whose importance is still largely theoretical. But its ideas are hardly less striking. General relativity is the modern theory of gravitation. Like special relativity, it pictures the world as a four-dimensional space-time continuum, but according to general relativity this is curved by the matter present in it. Particles and light rays are postulated to move along geodesics ("straightest possible" curves) in this four-space, and all reference to an absolute three-space as the standard of non-acceleration has disappeared. It is one of the marvels of this theory that, starting from such utterly different premises it nevertheless reproduces within experimental accuracy almost all the well-established results of Newton's (inverse square) gravitational theory. In the few cases where its predictions differ to a presently measurable extent from Newton's (as for the advance of the perihelia of the planets), general relativity has been borne out by observation. Furthermore, general relativity first led to the construction of many interesting cosmological models, such as closed and finite universes; it also implies the possibility of gravitational waves

and thus the need to quantize the gravitational field.

That gravity can be "explained" by theories as diverse as Newton's and Einstein's well illustrates the character of all physical theories: they are no more than *models* of certain parts of nature; they cannot aspire to be ultimate truths.

The theoretical basis of special relativity is Einstein's *special principle of relativity* which asserts that *all* the laws of physics are equally valid in *all* inertial frames of reference. This is an extension to the whole of physics of a relativity principle which the laws of mechanics have long been known to obey. Newton, as Galileo before him, illustrated this with the familiar example of a ship, "where all motions happen after the same manner whether the ship is at rest or is carried forward in a right line." The reason why Einstein's principle was revolutionary is that the known properties of light seem to contradict it at once. In our quasi-inertial terrestrial reference frame (which was assumed to coincide more or less with Maxwell's aether), light is propagated rectilinearly in all directions at constant speed. This fact is often called the *law of light propagation*. The validity of this law in all inertial frames would imply, for example, that a light signal emitted at the instantaneous coincidence of two observers O and O' who are moving uniformly relative to each other, each fixed in an inertial frame, spreads spherically with both observers considering themselves to remain permanently at the center of the sphere. Hence a light signal would always recede from an observer at the same speed, no matter how fast he chases it. The adoption of the special principle of relativity together with the law of light propagation thus seems to lead to absurdities. But, in fact, this is not so: it merely leads to the downfall of the classical ideas of space and time. It was part of Einstein's genius to recognize that these ideas were dispensable.

Two types of argument can be made in support of Einstein's principle. The first is experimental: all experiments devised to discover the frame of Maxwell's aether, such as the well-known MICHELSON-MORLEY EXPERIMENT (1887), failed to give positive results, though such results would have been well within range of observability. The second argument is theoretical, and rests on the unity of physics. For example, mechanics involves matter, which is electromagnetically constituted; electromagnetic apparatus involves mechanical parts; and so forth. If, then, physics cannot be separated into strictly exclusive branches, it would seem unlikely that the laws of different branches should have different transformation properties.

Consider now two observers O and O' like the ones mentioned earlier, and a light signal emitted at their coincidence. If each observer remains at the origin of a Cartesian reference system and sets his clock to read zero when the signal is emitted, the events on the light front must satisfy both the equations

$$x^2 + y^2 + z^2 - c^2 t^2 = 0$$

$$x'^2 + y'^2 + z'^2 - c^2 t'^2 = 0 \qquad (1)$$

where primes distinguish the space and time coordinates used by O' from those used by O. Now suppose the two observers arrange their corresponding y and z axes to be parallel, and their x axes to coincide. In classical mechanics, with this configuration of reference systems, the so-called *Galilean transformation equations*

$$x' = x - vt, \ y' = y, \ z' = z, \ t' = t \qquad (2)$$

relate the corresponding coordinates of any event. But under this transformation, the two equations (1) are not equivalent. Einstein showed that for these equations to be equivalent, the transformation equations must necessarily be

$$x' = \gamma(x - vt), \ y' = y, \ z' = z,$$

$$t' = \gamma(t - vx/c^2) \qquad (3)$$

where $\gamma = (1 - v^2/c^2)^{-\frac{1}{2}}$. These are the well-known *Lorentz equations* which constitute the mathematical core of the special theory of relativity. They replace equations (2), to which they nevertheless approximate when v is small. The most striking of equations (3) is the last. It implies that events with the same value of t do not necessarily correspond to events with the same value of t', which means that *simultaneity is relative*. Setting $x = 0$ in that equation also shows that the clock at the origin of O goes slow by a factor γ in the frame of O'. But, setting $x = vt$, we see that the clock at the origin of O' similarly goes slow in the frame of O. Setting $t = 0$ in the first of equations (3), we see that a rod, fixed in the frame of O' along the x' axis, appears shortened by a factor γ in the frame of O; this phenomenon too can be shown to be symmetric between the frames.

Another important property of equations (3) is that they leave invariant the differential quadratic

$$ds^2 = dx^2 + dy^2 + dz^2 - c^2 dt^2 \qquad (4)$$

which leads to the possibility of mapping events in a four-dimensional pseudo-Euclidean *space-time* in which an absolute *interval ds* exists, and in which the language and results of four-dimensional geometry can thus be applied. For example, a uniformly moving particle is described simply by a straight line in this space-time.

It was the first task of special relativity to review the existing laws of physics and to subject them to the test of the relativity principle by seeing whether they were invariant under Lorentz transformations. Any law found lacking had to be modified accordingly.

Since Newton's laws of mechanics are invariant under the transformation (2) and *not* (3), it was necessary to amend these laws so as to make them "Lorentz invariant." It was found possible to do this by retaining the classical laws of conservation of mass and momentum but postulating that the mass of moving bodies increases by the factor γ, a fact amply borne out by modern particle accelerators. This led to the theoretical discovery of the equivalence of mass and energy—most spectacularly exemplified by the atomic bomb.

In contrast to Newton's theory, Maxwell's vacuum electrodynamics was compatible with Einstein's theory. Lorentz, independently of Einstein, but without realizing the full significance of his result, had already discovered equations (3) as precisely those which leave Maxwell's equations invariant. In other words, Maxwell's equations already were "Lorentz invariant" and needed no modification. Nevertheless relativity has considerably deepened our understanding of Maxwell's theory. Other branches of physics, like kinematics, optics, hydrodynamics, thermodynamics, nonvacuum electrodynamics, etc., all underwent slight modifications to make them Lorentz invariant. Only Newton's inverse square gravitational theory proved refractory; several Lorentz invariant modifications of it were proposed but none were entirely acceptable.

Einstein eventually solved the gravitational problem in an unexpected way. He rejected Newton's absolute space as the cause of inertia on the grounds that "it is contrary to the spirit of science to conceive of a thing which acts but cannot be acted upon." His general theory of relativity ascribes to the space-time continuum discovered by special relativity the role of an inertial guiding field (free particles and light follow geodesics) but allows this field to be affected (curved) by the matter in it.

This extension was made possible by the so-called *principle of equivalence*. To Newton, an inertial frame was, primarily, the frame of "absolute space" in which the stars were assumed to be fixed, and, secondarily, any frame moving uniformly relative to absolute space. Thus an inertial frame exhibited its defining property, viz., that in it free particles move uniformly and rectilinearly (Newton's first law), only in the regions far from attracting masses. In 1907 Einstein changed this global definition to a local one: a local inertial frame is a freely falling non-rotating reference system. (The meaning of "local" is here determined by the extent to which the nonuniformity of the gravitational field is negligible.) Within the limits of each such frame Newton's laws of mechanics would be valid according to the classical theory; in particular, Newton's first law would be strictly satisfied. Now Einstein once again made the generalization from mechanics to the whole of physics. His principle of equivalence asserted that all the laws of

physics are the same in each local inertial frame. It is these frames, therefore, which are the proper province of the special principle of relativity. Special relativity now becomes a local theory. In recompense, we need no longer go to the tenuous interstellar regions for its strict validity.

An elementary consequence of the principle of equivalence is the bending of light in a gravitational field. For, if light travels rectilinearly in the local inertial frame, and *that* accelerates freely in the gravitational field, the light path is evidently curved in the field. No property of light other than its uniform motion in an inertial frame has been used in this argument. This, in turn, suggests that one might ascribe the bending of light to an inherent space curvature, rather than to the nature of light. In much the same way, the characteristic motion of free particles in a gravitational field suggests that they follow "natural" paths (geodesics) in a curved space. Their motion is independent of everything except their initial position and velocity, owing to the equality of "gravitational mass" (the analog of electric charge) and "inertial mass" (the measure of a particle's resistance to acceleration). It is this which makes the principle of equivalence possible. It should be noted, however, that for the geodesic law to be possible, space and time must be welded into four-dimensional space-time. Free motions could not be represented by geodesics in a *three*-dimensional curved space. For a geodesic is uniquely determined by a point on it and a direction at that point. But an initial point and an initial direction do *not* uniquely determine a free path in a gravitational field. *That* depends also on the initial speed. In space-time, on the other hand, a direction is equivalent to a (vector-) velocity. And it *is* the case in Newton's theory that an initial point and velocity uniquely determine a free path in a gravitational field. Note that all this depends on the equivalence of inertial and gravitational mass. This equivalence is an unexplained and inessential coincidence in Newton's theory; it is the *sine qua non* of Einstein's.

As we have seen, special relativity forces a four-dimensional metric structure [Eq. (4)] on the events within an inertial frame. By patching together the structures of all the local inertial frames, we obtain the structure of the world of general relativity. Locally, it can be regarded as flat. But it is evident that, if the very pleasing geodesic law of motion is to hold, the presence of matter must impress a curvature on this space-time. For example, the planets move in patently curved paths around the sun (in four-dimensions these are helicoidal rather than elliptical); for these paths to be geodesic, the space-time around the sun must be curved. Just how matter curves the surrounding space-time is expressed by Einstein's field equations

$$G_{ij} = -\frac{8\pi G}{c^4} T_{ij} \qquad (5)$$

which look deceptively simple. Technically, they represent ten second-order partial differential equations for the metric of space-time. This metric enters the 16 components of the "Einstein tensor" G_{ij}, of which only 10 are independent, for $G_{ij} = G_{ji}$. G is the constant of gravitation; T_{ij} is the so-called energy tensor of the matter, and its components represent a generalization of the classical concept of density.

The exact solution of Eq. (5) has been possible only in a limited number of physical situations. For example, in 1916 Schwarzschild gave the exact solution for the space-time around a spherical mass m (e.g., the sun):

$$ds^2 = (1 - a/r)^{-1} dr^2 + r^2 (d\theta^2 + \sin^2\theta \, d\phi^2)$$
$$- (1 - a/r)c^2 dt^2 \quad (6)$$

where $a = 2Gm/c^2$, r is a measure of distance from the central mass, t is a measure of time, and θ and ϕ are the usual angular coordinates. Note that when $m = 0$, Eq. (6) reduces simply to the flat space-time of Eq. (4), written in polar coordinates, and its geodesics would be straight lines (in space and time). But for Eq. (6), the geodesics in the plane $\theta = \pi/2$ are found to satisfy the equation

$$\frac{d^2 u}{d\phi^2} + u = \frac{Gm}{h^2} + \frac{3Gmu^2}{c^2} \quad (7)$$

where $u = 1/r$ and h is a constant. This differs formally from the classical orbit equation only by the presence of the last term, which is very small. But as a consequence of that term, the solution of Eq. (7) is

$$u = Gmh^{-2} (1 + e \cos p\phi),$$
$$p = 1 + 3G^2 m^2 h^{-2} c^{-2} \quad (8)$$

instead of the classical solution which has $p = 1$. Now r is a function in ϕ of period $2\pi/p$ instead of 2π, and therefore the orbital ellipse precesses. For the planet Mercury, for example, the secular precession predicted is $42''$ (seconds of arc), and this agrees well with observation. In the space-time defined by Equation (6) one also finds that light-signals which pass close to the central mass are bent by an angle twice as big as that predicted on a simple Newtonian corpuscular theory of light; and again observations bear out the relativistic prediction. The third "crucial" prediction, which has also been verified observationally, is the reddening of the light received from the surface of very dense stars.

Another more recently suggested test involves the timing of radar signals past the limb of the sun. According to general relativity, these should be slowed by the field of the sun, and this has been tentatively verified. Also in preparation are experiments in which a gyroscope will be carried in an artificial satellite around the earth. The gyroscope is, of course, subject to a great many classical perturbations, but general relativity has added to these a testable precession due to space-time curvature. Gravitational waves, if detected, would also support general relativity. Such detection has been reported by the pioneer in this field, J. Weber, but it has not yet been verified by other groups. If, indeed, the pulses observed by Weber are gravitational in origin, then the next puzzle is the source of the enormous gravitational energy apparently poured into space near the center of our galaxy.

Finally, we may note that whereas special relativity has long been an eminently practical science, general relativity has only recently been recognized for its practicability, and this especially in the realm of astrophysics. Apart from the need for general relativity in the explanation of cosmic dynamics and related topics (cosmology), such astrophysical phenomena as the evolution of super-massive stars, gravitational collapse, and quasars critically depend on general relativity for their explanation. For in connection with very strong gravitational fields, Newton's and Einstein's theories make qualitatively quite different predictions.

W. RINDLER

References

Bergmann, P. G., "Introduction to the Theory of Relativity," New York, Prentice-Hall, 1942.

Eddington, A. S., "Space, Time, and Gravitation, Cambridge, The University Press, 1920.

Einstein, A., et al., "The Principle of Relativity," New York, Dover, 1923.

Møller, C., "The Theory of Relativity," Oxford, Clarendon Press, 1972.

Pauli, W., "Theory of Relativity," London, Pergamon Press, 1958.

Rindler, W., "Essential Relativity," New York, Van Nostrand Reinhold Company, 1969.

Synge, J. L., "Relativity: The Special Theory," Amsterdam, North Holland, 1956; "Relativity: The General Theory," Amsterdam, North Holland, 1960.

Tolman, R. C., "Relativity, Thermodynamics, and Cosmology," Oxford, Clarendon Press, 1934.

Zeldovich, Ya. B., and Novikov, I. D., "Relativistic Astrophysics," Chicago, University of Chicago Press, 1971.

Cross-references: ACCELERATORS, PARTICLE; ASTROPHYSICS; ATOMIC ENERGY; DYNAMICS; GRAVITATION; MICHELSON-MORLEY EXPERIMENT; MÖSSBAUER EFFECT; TIME; VELOCITY OF LIGHT.

RELAXATION

By relaxation is understood the phenomenon that an observable time elapses between the moment when a system in equilibrium is subjected to a momentary change in condition and the moment when the system is again in equilibrium.

A good example of a system showing relaxa-

tion is an uncharged capacitor with a capacitance C connected in series with a resistance R, to which circuit a constant voltage U is applied at a time $t = 0$. The charge Q of the capacitor at time t is given by the differential equation

$$U = \frac{Q}{C} + R\frac{dQ}{dt} \qquad (1)$$

the solution of which is:

$$Q = CU(1 - e^{-\frac{t}{RC}}) \qquad (2)$$

Hence the charge Q does not follow the sudden change of U but shows an exponential increase towards the final value CU (see Fig. 1). The

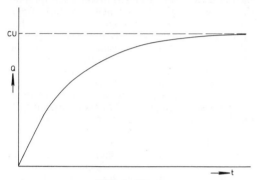

FIG. 1. Q vs t.

time $\tau = RC$ is referred to as the relaxation time of the system. Obviously τ governs both the rate of charging and the rate of discharge: if the capacitor with a charge Q_0 is shortcircuited via a resistance at the time $t = 0$, then the charge at time t is given by:

$$Q = Q_0 e^{-\frac{t}{\tau}}$$

Relaxation is met with in various fields of physics, e.g.:

(a) If a spring connected in parallel with a dash-pot is suddenly loaded with a constant force, it will take some time until this system is again in equilibrium.

(b) If an electrically or magnetically polarizable substance is suddenly placed in a constant electric or magnetic field, it will take some time until the electric or magnetic dipoles have orientated themselves in the field.

(c) If the irradiation of a phosphorescent substance is suddenly stopped, the phosphorescence does not cease immediately but continues for some time during which the intensity decreases exponentially.

An electrical analogy can be devised for all these cases. For instance, if in case (a) we substitute a voltage for the force, a charge for the displacement, the reciprocal of a capacitance for the spring constant f, and a resistance for the coefficient of friction η, we obtain exactly

the differential equation [Eq. (1)]. The relaxation time τ will then be $\tau = \eta/f$, which quantity depends on temperature since as a rule η greatly varies with temperature. Generally, the relaxation times in electrically and magnetically polarizable media also vary with temperature.

If we subject a system having relaxation properties to a periodically varying change in condition instead of one sudden change in condition, some characteristics are revealed which are likewise typical of relaxation. Let us again take the RC circuit as an example, this time applying to it a voltage $U = U_0 \sin \omega t$. Solution of the differential equation [Eq. (1)] yields the following expression for the charge Q of the capacitor:

$$Q = \frac{CU_0}{\sqrt{1 + \omega^2\tau^2}} \sin(\omega t - tg^{-1} \omega\tau)$$

The charge has a component Q' which is in phase with the voltage applied and a component Q'' which is shifted 90° in relation to the voltage applied. Q' and Q'', usually referred to as the real and the imaginary component of Q, respectively, are given by:

$$Q' = CU_0 \frac{1}{1 + \omega^2\tau^2}$$

$$Q'' = CU_0 \frac{\omega\tau}{1 + \omega^2\tau^2}$$

The variation of Q' and Q'' with $\omega\tau$ is shown in Fig. 2 where $\omega\tau$ has been plotted logarithmically in order to obtain symmetrical curves.

Q'' is a measure of the energy dissipated in the circuit per cycle; it has its maximum value at $\omega = 1/\tau$ and a negligibly small value at much higher and much lower frequencies.

Furthermore, Q'' reaches half its maximum value at $\omega = 3.73/\tau$ and $\omega = 0.27/\tau$ so that the half-width value $\Delta\omega$ of the Q'' curve expressed in angular frequency units is $3.46/\tau$. At $\omega = 1/\tau$, Q' just has half its maximum value.

Hence, by measuring Q' and Q'' vs frequency, we have various possibilities for determining the relaxation time.

If a dielectric solid is subjected to a periodically changing electric stress and the real (in-phase) and imaginary (out-of-phase) components of the dielectric constant of the substance are determined, curves will be found having a shape as shown in Figs. 2(a) and 2(b), from which the relaxation time can be determined. The mechanical relaxation time of an elastic solid can be determined in a similar manner.

In some cases, not one but several absorption peaks with the corresponding changes of the real component are found in this kind of experiment, from which it can be concluded that several relaxation mechanisms are involved. This phenomenon is frequently observed in polymers where the various components, such as short chains, long chains, cross-linked chains, etc.,

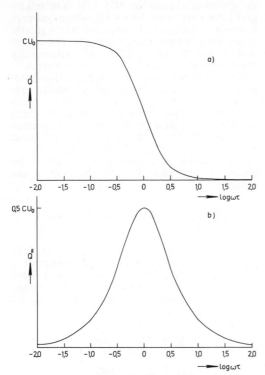

FIG. 2. Q' (a) and Q'' (b) vs log $\omega\tau$.

the interaction between the magnetic dipoles and their surroundings.

Now, if the direction of the magnetic field is suddenly changed, M will make a precessional motion about the new H due to the fact that the resulting angular momentum J is coupled to the magnetic moment M of the nuclei via the relation $\gamma = M/J$ where γ is the magnetogyric ratio of the nuclei.

The angular frequency of the precessional motion is given by:

$$\omega = \gamma H$$

On behalf of the precessional motion, the magnetic moment M has not only a longitudinal component M_l in the direction of the new magnetic field but also a transverse component M_t at right angles to the new magnetic field. Whereas it would seem logical to expect that M_l would increase and M_t decrease exponentially with the relaxation time T_1 due to the relaxation mechanism, in reality this is not so.

Experiments have shown that M_t decreases faster than the increase of M_l so that apart from the longitudinal relaxation time T_1 there must also be a separate transverse relaxation time T_2 which invariably is smaller than or equal to $2T_1$. The existence of a T_2 besides T_1 can be explained by the fact that apart from the return of individual magnetic moments of the nuclei to the direction of H (which is characterized by T_1), it is also possible for these individual magnetic moments—which together form M— to continue their precessional motion along the same conical shell though getting out of phase by mutual interaction. In the latter case, M_t decreases whereas M_l remains unchanged.

Just as with nonresonating systems, periodically changing quantities can be successfully introduced in resonating systems. In the case of a substance containing magnetic nuclei, this is done by applying, beside a stationary magnetic field H_z in the z-direction, also a periodically changing magnetic field $2H_1 \sin \omega t$ in the x-direction. This is known as a nuclear magnetic resonance experiment. In this case, a periodically changing magnetization intensity is created in the x-direction whose real (in-phase, dispersion) component M' and imaginary (out-of-phase, absorption) component M'' are given by:

$$M' = \gamma M_0 H_1 \frac{T_2^2 (\gamma H_z - \omega)}{1 + T_2^2 (\gamma H_z - \omega)^2 + \gamma^2 H_1^2 T_1 T_2}$$

$$M'' = \gamma M_0 H_1 \frac{T_2}{1 + T_2^2 (\gamma H_z - \omega)^2 + \gamma^2 H_1^2 T_1 T_2}$$

where M_0 is the magnetic moment when no periodically changing magnetic field is applied. These quantities can both be determined experimentally.

The variation of $M'/\gamma M_0 H_1 T_2$ and $M''/\gamma M_0 H_1 T_2$ has been plotted against $T_2 (\gamma H_z - \omega)$ in Fig. 3, it having been assumed that H_1 is so small that $\gamma^2 H_1^2 T_1 T_2$ is much smaller than

have different possibilities of moving and therefore have different relaxation times. There are also cases in which there is a more or less continuous distribution of relaxation times, and consequently, an absorption which is practically independent of frequency.

Since the above-mentioned electric circuit has no inductance (which corresponds to the masses of the particles in magnetic, electric and mechanical systems), there can be no resonance either.

As an example of a system having both resonance and relaxation properties, we will consider a liquid substance containing magnetic nuclei, e.g., hydrogen nuclei, which at the time $t = 0$ is placed in a magnetic field H. In this substance a magnetic moment M is built up in the direction of H by the fact that the original random orientation of the magnetic dipoles of the nuclei changes under the influence of the magnetic field into a distribution of such a nature that a resulting moment M arises in the direction of the magnetic field. M is determined by an equation analogous to Eq. (2), namely:

$$M = M_0 \left(1 - e^{-\frac{t}{T_1}}\right)$$

where M_0 is the final value of M and T_1 is a relaxation time known as longitudinal or spin-lattice relaxation time, which is associated with

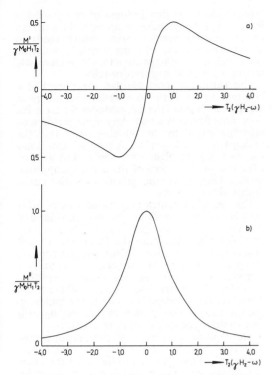

FIG. 3. Shape of the dispersion (a) and absorption (b) curves.

1. It will be seen that the curves differ considerably from those in Fig. 2. The absorption curve has its maximum at the value $\gamma H_z = \omega$ which value has nothing to do with the relaxation times but only with the concurrence of the precessional frequency γH_z of the magnetic moment in the magnetic field H_z with the frequency of the periodically changing magnetic field. Hence it is clearly a matter of resonance absorption. The half-width value $\Delta\omega$ of the absorption curve, expressed in terms of a frequency, is $2/T_2$. The $M'/\gamma M_0 H_1 T_2$ curve is the curve of anomalous dispersion, which at $\gamma H_z = \omega$ has just the value 0, which is invariably found with resonating systems. With increasing values of H_1 both curves get wider and wider and the absorption curve eventually becomes 0 throughout. This phenomenon is called saturation. T_1 and T_2 can be calculated in principle from curves plotted for different known values of H_1; in practice, pulse techniques have to be used, sometimes combined with Fourier transform techniques. Both relaxation times are very much dependent on temperature and on the phase of the substance under test.

The same phenomena are observed in the case of resonance of unpaired electrons, known as electron spin resonance.

Generally speaking, the investigation of relaxation times provides information on the surroundings of relaxing particles and thus can contribute to our knowledge about the structure of substances.

Furthermore, profound knowledge of relaxation times is essential in many instances to the control of physical processes (e.g., the creation of low temperatures by magnetic means) and physical techniques (e.g., the maser technique).

J. SMIDT

References

Farrar, Th. C., and Becker, E. D., "Pulse and Fourier Transform NMR," New York, Academic Press, 1971.
Van Krevelen, D. W., "Properties of Polymers," Amsterdam, Elsevier Publishing Company, 1972. (Part III and references mentioned there.)
Slichter, C. P., "Principles of Magnetic Resonance," New York, Harper & Row, 1965.

Cross-references: ABSORPTION SPECTRA; CAPACITANCE; CONDUCTIVITY, ELECTRICAL; ELECTRON SPIN; FOURIER ANALYSIS; LUMINESCENCE; MAGNETIC RESONANCE; MAGNETISM; RESONANCE.

REPRODUCTION OF SOUND

History In 1807 the British physicist Thomas Young designed the first device capable of making a graphic record of sound waves. His description of the principle of sound recording is as clear and valid today as it was then, and it may serve here:

"The situation of a particle at any time may be represented by supposing it to mark its path, on a surface sliding uniformly along in a transverse direction. Thus, if we fix a small pencil in a vibrating rod, and draw a sheet of paper along, against the point of the pencil, an undulated line will be marked on the paper, and will correctly represent the progress of the vibration."

The recording stylus of Young's device had to be touched directly with the sound source. The "phonautograph" developed by Léon Scott de Martinville in 1856 was able to record sound from the air, via a horn, parchment diaphragm, and hog-bristle stylus. Both the Young and Scott devices made a helical trace on a rotating cylinder. Neither recording could be played back because the recorded trace was not deep or stiff enough to guide the vibrations of a reproducing stylus.

In April 1877, Charles Cros deposited with the French Academy of Sciences a sealed package containing the description of a complete record-reproduce system. Cros planned to use metal records photoengraved from an original tracing in lampblack, but never carried out his plans. In the fall of that year, Edison constructed a "phonograph" whose recording stylus made indentations on tinfoil wrapped on a pre-grooved cylinder. Although these indentations were partly deformed by the playback stylus, a weak,

distorted, but intelligible version of the human voice could be reproduced.

Modern disc recording is closer to the Cros system than to Edison's; commercial recordings are stampings from a hardened mold. Virtually all original recordings for home use are first made on magnetic tape. They are then cut into a master disc made of a relatively soft material, lacquer, and end up as a metal stamper from which mass impressions can be made in a vinyl composition.

Modern Recording Systems Current recording media include magnetic tape, transparent film, and grooved discs. The most widely used is the disc.

If the disc cutter head is fed with constant electrical energy over the frequency spectrum, it will produce constant average velocity in the recording stylus. Since the wave length of the recorded signal is doubled with each lower octave, constant stylus velocity would produce impractically large groove excursions in the bass range. Progressive bass attenuation is therefore introduced below a frequency which has now been standardized at 500 hertz, called the *turnover* frequency, in such an amount that the amplitude of groove modulation for signals below this frequency remains the same at a given power. A compensatory boosting of the bass frequencies must be employed in the playback amplifier.

A second problem in disc recording has to do with surface noise introduced by irregularities in the record material and picked up by the needle. The noise is distributed fairly evenly over the frequency spectrum on the basis of energy per cycle. Since each higher octave covers twice the number of cycles, this noise may be considered primarily a treble phenomenon (see NOISE, ACOUSTICAL).

The signal to the recording cutter is again altered, this time by progressive treble boost. In playback, a compensatory treble attenuation is introduced which brings the recorded signal back to normal and at the same time significantly reduces the amount of surface noise. This system of recording *preemphasis* does not change the treble content of the final reproduced sound, but it increases the amplitude of the high-frequency groove modulations relative to the random surface irregularities in the recorded material.

These changes of frequency balance in the recorded signal are called *equalization*; the particular equalization curve is called the *recording characteristic.*

The Modern Disc Reproducing System A pickup, also called a cartridge, traces the groove modulations through a needle or stylus, whose vibrations are converted to an electrical signal. The most common types of electrical generator employed in cartridges are the ceramic (piezoelectric), moving magnet, moving coil, and variable reluctance. It is the task of the cartridge to translate faithfully the wave forms of the groove into an electrical signal. Some of the problems in cartridge design have to do with the stiffness of the moving needle system, which tends to wear the record, and with the mass of the needle tip, which tends to resonate with the semi-elastic record material at high frequencies.

The turntable must revolve the record at a constant speed. Periodic variations in this speed are called *flutter* (the onomatopoetic term for very slow flutter is *wow*). Any noise introduced into the signal by the moving parts (via the pickup) is called *rumble*. A pivoted arm holds the cartridge in place over the record groove, with the vibration axis of the cartridge approximately tangent to the groove over the entire radius of the record.

The amplifier, which may be on one or more chassis, has two sections: the *preamplifier* and the *power amplifier*. The former is a voltage amplifier which performs the functions of input program selection, tone control, volume control, compensation for the frequency equalization introduced in recording, and voltage amplification of the input signal to the point where it can drive the power amplifier. The latter builds up the electrical signal power so that the signal is able to drive the loudspeaker or speakers.

An amplifier is a device whose output energy is greater than, but in the same form as, the input signal energy. The amplifier must therefore borrow energy from an outside source, normally the electrical power line. There are many types of basic amplifying devices. The two that are used almost universally in sound reproduction are the vacuum tube and the transistor.

The loudspeaker converts the electrical output of the amplifier into acoustical energy, usually through a vibrating diaphragm. The loudspeaker and the cartridge, because they are mechanical devices with their own resonances and characteristic behavior, are more intransigent to precise control by the input signal than electronic circuits.

A reproducing system is designed for minimum noise, distortion, frequency discrimination over the audible spectrum, and transient ringing; speakers must also have adequate treble dispersion.

Stereophony Stereophonic sound is recorded on two separate channels from separate microphone inputs. Just as each lens of a stereoscopic camera takes a complete picture, each microphone channel picks up all of the sound, one from a right-oriented perspective and the other from a left-oriented perspective. When the two channels are played back through separate right and left speakers, more of the sense of the acoustical atmosphere of the concert hall is recreated; a corollary of this is an increased clarity of inner melodic voices. The ability of the listener to determine the apparent position of different musical instruments is a less important part of the stereo effect.

In stereo disc recording, one channel is, in effect, recorded on the left groove wall, and the

other channel on the right groove wall. The reproducing stylus must execute a complex motion containing both vertical and horizontal components in order to follow the modulations of both groove walls simultaneously. These complex movements are analyzed into two vectors by two separate generating elements, each at 45° to the vertical and on opposite sides. Each generating element produces the electrical signal for one channel.

Recent developments have been aimed at recapturing the acoustical atmosphere of the concert hall more accurately. In one system, additional speakers at the back and sides of the listening area are used to reproduce delayed signals that simulate reflections from more distant walls. Another system uses four separate channels, two to reproduce rear-hall sound at the rear of the listening room. As in two-channel stereo, there is sometimes a misplaced emphasis on directional effects at the expense of concert-hall ambience.

The ultimate design goal of sound reproducing equipment is not to create "better" sound, but to efface the imprint of the equipment, so that the original musical quality is recreated.

EDGAR VILLCHUR

References

Beranek, Leo L., "Acoustics," New York, McGraw-Hill Book Company, Inc., 1954.
Hunt, Frederick, V., "Electroacoustics," Cambridge, Harvard University Press, 1954.
Olson, Harry F., "Acoustical Engineering," New York, Van Nostrand Reinhold, 1957.
Villchur, Edgar, "Reproduction of Sound," New York, Dover Publications, Inc., 1965.
Villchur, Edgar, "Reproduction of Sound," *Phys. Today*, **5**, No. 9 (September, 1952).

Cross-references: ACOUSTICS; ARCHITECTURAL ACOUSTICS; MUSICAL SOUND; NOISE, ACOUSTICAL; PHYSICAL ACOUSTICS.

RESONANCE

The phenomenon which scientists call resonance can be identified in many different physical systems of widely varying sizes. For instance, a father who pushes his small child on a swing finds that with each successive push the swing goes higher. An astronomer who examines the spectrum of the sun notes the appearance of a series of dark lines superposed on the continuous red to violet band of colors. The solid state physicist who observes the amount of electromagnetic radiation transmitted through a waveguide at a particular microwave frequency finds it can be sharply reduced if certain materials are placed in the guide and a magnetic field is applied. All of these effects are examples of resonance, yet the actual physical mechanisms are different and the explanations require different

analytical procedures depending on whether the system is governed by classical or quantum theory.

In the case of the father pushing the swing, the resonance can be explained as a direct consequence of Newton's laws of classical mechanics. In simple terms, it occurs when an outside agent (the father) pushes the system (swing with child) with a periodic force having the same frequency as the natural frequency of the system itself. The natural frequency is the frequency with which the system oscillates if it is displaced from its normal position of equilibrium and then released to swing freely back and forth. If the external push is timed so as to be exactly in step with the natural frequency, one can think of the swing as being steadily accelerated in its natural direction of motion. When the natural direction of motion changes at the end points of the path so does the push. Elementary kinematics then predicts that such a steady acceleration will cause both the displacement and the maximum velocity to increase continuously and eventually become very large. It is this extreme magnitude of displacement and velocity which is the most noticeable aspect of resonance in a mechanical system. However, less apparent visually, yet equally important, is the rate of energy transfer between the source and the system at resonance. The external agent transfers energy in the form of mechanical work to the system. At resonance, the average rate of this energy transfer per cycle becomes a maximum. This property of maximum rate of energy transfer is of great value when analyzing the effect of radiation on microscopic systems such as atoms and nuclei whose physical behavior must be explained by the laws of quantum physics rather than classical physics. In these systems as in mechanical systems a necessary condition for resonance is that the frequency of the radiation must match a frequency which is in some way associated intrinsically with the system. But here the coordinates of position and velocity are no longer suitable ones to use in describing the response at resonance. Nevertheless, the resonant system is still characterized by the general property that the rate of energy transfer into it is a maximum. In order to bring out the essential features of resonance involving both the behavior of position and velocity and the rate of energy transfer, it is simplest to examine a mechanical system consisting of a mass on a spring with frictional damping.

Resonance in a Simple Mechanical Oscillator
We begin with a mass M attached to a fixed point by a spring with a force constant K and a damping resistance R. In addition the mass is acted upon by a periodic external force of frequency v, $F = F_0 \cos 2\pi v t$. The displacement of the mass from its normal equilibrium position is represented by x. The acceleration d^2x/dt^2 of the mass M is determined by the resultant of these three forces, all along the x-direction: $-Kx$, the elastic restoring force; $-R(dx/dt)$, the damping

force proportional to the instantaneous velocity dx/dt; and the external force $F_0 \cos 2\pi\nu t$. Newton's second law of motion, which states that resultant force = mass $\times$ acceleration, can be expressed by a second-order inhomogeneous linear differential equation:

$$M\frac{d^2x}{dt^2} + R\frac{dx}{dt} + Kx = F_0 \cos 2\pi\nu t \qquad (1)$$

However, in order to discuss resonance it is first necessary to describe the behavior of the spring system when no external driving force is being applied. If the mass is displaced from its normal equilibrium position and then released, it will move in simple harmonic motion with the natural frequency ν_1 given by

$$\nu_1 = \frac{1}{2\pi}\sqrt{\frac{K}{M} - \frac{R^2}{4M^2}}, \quad \left(\frac{K}{M} > \frac{R^2}{4M^2}\right) \qquad (2)$$

This result can be derived mathematically by setting the term on the right-hand side of Eq. (1) equal to zero thus making the equation homogeneous. It can be solved for $x(t)$ by standard methods (see references 1 and 2). The solution is:

$$x = Ae^{-(R/2M)t}\sin(2\pi\nu_1 t + \phi) \qquad (3)$$

where A and ϕ are constants depending on the initial position and velocity. For example, if the mass starts from a position $x = x_0$, with zero velocity, then $A = x_0$ and $\phi = 90°$, and Eq. (3) becomes

$$x = x_0 e^{-(R/2M)t}\cos 2\pi\nu \cdot t \qquad (4)$$

Since the solution is the product of a negative exponential function and a sinusoidal function, the amplitude of the displacement will diminish a little bit more with each succeeding cycle of oscillation and eventually the displacement becomes zero again. This is called a damped harmonic oscillation and is physically what we see any time a real spring or pendulum is disturbed and then allowed to oscillate freely. The damping of the oscillations can also be looked upon as representing a conversion of mechanical energy into heat which is proceeding at the instantaneous rate $R(dx/dt)^2$.

We now consider the solution of the inhomogeneous equation [Eq. (1)]. From the theory of linear differential equations, the solution of an inhomogeneous equation can be expressed as the sum of solutions of the homogeneous and inhomogeneous equation. Thus a general solution can be written down in which one term is the solution [Eq. (3)] while the second is the particular integral satisfying Eq. (1).

$$x = Ae^{-(R/2M)t}\sin(2\pi\nu_1 t + \phi)$$
$$+ \frac{F_0}{2\pi M}\frac{\cos(2\pi\nu t - \alpha)}{\sqrt{4\pi^2(\nu_0{}^2 - \nu^2)^2 + \dfrac{\nu^2 R^2}{M^2}}} \qquad (5)$$

where $\nu_0 = (1/2\pi)\sqrt{K/M}$ is the natural frequency for the undamped oscillator and α, the phase angle between the applied force and the displacement, is defined by

$$\tan\alpha = \frac{\nu R}{2\pi M(\nu_0{}^2 - \nu^2)} \qquad (6)$$

Since the first term in Eq. (5) becomes vanishingly small and can be neglected after a period of time has elapsed, it is called the transient part of the solution. The particular integral maintains a constant amplitude as long as the driving frequency does not change, and it is called the steady-state part of the solution.

The steady-state solution for the instantaneous velocity is also of great interest

$$\nu = \frac{dx}{dt} = \frac{F_0 \nu}{M}\frac{\cos(2\pi\nu t - \beta)}{\sqrt{4\pi^2(\nu^2 - \nu_0{}^2)^2 + \dfrac{R^2\nu^2}{M^2}}} \qquad (7)$$

where β, the phase angle between applied force and velocity, is defined by

$$\tan\beta = \frac{2\pi M(\nu^2 - \nu_0{}^2)}{\nu R} \qquad (8)$$

It is seen that both displacement and velocity have amplitudes which depend on the frequency of the applied force. The form of Eq. (5) and (7) is such that there must exist frequencies for which each achieves a maximum value. The frequencies which produce these maximum values can be found by differentiating the displacement or velocity function with respect to frequency, setting the derivative equal to zero, and solving for ν. In this way, it is deduced that the amplitude of x becomes a maximum when

$$\nu = \sqrt{\nu_0{}^2 - \frac{R^2}{8\pi^2 M^2}} \qquad (9)$$

while the amplitude of ν becomes a maximum when

$$\nu = \nu_0 \qquad (10)$$

This latter frequency ν_0 which is the natural frequency of the undamped oscillator is customarily referred to as the resonance frequency of the oscillator. The phase difference between the force and velocity at resonance is zero. Thus the velocity will achieve its largest magnitude in the part of the cycle when the push is greatest, confirming what we sense intuitively in pushing a swing. The displacement resonance occurs at a frequency slightly different from the resonance frequency, but the difference becomes smaller as R decreases. The velocity resonance is of significance in discussing energy because the rates of energy transfer into and out of the oscillator depend on velocity. The external periodic force is doing work on the oscillator at the instantaneous rate of $F\nu$, while the oscillator

is working against the damping force at the instantaneous rate of $-Rv^2$. Thus energy is being simultaneously absorbed and dissipated. Since the instantaneous rates vary periodically with time, it is more meaningful to calculate average rates per period and then compare. Such a calculation (see reference 2) shows that the average rate of energy absorption is exactly equal to the average rate of energy dissipation and has the magnitude $(F_0{}^2/2R) \cos^2 \beta$. At velocity resonance $\cos^2 \beta = 1$, and these rates of absorption and dissipation will have maximum magnitudes of $F_0{}^2/2R$.

Thus we find that a mechanical oscillator will resonate when a periodic external force with a frequency equal to the natural frequency of the oscillator acts on it. In addition, the rate of absorption of energy from the external source is a maximum at this same resonance frequency. This second property of maximum rate of energy absorption becomes useful in the discussion of resonance phenomena in systems where resonance cannot be described in terms of what happens to the state variables of position and velocity.

There is an exact analogue to this analysis in the electrical circuit consisting of an inductance L, a capacitance C, and a resistance R in series and driven by an alternating emf, $E_0 \cos 2\pi \nu t$. The differential equation for the variation of charge q with time is

$$L \frac{d^2 q}{dt^2} + R \frac{dq}{dt} + \frac{q}{c} = E_0 \cos 2\pi \nu t \qquad (11)$$

and resonance will occur under the same corresponding conditions as for the mechanical oscillator (see ALTERNATING CURRENTS).

Resonance in Coupled Systems A system of particles with n degrees of freedom in which the particles are coupled together by elastic restoring forces will possess a set of n natural or normal frequencies. If the motion is started with an arbitrary distribution of initial displacements and velocities, the subsequent time-dependent motion of each particle will appear as a superposition of all the normal frequencies. However, through a proper choice of initial conditions it is possible to excite any one of n so-called normal modes. A normal mode is characterized by all of the particles oscillating with one particular normal frequency. For each normal frequency there will be a corresponding normal mode. As an example, a coupled system of two identical particles has two normal frequencies, hence two normal modes. For the lower frequency the normal mode is one in which the particle displacements are exactly in phase with each other. For the higher frequency they are exactly out of phase with each other. If a periodic external force is applied with a frequency matching one of the normal frequencies, the entire system will be excited into resonance in the normal mode appropriate to that particular frequency. Just as with the simple mechanical oscillator, the magnitudes of the maximized amplitudes are limited

by whatever damping forces are acting and the rate of energy absorption equals the rate of energy dissipation. This mechanism is the basis for the excitation by resonance of standing waves in continuous elastic media such as solid structures and fluid columns. A standing wave is the configuration of the displacements of all the individual points when vibrating in a normal mode. A string held under tension between two fixed points will vibrate in a normal mode if a transverse frequency is applied which equals an integral multiple of the velocity of transverse waves in the string divided by twice the length. The instantaneous visual appearance of the standing wave corresponding to the lowest normal frequency is a sine curve with its point of maximum vibration, called an antinode, located midway between the fixed ends. This sine curve vibrates transversely back and forth between maximum positive and maximum negative displacements with the normal frequency. If the frequency is doubled, the corresponding standing wave has two antinodes separated by a point of no vibration, called a node, at the midpoint. Standing longitudinal sound waves can be set up in columns of air which are enclosed by tubes that are terminated by closed or open ends. A node will always be found at a closed end. An antinode will always be found just beyond the mouth of an open tube. The excitation of such standing waves by resonance with the appropriate external driving frequency results in an enhancement of the intensity of the sound. One of the most spectacular illustrations of the power of resonance was the destruction of the Tacoma Narrows Bridge on November 7, 1940 by large-amplitude torsional oscillations set up in its main span by strong cross winds.

Resonance Phenomena in Atomic-sized Systems The exact theory explaining the processes whereby systems composed of atoms absorb and emit energy is based on the principles of quantum theory. Nevertheless, such processes still show some physical analogy to resonance in a mechanical oscillator. A simple example is the single atom consisting of one or more electrons bound to a nucleus by predominantly electrostatic forces. Quantum theory predicts that the atom can exist only in a set of discrete energies in contrast to the continuous range of energies which in principle is available to a large-size satellite system such as the earth and moon. If the atom changes from a higher-energy state E_j to a lower-energy state E_i, energy in the form of electromagnetic radiation is given off and the frequency of the radiation ν_{ji} is related to the energy difference between the two states by the equation:

$$\nu_{ji} = \frac{E_j - E_i}{h} \qquad (12)$$

h is the well-known Planck constant of action and has a value of 6.625×10^{-27} erg sec. This frequency and others which connect discrete energy states consistent with the so-called selec-

tion rules for the atom can be pictured as a set of frequencies characteristic of the particular atom. By analogy with resonance in a mechanical oscillator absorption of energy at a maximum rate might be expected to occur when there is radiation incident on the atom with a frequency which matches one of these frequencies. In quantum mechanics, the meaningful index for such a process taking place is the probability that an energy transition will occur a time t after being exposed to the radiation. When calculated, this probability is found to be proportional to

$$\frac{1 - \cos 2\pi(\nu_{ij} - \nu)t}{(\nu_{ij} - \nu)^2} \qquad (13)$$

(see references 3 and 4).

Even though this probability function is not of the same mathematical form as the expression for rate of energy absorption derived in the section on "Resonance in a Simple Mechanical Oscillator," because of its dependence on $(\nu_{ij} - \nu)^2$ instead of $(\nu_0^2 - \nu^2)^2$, it can be looked upon as establishing a condition for a resonance type process. It predicts that the likelihood of resonance absorption becomes very large when the external frequency approaches something resembling a natural frequency of the atom. A distinctive example of this kind of resonance absorption is the phenomenon in the solar spectrum described in the introduction. The radiation from the hot core of solar gases is characterized by a continuous spectrum. In passing through the cooler gases of the sun's outer atmosphere, radiation will be absorbed at those frequencies which match frequencies of atomic transitions in the cool gas. These blocked out lines in the continuous spectrum show up as dark lines against the background. They are called Fraunhofer lines. The rare gas helium was first discovered as a consequence of these observations.

Another important class of atomic-scale resonance phenomena concerns the behavior of atoms and nuclei in static magnetic fields when subjected to radio frequency (rf) magnetic fields. If the frequency of the rf field matches the Larmor precession frequency of the particle's magnetic moment vector about the direction of the static field, a resonance absorption of energy from the rf field can occur. The phenomenon is called electron spin resonance (ESR) if the magnetic moment is associated with unpaired electron spins of the atom and nuclear magnetic resonance (NMR) if the moment is associated with the spin of the nucleus. The ESR frequency of an atom with a single unpaired electron spin of $1/2$ in a static magnetic field H is given by ν (in megahertz) = 2.80 H (in gauss). The NMR frequency of a proton is given by ν (in kilohertz) = 4.258 H (in gauss). During recent years magnetic resonance has proved to be a powerful experimental technique for obtaining information about the magnetic moments of atoms and nuclei and the strengths of internal magnetic

fields in solids. (See MAGNETIC RESONANCE and references 5, 6, and 7 for more details.)

ROBERT LINDSAY

References

1. Feynman, R. P., Leighton, R. B., and Sands, M., "Lectures on Physics," Vol. 1, Ch. 23, Addison-Wesley Publishing Co., 1963.
2. Lindsay, R. B., "Physical Mechanics," Third edition, Ch. 10, New York, Van Nostrand Reinhold, 1962.
3. Lindsay, R. B., "Influence of Environment on Transmission of Energy," *Am. J. Phys.*, **28**, 67–75 (1960).
4. Lindsay, R. B., and Margenau, H., "Foundations of Physics," Ch. 9, New York, John Wiley & Sons, 1936.
5. Pake, G. E., *Sci. Am.*, **199** 58 (August 1958).
6. Feynman, R. P., Leighton, R. B., and Sands, M., "Lectures on Physics," Vol. II, Chs. 34 and 35, Addison-Wesley Publishing Co., 1963.
7. Kittel, Charles, "Introduction to Solid State Physics," Fourth Edition, Chapter 16, New York, John Wiley & Sons, 1971.

Cross-references: ALTERNATING CURRENTS, DYNAMICS, ELECTRON SPIN, MAGNETIC RESONANCE, SOLAR PHYSICS.

RHEOLOGY

Rheology is the study of the response of materials to an applied force. It deals with the deformation and flow of matter.

Heraclitus, a pre-Socratic metaphysician, recognized in the fifth century B.C. that $\pi\alpha\nu\tau\alpha$ $\rho\epsilon\iota$, or "everything flows." Long before Heraclitus, the prophetess Deborah, fourth judge of the Israelites, had sung that "the mountains flowed before the Lord" in celebrating the victory of Barak over the Canaanites (1). Reiner (2) claims that the translation in the authorized version of the Bible that the mountains "melted" before the Lord misses the essential point of her wisdom, for Deborah recognized this early instance of a relaxation in the time scale provided by eternity; in recognition of her basic contribution to the primary literature of rheology, Reiner proposed the dimensionless quantity D (for Deborah) where

$$D = \frac{\text{time of relaxation}}{\text{time of observation}} = \frac{\tau}{t} \qquad (1)$$

The difference between solids and liquids is found in the magnitude of D. Liquids, which relax in small fractions of a second, have small D; solids, large D. A long enough time span can reduce the Deborah number of a solid to unity, and impact loading can increase D of a liquid. Viscoelastic materials are best characterized under conditions in which D lies within a few decades of unity.

Force Balance Equation When a force f is applied to a body, four things may happen. The

body may be accelerated, strained, made to flow, and slid along another body. If these four responses are added to each other, one can write for motion in one direction

$$f = m\ddot{x} + r\dot{x} + sx + f_0 \tag{2}$$

where m is the mass, r is a damping parameter related to viscosity, s to elasticity, and f_0 to the yield value. Evaluation of the coefficients m, r, and s involves the measurement of displacements, x, and their time derivatives in a manner which links these kinematic variables via an equation of state such as Eq. (2) to stress, σ (force per unit area), and its time derivatives.

Scope of Rheology In contrast to the discipline of mechanics wherein the responses of bodies to unbalanced forces are of concern, rheology concerns balanced forces which do not change the center of gravity of the body. Since rheology involves deformation and flow, it is concerned primarily with the evaluation of the coefficients r and s of Eq. (2). The coefficients account for most of the energy dissipated and stored, respectively, during the process of distorting a body.

Most rheological systems lie between the two extremes of ideality: the Hookean solid and the Newtonian liquid.

Measurements of Viscosity and Elasticity in Shear *Simple Shear.* Shear viscosity η and shear elasticity G are determined by evaluating the coefficients of the variables $\dot{x}$ and x respectively, which result when the geometry of the system has been taken into account. The resulting equation of state balances stress against shear rate $\dot{\gamma}$ (reciprocal seconds) and shear strain γ (dimensionless) as the kinematic variables. For a purely elastic, or Hookean, response,

$$\sigma = G\gamma \tag{3}$$

and for a purely viscous, or Newtonian, response

$$\sigma = \eta\dot{\gamma} \tag{4}$$

As a consequence, G can be measured from stress-strain measurements, and η from stress-shear rate measurements.

Elasticoviscous behavior is described in terms of the additivity of shear rates:

$$\dot{\gamma} = \frac{\sigma}{\eta} + \frac{\dot{\sigma}}{G} \tag{5}$$

whereas viscoelastic behavior is characterized by the additivity of stress according to Eq. (2):

$$\sigma = G\gamma + \eta\dot{\gamma} \tag{6}$$

See reference 3 for further information on rheological bodies.

Relaxation. Numerous attempts have been made to fit simplified mechanical models to the two behavior patterns described by Eqs. (5) and (6). One can picture the elastic element as a spring arrayed in a network parallel with the

viscous element to give essentially a (Kelvin) solid with retarded elastic behavior, wherein

$$\frac{\eta_k}{G_k} = \lambda \ \text{sec (retardation time)} \tag{7}$$

or as a series (Maxwell) network which flows when stressed or relaxes under constant strain:

$$\frac{\eta_m}{G_m} = \tau \ \text{sec (relaxation time)} \tag{8}$$

and transient experiments may be designed to measure these parameters singly. In real systems, a single relaxation (or retardation) time fails to account for experimental results. A distribution of relaxation times exists (see RELAXATION).

Dynamic Studies. When Eq. (2) is written in the form

$$\ddot{x} + 2k\dot{x} + \omega_1{}^2 x = 0 \tag{2b}$$

the equation suggests that the variation in stress be cyclic. Rheometers are designed so that the system may oscillate in free vibration of natural resonant frequency ω_1, or else so that a cyclic shearing stress of the form $f_0 \cos \omega t$ is impressed on the sample over a frequency range which spans ω_1. In neither case is the material strained beyond its range of linearity. Equation (2b) represents a damped harmonic oscillator, providing that the coefficients are constant (i.e., providing that they do not depend on the strain magnitude). Not all systems meet this requirement in the strict sense, with the result that one of the first consistency checks which the experimenter makes is for linearity. Doubling the amplitude of oscillation should double the stress and should not change the phase relationships between the cyclic stress and the deformation.

See RESONANCE and see reference 4 for more information on dynamic studies.

Time-temperature Equivalence *Steady-state Phenomena.* The creep of a viscoelastic body or the stress relaxation of an elasticoviscous one is employed in the evaluation of η and G. In such studies, the long-time behavior of a material at low temperatures resembles the short-time response at high temperatures. A means of superposing data over a wide range of temperatures has resulted which permits the mechanical behavior of viscoelastic materials to be expressed as a master curve over a reduced time scale as large as twenty decades, or powers of ten (see references 5 through 7).

Polymeric materials generally display large G values 10^{10} dynes/cm^2 or greater) at low temperatures or at short times of measurement. As either of these variables is increased, the modulus drops, slowly at first, then attaining a steady rate of roughly one decade drop per decade increase in time. If the material possesses a yield value, this steady drop is arrested at a level of G which ranges from 10^7 downward.

Dynamic Behavior. The application of sinus-

oidal stress to a body leads inevitably to the complex modulus G^*, where

$$G^* = G' + iG'' = G' + i\omega\eta' \qquad (9)$$

where G' is the in-phase modulus (σ/γ) which represents the stored energy, and G'' is the out-of-phase modulus $(\sigma/\dot{\gamma})$ representing dissipated energy (as its relation to η' suggests); the variable against which G' and η' are determined is the circular frequency ω. Superposition of variable temperature data or variable frequency data provides a master curve of the type described for the steady-state parameters.

Problems in Three Dimensions *State of Stress.* The forces and stresses applied to a body may be resolved into three vectors, one normal to an arbitrarily selected element of area and two tangential. For the yz plane the stress vectors are σ_{xx}, and σ_{xy}, σ_{xz}, respectively. Six analogous stresses exist for the other orthogonal orientations, giving a total of nine quantities, of which three exist as commutative pairs ($\sigma_{rs} = \sigma_{sr}$). The state of stress, therefore, is defined by three tensile or normal components (σ_{xx}, σ_{yy}, σ_{zz}) and three shear or tangential components (σ_{xy}, σ_{xz}, σ_{yz}). The shear components are most readily applicable to the determination of η and G.

Strain Components. For each stress component σ there exists a corresponding strain component γ. Even for an ideally elastic body, however, a pure tension does not produce a pure γ_{xx} strain; γ components exist which constrict the body in the y and z directions.

The complete stress-strain relation requires the six σ's to be written in terms of the six γ components. The result is a 6×6 matrix with 36 coefficients, k_{rs}, in place of the single constant. Twenty-one of these coefficients (the diagonal elements and half of the cross elements) are needed to express the deformation of a completely anisotropic material. Only three are necessary for a cubic crystal, and two for an amorphous isotropic body. These parameters are discussed in reference 8.

Similar considerations prevail for viscous flow, in which the kinematic variable is $\dot{\gamma}$.

RAYMOND R. MYERS

References

1. Judges 5:5.
2. Reiner, M., *Phys. Today*, 17, 62 (1964).
3. Reiner, Marcus, "Deformation, Strain and Flow," Second edition, London, H. K. Lewis & Co., 1960; "Lectures in Theoretical Rheology," Third edition, New York, Interscience Publishers, 1960.
4. Eirich, F. R., Ed., "Rheology, Theory and Applications," Five volumes, New York, Academic Press, 1956-1969.
5. Myers, R., Ed., *Transactions of Society of Rheology*, published annually 1957-1964, semiannually 1964-1966 and quarterly 1967-present.
6. Ferry, J. D., "Viscoelastic Properties of Polymers," Second Edition, New York, John Wiley & Sons, 1970.
7. Tobolsky, A. V., "Properties and Structures of Polymers," New York, John Wiley & Sons, 1960.
8. Alfrey, Turner, Jr., "Mechanical Behavior of High Polymers," New York, Interscience Publishers, 1948.

Cross-references: ELASTICITY, FLUID DYNAMICS, VISCOSITY.

ROTATION—CIRCULAR MOTION*

Circular or rotary motion is very common and is best exemplified by a wheel rotating on an axle or a particle revolving in a circle about an attracting center. The case of a fixed axis will be considered in this section. This and related topics are elaborated on in greater detail in most college physics texts; in particular, "University Physics" by F. W. Sears and M. W. Zemansky is recommended.

Consider, as in Fig. 1, a line fixed in the plane of the wheel or orbit and terminating at the axis

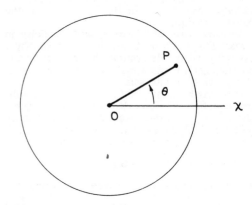

FIG. 1. Body rotating about a fixed axis through O.

of rotation. A second radial line is fixed in the body and also terminates on the axis. The angle between these two lines specifies the position or orientation of the orbiting particle P or a section of the rotating wheel. Certain equations are more simply written if this angle is expressed in radians, but revolutions or degrees are sometimes used.

If θ changes from θ_1 to θ_2 as time increases from t_1 to t_2, then the average angular velocity is defined as

$$\omega_{ave} = \frac{\theta_2 - \theta_1}{t_2 - t_1} = \frac{\Delta\theta}{\Delta t}.$$

*The author of this article died in 1971. Professor A. H. Weber of St. Louis University kindly revised the article to ensure its timeliness.

The instantaneous angular velocity ω is the value which this ratio approaches as $\Delta\theta$ and Δt become small. It is most advantageously expressed in radians per second.

Again, if ω is not constant but changes from ω_1 to ω_2 as t increases from t_1 to t_2, then the average angular acceleration is

$$\alpha_{\text{ave}} = \frac{\omega_2 - \omega_1}{t_2 - t_1} = \frac{\Delta\omega}{\Delta t}.$$

The instantaneous acceleration α is the limit which this ratio approaches as $\Delta\omega$ and Δt become small; α is most advantageously expressed in radians per second per second.

In calculus notation $\omega = d\theta/dt$ and $\alpha = d\omega/dt$. Inversely,

$$\theta = \int \omega dt$$

and if ω is known as a function of t, then the integration may be effected.

Also

$$\omega = \int \alpha dt$$

and may again be evaluated. A simple situation is for constant α, and this case is discussed fully in the reference cited.

Next, consider a particle in a circular orbit of radius r, or a particle in the plane of a wheel a distance r from the center but not necessarily on the rim. Such a particle moves along a circular arc of length $s = r\theta$, where θ must be in radians; s and r are both linear quantities and have the same units of length: e.g., meters. Here linear implies a length, not necessarily along a straight line, and is contrasted with an angular quantity which implies an angle of some sort. The equation $s = r\theta$ is the connection between linear and angular quantities and is the basis for a useful analogy between motion along a straight line and rotation about a fixed axis.

For this same particle moving in a circular arc, if s and θ change by Δs and $\Delta\theta$ and in the time Δt, then

$$\frac{\Delta s}{\Delta t} = r\frac{\Delta\theta}{\Delta t} \text{ or } v = r\omega.$$

By the same reasoning, $a = \alpha r$. Of course v is the instantaneous velocity along the arc (tangential to the arc) and a is the instantaneous tangential acceleration.

There is another component of acceleration involved in this circular motion. The linear velocity v is a vector quantity. Whenever v changes, in either magnitude or direction, there is an acceleration. The acceleration of the preceding paragraph, $a = \alpha r$, arises because the particle is changing the magnitude of its tangential velocity, that is the particle is either speeding up or slowing down. But of course v, being along the tangent, is always changing in direction, and this amounts to an acceleration too. Derivations of this acceleration can be found in various texts and it turns out to be $a = v^2/r = \omega^2 r$. This acceleration is directed inward along the radius (it is thus at right angles to the tangential acceleration) and is sometimes called radial acceleration or centripetal acceleration. (A more advanced treatment of orbital motion would employ the polar coordinates r, θ). Then if the particle moves along the radius, there would be still another acceleration along the radius, and the total radial acceleration in this notation is

$$\frac{d^2 r}{dt^2} = \omega^2 r.$$

The concept of kinetic energy is first developed in translational motion and is defined as $\frac{1}{2}mv^2$ where m is the mass of some particle moving with the velocity v. Kinetic energy is a scalar quantity and if there are two particles, their kinetic energies just add. Applying this to rotation, a rigid body rotating about a fixed axis, may be broken into small particles of mass m_1, $m_2, \cdots$ having velocities $v_1, v_2, \cdots$ respectively. The total kinetic energy is then

$$\tfrac{1}{2}m_1 v_1{}^2 + \tfrac{1}{2}m_2 v_2{}^2 \cdots$$

But $v_1 = \omega r_1$, $v_2 = \omega r_2$ where the ω is the same for all particles. So the kinetic energy equals

$$\tfrac{1}{2}m_1 \omega^2 r_1{}^2 + \tfrac{1}{2}m_2 \omega^2 r_2{}^2 \cdots = \tfrac{1}{2}(m_1 r_1{}^2$$
$$+ m_2 r_2{}^2 \cdots)\omega^2.$$

The quantity in the parentheses, usually denoted by I, is called the moment of inertia of the rotating body, and it plays the role for rotation that m, the inertia, plays for translation. Thus kinetic energy $= \frac{1}{2}I\omega^2$ in analogy to kinetic energy $= \frac{1}{2}mv^2$. The moments of inertia of various bodies are listed in tables.

Extending this analogy, linear momentum is defined as mv. This suggests that angular or rotational momentum could be defined as $I\omega$. This is a satisfactory definition of angular momentum for a rigid body, but a more general definition of angular momentum is $mvr \sin\theta$ where θ is the angle between v and r. Angular momentum is a very fundamental quantity because it remains constant for an isolated system. Also it is found to consist of integral multiples of a certain smallest amount of angular momentum. That is, angular momentum can be added to a body or taken from a body only in integral multiples of this smallest constant quantity. A photon for instance is found to possess a quantum of angular momentum. This

property of angular momentum is particularly important for small bodies such as rotating molecules.

Now these accelerations, which in turn imply changes in rotational kinetic energy and angular momentum, are brought about by the application of forces. Let us consider the two cases for the two components of the accelerations, the radial and the tangential components. We of course will use Newton's law $F = ma$ where F is the resultant force applied to m, a is the acceleration of m, and a is in the direction of F. Thus a radial acceleration is associated with a radial force and a tangential acceleration with a tangential force.

Case I. Force in the Radial Direction. Since there is no tangential force, the tangential acceleration is zero and the particle (or wheel) moves with constant angular velocity and constant tangential velocity. Further, for strictly circular motion, the acceleration is just $\omega^2 r$ directed toward the center and from Newton's second law, $F = m\omega^2 r$ also directed toward the center. This force is called the centripetal force and is the radial force which must be applied to a mass m in order to keep it moving in a circular path. If this force were not applied, the particle would not move in the circular path, but it would move along a straight line in accordance with Newton's first law.

There are many examples of this centripetal force. If a mass tied to a string is whirled in a circle, then this force must be applied to the mass by the string. If a car is rounding a curve, then the highway must exert on the car a force which is toward the center of the path. In either example, if the force is not exerted (that is, there is no force on the mass) the particle would move along a straight line rather than in a circle.

Case II. Force in the Tangential Direction. A particle speeding up or slowing down in its circular path has a tangential acceleration, a, which is related to its angular acceleration by $a = r\alpha$. Again by Newton's second law this requires a tangential force $F = ma = mr\alpha$. This can be extended to the case of many particles, as in a rotating wheel, by the following maneuvers. Multiply both sides by r obtaining $rF = mr^2\alpha$. The left hand side is recognized as the torque about the axis of rotation of the force F. Of course there is one such equation for each of the many particles in the wheel. Adding all such equations one gets on the left hand side just the total torque, usually denoted by L. On the right hand side, since α is the same for all particles, the summation will introduce a combination we have seen before and the sum is just $I\alpha$. So $L = I\alpha$ which is the rotational analog of $F = ma$. Thus torque L is the analog of F and, as before, I is the analog of m.

Centrifugal force is referred to in many text books and Coriolis force, while much less common, is sometimes mentioned. In contrast, some texts scrupulously avoid these two forces or show a greater distaste for centrifugal force than

CORIOLIS FORCE. An attempt will be made to reconcile these points of view. A key idea is the fact that different observers watching the same chain of events may record quite different observations and hence give quite different explanations. An inertial observer, that is, one at rest with respect to the fixed stars, and a rotating observer may do just that. Their explanations are equally valid; at least, the General Theory of Relativity admits both inertial and non-inertial observers on equal terms.

Consider first a ball tied to a string and whirled in a horizontal circle and then released. Any bystander is essentially an inertial observer and would see the ball fly off along the tangent in a straight line. Consider next the apparatus shown in Fig. 2. It consists of a horizontal turntable T

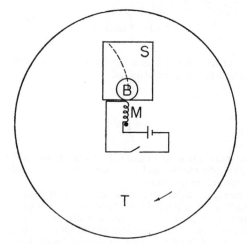

FIG. 2. Reprinted from *American Journal of Physics*, 27 (6), 429 (September, 1959).

on which there is a steel ball B and an electromagnet M. The ball rolls on a toy "magic slate," S, on which it leaves a trace of its path. The slate plays the role of a rotating observer and the trace left on it is a record of how it observes the motion. The procedure is to energize the magnet with the ball in contact with it, set the table into rotation and then release the ball. The dashed line represents the path followed. Notice that on the slate the ball starts rolling in a radial direction and then curves. The inertial observer sees a tangential motion of a released ball, while the rotating observer sees a radial motion.

Before the ball is released, the inertial observer says there is just one force acting on the ball, the tension in the string. This force on the ball is directed toward the center of the circle and is called centripetal force. The inertial observer also sees the ball accelerating toward the center and says that the centripetal force produces the centripetal acceleration. When the ball is released the centripetal force disappears, there is no force on the ball and the ball then travels in a straight line at constant speed.

In contrast, the rotating observer says that before the ball is released it is at rest. It has no motion and no acceleration with respect to the slate and is therefore in equilibrium. Hence two equal but opposite forces act on the ball. These two forces are a centripetal force applied by the magnet and a centrifugal force which acts radially outward. When the ball is released, the centripetal force ceases. This allows the centrifugal force, which continues to act, to accelerate the ball radially outward. Then follows a curvature of the path caused, according to the rotating observer, by the Coriolis force. This force appears when the ball acquires a velocity, v, with respect to the rotating observer and turns out to be always perpendicular to v. It is only the rotating observer who uses the concepts of centrifugal and Coriolis force. Notice also that while centrifugal and centripetal force are equal and opposite, they are not the action and reaction of Newton's Third Law as is implied in some texts. Actually since they act on the same body, they are equilibrants one of the other.

ARTHUR G. ROUSE

Cross-references: CENTRIFUGE, DYNAMICS.

S

SCHRÖDINGER EQUATION

The Schrödinger equation, first obtained in 1926[1], was an extension of de Broglie's hypothesis, proposed two years earlier,[2] that each material particle has associated with it a wavelength λ related to the linear momentum p of the particle by the equation

$$\lambda = \frac{h}{p} \tag{1}$$

where h is Planck's constant. Since any sinusoidally varying wave motion of amplitude ψ and wavelength λ satisfies the differential equation*

$$\nabla^2 \psi + \frac{4\pi^2}{\lambda^2} \psi = 0 \tag{2}$$

matter waves would obey the equation

$$\nabla^2 \psi + \frac{4\pi^2}{h^2} p^2 \psi = 0 \tag{3}$$

In particular, a particle of mass m with no forces acting on it has energy $E = \frac{1}{2}mv^2 = p^2/2m$, or $p^2 = 2mE$. Equation (3) may thus be written

$$\nabla^2 \psi + \frac{8\pi^2 m}{h^2} E \psi = 0 \tag{4}$$

This is the Schrödinger equation for a free particle. Of greater importance is the equation for a bound particle for which the binding force can be related to a potential energy V. In this case, the total energy of the particle is equal to the sum of the kinetic and potential energies, i.e., $E = p^2/2m + V$, or $p^2 = 2m(E - V)$. Equation (3) thus becomes

$$\nabla^2 \psi + \frac{8\pi^2 m}{h^2} (E - V)\psi = 0 \tag{5}$$

This is known as the time-independent Schrödinger equation. Its great utility lies in the fact that it enables one to calculate energy levels, or eigenvalues, of the energy E (see QUANTUM THEORY). The remarkable agreement of the results of the equation with experimental fact

$$*\Delta^2 \equiv \frac{\partial^2}{\partial x^2} + \frac{\partial^2}{\partial y^2} + \frac{\partial^2}{\partial z^2}.$$

has led to its being regarded as one of the fundamental equations of physics.

The more advanced formulation of the Schrödinger equation is based on the operator concept of quantum theory together with the Hamiltonian methods of classical mechanics. Specifically, to each dynamical variable q_i, there is a conjugate momentum p_i. The fundamental postulate of quantum mechanics states that for each pair (q_i, p_i), the equation

$$p_i \psi = -i\hbar \frac{\partial \psi}{\partial q_i} \tag{6}$$

holds, where $\hbar = h/2\pi$. That is, $-i\hbar\partial/\partial q_i$ is an operator, which, when applied to the wave function ψ, is equivalent to multiplying by p_i. In the Hamiltonian function $H(p_i, q_i)$, each p_i is replaced by its corresponding operator. The result is the Hamiltonian operator $H(-i\hbar\partial/\partial q_i, q_i)$, which, when it operates on the wave function, is equivalent to multiplying by the energy E, viz.,

$$H(-i\hbar\partial/\partial q_i, q_i)\psi = E\psi \tag{7}$$

This is the generalized form of the time-independent Schrödinger equation. It reduces to Eq. (5) when applied to a single particle, but it has the advantage that the application to systems of many particles can be carried out in a straightforward manner.

The time-dependent form of the Schrödinger equation is obtained by replacing E by its operator $E \rightarrow i\hbar\partial/\partial t$, so that

$$H\left(-i\hbar \frac{\partial}{\partial q_i}, q_i\right)\psi = i\hbar \frac{\partial}{\partial t} \psi \tag{8}$$

For applications of the various forms of the Schrödinger equation, the reader should consult the article on WAVE MECHANICS and references therein.

GRANT R. FOWLES

References

1. *Ann. Physik*, 79, 361, 489 (1926).
2. *Phil. Mag.*, 47, 446 (1924).

Cross-references: MATRIX MECHANICS, QUANTUM THEORY, WAVE MECHANICS, WAVE MOTION.

SECONDARY EMISSION

In its most general sense, secondary electron emission refers to the ejection of electrons from matter under the impact of rapidly moving particles such as electrons, ions, or neutral atoms. When the atoms of the material bombarded are in the gaseous state, the phenomenon is more commonly referred to as impact ionization. In practice, the term is mainly used in connection with the emission of electrons from solids under electron bombardment as in photomultipliers, and for the ejection of electrons at the cathode of gas discharge devices under the action of positive ions.

Historical Background Secondary emission from solids was first observed with electrons as incident particles. The effect was discovered by Austin and Starke in 1902 in the course of studies on the reflection of fast electrons from metals. Upon increasing the angle of incidence of the primary electrons away from the normal, Austin and Starke observed that the current into the target first decreased to zero and then actually reversed. They concluded that not only are the incident electrons reflected but other electrons are also ejected from the plate such that the total number leaving exceeds the number arriving. The effect was found to be strictly proportional to the number of primary electrons. Furthermore, it was found to be more pronounced for metals of high density, and it was observed to increase rapidly with the angle of incidence. Shortly thereafter, P. Lenard (1903) showed that the secondaries are emitted diffusely, that they possess low energies of the order of a few volts independent of primary energy or target material, that the yield goes through a maximum at a few hundred volts, and that the process occurs in insulators as well as metals. Lenard concluded that the formation process is fundamentally an atomic one and therefore largely independent of the state of aggregation. This deduction has been confirmed in recent years.

The emission of secondary electrons from solids under ion bombardment was first demonstrated in 1905 by J. J. Thomson and established to be very similar to the case of electron bombardment by C. Füchtbauer (1906). The secondaries were again found to have energies of a few volts, essentially independent of the nature of the bombarding ion, its velocity, or the properties of the solid bombarded. Shortly thereafter, N. R. Campbell (1911) established the same characteristics for the electrons emitted under α-particle bombardment, the so-called δ-rays.

Secondary Emission Under Electron Bombardment The basic features of the phenomenon as clarified by subsequent investigations may be summarized as follows. For all pure metals and elemental semiconductors free from surface oxides or gas contamination, the total yield δ, defined as the total number of electrons emitted per incident primary electron, never exceeds a

value of about 2. Out of this total, the number of backscattered electrons per incident primary η may be as high as 0.5 for high atomic number elements and energies in excess of a few kilovolts. The distinction between the two kinds of emitted electrons is based on their energy distribution. The true secondaries are characterized by their low energies, peaked at about 2 eV for all metals, and a Maxwellian-like energy distribution with a mean value close to 5 eV independent of primary energy. The backscattered electrons above about 50 eV emerge with energies all the way to the primary energy, but only a few per cent are truly elastically reflected, having lost no appreciable energy in the solid (as indicated in Fig. 1).

The backscattered fraction η is almost constant with changing primary energy for low atomic number elements ($Z \lesssim 30$), varying nearly linearly with Z from 0.04 for Be ($Z = 4$) to 0.28 for Ni ($Z = 28$). For heavier elements, η increases slowly with primary energy from values less than for Ni to limiting values as high as 0.45 for Pt ($Z = 78$) above 5 kV. The yield of low energy secondaries $\Delta = \delta - \eta$ starts from zero at a finite voltage in the neighborhood of 10 to 15 eV and rises to a maximum value in the range of 0.5 to 1.5 between 100 and 700 volts for all metals. Thereafter, it decreases steadily until at energies above a few kilovolts, Δ becomes less than the backscattered fraction η.

In sharp contrast to thermionic or photoelectric emission, neither the onset of emission nor the maximum yield is directly related to the work function of the metal. Instead, it has been found that the maximum yield Δ_m increases steadily within each period of the atomic table as successive electrons are added; the alkali metals have the lowest yield in each case as illustrated for the fourth period by Fig. 2.

The presence of surface impurities or oxides can increase the yield considerably, primarily owing to the fact that secondaries can travel larger distances in insulators than in metals, where they lose energy rapidly to the conduction electrons. Measurement of the yield for insulators, such as BaO, MgF_2, MgO, and KCl, have shown that yields of 6 to 10 or higher can be obtained for such materials depending on the method of preparation, the yields remaining well above unity even at primary energies of many kilovolts. It is for this reason that in technical applications in which it is desired to obtain the largest possible yields, one utilizes alloys which upon heat treatment form an oxide layer containing BeO or MgO on their surfaces. The most common of them are alloys of Cu-Be and Ag-Mg.

In addition to the larger mean free path for secondaries, such complex insulating surfaces often show an additional enhancement of their yield owing to internal electric fields, which act to increase the fraction of electrons able to escape, thus resulting in yields often many times

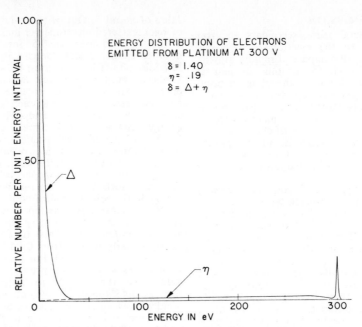

FIG. 1. Typical energy distribution of the electrons emitted from metals under electron bombardment by 300-V primaries; δ is the total yield, Δ the yield of true secondaries, and η the backscattered fraction.

those normally attainable. The presence of charging effects is characterized by a strong increase in the relative number of very low-energy secondaries. It is generally accompanied by a time delay in the emission process, which is long compared with that for normal secondary emission, which is completed in less than 10^{-12} second. In recent years, negative electron affinity materials that have wide band-gaps, such as GaP(Cs), and that achieve high yields with very fast response times have been successfully developed (B. F. Williams, 1970).

Secondary Emission Under Ion Bombardment As already noted, secondary emission under ion bombardment resembles closely the phenomenon under electron bombardment, especially for very high ion energies, when the velocities of the incident ions exceed the orbital velocities of electrons in the atoms of the solid. The principal difference is the somewhat larger yield for ions, brought about by their greater rate of energy loss and therefore ionization near the surface. For protons, the maximum yield is close to 4 occuring at an incident energy of about 100 kV. For α-particles or helium ions, the maximum yield is almost four times as large since the rate of ionization is proportional to the square of the effective charge. Another important difference in the case of fast ions is that all clean metals show closely the same yield at a given energy, because of a proportionality between the probability of secondary formation and absorption in all metals. Again, the presence of oxide layers can greatly enhance the attainable yield. For ions of very low velocity, the phenomenon becomes more complex since

the relative values of the ionization potential and the work function of the solid begin to play a dominant role. The electron-emission process is then determined primarily by the energy made available when an electron from the metal drops into the ionized outer level of the approaching ion, rather than by its kinetic energy and state of charge.

Theory In contrast to thermionic, photoelectric, and field emission, secondary emission under the impact of high-speed particles is an energetic process for which the usual free-electron model of a metal becomes inadequate. Furthermore, in the case of electrons falling on a solid, the strong inelastic scattering by the large number of more firmly bound electrons is the principal factor determining the depth at which the secondaries are formed. The theoretical description therefore consists of finding an expression for the ionization density as a function of depth, and then calculating the probability that the secondaries formed will reach the surface. When the primary particle velocity is high, the theory of Bohr and Bethe for the stopping of charged particles in gases may be used to calculate the scattering and ionization of the incident particles. In the special case of high-energy ions, scattering is negligible and a simple theory was formulated by E. J. Sternglass (1957) that explains the maximum in the yield as reflecting the maximum in the ionization probability for the atoms of the solid.

For the case of low-energy electrons incident on the surface, it is possible to arrive at an approximate expression for the mean depth at which the electrons have been completely scat-

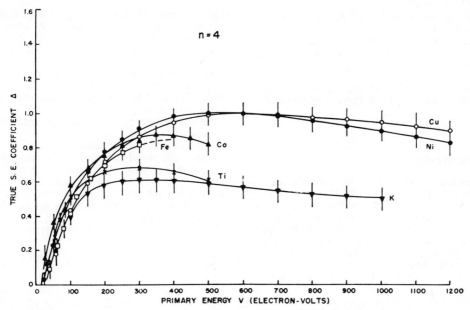

FIG. 2. Typical secondary-electron yield curves for metals. Data shown for elements in the 4th period of the atomic table.

tered and where most of the secondaries are formed. In view of the known rapid exponential absorption of the secondaries in metals, with a mean-free path of only a few atomic layers and an energy expenditure per secondary formed similar to that for gases (~30 eV), good agreement with the observed yields was obtained by E. J. Sternglass (1951). The shape of the yield curve is found to reflect the opposing effects of an increase in the number of secondaries formed and the decrease in their chance of reaching the surface as the primary energy is increased. In insulators, the escape probability is greater, thus leading to larger yields at high primary energies.

For the case of low-velocity rare-gas ions incident, the band-model of a metal can be used to calculate the energy available for the ejection of a conduction electron when a metallic electron neutralizes the incoming ion. The observed yield and energy distribution of the secondaries can then be accounted for rather well as shown by H. D. Hagstrum (1954). At the present time, the principal theoretical problem remaining is to establish the precise role of the surface potential barrier in determining the fraction of the secondaries able to escape.

Applications The principal application of secondary emission in the field of electronics has been in the amplification of weak electrical currents first suggested by J. Slepian in 1917. The most common use is in the intensification of photoelectrons by successive steps of multiplication in photomultiplier tubes, over-all gains of 10^7 being readily achieved at a very small loss in signal-to-noise ratio. The phenomenon also plays an important role in many types of television camera tubes such as the iconoscope and the image orthicon, and more recently in image-intensifying tubes based on secondary emission from a series of thin foils or plates containing microchannels coated with a high-resistance secondary emissive material. Other important applications exist in storage tubes, magnetrons, and high-gain multiplier receiving tubes. Secondary emission under ion bombardment is a fundamental process involved in most gas-discharge devices, and it is also believed to play an important role in high-voltage breakdown phenomena.

Most recently, secondary electron multipliers in the form of fine tubes (channeltrons) coated with internal layers of secondary emissive material have found increasing application as efficient particle detectors, especially in space research and mass spectroscopy.

E. J. STERNGLASS

References

Bruining, H., "Physics and Applications of Seconadry Electron Emission," New York, Pergamon Press, 1954.

Kollath, R., "Sekundärelektronen-Emission Fester Körper bei Bestrahlung mit Elektronen," in "Handbuch der Physik," Vol. XXI, pp. 232–303, Berlin, Springer, 1956.

Dekker, A. J., "Secondary Electron Emission," in Seitz, F., and Turnbull, D., Eds., "Solid State Physics," Vol. 6, pp. 251–311, New York, Academic Press, Inc., 1958.

Hachenberg, O., and Brauer, W., "Secondary Elec-

tron Emission from Solids," *Advan. Electron.*, **11**, 413 (1959).

Kaminsky, M., "Atomic and Ionic Impact Phenomena on Metal Surfaces," New York, Academic Press, 1965.

Cross-references: ELECTRON, PHOTOELECTRICITY, PHOTOMULTIPLIER TUBE, THERMIONICS.

SEISMOLOGY

Seismology, the study of earthquakes and attendant phenomena, provides the bulk of man's detailed knowledge of the earth's interior, largely as a result of investigations of the complex seismic waves which propagate throughout the earth following an earthquake. Analyses are based principally on ray theory for elastic body waves of the dilatational and shear types, and on wave theory for traveling elastic surface waves and their standing wave counterparts, the free oscillations of the earth. Seismological studies have, among other things, defined the configuration and structure of the earth's nonrigid outer core, the probably rigid inner core, the rigid mantle with its low-velocity layer at a depth of a few hundred kilometers, and the deeper regions of the earth's crust. In practice, the science includes widely diverse activities ranging from operation of unusual seismographs in the most remote locations of the earth to application of highly sophisticated mathematical techniques to problems involving complex earth models.

Excluding certain near-surface regions, the velocities of dilatational seismic waves range from about 5 km/sec in parts of the crust to a maximum of $13\frac{1}{2}$ km/sec at the base of the mantle; corresponding shear wave velocities range from 3 to 8 km/sec. The shortest periods of interest in the study of waves from distant earthquakes are of the order of 1/3 second (frequency = 3 Hz); the longest periods are about 53 minutes (frequency = $\sim$ 1 cycle/hour), and they correspond to a free oscillation of the earth in the fundamental spheroidal mode.

Free oscillations of measurable amplitudes are generated only by the largest earthquakes. Body and surface waves from large nuclear explosions and many earthquakes may be detected throughout the world; seismic waves from chemical explosions are adequate for exploration to depths of about 50 km or less. Seismic techniques are used extensively in petroleum exploration and for various other geologic purposes.

The largest earthquakes probably release between 10^{24} and 10^{25} ergs in the form of seismic waves, and the few largest shocks account for most of the energy released in this form. Mean annual release is estimated at 9×10^{24} ergs.

Earthquake size as determined by instruments is measured on a logarithmic scale called the Richter *magnitude* scale. In one variation of this scale, the very largest shocks have magnitudes slightly greater than $8\frac{1}{2}$. Energy in ergs is given empirically by $\log E = 11.4 + 1.5M$, where M is the magnitude. A noninstrumental scale for measuring earthquake effects at a given location is called the *intensity* scale; the popular Modified Mercalli version has divisions from I to XII. Whereas an earthquake may produce a range of intensities, it is in principle characterized by a single value of magnitude.

The frequency of occurrence of earthquakes increases by about a factor of 8 or 10 per unit of magnitude as the magnitude decreases. On the average, only about 25 shocks with a magnitude of 7 or more occur each year, but it has been estimated that there are at least one million earthquakes per year, most of them quite small. About 5000 to 10 000 of these are routinely located and studied.

Most earthquakes occur in certain narrow world-circling belts separated by relatively stable blocks. The circum-Pacific belt is by far the most important, accounting for about 80 per cent of the total activity. Other important features are the trans-Eurasian belt and the mid-ocean belt. The foci, i.e., the points of initiation of the first seismic waves, of most shocks are shallow, i.e., at depths of 60 km or less, but some are as deep as 700 km. Most large shocks are followed by a series of smaller aftershocks which occur in the same general region as the main shock. Aftershocks generally decrease in size and in frequency of occurrence with time but may persist for more than a year following a very large shock. Some earthquakes are preceded by one or a few foreshocks.

The most popular model of the earthquake mechanism is based on the elastic rebound theory which calls for gradual accumulation of elastic strain in a region prior to the release of the strain energy through rupture or by slippage along a preexisting fault. This model explains many features of many earthquakes but is clearly oversimplified and may not be applicable at all to deep shocks. Most of the seismic activity of the earth may be explained by the theory of plate tectonics. In the theoretical model, the earth's surface is made up of a small number of large plates of lithosphere some 100 km in thickness. These plates move about with relative velocities of the order of a few centimeters per year. The boundaries of the plates, where plate interactions occur, correspond to the major active seismic belts. The greatest seismic activity, the largest shocks, and the deepest shocks, occur at places where plates converge (the arcs such as Japan and Tonga), and one plate is thrust beneath another to depths at least as great as the depths of the deepest earthquakes. Where plates diverge (as along the Mid-Atlantic Ridge), or slide past one another (as along the San Andreas Fault in California), seismic activity is shallow, and although substantial, is usually not as great as that of the arcs. The global patterns of the focal mechanisms of earthquakes also fit, in general, the patterns of plate motion. Seismological evidence, in fact,

played an important role in the development of plate tectonics.

Precise prediction of earthquake occurrence in time and space is not now possible, but current and prospective research offer some promise.

In addition to transient seismic phenomena such as those due to earthquakes and explosions, there is a continuous background noise in the earth which is measurable with modern seismographs over a wide range of periods. For periods of about one second, ground amplitudes at very quiet locations are less than 1 millimicron. Between periods of 4 and 9 seconds, there is a sharp peak in the noise spectrum. The corresponding waves are called storm microseisms and are related, probably through ocean waves, to meteorological disturbances at sea.

Most modern seismographs are of the inertial type, depending upon measurement of the relative displacement between a point fixed to the earth and a mass loosely coupled to the earth. Other instruments measure relative displacement between two points in the earth. There are approximately one thousand seismograph stations in the world. Seismographs in limited numbers are also operated on the floor of the deep ocean and on the moon.

JACK OLIVER

References

Bullen, K. E., "Introduction to the Theory of Seismology," Third edition, Cambridge, Cambridge University Press, 1963.
Coulomb, J., and Jobert, G., "The Physical Constitution of the earth," New York, Hafner Publishing Co., 1963.
Eiby, E. A., "About Earthquakes," New York, Harper & Bros., 1957.
Ewing, M., Jardetzky, W. S., and Press, F., "Elastic Waves in Layered Media," New York, McGraw-Hill, 1957.
Gutenberg, B., and Richter, C. F., "Seismicity of the Earth," Princeton, N. J., Princeton University Press, 1949.
Hodgson, J., "Earthquakes and Earth Structure," Englewood Cliffs, N. J., Prentice-Hall, 1964.
Jeffreys, H., "The Earth," Cambridge, Cambridge University Press, 1962.
Richter, C. F., "Elementary Seismology," San Francisco, W. H. Freeman & Co., 1958.

Cross-references: GEOPHYSICS, VIBRATION, WAVE MOTION.

SEMICONDUCTOR DEVICES

Introduction Since the invention of the transistor (contraction for *trans*fer re*sistor*) by a research team of the Bell Laboratories in 1947, the transistor and related semiconductor devices have had an unprecedented impact on our society in general and on the electronics industry in

particular. Semiconductor devices have replaced tubes because they are more reliable and less expensive, they have better performance and use less power, and they lend themselves to integration into complex but readily manufacturable microelectronic circuits. Hence the true essence of these devices lies in their overwhelming potential to create for science and industry novel developments that could never have been derived from tubes alone. The semiconductor devices are now key elements in high-speed computers, in space vehicles and satellites, in modern communication and transportation systems, in biomedical equipment, and in pollution monitoring and controls.

Semiconductor devices[1] are intimately related to the energy band structures and transport properties of semiconductors and can be affected by electric field, magnetic field, temperature, pressure, and radiation. We shall be concerned mainly with devices associated with the electric effect in which the electrical conductivity of a semiconductor device is modulated by external electrical signals. One of the most important devices is the *p-n* junction, which is the basic building block of a semiconductor device. The other one is the junction transistor (also called bipolar transistor). The application of transistor theory and transistor technology[2] has broadened our knowledge and improved other semiconductor devices as well. Because of their importance, detailed discussions are given in two separate articles entitled DIODE and TRANSISTOR.

p-n Junction Devices *Semiconductor Controlled Rectifier.* A schematic diagram of the semiconductor controlled rectifier (SCR) is shown in Fig. 1(a). The four-layer *p-n-p-n* structure is intimately related to the junction transistor in which both electrons and holes are involved in the transport processes. The energy band diagrams for the forward "off" condition and the forward "on" condition are shown in Fig. 1(b) and (c) respectively. In the "off" condition most of the voltage drops across the center junction, while in the "on" condition all three junctions are forward-biased. The current-voltage characteristics of the forward and the reverse regions are shown in Fig. 1(d) for three different gate currents. The "forward" characteristic can be explained using the method of two-transistor analog. As the voltage increases from zero, the current will increase. This in turn will cause the current gains of both the *p-n-p* and *n-p-n* transistors to increase. Because of the regenerative nature of these processes, switching eventually occurs and the device is in its "on" state. As the gate current increases, one can reduce the threshold voltage at which the switching occurs. Because of its two stable states (on and off) and the low power dissipation in these two states, SCR has found unique usefulness as static switches, dc chopper, and electronic memory element.

Junction Field-Effect Transistor. The junction field-effect transistor (JFET) is a device based

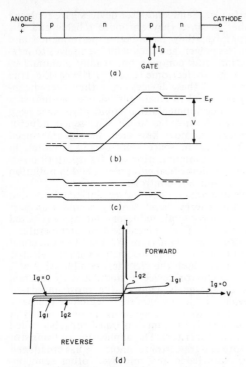

FIG. 1. (a) Semiconductor controlled rectifier (SCR). (b) Band diagram under forward "off" condition. (c) Band diagram under forward "on" condition. (d) Current-voltage characteristics.

on an entirely different physical principle from the junction transistor. While the junction transistor operates through the transport of injected minority carriers across the base, the JFET is basically a voltage-controlled resistor and its resistance can be varied by varying the width of the depletion layers extending into the channel Fig. 2(a). The device consists of a conductive channel provided with two ohmic contacts, one acting as a cathode (source) and the other as the anode (drain). The third electrode (or electrodes), the gate, forms a rectifying junction with the channel. The gate voltage controls the width of the depletion region, therefore varies the conductance of the channel. A typical I-V characteristic is shown in Fig. 2(b). We note that for a given V_G, the current increases initially with the drain voltage and then reaches a saturated value. The JFET is compatible with integrated circuit fabrication and can be operated into the microwave region.

Interface and Charge-transfer Devices *Metal-semiconductor (Schottky) Diode.* The metal-semiconductor diode, Fig. 3(a), is one of the earliest semiconductor devices. It was first investigated in 1874; and in 1938 Schottky suggested that the potential barrier could arise from stable charges in the semiconductor. The model is known as the Schottky barrier, and the energy band diagram at thermal equilibrium is

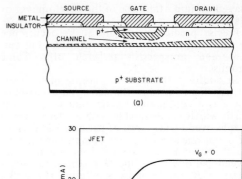

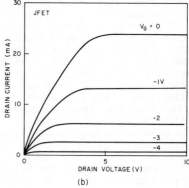

FIG. 2. (a) Junction field-effect transistor (JFET). (b) Typical I–V characteristics.

shown in Fig. 3(b). When a forward bias is applied (i.e., the metal electrode is positive with respect to the *n*-type semiconductor) electrons

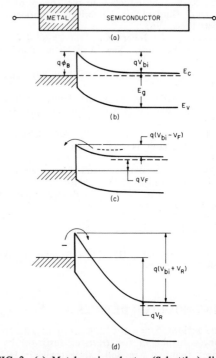

FIG. 3. (a) Metal-semiconductor (Schottky) diode. (b) Band diagram at equilibrium. (c) Forward bias. (d) Reverse bias.

will be injected thermionically from the semiconductor into the metal as shown in Fig. 3(c). Under reverse bias, Fig. 3(d), the current is small and is limited by the barrier height $q\phi_B$. The general I-V characteristic of a Schottky diode is very similar to that of a p-n junction. The main difference is that in usual Schottky diodes the current is due to majority carriers (i.e., electrons in n-type semiconductor) so that the storage time associated with minority carriers is negligibly small. This property makes Schottky diodes useful as microwave mixer and detector diodes as well as high-speed switching devices.

MIS Structure. A schematic diagram of a metal-insulator-semiconductor (MIS) structure is shown in Fig. 4(a). The band diagram for the structure immediately after the application of a biasing voltage is shown in Fig. 4(b). The semiconductor has a wide depletion region, because a negligible number of minority carriers are present. This is not a steady-state situation; nevertheless the surface will remain depleted for times of the order of a few seconds (for high-quality Si-SiO$_2$ interface) before thermally generated minority carriers accumulate at the insulator-semiconductor interface. Figure 4(c) shows the steady-state condition at which a saturated number of minority carriers have been collected at the interface. This is the inversion condition because there are more holes (minor-

ity carriers for n-type semiconductors) than electrons (majority carriers) at the semiconductor surface and the type of carriers at the surface is "inverted" as compared to the unbiased situation. The above band diagrams will now be used to discuss the following interface devices.

IGFET. The word IGFET stands for the *In*sulated-*G*ate *F*ield-*E*ffect *T*ransistor. The basic structure of an IGFET is shown in Fig. 5(a). The device consists of an n-type semiconductor substrate into which two p^+ regions, the source and drain, are formed. The metal contact on the insulator is called the gate electrode. Note that the gate is exactly the MIS structure discussed previously. When there is no voltage applied to the gate the source-to-drain electrodes correspond to two p-n junctions connected back to back. Therefore there is practically no current flowing from source to drain. When a sufficiently large negative voltage is applied to the gate such that a surface inversion layer [or channel as shown in Fig. 4(c)] is formed between the two p^+ regions, the source and the drain are thus connected by a conducting-surface p channel through which a large current can flow. The conductance of this channel can be modulated by varying the gate voltage. One may readily extend the discussion to an n-channel device by exchanging n for p and reversing the polarity of the voltage. A typical I-V characteristic of an IGFET is shown in Fig. 5(b) where V_G is the gate voltage and V_T is the threshold voltage, which is the minimum gate voltage required to invert the channel. We note that as the magnitude of the gate voltage increases,

(a)

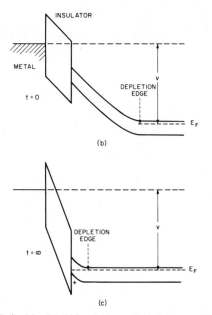

FIG. 4. (a) Metal-insulator-semiconductor (MIS) structure. (b) Band diagram under nonsteady-state condition. (c) Band diagram at steady state.

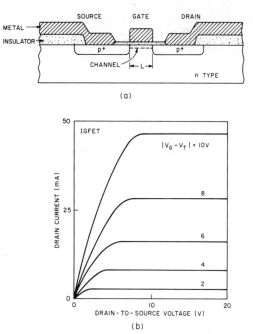

FIG. 5. (a) Insulated gate field-effect transistor (IGFET). (b) Typical I–V characteristic.

the drain current increases accordingly; and the general behavior is quite similar to that of a JFET, Fig. 2(b). IGFET is one of the most important semiconductor devices because of its many integrated circuit applications[3] including linear circuits, digital circuits, and semiconductor memories.

Charge-transfer Devices[4]. Charge-transfer devices belong to the MIS device family in which minority carriers are transferred from under one electrode to a closely adjacent electrode on the same semiconductor substrate when appropriate voltages are applied to the electrodes. Figure 6 shows three of the recently developed charge-transfer devices. Figure 6(a) is called the charge-coupled device (CCD). In the top figure the device is in a situation wherein a sufficiently large negative bias has been applied to all the electrodes to produce inversion [refer to Fig. 4(c)], and the center electrode has a slightly larger applied bias such that the center MIS structure is under depletion conditions [refer to Fig. 4(b)]. If minority carriers are introduced, they will collect at the surface in the potential minimum defined by the excess potential on the central electrode. If now the potential of the right-hand electrode is increased to exceed that of the central electrode, one obtains the potential distribution as shown in the bottom of Fig. 6(a). In this case, the minority carriers will be

transferred from the central to the right-hand electrode. Subsequently, the potential on the electrodes can be readjusted so that the quiescent storage site is located at the right-hand electrode. By continuing the above process, one can successively transfer the carriers along a linear array.

The bucket-brigade device is similar to the CCD in its operation and construction. A cross section of its structure is shown in Fig. 6(b) which is an array of IGFET bucket brigade in a two-phase arrangement. The charge storage sites are offset $p+$ regions under MIS capacitors. Initially $V_1 = V_2$ and minority carriers are stored in the first $p+$ region. When V_2 is made large enough to reduce the potential barriers between the $p+$ regions, charges can be transferred from the first $p+$ region to the second.

The surface-charge transistor is another version of the charge-transfer devices. As shown in Fig. 6(c), this structure is very similar to an IGFET except that the two $p+$ regions are replaced by two MIS structures using buried metal electrodes. Charge transfer is accomplished by lowering the potential barrier under the transfer gate to the point where charges can proceed through the transfer channel. Because of the ease of fabrication in integrated form, the aforementioned charge-transfer devices are useful as shift registers, image sensors, semiconductor memories, and in video cameras.

Microwave Devices[5] *Impatt Diode.* Impatt stands for *imp*act ionization *a*valanche *t*ransit *t*ime. Impatt diodes employ impact-ionization and transit-time properties of semiconductor structures to produce negative resistance at microwave frequencies (about 1 to 100 GHz with corresponding wavelength from 30 to 0.3 cm). A basic Impatt diode is a p-n junction as shown in Fig. 7(a), where it is biased into reverse avalanche breakdown. There is a high-field avalanche region at the $p+n$ junction where electron-hole pairs are generated. The generated holes quickly enter the $p+$ region; the generated electrons are injected into the drift region, Fig. 7(b). As the electric field changes periodically with time around an average value [Fig. 7(c)], the impact ionization rate per carrier follows the field change nearly instantaneously. However, the carrier density does not follow the field change in unison, because carrier generation depends also on the number already present. Even after the field has passed its maximum value, the carrier density keeps increasing because the carrier generation rate is still above the average value. The maximum carrier density is reached approximately when the field has decreased from the peak to the average value. Thus the ac variation of the carrier density lags the ionization rate by about 90°. The above situation is illustrated as the "injected" current in Fig. 7(d). The peak value of ac field (or voltage) occurs at $\theta = \pi/2$, but the peak of the injected carrier density occurs at $\theta = \pi$. The injected electrons then enter the drift region which they traverse at scattering-limited velocity. The induced external current is also shown in Fig. 7(d). From

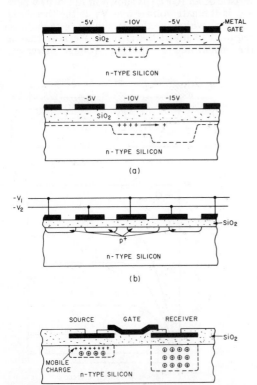

FIG. 6. Charge transfer devices: (a) Charge-coupled device (CCD). (b) Bucket-brigade device. (c) Surface-charge transistor.

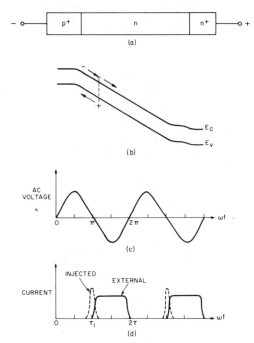

FIG. 7. (a) Impatt diode. (b) Band diagram under avalanche conditions. (c) AC voltage. (d) Injected and external current waveforms.

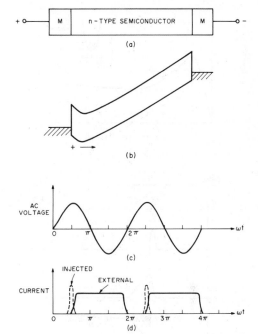

FIG. 8. (a) BARITT diode. (b) Band diagram under injection conditions. (c) AC voltage. (d) Injected and external current waveforms.

comparison of the ac field and the external current it is clear that the diode exhibits a negative resistance at its terminals.

Impatt diodes are among the most powerful solid-state sources of microwave power. Up to 1 W CW (continuous wave) power at 50 GHz has been obtained from an ion-implanted silicon Impatt diode, and up to about 35 per cent efficiency with more than 8 W at 5 to 10 GHz range has been obtained from Schottky-type GaAs Impatt diodes.

BARITT Diode[6]. BARITT stands for *bar*rier *i*njection *t*ransit *t*ime. BARITT diodes operate similarly to Impatt diodes in that the operating frequency is determined by the transit time across the drift region. However, in BARITT diodes the carriers are injected from a potential barrier instead of generated from the impact ionization. A typical BARITT diode structure is shown in Fig. 8(a) which is basically two Schottky diodes connected back to back. When a sufficiently large voltage is applied across the diode the central semiconductor can be completely depleted, and carriers can be injected from the forward-biased contact (or junction) into the drift region. The terminal voltage and current waveforms are also similar to that for Impatt diodes. The main difference is that the injection current peak occurs at the voltage peak, Fig. 8(c) and (d), so that the $\pi/2$ phase delay due to avalanche build-up is missing, and the efficiency of BARITT diodes is lower than that of Impatt diodes. However, because of its injection process, the shot noise of the BARITT

diode is expected to be considerably lower than the avalanche noise associated with Impatt diodes. It is thus expected that the BARITT diode will be useful as a low-noise microwave local oscillator.

Transferred Electron Devices. In GaAs and some other compound semiconductors, the energy band consists of a high-mobility low-energy valley and an adjacent low-mobility high-energy valley [inset of Fig. 9(a)]. When an electric field is applied, the electrons can gain energy and be transferred from the lower valley to the upper valley. In doing so, because of the reduction of mobility, the current is reduced as the field increases giving rise to a differential negative resistance as shown in Fig. 9(a).

The transferred-electron device can be operated in various modes. One of the modes, called the transit-time domain mode, is shown in Fig. 9(b). When the diode is biased above the threshold, E_T, periodic space-charge domains are launched at the negative terminal and propagate through the active region. A series of current pulses results, each spaced in time by the length of the active layer divided by the drift velocity. For a 10 μm sample, the frequency of oscillation is about 10 GHz. If one restricts the growing charge layer before it has had time to form a domain, one can operate the device in the limited-space-charge accumulation (LSA) mode. Over 1 W CW power at 10 GHz has been obtained from the domain mode and as high as 6 kW pulse power has been obtained from LSA modes.

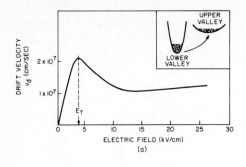

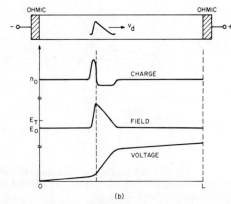

FIG. 9. (a) Drift velocity vs electric field in GaAs—inset shows electron transfer from lower valley to upper valley in the conduction band. (b) Schematic diagram of a transferred electron device, charge distribution (domain), field profile, and voltage variation along the active device length.

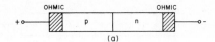

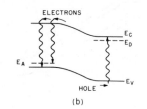

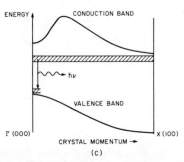

FIG. 10. (a) Light-emitting device. (b) Band diagram under forward bias. (c) Band structure vs crystal momentum, and a representation of the binding of holes and electrons in GaP and how the wavefunctions are distributed in k space as a result of the binding.

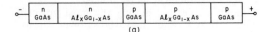

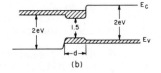

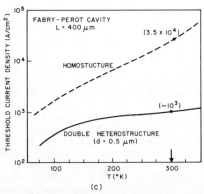

FIG. 11. (a) Double heterostructure laser. (b) Band diagram under forward bias. (c) Comparison of threshold current density for homostructure (ordinary p-n junction) and double heterostructure laser.

In addition to the above three devices, there are many other microwave devices including GaAs FET and Schottky diodes.

Optoelectronic Devices[7] *Light-emitting Diode.* A schematic p-n junction light-emitting diode (LED) is shown in Fig. 10(a). Under forward bias, Fig. 10(b), holes and electrons are diffused across the depletion region and may recombine. Provided that the bandgap is greater than about 1.8 eV (7000 Å wavelength), visible light may be generated in this recombination. Typical LED materials include $GaAs_{1-x}P_x$ (with bandgap 2.0 eV), GaP (2.4 eV), and SiC (3.0 eV). Free holes and electrons in GaP do not recombine radiatively because of the band structure, illustrated in Fig. 10(c), since the holes and electrons have different values of crystal momentum in k space. However, when a particle (such as nitrogen) becomes bound to an impurity center (such as phosphorus in GaP) it becomes localized in real space, and so spreads out in k space as illustrated in Fig. 10(c). This effect explains why the indirect bandgap materials can promote radiative recombination near their band edges. The LEDs are useful to perform many display functions such as solid-state indicator lamps, alphanumerics, and signals.

Semiconductor Laser. The GaAs p-n junction laser (*l*ight *a*mplification by *s*imulated *e*mission

of *r*adiation) has become the most efficient infrared source of coherent light. Using double heterojunction structure as shown in Figs. 11(a) and (b), the laser can be operated continuously at or above room temperature. A heterojunction is a junction formed between two semiconductors having different energy band gaps. The heterostructure can confine the carriers in the active region by the potential barriers, and can confine the light intensity within the active region by the sudden reduction of the refractive index outside the active region. These confinements will enhance the population inversion and provide significant quantum amplification in the active region; therefore, the threshold current density (i.e., the minimum current density to initiate lasing) is considerably lower than that required for a homostructure as shown in Fig. 11(c). The room-temperature semiconductor laser is compact and efficient, and is now finding its way into many ranging and communication systems.

S. M. SZE

References

1. For a general discussion of semiconductor devices, see, e.g., Sze, S. M., "Physics of Semiconductor Devices," New York, Wiley Interscience, 1969.
2. For an introductory discussion of planar technology and basic device physics, see Grove, A. S., "Physics and Technology of Semiconductor Devices," New York, John Wiley & Sons, 1967.
3. "Physical Design of Electronic Systems," Vol. III, "Integrated Device and Connection Technology," Baker, D., Koehler, D. C., Fleckenstein, W. O., Roden, C. E., and Sabia, R., Eds., Englewood Cliffs, N. J., Prentice Hall, Inc., 1971.
4. For a review on CCD and other relevant references, see Boyle, W. S., and Smith, G. E., "Charge-Coupled Devices–A New Approach to MIS Device Structures", *IEEE Spectrum* (July 1971).
5. For a review on microwave devices, see Brand, F. A., Ed., Special Issue on Microwave Semiconductors, *Proc. IEEE*, (August 1971).
6. Coleman, D. J., Jr., and Sze, S. M., "A Low-Noise-Metal-Semiconductor-Metal Microwave Oscillator," *Bell Syst. Tech. J.*, **50**, 1695 (1971).
7. For a review, see, e.g., Thomas, D. G., "Light-Emitting Diodes," *IEEE Trans. Electron Devices,* **ED-18**, 621 (1971).

Cross-references: DIODE (SEMICONDUCTOR); ENERGY LEVELS; SEMICONDUCTORS; SEMICONDUCTORS, INHOMOGENEOUS; SOLID-STATE PHYSICS; SOLID-STATE THEORY; TRANSISTOR.

SEMICONDUCTORS

Semiconductors are distinguished from other classes of materials by their characteristic electrical conductivity σ. The electrical conductivities of materials vary by many orders of magnitude, and consequently can be classified into the following categories: (1) the perfectly conducting superconductors, (2) the highly conducting metals ($\sigma \sim 10^6$ mho/cm), (3) the somewhat less conducting semimetals ($\sigma \sim 10^4$ mho/cm), (4) the semiconductors covering a wide range of conductivities ($10^3 \gtrsim \sigma \gtrsim 10^{-7}$ mho/cm), (5) the insulators also covering a wide range ($10^{-10} \gtrsim \sigma \gtrsim 10^{-20}$ mho/cm).

These low-conductivity materials are characterized by the great sensitivity of their electrical conductivities to sample purity, crystal perfection, and external parameters such as temperature, pressure, and frequency of the applied electric field. For example, the addition of less than 0.01 per cent of a particular type of impurity can increase the electrical conductivity of a typical semiconductor like silicon and germanium by six or seven orders of magnitude. In contrast, the addition of impurities to typical metals and semimetals tends to decrease the electrical conductivity, but this decrease is usually small. Furthermore, the conductivity of semiconductors and insulators characteristically *decreases* by many orders of magnitude as the temperature is lowered from room temperature to 1 K. On the other hand, the conductivity of metals and semimetals characteristically *increases* in going to low temperatures and the relative magnitude of this increase is much smaller than are the characteristic changes for semiconductors. The principal conduction mechanism in metals, semimetals, and semiconductors is electronic, whereas both electrons and the heavier charged ions may participate in the conduction processes of insulators. (See ELECTRICAL CONDUCTIVITY.)

It is customary to classify a semiconductor according to the sign of the majority of its charged carriers, so that a semiconductor with an excess of negatively charged carriers is termed *n*-type, and an excess of positively charged carriers is called *p*-type, while a material with no excess of charged carriers is considered to be perfectly compensated. Many of the important semiconductor devices depend on fabricating a sharp discontinuity between the *n*- and *p*-type materials, the discontinuity being called a *p-n* junction. (See SEMICONDUCTOR DEVICES, TRANSISTORS.)

Most semiconductors exhibit a metallic luster upon visual inspection; nevertheless, the visual appearance of materials does not provide an adequate criterion for the classification of materials, since the electrical conductivity of all materials is frequency-dependent. Visual inspection tends to be sensitive to the conductivity properties at visible frequencies ($\sim 10^{15}$ Hz). Although materials with a high optical reflectivity tend also to exhibit high dc conductivity, these two properties are not necessarily correlated in all semiconductors and metals. An example of a metal without metallic luster is ReO_3, a semitransparent reddish solid. On the other hand, most of the common semiconductors do exhibit metallic luster primarily because electronic excitation across their fundamental energy gaps can be achieved at infrared frequencies. At low frequencies, the principal conduction mechanism is free carrier conduction, which is important in metals and is present

to some extent in semiconductors which contain impurities or are found at elevated temperatures. On the other hand, interband transitions dominate the conduction process at very high frequencies. Interband transitions contribute to the conductivity by about the same order of magnitude in semiconductors, metals, and insulators.

Since the dc conductivity due to free carriers is characteristically low in semiconductors and insulators, the generation of free carriers by exposure to light at infrared, visible, and ultraviolet frequencies can lead to a large increase in the dc conductivity. This photoconductive effect, which is not observed in metals or semimetals, can be enormous in low-conductivity semiconductors (an increase in the dc conductivity of CdS by eight orders of magnitude is observed). (See PHOTOCONDUCTIVITY.)

Because of the extreme sensitivity of semiconductors to impurities, temperature, pressure, light exposure, etc., these materials can be exploited in the fabrication of useful devices, such as the crystal diode, the transistor, integrated circuits, photodetectors, and light switches. Semiconductor devices do, in fact, date back to the infancy of the electronics industry .when crystal sets were used for radio reception. With the development of reliable and efficient vacuum tubes, the interest in semiconductor devices waned for several decades. Renewed interest in crystal rectifiers was stimulated by the needs of the radar technology which developed during the World War II period at the M.I.T. Radiation Laboratory and at other laboratories. During this period and the immediate post-war years, intensive activity developed in the fabrication of very pure semiconducting materials as well as in the basic understanding of the energy level schemes and of the charged carrier transport in silicon and germanium. This intense activity culminated in the discovery of the transistor by Shockley, Bardeen, and Brattain in 1947, for which they were awarded the Nobel Prize in Physics (1956). With the invention of the transistor, the electronics industry rapidly incorporated semiconductor devices, and since the mid-1960s, solid-state components have largely replaced vacuum tubes in many technological applications, from the transistor radio to components for high-speed electronic computers.

The most common semiconductors are the elemental semiconductors silicon and germanium. Other common elemental semiconductors are diamond (carbon), gray tin, tellurium, selenium, and boron. Closely related to the group IV semiconductors diamond, silicon, germanium, and gray tin are the III-V compounds formed from elements in the third and fifth columns of the periodic table, such as InSb, InAs, GaAs, GaP, and GaSb. Another important class of inorganic semiconductors is the II-VI compounds, formed from elements in the second and sixth columns of the periodic table such as CdS, CdSe, CdTe, ZnS, ZnSe,

ZnTe, HgS, HgSe, and HgTe. Many other varieties of compound semiconductors are found, some of the more common varieties being the IV-IV compound SiC, the IV-VI compounds PbS, PbSe, PbTe, SnSe, SnTe, $Pb_x Sn_{1-x} Te$, $Pb_x Sn_{1-x} Se$, GeTe and the oxides MnO, NiO, SiO_2, SnO_2, GeO_2. Another class of semiconductors is the organic semiconductors, common examples being anthracene, tetracene, free radicals such as α α-diphenyl-β-picryl hydrazyl, biologically interesting materials such as the phthalocyanines, and various organic dyes.

Certain classes of semiconductors also possess other interesting properties. For example, the europium chalcogenides form a family of magnetic semiconductors, with EuO, EuS, and EuSe undergoing a ferromagnetic phase transition, while EuTe becomes antiferromagnetic below a Néel temperature of 9.8 K. Magnetic semiconductors are of particular interest because of the close coupling between the electrical and magnetic properties, such as electrical conductivity and the magnetic susceptibility. Some semiconductors have also been found to undergo a superconducting phase transition, as for example GeTe and SnTe for carrier concentrations of $\sim 10^{21}/cm^3$ and transition temperatures below 0.3 K.

Although most of the common semiconductor devices utilize crystalline materials, semiconductors are also found in the liquid and amorphous states. Of special interest is the fact that the electrical conductivity of an amorphous semiconductor tends to be much lower than that of its crystalline counterpart; the opposite situation prevails for amorphous and crystalline metals. Common semiconductors like silicon and germanium have been prepared in the amorphous state, although the major emphasis in recent years has been given to the amorphous chalcogenide glasses containing tellurium and selenium along with a host of other elements; these glasses have been utilized for switching and memory devices. (See SEMICONDUCTORS, INHOMOGENEOUS.)

Semiconductors tend to be hard and brittle and become ductile only at high temperatures. The hardness of semiconductors like diamond and SiC is utilized in the manufacture of industrial abrasives. Because of this hardness, high-quality optical surfaces on semiconductors can be achieved using lapping and etching techniques.

Because of the industrial demands for the fabrication of high-quality, high-purity semiconductors, a great deal of attention has been given to the development of a sophisticated semiconductor technology. To illustrate the present state of the art, it is now possible to grow single crystals of germanium with uncompensated impurity concentrations of $2 \times 10^{10}/cm^3$, which corresponds to less than one charged impurity in 10^{12} germanium atoms; this is probably the purest and most perfect crystalline material of any type that is now available.

A number of techniques have been employed

in growing single crystals of semiconductors. To produce single crystals of large size, it is common to pull the crystal from the melt by the Czochralski technique. These large boules are then cut up into wafers and appropriate impurities are diffused into the material to produce the desired device structures.

For some specific applications, it is necessary to achieve greater control in the carrier concentration than is possible with diffusion techniques, as, for example, in the production of heterojunction devices. In such cases, liquid-phase epitaxial growth is employed, using as a substrate either the same semiconductor or another material of similar lattice constant and thermal expansion coefficient. For example, in the fabrication of sharp p-n junctions in GaP for light-emitting-diode applications, a wafer of GaP grown by the Czochralski technique is used as a substrate and epitaxial layers of n- and p-type GaP are then sequentially deposited by liquid-phase epitaxy.

To produce crystals of the highest purity and crystalline perfection, the method of chemical vapor deposition is often employed. For certain semiconductors, such as SiC and SnO_2, single crystals can be prepared only by chemical vapor deposition. Although the growth rate by this technique is slow, chemical vapor deposition has been utilized in the fabrication of specific microcircuits in order to exploit the flexibility that this technique provides for varying the type and concentration of dopants which are introduced. Furthermore, chemical vapor deposition can be utilized in the growth of certain mixed compound semiconductors. For example, $GaAs_{.6}P_{.4}$, which is a desirable light-emitting-diode material, is difficult to prepare by conventional means but can be prepared using as a substrate a wafer of GaP, which can be grown easily by the Czochralski technique: on this substrate a graded growth of $GaP_{1-x}As_x$ proceeds by chemical vapor deposition until the desired composition is achieved. (See CRYSTALLIZATION.)

To develop an understanding of the electrical conduction in semiconductors, it is necessary to examine the conduction mechanisms appropriate to these materials. The flow of electric current depends on the acceleration of charges by the externally applied electric field. Only those charges that resist collisions or scattering events are effective in the conduction process. Because of collisions, charged particles in a solid are not accelerated indefinitely by the applied field, but rather, after every scattering event, the velocity of a charged particle tends to be randomized. Thus, the acceleration process must start anew after each scattering event and charged particles achieve only a finite velocity along the electric field $\mathbf{E}$, the average value of this velocity being denoted by $\mathbf{v}_D$, the drift velocity. The effectiveness of the charge transport by a particular charged particle is expressed by the mobility μ which is defined as $\mu = v_D/E$. The mobility of a particle with charge e and

mass m can be related directly to the mean time between scattering events τ (also called the relaxation time) by the expression $\mu = e\tau/m$. The electrical conductivity σ depends on the mobility of the charged carriers as well as on their concentration n, and is simply written as $\sigma = ne\mu$ where e is the charge of the carriers. The advantage of expressing the conductivity in this form is the explicit separation into a factor n which is highly sensitive to external parameters such as temperature, pressure, optical excitation, irradiation, and into another factor μ which depends characteristically on scattering mechanisms and on the electronic structure of the semiconductor.

The classical theory for electronic conduction in solids was developed by Drude in 1900. This theory has since been reinterpreted to explain why all contributions to the conductivity are made by electrons which can be excited into unoccupied states (Pauli principle) and why electrons moving through a perfectly periodic lattice are not scattered (wave-particle duality in quantum mechanics). Because of the wavelike character of an electron in quantum mechanics, the electron is subject to diffraction by the periodic array, yielding diffraction maxima in certain crystalline directions and diffraction minima in other directions (See DIFFRACTION BY MATTER.) Although the periodic lattice does not scatter the electrons, it nevertheless modifies the mobility of the electrons through introduction of an effective mass m^* so that $\mu = e\tau/m^*$. A sensitive technique for the measurement of the effective mass and its anisotropy is the cyclotron resonance technique. (See CYCLOTRON RESONANCE.) In terms of the effective mass approximation, which provides a good description for the transport properties of many common semiconductors, the effect of a periodic potential on a conduction electron can be approximately taken into account by considering the electron to move with an effective mass m^* and in a medium with dielectric constant ϵ. For many of the common semiconductors, the effective mass of the carriers is characteristically lighter than the free electron mass m_0, though low-mobility semiconductors containing transition metal atoms (d-bands) tend to have carriers with large effective masses, often larger than m_0. (See SOLID-STATE PHYSICS.)

Although the perfectly periodic lattice does not scatter electrons, an electron in a solid does, in fact, experience scattering events through a variety of mechanisms. At room temperature and above, the principal scattering mechanism is due to lattice vibrations, which arise from the thermal motion of the lattice. Lattice vibrations cause a displacement of the atoms from their equilibrium positions, thereby destroying the perfect periodicity of the lattice.

The effectiveness of lattice vibrations (or phonons) in scattering electrons depends to some extent on the *type* of phonon which is involved in the scattering event. Phonons are

classified as either *acoustic* (atoms on adjacent sites vibrate *in* phase) or *optical* (atoms on adjacent sites vibrate *out of* phase). Materials with only one atom/unit cell have only acoustic branches, three in number, while materials with multiple atoms/unit cell have, in addition to the three acoustic branches, three optical branches for every additional atom/unit cell. Every acoustic and optical phonon branch is further classified according to whether the lattice vibrations are along the direction of propagation of the lattice mode (longitudinal) or perpendicular to this direction (transverse). Phonons exhibit dispersion relations whereby the phonon frequency ω_q depends on the wave vector $\mathbf{q}$ for the lattice mode. Of particular interest are those ranges of $\mathbf{q}$ where ω_q varies slowly with q, thereby producing a high density of phonon states. Those phonons which have a high density of states (such as acoustic phonons near the Brillouin zone boundary, and the optical phonons) are most effective in scattering electrons. Since less thermal energy is required to excite an acoustic phonon than an optical phonon, it is the acoustic phonons which play a leading role in the scattering process at intermediate temperatures. At very low temperatures, the thermal energy is too small to excite significant numbers of phonons of any sort, so electron scattering is dominated by mechanisms involving crystalline imperfections such as lattice vacancies, interstitial atoms, impurity atoms, and crystal boundaries; these crystalline imperfection mechanisms do not contribute significantly to electron scattering at room temperature in solids which have a high degree of crystalline perfection and purity. On the other hand, for amorphous semiconductors, these imperfection scattering mechanisms are relatively important, even at temperatures where there are a significant number of thermally excited phonons. (See PHONONS.)

In considering the mobility of carriers in the vicinity of room temperature, it is clear that the increased probability of exciting phonons with increasing temperature T results in more frequent electron scattering events with increasing T, and consequently a decline in the electron mobility with increasing T. However, this decrease in mobility varies relatively slowly with T, having a power law dependence on T.

On the other hand, the temperature dependence of the carrier density in semiconductors is a strongly increasing function of temperature, which is closely related to the existence of a thermal activation energy E_t, or energy barrier which restricts potential carriers to bound, nonconducting states. This energy barrier can be overcome by the thermal or optical excitation of carriers, and the carrier density, n, excited at a given temperature is given by a Boltzmann factor $n = n_0 \exp(-E_t/2kT)$, where n_0 is the density of available bound carriers and k is Boltzmann's constant. With $E_t \sim 1$ eV for typical semiconductors, it is evident that $E_t \gg$ $2kT$ at room temperature, so the carrier density is a rapidly increasing function of temperature. On the other hand, the carrier density of metals and semimetals is essentially independent of T, so the entire temperature dependence of the electrical conductivity is related to the mobility through the temperature-dependent scattering time τ.

The origin of the energy barrier for carrier generation is directly connected with the energy levels for electrons in a solid. Considering electrons in a solid from a tight-binding point of view, the discrete energy levels of the free atom broaden in the solid to form energy bands. For materials which are well described by the tight-binding approximation, the width of the energy bands is sufficiently small so that an energy gap between the energy bands is formed; in the forbidden energy gap there are no bound states. Of particular importance to the conduction properties of a solid is the fact that *all* of the available states in each band would be filled if each atom were to contribute exactly two electrons, thereby causing every solid with an odd number of electrons per atom to be metallic, while solids with an even number of electrons per atom would be insulating or semiconducting. The occurrence of energy bandgaps is also a consequence of the weak binding approximation, whereby the periodic potential itself is responsible for creating bandgaps through the mixing of states separated by a reciprocal lattice vector. (See ENERGY LEVELS.)

The solution of Schrödinger's equation to obtain the electronic energy levels of a semiconductor can be carried out in an approximate way by exploiting the translational symmetry of the perfectly periodic lattice. Through the translational symmetry, phase factors of the form $e^{i\mathbf{k}\cdot\mathbf{R}_n}$ are introduced as eigenvalues of the operator for translation by a lattice vector $\mathbf{R}_n$, where the wave vector $\mathbf{k}$ assumes the role of the quantum number labeling the various translational states. Since the Hamiltonian for an electron in a periodic solid is invariant under translations by a lattice vector, the energy eigenvalues of Schrödinger's equation are also labeled by the quantum number $\mathbf{k}$. In fact, a knowledge of the dispersion relation for electrons in a solid $E(\mathbf{k})$ uniquely determines the conduction properties of the solid; for this reason, a great deal of attention has been given to the detailed study of the energy band structure of semiconductors.

Semiconductors are classified according to whether they are direct- or indirect-gap semiconductors. For a direct-gap semiconductor, the maximum energy of the occupied valence band occurs at the same value of $\mathbf{k}$ as the minimum energy of the unoccupied conduction band. Typical direct-gap semiconductors are InSb and GaAs; these materials have their energy extrema at $k = 0$. On the other hand, for indirect-gap semiconductors, the conduction band minima and the valence band maxima

occur at different wave vectors. Typical indirect gap semiconductors are silicon and germanium. Both of these semiconductors have valence band maxima at $k = 0$, but the conduction band minima for germanium are located at the Brillouin zone boundary along a (111) direction and for silicon are located along a (100) direction about 85 per cent of the distance out to the zone boundary.

Whereas the minimum energy gap is the threshold for thermal excitation in the case of both direct- and indirect-gap semiconductors, the response to optical excitation is different for the two types of semiconductors. Optical transitions involve only a very small change in k because the wavelength of light is very large compared with atomic spacings in a solid. Since optical transitions are direct (essentially k-conserving), it is necessary to either absorb or emit a phonon with wave vector $(\mathbf{k_c} - \mathbf{k_v})$ to excite carriers optically in an indirect-gap semiconductor, where $\mathbf{k_c}$ and $\mathbf{k_v}$ correspond to the wave vectors for the conduction and valence band extrema, respectively. Measurement of the threshold for phonon-assisted absorption provided one of the earliest determinations of the phonon frequencies in a semiconductor. More accurate measurements of phonon frequencies in semiconductors are now made using the techniques of phonon-assisted tunneling, Raman scattering, and inelastic neutron scattering. (See TUNNELING, RAMAN EFFECT.)

The different response of the optical carrier excitation process can be utilized in the identification of an energy gap as direct or indirect. For a direct-gap semiconductor, the onset of optically induced interband transitions across an energy gap E_g is marked by a photon energy dependence of the optical absorption coefficient α, which is $\sim (\hbar\omega - E_g)^{1/2}$. On the other hand, the threshold for interband transitions in an indirect-gap semiconductor has a characteristic photon energy dependence $\alpha \sim (\hbar\omega - E_t \pm \hbar\omega_q)^2$ in which E_t represents the indirect energy gap; for indirect transitions, the threshold occurs at a lower photon energy when a phonon of energy $\hbar\omega_q$ is absorbed than when it is emitted. Furthermore, the magnitude of the absorption coefficient for a direct-gap semiconductor is as much as two or three orders of magnitude larger than for an indirect-gap semiconductor at the threshold for the optical excitation of carriers. In the optical excitation process, electrons are introduced into the conduction band and empty states (holes) are left behind in the valence band. Both electrons and holes contribute to the electrical conductivity. Furthermore, the electron is attracted to the hole it left behind thereby forming an exciton state.

The actual calculation for the energy bands of solids is complicated by the band degeneracies which occur at high symmetry points in the Brillouin zone because of the rotational point symmetry of the crystal structure. These band

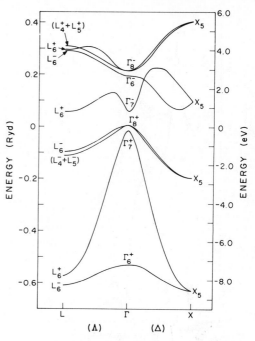

FIG. 1. Electronic band structure for Ge. The zero of energy is taken at the highest point in the valence band (Γ_8^+). The lowest level in the conduction band occurs at the Brillouin zone boundary (L_6^+).

degeneracies are evident in the $E(\mathbf{k})$ diagram for germanium shown in Fig. 1. Of particular interest is the band degeneracy of the valence band at $\mathbf{k} = 0$, which is typical of semiconductors which crystallize in the diamond and zincblende crystal structures. Further complications arise because these semiconductors contain two atoms per unit cell; as a result, the covalently bonded electrons form filled bonding states in the valence band, leaving the higher-lying antibonding states in the conduction band unoccupied. The basic difference between the energy band structure for a semiconductor as contrasted with a semimetal or metal is the existence of a forbidden energy gap for all $\mathbf{k}$ values. In a semimetal or metal, the maximum energy for a valence band state is larger than the minimum energy for a conduction band state, so band overlaps can occur. In a semimetal, the number of holes is equal to the number of electrons, but this need not be the case in a metal.

The figure of merit for a given energy band calculation can be determined by calculation of the frequency-dependent dielectric constant which these bands imply. The good agreement shown in Fig. 2 between the calculated (points) and experimental (curves) dielectric constants indicates confidence in the major features of the energy band structure given in Fig. 1.

It is of interest to observe that the crystal

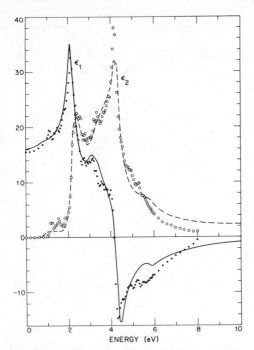

FIG. 2. The frequency-dependent complex dielectric constant ($\epsilon_1 + i\epsilon_2$). The curves are experimental results and the points represent a numerical calculation based on the energy bands shown in Fig. 1.

structure affects the electrical properties of a material, insofar as solids formed from a particular atomic species may be conducting or semiconducting, depending on the crystal structure. Trigonally bonded carbon forms graphite, which is highly conducting in the layer planes, while tetrahedrally bonded carbon forms the semiconductor, diamond.

The electronic energy levels of a semiconductor may be examined with profit from the chemical-bonding point of view. The elemental semiconductors, silicon, germanium, gray tin, and diamond, all crystallize in the diamond structure, in which identical atoms are located at the center and corners of a regular tetrahedron. Each group IV atom contains four valence electrons, thereby occupying exactly eight of the valence states having about equal energy. Through covalent bonding, each atom achieves a filled valence shell by sharing one electron with each of its four neighboring atoms at the corners of the tetrahedron. This strong covalent bonding is responsible for the mechanical hardness of these semiconductors. In diamond, the valence electrons are in the $n = 2$ shell, in silicon in the $n = 3$ shell, in germanium in the $n = 4$ shell, in gray tin in the $n = 5$ shell. Less energy is required to break a bond as we move down the periodic table from diamond to gray tin. The breaking of bonds freeing carriers for electronic conduction can be conveniently accomplished

by thermal or optical excitation. The semiconducting properties of some amorphous materials can be most easily understood in terms of chemical bonding.

The introduction of impurities from group V (or group III) of the periodic table into the diamond structure leads to carrier generation for electrical conduction. For example, antimony has 5 valence electrons, which is one more than is necessary to satisfy the covalent bonding requirements of the diamond structure. Thus, only a small amount of energy is necessary for the liberation of this weakly bound electron from the positively charged Sb^+ ion. Impurities which contribute electrons to the conduction process are called donors and usually result in an excess of negatively charged carriers, thereby yielding an n-type semiconductor. The presence of impurities destroys the perfect periodicity of the lattice and produces energy states within the energy gap between the normally occupied valence band and the normally unoccupied conduction band. The weakly bound donor electrons occupy states close to the conduction band minima and can be treated with considerable success within the effective mass approximation by a hydrogenic model for the Coulombic attraction of the donor electron to the positively charged donor ion. In this approximation, the energy levels of the donor states are given by the bound hydrogenic states $E_n = - m^* e^4 / 2\hbar^2 n^2 \epsilon^2$, where $n = 1, 2, \cdots$, ϵ is the static dielectric constant of the semiconductor, and the donor levels are measured relative to the lowest-lying conduction band states. Ionization of this bound donor to the conduction band by thermal or optical excitation results in electronic conduction. Since the effective masses for such donors tends to be small (group V donors in germanium have $m^* \simeq 0.1 m_0$) and the dielectric constant large (in germanium $\epsilon \simeq 16$), the hydrogenic donor levels are shallow (within $\sim 6 \times 10^{-3}$ eV from the conduction band minima). Furthermore, the small effective masses and large dielectric constant result in a large effective Bohr radius $r_B = \hbar^2 \epsilon / m^* e^2$, so the donor electrons are not localized within the unit cell of the donor ion, but rather extend over many unit cells.

Introduction of group III impurities, such as indium into silicon, results in a p-type semiconductor since the group III impurities have a deficiency of one electron for the fulfillment of the bonding requirement. Since the covalent bonding in these semiconductors is strong, an electron deficiency at an impurity site results in the acquisition of an electron from a covalent bond elsewhere in the material. The covalent bond with an electron deficiency represents an effective positive charge (or acceptor state) which can hop from one covalent bond to another, thereby representing the flow of positive charge, which is characteristic of p-type semiconductors. Acceptor states, like donor states, tend to lie within the forbidden semi-

conducting energy gap; and weakly bound acceptors characteristically have energy levels which lie just slightly above the valence band maximum energy.

Since impurity atoms in typical semiconducting crystals tend to be relatively isolated from each other, the degree of ionization of the impurity atoms and hence the concentration of n- and p-type carriers can be determined from the law of mass action:

$$np = 4 \left(\frac{kT}{2\pi\hbar^2} \right)^3 (m_e m_h)^{3/2} \, e^{-E_t/kT}$$

where n and p are the concentration of electrons and holes and m_e and m_h are the corresponding effective masses. This relation is generally valid whether the carriers are produced exclusively by thermal excitation (an *intrinsic* semiconductor) or by the introduction of impurities (an *extrinsic* semiconductor). If the semiconductor is intrinsic, then $n = p$ and the Fermi level or chemical potential is determined by

$$E_F = \tfrac{1}{2} E_t + \tfrac{3}{4} kT \ln (m_h/m_e).$$

In these relations, the appropriate energy gap is the thermal energy gap E_t, which is smaller than the direct-band gap E_g, for indirect-gap semiconductors such as silicon and germanium. For extrinsic semiconductors, the Fermi level may be pinned to an impurity band of donors or acceptors within the band gap or may even lie in the valence or conduction bands, in which case the semiconductor is called *degenerate*.

In practice most semiconducting crystals contain measurable concentrations of impurities, whether or not these impurities are introduced intentionally. At high temperatures, the therm-

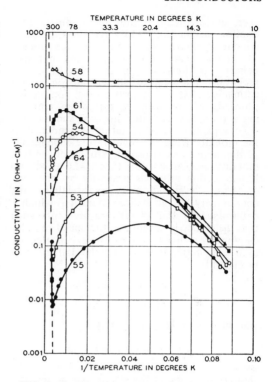

FIG. 3. Conductivity versus absolute temperature for a set of arsenic-doped germanium samples indicated in the figure by sample numbers. The data were taken by Debye at Bell Laboratories. The dashed line represents intrinsic conductivity. (After Conwell)

ally excited carriers tend to dominate the conduction process and the semiconductor behaves as an intrinsic semiconductor; how-

TABLE 1. ROOM TEMPERATURE PROPERTIES OF SOME SEMICONDUCTORS

Material	Band Gap (eV)	Electron Mobility (cm² volt⁻¹ sec⁻¹)	Hole Mobility (cm² volt⁻¹ sec⁻¹)	Dielectric Constant, $\epsilon = n^2$	Lattice Constant (Å)	Density (g/cm³)	Melting Point (°C)
Si	1.15	1900	480	11.8	5.42	2.4	1412
Ge	0.65	3800	1800	16.0	5.646	5.36	938
GaAs	1.35	8500	400	13.5	5.65	5.31	1280
GaSb	0.69	4000	650	15.2	6.095	5.62	728
InSb	0.17	70000	1000	16.8	6.48	5.775	525
SiC	3.0	60	8	10.2	4.35	3.21	2700
PbS	0.37	800	1000	17.9	7.5	7.61	1114
ZnO	3.2	190	–	8.5	(a) 3.24 (c) 5.18	5.60	1975
CdS	2.4	200	–	5.9	5.83	4.82	685
HgTe	0.2	22000	160		6.429	8.42	670
C (diamond)	5.3	1800	1600	16.5	3.56	3.51	3800
Te	0.38	1100	700	∥ 38.0 ⊥ 23.0	(a) 4.45 (c) 5.93	6.25	452
Se (amorphous)	1.8	0.005	.015	6.6	–	4.82	–
Se (crystalline)	2.6	–	1	∥ 13.3 ⊥ 8.0	(a) 4.36 (c) 4.95	4.79	217

ever, at low temperatures the impurity conduction mechanism is dominant and the semiconductor behaves as an extrinsic semiconductor. The passage between intrinsic and extrinsic behavior is illustrated in the plot of ln σ vs reciprocal temperature shown in Fig. 3 for germanium. At low temperatures, conduction proceeds via impurity states, often employing a thermally activated hopping mechanism.

To separate the temperature dependence of the mobility from the temperature dependence of the carrier concentration, studies of the Hall mobility are carried out. (See HALL EFFECT.) If conduction proceeds primarily by one type of carrier, the Hall mobility μ_H is related to the conductivity by the Hall constant R_H, which is determined by Hall effect measurements, such that $\mu_H = c|R_H|\sigma$ where c is the speed of light. On the other hand, if two carriers participate in the conduction process, then the Hall constant is related to

$$R_H = \frac{1}{ec} \frac{(p\mu_h^2 - n\mu_e^2)}{(p\mu_h + n\mu_e)^2}$$

and the conductivity is given by

$$\sigma = e(n\mu_e + p\mu_h).$$

By studying the temperature dependence of the Hall constant and of the electrical conductivity, the carrier densities and mobilities of the two types of carriers can be determined. A summary of the relevant parameters for some of the more common semiconductors is given in Table 1.

MILDRED S. DRESSELHAUS

References

Kittel, C., "Introduction to Solid State Physics," 4th edition, New York, John Wiley & Sons, 1971.
Shockley, W., "Electrons and Holes in Semiconductors," Englewood Cliffs, N.J., Prentice-Hall, 1950.

Cross-references: DIODE (SEMICONDUCTOR); ENERGY LEVELS; PHONONS; SEMICONDUCTOR DEVICES; SEMICONDUCTORS, INHOMOGENEOUS; SOLID-STATE PHYSICS; SOLID-STATE THEORY; TRANSITORS.

SEMICONDUCTORS, INHOMOGENEOUS

It is never possible to produce a perfectly homogeneous crystal in the laboratory by any method of preparation, and although the inhomogeneities can be refined out to some extent after manufacture, a small proportion will always remain and these may still seriously affect the electrical properties of the crystal. On the other hand, it may be just these nonuniform properties that are required in a device, so the inhomogeneities may be deliberately added during or after the basic crystal manufacture.

Types of Defect The main types of defect which contribute to the inhomogeneity are (1) interstitial impurities in which the impurity atoms are wedged between the atoms of the host lattice, and substitutional impurities which replace the atoms of the host lattice. Donor impurities, e.g., As in Ge, have more valence electrons than the host atoms, resulting in a number of electrons weakly bound to these sites. Acceptor impurities, e.g., Ga in Si, have fewer valence electrons than the host atoms and act as hole traps. (2) Frenkel defects are vacancy-interstitial pair defects which occur when a host atom moves from its lattice site into an interstitial site. The interstitial may migrate to the surface leaving behind a Schottky defect which can behave as an electron or a hole trap. (3) Edge dislocations may be thought of as occurring when an extra half-plane of lattice sites is introduced between two existing planes. The edge of the half-plane is surrounded by a cylindrical region of positive spacecharge with no conduction electrons, and acts as a scatterer or as a region of zero conductivity. A grain boundary is caused by a small nonzero angle between the lattice planes on each side of the boundary, and its electrical characteristics depend on the nature of the bulk material. For example, in Ge or Si doped with Ag the boundary may act as a highly conducting region in an insulating bulk, but in ordinary Ge or Si it may be insulating. (4) Plastic deformations can alter the electrical properties of crystals. For example, regions of high deformation in Ge tend to become p-type, and trapping levels are also produced in n-type material. (5) The surface of a semiconductor may possess energy states which may not be characteristic of the bulk material. These are due to imperfections at the surface or chemical contamination due to the adsorption of electronegative impurities onto the surface, and result in a natural rectification effect in n-type Ge. It was the study of these surface states that led to the discovery of transistor action (see Ref. 1). Surface states can cause trouble in measurements of the bulk properties of the material.

Any of the above defects may be distributed randomly over the sample, or they may cluster in parts of the material to make it macroscopically nonuniform. It is usually convenient to classify the spatial distribution of the inhomogeneities into three types: the microscopic case in which the distribution fluctuates on a scale compared with the mean free path of the carriers; the intermediate case in which the fluctuations are large compared with this path but small compared with the sample size; the macroscopic case in which the fluctuations are on the scale of the sample size. Even under the most ideal conditions of uniform crystal doping the impurity atoms will be distributed with a Poisson distribution. This statistical inhomogeneity is important in small volumes of material with low impurity density and when point contacts are

made. (See Ref. 2 for fuller details of this classification.)

Properties and Manufacture of Junctions For two substances having almost the same lattice constant, e.g., CdS and ZnS, the resulting semiconducting alloy will not be ordered, and at best there will be microscopic spatial fluctuations of the densities. In thermal equilibrium the conduction band and valence band edges will vary contravariantly about the Fermi level and the system will be electrically neutral. For example in a HgSe-HgTe alloy the larger intrinsic gap occurs where more Se atoms are present. On the other hand, if there is a spatial fluctuation of impurity density, then in thermal equilibrium the band edges vary covariantly and the spacecharge depends on position. An extreme example of this second case is the *p-n* junction. One part of a crystal can be doped uniformly with an excess of acceptors and the other part can be doped uniformly with an excess of donors. The resulting junction can be graded slowly from *n*- to *p*-type, or it can be abrupt in which case the width of the junction is much less than the width of the spacecharge layer. Such an arrangement is the basic component of the rectifier and the multicontact transistors. For a given doping profile it is possible to calculate the current-voltage-capacitance characteristics of the device. The reverse calculation—finding a suitable doping profile for given characteristics—is much more complicated but potentially very useful industrially for the manufacture of devices without wastage. Work is currently being done in this field.

The main methods of junction manufacture are as follows. (1) In the diffusion method the impurities are introduced from a gaseous phase surrounding the crystal at a high temperature. The advantage of this method is that since different impurity types diffuse at different rates, graded junctions can be made which are useful in, for example, drift transistors. (2) The alloying method is similar to diffusion except that the impurities are introduced from the solid form. The doping substance can be applied to several faces of a crystal and then heated. This method is useful for making abrupt junctions. (3) In the Czochralski method single crystals can be grown by drawing them from the melt and rotating at the same time. Junctions can be made by changing the impurity content of the melt as the drawing takes place. (4) In the ion implantation technique the doping material is introduced in the form of an accelerated ion beam. The depth and profile of the doping are better controlled and more reproducible than in the diffusion method. Annealing is often necessary after implantation to remove any radiation damage, but annealing temperatures are less than those for diffusion, so the profile is unharmed. (See Ref. 3 for further details of this technique.)

Accidental Inhomogeneities Because the presence of impurities affects the freezing temperature, a continuous impurity gradient is generally seen in crystals grown from the melt. This phenomenon can be turned into an advantage in the fractional crystallization process, and the impurity gradients are not too steep unless the volume of the melt is small. Cores of high-density impurity concentration can often be seen in pulled rotated crystals and are caused by planar facets forming at the solid-liquid interface. For example, when Se is introduced into InSb in this way and the crystal is not pulled in the [III] direction, facets of high-density Se are found near the edges of the crystal which can then be removed to leave a fairly homogeneous crystal with a lower impurity concentration. Cells of high impurity concentration can appear in crystals due to constitutional supercooling in which impurities which lower the melting point are pushed into the liquid through the interface. If the liquid is not adequately stirred, then a reduction of the temperature causes solidification of the liquid some distance ahead of the higher concentration, leaving it trapped to form a high-concentration cell. Cellular structures are also formed at the liquid-solid interface if the pulling speed is too fast. Striations can occur in planes perpendicular to the pulling axis if the growth rate is not uniform. These striations can form an almost periodic variation of impurity concentration, and can be caused by minute fluctuations in the growth rate and by vibration in the pulling mechanism. Striations can occur if the crystal and crucible are rotating to facilitate stirring when there is a small temperature gradient perpendicular to the pull of the crystal, since each point of the interface is then subjected to a periodic change in temperature. Even with no rotation, fluctuations in the temperature of the melt can cause striations. Experiments on InSb crystal growth show that even changes of less than 1°C can cause nonuniformity if the rate of change of temperature is sufficiently large. Such an effect can be caused by the switching on and off of the temperature control mechanism. (See Ref. 4 for details of the experiments and for detailed photographs of inhomogeneities.) Finally the method of zone melting purification usually leaves the substance in a polycrystalline form in which uncontrollable junction effects occur at the interior grain boundaries.

Electrical Properties The electrical properties of semiconductors depend to a greater or lesser degree on the presence of inhomogeneities. The main effects are as follows. (1) Magnetoresistance, defined as the fractional change in resistivity when a magnetic field is applied, is the most strongly dependent on inhomogeneity. In contrast to the homogeneous case, the transverse magnetoresistance (in which the current is perpendicular to the field) for an inhomogeneous semiconductor does not saturate at high field, the longitudinal magnetoresistance is not zero, and negative magnetoresistance is often seen at room temperature. The magnetoresistance effect

is anisotropic and has been found to depend on the pulling direction and pulling rate of the crystal. The nonsaturation effect is particularly noticeable in PbTe with even minute deviations from homogeneity, and experiments with InSb show that the transverse effect may vary by two orders of magnitude for specimens cut in different directions from the same crystal. (See Ref. 5 for further details.) (2) The Hall effect is not so strongly affected by the presence of inhomogeneities, but those in the form of junctions and striations can reduce the measured Hall mobility below the true mobility. In general the measured Hall coefficient is a function of the off-diagonal and diagonal components of the magnetoresistivity tensor and will be anisotropic for inhomogeneous semiconductors. (3) Helicon waves, which are low-frequency circularly polarized waves in metals and semiconductors, are damped when the material is inhomogeneous. This is because the skin depth of the waves for high magnetic fields is inversely proportional to the resistivity for the current perpendicular to the field, and this resistivity does not saturate for inhomogeneous material. (4) Peltier heat transport by circulating thermoelectric currents arises in the presence of inhomogeneities, and this effect may be quite large in some heavily doped semiconductors. It can be shown that for a semiconductor containing randomly placed inhomogeneities that an upper limit exists for the thermoelectric figure of merit. This limit does not exist for homogeneous material, and can be as low as unity for alloys containing cellular growths.

Detection of Inhomogeneities The anisotropy of the Hall coefficient and magnetoresistance effect can be used to indicate the presence of inhomogeneities. Variations of resistivity measurement throughout the crystal will indicate the inhomogeneous structure and although very small-scale fluctuations may not be detected by this method, techniques for mapping resistivity down to distances of 0.025 mm have been developed. Resistivity changes and the presence of junctions can be indicated using the bulk photovoltaic effect in which a point between the contacts is illuminated. A voltage appears which is roughly proportional to the gradient of the resistivity at the illumination point. The presence of junctions may also be revealed by allowing a suspension of $BaTiO_3$ to dry on the face of the crystal—the particles tend to deposit on high-field regions. Different regions of n- and p-type can be revealed using the thermoelectric tester in which a hot probe becomes positive for n-type material. However, this test is very sensitive to thin surface layers and may give contradictory results. Electrolyte etching may also indicate regions of p-type material because these regions may etch faster than n-type regions at low voltages. It should be possible to get some indication of inhomogeneity by measuring the noise due to the generation and recombination of charge carriers, but methods of calculating the effect of inhomogeneities in this case are not yet fully developed. (See Ref. 6 for details of noise calculations in inhomogeneous semiconductors.)

E. A. B. COLE

References

1. Bardeen, J., *Phys. Rev.*, **71**, 717 (1947).
2. Herring, C., *J. Appl. Phys.*, **31**, 1939 (1960).
3. Dearnaley, G., *Rep. Prog. Phys.*, **32**, 405 (1969).
4. Albon, N., *J. Appl. Phys.*, **33**, 2912 (1962).
5. Weiss, H., *Semiconductors and Semimetals*, **1**, 315, (1966).
6. Cole, E. A. B., *Physica*, **45**, 598 (1970).

General References

Bate, R. T., *Semiconductors and Semimetals*, **4**, 459, (1968).
Dunlap, W. C., "An Introduction to Semiconductors," New York, John Wiley & Sons, 1957.

Cross-references: CONDUCTIVITY, ELECTRICAL; CRYSTALLIZATION; ENERGY LEVELS; HALL EFFECT AND RELATED PHENOMENA; SEMICONDUCTORS; SEMICONDUCTOR DEVICES; SOLID-STATE PHYSICS; TRANSISTOR.

SERVOMECHANISMS

Definition—A servomechanism is a feedback control system in which the difference between a reference input $r(t)$ and some function of a controlled output $c(t)$ is used to supply an actuating signal $e(t)$ to a controller and a controlled system. The actuating signal is amplified in the controller and is used to vary the output of the controlled system in such a manner that the difference between input and output is reduced to zero. A simple block diagram representation of a servomechanism is shown in Fig. 1.

The controlled system may consist of a mechanical structure, a chemical process, a heating system, an electric supply or any system in which a variable can be measured and controlled. The reference input may be a reference level, a sinusoidal or a polynomial function of time, or a discrete, sampled, or programmed set of values. The difference detector is usually matched to the form of the output and input signals. The controller contains signal amplifiers and may also contain power amplifiers which furnish power to an actuating device from an external power source. Actuating devices vary with the con-

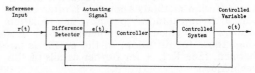

FIG. 1. Block diagram of a servomechanism with unity feedback.

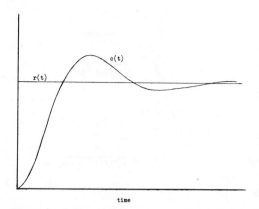

FIG. 2. Transient response of a type I servomechanism to a step input.

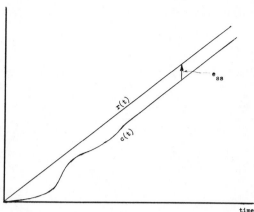

FIG. 3. Response of type I servomechanism to a
ramp input.

trolled system. Actuating devices to position or
move mechanical structures may be electromechanical, hydraulic, or pneumatic.

The controller is designed to control a system
with known dynamic properties to respond to a
specified type of input signal with a specified
steady-state and transient performance. The controller may be digital or analog and may be
designed for nonlinear or linear operation or
may have a linear operating region of actuating
signals and a nonlinear saturation zone. Nonlinear systems can be designed with better per-

formance characteristics than linear systems,
but linear systems are easier to analyze. A simple
linear system with unity feedback will be
described.

Linear servomechanisms are analyzed in terms
of their transfer function, which can be obtained
by taking the Laplace transform of the differential equations of the open loop system with zero
initial energy storage. The transfer function is
the ratio of the Laplace transform of the output
to the Laplace transform of the actuating signal.

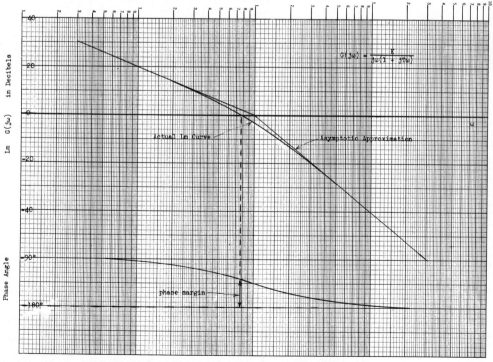

FIG. 4. Bode plots of simple type I servomechanism.

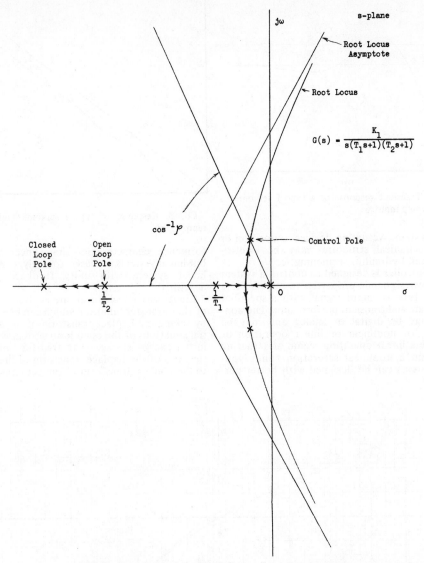

FIG. 5. Root locus plot of typical type I servomechanism.

$$G(s) = \frac{C(s)}{E(s)}$$

In most cases, $G(s)$ is or can be approximated as a rational algebraic function and can be expressed in the following form.

$$G(s) = \frac{K_n(T_1s + 1)(T_2s + 1) \cdots \left[\dfrac{s^2}{\omega_1^2} + \dfrac{2\zeta_1}{\omega_1}s + 1\right] \cdots \left[\dfrac{s^2}{\omega_2^2} + \dfrac{2\zeta_2}{\omega_2}s + 1\right] \cdots}{s^n(T_as + 1)(T_bs + 1) \cdots \left[\dfrac{s^2}{\omega_a^2} + \dfrac{2\zeta_a}{\omega_a}s + 1\right] \cdots \left[\dfrac{s^2}{\omega_b^2} + \dfrac{2\zeta_b}{\omega_b}s + 1\right] \cdots}$$

The value of the exponent n is used to classify the type of servomechanism. For $n = 0$ (a type 0 servomechanism), the system is often called a regulator or governor, rather than a servomechanism, the distinction being that a servomechanism must contain integration in its transfer function ($n \geq 1$) in order to be able to

reduce its steady-state error for a position input to zero.

The control ratio is the closed-loop counterpart of the transfer function.

$$\frac{C(s)}{R(s)} = \frac{G(s)}{1 + G(s)}$$

The ratio of error (or actuating signal) transform to the input signal transform is given by

$$\frac{E(s)}{R(s)} = \frac{1}{1 + G(s)}$$

The characteristic equation for the closed loop system is given by

$$1 + G(s) = 0$$

For a stable system, there must not be any roots of the characteristic equation in the right half of the complex s plane. A stable system usually has a pair of complex roots much closer to the imaginary axis than any of the other roots. These roots, known as the control poles, are largely responsible for the transient performance of the servomechanism. The controller may contain compensating networks which introduce zeros to cancel undesirable poles and substitute desirable poles.

Transient performance is often given in terms of the output response to a unit step input—the response frequency, overshoot, and settling time being specified. A value of $\zeta = 0.4$ in the control poles usually limits the transient overshoot to 25 per cent.

Steady-state performance may be specified in terms of the steady-state error during a steady ramp input.

$$r(t) = \omega_i t$$

For a type I servomechanism ($n = 1$)

$$e_{ss} = \lim_{s \to 0} sE(s)$$

$$= \frac{\omega_i}{K_1}$$

For a type II servomechanism ($n = 2$), the steady-state error for a steady ramp input is theoretically zero.

Servomechanisms can be complicated systems with multiple loops, feedback functions, nonlinear or time-varying components, adaptive elements, and undesired random-variable inputs. Special design techniques have been developed to handle these systems.

A very widely used design technique for linear servomechanisms is the Bode plot. The log modulus of the transfer function,

$$Lm[G(j\omega)] = 20 \log_{10} |G(j\omega)|$$

and the corresponding phase angle of $G(j\omega)$ are plotted vs frequency on semilog paper. Straight-line asymptotic approximations for the log modulus plots are usually sufficiently accurate. The phase margin, defined as the amount of phase lag less than $180°$ of $G(j\omega)$ when $Lm[G(j\omega)] = 0$ decibels, is the basic design quantity. A phase margin of $45°$ corresponds to control poles with a $\zeta = 0.4$ and a 25 per cent transient overshoot.

A useful tool in the design and analysis of servomechanisms is the root locus plot. The loci of the roots of the closed loop characteristic equation are plotted as the gain is varied. The gain is adjusted until the control poles have a value of ζ corresponding to the desired transient response.

STEPHEN J. O'NEIL

References

Eveleigh, V. W., "Introduction to Control System Design," New York, McGraw-Hill Book Co., 1972.
Melsa, J., and Schultz, D., "Linear Control Systems," New York, McGraw-Hill Book Co., 1969.
Raven, F., "Automatic Control Engineering," New York, McGraw-Hill Book Co., 1968.
Elgood, O., "Control Systems Theory," New York, McGraw-Hill Book Co., 1967.
Truxal, J. G., Ed., "Control Engineers' Handbook," New York, McGraw-Hill Book Co., 1958.
Truxal, J. G., Ed., "Automatic Feedback Control Systems Synthesis," New York, McGraw-Hill Book Co., 1955.
D'Azzo, J. J., and Houpis, C. H., "Feedback Control System Analysis and Synthesis," New York, McGraw-Hill Book Company, 1960.
Del Toro, V., and Parker, S. R., "Principles of Control Systems Engineering," New York, McGraw-Hill Book Company, 1960.
Ragazzini, J. R., and Franklin, G. F., "Sampled-Data Control Systems," New York, McGraw-Hill Book Company, Inc., 1958.
Newton, G. C., Jr., Gould, L. A., and Kaiser, J. F., "Analytical Design of Linear Feedback Controls," New York, John Wiley & Sons, Inc., 1957.

Cross-references: CYBERNETICS, FEEDBACK.

SHOCK WAVES

Infinitesimal disturbances in a fluid medium are propagated with a characteristic speed known as the sound speed. When the restriction on the amplitude of the disturbance is lifted, the linear approximation breaks down and the velocity of propagation becomes dependent on the amplitude of the disturbance. Another feature of this phenomenon is that the forward gradient of the disturbance rapidly steepens until it becomes a discontinuity and propagates as such. A *shock wave* is then a discontinuity in the physical properties of a fluid medium which propagates through the medium at supersonic

velocity without further change. The strength of the shock is defined by the Mach number, the ratio of its velocity to the undisturbed sound speed. Such waves are generated by the detonation of explosive material, by high-speed aircraft and missiles, and by earthquakes and similar natural phenomena.

Since all media are necessarily discrete, a true discontinuity is inconceivable but, as the thickness of the shock transition corresponds to only a few mean free paths in a gas (or internuclear distances in a solid), the transition can be treated as a discontinuity to the same extent that the medium can be regarded as continuous. In comparison with an adiabatic or isentropic change, the shock wave is an irreversible process and hence leads to an increase in the entropy of the material. The pressure, density and temperature of the medium are all raised on passage through the shock and the flow velocity is reduced. The latter is easily understood by observing that, with respect to the moving front, the molecules enter with an ordered flow motion at supersonic speed and the transport processes in the front transform a major fraction of this ordered flow into the random temperature or kinetic motions of the molecules.

The extent to which the various properties change through the transition depends on the magnitude or strength of the shock and on the thermodynamic properties of the fluid. For an essentially incompressible material such as a liquid or solid, the major change normally occurs in the pressure variable, whereas, for a gaseous medium, the most significant change is in the temperature. Although shock waves in solid and liquid materials have been used to study physical properties at high pressures, (see PRESSURE, VERY HIGH), the method is rather limited by the small test times available before the interaction of other wave phenomena which prevent the attainment of thermodynamic equilibrium, and it is in gases that shock waves have proved of most interest.

The detailed behavior of the shock transition is in itself a most important subject for study since shock waves are associated with the flight of supersonic aircraft and with the re-entry of ballistic missiles into the earth's atmosphere. In addition to their own intrinsic interest, shock waves are important for another reason. Since the transition involves the translational motions of the molecules, energy must eventually be transferred into other modes before the system reaches equilibrium. These subsequent RELAXATION processes involve the rotation, vibration, chemical reaction, electronic excitation and even ionization of the molecules if the shock is sufficiently strong. The shock phenomenon thus provides an excellent method for studying energy transfer processes. For chemical reactions in particular, the shock wave provides a source of heat which is essentially instantaneous and is completely homogeneous. Also, provided the thermodynamic properties of the medium are known, the temperature is completely defined by a determination of the shock velocity.

Although shock waves can be created in a large number of ways, including the detonation of high explosives and the use of wind tunnels, the simplest technique makes use of the *shock tube,* discovered in 1899 by Vieille. A long tube of uniform cross section is divided into two parts by a thin diaphragm and gas is admitted to these at different pressures. If the diaphragm is ruptured in some way, a shock wave is generated in the low pressure gas and a corresponding rarefaction, or expansion, wave in the driver gas. Because the motion is restricted to a single dimension by the containing walls, the strength of the shock does not decrease with distance as it would in a three-dimensional expansion and the relaxation processes become simple functions of distance behind the front. This extremely simple piece of equipment can generate temperatures up to 20 000 K since the strength (or velocity) of the shock depends only on the pressure ratio across the diaphragm immediately prior to rupture and on the thermodynamic properties of the gases in the two sections.

The disadvantage of all shock tube work is that the front moves so rapidly and subsequent wave interactions follow so soon afterwards, that the available testing time is very short, often as low as $100 \mu sec$. In addition, the total quantity of gas involved is small so that detectors suitable for following the subsequent relaxation processes demand high time resolution and high sensitivity coupled with a suitable physical design which prevents any significant interference with the flow of the gas. Optical devices fit these requirements well, and interferometry, schlieren techniques, ultraviolet, visible and infrared spectrophotometry, and x-ray densitometry have all been used. At the highest temperatures, the shock heated gases become luminous and the shock tube has been used as a spectroscopic source to simulate conditions in stellar atmospheres.

Shock waves can also be created in highly ionized media where the forces are Coulombic in origin and the shocks are termed "collisionless." In this situation, shock waves lie more properly in the realm of plasma physics.

JOHN N. BRADLEY

References

Bradley, J. N., "Shock Waves in Chemistry and Physics," London and New York, Methuen & Co., Ltd., and John Wiley & Sons, Inc., 1962.

Courant, R., and Friedrichs, K. O., "Supersonic Flow and Shock Waves," New York, Interscience Publishers, Inc., 1948.

McChesney, M., "Shock Waves and High Temperatures," *Sci. Am,.* **208**, 109 (1963).

"Shock Tube Research: Proceedings of the Eighth

International Shock Tube Symposium, Imperial College, London, 5–8 July 1971," Stollery, J. L., Gaydon, A. G., and Owen, P. R., Eds., London, Chapman and Hall, 1971.

Zeldovich, Ya. B., and Raizer, Yu. P., "Physics of Shock Waves and High Temperature Hydrodynamic Phenomena," Vols. 1 and 2, New York, Academic Press, 1967.

Cross-references: AERODYNAMICS,   FLUID   DYNAMICS.

SIMPLE MACHINES*

Over the years, the ability of man to think has enabled him to find new ways to perform laborious tasks. He developed the lever, ropes, and the inclined plane, modifications of which have resulted in the use of pulleys, wheels and axles, the wedge, and the screw.

Levers   A lever consists of a bar of nearly rigid material, either straight or bent, a fulcrum (F), a weight (W), and a force (P). The components F, W, and P can be applied, in any position relative to each other, to the bar as shown in Fig. 1. Levers are used to move large forces

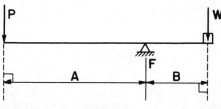

FIG. 1.

(weights) by means of smaller forces or are used to either amplify or diminish arc motion (Fig. 2). The arms A and B must be perpendicular to the lines of actions (directions) of their respec-

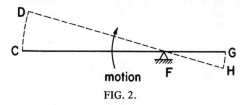

FIG. 2.

tive forces P and W. Then by a balanced moment equation about F,

$$PA = WB$$

The mechanical advantage of a lever, which defines the ability of an available force P to overcome a resisting force W is given by the ratio

*Author deceased.   Article is reprinted from first edition.

of W/P or A/B and results in the expression

$$\text{Mechanical advantage} = \frac{W}{P} = \frac{A}{B}$$

Figure 2 illustrates the use of a lever to amplify (or decrease) motion. When bar CG rotates about F, point G moves through the arc GH, end C will move through the arc CD and

$$\frac{\overline{CD}}{\overline{CF}} = \frac{\overline{GH}}{\overline{FG}}$$

Pulleys   In pulley systems, forces are transmitted by ropes used in conjunction with pulley wheels and axles. As noted from the lever examples, a wheel and axle is an adaptation of a lever rotating about its fulcrum.

Considering a frictionless system of pulleys, the force (pull) in any part of a continuous rope is constant and equal to P. Then, by establishing the number of supporting forces (ropes) and the weight W which is being moved, $nP = W$ where n is the number of supporting ropes. In Fig. 3,

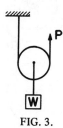

FIG. 3.

two forces (ropes) support the weight W, hence $2P = W$ and $P = W/2$. In Fig. 4, four forces (ropes) support the weight W, then $4P = W$ and $P = W/4$. In Fig. 5, five forces (ropes) support W, then $5P = W$ and $P = W/5$.

The mechanical advantage of a pulley system is the ratio of the weight to be moved to the applied pull in the rope or $W/P = n$, the same as the number of supporting ropes. In Fig. 3, $W/(W/2) = 2$ or for Fig. 4, the mechanical advantage is $W/(W/4) = 4$. In Fig. 5, the mechanical advantage is $W/(W/5) = 5$.

Pulley systems can be analyzed by the use of the *work* (refer to the section on WORK, POWER AND ENERGY) done by the force P and its relation to the work done by W. The displacement (in Fig. 4) of P is four times that of W. Then the work done by P is $4PS$ where $4S$ is the distance that P moves. The work done by W is WS. The mechanical advantage is $4S/S = 4$ and $4P = W$ as above.

Differential Pulley   The differential pulley makes use of two pulleys of different radii r_1 and r_2 attached to each other and rotating about a common axle. An endless chain connects the dual pulley to a second free pulley wheel as shown in Fig. 6. The chain and the corresponding

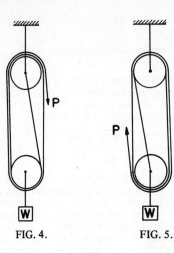

FIG. 4.   FIG. 5.

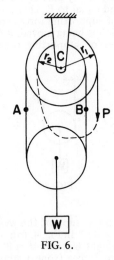

FIG. 6.

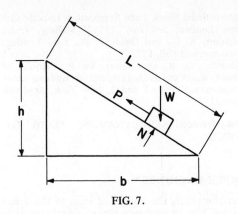

FIG. 7.

teeth on the dual pulleys prevent slipping between the chain and pulleys.

From the previous analysis of pulleys, a force equal to $W/2$ acts in the chain at points A and B. A moment equation about the axle C then gives

$$Pr_1 + \frac{W}{2}r_2 = \frac{W}{2}r_1$$

from which

$$P = \frac{W(r_1 - r_2)}{2r_1}$$

The mechanical advantage of the differential pulley is the ratio W/P.

The Inclined Plane The inclined plane, as a simple machine, is presumed to be rigid and smooth. The weight (W), which moves along the incline, is a vertically downward force partially supported (N) by the frictionless plane. If the weight W is to be at rest on the incline, Fig. 7,

the force system must be balanced in directions normal and parallel to the inclined plane. Balancing the forces parallel to the incline,

$$P = W\frac{h}{L} \quad \text{or} \quad PL = Wh$$

This is equivalent to a work equation where P is displaced a distance L and W is lifted a distance h.

When the force P acts to the left in a *horizontal* direction, P moves an equivalent distance of b, then

$$Pb = Wh$$

The mechanical advantage, as before, is the ratio $W{:}P$ or $L{:}h$ where the force is parallel to the incline. A *wedge* is equivalent in its analysis to an inclined plane. When t is the thickness of a wedge, $P{:}W{::}t{:}L$.

The Screw The screw is an inclined plane wrapped around a cylinder in such a way that the height h is parallel to the axis of the cylinder. If p is the height of travel in one circumference of the screw thread and r is the radius of the thread and friction is neglected, by the work method of analysis

$$P{\cdot}2\pi r = Wp$$

The mechanical advantage is

$$\frac{W}{P} = \frac{2\pi r}{p}$$

Gears and Gear Trains A gear is a wheel with projections uniformly spaced around its circumference. It is usually meshed with a second similar wheel of a different diameter so that the circumferential forces and rotational speeds are different. Figure 8 shows two meshed gear wheels, the teeth of which are not shown. From a balanced moment equation,

$$PR_1 = Wr_1$$

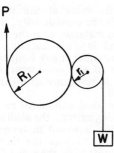

FIG. 8.

then

$$\frac{W}{P} = \frac{R_1}{r_1}$$

and the mechanical advantage is the ratio of W/P or R_1/r_1.

Gear trains consisting of more than two gear wheels have the same relationships. In Fig. 9,

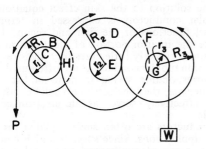

FIG. 9.

letting the wheels be represented by letters, then

$$PR_1 R_2 R_3 = Wr_1 r_2 r_3$$

and the mechanical advantage is

$$\frac{W}{P} = \frac{R_1 R_2 R_3}{r_1 r_2 r_3}$$

By inspection and understanding that the points of contact, such as point H, have a common speed, the directional relations can be determined. If wheels B and C are rotating counterclockwise, D and E rotate clockwise, and F and G rotate counterclockwise.

Spur gears are those which have their teeth cut parallel to the parallel axes of rotation. Bevel gears are used when their axes of rotation intersect and have their teeth cut on the conical surfaces with their apex at the point of intersection of their axes. Their speed ratios are inversely proportional to their pitch diameters, number of teeth, or their number of revolutions. Referring to Fig. 9,

$$\frac{\text{rpm of } E}{\text{rpm of } F} = \frac{2R_3}{2r_2} = \frac{R_3}{r_2}$$

When a screw meshes with a cogged wheel, it is known as a *worm and worm wheel*. When the worm has a single continuous thread, one revolution of the worm will cause the wheel to rotate equivalent to a circumferential distance equal to the distance between two consecutive teeth. Thus a worm must rotate 48 revolutions if a worm wheel with 48 teeth is to rotate one revolution. The same relationship is true if speeds are considered.

Efficiencies of Simple Machines The efficiency of a machine is defined as the ratio of the output to the input. The efficiency of a lever is relatively high since the only loss will occur at the fulcrum. Assuming a frictional moment of 5 per cent of the weight moment, then

$$PA = (W + 0.05W)B$$

and the efficiency (per cent) = $(W/1.05W)(100)$. For pulley systems, the efficiencies are rather low because of the frictional resistances at the pulley wheels. A "rule of thumb" states that the weight W shall be increased by 10 per cent for each wheel over which any rope passes. Thus if there are four pulley wheels, the efficiency (per cent) = $[W/(W + 0.4W)](100)$. Differential pulleys have efficiencies approximating 30 per cent due to the large amount of friction present. The efficiency of an inclined plane is given by the expression

$$\text{Efficiency (per cent)} = \frac{h}{h + fb} 100$$

for the case where the applied pull tends to move the block up the incline (Fig. 7) and f is the coefficient of friction between the incline and the block.

JOHN W. BRENEMAN

Cross-references: FRICTION, MECHANICS.

SKIN EFFECT

For a steady unidirectional current through a homogeneous conductor, the current distribution over the cross section is uniform. However, for an alternating current, the current is not uniformly distributed over the cross section but is displaced more and more to the surface as the frequency increases. For high frequencies, practically the entire current is concentrated in a thin layer at the surface or "skin" of the conductor. This phenomenon has commonly come to be called the "skin effect."

For a physical explanation of this phenomenon, consider a cylindrical conductor that is carrying a steady unidirectional current. The current distribution over the cross section is uniform. A magnetic field is set up by the current in which the magnetic flux lines within and around the conductor are symmetrical to the conductor axis, i.e., they are in concentric

circles. Consider the conductor to be composed of very small circular filaments of equal area which carry equal fractions of the total current. Consider a filament A near the axis of the conductor and another filament B near the surface. The flux linking A is greater than that linking B. If the steady unidirectional current is changed to an alternating current, the magnetic field which is set up by the current must reverse itself periodically with the result that the flux linkages change with time. Self-induced electromotive forces (emf's) are created within the conductor due to these flux changes. These emf's tend to generate currents (eddy currents) which oppose the main current. Because the emf created in filament A is greater than that in B due to a greater flux linkage, the net or resulting current in A becomes less than in B. The current in the conductor is no longer uniform but is displaced toward the surface. The current density becomes greater at the surface and decreases toward the center. This current displacement becomes more pronounced the higher the rate of change of flux.

The total resistance offered by the conductor to alternating current is greater than to a steady unidirectional current because of skin effect. When the current is displaced from the center of the conductor and crowded into the area near the surface, the effective cross section of the conductor is reduced, thereby increasing its resistance. The resistance of the conductor increases with frequency

The equations which mathematically describe skin effect can be derived from Maxwells' equations for electrodynamic problems. However, exact solutions have been obtained for only a few simple shapes of conductor. Shapes which have been amenable to analysis include the cylindrical conductor, tubular conductor, flat conductor, surface plated flat, cylindrical and tubular conductor, and coaxial conductor. Even then it is necessary to consider conductors whose material properties do not change with time or temperature.

The first theoretical explanation of skin effect for wires of circular cross section was given by Lord Kelvin in 1887. Early investigators were Kennelly, Laws, and Pierce,[2] who conducted comprehensive experiments on skin effect, and Dwight[3] who obtained solutions for skin effect in tubular and flat conductors. Many other investigations have been made since that time.

The solution to the skin effect equation for a flat or plane conductor carrying a sinusoidal alternating current shows that the current density is maximum at the surface and decreases exponentially in magnitude with distance from the surface into the conductor. Also, as the distance from the surface increases, the current lags in time-phase further and further behind the current at the surface. A quantity $\delta = (2/\sigma\omega\mu)^{1/2}$ is often called the "skin thickness" since it corresponds to the distance from the surface in which the current density drops to $1/e$ of its value at the surface. In this equation, σ is the conductivity, μ is the permeability of the material, ω is the frequency. The resistance and internal reactance of the plane conductor are equal at any frequency. Also, the ac resistance of the conductor is exactly the same as the dc resistance of a plane conductor of thickness δ.

For a cylindrical conductor carrying a sinusoidal alternating current, the solution to the skin effect equation is found in terms of the zeroorder Bessel function of the first kind. If the frequency is quite high, the exact formulation in terms of Bessel functions reduces to the simple exponential solution for flat or plane conductors. A useful engineering approximation for the ratio of ac to dc resistance is $R_{ac}/R_{dc} = a/2\delta$ where a is the radius of the conductor and $\delta \leqslant 0.1a$. The exact ratio in terms of Bessel functions must be used to obtain a solution for low frequencies or small conductors where $0.1a < \delta < a$. At radio frequencies, there is practically no magnetic field inside the conductor, so the reactance is negligible.

The solution to the skin effect equation for tubular conductors is expressed in terms of Bessel functions of the first and second kind. Since the interior portion of a cylindrical conductor carries very little current at high frequencies, thin tubular conductors are often used with a corresponding saving in material. At these frequencies, the tube acts like a solid conductor and effectively serves as an electromagnetic shield.

Conductors are often surface plated for specific applications. Since silver has high conductivity, resonant cavities and wave guides which operate at very high frequencies are silver plated to reduce I^2R loss since most of the current is concentrated at the surface. Analyses have been made of a number of surface plating combinations to determine what effect such coatings have on the over-all resistance.

The skin effect phenomenon has a very practical application in induction heating. Since the current is concentrated near the surface, a highly selective heating source is created in the surface itself. Advantage is taken of this phenomenon and electromagnetic induction to create a heating method which requires no external heat source and no physical contact with the energy source, the induction coil.

Consider an induction coil carrying alternating current which is wound uniformly around a metal cylinder. Eddy currents are induced in the metal and tend to concentrate near the surface. The problem is similar to that of the cylindrical conductor previously described except that the induced currents are in concentric circles at right angles to the axis of the cylinder instead of being in the axial direction. The solution of the skin effect equation is in terms of the first-order Bessel function instead of the previous zero-order function.

At sufficiently high frequencies, the properties

of individual electrons must be considered. The inertia of the electrons leads to relaxation effects and to "anomalous skin effect" if the skin thickness becomes smaller than the mean free path of the conduction electrons. In metals that are in the superconducting state, skin effect exists but is affected by the number of superconducting electrons and radiation and absorption processes. An excellent review of these topics is presented in the three-part article by Casimir and Ubbink.[10]

JOHN C. CORBIN, JR.

References

1. Thomson, W., "Mathematical and Physical Papers," Vol. 3, p. 493, Cambridge, Cambridge University Press, 1890.
2. Kennelly, A. E., Laws, F. A., and Pierce, P. H., "Skin Effect in Conductors," *Trans. AIEE*, **34**, 1953 (1915).
3. Dwight, H. B., "Skin Effect in Tubular and Flat Conductors," *Trans. AIEE*, **37**, 1379 (1918).
4. Ramo, S., and Whinnery, J. R., "Fields and Waves in Modern Radio," Ch. 6, New York, John Wiley & Sons, 1953.
5. McLachlan, N. W., "Bessel Functions for Engineers," Ch. 8, London, Oxford University Press, 1955.
6. Flugge, S., Ed., "Handbuch der Physik," Vol. XVI, "Electric Fields and Waves," p. 182, Berlin, Springer-Verlag, 1958.
7. Moon, P., and Spencer, D. E., "Foundations of Electrodynamics," Ch. 7, New York, Van Nostrand Reinhold, 1960.
8. Simpson, P. G., "Induction Heating," New York, McGraw-Hill Book Co., 1960.
9. Corbin, J. C., "The Influence of Magnetic Hysteresis on Skin Effect," Aerospace Research Laboratories Report 65-167, August 1965 (U.S. Air Force Publication).
10. Casimir, H. B. G. and Ubbink, J., "The Skin Effect; I. Introduction–The Current Distribution for Various Configurations; II. The Skin Effect at High Frequencies; III. The Skin Effect in Superconductors," *Philips Technical Review*, **28**, 271–283, 300–315, 366–381 (1967).

Cross-references: ALTERNATING CURRENTS; CONDUCTIVITY, ELECTRICAL; INDUCTANCE; INDUCED ELECTROMOTIVE FORCE.

SOLAR CONSTANT AND SOLAR SPECTRUM

The solar constant is the amount of total solar energy of all wavelengths received per unit time per unit area exposed normally to the sun's rays at the average distance of the earth and in the absence of the earth's atmosphere. The solar spectrum as understood here is the distribution of the same energy as a function of wavelength. The spectrum of the sun extends from x-rays of wavelength 1 Å or below to radio waves of wavelength 100 meters and beyond. Measurements have been made in recent years to cover the entire range. However, for most applications of physics and related fields a more limited range alone need be considered. Ninety-nine per cent of the solar energy is in the range 0.276 μm (1 μm = 10^{-6} m) to 4.96 μm, and 99.9 per cent of the energy is in the range 0.217 μm to 10.94 μm.

The solar irradiance, total and spectral, is important 'for different branches of physical sciences. The production of solar energy depends on the processes in the interior of the sun. The energy received from the sun yields information about these processes, and about the absorption and reradiation in the intervening space, mainly in the reversing layer of the sun. Comparison of the spectrum outside the earth's atmosphere with that on the ground leads to a knowledge of the absorptive processes in the atmosphere. The sun is an average star, the only one about which detailed knowledge is available at present, and hence the sun's radiation serves as a stepping stone to the science of the stars. Almost all the major topics in geophysics and meteorology, many problems such as heat balance of the earth, physics of the upper atmosphere, fluctuations in the radiation belts, albedo of the earth, and weather forecasting, are closely related to the total and spectral energy received from the sun. There are also many applications in space-age technology. Solar irradiance is the main factor which controls the thermal balance of spacecraft and the output of solar cells. Ultraviolet radiation may degrade spacecraft surfaces or damage insulation materials and optical elements. In some experiments on board satellites, knowledge of the solar irradiance is needed as a standard of calibration for earth-emitted radiation. Spacecraft control systems have to take into account the radiation torques caused by the sun. Thus the solar constant and solar spectrum are standard physical constants which are needed in many areas of physics, astronomy, astrophysics, meteorology, satellite technology, etc.

The energy from the sun has been the topic of research for a long period of time. As is well known, the science of spectroscopy began with Isaac Newton's discovery in 1666 that the white light of the sun is composed of many colors. Infrared was discovered in 1800 when William Herschel probed the dark region beyond the red end of the solar spectrum with a sensitive thermometer. Shortly afterwards followed the discovery of absorption lines in this spectrum by Wollaston in 1802 and by Fraunhofer in 1814. The first known quantitative measurement of the sun's energy was made by Pouillet in 1838. He filled a blackened vessel with water, exposed it to the sun's rays, and measured the rate of rise of temperature. Pouillet determined the value of the solar constant to be 1.7633 calories per square centimeter per minute (1230 W · m^{-2}). This work was continued by several others, notably by K. J. Ångström in

Sweden after whom the Ångström pyrheliometer is named, and by S. P. Langley at the Smithsonian Institution in Washington, D.C. In 1901 Hann's standard work on meteorology quoted without preference three values of the solar constant then currently accepted: Pouillet's, 1.76; Langley's, 3.02; and Ångström's 4.00 cal·cm^{-2}·min^{-1}. Following the lead of Pouillet the solar constant is expressed in cal·cm^{-2}·min^{-1} in all of the earlier literature; the preferred unit at present is W·m^{-2}. One cal·cm^{-2}·min^{-1} = 679.3 W·m^{-2}.

Work done during this century has helped to narrow down the margin of uncertainty and to map the spectrum more completely and accurately. The most extensive series of measurements were those done by C. G. Abbot and his co-workers of the Smithsonian. This work was begun at the turn of the century and was continued for over 50 years from many different locations around the globe. The basic instrumentation consisted of a spectrobolometer which measures solar spectral irradiance on a relative scale and a water-flow pyrheliometer which measures the total energy on an absolute scale. The readings of the bolometer are made absolute by integrating the area under the curve, adding corrections for the two ends of the spectrum (wavelengths less than 0.346 μm and greater than 2.4 μm) undetected by the bolometer but measured by the pyrheliometer, and equating the total area to that measured by the pyrheliometer. These readings are repeated for different values of air mass and extrapolated to zero air mass by Bouguer's law. Air mass is defined as the ratio of the equivalent path in air of the sun's rays for a given zenith angle to that when sun is at the zenith; it is equal to the secant of the zenith angle if atmospheric refraction effects are ignored. By Bouguer's law the logarithm of the irradiance at any wavelength varies linearly with air mass. The value of the solar constant is obtained by integrating the area under the zero air mass spectrobolometer curve and adding the corrections for the two ends of the spectrum.

The Smithsonian method measures the energy of the whole solar disc. It was adopted by most workers in this field. With the development of high dispersion grating spectrometers and blackbody standards of radiance, a slightly different method was adopted by some observers, notably by M. Nicolet in Belgium and by D. Labs and H. Neckel in Germany. The center of the solar disc is focused on the spectrograph slit, the spectral radiance is measured at many different wavelengths in the continuum between Fraunhofer lines, corrections are made for solar limb darkening and Fraunhofer absorption, spectral data from the Smithsonian and other observers are added for rather wide ranges of wavelength at the two ends of the spectrum, spectral values are extrapolated to zero air mass, and the integral is obtained.

Among values of the solar constant which gained wide acceptance for several years were those proposed by Nicolet in 1951, 1380 W·m^{-2}, and by F. S. Johnson in 1954, 1395 W·m^{-2}. Both authors had also published detailed solar spectrum curves. Johnson's data were mainly used in the United States and Nicolet's in Europe. The two spectral curves show wide differences, especially in the UV near 0.3 μm where Johnson's values are higher by about 30 per cent and in the IR near 2 μm where Nicolet's values are higher by about 25 per cent. A major difficulty in all ground-based measurements is water-vapor absorption and aerosol scattering. Both of these are large and change considerably in the course of a day, so the extrapolation to zero air mass is open to large uncertainties. In the IR, where the absorption due to water vapor is a major source of error, many authors had assumed the solar spectral curve to be that of a 6000 K blackbody.

In recent years several attempts have been made to measure the solar constant and the solar spectrum from above all or almost all of the atmosphere. The solar constant is determined directly with instruments which measure total irradiance, thus insuring higher accuracy than is possible with the earlier techniques, or integrating spectral irradiance curves extrapolated to zero air mass. A Convair 990 jet aircraft flying at 11.6 km was used by a group of experimenters from NASA's Goddard Space Flight Center (GSFC). At this altitude the instruments are above 80 per cent of the permanent gases and above all of the dust, haze, and smoke of the atmosphere; more importantly, they are above all but 0.1 per cent of the water vapor. Four total irradiance instruments were used: a wire-wound cone radiometer, which measures the incident solar energy in terms of electrical energy required to produce the same change in resistance in the wire; two Ångström pyrheliometers, which measure the solar irradiance on the International Pyrheliometric Scale (IPS 56); and a normal incidence radiometer, which is calibrated with reference to a blackbody. Two types of jet aircraft, Convair 990 and U.S. Air Force B-57B, and the NASA rocket aircraft X-15 served as the observing platforms for several series of measurements made by a joint team of the Eppley Laboratory and the Jet Propulsion Laboratory. The X-15 aircraft reaching an altitude of 85 km provided the first direct measurements of the sun's energy from above the ozone of the atmosphere. The detector was a wire-wound thermopile, calibrated on IPS 56. Measurements from balloons at altitudes 30 km and above were made by research teams of the University of Denver, the University of Leningrad, U.S.S.R., and the Jet Propulsion Laboratory. The detectors were thermopiles calibrated on IPS 56 for the first two and an electrically compensated cavity radiometer for the third. At the balloon altitude the instruments are above all but one per cent of the earth's atmosphere. Another set of data, totally free from atmospheric effects, was obtained by a cavity radiom-

eter mounted on the Mars Mariner probe. All of these measurements made at high altitudes and with total irradiance instruments gave converging evidence that the values derived earlier by Nicolet or Johnson from groundbased measurements were too high.

High-altitude solar spectral irradiance data are available mainly from the measurements made on board the Convair 990 at 11.6 km by the NASA GSFC experimenters. The instrumentation consisted of two high-dispersion monochromators, one a Perkin-Elmer, with a lithium fluoride prism for the range 0.3 to 4.0 μm, the other a Zeiss, with a double quartz prism for the range 0.3 to 1.6 μm, a filter radiometer (0.3 to 1.2 μm), a polarization-type interferometer (0.3 to 2.5 μm), and a Michelson-type interferometer (2.6 to 15 μm). These instruments represented some of the best available in precision spectroradiometry. The window material for the aircraft was selected to suit the wavelength range of each instrument, Irtran 4 for the Michelson, sapphire for the Perkin-Elmer and dynasil or infrasil quartz for the other three. Light from the whole solar disc was made to shine on the entrance aperture of each instrument. Corrections for the residual atmosphere above the aircraft were made by applying Bouguer's law. The instruments were calibrated with reference to standards of spectral irradiance, NBS-type lamps for the range below 2.6 μm and high-temperature blackbodies for the longer wavelengths. The Goddard experimenters derived a detailed solar spectral irradiance curve based on these measurements. The area under the curve was found to be almost identical with the value of the solar constant derived from their total irradiance data.

The other highly valuable series of high-altitude spectral measurements are those made by the Eppley-JPL team on board CV 990, B-57B, and X-15 aircraft. The instrument was a 12-channel filter radiometer which gave integrated values of solar irradiance over bandwidths of 500 Å or more. The standard of reference was IPS 56. These results provided a strong confirmation for the Goddard spectral curve.

The value of the solar constant based on all of the high-altitude measurements of recent years is 1353 W $\cdot$ m^{-2}. In thermal units the value is 1.940 cal $\cdot$ cm^{-2} $\cdot$ min^{-1}. The solar spectral irradiance for zero air mass at the average sun-earth distance is shown in Table 1 and Fig. 1. The probable error in these values is less than 1.5 per cent for the solar constant and less than 5 per cent for spectral irradiance. The solar constant value is 3 per cent lower than the one proposed by Johnson, but very close to the different values proposed in earlier years by C. G. Abbot and his co-workers at the Smithsonian.

These values are the standards recommended by an ad hoc Committee which made a critical evaluation of all available literature on the subject. The committee was sponsored by the NASA Space Vehicles Design Criteria Office and the Institute of Environmental Sciences. They have been proposed as design values by NASA and as engineering standards by IES-ASTM.

Table 1 is an abridged version of more detailed tables published in the original documents.[4,9] These tables cover the wavelength range 50 Å to 6 m and give the spectral irradiance at closer wavelength intervals. The values of E_λ are averages over small bandwidths centered at that wavelength. Bandwidths are 0.01 for $0.3 < \lambda < 0.75$; 0.05 for $0.75 < \lambda < 1.0$; and 0.1 for $\lambda > 1.0$ (all units in μm). This gives the solar spectrum independent of the Fraunhofer

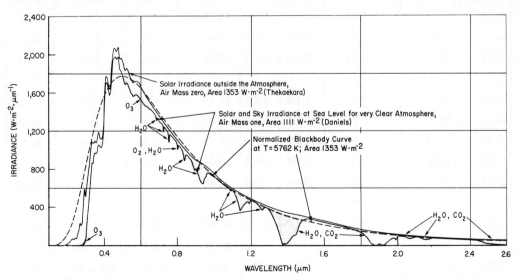

FIG. 1. Solar spectral irradiance outside the earth's atmosphere at 1 A.U. (ASTM standard), normally incident solar irradiance at ground level on very clear days and blackbody spectral irradiance curve at $T = 5762$K.

TABLE 1   SOLAR SPECTRAL IRRADIANCE OUTSIDE THE EARTH'S ATMOSPHERE AT THE
MEAN SUN-EARTH DISTANCE (ASTM STANDARD CURVE.)

λ - WAVELENGTH IN μm

E_λ - SOLAR SPECTRAL IRRADIANCE AVERAGED OVER SMALL BANDWIDTH CENTERED AT λ, IN $W \cdot m^{-2} \cdot \mu m^{-1}$

$D_{o-\lambda}$ - PERCENTAGE OF THE SOLAR CONSTANT ASSOCIATED WITH WAVELENGTHS SHORTER THAN λ

SOLAR CONSTANT - 1353 $W \cdot m^{-2}$

λ	E_λ	$D_{o-\lambda}$	λ	E_λ	$D_{o-\lambda}$	λ	E_λ	$D_{o-\lambda}$
0.115	.007	1×10^{-4}	0.43	1639	12.47	0.90	891	63.37
0.14	.03	5×10^{-4}	0.44	1810	13.73	1.00	748	69.49
0.16	.23	6×10^{-4}	0.45	2006	15.14	1.2	485	78.40
0.18	1.25	1.6×10^{-3}	0.46	2066	16.65	1.4	337	84.33
0.20	10.7	8.1×10^{-3}	0.47	2033	18.17	1.6	245	88.61
0.22	57.5	0.05	0.48	2074	19.68	1.8	159	91.59
0.23	66.7	0.10	0.49	1950	21.15	2.0	103	93.49
0.24	63.0	0.14	0.50	1942	22.60	2.2	79	94.83
0.25	70.9	0.19	0.51	1882	24.01	2.4	62	95.86
0.26	130	0.27	0.52	1833	25.38	2.6	48	96.67
0.27	232	0.41	0.53	1842	26.74	2.8	39	97.31
0.28	222	0.56	0.54	1783	28.08	3.0	31	97.83
0.29	482	0.81	0.55	1725	29.38	3.2	22.6	98.22
0.30	514	1.21	0.56	1695	30.65	3.4	16.6	98.50
0.31	689	1.66	0.57	1712	31.91	3.6	13.5	98.72
0.32	830	2.22	0.58	1715	33.18	3.8	11.1	98.91
0.33	1059	2.93	0.59	1700	34.44	4.0	9.5	99.06
0.34	1074	3.72	0.60	1666	35.68	4.5	5.9	99.34
0.35	1093	4.52	0.62	1602	38.10	5.0	3.8	99.51
0.36	1068	5.32	0.64	1544	40.42	6.0	1.8	99.72
0.37	1181	6.15	0.66	1486	42.66	7.0	1.0	99.82
0.38	1120	7.00	0.68	1427	44.81	8.0	.59	99.88
0.39	1098	7.82	0.70	1369	46.88	10.0	.24	99.94
0.40	1429	8.73	0.72	1314	48.86	15.0	4.8×10^{-2}	99.98
0.41	1751	9.92	0.75	1235	51.69	20.0	1.5×10^{-2}	99.99
0.42	1747	11.22	0.80	1109	56.02	50.0	3.9×10^{-4}	100.00

structure which different instruments present differently according to their resolution. In the wavelength range 0.3 to 15 μm, which contains nearly 99 per cent of the solar energy, the E_λ values are from the NASA GSFC results, modified slightly for $0.3 < \lambda < 0.7$ in the light of the Eppley-JPL data. At the two extreme ends of the spectrum results from other sources have been used, namely data from experiments on board satellites and rockets for $\lambda < 0.3$ μm [5,6] and compilations of brightness temperature of the sun observed by many different experimenters.[7]

In Fig. 1 are shown two solar spectral curves and a blackbody curve. This figure was prepared by G. Daniels for a NASA monograph of the Space Vehicles Design Criteria series, SP8084, "Surface Atmospheric Extremes." The upper curve gives the solar spectrum outside the atmosphere and is based on the data of Table 1. The lower curve gives the spectrum at sea level on a very clear, dry day (about 2 mm of precipitable water vapor), based on measurements by Daniels. This is the irradiance due to the sun and sky, with the sun at the zenith, and represents about the maximum obtainable at sea level. The annual average H_2O in midlatitudes is about 19 mm of precipitable water vapor, and hence the absorption bands due to H_2O would be considerably stronger on most days. The dashed line gives a normalized blackbody curve for temperature 5762 K. This is the temperature of the sun as computed from the Stefan-Boltzmann equation, $S = \sigma T^4 r^2 / R^2$, where S is the solar constant 1353 W $\cdot$ m^{-2}; σ is the Stefan-Boltzmann constant, 5.669×10^{-8} W $\cdot$ m$^{-2} \cdot$ deg^{-4}; r is the radius of the solar disc, 6.960×10^8 m; R is the mean sun-earth distance, 1.496×10^{11} m.

The temperature of the sun may also be defined in other ways. From Wien's displacement law, $T\lambda_{max} = C$, the temperature is 6166 K. λ_{max} of the solar spectral curve, which cannot be clearly defined because of Fraunhofer absorption, is taken to be 0.47 μm. The Wien constant is 2.898×10^{-3} m $\cdot$ deg. The effective blackbody temperature of the sun is 5631 K. The effective blackbody temperature is that temperature of the normalized blackbody curve (normalized so that the area under the curve is equal to 1353 W $\cdot$ m^{-2}) for which the area enclosed between the blackbody curve and the solar spectral curve is a minimum. Another definition of the sun's temperature, highly useful in solar physics, is the brightness temperature, which varies with wavelength. It is computed by obtaining the spectral radiance of the sun from the spectral irradiance at one astronomical unit and applying Planck's equation which gives spectral radiance of a blackbody as a function of wavelength and temperature. The brightness temperature of the sun, which is relatively high in the x-ray range, drops to a minimum of about 4540 K at 0.15 μm; it rises to a high value near 6000 K in the visible and near IR; in the IR the temperature

falls slowly, reaching a minimum about 4360 K at 50 μm, and then rises to relatively higher values in the microwave region.

The solar constant as stated above is defined for the distance of one astronomical unit (A.U.). The values of solar irradiance when the earth is at the perihelion on January 3 and the aphelion on July 4 are respectively 1399 W $\cdot$ m^{-2} and 1309 W $\cdot$ m^{-2}. The total solar energy received by the earth-atmosphere system per year is 5.45×10^{24} joules or 1.3×10^{24} calories. The irradiance at 1 A.U. leads to an evaluation of the total energy radiated by the sun. The sun radiates energy at the rate of 3.805×10^{26} W. From the relativistic equivalence of mass and energy, the rate of diminution of the mass of the sun is 4.234×10^{12} gm per second. A question might be asked how far this loss of mass in conversion of hydrogen to helium would cause a diminution of solar radiance. The loss is very small compared to the mass of the sun, 1.989×10^{33} gm. If the exponential decay of hydrogen were the only factor, assuming that three-fourths of the sun's mass is hydrogen, it can be shown that the solar radiance would decrease by 0.1 per cent in 8×10^5 years. But other factors such as increased reaction rate due to helium accumulation are involved, and astrophysical theory postulates a secular increase rather than decrease in solar irradiance.

A related question is, what short-term changes, if any, are there in the solar constant and solar spectral irradiance? There are significant changes in the very long wavelength range 6 mm to 6 m with sunspot maxima and minima and with major solar activity.[3] Rocket and satellite experiments in recent years have shown changes also in the x-ray and UV range below 0.3 μm.[5,6] As regards the solar spectrum in the visible and IR and the solar constant, there is a large amount of conflicting experimental data,[1] so it is difficult to state the magnitude of the variations and their relation to sunspot cycles, solar rotation, and other solar phenomena. It would seem that the variations are of the order of one per cent and within the margin of uncertainty in our present knowledge of the solar constant and solar spectrum. With improved techniques in measuring radiant energy, both spectral and total, and better definition of the standard scales of radiometry, it is to be expected that solar energy and its variations will be determined to a considerably higher order of accuracy. This will lead to a better understanding of the sun as a star and its influence on terrestrial phenomena, on weather, in the upper atmosphere, and in oceanography.

MATTHEW P. THEKAEKARA

References

1. Abbot, C. G., "The Sun and the Welfare of Man," Chapter VII, "Solar Variation and Weather," Washington, D.C., Smithsonian Institution, 1929.

2. Abetti, G., "The Sun," London, Faber and Faber, 1955.

3. Allen, C. W., "Astrophysical Quantities," London, The Athlone Press (University of London), 1964.

4. Anon., "Solar Electromagnetic Radiation," NASA Space Vehicles Design Criteria, SP-8005 Revised, NASA, Washington, D.C., 1971.

5. Heath, D. F., "Observations on the Intensity and Variability of the Near Ultraviolet Solar Flux from the Nimbus III Satellite," *J. Atmospheric Sciences*, **26** (5), 1157–1160 (Sept. 1969).

6. Hinteregger, H. E., "The Extreme Ultraviolet Solar Spectrum and Its Variation During a Solar Cycle," *Ann. Géophysique*, **26** (2), 547–554 (1970).

7. Shimabukoro, F. J., and Stacey, J. M., "Brightness Temperature of the Quiet Sun at Centimeter and Millimeter Wavelengths," *Astrophys. J.*, **152** (6), 777–782 (June 1968).

8. Thekaekara, M. P., Kruger, R., and Duncan, C. H., "Solar Irradiance Measurements from a Research Aircraft," *Appl. Optics*, 8 (8), 1713–1732 (Aug. 1969).

9. Thekaekara, M. P., ed., "The Solar Constant and the Solar Spectrum Measured from a Research Aircraft," NASA TR R-351 (Washington, D. C.), Oct. 1970.

10. Thekaekara, M. P., and Drummond, A. J., "Standard Values for the Solar Constant and its Spectral Components," *Nature, Physical Sciences*, **229** (1), 6–9 (Jan. 4, 1971).

Cross-references: METEOROLOGY; INFRARED RADIATION; RADIATION, THERMAL; SOLAR ENERGY SOURCES; SOLAR ENERGY UTILIZATION; SOLAR PHYSICS; SPECTROSCOPY.

SOLAR ENERGY SOURCES*

The existence and persistence of biological life on our planet during the last two or three billion years informs us that the solar light intensity has been very steady for at least that length of time. This in turn points to the fact that the source of solar power must be nuclear energy. Any other source (chemical, gravitational, etc.) would have been exhausted long ago.

The detailed mechanism responsible for solar energy production was identified some thirty years ago. The energy is liberated when, through various networks of reactions, four hydrogen atoms (H) are combined to form one helium atom (He). The difference of mass between the four hydrogen atoms and the helium atom ($\simeq 5 \times 10^{-26}$ gram, corresponding to 26.740 MeV) is then liberated, mostly in the form of gamma rays (about 96 per cent), but also partly in the form of neutrinos (about 4 per cent). The gamma rays (γ) are quickly transformed into heat while the neutrinos (ν) escape immediately and are lost as far as solar heating is concerned. Some 4.7 billion years ago the mass of gas

*Editor was unable to locate author. Article is reprinted from first edition.

which was to become the sun was somehow detached from a bigger mass and started to condense under its own weight. From the outside, the stellar mass looked red and was a lot more brilliant than the present sun. The particles composing the gas were mostly hydrogen atoms (about 90 per cent of the atoms), helium (about 9 per cent), then carbon, nitrogen, and oxygen (less than 1 per cent), and finally traces of many other elements including some metals such as iron. As the contraction proceeded the gas grew hotter. When the temperature reached about one million degrees centigrade, thermonuclear reactions between the atoms in the gas started to occur and to liberate nuclear energy. As the power released by these reactions became comparable to the power radiated away by the sun, the contraction stopped, the temperature remained constant and nuclear energy took over the burden of keeping the sun warm. The period of contraction had lasted about 10^7 years. By then the sun had taken its present yellowish appearance and had approximately its present-day brilliance. It had become a so-called main-sequence star.

The transformation of hydrogen into helium then mainly involved the following set of reactions. First in a collision between two hydrogen atoms (^{1}H) a nuclear reaction takes place and an atom of deuterium (^{2}H, heavy hydrogen) is formed. This reaction is by far the slowest that we shall meet. It essentially governs the rate of solar energy generation. Next the deuterium reacts with another hydrogen to form an atom of helium 3 (^{3}He, the light isotope of helium); then two helium 3 thus formed react together to form one helium 4 (^{4}He) isotope and to release two hydrogen atoms. (The collision between helium 3 and hydrogen yields nothing.) The chain (called the proton-proton or PP I chain) is summarized in Table 1.

TABLE I. THE PROTON-PROTON CHAINS

PP I
$$^1H + {}^1H \rightarrow {}^2H + e^+ + \nu$$
$$^2H + {}^1H \rightarrow {}^3He + \gamma$$
$$^3He + {}^3He \rightarrow {}^4He + 2\,^1H$$

or
$$^3He + {}^4He \rightarrow {}^7Be + \gamma$$

PP II
$$^7Be + e^- \rightarrow {}^7Li + \nu$$
$$^7Li + {}^1H \rightarrow {}^8Be + \gamma$$
$$^8Be \rightarrow 2\,^4He$$

or
$$^7Be + {}^1H \rightarrow {}^8B + \gamma$$

PP III
$$^8B \rightarrow {}^8Be^* + e^+ + \nu$$
$$^8Be^* \rightarrow 2\,^4He$$

PP IV
$$^{12}C + {}^1H \rightarrow {}^{13}N + \gamma$$
$$^{13}N \rightarrow {}^{13}C + e^+ + \nu$$
$$^{13}C + {}^1H \rightarrow {}^{14}N + \gamma$$
$$^{14}N + {}^1H \rightarrow {}^{15}O + \gamma$$
$$^{15}O \rightarrow {}^{15}N + e^+ + \nu$$
$$^{15}N + {}^1H \rightarrow {}^{12}C + {}^4He$$

γ represents gamma rays; ν represents neutrinos

As the concentration of helium increases, another reaction becomes important, the reaction between one helium 3 and one helium 4, resulting in the production of one beryllium 7 (^{7}Be) isotope. In this reaction, the beryllium atom captures a free electron in the stellar gas and decays into a lithium 7 (^{7}Li) atom. Then the lithium 7 atom captures a hydrogen atom, thereby forming a beryllium 8 (^{8}Be) atom. This atom is highly unstable. It rapidly breaks into two helium 4. This forms the PP II chain (see Table 1).

In the present sun, 40 per cent of the energy comes from the PP I chain and 56 per cent from PP II. The central temperature is about sixteen million degrees and the central density 180 g/cm^3. (The density of water is 1 g/cm^3.)

A third chain is started if the beryllium 7 atom absorbs a hydrogen atom before it has time to decay. A boron 8 (^{8}B) atom is thus formed which quickly decays to beryllium 8. The beryllium 8 breaks apart releasing two helium 4 atoms. The contribution of this chain to the total energy generation is negligible (0.05 per cent). Its interest lies in the fact that with the decay of the beryllium 8, a neutrino (ν) with a mean energy of about 7 MeV is emitted. The other branches are also accompanied with neutrino emission but with mean energy less than 2 MeV. High-energy neutrinos are far easier to detect than low-energy neutrinos. Later we shall discuss a project already underway which should bring about the detection of solar neutrinos.

Finally, the fourth mode of hydrogen to helium conversion in the sun is the famous carbon cycle. First an atom of carbon 12 (^{12}C) captures hydrogen to produce nitrogen 13. Then nitrogen 13 (^{13}N) decays to carbon 13. Carbon 13 (^{13}C) forms nitrogen 14 (^{14}N) and oxygen 15 (^{15}O) by absorbing successively two hydrogens. Oxygen 15 decays to nitrogen 15 (^{15}N). Nitrogen 15 captures a last hydrogen and breaks into carbon 12 and helium 4. Carbon 12 is thereby returned to the gas, ready to start the cycle again.

Until a few years ago, this cycle was thought to be the main source of energy generation in the sun. Better solar models made with more accurate evaluation of the opacity of the solar material have shown that only about 4 per cent of the sun's brightness comes from this cycle.

As mentioned before, the sun has been in the process of converting hydrogen into helium for the past 4.5 billion years or so. Now the number of helium atoms in the center reaches 30 per cent from the 10 per cent that was there originally. As this number keeps on increasing, a bigger and bigger fraction of the solar energy will come from the carbon cycle. In a few billion years, as the core gets depleted of hydrogen, the sun will slowly start warming up again. A thin shell of hydrogen surrounding the helium core will get hot enough to generate energy, this time almost entirely through the carbon cycle. As this process goes on, the envelopes will start expanding at a rather fast rate; the sun will be entering its red giant phase. The surface, somewhat cooler than it is now, but still at temperature above the melting and vaporizing point of all material, will gradually swallow Mercury, Venus, the earth, and possibly Mars and Jupiter. Humanity will have learned to escape the doomed solar system or it will be destroyed. However since these events will take place in a few billion years, there is still time . . .

Eventually the central temperature will reach the one hundred million degree mark and the central helium will be ignited. The collision of two helium 4 nuclei induces the formation of one beryllium 8 atom which, however, soon breaks apart into its initial components.

However, as this sequence of combination and dissociation goes on (similar to processes in atomic and molecular gases), an equilibrium concentration of beryllium builds up. Occasionally one of these atoms will hit another helium 4 and form a carbon atom. The over-all reaction is labelled $3\,^4\text{He} \rightarrow\, ^{12}\text{C}$. It will provide energy for the sun for a few tens of millions of years.

Eventually, when helium is exhausted the sun will keep on warming its center and will burn its carbon and then its oxygen (both of these elements are products of the helium burning stage). Soon it will have no more energy sources to draw on. It will start cooling and contracting—first becoming a white dwarf, then shining no more, and losing all contact with the external world except through its gravitational field.

How and how well do we know that? What is the basis of our exploration of the past, the present, and the future of our sun? In our hands we have two different tools: physics and astronomy. Laboratory experiments are the foundation of our understanding of matter at our scale—the atomic scale and the nuclear scale. From these experiments, theories have been constructed which we believe can be applied in extraterrestrial settings. Astronomical observations are the basis of our cognizance of extraterrestrial settings.

From observations made on the sun we can obtain its mass, its radius, its luminosity, and the chemical composition of the surface. From other individual stars, we get even less information. However from statistical studies made on stars, and in particular on star clusters, we obtain most of our knowledge of stellar evolution (the same way one can investigate the pattern of growth of trees by walking in a forest).

The two main observational characteristics of a star are its color and its absolute brightness (i.e., how much energy it pours out). Families of stars of similar or related brightness and color have been identified for a long time. The most important groups of stars are called main sequence stars, red giants, and white dwarfs. After many years of patient labor involving the working out of stellar models from our knowledge of hydrodynamics, atomic and nuclear physics, and the comparison of these models with actual stars or groups of stars, the pattern of evolution has become apparent. After a period of contraction,

a star spends most of its life as a main-sequence star (such as the present sun), then it becomes a red giant, and eventually after shedding out some of its mass, it becomes a white dwarf.

The story of our sun described in the first pages of this text is based on such evidences. How solid such evidences are, one never really is certain, but in view of the enormous amount of observations properly explained this way, one feels confident.

Another piece of information about the sun should become available within a few years. As mentioned before, a fraction of the solar energy is used to generate neutrinos. These neutrinos come from the hot furnace in the center of the sun and escape immediately. A program for the detection of these neutrinos has been underway for some time. The neutrinos are extremely difficult to detect and consequently the experiment is a highly involved one. If the experiment is successful, it will give us first hand information about the solar interior. First we shall get direct confirmation of the nuclear origin of solar energy; second we shall obtain a very accurate determination of the solar temperature. Should this measurement be very different from our present estimation we would have to worry about our knowledge of stellar structure and possibly be on the way toward exciting new discoveries.

HUBERT REEVES

References

Schwarzschild, M., "Structure and Evolution of Stars," Princeton, N.J., Princeton University Press, 1958.

Stromgren, B., "The Sun as a Star," in "The Sun," Chicago, The University of Chicago Press, 1953.

Rudaux, L., and DeVancouleurs, G., "Larousse Encyclopedia of Astronomy," New York, Prometheus Press, 1962.

Aller, L. H., "Astrophysics," Vol. II, New York, The Ronald Press Co., 1954.

Reeves, H., "Stellar Energy Sources," in Aller, L. H., and McLaughlin, D., Eds., "Stars and Stellar Systems," Chicago, University of Chicago Press, 1964.

Schatzman, Evry., "Origine et Evolution des Mondes," Paris, Editions Albin Michel, 1960.

Menzel, D. H., "Our Sun," Philadelphia, Blakiston Co., 1958.

Cross-references: ASTROPHYSICS, NEUTRINO, NUCLEAR REACTIONS, NUCLEONICS, SOLAR PHYSICS.

SOLAR ENERGY UTILIZATION

The use of solar energy is likely to become of increasing importance both on earth, because of the rapidly diminishing supplies of fossil fuels, and in man's expanding adventures into space. The problem of economically using solar energy for various terrestrial needs has challenged us for many years, but there are still only a few economically attractive applications. Technolog-ical advances may well change this situation and help satisfy mankind's growing appetite for more and more energy. The launching of the first earth satellite opened up a completely new era for solar energy utilization. For space applications, reliability and weight are generally much more important than the cost of the power system itself. Silicon photovoltaic power supplies already have found extensive use on satellites and space vehicles.

The Sun as an Energy Source Our sun is a typical main sequence dwarf of spectral class G-2. In almost every respect (size, luminosity, mass, etc.), it is an average star. The mean distance from the earth is 93 004 000 miles, at which distance the sun subtends an angle of 31 minutes 59 seconds.

The sun's total radiation output is approximately equivalent to that of a blackbody at $10\,350°R$ $(5750\ K)$. However, its maximum intensity occurs at a wavelength which corresponds to a temperature of $11\,070°R$ $(6150\ K)$ as given by Wien's displacement law. Figure 1(a) presents the intensity of solar radiation outside the earth's atmosphere as a function of wavelength. The total irradiance at the mean sun-earth distance is approximately $442\ Btu/hr\ ft^2$ $(0.140\ watts/cm^2)$. Figure 1(b) shows how the energy in the sun's spectrum is distributed.

Sunlight passing through the atmosphere suffers both absorption and scattering. The solar irradiance reaching the earth depends upon the total air mass through which the sun's radiation passes and, of course, weather conditions. Figure 1(c) shows a typical plot of the solar irradiance at the earth's surface. For some applications, the radiation from the sky is also important. The day sky exhibits wide variations in brightness and in spectral distribution, depending upon the sun's position, weather conditions, and the "receiver's" orientation.[1] Table 1 presents typical values of direct and diffuse solar radiation for several different atmospheric conditions. A great deal of study has been made of the variation of the solar irradiance at the earth's surface with weather, atmospheric conditions, zenith angle of the sun, etc.[2,3]

Uses for Solar Energy Table 2 lists most types of application of solar energy of interest today. They are grouped according to the form of energy required by the application. As an example, supplying electrical power for space vehicles requires a conversion from solar to electrical energy which may be a one-step process with photovoltaic cells (solar cells) or a multistep process. A typical multistep process might involve conversion of solar energy to thermal energy by using a parabolic mirror to heat a working fluid in a boiler, then conversion to mechanical energy using a Stirling engine, and then conversion to electrical power using a generator. Reference 4 discusses each of these applications and comments on their economic feasibility. The interested reader is directed to

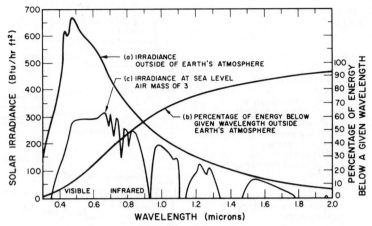

FIG. 1. Spectral distribution of solar energy.

TABLE 1. VALUES OF DIRECT AND DIFFUSE SOLAR RADIATION[a]

Solar Altitude α (degrees)	Optical air-mass path,[b] m ~ cscα	Standard, Cloudless Atmosphere			Industrial, Cloudless Atmosphere			Through Complete Overcasts, Blue Hill, Average Total Insolation on Horizon			
		Direct, Perpendicular Radiation I (B/hr ft^2)	Diffuse on Horizontal I_z, Difference (B/hr ft^2)	Total on Horizontal W_z, (B/hr ft^2)	Direct, Perpendicular Radiation I (B/hr ft^2)	Diffuse on Horizontal I_z Difference (B/hr ft^2)	Total on Horizontal W_z, (B/hr ft^2)	Cirrostratus W_z, (B/hr ft^2)	Altocumulus W_z, (B/hr ft^2)	Stratocumulus W_z, (B/hr ft^2)	Fog W_z (B/hr ft^2)
5	10.39	67	7	13	34	9	12	–	–	–	–
10	5.60	123	14	35	58	18	28	–	–	15	10
15	3.82	166	19	62	80	24	45	50	35	25	15
20	2.90	197	23	90	103	31	64	70	50	35	20
25	2.36	218	26	118	121	38	89	95	65	40	20
30	2.00	235	28	146	136	44	112	120	75	50	25
35	1.74	248	30	172	148	48	133	145	90	60	30
40	1.55	258	31	197	158	52	154	165	105	70	35
45	1.41	266	32	220	165	55	172	185	115	80	40
50	1.30	273	33	242	172	58	190	205	130	85	40
60	1.15	283	34	279	181	63	220	235	150	100	45
70	1.06	289	35	307	188	69	246	260	160	110	50
80	1.02	292	(35)	(322)	195	–	–	–	–	–	–
90	1.00	294	(36)	(328)	200[c]	–	–	–	–	–	–

[a]Data assembled by F. A. Brooks. "B" in the headings stands for British thermal units (Btu).
[b]Smithsonian Meteorological Tables, 6th rev. ed., p. 422, 1951.
[c]192 would be more consistent with the curve from 70° down.

this and other references listed at the end of this article for these details.

Considerations in the Conversion of Solar Energy to Other Forms Table 2 indicates that most of the applications of solar energy require that the energy be delivered in one of four forms: thermal, electrical, mechanical, or chemical. It is of interest, then, to examine the techniques and limitations of converting solar energy to these other forms.

Table 3(a) shows several methods of directly converting solar energy to these other forms. Table 3(b) shows other conversion steps that might be used in a multistep process. The devices described in Table 3(b) make use of

processes which are well known and not restricted to solar energy utilization. Those in Table 3(a), on the other hand, are of prime interest to the present discussion.

Conversion of Solar Energy to Thermal Energy. Many of the systems which utilize solar energy first collect the energy and its heat. A solar heat collector intercepts radiation, converting this to thermal energy, and transfers this heat to a working fluid. Some collectors use mirrors or lenses to achieve high flux densities (concentrating collectors) while others do not (flat-plate collectors).

Flat-plate Collectors. The most common flat-plate collector consists of a metal plate painted

TABLE 2. SOME APPLICATIONS OF SOLAR ENERGY

Form of Energy Required	Application
Thermal	Concentration of brine
	Cooking
	Cooling and refrigeration
	Dehumidifying of buildings
	Distillation of water
	Drying of materials, fruits, grain, etc.
	Heating of buildings
	Heating of water
	Heating of materials to high temperatures
	Salt making
Electrical	Supplying power for special uses
	Supplying space vehicle power
Mechanical	Pumping water
Chemical	Producing food
	Producing fuel
Optical	Natural lighting
	Phosphorescent markers

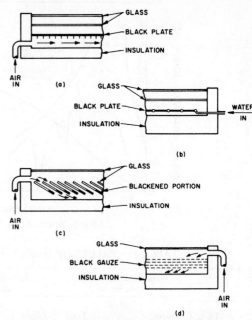

FIG. 2. Four flat-plate collector designs.

black on the side facing the sun and thermally insulated on the edges and back. Above the plate, spaced an inch or so apart, are one or more glass or plastic covers to reduce upward heat losses. The absorbed energy is transferred to water or some other working fluid in tubes which are in thermal contact with the absorber plate or by circulating air past the absorber. Figure 2 displays several flat-plate collector designs.[5] Design b is the conventional type described above; a uses air instead of water for heat transfer. In c, the glass-shingle collector,

TABLE 3. MATRIX OF A FEW ENERGY CONVERSION DEVICES

(a) Direct Conversion from Solar Energy

To \ From	Solar
Chemical	(Photochemical reactions)
Electrical	Photovoltaic cell
Mechanical	Photon "sail"
Thermal	Flat-plate collector
	Concentrator-boiler

(b) Other Conversion Steps

To \ From	Chemical	Electrical	Mechanical	Thermal
Chemical	–	Electrolysis	(Mechanical activation of chemical processes)	(Endothermic reactions) (Thermal dissociation)
Electrical	Fuel cell battery	–	Generator	Thermopiles Thermionic diodes MHD devices
Mechanical	(Equilibrium volume and pressure)	Motor Solenoid	–	Turbine Positive displacement engine
Thermal	(Combustion)	Resistance heaters	Friction brake	–

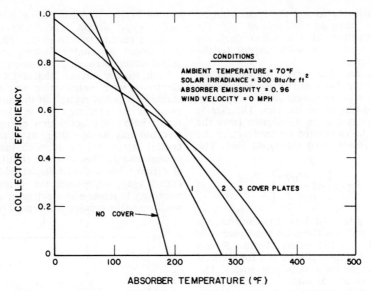

FIG. 3. Calculated performance of flat-plate collectors showing effect of multiple glass covers.

heat is absorbed on the blackened bottom third of tilted glass plates and transferred to the air drawn down through these shingles. In d, solar energy is absorbed on black gauze. The flat-plate collector is a simple, rugged device which, without orientation mechanisms, can efficiently collect solar energy at moderate temperature levels.

The results of some comparative calculations of conventional collectors are shown in Fig. 3. The emissivity and absorptance of the absorber plate was assumed to be 0.96, and the curves were plotted for zero, one, two, and three cover plates of typical single-strength window glass. It is seen that for high efficiencies (with correspondingly low collector temperatures), it might be preferable to have only one or two covers. As an example, a two-cover collector is preferable to a three-cover collector out to a temperature of about 200 F (for the case analyzed); it is only at higher temperatures that the decrease in upward losses made by using one more cover is greater than the transmission loss of that cover.

Concentrating Collectors. An optical system using lenses or mirrors can be used to concentrate solar radiation into a very small area. If this energy is received into a cavity or absorbed on a metal plate, heat is generated and very high temperatures may be obtained.

The concentration ratio C is defined as the ratio of the flux density within the image of the sun formed by the optical system to the actual flux density reflected from the mirror. For a parabolic mirror, C is given by[7]

$$C = 46.1 \times 10^3 \sin^2 \theta \qquad (1)$$

where θ is the rim angle of the mirror as defined by the sketch in Fig. 4. Figure 4 plots Eq. (1)

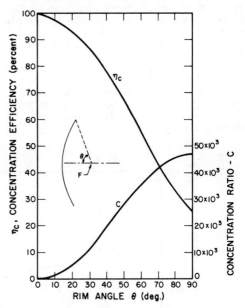

FIG. 4. Concentration ratio and concentration efficiency as a function of rim angle for a paraboloidal reflector.

and also a parameter called concentration efficiency which is defined as the ratio of the power received within the sun's image to the total power reflected by the mirror. For the parabolic mirror, the concentration efficiency is given by

$$\eta_c = \left(\frac{1 + \cos \theta}{2} \right)^2 \qquad (2)$$

The concentration ratio and the concentration efficiency are strongly influenced by the geometric perfection of the mirror and the location of the absorber with respect to the focus of the mirror.[8]

Consider an example where the energy reflected from a parabolic mirror is collected by an ideal cavity receiver having an opening equal to the image diameter of the sun. The rate at which heat energy can be withdrawn from the cavity, P, can be calculated by subtracting the radiative heat losses from the input flux. The result is:

$$P = \eta_c A \left[rH - \frac{\sigma T^4}{c} \right] \qquad (3)$$

where A is the projected area of the mirror, r is its reflectance and H is the solar irradiance. T is the temperature of the cavity. Figure 5 uses Eq. (3) to plot the ratio of P/A as a function of cavity temperature for several rim angles. The intersection of the curves with the abscissa show the maximum attainable temperature for various rim angles, corresponding to $P = 0$ in Eq. (3).

A variety of optical systems has been studied for use as solar concentrators with various absorbers.[9-11] The parabolic mirror-cavity receiver example, however, is indicative of the ultimate performance attainable.

Conversion of Solar Energy to Electrical Energy. The PHOTOVOLTAIC EFFECT, particularly in silicon, has become very important to solar energy utilization. In the silicon "solar cell," photons create hole-electron pairs by removing electrons from valence bonds. This occurs in the junction region between p-type and n-type silicon where the electric field causes a current to flow in the cell. Equilibrium is restored by charge flowing around an external circuit through a load resistor.[12]

Each silicon nucleus shares its four valence electrons with neighboring nuclei forming a stable tetrahedral crystal. In the junction region, most of the electrons are in the lower filled band, below the forbidden energy band. The electron may be thought of as either bound to a crystal lattice region or, with the addition of enough energy, free to move about and conduct electricity. The width of the forbidden region, or energy gap, represents the threshold energy necessary to remove an electron from the bound position to the conduction band. For silicon, it is

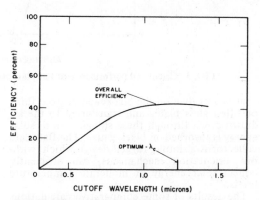

FIG. 6. Maximum solar conversion efficiency of an ideal quantum converter.

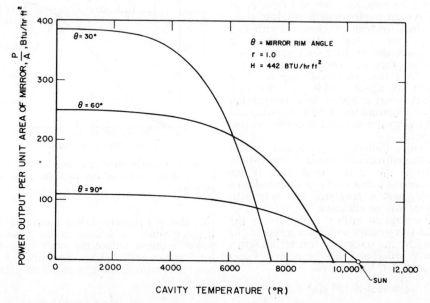

FIG. 5. Maximum power output from an ideal parabolic mirror-cavity absorber as a function of operating temperature.

approximately 1.1 eV. It follows that only photons of 1.1 eV or over can create hole-electron pairs in silicon. Higher-energy photons can create hole-electron pairs with the excess energy being dissipated as heat (see ENERGY LEVELS and SEMICONDUCTORS).

Since one hole-electron pair is created for each photon possessing sufficient energy to do so, the ultimate efficiency that might be achieved depends upon the threshold energy at which the hole-electron conversion takes place and upon the spectrum of the radiation. Figure 6 is the plot of the maximum power conversion efficiency as a function of threshold level. It assumes that all of the photons whose energy is greater than or equal to the threshold energy are converted into hole-electron pairs at the potential of the energy gap.*

Some of the factors which limit the efficiency in a practical cell include:

(1) Some hole-electron pairs recombine before they can be separated by the field in the junction,

---

*Several schemes have been proposed to get around the band gap limitation by using three or more semiconductors sandwiched with the widest-gap semiconductor on top—utilizing the highest-energy photons, a medium-gap material using the next lower energy, etc. It has also been proposed that it might be possible to continuously vary the material so that a variable band gap is achieved. Other schemes which utilize dichroic mirrors to separate the spectrum into two beams of different spectral content to shine on two separate sets of cells with different band gaps have also been proposed.

(2) Reflection losses from the front surface,

(3) Loss due to electrical resistance within the cell, and

(4) Loss due to leakage across the barrier (diode current).

In full sunlight a good silicon cell will develop approximately 0.6 volt, open circuit, and will operate at a conversion efficiency of 10 to 12 per cent.

Figure 7 is a photograph of one of the solar panels used on the Ranger Spacecraft developed for NASA's Jet Propulsion Laboratory. The panel contains 72 strings of 68 cells each to provide 100 watts output at approximately 30 volts. The use of optical filters to cover the cells results in a lower cell temperature, hence higher efficiency, and provides improved resistance to radiation damage.[13] It is also possible to improve the power output per unit weight of a solar panel by using lightweight mirrors to concentrate sunlight on the cells.[14]

Conversion of Solar to Mechanical Energy. Solar radiation incident upon a reflecting surface exerts a radiation pressure of approximately 0.8×10^{-4} dynes/cm^2 or 1.7×10^{-7} lb/ft^2. Although impractical for terrestrial applications, the use of radiation pressure for space propulsion (solar sailing) may prove to be worthwhile for some missions.[15]

Conversion of Solar Energy to Chemical Energy. It has been estimated that only a few tenths of a per cent of a year's supply of incident solar energy is stored in an average farm crop. Research into the mass production of algae has been directed toward tenfold greater yields; research in other types of plants, toward

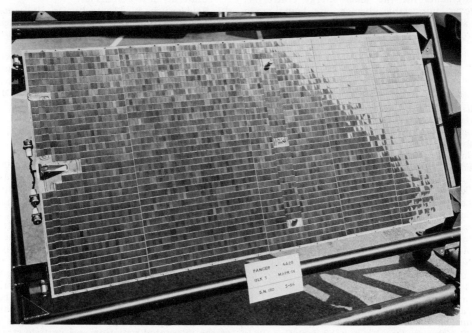

FIG. 7. Ranger spacecraft solar cell panel. (*Photograph courtesy Electro-Optical Systems, Inc.*

the end of increasing photosynthetic efficiency, is also being conducted.

The existence of photosynthesis raises the hope that other photochemical reactions will be found which can be effectively used to obtain chemical energy from the sun. What is needed is a reversible endothermic photochemical reaction which can utilize a large portion of the sun's spectrum. Most photochemical reactions evolve heat instead of absorbing it, or they reverse so quickly that the energy is lost even during exposure to sunlight.

Water is photochemically decomposed into hydrogen and oxygen by ultraviolet light, though at very low efficiency.[16] A fuel cell could be used to obtain electricity from the stored gases, or mechanical energy could be obtained in an engine. While this process is not presently of economic importance, it serves to demonstrate the possibilities. Unfortunately, 50 per cent of the sun's energy is at wavelengths too long to be of much use for photochemical reactions, since the energy per photon is too low. All molecules which undergo photochemical change have a minimum threshold energy required to create a bond rupture. If a quantum is absorbed with energy above this threshold, the excess energy is dissipated (as kinetic, vibrational, etc.) and usually does not contribute to the conversion to chemical energy. The maximum theoretical efficiency of conversion of solar to chemical energy can be evaluated with the help of Fig. 6 providing the cutoff wavelength is known.

At the present time, there is not one system known which comes close to fulfilling all of the requirements for the ideal energy converter; however, important advances are being made and some chemical systems show a great deal of promise.[17]

A. M. ZAREM
DUANE D. ERWAY

References

1. Kruse, P. K., McGlauchlin, L. D., and McQuistan, R. B., "Elements of Infrared Technology," pp. 76, 77, New York, John Wiley & Sons, 1962.
2. Brooks, F. A., and Miller, W., "Availability of Solar Energy," in Zarem, A. M., and Erway, D. D., Eds., "Introduction to the Utilization of Solar Energy," pp. 30–57, New York, McGraw-Hill Book Co., 1963.
3. Landsberg, H. E., "Solar Radiation at the Earth's Surface," *Solar Energy J.*, 5(3), 95 (1961).
4. Zarem, A. M., and Erway, D. D., "Introduction to the Utilization of Solar Energy," New York, McGraw-Hill Book Co., 1963.
5. Nollel, H. C., "Residential Uses of Solar Energy," *Proc. World. Symp. Appl. Solar Energy, Phoenix, Ariz.*, 1955, 103 (1956).
6. Erway, D. D., "Collection of Solar Energy," in Zarem, A. M., and Erway, D. D., Eds., "Introduction to the Utilization of Solar Energy," pp. 89–100, New York, McGraw-Hill Book Co., 1963.
7. Hiester, N. K., Tietz, T. E., Loh, E., and Duwez, P., "Theoretical Considerations on Performance of Solar Furnaces," *Jet Propulsion*, 27, 507 (1957).
8. Duwez, Pol, "Concentration of Solar Energy," in Zarem, A. M., and Erway, D. D., Eds., "Introduction to the Utilization of Solar Energy," pp. 121–123, New York, McGraw-Hill Book Co., 1963.
9. Fisher, J. H. *et al.*, "An Analysis of Solar Energy Utilization," Vol. II, pp. 45–98, Wright Air Development Center Report 59-17, 1959 [available through the Defense Document Center (DDC)].
10. McClelland, D. H., "Solar Concentrators for High Temperature Space Power Systems," in Snider, N. W., Ed., "Space Power Systems," p. 129, New York, Academic Press, 1961.
11. Giutronich, J. E., "The Design of Solar Concentrators using Toroidal, Spherical, or Flat Components," *Solar Energy J.*, 7(4), 162–166 (1963).
12. Prince, M. B., "Silicon Solar Energy Converters," *J. Appl. Phys.*, 26, 534–540 (1955).
13. Hamilton, Robert C., "Ranger Spacecraft Power System," in Snider, N. W., Ed., "Space Power Systems," p. 19, New York, Academic Press, 1961.
14. Menetrey, W. R., "Space Applications of Solar Energy," in Zarem, A. M., and Erway, D. D., Eds., "Introduction to the Utilization of Solar Energy," pp. 373–378, New York, McGraw-Hill Book Co., 1963.
15. Garwin, Richard L., "Solar Sailing–A Practical Method of Propulsion within the Solar System," *Jet Propulsion*, 28(3), 188 (1958).
16. Daniels, F., and Duffie, J. A., "Solar Energy Research," pp. 119–219, Madison, Wisconsin, University of Wisconsin Press.
17. Rabinowitch, E., "Photochemical Utilization of Light Energy," *Solar Energy J.*, 52 (September 1961, special issue).

Cross-references: ENERGY LEVELS; INFRARED RADIATION; PHOTOCHEMISTRY; PHOTOVOLTAIC EFFECT; REFLECTION; SEMICONDUCTORS; SOLAR ENERGY SOURCES; SOLAR PHYSICS; WORK, POWER, AND ENERGY.

SOLAR PHYSICS

The main activity of solar physics is the interpretation of the observed flow of energy away from the sun. Most of the sun's energy output appears as a nearly constant flux of electromagnetic radiation in the photographic, visual, and infrared regions of the spectrum, but extraordinary variations are characteristic of the x-, ultraviolet, and radio radiation. A small part of the sun's energy flows outward in highly variable streams of particles (mainly protons and electrons). Since the sun appears as a rather large disk, the observations forming the bases for the solar physicist's interpretations often refer to small areas of the solar surface, as well as the integrated radiation and particle streams

from the entire sun. A reasonably good solar telescope can subdivide the apparent disk of the sun into about three million smaller elements of area. Streams of particles and radiation from each of these elements should be recorded, with all possible detail and precision, nearly continuously for a complete observational record. A close approach to such observational perfection probably is unattainable, perhaps it is unnecessary, but the fragmentary and incomplete nature of all solar observations continues to be a serious barrier in the search for a satisfactory general theory of the sun. Some progress has been made, but until an adequate theory is developed, it is best to consider the physics of the sun by reviewing the observations of possible importance.

The radius, mass, and luminosity of the sun are fundamental in the physical interpretation of the sun. Luckily, they can all be deduced with reasonable directness from observations. In principle, the radius of the sun can be obtained directly from angular and linear observations made on earth, but a number of practical difficulties limit the attainable precision. Somewhat devious methods, invoking gravitational theory, give more consistent results that converge on the value,

Radius of the sun, $R = 6.9598 \pm 0.007 \times 10^{10}$ cm

The mass of the sun is also derived from the application of gravitational theory: first, to the measurement of the mass of the earth; then, by way of the moon and planets, to the sun; with the result,

Mass of the sun, $M = 1.989 \pm 0.002 \times 10^{33}$ grams

A measurement of the total radiation received at the earth's distance from the sun is the basic observation from which its luminosity can be found (once the distance to the sun, and the radius of the sun are known). This measurement is extremely difficult and is seriously distorted by the earth's atmosphere, but the value

Luminosity of the sun, $L = 3.90 \pm 0.04 \times 10^{33}$

ergs/sec

can be derived from long, independent series of observations.

An additional parameter, or series of numbers, is essential for the construction of an adequate theoretical model sun. These are the abundances of the chemical elements. For convenience, abundances are stated in terms of the abundance of hydrogen. In the sun, the relative abundances of the important constituents are

$$\left.\begin{array}{l} \text{Hydrogen} = 1.00 \\ \text{Helium} = 0.23 \\ \text{Z (all other elements)} = 0.02 \end{array}\right\} \begin{array}{l} Q, \text{the relative} \\ \text{chemical} \\ \text{abundance} \end{array}$$

The values of L, M, R, Q, deduced from observation for the sun, are somewhere near the middle of ranges of these quantities as derived for other stars. It is, therefore, sometimes said that the sun is an average star, but for the stars inside an imaginary spherical shell surrounding the sun, with a radius so small that it is reasonably certain that all stars within the enclosed volume have been observed, a different interpretation is valid. Most of the stars close to the sun are cool, red, dwarf stars, probably the most numerous of all stellar varieties. Only ten of the fifty-five nearest stars can be seen with the eye alone. Only three of these stars are brighter than the sun, most are exceedingly faint. Stars brighter than the sun are extremely rare, and the sun is outstanding in all of its properties.

Although the sun's $L, M, R,$ and Q can be fitted into a coherent physical theory which, starting with a nuclear energy source (see SOLAR ENERGY SOURCES) near the sun's center, can trace the outward flow of energy from the deep interior, through complicated transformations, until a quantity and quality of radiation is predicted at the solar surface that agrees closely with observation; only the most primitive beginning has been made on a theory of the phenomena that occur in the observable regions of the sun: the photosphere, the chromosphere, and the corona.

The photosphere of the sun is the surface observed directly by the eye through a protective dense black glass screen. In very transparent skies with the help of special telescopes or at times of total solar eclipses, the chromosphere and corona may also be observed visually. All three of these layers show structures in widely different sizes and rates of change. The theoretical problems connected with the photosphere-chromosphere and the chromosphere-corona interfaces are nearly intractable, and the individual layers are understood only slightly better.

Nearly three centuries of telescopic observation of the solar photosphere define this part of the sun as that imaged on a photographic plate, or seen by the eye, using the light in a spectral band at least 1000Å wide, centered near 5000Å in the blue-green part of the spectrum. The portion of the sun thus recorded is a spherical shell, 5×10^8 cm thick, whose outer radius is the edge of the apparent solar disk, 7×10^{10} cm from the sun's center. Good photospheric photographs show a granulation composed of small (10^8 cm, or less) bright, circular, or hexagonal, structures all over the sun except extremely near the edge. These are the tops of convection cells that carry much of the solar energy. They are a few hundred degrees hotter than the five-thousand-plus degrees absolute that is consistent with the sun's assigned total luminosity. Occasionally, small dark spots (pores) appear among the granulations, and still more infrequently, a pore will develop into a larger dark complex, a sunspot region. Spot regions are some thousands of degrees cooler than the granulated photosphere

in which they are immersed. They mark the locations of sizable magnetic fields, and the spot regions may cover some tenths of the sun's disk. Since the spot regions are nearly fixed on the solar surface, they may also be used as markers for the measurement of the rate of rotation of the sun.

The angular rate of rotation, deduced from sunspot, or spectroscopic, observations, varies from the sun's equator to its poles. It is greatest on the equator, there corresponding to a period of rotation of twenty-five days. At the pole the period of rotation is nearly thirty-five days.

Sunspots are the main sources of difficult problems of the photosphere. How can the refrigeration of the spot regions be explained? What is the origin of the magnetic fields? How is the distribution of angular velocities established, and how is it maintained?

The chromosphere is most easily observed at times of total solar eclipse. It appears as a red-purple narrow irregular ring just after the beginning and again just before the ending of totality. The average thickness of the chromospheric layer is 10^9 cm, but it is so tenuous that it is undetectable under conditions satisfactory for observation of the photosphere. For the daily observation of the chromosphere, a filter transmitting a spectral band not wider than 1 Å must be used to produce monochromatic solar images, and the center of the spectral band transmitted by the filter must be adjusted to coincide with the center of an emission line that appears strongly in the spectrum of the chromosphere. Nearly all observations of the chromosphere are made with light from the center of just two spectrum lines: the H-alpha line of hydrogen in the red part of the spectrum; and the K line of ionized calcium in the ultraviolet. The pictures show the chromosphere as a continually seething part of the solar atmosphere, subject to spectacularly sudden changes in the neighborhood of sunspots. The changes in the chromosphere and the dominating changes that occur in the underlying sunspots are considered together as the phenomenon of *solar activity*.

Long before regular observation of the chromosphere became possible, records of the numbers of sunspots had led to the discovery of a ten-year cycle of variation. As solar observation has become more nearly continuous, nearly every aspect of the sun's activity has revealed cyclical behavior closely synchronized with the variation in the numbers of spots. This is especially true for the changes in the chromosphere. The solar flares and extensive systems of solar prominences in the chromosphere are apparently organized and controlled by the magnetic fields rooted in the sunspot regions.

However, the smallest structures in the chromosphere are not obviously connected with sunspot activity. The smallest features in undisturbed solar areas far from the dominance of

spot regions undergo damped oscillations that are nearly periodic with characteristic times of about three hundred seconds. Perhaps these motions are enforced by the somewhat slower changes observed in the photospheric granulations on which the chromospheric structures are based.

Like the chromosphere, the corona can only be observed with the unaided eye at the time of a total solar eclipse, but with telescopic, spectroscopic, and other instrumental aids, it can be observed every day. It is the most extensive of the divisions of the sun's atmosphere, its outer limits lying somewhere beyond the distance of the earth from the sun where the corona becomes indistinguishable from the interplanetary medium. The corona changes both gradually and suddenly in rather sensitive connection with the spot regions. It is the principal source of the sun's x-rays, extreme ultraviolet, and radio emission, and the combination of satellite observations near the short-wavelength limit of the solar spectrum and radio observations at the other end of the spectrum results in an attractive qualitative picture of solar activity.

At times of solar flare outbursts in the spot regions, observations in the two ends of the solar spectrum can be interpreted as indicating motion of an unknown disturbance, starting away from the sun with the beginning of the flare and moving outward through the chromosphere and the corona. Frequently, streams of particles associated with the flare activity reach earth, and are detected as cosmic rays and by their secondary effects such as terrestrial magnetic storms, but many of the changes induced in the corona by activity in spot regions seem to be connected with variations in local solar magnetic fields and not with streams of particles.

It should be evident from this brief synopsis of some of the general results of intensive observation of the sun for more than a century that solar theory is in a reasonably satisfactory state only for those parts of the sun that have not been observed. The problems for which theoretical help is badly needed to understand observed phenomena are derivatives of two main questions that are not necessarily unrelated: (1) What is the explanation of the observed variation of angular rotation from the sun's equator to its poles? (2) What are the physical bases of sunspot phenomena?

New results, flooding from new observatories and the exploratory applications of rockets and space technologies to solar studies have emphasized the persistence of unsolved problems and the remarkable opportunities for contributions to observational and theoretical solar physics.

ORREN C. MOHLER

References

Kuiper, G. P., Ed., "The Sun," Chicago, University of Chicago Press, 1953.

Thomas, R. N., and Athay, R. G., "Physics of the Solar Chromosphere," New York, Interscience Publishers, 1961.

Smith, H., and E., "Solar Flares," New York, The Macmillan Co., 1963.

Gamow, G., "A Star Called the Sun," New York, Viking Press, 1964.

Bray, R., and Loughhead, R., "Sunspots," London, Longmans, 1964.

Zirin, H., "The Solar Atmosphere," Waltham, Mass., Blaisdell Publ. Co., 1966.

Tandberg-Hanssen, E., "Solar Activity," Waltham, Mass., Blaisdell Publ. Co., 1967.

Bray, R., and Loughhead, R., "The Solar Granulation," London, Chapman and Hall, Ltd., 1967.

Cross-references: ASTROMETRY, ASTROPHYSICS, SOLAR ENERGY SOURCES.

SOLID-STATE PHYSICS

Solid-state physics is the study of the crystallographic, electronic, and magnetic properties of solids, primarily of crystalline solids. It concerns itself not only with the inherent nature of solids considered as a collection of atoms, but also with the interaction of solids with mechanical forces, with sources of heat, with electromagnetic fields, with bombarding particles, and the like. It includes both theoretical and experimental aspects of solids. It is a broad field, merging with such associated sciences as chemistry and biology and such technologies as metallurgy, ceramics, and electrical engineering; the boundaries between solid-state physics and these associated disciplines are not well defined.

The atoms which comprise a solid can be considered, for many purposes, to be hard balls which rest against each other in a regular repetitive pattern called the crystal structure. Most elements have simple crystal structures of high symmetry but many compounds have complex crystal structures of low symmetry. The determination of crystal structures, of atom location in the crystal, and of the dependence of many physical properties upon the inherent characteristics of the perfect solid is an absorbing study, one which has occupied the lives of numerous geologists, mineralogists, physicists, and other scientists for many years. (See CRYSTALLOGRAPHY.)

The rigid, hard-ball model is not adequate to explain many properties of solids. To begin with, solids can be deformed by finite forces, thus solids must not be completely rigid. Furthermore, atoms in a solid possess vibrational energy, so the atoms must not be precisely fixed to mathematically defined lattice points. This deformability of solids is built into the model by the assignment of deformable bonds (springs) between nearest atom neighbors. This ball-and-spring model has many successes; one important early use was that of Einstein to devise a reasonably successful theory of specific heats. Later incorporation by Debye of coupled motion of groups of atoms led to an even more successful theory.

Several measures exist of the strength of these bonds. One is the size of the elastic constants—for most solids Young's modulus is about 10^{11} newtons/m^2. The other is the frequency of vibration of the atoms; values around 10^{13} to 10^{14} Hz are found.

The lack of perfection occasioned by elastic deformation of solids is but one of many kinds of crystalline imperfections. By the way crystals are produced, either in the laboratory or in nature, defects in structure exist, often in profusion. These defects may be characterized by three principal parameters—their geometry, size, and energy of formation.

All real crystals have atoms which occupy external surface sites and which do not possess the correct number of nearest neighbors as a consequence. Thus a surface is a seat of energy and is characterized by a SURFACE TENSION. Furthermore, internal surfaces exist, grain boundaries and twin boundaries across which atoms are incorrectly positioned. In a crystal of reasonable size, say 1 cm^3, these two-dimensional defects, called *surface defects*, contain only about 1 atom in 10^6, a rather small fraction. Even so, surfaces are important attributes of solids.

Some defects have extent in only one dimension—*line* defects. The most prominent of these, the dislocation, is a line in the crystal along which atoms have either an incorrect number of neighbors or neighbors which have not the correct distance or angle. In 1 cm^3 of a real crystal one might find a wide variation of length of dislocations present—from near zero to perhaps 10^{11} cm.

Defects which have extent of only about an atomic diameter also exist in crystals—the *point defects*. Vacant lattice sites may occur—*vacancies*. Extra atoms—*interstitials*—may be inserted between regular crystal atoms. Atoms of the wrong chemical species—*impurities*—may also be present.

The properties of defects are intimately related to their energy of formation. A standard against which this energy can be compared is provided by the energy of sublimation—the energy necessary to separate the ions of a solid into neutral, noninteracting atoms. This energy is about 81 000 cal/mole for a typical metal, Cu, at room temperature, about 3.5 eV per atom. Energies of surfaces, both free surfaces and grain boundaries, are about 1000 ergs/cm^2, about 1 eV per surface atom. Dislocation energies are of similar size per atom length of dislocation, about 1 to 5 eV, so the energy of a dislocation is about 10^{-4} ergs/cm of length. Point defects, too, possess an inherent energy of about 1 eV each. Vacancies in Cu have an energy of about 1 eV, self-interstitials 2 or 3 eV.

The energies per atom of these various defects, surface, line, and point, are all much larger than the average thermal energy per atom in a solid at reasonable temperatures. This thermal energy,

kT, is only about 1/40 eV at room temperature. Thus, defects can be produced only by conditions which exist during manufacture of crystals, by external means such as plastic deformation or particle bombardment, or by large local fluctuations in thermal energy away from the average.

The total amount of energy which is bound up in ordinary concentrations of these defects is not large compared to the total thermal energy of a solid at normal temperatures. All the vacancies in equilibrium in Cu, even at the melting point, comprise less than 10 cal of energy per mole, much less than the enthalpy at 1357 K (the melting point) of more than 7000 cal/mole. In a material with very heavy dislocation density, 10^{12} cm/cm^3, the total dislocation energy is only a few calories per mole. And the total energy of a free surface of a compact block of 1 mole of Cu is even less, about 10^{-3} cal. Thus the inherent energy of these defects is not large; even so they are immensely important in controlling many phenomena in crystals.

Crystallographic defects need not remain stationary in the crystal; they may move about with time. Some of these movements may reduce the overall free energy of the solid, others (these are chiefly movement of the point defects) may simply be the wandering of random walk. Since these movements require the surmounting of a potential barrier much larger than kT, the motion of defects depends upon rather large local fluctuations in energy. Consequently, their rate of motion depends on temperature through a Boltzmann factor $\exp(-\Delta H/RT)$, where ΔH is the enthalpy increase necessary to move the defect from the lowest energy site to the top of the barrier.

A convenient description of the crystalline structure of solids is thus seen to consist of successive stages of approximation. First the mathematically perfect geometrical model is described, then departures from this perfect regularity are permitted. The deformability of solids is allowed for by letting the force constants between adjacent atoms be finite, not infinite. Then misplacement of atoms is permitted and a variety of crystalline irregularities, called defects, is described. Some of these defects have intrinsic features which affect properties of the crystal, others affect the properties by their motion from site to site in the crystal. In spite of their relatively small number, defects are of immense importance.

The electronic structure of solids is determined, in principle, solely by the electronic structure of the free atoms of which the solid is composed. Since the free atom structure is known rather well, especially for atoms of lower atomic number, the electronic structure of solids should be readily calculable, even though the calculation might be tedious. Such is not the case; a wide variety of interactions occur between the electrons on adjacent atoms as they approach the equilibrium distance characteristic of solids. These interactions are of such complex nature that they cannot be concisely defined and involve such a host of charged particles, electrons, and ion cores, that only approximate calculations can usually be made. Nevertheless, the use of approximate models allows many general features of the electronic structure to be deduced, especially when close interplay between theory and experiment is established. As for the crystalline structure of solids, two stages are useful in understanding the electronic structure. First the perfect electronic structure is defined, then irregularities in this structure, again termed defects, are described. Although both the geometry and energy of crystalline defects are defined, description of the geometry of the charge distribution of many of the electronic defects is not possible and one must generally be content with description of the formation energy of the defect.

The nuclei of the atoms in a solid and the inner electrons form ion cores with energy levels little different from corresponding levels in free atoms. The characteristics of the valence electrons are modified greatly, however. The state functions of these outer electrons greatly overlap those of neighboring atoms and restrictions of the Pauli Exclusion Principle and the Uncertainty Principle force modification of the state functions and development of a set of split energy levels rather than the single-level characteristic of isolated atoms. This set of split levels becomes a quasi-continuous band of levels of width several electron volts for most solids. Importantly, unoccupied levels of the atoms are also split into bands. The electronic characteristics of solids are determined by the relative position in energy of the occupied and unoccupied levels as well as by the characteristics of the electrons within a band.

The solid is called a *metal* if excitation of electrons from the highest filled levels to the lowest unoccupied levels can occur with infinitesimal expenditure of energy. Thus excitation can occur by means of many external forces such as electric fields, heat, light, radio waves. Metals are therefore good conductors of electricity and of heat, they are opaque to light, and they reflect radio waves.

Some solids have wide spacing between the occupied and unoccupied energy states—2 eV or more. Such solids are called *insulators* since normal electric fields cannot cause extensive motion of the electrons. Examples are diamonds, sodium chloride, sulfur, quartz, mica. They are poor conductors of electricity and heat and are usually transparent to light (when not filled with impurities or defects).

Solids with conductivity properties intermediate between those of metals and insulators are called *semiconductors*. For them, the excitation energy lies in the range 0.1 to about 2 eV. Thermal fluctuations are sufficient to excite a small, but significant, fraction of electrons from

the occupied levels (the valence band) into the unoccupied levels (the conduction band). Both the excited electrons and the empty states in the valence band (aptly called holes) may move under the influence of an electric field, providing a means for conduction of current. Such electron-hole pairs may be produced not only by thermal energy, but also by incident light, providing photo-effects. The inverse process, emission of light by annihilation of electrons and holes in suitably prepared materials, provides a highly efficient light source (light-emitting diodes).

Crystallographic defects, in general, are also electronic defects. In metals, they provide scattering centers for electrons, increasing the resistance to charge flow. The resistance wire in many electric heaters, in fact, consists of an ordinary metal such as iron with additional alloying elements such as nickel or chromium providing scattering centers for electrons. In semiconductors and insulators, however, alloying elements and defects provide an even greater variety of effects, since they can change the electron-hole concentrations drastically in addition to providing scattering centers. The entire semiconductor device industry is based on alloying of silicon, germanium, and compound semiconductors with selected impurities in carefully controlled concentration and geometry.

Most materials of importance to us are nearly perfect crystals containing a relatively small fraction of atoms associated with defects. However, some materials depart greatly from crystallinity, glass and plastics being notable examples. Although their electronic structure cannot be understood as well as that of crystals, they possess properties of conductivity, dielectric constant, strength, and the like similar to those of crystals. Thus they are of great practical use; glass, of course, having been used for centuries and plastics for about a hundred years. Of more recent interest is a class of noncrystalline semiconductors called *amorphous* semiconductors. The electronic bands of these materials, poorly understood, nevertheless provide semiconducting characteristics which may be of value in electronic devices.

Solids are useful because of their interaction with external forces or stimuli such as electric and magnetic fields, heat, and mechanical forces. Yet among all of these interactions none is more important than the interrelations between matter and light. The earth is warmed by the sun, photosynthesis provides food, vision is the most important of our senses. Yet the physics and chemistry of the absorption processes on which these phenomena depend are only partially understood. That generation of light is also of great importance may be seen from the fact that about 25 per cent of all electrical energy consumed in the United States is used in production of light. Small wonder that immense effort is being spent on increasing lighting efficiency by high-pressure arc discharge lamps, by more efficient phosphors for fluorescent tubes, and by improved devices using cathodoluminescence and electroluminescence. Unfortunately, little chance seems possible to increase efficiency of visible light production from incandescent lamps, an efficiency which does not exceed 10 per cent at best.

The interaction of light with matter is so important that a chief hallmark of physics in this century is the extraordinary development of spectroscopy and its application to processes in solids. First came investigation of emission and absorption of radiation from free atoms. Later investigations have included emission and absorption of radiation by atoms in solids, MASER and LASER phenomena, Mössbauer spectroscopy, nuclear magnetic resonance, x-ray diffraction, infrared spectroscopy, fluorescence, the Raman effect, microwave emission and absorption, and many other effects. These investigations have led not only to an increasingly detailed perception of the nature of solids, but also to a host of practical devices such as electric lights, LASER generators and amplifiers, and x-ray generators.

MAGNETISM is basically an inherent property of the electrons in a perfect crystal. It is of importance both for the insights which magnetic studies provide into the intrinsic properties of materials and for its practical importance. Two weak effects, DIAMAGNETISM and PARAMAGNETISM, are purely of academic importance. The basic properties of ferromagnets (saturation magnetization, Curie temperature, magnetostriction, crystalline anisotropy) are inherent properties of the perfect lattice. The technological application of ferromagnets, however, demands careful control of defects, which exert strong influence on such properties as hysteresis loss, permeability, and coercive force. (See FERROMAGNETISM.)

The physics of computers is a newer application of solids. Not only do the active computational devices depend on ever-increasing sophistication of semiconductor devices, but also the pressure for memory cores of smaller physical size, faster readout time, and lower power consumption puts great demands on continued development of magnetic materials.

Summarizing in a sentence: Solid-state physics, in its broadest sense, is the study of the perfect and imperfect crystalline and electronic properties of solids, ranging from attempts to understand these phenomena from the most fundamental point of view to the edge of the technological applications of solids.

CHARLES A. WERT

References

van Vlack, L., "Elements of Materials Science," Second edition, Reading, Mass., Addison-Wesley Publishing Co., 1964.

Wert, C., and Thomson, R., "Physics of Solids,"

Second edition, New York, McGraw-Hill Book Co., 1970.

Ziman, J. M., "Electrons and Phonons," Oxford, Clarendon Press, 1970.

Seitz, F., and Turnbull, D ., "Solid State Physics, " New York, Academic Press, 1955.

Scientific American (Nearly every issue has some reference to a property of solids or some application. See especially issues on Materials, September 1967, and Light, September, 1968).

Cross-references: CRYSTALLOGRAPHY, DIAMAGNETISM, ENERGY LEVELS, FERROMAGNETISM, HEAT CAPACITY, MAGNETISM, PARAMAGNETISM, SEMICONDUCTORS, SOLID-STATE THEORY, SURFACE TENSION.

SOLID-STATE THEORY

True solids possess long-range order not found in other phases of matter. The (approximate) periodicity of the potential in solids makes possible detailed investigations by powerful mathematical techniques which cannot be used in other condensed systems. Studies of phenomena related to the almost periodic potential comprise the bulk of modern solid-state theory. Research on local deviations from periodicity, "imperfections," constitutes a sizable minority activity.

The one-electron problem in a truly periodic potential can be considered solved, in principle, with one reservation. Fast digital computers make the calculation of the "band structure," i.e., the dependence of electron energy on wave vector, $\epsilon(k)$, a matter of perhaps half an hour on a large computing machine. The reservation refers to the uncertainty in knowledge of the potential to be furnished to the computing machine. Self-consistent methods have been constructed, but the treatment of "exchange" is not completely satisfactory. As knowledge of experimental parameters for specific crystals becomes more precise, so do the theoretical band structures. Accordingly calculations of other measurable properties in those systems are becoming more quantitative.

Of course, electrons in a solid do interact, and a one-electron theory cannot describe the correlation effects. Many-body theory to describe the collective behavior of the electrons is being investigated by many workers.

The basic calculation of the dispersion of PHONONS (quanta of the vibrational field), i.e., the frequency of normal modes of oscillation vs their wave vectors, $\omega(q)$, is not as simple as for the electrons in a periodic potential. Not only are the interatomic forces difficult to specify, but there exist peculiarities, the Van Hove singularities, in the density of states. Phonons also interact with each other, since the vibrational motion is not truly harmonic. Considerable activity is currently associated with these problems.

More difficult still are the questions which arise when the electron system and the phonons interact. Most theoretical work on pure systems is based on (1) a description of the electrons as if the potential were actually periodic, i.e., as if no phonons or even zero-point vibration were present, and (2) a description of the lattice vibration which ignores the electronic state of the crystal. For many purposes, this approximation is not as crude as it appears at first sight; if the electronic wave function actually is coherent over many atomic positions, and frequently it is, then the lattice vibration is indeed insensitive to small changes in the electronic state, and vice versa. Thus in a metal under ordinary conditions, one may ignore not only any change in the dispersion curve, but also any effect on the distribution function of phonons as the electronic state is changed, say by an electric field. In a semiconductor like Ge, the "phonon drag" problem may require that the electron and phonon distributions in the presence of a driving force be considered self-consistently, even though $\epsilon(k)$ and $\omega(q)$ may be treated as unchanged. Even this problem is not simple.

When imperfections are present, such as vacancies, impurities, or dislocations, it is necessary to consider the possibility of localized modes being created in the vicinity of these imperfections; i.e., modes of lattice vibration of frequency ω may exist near the imperfections which could not exist in the perfect crystal. Furthermore there may occur a concentration of lattice modes of vibration in a certain frequency range, in the vicinity of the imperfections (resonant modes).

In addition, in some systems such as ionic crystals, it is necessary to go one step further, and consider "relaxation" of the lattice after an imperfection changes its electronic state. The motion of the neighboring atoms leads to a further change in the electronic wave function, sometimes even its symmetry, with large effects on the optical properties.

In the perfect crystal there exist simple selection rules based on momentum conservation which relate the initial and final values of the wave vector of the excited electron upon optical excitation. In many cases, however, theory predicts "indirect" transitions, in which a phonon is simultaneously excited or absorbed. Theory has also developed to account for numerous new effects in optical properties of solids, such as nonlinear optical effects, laser action, 2-electron transitions, and 2-photon effects.

The mechanical properties of solids are now understood at a far more fundamental level than they were at mid-century through development of the theory of dislocations. Many new phenomena have been interpreted or predicted, such as spiral growth, "climb," dislocation networks, "whiskers," and decoration with colloidal particles. This has been a most active field of research (see SOLID-STATE PHYSICS).

Magnetic behavior continues to receive much attention. Nuclear and electron resonance phenomena have been powerful techniques for investigating the magnetic structure of solids (see MAGNETIC RESONANCE); likewise the Mössbauer effect. Furthermore, the use of high magnetic fields has elucidated phenomena for which investigative methods were not available earlier. The theory of these phenomena has kept pace with them, if not preceded them. The theory of FERROMAGNETISM continues to occupy a major field of activity. The specific interaction among electrons which gives rise to the ferromagnetic behavior may not be predictable for a given system, but the general outlines of several theories are reasonably well understood.

The existence of SUPERCONDUCTIVITY, which represented such a mystery for so long, has now been explained in terms of electron-phonon interaction. Much detailed work going beyond the BCS theory is being done. Inter alia, people are trying to see if other interactions could likewise give rise to the existence of superconductivity. There is some speculation that high-temperature superconductors might exist.

In the theory of transport phenomena there are attempts at more sophisticated theory than the conventional one-electron Boltzmann equation will allow. Density matrix methods are applied, for example, and scattering probabilities are computed without making use of such approximations as spherical energy surfaces and Born approximation, and the importance of Umklapp processes is now better appreciated.

The study of quasi particles continues to grow, and we have names and descriptions for helicons, excitons, magnons, phonons, polarons, polaritons, and plasmons. Much modern theory is devoted to considerations of the existence and the propagation of these quasi particles, which are quantized elementary excitations of a solid and are characterized by an energy, wave vector, and polarization. As they become better understood interactions among them are increasingly investigated, e.g., exciton fission and fusion, and magnon-phonon interactions.

Several areas of solid-state theory have developed great interest in recent years. The theory of CRITICAL PHENOMENA, e.g., the temperature rate of approach to critical points, is one example. Another is the study of amorphous nonmetallic solids, e.g., the density of states in the "forbidden" gap, and the idea of a "mobility gap." Another is the metal-insulator phase transition. Still another is the study of magnetic alloys, e.g., the Kondo effect. Increasing also is the attempt to apply solid-state theory, or theoretical techniques, to the study of biological systems.

Recent advances in theoretical techniques are the use of fast computing machines, of course, as well as the increasing application of group theoretical methods to exploit and describe symmetries other than translational, and Green's functions and quantum field theoretical methods in many-body problems.

Work on solid-state theory is widespread. Notable is the work in the United States, the Soviet Union, Japan, and England, but many other localities are contributing also.

DAVID L. DEXTER

References

Kittel, C., "Introduction to Solid State Physics," Fourth 'edition, New York, John Wiley & Sons, 1972.

Seitz, F., and Turnbull, D., Eds., "Solid State Physics," Vols. 1–26, New York, Academic Press, Inc.

Cross-references: CRITICAL PHENOMENA, ENERGY LEVELS, EXCITONS, FERMI SURFACE, FERROMAGNETISM, MAGNETIC RESONANCE, MAGNETISM, PHONONS, SEMICONDUCTORS, SOLID-STATE DEVICES, SOLID-STATE PHYSICS, SUPERCONDUCTIVITY, TUNNELING.

SONAR*

The term SONAR is a coined word derived from the phrase SOund NAvigation and Ranging. The term generally refers to the principles employed in the design and operation of systems that utilize acoustic energy transmitted in an ocean medium; while the systems themselves are referred to as sonar systems. Thus, sonar may be defined as a branch of applied acoustics concerned with the utilization of the ocean as the transmitting medium.

The problem of sonar is threefold: (a) understanding the transmission of acoustic energy through the transmitting medium, (b) developing sources which convert mechanical or electrical energy into acoustic energy, and (c) developing receivers which convert the acoustic energy back into mechanical or electrical energy.

Whenever a body vibrates in a fluid, longitudinal waves are formed, which propagate outward from the vibrating body. The particles of the fluid are set in motion, and temporary stresses are produced which increase and decrease during each vibration. The motion of the particles gives the fluid kinetic energy while the stresses induce potential energy. The sum of the two energies is called acoustic energy.

Traditionally, the starting point for a discussion of the transmission of acoustic energy in a fluid is to assume a point source radiating acoustic energy in an ideal homogeneous nonabsorptive medium of infinite extent. Under these assumptions, the energy from the source will radiate outwards with the wave front forming a

---

*The opinions and assertions contained herein are the private ones of the writer, and are not to be construed as official, or as reflecting the views of the Navy Department or the Naval Service at large.

spherical shell. As the radius of the shell increases, the sound intensity decreases. In practice it is customary to express the sound intensity by means of a logarithmic scale. The most generally used logarithmic scale is the decibel. The intensity level in decibels of a sound of intensity I is defined as 10 log (I/I_0) where I_0 is a reference intensity. The intensity level can also be expressed as 20 log (P/P_0) where P is the pressure and P_0 the reference pressure, usually 1 dyne/cm^2 in underwater acoustics. In this discussion the terms in all equations are expressed in decibels. The decrease in intensity as the shell increases in radius is called the spreading loss. The spreading loss from a unit range of R_0 to a range of R is 10 log [(intensity at R_0)/(intensity at R)] = 10 log $(R^2/1^2)$ = 20 log R. In most applications the use of such a simple model has been inadequate.

A more realistic model considers the following factors: the water-earth interface (bottom), the water-atmosphere interface (surface), the absorption of acoustic energy in the medium, the presence of foreign material in the medium, and the distribution of sound speed. Considered as an acoustic medium, the waters of the ocean form a thin layer on the earth's surface. Some of the acoustic energy radiated into this layer by a source will reach either the surface or the bottom. At either of these surfaces abrupt discontinuities in acoustic properties occur. Because of these discontinuities part of the intercepted energy is reflected, part may be transmitted across the interface, and part may be scattered within the medium. Since the transmission of an acoustic wave in water is accompanied by a compression and expansion of the medium, friction will occur between water molecules. This friction results in the conversion of some of the acoustic energy into thermal energy. In addition to this frictional, or viscous, loss there is another loss of energy in seawater related to the salts which continuously undergo chemical changes because of pressure fluctuations. Energy losses associated with both of these phenomena are called absorption losses. Due to the presence of foreign bodies in the volume of water, reflection and scattering are not limited to the surface and bottom boundaries. Foreign matter and biological content vary widely in size and acoustic characteristics. All ocean waters contain such bodies which modify the direction in which the acoustic energy is transmitted. In sufficient number they may also modify and increase the total absorption loss. The effect of variations in sound speed is to bend the wave front in the direction of the lower speed. This bending of the wave front is referred to as refraction. Both refraction and reflection can result in the guiding of acoustic energy in certain directions.

The factors above affect the propagation of acoustic energy in seawater in two different ways. The first results in a spreading loss already mentioned, and the second results in a loss referred to as attenuation. Attenuation consists of both the scattering and absorption losses. The spreading and attenuation are related to the distance the acoustic energy travels in different ways. An important difference is that the spreading loss frequently is relatively independent of frequency while the attenuation is a function of frequency.

There are three basic types of sonar systems: direct listening systems, echo-ranging systems, and communication systems.

In direct listening the acoustic energy is radiated by the target, which is the primary source. The acoustic transmission is a one-way process. In their more elementary forms, direct listening sonar systems may be nondirectional and only give a warning that a primary source is in the vicinity of the searching vehicle; or directional, and permit determination of the bearing of individual primary sources relative to the listening platform. They generally do not give range. Direct listening is limited by the magnitude of the signal when it reaches the receiving point and the magnitude of the interfering noise which tends to obscure its reception.

In echo ranging, the sonar system projects acoustic energy into the water with the expectation that this energy will strike a target and enough of the energy will be reflected back to the searching platform so that it can be recognized as a target echo. The primary source of acoustic energy is in the searching platform, with the target, upon reflection of the energy, becoming a secondary acoustic source. The transmission of the energy is a two-way process. Echo-ranging sonar systems permit a determination of the bearing of a silent target, and by timing the echo-signal transmission and by knowing the speed of sound in seawater, a range may also be obtained. Echo ranging is limited by the relative magnitudes of the signal and of the locally generated interference. In some cases the sonar performance is limited by reverberation, which is the acoustic energy returning by reflectors other than the target of interest.

Acoustically, sonar communications systems are similar to direct listening systems in that they utilize a one-way transmission path. Instrumentally, they are similar to echo-ranging systems, one located at each of the two points between which communications is to be established. In these systems coded pulses or voice modulated signals are transmitted by one system and received by the other.

To hear a target by direct listening, it is necessary that the acoustic level of the target less the transmission loss along the acoustic path from the target to the listening equipment be equal to or greater than the level of the background noise. This may be expressed as $L - H \geqslant N$ where L is the source level of the target, H is the one-way transmission loss, and N is the noise level. The size of this inequality depends upon operator skill, signal processing, and method of presentation. It is called the signal excess, E. This inequality can be written as an equation

where $E = L - H - N$. This equation is called the direct-listening sonar equation for an omni-directional listening hydrophone. When using directional hydrophones a factor called the directivity index must be added to the right-hand member of the equation. The source level, L, is a measure of the amount of acoustic energy put into the water by the target vehicle and is equal to 10 log (sound intensity at unit distance from the source). The transmission loss, H, is the sum of the losses related to refraction, surface and bottom reflection, absorption, and scattering. The noise, N, results from unwanted acoustic energies arriving from many different sources and normally consists of thermal, ambient, and self noises.

To see a target by echo ranging it is necessary that the acoustic level of the primary source less twice the transmission loss along the acoustic path from source to target plus the target strength be equal to or greater than the noise. This may be expressed, for a nondirectional receiver against a noise background, as $L - 2H + T \geqslant N$ where T is the target strength, a function of the reflecting characteristics of the target. Against a reverberation background the inequality becomes $L - 2H + T \geqslant R$ where R is the reverberation level. As in the case of direct listening, the inequalities can be expressed in terms of the signal excess as $E_N = L - 2H + T - N$ or $E_R = L - 2H + T - R$ where E_N and E_R are the signal excesses for noise and reverberation. The noise, N, comes from own-ship's noise and target noise. Reverberation, R, is the energy that is returned from the outgoing acoustic energy to the receiving equipment after having been reflected from reflectors in the medium other than the target. Reverberation sources usually are backscattering from the surface, bottom, and foreign particles in the water.

ERNEST R. ANDERSON

References

Albers, V. M., "Underwater Acoustics Handbook," Pennsylvania State University Press, 1960.

Horton, J. W., "Fundamentals of Sonar," U.S. Naval Institute, 1959.

Kinsler, L. E., and Frey, A. R., "Fundamentals of Acoustics," New York, John Wiley & Sons, Inc., 1962.

Officer, C. B., "Introduction to the Theory of Sound Transmission," New York, McGraw-Hill Book Co., Inc., 1958.

Cross-references: ACOUSTICS, ELECTROACOUSTICS, NOISE, ULTRASONICS.

SPACE PHYSICS

Space physics is usually taken to be the physics of phenomena naturally occurring in space, but frequently space is not clearly defined. It normally includes at least the outer portions of planetary atmospheres (in which densities are low enough to permit satellite flight), the outer portion of the sun's atmosphere, and interplanetary space. It frequently also includes galactic space and intergalactic space. It is also frequently taken to include planetary studies and the study of the earth's atmosphere at altitudes above those attainable by balloons. With such a broad coverage, there are many special areas of study included within the scope of space physics, and several of these are described separately; for example, see ASTROPHYSICS, COSMIC RAYS, IONOSPHERE, PLANETARY ATMOSPHERES, RADIATION BELTS, RADIO ASTRONOMY, and SOLAR PHYSICS.

Earth's Outer Atmosphere The earth's atmosphere extends far out into space, something which would not necessarily be expected on the basis of atmospheric properties near the earth's surface. There are two factors involved in this great extension. First, above 100 km, the atmospheric temperature increases rapidly with altitude, causing an outward expansion of the atmosphere far beyond that which would have occurred had the temperature stayed within the bounds observed at the earth's surface. Second, above about 100 km, the atmosphere is sufficiently rarefied so that the different atmospheric constituents attain diffusive equilibrium distributions in the gravitational field; the lighter constituents then predominate at the higher altitudes and extend farther into space than would an atmosphere of more massive particles. This effect is enhanced by the dissociation of some molecular species into atoms. The pressure p at altitude h, in terms of the pressure p_0 at the earth's surface, is given by

$$p = p_0 \exp \left(- \int_0^h \frac{\overline{m}g \, dh}{kT} \right) \qquad (1)$$

where $\overline{m}$ is the average mass of the atmospheric particles, g is the acceleration of gravity, k is the Boltzmann constant, and T is the atmospheric temperature. It is clear from this expression that the high temperatures and low particle masses above 100-km altitude act to maintain pressures at still higher altitudes in excess of those that would exist if the temperature and molecular weight were constant with altitude. Where diffusion equilibrium prevails, Eq. (1) applies to each constituent separately, provided $\overline{m}$ is replaced by the particle mass for the particular constituent under consideration and p_0 is the partial pressure at some reference altitude where h is taken to be equal to zero.

The composition of the atmosphere does not change much up to 100 km; there is a region of maximum concentration of ozone (still a very minor constituent) near 20 to 30 km (see PLANETARY ATMOSPHERES), the relative concentration of water vapor falls markedly from its average sea-level value up to 10 or 15 km, and the relative abundance of atomic oxygen begins to become appreciable on approaching 100 km,

due to photodissociation of oxygen by ultraviolet sunlight. Above 100 km, atomic oxygen rapidly increases in importance, due to the combined influence of photodissociation and diffusive separation in the gravitational field; above 200 km, atomic oxygen is the principal atmospheric constituent for several hundred kilometers. However, helium is even lighter than atomic oxygen, so its concentration falls less rapidly with altitude, and it finally replaces atomic oxygen as the principal atmospheric constituent above some altitude which varies with the sunspot cycle between 600 and 1500 km. At still higher altitudes, atomic hydrogen finally displaces helium as the principal constituent. The hydrogen extends many earth radii out into space and constitutes the telluric hydrogen corona, or geocorona.

The temperature of the upper atmosphere, and hence its density, varies with the intensity of solar ultraviolet radiation, and this in turn varies with the sunspot cycle and with solar activity in general. The solar radio-noise flux is a convenient index of solar activity, since it can be monitored at the earth's surface. The minimum nighttime temperature of the upper atmosphere above 300 km has been expressed in terms of the 27-day average of the solar radio-noise flux $\bar{S}$ at 8-cm wavelength, as follows,[4]

$$T = 280 + 4.6\bar{S}$$

This varies from about 600 K near the minimum of the sunspot cycle to about 1400 K near the maximum of the cycle. The maximum daytime temperature is about one-third larger than the nighttime minimum.

Magnetosphere The magnetosphere is that region of space in which the geomagnetic field dominates the motion of charged particles. Near the surface of the earth, the geomagnetic field resembles that of a dipole; the best-fit dipole is off center about 440 km and is inclined about 11° to the earth's axis of rotation. Well out into space, the field is severely deformed so that it no longer resembles a dipole field. The most apparent deformation is that due to a plasma of charged particles flowing away from the sun, a flow generally referred to as the solar wind. When the kinetic energy of the directed flow of the solar wind exceeds the energy density of the geomagnetic field, the plasma displaces the field. The diamagnetic properties of the flowing plasma tend to compress and confine the geomagnetic field,[2] at least on the side facing the sun (there is conjecture that on the side away from the sun the geomagnetic field might be indefinitely extended). Calculations indicate that the surface of the magnetosphere facing the sun is roughly hemispherical, with dimples over the earth's magnetic poles. Observations by space probes indicate that the distance that the geomagnetic field extends towards the sun is about 10 earth radii.[3]

The magnetosphere is a region within which many geophysical phenomena occur. Most deeply embedded within it are the plasmasphere and the Van Allen belts (see RADIATION BELTS). The plasmasphere consists of an upward extension of the ionosphere and hence it is made up of relatively low-energy particles; it has a sharp outer boundary that exhibits a diurnal pattern of movement. Beyond the plasmasphere there is virtually no low-energy plasma. The Van Allen belts consist of high-energy particles, both electrons and ions. The inner belt consists of protons with energies in the 10 to 100 MeV range and it is centered about half an earth radius above the geomagnetic equator. The outer belt consists of electrons with energies from 1 keV to 5 MeV that fill most of the magnetosphere almost out to the auroral zone. The tail of the magnetosphere is divided into two parts with oppositely directed field—one half with field lines directed away from the sun and connecting with the south polar region of the earth, and one half with field lines directed toward the sun and connecting with the north polar region of the earth. The neutral sheet separates the two regions of oppositely directed field, and the plasma sheet is a broader region extending on both sides of the neutral sheet in which there is a significant number of energetic ionized particles.

The solar plasma that compresses the geomagnetic field and limits the magnetosphere flows away from the sun at a velocity that might be described as hypersonic—the ordered velocity greatly exceeds the average random thermal velocity of the particles. Although the medium is so rarefied that collisions are rare, the particles can interact with one another through the agency of magnetic fields contained within the plasma. As a result, a collisionless shock wave develops in the flow before it reaches the surface of the magnetosphere.[8] Space probes have shown that the shock front lies about 4 earth radii beyond the surface of the magnetosphere in the direction of the sun.[3]

Aurorae are luminosities in the upper atmosphere at high latitudes caused by energetic particles, mainly electrons, that flow from the outer magnetosphere into the atmosphere. The cause of this electron bombardment from the magnetosphere is a long-standing scientific mystery. There is an obvious relationship to solar activity, but the mechanism that relates these two phenomena remains unknown (see AURORA AND AIRGLOW).

Interplanetary Space Up until about 1954, interplanetary space was thought to be essentially a perfect vacuum, devoid of interesting physical phenomena except for occasional sporadic events such as the ejection of gas clouds by the sun or the passage of comets. It is now recognized that interesting physical phenomena are always present. The solar corona expands continually, giving rise to a steady outstreaming into interplanetary space of ionized gas from the sun. As was mentioned above, this outflow of ionized gas is generally referred to as the solar wind.

The steady outflow of particulate matter from the sun was first recognized by Biermann in 1954 on the basis of the deflection of comet tails away from the sun—a deflection that was too great to be explained on the basis of light pressure. Biermann at first overestimated the strength of the outflow, because of an underestimate of the strength of the interaction between the solar plasma and the cometary plasma. The solar wind was first observed directly and measured with some accuracy in the spacecraft Mariner II.[7] This showed that the concentration of solar material near the earth was of the order of 5 protons/cm³, along with a corresponding concentration of electrons, moving with a velocity of about 500 km/sec.[7]

Parker[5] has given the most satisfactory explanation of the solar wind, describing it as a continuous hydrodynamic expansion of the solar corona, with a continuous heat input into the outflowing gas for a substantial distance near the sun. The flow can be compared to the flow of gas through a rocket nozzle, where, in the case of the sun, gravity plays the role in restricting the gas flow that the throat plays in the rocket nozzle. Parker has also shown that the outflowing, electrically conducting gas must pull the solar magnetic field out radially and that the rotation of the sun must twist the radial pattern into a spiral. This provides a magnetic connection, or a guiding path, from the western portion of the sun to the earth for any cosmic radiation produced in solar flares, something that is confirmed by observation.

A surprising property of interplanetary space, as observed by space probes, is the irregularity of the magnetic field. Although the average orientation of the field agrees with the spiral pattern predicted by Parker, many irregularities are present.[3] The magnetic field energy density is mainly due to the irregular fields, and it is approximately equal to the thermal energy of the solar wind particles, which is approximately 1 per cent of the energy of ordered flow. The real significance of these observations seems not to have been recognized at this writing.

A satisfying concept for the termination of the solar wind at some finite distance from the sun has been provided by Axford et al.[1] As the solar wind moves outward from the sun, its concentration falls according to an inverse square law, and the dynamic pressure that can be generated by stopping it falls accordingly. At some point, it must become so attenuated that its continued outward hypersonic flow will be stopped by the galactic magnetic field. At this point, there must be a shock front and a conversion of ordered energy of flow to disordered thermal energy. The heated gas beyond the shock front should cool mainly by charge exchange between the high-temperature protons from the solar wind and cool hydrogen atoms from galactic space. After charge exchange, the hydrogen atoms will carry the energy away. The cool proton gas left behind is less electrically conducting than was the hotter gas, and the magnetic field is gradually

released from the proton gas, allowing the magnetic field lines to merge and the proton gas to drift out into galactic space.

The hydrogen atoms that are heated beyond the shock front have high enough velocities to penetrate far into the solar system, even to the vicinity of the earth's orbit, before becoming ionized by solar ultraviolet radiation. The hydrogen atoms within a few astronomical units from the sun scatter hydrogen Lyman-alpha radiation emitted by the sun, and this scattered radiation can be detected with instrumentation flown in rockets. The rocket observations can be used to determine the concentration of the high-velocity neutral hydrogen atoms in interplanetary space, and this in turn can be interpreted in terms of the distance from the sun to the shock front beyond which the hydrogen originates. Patterson et al.[6] have shown that this interpretation indicates that the distance to the shock front is about 20 astronomical units (AU). The solar magnetic field spirals around about three times in this distance, and in the outer portion of the solar system, the magnetic field lines in the plane of the ecliptic are approximately circular, with the sun at the center.

Such a pattern of magnetic field in the solar system can be expected to produce significant anisotropies in the cosmic radiation, whether of solar or galactic origin. This is most pronouncedly true when cosmic radiation is released from a point on the sun that is connected by a magnetic field to the vicinity of the earth, in which case the cosmic radiation appears to approach the earth's magnetosphere from a point forty or fifty degrees to the west of the sun. A weak anisotropy is produced in the low-energy galactic cosmic radiation, and the anisotropy becomes smaller for the higher energy radiation.

Moon The nature of the interaction of the solar wind with a planetary body depends upon a number of factors including the conductivity of the planet, the characteristics of its atmosphere, and the presence of a planetary magnetic field, with each of these able under certain conditions to cause the deflection of the solar wind around the planet. In the case of the moon, there is neither atmosphere nor magnetic field to stop the solar wind, and the conductivity of the moon, mainly near the surface, controls the interaction.[9] Spacecraft observations have shown that the solar wind impinges directly on the lunar surface,[10,11] thus indicating that the moon is a poor conductor at its surface.

Measurements on the lunar surface have shown that magnetic field variations in the solar wind are magnified near the lunar surface on the sunward side. This indicates significant conductivity somewhere in the lunar interior, which permits the induction of internal currents that resist the field charge, causing an enhancement of the field charge near the lunar surface.

Planets There is great diversity among the planets and their influences upon physical phenomena occuring in space. Mercury, the

closest planet to the sun, has no atmosphere. Its interaction with the solar wind may resemble that of the moon, although it is entirely possible that it is sufficiently conductive to produce a different type of interaction. If sufficiently conducting, currents may be induced that produce magnetic field increases on the windward side sufficient to cause the deflection of the solar wind flow around the planet. In this case, a shock front would appear in the flow surrounding the front side of the planet, more or less like the shock around the front of the earth's magnetosphere. However, until such time as spacecraft observations are made near the planet, this must remain conjectural.

Venus has a massive atmosphere, while that of Mars is thin, but still sufficient to produce an ionosphere; neither has sufficient magnetic field to deflect the solar wind. The solar wind interacts with the conducting atmosphere in such a way as to produce a shock wave in the solar wind and a deflection of the flow around the planet, but the details of the interactions are not entirely clear. Both planets have warm thermospheres, though not so warm as the earth's. The interaction between the solar wind and the atmosphere is not satisfactorily understood, but it is clear from observation that the interaction produces a shock wave in the solar wind.

Jupiter has a massive magnetic field and hence the solar wind must be kept well away from the planet. Jupiter is a strong source of radio noise, some of it triggered by its satellite Io. The radio noise is taken as evidence that Jupiter has a belt of trapped radiation much more intensive than the Van Allen radiation belt around the earth, so powerful that spacecraft may not be able to penetrate within a half-dozen planetary radii of Jupiter without undergoing radiation damage that might disable the spacecraft.

FRANCIS S. JOHNSON

References

1. Axford, W. I., Dessler, A. J., and Gottlieb, B., "Termination of Solar Wind and Solar Magnetic Field," *Astrophys. J.*, 137, 1268-1278 (1963).
2. Beard, D. B., "The Solar Wind Geomagnetic Field Boundary," *Rev. Geophys.*, 2, 335-366 (1964).
3. Ness, S. F., Scearce, C. S., and Seek, J. B., "Initial Results of Imp I Magnetic Field Experiment," *J. Geophys. Res.*, 69, 3531-3569, (1964).
4. Nicolet, M., "Solar Radio Flux and Temperature of the Upper Atmosphere," *J. Geophys. Res.*, 68, 6121-6144 (1963).
5. Parker, E. N., "Interplanetary Dynamical Processes," pp. 272, New York, Interscience Publishers, 1963.
6. Patterson, T. N. L., Johnson, F. S., and Hanson, W. B., "The Distribution of Interplanetary Hydrogen," *Planetary Space Sci.*, 11, 767-778 (1963).
7. Snyder, C. W., Neugebauer, M., and Rao, U. R., "The Solar Wind Velocity and Its Correlation with Cosmic Ray Variations and with Solar and

Geomagnetic Activity," *J. Geophys. Res.*, 68, 6361-6370 (1963).
8. Spreiter, J. R., and Jones, W. P., "On the Effect of a Weak Interplanetary Field on the Interaction between the Solar Wind and the Geomagnetic Field," *J. Geophys. Res.*, 68, 3555-3565 (1963).
9. Johnson, F. S., and Midgley, J. E., "Notes on the lunar magnetosphere," *J. Geophys. Res.*, 73, 1523-1532 (1968).
10. Ness, N. F., Behannon, K. W., Scearce, C. S., and Cantarano, S. C., "Early results from the magnetic field experiment on lunar Explorer 35," *J. Geophys. Res.*, 72, 5769-5778 (1967).
11. Sonett, C. P., and Colburn, D. S., "Establishment of a lunar unipolar generator and associated shock and wake by the solar wind," *Nature*, 216, 340-343 (1967).

Cross-references: ASTROPHYSICS, AURORA AND AIRGLOW, COSMIC RAYS, IONOSPHERE, IONIZATION, PLANETARY ATMOSPHERES, RADIO ASTRONOMY, SOLAR PHYSICS.

SPARK AND BUBBLE CHAMBERS

When particles such as protons, neutrons, or mesons, occurring naturally in the cosmic radiation or produced copiously by accelerators, move through matter, they can produce nuclear interactions which are studied in nuclear and high-energy or particle physics. Electrically charged particles also produce pairs of electrons and positively charged ions in frequent *atomic* collisions, which are used to detect and trace the paths taken by incident and outgoing particles in the nuclear collisions.

In spark chambers, the electrons freed in a gas are accelerated by electric fields between electrodes, so that in further atomic collisions they can free additional electrons, leading to electron avalanches. Space charge effects, also due to the positively charged ions, and energetic photons due to excitation of atoms contribute additional avalanches. "Streamers" result which increase in length until they reach the electrodes at which point spark breakdown occurs, the location of which is recorded. The necessary high voltage potential is applied to the electrodes only after passage of a particle, making spark chambers quite insensitive to background radiation, but allowing them to be triggered by interaction events under investigation.

Parallel-plate spark chambers consist of a number of spark gaps formed by metal plates or foils separated by plastic rectangular frames. Chambers consisting of concentric cylindrical electrodes have also been built. The gaps of 2 to 15 mm must be maintained to accuracies of a few per cent over the full area, up to 10 m^2, of the plates. In thick, heavy metal plates, entering particles can be absorbed by ionization losses so that their ranges and thus energies can be measured, or they can produce electron showers or nuclear interactions. More often, however, thin

aluminum foils are preferred merely to track particles originating, for instance, from a liquid hydrogen or deuterium target; high-energy collisions of elementary particles with individual protons or with the one neutron in deuterons are much easier to interpret than events in heavier nuclei where interaction products can undergo secondary collisions.

The spark gaps are usually filled with a gas near normal pressure. Operation at higher gas pressures, and perhaps with liquids, is also possible if the origins of interactions are to be viewed or if very high accuracy for spark location is required. Most frequently used is a mixture of 90 per cent neon and 10 per cent helium which usually is continuously recirculated for purification. If every electron produces α additional electrons per centimeter of drift space, then an avalanche containing about 10^8 electrons can develop if a minimum drift space (or minimum gap width) $d = 20/\alpha$ cm is available. From this "Raether criterion" many operating features of a spark chamber can be predicted. α is the "first Townsend coefficient" which depends on the gas used and on the ratio E/p of applied electric field to gas pressure. For instance, for neon at atmospheric pressure and for a field of 10 kV/cm, $\alpha = 65$. Thus $d \geqslant 3$ mm. If the Raether condition is not met, sparks are not intense or are not formed at all. To obtain spark efficiencies near 100 per cent in a gap, the rise time, duration, and height of the voltage pulse must also be adjusted carefully, especially when many tracks are to be formed simultaneously.

The sensitive time in a spark chamber is defined by the maximum period between arrival of an event to be recorded and application of the voltage trigger pulse. It must be short enough to avoid recording of background events and can be decreased by application of a clearing field of 100 to 200 V/cm between pulses or by an admixture of, for instance, 1 per cent sulfur dioxide or alcohol to the gas filling. For multiplate chambers the sensitive time can be $\geqslant 1$ μsec. The number of events that can be recorded per unit time depends on the repetition time for the whole apparatus. If the sparks are photographed, this time is $\geqslant 0.1$ sec. TV vidicon cameras can be used, where the image focused on a photoconductive surface is scanned by an electron beam and the information stored on magnetic tape or fed directly into a digital computer. The Plumbicon operates similarly but with better space resolution. Repetition times $\geqslant 30$ msec can be expected. The space resolution or accuracy of 0.2 to 1 mm obtainable with a spark chamber is defined by the displacement between actual passage of a particle and resulting spark. An angle $<45°$ between direction of travel of the particle and electrode surface usually results in insufficient accuracy. Accuracy is also affected by time delay of high-voltage pulse, gas properties, Larmor precession in magnetic fields, etc.

Besides emitting light, sparks also emit sound the travel time of which can be recorded, as in acoustic chambers, and of course constitute electric currents used in wire spark chambers, where wires (often aluminum), $\geqslant 100$ μm in diameter and 1 to 2 mm apart, are stretched and fastened across plastic frames to form planes or cylinders. A spark between two wires in two planes produces a current which can be "read out," for instance, after letting it pass through a computer-type ferrite core at the end of every wire, or after causing a sound wave in a magnetostrictive cobalt-iron wire placed across all the ends of the wires in a plane, or after charging a capacitor, the latter being insensitive to magnetic fields. So far magnetostrictive read-out is the cheapest, requiring less electronic circuitry. For unambiguous determination of the location of two or more tracks, three sets of planes with wires at different angles are needed. Wire spark chambers probably are now the most widely used because they are relatively inexpensive, highly efficient, have repetition times $\geqslant 2$ msec, and supply digitized information on coordinates. Besides magnetic tape records, it is possible to put at least a fraction of the data pulses into a digital computer on line to the read-out system and display output data on an oscilloscope in the form of tables or histograms so that experiments can be continuously monitored.

In wide-gap chambers the electrodes are up to 60 cm apart so that under proper conditions, including a pulse of several hundred kilovolts, a long spark is produced which follows the path of a particle if inclined $>45°$ to the electrode surface. In a magnetic field the track becomes part of a circle.

In the streamer chamber the duration of the high-voltage pulse is kept so short that a spark cannot develop, but individual streamers, a few millimeters long, are formed from electron avalanches and are photographed end-on, parallel to the direction of the electric field, through wire electrodes. Vidicon viewing usually requires image intensification. Particles must travel at *small* angles to the electrode planes. The density of the streamers along a track is a measure for the velocity of a particle, which decreases with increasing ionization density.

In the newly developed multiwire proportional chambers, gas amplification proceeds only to the point of avalanche formation. Between planes of tungsten or other metal wires ($\geqslant 10$ μm diameter) a dc potential difference of a few thousand volts is maintained. The electric field is highest near the fine wires where an avalanche due to a free electron can form and produce a signal which must be amplified at the end of the wire before further transmission. For higher ionization densities, several avalanches form near a wire so that a proportionally stronger signal will be transmitted. Repetition time is about 1 μsec, several orders of magnitude faster than for other types of chambers. Since the high voltage is applied continuously and since they

respond in $\geqslant 2 \times 10^{-2}$ μsec, multiwire proportional chambers can be used to trigger other chambers. They are practically 100 per cent efficient for any number of particles and their read-out is not sensitive to magnetic fields.

At high-energy accelerators, experimental arrangements can involve many kinds of electronic detectors simultaneously. A "spectrometer facility" might make use of a large magnet to determine particle momenta from track curvatures. The magnet gap may contain a liquid-hydrogen target, surrounded and followed by spark chambers. Additional equipment can be mounted outside the magnet, forming "arms" of the spectrometer. Events produced in the target by a beam of particles are selected by coincidences in a trigger system, combining scintillators, Čerenkov counters, or multiwire proportional chambers, and very fast associated circuitry. The whole apparatus is monitored by an on-line computer and all data are stored on magnetic tape for further analysis. High-statistics experiments involving events with many secondary particles distributed over large solid angles are possible with this very powerful technique.

For comparison, the liquid in bubble chambers can act as a target so that the origins of events, as well as secondary events occurring nearby, are visible over a full 4π-solid angle. Excellent space resolution of 0.05 to 0.15 mm is provided, depending on the size of a chamber. However, sensitive times are $\geqslant 0.5$ msec, much longer than for spark chambers, and repetition times usually >50 msec, depending on size. Furthermore, bubble chambers cannot be triggered for selected events. For these reasons high-statistics experiments are not feasible. The spark and bubble chamber techniques have complemented each other very well, the discoveries with one technique often stimulating further research with the other. For example, neutrino interactions were first studied with spark chambers, but neutrino interactions in hydrogen and deuterium will be studied with the very large bubble chambers now nearing completion. On the other hand, many of the hundreds of strongly interacting particles were first discovered in bubble chambers and then their properties were further investigated in spark chamber experiments.

A bubble chamber consists of a pressure vessel filled with a liquid, kept at proper temperature and pressure, which becomes superheated when expanded by means of a piston or diaphragm. A low-energy electron (δ-ray), produced at this time by an atomic collision of a particle passing through the liquid, generates a number of ion pairs which upon recombination cause local heating, or a heat spike, so that a bubble can begin to grow. The heat spike would diffuse in < 1 μsec, which is insufficient to trigger the expansion system. The number of electrons, and therefore bubbles produced per unit length, again depends on the particle's velocity. After a time $\geqslant 0.3$ msec bubbles grow large enough to

be photographed. The liquid is then immediately compressed to reliquefy the bubbles. This produces some heat which must be carried off by conduction and convection through the liquid and exchanged at cooling surfaces. At least three glass or quartz windows are provided for complete stereoscopic viewing with camera lenses of high quality, to match the available space resolution. The available depth of the chamber must also be fully covered by the lenses, requiring small apertures and sensitive photographic film. While bubbles in heavy liquids can be dark-field illuminated at 90° to the viewing axis, cryogenic liquids have low indices of refraction and require dark- or bright-field illumination at small angles. Of particular interest is the wide application of a specially developed Scotchlite reflecting light within a narrow cone into the photographic lens located at the center of a ring-shaped light source. Usually, bubble chambers are mounted inside magnets providing fields as high as 40 kilogauss. Recently, very large magnets have employed superconducting niobium-titanium wires embedded in and stabilized by copper. Thus large amounts of electric power are saved, which will soon amortize the initial investment for required helium refrigerators operating at 4.2 K.

In heavy-liquid bubble chambers, mixtures of propane and freon are generally used, which due to their short radiation lengths are especially important for detection of gamma rays by conversion to electron pairs. They are operated near room temperature at pressures up to 20 atm and must be expanded by about 3 per cent requiring very powerful actuating systems for expansions. Studies of interactions in liquid hydrogen or deuterium avoid complications due to heavy nuclei, but require cryogenic techniques at operating temperatures between 25 and 30 K. Cryogenic bubble chambers are expensive and require careful safety precautions and relatively large operating staffs. They are expanded by $\leqslant 1$ per cent from pressures $\leqslant 8$ atm. Liquid neon or neon-hydrogen mixtures can also be used for gamma-ray detection. "Track-sensitive targets" are under development, consisting of transparent plastic containers filled with hydrogen or deuterium mounted in a bubble chamber filled with neon-hydrogen and expanded simultaneously with the chamber. A cryogenic bubble chamber requires multilayered aluminized plastic insulation in a vacuum chamber which may be shared with the magnet if it is superconducting. Cryogenic bubble chambers containing as much as 30 m^3 of liquid are under construction.

Also of interest are sonic chambers which are expanded >20 times per second by producing a standing sound wave between two plates in the liquid. Sonic chambers, as well as other rapid-cycled chambers are especially useful at rapid-pulsed linear accelerators, in contrast with synchrotrons where expanding a chamber two or three times during the less frequent accelerator pulse is usually sufficient.

Bubble chamber and spark chamber photographs store a large amount of data which must be extracted by first scanning the film for events that may satisfy the requirements of a particular experiment. For simple interactions computer-guided pattern recognition methods may be applied in conjunction with human intervention and interrogation, combining the scanning and subsequent measuring processes. More often the scanned film is transferred to measuring machines of varying complexity where positions of bubble or spark images are measured with commensurate accuracy. As an example, on a flying-spot digitizer, a light spot, 15 μm in diameter, scans a photograph in a few seconds. A bubble image causes a signal in a photomultiplier, which is compared with time pulses similarly produced by a grating scanned by a synchronized light spot, locating the image with respect to fiducial marks. Hundreds of events per hour can thus be measured with excellent precision. In the spiral reader a fine slit spirals over the photograph, again producing light signals. A flying-image digitizer finished in 1973 will scan many different portions of a photograph simultaneously so that thousands of events can be processed per hour. The processing of spark or bubble chamber data requires large amounts of computer time, on-line to scanning and measuring equipment and off-line for spatial reconstruction of events from the three or more stereoscopic views, for kinematic fitting and selection of probable events, and finally for interpretation of results.

R. P. SHUTT

References

Shutt, R. P., Ed., "Bubble and Spark Chambers," Vols. I and II, New York and London, Academic Press, 1967.
Allkofer, O. C., "Spark Chambers," Munich, Verlag Karl Thiemig KG, 1969.
Charpak, G., "Evolution of the Automatic Spark Chambers," *Ann. Rev. Nuclear Sci.*, **20** (1970).

Cross-references: ACCELERATORS, PARTICLE; NUCLEAR INSTRUMENTS; NUCLEAR RADIATION; NUCLEAR REACTIONS.

SPECTROSCOPY*

Spectroscopy is the branch of science in which the interaction of energy between electromagnetic radiation and matter is investigated. It is one of the few branches of science which yield directly, accurate information concerning the nature of substances in their own environment. It has been until recently practically the only experimental method for obtaining extraterrestrial information. Its importance as a major experimental method in physics, chemistry, and the biological sciences, can be demonstrated by the wide range of problems which can be solved with its techniques.

The broad field of spectroscopy can be subdivided in various ways, e.g., according to the energy (or frequency) range of the electromagnetic radiation studied or according to the nature of the transition involved. Several processes which result in absorption or emission of energy may occur within an atom or molecule, but fortunately each process is associated with a fairly definite frequency range, with very little overlap. Figure 1 is a schematic representation of the electromagnetic spectrum in which the various regions and the type of transitions which occur in each are indicated.

At very high energies or high frequencies, the transitions involve changes in the atomic nucleus and are independent of the environment of the nucleus. At slightly lower energy, inner shell electronic transitions occur. Irradiation of a sample with x-rays results in expulsion of electrons from the inner shells and then emission of x-rays as the electrons return to their normal states (x-ray fluorescence). The frequency of the x-rays emitted is independent of the state of chemical binding and depends only on the atom.

Irradiation with still lower-energy photons results in electronic transitions in the valence shell. The frequency of the radiation emitted when outer-shell electrons, which have been excited either thermally or by electric arc, return to their ground states depends on the element involved and is usually independent of chemical state. The x-ray fluorescence mentioned above and the emission spectra in the ultraviolet and visible regions are very useful in identification of elements present in a sample. Atomic emission spectra are also useful in determination of electronic energy levels in atoms and in determination of composition and other properties of stars, planets and comets.

With the exceptions of flame spectroscopy and the emission from upper atmospheres, molecules are not usually sufficiently stable at the high temperatures required for thermal excitation of outer-shell electrons and, therefore, do not emit radiation in far ultraviolet, ultraviolet and visible regions. However, molecules do *absorb* radiation in the far ultraviolet, ultraviolet, and occasionally in the visible regions, as a result of the excitation of outer shell electrons. The absorption spectra in these regions are useful in studying the electronic states of small or unsaturated molecules and in the analysis of unsaturated organic compounds and inorganic complex ions. The energy absorbed by the molecules is usually rapidly converted to vibrational, rotational, or translational energy, but occasionally emission occurs (fluorescence and phosphorescence).

In the infrared region, changes in vibrational

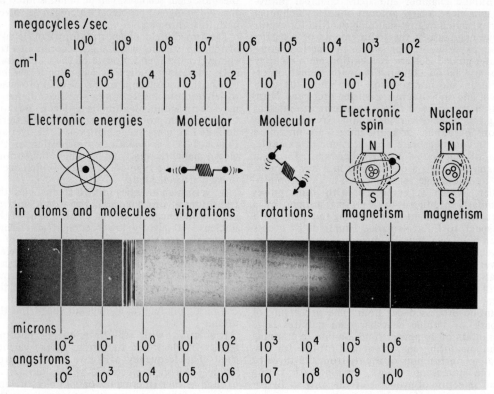

FIG. 1. Schematic representation of the electromagnetic spectrum in which the spectral regions and types of transitions are shown.

spectra. (Vibrational emission spectra have only recently begun to be studied in detail.) At still lower frequencies, in the far infrared and microwave regions, pure rotational transitions are observed.

Radiation in the microwave and radiofrequency ranges is used for studying the very low-energy transitions which result from reorientations of nuclear and electron spins in an applied magnetic field, i.e., for nuclear and electron magnetic resonance studies.

The occurrence of an energy change depends on the ability of the molecule or atom to interact with the electromagnetic radiation. In general, energy is absorbed only if the energy of the incident radiation is precisely the same as the amount required for the transition to take place.

Certain other criteria must also be satisfied. For example, the criterion for the absorption or emission of vibrational energy by a molecule in the infrared region is that a change in the electric dipole moment of the vibrating species must occur during the vibration. That is, not only must the energy of the incident radiation equal the energy of the vibration, but also the vibration must produce a temporary displacement of the electrical center of gravity. For a pure rotational energy change, the molecule

must possess a permanent electric dipole moment. Nor do transitions take place between all different energy levels. The number of transitions allowed is limited by selection rules which can be justified theoretically on the basis of the limitations which must be introduced in order to obtain acceptable solutions for the wave equations. For example, pure rotational energy changes are limited to transitions between adjacent levels. The selection rules are occasionally defied, but the intensity of such a forbidden transition is usually low. Selection rules for linear molecules are fairly simple, but as the symmetry of the molecule decreases, the complexity of the selection rules increases.

Raman spectroscopy is an important exception to the rule that incident photons must possess exactly the correct amount of energy for the transition to occur. Under certain circumstances, frequencies in the visible or ultraviolet regions may be partially absorbed and cause the molecule to vibrate or rotate. The photon is then re-emitted with a new frequency, the Raman line, which is lower than the original and equal to the difference between the incident frequency and the vibrational frequency (see RAMAN EFFECT AND RAMAN SPECTROSCOPY).

The term "spectroscopy" has also been applied

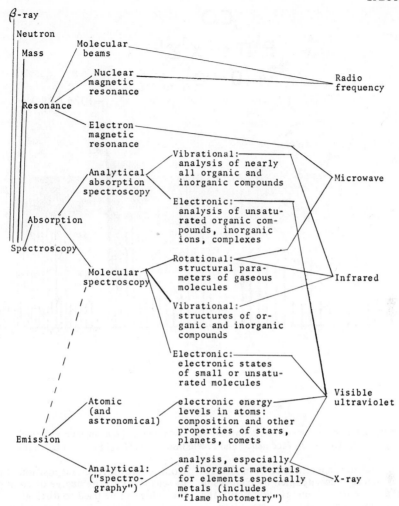

FIG. 2. Fields of spectroscopy (reproduced with permission from R. Bauman, "Absorption Spectroscopy," New York, John Wiley & Sons, 1962).

to some fields which do not involve electromagnetic radiation, but which use techniques similar to those of spectroscopy to separate a beam of particles according to their energy or other property. In β-ray spectroscopy, the energies of electrons emitted from nuclei are studied. In mass spectroscopy, charged particles are separated as a function of ratio of charge to mass. Figure 2 gives a summary of the fields of spectroscopy.

In order to indicate the broad scope of spectroscopy, some of the types of information which can be obtained and the experimental methods used to obtain them will be indicated. Studies in the ultraviolet, visible, infrared, microwave and radio-frequency regions have all found use in qualitative and quantitative analysis and in the determination of the geometry of simple molecules.

ATOMIC SPECTRA, which historically contributed extensively to the development of the theory of the structure of the atom and led to the discovery of the electron and nuclear spin, provide a method of measuring ionization potentials, a method for rapid and very sensitive qualitative analysis, a method for quantitative spectrochemical analysis, and data for the determination of the dissociation energy of a diatomic molecule. Information about the type of coupling of electron spin and orbital momenta in the atom can be obtained from the spectra obtained with an applied magnetic field. Other applications include the use of atomic spectra to obtain information about certain regions of interstellar space from the microwave frequency emission by hydrogen and the use of atomic spectra to examine discharges in thermonuclear reactions.

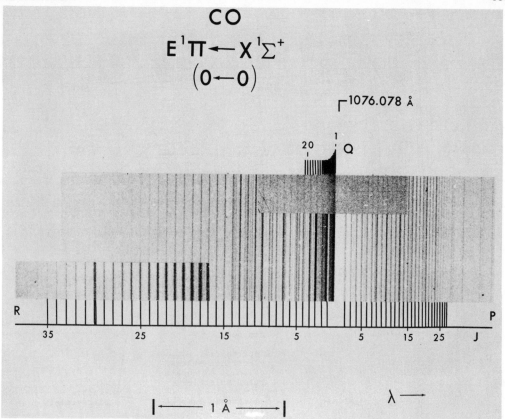

FIG. 3. High-resolution vacuum-ultraviolet absorption spectrum of the E singlet $\pi \leftarrow$ X singlet Σ^+ transition in CO. (Courtesy of S. G. Tilford, J. Vanderslice, and P. Wilkinson, U.S. Naval Research Laboratories).

Molecular electronic spectra arise from changes in electronic energy accompanied by changes in vibrational and rotational energy. Were only the electronic energy changed during a transition, as in atomic spectra, a single line would be observed. Instead, for each electronic transition a system of bands is observed, each of which is composed of a group of lines. These lines result from the changes in rotational energy in each pair of the vibrational energy levels associated with the upper and lower electronic states (see Fig. 3) and MOLECULAR SPECTROSCOPY).

Data obtained from vibrational analysis of band systems of diatomic molecules and radicals can be used to determine the anharmonicity of the vibrational motion, approximate values for the dissociation energy of the species studied, and force constants of the upper and lower electronic states, to calculate the value of α in the Morse equation, and to assist in the statistical calculation of thermodynamic functions. Measurement of the relative intensities of adjacent rotational lines in a band of an electronic transition can lead to the determination of the nuclear spin quantum number.

Electronic transitions in polyatomic molecules have been classified according to the type of orbital occupied in the upper and lower elec-

tronic energy levels. The position of the band and its sensitivity to the degree of conjugation in the molecule can be used to distinguish between the possible types of transition and hence to elucidate the nature of the bonding involved. Knowledge of the effects of conjugation and substitution on electronic spectra of organic molecules leads to the use of electronic spectra in identification of characteristic groups. Study of electronic absorption spectra is valuable not only in qualitative and quantitative analysis, but also in the investigation of steric hindrance, isomerism, and intermolecular interactions such as charge-transfer phenomena.

In the infrared region, considerable work has centered on associating a particular frequency with a characteristic group or structural unit for application in qualitative analysis. Internuclear distances, bond angles, spectral moments of inertia, and force constants are some of the more fundamental quantities which can be determined by infrared and Raman spectroscopy. These methods have also been useful in statistical calculation of thermodynamic quantities, such as entropy and heat capacity. They have proved very valuable in quantitative analysis, especially in cases for which chemical analysis is difficult or inapplicable. Figure 4 shows the changes in

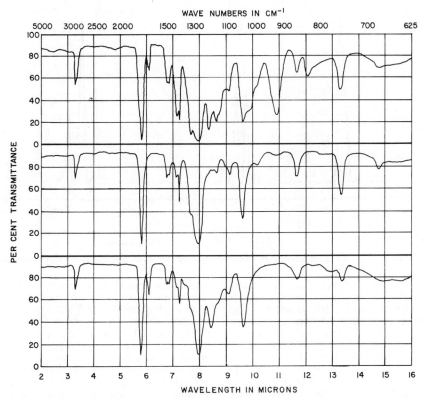

FIG. 4. The infrared spectra of successive distillation fractions of a mixture of the ethyl esters of maleic and fumaric acids.

the infrared spectrum of a mixture of ethyl esters of maleic and fumaric acids on fractional distillation. The Raman spectrum of allene showing rotational structure is given in Fig. 5.

Spectroscopy in the microwave region includes

the study of pure rotational changes and electron spin resonance phenomena. In addition to its qualitative and quantitative applications, micro-wave spectroscopy provides probably the most accurate method of determining internuclear

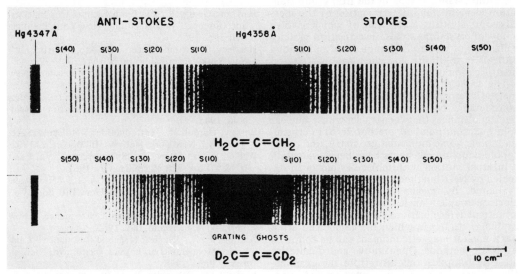

FIG. 5. The Raman spectrum of allene showing rotational structure.

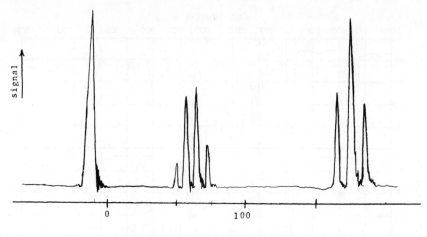

FIG. 6. High-resolution NMR spectrum of ethyl alcohol showing spin-spin splitting of the three resonance lines.

distances of linear, symmetric top and simple asymmetric top molecules and bond angles for the last two types of molecules. (In some of these determinations, the use of isotopes is necessary.) It provides a method of evaluating the quadrupole coupling constant and gives values of electric dipole moments with accuracy equal to or better than that obtained by the best of the dielectric constant methods. Microwave studies have also been made on the potential energy barriers opposing rotation in liquid and solid samples (see MICROWAVE SPECTROSCOPY).

The microwave region is almost always chosen for electron spin resonance studies, but some work has been done at radio frequencies. Some of the principal applications of the electron spin resonance technique are the determination of nuclear spin quantum numbers, elucidation of electronic states of ions in the iron group transition elements, and determination of the spectroscopic splitting factor (all of which involve study of crystalline solids, investigation of delocalization of electrons in molecules and among radicals in solution), and chemical analysis and identification of unstable free radicals.

The variety of problems for which nuclear magnetic resonance spectroscopy is applicable is considerable. Nuclear magnetic moments, internuclear distances (between nuclei whose nuclear spin quantum numbers are not zero) in crystalline solids, some molecular geometry, and quadropole coupling constants have been evaluated.

Internal motion with molecules has been detected by NMR methods and the energy barriers evaluated. By means of chemical shifts and electron-coupled nuclear spin-spin interaction, structural determinations can be made. Chemical exchange studies in which the exchanged atom has a nuclear magnetic moment can be followed by NMR methods. Quantitative and qualitative analytical applications arise from the examination of the number, spacing, position and inten-

sity of the lines in the spectrum. Figure 6 shows the spin-spin splitting of the three resonance lines in a high-resolution NMR spectrum of ethyl alcohol.

The unusual power of spectroscopic methods in scientific research is perhaps best emphasized by the diversity of their application in other fields—from measurement of intermolecular interaction forces, observation and study of properties of unstable species which cannot be captured, determination of temperatures and composition of astronomical bodies, to study of microorganisms.

ELLIS R. LIPPINCOTT
LINDA S. WHATLEY

References

Harrison, George R., and Lord, Richard C., "Practical Spectroscopy," Second edition, New York, Prentice-Hall, Inc., 1965.

Herzberg, G., "Atomic Spectra and Atomic Structure," New York, Dover Publications, 1944.

Herzberg, G., "Spectra of Diatomic Molecules," New York, Van Nostrand Reinhold, 1950.

Herzberg, G., "Infrared and Raman Spectra of Polyatomic Molecules," New York, Van Nostrand Reinhold, 1945.

Barrow, Gordon M., "Introduction to Molecular Spectroscopy," New York, McGraw-Hill Book Co., 1962.

Walker, S., and Straw, H., "Spectroscopy," Vol I and II, New York, The Macmillan Co., 1962.

Townes, C. H., and Schawlow, A. L., "Microwave Spectroscopy," New York, McGraw-Hill Book Co., 1955.

Pake, George E., "Paramagnetic Resonance," New York, W. A. Benjamin, Inc., 1962.

Andrew, E. R., "Nuclear Magnetic Resonance," Cambridge Monographs on Physics, Cambridge, The University Press, 1958.

Pople, J. A., Schneider, W. G., and Bernstein, H. J.,

"High Resolution Nuclear Magnetic Resonance," New York, McGraw-Hill Book Co., 1959.

Clark, George L., Ed., "Encyclopedia of Spectroscopy," New York, Van Nostrand Reinhold, 1960.

Rao, C. N. R., "Ultraviolet and Visible Spectroscopy," London, Butterworths, 1961.

Cross-references: ABSORPTION SPECTRA; ATOMIC SPECTRA; ELECTRON SPIN; ENERGY LEVELS; LIGHT; MASS SPECTROMETRY; MICROWAVE SPECTROSCOPY; MOLECULAR SPECTROSCOPY; RAMAN EFFECT AND RAMAN SPECTROSCOPY.

SPIN WAVES (MAGNONS)

General Properties In magnetically ordered solids such as ferromagnets, antiferromagnets, and ferrimagnets, the spins of the magnetic ions are oriented along certain preferred directions. Coherent deviations of the spins from their preferred direction which propagate in space and time with wave-like characteristics are called spin waves. They were first studied by F. Block in 1930.[1] Spin waves are similar to lattice waves in solids. The departure of the spin vector from its preferred direction is analogous to the atomic displacement of a lattice vibration. The spins of a ferromagnetic insulator, for example, may be pictured classically as precessing about the direction of magnetization as illustrated in Fig. 1. The

FIG. 1. In the top of the figure the spins are illustrated in perspective. The bottom shows the circular precession of each spin with the wave-like motion drawn through the ends of the spin vectors.

radius of the precessional circle is proportional to the amplitude of excitation of the spin wave and the phase on the precessional circle varies in a wave-like manner. Spin waves are characterized by a propagation vector k and a frequency vs wave-vector dispersion law $\nu(k)$. According to quantum theory, spin waves are elementary (Bose) excitations called magnons which possess linear momentum $\hbar k$, a quantum of energy $h\nu(k)$, and one $(\hbar)$ unit of spin angular momentum. At low temperatures the magnetic contribution to thermodynamic quantities such as internal energy, specific heat, magnetization, and thermal conductivity is determined by the number and energy of thermally excited magnons. Spin waves have been observed and studied by a variety of experimental techniques. Some of the important physical phenomena associated with spin-wave excitations are presented in Table 1.

Microscopic Theory of Spin Waves Magnetic ordering in solids is a consequence of the Pauli exclusion principle, which leads to a dependence of the coulomb energy on the spin directions of the electrons comprising a quantum-mechanical system. The energy associated with this effect is called the exchange energy, and it may be represented by an exchange Hamiltonian[9]

$$\mathcal{H} = -\frac{1}{2} \sum_{\ell \neq m} J(\ell, m)\, S_\ell \cdot S_m, \qquad (1)$$

where S_ℓ is the spin operator of a magnetic ion located at the lattice position R_ℓ. The exchange integrals $J(\ell, m)$ depend on $R_\ell - R_p$ but are nonnegligible only for $|R_\ell - R_p|$ less than a few atomic lattice spacings. For a ferromagnet the J's are predominantly positive so that the minimum exchange energy results for a ground state $|\psi_g\rangle$ in which all spins are parallel. For the antiferromagnet or ferrimagnet the J's are predominantly negative leading to minimum energy for approximately antiparallel (or complex) spin arrangements in the ground state. The low-lying excited states $|\psi_k\rangle$ of the exchange Hamiltonian are spin waves which correspond to a uniform probability of finding one quantum of spin disorder in the system. For a ferromagnet the magnon state is

$$|\psi_k\rangle = \frac{1}{\sqrt{N}} \sum_\ell e^{ik \cdot R_\ell}\, S_\ell^- |\psi_g\rangle \qquad (2)$$

where S_ℓ^- is the operator which lowers the spin at R_ℓ by one unit. These states are solutions of the exchange Hamiltonian only when the number of spin waves in the system is small. Neglect of magnon-magnon interactions is referred to as the spin-wave approximation. This approximation is valid at low temperatures where the energy of the system associated with the magnons is

$$\mathcal{E} = \sum_k \bar{n}_k\, h\nu(k) \qquad (3)$$

with $\bar{n}_k$ the number of thermally excited magnons. The quantity $\bar{n}_k$ is given by the Bose distribution function. The fractional decrease ΔM in the saturation magnetization M with increasing temperature is given by $\Delta M/M \propto \sum_k n_k$ which is proportional to $T^{3/2}$ for magnons whose dispersion law is of the form $h\nu(k) \propto k^2$ for small k. For a simple cubic ferromagnet with only nearest-neighbor exchange integrals the dispersion law is of the form

$$h\nu(k) \propto JM(T)(3 - \cos k_x a - \cos k_y a - \cos k_z a) \qquad (4)$$

where k_α are the cartesian components of the wave vector, a is the lattice spacing, and $M(T)$ is the temperature-dependent saturation magneti-

TABLE 1. MAGNON-PARTICLE INTERACTIONS

Particles	Effect	Source of Interaction	Information	References
Neutron	Neutron inelastic scattering	Dipole-dipole	Magnon dispersion and relaxation, critical behavior of the magnetization	2 3
Electron	Electron-magnon interaction	Exchange interaction	Thermodynamic transport and optical properties in magnetic semiconductors	4
Photon	Raman scattering Infrared absorption Magnon sidebands	Spin-orbit interaction Symmetry-breaking interactions	Magnon dispersion and relaxation	5 6 7
Phonon	Magnon-phonon interactions Magnetostatic waves	Dependence of exchange on lattice position	Magnetoelastic dispersion law, parametric processes	8
Magnon	Magnon-magnon interactions	Nonlinearity of the spin Hamiltonian	Magnon-lifetime Parametric processes	8

zation. The low-temperature specific heat is also proportional to $T^{3/2}$.

The exchange Hamiltonian described above applies to magnetic insulators in which the magnetic electrons are localized at lattice sites. An appropriate quantum-mechanical Hamiltonian for magnetic metals in which the magnetic electrons are itinerant can be defined. Long-wavelength spin waves in metallic systems have essentially the same qualitative features as those of insulating magnets with localized electrons. Short-wavelength magnons in metals, however, have a short lifetime due to decay into electron-hole pairs called Stoner excitations.[10]

Antiferromagnets In a simple two-sublattice antiferromagnet the spins on one sublattice are oriented opposite to those of the other sublattice so that the net magnetization of the solid vanishes. Two degenerate spin-wave branches occur for such systems. The spin waves of either branch involve excitations of the spins of both sublattices but in different proportions. The degeneracy of the two spin-wave branches is removed by an external magnetic field. The frequency of one branch is raised while that of the other is lowered. At a critical magnetic field called the spin-flop field, the frequency of the lower branch vanishes. For external fields in excess of the spin-flop field the spin system is unstable and the spins reorient approximately perpendicular to the external field. Long-wavelength spin waves can be excited by electromagnetic radiation with a frequency equal to the spin-wave frequency. This phenomenon is called antiferromagnetic resonance (AFMR) and ferromagnetic resonance[8] (FMR) in antiferromagnets and ferromagnets, respectively.

Special Types of Spin Waves In real crystals effects of impurities and surfaces lead to spin-wave oscillations having local properties. These localized excited states of the spin system are called localized magnons[11] (the amplitude of the spin deviation is localized near an impurity atom), and surface magnons (the excitation is localized near the surface of a magnetic solid but propagates parallel to the surface[12]).

Phenomenological Theory In a complete description of the magnetic system there exists, in addition to the exchange interaction, contributions which are relativistic in origin (dipole-dipole, spin-orbit). These interactions are weak but long range, and they are important in kinetic and relaxation processes, and microwave absorption at low frequencies.

Long-range interactions are most frequently treated by using a phenomenological theory of spin waves.[8] In this treatment spin waves are introduced as wave oscillations of the magnetic moment around the equilibrium value $\mathbf{M}(\mathbf{r})$. In this description the properties of the ferromagnet are described by Maxwell's equations and the equation of motion for the magnetization. Among the predictions of this model are magnetostatic modes of oscillations (magnetic modes principally characterized by the dipolar energy) and standing spin waves (dominated by the exchange contribution).[8] These long-wavelength modes have been studied by ferromagnetic resonance techniques. Ferromagnetic resonance of the $k = 0$ (homogeneous resonance) was first investigated by Griffiths[13] and is an important method for characterizing magnetic materials. The exchange interaction can be determined from measurements of the standing spin wave frequencies.[14]

R. E. De Wames
T. Wolfram

References

1. Block, F., *Z. Physik*, **61**, 206 (1930).
2. Sinclair, R. N., and Brockhouse, B. N., *Phys. Rev.*, **120**, 1638 (1960).

3. Marshall, W., "Critical Phenomena," Proceedings of a conference held in Washington, D.C., April 1965; Edited by M. S. Green and J. V. Sengers, National Bureau of Standards, Miscellaneous Publication 273.
4. Hass, C., *CRC*, **VI**, Issue 1, p. 47 (March 1970).
5. Fleury, P. A., Porto, S. P., Chiesman, L. E., and Guggenheim, H. J., *Phys. Rev. Letters*, **17**, 84 (1966).
6. Halley, J. Woods, and Silvera, I., *Phys. Rev. Letters*, **15**, 654 (1965).
7. Green, R. L., Sell, D. D., Yen, W. M., Schawlow, A. L., and White, R. M., *Phys. Rev. Letters*, **15**, 656 (1965).
8. Akheizer, A. I., Bar'Yakhtar, V. G., and Peletminskii, S. V., "Spin-Waves," Amsterdam, North-Holland Publishing Co., 1968.
9. Heisenberg, W., *Z. Physik*, **49**, 619 (1928).
10. Izuyama, T., Kim, D. J., and Kubo, R., *J. Phys. Soc. Japan*, **18**, 1025 (1963).
11. Wolfram, T., and Callaway, *Phys. Rev.*, **130**, 2207 (1963).
12. De Wames, R. E., and Wolfram, T., *Phys. Rev.*, **185**, 720 (1969).
13. Griffiths, J., *Nature*, **158**, 670 (1947).
14. Seavey, M., and Tannenwald, P., *Phys. Rev. Letters*, **1**, 168 (1958).

Cross-references: ANTIFERROMAGNETISM, FERRIMAGNETISM, FERROMAGNETISM, MAGNETISM.

STATES OF MATTER

In writing about the "states of matter" it would seem reasonable to begin by deciding what is meant by "matter" and by "state." Let, then, a short space be devoted to those questions.

As for "matter" consider it this way. Consider a brazen sphere, cube, and pyramid. What have they in common? They are brazen, or "of bronze." Now let the sphere be brazen, the cube golden, the pyramid of iron. What have they now in common? They are all metallic, or "of metal." Now let the sphere be brazen, the cube wooden, and the pyramid of earthenware. What have they in common? They are all solid, or "of solid stuff." Finally, let the sphere be brazen, the cube water, the pyramid outlined with smoke in the air. What have they in common? They are all material, or "of matter." So matter is that which is common to all material objects, but is not involved with immaterial things—the binomial theorem, for instance, or the right-angled isosceles triangle is not, as an abstract idea, material. This argument shows us, moreover, that we never have any experience of matter in the abstract. It is always "this ingot of iron," "that block of stone," "the pile of clay over there." However, just as, while we never see "man" but always John Jones or Sam Smith or some such individual, it is convenient to talk about the abstraction "man"; even so, the abstraction "matter" can be a convenient one.

As for "states," suppose we think this way. What is it that, above all else, distinguishes material objects? Is it not that they are tangible? For, on the one hand, a rainbow is visible, but we should not call it "material"; on the other hand, if we had something invisible, but which we could feel, we should declare it to be "material." So tangibility, it would seem, is the criterion. Now as to tangibility we might divide objects into: (a) unyielding, (b) yielding but quite tangible, and (c) hardly tangible. And these three classes, of course, we call solid, liquid, and vapour or gas: the three states of matter in which we are interested. This argument shows why we distinguish matter primarily into these classes, and not, for instance, according to color. It is because it is above all else tangibility in which we are interested.

It is true, of course, that the division into three classes will leave some doubtful cases at the borders, just as does the division of living things into animal and vegetable. And we can always deal with a thing according to the aspect which predominates in the circumstances in which we are interested, so that we might think of pitch, say, as a solid at one time, a liquid at another.

Gases A gas, of course, must be kept in some container, and it tends to expand the container, unless prevented from outside. We say that it exerts pressure; for instance, the pressure of air near sea level is about 14.7 psi, or just over 1×10^6 dynes/cm^2. It is found that the pressure of a given amount (by weight) of a gas in a container depends on the volume of the container, and on the temperature. The relation may be a very complicated one, but at sufficiently low pressure and sufficiently high temperatures, it is approximately true for all gases that

$$\frac{PV}{T} = \text{Constant}$$

P represents the pressure of the gas, V the volume and T the temperature measured from absolute zero, which is at $-273°C$ or $-460°F$, approximately. This kind of equation is called an equation of state, and this particular one is the law of ideal gases, and it is said that a gas behaving thus is an ideal gas. Actually, of course, there is no such thing as an ideal gas, but any gas under suitable conditions will behave nearly ideally.

Liquids It is sometimes said that there is no simple equation for liquids corresponding to the ideal law for gases. However, it is close to the truth, under many circumstances, to write

$$V = \text{Constant}$$

i.e., the volume of the liquid is constant independently of pressure and temperature. In fact, this is not true; the liquid is compressed a little by pressure, and the volume usually increases a little with increasing temperature. Nevertheless, this simple law is probably as close to the truth

as is the law of ideal gases in many of the circumstances in which it is used.

Solids Likewise a simple law can be given for solids, i.e.,

$$L = \text{Constant}$$

L being the length of the line joining any two points in the solid. That is to say, not only does the volume not change, but neither is the solid distorted by any action on it. Again, this is only an approximation to the truth, and probably about as valid.

Changes of State We often tend to think of a given kind of stuff as being in a particular state; for instance we think of water as liquid, iron as solid, and air as gas. However we know that almost anything may exist in any of the states; water, for instance may be liquid, solid, or vapor. The ways in which things change from one state into another can be very interesting. (In books on THERMODYNAMICS, it may be mentioned here, in which these things are discussed in great detail, the word "phase" is often used instead of "state" as used here.) In general, the division between the different states depends on the pressure and temperature of the sample. Increasing the temperature makes the material go to a "looser" state; e.g., if ice is heated somewhat, it melts, and if the water is heated more, it evaporates. Increasing the pressure tends to squeeze the material into a "denser" state, either liquid or solid according to circumstances.

The way in which the state of a given material, say water, varies with pressure and temperature can be shown well in a graph such as that in Fig. 1. Every point on the graph will represent a

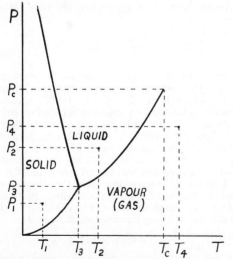

P
P_c
P_4
P_2
SOLID
LIQUID
P_3
P_1
VAPOUR
(GAS)
T_1 T_3 T_2 T_c T_4 T

FIG. 1. Phase diagram: plot of pressure vs temperature for a typical material.

certain combination of pressure and temperature, in the way of analytic geometry. The graph is divided into regions marked "solid," "liquid" and "vapor." At temperatures and pressures

such as T_1 and P_1, which give a point in the region marked "solid," the material is solid. Likewise at temperatures and pressures such as T_2 and P_2, giving a point in the "liquid" region, the material is liquid. And at temperatures and pressures such as T_4 and P_4, it is a vapor. Thus, this graph indicates the whole behavior of the material with respect to temperature and pressure. Note that the line dividing the "liquid" from the "vapor" region just ends at a point at temperature T_c and pressure P_c. These are called the "critical point," and the "critical temperature" and "critical pressure", respectively. At temperatures higher than critical, there is no distinction between liquid and vapor. For water, the critical temperature is $374°C$; critical pressure, 219 atmospheres.

It can be seen that three parts of the curve meet as it were, at the point given by T_3 and P_3. This point is called the "triple point." For water, the triple point is at about $0.01°C$ and 4.6 mm of mercury. Note that if you warm a solid at pressures lower than the pressure at the triple point, it will change to vapor without first melting to a liquid at all. Such "dry evaporation" is called "sublimation." For carbon dioxide, for instance, the pressure at the triple point is about 5.1 times atmospheric. Thus, solid carbon dioxide, i.e., "dry ice," when allowed to warm up at atmospheric pressure, sublimes directly into vapor, as is well known. A process the reverse of sublimation happens when frost forms on cold objects without any intervening stage of liquid.

Vapor Pressure In Fig. 1, along the curve joining the triple point and critical point, the "liquid" and "vapor" regions meet; i.e., liquid and vapor can exist together. Note, however, that at a given temperature, they exist together only at a certain pressure. This pressure is called the vapor pressure of the liquid at the temperature concerned.

An analogous thing could be said about liquid and solid, or solid and vapor, along the appropriate curves.

Vapor Pressure and Relative Humidity In a certain volume, say one cubic foot, of air, there is, along with the air, ordinarily a small amount of water vapor. Suppose that this same amount of water vapor were put into a vessel of the same volume, i.e., one cubic foot, which contained nothing else at all. There would be a small pressure, perhaps about 1/50 of atmospheric pressure. This pressure is called the partial pressure of the water vapor.

The ratio of the partial pressure of water vapor in the air to the vapor pressure of water at the temperature of the air is called the relative humidity. (There is a bit of approximation here, because water vapor is not really an ideal gas.) For instance, at $70°F$ or $21°C$, the vapor pressure of water is about 20 mm of mercury. (Standard atmospheric pressure is 760 mm of mercury.) If the actual partial pressure of water vapor were 10 mm the relative humidity would be 0.5 or 50 per cent.

Changes of Volume and Shape of Liquids and Solids The "equations of state" proposed above for liquids and solids are really too drastic; they ordinarily expand when heated. Typically, the volume of a liquid increases by 0.05 per cent for each degree Fahrenheit increase in temperature. (About 0.09 per cent for each degree C.) (Water may be anomalous in this, as well as other, respects.) They are compressed by the application of pressure; typically, the volume is decreased by 0.01 per cent for each atmosphere of pressure.

Solids are generally compressed only about 1/50 as much as liquids by the same pressure. It is more interesting to know how much force is needed to stretch a bar of solid material. For steel, it takes about 30 000 pounds force for each square inch of cross section of the bar to stretch it by 0.1 per cent. (About 2×10^9 dynes for a bar of cross section 1 cm^2.) For other solids, the force needed is mostly less, typically one-third to one-tenth of that.

The Surface of Liquids A liquid, if it does not fill the container entirely, has an exposed surface. If an attempt is made to stretch the surface, for instance by withdrawing a horizontal piece of wire from the liquid, the surface acts as if it were an elastic sheet. The force necessary to stretch a unit length of surface is called the SURFACE TENSION. For instance, the surface tension of pure water around room temperature is about 72 dynes/cm. The addition of impurities, e.g., soap to water, reduces the surface tension greatly. The rising of liquids in fine tubes or in porous materials is connected with surface tension.

Molecular Theory of the States of Matter The molecular theory considers all matter to be built up of molecules in some arrangement (or lack thereof!), each molecule, in turn, consisting of one or more atoms. The molecules attract one another with forces of electrical origin, and thus may stick together. However, they are also in motion or at least vibration, and this tends to make them break apart. The motion increases with increasing temperature, hence the structure "loosens." In a gas, around atmospheric pressure and room temperature, the molecules are about 3×10^{-7} cm apart; the forces between them are very small and they move almost freely and randomly. In so doing, they bombard the walls of the vessel; the effect of this bombardment is the pressure.

In a liquid or solid, the molecules are typically only about one-tenth as far apart. The forces then hold the molecules together; their motion is reduced to a vibration which never gets them far from one place. Occasionally, one molecule gets an extra hard push and flies away; this is evaporation or sublimation. According to the nature of the molecules, they may pile together as would a heap of spheres, or they may stick together in chains or other arrangements.

In a liquid the distance between molecules is about the same as in a solid. The different behavior may be because of a few "holes" in the liquid, i.e., places, a few per cent in all, where a molecule is missing. These spaces allow the liquid to flow, just as on a checker board when a few of the men are missing, the whole pattern can be moved by shifting men into and out of the holes. Of course this takes time, and it shows up in the viscosity or "slowness" of liquids. Molasses, for instance, is very viscous, water not very.

Various Kinds of Solids In solids as was mentioned above, the molecules may be packed, arranged in chains, etc. Corresponding to these are the classes: metals, polymers, etc. Sometimes these are all spoken of as different states of matter, but from the present viewpoint it seems better to call them special kinds of solid.

H. L. ARMSTRONG

References

General

Slater, J. C., "Introduction to Chemical Physics," New York, McGraw-Hill Book Co., 1939.

On the Forces which Hold Matter Together

Moelwyn-Hughes, A. E., "States of Matter," London, Oliver and Boyd, 1961.

On Thermodynamics

Pippard, A., "Elements of Classical Thermodynamics," Cambridge, Cambridge University Press, 1957.

Porter, A. W., "Thermodynamics," London, Methuen, and New York, John Wiley & Sons, 1951.

Cross-references: COMPRESSIBILITY, GAS; CONDENSATION; GAS LAWS; KINETIC THEORY; LIQUID STATE; PHASE RULE; SOLID-STATE PHYSICS; VAPOR PRESSURE AND EVAPORATION.

STATIC ELECTRICITY

Until it was accepted that galvanic currents are identical with moving electric charges, *static electricity* referred to all electric charges that were stationary or nearly so, including such charges as those on Leyden jars and pyroelectric crystals. Nowadays the meaning encompasses only the more or less immobilized electrification due to (1) charge redistributed on a single body through *induction* caused by the presence of charge on neighboring bodies; (2) charge transferred from one material (solid or liquid) to another by *contact* and subsequent separation; (3) charge accumulated on a body (solid or liquid) by *deposition* of electrons or ions from the surrounding atmosphere, as in charging by corona, flame, or radiation. One generally excludes separation and redistribution of charge in pyroelectrics, piezoelectrics, thermoelectrets, photoelectrets, capacitors, and electrolytic cells.

In scientific and technical work, it is often important to control static electricity, either to exploit its effects or to avoid them. For convenience we divide the problem into *generation* of charge and *dissipation* of charge. So far as

generation is concerned, *induced electrification* is largely understandable in terms of classical physics; the fundamentals are well understood, and the applications are straightforwardly made as part of electrical engineering and safety engineering (see ELECTRICITY). *Contact electrification*, on the other hand, is far from being understood, and immediately comes to frontier problems in the modern theory of liquids and solids. *Deposition electrification* [from a gaseous ion cloud] is in an intermediate position. The fundamental processes of electrical discharge in gases are understood in principle, but real situations are so complex that theory is of limited use. As far as dissipation is concerned, the origin of the charge is largely irrelevant; a wide variety of physical and chemical processes of all degrees of complexity enter in analyzing the decay or neutralization of static charge.

Generation *Induction Charging.* Induction phenomena, as mentioned, are adequately described as a branch of classical electrostatics. Hence we devote the main part of our discussion here to the more poorly understood topic of contact phenomena, plus a brief overview of deposition from corona discharges or other ion clouds.

Contact Charging. When two materials differing at their surfaces in chemical composition, or even temperature or state of strain, are placed in contact, charge tends to flow from one to the other until their electrochemical potentials are identical. If the materials are subsequently separated, some portion of the transferred charge is retained, the potential difference between the materials increasing as the capacitance decreases. As a rule, this net transfer produces no noteworthy effects; in fact, a sensitive electrometer is ordinarily needed to measure it. With metal-metal contacts, the charge retained is invariably very small and is not detected by the senses. With metal-insulator or insulator-insulator contacts, the charge transferred while the materials remain in contact may be large, but it decreases during separation to an unimportant amount unless the insulator has quite high resistivity. At the speeds encountered in ordinary events, say about 100 cm/sec, the charge leaks back too fast to give noticeable effects whenever the resistivity of the more poorly conducting material falls below about 10^9 ohm-cm. At higher speeds, static effects become noticeable even at low resistivity, whereas at lower speeds they appear at very high resistivity.

The combination of moderate or high speed and high resistivity frequently produces large enough charge transfer that the surrounding medium breaks down electrically. In air at atmospheric pressure, the requisite charge densities on a uniformly charged plane conducting surface are about 8 esu (statcoulombs/cm^2) or 25 $\mu C/m^2$, to give a field of about 30 kV/cm just above the surface. This density represents about 2×10^{10} electronic charges per square centimeter, so that only one in perhaps 10^5

surface atoms is charged even at the highest electrifications ordinarily occurring.

For practical purposes, the phenomena of interest in static electrification are the forces of attraction or repulsion resulting from excess charge (e.g., in textile processing, ore separating, and electrostatic copying), the occurrence of sparks and their consequences (e.g., in transfer of flammable liquids, or in processing of photographic films), and so on. From a fundamental point of view, these phenomena are simply consequences of transfer of charge and its subsequent behavior. Hence we may take as the central question in static electrification the following: Given two materials of specified chemical composition and physical state, what is the charge—in sign and amount—transferred when they are placed in contact under specified mechanical and ambient conditions, and then separated?

At the present stage of theory of matter, an answer is available only for some very special situations. For the rest of the cases, we must content ourselves with trying to get some guidance from crude models of the type to be described below. For brevity let us restrict our considerations to solid-solid contacts, even though liquid-solid contacts are almost as important technologically. Furthermore let us as a rule consider bodies that are uncharged before contact. We assume first that a certain charge q_0 is transferred between two objects while they are touching. For many materials, q_0 will increase with duration of contact towards an equilibrium value q_∞. We designate as α the degree of attainment of this value, writing $q_0 = \alpha q_\infty$. We should expect q_∞ to depend on the chemical nature of the materials, as well as on the mechanical nature of the contact i.e., on the size and shape of the objects, and the normal force between them. Let us write q_∞ as a factor b ("b" for band structure, in the case of solids) dependent on the electrochemical properties of the materials, multiplied by a factor g ("g" for geometry) dependent on the mechanical parameters of the contact. Upon separation some of the charge returns to its origin, either through conduction processes such as tunneling, or through atmospheric breakdown; let us call f that fraction of the initial charge q_0 that remains to give the observed charge $q = q_0 f$. Upon combining all these relations, we get a four-factor formula

$$q = \alpha bgf$$

The utility of this expression can be assessed only by experience. Note that α and f are both positive numbers between zero and unity, and that g is intrinsically positive; the sign of the charge enters in b.

An important qualitative consequence of the above scheme is the existence of a *triboelectric series*, i.e., a listing of materials such that any one in it becomes positive when rubbed against another lower in the series. When the materials, the ambient conditions, and the mode of contact

are reasonably well defined, such series are generally conceded to exist. An example is the following: Wool, nylon, viscose rayon (regenerated cellulose), cotton, silk, cellulose acetate, polymethylmethacrylate, polyvinylalcohol, polyethylene, polytetrafluoroethylene. In principle, one ought to be able to predict the position of a given substance from its chemical properties, but as yet the attempts have been more suggestive than successful.

So far as quantitative results are concerned, prediction of α and b is possible in principle when detailed information is available on the energy levels of the materials. As yet, only metal-metal systems have been found to be simple enough to be analyzed successfully. With insulators, surface states of high complexity may occur.

Prediction of g is made, one hopes, by estimating the area of "true contact," namely, the area wherein atomic fields interpenetrate. The size of this area depends on the roughness of the contacting objects and on the normal forces between the objects up to the point where the area of "true contact" approaches a maximum approximately equaling the area of apparent contact. In the case of rolling contacts (and some sliding contacts) between cylinders and spheres, the area of apparent contact increases with normal force, in a fashion well understood for elastic deformation and pretty well understood for plastic deformation. Thus it is not uncommon in such cases to find reports of fractional-power dependence on normal force between contacting objects, the power taking values from near zero to unity. In the case of sliding contacts where one or both objects are planar, the "true contact" can apparently be increased by two or three orders of magnitude, as deduced from the much larger charge transfers sometimes observed in "frictional electrification," a not precisely defined concept in which "rubbing"—as opposed to mere "touching"—predominates. Here effects beyond mere "contact" enter, such as local heating, wear, and material transfer; then the Helmholtz theory that sliding simply serves to multiply the contact region loses much of its utility. Even so, in many cases of rolling or sliding contact, the effective area for given normal force is proportional to the *length* of the stroke.

Prediction of f is made, in the absence of atmospheric breakdown, by analyzing the time scale of the experiment. We expect f to be a function of the ratio of T, a time characteristic of the speed of separation, to τ, a relaxation time characteristic of the material of higher resistivity. The separation time T may be taken as l_0/v, where v is a speed of separation, and l_0 is some characteristic length; the relaxation time τ should be related to the time constant for redistribution of charge in a medium of dielectric constant ϵ and volume resistivity ρ. We have then $T/\tau = (l_0/v)/(\epsilon\rho)$, and we see that velocity may be traded for resistivity, since $f = f(T/\tau) = f(l_0/\epsilon\rho v)$. For ordinary materials at ordinary speeds, f is very small for ρ lower than 10^9 ohm-cm. For metal-metal contacts in particular, where $\rho \sim 10^{-5}$ ohm-cm, static effects disappear, their only remnant being the slight transfer due to contact potential difference at the last points of contact. In the presence of atmospheric breakdown, a saturation value of charge q is reached, the magnitude depending on the properties of the surrounding atmosphere. Estimating f here is largely a matter of bookkeeping, and without much point.

Deposition Charging. When a gas is exposed to a high electric field set up between a pair of electrodes, it breaks down to produce a continuous electrical discharge when a threshold voltage between the electrodes is reached. This critical voltage depends on the nature of the gas, its density, and the geometry of the electrodes. To maximize field strength at a given potential, one of the electrodes at least should have a very small radius of curvature, as with a set of points or a fine wire. In a typical application in electrophotography, a cylindrical wire of 0.1 mm diameter might be mounted at a distance of 1 cm from a flat grounded surface. The threshold voltage to start the discharge would be about 3 kV, and the operating voltage might be about 5 kV, to yield a corona current of say 100 μA per cm electrode length. The threshold voltage is nearly proportional to air density, and hence to pressure at constant temperature. It increases with increasing diameter of the wire. Details may be found in references on electrical discharges in gases. A cloud of charge can be produced by flames or by ionizing radiation as well as by corona discharge. But the large and controllable amounts of charge available in the corona have made it by far the most common source.

A plane surface (or other large surface) maintained in the neighborhood of the wire at a potential different from it will eventually accumulate electrostatic charge from the corona until the field between the wire and the surface vanishes. In practice one waits only long enough to charge the surface to several hundred volts, corresponding to 10^{11} to 10^{12} electron charges/cm^2. A particle in the charge cloud and hence in an electric field will pick up charge Q to the limiting amount

$$Q = pE_{\text{corona}} a^2,$$

where a is the "diameter" of the particle, E_{corona} is the electric field strength in the region of the corona, and p is a factor—of the order of unity—dependent on the dielectric properties of the particles and on the properties of the corona discharge. Since the electric force on the particle equals the charge times the electric field strength, and since the viscous drag in the Stokes' law regime is proportional to the diameter and the viscosity of the medium, the terminal velocity of a particle within the corona is proportional to the electrical field strength and the diameter, and inversely proportional to the viscosity.

Dissipation Charge may be dissipated by currents within the body of the object or over its surface, or by currents within the medium in which the object is immersed. Charge in the interior of a body ultimately reaches the boundaries, decaying exponentially with a well-defined time constant $\epsilon\rho$. Charge on the surface of a body moves to attain an equilibrium distribution, decaying in a complicated fashion that is only approximately described by a time constant proportional to $\epsilon\rho$. Currents within the medium surrounding the object are described by the laws of electrical conduction in liquids or gases, as the case may be, in all their complexity.

Control of Static Electrification Effects of static charge, beneficial or harmful, can be controlled by influencing either the production of charge or its neutralization.

Production of Charge. In the case of induced electrification, the fields between objects may be controlled by altering the potentials of neighboring conductors, usually by screening and grounding. In the case of contact electrification, the four-factor formula may be used as a basis for discussion:

Control of α: The only practical control is through fixing of the charge state of the object. (We must accordingly generalize our analysis to include objects initially charged.) If one object has lost so much charge that it can lose no more upon contact with another object, this second object will remain in its initial charge state. (As an illustration, a yarn running through an insulating or insulated guide may not pick up more charge after a brief initial period in which the guide electrically "saturates.")

Control of b: In principle, the electrochemical potential for one given material may be matched against that for some other material so that charge transfer between the two is negligible; in practice the potentials cannot be controlled closely enough, particularly over a range of ambient and mechanical conditions. More significantly, objects usually must work against a variety of materials which will have a variety of electrochemical potentials. There have been proposed composite surfaces wherein a material high in the triboelectric series is interspersed with one low in the series to give a small average electrification. The efficacy of such blending is high in some applications.

Control of g: Decrease of the normal force almost always produces a decrease in charge transfer. In cases where the dependence follows a fractional power law, it may not be useful to go to great lengths to decrease the normal force to very small values. With respect to path length, action is obvious though seldom practical. If the nature of the contact can be changed somewhat, however, by modifying the extent of slip between contacting objects, the amount of charge transferred can sometimes be modified drastically.

Control of f: In practice, charge transfer is reduced by decreasing the product $\epsilon\rho v$. It is difficult to alter the dielectric constant by more than a small factor and hence to affect the rate of dissipation strongly in this way. The resistivity, on the contrary, may be changed greatly, either by changing the molecular structures of the body (say by grafting conducting segments onto polymers) or by adding conducting materials to the surface of the object (say by adding moisture or various antistatic agents). With hydrophilic materials, one traditionally alters the moisture content of the surrounding air, with that of the object following. The resistivity varies as a high negative power of the moisture content, and a change in relative humidity of a few per cent may bring about a tenfold difference in charge observed at a given time, or a tenfold difference in the time required to attain a given charge state. In a few special applications, the resistivity may be lowered by increasing the temperature. The factor v can be decreased by simply slowing down the process, of course, and also by changing the mode of contact, say from sliding to rolling (with concomitant change in g), or by lowering the relative speed of the two contacting objects.

In the case of deposition electrification, the relation $Q \sim E_{\text{corona}} a^2$ shows that the limiting charge can be increased through increase of the electric field strength by increasing the voltage difference across the electrodes, or decreasing the distance between them, on the one hand; and working with larger particles, on the other hand. In practice the ultimate values are seldom approached, and the relevant design factors are those determining the time required for charging and for moving particles along a trajectory. We note in general that gravitational and inertial forces vary as the cube of the diameter, electrical forces as the square, and viscous forces as the first power. It is inappropriate to pursue these matters further here.

Neutralization of Charge. Surplus charge inexorably is neutralized, since the resistivities of even the best nongaseous insulators seldom exceed 10^{18} ohm-cm or so, and since natural radioactivity and cosmic rays produce mobile ions in surrounding fluids. When it is desired to hasten neutralization, charge must be supplied by other means. The conductivity of the body can be increased, especially at the surface, according to some of the ideas expressed earlier. More commonly, charge can be supplied through the surroundings. The medium in which the object is immersed can sometimes be rendered conductive by the electric field set up by the body itself, especially at surface regions of small radius of curvature, for example, at the points of tinsel or needles. Although the charge cannot be completely eliminated in this way, it can be made quite small if the ambient pressure can be brought near the minimum in the Paschen law for electrical breakdown in gases.

More often the surrounding atmosphere is ionized with the aid of external agents. Various commercial static eliminators have been developed to produce glow or spark discharges from high-tension wires or points. Electromagnetic

radiation, in the form of x-rays or gamma rays, will ionize surrounding media, but it is often objectionable because of its hazards to personnel. Particle radiation, in the form of alpha or beta rays is very effective in producing ions, and is easier to control with respect to health hazard. Plutonium 240 with a half-life of 6600 years and americium 241 with a shorter half-life of 462 years are alpha emitters nearly free from gamma rays. They are modern substitutes for the nearly gamma-free polonium 210 with half-life of 138 days, and the gamma-active radium 226 with half-life of 1620 years. Flames produce copious ionization, but their action is usually only ancillary, as in flame-driers at the take-off of some printing presses.

D. J. MONTGOMERY
R. G. CUNNINGHAM

References

Montgomery, D. J., "Static Electrification of Solids," *Solid State Physics*, 9, 139 (1959). Though somewhat dated, serves as a *vade-mecum* for neophytes.

Harper, W. R., "Contact and Frictional Electrification," London, Oxford University Press, 1967. Treats with insight and care many of the significant phenomena in contact charging.

Gross, B., "Charge Storage in Dielectrics," Amsterdam and New York, Elsevier Publishing Co., 1964. Contains excellent section of annotated references.

Dessauer, J. H., and Clark, H. E., eds., "Xerography and Related Processes," London and New York, The Focal Press, 1965. Contains several chapters on fundamentals of electrostatics and on applications thereof to electrostatic printing.

Schaffert, R. M., "Electrophotography," London and New York, The Focal Press, 1965. Contains an analysis of the theory behind electrophotographic processes, and includes extensive lists of patents.

de Geest, W., ed., "Advances in Static Electricity" (Proc. 1st Internat. Conf. on Static Electricity, Vienna, 1970), Brussels, Auxilia, 1970. Comprises reports over a wide range of fundamental and applied electrostatic phenomena.

Danes, E. K., ed., Conference Series No. 11, Proceedings of the 3rd Conference on Static Electrification, 1971. The Institute of Physics and the Physical Society, London and Bristol, 1972. Comprises largely state-of-the-art accounts of industrial applications of static electrification in solids and liquids.

Haase, H., "Statische Elektrizität als Gefahr" [Static Electricity as a Hazard], Weinheim/Bergstrasse, Verlag Chemie, 1968. Treats measurement and control of static electricity in practical situations.

Challande, R., ed., Association Nationale de la Recherche Technique, "Mesure et Elimination de l'Electricité Statique Nuisible" [Measurement and Elimination of Harmful Static Electricity], Paris, Eyrolles Editeur, 1973. (See preceding item.)

Cookson, A. H., ed., "Bibliography on Static Electrification," in "Digest of Literature on Dielectrics," Vol. 34, Chap. 11, 1970, Washington, D. C., National Academy of Sciences, 1972. Contains about 500 references to the literature.

Ralston, O. C., "Electrostatic Separation of Mixed Granular Solids," Amsterdam and New York, Elsevier Publishing Co., 1961. Contains little fundamental analysis, but is valuable for its practical content, including a long list of patents.

Cross-references: CONDUCTIVITY, ELECTRICAL; DIELECTRICS; ELECTRICAL DISCHARGES IN GASES; ELECTRICITY; SOLID-STATE PHYSICS.

STATICS

Statics is the branch of MECHANICS which studies the conditions of equilibrium of forces acting on particles or rigid bodies, or on inextensible cords, belts and chains. Hydrostatics, the study of the equilibrium of fluids, is usually not regarded as a part of statics in the conventional sense of the term.

Statics is the oldest branch of mechanics, some of its principles having been used by the ancient Egyptians and Babylonians in their constructions of temples and pyramids. As a science it was established by Archytas of Taras (ca. 380 B.C.) and primarily by Archimedes (287–212 B.C.); it was further developed by medieval writers on the "science of weights" such as Jordanus de Nemore (thirteenth century) and Blasius of Parma (fourteenth century). In the sixteenth century, it was revived by Leonardo da Vinci, Guido Ubaldi and especially by Simon Stevin (1548–1620) who laid the foundations of modern statics (inclined plane, equilibrium of pulleys, parallelogram of forces).

Although the laws of statics can in principle be derived from those of dynamics as a limiting case for vanished velocities or accelerations, statics has been developed, since the end of the eighteenth century, independently of dynamics. Its fundamental notion, like that of dynamics, is the concept of *force*, representing the action of one body on another and characterized by its point of application, its magnitude and its direction (line of action) or briefly by a VECTOR f. Two equal and opposite forces whose lines of action are parallel and non-coinciding are said to form a *couple*. The *moment* or *torque* m_0 of a force f about a point O is a vector whose magnitude is the product of the magnitude of f and the length of the perpendicular distance of O from the line of action of f, or in VECTOR notation $m_0 = r \times f$ (vector product), where r denotes the vector from O to the point of application of f.

The following four principles may serve as the basic postulates for statics. (1) *The principle of composition (addition) of forces*: two forces, f_1 and f_2, with a common point of application A can be replaced by a third force, the resultant f, which is obtained graphically (geometrically) as the diagonal, from A, in the parallelogram determined by the two given forces, or analytically (algebraically) as the vector whose components, usually with reference to a rectangular reference system, are the sum of the correspond-

ing components of the two given forces, $f_x = f_{1x} + f_{2x}$, etc. (vector addition). The resultant of more than two forces is independent of the order of addition. (2) *The principle of transmissibility of force*: the point of application of force acting on a rigid body can be transferred to any point on the line of action of the force provided the point is rigidly connected with the body (sliding vector). (3) *The principle of equilibrium*: the necessary and sufficient condition for the EQUILIBRIUM, that is, absence of accelerated motion, of a particle is the vanishing of the resultant of all forces acting on the particle, or $\mathbf{F} = \sum \mathbf{f}_i = 0$. The condition for the equilibrium of a rigid body is the vanishing of the resultant of all forces as well as the vanishing of the resultant of their moments about an arbitrary point O, or $\mathbf{M_O} = \sum (\mathbf{r}_i \times \mathbf{f}_i) = 0$. If $\mathbf{F} = 0$, $\mathbf{M_O}$ is independent of the choice of O. (4) *The principle of action and reaction* (Newton's third law): the force exerted by one body on another is equal and opposite to that exerted by the second body on the first and both forces lie along the same line of action.

These principles imply the following results. Two parallel forces can be added if additional compensating forces are introduced. Any set of coplanar forces, with the exception of couples, can be reduced to a single resultant. The sum of the moments of any two intersecting forces about any point in their plane equals the moment of their resultant about the same point (Varignon's Theorem). Any system of forces acting on a rigid body can be reduced, in an infinite number of ways, to a single resultant $\mathbf{F}$ and a single couple $\mathbf{M}$. In all these reductions $\mathbf{F}$ is uniquely determined but $\mathbf{M}$ depends on the position of $\mathbf{F}$. There is one, and only one, line of action for $\mathbf{F}$, called *Poinsot's central axis of the system*, for which $\mathbf{M}$ is parallel to $\mathbf{F}$. Hence every system of forces is equivalent to a *wrench* as this particular force-couple combination is called.

Statical analysis of framed structures or trusses, collections of straight members pinned or jointed together at the ends, is based on the preceding theorems. Such structures rest upon supports whose reactions or pressures have usually to be determined in practical applications. The equilibrium conditions, according to (3), are two vector equations or, equivalently, six scalar equations and hence can be solved for no more than six unknowns (the reactions at supports and connections). If the reactions involve more than six unknowns, some of the reactions are statically indeterminate; if less, the body is said to be unstable. In case the unknown reactions arise from constraints, i.e., conditions restricting possible motions, a convenient method for the elimination of unknown reactions is the use of the *principle of virtual work* according to which the total virtual work (work due to a possible small displacement which need not necessarily take place) of the external forces acting on the body vanishes for any virtual displacement of the body. In general, internal forces, holding together the various parts of the structure, also have to be taken into account, e.g., for trusses which consist of straight members connected by joints.

In particular, parallel forces can always be replaced by a single resultant whose point of application is called the *center of the system of parallel forces*; it is invariant if all forces change their directions but remain parallel to each other. In this case the sum of the moments of these forces about any point equals the moment of their resultant about the same point; in particular, the sum of the moments about any point on the resultant is zero (generalization of the law of the lever). An important case of this kind is that of the earth's gravitational forces which act at a given place in practically parallel lines on every element of a not too voluminous body. The center of the system of forces, in this case, is the *center of gravity* and is identical with the center of mass or *centroid* which can easily be determined by summation for a system of discrete particles or by integration for continuous masses.

The study of friction, the resistance of a surface to the motion of a body upon it, belongs properly to applied mechanics. Since however many problems in statics involve, at least, considerations concerning *static friction* (the frictional force which just prevents motion), the study of FRICTION is often included in the science of statics.

MAX JAMMER

Cross-references: DYNAMICS, FLUID STATICS, FRICTION, MECHANICS.

STATISTICAL MECHANICS

The object of statistical mechanics is the explanation of the macroscopical physical phenomena as consequences of the laws of motion of the atoms and molecules. Equivalently, statistical mechanics can be defined as the mechanics of systems of a very large number of degrees of freedom. Whereas in "ordinary" mechanics even the three-body problem cannot be solved exactly, statistical mechanics takes advantage of the large number N of degrees of freedom and tries to formulate exact *asymptotic* results in the limit $N \to \infty$ (in a certain well-defined way).

The fundamental laws of motion of the atoms and molecules are those of quantum mechanics; however, in many statistical mechanical problems, classical mechanics provides a sufficient approximation.

In ordinary classical mechanics, a problem is completely specified when the initial positions and momenta of all its particles are specified. Such information is impossible to obtain, and moreover is completely useless, for systems consisting of about 10^{24} particles. The only initial

data which are interesting for such systems are of a macroscopic nature: density, local velocity, temperature at each point of a fluid, correlations between the density fluctuations in two points of the system, etc. There is a very large number of microscopic initial configurations of the molecules which is compatible with a given macroscopic specification. Hence, in order to describe such systems, Gibbs introduced the concept of an *ensemble*. This is defined as a set of a very large number of systems, all dynamically identical with the system under consideration (i.e., having the same Hamiltonian H), differing in the initial conditions of the molecules but compatible with the macroscopic specification of the system.

The natural mathematical framework of such a description is the *phase space*, a many-dimensional space whose coordinates are the positions $x_1, \cdots, x_N$ (shortly: x) and the momenta $p_1, \cdots, p_N$ (shortly: p) of all the particles of the system. A point in phase space therefore represents a complete dynamical system in a definite microscopic configuration. A Gibbs ensemble corresponds to a cloud of points in phase space, which can usually be considered as a continuous distribution. The basic concept is therefore the *distribution function* in phase space $\rho(x, p; t)$, giving the density of the ensemble as a function of the positions and momenta of the particles (i.e., of the coordinates of the phase space) at time t. The connection between microscopic and macroscopic physics is then given by the following assumption: The observable value of a dynamical property of the system, (e.g., density, local velocity, average energy, etc.), $\bar{A}(t)$, is the average value of the corresponding microscopic dynamical function $A(x, p)$, weighted by the distribution function:

$$\bar{A}(t) = \int dx \int dp \, A(x, p) \rho(x, p; t) \qquad (1)$$

Practically all functions $A(x, p)$ of physical interest are sums of functions involving only one or two particles. Hence it follows from Eq. (1) that the functions of real importance are the integrals of $\rho(x, p; t)$ over all but one or two particles: these are called reduced (one- or two-body) distribution functions. Their main importance comes from the fact that they remain finite in the limit $N \to \infty$.

The evolution of the system in time is described by the change in time of the distribution function. According to the laws of classical mechanics, the latter obeys a partial differential equation called the *Liouville equation*:

$$\frac{\partial \rho}{\partial t} + \sum_{i=1}^{N} \left[\frac{\partial H}{\partial p_i} \frac{\partial \rho}{\partial x_i} - \frac{\partial H}{\partial x_i} \frac{\partial \rho}{\partial p_i} \right] \equiv \frac{\partial \rho}{\partial t} + [\rho, H] = 0$$

$$\qquad (2)$$

The bracketted expression $[\rho, H]$ is called the Poisson bracket of the Hamiltonian H and the distribution function. The purpose of classical statistical mechanics is the solution of the Liouville equation in the limit $N \to \infty$.

In quantum statistical mechanics, the conceptual situation is much the same, but it is more complicated because of the proper statistical character of the quantum description of even a single system. Indeed, due to the HEISENBERG UNCERTAINTY PRINCIPLE, the momentum and the position of a particle can never be measured simultaneously with arbitrary accuracy. Hence the concept of a phase space has no meaning in quantum mechanics. The maximum information which can be obtained about a single system (in a "pure" state) is contained in its wave function $\Psi(x; t)$. The observable value of a dynamical variable in such a state is given in terms of the corresponding operator $\hat{A}$ by the expression

$$\bar{A}(t) = \int dx \, \psi^*(x; t) \hat{A} \psi(x, t) \qquad (3)$$

To this statistical aspect of quantum mechanics is added the proper indeterminism of statistical mechanics. Suppose the wave function of a single system (n) can be expanded in a series of orthonormal functions $\varphi_i(x)$ [see WAVE MECHANICS]

$$\Psi^{(n)}(x; t) = \sum_i a_i^{(n)}(t) \varphi_i(x) \qquad (4)$$

In the statistical mechanical description, the single system is replaced by an ensemble, in which each system (n) is weighted by a density p_n. The role of the classical distribution function is now played by the *density operator* ρ introduced by J. von Neumann (1932). The matrix elements of this operator in the present representation are defined by

$$\rho_{ij} = \sum_n p_n a_j^{*(n)} a_i^{(n)} \qquad (5)$$

the sum over n running over all the systems of the ensemble.

The averaging prescription which replaces Eqs. (1) and (3) is now:

$$\bar{A}(t) = \text{Trace } \rho A \qquad (6)$$

It is easily seen that this rule embodies the double averaging necessary for quantum and statistical mechanics. The evolution in time of the density operator is given by von Neumann's equation:

$$\frac{\partial \rho}{\partial t} + \frac{1}{i\hbar} [\rho H - H\rho] \equiv \frac{\partial \rho}{\partial t} + \frac{1}{i\hbar} [\rho, H] = 0 \quad (7)$$

H again being the (quantum) Hamiltonian of the system. The classical Poisson bracket has been replaced by $(i\hbar)^{-1}$ times the commutator of the operators ρ and H.

Quantum statistical mechanics shares with the usual quantum mechanical many-body problem the following characteristic feature. It is known that in a system of several identical particles, the latter are undistinguishable. In order to satisfy this requirement, the wave function of the system must be either symmetrical or antisymmetrical with respect to a permutation of any two particles. This symmetry requirement introduces the classification of quantum statistical systems into systems of *bosons* (Bose-Einstein statistics, symmetric wave functions) and systems of *fermions* (Fermi-Dirac statistics, antisymmetric wave functions). The purpose of quantum statistical mechanics is the solution of Eq. (7) with the proper symmetry condition.

The simplest solutions of Eqs. (2) or (7) are the time-independent solutions: these are functions of the Hamiltonian H alone. They describe systems in equilibrium. A particular function of the Hamiltonian is the *canonical distribution*:

$$\rho = Ce^{-H/kT} \qquad (8)$$

where C is a normalization constant and k is called the Boltzmann constant. It can be shown that this distribution represents a system in thermodynamical equilibrium at temperature T. The main result in classical equilibrium statistical mechanics is the following. Consider the function

$$Z(V, T) = (N! \, h^{3N})^{-1} \int dp \int dx \, e^{-H(p,x)/kT} \qquad (9)$$

the integration extending over the whole volume occupied by the system in phase space. $Z(V, T)$, as a function of the volume and of the temperature T, is called the *partition function*. It can be shown that the Helmholtz free energy $F(V, T)$ of the system [see THERMODYNAMICS] is given by

$$F(V, T) = -kT \ln Z(V, T) \qquad (10)$$

The importance of this formula lies in the fact that the knowledge of a thermodynamic potential such as $F(V, T)$ enables one to calculate all thermodynamic properties (pressure, entropy, specific heat, etc.) by simple differential operations. A completely analogous result holds in quantum statistical mechanics.

Although the basic problem of equilibrium statistical mechanics is solved in principle (i.e., it is reduced to quadratures), the explicit evaluation of the $6N$-fold integral occuring in the partition function poses a formidable mathematical problem. Only in the case of systems of noninteracting degrees of freedom can one calculate the partition function exactly. Moreover, essentially three main groups of systems of interacting particles are thoroughly understood at the present time. All of these systems are characterized by the following Hamiltonian:

$$H = H_0 + \lambda V \qquad (11)$$

where H_0 is the Hamiltonian of a set of independent particles, whereas V describes the interactions and λ characterizes the size of the interactions. The three cases mentioned are the following:

(a) *Weakly coupled gases*. These are systems in which the interparticle interactions are weak; the partition function can then be expanded in a power series in λ.

(b) *Dilute gases*. In real gases, the particles interact through forces which have a very short range (the molecules can usually be idealized as hard spheres). In a dilute gas the molecules move most of the time in straight lines and occasionally suffer collisions, which are more and more frequent and involve more and more particles simultaneously as the density of the gas increases. H. D. Ursell (1927) and J. E. Mayer (1937) have shown that the partition function, and hence the pressure, can be expanded as a power series in the density; the result is the famous *virial equation of state* (or *cluster expansion*). The original derivation of this equation made extensive use of a diagram technique, a procedure which establishes a one-to-one correspondence between certain mathematical expressions and certain graphs; such diagram techniques proved to be of major importance in modern perturbation theory. The coefficients of the various powers of the density (or virial coefficients) are expressed in terms of so-called cluster integrals, describing correlations of various types between a given number of particles (see KINETIC THEORY).

As the density increases, the cluster expansion breaks down and more powerful methods have to be used. The statistical theory of liquids is now well accepted, but it is based on more or less ad hoc assumptions, the justification of which from first principles is impossible. The advent of fast computers played a very important role in this field. The development of the methods of molecular dynamics allows one to perform detailed "numerical experiments" in order to determine the structure of complicated many-body problems (up to 1000 particles interacting with realistic potentials).

The theory of critical phenomena is one of the "hot points" of present research. The problem here is to understand the occurrence of singularities in a number of physical phenomena as well as the relations among them. Although no final solution of this problem has been reached as yet, considerable progress has been made in recent years. (See CRITICAL PHENOMENA.)

(c) *Plasmas*. The ionized gases, or plasmas, have a radically different behavior as compared to "usual" gases. This is due to the long range of the Coulomb forces. As a result, one cannot speak of collisions in the ordinary sense: the interactions have a markedly collective character, involving many particles simultaneously. Mathematically, the various virial coefficients turn out to be divergent. J. E. Mayer (1950) has shown that by rearranging the cluster expansion

and by performing summations of certain sub-series, one can obtain a convergent equation of state for a plasma, the first term of which agrees with the one calculated by Debye and Hückel in their famous theory of electrolytes (which is semiphenomenological) (see PLASMAS).

Whereas equilibrium statistical mechanics is in a state where the difficulties are mainly mathematical, nonequilibrium statistical mechanics is still in a state where the principles and the ideas are not yet completely clarified and unified. Most of our present knowledge has been achieved in the last thirty years, and this field is still in rapid growth.

The main problem here is to understand the basic paradox of irreversibility: whereas the laws of mechanics are invarient with respect to an inversion of time, the macroscopic evolution (e.g., heat conduction, dissipative phenomena, etc.) is irreversible. In older theories (Boltzmann), it was argued that due to the large number of particles and their complicated motions, one could invoke a probabilistic argument which, superposed to mechanics, would readily yield an explanation of irreversibility.

There exist at present a few formalisms for the treatment of nonequilibrium mechanics (they are all equivalent). The basic idea in the modern theories is to avoid the probability arguments.

In a recent and quite illuminating version of nonequilibrium statistical mechanics, the theory is presented as follows. The distribution function $\rho(x, p; t) \equiv \rho(t)$ can be split into two terms

$$\rho(t) = \bar{\rho}(t) + \hat{\rho}(t) \qquad (12)$$

If a certain number of very mild symmetry requirements are imposed [such as: $\bar{\rho}(t)$ must remain at all times in the subspace $\bar{\rho}$ as it evolves under the laws of exact mechanics], and if certain conditions on the nature of the interactions and the size of the system are met, the separation is unique. It can then be shown that the component $\bar{\rho}(t)$ has a "kinetic behavior." The reduced one-particle function determined from it, $\bar{F}_1(x, p; t)$, obeys a *closed* equation, independently of the correlations. This closed equation, called the *kinetic equation*, describes the approach of the system to thermal equilibrium. At least in the three limiting cases mentioned above (weak coupling, dilute gases, plasma limit) the approach is purely irreversible. For dilute gases the kinetic equation is none other than the classical Boltzmann equation.

As for the complementary (and complicated) component $\hat{\rho}(t)$, it can be shown that, even if present, it does not contribute to the calculation of some important physical quantities, such as the static transport coefficients (see below). For all these problems the kinetic equation provides a complete and self-contained description.

One of the practical purposes of nonequilibrium statistical mechanics is the calculation of transport coefficients (thermal and electrical conductivity, viscosity, etc.) from molecular data. This can be done by starting from the kinetic equations. Alternatively, it has been shown recently (M. S. Green, R. Kubo) that a compact expression for most transport coefficients can be obtained from general arguments. The "Kubo formulas" express these coefficients in terms of an autocorrelation function of two microscopic currents (electrical currents, heat flow, etc.) averaged over the equilibrium distribution function. These two equivalent approaches can be combined in order to form a basis for the rigorous calculation of transport coefficients (see TRANSPORT THEORY).

Many other important results have been obtained recently in statistical mechanics; they cannot be reviewed in such a short article. The interested reader is referred to the existing textbooks, such as those given below.

RADU C. BALESCU

References

Huang, K., "Statistical Mechanics," New York, J. Wiley & Sons, 1963.

de Boer, J., and Uhlenbeck, G. E., Eds., "Studies in Statistical Mechanics," Vol. 1, New York, Interscience Publishers, 1962.

Prigogine, I., "Non Equilibrium Statistical Mechanics," New York, Interscience, 1963.

Balescu, R., "Statistical Mechanics of Charged Particles," New York, Interscience Publishers 1963.

Stanley, H. E., "Introduction to Phase Transitions and Critical Phenomena," London, Oxford University Press, 1971.

Balescu, R., and Wallenborn, J., "On the structure of the time evolution process in many-body systems," *Physica*, 54, 477 (1971).

Cross-references: BOLTZMANN'S DISTRIBUTION LAW, BOSE-EINSTEIN STATISTICS AND BOSONS, CRITICAL PHENOMENA, FERMI-DIRAC STATISTICS AND FERMIONS, KINETIC THEORY, HEISENBERG UNCERTAINTY PRINCIPLE, LIQUID STATE, MATHEMATICAL PRINCIPLES OF QUANTUM MECHANICS, PLASMAS, STATISTICS, THERMODYNAMICS, TRANSPORT THEORY, WAVE MECHANICS.

STATISTICS

Statistics has been called the art and science of making reasonable decisions in the face of uncertainty or incomplete information. Such a wide ranging description suggests that the basic procedures of statistics must be very much involved with what is usually called simply the scientific method. This is indeed the case. A scientist builds a theory (model) that he hopes will explain some aspects of nature. He deduces from this theory predictions which he then checks against experimental data, thus confirm-

ing or repudiating his theory. When the theory has factors of uncertainty built into it, by way of probabilities, statistical methods must come into play.

Suppose we let X be a *random variable*. That is, X stands for the outcome of a certain experiment. We call the collection E of all possible values for X (i.e., the collection of all possible outcomes of the given experiment) the *sample space* for the random variable. We may well be uncertain as to which of the possible values of X will actually occur. But, in such a case, we can imagine a *probability distribution* for X. If E is a discrete set, this probability distribution assigns a probability to each point in E. If E is not discrete (e.g., E might be an interval on the real line) this probability distribution assigns probabilities to certain sets by way of a *probability density function*. The probability assigned to a set A is obtained by integrating the probability density function over A, much as integrating a mass density function yields a mass. We think of the probability assigned to a point or to a set as the long-run relative frequency with which that point or some point in that set will occur in repeated trials of the experiment. If we make n independent runs of the given experiment, we obtain the outcome $(X_1, X_2, \cdots, X_n)$ which is called a *random sample* for X. The process of drawing conclusions about the probability distribution from information about a sample is called *statistical inference*.

Quantities that we may compute from a given sample to be used in this process are called *statistics*. Some of the useful statistics that may be found for a sample are the mean, median, mode, range, and standard deviation. This last is the positive square root of the variance S^2 which is given by

$$S^2 = \frac{1}{n} \sum_{i=1}^{n} (X_i - \bar{X})^2$$

where $\bar{X}$ is the sample mean. Any statistic is itself a random variable in the sense that its value is obtained by performing an experiment— the experiment of drawing a random sample for X and then computing the value of the statistic from these sample values.

On the other hand, any probability distribution for a random variable will, itself, usually have a mean, median, mode, range, and standard deviation. Such numerical properties of probability distributions are called *parameters*. Parameters are *not* statistics.

A standard example of this situation would be the case where $X_1, X_2, \cdots,$ and X_n are repeated measurements of some physical quantity and there is a random error in our measurement. (In this case, the standard deviation is often called the standard error.) The mean $\bar{X}$ of all our measurements would be a statistic and we would probably use $\bar{X}$ to estimate the underlying true value we are trying to measure. This unknown true value would be a parameter of the distribution for our measurements.

This is an instance of a broad class of problems where we wish to *estimate* one or more *parameters*. Another instance would be an opinion poll. The pollster is estimating certain parameters (the proportions of people in the population at large that would respond in certain ways to his questions) on the basis of the responses of people in his sample.

If θ is an unknown parameter for a random variable X and $(X_1, X_2, \cdots, X_n)$ is a random sample for X, we may consider a certain statistic $\hat{\theta}$, which will be a function of the sample values, as an *estimator* for θ. We would call θ an *unbiased* estimator if θ is the mean of the probability distribution for $\hat{\theta}$. The variance of the distribution for $\hat{\theta}$ is a measure of the *efficiency* of the estimator. A *best* estimator is one which is unbiased and of minimum variance (i.e., as efficient as possible) for the given sample size.

It is often desirable to give an *interval estimate* for an unknown parameter instead of giving a *point estimate* as above. Suppose it is possible to find two functions L and U which have the property that, no matter what the value of the unknown parameter θ, the probability that θ will be between L $(X_1, X_2, \cdots, X_n)$ and U $(X_1, X_2, \cdots, X_n)$ is, say, 0.95. If we then observe the sample values $X_1 = x_1, X_2 = x_2, \cdots,$ and $X_n = x_n$, we say that the interval from $L(x_1, x_2, \cdots, x_n)$ to $U(x_1, x_2, \cdots, x_n)$ is a 95 per cent *confidence interval* for θ. Similar interpretations are given for other levels of confidence or for one-sided confidence intervals.

Aside from problems of parameter estimation, there is the broad question of which probability distributions seem feasible in view of some experimental data. The classical *Neyman-Pearson theory* of hypothesis testing is a widely accepted approach to such questions. Any assertion about a probability distribution may be considered to be a *statistical hypothesis*. In many scientific endeavors, the basic questions can be put in terms of deciding between competing statistical hypotheses. For example, we might wish to decide between the hypothesis H_0 that a new medical treatment produces no higher a proportion of cures than an older treatment, and the hypothesis H_1 that the new treatment increases the proportion of cures. Or we might consider the hypothesis H_0 that a rate of radioactive decay is independent of the temperature, against the hypothesis H_1 that it is not. Or we might want to look at the hypothesis H_0 that the proportion of physicists who are unemployed is no higher this year than it was last, against the hypothesis H_1 that it has increased.

When we wish to decide between two hypotheses H_0 and H_1 about the probability distribution for a random variable X, we usually may arrange it so that we base our decision on the observation of a random sample for X. A *test* for the given hypotheses will be a specification of the conditions under which we will accept one of the hypotheses and reject the other. Since there are only two hypotheses, H_0

and H_1, being considered, such a test is given completely by specifying exactly which samples will cause us to reject H_0. The collection of such samples is called the *critical region* for the test. If H_0 happens to be true and yet when we draw our sample and use the test we find that we reject H_0 (and thus accept H_1), then we have commited an error. Such a mistake is traditionally called an *error of the first kind*. To accept H_0 when actually H_0 is false is to commit an *error of the second kind*. In some cases, it is possible to compute the probability of rejecting H_0 when H_0 is true. This probability is called the *significance level* of the test. Thus, to say that we reject H_0 at the 1 per cent significance level is to say that our observations led us to reject H_0 using a test which has the property that it will reject H_0 only 1 per cent of the time when H_0 is true. When it is not possible to compute the probability of rejecting H_0 given that H_0 is true, it is customary to take the *significance level* of the test to be the maximum possible probability of rejecting H_0 when H_0 is true. If both H_0 and H_1 are concerned with the value of a parameter θ we may judge the value of a proposed test by considering its *power function* f. $f(y)$ is defined to be the probability of rejecting H_0 when y is the true value of θ. For an effective test we would want $f(y)$ to be small for values of y such that $\theta = y$ makes H_0 true, and large for values of y such that $\theta = y$ makes H_1 true. The function whose value at y is $1 - f(y)$ is sometimes called the *characteristic function* for the test.

We note that in view of the intimate connections between the mathematical models we are using, the decisions we want to make, and the experiments we carry out, it is of the utmost importance to plan our experiment in a manner which takes these factors into consideration. There are cases on record where large-scale experiments have been carried out without such planning and were of such a nature that no decision could be made on the basis of the experiment—no matter what the data came out to be. Common sense dictates that planning should take place *before* the experimentation. The broad field of study known as *design of experiments* attempts to give guidance in such planning.

Most of the ideas about estimation and hypothesis testing are useful only when used in conjunction with facts from the theory of probability distributions. Some of the most useful distributions can be described as follows. If X is the number of "successes" in n independent trials where the probability of a "success" on each trial is p, then X is said to have the *binomial* distribution $B(n, p)$. If X has the probability density function

$$f(x) = \frac{1}{\sigma \sqrt{2\pi}} e^{-(1/2)[(x - \mu)/\sigma]^2}$$

where μ (the mean of the distribution) and σ (the standard deviation of the distribution) are

real numbers with σ positive, then X is said to have the *normal distribution* $N(\mu, \sigma^2)$. If

$$Y = \sum_{i=1}^{n} X^2$$

where $(X_1, X_2, \cdots, X_n)$ is a random sample for X and X is $N(0, 1)$, then Y is said to have the *chi-square distribution* $\chi^2(n)$ with n degrees of freedom. If X is $N(\mu, \sigma^2)$ and $\overline{X}$ and S are the mean and standard deviation for a random sample of size n for X, then

$$T = \frac{\overline{X} - \mu}{S/\sqrt{n - 1}}$$

has the *Student's distribution* $t(n - 1)$ with $n - 1$ degrees of freedom. If Y is $\chi^2(n)$ and Z is $\chi^2(m)$ and Y and Z are independent, then $W = (Y/n)/(Z/m)$ has the *F-distribution* $F(n, m)$ with n and m degrees of freedom. Handbooks of mathematics and statistics usually contain tables that give certain probabilities for these standard distributions. Often these tables give only *critical values* that are the most useful. These are the values that cut off, on one side or the other, intervals over which, say, 5 per cent or 1 per cent of the probability lies.

Measurements that involve random errors are often observed to have distributions that are normal or approximately so. (In fact, a probability density function for a normal variable is often called a *Gaussian error function*.) Many other quantities that have approximately normal distributions seem to occur in nature. But even if this did not happen, normal distributions would be extremely useful because of the following powerful result which is called the *central limit theorem*: If X has a mean μ and a standard deviation σ, and $\overline{X}$ is the mean of a random sample of size n for X, then $(\overline{X} - \mu)/(\sigma/\sqrt{n})$ has a distribution which is approximately $N(0, 1)$ when n is large. Notice that there is no assumption about the underlying distribution for X aside from the fact that μ and σ exist. Many standard statistical techniques rely heavily on the central limit theorem. These techniques would be part of what is called *large-sample theory* as opposed to *small-sample theory* where other results must be used. Many useful small-sample techniques are concerned with so-called *nonparametric tests*, which involve hypotheses which are not stated in terms of the values of certain parameters.

Student's distributions are of special importance in small-sample theory. Chi-square distributions are useful for certain *goodness-of-fit* tests which include standard procedures for handling *contingency tables*. F distributions come into play in *analysis of variance* where the underlying variables are assumed to be normal and we are interested in detecting differences between their means.

Since statistical methods are so closely intertwined with basic questions about scientific methods it is not surprising to find that there

are controversies about these methods. The *decision theoretic* approach to statistics questions some of the basic ideas of classical hypothesis testing and suggests that, where possible, we should take into account the *cost* of committing the different kinds of errors we may make. Here the proper approach would be to design a procedure that would, in some sense, minimize our expected loss. In a laboratory situation, however, it may be difficult to assign costs to the sorts of errors. In managerial or social situations it may make a great deal of sense to consider seriously how much we will lose if we follow certain paths.

Statistics relies heavily on the theory of probability, and the question of the exact nature (or natures) of probability is an old one in the philosophy of science. A growing group of theoretical and practicing statisticians takes a somewhat different view of probability than is usual. These people call themselves *Bayesians* or *subjectivists* and believe that it is most useful to consider a probability to be a subjective, personal thing which is based on an individual's knowledge (and ignorance) and is subject to modification (via what is known as Bayes theorem) in view of empirical information. We may determine an individual's probability for an event by offering him bets and discovering at what odds he will take either side of the bet. A Bayesian point of view has considerable impact on the question of what constitutes an acceptable statistical procedure and articles about this impact are common in the current literature.

This ferment in statistics happens to coincide in time with a great increase in the use of statistical methods in the natural and social sciences. With the continual pressures caused by a reconsideration of the foundations and a demand for useful tools for applications, the field of statistics will continue to grow in both depth and usefulness.

FRANK L. WOLF

References

Feller, W., "An Introduction to Probability Theory and its Applications," Vol. 1, 3rd ed., New York, John Wiley & Sons, 1968.

Hicks, C. R., "Fundamental Concepts in the Design of Experiments," New York; Holt, Rinehart, and Winston, 1965.

Hogg, R. V., and Craig, A. T., "Introduction to Mathematical Statistics," 3rd ed., New York, Macmillan, 1970.

Lindgren, B. W., "Statistical Theory," 2nd ed., New York, Macmillan, 1968.

Owen, D. B., "Handbook of Statistical Tables," Reading, Mass., Addison-Wesley, 1962.

Wolf, F. L., "Elements of Probability and Statistics," 2nd ed., New York, McGraw-Hill, 1974.

Cross-references: CALCULUS OF PHYSICS; MEASUREMENTS, PRINCIPLES OF; MATHEMATICAL PRINCIPLES OF QUANTUM MECHANICS.

STRONG INTERACTIONS

Only two types of fundamental interaction operate in classical physics, which account for all macroscopic and chemical phenomena including atomic structure. There are the gravitatonal forces which control the motion of bulk matter, which is electrically neutral—particularly the motion of the planets in the solar system. Then there are the electromagnetic forces which govern the motion of the electrons in atoms, and also give rise to the interactions between atoms and, hence, form the basis of all chemical reactions.

An atom has a radius of about 10^{-10} m. In an atom, a cloud of electrons orbit about a central nucleus with a radius of about 10^{-14} m. These nuclei are made up of nucleons—protons and neutrons. The total charge, which is determined by the number of protons, fixes the chemical nature of the atom. The nuclei are extremely stable, remaining unchanged through the most violent chemical reactions. The gravitational forces within a nucleus are completely negligible compared with the electrical repulsion between the charges on the tightly packed protons. Since the electrical forces tend to blow the nucleus apart, it follows that a completely new, specifically nuclear, force must be operating to form these stable structures. This force is of short range, only effective when the nucleons are less than 10^{-14} m apart. Within this range, it is strong enough to overcome the powerful electrical repulsions. It is known as the *strong nuclear interaction*, to distinguish it from the other specifically nuclear interaction—the *weak* interaction—which causes the spontaneous disintegration of subnuclear particles (see WEAK INTERACTIONS). It is the strong nucleon interaction which is the source of energy in nuclear weapons and in nuclear reactors.

To investigate the workings of the strong nuclear interaction a beam of high-energy protons from a proton accelerator is directed at a target of liquid hydrogen (more protons) and scattered. At low energies, below 300 MeV in the laboratory, the protons are merely deflected by the strong nucleon-nucleon interaction. Above this energy, new particles are produced in the collision. The first to appear are the π-mesons, or pions. As the energy increases, more and more particles are found. The least massive are stable as far as the strong interaction is concerned, but they disintegrate through the weak interaction with mean lifetimes of about 10^{-10} second. The more massive particles decay via the strong interaction into other strongly interacting particles in about 10^{-23} second. These are tabulated in the article on ELEMENTARY PARTICLES.

Because of the strength of this interaction, it has not been possible to discover the details of the corresponding dynamics. However, considerable progress has been made by studying the conservation laws which govern the collisions of strongly interacting particles.

The subnuclear particles are specified according to their properties which correspond to those physical quantities which are conserved (i.e., do not change) in any collision which is dominated by the strong interaction. These are typically the mass, which contributes to the energy, and the spin which is part of the total angular momentum. If a particle has spin J (in units of $h/2\pi$) there are $2J + 1$ possible states, corresponding to the orientations of the spin axis allowed by quantum mechanics. These states are distinguished by the magnitude of the component J_z which ranges by integers from $+J$ to $-J$.

Other conserved quantities are the electric charge, the so-called hypercharge, and the baryon number. These are also tabulated in the article ELEMENTARY PARTICLES.

These subnuclear particles appear in multiplets of nearly equal mass, but differing charge. Thus there are three pions (positive, negative and neutral) and two nucleons, one positive (the proton) and one neutral (the neutron). These are closely analogous to the $2J + 1$ spin states of a particle of spin J and may be explained by attributing to each mass multiplet a spin I (isotopic spin) in an abstract space. The different charge states are then interpreted as the different "orientations" in this abstract space and are specified by the $2I + 1$ values of the component I_3. Thus the pion has isotopic spin 1, with the three charge states specified by $I_3 = \pm1$, 0. The nucleon has isotopic spin $I = 1/2$, with two

charge states $I_3 = \pm 1/2$. Isotopic spin is conserved in strong interactions, just as total angular momentum is conserved. The conservation of angular momentum is related to the invariance of the whole colliding system with respect to its orientation in space. The conservation of isotopic spin is similarly equivalent to the statement that the strong interactions are invariant under a group of two-dimensional unitary transformations, known to group theorists as SU(2).

It has been conjectured that the strong interactions are approximately invariant under a wider group of three-dimensional unitary transformations, SU(3), which combines the notion of isotopic spin with that of hypercharge. According to this theory, the isotopic multiplets of particles of the same spin J can be combined into supermultiplets of roughly similar mass, which form hexagonal or triangular patterns when they are exhibited on a graphical plot of I_3 against Y. By 1963, three such supermultiplets had been established. They form octets of particles, with $J = 0, \frac{1}{2}$ and 1. (These are $\pi^+ \pi^- \pi^0 \eta^0 K^+ K^0 K^- \bar{K}^0$; $\Sigma^+ \Sigma^- \Sigma^0 \Lambda^0 p n \Xi^- \Xi^0$; $\rho^+ \rho^- \rho^0 \phi^0 K^{*+} K^{*0} K^{*-} \bar{K}^{*-}$.) At that time, the known particles of spin $J = 3/2$ formed a tenfold triangular multiplet, with one particle missing—the Ω^-. This missing particle was an isotopic singlet ($I = 0$) with hypercharge minus two. It had remarkable physical properties very well defined so that its mass, mode of production, mean life time, and decay could all be predicted. This

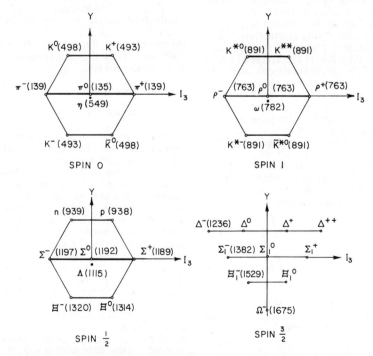

FIG. 1. The well-established SU(3) multiplets. In each of these, particles lying together on horizontal lines form sub-multiplets of SU(2) (isotopic spin). The figures in brackets indicate the masses of the particles in MeV/c^2.

particle was discovered in 1964 exactly as forecasted, thus confirming the wider unitary scheme.

This scheme provides a kind of "periodic table" for the subnuclear particles, which can clearly no longer be reasonably regarded as "elementary." Since the periodic table of the elements follows from their electronic structure, it is natural to ask if the regularities discovered among the subnuclear particles can be similarly explained in terms of their being composed of some yet more basic entities. If so, unitary symmetry implies that these should be a triplet of particles of nearly equal mass—called QUARKS—composed of an isotopic doublet and an isotopic singlet, and that the multiplets of subnuclear particles are combinations of quarks with specified symmetry properties. If these quarks are assumed to have an ordinary spin of $\frac{1}{2}$, they also provide a very natural explanation of the spins of all the particles appearing in Fig. 1. However, in order for the currently known particles to have integer charges (in units of the electron charge) the quarks must have fractional charges of $\frac{2}{3}$ and -$\frac{1}{3}$. This is a revolutionary idea and nothing of the kind has yet been seen with presently operating proton accelerators (about 70 GeV), but they may be discovered in the Intersecting Storage Rings at CERN or at the 400 GeV machine now in operation at Batavia, Illinois.

The establishment of "unitary symmetry" for strong interactions has been a great step forward in our understanding of the nuclear world, but it leaves many questions unanswered. We still have no knowledge of the detailed working of the dynamics of the strong interaction. We do not know, for example, why the particles have the masses that they do. If the states of lowest mass are made of simple combinations of quarks, we do not even know whether the higher-mass states are made of more complicated combinations or by the original quarks gaining energy by a general rotational motion. Progress here too is likely to come from the new proton accelerators which will enable physicists to study collisions at higher and higher energies, and which are sensitive to the structure of matter at smaller and smaller distances, enabling us to study in terrestial laboratories matter as it exists at the centers of the most massive stars.

P. T. MATTHEWS

Reference

Matthews, P. T., "The Nuclear Apple," Chatto and Windus, 1971.

Cross-references: ELECTRON, ELEMENTARY PARTICLES, NEUTRINO, NEUTRON, PROTON, QUARKS, WEAK INTERACTIONS.

SUPERCONDUCTIVITY

This article describes the experimental facts relating to superconductivity, our present theoretical understanding, and some practical applications. No attempt is made to follow historical order or to provide an exhaustive treatment; the references at the end of the article will help those who wish to pursue the subject further.

The most spectacular property of a superconductor is the total disappearance of its electrical resistance when it is cooled below a critical temperature T_c. Very careful measurements show that the electrical resistance of a superconductor is at least a factor 10^{17} smaller than the resistance of copper at room temperature and may therefore for all practical purposes be taken to be zero. Some 25 elements and a vast number of alloys and compounds have so far been discovered to be superconducting; examples are In, Sn, V, Mo, Nb-Zr alloys and $Nb_3 Sn$. Transition temperatures range from a few thousandths of a degree Kelvin (for certain Nb-Mo alloys) all the way to about 23K for $Nb_3 Ge$.

Another important property is the destruction of superconductivity by the application of a magnetic field equal to or greater than a critical field H_c. This H_c, for a given superconductor, is a function of the temperature given approximately by

$$H_c = H_0(1 - T^2/T_c^2) \qquad (1)$$

where H_0, the critical field at 0 K, is in general different for different superconductors and has values from a few gauss to a couple of thousand gauss. For applied magnetic fields less than H_c, the flux is excluded from the bulk of the superconducting sample, penetrating only to a small depth λ into the surface. The value of λ (called the penetration depth) is in the range 10^{-5} to 10^{-6} cm. Thus the magnetization curve for a superconductor is

$$B \text{ (inside)} = 0 \qquad \text{for } H < H_c$$

$$B \text{ (inside)} = B \text{ (outside) for } H > H_c$$

This magnetization behavior is reversible and cannot therefore be explained entirely on the basis of the zero resistance. The reversible magnetization behavior is called the Meissner effect.

The existence of the penetration depth λ suggests that a sample having at least one dimension less than λ should have unusual superconducting properties, and such is indeed the case. Thin superconducting films, of thickness d less than λ, have critical fields higher than the bulk critical field, approximately in the ratio of λ to d. This result follows qualitatively from the thermodynamics of the Meissner effect: the metal in the superconducting state has a lower free energy than in the normal state, and the transition to the normal state occurs when the energy needed to keep the flux out becomes equal to this free energy difference. But in the case of a thin film with $d < \lambda$, there is partial penetration of the flux into the film, and thus one must go to a higher applied field before the free energy difference is compensated by the magnetic energy.

It is clear that the existence of the critical field also implies the existence of a critical transport electrical current in a superconducting wire, i.e., that current I_c which produces the critical field H_c at the surface of the wire. For example, in a cylindrical wire of radius r, $I_c = \frac{1}{2} r H_c$. This result is called the Silsbee rule.

All of the above properties distinguish superconductors from "normal" metals. There is another very important distinction, which contains a clue to understanding some of the properties of superconductors. In a normal metal at 0 K, the electrons, which obey Fermi statistics, occupy all available states of energy below a certain maximum energy called the Fermi energy ζ. Raising the temperature of the metal causes electrons to be singly excited to states just above Fermi energy. There is for all practical purposes a continuum of such excited energy states available above the Fermi energy.

The situation is quite different in a superconductor; in a superconductor, the lowest excited state for an electron is separated by an energy gap Δ from the ground state. The existence of this gap in the excitation spectrum has been confirmed by a variety of experiments: electronic heat capacity, thermal conductivity, ultrasonic attenuation, far infrared and microwave absorption, and tunneling. It is to be noted that the excitation of electrons across the gap by photons requires a minimum energy of 2Δ, which is consistent with the description of the superconducting ground state in terms of Cooper pairs, as described further below. The energy gap decreases monotonically with increasing temperature, having a value $\Delta_0 \sim 1.75 \, kT_c$ at 0 K (where k is the Boltzmann constant) and vanishing at T_c (see ENERGY LEVELS).

The superconducting state has a lower entropy than the normal state, and therefore one concludes that superconducting electrons are in a more ordered state. Without, for the present, inquiring more deeply into the nature of this ordering, one can state that a spatial change in this order produced say by a magnetic field will occur, not discontinuously, but over a finite distance ξ, which is called the *coherence length*. The coherence length represents the range of order in the superconducting state and is typically about 10^{-4} cm, though we shall see later that it can in some superconductors take much lower values and lead to some remarkable properties.

Measurements of the transition temperature on different ISOTOPES of the same superconductor showed that T_c is proportional to $M^{-1/2}$, where M is the isotopic mass. This isotope effect suggests that the mechanism underlying superconductivity must involve the properties of the lattice, in addition to those of the electrons. Another indication of this is given by the behavior of allotropic modifications of the same element: white tin is superconducting, while grey tin is not, and the hexagonal and face-centered cubic phases of lanthanum have different transition temperatures. A third, and most striking, indication is that the current vs

voltage characteristic of a superconducting tunneling junction shows a structure which is intimately related to the phonon spectrum of the superconductor.

The superconducting properties of alloys present a bewildering variety of phenomena. They show a great deal of magnetic hysteresis, with little indication of a perfect Meissner effect. The Silsbee rule is inapplicable, and the resistive transition occurs at fields generally very much higher than in pure superconductors. For example, a wire of Nb_3Sn can carry a current of 10^5 amperes/cm^2 in an applied field of 100 kilogauss, while a similar wire of lead would carry about 10^3 amperes/cm^2 in a field of only 100 gauss. When experiments are done using well-annealed (preferably single-crystal) alloys, it is found that the critical currents drop considerably, and the magnetic behavior becomes reversible but still quite unlike that of pure superconductors. The flux is excluded from the interior of the sample up to a well-defined field H_{c1}. When the applied field is raised further, flux begins to penetrate, even though the resistance remains zero, until a second critical field H_{c2} is reached, at which the flux penetration is complete, and normal resistance is abruptly restored.

The theory of superconductivity has developed along two lines, the phenomenological and the microscopic. The phenomenological treatment was initiated by F. London, who modified the Maxwell electromagnetic equations so as to allow for the Meissner effect. His theory explained the existence and order of magnitude of the penetration depth, and gave a qualitative account of some of the electrodynamic properties. The treatment was extended by V. L. Ginzburg and L. D. Landau, and by A. B. Pippard, who in particular emphasized the concept of the range of coherence. A. A. Abrikosov used these ideas to develop a model for alloy superconductors. He showed that if the electronic structure of the superconductor were such that the coherence length ξ becomes smaller than the penetration depth λ, one would get magnetic behavior similar to that observed in alloys, with two critical fields H_{c1} and H_{c2}. In particular, Abrikosov's work, as extended by others, showed that the state of such a superconductor in applied fields between H_{c1} and H_{c2} (called the *mixed state*), consists of a triangular lattice of magnetic flux lines uniformly penetrating the superconductor. The core of each flux line, of approximate radius ξ, consists essentially of normal material, while the surrounding regions are superconducting. Each flux line core is surrounded by persistent supercurrents, and contains a quantum of flux $\phi_0 \equiv h/2e \simeq 2 \times 10^{-7}$ gauss-cm^2. The existence of such a lattice of flux lines received brilliant experimental confirmation through the work of Essmann and Traüble, who used a Bitter technique involving ferromagnetic powder to show up the magnetic lattice on the surface of a superconductor in the mixed state. Such superconductors which show mixed-state behavior are called *type II super-*

conductors, while those which show the usual Meissner effect up to the critical field H_c are called *type I superconductors*. The problem of high critical currents in unannealed (or otherwise metallurgically imperfect) alloys and compounds is more complicated because it involves the interaction between the microscopic metallurgical structure and the superconducting properties. This is an area of great research activity because of the technological implication to be mentioned later.

The microscopic theory of superconductivity was initiated by H. Fröhlich, who first recognized the importance of the interactions of electrons with lattice vibrations and in fact predicted the isotope effect before its experimental observation. The detailed microscopic theory was developed by J. Bardeen, L. N. Cooper, and J. R. Schrieffer in 1957, and represents one of the outstanding landmarks in the modern theory of solids. The BCS theory, as it is called, considers a system of electrons interacting with the PHONONS, which are the quantized vibrations of the lattice. There is a screened coulomb repulsion between pairs of electrons, but in addition there is also an attraction between them via the electron-phonon interaction. If the net effect of these two interactions is attractive, then the lowest energy state of the electron system has a strong correlation between pairs of electrons with equal and opposite momenta and opposite spin and having energies within the range $k\theta$ (where θ is the Debye temperature) about the Fermi energy. This correlation causes a lowering of the energy of each of these Cooper pairs (named after L. N. Cooper who first pointed out their existence on the basis of some general arguments) by an amount 2Δ relative to the Fermi energy. The energy 2Δ may be regarded as the binding energy of the pair, and is therefore the minimum energy which must be supplied in order to raise a pair of electrons to excited states. We see thus that the experimentally observed energy gap follows from the theory. The magnitude Δ_0 of the gap at 0 K is

$$\Delta_0 \approx 2k\theta \exp\left(-\frac{1}{NV}\right)$$

where N is the density of electronic states at the Fermi energy and V is the net electron-electron interaction energy. The superconducting transition temperature T_c is given by

$$3.5\,kT_c \approx 2\Delta_0$$

It has been shown that the BCS theory does lead to the phenomenological equations of London, Pippard, and Ginzburg and Landau, and one may therefore state that the basic phenomena of superconductivity are now understood from a microscopic point of view, i.e., in terms of the atomic and electronic structure of solids. It is true, however, that we cannot yet, *ab initio*, calculate V for a given metal and therefore predict whether it will be superconducting or not. The difficulty here is our ignorance of the exact wave functions to be used in describing the electrons and phonons in a specific metal, and their interactions. However, we believe that the problem is soluble in principle at least.

The range of coherence follows naturally from the BCS theory, and we see now why it becomes short in alloys. The electron mean free path is much shorter in an alloy than in a pure metal, and electron scattering tends to break up the correlated pairs, so that for very short mean free paths one would expect the coherence length to become comparable to the mean free path. Then the ratio $\kappa \approx \lambda/\xi$ (called the Ginzburg-Landau parameter) becomes greater than unity, and the observed magnetic properties of alloy superconductors can be derived. The two kinds of superconductors, namely those with $\kappa < 1/\sqrt{2}$ and those with $\kappa > 1/\sqrt{2}$ (the inequalities follow from the detailed theory) correspond respectively to type I and type II superconductors.

As the implications of the BCS theory were better understood, and its relationship to the Ginzburg-Landau and London theories further clarified, during the past few years, a profound and very beautiful new understanding of the nature of the superconducting state has been obtained. F. London had in his earliest work described the superconducting state as a *macroscopic quantum state*, and used a many-body wave function to describe this state. But it has now become clear that, while the full statistical-mechanical description of the condensation of the electrons into the superconducting state is indeed very complicated, the resulting macroscopic quantum state can be described by a complex "wave function" $\Psi(\underset{\approx}{r}, t)$ which is a function of position $\underset{\approx}{r}$ and time t. The amplitude of Ψ gives the fraction of the electron fluid which is in the condensed superconducting state, and its phase contains information about its dynamics. One notes the formal similarity with the Schrödinger wave function of a free particle,

$$\psi = \psi_0 \exp \frac{i}{\hbar}(px - Et)$$

where p is the momentum and E is the energy. The wave function of the superconductor, which is referred to usually as its *order parameter*, can be written

$$\Psi = \Psi_0 \exp(i\phi)$$

where for a uniform superconductor Ψ_0 is a constant and ϕ is in general a function of space and time, and also involves the magnetic field or more precisely the vector potential. The single-valuedness of the order parameter leads to the quantization of magnetic flux in units of ϕ_0, defined earlier, in any area which is fully surrounded by a superconducting region, such

as the core of an Abrikosov flux line or a super-conducting ring carrying a persistent current. It should be mentioned here that this concept of a complex order parameter provides a funda-mental link between superfluid helium and superconductivity, which are now seen as two manifestations of the basic phenomenon of SUPERFLUIDITY, even though the microscopic origins are quite different in the two cases. In terms of the order parameter, one can now give a unified description of similar phenomena in the two areas, such as critical velocities, quan-tized flux/vortex lines, and the influence of magnetic field/rotation.

B. Josephson's important contribution was to recognize the implications of the complex order parameter for the dynamics of the supercon-ductor, and in particular when one considers a system consisting of two bulk superconductors 1 and 2 connected by a "weak link." The basic requirement for the weak link is that the ampli-tude of the order parameter there should be substantially smaller than in the bulk regions. Experimentally such a situation has been real-ized in a variety of ways: two evaporated films separated by a thin (< 20 Å) oxide layer, a light point contact between two bulk superconduc-tors, a single hourglass-shaped evaporated film, with the constriction of dimensions small com-pared to the coherence length, or indeed even a bare niobium wire with a pendant frozen blob of soft solder, where the weak links, indetermi-nate in number, were formed by solder bridges through pinholes in the surface oxide. Collec-tively, all such weak link junctions are referred to as *Josephson junctions*.

The electrodynamic behavior of such a Joseph-son junction can be described at several levels of sophistication: as the solutions of the time-dependent Schrödinger equations for ψ_1 and ψ_2 with an assumed weak coupling between 1 and 2, by perturbation-theoretic methods, or by Green's function methods. All methods fortu-nately give the same two simple equations, the famous Josephson equations:

$$j = j_0 \sin\left(\phi_2 - \phi_1 - \frac{2e}{\hbar}\int_1^2 A\,dx\right). \quad \text{(J1)}$$

$$\frac{\partial}{\partial t}\left(\phi_2 - \phi_1 - \frac{2e}{\hbar}\int_1^2 A\,dx\right)$$

$$= -\frac{1}{\hbar}(\mu_2 - \mu_1) = \frac{2eV}{h}. \quad \text{(J2)}$$

where for simplicity a one-dimensional junction has been treated. In the above equations j is the supercurrent through the junction, ϕ is the phase of the order parameter, A is the vector potential, μ is the chemical potential, V is the voltage bias across the junction, and e and h have their usual meanings. The subscripts 1 and 2 refer to the bulk superconductors on either side of the weak link respectively.

From Eq. (J1) and (J2) one can see easily that, in the absence of a magnetic field, i.e., $A = 0$, a maximum supercurrent j_0 can flow (which is a function of the junction parameters), and the application of a constant bias voltage V to the junction produces an alternating current at a fre-quency $\nu_J = 2eV/h$. These two effects consti-tute the dc and ac *Josephson effects* respectively. In addition, when a Josephson junction biased at a voltage V is exposed to electromagnetic radiation at frequency f, the beating of the two frequencies f and ν_J produces a zero-frequency current component, and consequently a con-stant-voltage step in the dc junction current, whenever $\nu_J = nf$ where n is an integer. Thus, at values of the voltage $V_n = nhf/2e$, the current-voltage characteristic of the junction shows vertical current steps.

Space does not permit a detailed discussion here of the various effects of a magnetic field on Josephson junctions in different circuit con-figurations. But it is apparent from Eq. (J1) that the integral on the right can in certain configurations be made to correspond to the magnetic flux through a portion of the circuit. Then j would show an oscillatory dependence upon the field, going through one cycle each time the flux changes by one quantum ϕ_0. For example, in the case of two junctions in parallel enclosing an area A, the maximum supercurrent goes through a cycle as the applied field changes by ϕ_0/A. If A is of the order of a square centimeter it is obvious from the magnitude of $\phi_0 \sim 2 \times 10^{-7}$ cm^2 – gauss that field changes of less than a microgauss can be detected.

Both the dc and ac Josephson effects have found some exciting and novel applications. The high sensitivity to magnetic field of the dc Josephson current in certain circuit configura-tions has been used to develop a family of devices called "squids" (superconducting quan-tum interferometric device) which are used to measure extremely small currents, voltages, and magnetic fields. The ac effect has been used to obtain a very precise measurement of $2e/h$ and thence the fine structure constant α, in terms of the standard volt and a frequency, by D. N. Langenberg and his collaborators. Their work has helped to resolve a number of discrepancies between experiment and the predictions of quantum electrodynamics. It now appears likely that the U.S. legal volt will be maintained in terms of the Josephson frequency by the National Bureau of Standards, using the relation

$$1\mu\text{V} = 483.593718 \pm 0.000060 \text{ MHz}$$

as determined by Langenberg et al.

The intriguing question of how high a transi-tion temperature is possible has not yet been given a satisfactory theoretical answer. The BCS theory suggests as an upper limit the Debye temperature, which is a few hundred degrees Kelvin for most materials; but actual T_c's are a tenth of this or less. The experimental search

for high-temperature superconductors has been led by B. T. Matthias and his collaborators, who were responsible for the Nb_3 (AlGe) which has one of the highest T_c's so far known, 21 K. It appears that as one progressively modifies a given material in the direction of higher T_c's, lattice instabilities set in which inhibit the superconductivity. Matthias believes that these instabilities can be avoided by using metastable high-temperature phases of complex alloys and compounds.

There have been several attempts at technological applications of superconductors. The most spectacularly successful one is the use of certain type II superconductors like Nb-Zr and Nb-Ti alloys, and $Nb_3 Sn$, in making electromagnets. In a conventional electromagnet employing normal conductors, the entire electric power applied to the magnet is consumed as Joule heating. For a magnet to produce 100 kilogauss in a reasonable volume, the power requirement can run into megawatts. In striking contrast, a superconducting magnet develops no Joule heat because its resistance is zero. Indeed, if such a magnet has a superconducting shunt placed across it after it is energized, the external power supply can be removed, and the current continues to flow indefinitely through the magnet and shunt, maintaining the field constant. Superconducting magnets have already been constructed producing fields of over 100 kilogauss in usable volumes. There is a natural upper limit to the critical field possible in such superconductors, given by the paramagnetic energy of the electrons (due to their spin moment) in the normal state becoming equal to the condensation energy of the Cooper pairs in the superconducting state. This leads to a limit of about 360 kilogauss for a superconductor with a T_c of 20K.

The possibility of a persistent current in a superconducting ring, and the sharpness and speed of the change in resistance at the superconducting to normal transition, have led to consideration of superconductors for memory and logic circuits in computers. Further work, mainly of a technological nature, is needed before practical superconducting computers can be built.

B. S. CHANDRASEKHAR

References

Lynton, Ernest A., "Superconductivity," New York, John Wiley & Sons 1969 (3rd edition). A concise, extremely readable book in which most of the ideas in this article are elaborated.

Shoenberg, D., "Superconductivity," New York, Cambridge University Press, 1952. An excellent account of the field up to about 1952.

London, F., "Superfluids," Vol. I, New York, John Wiley & Sons, 1950. A classic account of the early theory of superconductivity; it and its companion Volume II on superfluid helium should be required reading for every cryophysicist.

Rose-Innes, A. C., and Rhoderick, E. H., "Introduction to Superconductivity," New York, Pergamon, 1969. About the same level as Lynton, but some topics discussed in more detail; all equations are given in mks units, which should please some.

There are several books on the modern theory of superconductivity, some of which are Schrieffer, J. Robert, "Theory of Superconductivity," New York, W. A. Benjamin, 1964; Rickayzen, G., "Theory of Superconductivity," New York, Interscience, 1965; de Gennes, P. G., "Superconductivity of Metals and Alloys," New York, W. A. Benjamin, 1966; Kuper, C. G., "An Introduction to the Theory of Superconductivity," New York, Oxford University Press, 1968; Saint-James, D., Sarma, G., and Thomas E. J., "Type II Superconductivity," New York, Pergamon, 1969.

R. D. Parks, ed., "Superconductivity," Volumes I and II, New York, Marcel Dekker, 1969. A truly encyclopedic treatment of the subject, written by about thirty international experts.

Rev. Mod. Phys., 36, 1-331 (1964). This contains the proceedings of an international conference on superconductivity held in 1963.

Chilton, F., ed., "Superconductivity," Amsterdam, North-Holland, 1971. This contains the proceedings of an international conference on superconductivity held in 1969.

Proceedings of the LT conferences, various publishers. These contain papers, many of them on superconductivity, from the biennial International Conference on Low Temperature Physics.

"Advances in Cryogenic Engineering," New York, Plenum. This is an annual series containing the proceedings of the annual cryogenic Engineering Conference, dealing with many applications of superconductivity and techniques of low temperatures.

Physics Today, August 1971 (vol. 24, no. 8) New York, American Institute of Physics. A special issue devoted to low temperature physics, with articles on the search for high-temperature superconductors by B. T. Matthias, Josephson effect by J. Clarke, and superconducting magnets by J. K. Hulm, D. J. Kasun and E. Mullan.

Electronics, March 1, 1971, New York, McGraw-Hill. Contains articles on Josephson junctions and their applications by O. Doyle, A. Longacre, and D. N. Langenbert, T. G. Finnegan, and A. Denenstein.

Cross-references: CONDUCTIVITY, ELECTRICAL; ELECTRON SPIN; ENERGY LEVELS; FERMI-DIRAC STATISTICS AND FERMIONS; HEAT CAPACITY; HEAT TRANSFER; MAGNETISM; PHONONS; SEMICONDUCTORS; SOLID-STATE PHYSICS; SUPERFLUIDITY.

SUPERFLUIDITY

Superfluidity is a term used to describe a property of condensed matter in which a resistance-less flow of current occurs. The mass-four isotope of helium in the liquid state plus some twenty-five metallic elements are presently known to exhibit this phenomenon. In the case

of liquid helium, these currents are hydrodynamic; for the metallic elements, they consist of electron streams. The effect occurs only at very low temperatures in the vicinity of the absolute zero ($-273.16°C$ or 0 K). In the case of helium, the maximum temperature at which the effect occurs is about 2.2 K; for metals the highest temperature is in the vicinity of 23 K.

If one of these metals (called superconductors) is cast in the form of a ring and an external magnetic field is applied perpendicular to its plane and then removed, a current will flow round the ring induced by Faraday induction. This current will produce a magnetic field, proportional to the current, and the size of the current may be observed by measuring this field. Were the ring (e.g., one made of Pb) at a temperature above 7.2 K, this current and field would decay to zero in a fraction of a second. But with the metal at a temperature below 7.2 K before the external field is removed, this current shows no signs of decay even when observations extend over a period of a year. As a result of such measurements, it has been estimated that it would require 10^{99} years for the supercurrent to decay! To the best of our knowledge, therefore, the lifetime of these "persistent" currents is infinite. The persistent or frictionless currents in superconductors are not a recent discovery; they were observed first over 60 years ago (see SUPERCONDUCTIVITY).

In the case of liquid helium, these currents are, as mentioned, hydrodynamic, i.e., they consist of streams of neutral (uncharged) helium atoms flowing in rings. Since, unlike electrons, the helium atoms carry no charge, there is no resulting magnetic field. This makes such currents much more difficult to create and detect. Nevertheless, as a result of research carried out here and in England in the past ten or eleven years, the existence of these supercurrents in liquid helium has definitely been proved. These currents have been observed (1964) for periods as long as 12 hours, a time of the order of 10^3 shorter than is the case for electron currents. Nevertheless, our present belief is that these hydrodynamic currents also possess an infinite lifetime.

As mentioned, the empirical discovery of infinite-lifetime electron currents is of considerable antiquity, and from the beginning, many attempts have been made to explain the effect theoretically. Until recently all such attempts have failed completely, and as a matter of fact, the theoretical picture is still not completely satisfactory. Nevertheless, immense progress in this direction has occurred in the past two decades largely as the result of work in the U.S.A., England and Russia.

Although superfluidity in liquid helium is important to our basic understanding of the phenomenon, it is the effect in superconductors which arouses the most interest. This is due, in part at least, to the possible practical applications to which the effect might lead. In ordinary conductors (e.g., copper), the flow of an electric current is always accompanied by energy dissipation. The supercurrents propagate with no such power loss; superconducting transmission lines would be an economic advance of the first order. However, they would require "room temperature" superconductors, and unfortunately, modern theories, while they do not absolutely prohibit such, render their occurrence most unlikely.

In other ways, however, superconductors have already proved of practical value. Since the currents once created are there for all time, they have fairly obvious use as memory elements in computers. Again the persistent currents form a sort of super gyroscope more perfect than any so far devised. In recent years alloy superconductors have been found (e.g., Nb_3Sn) which can support persistent currents even in the presence of intense magnetic fields of the order of 100 000 gauss. It is, generally speaking, a property of elemental superconductors that the persistent current is quenched in fields of a few hundred gauss; the situation in some alloys like the above is very different.

This has led to the development of intense field solenoidal magnets which maintain their magnetic fields with zero energy dissipation. A conventional electromagnet of the same size would consume many hundreds of kilowatts. This discovery has important consequences in several areas of physics.

Both aspects of superfluidity find their theoretical explanation in what is called a two-fluid theoretical model. We suppose that liquid helium and superconductors are quantum systems possessing a zero energy ground state plus a series of available states of higher energy called normal or excited states. The occupancy of the ground state is zero above the superfluid transition temperature (2.2 K for liquid helium) but grows steadily as the temperature is lowered. At absolute zero, the whole system is in the ground state. At any finite temperature, below transition, the system is in a mixture of ground and excited states. It is the particles in the ground state which form the persistent current.

A simple, though not entirely accurate, *raison d'etre* for the persistent currents lies in the fact that in the ground state, all the very many particles possess the same single wave function. It follows from this that such particles are not easily scattered out of the ground state—a finite amount of energy is required. Such an assembly will not readily interact with outside particles including those in excited states. Since fluid friction or viscosity is due to particle momentum interchange between neighboring layers of liquid, it follows that particles in the ground state will possess zero viscosity. This, in turn, means frictionless flow.

An assembly of particles obeying Bose-Einstein statistics will, below a certain temperature, possess a ground state like the one postulated above. It is known that Bose-Einstein statistics

apply only to particles which possess zero (or integral) spin. The neutral He^4 atom possesses zero spin. The isotope He^3 (spin $\frac{1}{2}$) does not; and, in fact, liquid He^3 is not a superfluid. But this is also true of electrons which possess half integral spin and obey a very different statistic (Fermi-Dirac). In this statistic no more than two electrons can possess the same wave function. Hence a ground state, in the above sense, can clearly not exist. Thus according to our model, superfluid flow of electrons cannot occur—but it does!

A way out of this dilemma was suggested nearly 30 years ago. Namely, combine the electrons in pairs, with opposite spins. The resulting "particle" is then a boson and may properly reside in the ground state. The reason why this idea was not accepted by theoretical physicists until recently was because no mechanism could be found by which the electrons could be induced to form pairs. It turns out that the required mechanism arises as a result of a phonon (quantized lattice wave) emitted by one electron and absorbed by another at some other place. This couples the two together.

As mentioned, none of the current theories clearly explains persistent currents. It is not at all evident that their lifetimes should be infinite. It is thought by some that a better formulation for statistical mechanics than presently exists may be necessary before this becomes possible.

A system of persistent currents distinguished by the fact that many particles possess the same wave function constitutes a quantum effect on a hitherto unknown macroscopic scale. In other words, superfluids should exhibit quantum effects of such size that they are readily amenable to experimentation. Two such effects, one in each of the superfluids, have been found. A long thin cylinder with a hole along the axis (i.e., a tube) is similar to the previously mentioned superconducting ring in that persistent currents may also be produced in it. If the length of the cylinder is large compared to the diameter of the hole, the "trapped" magnetic field due to the persistent current is substantially uniform. The flux is the product of this field by the area of the hole.

As a consequence of the fact that the particles producing the current all possess the same wave function, it may be shown that this flux is quantized in integral multiples of hc/q ($h =$ Planck's constant, $c =$ velocity of light, $q =$ charge on the particles).

This prediction has been confirmed experimentally (1961). Further, these experiments show that $q = 2e$, where e is the charge on an electron. Thus the pair hypothesis is very nicely proven.

An interesting consequence of the above effect is that it is impossible to have any field (below a certain value depending on the size of the hole) at all in the cavity. Thus the measurements show that $hc/q \cong 2 \times 10^{-7}$ so that with a hole 1μ in diameter, a field less than about 13 gauss

could not exist. We should therefore have a truly field-free space.

A very similar situation, due fundamentally to the same cause, exists for the hydrodynamic currents in liquid helium. In this case, it is the hydrodynamic "circulation" which is quantized in units of h/m ($h =$ Planck's constant, $m =$ helium atom mass). By circulation we mean $\oint \mathbf{v} \cdot \mathbf{dl}$ where $\mathbf{v}$ is the velocity of the atom in the ring-current and $\mathbf{dl}$ is a line element of the periphery of the ring. This effect has also been observed in laboratory experiments (1958).

There is also a surprising consequence connected with this effect. Suppose the helium being rotated in its containing vessel at a temperature above 2.2 K. Here the helium is "classical" and would rotate, like any other familiar liquid, at the same angular velocity as the vessel. Suppose, now, that the helium was cooled down to near 0 K with the vessel still rotating. If the initial speed were less than that required to produce one quantum of circulation, the rotating helium would come to rest while the container continued to rotate!

This is analogous to the behavior of the magnetic flux on the superconductor, the angular velocity being the quantity analogous to the magnetic field. To be sure, the above experiment has, to date, not been performed, but this is entirely due to difficulties with the existing instrumentation. With advances in technique, it seems very likely that the experiment can eventually be performed, and there is little doubt that the result perdicted will be observed.

C. T. LANE

Cross-references: BOSE-EINSTEIN STATISTICS AND BOSONS; CONDUCTIVITY, ELECTRICAL; ELECTRON SPIN; FERMI-DIRAC STATISTICS AND FERMIONS; PHONONS; SUPERCONDUCTIVITY.

SURFACE PHYSICS*

Thermodynamics and Simplified Models of Surfaces The reversible work required to create a unit area of solid surface at a constant volume, temperature and chemical potential is customarily called the surface tension and denoted as γ. The Helmhotz free energy per unit area of surface, f_s, is thus:

$$f_s = \gamma + \sum_i \mu_i \Gamma_i$$

where μ_i and Γ_i are respectively the chemical potential and excess surface density of the ith component. For one-component systems, $\gamma = f_s$, Γ_i then being 0. For a liquid, γ is equal to the surface stress; in a solid, this is not true, and in fact, components of the surface stress tensor may be zero or of either sign. The above defini-

*Editor was unable to locate author. Article is reprinted from first edition.

tions are somewhat inadequate for a general surface. The ambiguities in the definition of surface properties have been treated by Gibbs and discussed in several places.[1,2]

Crudely the surface tension arises from the fact that the surface atoms are bound to fewer neighbors than are atoms in the bulk phase. Assuming neighbor-neighbor interactions and no surface distortion, one may estimate γ by counting broken bonds which yields, for a close packed surface, $A\gamma \approx \frac{1}{4} (L_0/N)$ where A is the area per surface atom, L_0 is molar heat of sublimation and N is Avagadro's number. These assumptions are obviously inadequate, and the estimate gives only the order of magnitude of γ which for metals is on the order of several hundred to several thousand ergs per square centimeter.

For a crystal, γ is a function of the crystallographic orientation of the surface. A surface with a mean orientation the same as that of a low index face is usually thought to be smooth. For surfaces inclined with respect to low index planes there will be atomic planes which terminate on the surface at steps. In the crude picture, additional broken bonds are associated with the steps and thus the energy will be higher than for a closepacked plane. Again, counting broken bonds, and assuming steps widely separated so as not to interact, leads to:

$$\gamma(\theta) = \gamma_0 \cos\theta + \alpha \sin|\theta|; \theta \ll 1$$

where γ_0 is the surface tension of the low index face, α is proportional to the energy per step, and $\gamma(\theta)$ is the surface tension for a surface inclined by an angle θ from the low index face. Thus, on a polar plot of $\gamma(\theta)$ vs the orientation of the normal to the surface, there will be cusps at the orientations of close-packed planes. At finite temperature, the cusps disappear because of entropy considerations.

The surface tension is changed by adsorption on the surface in accordance with Gibbs' adsorption equation:

$$d\gamma = -s_s dT - \sum_i \Gamma_i d\mu_i$$

where s_s is the specific surface entropy. Thus, at constant temperature, introduction of a component which is adsorbed on the surface reduces γ and generally changes the shape of the γ plot since the Γ_i depend on the orientation of the surface.

The equilibrium shape of a crystal depends on the orientation dependence of γ and may be determined graphically by the Wulff construction. In the polar plot of the γ diagram mentioned above, one constructs planes perpendicular to all radius vectors at the point at which they intersect the γ plot. Then the figure containing all points which may be reached from the origin without crossing any such plane has the same shape as the equilibrium crystal. Her-

ring[1] has discussed proofs of the Wulff construction and possible equilibrium shapes of crystals.

A smooth surface of an orientation not represented in the Wulff equilibrium shape will be able to reduce its surface energy by developing facets, keeping the same mean orientation. Such faceting may be observed if the kinetics allow it in reasonable time and if other processes such as selective evaporation or chemical reactions do not allow the development of the equilibrium surface. When faceting driven by the surface energy is observed, it should yield information about the anisotropy of γ.

Atoms may be transported from one surface site to another by (1) transport through a vapor phase, (2) diffusion through the bulk, and (3) surface diffusion. Only the last is considered briefly here. The surface self-diffusion is thermally activated and often is much faster than bulk diffusion and vapor transport. The situation is somewhat complicated by the fact that atoms may occupy a variety of sites on a surface, i.e., (1) as an adatom on an otherwise smooth surface, (2) as an atom on a step, (3) as an atom at a jog in the step, (4) as an atom in a step, or (5) as an atom within a smooth layer. A diffusing atom will occupy each type of these sites in its motion over the surface, and for each type, there will be a different average jump frequency. In a given experimental situation, the diffusion will depend on the population of atoms in the various sites which may not be in equilibrium. Furthermore, the diffusion will not necessarily be isotropic in the plane of the surface and will be affected by absorbed impurities.

The surface self diffusion is measured experimentally by observing development of grain boundary grooves, smoothing of scratches, thermal faceting, blunting of field-emission microscope tips, by radioactive tracer techniques and by field ion-microscopy. N. A. Gjostein[3] has written a review of surface diffusion and has summarized available experimental data.

Atomic Structure of Surfaces In the previous paragraphs, reference has been made to surface structures as if they resulted by simply terminating the bulk structure along a plane with perhaps some terraces, steps and jogs. Recently, mainly through slow electron diffraction experiments, considerable detailed information concerning actual structures has become available. Within several atomic layers of the surfaces, real structures may differ from those of the bulk by small distortions or may be completely "reconstructed." Elizabeth A. Wood has proposed conventions for describing surface structures which are followed here.[4] The region of the material in which the structure is periodic in the direction normal to the surface (the structure is triperiodic) is the substrate. The region in which the structure is diperiodic is called the selvedge. Whereas in a triperiodic structure unit cells are arranged in one of the fourteen Bravais lattices, in a diperiodic structure unit meshes are arranged in one

TABLE 1 (TAKEN FROM WOOD'S PAPER)[a]

Shape of Mesh	Lattice Symbol[b]	Choice of Axis	Nature of Axis and Angles	Name of Corresponding System
General parallelogram	p	$a < b$	$a \neq b$ $\gamma \neq 90°$	Oblique
Rectangular	p c	Shortest two mutually perpendicular vectors $a < b$	$a \neq b$ $\gamma \neq 90°$	Rectangular
Square	p	Shortest two mutually perpendicular vectors	$a = b$ $\gamma = 90°$	Square
120° angle rhombus	p	Shortest two vectors at 120° to each other	$a = b$ $\gamma = 120°$	Hexagonal

[a]From Wood, Elizabeth A., "Vocabulary of Surface Crystallography," *J. Appl. Phys.*, **35**, 1306 (1964).
[b]p refers to a primitive mesh and c to a centered one.

of five nets. The five nets are described in Table 1.

Most of the usual crystallographic notation of triperiodic structures can be carried over to diperiodic systems with only obvious modifications. These are listed by Wood. The reciprocal lattice becomes a family of rods normal to the net. The Miller indices of rows are customarily given in terms of the substrate, and since surface structures often have large unit meshes, fractional Miller indices are used.

The surface structure usually bears a close relationship to the substrate, and this fact is used in a convenient notation to designate the surface structure. The orientation of the substrate plane parallel to the surface is specified first, then the ratios of the lengths of unit mesh vectors of the surface structures and of the substrate plane, and finally the chemical symbol of any adsorbed atoms if present. As an example, Ni(110) 3 × 1 – O refers to a surface structure on the (110) face of nickel with unit mesh vectors parallel to the substrate, with

$$|\vec{a}_{surface}|/|\vec{a}_{substrate}| = 3,$$

and $\vec{b}_{surface}|/|\vec{b}_{substrate}| = 1$

and containing adsorbed oxygen. If the two ratios above are the same, only their common value is given.

The surface structure of several materials and adsorbed layers on them have been investigated by low-energy electron diffraction techniques. Summaries of the results and references to them are given by J. J. Lander[5] and in reference 6.

Surfaces of the dense planes of metals, layered materials such as graphite and cleavage planes of ionic crystals generally differ by only small distortions from the corresponding bulk structures. As examples: Peria and Johnson[7] find that the low-energy electron diffraction from the cleavage plane of MgO is best fit by displacing the second layer of magnesium ions 0.35 Å toward the surface, the oxygen ions remaining fixed; Germer and Mac Rae[8] suggest that the spacing between the first and second atomic

layers of clean nickel is 5 per cent greater than in the bulk material. These results should perhaps be considered as tentative since a completely satisfactory understanding of the scattered intensities in slow electron diffraction experiments is not yet available.

Covalently bonded materials are more likely to have "reconstructed" surface structures as might be expected from the unfavorable energy of structures with broken bonds. There may be a wide variety of such structures for surfaces of each orientation, and prediction of such structures from first principles is as yet impossible. Interesting examples of such structures are the surfaces of freshly cleaved and then annealed silicon. In a (111) surface cleaved at room temperature in vacuum, alternate "rows of top layer atoms are brought into the adjacent rows and given double bonds to the atoms already there. The broken bonds of atoms in the row below are then restored by displacing these atoms to form paired rows."[9] It is interesting that this structure has twofold rotational symmetry on a substrate of threefold symmetry. At 700°C, the structure is "reconstructed" to a more stable one, Si (111)−7 or Si (111)−5 which are made up of "warped benzene rings," each unit having three atoms from both the first and second layers of atoms. The outer layer contains only about three-fourths as many atoms as the freshly cleaved structure, and therefore diffusion of atoms out of the surface is required for its formation.

The variety and complexity of actual surface structures illustrates the serious shortcoming of those calculations of surface properties based on simplified models.

Electronic Structure The electronic structure in the vicinity of the surface differs from that which would result from simply terminating the crystal along a plane and allowing no subsequent relaxation. In a metal, the electronic charge distribution does not end abruptly at the surface, but decreases smoothly and extends beyond the boundaries of the Wigner-Seitz cells of the surface atoms. This leads to a surface dipole layer, negative on the outside, which,

along with the image potential, is the major contribution of the surface to the work function of the metal. This contribution is the order of a few tenths of an electron volt and is the order of 10 per cent of the observed work function. The larger contributions are due to the bulk properties and are not discussed here. In a metal, the thickness of the region in which the electron density differs from its bulk value is on the order of the interatomic spacing, which is of course the order of the wavelength of the most energetic conduction electrons. This smooth decrease of the charge density at the surface is a result of a compromise between the higher electrostatic energy of the dipole layer and the kinetic energy it would require to make a steeper boundary. This same compromise will make the boundary of the electron distribution smoother in the directions parallel to the surface than the boundary of the ion cores. The hill and valley structure of atomically rough surfaces then gives an additional dipole layer with the positive side outward. Thus, rougher surfaces have lower work functions than more closely packed, smoother surfaces.

The electronic distribution makes a contribution to the surface energy, but realistic calculations are very difficult and the usual discussions are for a free electron gas model. Because the conduction electrons adjust easily to the potential at the surface, metals have surface energies of only $\frac{1}{2}$ to $\frac{2}{3}$ that which would be predicted from the sublimation energy. For both the surface energy and the work function, the lattice potential and correlation and exchange terms are important. The theoretical approaches to these problems are reviewed by Ewald and Juretschke[10] and by Herring.[11]

For the half-infinite crystal with a periodic potential, there is the possibility that there are localized states on the surface with energies within the band gaps of the bulk structure. The wave functions of these states are exponentially damped on both sides of the surface. The area density of such states should be the same order as the density of surface atoms. They are called Tamm states after I. Tamm who first investigated them for a one dimensional Kronig-Penney model. The conditions for the existence of surface states for actual crystals are not completely clear, but in some models they appear if the energy bands of the bulk overlap or if the surface atomic structure is different from the bulk, resulting in a potential trough. Discussions of both theoretical and experimental aspects of surface states can be found in the papers of reference 6.

Surface states are particularly important in semiconductors, and there has been extensive work on Germanium crystals[12]. They are of two types: (1) "fast" states which occur on atomically clean surfaces or at the interface between the semiconductor and its oxide layer, which are thus in good electrical contact with the bulk, and which therefore may adjust their occupation in the order of 10^{-6} to 10^{-8} second following a disturbance; and (2) "slow" states on the outer surface of the oxide layer and for which changes in the occupation after a disturbance are much slower. The observed density of the "fast" states is a few orders of magnitude smaller than the surface density of atoms so they are not truly Tamm states, but may be due to imperfections or deformations of the surface.

There will be a surface space charge region which shields any charge localized in the surface states and which will, because of the low density of free carriers in the semiconductor, extend into the bulk to depths usually the order of 10^{-5} cm. The energy bands bend through this region in order to give the requisite shielding charge. The bending of the bands will lead to regions in which the conductivity type (n or p) may be opposite that of the bulk (i.e., an inversion layer) or in which the conductivity is more strongly of the same type as the bulk (i.e., an accumulation layer) or, finally, in an intermediate case, in a region where the conductance of the specimen is decreased, called an exhaustion layer. The energies, densities, and trapping and recombination cross sections of the surface states can be investigated by measurements of various electrical properties. The discussion of these investigations is beyond the scope of this article and the reader is referred to reviews by Watkins,[12] Law,[13] and by Zemel.[14]

M. B. WEBB

References

1. Herring, C., in Gomer and Smith, Eds., "Structure and Properties of Solid Surfaces," Chicago, Ill., University of Chicago Press, 1952.
2. Mullens, W. W., in "Metal Surfaces," ASM, 1962.
3. Gjostein, N. A., in "Metal Surfaces," ASM, 1962.
4. Wood, E. A., *J. Appl. Phys.*, **35**, 1306 (1964).
5. Lander, J. J., *Surface Sci.*, **1**, 125 (1964).
6. *Surface Science*, **2** (1964). This entire volume contains the proceedings of the International Conference on the Physics and Chemistry of Solids (1964).
7. Johnson, D. C., Ph.D. thesis, University of Minnesota, 1964 (unpublished).
8. Mac Rae, A. U., and Germer, L. H., *Ann. N.Y. Acad. Sci.*, **101**, 627 (1963).
9. Lander, J. J., Gobeli, G. W., Morrison, J., *J. Appl. Phys.*, **34**, 2298 (1963).
10. Ewald, P. P. and Juretschke, H., in Gomer and Smith, Eds., "Structure and Properties of Solid Surfaces," Chicago, Ill., University of Chicago Press, 1952.
11. Herring, C., in "Metal Interfaces," A.S.M., 1952.
12. Watkins, T. B., "Progress in Semiconductors," New York, John Wiley & Sons, Vol. 5, 1960.
13. Law, J. T., in Hannay, Ed., "Semiconductors," New York, Van Nostrand Reinhold, 1959.
14. Zemel, J. N., *Ann. N.Y. Acad. Sci.*, **101**, 830 (1963).

Cross-references: CRYSTALLOGRAPHY, SOLID-STATE PHYSICS, SOLID-STATE THEORY, SURFACE TENSION.

SURFACE TENSION

Surface tension results from the tendency of a liquid surface to contract. It is given by the tension σ across a unit length of a line on the surface of a liquid. The surface tension of a liquid depends on the temperature and diminishes as temperature increases and becomes 0 at the critical temperature. For water σ is 0.073 newtons/m at 20°C, and for mercury it is 0.47 newtons/m at 18°C.

Surface tension is intimately connected with capillarity, that is, rise or depression of liquid inside a tube of small bore when the tube is dipped into the liquid. Another factor which is related to this phenomenon is the angle of contact. If a liquid is in contact with a solid and with air along a line, the angle θ between the solid-liquid interface and the liquid-air interface is called the angle of contact (Fig. 1). If $\theta = 0$, the liquid is said to wet the tube thoroughly. If θ is less than 90°, the liquid rises in the capillary, and if θ is greater than 90°, the liquid does not wet the solid but is depressed in the tube. For mercury on glass, the angle of contact is 140°, so that mercury is depressed when a glass capillary is dipped into mercury. The rise h of the liquid in the capillary is given by $h = 2\sigma \cos \theta / r\rho g$, where r is the radius of the tube, ρ the density of the liquid, and g is the acceleration due to gravity.

Surface tension can be explained on the basis of molecular theory. If the surface area of liquid is expanded, some of the molecules inside the liquid rise to the surface. Because a molecule inside a mass of liquid is under the forces of the surrounding molecules while a molecule on the surface is only partly surrounded by other mole-cules, work is necessary to bring molecules from the inside to the surface. This indicates that force must be applied along the surface in order to increase the area of the surface. This force appears as tension on the surface and when expressed as tension per unit length of a line lying on the surface, it is called the surface tension of the liquid.

The molecular theory of surface tension has been dealt with since the time of Laplace (1749–1827). As a result of the clarification of the nature of intermolecular forces by quantum mechanics and of the recent development in the study of molecular distribution in liquids, the nature and the value of surface tension have come to be understood from a molecular point of view.

Surface tension is closely associated with a sudden but continuous change in the density from the value for bulk liquid to the value for the gaseous state in traversing the surface (Fig. 2). As a result of this inhomogeneity, the stress across a strip parallel to the boundary—p_N per unit area—is different from that across a strip perpendicular to the boundary—p_T per unit area. This is in contrast with the case of homogeneous fluid in which the stress across any elementary plane has the same value regardless of the direction of the plane.

The stress p_T is a function of the coordinate z, the z-axis being taken normal to the surface and directed from liquid to vapor. The stress p_N is constant throughout the liquid and the vapor. The figure shows the stress p_N and p_T. The stress $p_T(z)$ as function of z is also shown on the left side of the figure.

The surface tension is given by integrating the

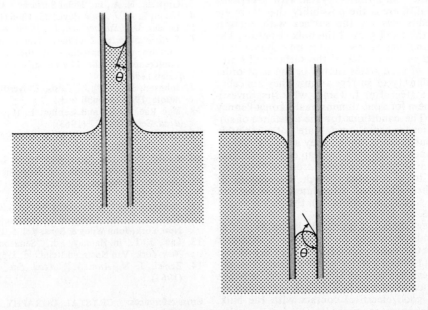

FIG. 1. Capillarity.

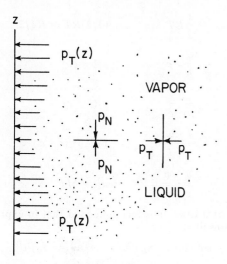

FIG. 2. Stress relationships in surface tension.

difference $p_N - p_T(z)$ over z:

$$\sigma = \int_{\text{(liquid)}}^{\text{(vapor)}} [p_N - p_T(z)]\, dz$$

A statistical mechanical treatment of the system leads to the expression of p_N and p_T in terms of intermolecular forces, density distribution, and the distribution of other molecules around a molecule which is located at a position z. The change of the number density and the distribution of other molecules around a central molecule at z are problems which have not yet been completely solved. Some simplifying assumptions such as to assume the transition layer to be a mathematical surface of density discontinuity have made the theory more amenable to numerical calculations. It can be said that so far as such simple liquids as liquid argon are concerned, the values of surface tension have been calculated theoretically in fair agreement with observed values.

AKIRA HARASIMA

References

Hirschfelder, J. O., Curtiss C. F., and Bird, R. B., "Molecular Theory of Gases and Liquids," p. 336, New York, John Wiley & Sons, 1954.

Harasima, A., "Molecular Theory of Surface Tension," in Prigogine, Ed., "Advances in Chemical Physics," Vol. I, New York, Interscience Publishers, 1958.

Ono, S., and Kondo, S., "Molecular Theory of Surface Tension in Liquids," in Flügge, S., Ed., "Encyclopedia of Physics," Vol. X, "Structure of Liquids," p. 134, Berlin, Springer, 1960.

Kirkwood, J. G., "Theory of Liquids," p. 127, New York, Gordon and Breach, 1968.

Cross-references: LIQUID STATE, STATISTICAL MECHANICS.

SYMBOLS, UNITS, AND NOMENCLATURE IN PHYSICS

Introduction International communication and cooperation in science continue to grow in importance. Not the least important aspect of this cooperation is uniformity of international usage of symbols, units, and nomenclature in physics. The proliferation of research in countries throughout the world makes the problem of uniformity of usage a vital one in the dissemination of scientific literature, for it is obvious that much time and effort can be wasted in misunderstandings arising from terminology.

The recommendations given here are primarily those of the Commission on Symbols, Units and Nomenclature of the International Union of Pure and Applied Physics* as approved by the General Assemblies of IUPAP, 1960–1972. There is agreement on these recommendations among the following international organizations:

(1) International Organization for Standardization;

(2) General Conference on Weights and Measures;

(3) International Union of Pure and Applied Chemistry;

(4) International Electrotechnical Commission, Technical Committees 24, 25;

(5) International Commission on Illumination.

Physical Quantities—General Recommendations A physical quantity, represented by a symbol, is equivalent to the product of a *numerical value* and a *unit*. For dimensionless physical quantities, the unit often has no name or symbol and is not explicitly indicated.

EXAMPLES:

$$E = 200\text{ J} \qquad n_{\text{qu.}} = 1.55$$
$$F = 27\text{ N} \qquad f = 3 \times 10^8\text{ Hz}$$

Symbols for Physical Quantities—General Rules. (1) *Symbols for physical quantities* should be *single letters* of the Latin or Greek alphabet with or without modifying signs: subscripts, superscripts, dashes, etc.

REMARK: (a) An exception to this rule consists of the two-letter symbols, which are sometimes used to represent dimensionless combinations of physical quantities. If such a symbol, composed of two letters, appears as a factor in a product, it is recommended to separate this symbol from the other symbols by a dot or by brackets or by a space.

(b) Abbreviations, i.e., shortened forms of names or expressions, such as p.f. for partition function should not be used in physical equations. These abbreviations in the text should be written in ordinary Roman type.

(2) *Symbols for physical quantities* should be printed in *italic* (i.e., sloping) *type*.

---

*UIP 11 (SUN 65-3), 1965.

REMARK: Subscripts and superscripts should be in italic type when they are symbols for physical quantities or when they are running indices: e.g., C_p where p represents pressure but C_g where g means gas; F_{ik} where i and k are running indices but E_k where k means kinetic.

(3) *Symbols for vectors and tensors*: Special type fonts are recommended for these quantities but not for their components:

(a) Vectors should be printed in boldface type.

(b) Tensors of the second rank should be printed in sans serif type.

Simple Mathematical Operations. (1) *Addition and subtraction* of two physical quantities are indicated by

$$a + b \quad \text{and} \quad a - b$$

(2) *Multiplication* of two physical quantities may be indicated in one of the following ways:

$$ab \quad a\ b \quad a \cdot b \quad a \times b$$

REMARK: The various products of vectors and tensors may be written in the following ways:

Scalar product of vectors **A** and **B**: **A** · **B**
Vector product of vectors **A** and **B**: **A** × **B**
Dyadic product of vectors **A** and **B**: **AB**
Scalar product of tensors S and T
$(\sum_{ik} S_{ik} T_{ki})$ S : T
Tensor product of tensors S and T
$(\sum_k S_{ik} T_{kl})$ S · T
Product of tensor S and vector **A**
$(\sum_k S_{ik} A_k)$ S · **A**

(3) *Division* of one quantity by another quantity may be indicated in one of the following ways:

$$\frac{a}{b} \quad a/b \quad a\ b^{-1} \quad a(1/b)$$

These procedures can be extended to cases where one of the quantities or both are themselves products, quotients, sums or differences of other quantities

If necessary, brackets have to be used in accordance with the rules of mathematics.

If the solidus is used to separate the numerator from the denominator and if there is any doubt where the numerator starts or where the denominator ends, brackets should be used.

EXAMPLES:

Expressions with a Horizontal bar	Same Expressions with a Solidus
$\dfrac{a}{bcd}$	a/bcd
$\dfrac{2}{9} \sin kx$	$(2/9) \sin kx$

$\dfrac{1}{2} RT$	$(1/2)RT$ or $RT/2$
$\dfrac{a}{b} - c$	$a/b - c$
$\dfrac{a}{b - c}$	$a/(b - c)$
$\dfrac{a - b}{c - d}$	$(a - b)/(c - d)$
$\dfrac{a}{c} - \dfrac{b}{d}$	$a/c - b/d$

REMARK: It is recommended that in expressions like:

$$\sin\{2\pi(x - x_0)/\lambda\}, \quad \exp\{(r - r_0)/\sigma\},$$
$$\exp\{-V(r)/kT\}, \sqrt{(\epsilon/c^2)}$$

the argument should always be placed between brackets, except when the argument is a simple product of two quantities, e.g., sin kx. When the horizontal bar above the square root is used no brackets are needed.

Units—General Recommendations   *Symbols for Units—General Rules.* (1) *Symbols for units* of physical quantities should be printed in *roman* (upright) *type*.

(2) *Symbols for units* should not contain a final full stop and should remain unaltered in the plural, e.g., 7 cm and *not* 7cms.

(3) *Symbols for units* should be printed in *lower case* roman (upright) type. However, the symbol for a unit, derived from a proper name, should start with a capital roman letter, e.g., m (meter); A (ampere); Wb (weber); Hz (hertz).

Mathematical Operations. (1) *Multiplication* of two units may be indicated in one of the following ways:

$$\text{newton meter: } \text{N} \cdot \text{m (preferred)}, \text{N m}$$

(2) *Division* of one unit by another unit may be indicated in one of the following ways:

$$\text{meter per second: } \frac{\text{m}}{\text{s}}, \text{m/s}, \text{m s}^{-1}$$

or by any other way of writing the product of m and s^{-1}. Not more than one solidus should be used, e.g., not J/K/mol, but J/K · mol.

Numbers and Figures (1) *Numbers* should be printed in *upright type.*

(2) *Division* of one number by another number may be indicated in the following ways:

$$\frac{136}{273.15} \quad 136/273.15$$

or by writing it as the product of numerator and the inverse first power of the denominator.

In such cases, the number under the inverse power should always be placed between brackets.

REMARK: When the solidus is used and when there is any doubt where the numerator starts or the denominator ends, brackets should be used, as in the case of physical quantities.

(3) To facilitate the reading of large numbers, the figures may be grouped in *groups of three*, but no comma should be used, since European convention uses the comma as a decimal point.
EXAMPLE:

2 573 421 736.01

Symbols for Chemical Elements, Nuclides, and Particles (1) *Symbols for chemical elements* should be written in *roman* (upright) *type*. The symbol is not followed by a full stop.
EXAMPLES:

Ca   C   H   He

(2) A nuclide is specified by the chemical symbol and the mass number, which should appear as a left superscript, e.g., ^{14}N. The atomic number may be shown too as a left subscript, e.g., $_7^{14}N$, if needed. The right superscript position may be used to indicate a state of ionization, e.g., Ca^{2+}, OH^-, or a state of excitation, e.g., $^{110}Ag^m$, $^4He^*$. The right subscript position is used to indicate the number of atoms of the specified nuclide or chemical element in a molecule, e.g., H_2SO_4.

(3) Symbols for particles and quanta

neutron	n
triton	t
leptons	e (electron), ν (neutrino), μ (muon)
mesons	π (pion), K, η
baryons	$\Lambda, \Sigma, \Xi, \Omega$
proton	p
helion	h
α-particle	α
deuteron	d
photon	γ

The charge of particles may be indicated by adding the superscript +, -, or 0.
EXAMPLES:

$\pi^+, \pi^-, \eta^0, p^+, p^-, e^+, e^-$

If in connection with the symbols p and e no charge is indicated, these symbols should refer to the positive proton and the negative electron respectively. The bar or tilde above the symbol of a particle is ofted used to indicate the antiparticle of that particle (e.g., $\bar{\nu}$ for antineutrino).

Quantum States (1) A symbol indicating the quantum state of a *system* such as an atom should be printed in capital roman (upright) type. The right subscript indicates the total angular momentum quantum number, and the left superscript indicates the multiplicity.

EXAMPLE:

$$^2P_{3/2}(J = \frac{3}{2}, \text{spin-multiplicity: 2})$$

(2) A symbol indicating the quantum state of a single *particle* such as an electron should be printed in lower-case roman (upright) type. The right subscript may be used to indicate the total angular momentum quantum number of the particle.
EXAMPLE:

$p_{3/2}$(electron state)

(3) The letter symbols corresponding to the *angular momentum quantum numbers* should be:

0 S, s	4 G, g	8 L, l
1 P, p	5 H, h	9 M, m
2 D, d	6 I, i	10 N, n
3 F, f	7 K, k	11 O, o

Nomenclature (1) *Use of the words specific and molar.* The word "specific" in English names for physical quantities should be restricted to the meaning "divided by mass."
EXAMPLES:

Specific volume	volume/mass
Specific energy	energy/mass
Specific heat capacity	heat capacity/mass

The word "molar" in the name of an extensive physical quantity should be restricted to the meaning "divided by amount of substance."
EXAMPLE

molar volume   volume/amount of substance

(2) *Notation for covariant character of coupling:*

S Scalar coupling	A Axial vector coupling
V Vector coupling	P Pseudoscalar coupling
T Tensor coupling	

(3) *Abbreviated notation for a nuclear reaction.* The meaning of the symbolic expression indicating a nuclear reaction should be the following:

$$\text{Initial nuclide} \begin{pmatrix} \text{incoming particle or quantum} & \text{outgoing particle(s) or quanta} \end{pmatrix} \text{Final nuclide}$$

EXAMPLES:

$^{14}N(\alpha, p)^{17}O$ $^{59}Co(n, \gamma)^{60}Co$

$^{23}Na(\gamma, 3n)^{20}Na$ $^{31}P(\gamma, pn)^{29}Si$

(4) *Character of transitions.* Multipolarity of transition:

Electric or magnetic monopole	E0 or M0
Electric or magnetic dipole	E1 or M1
Electric or magnetic quadrupole	E2 or M2
Electric or magnetic octupole	E3 or M3
Electric or magnetic 2^n pole	En or Mn

(5) *Nuclide:* A species of *atoms*, with specified atomic number and mass number should be indicated by the word *nuclide*, not by the word *isotope*.

Different nuclides having the same atomic number should be described as *isotopes*.

Different nuclides having the same mass number should be described as *isobars*.

SI Units The General Conference on Weights and Measures, to which the United States adheres by treaty, has established the International System of Units, called SI units. The seven base quantities of this system and the corresponding units and their symbols are:

length	meter	m
mass	kilogram	kg
time	second	s
electric current	ampere	A
thermodynamic temperature	kelvin	K
luminous intensity	candela	cd
amount of substance	mole	mol

The units radian (rad) for plane angle and steradian (sr) for solid angle are described as supplementary units and are normally treated as though they were base units, although the corresponding quantities may be treated as dimensionless. The coherent SI unit system consists of the above units plus all of the units derived from them by multiplication and division without introducing numerical factors.

A number of derived units have been given special names and symbols.

Decimal multiples of the coherent base and derived SI units are formed by attaching to these units the following prefixes.

Factor by which the Unit is Multiplied	Prefix Name	Symbol
10^{12}	tera	T
10^9	giga	G
10^6	mega	M
10^3	kilo	k
10^2	hecto	h
10	deca	da
10^{-1}	deci	d
10^{-2}	centi	c
10^{-3}	milli	m
10^{-6}	micro	μ
10^{-9}	nano	n
10^{-12}	pico	p
10^{-15}	femto	f
10^{-18}	atto	a

The symbol of a prefix forms, with the unit symbol to which it is directly attached, a compound symbol which may have a positive or negative exponent, and which may be combined with other unit symbols. Thus:

$$1 \text{ cm}^3 = (10^{-2}\text{ m})^3 = 10^{-6}\text{ m}^3 \neq 10^{-2}\text{ m}^3$$

$$1 \text{ C} \cdot \mu\text{s}^{-1} = 1 \text{ C}(10^{-6}\text{ s})^{-1} = 10^6 \text{ C/s}.$$

Note 1. Because the base unit kilogram contains the prefix "kilo," the other prefixes are attached to the name "gram," e.g., milligram (mg) instead of microkilogram (μkg).

Note 2. Compound prefixes should not be used, e.g., use nanometer (nm) and not millimicrometer (mμm).

There are additional units, not part of the coherent system, which are generally accepted for use with the SI units or accepted for use in special fields.

Quantity	Name of SI Derived Unit	Symbol	Expressed in Terms of SI Base or Derived Units
frequency	hertz	Hz	$1 \text{ Hz} = 1 \text{ s}^{-1}$
force	newton	N	$1 \text{ N} = 1 \text{ kg} \cdot \text{m/s}^2$
pressure and stress	pascal	Pa	$1 \text{ Pa} = 1 \text{ N/m}^2$
work, energy, quantity of heat	joule	J	$1 \text{ J} = 1 \text{ N} \cdot \text{m}$
power	watt	W	$1 \text{ W} = 1 \text{ J/s}$
quantity of electricity	coulomb	C	$1 \text{ C} = 1 \text{ A} \cdot \text{s}$
electromotive force, potential difference	volt	V	$1 \text{ V} = 1 \text{ W/A}$
electric capacitance	farad	F	$1 \text{ F} = 1 \text{ A} \cdot \text{s/V}$
electric resistance	ohm	Ω	$1 \ \Omega = 1 \text{ V/A}$
electric conductance	siemens	S	$1 \text{ S} = 1 \ \Omega^{-1}$
flux of magnetic induction, magnetic flux	weber	Wb	$1 \text{ Wb} = 1 \text{ V} \cdot \text{s}$
magnetic flux density, magnetic induction	tesla	T	$1 \text{ T} = 1 \text{ Wb/m}^2$
inductance	henry	H	$1 \text{ H} = 1 \text{ V} \cdot \text{s/A}$
luminous flux	lumen	lm	$1 \text{ lm} = 1 \text{ cd} \cdot \text{sr}$
illuminance	lux	lx	$1 \text{ lx} = 1 \text{ lm/m}^2$

Quantity	Name of Unit	Unit Symbol	Magnitude in SI Units
time	minute	min	60 s
	hour	h	3600 s
	day	d	86400 s
plane angle	degree	°	$\pi/180$ rad
	minute	′	$\pi/10\ 800$ rad
	second	″	$\pi/648\ 000$ rad
volume	litre	l	1 l = 1 dm^3
mass	tonne	t	1 t = 10^3 kg
energy	electronvolt	eV	approx. 1.60219 × 10^{-19} J
mass of an atom	atomic mass unit	u	approx. 1.66053 × 10^{-27} kg
length	astronomical unit	AU	149 600 × 10^6 m
	parsec	pc	approx. 30 857 × 10^{12} m

The following units are accepted by the International Committee of Weights and Measures for use with the SI units for a limited transitional period: angstrom (1 Å = 10^{-10} m), barn (1 b = 10^{-28} m^2), bar (1 bar = 10^5 Pa), standard atmosphere (1 atm = 101 325 Pa), curie (1 Ci = 3.7 × 10^{10} s^{-1}), roentgen (1 R = 2.58 × 10^{-4} C/kg), rad (1 rad = 10^2 J/kg).

Other Unit Systems The cgs system of units, based on the centimeter, gram, and second, as units in mechanics, is a metric system which continues to be used in some branches of physics. In daily life the customary units in the United States are those based on the foot, pound-force,

and second, but these units are almost never used in physics except for the description of equipment, e.g., a 2-inch pipe.

Symbols and Units for Physical Quantities The table below provides an extensive but not exhaustive list of physical quantities with recommended symbols and with the symbol for the SI unit of each quantity. It is understood that deviations from the recommended quantity symbols may sometimes be necessary or desirable. On the other hand, the unit symbols are *standard* symbols for the units they represent, although other units with other symbols may, of course, be used.

Table of Symbols for Physical Quantities

Quantity	Symbol	International Symbol for Unit
SPACE AND TIME		
length	l	m
breadth	b	m
height	h	m
radius	r	m
diameter: $d = 2r$	d	m
path: $L = \int ds$	L, s	m
area	A, S	m^2
volume	$V, (v)$	m^3
plane angle	$\alpha, \beta, \gamma, \theta, \vartheta, \phi$	rad
solid angle	ω, Ω	sr
wave length	λ	m
wave number: $\sigma = 1/\lambda$	σ	m^{-1}
circular wave number: $k = 2\pi/\lambda$	k	m^{-1}
time	t	s
period	T	s
frequency: $\nu = 1/T$	ν, f	Hz
circular frequency: $\omega = 2\pi\nu$	ω	s^{-1}
velocity: $v = ds/dt$	c, u, v	m/s
angular velocity: $\omega = d\phi/dt$	ω	rad/s
acceleration: $a = dv/dt$	a	m/s^2
angular acceleration: $\alpha = d\omega/dt$	α	rad/s^2
gravitational acceleration	g	m/s^2
standard gravitational acceleration	g_n	m/s^2
speed of light in vacuum	c	m/s
relative velocity: v/c	β	

| | | International Symbol for |
Quantity	Symbol	Unit

MECHANICS

mass	m	kg
density: $\rho = m/V$	ρ	kg/m^3
reduced mass	μ	kg
momentum: $p = mv$	$\mathbf{p}, p$	kg · m/s
moment of inertia: $I = \int r^2\, \mathrm{d}m$	I, J	kg · m^2
force	$\mathbf{F}, f$	N
weight	G, W	N
moment of force	$\mathbf{M}, M$	N · m
pressure	p	Pa
normal stress	σ	Pa
shear stress	τ	Pa
gravitational constant: $F(r) = Gm_1 m_2/r^2$	G	N · m^2/kg^2
modulus of elasticity, Young's modulus: $\sigma = E\Delta l/l$	E	N/m^2
shear modulus: $\tau = G\,\mathrm{tg}\,\gamma$	G	N/m^2
compressibility: $\kappa = -(1/V)\mathrm{d}V/\mathrm{d}p$	κ	m^2/N
bulk modulus: $K = 1/\kappa$	K	N/m^2
viscosity	η	Pa · s
kinematic viscosity: $\nu = \eta/\rho$	ν	m^2/s
friction coefficient	f	—
surface tension	γ, σ	N/m
energy	E, U	J
potential energy	V, E_p	J
kinetic energy	T, E_k	J
work	W, A	J
power	P	W
efficiency	η	—
Hamiltonian function	H	J
Lagrangian function	L	J
relative density	d	—

MOLECULAR PHYSICS

number of molecules	N	
number density of molecules: $n = N/V$	n	m^{-3}
Avogadro's constant	$N_0, (L)$	mol^{-1}
molecular mass	m	kg
molecular velocity vector with components	$\mathbf{c}, (c_x, c_y, c_z)$	m/s
	$\mathbf{u}, (u_x, u_y, u_z)$	m/s
molecular position vector with components	$\mathbf{r}, (x, y, z)$	m
molecular momentum vector with components	$\mathbf{p}, (p_x, p_y, p_z)$	kg · m/s
average speed	$\bar{c}, \bar{u}$	m/s
most probable speed	$\hat{c}, \hat{u}$	m/s
mean free path	l	m
molecular attraction energy	ϵ	J
interaction energy between molecules i and j	ϕ_{ij}, V_{ij}	J
velocity distribution function: $n = \int f\, \mathrm{d}c_x \mathrm{d}c_y \mathrm{d}c_z$	$f(c)$	—
generalized coordinate	q	—
generalized momentum	p	—
volume in γ phase space	Ω	—
Boltzmann's constant	k	J/K
$1/kT$ in exponential functions	β	J^{-1}
gas constant per mole	R	J/mol · K
partition function	Q, Z	—
diffusion coefficient	D	m^2/s
thermal diffusion coefficient	D_T	m^2/s
thermal diffusion ratio	K_T	—
thermal diffusion factor	α_T	—

Quantity	Symbol	International Symbol for Unit

MOLECULAR PHYSICS (*Cont.*)

Quantity	Symbol	Unit
characteristic temperature	Θ	K
Debye temperature: $\Theta_D = h\nu_D/k$	Θ_D	K
Einstein temperature: $\Theta_E = h\nu_E/k$	Θ_E	K
rotational temperature: $\Theta_r = h^2/8\pi^2 Ik$	Θ_r	K
vibrational temperature: $\Theta_v = h\nu/k$	Θ_v	K

THERMODYNAMICS

Quantity	Symbol	Unit
quantity of heat	Q	J
work	W, A	J
temperature	$t, (\vartheta)$	K
thermodynamic temperature	$T, (\Theta)$	K
entropy	S	J/K
internal energy	U	J
Helmholtz function: $F = U - TS$	F, A	J
enthalpy: $H = U + pV$	H	J
Gibbs function: $G = U + pV - TS$	G	J
linear expansion coefficient	α_l	K^{-1}
cubic expansion coefficient	α, γ	K^{-1}
thermal conductivity	λ	$W/m \cdot K$
specific heat capacity	c_p, c_v	$J/kg \cdot K$
heat capacity	C_p, C_v	J/K
Joule-Thomson coefficient	μ	$K \cdot m^2/N$
ratio of specific heats	γ, κ	—

ELECTRICITY AND MAGNETISM

Quantity	Symbol	Unit
quantity of electricity	Q	C
charge density	ρ	C/m^3
surface charge density	σ	C/m^2
electric potential	V, Φ	V
electric field strength	$\mathbf{E}, E$	N/C, V/m
electric displacement	$\mathbf{D}, D$	C/m^2
capacitance	C	F
permittivity: $\epsilon = D/E$	ϵ	F/m
permittivity of vacuum	ϵ_0	F/m
relative permittivity: $\epsilon_r = \epsilon/\epsilon_0$	ϵ_r	—
dielectric polarization: $\mathbf{D} = \epsilon_0 \mathbf{E} + \mathbf{P}$	$\mathbf{P}, P$	C/m^2
electric susceptibility	χ_e	—
polarizability	α, γ	$C \cdot m^2/V$
electric dipole moment	$\mathbf{p}, p$	$C \cdot m$
electric current	I	A
electric current density	j, J	A/m^2
magnetic field strength	$\mathbf{H}, H$	A/m
magnetic induction	$\mathbf{B}, B$	T
magnetic flux	Φ	Wb
permeability: $\mu = B/H$	μ	H/m
permeability of vacuum	μ_0	H/m
relative permeability: $\mu_r = \mu/\mu_0$	μ_r	—
magnetization: $\mathbf{B} = \mu_0(\mathbf{H} + \mathbf{M})$	$\mathbf{M}, M$	A/m
magnetic susceptibility	χ_m	—
electromagnetic moment	$\boldsymbol{\mu}, \mu, \mathbf{m}, m$	$A \cdot m^2$
magnetic polarization: $\mathbf{B} = \mu_0 \mathbf{H} + \mathbf{J}$	$\mathbf{J}$	T
magnetic dipole moment	$\mathbf{j}, j$	$Wb \cdot m$
resistance	R	Ω
reactance	X	Ω
impedance: $Z = R + iX$	Z	Ω
admittance: $Y = 1/Z = G + iB$	Y	S
conductance	G	S
susceptance	B	S
resistivity	ρ	$\Omega \cdot m$

Quantity	Symbol	International Symbol for Unit
ELECTRICITY AND MAGNETISM (*Cont.*)		
conductivity: $1/\rho$	γ, σ	S/m
self-inductance	L	H
mutual inductance	M, L_{12}	H
phase number	m	–
loss angle	δ	rad
number of turns	N	–
power	P	W
Poynting vector	$\mathbf{S}, S$	W/m^2
magnetic vector potential	$\mathbf{A}$	Wb/m
LIGHT, RADIATION		
quantity of light	$Q(Q_v)$	lm · s
luminous flux	$\Phi(\Phi_v)$	lm
luminous intensity	$I(I_v)$	cd
illuminance	$E(E_v)$	lx
luminance	$L, (L_v)$	cd/m^2
luminous exitance	M	lm/m^2
radiant energy	$Q, W, (Q_e)$	J
radiant flux	$\Phi, (P, \Phi_e)$	W
radiant intensity	$I, (I_e)$	W/sr
irradiance	$E, (E_e)$	W/m^2
radiance	$L, (L_e)$	W/sr · m^2
radiant exitance	$M, (M_e)$	W/m^2
absorptance	$\alpha(\lambda)$	–
reflectance	$\rho(\lambda)$	–
transmittance	$\tau(\lambda)$	–
linear attenuation coefficient	μ	m^{-1}
linear absorption coefficient	a	m^{-1}
refractive index	n	–
Stefan-Boltzmann constant: $M = \sigma T^4$	σ	W/m^2 · K^4
luminous efficacy: Φ_v/Φ_e	K	lm/W
luminous efficiency: $K/K_{\max}$	V	–
ACOUSTICS		
velocity of sound	c	m/sec
sound energy flux	P	W
reflection factor	ρ	–
acoustic absorption factor: $1 - \rho$	$\alpha, (\alpha_a)$	–
transmisssion factor	τ	–
dissipation factor: $\alpha - \tau$	δ	–
loudness level	$L_N, (\Lambda)$	–
reverberation time	T	s
specific acoustic impedance	$Z_s, (W)$	N · s/m^3
acoustic impedance	$Z_a, (Z)$	N · s/m^5
mechanical impedance	$Z_m, (\omega)$	N · s/m
ATOMIC AND NUCLEAR PHYSICS		
atomic number, proton number	Z	–
mass number	A	–
neutron number: $N = A - Z$	N	–
elementary charge	e	C
electron mass	m, m_e	kg
proton mass	m_p	kg
neutron mass	m_n	kg
meson mass	m_π, m_μ	kg
atomic mass	m_a	kg
(unified) atomic mass constant: $m_u = m_a(^{12}C)/12$	m_u	u
magnetic moment of atom or nucleus	μ	A · m^2

Quantity	Symbol	International Symbol for Unit

ATOMIC AND NUCLEAR PHYSICS (*Cont.*)

Quantity	Symbol	Unit
magnetic moment of proton	μ_p	$A \cdot m^2$
magnetic moment of neutron	μ_n	$A \cdot m^2$
magnetic moment of electron	μ_e	$A \cdot m^2$
Bohr magneton	μ_B	$A \cdot m^2$
Planck constant $\left(\dfrac{h}{2\pi} = \hbar\right)$	h	$J \cdot s$
principal quantum number	n, n_i	−
orbital angular momentum quantum number	L, l_i	−
spin quantum number	S, s_i	−
total angular momentum quantum number	J, j_i	−
magnetic quantum number	M, m_i	−
nuclear spin quantum number	I, J	−
hyperfine quantum number	F	−
rotational quantum number	J, K	−
vibrational quantum number	v	−
quadrupole moment	Q	m^2
Rydberg constant	R_∞	m^{-1}
Bohr radius: $a_0 = 4\pi\epsilon_0\hbar^2/m_e e^2$	a_0	m
fine structure constant: $\alpha = e^2/4\pi\epsilon_0\hbar c$	α	−
mass excess: $m_a - Am_u$	Δ	kg
mass defect	B	kg
packing fraction: Δ/Am_u	f	−
nuclear radius	R	m
nuclear magneton	μ_N	$A \cdot m^2$
g-factor of nucleus: $\mu = gI\mu_N$	g	−
gyromagnetic ratio: $\gamma = \mu/I\hbar$	γ	$A \cdot m^2/J \cdot s$
Larmor (circular) frequency	ω_L	s^{-1}
cyclotron (angular) frequency	ω_c	s^{-1}
level width	Γ	J
mean life	τ	s
reaction energy	Q	J
cross section	σ	m^2
macroscopic cross section	Σ	m^2
impact parameter	b	m
scattering angle	$\vartheta, \theta, \varphi$	rad
particle flux density	φ	$s^{-1} \cdot m^{-2}$
particle fluence	Φ	m^{-2}
energy flux density	ψ	W/m^2
energy fluence	F	J/m^2
internal conversion coefficient	α	−
half-life	$T_{1/2}$	s
decay constant, disintegration constant	λ	s^{-1}
activity	A	s^{-1}
Compton wavelength; $\lambda c = h/mc$	λc	m
electron radius: $r_e = e^2/mc^2$	r_e	m
linear attenuation coefficient	μ, μ_l	m^{-1}
atomic attenuation coefficient	μ_a	m^2
mass attenuation coefficient	μ_m	m^2/kg
linear stopping power	S, S_l	J/m
atomic stopping power	S_a	$J \cdot m^2$
linear range	R, R_l	m
recombination coefficient	α	m^3/s
linear ionization by a particle	N_{il}	m^{-1}
total ionization by a particle	N_i	−
number of neutrons per fission	ν	−
number of produced neutrons per absorption	η	−
absorbed dose	D	J/kg
linear energy transfer	L	J/m

Quantity	Symbol	International Symbol for Unit

CHEMICAL PHYSICS

Quantity	Symbol	Unit
amount of substance	n, ν	mol
molar mass of substance B	M_B	kg/mol
molar concentration of substance B	c_B	mol/m³
mole fraction of substance B	x_B	—
molar internal energy	$U_m, (E_m)$	J/mol
mass fraction of substance B	w_B	
molality of solute component B	m_B	mol/kg
chemical potential of component B	μ_B	J/mol
activity of component B	λ_B	—
relative activity	a_B	—
activity coefficient of component B	f_B	—
osmotic pressure	Π	Pa
osmotic coefficient	g, ϕ	—
stoichiometric number of component B	ν_B	—
affinity	A	J/mol
equilibrium constant	K_p	Pa
charge number of ion	z	—
Faraday constant	F	C/mol
ionic strength	I	mol/kg
fugacity of component B	f_B	Pa
electrolytic conductivity	σ, κ, γ	S/m
transport number	t	—
degree of dissociation	α	—

Mathematical Symbols

GENERAL SYMBOLS

equal to	$=$
not equal to	$\neq$
identically equal to	$\equiv$
corresponds to	$\triangleq$
approximately equal to	$\approx$
proportional to	$\sim, \propto$
approaches	$\rightarrow$
greater than	$>$
less than	$<$
much greater than	$\gg$
much less than	$\ll$
greater than or equal to	$\geq$
less than or equal to	$\leq$
plus	$+$
minus	$-$
plus or minus	$\pm$
a raised to the power n	a^n
magnitude of a	$|a|$
square root of a	$\sqrt{a}, \sqrt[]{a}, a^{1/2}$
mean value of a	$\bar{a}, \langle a \rangle \langle a \rangle_{av}$
factorial p	$p!$
binomial coefficient: $n!/p!(n-p)!$	$\binom{n}{p}$
infinity	∞

LETTER SYMBOLS AND LETTER EXPRESSIONS FOR MATHEMATICAL OPERATIONS

These should be written in roman (upright) type

exponential of x	$\exp x, e^x$
base of natural logarithms	e

logarithm to the base a of x	$\log_a x$
natural logarithm of x	$\ln x$
common logarithm of x	$\lg x, \log x$
summation	Σ
product	Π
finite increase of x	Δx
variation of x	δx
total differential of x	dx
function of x	$f(x), \mathrm{f}(x)$
limit of $f(x)$	$\lim_{x \to a} f(x)$

TRIGONOMETRIC FUNCTIONS

sine of x	$\sin x$
cosine of x	$\cos x$
tangent of x	$\tan x$
cotangent of x	$\cot x$
secant of x	$\sec x$
cosecant of x	$\operatorname{cosec} x$

REMARKS: (a) It is recommended to use for the *inverse trigonometric functions* the symbolic expressions for the corresponding trigonometric function preceded by the letters: arc.

EXAMPLES:

$$\arcsin x, \quad \arccos x, \quad \arctan x, \text{ etc.}$$

(b) It is recommended to use for the *hyperbolic functions* the symbolic expressions for the corresponding trigonometric function, followed by the letter: h.

EXAMPLES:

$$\sinh x, \quad \cosh x, \quad \tanh x, \text{ etc.}$$

(c) It is recommended to use for the *inverse hyperbolic functions* the symbolic expression for the corresponding hyperbolic function preceded by the letters: ar.

$$\text{arsinh } x, \quad \text{arcosh } x, \text{ etc.}$$

COMPLEX QUANTITIES

imaginary unit ($i^2 = -1$)	i, j
real part of z	Re z, z'
imaginary part of z	Im z, z''
modulus of z	$\lvert z \rvert$
argument of $z : z = \lvert z \rvert \exp i\varphi$	arg z, φ
complex conjugate of z	$z*$, $\bar{z}$

VECTOR CALCULUS (SEE ALSO P. 916)

absolute value of **A**	$\lvert \mathbf{A} \rvert$, A
differential vector operator	$\partial/\partial \mathbf{r}$, ∇
gradient of φ	grad φ, $\nabla\varphi$
divergence of **A**	div **A**, $\nabla \cdot \mathbf{A}$
curl of **A**	curl **A**, rot **A**, $\nabla \times \mathbf{A}$
Laplacian of φ	$\Delta\varphi$, $\nabla^2\varphi$
d'Alembertian of φ	$\square\varphi$

MATRIX CALCULUS

transpose of matrix A	$\tilde{A}_{ij} = A_{ji}$ $\tilde{A}$
complex conjugate of A	$(A*)_{ij} = (A_{ij})*$ $A*$
Hermitian conjugate of A	$(A^\dagger_{ij}) = A_{ji}^*$ $A^\dagger$

HUGH C. WOLFE

Cross-reference: CONSTANTS, FUNDAMENTAL.

SYNCHROTRONS

The term synchrotron has come to mean "a ring shaped device for accelerating charged particles, e.g., electrons, protons, or heavier ions, to relativistic energies by the repeated passage of the particles, at essentially constant radius, through a time-varying electric field which alternates in direction at a fixed or variable frequency." Special examples are: (1) weak focusing synchrotrons, ie., constant gradient (CGS); (2) alternating-gradient synchrotrons (AGS); (3) fixed-field alternating-gradient synchrotrons (FFAG), or azimuthally varying-field synchrotrons (AVF); (4) separated-function, alternating-gradient synchrotron (SFAGS). All these machines have evolved from the early accelerators invented by E. O. Lawrence (cyclotron–1930), D. W. Kerst (betatron–1940), the synchronous acceleration principle discovered by E. M. McMillan and V. Veksler (1945), and the alternating-gradient strong focusing principle of Christofilos (1950), and Livingston, Courant and Snyder (1952); and the separated-function concept of M. G. White (1952) and T. Kitagaki (1953).

There are basically six components or functions which a synchrotron must provide: (1) A source of particles, e.g., electrons or protons

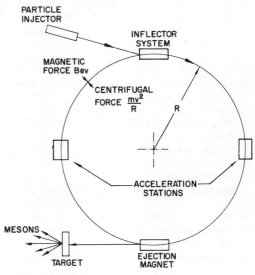

FIG. 1. Synchrotron.

with energy and direction suitable for injection; (2) a vacuum chamber; (3) a magnet to bend particles in a circle; (4) focusing of particles; (5) acceleration of particles; (6) ejection of particles.

Ion Source Electrons or ions to be accelerated are generally produced in an external device by a hot cathode or a gaseous discharge and then, after being electromagnetically focused into a narrow pencil, they are accelerated up to several tens of MeV before injection into the synchrotron magnet gap. The optimum injector energy depends upon a number of factors, e.g., minimum magnet field strength at which the magnetic field shape will produce satisfactory focusing, space charge limitations, design of the radio-frequency acceleration system, and "inflection" problems associated with bending the particles into orbit. Generally speaking, a fairly high injector energy is preferred since most of the above problems are eased as the injector energy increases. Very close tolerances must be placed on the energy and angular spread of the injected beam; otherwise the particles will strike the walls of the vacuum chamber after only a few turns. Injector accelerators generally in use are: (1) Cockroft Walton (750 kV); (2) Van de Graaff (3 to 5 MeV); (3) linear accelerators (15 to 200 MeV).

Injection into extremely high energy synchrotrons, such as the 200/500 GeV National Accelerator Laboratory machine or the similar device now under design at CERN (Geneva, Switzerland), is accomplished in three steps: A 750 KeV Cockcroft-Walton, followed by a 200 MeV linear accelerator, followed by an 8 GeV, fast-cycling booster synchrotron which pulses at 15 Hz and injects into the final, separated-function synchrotron. The use of the intermediate booster synchrotron permits a smaller mag-

TABLE 1. SOME TYPICAL SYNCHROTRONS[a]

	Princeton Heavy Ion Accelerator, Princeton, N.J.	Cornell Electron Synchrotron, Ithaca, N.Y.	Brookhaven National Laboratory, Upton, L.I.	National Accelerator Laboratory, Batavia, Ill.
1. Focusing scheme	CGS	AGS	AGS	SFAGS
2. Particle	neon	electrons	protons	protons
3. Maximum energy, GeV	9 (Ne^{7+})	12.0	33	200/500
4. Pulse rate, per min	1110	3600	30	15/6
5. Particles per pulse	10^5	3×10^{10}	10^{13}	5×10^{13}
6. Particles per sec	2×10^6	1.8×10^{12}	5×10^{12}	10^{13}
7. Orbit diameter, m	25	250	257	2000
8. Magnet wt., kG (tons)	3.8×10^5 (415)	1.1×10^5 (125)	4×10^6 (4400)	8.9×10^6 (9850)
9. Magnet power, kW (ave)	2500	1078	5000	28 000
10. Vacuum chamber, cm (aperture)	18×6	5.5×2.5	13×6	12×5
11. Acceleration system	4 drift tubes 4 ferrite cavities	6 cavities	10 4-gap cavities	16 cavities
12. Acceleration frequency, MHz	1.0–30.0	714.0	2.5–4.5	53.08–53.10
13. rf cycles per revolution	8–10–12–16	1800	12	1113
14. Energy gain per turn, keV	60	2×10^4	192	2.5×10^3
15. rf power, peak kW	320	2000	1400	1800
16. rf power, ave kW	80	400	350	800
17. Magnetic field (injection) gauss	300	50	251	396
18. Magnetic field (max) gauss	13 900	3960	13 100	9000/22 500
19. Injector, MeV	Van de Graaff 4.0	Linac 150	Linac 400	Linac 200
20. Booster Injector, GeV	none	none	none	synchrotron 8

[a]Parameters listed for a given synchrotron do not necessarily occur simultaneously but represent maximum capabilities.

netic aperture in the final magnet and also raises the injection field to a level at which variations in remanent fields play no disturbing role.

Vacuum Chamber Since particles are scattered by collision with air molecules, it is necessary to provide a good vacuum over the entire region traversed by the particles while they are undergoing acceleration. The most critical period is when the particles are at low velocity, for then the Rutherford nuclear scattering and small angle atomic scattering are most probable. A vacuum of 10^{-6} mm of Hg is generally quite sufficient to reduce gas scattering losses to negligible proportions for electrons, protons, and deuterons.

For heavy ions, e.g., neon or heavier, the vacuum requirements are much more severe since the ion, if only partially ionized, can either lose or gain electrons by collisions with the residual gas and consequently be immediately lost to the walls. The dependence of beam attenuation on ion species, velocity, gas pressure, and synchrotron parameters is quite complex. As an example of the heavy ion vacuum requirement, the Princeton Heavy Ion

Synchrotron (see Table 1) successfully accelerated neon (Ne^{7+}) at a pressure of 4×10^{-8} Torr, but the beam was attenuated by a factor of 100. Calculations show that this synchrotron, at a pressure of 10^{-9} Torr, could accelerate any ion in any charge state with very little attenuation. A vacuum of even 10^{-10} Torr is now feasible.

In order that the vacuum chamber walls should not interfere with the magnetic field, or its space and time derivatives, it is necessary to employ either insulating walls of ceramic or laminated metal structures made vacuum tight by an outer skin of epoxy fibre glass. A thin-walled stainless steel pipe is satisfactory for slowly varying magnetic fields as in the Brookhaven synchrotron or the National Accelerator Laboratory final ring.

Bending A particle of rest mass m_0, charge $Z \cdot e$, and kinetic energy T, moving in a direction perpendicular to a magnetic field of B gauss, will move in a circle of radius R given by:

$$B \cdot R = \frac{1}{2.8 Z} (T^2 + 2TE_0)^{1/2}$$

(kilogauss, meters, MeV)

where $E_0 = m_0 c^2$, the rest energy of the parti-cle. From this equation it can be seen that as the particle energy is increased from a very low initial energy to the final energy of several thou-sand MeV, the product $B \cdot R$ must increase manyfold. If B is held constant in time during the acceleration cycle and if the space average of B is also relatively constant, then R must in-crease with energy thus leading to the need for a very large radial aperture over which the field must be maintained. This is the case with cyclo-trons. The radial aperture can be drastically re-duced in either of two ways: (1) time modulate (e.g., pulse) the magnetic field so that it in-creases from a few tens or hundreds of gauss at ion injection time up to 10 to 20 kilogauss at which field the maximum particle energy is reached; (2) shape the magnetic field such that it increases sharply with increasing radius. The latter approach, while seemingly obvious, actu-ally requires a very sophisticated angular and radial variation of the field in order to retain focusing in the direction parallel to the mag-netic field. (It has been done by L. H. Thomas, 1938; Ohkawa, 1955; Kolomenskji, Petukhov, and Rabinovitch, 1955; Symon, 1955.) Accel-erators based on this time-independent but spatially varying field are generally referred to as FFAG or Spiral Sector Ring Accelerators. Their major utility appears to be in the field of high ion currents, which they can achieve by virtue of their non-pulsed character, but they appear to be practicable up to only a few thou-sand MeV of energy since they still require con-siderable radial aperture. By far the most widely exploited type of synchrotron is that first men-tioned, i.e., the time-varying magnetic field, which holds the particles at an essentially con-stant radius while gaining energy. This tech-nique, which leads to a simpler magnet design and a minimum of weight, will be described in detail in the remainder of this article.

Focusing A magnetic field which is per-fectly uniform over the entire circular path of the particle and over the radial aperture leads to stable motion only for radial displacements of the particle. Particles displaced parallel to B (i.e., out of the orbit plane) are not refocused back on to the original circle and are quickly lost to the chamber walls. This can be readily understood by noting that motion parallel to B generates no $e\mathbf{V} \times \mathbf{B}$ force, and therefore such motion persists until the particle strikes the chamber walls. However, by deliberately intro-ducing curved lines of force, it is possible to produce $e\mathbf{V} \times \mathbf{B}$ forces whose net effect results in restoring forces for all displacements from the ideal circular orbit. Oliphant's (1945) pio-neering proton synchrotron in Manchester, Eng-land achieved weak focusing by employing a small, constant, radial *decrease* of magnetic field with *increasing* radius (constant-gradient synchrotron, GGS). Subsequent to the use of this principle in several large synchrotrons there has evolved a wide variety of field shapes which have a much stronger focusing action. All these strong-focusing fields are characterized by rapid spatial changes in the field strength, periodic re-versal of sign of field gradients and even of the field itself. The most widely employed alter-nating gradient scheme is one in which a magnet sector that focuses *radially*, but defocuses *axi-ally*, is followed by a sector which has the re-verse property, i.e., *defocuses* radially and fo-cuses axially. The net effect is strong focusing in *both* directions. There is a close analogy be-tween alternating-gradient synchrotron focusing and an alternating series of convergent and di-vergent optical lenses whose net action is focus-ing. As a result of this arrangement of magnetic lenses, it is possible to use larger field gradients than in the weak-focusing case and thereby to achieve very strong focusing action. For ex-ample, an alternating-gradient 35 000-MeV ac-celerator, 560 feet in diameter, requires a vac-uum chamber with a cross section of only 2.7 $\times$ 6 inches, whereas a weak-focusing, constant-gradient synchrotron would require at least ten times more aperture for equivalent performance.

The separated-function synchrotron (SFAGS) also employs alternating gradient focusing, but the bending function of the magnet is separate from the focusing. This is achieved by employ-ing separate quadrupole and sextupole magnets for focusing only, while the bending magnets, having zero radial gradient, provide no focusing. The advantage of this separation lies in the pos-sibility of achieving much higher bending fields than in a combined function magnet. For ex-ample, the National Accelerator Laboratory separated-function main ring is designed to op-erate at 22 kG whereas the usual AGS is limited to about 13 kG. The SFAGS principle also per-mits the exploitation of very high field, super-conducting, iron-free bending magnets which do not lend themselves to the combined-func-tion approach. Brookhaven National Labora-tory is currently designing a superconducting, separated-function, combination intersecting storage ring and accelerator (ISA) which is to operate at 40 kG. Counter-rotating beams of 200 GeV protons will collide head-on releasing 400 GeV in the center-of-mass, or the equiva-lent of 80 000 GeV in a one-way machine with the target nucleus at rest.

Acceleration The increase in particle energy actually takes place when the circling charged particles pass through electric fields spaced around the circumference of the magnet. These fields must be time varying since a complete, repetitive traversal of a static field leads to zero energy gain. The usual arrangement is one in which the acceleration electrodes are excited by a sinusoidal voltage whose frequency is a harmonic (one to several thousand) of the par-ticle rotation frequency and whose amplitude is such that particles can gain sufficient energy to match the rising magnetic field. Because of the principle of synchronous phase stability, discovered by McMillan and Veksler, particles

with a wide spread in phase angle relative to the radio frequency are captured in stable "buckets" in phase space and are accelerated at just the correct rate, on the average, to stay in the middle of the vacuum chamber. Of course, the frequency of the accelerating field must be steadily and precisely increased as the particle rotation frequency increases. In some weak-focusing synchrotrons, this is one of the most difficult engineering tasks.

Electron synchrotrons pose special problems for the radio-frequency system. Because it is easy to inject electrons with a velocity very close to the velocity of light, the frequency of the required acceleration voltage is constant. This greatly simplifies the rf high voltage system and associated controls as compared with a proton synchrotron. However, a steep price is paid since relativistic electrons copiously radiate electromagnetic energy when traveling in a circle. [Radiation loss = $8.85 \times 10^4 (W^4/R)$ (eV/turn) where W is particle energy in GeV and R is magnet radius in meters.] For example, the Cornell electron synchrotron (see Table 1) radiates 20 MeV/turn at 12.0 GeV. This energy must be replaced by the rf cavities during each revolution in addition to increasing the kinetic energy of the electrons by a relatively small amount.

Ejection When the particles have been accelerated to full energy, they are caused either to run into an internal target or they are ejected by one of several schemes which usually involve exciting strong radial betatron oscillations with the last oscillation carrying the particles into an ejection magnet which deflects the beam clear of the synchrotron magnet structure.

In Table 1 are listed the important parameters of several typical existing synchrotrons. The principles discussed above for the separated-function, alternating-gradient synchrotron (SFAGS) are believed to be capable of extension to extremely high energy limited only by financial considerations. For protons and heavier particles, the electromagnetic radiation loss, which sets a practical limit for electron synchrotrons at about 60 GeV, will not be troublesome at any conceivable energy.

MILTON G. WHITE

References

Livingood, J. J., "Cyclic Particle Accelerators," New York, Van Nostrand Reinhold, 1961.

Livingston, M. S., and Blewett, J. P., "Particle Accelerators," New York, McGraw-Hill Book Co., 1962.

Wilson, R. R., and Littauer, R., "Accelerators, Machines of Nuclear Physics," Science Study Series, Garden City, N. Y., Doubleday Anchor, 1960.

Green, G. K., and Courant, E. D., in F. Flügge, Ed., "Handbuch der Physik," Vol. 44, Berlin, Springer Verlag, pp. 218–340, 1959.

Cross-references: ACCELERATORS, VAN DE GRAAFF; ACCELERATORS, LINEAR; ACCELERATORS, PARTICLE; BETATRON; CYCLOTRON; IONIZATION.

T

TELEMETRY

The terms telemetry and telemetering imply both distance and measurement, but beyond this there is not universal agreement regarding the use and meaning of the terms. The American Standards Association defines telemetering as: "The measurement with the aid of intermediate means which permit the measurement to be interpreted at a distance from the primary detector." The distance involved may be anywhere from a few inches in the case of certain test projectiles to many millions of miles in the case of space probes to other planets. Other terms such as data transmission system or data link are frequently used. A distinction in terminology is sometimes made between the transmission of a measurement for observation and interpretation and the transmission of a measurement to directly govern a controlling action. In modern applications, the quantity transmitted may not be a measurement at all, but the result of some complex calculation based on numerous measurements over a time interval.

The dominant transmission means for telemetry has been electrical, and a few applications were already reported during the first half of the nineteenth century. During the latter half of the century, applications included regular transmission of meteorological and other measurements. During the early part of the twentieth century, there were extensive applications of telemetry in connection with the Panama Canal followed by applications in many other areas such as electrical power and pipeline distribution systems. Soon after 1930, telemetry through the transmission medium of radio links was in use for meteorological measurements from small unmanned balloons. Soon after 1940, the first radio telemetering systems for testing aircraft were being designed and used. This occurred in response to the need for more complete and reliable measurement during experimental flights of high-performance military aircraft than could be provided by onboard recorders and pilot's observation. By 1945, radio telemetry was being used for measurements in the then small rockets, and before the end of the decade, telemetry carried by rocket vehicles was being used to investigate the upper reaches of the earth's atmosphere. Subsequently, the development of advanced radio telemetering systems has been spurred by the well-known rapid development

of the field of rocket-propelled vehicles. Recently, telemetry has seen rapidly increasing application in geophysical and biomedical research.

It is sometimes convenient to divide telemetry applications into two areas which might be called operational and test. By operational we mean the application of telemetry as a permanent part of some system, in which case the telemeter must be compatible with the rest of the system in such aspects as cost, reliability, and maintainability. By test we mean the temporary application of telemetry to obtain test information during the developmental phase of some system, in which case the telemeter need not be completely compatible with the rest of the system.

Telemetry systems for industrial purposes tend to fall more under the operational area and formed the majority of applications before 1940. Industrial telemetering systems have been frequently characterized by modest requirements for speed of response and accuracy which fall well within the physical limitations of the transmission link (frequently wire circuits) and are therefore accomplished by rather straightforward and uncomplicated signal handling methods. On the other hand, these applications have been characterized by demanding requirements for low first cost and high reliability during long periods of unattended operation. Geophysical (including oceanographic) applications often have similar requirements. Industrial telemetry is well exemplified by the many thousands of telemeters in constant use by the electrical power industry throughout the world to measure electrical quantities and plant conditions.

The majority of aerospace telemetry during the last thirty years has been in the test area. Because of the destructive nature of tests and/or the difficulty in repeating them and because of the marginal nature of many of the systems being tested, aerospace telemetry has been characterized by demanding requirements for speed of response, accuracy, and number of channels which are frequently not well within the physical limitations of the radio transmission link. This together with severe weight and space restrictions and difficult environmental conditions for equipment operation has resulted in a field of telemetry activity more or less separate from the industrial area. Much attention has been given

to the statistical efficiency of signal processing in the presence of random errors of various kinds and to the specialized hardware techniques needed to satisfy space, weight, power supply, and environmental conditions. The recent advent of long-lived satellites and space probes, including many systems whose mission is wholly dependent on telemetered measurements, has greatly emphasized telemetry reliability considerations.

The deeper understanding of the nature of measurement and information that has occurred during the last three decades by application of statistical methods has had its effect on the telemetering field. In the beginning, the design and classification of telemetering systems tended to be in terms of the physical quantity measured, the physical quantities used for transmission and interpretation, and the transducers for conversion between these physical quantities, i.e., in terms of the hardware. Terms such as current, voltage, frequency, ratio, phase, impulse, etc., were and are used to describe some systems. Multiplexing (the transmission of many measurements over the same channel) was either frequency division (assignment of a frequency band to each measurement, non-overlapping with those of the others) or time division (assignment of a periodic time interval to each measurement, non-over-lapping with those of of the others).

The statistical systems point of view in telemetry is concerned with *what* is done to the signal rather than *how* it is accomplished physically. From this point of view a telemetering system may do any or all of the following in logical sequence: (1) make a measurement; (2) abstract from the measurement in the form of a signal those characteristics which are needed for the eventual interpretation or decision; (3) store this signal; (4) code (modulate) this signal to give it greater immunity to the errors in the transmission link; (5) receive the signal; (6) store the signal; (7) decode (demodulate) the received signal to best preserve those characteristics which are needed for interpretation and decision; (8) store the result. A measurement is said to have been made on a system if after the measurement, the uncertainty regarding the quantitative state of the system is less than the uncertainty existing before the measurement. Uncertainty in the sense of information theory has an exact quantitative measure in terms of the probability distributions involved and can be replaced by a cost index when a cost criterion is available. Similarly, a measurement is said to have been telemetered when there is a reduction in uncertainty or cost on the basis of the data produced by the telemetering system.

Current radio telemetering systems use many methods of modulation in various combinations. These include amplitude, phase, frequency, pulse amplitude, pulse position, pulse duration, pulse frequency, and pulse code. Multiplexing is sometimes accomplished by more general orthogonal methods than frequency- and time-division.

With the advent of solid-state active circuit components and, most recently, of microelectronic techniques there has been a revolution in telemetry hardware. The practicability of complex circuits made possible by solid-state components, the use of digital computers for data processing, and developments in improved coding and demodulation methods have brought about considerable use of pulse-code modulation telemetering systems during the last two decades.

In current aerospace applications, the telemetry function is often an integral part of a combined telecommunication and navigation system, such as the USBS (Unified S-Band System) and SGLS (Space-Ground-Link System).

LAWRENCE L. RAUCH

References

Borden, P. A., and Mayo-Wells, W. J., "Telemetering Systems," New York, Van Nostrand Reinhold, 1959.

Stiltz, H. L., Ed., "Aerospace Telemetry," Vols. I and II, Englewood Cliffs, N.J., Prentice-Hall, 1966.

Filipowsky, H. F., and Muehldorf, E. I., "Space Communication Systems," Englewood Cliffs, N.J., Prentice-Hall, 1965.

Middleton, D., "Statistical Communication Theory," New York, McGraw-Hill Book Company, 1960.

Cross-references: FEEDBACK; MEASUREMENT, PRINCIPLES OF; MODULATION.

TEMPERATURE AND THERMOMETRY

Temperature is the degree of hotness or coldness as measured on a definite scale; it is that property of an object which determines the direction of heat flow when the object is placed in contact with another. The concept serves as a measure of the average kinetic energy of the molecules of an object due to heat agitation. Human sensory organs can furnish an approximate indication of air temperature or of the temperature of an object. However, this indication can be strongly affected by factors such as moisture in the air or the heat conductivity of the object. Thermometry is the measurement of temperature and utilizes changes in some property of an object as an indicator. Changes in pressure, volume, length, electrical resistance, and electrical potential have all been used in thermometers.

Temperature Scales Many different scales have been used in measuring temperatures. The most common of them are Celsius or centigrade, Fahrenheit, Réaumur, Kelvin or centigrade absolute, and Rankine. Symbols used for the units on these scales are $°C$, $°F$, $°R$, K and $°R$, respectively. The Kelvin scale is noteworthy because it is essentially the true thermodynamic scale. The scales are all based on one primary reference point, which represents the temperature at which a sharp change occurs. This temperature is assigned a number and serves as a starting point. A second reference point determines the size of

the degree. All of these scales use the same primary reference point called the "ice-point". This is the temperature at which pure macroscopic ice crystals are at equilibrium with pure, liquid water under air saturated with moisture and at standard atmospheric pressure (1.01325 bar or 1.013 250 dynes/cm^2). For the various scales this point is assigned numerical values as follows: 0°C, 32°F, 0°Réaumur, 491.7°Rankine, and 273.15 K. The value of 273.15 K is set so as to bring the scale as close as possible to the true thermodynamic scale. It is based on the use of 273.16 K for the triple point of water as an international standard (see STATES OF MATTER). The secondary point is that temperature at which the vapor pressure of pure water is equal to standard atmospheric pressure. The temperature interval between the primary and secondary points is divided into degrees, and the number of them between the two points is 100 Celsius degrees, 180 Fahrenheit degrees, 80 Réaumur degrees, 180 Rankine degrees, and 100 Kelvin degrees. When working above the secondary point or below the primary point, an attempt is made to keep the degrees the same size as those between the fixed points. The Fahrenheit and Rankine degrees are five-ninths as big as the Kelvin and Celsius or centigrade degrees.

Conversion from Scale to Scale The conversion of a temperature reading from one scale to another requires remembering that the degrees are not always the same size and that the zero mark does not represent the same temperature on the different scales. Methods or formulas for the conversions can then be derived.

To convert a reading from degrees centigrade to degrees Fahrenheit, multiply by 9/5 and then add 32.

To convert a reading from Fahrenheit to centigrade, subtract 32 and multiply by 5/9.

To convert a reading from centigrade to Kelvin, add 273.15.

To convert a reading from Kelvin to centigrade, subtract 273.15.

To convert a reading from Fahrenheit to Rankine, add 459.7.

To convert a reading from Rankine to Fahrenheit, subtract 459.7.

To convert a reading from centigrade to Réaumur, multiply by 4/5.

To convert a reading from Réaumur to centigrade multiply by 5/4.

Similar formulas can be derived for conversions not shown above, or the calculation can be made in steps, using the conversions above to go from one scale to another until the desired reading is obtained. If a large number of readings must be converted, the use of a table such as may be found in handbooks is preferable both from the standpoint of avoiding mistakes and as a time saving device.

Reference Temperatures The International Practical Temperature Scale of 1968, as adopted by the Comité Intèrnational des Poids et Mésures (International Committee on Weights and Measures) established a series of reference temperatures to assure uniformity in measurements when using various types of precision thermometers. This is necessary because of the lack of uniformity in changes in volume or length or electrical properties with respect to changes in temperature. The standard instrument between 13.81 K and 630.74°C is the platinum resistance thermometer. The standard instrument from 630.74°C to 1064.43°C is the platinum–10 per cent rhodium/platinum thermocouple. Above 1064.43°C, the International Practical Temperature is defined by the Planck law of radiation. For calibration, certain fixed points have been selected, and these are given in Table 1.

Utilization of Temperature Scales The centigrade or Celsius scale is very widely used for scientific studies, and most thermometers for exacting work are calibrated in this scale. It was invented in 1742 by Anders Celsius and, though the name centigrade is still widely accepted, the preferred name is Celsius. The Fahrenheit scale is used in every day life in the United States and England, and is the usual scale for engineering and medical practice in those countries. The Réaumur scale is in limited use in France, Germany, and Russia. The Rankine scale is used in some engineering work, particularly where an absolute scale is needed for such things as the calculation of the theoretical efficiency of engines. The Kelvin scale was originated by Lord Kelvin and was based on a consideration of the second law of thermodynamics. This leads to a temperature scale with the zero point at the temperature at which all the thermal motion of the atoms stops. By using this as the zero point or absolute zero and another reference point to determine the size of the degrees, a scale can be defined. The Comité Consultative of the International Committee of Weights and Measures selected 273.16 K as the value for the triple point of water. This set the ice-point at 273.15 K.

Thermodynamic Scale Thermodynamically speaking, the thermal efficiency E of an engine is equal to the work W derived from the engine divided by the heat supplied to the engine Q_2. If Q_1 is the heat exhausted from the engine,

$$E = (W/Q_2) = (Q_2 - Q_1)/Q_2 = 1 - (Q_1/Q_2)$$

where W, Q_1, and Q_2 are all in the same units. A Carnot engine is a theoretical one in which all the heat is supplied at a single high temperature and the heat output is rejected at a single temperature. The cycle consists of two adiabatics and two isothermals (see CARNOT CYCLES AND CARNOT ENGINES). Here the ratio Q_1/Q_2 must depend only on the two temperatures and on nothing else. The Kelvin temperatures are then defined by the relation

$$\frac{Q_1}{Q_2} = \frac{T_1}{T_2}$$

TABLE 1. DEFINING FIXED POINTS OF THE IPTS-68[a]

	Assigned Value of International Practical Temperature	
Equilibrium State	T_{68}(K)	t_{68}(°C)
Equilibrium between the solid, liquid, and vapor phases of equilibrium hydrogen (triple point of equilibrium hydrogen)	13.81	−259.34
Equilibrium between the liquid and vapor phases of equilibrium hydrogen at a pressure of 33 330.6 N/m² (25/76 standard atmosphere)	17.042	−256.108
Equilibrium between the liquid and vapor phases of equilibrium hydrogen (boiling point of equilibrium hydrogen)	20.28	−252.87
Equilibrium between the liquid and vapor phases of neon (boiling point of neon)	27.102	−246.048
Equilibrium between the solid, liquid, and vapor phases of oxygen (triple point of oxygen)	54.361	−218.789
Equilibrium between the liquid and vapor phases of oxygen (boiling point of oxygen)	90.188	−182.962
Equilibrium between the solid, liquid, and vapor phases of water (triple point of water)[c]	273.16	0.01
Equilibrium between the liquid and vapor phases of water (boiling point of water)[b,c]	373.15	100
Equilibrium between the solid and liquid phases of zinc (freezing point of zinc)	692.73	419.58
Equilibrium between the solid and liquid phases of silver (freezing point of silver)	1235.08	961.93
Equilibrium between the solid and liquid phases of gold (freezing point of gold)	1337.58	1064.43

[a]Except for the triple points and one equilibrium hydrogen point (17.042 K) the assigned values of temperature are for equilibrium states at a pressure p_0 = 1 standard atmosphere (101 325 N/m²). In the realization of the fixed points, small departures from the assigned temperatures will occur as a result of the differing immersion depths of thermometers or the failure to realize the required pressure exactly. If due allowance is made for these small temperature differences, they will not affect the accuracy of realization of the scale.

[b]The equilibrium state between the solid and liquid phases of tin (freezing point of tin) has the assigned value of t_{68} = 231.9681 °C and may be used as an alternative to the boiling point of water.

[c]The water used should have the isotopic composition of ocean water.

where Q_1/Q_2 is the ratio of the heats rejected and absorbed, and T_1/T_2 is the ratio of the Kelvin temperatures of the reservoir and the source. If one starts with a given size for the degree, then the equation completely defines a thermodynamic temperature scale.

A series of Carnot engines can be postulated so that the first engine absorbs heat Q from a source, does work W, and rejects a smaller amount of heat at a lower temperature. The second engine absorbs all the heat rejected by the first one, does work and rejects a still smal-

ler amount of heat which is absorbed by a third engine, etc. The temperature at which each successive engine rejects its heat becomes smaller and smaller, and in the limit this becomes zero so that an engine is reached which rejects no heat at a temperature which is absolute zero. A reservoir at absolute zero cannot have heat rejected to it by a Carnot engine operating between a higher temperature reservoir and the one at absolute zero. This can be used as the definition of absolute zero. Absolute zero is then such a temperature that a reservoir at that temperature cannot have heat rejected to it by a Carnot engine which uses a heat source at some higher temperature.

Thermometry The measurement of temperature can be accomplished by many devices with varying degrees of accuracy or convenience. Among the instruments most frequently used are those based on (1) expansion of a solid, a liquid, or a gas; (2) change of pressure in a gas or vapor kept at a constant volume; (3) the thermoelectric effect; (4) changes in electrical resistance; and (5) changes in the character of thermal radiation.

The familiar mercury-in-glass thermometer utilizes the expansion of mercury which expands much more rapidly than does its glass container. For a wider temperature range, alcohol, usually colored for easier visibility, can be substituted. Maximum thermometers, such as the clinical thermometer, have a very narrow constriction just above the bulb so that if the temperature goes down, the mercury column breaks at the constriction leaving the column in the tube above the constriction to indicate the highest temperature reached. A minimum thermometer can be built by including a small rider or index. As the liquid in the thermometer contracts, the rider is pulled towards the bulb, its end staying just at the surface of the liquid. If temperature goes up, the liquid flows past the index, leaving it to indicate the lowest temperature reached.

Gases are used as the working fluid in two types of thermometer. One holds the pressure constant, and the change in volume provides the temperature indication. The other is usually more convenient to use. In it the volume of the gas is held constant, and changes of pressure indicate temperature changes. Gases which are close to ideal gases are used, and corrections can be made for nonideal behavior so that the readings follow the absolute thermodynamic scale. This constant volume type has been adopted as the practical standard for the measurement of temperature.

A bimetallic strip can be made from small strips of two different metals welded or riveted together side by side. If the two have different coefficients of expansion, changes in temperature will cause the bimetallic strip to bend as one metal expands more than the other. This can be used to move a pointer over a scale. By using the motion of one end of the strip to open and close electrical contacts, a thermostat results for electricity controlling devices such as furnaces, ovens, or air conditioning units.

The thermoelectric effect can be used to measure temperature because the difference in potential created at a junction varies as a smooth function of temperature. The junction or sensor can be made very small and with low heat capacity so that such a thermocouple can be used for the precise indication of rapid changes in temperature.

Resistance thermometers require a wire or strip of metal and a circuit for determining changes in the resistance of the strip or wire as temperature changes.

An optical pyrometer measures the thermal radiation from a hot object over a narrow wavelength region and uses this radiation as a measure of temperature. Measurements are made by comparing brightness with that of a standard or by using photoelectric detectors. Such pyrometers can be used for temperatures far above those which can be measured by other methods (see PYROMETRY, OPTICAL). Radiation pyrometers measure the total thermal radiation and use this as an indication of temperature. They tend to be less accurate than optical pyrometers.

Each type of thermometer has its own advantages and disadvantages, and the choice of which to use must be made on the basis of the requirements of each particular application.

ROBERT M. BESANÇON

References

Herzfeld, Charles M., Ed., "Temperature: Its Measurement and Control in Science and Industry," Vol. 3, Parts I and II (1962) and Part III (1963), New York, Van Nostrand Reinhold.

Thekaekara, Matthew P., "Radiation Scales on Which Standard Values of the Solar Constant and Solar Spectral Irradiance are Based," paper for IES, ASTM, AIAA Space Simulation Conference, New York, April 30 to May 4, 1972.

Thomas, W., Zander, W., Wagenbreth, H., and Otto, J., "Bericht über die Tätigkeit der PTB in Jahre 1966," Abt. 3, No. 134, Braunschweig 1967.

Benedict, R. P., "The International Practical Temperature Scale of 1968," *Leeds Northrup Tech. J.*, **IVa**(6) (1969).

Anon, "International Practical Scale of 1968," Foreword by C. R. Barber, *Metrologia*, **5**, 35 (1969).

Cross-references: CARNOT CYCLES AND CARNOT ENGINES; EXPANSION, THERMAL; GAS LAWS; HEAT; PYROMETRY, OPTICAL; RADIATION, THERMAL; STATES OF MATTER; THERMOELECTRICITY.

TENSORS AND TENSOR ANALYSIS

Introduction Tensors and tensor analysis represent a powerful and useful part of mathematical physics. Tensors include such familiar objects of physical interest as ordinary scalars and vectors. They also include more complicated objects and are basic to a full understanding of advanced

subjects such as electromagnetic theory and general relativity. Consequently, tensors often possess an aura of mystery and a special mystique that they do not always deserve. The reader is referred to the articles on VECTOR PHYSICS, ELECTROMAGNETIC THEORY, and RELATIVITY appearing elsewhere in this encyclopedia.

The concept of tensor can be traced back to such men as Karl Gauss, George Riemann, and Elwin Christoffel in the last century. The algebra and calculus of tensors can be traced back to Gregorio Ricci and his pupil Tullio Levi-Civita early in this century. Their names appear frequently in connection with specific concepts or special tensors. The books by Levi-Civita[1] and Eisenhart[2] in the general references at the end of this article will provide a more complete history of this subject.

The word *tensor* means "to stretch" and thus is related to the concepts of stress and strain appearing in the theory of elasticity and deformable bodies. Dyadics, which were used more frequently in the last century, may be considered to be almost synonymous with the more modern concept of tensors and to be superseded by them. Tensors and tensor analysis are important in both mathematics and physics and are gaining importance in many fields of engineering and technology. See the excellent book by Sommerfeld[3] for applications to the mechanics of deformable bodies, and the book by Page[4] for more information about dyadics.

Tensors, Rank, and Dimensionality Before wondering about the physical interpretation of a tensor, which depends entirely on the problem at hand, consider its mathematical description. The number of components in a given tensor depends on both its rank R and on its tensor dimensionality D. The lowest rank R that a tensor may have is 0. The number of components possessed by a tensor of rank 0 is always 1, no matter what the dimensionality D of the tensor may be. A common name for such a tensor is "scalar." So, an n-dimensional scalar is a one-component tensor of rank zero. One example of a scalar quantity is a thermometer reading representing temperature. A second example is ordinary mass—but not the gravitational weight associated with the mass which is, in fact, a downward-pointing force vector.

The next rank that a tensor may have is 1. The number of components possessed by a tensor or rank 1 is always n, the dimensionality of the tensor. Thus, in two-dimensional space, a tensor of rank 1 has 2 components; in three-dimensional space, 3 components; and so on. Again, a common name for such a tensor is "vector." So an n-dimensional vector is an n-component tensor of rank 1. The first example of a vector that comes to mind is velocity.

The next rank that a tensor may have is 2. The number of components possessed by a tensor of rank 2 is always n^2, the square of the dimensionality of the tensor. Thus in two-dimensional space a tensor of rank 2 has 4 components; in

three-dimensional space, 9 components, and so on. A tensor of rank 2 is the first that normally would be called a true tensor.

These facts may be summarized. For what are called complete tensors the general result is that the number of components in a tensor of rank R and dimensionality D is given by the formula $Z = D^R$.

One kind of incomplete tensor is called an "antisymmetric tensor." Such a tensor always has some zero components. The number of independent nonzero components in an antisymmetric tensor in n-dimensional space is given by $\frac{1}{2}n(n-1)$.

It is convenient that in three dimensions an antisymmetric tensor of rank 2 has only three nonzero components. This coincidence gives rise to this tensor's interpretation as a kind of vector or "pseudovector." A familiar example of an antisymmetric tensor that may be thought of as a vector is magnetic field strength **H** and the associated magnetic induction **B**. A second example is angular momentum **L**. It is this last association that has given the name axial vector to this general class of pseudovector. The coincidence is related to the fact that in three dimensions the number of planes (defined by pairs of coordinates $x, y; x, z; y, z$) is the same as the number of coordinates x, y, z. In any other dimension this does not happen, but the number of independent planes still is equal to the number of tensor components. Thus, in two dimensions, there is only one plane $(1, 2)$ and one tensor component, while in four dimensions, there are six independent planes $(1,2; 1,3; 1,4; 2,3; 2,4; 3,4)$ and six components. Finally, Table 1 summarizes the number of components of simple tensors for spaces with dimensions up to five. Notice that the number of components of the symmetric and antisymmetric tensors of a given rank sum up to the maximum number for that rank. For more details on the elementary properties of vectors and tensors the reader is referred to the book by Lass[5] in the general references.

Algebra of Tensors As a general rule, the algebra that has been developed for matrices may be used with tensors. In fact, second-rank tensors look like square matrices; first-rank

TABLE 1. NUMBER OF COMPONENTS OF A TENSOR

	Dimensions				
	1	2	3	4	5
Scalar	1	1	1	1	1
Vector	1	2	3	4	5
Axial vector	1	2	3	4	5
Tensor—second rank	1	4	9	16	25
Symmetric tensor	1	3	6	10	15
Antisymmetric tensor	0	1	3	6	10
Tensor—third rank	1	8	27	64	125

tensors (vectors) look like 1 by n matrices. In any given situation, tensors and matrices may be multiplied together to achieve a purpose such as transforming the tensor by a linear operator. In these instances the tensor components may express the physical aspects of the problem and the matrix components the more mathematical aspects of the problem. The reader may find more information on this subject in the article on MATRICES appearing elsewhere in this encyclopedia.

All vectors are tensors, but not all tensors are vectors. A vector A_i has the transformation law:

$$A_j' = \ell_{ij} A_i,$$

whereas a tensor K_{ik} has a transformation law:

$$K_{jl}' = \ell_{ij} \ell_{kl} K_{ik}.$$

Here the symbol ℓ_{ij} or ℓ_{kl} represents the transformation matrix taking A_i or K_{ik} from the unprimed to the primed coordinate system. The n^2 elements of the matrix ℓ_{ij} are derived from the direction cosines of the unit vectors in one system of coordinates with respect to the unit vectors in the other.

A tensor K_{ik} or K_{jl}' represents a physical object. The double index ik or jl, while similar to ij or kl for the matrix ℓ, refers to the axes in one system of coordinates. Accordingly, they are different in nature even though they may have the same form.

Covariance and contravariance refer to the transformation properties of vectors and tensors. These concepts are essential to a complete understanding of vector and tensor analysis. The rules of manipulation of the vector or tensor indices, which designate whether a vector is covariant or contravariant or whether a given tensor is covariant, contravariant, or mixed in its transformation properties, are well documented along with other mathematical and formal aspects in many textbooks. One of the best of these is Sokolnikoff[6] listed in the general references. An approach that emphasizes the relationship between the concept of reciprocal lattices (long familiar to solid-state physicists and crystallographers) and the fact that the covariant and contravariant versions of the same vector reside in different coordinate systems is explained in Stratton[7] and illustrated in Eisele and Mason[8]. In many problems the value of retaining the distinction between covariance and contravariance vanishes because, for cartesian coordinates, a coordinate lattice and its reciprocal lattice are one and the same. It follows that the covariant and contravariant components of a vector or tensor will be identical in magnitude and direction.

Calculus of Tensors Numerous applications of tensor analysis can be found in texts dealing with special and general relativity. In fact, it would not be too inaccurate to say that the subject of tensor calculus grew up with general relativity. The small book by Einstein[9], and another by Møller[10] provide further background on the subject of relativity. Deserving special consideration as an extremely simple introduction to the manipulation of tensors and their calculus is the book by Lieber and Lieber[11].

The concepts of covariance and contravariance reappear in tensor calculus in a new and more general form than previously mentioned in connection with reciprocal lattices. The archetype contravariant vector is taken as the position vector $\mathbf{r} = (x^1 \cdots x^n)$ or differential components of $d\mathbf{r}$. It obeys the transformation:

$$dx'^i = M^i{}_j dx^j = \frac{\partial x'^i dx^j}{\partial X^j},$$

or $A'^i = M^i{}_j A^j$. Contravariant tensors of higher rank follow a similar pattern of index and prime placement. The archetype covariant vector is taken as a vector generated by the gradient operator and obeys the transformation

$$\frac{\partial \phi}{\partial x'^i} = N^j{}_i \frac{\partial \phi}{\partial x^j} = \frac{\partial x^j}{\partial x'^i} \frac{\phi}{\partial x^j},$$

or $B'_i = N^j{}_i B_j$. Covariant tensors of higher rank follow a similar pattern of index and prime placement. A mnemonic device "co-lo-prime-below" has been introduced by Lieber and Lieber[11] to aid in remembering the difference between the two classes of tensors.

The metric tensor g_{ij} or $g^i{}_j$, which has a special meaning in relativity, is introduced in differential geometry in connection with the definition of differential line element:

$$ds^2 = g_{ij} dx^i dx^j.$$

Its forms for three-dimensional cartesian and spherical coordinates respectively, are:

$$\begin{vmatrix} 1 & 0 & 0 \\ 0 & 1 & 0 \\ 0 & 0 & 1 \end{vmatrix} \quad \text{and} \quad \begin{vmatrix} 1 & 0 & 0 \\ 0 & r^2 & 0 \\ 0 & 0 & r^2 \sin^2 \theta \end{vmatrix}$$

The Kronecker delta and the Levi-Civita symbols are defined as:

$$\delta_{ij} = 1 \text{ if } i = j$$
$$0 \text{ if } i \neq j$$

and

$$\epsilon_{ijk} = +1 \text{ if } i, j, k = 1, 2, 3 \text{ or a cyclic permutation}$$
$$-1 \text{ if } i, j, k = 3, 2, 1 \text{ or a cyclic permutation}$$
$$0 \text{ if any two or three of } i, j, k \text{ have the same value.}$$

The delta symbol is useful in discarding cross-product terms that vanish under conditions of orthogonality and in indicating unity in the normalization process. The epsilon symbol is

useful in simplifying multiple vector products and revealing their true tensor nature. Thus for example in tensor component form:

$C = A \times B$ becomes $C_i = \epsilon_{ijk} A_j B_k$,

$A \cdot (B \times C)$ becomes $\epsilon_{ijk} A_i B_j C_k$, and

$A \times (B \times C)$ becomes $\epsilon_{ijm} \epsilon_{klm} A_j B_k C_l$.

JOHN A. EISELE
ROBERT M. MASON

References

1. Levi-Civita, T., "The Absolute Differential Calculus," London, Blackie and Son, Limited, 1947.
2. Eisenhart, L., "Riemannian Geometry," Princeton, N.J., Princeton University Press, 1949.
3. Sommerfeld, A., "Mechanics of Deformable Bodies," Translated by G. Knerti, New York, Academic Press, Inc., 1950.
4. Page, L., "Introduction to Theoretical Physics," 3rd Ed., New York, Van Nostrand Reinhold, 1952.
5. Lass, H., "Vector and Tensor Analysis," New York, McGraw-Hill Book Company, Inc., 1950.
6. Sokolnikoff, I., "Tensor Analysis," New York, John Wiley & Sons, Inc., 1964.
7. Stratton, J., "Electromagnetic Theory," New York, McGraw-Hill Book Company, Inc., 1941.
8. Eisele, J., and Mason, R., "Applied Matrix and Tensor Analysis," New York, John Wiley & Sons, Inc., 1970.
9. Einstein, A., "The Meaning of Relativity," 5th Ed., Princeton, N.J., Princeton University Press, 1955.
10. Møller, C., "The Theory of Relativity," Oxford, Clarendon Press, 1952.
11. Lieber, L., and Lieber, H., "The Einstein Theory of Relativity," New York, Holt, Rinehart, and Winston, 1945.

Cross-references: ELECTROMAGNETIC THEORY, MATRICES, QUANTUM MECHANICS, RELATIVITY, VECTOR PHYSICS.

THEORETICAL PHYSICS

A division of physics into the two broad categories of theoretical and experimental physics is very common. Both, of course, share the general aim of physics to describe and correlate the results of past experiments, to predict the numerical results of experiments yet to be performed, and to develop concepts and methods which enable one to encompass many diverse and related phenomena into a single coherent description. The questions which one can ask of a physical theory are therefore of a "how" type, for example, "How long will it take a falling stone to reach the ground?" or "How many degrees would the temperature of the water in this pail drop if I were to leave it on this block of ice for one hour?" Questions of a "why" type such as, "Why does the stone fall toward the earth when I release it?" are presumed to be of the type which cannot legitimately be asked of physics. In general terms, the role of theoretical physics is the development of concepts which can be represented by mathematical symbols and then manipulated by using the wide variety of mathematical tools available; hence, the principal characteristic of theoretical physics is the importance of mathematics in its formulation and methods. The intermediate stages of a typical calculation generally cannot be checked at every step by a corresponding experiment. The value of a particular theory can therefore only be justified by how well the final results predicted by it agree with experiment. Occasionally it has been found that two quite different theories will agree equally well with experiment; then the choice between them has been made on another basis, usually by favoring the simpler one.

Theoretical physics as a career in itself became important only in this century. Pioneers in the development of physics such as Galileo and Newton did notable experiments in addition to the creation of useful mathematical methods. Much of the initial theoretical effort was devoted to MECHANICS and culminated in the development of Lagrange's and Hamilton's equations of motion. An important synthesis occurred later when it was found to be possible to write Maxwell's equations for electromagnetism in the same Hamiltonian form which had been devised for mechanics. Consequences of the rise of the atomic theory of matter were such subjects as KINETIC THEORY and STATISTICAL MECHANICS in which the bulk properties of materials are calculated as averages of mechanical and electrical characteristics of a large number of atomic and molecular particles. QUANTUM MECHANICS, as a method of dealing with the wave properties of matter, was developed during the first thirty years or so of this century and made it possible to calculate individual atomic properties which had become measurable as a result of greatly improved experimental techniques. The older forms of mechanics, which had been so successful up to then, survived as a limiting case of the newer quantum mechanics. At about this same time, theoretical physics became a recognized specialty and the number of theoretical physicists has subsequently greatly increased. Present day theoretical physicists work both on the solution of specific problems of practical interest by known methods, and on the development of new theories appropriate to the description of the large amount of newly obtained experimental data. For convenience, theoretical physics can be divided into subject matter fields such as mechanics, electrodynamics, statistical mechanics, quantum mechanics, quantum field theory, and relativity. Another convenient subdivision is into macroscopic and microscopic theories. A macroscopic theory generally deals solely with relations among the measured properties of matter in bulk such as its heat capacity and electrical conductivity; thermodynamics is such

a theory. In a microscopic theory, on the other hand, one tries to account for these large scale features in a more "fundamental" way by obtaining them from atomic properties. Related to this approach is the unsolved question of whether the fundamental numerical constants of nature, such as the electric charge and the mass of the electron, must be left entirely to experimental determination or may some day be calculable directly from a suitable general theory.

Experimental physics and theoretical physics are constantly influencing each other. Theory is strongly dependent upon experiment because the results of experiments provide the motivation to develop a new theory or to try to combine several existing theories into a more complete and general one. In turn, theory makes important contributions by suggesting new experiments which can serve to check various aspects of the theory or by predicting a previously unknown effect. Much of the effort of theoretical physicists is devoted to the extension and investigation of their theories in an attempt to predict such new effects. If these are confirmed by experiment, they increase one's confidence in the theory. Experimental results which differ from theoretical predictions show the necessity of improving the theory—sometimes the disagreement is so great that radical revisions are necessary. A few experiments have become known as "crucial" experiments because they have provided an unambiguous comparison between the basic foundations of an accepted theory and experiment. A famous example is the MICHELSON-MORLEY EXPERIMENT on the dependence of the speed of light upon the direction of motion of the earth in its orbit. The flat disagreement between the results of this experiment and the predictions of the then current theory led Einstein to make his searching reexaminations of the fundamental concepts of space and time which resulted in his development of the theory of relativity. It is common practice for experimenters to try to find empirical formulas which will describe their results, and it is a constant challenge to theory to account for and to derive these formulas. Such formulas are common in SPECTROSCOPY, and their simplicity as compared to the complexity of the measurements inspired many efforts to calculate them; the first success of this kind was attained by Bohr in his quantum theory of the spectrum of hydrogen. Occasionally, use has been made of "thought experiments." As the name implies, these are not actually performed but are imagined and then analyzed in detail. For example, Heisenberg considered the use of a microscope as an instrument for measuring the position of a particle, paying particular attention to the effect of the interaction between the particle and the light which scatters the incident light into the microscope thus enabling the particle to be located. Considerations such as these were extensively used in the early development of quantum mechanics for the formulation of the

"uncertainty principle" which is a statement of the inherent limitations on the accuracy of simultaneous measurements of related variables such as position and momentum.

Generally, theoretical physicists spend much of their time trying to solve specific problems. Often a problem arises from the need to fit the results of a given experiment into the established theory. Many problems are devised by the theoretical physicist himself, since experience has shown that progress in theory has rarely been accomplished by means of a single brilliant stroke of exceptional generalization, but rather by the slower process of solving bits at a time. It is only later that these various problems and their solutions can be combined into a more general problem in which the previous ones are now special cases of the new formulation. A particular situation may require new methods, and it is only by handling simplified cases at first that one can obtain enough experience and facility to enable the more complex case of ultimate interest to be finally solved. Accordingly, much of the training of physicists involves solving specific problems which are incorporated into textbooks. An important attribute of a competent theoretical physicist, which is much more profound than being able to solve an already existing problem, is the ability to formulate useful and significant problems, i.e., the ability to ask the right questions.

Virtually all theoretical problems involve a high degree of idealization. Quite often, the experimental situation involves very many variables and specific details of widely varying importance. The initial task of the theoretical physicist is to try to estimate which variables are of principal significance so that he can then decide which can be safely neglected in his analysis. For example, a volume of interest may often be regarded as so large that its boundaries can be assumed to be infinitely far away so that their effects are negligible. In essence, then, what is sought is a reasonable and tractable approximation that is a fairly good substitute for the actual state of affairs. Arguments involving whatever properties of symmetry the system may have often play an important role in the approach to a problem. If, for example, it can be assumed that the distribution of mass in the earth depends only on the distance from the center and not on the particular direction in which one proceeds from the center, then the gravitational attraction of the earth will also not depend on direction but will involve only the distance from the center. Using this consequence of the geometrical symmetry, it is possible to simplify the problem by restricting one's attention only to those possible solutions which do not depend on any angle or direction. Although there exist a wide variety of formal methods of solution which have been devised through the years, one should also recognize how great the importance of experience has been as is shown by the many successful uses of intuition,

hunches, and inspired guesses. Sometimes, one is somewhat inexplicably led to try a particular solution, which, upon test, turns out to be either the correct solution to the problem or so near to it that it is a relatively simple matter to adjust the trial solution to make it correct. At times, these trials are based on the knowledge that a uniqueness theorem exists, i.e., it has been shown previously that a particular equation has only one possible solution. One can then be confident that, no matter how devious the means may have been by which the solution was obtained, it is the only possible one and it is not necessary to spend one's time considering other possibilities. Many problems can be solved by using a general solution which has been found for a more general problem and then reducing this solution to the specific one needed at the moment by making it satisfy the appropriate conditions at the boundaries of regions concerned; these boundary conditions then suffice to determine specific numerical values of parameters which appear in the mathematical form of the general solution and which previously had to be left undetermined.

Somewhat related to the value of intuition is the extensive use which is made of analogies in the solution of certain problems. It is often quite surprising how many diverse subjects and topics can be described by exactly the same form of mathematical equations; this is an example of the unifying role of theoretical physics. From a practical point of view, methods and concepts which have proved useful in one field can then be transferred bodily over into another, without, in many cases, it being necessary to change the terminology. As an example, many problems in coupled vibrating mechanical systems have been successfully treated by using methods which were originally developed to cope with coupled oscillating electrical circuits. Similarly, the motion of electrons through the lattice of ions in a metal can be related to the propagation of waves along a chain of masses connected by springs.

From a purely mathematical point of view, the student of theoretical physics soon finds that very many problems cannot be solved exactly in terms of simple or well-known mathematical functions. Although, in principle, these problems could all be solved by numerical methods, it is often of more interest and value to have a mathematically simple form for the solution. Consequently, the use of approximations is very extensive. This often consists of an expansion of a solution in a power series and of keeping only the first few terms since the others are of negligible magnitude. Sometimes only a knowledge of the order of magnitude of a quantity is sufficient, and this can be estimated quite well in spite of the impossibility of obtaining an exact solution, which in itself may be so complicated as to obscure the underlying features. In recent years, the development and availability of high-speed computers has been of great value for theory. The computers enable one to obtain numerical solutions of problems which previously were not solved because conventional numerical methods would simply take too long. Computer solutions have also proved useful in indicating the direction which should be taken by analytical methods and in suggesting appropriate types of approximations.

ROALD K. WANGSNESS

References

The following list of selected references should enable an interested reader to obtain a more detailed picture of the scope and methods of theoretical physics. Many of the points mentioned above are discussed in more detail in these books and other examples of specific problems are described and analyzed.

Einstein, A., and Infeld, L., "The Evolution of Physics," New York, Simon and Schuster, 1937.

Lindsay, R. B., and Margenau, H., "Foundations of Physics," New York, John Wiley & Sons, Inc., 1936.

Wangsness, R. K., "Introduction to Theoretical Physics: Classical Mechanics and Electrodynamics," New York, John Wiley & Sons, Inc., 1963.

Wangsness, R. K., "Introductory Topics in Theoretical Physics: Relativity, Thermodynamics, Kinetic Theory, and Statistical Mechanics," New York, John Wiley & Sons, Inc., 1963.

Bohm, D., "Quantum Theory," New York, Prentice-Hall, Inc., 1951.

Cross-references: FIELD THEORY; HEISENBERG UNCERTAINTY PRINCIPLE; KINETIC THEORY; MATHEMATICAL PHYSICS; MATRIX MECHANICS; MEASUREMENTS, PRINCIPLES OF; MECHANICS; QUANTUM THEORY; RELATIVITY; SPECTROSCOPY; STATISTICAL MECHANICS.

THERMIONICS*

Thermionics is the science of the emission of electricity from solids induced by high temperature.

While thermionic emission was undoubtedly observed long ago in the discharge of electrified particles near heated solids and considerably studied in the last half of the nineteenth century, not much progress in understanding it was made because fundamental concepts of the electric current were lacking. At the beginning of the present century the existence of the electron was established, and since then thermionics progressed rapidly both in theory and applications so that now it is basic to many large industries. As a measure of its growth, there are now in use probably two billion thermionic tubes in a host of different applications, and the basic theory of thermionics is largely worked out.

*Author deceased. Article is reprinted from first edition.

Among the early workers with currents from hot electrodes were Hittorf (1869–1883) and Goldstein (1885), both drawing quite large currents, and Elster and Geitel (1882–1889) who worked with very small currents, both positive and negative, in their research on the phenomenon. Edison (1883) in his work on the incandescent lamp discovered current emitted from the hot carbon filament and proposed a use for it in a patent granted to him. This emission became known as the "Edison Effect." None of these men, however, knew what they had, supposing that they dealt with ions such as occur in electrolysis or gas discharges. It was not until 1897–1899 that the work of J. J. Thomson showed that the negative carriers of cathode rays were a new species of particle with mass about 1700 times smaller than that of the hydrogen ion. This was the electron. Drude (1900) suggested that electrons rather than metallic ions are the carriers of current in metals, and Thomson proposed that they are also the negative charges emitted by hot metals. O. W. Richardson made a study on this basis (1901) and derived two forms of the "Richardson equation" relating the emitted current density i to the absolute temperature T of the metal and a property of the metal expressed by the letter b. The equations are

$$i = A_1 T^{1/2} \exp\left(-\frac{b_1}{T}\right) \tag{1}$$

and

$$i = A_2 T^2 \exp\left(-\frac{b_2}{T}\right) \tag{2}$$

A_1 and A_2 are arbitrary constants, exp (z) stands for the base of natural logarithms $e = 2.718$ raised to the exponent or power z, and b relates to the work required to remove an electron from the inside to the outside of the metal surface. The derivation of Eq. (1) was made using classical mechanics and the Maxwell-Boltzmann distribution of energies, later shown not to hold for free electrons within a metal. Equation (2) was based on the experimental fact that the electrons do not share in the specific heat of the metal. The formula even now retains essentially its original form [Eq. (2)], with expressions for the constants given in terms of known quantities. Richardson verified the form of his formula by careful experimental tests. Neither he nor subsequent workers would discriminate between the two forms, but the second is thought to be on a better theoretical basis. Richardson also introduced the term "thermionic."

W. Schottky (1919) and S. Dushman (1923) derived an expression for the constant A_2 in Eq. (2):

$$A = \frac{2T_1 k^2 m e}{h^3} = 60.2 \text{ amperes/cm}^2 \text{ deg}^2 \tag{3}$$

Here k is Boltzmann's constant, m is the mass and e the charge of the electron, and h is Planck's constant. Later derivations of the expression take into account the Sommerfeld (1928) theory of metallic conduction, the Pauli exclusion principle, and the spin of the electrons to yield a value of A of 120 amperes/cm^2 deg^2. The value of the exponent becomes

$$\frac{b}{T} = \frac{e\phi}{kT} = \frac{W_a - W_1}{kT} \tag{4}$$

Here ϕ is called the work function of the metal, usually expressed as a measured quantity in volts; W_a is the work of moving the electron out against the surface barrier, and W_i is the energy the electron may have had inside the metal. There is in addition a factor introduced to account for the reflection r of electrons at the inner surface of the metal. The present form of the Richardson equation is then, according to Nordheim (1929)

$$i = A(1 - r) \exp\left(-\frac{e\phi}{kT}\right) \tag{5}$$

The exponential term of the expression has been amply verified over a large temperature range. The work function ϕ is known for a large number of metals. It tends to be larger for metals in which the atoms are packed closely together, smaller for open lattice metals, the range being about 1.5 to 6 volts. It is slightly higher on dense crystal faces than on open ones. The constant A may appear to vary by a large amount from its theoretical value of 120, in the range of 10 to 100 for pure metals. Actually, it is not that A is different but that ϕ varies with temperature. The pure metal that is most often used as a thermionic emitter where ruggedness and high voltage are involved is tungsten, because of its strength and high melting point. For it, the values of ϕ and apparent A are about 4.5 volt and 100 amperes/cm^2 deg^2. Molybdenum, tantalum and niobium are others used in special applications.

The thermionic properties of a metal surface are profoundly changed by thin films of foreign materials. This is the basis of the thoriated tungsten emitter used in small- and medium-size vacuum tubes by Langmuir and Rodgers in 1914. The filament is made of tungsten having a small additive of thorium. In the heat treatment, some of the thorium diffuses to the surface where it forms a quite stable deposit that is less than one atom deep. The work function of this surface is less than that of either thorium or tungsten, about 2.6 volts, and A is about 3 ampere/cm^2 deg^2. Where the tungsten filament is normally operated near 2700 K the thoriated tungsten yields a comparable emission current density at 1800 to 2000 K, with a very considerable saving in heating power. The surface is less rugged than that of pure tungsten.

By far the larger number of vacuum tubes use the oxide-coated filament, described by Wehnelt

(1904). On a metallic base that is usually a nickel alloy is deposited a relatively thick coating of the mixed oxides of barium, strontium and calcium. Certain activation processes yield a surface with work function ϕ in the region of 1 volt. In spite of the small and variable value of the factor A, in the range of .01, the low work function provides a surface of high emission so that it can be used at the temperature of near 1000°K, giving still higher thermal efficiency than the thoriated tungsten. The mechanism of electron emission from this surface is considerably different from that of the pure metal. The oxide layer is normally an insulator at room temperature that becomes a semi-conductor at the operating temperature. The oxides are partly dissociated so that there are metal atoms, particularly of barium, in the body of the layer and on its surface. The surface barium probably contributes to the low work function. The body barium is presumably ionized so that it contributes conduction electrons in the semi-conductor. At the metal-oxide interface, there is another low work function surface so that electrons can pass from the metal base into the oxide, to be available for emission at the outer surface. With this modified mechanism, the emission equation still essentially holds. The reason is largely that the Boltzmann factor exp $(e\phi/kT)$ varies so rapidly with temperature that it renders other factors of little consequence experimentally.

So far it has been assumed that there is another electrode nearby with high enough positive voltage on it so that all of the emitted electrons are drawn to it. The current is then said to be saturated. In this condition, the current can still increase slowly with increasing voltage. The reason is that the strong electric field at the surface of the metal penetrates between the surface atoms and helps the electrons escape. The actual current then is increased above the saturation current by a factor exp 4.40 $(F^{1/2}/T)$ determined by Schottky in 1914, where F is the field strength in volts per centimeter, as verified with the refractory metals. With thoriated tungsten, the increase is more rapid than this, and with the oxide cathodes, the increase is so rapid that it is hard to say when saturation sets in.

At still higher surface fields, of the order 10 million volts/cm, another emission effect sets in, whereby the electrons are drawn out of even the cold metal. This is FIELD EMISSION, q.v.

At voltages below that required for saturation, the repulsion between the negatively charged electrons tends to limit the current. This is the space charge region, the condition in which most thermionic devices work. The current then is fairly insensitive to temperature and other conditions at the cathode so long as the anode voltage is well below the saturation value. In this condition, the current can be controlled by grids and other means. The space charge limited current between a plane emitting cathode and an anode at the distance d from it and at voltage,

V, each of area 1 cm², is given fairly closely by the expression

$$i = 2.33 \times 10^{-6}\, V^{3/2}/d^2 \text{ amperes} \qquad (6)$$

derived by Child (1911) and by Langmuir (1913). The equation is modified for a cylindrical structure, but the $V^{3/2}$ factor applies to any structure.

When the potential between emitter and plate is reversed so as to become retarding for electrons, the current is limited to the number of electrons with enough energy to overcome the retarding potential and is not limited by space charge. The current i_r is then related to the saturation current i_s by the expression

$$i_r = i_s \exp\left(-11600\,\frac{V_r}{T}\right) \qquad (7)$$

T being the temperature of the emitter and V_r the retarding potential. This may be written

$$\log i_r = -5030\,\frac{V_r}{T} + \log i_s. \qquad (8)$$

Besides giving a means of determining the temperature of the emitter as shown by Germer (1925), the formula also is the basis of electronic devices with logarithmic response.

The emission of positive ions from hot bodies seemed, before the existence of the electron was recognized, to be as important as the negative emission, and much work was devoted to it. It turned out eventually that it was not an important property of the body of the emitter but rather one of surface impurities. Richardson (1903-1914) showed that the positive ions given off by hot metals were ionized alkali atoms, and with a simple mass spectrometer he determined that they were mostly potassium coming originally from the glass envelope of the tube. Later studies have amply verified this finding, and the reason for it is now understood. A surface atom on a hot metal will be evaporated as a positive ion if the ionization potential of the atom is less than the work function of the metal, the metal then retaining the electron. This condition is satisfied with high work function metals as a base and with potassium, rubidium, cesium and possibly sodium as the impurity atoms.

There have been few practical applications of the positive ion emission beyond that of Kunsman (1927), but it has been useful in certain experimental researches such as those of Langmuir and Kingman (1925).

J. B. JOHNSON

References

Richardson, O. W., "Emission of Electricity from Hot Bodies," New York, Longmans, Green & Co., 1916, 1921.

Reimann, A. L., "Thermionic Emission," New York, John Wiley & Sons, Inc., 1934.

Millman, J., and Seely, S., "Thermionics," New York, McGraw-Hill Book Co., 1941.

de Boer, J. H., "Electron Emission and Adsorption Phenomena," New York, The Macmillan Co., 1935.

Dushman, S., "Thermionic Emission," *Rev. Mod. Phys.*, **2**, 381 (1930).

Becker, J. A., "Thermionic Electron Emission," *Rev. Mod. Phys.*, **7**, 95–128 (1935).

Herring, C., and Nichols, M. H., "Thermionic Emission," *Rev. Mod. Phys.*, **21**, 185–270 (1949).

Cross-references: ELECTRON, ELECTRON TUBES, FIELD EMISSION, IONIZATION, PHOTOELEC-TRICITY.

THERMODYNAMICS

Classical Thermodynamics is a theory which on the basis of four main laws and some ancillary assumptions deals with general limitations exhibited by the behavior of macroscopic systems. Phenomenologically it takes no cognizance of the atomic constitution of matter. All *mechanical* concepts such as kinetic energy or work are presupposed. Thermodynamics is motivated by the existence of dissipative mechanical systems. A *thermodynamic system* K may be thought of as a collection of bodies in bulk; when its condition is found to be unchanging in time (on a reasonable time scale) it is *in equilibrium*. It is then characterized by the values of a finite set of say n physical quantities, it being supposed that none of these is redundant. Such a set of quantities constitutes the *coordinates* of K, denoted by $x(=x_1, \cdots, x_n)$. Any set of values of these is a state $\mathfrak{S}$ of K. In virtue of these definitions, K is in a state only when it is in equilibrium. The passage of K from a state $\mathfrak{S}$ to a state $\mathfrak{S}'$ is a *transition* of K. A transition is *quasi-static* if in its course it goes through a continuous sequence of states, and if the forces which do work on the system are just those which hold it in equilibrium. A transition is *reversible* if there exists a second transition which restores the initial state, the final condition of the surroundings of K being the same as the initial condition. Reversible transitions are assumed to be quasi-static.

An enclosure which is such that the equilibrium of a system contained within it can only be disturbed by mechanical means is *adiabatic*, otherwise it is *diathermic*. For instance, stirring, or the passage of an electric current, constitute "mechanical means." A system K_0 in an adiabatic enclosure is *adiabatically isolated* but this does not preclude mechanical interactions with the surroundings. Its transitions are then called adiabatic.

For the time being, the masses of all substances present will be supposed fixed, and to achieve simplicity it will be given that (1) there are no substances present whose properties depend on their previous histories; (2) capillary forces as well as long-range interactions are absent. Further it will be supposed that of the n coordinates of K just $n - 1$ have geometrical character (*deformation coordinates*, e.g., volumes of enclosures), so that the work done by K in a quasi-static transition is

$$\int dW = \int \sum_{k=1}^{n-1} P_k(x)dx_k \qquad (1)$$

Such a system will be called a *standard system* ($n - 1$ enclosures in diathermic contact, each containing a simple fluid, may serve as example, x_n being any one of the pressures).

The Zeroth Law Suppose two systems $K_A(x)$ and $K_B(y)$ to be in mutual diathermic contact. Experience shows that the states $\mathfrak{S}_A$ and $\mathfrak{S}_B$ cannot be assigned arbitrarily, but that there exists a necessary relation of the form

$$f(x;y) \equiv f(x_1, \cdots, x_n; y_1, \cdots, y_m) = 0 \qquad (2)$$

between them. If K_C is a third system, its diathermic equilibrium with K_B on the one hand, or with K_A on the other, is governed by conditions

$$g(y;z) = 0 \qquad (3)$$

and

$$h(z;x) = 0 \qquad (4)$$

respectively. That these three functions are not independent is expressed by the *Zeroth Law*: *If each of two systems is in equilibrium with a third system then they are in equilibrium with each other.* It follows that any two of Eqs. (2) through (4) imply the third, i.e., they must be equivalent to equations of the form

$$\xi(x) = \eta(y) = \zeta(z) \qquad (5)$$

Thus with each system there is now associated a function, its *empirical temperature function*, such that two systems can be in equilibrium if and only if their *empirical temperatures* (i.e., the values of their empirical temperature functions) are equal. Write $t = \xi(x)$ so that one has the *equation of state* of K_A. Also, t may be introduced in place of any one of the x_k. Note that the empirical temperature is not uniquely determined since $t_A = t_B$ may be replaced by $\phi(t_A) = \phi(t_B)$ where the function ϕ is monotonic but otherwise arbitrary: one has a choice of *temperature* scales. For a system not in equilibrium, temperature is not defined.

The First Law It is obvious that one can do mechanical work upon a system (say by stirring) while its initial and final states are the same. (Nothing is being said about the surroundings!) In this sense mechanical energy is not conserved. One might however hope that it is conserved at least in a restricted class of transitions. That this is so is asserted by the

First Law: The work W_0 done by a system K_0 in an adiabatic transition depends on the terminal states alone. Thus if $\mathfrak{S}'(x')$, $\mathfrak{S}''(x'')$ are the terminal states

$$W_0 = F(x'; x'')$$

If $\mathfrak{S}'''(x''')$ is a third state, and the previous transition proceeds via $\mathfrak{S}'''$, W_0 must not depend on x''', i.e.,

$$F(x'; x''') + F(x'''; x'') \equiv F(x'; x'')$$

It follows that there must exist a function $U(x)$, defined to within an arbitrary additive constant, such that

$$F(x'; x'') = U(x') - U(x'')(= -\Delta U \text{ say})$$

$U(x)$ is the *internal energy function* of K. (To make sure that U is in fact defined for all states, one assumes that *some* adiabatic transition always exists between any pair of given states.) The energy of a compound standard system is the sum of the energies of its constituent standard systems. Further, U must be a monotonic function of t, and it is convenient to choose the scale of t such that $\partial U/\partial t > 0$.

When the transition from $\mathfrak{S}'$ to $\mathfrak{S}''$ is adiabatic, $W_0 + \Delta U$ vanishes by definition of U. If the transition is not adiabatic and W is the work done by K, the quantity

$$\Delta U + W (=Q, \text{ say}) \qquad (6)$$

will in general fail to vanish. Q is then called the *heat absorbed* by K. Every element of a quasi-static adiabatic transition is subject to $dQ = 0$, i.e., by Eqs. (1) and (6), to the differential equation

$$\sum_{k=1}^{n-1} \left(P_k(x) + \frac{\partial U(x)}{\partial x_k} \right) dx_k + \frac{\partial U}{\partial t} dt = 0 \qquad (7)$$

The Second Law Experiment shows that if $\mathfrak{S}'$ and $\mathfrak{S}''$ are arbitrarily prescribed states, then it may be that no adiabatic transition from $\mathfrak{S}'$ to $\mathfrak{S}''$ exists. When this is the case one says that $\mathfrak{S}''$ is inaccessible from $\mathfrak{S}'$, but $\mathfrak{S}'$ is then accessible from $\mathfrak{S}''$, as has been already assumed. The states may of course happen to be mutually accessible. The existence of states adiabatically inaccessible from a given state is asserted precisely by the *Second Law: In every neighbourhood of any state $\mathfrak{S}$ of an adiabatically isolated system, there are states inaccessible from $\mathfrak{S}$*. (This formulation of the Second Law is known as the *Principle of Carathéodory*.) A fortiori this law applies to quasi-static transitions, i.e., those which satisfy Eq. (7). It asserts there are states $\mathfrak{S}''$ near $\mathfrak{S}'$ such that no functions $x_k(t)$ exist which satisfy Eq. (7) and whose values when $t = t''$ are just x_k'', $(k = 1, \cdots, n - 1)$. It is merely a mathematical problem (the Theorem of Carathéodory) to prove that this is the case if and only if there exist

functions $\lambda(x)$ and $s(x)$, $(x_n \equiv t)$ such that the left-hand member is identically equal to λds, where ds is the total differential of s. Thus, the Second Law entails that

$$dQ = dU + dW = \lambda \, ds \qquad (8)$$

(dQ is of course not a total differential). s is called the *empirical entropy function of* K. It is not uniquely determined, since it may be replaced by any monotonic function of s. If two standard systems K_A and K_B in diathermic contact make up a compound system K_C, $dQ_C = dQ_A + dQ_B$, i.e., because of Eq. (8),

$$\lambda_A ds_A + \lambda_B ds_B = \lambda_c ds_c$$

By including s_A, s_B and the common empirical temperature t among the coordinates of K_C, one infers that

$$\lambda_A = T(t)\theta_A(s_A), \quad \lambda_B = T(t)\theta_B(s_B),$$

$$\lambda_C = T(t)\theta(s_A, s_B)$$

The common function $T(t)$ is called the *absolute temperature function*, while

$$S_A(s_A) = \int \theta_A(s_A) ds_A$$

is the *metrical entropy* of K_A. The "element of heat" dQ of any standard system thus splits up into the product of a universal function of the empirical entropy and the total differential $dS(x)$ of the metrical entropy function:

$$T \, dS = dU + dW \qquad (9)$$

By multiplying T by a constant and dividing S by the same constant, T can be arranged to be positive.

If one now chooses $x_n = S$ and recalls that the $x_k(k < n)$ are freely adjustable, the Second Law would be violated if S were also adjustable at will (by means of non-static adiabatic transitions.) Taking continuity requirements into account, it follows that S can either never decrease or never increase. The single example of the sudden expansion of a real gas shows that it can never decrease. One has the *Principle of Increase of Entropy: The entropy of an adiabatically isolated system can never decrease*.

The Third Law It is known from experiment that for given values of the deformation coordinates, the energy function has a lower bound U_0. The question arises whether the entropy S has an analogous property. It is found in practice that the specific heats $\partial U/\partial T$ of all substances appear to go to zero at least linearly with T as $T \to 0$. This ensures that the function S goes to a finite limit S_0 as $T \to 0$. Experiment shows however further that as $T \to 0$, the derivatives of S with respect to the deformation coordinates also go to zero. In contrast with U_0, S_0 has therefore the remark-

able property that it is independent of the deformation coordinates. One thus arrives at the *Third Law: The entropy of any given system attains the same finite least value for every state of least energy*. One immediate consequence of this is that the so-called *classical ideal gas* (the product of whose volume V and pressure P is proportional to T) cannot exist in nature. Further, no system can have its absolute temperature reduced to zero. The Third Law is therefore a statement about the properties of functions, not of systems, at $T = 0$.

The practical applications of the theory just outlined divide themselves into two broad classes: (1) those which are based on the existence and properties of the functions U and S and some others related to them—all "thermodynamic identities" being merely the integrability condition for the total differentials of these functions; and (2) those which are based on the Principle of Increase of Entropy: the entropy of the actual state of an adiabatically enclosed system being greater than that of any neighbouring "virtual" state.

The most important of the auxiliary functions just mentioned are
the *Helmholtz Function:*

$$F = U - TS \qquad (10)$$

the *Gibbs Function:*

$$G = U - TS + \sum_{k=1}^{n-1} P_k x_k \qquad (11)$$

the *enthalpy:*

$$H = U + \sum_{k=1}^{n-1} P_k x_k \qquad (12)$$

sometimes called *thermodynamic potentials.* Then, e.g.,

$$dF = -S \, dT - dW$$

F therefore contains all available quantitative information about K, since

$$S = -\frac{\partial F}{\partial T}, \quad \text{and} \quad P_k = -\frac{\partial F}{\partial x_k} \qquad (13)$$

The same is true of G for instance, since

$$S = -\frac{\partial G}{\partial T}, \quad \text{and} \quad x_k = \frac{\partial G}{\partial P_k}$$

F and G are naturally taken as functions of $x_1, \cdots, x_{n-1}, T$ and of $P_1, \cdots, P_{n-1}, T$, respectively. At times one speaks of F as the "Helmholtz free energy" and of G as the "Gibbs free energy." In an *isothermal* reversible transition, the amount W of work done by a system is equal not to the decrease of its energy U but to the decrease $-\Delta F$ of its (Helmholtz) free energy. In the presence of internal sources

of irreversibility

$$W < -\Delta F$$

In considering physicochemical equilibria, that is to say, if one is interested in the internal constitution of a system in equilibrium when changes of phase and chemical reactions are admitted, one introduces the *constitutive coordinates* n_i^α; this being the number of moles of the ith constituent C_i in the αth phase. The definitions of Eqs. (10) through (12) remain unaltered, for the n_i^α do not enter into the description of the interaction of the system with its surroundings. Let an amount dn_i^α of C_i be introduced quasistatically into the αth phase of the system. The work done on K shall be $\mu_i^\alpha dn_i$. The quantity μ_i^α so defined is the *chemical potential* of C_i in the αth phase. It is in general a function of all the coordinates of K. Then, identically,

$$dG = \sum_{k=1}^{n-1} x_k dP_k - S \, dT + \sum_i \sum_\alpha \mu_i^\alpha dn_i^\alpha$$

Integrability conditions such as

$$\partial \mu_i^\alpha / \partial T = -\partial S / \partial n_i^\alpha$$

are applications of the first kind. On the other hand, the minimal property of G, derived from the maximal property of S, requires that

$$\sum_i \sum_\alpha \mu_i^\alpha dn_i^\alpha = 0$$

when all virtual states differ only in the values of the constitutive coordinates. If the system is chemically inert, the dn_i^α are subject only to the requirements of the conservation of matter. One then concludes that if there are c constituents and p phases, i.e., $n + pc$ coordinates in all, then the number f of these to which arbitrary values may be assigned is

$$f = c - p + n$$

This typical application of the second kind is the Gibbs PHASE RULE (for inert systems.) This rule is often stated merely for systems with only two external coordinates ($n = 2$, e.g., $x_i = P$, $x_2 = T$). There must then be no internal partitions within the system nor may it, for instance, contain magnetic substances in the presence of external magnetic fields.

The beauty and power of phenomenological thermodynamics lies just in the generality and paucity of its basic laws which hold independently of any assumptions concerning the microscopic structure of the systems which they govern. Its quantitative content is limited to conditions of equilibrium. Its conceptual framework is too narrow to permit the description of the temporal behavior of systems, except in as far as it makes it possible to decide which one of any pair of states of an adia-

batically enclosed system must have been the earlier state.

Statistical thermodynamics seeks to remedy these deficiencies by making specific assumptions about the microscopic structure of the system K, and relating its macroscopic behaviour to that of its atomic constituents. K is then to be regarded as an *assembly* of a very large number of particles, which, on a non-quantal level, is a mechanical system with, say, N degrees of freedom. A *microstate* of K is a set of values of its N coordinates and its N conjugate momenta. It is out of the question to measure all these at a given time. One therefore constructs a *representative ensemble* $\mathcal{E}_K$ of K, which is an abstract collection of a very large number of identical copies of K. At any time t, the members of $\mathcal{E}_K$ will be in different microstates. Let the fractional number of members of the ensemble whose microstates lie in the range dp, dq about p, q be $\phi\, dp\, dq$. Then ϕ is the *probability-in-phase*, and with $d\Gamma = dp\, dq$

$$\int \phi\, d\Gamma = 1 \qquad (14)$$

The reason for this terminology is implicit in the *Postulate: The probability that a given assembly* K *will, at time t, be in a microstate lying in the range* $d\Gamma$ *about p,q, is equal to the probability* $\phi\, d\Gamma$ *that the microstate of a member of* $\mathcal{E}_K$, *selected at random at time t, lies in the same range.*

The mean value $\langle f \rangle$ of a dynamical quantity f is defined to be

$$\langle f \rangle = \int f\phi\, d\Gamma$$

If N is sufficiently large, fluctuations about the mean will usually be negligible.

When K is in equilibrium ϕ must be constant in time, and this will be the case if it is a function of the (time-independent) Hamiltonian H of K. Ensemble averages are now assumed to coincide with temporal averages. When, in particular, K is in diathermic equilibrium with its surroundings one can show that ϕ must have the form

$$\phi = \exp[(\Phi - H)/\theta] \qquad (15)$$

where Φ and θ are independent of p,q. Then

$$\theta\langle \ln \phi \rangle = \Phi - \langle H \rangle \qquad (16)$$

and, because of Eq. (14)

$$d \int \exp[(\Phi - H)/\theta]\, d\Gamma = 0 = \langle d[(\Phi - H)/\theta] \rangle$$

where d refers to a variation of the macroscopic coordinates of K. Using Eq. (16) and its variation, the relation

$$-\theta d\langle \ln \phi \rangle = d\langle H \rangle - \langle dH \rangle \qquad (17)$$

follows. Now $\langle H \rangle$ ($=\overline{U}$, say) is the total energy of the assembly, while $\langle dH \rangle$ is the average of the change of the potential energy, i.e., the work $-dW$ done by the external forces on K. If one writes

$$\overline{S} = -k\langle \ln \phi \rangle$$

where k is a constant, Eq. (17) becomes

$$k^{-1}\theta\, d\overline{S} = d\overline{U} + dW$$

This is identical with the phenomenological relation of Eq. (9) if one formally identifies S with $\overline{S}$, U with $\overline{U}$ and θ with kT. In this way, contact with the phenomenological theory has been established, and the quantities characteristic of the one theory have been *correlated* with that of the other. With this correlation, or interpretation, Φ becomes F. However, because of Eqs. (14) and (15)

$$F = -kT \ln \int \exp(-H/kT)d\Gamma$$

so that if only H is known, the integral on the right (the *partition function*), and thus F, can be calculated. The equation of state of a real gas can thus in principle be obtained from a knowledge of the forces operating within the assembly. This illustrates how the additional information put into the theory yields a correspondingly greater output. Phenomenologically such an equation of state might be written as

$$PV = \sum_{n=1}^{\infty} B_n(T)\, V^{1-n}$$

but here each of the *virial coefficients* B_1, B_2, $\cdots$ must be measured separately.

If the quantum mechanical behavior of matter is taken into account, the fact that one cannot assign precise simultaneous values to canonically conjugate quantities must produce modifications of the details of the statistical theory. However, it is not necessary to consider these here.

H. A. BUCHDAHL

Reference

Buchdahl, H. A., "The Concepts of Classical Thermodynamics," Cambridge, England, The University Press, 1966.

Cross-references: ENTROPY, HEAT CAPACITY, PHASE RULE, PHYSICAL CHEMISTRY.

THERMOELECTRICITY

Thermoelectricity is the subject dealing with the interaction between temperature gradients and electrical potential differences in solid or liquid

materials. In the absence of a magnetic field there are three thermoelectric effects—the Seebeck, Peltier, and Thomson effects.

The Seebeck effect was discovered by T. J. Seebeck in 1822. Consider a circuit made up of two different materials as shown in Fig. 1. The

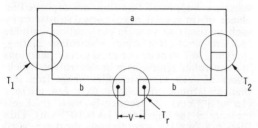

FIG. 1. A thermoelectric circuit composed of two different materials, a and b. The regions enclosed in circles are assumed isothermal at the temperatures shown.

regions around the junctions are assumed isothermal at temperatures T_1, T_2, and T_R. If $T_1 \neq T_2$, a voltage V is observed. If the two materials a and b are homogeneous, the voltage V does not depend on T_R or on the temperature distribution along either material, but only on the temperature difference between the junctions. For small temperature differences, the voltage is proportional to the temperature difference

$$V_{ab} = \alpha_{ab}(T_1 - T_2) \qquad (1)$$

where α_{ab} is called the Seebeck coefficient of the couple. (It has often been called the thermoelectric power, but this is a poor name since it does not have the dimensions of power.)

The Peltier effect was discovered by J. C. A. Peltier in 1834. In any conductor in which an electric current exists, heat is produced called the Joule heat which is given by

$$P_j = J^2 \rho \qquad (2)$$

where P_j is the rate of Joule heat production per unit volume, J is the current density, and ρ is the electrical resistivity. At a junction between dissimilar materials, one finds an additional heat evolved or absorbed when current is present. This additional heat is called the Peltier heat and is given by

$$P_p = \pi_{ab}J_{ab} \qquad (3)$$

where P_p is the rate of Peltier heat production per unit cross-sectional area of the junction and π_{ab} is the Peltier coefficient of the junction. Note that the Joule heat is always given off, whereas the Peltier heat may be absorbed or given off depending on the direction of the electric current.

The Thomson effect was predicted by William Thomson (later Lord Kelvin) in 1854 and experimentally established by him several years later.

He found that a material in which there was a temperature gradient and electrical current gave off or absorbed heat in addition to the Joule heat. The difference between the total heat given off and the Joule heat is called the Thomson heat. It is given by

$$P_t = -\tau J \nabla T \qquad (4)$$

where P_t is the rate of Thomson heat production per unit volume, τ is the Thomson coefficient of the material, and ∇T is the temperature gradient. Note that if either the temperature gradient or the electrical current is reversed in direction, then the Thomson heat reverses also, i.e., if Thomson heat originally was absorbed, then with a reversal of either the temperature gradient or the current density it will be emitted.

The three thermoelectric coefficients are related by the Kelvin relations

$$\pi_{ab} = T\alpha_{ab} \qquad (5a)$$

$$\tau_a - \tau_b = T(d\alpha_{ab}/dT) \qquad (5b)$$

where T is the absolute temperature.

It should be noted that the Seebeck and Peltier coefficients as defined here involve two different materials, while the Thomson coefficient involves only one. There are two ways in which Seebeck coefficients for a single material are defined. (1) The relative Seebeck coefficient is defined as the Seebeck coefficient of a couple composed of the given material and a specified standard material such as platinum, lead, or copper. (2) The absolute Seebeck coefficient at temperature T_1 is defined by

$$\alpha_a(T_1) \equiv \int_0^{T_1} (\tau_a/T)dT \qquad (6)$$

Since the Seebeck coefficient of a couple is zero at absolute zero temperature, integration of Eq. (5b) yields

$$\alpha_{ab} = \alpha_a - \alpha_b$$

At room temperature, metals have Seebeck coefficients in the range from a few tenths to as high as 40 μV/°C for some alloys. Semi-metals such as bismuth have Seebeck coefficients ranging from about 20 to 40 μV/°C, while semiconductors have Seebeck coefficients from a few microvolts per degree Celsius to as high as 1 mV/°C.

The Seebeck effect is widely used to measure temperature. The thermoelectric circuit, usually called a thermocouple, is made by welding together wires of pure metal or metallic alloys such as copper with constantan, chromel with alumel, or platinum with a platinum-rhodium alloy. For the measurements of very small temperature differences, it is possible to put a number of thermocouples in series so that the voltages add, as shown in Fig. 2. This device is called a thermopile.

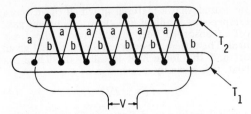

FIG. 2. A thermopile made from materials a and b. All of the upper junctions are at temperature T_2 and all of the lower ones are at temperature T_1.

Devices have also been built utilizing the Seebeck effect to generate electricity directly from a heat source and utilizing the Peltier effect for refrigeration or heat pumping. In these applications the thermoelectric materials are semiconductors, such as Bi_2Te_3, PbTe or GeTe, with a diameter of 0.3 to 1.3 cm and a length of 0.3 to 2 cm. The introduction of a magnetic field into a material may change its Seebeck, Peltier, and Thomson coefficients; it also produces several new effects, called galvanomagnetic and thermomagnetic effects. These include the Nernst, Ettingshausen, and Righi-Leduc effects. In these effects, the electric current or electrical potential difference, the magnetic field, and the temperature gradient or heat flow are all mutually perpendicular. These effects have also been used as a basis for devices which will pump heat or generate electricity directly from a temperature gradient (see HALL EFFECT AND RELATED PHENOMENA).

ROLAND W. URE, JR.

References

Heikes, R. R., and Ure, R. W., Jr., "Thermoelectricity: Science and Engineering," New York, Interscience Publishers, 1961.

MacDonald, D. K. C., "Thermoelectricity: An Introduction to the Principles," New York, John Wiley & Sons, 1962.

Goldsmid, H. J., "Applications of Thermoelectricity," London, Methuen & Co., Ltd., 1960.

Domenicali, C. A., *Rev. Mod. Phys.*, **26**, 237 (1954).

Joffe, A. F., *Sci. Am.*, **199**, 31 (November 1958).

Angrist, S. W., *Sci. Am.*, **205**, 45 (December 1961).

Wolfe, R., *Sci. Am.*, **210**, 70 (June 1964).

Ure, R. W., Jr., "Thermoelectric Effects in III-V Compounds," in "Semiconductors and Semimetals," edited by R. K. Willardson and A. C. Beer, New York, Academic Press, 1972, Vol. 8, p. 67–102.

Harman, T. C., and Honig, J. M., "Thermoelectric and Thermomagnetic Effects and Applications," New York, McGraw-Hill Book Co., 1967.

Cross-references: CONDUCTIVITY, ELECTRICAL; HALL EFFECT AND RELATED PHENOMENA; TEMPERATURE AND THERMOMETRY.

THIN FILMS

General The term "thin films" is used for a wide variety of physical structures. Self-supporting solid sheets usually are called foils when thinned from thicker material by such methods as rolling, beating, or etching; and films, when obtained by stripping a deposited layer from its substrate. Supported thin films are deposited on planar or (in special cases) curved substrates by such methods as vacuum evaporation, cathode sputtering, electroplating, electroless plating, spraying, and various chemical surface reactions in a controlled atmosphere or electrolyte. Thicknesses of such supported films range from less than an atomic monolayer to a few microns ($1\mu = 10^{-4}$ cm). A frequently used thickness measure is the angstrom ($1\text{Å} = 10^{-8}$ cm). Thin films not forming a continuous sheet are called "island films." Particularly, noble metals may condense as islands of considerable thickness (up to $\sim 10^2 \text{Å}$).

In scientific studies and technical applications, the use of well-controllable deposition methods such as vacuum evaporation and cathode sputtering are generally preferred. The film structure is markedly influenced by such deposition parameters as substrate composition and surface structure, source and substrate temperatures, deposition rate, and composition and pressure of the ambient atmosphere (where applicable). In general, the structure of films is more disordered than the corresponding bulk material. Smaller grains, higher dislocation concentrations, and deviations from stoichiometry are typical, and films approach bulk structure only as a limiting case. Under certain growth conditions, films exhibit preferential crystal orientations or even epitaxy. (Epitaxy means that the film structure is determined by the crystal structure and orientation of the underlying substrate.)

Solid thin films are common study objects in most phases of solid-state physics. They supply the samples for the study of general structural and physical properties of solid matter where special beam methods require small quantities of material or extremely thin layers, as for instance in transmission electron microscopy and diffraction, NEUTRON DIFFRACTION, UV spectroscopy, and X-RAY DIFFRACTION and SPECTROSCOPY. Thin films represent the best means for studying physical effects, where these effects are caused by the extreme thinness of the material itself. Examples are the rotational switching of ferromagnetic films, electron tunneling phenomena, electromagnetic skin effects of various kinds, and certain optical interference phenomena (see FERROMAGNETISM, SKIN EFFECT and TUNNELING). Films also are convenient vehicles for the investigation of nucleation and crystal growth, and for states of extremely disturbed thermodynamic equilibrium.

Presently, films find three major industrial uses: the decorative finishing of plastics, optical coatings of various kinds (mainly antireflection

coatings, reflection increasing films, multilayer interference filters, and fluorescent coatings), and in electronic components from transistors or resistor-capacitor networks to such specialized devices as magnetic storage bits, photosensors, and cryotrons. The restricted space only permits the discussion of a few selected research and application areas.

Nucleation, Growth and Mechanical Properties of Films In vacuum evaporation, molecules or atoms of thermal energy are deposited at a uniform angle of incidence and under well-defined environmental conditions. Most nucleation and growth studies, therefore, have been made on evaporated films. A particle approaching the substrate enters close to its surface a field of attracting short-range London forces with an exchange energy proportional to $-1/r^6$. At a still shorter distance r, repulsive forces proportional to $e^{-r/constant}$ resist the penetration of the electron clouds of the surface atoms. Due to the atomic or crystalline structure of the substrate, this potential field exhibits periodicity or quasiperiodicity in the substrate plane. The freshly condensed particles migrate over the surface with a jump frequency $i_D \propto \exp(-Q_D/kT)$, or desorb with a frequency $i_{ad} \propto \exp(-Q_{ad}/kT)$, where the activation energy Q_D is often approximately one-fourth of Q_{ad}. Permanent condensation occurs in most cases at distinct nucleation centers which may consist of deep potential wells of the substrate, clusters of condensed particles, or previously deposited "seed" particles of a different material. The number of nuclei formed in the second case is strongly temperature and rate dependent.

Most metals always condense in crystalline form, but the grain size is extremely small at low temperatures (on the order of a few angstroms) and increases markedly with increasing substrate temperatures. Grain size decreases with increasing deposition rates. The condensation of amorphous or quasi-liquid phases at low temperatures has been observed for such metals as antimony and bismuth and a few dielectrics. Some of these materials, on annealing, pass through otherwise unobserved, and probably metastable, phases.

Stresses of considerable magnitude are often observed in deposited films. The main causes of these stresses are a mismatch of expansion coefficients between substrate and film, enclosed impurity atoms, a high concentration of lattice defects and, in very thin films, a variety of surface effects. Often, the stresses resulting from lattice defects can be minimized by the choice of a higher substrate temperature during deposition, or they can be reduced by a post-deposition anneal. Metal films frequently exhibit tensile strengths which are considerably larger than those of the corresponding bulk materials.

Thin-film Optics Deposited metal mirrors probably represent the oldest optical application of films. High-quality mirrors usually are produced by the vacuum evaporation of aluminium on an appropriately shaped glass substrate. Often, a glow-discharge cleaning of the substrate or a chromium undercoat is first applied to increase the adhesion of the aluminium. After deposition, the aluminium is protected by anodic oxidation or an evaporated overcoat of SiO, SiO_2, or Al_2O_3.

For SiO, maximum reflectance in the visible spectral region is achieved at a thickness of about 1400Å. Rapid SiO evaporation reduces the reflectance at shorter wavelengths.

Single or multilayer coatings find increasing use as optical interference filters. These film stacks may consist solely of transparent films of different refractive indices n_f, or a combination of absorbing and nonabsorbing layers. Common low-index materials for glass coatings in the visible region of the spectrum are MgF_2 (n_f = 1.32 to 1.37), and cryolite Na_3AlF_6 (n_f = 1.28 to 1.34); high-index materials are SiO (n_f = 1.97), ZnS ($n_f \approx 2.34$), TiO_2 (n_f = 2.66 to 2.69) and CeO_2 (n_f = 2.2 to 2.4). The indices are given for the sodium D line. Various semiconductors are used for infrared coatings.

At each air-film, film-film, or film-substrate interface, the incident light amplitude is split into a reflected and a transmitted fraction according to the Fresnel coefficients

$$f_{j-1} = (\hat{n}_{j-1} - \hat{n}_j)/(\hat{n}_{j-1} + \hat{n}_j) \text{ and }$$

$$g_{j-1} = 2\hat{n}_{j-1}/(\hat{n}_{j-1} + \hat{n}_j)$$

where j and $j - 1$ denote the number of the optical layer counted from the side of the incident beam. $\hat{n}_j = \hat{n}/\cos \Theta_j$ for p polarization or $\hat{n}_j = \hat{n}_j \cos \Theta_j$ for s polarization is the effective refractive index, and $\hat{n}_j = n_j - ik_j$ the refractive index of the j layer.

$$\cos \Theta_j = \sqrt{(\sqrt{p_j^2 + q_j^2} + p_j)/2}$$
$$- i\sqrt{(\sqrt{p_j^2 + q_j^2} - p_j)/2}$$

$$p_j = 1 + (k_j^2 - n_j^2)\,[n_0 \sin \theta_0/(n_j^2 + k_j^2)]^2$$

$$q_j = -2n_j k_j\,[n_0 \sin \theta_0/(n_j^2 + k_j^2)]^2$$

The symbol θ_0 is the angle of incidence in the incident medium.

For nonabsorbing film stacks ($k_i = 0$; $i = 1$, $2 \cdots$, $m + 1$), the over-all reflectance and transmittance may be obtained by summing the multiple coherent reflections between the film boundaries. A more general treatment based on electromagnetic theory yields for amplitude reflectance and transmittance the recursion formulas

$$r_{(j-1)-} = (f_{j-1} + r_{j-} \exp(-2i\,\hat{\Phi}_j))/$$
$$(1 + f_{j-1}r_{j-} \exp(-2i\,\hat{\Phi}_j))$$

and

$$t_{(j-1)-} = (g_{j-1} t_{j-} \exp{(-i\,\hat{\Phi}_j))}/$$

$$(1 + f_{j-1} r_{j-} \exp{(-2i\,\hat{\Phi}_j))}$$

$\hat{\Phi}_j = \Phi_j \cos\Theta_j$ is the effective phase thickness. $\Phi_j = (2\pi/\lambda)\tilde{n}_j l_j$ where λ is the wavelength in vacuo and l_j is the geometrical film thickness. The recursion is started on the side of emergence, using the initial conditions $r_{m-} = f_m$ and $t_{m-} = g_m$. Intensities are given by $R = |r_{0-}|^2$ and $T = (\Re \tilde{n}_{m+1}/n_0)\,|t_{0-}|^2$ where $\Re$ denotes "real part of." If A_j is the absorption in the layer j, $R + T + \Sigma_j A_j = 1$.

A single antireflection coating of $\lambda/4$ optical thickness $n_f l_f$ yields zero reflectance at $n_f = \sqrt{n_{\text{glass}}}$. A double layer coating of $\lambda/4$ films requires $n_2/n_1 = \sqrt{n_g}$. The transmission of a Fabry-Perot interference filter consisting of a dielectric spacer layer between two partially reflecting metal films is given by $I/I_0 = [(1 + A/T)^2 + (4R/T^2)\sin^2{(\delta - \Phi)}]^{-1}$ where $\Phi = 2\pi nl\cos\theta/\lambda$. R, T, and A are the reflection, transmission and absorption coefficients of the reflecting layers. The refractive index and thickness of the spacer film are n and l. θ is the angle of refraction in the spacer, and δ is the phase change for reflections at the spacer-metal film interfaces. $(I/I_0)_{\max} = (T/(1-R))^2$ and $(I/I_0)_{\min} = (T/(1+R))^2$. The band pass half-width is $\Delta\lambda_{1/2} \simeq \lambda\,(1-R)/m\pi R^{1/2}$ for the interference order m $(m\pi = \Phi)$. More complex coatings and filters, and their various applications, cannot be discussed here. It should be mentioned, however, that films play a very important role today in the accurate determination of the optical constants of many materials, but particularly of metals (see REFLECTION).

Film Electronics Deposited dielectric film materials in common use are SiO_2, Al_2O_3, Si_3N_4, and various glasses. Thin capacitive layers in the 100 to 500 Å thickness region are often produced by the anodization of tantalum and aluminum to Ta_2O_5 or Al_2O_3, respectively. The breakdown strength and dielectric constant of films approach bulk values, but might be reduced by surface roughness, structural faults, and lower density. According to the Lorentz-Lorenz formula, the dielectric constant D changes with reduced density ρ as $dD/d\rho = 3C/(1 - C\rho)^2$, where C is a constant depending on the material. On metal-dielectric-metal films, quantum mechanical tunneling through the dielectric film becomes observable below a dielectric thickness of about 100 Å. For applied voltages less than the metal-insulator work function ϕ, the tunneling current density J is proportional to the applied voltage V, demonstrating that the low-voltage tunneling resistance is ohmic. $J = (qV/h^2 s)(2m^*\phi)^{1/2}\,\exp{[-(4\pi s/h)(2m^*\phi)^{1/2}]}$. At high applied voltages $(qV > \phi)$, the current increases very rapidly: $J = (q^2 V^2/8\pi h\phi_s^2)\exp{[-(8\pi s/3hqV)(2m^*)^{1/2}\phi^{3/2}]}$. s is the insulator thickness, m^* the electronic effective mass, and q the electron charge. Thicker dielectric films may exhibit in high fields appreciable Schottky or avalanche currents when they are greatly disordered.

Polycrystalline metal films generally show, due to their low structural order, a larger resistivity than the bulk material. According to Matthiessen's rule, the total resistivity can be expressed as $\rho = \rho(t) + \rho(i)$ where $\rho(t)$ is the temperature-dependent resistivity associated with scattering by lattice vibrations, and $\rho(i)$ is a temperature-independent resistivity caused by impurity or imperfection scattering. Very thin specimens with a thickness comparable to the electron mean free path show a $\rho(i)$ rapidly increasing with decreasing thickness. This increase is caused by an increasing contribution of non-specular electron scattering at the film surfaces. By annealing a metal film, $\rho(i)$ might be reduced permanently. A large $\rho(i)$ results in a small temperature coefficient α.

Many known superconductors can be deposited as super-conductive films (see SUPERCONDUCTIVITY). Through thin-film experiments, the energy gap in semiconductors can be measured, and material parameters, such as the penetration depth of magnetic fields, can be studied at dimensions less than the coherence range.

Studies of semiconductor films have shown many facets. The properties of epitaxial films have mainly been investigated on Ge and Si, and to a lesser degree on III-V compounds. Much work has been done on polycrystalline II-VI films, particularly with regard to the stoichiometry of the deposits, doping and post-deposition treatments, conductivity and carrier mobility, photo-conductance, fluorescence, electroluminescence, and metal-semiconductor junction properties. Among other semiconductors, selenium, tellurium, and a few transition metal oxides have found some interest.

Film resistors, capacitors, and interconnected R-C net-works on planar glass or ceramic substrates are finding widespread industrial use. Common resistor materials are carbon, nichrome and tin oxide in individual components; and nichrome, tantalum nitride, SiO-chromium cermet and cermet glazes in planar networks. Gold, copper, aluminum, or tantalum are used for termination lands, connection leads, and capacitor plates. SiO_2, Al_2O_3 and Si_3N_4 serve as film capacitor dielectrics and crossover insulation. The geometrical configuration of the desired component or circuit pattern is obtained either by deposition through mechanical masks or by removing from a continuous sheet the undesired portions after the deposition process is completed. This removal is frequently accomplished by a combination of photolithographic and etch processes.

The minimum length l and width w of a resistor are calculated from the given resistance R, the sheet resistance $\Re$ in ohms per square, dissipated power P, and permissible power dissipa-

tion per square inch $\mathscr{P}$ by use of the formulas $w = \sqrt{(P \cdot \mathscr{R})/\mathscr{P} \cdot R}$ and $l = wR/\mathscr{R}$. The capacitance of film capacitors is given by $C = 0.225 D(N-1)A/t$, where C is the capacitance in picofarads, D the dielectric constant, N the number of plates, A the area in square inches, and t the dielectric thickness in inches.

Thin-film semiconductor devices have been slow to reach the production stage, mainly due to difficulties in controlling the film surface and interface properties. Various barrier layer diodes have exhibited impressive rectification ratios, but limited breakdown strength and low speed due to their large specific capacitance. Of the many film TRANSISTOR concepts proposed, the insulated gate field effect device looks the most promising and manufacturable. Its structure consists of a minute metal-dielectric-semiconductor capacitor. The semiconductor strip carries current between two terminals called source and drain. A field applied between metal "gate" and source modulates the semiconductor conductance and consequently the source-drain current. Usable semiconductor materials with a sufficiently low concentration of interface states are CdS, CdSe, and tellurium. These devices exhibit pentode-like characteristics with voltage gains ranging from 2.5 at 60 MHz to 8.5 at 2.5 MHz. The gain band width product G.B., which is equal to the transconductance divided by 2π times the gate capacitance, reaches values of about 20 MHz. It is determined by $G.B. = \mu_d V_D / 2\pi L^2$, where μ_d is the effective drift mobility of the electrons, V_D the source-drain potential, and L the source-drain spacing which is usually chosen between 5 and 50μ. Special film semiconductor devices in industrial use are various types of photodetectors.

Magnetic Films Magnetic thin films of nickel-iron (usually deposited at an $80:20$ composition by weight) exhibit a number of unusual properties, which have led to many experimental and theoretical studies, as well as to important applications in binary storage and switching, magnetic amplifiers, and magneto-optical Kerr-effect displays.

Such "Permalloy" films have two stable states of magnetization, corresponding to positive and negative remanence. When deposited in a magnetic field or at an oblique angle, they exhibit uniaxial anisotropy. In practice, this anisotropy shows some dispersion, since it results from the alignment of local lattice disturbances. The stable states result from the minimization of the free energy $E = MH_L \cos\theta - MH_T \sin\theta + K\sin^2\theta$, where the last term represents the anisotropy energy, and θ is the angle between the magnetization M and the easy axis. From an inspection of the derivatives of this equation follows the hard-direction straight-line and the easy-direction square hysteresis loops of anistropic films. In the latter case, the magnetization is always either $+M$ or $-M$, and the change occurs at $H_L = \pm H_K$. The transitions from unstable to stable

states occur at $\partial^2 E/\partial\theta^2 = 0$, resulting in a critical curve $H_L^{2/3} + H_T^{2/3} = H_K^{2/3}$ which has the form of an asteroid enclosing the origin (see MAGNETISM).

An important feature of magnetic films is the high speed with which the state of magnetization can be reversed. Dependent on film properties and magnetic fields, three modes of magnetization reversal occur: Domain wall motion, incoherent rotations, and the extremely fast coherent rotation of the magnetization. Wall-motion switching is expected when the driving fields are smaller than the critical values.

More recently, various magnetic garnet films have gained importance in research and industrial applications.

RUDOLF E. THUN

References

Dushman, S., "Scientific Foundations of Vacuum Technique," Second edition, New York, John Wiley & Sons, 1962.

Holland, L., "Vacuum Deposition of Thin Films," New York, John Wiley & Sons, 1958.

Keonjian, Edward, Ed., "Microelectronics," New York, McGraw-Hill, 1963.

Hass, G. Ed., "Physics of Thin Films," Vols. I to VI, New York, Academic Press, 1963 to 1971.

Neugebauer, C. A., et al., Ed., "Structure and Properties of Thin Films," New York, John Wiley & Sons, 1959.

Mayer, H., "Physik dünner Schichten, I and II," Stuttgart, Wissenschaftliche, 1950 and 1955.

Heavens, O. S. "Optical Properties of Thin Solid Films," London, Butterworths, 1955.

Series: "Vacuum Technology Transactions," New York, Pergamon Press, 1955–1963.

Walter, H., in Flügge, S., Ed., "Handbuch der Physik," Vol. 24, Berlin, Springer, 1956.

Maissel, L. I., and Glang, R., Eds., "Handbook of Thin Film Technology," New York, McGraw-Hill, 1970.

Cross-references: CONDUCTIVITY, ELECTRICAL; ELECTRON MICROSCOPE; FERROMAGNETISM; MAGNETISM; NEUTRON DIFFRACTION; SEMICONDUCTORS; SKIN EFFECT; SPECTROSCOPY; SUPERCONDUCTIVITY; TRANSISTOR; TUNNELING; X-RAY DIFFRACTION.

TIME

Too many interpretations of the concept of time are based on one of the following two kinds of oversimplification. Philosophers have speculated about time on the premise that it is a primary notion and can be abstractly defined without bothering about the implementation of the definition. Conversely, the physicists, before Einstein, had a tendency to take time for granted and to use it as a parameter without further questioning its definition. Phychologists may have been the first to make a step in the right

direction by trying to relate the concept of time to actual perceptions.

Nowadays, the physicist has become aware of the necessity of providing operational definitions of the concepts he uses, and it is generally acknowledged that the very concept of time depends upon the possibility of the repetition of events that may be considered identical or, at least, that have a common recognizable feature. However, the far-reaching implications of this idea are seldom realized, and it is not infrequent to read otherwise respectable discussions based on a notion so "obvious" that its vagueness remains completely unsuspected, namely, the notion of a "clock."

Assigning to time the character of a self-contained concept and assuming the existence of appropriate "clocks" showing the flow of this "time" is putting the cart before the horse. In a more refined approach, an a priori time concept is accepted and principles are formulated by virtue of which a motion taking place in some specified conditions is uniform. But even such a procedure amounts to a self-deception, as the actual definition of time is then camouflaged behind those "principles." (For example, the essential of the definition of time in classical mechanics lies in Newton's first law). In brief, the true primary operation is the *arbitrary choice* of a repeatable phenomenon that may be used in the definition of a clock. The rate of flow of "time" is then implied by this choice, that is, the choice of the fundamental clock *is* the definition of time.

For practical purposes, it is appropriate to limit the freedom inherent in the choice of a clock by specifying convenient properties to be imposed on the resulting time scale. The main such properties are the availability of a sufficiently perennial master "clock" and the possibility of devising wieldy secondary clocks, for everyday use, that give reproducible and consistent readings endowed with a property of additivity. The first master clock that suggested itself to mankind was provided by the rotation of the earth on its axis and around the sun. The unit of time thus defined and its aliquot parts gave birth to the first astronomical time scales (mean solar day, tropical year), which served as a background for the development of classical mechanics and astronomy. A large number of phenomena were discovered (e.g., the beats of a good watch) that bear a linear relationship to that time scale. Any of the "linear systems" involved could be used as a secondary clock. Then, when the measuring techniques improved, it appeared that the mutual linearity of those phenomena was only an approximation. This discovery brought about a mild crisis of the metrology of time. The crisis was readily dismissed by stating that the rotation of the earth was not really uniform (as compared to "more accurate" clocks). In fact, the situation had a deeper purport: two descriptions of the fundamental

master clock, that had been hitherto considered equivalent, appeared to be inconsistent, and the question of the *choice* of the clock was brought to the foreground again. The difficulty was temporarily settled in 1955 by relating the astronomical time scale to one particular period (tropical year 1900.0 = 31 556 925.975 seconds), and the following new permanent definition was adopted at the October, 1967, meeting of the 13th General Conference on Weights and Measures: "The second is the duration of 9 192 631 770 periods of the radiation corresponding to the transition between the two hyperfine levels of the fundamental state of the atom of cesium 133." This definition, which is in full agreement with the preceding one, has two advantages: It can readily be implemented by a so-called atomic clock, and it yields a standard which is reproducible to 1 part in 10^{11} or better.

Newtonian time, a basic feature of the whole body of classical mechanics, is practically the astronomical time, operationally defined as above, complemented by the following extra postulate. Let any single observer, standing still on earth, determine the (improved as above) astronomical time scale; the time scale so obtained is then to be used by every "observer," whatever his motion with respect to the first one. This postulate expresses, for each "observer," one choice of the master clock among infinitely many possible choices and as such it is legitimate. When it was stated, it was also consistent with the contemporaneous physical knowledge. Later on, the physicists grew accustomed to certain properties derived from the choice of Newtonian time and space and from other postulates of mechanics and electromagnetism, until a calamity happened which was similar to what has befallen astronomical time: the improvement of the measuring techniques showed that one empirical fact (namely, that the velocity of light in the laboratory frame of reference is independent of the motion of the emitter) was not compatible with all of those properties. Again a choice was necessary. The analysis of special relativity disclosed which of the properties at stake were incompatible. The decision as to which to drop was largely a matter of convenience. Einstein's choice (justified by strong operational reasons) was to drop the universality of time and space in order to retain more physical postulates. From then on, time and space ceased to be absolute concepts (see RELATIVITY). It is worth mentioning that the presence of such a fundamental choice at the basis of the special-relativistic theory of time is not always recognized.[1]

As the choice of the master clock may not be made any more by one "observer" on behalf of another one, the choice has to be decided upon for each "observer" separately. Special relativity's specification is that each inertial "observer" shall use the time scale defined by means of a conventional atomic "clock" at rest with

respect to himself. This procedure leads to the concept of proper time, which enjoys a mathematically invariant character and plays, for inertial systems, the part formerly played by the universal time (see RELATIVITY).

When it comes to comparing the descriptions of the universe as made by "observers" whose motions relative to an inertial frame involve an acceleration, use is generally made of "general covariance," which permits a straightforward generalization of proper time. The relevant mathematical framework is that of general RELATIVITY. However, the interpretation of the general-relativistic proper time in terms of everyday experience involves instantaneous inertial frames, which are not embodied by any material system in this kind of problem. Therefore, the explicit relationship between proper time and the time actually measured by a material device called a clock is by no means clear.[2] In fact, the use of proper time in accelerated systems again implies a choice of the master clock, and in the present instance the choice has the drawback of being fairly abstract. Notwithstanding the largely widespread opinion, general covariance may not be the most convenient tool for the study of time in noninertial frames of reference. The problem of time measurements in such frames is an open problem, on which practically everything remains to be done.

Although quantum mechanics has not brought a revolution in the conception of time (which remains an evolution parameter in the physical equations), it has suggested one approach which, if it ever turns out to be fruitful, would seriously upset the current notion of time. This approach consists of an attempt to quantize space-time itself, i.e., to assign to space and time jointly a discontinuous structure, involving elementary lengths and durations, instead of simply quantizing phenomena in a continuous spacetime framework. As no consistent formalism of practical use has been developed so far along these lines, it suffices to mention a couple of recent references.[3,4]

JACQUES E. ROMAIN

References

1. Romain, J. E., *Nuovo Cimento*, **30**, 1254 (1963).
2. Romain, J. E., *Rev. Mod. Phys.*, **35**, 376 (1963); *Advances in Astronautical Sciences*, **13**, 616 (1963); *Nuovo Cimento*, **31**, 1060 (1964); **33**, 1576 (1964); **34**, 1544 (1964).
3. Finkelstein, D., *Phys. Rev.*, **184**, 1261 (1969) "International Seminar on Relativity and Gravitation," Technion City, Israel, July, 1969 (Gordon and Breach, 1971), p. 159.
4. Cole, E. A. B., *Nuovo Cimento*, **A66**, 645 (1970).

Cross-references: ATOMIC CLOCKS, QUANTUM THEORY, RELATIVITY.

TRANSFORMER*

In elementary form, a transformer consists of two coils wound of wire and inductively coupled to each other. When alternating current at a given frequency flows in either coil, an alternating electromotive force (emf) of the same frequency is induced in the other coil. The value of this emf depends on the degree of coupling and the magnetic flux linking the two coils. The coil connected to a source of alternating emf is usually called the primary coil, and the emf across this coil is the primary emf. The emf induced in the secondary coil may be greater than or less than the primary emf, depending on the ratio of primary to secondary turns. A transformer is termed a step-up or a step-down transformer accordingly.

Most transformers have stationary iron alloy cores, around which the primary and secondary coils are placed. Because of the high permeability of iron alloys, most of the flux is confined to the core, and tight coupling between the coils is thereby obtained. So tight is the coupling between the coils in some transformers that the primary and secondary emf's bear almost exactly the same ratio to each other as the turns in the respective coils or windings. Thus, the turns ratio of a transformer is a common index of its function in raising or lowering potential.

A simple transformer coil and core arrangement is shown in Fig. 1. The primary and

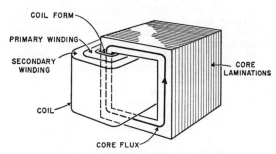

FIG. 1. Transformer coil and core.

secondary coils are wound one over the other on an insulating coil tube or form. The core is laminated to reduce eddy currents. Flux flows in the core along the path indicated, so that all the core flux links both windings. In a circuit diagram, the transformer is represented by the symbol of Fig. 2.

In order for a transformer to deliver secondary emf, the primary emf must vary with respect to time. A dc potential produces no voltage in the

*Figures 1, 2, 4, and 5 and information contained in this article are based on the book "Electronic Transformers and Circuits" by Reuben Lee, New York, John Wiley & Sons, Inc., and are used with permission of the publisher.

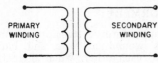

FIG. 2. Simple transformer.

secondary winding or power in the load. If both varying and dc potentials are impressed across the primary, only the varying part is delivered to the load. This comes about because the electromotive force e in the secondary is induced in that winding by the core flux ϕ according to the equation

$$e = -\frac{N\,d\phi}{dt}$$

This equation may be stated in words as follows: The voltage induced in a coil is proportional to the number of turns and to the time rate of change of magnetic flux linking the coil. This rate of change of flux may be large or small. For a given potential, if the rate of change of flux is small, many turns must be used. Conversely, if a small number of turns is used, a large rate of change of flux is necessary to produce a given potential.

Without transformers, modern industry could not have reached its present state of development. The highest potentials which are economically feasible in ac generators are of the order of 20 kV. Transmission of power over long distances is most economical at high potentials which have reached levels of 750 kV and over. The higher the potential of the transmission line, the greater is the amount of power that can be transmitted over a given line conductor. The upper limit of potential is determined by insulation. Insulation research and development have resulted in completely surge-proof transformers, and have made possible power systems which are capable of withstanding lightning surges. At the utilization end of power systems, potential is successively lowered by means of step-down transformers to make power available in safe, useful form. Instrumentation and control of electrical power also require special forms of transformers.

An ideal transformer is defined as one which neither stores nor dissipates energy. Departures from the ideal transformer are caused by:

(1) Winding resistance and capacitance,
(2) Leakage inductance (due to flux which does not link both windings),
(3) Core hysteresis and eddy current losses,
(4) Magnetizing current.

Factors (1) and (2) above contribute to regulation, or the difference between secondary emf at no-load and full-load. This property is most important with variable load. Although no actual transformer is ideal, some transformers very nearly approach it. For example, in a 50-kVA rectifier transformer winding resistance amounts to 1 per cent, and leakage reactance 3 per cent, of the applied emf; core loss is 0.6 per cent of

rated power, and magnetizing current is 2 per cent of rated current. Efficiency (output power divided by input power) is 98.4 per cent for this transformer.

Transformers are needed in electronic apparatus to provide the different values of potential for proper vacuum, gas or solid-state device operation, to insulate circuits from each other, to furnish high impedance to alternating current but low impedance to direct current, to change from one impedance level to another, to connect balanced lines to unbalanced loads, and to maintain or modify wave shape and frequency response at different potentials. Electronic transformers differ from power frequency transformers in the range of impedance levels, frequencies, size and weight. Categories of electronic transformers are: (1) Power, (2) frequency range, and (3) pulse.

Electronic power transformers are generally used to supply rectifiers at potentials ranging from 150 volts to 750 kV. Recent years have seen the widespread use of inverter transformers which convert dc potentials to higher dc potentials in conjunction with semiconductor or gas-filled devices. A simplified circuit is that of Fig. 3. Here the transformer output is a

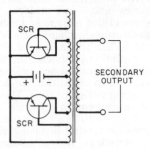

FIG. 3. Solid-state controlled rectifier and transformer for dc to ac inverter.

rectangular alternating wave which is often rectified again to produce dc output at increased potential.

Frequency range transformers are used in applications where the frequency varies, including audio, video, carrier and control frequencies. Such frequencies vary from a fraction of 1 Hz to uhf (300 to 3000 MHz). Transformers may be wide-band or narrow-band in frequency response, and the core material changes accordingly. In wide-band transformers, the ratio of lowest frequency to highest frequency may be as great as 10^5. For such a wide band, the core material consists of nickel alloy laminations of high permeability which maintain uniform secondary voltage at the lowest frequency; also, this material makes possible low leakage inductance and winding capacitance, both of which are essential to good response at the highest frequency.

Narrow-band applications use mostly high frequencies and operate over a small percentage

of the carrier frequency (e.g., 50 to 55 MHz). At radio frequencies, air-core transformers are used. Primary and secondary windings may be coaxial or concentric, with provision for adjusting the coupling between them. A circuit often used at radio frequencies is shown in Fig. 4. Primary and secondary circuits are tuned to

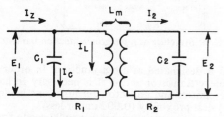

FIG. 4. Tuned air-core transformer.

resonance at the carrier frequency, and the response is shown in Fig. 5 for three conditions

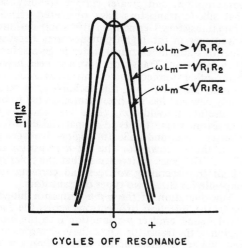

CYCLES OFF RESONANCE

FIG. 5. Response curves for circuit of Fig. 4.

of coupling. Here

L_1 = self-inductance of primary coil
L_2 = self-inductance of secondary coil
L_m = mutual inductance between coils
k = coefficient of coupling = $L_m/\sqrt{L_1 L_2}$
f = carrier frequency
ω = $2\pi f$

It can be shown that maximum output occurs when

$$2\pi f L_m = \sqrt{R_1 R_2}$$

and the value of the coupling coefficient that produces this output at resonance is known as the critical value. Undercoupling produces less output than critical. A certain degree of overcoupling may be advantageous, in that it causes a broad-nosed response curve such as the slight double hump in the response marked $\omega L_m >$ $\sqrt{R_1 R_2}$. With modulated carriers, this response

would offer very little attenuation to sidebands formed by the carrier and audio frequencies; yet the circuit would reject unwanted signals in adjacent carrier channels.

In tuned circuits like these, cores of powdered iron or ferrites are often used to tune the coils, minimize size, and obtain better performance than would be possible with air-core coils. The kind of core material used depends upon the frequency and Q (= $2\pi f L_1/R_1$) required. In general, the higher the frequency, the lower the permeability of the core material. Ferrites are available that range in permeability from $\mu = 10^4$ for use at low frequencies to $\mu = 10$ for use at 60 MHz.

Pulse transformers are used in radar modulators and computers. In radar applications, the pulses are usually rectangular and occur repetitively. Pulse widths range from 0.1 to 200 μsec. Peak ratings are large, from 100 to 50 000 kW. Secondary emf may range up to 300 kV for operation of high-power magnetrons and klystrons. Computer transformers are usually small, have ferrite cores and operate from current pulses to drive core matrices.

Advances in transformer technology depend largely on development of new core and insulation materials, conductor arrangements, measuring techniques and methods of application. By these means, transformers come into use at higher frequencies, with better balance, smaller size or higher power than formerly thought possible.

REUBEN LEE

References

M.I.T. Electrical Engineering Staff, "Magnetic Circuits and Transformers," New York, John Wiley & Sons, 1943.

Lee, Reuben, "Electronic Transformers and Circuits," Second edition, New York, John Wiley & Sons, 1955.

"Standard on Low Power Wideband Transformers," No. 111, Institute of Electrical and Electronic Engineers, Box A, Lenox Hill Station, New York, 1964.

"Standard on Computer Pulse Transformers No. 272," I.E.E.E. New York, 1970.

Bright, R. Louis, Pittman, G. Frank, Jr., and Royer, George H., "Transistors as On-Off Switches in Saturable-Core Circuits," *Elec. Mfg.* (December 1954).

Dewan, S. B., and Duff, D. L., "Analysis of Energy Recovery Transformer in DC Choppers and Inverters," *IEEE Trans. on Magnetics*, March 1970.

Lord, H. W., "Pulse Transformers," *IEEE Trans. on Magnetics*, March 1971.

Polydoroff, W. J., "High Frequency Magnetic Materials," New York, John Wiley & Sons, 1960.

Snelling, E. C., "Ferrites for Linear Applications," *IEEE Spectrum*, January 1972.

Cross-references: ALTERNATING CURRENTS, ELECTRICITY, INDUCED ELECTROMOTIVE FORCE, INDUCTANCE, MAGNETISM, PULSE GENERATION, RECTIFIERS.

TRANSISTOR

Few inventions have had as much impact on the electronics industry as the invention of the transistor. Even though the first transistors differed greatly in structure and method of fabrication from those which are in use today, many of the advantages were immediately recognized. Because it was the first workable solid-state amplifier with no physical mechanism which would wear out during its life and because it was relatively simple to fabricate, it immediately became apparent that the transistor would replace a large fraction of the vacuum tubes which were used in radios and electronic systems.

The point-contact transistor[1] was invented by J. Bardeen and W. H. Brattain at Bell Telephone Laboratories in 1948. Its structure (Fig. 1)

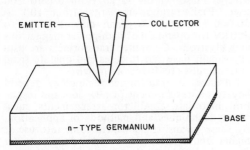

FIG. 1. Point-contact transistor.

consists of a piece of n-type germanium about $0.1 \times 0.1 \times 0.01$ cm on which are placed two sharpened points (a beryllium-copper emitter and a phosphor-bronze collector) approximately 0.005 cm apart. Each of these points exhibits rectifying diode type current-voltage characteristics. The operation of the transistor depends on the injection of holes into the n-type material through the forward-biased emitter point and the collection at the reverse-biased collector point. The third electrode in the transistor is a low resistance, nonrectifying contact made to the n-type germanium and is designated the base electrode. Power gain is achieved in this structure because the collector current increases at a rate equal to two or three times the emitter current and because the reverse-biased collector terminals can be matched in a circuit to a higher impedance load than the input emitter impedance.

The junction transistor[2,3] exhibits definite advantages over the point-contact transistor and has obsoleted this latter type. In a junction transistor, the rectifying characteristics are obtained within the bulk of the semiconductor crystal by placing different types of impurities at different points in the crystal. The structure of an n-p-n junction transistor is illustrated in Fig. 2. The emitter and collector regions have an excess of n-type impurities while the base region has an excess of p-type impurities. The transition from p-type material to n-type material is designated as a p-n junction. In order to achieve transistor action it is necessary to have the emitter and collector p-n junctions in close physical proximity (0.002 cm or less).

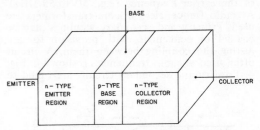

FIG. 2. Structure of n-p-n grown-junction transistor.

Junction transistors are generally made from germanium or silicon crystals. Germanium technology preceded silicon by approximately five years, but silicon offers several advantages—operation at higher temperatures, lower power consumption, and greater surface stability—so that silicon transistors have obsoleted germanium transistors. Germanium offers only definite advantages in the high-frequency area because electrons and holes travel faster in germanium than in silicon. Transistors have also been made from other semiconductor materials such as gallium arsenide,[4] but this technology is relatively new and has not been demonstrated to be as useful. In addition, there are also p-n-p transistors where the type of material used for emitter, base, and collector regions is reversed from those shown for the n-p-n transistor in Fig. 2. The basic difference is that the polarity of all the operating voltages and currents are opposite for these two types of transistors.

The operation of the n-p-n transistor hinges upon the injection of electrons across the forward biased emitter p-n junction into the base region of the transistor. Once these electrons are injected across the junction they diffuse across the base and arrive at the reverse-biased collector junction. While the emitter junction acts as a source for these electrons, the reverse-biased collector junction acts as a sink for them. We measure the efficiency of such transistor by the current multiplication factor α_F defined as

$$\alpha_F = -\frac{\partial I_C}{\partial I_E} \qquad (1)$$

where I_C is the collector current and I_E is the emitter current. In most junction transistors α_F is between 0.95 and 1.00.

The junction transistor can be connected in a circuit so that any one of its three terminals is the common terminal. Figure 3 shows an n-p-n transistor connected in the common emitter configuration with typical operating voltages and currents. Note that in this connection a small incremental increase in base current produces a sizeable increase in collector current.

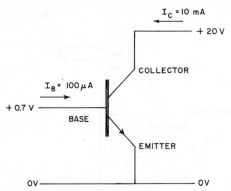

FIG. 3. Circuit symbol and typical potentials for *n-p-n* silicon junction transistor.

This ratio is defined as

$$h_{FE} = -\frac{\partial I_C}{\partial I_B} = \frac{\alpha_F}{1 - \alpha_F} \qquad (2)$$

Typical values of h_{FE} are between 20 and 200.

There are many types of junction transistors. dependent on the specific method of fabrication chosen. In all cases *n*-type impurities such as phosphorus, arsenic, or antimony, and *p*-type impurities such as boron, indium, gallium, or aluminum are introduced into the appropriate regions of the transistor. In a grown-junction transistor,[5] the impurities are introduced at the time that the silicon or germanium crystal is being fabricated. In an alloy-junction structure[6], the impurities are introduced by melting a pellet of the appropriate doping material on the surface of the semiconductor and regrowing the crystal. Diffused junction transistors[7,8] are produced by placing the semiconductor material in a furnace at an elevated temperature in an atmosphere containing the desired doping element. The doping material then diffuses[9] into the semiconductor crystal and substitutionally replaces some of the silicon or germanium atoms in the crystal lattice. A region of the opposite type can be created by overcompensating, diffusing into the same region the other type of impurity to a concentration in excess of that previously diffused.

Figure 4 shows the structure for a silicon

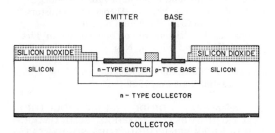

FIG. 4. Cross-sectional view of silicon *n-p-n* planar transistor.

planar transistor.[10] This transistor is produced by diffusing boron impurities into *n*-type silicon in order to create the *p*-type base region and later diffusing phosphorus to create the *n*-type emitter region. Note that the surface of the transistor is covered by a layer of silicon dioxide (quartz) which acts as a protection for the exposed *p-n* junctions; such layer assures a very high-reliability transistor.

This transistor is also economical to fabricate because mass processing techniques can be utilized; several hundred identical transistors can be produced on a slice of silicon approximately one inch in diameter. The precise geometrical control achieved by using diffusion techniques results in very reproducible electrical characteristics. In order to fabricate a planar transistor we take advantage of the fact that boron and phosphorous do not diffuse through the protecting silicon layer. Hence, it is possible to cover an entire slice of silicon with the oxide and cut holes in the oxide of a geometrical pattern corresponding to that of the desired diffusions. The same techniques can also be used for making integrated circuits.[11] In an integrated circuit, the transistors, diodes, resistors, and capacitors are produced on the same slice of silicon by properly controlled diffusion methods.

During the last few years there has been greatly increased usage of field effect transistors, of which the MOS (metal-oxide-semiconductor) transistor is most popular. In these transistors a conducting channel of either electrons or holes is established between two regions, called source and drain, to which ohmic low resistance contacts are made. Control of the source-to-drain current is achieved by applying a potential to the gate electrode, which affects the width of the conducting channel and/or the number of mobile carriers in the channel. Power gain is achieved between the gate-source input terminals and the drain-source output because of the high input impedance.

In a diffused junction field-effect transistor the gate is a reverse-biased *p-n* junction. In an *n*-channel enhancement mode MOS transistor (see Fig. 5) the gate electrode is a metallized region separated from the semiconductor by an insulating oxide layer. Application of a positive gate potential to the MOS transistor creates an electron-rich region in the semiconductor (effectively converts the surface of the semiconductor from *p*-type to *n*-type) which serves as a conducting path (*n*-type channel) between the source and the drain. Increasing the gate bias widens the channel and also increases the source to drain electron flow.

MOS transistors are used extensively for integrated circuits because they require a minimum number of fabrication steps and can be manufactured at high yields. The transistor of Fig. 5, for example, requires only a single *n*-type diffused region of noncritical dimensions. There are also depletion mode transistors, where the *n*-type channel is permanently established and

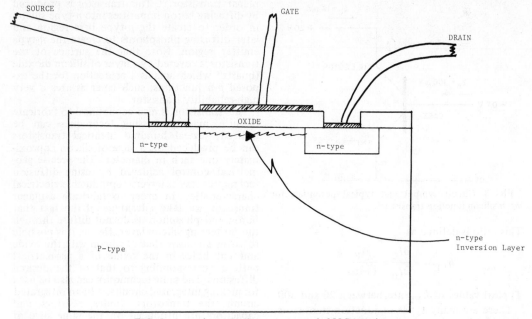

FIG. 5. An *n*-channel enhancement mode MOS transistor.

the gate bias (negative) is used to decrease and eventually cut off the drain-to-source current flow.

Transistors are now being used extensively in all electronic equipment. As amplifiers they are useful up to frequencies of several gigahertz and at power levels of several hundred watts. However, one of the largest applications of transistors has been as a switch in computers. The electrical characteristics of a transistor are nearly ideal for this type of application in that they closely simulate a relay in its open and closed positions. Essentially all computers in use today are completely transistorized.

L. B. VALDES

References

1. Bardeen, J., and Brattain, W. H., "The Transistor: A Semiconductor Triode," *Phys. Rev., 74*, 230–231 (July 15, 1948).
2. Shockley, W., "The Theory of *p-n* Junctions in Semiconductors and *p-n* Junction Transistors," *Bell System Tech. J., 28*, 435–489 (July, 1949).
3. Shockley, W., Sparks, M., and Teal, G. K., "*p-n* Junction Transistors," *Phys. Rev., 83*, 151–162 (July 1, 1951).
4. Jones, M. E., and Wurst E. C., Jr., "Recent Advances in Gallium Arsenide Transistors," *IRE Intern, Conv. Record,* 9, Pt. 3, 26–29 (1961).
5. Wallace, R. L., and Pietenpol, W. J., "Some Circuit Properties and Applications of *n-p-n* Transistors," *Proc. IRE*, 39, 753–767 (July 1951).
6. Saby, J. S., "Fused Impurity *p-n-p* Junction Transistors," *Proc. IRE*, 40, 1358 (November, 1952).
7. Lee, C. A., "A High-Frequency Diffused Base Germanium Transistor," *Bell System Tech. J.*, 35, 23–24 (January, 1956).
8. Tanenbaum, M., and Thomas, D. E., "Diffused Emitter and Base Silicon Transistors," *Bell System Tech. J.*, 35, 1–22 (January, 1956).
9. Fuller, C. S., and Ditzenberger, J. A., "Diffusion of Donor and Acceptor Elements in Silicon," *J. Appl. Phys.*, 27, No. 5, 544–553 (May, 1956).
10. Hoerni, J. A., IRE Electron Devices Meeting, Washington, D.C., October, 1961.
11. Moore, G. E., "Semiconductor Integrated Circuits," "Microelectronics," pp. 262-359, New York, McGraw-Hill Book Company, Inc., 1963.

General References

Shockley, W., "Electrons and Holes in Semiconductors," New York, Van Nostrand Reinhold, 1950.
Dunlap, W. C., "An Introduction to Semiconductors," New York, John Wiley & Sons, 1957.
Shive, J. N., Bridgers, H. E., Scaff, J. H., and Biondi, F. J., "Transistor Technology," Vols. I, II, III, New York, Van Nostrand Reinhold, 1958.
Valdes, L. B., "The Physical Theory of Transistors," New York, McGraw-Hill Book Co., 1961.
Hunter, L. P., "Handbook of Semiconductor Electronics," Second edition, New York, McGraw-Hill Book Co., 1962.
Spenke, E., "Electronic Semiconductors," New York, McGraw-Hill Book Co., 1958.

Cross-references: DIODE (SEMICONDUCTOR), ELECTRON TUBES, RECTIFIERS, SEMICONDUCTOR DEVICES, SEMICONDUCTORS, SOLID-STATE PHYSICS.

TRANSPORT THEORY (Radiative Transfer)*

When light passes through an atmosphere, it may be scattered and absorbed. When neutrons move through a medium, collisions with the nucleii of the material may result in absorption of the neutrons, changes in their direction and energy, and sometimes, by the fission mechanism, production of more neutrons.

These two phenomena are examples of transport processes. The problem of specifying the radiation field in an atmosphere stems back to Rayleigh's investigations on the illumination of a sunlit sky. The astrophysicists refer to this general subject as *radiative transfer* and have studied it for well over half a century. Interest in neutron transport has perforce been of more recent origin.

If light is thought of as consisting of photons, then there is seen to be a very strong similarity between neutron transport and radiative transfer. The former process is both complicated and made more interesting by the possibility of fission in various materials. Other physical phenomena, such as the passage of γ-rays through a medium, possess many characteristics of the two processes that have been mentioned.

Fortunately, it is possible to develop a mathematical structure which encompases all these phenomena. The situation is similar to that in classical diffusion theory, where the same mathematical equations may be interpreted, for example, to yield information concerning the distribution of heat in a metal or the flow of one material into another. The equations describing particle transport are, however, of a much more complicated nature than many of those of classical physics and are only now beginning to yield to the techniques of the mathematicians.

All the transport processes described above have the property that the moving particles involved may be thought of as interacting or colliding with fixed centers or nucleii of the material through which they are passing. The moving particles do not collide with each other. The interactions, in the situations which we will consider, are strictly independent and local events—a particle is affected only by a scattering center in its immediate neighborhood. Most important is the fact that a probability for such an interaction may be assigned:

Probability of interaction in moving a distanceΔ

$$= \Sigma\Delta + \text{(terms of higher order in } \Delta) \quad (1)$$

The quantity Σ, called the *macroscopic cross section*, is dependent upon the kind and density of the medium, the type of moving particle

*This work was supported in part by the United States Atomic Energy Commission. Reproduction in whole or in part is permitted for any purpose of the U.S. Government.

(photon, neutron, etc.), the particle energy, etc. Determination of Σ is a complicated problem of experimental and theoretical physics.

An interaction or collision may result in a change in the direction of the moving particle (scattering), disappearance of the particle (absorption), or production of new particles of the same kind (fission). Scattering may produce no energy loss (elastic), or it may involve energy loss (inelastic). Such interactions may affect the transport medium, though for most purposes this change may be neglected. Again, the actual physical determination of the result of a collision is frequently a difficult task. Such information, together with the quantity Σ, must be considered for our purposes as already known.[7]

The central problem of transport theory as we view the subject, may now be formulated. Given a physical medium with all parameters, such as the macroscopic cross section and the results of interaction, specified, let a population of particles of given kind, direction, energy, etc., be present in the material at initial time, $t = 0$. Let any internal or external sources of such particles be given. Describe as a function of position, direction, energy, etc., the expected particle population at any time $t > 0$.

Clearly, the transport process is probabalistic in nature. It is customary, because of the difficulty of the subject, to study expected value theory, although some investigations of a more detailed type have been made. Often the term "expected" is dropped in discussion so that "expected flux" becomes simply "flux," etc. It is important to remember that this is done only as a matter of convenience in writing.

From Eq. (1) further information concerning the probability of collision may be obtained. Write

$p(x) = $ Probability that a particle moves a

distance x without collision   (2)

Then,

$$p(x + \Delta) = (1 - \Sigma\Delta)\, p(x) + \text{(terms of higher order in } \Delta) \quad (3)$$

Equation (3) gives

$$\frac{dp}{dx} = -\Sigma p(x)$$

and, if Σ is constant,

$$p(x) = e^{-\Sigma x} \quad (4)$$

This is the well-known exponential law.

To find the average distance a particle moves without collision observe that

$F(x) = $ Probability that the *first* collision

occurs at some $X \le x$ (5)

$$= 1 - e^{-\Sigma x}$$

Then the average or expected value of X is

$$E(X) = \int_0^\infty x \, dF(x) = \int_0^\infty \Sigma x e^{-\Sigma x} \, dx \quad (6)$$

$$= \frac{1}{\Sigma}$$

This average distance between collisions is referred to as the *mean free path*, usually denoted λ.

Suppose the half space $x > 0$ is filled with a medium characterized by constant macroscopic cross section Σ. If a flux of N_0 particles impinges perpendicularly on $x = 0$, then the expected flux at $x = d$ of particles *which have made no collision* is, from Eq. (4),

$$N(d) = N_0 e^{-\Sigma d} \quad (7)$$

When the collision process involves only absorption, $N(d)$ is the *total* expected flux at $x = d$, but if scattering and fission processes occur $N(d)$ may be quite different from the total flux. These physical events complicate transport theory greatly.

Some idea of the complexities introduced by the fission process may be obtained by study of a very simple mathematical model in which particles are allowed to move only to the right or left in a rod (i.e., a line segment) of length a. Suppose that in an interaction the colliding particle disappears and two new ones emerge, one moving left and one moving right (binary fission). All particles have the same speed c, and Σ is constant. Finally, assume that the process is such that the average particle density is the same at one time as it is at any other, so that time dependence may be neglected. Denote by $cu(x)$ and $cv(x)$ the right and left fluxes at x.

Then[8]

$$u(x + \Delta) = (1 - \Sigma\Delta)u(x) + \Sigma\Delta \, u(x)$$

$$+ \Sigma\Delta \, v(x) + (\text{higher order terms in } \Delta) \quad (8)$$

which leads to

$$\frac{du}{dx} = \Sigma v \quad (9)$$

Similarly

$$-\frac{dv}{dx} = \Sigma u \quad (10)$$

If one left-moving particle per second is introduced at $x = a$, with no source at $x = 0$, then

$$u(0) = 0, \quad cv(a) = 1, \quad (11)$$

and the system of Eqs. (9) through (11) yields

$$cu(x) = \frac{\sin \Sigma x}{\cos \Sigma a}, \quad cv(x) = \frac{\cos \Sigma x}{\cos \Sigma a}, \quad 0 \leqslant x \leqslant a$$

$$(12)$$

These results are obviously quite different from any that would be given by a simple attenuation law such as Eq. (7). Indeed, because of the fission assumed, a collision results in an increase, rather than a decrease, in the particle population. The case $a = \pi/2\Sigma$ is of especial interest. For a rod of that length neither $u(x)$ nor $v(x)$ is defined. Physically, the system is just *critical*. A time-independent population cannot prevail with the source specified. Equations (9) and (10) no longer hold when $a \geqslant \pi/2\Sigma$.

This observation does not imply that supercritical systems cannot be analyzed. To do so requires explicit introduction of the time variable.[8] Equations (9) and (10) are replaced by

$$\frac{1}{c}\frac{\partial u}{\partial t} + \frac{\partial u}{\partial x} = \Sigma v(x, t) \quad (13)$$

$$\frac{1}{c}\frac{\partial v}{\partial t} - \frac{\partial v}{\partial x} = \Sigma u(x, t) \quad (14)$$

with suitable boundary and initial conditions. For large times it may be shown that the solutions to these equations can be written *approximately* as

$$u(x, t) \doteq u_0(x) \, e^{\alpha t}, \, v(x, t) \doteq v_0(x) \, e^{\alpha t}$$

$$(15)$$

for some α. When $a > \pi/2\Sigma$, α is positive so that the particle fluxes build up exponentially in time. This exponential increase is observed in actual experiments involving fissionable materials. When the particle population in a system is just sustained without introduction of additional particles (sources) the system is just critical (see CRITICAL MASS).

It is possible to consider other relatively simple mathematical models of transport phenomena and from them to determine much valuable information. Any attempt to solve a "realistic" physical problem, however, usually results in great difficulties. The general transport equation is of the form

$$\frac{DN}{Dt}(\bar{r}, \bar{v}, t) = -\Sigma(\bar{r}, \bar{v}, t) N(\bar{r}, \bar{v}, t)$$

$$+ \int_{\bar{v}'} K(\bar{r}, \bar{v}' \to \bar{v}, t) \Sigma(\bar{r}, \bar{v}', t) N(\bar{r}, \bar{v}', t) \, d\bar{v}'$$

$$+ S(\bar{r}, \bar{v}, t) \quad (16)$$

subject to boundary and initial conditions dependent upon the geometry. In Eq. (16), $\frac{D}{Dt}$ is the total time derivative, $\bar{v}$ is the velocity, and K is a function that gives the density of particles emerging at velocity $\bar{v}$ from a collision at $\bar{r}$ at time t involving a particle moving at velocity $\bar{v}'$. Sources are represented by S. It is clear that Eq. (16), while linear, has a much more complicated structure than many of the

classical equations of mathematical physics. Little is known of the mathematical properties of its solutions.

The complexity of the general transport operator, coupled in some cases with the urgencies of designing atomic weapons, nuclear reactors, etc., has resulted in a plethora of approximate methods for its treatment.[1,4,5,7] It should be pointed out that no such scheme can possibly give satisfactory results without good knowledge, either experimental or theoretical, of the physical parameters involved. Great efforts have been made toward accurate determinations of Σ and K.

A very simple approximation to transport theory may be obtained by considering all particles of the same energy, with K a constant. Truncated expansion in Legendre polynomials of the angular dependence of pertinent functions then yields neutron diffusion theory. The resultant equation is identical in structure to the heat equation, allowing classical solutions to be used in many problems. This approximate theory is valid only under quite stringent conditions, but it often gives surprisingly good results. Variants of simple neutron diffusion theory are numerous, including age theory and n-velocity group theory to account for energy changes, and the P_n-approximation, in which more terms of the Legendre series are retained. Non-constant K may also be included. A method of calculating the integral in Eq. (16) by Gaussian quadrature is closely connected with the P_n-approximation.[3]

The advent of the high-speed computing machine has made finite difference schemes for solving the transport equation quite feasible. One of the most successful is the so-called S_n-method, characterized by the fact that angular dependence of the flux is assumed to be piecewise linear.[1]

Another popular attack on transport problems is via the Monte Carlo method.[6] There, the particle motion is actually simulated by machine computation. Particles suffer collisions, change direction, lose energy, etc., according to specified probabilities. The machine traces the history of a single particle from its appearance in the system until the particle leaves or is no longer of interest. Events in the particle's history are allowed to happen randomly, the computing machine deciding on the event according to a preassigned (and presumably physically correct) probability distribution. This method is hence stochastic in nature, although expected values are usually taken after a sufficiently large particle population has been examined. The Monte Carlo technique is often used when the geometry of the problem is complicated.

A completely different approach, of both analytical and computational interest, to the over-all problem of particle transport has been used rather extensively over the last thirty years by the astrophysicists. It is used to a lesser extent by workers in neutron physics. This device, called the "method of invariance" or "invariant imbedding," focuses attention on the particles *emergent* from the medium.[3,8] Equations are derived by considering the relationship between the flux out of a system and the corresponding flux emergent from a slightly larger system. Invariant imbedding has several computational advantages, especially when the emergent flux is the quantity of primary physical interest. The imbedding equations are nonlinear, but in some ways are easier to handle than equations like Eq. (16). At present, the method can be successfully applied only to systems with considerable symmetry.

A still more recent development is the method of singular eigenfunctions. This is a very powerful device, allowing many difficult problems of classical transport theory to be solved quite easily. Unfortunately, it seems to be effectively applicable to only relatively simple models.[2]

Transport theory is still a relatively young subject. Much remains to be accomplished, both from the viewpoint of the physicist and from that of the mathematician.

G. MILTON WING

1. Bell, G. I., and Glasstone, S., "Nuclear Reactor Theory," New York, Van Nostrand Reinhold Co., 1970.
2. Case, K. M., and Zweifel, P. F., "Linear Transport Theory," Reading, Mass., Addison-Wesley Publishing Co., 1967.
3. Chandrasekhar, S., "Radiative Transfer," Oxford, Clarendon Press, 1950.
4. Davison, B., "Neutron Transport Theory," Oxford, Clarendon Press, 1957.
5. Kourganoff, V., and Busbridge, I. W., "Basic Methods in Transfer Problems," Oxford, Clarendon Press, 1952.
6. Richtmyer, R. D., "Monte Carlo Methods," *Proceedings of the Symposia in Applied Mathematics*, 11, 190–205 (1961).
7. Weinberg, A. M., and Wigner, E. P., "The Physical Theory of Neutron Chain Reactors," Chicago, The University of Chicago Press, 1958.
8. Wing, G. M., "An Introduction to Transport Theory," New York, John Wiley & Sons, 1962.

Cross-references: COLLISIONS OF PARTICLES, CRITICAL MASS, CROSS SECTIONS AND STOPPING POWER, FISSION, HEAT TRANSFER.

TRANSURANIUM ELEMENTS

The transuranium elements are those elements heavier than uranium, element 92. They are all radioactive and, in general, have half-lives too short to have existed in nature since their original creation. They were all discovered and produced by nuclear synthesis. The presently known (1973) transuranium elements have the following names and symbols: 93, neptunium (Np); 94, plutonium (Pu); 95, americium (Am); 96, curium (Cm); 97, berkelium (Bk); 98, cali-

fornium (Cf); 99, einsteinium (Es); 100, fermium (Fm); 101, mendelevium (Md); 102, nobelium (No); 103, lawrencium (Lr); 104, rutherfordium (Rf); and 105, hahnium (Ha).

The heaviest elements of the periodic system with atomic numbers 89 (actinium) through 103 (lawrencium) are members of the actinide series, analogous to the lanthanide series or rare earths (atomic numbers 57 through 71). An inner electron shell, consisting of fourteen $5f$ electrons, is filled in progressing across the series. The electronic configurations of the actinide transuranium elements are given in Table 1.

TABLE 1. ELECTRONIC CONFIGURATIONS (BEYOND RADON) FOR GASEOUS ATOMS OF ACTINIDE TRANSURANIUM ELEMENTS

Atomic No.	Element	Electronic Configuration[a]
93	Neptunium	$5f^4 6d 7s^2$
94	Plutonium	$5f^6 7s^2$
95	Americium	$5f^7 7s^2$
96	Curium	$5f^7 6d 7s^2$
97	Berkelium	$5f^9 7s^2$
98	Californium	$5f^{10} 7s^2$
99	Einsteinium	$5f^{11} 7s^2$
100	Fermium	$5f^{12} 7s^2$
101	Mendelevium	$(5f^{13} 7s^2)$
102	Nobelium	$(5f^{14} 7s^2)$
103	Lawrencium	$(5f^{14} 6d 7s^2$ or $5f^{14} 7s^2 7p)$

[a]Configurations in parentheses have not been determined experimentally.

Since the actinide series is completed with lawrencium, element 103, the succeeding "transactinide" elements with atomic numbers 104 through 108 should be chemical homologs to the known elements with atomic numbers 72 (hafnium) to 76 (osmium). This analogy should continue in the still heavier transuranium elements, and element 118 should be a noble gas. Some typical predicted electronic configurations for transactinide elements are given in Table 2.

Chemically the transuranium elements which are members of the actinide series are very similar, although the observed differences are those expected and anticipated from, their unique position in the periodic system as part of a second rare-earth series. All have trivalent ions, which form inorganic complex ions and organic chelates. Also in common are acid-insoluble trifluorides and oxalates, soluble sulfates, nitrates, chlorides, and perchlorates. Neptunium, plutonium, and americium have several higher oxidation states in aqueous solution (similar to uranium), but the stability of these states relative to the common trivalent ion becomes progressively less as one proceeds to the higher atomic numbers. This is a direct consequence,

TABLE 2. PREDICTED ELECTRONIC CONFIGURATIONS (BEYOND RADON) FOR GASEOUS ATOMS OF SOME TRANSACTINIDE ELEMENTS

Element	Electronic Configuration
104	$5f^{14} 6d^2 7s^2$
105	$5f^{14} 6d^3 7s^2$
106	$5f^{14} 6d^4 7s^2$
107	$5f^{14} 6d^5 7s^2$
108	$5f^{14} 6d^6 7s^2$
112	$5f^{14} 6d^{10} 7s^2$
114	$5f^{14} 6d^{10} 7s^2 7p^2$
118	$5f^{14} 6d^{10} 7s^2 7p^6$
120	$5f^{14} 6d^{10} 7s^2 7p^6 8s^2$
126	$5f^{14} 5g^2 6d^{10} 6f^2 7s^2 7p^6 8s^2 8p^2$

indeed an identifying feature, of the actinide role as a second rare-earth type transition series.

One of the most important methods for study and elucidation of chemical behavior of the actinide elements has been ion-exchange chromatography. Adsorption on and elution from ion-exchange columns have made possible the identification and separation of trace quantities of all of the actinides. The behavior of each actinide transuranium element in this respect is very similar to its analogous rare-earth element. This has made it possible to detect as little as one or two atoms when this small a number has been made in some of the transmutation experiments.

The concept of atomic weight in the sense applied to naturally occurring elements is not applicable to the transuranium elements, since the isotopic composition of any given sample depends on its source. In most cases, the use of the mass number of the longest-lived isotope in combination with an evaluation of its availability has been adequate. Good choices at present are neptunium, 237; plutonium, 242; americium, 243; curium, 248; berkelium, 249; californium, 249; einsteinium, 254; and fermium, 257.

Brief descriptions of the transuranium elements follow:

Neptunium (Np, atomic number 93, after the planet Neptune.) Neptunium was the first of the synthetic transuranium elements to be discovered; the isotope ^{239}Np was produced by McMillan and Abelson in 1940 at Berkeley, California, as the result of the bombardment of uranium with cyclotron-produced neutrons. The isotope ^{237}Np (half-life 2.14 $\times$ 10^6 years) is currently obtained in kilogram quantities as a by-product of nuclear power reactions. Trace quantities of the element are actually found in nature owing to transmutation reactions in uranium ores produced by the neutrons which are present.

Neptunium metal has a silvery appearance, is chemically reactive, melts at 637°C, and exists

in at least three structural modifications: α-neptunium, orthorhombic, density = 20.45 g/cm^3; β-neptunium (above 280°C), tetragonal, density (313°C) = 19.36 g/cm^3; γ-neptunium (above 577°C), cubic, density (600°C) = 18.0 g/cm^3.

Neptunium gives rise to five ionic oxidation states in solution: Np^{3+} (pale purple), analogous to the rare earth ion Pm^{3+}, Np^{4+} (yellow-green), NpO_2^+ (green-blue), NpO_2^{2+} (pale pink), and NpO_5^{3-} (green). These oxygenated species are in contrast to the rare earths which exhibit only simple ions of the (II), (III), and (IV) oxidation states in aqueous solution. The element forms tri- and tetrahalides such as NpF_3, NpF_4, $NpCl_3$, $NpCl_4$, $NpBr_3$, NpI_3, and oxides of various compositions such as are found in the uranium-oxygen system, including Np_3O_8 and NpO_2.

Plutonium (Pu, atomic number 94, after the planet Pluto.) Plutonium was the second transuranium element to be discovered; the isotope ^{238}Pu was produced in 1940 by Seaborg, McMillan, Kennedy, and Wahl at Berkeley, California, by deuteron bombardment of uranium in the 150-cm cyclotron. By far of greatest importance is the isotope ^{239}Pu (half-life 24 400 years), which is fissionable with thermal neutrons and produced in extensive quantities in nuclear reactors from the abundant nonfissionable uranium isotope ^{238}U:

$$^{238}U(n,\gamma) \; ^{239}U \xrightarrow{\beta^-} \; ^{239}Np \xrightarrow{\beta^-} \; ^{239}Pu$$

Plutonium (in the form of ^{239}Pu) has assumed the position of dominant importance among the transuranium elements because of its successful use as an explosive ingredient in nuclear weapons and the place which it holds as a key material in the development of industrial utilization of nuclear energy, one pound being equivalent to about 10 000 000 kWh of heat-energy equivalent. In certain nuclear reactors called breeder reactors, it is possible to create more new plutonium from ^{238}U than plutonium consumed in sustaining the fission chain reaction. Because of this, plutonium is the key to unlocking the enormous energy reserves in the nonfissionable isotope ^{238}U.

Plutonium (in the form of ^{239}Pu) also exists in trace quantities in naturally occurring uranium ores. It is formed in much the same manner as neptunium, by irradiation of natural uranium with the neutrons which are present. Much smaller quantities of the longer-lived isotope, ^{244}Pu, (half-life 83 000 000 years), have been found in nature; in this case it may represent the small fraction remaining from a primordial source or it may be due to cosmic rays.

Much of the early work on the determination of the chemical and physical properties of plutonium has been done employing the isotope ^{239}Pu. However, the relatively high specific alpha particle radioactivity of this isotope leads to difficulties caused by radiation damage and self-heating of the material under investigation. Hence, the longer-lived isotope ^{242}Pu (half-life 390 000 years) is better suited for such investigations; this isotope is rather readily available in high isotopic purity as the result of successive neutron capture reactions when plutonium is irradiated over sufficiently long periods of time in very high neutron flux reactors:

$$^{239}Pu \, (n,\gamma) \; ^{240}Pu \, (n, \gamma) \; ^{241}Pu \, (n, \gamma) \; ^{242}Pu$$

The still longer-lived ^{244}Pu is even better suited for such investigations, but the difficulty of producing it limits its availability; in this case the neutron capture reactions must continue for two additional steps:

$$^{242}Pu \, (n, \gamma) \; ^{243}Pu \, (n, \gamma) \; ^{244}Pu$$

and the yield is drastically reduced owing to the short half-life of ^{243}Pu (4.96 hours).

Plutonium metal can be prepared, in common with neptunium and uranium, by reduction of the trifluoride with alkaline-earth metals. The metal has a silvery appearance, is chemically reactive, and melts at 640°C. It exhibits six crystalline modifications: α-plutonium, primitive monoclinic, below 115°C; β-plutonium, monoclinic, 115 to 185°C; γ-plutonium, face-centered orthorhombic, 185 to 310°C; δ-plutonium, face-centered cubic, 310 to 452°C; δ'-plutonium, tetragonal, 452 to 480°C; and ε-plutonium, body-centered cubic, 480°C up to the melting point.

Plutonium also exhibits five ionic valence states in aqueous solutions: Pu^{3+} (blue-lavender), Pu^{4+} (yellow-brown), PuO_2^+ (pink), PuO_2^{2+} (pink-orange), and PuO_5^{3-} (blue-green). The ion PuO_2^+ is unstable in aqueous solutions, disproportionating into Pu^{4+} and PuO_2^{2+}; the Pu^{4+} thus formed, however, oxidizes the PuO_2^+ into PuO_2^{2+}, itself being reduced to Pu^{3+}, giving finally Pu^{3+} and PuO_2^{2+}.

Plutonium forms binary compounds with oxygen: PuO, PuO_2, and intermediate oxides of variable composition; with the halides: PuF_3, PuF_4, $PuCl_3$, $PuBr_3$, PuI_3; with carbon, nitrogen, and silicon: PuC, PuN, $PuSi_2$; in addition oxyhalides are well known: PuOCl, PuOBr, PuOI.

Because of the high rate of emission of alpha particles, and the physiological fact that the element is specifically absorbed by bone marrow, plutonium, like all of the transuranium elements, is a radiological poison and must be handled with special equipment and precautions.

Americium (Am, atomic number 95, after the Americas.) Americium was the fourth transuranium element to be discovered; the isotope ^{241}Am was identified by Seaborg, James, Morgan, and Ghiorso late in 1944 at the wartime Metallurgical Laboratory (now the Argonne National Laboratory) of the University of Chicago as the result of successive neutron capture

reactions by plutonium isotopes in a nuclear reactor:

$$^{239}\text{Pu}\,(n,\gamma)\,^{240}\text{Pu}\,(n,\gamma)\,^{241}\text{Pu}\xrightarrow{\beta^-}\,^{241}\text{Am}$$

Americium is produced in kilogram quantities. Since the isotope ^{241}Am can be prepared in relatively pure form by extraction as a decay product over a period of years from plutonium containing ^{241}Pu, this isotope has been used for much of the chemical investigation of this element. Better suited is the isotope ^{243}Am owing to its longer half-life (7.4×10^3 years as compared to 433 years for ^{241}Am). A mixture of the isotopes ^{241}Am, ^{242}Am, and ^{243}Am can be prepared by intense neutron irradiation of ^{241}Am according to the reactions ^{241}Am (n,γ) ^{242}Am (n,γ) ^{243}Am. Nearly isotopically pure ^{243}Am can be prepared by the reactions ^{242}Pu (n,γ) ^{243}Pu $\xrightarrow{\beta^-}$ ^{243}Am, and the ^{243}Am can be chemically separated.

Americium can be obtained as a silvery white reactive metal by reduction of americium trifluoride with barium vapor at $1300°C$. It appears to be more malleable than uranium or neptunium and tarnishes slowly in dry air at room temperature. The density is 13.67 g/cm^3 with a melting point at $1176°C$. It has a double hexagonal-close-packed crystalline structure at temperatures up to $1079°C$ (α-americium) and a face-centered cubic structure above $1079°C$ (β-americium).

The element exists in four oxidation states in aqueous solution: Am^{3+} (light salmon), AmO_2^+ (light tan), AmO_2^{2+} (light tan), and a fluoride complex of the 4+ state (pink). The trivalent state is highly stable and difficult to oxidize. AmO_2^+, like plutonium, is unstable with respect to disproportionation into Am^{3+} and AmO_2^{2+}. The ion Am^{4+} may be stabilized in solution only in the presence of very high concentrations of fluoride ion, and tetravalent solid compounds are well known. Divalent americium has been prepared in solid compounds; this is consistent with the presence of seven $5f$ electrons in americium (enhanced stability of half-filled $5f$ electron shell) and is similar to the analogous lanthanide, europium, which can be reduced to the divalent state.

Americium dioxide, AmO_2, is the important oxide; Am_2O_3 and, as with previous actinide elements, oxides of variable composition between $\text{AmO}_{1.5}$ and AmO_2 are known. The halides AmF_2 (in CaF_2), AmF_3, AmF_4, AmCl_2, AmCl_3, AmBr_2, AmBr_3, AmI_2, and AmI_3 have also been prepared.

Curium (Cm, atomic number 96, after Pierre and Marie Curie.) Although curium comes after americium in the periodic system, it was actually known before americium and was the third transuranium element to be discovered. It was identified by Seaborg, James, and Ghiorso in the summer of 1944 at the wartime Metallurgical Laboratory in Chicago as a result of helium-ion bombardment of ^{239}Pu in the Berkeley, California, 150-cm cyclotron. It is of special interest because it is in this element that the first of the transition series of actinide elements is completed.

The isotope ^{242}Cm (half-life 163 days) produced from ^{241}Am by the reactions ^{241}Am (n,γ) ^{242}Am $\xrightarrow{\beta^-}$ ^{242}Cm was used for much of the early work with macroscopic quantities, although this was difficult due to the extremely high specific alpha activity. A better, but still far from ideal, isotope for the investigation of curium is ^{244}Cm. Its somewhat longer half-life of 18 years still presents a problem of relatively high specific alpha activity, but it has been used extensively because of its availability as the result of production by the reactions ^{243}Am (n,γ) ^{244}Am $\xrightarrow{\beta^-}$ ^{244}Cm. Much better suited for such investigations are the longer-lived isotopes ^{247}Cm (half-life 16 000 000 years) and ^{248}Cm (half-life 350 000 years) which are becoming available in increasing quantities as the result of their production in high neutron-flux reactors through the successive capture of neutrons in the reactions ^{244}Cm (n,γ) ^{245}Cm (n,γ) ^{246}Cm (n,γ) ^{247}Cm (n,γ) ^{248}Cm; the difficulties of this long production chain are compounded by the necessity of separating the ^{247}Cm and ^{248}Cm from the remaining lower mass-number isotopes by mass spectrometric methods in order to obtain final products of the desired low specific alpha activity. ^{248}Cm is also produced in relatively high isotopic purity as the alpha-decay daughter of ^{252}Cf.

Curium metal resembles americium metal in crystal structure (α and β modifications) but melts at the considerably higher temperature of $1340°C$. It can be prepared by heating curium trifluoride with barium vapor at $1350°C$.

Curium exists solely as Cm^{3+} (colorless to yellow) in the uncomplexed state in aqueous solution. This behavior is related to its position as the element in the actinide series in which the $5f$ electron shell is half filled, i.e., it has the especially stable electronic configuration, $5f^7$, analogous to its lanthanide homolog, gadolinium. Similarly to americium (IV) a curium (IV) fluoride complex ion exists in aqueous solution. Solid compounds include Cm_2O_3, CmO_2 (and oxides of intermediate composition), CmF_3, CmF_4, CmCl_3, CmBr_3, and CmI_3.

Berkelium (Bk, atomic number 97, after Berkeley, California.) Berkelium, the eighth member of the actinide transition series, was discovered in December 1949, by Thompson, Ghiorso, and Seaborg and was the fifth transuranium element synthesized. It was produced by cyclotron bombardment of ^{241}Am with helium ions at Berkeley, California.

The only isotope available in weighable quantities for the study of the chemical and physical properties of berkelium is ^{249}Bk (half-life 314 days) produced in limited quantity by the neutron irradiation of somewhat rare ^{248}Cm by the reactions ^{248}Cm (n,γ) ^{249}Cm $\xrightarrow{\beta^-}$ ^{249}Bk. This

isotope is difficult to work with because of its relatively high specific beta particle radioactivity and because of continuous self-contamination with its daughter ^{249}Cf radioactivity.

Berkelium metal can be prepared by the reduction of BkF_3 with lithium at 1025°C. It exists in a double hexagonal-close-packed phase (presumably the low temperature phase) and a face-centered cubic phase and melts at 986°C.

Berkelium exhibits two ionic oxidation states in aqueous solution, Bk^{3+} (yellow-green) and somewhat unstable Bk^{4+} (yellow) as might be expected by analogy with its rare-earth homolog terbium. Solid compounds include Bk_2O_3, BkO_2 (and presumably oxides of intermediate composition), BkF_3, BkF_4, $BkCl_3$, $BkBr_3$, and BkI_3.

Californium (Cf, atomic number 98, after the state and University of California.) Californium, the sixth transuranium element to be discovered, was produced by Thompson, Street, Ghiorso, and Seaborg in January 1950, by helium-ion bombardment of microgram quantities of ^{242}Cm in the Berkeley 150-cm cyclotron.

The best isotope for the investigation of the chemical and physical properties of californium is ^{249}Cf (half-life 352 years), produced in pure form as the beta-particle decay product of ^{249}Bk, which is available in only limited quantity because its production from lighter isotopes requires multiple neutron capture over long periods of time in high neutron-flux reactors. Mixtures of californium isotopes produced by reactions such as ^{249}Bk (n, γ) ^{250}Bk $\xrightarrow{\beta}$ ^{250}Cf (n, γ) ^{251}Cf (n, γ) ^{252}Cf are also used but these have the disadvantage of high specific radioactivity, especially the spontaneous fission decay of ^{252}Cf.

Californium metal can be prepared by the reduction of CfF_3 with lithium. It is quite volatile and can be distilled at temperatures of the order of 1100 to 1200°C. It appears to exist in two different cubic crystalline modifications.

Californium exists mainly as Cf^{3+} in aqueous solution (emerald green), but it is the first of the actinide elements in the second half of the series to exhibit the (II) state, which becomes progressively more stable on proceeding through the heavier members of the series. It also exhibits the (IV) oxidation state in CfF_4 and CfO_2 which can be prepared under somewhat intensive oxidizing conditions. Solid compounds also include Cf_2O_3 (and higher intermediate oxides), CfF_3, $CfCl_3$, $CfBr_2$, $CfBr_3$, CfI_2, and CfI_3.

Einsteinium (Es, atomic number 99, after Albert Einstein.) Einsteinium, the seventh transuranium element to be discovered, was identified by Ghiorso et al. in December 1952, in the debris from a thermonuclear explosion in work involving the University of California Radiation Laboratory, the Argonne National Laboratory, and the Los Alamos Scientific Laboratory. The isotope produced was the 20-day ^{253}Es, originating from beta decay of ^{253}U and daughters.

Einsteinium can be investigated with macroscopic quantities using the isotopes ^{253}Es (half-life 20.5 days), ^{254}Es (half-life 276 days), and ^{255}Es (half-life 38.3 days), whose production by the irradiation of lighter elements is severely limited because of the required long sequence of neutron capture reactions over long periods of time in high-neutron-flux reactors. Most of the investigations have used the short-lived ^{253}Es because of its greater availability, but the use of ^{254}Es will increase as it becomes more available. In any case the investigation of this element is very difficult due to the high specific radioactivity and small available quantities of the isotopes.

Einsteinium metal, which is quite volatile, can be prepared by the reduction of EsF_3 with lithium and has a face-centered cubic crystal structure.

Einsteinium exists in normal aqueous solution essentially as Es^{3+} (green) although Es^{2+} can be produced under strong reducing conditions. Solid compounds such as Es_2O_3, $EsCl_3$, $EsOCl$, $EsBr_2$, $EsBr_3$, EsI_2, and EsI_3 have been made.

Fermium (Fm, atomic number 100, after Enrico Fermi.) Fermium, the eighth transuranium element to be discovered, was identified by Ghiorso et al. early in 1953 in the debris from a thermonuclear explosion in work involving the University of California Radiation Laboratory, the Argonne National Laboratory, and the Los Alamos Scientific Laboratory. The isotope produced was the 20.1-hour ^{255}Fm, originating from the beta decay of ^{255}U and daughters.

No isotope of fermium has yet been isolated in weighable amounts and thus all the investigations of this element have been done with tracer quantities. The longest-lived isotope is ^{257}Fm (half-life about 80 days) whose production in high-neutron-flux reactors is extremely limited because of the very long sequence of neutron-capture reactions that is required.

Despite its very limited availability, fermium, in the form of the 3.24-hour ^{254}Fm isotope, has been identified in the "metallic" zerovalent state in an atomic-beam magnetic resonance experiment. This established the electron structure of elemental fermium in the ground state as $5f^{12}7s^2$ (beyond the radon structure).

Fermium exists in normal aqueous solution almost exclusively as Fm^{3+} but strong reducing conditions can produce Fm^{2+} which has greater stability than Es^{2+} and less stability than Md^{2+}.

Mendelevium (Md, atomic number 101, after Dmitri Mendeleev.) Mendelevium, the ninth transuranium element to be discovered, was first identified by Ghiorso, Harvey, Choppin, Thompson, and Seaborg in early 1955 as a result of the bombardment of the isotope ^{253}Es with helium ions in the Berkeley 150-cm cyclotron. The isotope produced was ^{256}Md which decays by electron capture to ^{256}Fm, which in turn decays predominantly by spontaneous fission with a half-life of 2.6 hours. This first

identification was notable in that only of the order of one to three atoms per experiment were produced. The extreme sensitivity for detection depended on the fact that its chemical properties could be accurately predicted as eka-thulium and there was a high sensitivity for detection because of the spontaneous fission decay.

All of the isotopes of mendelevium, which include the relatively long-lived ^{258}Md (half-life 56 days), are produced by the bombardment of lighter elements with charged particles provided by accelerators. The chemical properties have, of necessity, been determined solely by the use of the tracer method. Mendelevium has the ions Md^{3+} and Md^{2+} in aqueous solution with the former somewhat more stable than the latter.

Nobelium (No, atomic number 102, after Alfred Nobel.) The discovery of nobelium, the tenth transuranium element to be discovered, corresponds to a complicated history. For the first time scientists from countries other than the United States embarked on serious efforts to compete with the United States in this field. The reported discovery of element 102 in 1957 by an international group of scientists working at the Nobel Institute for Physics in Stockholm, who suggested the name nobelium, has never been confirmed and must be considered to be erroneous. Working at the Kurchatov Institute of Atomic Energy in Moscow, G. N. Flerov and co-workers in 1958 reported a radioactivity which they thought might be attributed to element 102 but a wide range of half-lives was suggested and no chemistry was performed. As the result of more definitive work performed in 1958, Ghiorso, Sikkeland, Walton, and Seaborg reported an isotope of the element produced by bombarding a mixture of curium isotopes with ^{12}C ions in the then-new Heavy Ion Linear Accelerator (HILAC) at Berkeley. They described a novel "double recoil" technique which permitted identification by chemical means of any daughter isotope of element 102 that might have been formed. The isotope ^{250}Fm was identified conclusively by this means, indicating that its parent should be the isotope of element 102 with mass number 254 produced by the reaction of ^{12}C ions with ^{246}Cm. However, another isotope of element 102, with half-life 3 seconds, also observed indirectly in 1958, and whose alpha particles were shown to have an energy of 8.3 MeV by Ghiorso and co-workers in 1959, was shown later by G. N. Flerov and co-workers (working at the Dubna Laboratory near Moscow) to be due to an isotope of element 102 with mass number 252 rather than 254; in other words two isotopes of element 102 were discovered by the Berkeley group in 1958 but the correct mass number assignments were not made until later. On the basis that they identified the atomic number correctly, the Berkeley scientists probably have the best claim to the discovery of element 102; they suggest the retention of nobelium as the name for this element.

All isotopes of nobelium are short-lived and are produced by the bombardment of lighter elements with charged particles; thus all of the chemical investigations have been done on the tracer scale. These have demonstrated the existence of No^{3+} and No^{2+} in aqueous solution with the latter much more stable than the former. The stability of No^{2+} is consistent with the expected presence of the completed shell of 14 $5f$ electrons in this ion.

Lawrencium (Lr) atomic number 103, after Ernest O. Lawrence.) Lawrencium was discovered in 1961 by Ghiorso, Sikkeland, Larsh, and Latimer using the Heavy Ion Linear Accelerator (HILAC) at the University of California at Berkeley. A few micrograms of a mixture of ^{249}Cf, ^{250}Cf, ^{251}Cf, and ^{252}Cf were bombarded with ^{10}B and ^{11}B ions to produce an isotope of element 103 with a half-life measured as eight seconds and decaying by the emission of alpha particles of 8.6 MeV energy. Ghiorso suggested at that time that this radioactivity might be assigned the mass number 257. G. N. Flerov and co-workers have disputed this discovery on the basis that their later work suggests a greatly different half-life for the isotope with the mass number 257. Subsequent work by Ghiorso and co-workers proves that the correct assignment of mass number to the isotope discovered in 1961 is 258, and this later work gives four seconds as a better value for the half-life.

All isotopes of lawrencium are short-lived, are produced by bombardment of lighter elements with charged particles, and all chemical investigations have been performed in the tracer scale. These have demonstrated that the normal oxidation state in aqueous solution is the (III) state, corresponding to the ion Lr^{3+}, as would be expected for the last member of the actinide series.

Rutherfordium (Rf, atomic number 104, after Lord Ernest Rutherford.) Rutherfordium, the first transactinide element to be discovered, was probably first identified in a definitive manner by Ghiorso, Nurmia, Harris, K. Eskola, and P. Eskola in 1969 at Berkeley. Flerov and co-workers have suggested the name kurchatovium (after Igor Kurchatov with symbol Ku) on the basis of an earlier claim to the discovery of this element; they bombarded, in 1964, ^{242}Pu with ^{22}Ne ions in their cyclotron at Dubna and reported the production of an isotope, suggested to be ^{260}Ku, which was held to decay by spontaneous fission with a half-life of 0.3 second. After finding it impossible to confirm this observation, Ghiorso and co-workers reported definitive proof of the production of alpha particle emitting ^{257}Rf and ^{259}Rf, demonstrated by the identification of the previously known ^{255}No and ^{253}No as decay products, by means of the bombardment of ^{249}Cf with ^{12}C and ^{13}C ions in the Berkeley HILAC.

All isotopes of rutherfordium are short-lived and are produced by bombardment of lighter elements with charged, heavy-ion particles. The isotope ^{261}Ru (half-life 65 seconds) has made it possible, by means of rapid chemical experiments, to demonstrate that the normal oxidation state of rutherfordium in aqueous solution is the (IV) state corresponding to the ion Rf^{4+}. This is consistent with expectations for the first transactinide element which should be a homolog of hafnium, an element that is exclusively tetrapositive in aqueous solution.

Hahnium (Ha, atomic number 105, after Otto Hahn.) Hahnium, the second transactinide element to be discovered, was probably first identified in a definitive manner in 1970 by Ghiorso, Nurmia, K. Eskola, Harris, and P. Eskola at Berkeley. They reported the production of alpha particle emitting ^{260}Ha, demonstrated through the identification of the previously known ^{256}Lr as the decay product, by bombardment of ^{249}Cf with ^{15}N ions in the Berkeley HILAC. Again the Berkeley claim to discovery is disputed by Flerov and co-workers who earlier in 1970 reported the discovery of an isotope held to be element 105, decaying by the less definitive process of spontaneous fission, produced by the bombardment of ^{243}Am with ^{22}Ne ions in the Dubna cyclotron; later work by Flerov has confirmed the alpha particle emitting isotope of element 105 reported by Ghiorso and workers. Flerov has suggested Nielsbohrium (after Niels Bohr, symbol Ns) as the name for element 105.

All the isotopes of element 105 are short-lived and are produced by bombardment of lighter elements with charged, heavy-ion particles. The isotope ^{262}Ha (half-life 40 seconds) makes it possible, with rapid chemical techniques, to study the chemical properties of hahnium. It should exhibit the (V) oxidation state like its homolog tantalum.

Superheavy Elements Although the transactinide elements immediately beyond hahnium are predicted to have very short half-lives, theoretical considerations suggest increased nuclear stability, compared to preceding and succeeding elements, for a range of elements around atomic numbers 110, 115, 120, or 125. The elements with atomic numbers 114 or 126 seem to show special promise of such relative stability, i.e., relatively long half-lives. It should be possible to synthesize isotopes of such "superheavy" elements through bombardments of heavy-element targets with intense beams of very heavy ions accelerated in specially constructed heavy-ion accelerators.

The transactinide elements with atomic numbers 104 to 118 clearly should be placed in an expanded periodic table under the row of elements beginning with hafnium, number 72, and ending with radon, number 86. This arrangement allows prediction of the chemical properties of these transactinide elements and it is suggested that they will have an element-by-element chemical analogy with the elements immediately above them in the periodic table. In other words, rutherfordium should chemically be like hafnium, hahnium like tantalum, element 106 like tungsten, 107 like rhenium, and so on across the periodic table to element 118, which should be a noble gas like radon. Beyond element 118, the elements 119, 120, and 121 should fit into the periodic table under the elements francium, radium, and actinium (atomic numbers 87, 88, and 89). At about this point there should start another, but a special kind of inner transition series perhaps similar in some respects to the actinide series. However, this series, which may be termed the "superactinide" series, will be different in that it will contain 32 elements, corresponding to the filling of the 18 member inner 5g and 14 member inner 6f shells. After the filling of these shells the still higher elements should again be placed in the main body of the periodic table.

GLENN T. SEABORG

References

Keller, Cornelius, "The Chemistry of the Transuranium Elements," "Kernchemie in Einzeldarstellungen," Vol. 3, Germany, Verlag Chemie GmbH, 1971.

Seaborg, Glenn T., "Man-Made Transuranium Elements," Englewood Cliffs, N.J., Prentice-Hall, Inc., 1963.

Cross-references: ATOMIC PHYSICS; CYCLOTRON; ELEMENTS, CHEMICAL; ISOTOPES; NUCLEAR REACTIONS; NUCLEAR REACTORS; RADIOACTIVITY; RARE EARTHS.

TUNNELING

Tunneling is a quantum mechanical process without a classical analog. An electron (or other quantum mechanical particle) incident upon a potential barrier whose height is larger than the kinetic energy of the electron will penetrate (tunnel) a certain distance into the barrier. This is most easily visualized by considering the one-dimensional Schrödinger equation for the wave function $\psi(x)$ of such an electron:

$$-\frac{\hbar^2}{2m}\frac{\partial^2 \psi}{\partial x^2} + V(x)\psi = E\psi \qquad (1)$$

If V varies relatively slowly with distance, the solution of Eq. (1) can be approximated by

$$\psi \approx \psi_0 \exp\left[\pm i \frac{\sqrt{2m}}{\hbar}\sqrt{E - V(x)}\, x\right] \qquad (2)$$

The nonclassical case is the one where the electron energy E is smaller than the potential $V(x)$. Then ψ is no longer an oscillating wave, but it is real and decays exponentially with dis-

tance into the barrier. The penetration probability through a given barrier is equal to the ratio of the probability density $|\psi(x)|^2$ at the exit from the barrier to its value at the entrance. Equation (2) shows that this probability is exponentially dependent on barrier height and thickness. The tunneling takes place at constant electron energy as there is no scattering involved.

A more accurate solution of Eq. (1), which adequately describes many real situations, may be calculated by the Wentzel, Kremers, Brillouin (WKB) approximation. The tunneling probability through a barrier then becomes

$$P \approx \exp\left[-2 \int_{x_1}^{x_2} \frac{\sqrt{2m}}{\hbar} \sqrt{V(x) - E} \, dx \right] \tag{3}$$

An idea of the magnitude of the tunneling probability may be obtained by calculating the value of Eq. (3) for a rectangular barrier 1 eV higher than the particle energy and 25 Å wide. The result for an electron is $P \approx 10^{-11}$; for a proton, $P \approx 10^{-400}$.

Tunneling can occur in many physical situations. The simplest case is that of FIELD EMISSION. This is the emission of electrons from a solid by the application of very high fields. The energy-band diagram for such a system is shown in Fig. 1.

The electrons in a metal surrounded by vacuum can be regarded as an ensemble of quasi-free electrons held in a potential well by the positive charges of the metal ions. The depth of the well is called the electron affinity χ. The potential well is filled with electrons up to the Fermi level (E_F) and consequently electrons at this level "see" a barrier $\phi_M = \chi - E_F$ (work function) surrounding them. They can tunnel a short distance into the walls of the potential well, but of course cannot escape from it.

If a high positive field ξ is applied to the metal (e.g., by applying a potential difference between the metal under consideration and an adjacent piece of metal), the potential energy distribution is that shown in Figure 1. There now exists a barrier through which, under appropriate conditions, the electrons may tunnel. The minimum

height of the barrier is ϕ_M, and its width is approximately ϕ_M/ξ so that the current becomes

$$I \propto P \approx \exp\left[-2 \frac{2}{3} \frac{\sqrt{2m}}{\hbar} \sqrt{\phi_M} \frac{\phi_M}{\xi} \right]$$

$$\approx \exp\left[-10^8 \frac{\phi_M^{3/2}}{\xi} \right] \tag{4}$$

if ϕ_M is given in units of electron volts and ξ in units of volts per centimeter. Since ϕ_M generally has a value between 2 and 5 eV, an electric field of the order of 10^7 volts/cm is required before appreciable numbers of electrons will be emitted into vacuum.

Figure 1 is a somewhat simplified picture of an actual metal-vacuum interface. An electron outside the metal experiences a polarization force towards the metal, the so-called image force. While this is not a true potential, it may nevertheless be included in the potential energy diagram as a rounding-off of the well edge. When the field is applied, this will mean that the barrier is lowered and so the tunneling probability is increased. Particularly at high fields this will cause a departure from the simple current relationship described above. If these effects are included in the calculation, good agreement can be obtained with experimental results.

Current flow at a metal-insulator interface may be treated in the same way as that at a metal-vacuum boundary. The potential barrier height is now given by the distance from the metal Fermi level to the bottom of the insulator conduction band, which is usually smaller than the work function. Also the dielectric constant of the insulator will have to be taken into account (e.g., in the image force). These modifications do not change the basic current-voltage relationship [Eq. (4)] which has also been verified experimentally.

There may be localized electronic states in the barrier region, either due to impurities in the insulator layer or due to adsorbed molecules at the metal-insulator or metal-vacuum interfaces. An electron in the metal at the energy of the impurity state will then have a higher probability of tunneling to the impurity state and from there to the other side of the barrier than the probability of tunneling directly through the barrier. This means that when the applied voltage raises the Fermi level in the metal to the energy of impurity states in the barrier, there will be a sudden increase in current. The current-voltage relationship can thus be used to study the distribution of impurity states.

In case of a very thin insulator layer (< 60Å) bounded on both sides by metallic regions, high fields are no longer required for tunneling. The band structure may be approximated by the square potential barrier discussed initially. The top of the barrier is again formed by the con-

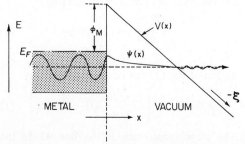

FIG. 1. Simplified energy-band diagram for field emission from a metal. $\psi(x)$ represents the wave function of an electron with energy E.

duction band of the insulator, modified appropriately by image force considerations. In equilibrium, there will be equal numbers of electrons tunneling in both directions through the insulator; no net current flows.

When a potential difference is applied, one tunneling direction is favored and net current flows. For small potential differences (much less than the barrier heights) the tunneling probability does not vary with applied field and the current flowing will be proportional to the difference in number of electrons available on the two sides of the barrier at the same energies. These numbers are in turn closely related to the density of electronic states in the metals at these energies. The tunneling current may therefore be used to investigate the density of states in certain materials, where this quantity changes rapidly with energy.

This technique for determining the density of states has been put to particularly good use in the case of superconductors. The fact that the superconductor has an energy gap in the density-of-states function at the Fermi level leads to nonlinearities and negative resistance regions in the current-voltage characteristics. This has become the most accurate method of measuring the energy gap of superconductors as a function of temperature, magnetic field and other variables. More complicated phenomena, such as simultaneous tunneling of two electrons as a pair, have also been observed. This forms the basis for the Josephson effects.

Other nonlinearities are observed at small voltages in junctions made of normal as well as superconducting metals. These are due to inelastic tunneling where the electron changes energy during tunneling by interaction with lattice excitations; e.g., it may emit or adsorb a phonon. Emission can only take place if the applied voltage is larger than the phonon energy so that a step in the current (or its derivative) is expected at that voltage. This is observed experimentally at low temperatures. It has become one of the best tools for quantitative study of the properties of electrons and phonons in metals. In some cases, anomalies are also observed at zero voltage and they may be due to magnetic interactions.

Tunneling out of a three-dimensional well is treated similarly to tunneling through the one-dimensional barrier. The exact exponential dependence will be different from Eq. (2) and depend on the form of the barrier. One type of three-dimensional well is formed by an impurity in a semiconductor or insulator which may form a bound state in the region of the forbidden gap. An electron can only tunnel out of such a state when a high field is applied, analogous to field emission from metals.

A different type of three-dimensional potential well is found in the atomic nucleus. A combination of short-range nuclear attraction and Coulomb repulsion forms a potential barrier of the type shown in Fig. 2. Many heavy radio-

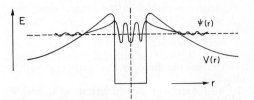

FIG. 2. Model of the nucleus, with $\psi(r)$ the wave function of an α-particle.

active nuclei contain α-particles with high enough kinetic energy to tunnel through the barrier (α-decay). Because of the much heavier mass and high barrier energy, the barrier must be considerably thinner than for an electron ($\sim 10^{-12}$ cm). Again calculations for a Coulomb barrier agree well with experimental observations of the energy dependence of the decay time (Geiger-Nuttall relation).

Tunneling of entire atoms can take place in solids, particularly when there are two possible equilibrium states (potential minima) at equal energy for the atoms which are separated by a small distance and low potential barrier. Examples of this are ferroelectric crystals of the hydrogen-bonded type (e.g., KH_2PO_4). The hydrogen atom has two possible positions in the hydrogen bond, near one or the other of the adjacent atoms. In the ferroelectric phase, all hydrogen atoms occupy the same potential well and a reversal of polarization direction is accomplished by a switch from one well to the other.

Electron tunneling is also observed in semiconductors (Zener tunneling), but in this case the situation cannot be represented by the kind of barrier discussed previously. The band structure of a semiconductor under a large applied field is shown in Fig. 3. There exists no set of real energy states connecting the two regions, and an electron must always make a discontinuous step in passing from the valence band to the conduction band. Still the tunneling probability may be calculated with an approximation equivalent to that used for the simple barrier, and except for a numerical factor, the result is the same as Eq. (4) with ϕ_M replaced by E_G.

Conduction of this type is observed in very narrow p-n junctions under reverse bias (Zener breakdown) or in insulators where there are no

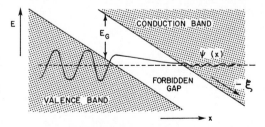

FIG. 3. Band structure of a semiconductor or insulator under an applied field.

free carriers available. In the former case, there is a large built-in field even at zero external voltage which is produced by the difference in the electrochemical potentials of the n- and p-regions. A small additional voltage (1 to 2 volts) raises the field to the value required for tunneling.

In still narrower p-n junctions ("tunnel diodes") tunneling readily takes place even where no applied voltage exists. As in the case of the very thin insulator, the electrons tunneling in opposite directions then just cancel one another out. The current-voltage curve of such a junction is drawn in Fig. 4. The band structure con-

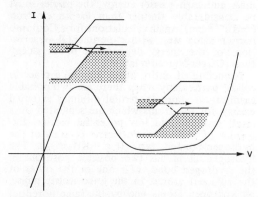

FIG. 4. Current-voltage characteristic of a tunnel diode. The two inserts depict the band structure at the maximum tunnel current and at the valley where tunneling is no longer possible.

figurations at two values of forward bias are also shown. Net tunneling current will flow in either direction of applied voltage, as long as there are electrons on one side opposite empty states of the same energy on the other side. Under large forward current this condition is no longer fulfilled, as the bottom of the conduction band on the n-type side comes opposite the forbidden energy gap on the p-type side. This means that

the current passes through a maximum value and then decreases towards zero with increasing forward bias. At still larger bias, the conventional forward diode current becomes dominating.

In actual diodes, the current never decreases completely to zero. There always exist impurity states in the forbidden gap to which an electron of appropriate energy may tunnel and from which it may drop into an empty state in the valence band giving up energy to localized lattice vibration. Alternatively, the electron need not actually occupy the impurity state but can tunnel "inelastically" directly to the valence band while simultaneously giving up the difference energy to the impurity atom and its vibration.

DIETRICH MEYERHOFER

References

Franz, W., in Flügge, S., Ed., "Handbuch der Physik," Vol. XVII, pp. 201–219, Berlin, Springer-Verlag 1956.

Fisher, J. C., and Giaever, I., J. Appl. Phys., **32**, 172 (1961).

Kane, E. O., J. Appl. Phys., **32**, 83 (1961).

Burstein, E., and Lundqvist, S., Eds., "Tunneling Phenomena in Solids," New York, Plenum Press, 1969.

Duke, C. B., "Tunneling in Solids," New York, Academic Press, 1969.

McMillan, W. L., and Rowell, J. M., in Parks, R. D., Ed., "Superconductivity," pp. 561 ff, New York, Marcel Dekker, 1969.

Kurtin, S., McGill, T. C., and Mead, C. A., Phys. Rev. Letters, **25**, 756 (1970).

Gadzuk, J. W., J. Appl. Phys., **41**, 286 (1970).

Cross-references: ENERGY LEVELS, FIELD EMISSION, RADIOACTIVITY, SCHRÖDINGER EQUATION, SEMICONDUCTORS, SOLID-STATE PHYSICS, SOLID-STATE THEORY, SUPERCONDUCTIVITY, THIN FILMS.

U

ULTRASONICS*

Ultrasonic Waves Ultrasonic waves are sound waves above the frequency normally detectable by the human ear, that is above about 20 kHz. The particles of matter transmitting a *longitudinal* wave move back and forward about mean positions in a direction parallel to the path of the wave. Alternate compressions and rarefactions in the transmitting material exist along the wave propagation direction. In *shear* waves, the particles move perpendicularly to the direction of wave propagation. In surface waves in seismological studies and in waves through thin stock, the *Rayleigh* and *Lamb* waves respectively, the particles undergo much more complicated vibratory motions than in longitudinal and transverse waves (see WAVE MOTION).

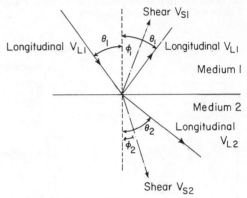

FIG. 1

TABLE 1. APPROXIMATE SOUND VELOCITIES

	In Water (m/sec)	In Steel (m/sec)
Longitudinal	1.5×10^3	6×10^3
Transverse	Cannot be supported	3×10^3
Rayleigh	Cannot be supported	3×10^3

In most practical applications of ultrasonics, pulses or packets containing a number of oscillation cycles are sent through the solid or liquid under investigation. A longitudinal wave pulse, when incident on the boundary between two materials having different sound velocities, is transformed into reflected and refracted shear and longitudinal waves. Snell's law governs the angles of REFLECTION and REFRACTION for both types of waves. It states that

$$\frac{\sin \theta}{V} = \text{Constant}$$

where θ is the angle the beam makes with a normal to the intervening surface and V is the sound velocity. Therefore, in Fig. 1,

$$\text{Constant} = \frac{\sin \theta_1}{V_{L1}} = \frac{\sin \theta_2}{V_{L2}} = \frac{\sin \phi_2}{V_{S2}} = \frac{\sin \phi_1}{V_{S1}}$$

*Editor was unable to locate author. Article is reprinted from first edition.

Transducers In general, a transducer is a device to convert electrical energy into mechanical vibrations which are then directed into the specimen. The transducer also commonly reconverts received mechanical oscillations back again into electrical signals for amplification and recognition. Transducers are usually piezoelectric, ferroelectric or magnetostrictive in nature.

The application of a voltage across a piezoelectric crystal causes it to deform with an amplitude of deformation proportional to the voltage. Reversal of the voltage causes reversal of the mechanical strain. Until recently, the only piezoelectric transducer in general use was quartz, but now several synthetic ceramic materials are employed.

Ferroelectric crystals are also electrostrictive. Barium titanate has an electrical mechanical conversion efficiency about one hundred times that of quartz. Unlike the piezoelectric mode of oscillation, in ferroelectric crystals application of a voltage in either direction across the crystal causes expansion of the crystal. This mode can however be converted to the piezoelectric by biasing the expansion in one direction either by application of a strong dc field or more commonly by cooling the ferroelectric crystal through its Curie temperature while it is under the influence of a strong electric field (order of 10^6 volts/m).

Transducer crystals are normally cut to a resonant frequency, the thickness being one-half the acoustic wavelength. A bond between the crystal transducer and the specimen matches the

acoustic impedance and carries the acoustic power into the latter. Backing layers may be fixed to the rear surface of the transducer. These layers are chosen to reflect power forward into the crystal and specimen in some technological applications. They may also be chosen to absorb power so as not to complicate signals received in material testing applications.

Ultrasonic Testing Most ultrasonic test equipment employs pulses of high-frequency sound (>1 Mhz), the pulse width being adjustable between 0.1 and 1.0 μsec and the repetition rate between 60 and 1000 pulses per second. Figure 2 shows a typical block diagram.

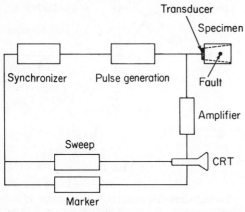

FIG. 2

The synchronizer triggers a pulse in the generation circuit. This is converted to an acoustic pulse by the transducer crystal. The synchronizer also starts the sweep circuit of the cathode ray tube (CRT) and the marker circuit, the latter making marker pips along the time base. Separate transducer crystals may be used for transmission and reflection, or one crystal may be made to carry out both functions. The echo from the back face of the specimen block arrives twice the transmission time after the initial pulse. The marker pips can then be calibrated in depth. A fault will show up as an extra echo whose depth into the specimen can be read from the marker pip which coincides with its position on the screen of the CRT.

The transducer is coupled to the specimen under test by an oil or adhesive. In high-speed testing or in cases where rough surfaces are encountered, the specimen may be immersed in a liquid or a stream of liquid passed between the transducer and the specimen in order to give sonic coupling.

Examples of Ultrasonic Testing. Solid objects of thickness greater than about half an inch may be tested for inhomogeneities. Special techniques also exist for sheet testing. Heavy forgings, crank shafts, rails, concrete structures and a host of other manufactured objects are now regularly scanned for porosity or internal faults.

The frequencies employed are normally from 1 to 5 Mhz for steel objects, about 0.5 Mhz for many plastics and 0.1 Mhz for concrete.

In a medical application of ultrasonic techniques, the subject is immersed in water and the transducer is scanned in a circular path round the axis of the torso or limb under detailed examination. Echoes are recorded on the CRT which is also circularly scanned (like the P.P.I. radar system). A long persistence screen gives a complete record of the scanned portion of the body. Gallstones, tumors, cancers and other pathological conditions are revealed.

Sophisticated scanning arrays are used in SONAR underwater detection. Frequencies must be low because of the high attenuation in water (at 100 kHz attenuation $\approx$ 60 dB/km), and this limits definition. Sea noises, fish and underwater refraction by layers at different temperatures introduce difficulty of interpretation into the echo patterns. Depth recording is now accomplished by the use of many sending and receiving transducers coupled to a computing system which interprets differences of arrival times in terms of variation of path length and ultimately of depth. Continuous records of the ocean bed or the depth of surface ice can be made.

Systems similar in principle to Sonar are also employed to give continuous records of manufactured plate thickness and to control the filling of enclosed tanks.

Examples of the Use of Ultrasonic Power. Londitudinal ultrasonic waves can be produced at sufficient intensity to cause changes in materials of industrial importance. In many cases, standing waves are set up in a containing vessel with resulting periodic variation of vibration amplitude. In almost all cases ceramic transducers are used. Emulsifying, mixing, dispersing, degassing and cleaning applications generally employ unfocused acoustic radiation. In welding, soldering, drilling, machining and the neurosurgical controlled damage of brain tissue, on the other hand, a focused acoustic beam is always used.

Focusing may be done by the use of either an acoustic horn or by an acoustic lens. Figure 3

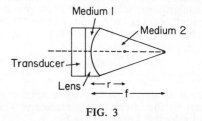

FIG. 3

shows the principle of a simple plano-concave lens whose radius of curvature r is given by

$$r = f\left(\frac{n-1}{n}\right)$$

where n, the index of refraction, is the ratio of velocities in the lens and adjacent medium:

$$n = \frac{V_1}{V_2}$$

Fundamental Research in Physics by Ultrasonics *Acoustic Velocity.* The acoustic velocity in a material is fundamentally related to the binding forces between the atoms or molecules. Measurement of the velocity is made by a pulse technique or by vibrating a specimen of known dimensions in one of its fundamental modes of oscillation and recording the frequency.

Acoustic Attenuation. Attenuation measurements are made by recording the decay in oscillation amplitude with time of a solid material set to ring in one of its natural modes. Attenuation may also be measured from the amplitude of successive echoes passing through the material.

Under the influence of thermal activation, impurity elements or defects may switch position in a crystal lattice. This they do in a definite RELAXATION time, which is related exponentially to the temperature and to the difference in energy of the defect in its two positions. Now if the switching of position of the defect also causes a difference in dimension of the specimen, then a maximum in attenuation is found when the period of an applied acoustic stress just matches the thermal relaxation time. A whole spectrum of relaxation attenuation maxima has been found in solids. Each is related to a definite internal process, each with its characteristic energy difference. Perhaps the best known of these is the relaxation maximum given by the diffusion of carbon atoms in iron from which the activation energy for carbon diffusion can be calculated (Snoek peaks).

Dislocations are line defects in crystalline material the movement of which is involved in all cases of plastic deformation. Acoustic waves vibrate the dislocations, and in general, the more freely the dislocation moves, the greater is the acoustic beam attenuated. Attenuation measurements thus give information on how well the dislocation is locked in position in the solid, i.e., on how strong the material is. Pinning down of the dislocations may be effected by alloying or by radiation with high-energy particles which cause internal damage. Measurement of acoustic attenuation is therefore encountered in such studies.

Electrons in metals also attenuate acoustic waves if the frequencies are sufficiently high ($>$ 5 MHz) and the temperature sufficiently low ($>$ 10K) so that the acoustic wavelength is comparable with the mean free path of the electrons. Attenuation measurements give information on relaxation times of electrons, and hence their energies, and are therefore concerned in the study of Fermi surfaces in metals. Such studies are intimately related to the phenomena of electrical and heat conductivity.

The onset of superconductivity in some metals and alloys at low temperatures is characterized by a fall to zero electrical resistance and also by a sharp fall in high-frequency acoustic attenuation.

In nonmetallic crystalline materials, thermal vibrations or PHONONS interact with one another and limit heat conductivity. Measurements of high-frequency attenuation are now giving information on phonon-phonon interactions. Such information may lead to the elucidation of the spectrum of thermal vibrations in all materials above the absolute zero of temperature.

T. S. HUTCHISON

References

Goldman, R. G., "Ultrasonic Technology," New York, Van Nostrand Reinhold, 1962. Gives techniques used in ultrasonics.

Hutchison, T. S., "Ultrasonic Absorption in Solids," *Science*, **132** (Sept. 9, 1960). Treats the physics of ultrasonic studies.

Dransfeld, K., *Sci. Am.*, **208**, No. 6, 6 (1963). Information on recent high-frequency studies.

Cross-references: CONDUCTIVITY, ELECTRICAL; FERMI SURFACE; FERROELECTRICITY; HEAT TRANSFER; MAGNETOSTRICTION; OSCILLOSCOPE; PHONONS; REFLECTION; REFRACTION; RELAXATION; SOLID-STATE PHYSICS; SONAR; SUPERCONDUCTIVITY; VIBRATION; WAVE MOTION.

ULTRAVIOLET RADIATION

Ultraviolet radiation comprises the region of the electromagnetic spectrum extending from the violet end of the visible, wavelength 4000Å, to the beginning of X-RAYS, arbitrarily taken as 100Å, a span of more than five octaves. The unit of wavelength generally used for the ultraviolet is $Å = 10^{-8}$ cm; it is named after A. J. Ångström, Swedish pioneer in SPECTROSCOPY, who made in 1868 the first accurate measurements of the wavelengths of spectral lines. Although still occasionally heard, the term ultraviolet rays has become obsolete. Ultraviolet light, however, is an expression which is usually acceptable even though ultraviolet cannot ordinarily be seen by the eye.

The ultraviolet is subdivided into several parts: The near ultraviolet, 4000 to 3000Å, present in sunlight, producing important biological effects, but not detectable by the eye; the middle ultraviolet, 3000 to 2000Å, called by biologists the far ultraviolet, not present in sunlight as it reaches the earth's surface, but well transmitted through air; the long range 2000 to 100Å known as the extreme ultraviolet, abbreviated XUV, since it connects the ultraviolet and x-rays. The XUV is known also as the vacuum ultraviolet, because it is not transmitted through air, and is sometimes called the far ultraviolet. The portion

of the XUV from 2000 to 1350Å is known as the Schumann region, after its discoverer.

The boundary, 100Å, between XUV and x-rays is arbitrary; it is often preferred to make the distinction on the basis of the method of production and analysis. Radiation is called x-rays if produced by the classical x-ray tube in which bombardment by electrons removes inner-shell electrons from atoms of the target material, with radiation emitted when outer electrons fall back; x-rays are also generated by the BREMS-STRAHLUNG process when fast electrons are suddenly decelerated. In sparks, arcs, and electrical discharges through gases, the classical sources of ultraviolet, it is the outer electrons of either neutral atoms or ions that are excited; the radiation occurs when the outer electrons are recaptured and fall back to their ground states (see ELECTRICAL DISCHARGES IN GASES).

Ultraviolet radiation was discovered by Ritter in 1801; he found that silver chloride was blackened, as it is by visible light, if placed beyond the violet end of the sun's spectrum, where nothing can be seen. Stokes, in 1862, using a prism of quartz rather than glass, observed to a short-wavelength limit of 1830Å radiation produced by a spark discharge between aluminum electrodes by using a fluorescent plate detector. The break-through further into the ultraviolet was made between 1885 and 1903 by Victor Schumann, an instrument maker and machine shop owner of Leipzig. Schumann realized that there are three reasons why ultraviolet of shorter wavelengths had not been detected: (1) air is opaque, (2) quartz prisms and lenses do not transmit, (3) ordinary photographic emulsions are not sensitive, because of absorption by gelatin. He overcame these difficulties by constructing the first vacuum spectrograph, using optics of crystal fluorite instead of quartz, and by making photographic plates with almost no gelatin, now known as Schumann plates. Theodore Lyman of Harvard University, soon passed the limit, 1300Å, reached by Schumann, by constructing a vacuum spectrograph with a reflection-type concave diffraction grating instead of the fluorite prism and lenses. He discovered the Lyman series of hydrogen, the most fundamental spectral series of the simplest and most abundant element, with first line, Lyman-alpha, at 1215.67Å and series limit at 911.7Å. Further progress reaching 140Å was made by R. A. Millikan and his students at the California Institute of Technology with the aid of a "hot" spark in vacuum. Finally Osgood, in 1927, closed the gap to x-rays by combining the hot spark and a grating used at grazing incidence; in the same year, Dauvillier reached 121Å in the XUV from the x-ray side, using an x-ray tube with a spectrometer utilizing a crystal of large lattice constant, made from a fatty acid.

Ultraviolet radiation is emitted by almost all light sources, to some extent. In general, the higher the temperature or the more energetic the excitation, the shorter are the wavelengths.

Tungsten lamps in quartz envelopes radiate in the ultraviolet in accordance with Planck's law, slightly modified by the emissivity function of tungsten. Because of its high temperature, 3800K, the crater of an open carbon arc is an excellent source of ultraviolet extending to the air cutoff. Electrical discharges through gases produce intense ultraviolet emission, mainly in lines and bands. The most widely used is the quartz mercury arc; when the Hg pressure is allowed to rise to several atmospheres, the intensity becomes great, and the spectrum is a quasi continuum. For the shortest wavelengths, still higher temperatures are required, as produced by discharging a large capacitor at some 50 kV between metal electrodes in vacuum. This violent discharge vaporizes atoms from the electrodes, then strips off as many as 10 or 15 outer electrons. The emission line radiation emitted when these highly ionized atoms recapture electrons extends to very short wavelengths. A similar short-XUV "spark" can also be produced by focusing a high-power laser beam on a metal surface. Another source producing highly ionized atoms and emission lines in the XUV is the magnetically compressed plasma such as produced by the devices known as zeta and theta pinch, which reaches a temperature of half a million degrees. Still another useful source is the synchrotron, in which electrons are accelerated in circular paths through several hundred MeV. The electromagnetic radiation produced by the great centripetal acceleration is plane-polarized continuum radiation, whose peak lies well below 100Å. For great XUV intensity, however, no man-made source has equaled the atomic bomb.

Solids, liquids, and gases usually transmit well in the near ultraviolet but always become opaque somewhere in the middle or extreme ultraviolet. Among solids, both crystal and fused quartz transmit to a short wavelength limit between 2000 and 1500Å, depending on purity; CaF_2 (fluorite), to 1230Å; MgF_2 to 1140Å; and LiF, the most transparent known solid, to 1050Å. These materials are invaluable for constructing lenses and prisms for ultraviolet instruments.

Solids in the form of very thin films transmit to some extent throughout the XUV, but the thickness must be less than a few thousand Ångstroms. Certain thin films are useful as optical filters; Al, for example transmits from 837Å corresponding to its plasmon frequency, to its x-ray L-edge at 170Å, and to a small extent as far as 150Å. Films of plastics, such as collodion of 300Å thickness, transmit fairly well below 500Å; they are useful as windows for low-pressure gas retention.

Gases vary greatly in their absorption characteristics. Molecular oxygen causes air to become opaque below about 1850Å, because of absorption in the Schumann-Runge band system, followed by continuous absorption from 1750 to 1290Å, and strong irregular absorption to shorter wavelengths. Molecular nitrogen, how-

ever, is relatively transparent all the way to 1000Å. Hydrogen absorbs in the Lyman series lines, and in an ionization continuum beyond the series limit, 911.7Å. Of all the gases, helium is the most transparent; absorption first takes place in the resonance lines, the longest lying at 584Å, and in a continuum beyond the series limit, 504Å. More complicated molecular gases, such as CO_2, NO, and N_2O are rather opaque throughout most of the XUV. Water vapor is much like O_2 with absorption commencing below 1850Å.

Reflection occurs for ultraviolet, just as for visible radiation. In general, the reflectance becomes less, as the wavelength decreases. Aluminum is the best reflector over much of the long-wavelength region; when properly prepared, by rapid evaporation of the pure material in an excellent vacuum, the reflectance is greater than 90 per cent to 2000Å, and can be maintained to 80 per cent at 1200Å by overcoating with a thin layer of MgF_2 to prevent growth of Al_2O_3. Below 1000Å, platinum is best with a reflectance of about 20 per cent at 600Å, but only about 4 per cent at 300Å.

Ultraviolet can be detected in a variety of ways, making use of effects produced when it is absorbed by matter, e.g., fluorescence with re-radiation of longer wavelengths; chemical reactions in solids; dissociation of gas molecules, with ensuing reactions; ionization of gases; emission of photoelectrons from surfaces of solids. In general, the shorter the wavelength, the more energetic is the reaction. This is in accordance with Einstein's law, $E = h\nu$, giving the energy of a photon in terms of Planck's constant, h, and its frequency ν (velocity of light ÷ wavelength). Thus, ultraviolet photons range up to about 10 000 times more energetic than visible photons, and effects produced by them are much easier to observe.

The simplest way to detect and measure ultraviolet radiation is by making use of the fluorescence process, converting the ultraviolet into visible radiation which can be seen, or into near ultraviolet which is easily photographed or measured with conventional photomultipliers. Calcium tungstate, for example, is an excellent converter for the middle ultraviolet. Materials much used for the extreme ultraviolet are oil and sodium salicylate. The latter is especially valuable because its quantum efficiency of fluorescence is high and is nearly independent of wavelength. An ordinary photomultiplier, with its glass window coated with a layer of sodium salicylate becomes a sensitive radiometer for use throughout the entire ultraviolet.

Ordinary photographic emulsions containing gelatin as a binder are useful only to about 2500Å; they can be sensitized easily by overcoating with oil or sodium salicylate. Eastman Kodak spectroscopic-type plates and films are available with ultraviolet sensitization, produced by overcoating with a fluorescent lacquer. Nearly gelatin-free Schumann-type emulsions combine greater sensitivity and higher resolving power than fluorescence-sensitized emulsions; they are available as Eastman Kodak 104 (formerly called SWR), the higher-speed 101, and Kodak Pathé SC5 and 7. All types must be handled so that the delicate emulsion surface is never touched.

Ultraviolet radiation is easily detected and measured directly by means of photomultipliers if they are equipped with ultraviolet transmitting windows or are used without an envelope in a vacuum. Almost all materials emit photoelectrons to some extent when ultraviolet-irradiated, but in applications, the problem is usually to devise a photocathode surface that has extremely high efficiency in a certain spectral region and is insensitive in others. When constructed with ultraviolet-transmitting envelopes, the various visible-sensitive photocathodes respond well throughout the ultraviolet. For applications in the presence of sunlight, however, it is often necessary to use a "solar blind" surface, having negligible sensitivity longward of 2900Å; one of the best surfaces is RbTe, with quantum efficiency of $< 10^{-3}$ at $\lambda > 3000$Å and ≈ 0.1 at $\lambda < 2600$Å.

For use at wavelengths shorter than 1300Å the best photocathodes are simple metal surfaces, such as tungsten, used directly in vacuum. Most metals exhibit a strong internal photoelectric effect at $\lambda < 1500$Å, which reaches a high value of about 15 per cent at 1000Å. This high work function results in low sensitivity to long-wavelength stray light, and low noise. By coating the metal cathode with LiF, MgF_2, or other compounds, the spectral response curve can be greatly modified and the long wavelength cut-off displaced, to adapt the detector for special applications. Metal photocathodes are available in electrostatically focused photomultipliers with photocathode and dynodes of Be-Cu or stainless steel, and magnetically focused strip-photomultipliers with tungsten photocathodes. The sensitivity is little changed by repeated exposure to air.

Ionization chambers and Geiger counters form another useful class of detectors of XUV radiation. Knowledge of the ionization efficiency of the gas makes it possible to use them for measurement of absolute energy. One of the most useful is filled with NO, responding from the ionization limit, 1350Å, to the transmission limit of the LiF window, 1050Å. To shorter wavelengths, it is possible to use Geiger counters without a window, by maintaining a slight positive gas pressure inside the tube. When filled with a rare gas, they count all incident photons of wavelengths shorter than the ionization limit of the gas, since the gas ionization efficiency is 100 per cent.

Ultraviolet radiation can, of course, be detected with a thermocouple, by direct conversion of its energy into heat. Because of low sensitivity, this fundamental absolute method of energy measurement is resorted to only when no other method is available, for example, in order to

establish that the ionization efficiency of the rare gases is 100 per cent for radiation below their series limits.

Mankind's principal source of energy, the sun, emits strongly throughout the ultraviolet, but only the near ultraviolet reaches the surface of the earth. Wavelengths shorter than 2900Å are absorbed by a layer of ozone (O_3) with center at an altitude of about fifteen miles.

The principal action of solar ultraviolet is to produce sunburn, or erythema, but it is only the shortest wavelengths penetrating the ozone layer which have this action. Since the effective band is centered at 2967Å and extends to about 3100Å, sunlight becomes rapidly more effective in burning the skin when the subject goes to a high altitude and when the sun lies high in the sky. Excessive exposure is known to be a cause of skin cancer.

The normal eye does not sense the sun's ultraviolet, although it does have a small sensitivity below 4000Å. Young eyes transmit more than old, and do, indeed, detect ultraviolet from 4000Å to about 3130Å as a faint, bluish sensation, but sharp images are not formed without special corrective lenses, on account of the chromatic aberration of the eye's optical system. To shorter wavelengths, ultraviolet is absorbed by the cornea and causes fluorescence, which is seen as a general haze. Excessive exposure to wavelengths short of 3000Å, however, causes conjunctivitis, a painful burn of the cornea. For this reason, it is extremely important to wear glass goggles, when in the presence of intense sources of middle ultraviolet radiation. Similarly, on snowfields and glaciers, goggles must be worn to prevent the form of conjunctivitis known as snow blindness.

A new and unfortunate action of solar ultraviolet is the production of Los Angeles-type smog, containing molecules which irritate the eye and causes damage to plants. The photochemical processes are complicated and are not as yet completely understood. It is well established, however, that the principal atmospheric contaminants involved are nitrogen oxide, nitrogen dioxide, and various organic molecules present in gasoline engine exhausts. The initial process appears to be the absorption of solar ultraviolet by NO_2, which produces O and NO. The principal reactions, however, are the photolysis of mixtures of nitrogen oxides and hydrocarbons in air, caused by absorption of solar ultraviolet. The products of the reactions are ozone, aldehydes, acrolein, acetone, and peroxyacyl nitrates and nitrites (PAN); among these, formaldehyde, acrolein, and PAN are specific eye irritants. One principal phytotoxicant is ozone, which produces a mottling or bleaching of the upper surfaces of leaves; various others cause a bronzing or glazing of the underneath surfaces of leaves. Obviously, solar ultraviolet cannot be eliminated; photochemical smog relief must come from the chemist.

The principal present-day application of ultraviolet radiation is in increasing the efficiency of conversion of electrical energy into light. The fluorescent lamp utilizes a coating of a crystalline substance, such as manganese-activated zinc silicate, on the inside wall of a mercury arc lamp, to convert the middle- and near-ultraviolet radiation from the mercury vapor column into visible light and thus add to the visible-line spectrum emission of the mercury. The efficiency of fluorescent lamps may reach values 2.5 times greater than those of commonly used incandescent tungsten lamps.

Another widespread use of ultraviolet is in "black lighting," largely for the theater. By introducing an ultraviolet-transmitting, visible-opaque filter over a carbon arc projector, an intense ultraviolet beam can be projected onto the stage. There it causes different materials to glow brilliantly, with color determined by the particular dye molecule.

As a technical industrial tool, ultraviolet spectroscopic analysis has become of extreme importance. In the production of steel, for example, a sample can be analyzed in minutes, by introducing it into a source electrode, and analyzing the radiation with a multichannel spectrometer. Different exit slits select the strongest and most sensitive emission lines of the various elements present; with photomultipliers, their intensities are measured and converted at once to give the composition of the steel.

Among various biological and medical applications of middle-ultraviolet radiation, perhaps the most important are its uses to kill bacteria and fungi in hospitals and especially in operating rooms to eliminate the hepatitis virus from blood plasma, to keep foods sterile, and to treat skin diseases. Rickets and certain other diseases, can be cured by exposure of the body to ultraviolet, which produces vitamin D. Similarly, vitamin D is produced in milk by ultraviolet irradiation.

The middle- and extreme-ultraviolet radiation from the sun, although not able to reach the earth's surface, nevertheless affects man and his activities through its powerful influence on the upper atmosphere. First knowledge of the sun's ultraviolet spectrum was obtained in 1946, when a spectrograph was flown in a V-2 rocket by the U.S. Naval Research Laboratory and the solar spectrum was recorded from 3000 to 2200Å. In the twenty-seven years since this event, great progress has been made in studying, from rockets and orbiting vehicles, the true solar spectrum, the reactions produced in the atmospheric gases when the sun's short wavelengths are absorbed, and the physical processes in the solar atmosphere giving rise to these radiations. Grouped together broadly as a space science, they comprise several fields, such as aeronomy, solar physics, solar-terrestrial relationships, and ionospheric research. In the years to come, it is certain that orbiting observatories will monitor the ultraviolet and x-ray emissions from the sun, just as the great ground-based observatories study in visible and near-ultraviolet light the phenomena taking place in its atmosphere.

As affecting our present-day way of life, per-

haps the most important action of solar short-ultraviolet and soft x-rays is in producing the several ionospheric layers; acting as mirrors, they reflect radio waves and so make possible radio communication over great distances. Far more important for mankind, however, is the solar radiation in the Schumann region, 2000 to 1300Å. It is upon this radiation that the human race relies for survival; absorption of these wavelengths by molecular oxygen in the high atmosphere gives rise to atomic oxygen, which then reacts with molecular oxygen to form ozone. It is this permanent layer of ozone which protects all forms of terrestrial life from the lethal effects of the sun's middle-ultraviolet radiation.

RICHARD TOUSEY

References

1. Green, Alex S., Ed., "The Middle Ultraviolet: Its Science and Technology," New York, John Wiley & Sons, Inc., 1966.
2. Samson, J. A. R., "Techniques of Vacuum Ultraviolet Spectroscopy," New York, John Wiley & Sons, 1967.

Cross-references: BREMSSTRAHLUNG, ELECTRICAL DISCHARGES IN GASES, PHOTOELECTRICITY, PHOTOMULTIPLIER, PLASMAS, SPECTROSCOPY, SYNCHROTRON, X-RAYS.

V

The term "vacuum," which strictly implies the unrealizable ideal of a space entirely devoid of matter, is used in a relative sense in vacuum technique to denote gas pressure below the normal atmospheric pressure of 760 torr (1 torr = 1 mm of mercury = 133 pascal). The degree or quality of the vacuum attained is indicated by the total pressure of the residual gases in the vessel which is pumped. Table 1 shows the accepted terminology in denoting degrees of vacuum together with the pressure range concerned, the calculated molecular density (from the equation $p = nkT$ where p is the pressure, n is the molecular density, i.e., number of molecules per cubic centimeter, k is Boltzmann's constant, and T is the absolute temperature taken to be 293 K or 20°C) and the mean free path λ from the approximate equation for air: $\lambda = 5/p$ cm, where p is the pressure in millitorr.

Vacuum Pumps There are several types of vacuum pumps. The two most widely used are the mechanical rotary oil-sealed pump and the vapor pump. The former provides a medium vacuum and works relative to the atmosphere; the vapor pump, on the other hand, provides a high or very high vacuum and operates relative to a medium vacuum provided by a rotary pump, referred to as a backing pump in this connection. Thus, the most widely used high-vacuum system able to establish an ultimate pressure of about 10^{-6} torr or below consists of a vapor pump backed by a rotary pump.

Four or five patterns of rotary oil-sealed pump exist, but they have in common the fact that the volume between a rotor (or rotating plunger) and a stator is divided into two-crescent-shaped sections which are isolated from one another as regards the passage of gas. Further, they are furnished with an intake port and a discharge outlet valve to the atmosphere. On revolution of the rotor (speeds of 450 to 700 rpm are used) gas is swept from the intake port, compressed, and discharged to the atmosphere via the one-way outlet valve. The mechanism is immersed in a low-vapor-pressure oil for sealing and lubrication in a small pump; larger units have a separate oil reservoir and feed device. A spring-loaded vane type of rotary oil-sealed pump is shown in Fig. 1(a). A single-stage pump of this kind provides an ultimate pressure of about 10^{-2} torr; a two-stage one with two units in cascade will give an ultimate of about 10^{-4} torr. Rotary pumps with speeds from 20 to 20 000 liters/min are commercially available, the smallest being driven by an $\frac{1}{8}$-hp motor, the largest requiring a 40-hp motor.

These pumps handle permanent gases efficiently. Condensable vapors, e.g., water vapor, are not satisfactorily pumped because they may liquefy during the compression part of the rotation. To prevent this, gas ballast is a common provision whereby air from the atmosphere is admitted to the pump through a simple, adjustable screw valve to the region between the rotor and stator just before the discharge outlet valve. The amount of extra air admitted is readily adjusted to provide a compressed gas-vapor mixture which opens the discharge valve before vapor condensation occurs. Gas ballasting will clearly increase significantly the ultimate pressure provided by the pump, but this is not important since the gas-ballast valve can be closed after initial pumping has removed most of the water vapor.

Vapor pumps are of two main types: vapor diffusion pumps and vapor ejector pumps. Both employ vapor (of either mercury or a low-vapor-pressure oil) issuing from a nozzle as a means of

TABLE 1. DEGREES OF VACUUM AND PRESSURE RANGES

Degree or Quality of Vacuum	Pressure Range (torr)	Molecular Density, n (molecules/cm^3)	Mean Free Path, λ (cm)
Coarse or rough vacuum	760–1	2.69×10^{19}–3.5×10^{16}	6.6×10^{-6}–5×10^{-3}
Medium vacuum	1–10^{-3}	3.5×10^{16}–3.5×10^{13}	5×10^{-3}–5
High vacuum	10^{-3}–10^{-7}	3.5×10^{13}–3.5×10^{9}	5–5×10^{4}
Very high vacuum	10^{-7}–10^{-9}	3.5×10^{9}–3.5×10^{7}	5×10^{4}–5×10^{6}
Ultrahigh vacuum	$<10^{-9}$	$<3.5 \times 10^{7}$	$>5 \times 10^{6}$

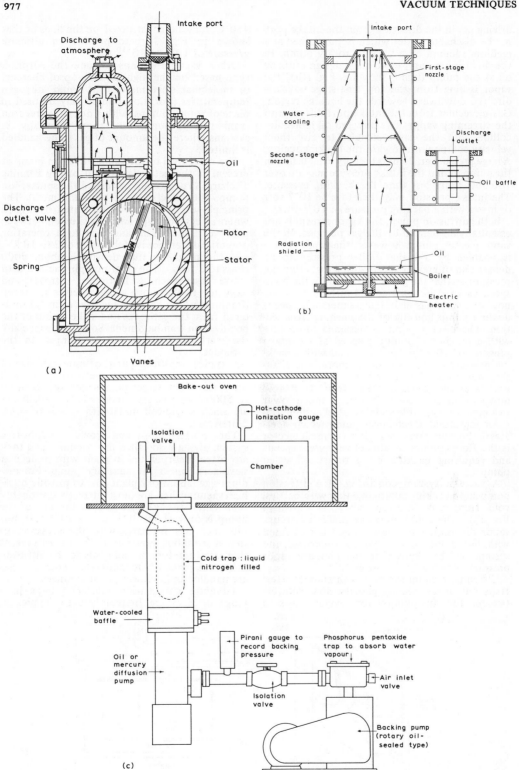

FIG. 1. (a) A spring-loaded vane type of rotary oil-sealed pump. (b) A two-stage or diffusion pump. (c) A diffusion pump-rotary backing pump vacuum system.

driving gas in the direction from the intake port to the discharge outlet which is maintained at a medium vacuum by a backing rotary pump. In the diffusion pump [a two-stage design utilizing oil as the pump fluid is shown in Fig. 1(b)] the vapor issuing from the top, first-stage nozzle is directed downward towards the backing region. Gas molecules from the intake port diffuse into the streaming vapor. The directed oil molecules collide with the gas molecules to give them velocity components toward the backing region. A large pressure gradient is thereby established in the pump so that the intake pressure may be over 100 000 times less than the backing pressure. The intake pressure may therefore be 10^{-6} torr or lower with a backing pressure of 10^{-1} torr.

In the diffusion pump, the vapor stream is not essentially influenced by the gas pumped. In the vapor ejector pump, however, the vapor stream is enabled by a higher boiler pressure to be denser and of greater speed with a higher intake pressure, so that the gas is entrained by the high-speed vapor. Viscous drag and turbulent mixing now carry the gas at initially supersonic speeds down a pump housing of diminishing cross section. The ejector pump is designed to operate with a maximum pumping speed at an intake pressure of 10^{-1} to 10^{-3} torr and with a backing pressure of 0.5 to 1 torr or more. The diffusion pump, on the other hand, is designed to have a fairly constant speed from 10^{-3} torr down to an ultimate 10^{-6} torr or much lower in a modern, bakeable stainless steel system.

An important mechanical pump which operates in the same pressure region as the oil ejector is the Roots pump, capable of very great speeds and requiring backing by a rotary oil-sealed pump.

A vacuum system consisting of a diffusion pump and a backing pump, together with baffles, cold traps and isolation valves, is shown in Fig. 1(c). The cold trap is essential if a mercury vapor diffusion pump is used and is best filled with liquid nitrogen ($-196°C$); otherwise, the system will be exposed to the mercury vapor pressure, which is 10^{-3} torr at $18°C$.

Ultrahigh-vacuum systems with stainless steel traps and metal sealing gaskets, and bakeable (except for the pumps) for several hours to

$450°C$, may be constructed on the lines of that shown in Fig. 1(c) to provide an ultimate pressure of 10^{-9} to 10^{-10} torr.

Other vacuum pumps include the sorption type based on the high gas take-up of charcoal or molecular sieve material at liquid nitrogen temperatures. Sorption pumps may be used in place of rotary pumps, with a desirable freedom from rotary pump oil vapor, especially in systems where the amount of gas to be handled is limited.

The chief rival to the vapor diffusion pump at present is the getter-ion pump of the Penning discharge type, sometimes called the sputter-ion pump, with electrodes of titanium metal. The principle of operation is illustrated by Fig. 2 where an egg-box type anode is situated between plane cathodes. The anode-cathode operating potential difference is of the order of 2 to 10 kV, and the magnetic flux density is about 3000 gauss (0.3 tesla). The chief pumping action with active gases such as hydrogen, nitrogen and oxygen is to the anode which receives deposited titanium (which has very high gas affinity) sputtered from the cathodes under the action of the positive ion bombardment. Some gas, especially the inert gases like argon, is pumped to the cathodes.

A typical multicell pump of moderate size of this type has a pumping speed of about 250 liters/sec. Much larger pumps with speeds of up to 5000 liters/sec are commercially available, as are small single-cell units with speeds of some 2 liters/sec.

The sputter-ion pumps provide a vapor-free system giving a so-called dry vacuum, and they are often incorporated in plant with molecular sieve sorption as the auxiliary pump. For medium-size laboratory plant able to provide ultrahigh vacuum they are most attractive. Probably their chief disadvantage is that the life of the pump is only about 40 hours at 10^{-3} torr, but this increases inversely with the pressure, so that it is 40 000 hours at 10^{-6} torr. At present they are therefore strong rivals to the diffusion pump for plant where moderate amounts of gas are handled in the lower pressure ranges.

Titanium sublimation (getter) pumps in a range of sizes are frequently used. Typically,

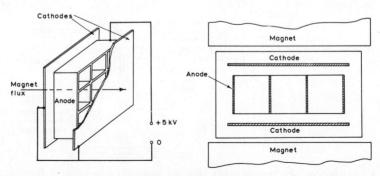

FIG. 2. A sputter-ion pump.

the titanium is sublimed from an electrically heated tungsten or tantalum alloy filament loaded with titanium wire to become deposited on the interior wall of the surrounding casing, which may be air-cooled, water-cooled, or in specialized cases, refrigerated with liquid nitrogen. The sorption of the active gases by the titanium provides high-speed pumping. Apart from their use as auxiliary pumping devices (particularly in the ultrahigh vacuum region), frequently adopted practice is to use such pumps in combination with a sorption pump and a sputter-ion pump. The molecular-sieve type of sorption pump is able to reduce the pressure from the atmospheric value to about 10^{-2} torr; the lifetime of the sputter-ion pump is seriously reduced if it is frequently switched on at pressures above about 10^{-4} torr. The titanium sublimation pump used as an intermediary between the sorption pump and the sputter-ion pump overcomes this difficulty, and moreover, provides enhanced pumping action to the sputter-ion pump by virtue of its deposited titanium film. The usual sequence is to utilize the sorption pump, then the titanium sublimation pump, and finally the sputter-ion pump.

The turbomolecular pump, introduced in 1958 by Becker as a significant advance on the older molecular drag pumps originated by Gaede in 1913, Holweck in 1923, and Siegbahn in 1944, operates relative to a backing pressure of about 10^{-1} torr and provides an inlet pressure of 10^{-8} torr and down to 5×10^{-10} torr and below, provided that suitable bake-out is practiced. In the turbomolecular pump, the rotor consists of a special arrangement of separated, slotted discs on a ball-bearing-mounted shaft. These discs are interleaved between similar stationary slotted vanes attached to the cylindrical housing. The rotor is driven at speeds of 16 000 rpm or greater to achieve movement of the gas from the inlet to the discharge outlet by virtue of a complex entrainment and drag of the gas within the wedge-shaped channels formed between the angled slots in the adjacent rotor and stator discs. As back-streaming is virtually absent (there is no pump fluid as in a vapor pump, only a modest amount of lubrication on the shielded axle bearings), turbomolecular pumps in a range of sizes are being increasingly used on systems demanding the production of fluid-free high and ultrahigh vacuum. Examples are particle accelerators where very low pressures are needed and turbomolecular pumps are used in conjunction with sputter-ion pumps after the initial pumping by conventional mechanical rotary gas-ballast pumps, and in modern electron microscopes and other specialized instruments utilized in surface science studies, especially where high-speed pumping with freedom from oil contamination at pressures below 10^{-6} is demanded.

Cryogenic pumping is presently receiving much attention. Here, basically, the provision is, within an initially evacuated system, a surface which is at such a low temperature that gas impinging on it is condensed. For example, if the surface is maintained at the temperature of liquid helium ($-269°C$), all other gases have insignificantly low vapor pressures at this temperature and molecules of these gases impinging on the surface would remain there. A pumping speed for nitrogen of nearly 12 liters sec^{-1} cm^{-2} of cooled surface is hence theoretically possible. Liquid nitrogen, together with molecular sieve and other sorbent surfaces, and also liquid-hydrogen ($-253°C$, at which the vapor pressure of solid nitrogen is 10^{-10} torr) and liquid-helium cooled metallic surfaces are being actively investigated with the possibility of providing very high pumping speeds (10^6 liters/sec is not out of question) in space simulators and other plant.

Vacuum Gauges A considerable problem in vacuum technique is that there is only one straightforward gauge able to measure low gas pressures absolutely in the sense that its calibration is independent of the nature of the gas and can be directly referred to millimeters of mercury: the McLeod gauge (Fig. 3).

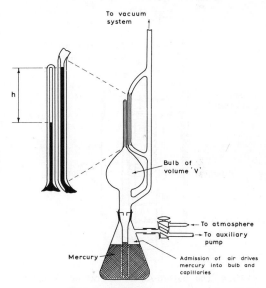

FIG. 3. The McLeod gauge.

The McLeod gauge is a compression device, i.e., the gas is compressed from an initial bulb volume V into a small diameter capillary tube of volume v per unit length so that it occupies a length h of this capillary. With the setting indicated in Fig. 3, the pressure p is given by the equation

$$p = \frac{v}{V} h^2$$

where p is in torr if h is in millimeters and with v and V in the same units.

This gauge is clumsy, contains mercury and

does not record correctly the partial pressure due to any condensable vapors present. Indeed, it is best to avoid it on most vacuum systems, but it is a virtually indispensable reference gauge for calibration work.

There are several alternatives, but none of them are absolute gauges and their calibrations all depend on the nature of the gas. Of the many possibilities, the thermal conductivity gauges of the Pirani and thermocouple types are useful within the pressure range from 10^{-4} to 10 torr, and operate by virtue of the dependence of the thermal conductivity of a gas on the pressure at low pressures. Two types of ionization gauge are valuable below 10^{-3} torr. The first of these is the Penning cold-cathode gauge with a range from 5×10^{-3} to 10^{-7} torr which has been extended in the inverted magnetron type (Redhead gauge) to 10^{-11} torr or below. The second is the hot-cathode ionization gauge of which the most widely used pattern is the Bayard-Alpert gauge (Fig. 4) which has become almost indispensable

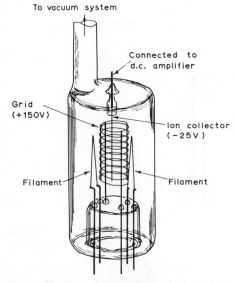

To vacuum system

Connected to d.c. amplifier

Grid (+150V)

Ion collector (−25V)

Filament   Filament

FIG. 4. The Bayard-Alpert hot-cathode ionization gauge.

as a measuring instrument on ultrahigh-vacuum systems and has a range from 10^{-3} to 5×10^{-11} torr.

Within the hot-cathode ionization gauge, positive ions are created by impact with the residual gas molecules of the thermally emitted electrons in their paths to the positive grid (at about + 150 volts w.r.t. the thermionic filament). These positive ions are attracted to the negative ion collector (at − 25 to − 50 volts) where the positive ion current as recorded by a calibrated dc amplifier is directly proportional to the gas pressure for a given gas and electron current. In order to minimize electron emission from the collector (indistinguishable from the arrival of positive

ions) brought about by its irradiation with x-rays produced on arrival of electrons at the positive grid, this collector is made of a thin central wire of insignificant interception of x-rays in the Bayard-Alpert gauge.

Such a gauge will typically have a sensitivity for nitrogen of about 20 $torr^{-1}$, i.e., the positive ion current will be 20 μA with an electron current of 1 mA at a nitrogen pressure of 10^{-3} torr and it will decrease in direct proportion to the pressure.

These ionization gauges of both the hot- and cold-cathode varieties have a pumping action due to removal of positive ions to the collector and to the glass walls. This pumping action has been utilized in small glass systems to create an ultra-high vacuum. Initially, a pressure of 10^{-7} torr or below is established by a diffusion pump in the thoroughly baked ionization gauge. The gauge is then isolated from the pumps by a bakeable metal or greaseless glass valve. Subsequent operation of the gauge then reduces the pressure to the order of 10^{-10} torr. This technique, introduced by Alpert in 1950, has now been replaced by plant employing mercury or oil diffusion pumps with bakeable cold traps and metal gasket sealing, by the use of sputter-ion pumps and by cryopumping.

In the measurement of gas pressure the determination of the partial pressures of the constituent gases is often as important as a knowledge of the total pressure. Gas analyzers for this purpose are based on the mass spectrometer of the magnetic deflection type, on the radio-frequency mass spectrometer, and on the quadrupole mass spectrometer. These gas analyzers also play an important part in leak detection techniques.

The applications of vacuum techniques are numerous and include the vacuum coating of substrates with metallic and insulating films in the production of optical mirrors, electrical resistors and capacitors, microminiature solid-state circuits, antireflection and enhanced reflection coatings on glass, conducting glass, interference filters, sorption and chemically reactive layers, etc. Further important fields of activity are the electron tube industry, vacuum drying and freeze drying, vacuum impregnation, distillation and molecular distillation, vacuum metallurgy including metal degassing, and space simulation.

J. YARWOOD
K. J. CLOSE

References

Dushman, S., "Scientific Foundations of Vacuum Technique," New York, John Wiley & Sons, Inc., 1962; second edition revised by Lafferty, J. M., Ed.

Yarwood, J., "High Vacuum Technique," London, Chapman and Hall, Ltd., 1967.

Power, B. D., "High Vacuum Pumping Equipment," London, Chapman and Hall Ltd., 1966.

Cross-references: DIFFUSION IN LIQUIDS, IONIZATION, KINETIC THEORY.

VAPOR PRESSURE AND EVAPORATION

Vapor Pressure Vapor pressure is the term applied to the driving force behind the apparently universal tendency for liquids and solids to disperse into the gaseous phase. All known liquids and solids possess this fundamental property, although in some cases it is too minute to be measurable. A typical liquid will exert a vapor pressure which is constant and reproducible. This pressure is dependent only upon the temperature of the system, and increases with increasing temperatures.

The molecular theory explains the phenomenon of vapor pressure through molecular activity. The molecules of a liquid are in rapid motion, even though they are in contact with each other. This motion or activity increases with temperature. At the vapor-liquid interface, this motion results in diffusion of some molecules from the liquid into the vapor. The attraction between molecules is strong, and some of the molecules dispersed into the vapor return to the liquid. The net number of molecules escaping produces the vapor pressure. For all practical purposes, this vapor pressure can be assumed constant whether the system is at equilibrium or not, due to the extremely high rate of molecular diffusion at the interface of the two phases.

In solids, the attractive forces of the molecules are so dominant that each is more or less frozen in place. Some diffusion does occur, however, as evidenced by the evaporation of ice, the odor of moth balls, and the slow diffusion or alloy formation of some metals kept in intimate contact. This vapor pressure increases with temperature, but is also a function of the molecular arrangement of the solid. As some solids such as sulfur are heated and molecular rearrangements take place, forming another allotrope of the same element, the vapor pressure changes sharply as this rearrangement occurs.

Vapor pressure can only be exhibited when the molecular activity is at a low enough level to permit continuous contact of the molecules and thus formation of a liquid. The maximum temperature at which this is possible is a fundamental property and is called the *critical temperature*. Above this temperature the material cannot be compressed to form a liquid, and only one phase results. This temperature is $374.0^\circ C$ ($705.4^\circ F$) for water and $-240.0^\circ C$ ($-399.8^\circ F$) for hydrogen.

The fundamental relationship between temperature and vapor pressure can be derived from thermodynamic laws. With certain limiting assumptions, the Clausius-Clapeyron equation is most often applied:

$$\frac{dp}{dT} = \frac{qP}{RT^2}$$

$\dfrac{dp}{dt}$ = slope of vapor pressure vs temperature

curve at the point in question in cm mercury per $^\circ C$

q = heat of vaporization in calories per gram mol

P = pressure in cm of mercury

R = gas constant in calories per $^\circ C$ per gram mol

T = temperature in Kelvin

Because of these limiting assumptions, the integrated form of this equation is used in practice primarily as a guide to develop methods of correlating and plotting vapor pressure data.

The vapor pressure of a solution containing a nonvolatile substance (e.g., salt in water) is lower than that of the pure liquid. This phenomenon can be explained by interference with the liquid molecular activity by the dissolved substances. The relationship between this vapor pressure depression and the concentration of the dissolved substance is valid for most substances at low concentrations. It was found to be dependent on the relative numbers of molecules of the solute and the solvent, and allowed accurate determinations of molecular weights of unknown solutes. If the Clausius-Clapeyron equation given above is combined with the above concentration relationship, it can be shown that:

$$\Delta T = \frac{RT^2}{q} \cdot C$$

where ΔT is the elevation of the boiling point. and C is the mol ratio of solute to solvent. This defines the effect of any solute on the vapor pressure exhibited by any solvent of latent heat q.

In the same manner, the vapor pressure of one component of a solution of two liquids has a different relationship with temperature than if it were pure. For many liquid mixtures, such as most hydrocarbon mixtures, the vapor pressures of the components vary directly from that exhibited in the pure form as their molar concentration in the solution. This relationship is known as Raoult's law:

$$\text{Partial pressure} = P_0 x$$

where x is the molar concentration of the component in the liquid and P_0 is the vapor pressure of the pure component at the same temperature as the mixture. A mixture following this rule is called an *ideal* solution, and its total volume is the sum of its components' volume.

If the gas phase above the liquid is also "ideal," the partial pressure of a component in this phase is equal to the total system pressure times the mole fraction of the component in the gas phase. This is called Dalton's law:

$$\text{Partial pressure} = P_t y$$

Combining these two formulas, it can be seen that:

$$\frac{y}{x} = \frac{P_0}{P_t} = K$$

for any particular temperature. This relationship can largely define many very complex liquid mixtures if the pressures used in the correlation are corrected by experimental data for deviation from the ideal.

A different relationship results if two liquids are relatively immiscible in each other. Molecular interference is minimal, and the total pressure exerted is equal to the sum of that of the individual pure components. The fundamental property of vapor pressure is thus dependent on temperature and composition of the material considered. These known and reproducible relationships have great technical application.

Vapor pressure relations can be used to determine heats of solution, heats of sublimation, and heats of fusion. Problems dealing with the solution of gases in liquids and adsorption of gases by solids are best handled by vapor pressure concepts. In dealing with solutions of miscible liquids, the most simple and useful relationship involves plotting the mole fraction y of one component in the vapor against x, the mole fraction of the component in the liquid. The ratio of y/x is called the phase equilibrium constant K and is used for definition of bubble points and dew points of simple and complex hydrocarbon mixtures over temperature and pressure ranges to near the critical.

Some equations of state also define vapor pressure relationships. One of the most recognized is that developed by Benedict, Webb, and Rubin due to its ability to predict P-V-T properties in the two-phase region and to describe behavior of the superheated vapor. See *J. Chem. Phys.*, **8**, 334 (1940); ibid., **10**, 747 (1942); and *Chem. Eng. Progr.*, **47** (1951).

Evaporation The above effects of mixtures and of solutes on vapor pressure of a component are the very reasons why continuous generation of vapor (or *evaporation*) is the major tool of most process separations.

These effects permit us to separate salts from solutions, to separate liquid components from mixtures, and to use the energy relationships in process control of all kinds.

When molecules of a liquid do leave the surface and become vapor, they do so by overcoming the rather large attractive forces existing when they were in the liquid state. These forces were large since the molecules were in very close proximity in the liquid. Overcoming these attractive forces requires *energy*, heat energy, this is named the "*latent heat*" or "heat of vaporization" of the fluid. In general, this is in terms of heat units per weight unit of material, such as Btu per pound, or calories per gram. In magnitude, latent heat will decrease as the liquid temperature increases or as the kinetic energy of the molecules increases. At the critical temperature, there is no latent heat—the molecules are in such an excited state that formation of a liquid is not possible.

For continuous evaporation, a continuous supply of energy is required. An available utility such as steam is a typical source.

Depending on the process, the evaporation is done:

(1) In equipment named "evaporators" such as the popular LTV of forced or natural circulation design used in acid concentration, salt production, sugar solution concentration and others.

(2) In processing distillation towers in a stepwise manner, tray to tray, resulting in a slight change in composition at each tray until required terminal conditions of overhead and bottom composition are reached.

(3) In reactors of various designs where one or more components are driven off, frequently by the heat of reaction.

(4) In "cooling towers" where the desired effect is not the separation or concentration of components but the use of the latent heat of evaporating water to remove unwanted process heat.

(5) In all steam generating boilers.

(6) In any process step where a liquid/vapor phase change occurs.

The concentration and energy relationships discussed before apply.

Evaporation is thus the most widely used tool of nature and of industry. For this reason, an intimate knowledge of the theory of heat transfer, of the large quantity of experimental data available, and of the more sophisticated methods of utilizing equations of state to correlate these data, are all essential to understand and properly develop almost any industrial process.

DOUGLAS L. ALLEN

Cross-references: GAS LAWS, HEAT TRANSFER, KINETIC THEORY, LIQUID STATE, MOLECULES AND MOLECULAR STRUCTURE, SOLID-STATE PHYSICS.

VECTOR PHYSICS

The Emergence of Vectors in Physics A physical variable whose values can be specified by single numbers is called a *scalar concept*. The number 212 on the Fahrenheit thermometer specifies the boiling temperature of water at standard pressure. Temperature then is a scalar concept. By contrast, even when a suitable reference frame has been selected, the instantaneous velocity of a rocket is not fully described by stating that its speed is 2000 mph. If one also designates the *direction* of the motion (say by stating that it heads northeast and climbs at elevation 60°), then the velocity is unambiguously described. Velocity is an example of a *vector concept*.

Some of the special properties of vector concepts have been recognized for hundreds of years, e.g., the ancient fact that forces combine according to the familiar parallelogram law (see article on STATICS). Mathematical tools for

dealing with directed quantities in three dimensions are outstanding products of nineteenth century mathematics. It now seems entirely natural to express key propositions of classical physics using vector algebra and vector calculus. A few decades ago, however, this was a controversial subject. Between 1891 and 1894, Peter G. Tait, Oliver Heaviside, Josiah Willard Gibbs, and others published fiery articles (still exciting reading) in the British journal *Nature*. Tait was a devoted promoter of quaternions, developed by his mentor, William Rowan Hamilton, as the proper tool for spatial physics. Gibbs, familiar with the work of Hamilton and also the more general theories of H. Grassmann, had devised his own treatment of physical problems. Heaviside was an indomitable advocate of the views of Gibbs. All of these men left their imprint on mathematics and physics. The notation of Gibbs, which mainly is followed here, has been particularly influential in the contemporary applications of vector mathematics.

Vector Algebra To the question, "What is a vector?," one may give several reasonably respectable elementary answers. A vector is an arrow of a particular length and direction. A vector is a class of equivalent arrows. A vector is an ordered pair of points. A vector is a class of equivalent ordered pairs of points. A vector is an ordered triple of numbers. A vector is an ordered sequence of n numbers (which is called a scalar if $n = 1$!). A vector is one of the undefined elements of a vector space. Each answer makes sense in its own context. The last answer provides a pattern which includes the others and offers the quickest approach to the albegra of vectors.

A *vector space* is an algebraic structure whose elements are called vectors (usually denoted here by boldface type: **A**, **B**, **C**, etc.), whose two operations are called *addition* and *multiplication by numbers* (we use real numbers throughout), and for which certain postulates are satisfied. These postulates should be regarded as a catalog of fundamental properties of such a structure. Other properties may be derived from them. The postulates may be stated as follows:

(1) For every pair of vectors **A**, **B** there is a vector sum such that

$$\mathbf{A} + \mathbf{B} = \mathbf{B} + \mathbf{A}$$

(2) For every triple of vectors, **A**, **B**, **C**, we have the equality

$$(\mathbf{A} + \mathbf{B}) + \mathbf{C} = \mathbf{A} + (\mathbf{B} + \mathbf{C})$$

(3) There is a null vector **O**, such that for every vector **A**,

$$\mathbf{A} + \mathbf{O} = \mathbf{A}$$

(4) Every vector **A** has an opposite vector $-\mathbf{A}$, such that

$$\mathbf{A} + (-\mathbf{A}) = \mathbf{O}$$

(5) For every number c and every vector **A** there is a vector $c\mathbf{A}$ such that

$$c\mathbf{A} = \mathbf{A}c$$

(6) For every pair of numbers c, c' and every vector **A**,

$$(c + c')\mathbf{A} = c\mathbf{A} + c'\mathbf{A}, \qquad c(c'\mathbf{A}) = (cc')\mathbf{A}$$

(7) For every pair of vectors **A**, **B** and every number c,

$$c(\mathbf{A} + \mathbf{B}) = c\mathbf{A} + c\mathbf{B}$$

(8) The particular product $1\mathbf{A}$ is equal to **A**.

The geometric and physical significance of this list of algebraic properties is more clear when one considers suitable definitions of the two operations for particular vector spaces. For example, if the vectors represent forces, and hence are drawn as arrows, addition is composition of forces by the parallelogram rule, while multiplication by a number is merely an alteration of the magnitude (denoted by vertical bars) of the force according to the rule: $|c\mathbf{F}| = |c||\mathbf{F}|$. Multiplication by a negative number reverses direction. As a second example, if the vectors are triples of numbers (as in statics when components are listed), the two operations are at once defined thus:

$$(a_1, a_2, a_3) + (b_1, b_2, b_3)$$
$$= (a_1 + b_1, a_2 + b_2, a_3 + b_3)$$
$$c(a_1, a_2, a_3) = (ca_1, ca_2, ca_3)$$

One can easily verify that triples satisfy all eight postulates.

Two additional operations are of particular importance in physics. First, an *inner product* associates with each pair of vectors **A**, **B** a number, designated by $\mathbf{A} \cdot \mathbf{B}$, such that for all vectors **A**, **B**, **C** and every number c, the following identities hold:

(9) $\mathbf{A} \cdot \mathbf{B} = \mathbf{B} \cdot \mathbf{A}$
(10) $\mathbf{A} \cdot (\mathbf{B} + \mathbf{C}) = \mathbf{A} \cdot \mathbf{B} + \mathbf{A} \cdot \mathbf{C}$
(11) $c(\mathbf{A} \cdot \mathbf{B}) = (c\mathbf{A}) \cdot \mathbf{B}$

A final postulate for a vector space with inner product (called a *euclidean vector space*) is

(12) $\mathbf{A} \cdot \mathbf{A} = 0$ if and only if $\mathbf{A} = \mathbf{O}$, and
$\mathbf{A} \cdot \mathbf{A} > 0$ if and only if $\mathbf{A} \neq \mathbf{O}$.

The physical concept of work provides a strong motivation for the usual definition of inner product. A force **F** and a displacement **S** are assigned a work $|\mathbf{F}||\mathbf{S}| \cos(\mathbf{F}, \mathbf{S})$ where $(\mathbf{F}, \mathbf{S})$ is the angle between vectors parallel to **F** and **S**. The defining formula for inner products of arrows is taken to be

$$\mathbf{A} \cdot \mathbf{B} = |\mathbf{A}||\mathbf{B}| \cos(\mathbf{A}, \mathbf{B})$$

Similarly, for triples

$$(a_1, a_2, a_3) \cdot (b_1, b_2, b_3) = a_1b_1 + a_2b_2 + a_3b_3$$

To prove that these two definitions satisfy postulates (9) through (12) is by no means trivial.

Similarly, an *outer product* associates with

each ordered pair of vectors **A**, **B** a vector designated by **A X B**, and possesses the following key properties. For all vectors **A**, **B**, **C** and every number c,

(13) $\mathbf{A} \mathbf{X} \mathbf{B} = -\mathbf{B} \mathbf{X} \mathbf{A}$

(14) $\mathbf{A} \mathbf{X} (\mathbf{B} + \mathbf{C}) = \mathbf{A} \mathbf{X} \mathbf{B} + \mathbf{A} \mathbf{X} \mathbf{C}$

(15) $(c\mathbf{A}) \mathbf{X} \mathbf{B} = c(\mathbf{A} \mathbf{X} \mathbf{B})$

(16) $\mathbf{A} \mathbf{X} (\mathbf{B} \mathbf{X} \mathbf{C}) = (\mathbf{A} \cdot \mathbf{C})\mathbf{B} - (\mathbf{A} \cdot \mathbf{B})\mathbf{C}$

The physical concept of moment of a force about a point leads naturally to a definition of outer product for arrows. Let **F** be a vector representing a force acting at a point Q and for some point P let **R** denote the arrow PQ. The moment **M** of the force about the point P has magnitude given as follows:

$$|\mathbf{M}| = |\mathbf{R} \mathbf{X} \mathbf{F}| = |\mathbf{R}||\mathbf{F}| \sin(\mathbf{R}, \mathbf{F})$$

If $\sin(\mathbf{R}, \mathbf{F}) \neq 0$, the direction of **M** is perpendicular to the plane of the point P and the arrow **F**. We then write

$$\mathbf{M} = \mathbf{R} \mathbf{X} \mathbf{F} = [|\mathbf{R}||\mathbf{F}| \sin(\mathbf{R}, \mathbf{F})]\mathbf{N}$$

where **N** is a vector of magnitude 1 (a *unit vector*) perpendicular to the **PF** plane. The sense of **N** is usually taken so that the rotation of **R** into the direction of **F** determines **N** by the right-hand rule. And for triples:

$$(a_1, a_2, a_3) \mathbf{X} (b_1, b_2, b_3)$$

$$= (a_2 b_3 - a_3 b_2, a_3 b_1 - a_1 b_3, a_1 b_2 - a_2 b_1)$$

For either of these models (arrows or triples), property (16) is quite remarkable. By applying it in two different ways to $\mathbf{A} \mathbf{X} [\mathbf{A} \mathbf{X} (\mathbf{A} \mathbf{X} \mathbf{B})]$, the reader may show, with the aid of property (13), that $\mathbf{A} \cdot \mathbf{A} \mathbf{X} \mathbf{B}$ vanishes for all vectors **A**, **B**. Property (16) also leads easily to the Jacobi identity:

$$\mathbf{A} \mathbf{X} (\mathbf{B} \mathbf{X} \mathbf{C}) + \mathbf{B} \mathbf{X} (\mathbf{C} \mathbf{X} \mathbf{A}) + \mathbf{C} \mathbf{X} (\mathbf{A} \mathbf{X} \mathbf{B}) = \mathbf{O}$$

For the purposes of simple physical or geometric applications, the transition from arrows to triples is immediate. For a given reference frame, one lets (a_1, a_2, a_3) denote the three components (parallel to axes) of the arrow **A**. These components may be computed by use of the inner product formula. Let $\mathbf{i}_1, \mathbf{i}_2, \mathbf{i}_3$ be unit vectors parallel to three mutually perpendicular positive coordinate axes. Then, relative to these chosen axes, an arrow **A** has components as follows;

$$a_1 = \mathbf{A} \cdot \mathbf{i}_1, \quad a_2 = \mathbf{A} \cdot \mathbf{i}_2, \quad a_3 = \mathbf{A} \cdot \mathbf{i}_3$$

Note that for each subscript j, since $|\mathbf{i}_j| = 1$, we have

$$a_j = |\mathbf{A}| \cos(\mathbf{A}, \mathbf{i}_j)$$

The preceding formula is used in statics for computing components of a force. One may think of each arrow **A** as represented by the triple (a_1, a_2, a_3) of its components. In fact, one can make the merger complete by resolving each arrow into a sum of arrows parallel to the chosen axes:

$$\mathbf{A} = a_1 \mathbf{i}_1 + a_2 \mathbf{i}_2 + a_3 \mathbf{i}_3$$

In this article, arrows and triples appear as alternate but related representations of physical concepts. For details on the ideas of this section see reference 5.

Vector Concepts in Elementary Geometry and Kinematics In particle kinematics the most primitive ideas are position and displacement. Relative to an origin O the arrow OP is called the *position vector* of a particle at the point P. The displacement from P to P' is described by the arrow $\mathbf{D} = PP'$. One can easily see that $OP + PP' = OP'$, or $\mathbf{R} + \mathbf{D} = \mathbf{R}'$. It is natural now to introduce the notation of vector subtraction:

$$\mathbf{R}' - \mathbf{R} = \mathbf{R}' + (-\mathbf{R}) = \mathbf{D}$$

Hence, in vector geometry, a *displacement is equal to a difference of position vectors*. For a time interval Δt we often write the displacement as $\Delta \mathbf{R}$.

From the definitions of arrow operations, a number of geometric conclusions may be drawn:

(1) Non-null vectors **A**, **B** are *parallel* (or antiparallel) if and only if $\mathbf{A} \mathbf{X} \mathbf{B} = \mathbf{O}$.

(2) Non-null vectors **A**, **B** are *perpendicular* if and only if $\mathbf{A} \cdot \mathbf{B} = 0$.

(3) An *equation for a plane* through a fixed point P' with position vector **R**' and normal to a fixed vector **N** is given by $(\mathbf{R} - \mathbf{R}') \cdot \mathbf{N} = 0$. This means for any point $P \neq P'$ on the plane, the arrow P'P is perpendicular to **N**.

(4) Similarly, an *equation for a line* through P' parallel to **N** is given by $(\mathbf{R} - \mathbf{R}') \mathbf{X} \mathbf{N} = \mathbf{O}$.

For further applications of vectors to elementary geometry, see reference 15 or Appendix 2 of reference 5. Note that if one treats the position vector of P as a triple (x_1, x_2, x_3), using coordinates, instead of as an arrow, the results just described are still valid.

If we define *velocity* as displacement per time, then we may represent the vector **V** as a derivative:

$$\mathbf{V} = \lim_{\Delta t \to 0}(\Delta \mathbf{R}/\Delta t) = d\mathbf{R}/dt$$

Similarly, acceleration **A** is defined by $\mathbf{A} = d\mathbf{V}/dt$. Here again, when a reference frame has been chosen, one may employ triples:

$$\mathbf{V} = (dx_1/dt, dx_2/dt, dx_3/dt)$$

$$\mathbf{A} = (d^2 x_1/dt^2, d^2 x_2/dt^2, d^2 x_3/dt^2)$$

In numerous physical applications, the use of vectors for geometric descriptions is effective. Consider a gas escaping through a surface element of area Δa. Call the outward unit vector normal to the surface element **N**. The area element may be treated as a vector

$$\Delta \mathbf{A} = (\Delta a)\mathbf{N}$$

If the velocity of escape is uniformly **V**, the outward flux (in particles per second) is given

by

$$\Delta(\text{flux}) = \rho \mathbf{V} \cdot \Delta \mathbf{A}$$

where ρ is number of particles per unit volume. Formulas for efflux under more general conditions may be found in books on kinetic theory, or in reference 5.

For a rigid body spinning about a fixed axis, the angular velocity is a vector $\boldsymbol{\omega}$ directed along the axis of rotation according to the right-hand rule. Its time derivative is the angular acceleration $\boldsymbol{\alpha}$. If we take the origin of position vectors on the axis, the induced velocity and acceleration for a point of position vector $\mathbf{R}$ are given by

$$\mathbf{V} = \boldsymbol{\omega} \textbf{ X } \mathbf{R}$$

$$\mathbf{A} = \boldsymbol{\alpha} \textbf{ X } \mathbf{R} + \boldsymbol{\omega} \textbf{ X } (\boldsymbol{\omega} \textbf{ X } \mathbf{R})$$

The second term in the acceleration formula is called *centripetal acceleration*. Note that when $\alpha = \mathbf{O}$, $\mathbf{A} = \boldsymbol{\omega} \textbf{ X } \mathbf{V}$ (see article on ROTATION — CIRCULAR MOTION). The preceding formula for centripetal acceleration in uniform circular motion has an interesting rotational analogue:

$$\boldsymbol{\alpha} = \boldsymbol{\omega}_p \textbf{ X } \boldsymbol{\omega}_s$$

The subscripts stand, respectively, for precession and spin. This new formula describes uniform precession for gyroscopic motion (See article on GYROSCOPE).

Vector Concepts in Dynamics Newton's second law (see article on DYNAMICS) may be summarized in vector equations:

$$\mathbf{F}_1 + \mathbf{F}_2 + \cdots + \mathbf{F}_n = (d/dt)(m\mathbf{V}) = m\mathbf{A}$$

The addition in the left member is vector addition. The product in the right member is multiplication of a vector by a number. The left member may be written as

$$\sum_1^n \mathbf{F}_i = \overline{\mathbf{F}}$$

where $\overline{\mathbf{F}}$ denotes a resultant force. The abbreviated equation of motion

$$\overline{\mathbf{F}} = m\mathbf{A}$$

where $\overline{\mathbf{F}}$ and $\mathbf{A}$ stand for arrows, provides an expressive condensation of a basic physical proposition. The same equation serves as the key to analytical procedures if triples are used instead of arrows:

$$(\overline{f}_1, \overline{f}_2, \overline{f}_3) = m(d^2 x_1/dt^2, d^2 x_2/dt^2, d^2 x_3/dt^2)$$

This vector equation yields three component equations:

$$\overline{f}_i = m \, d^2 x_i/dt^2, \quad i = 1, 2, 3$$

In vector physics, the arrow representation of vector concepts repeatedly provides an easily visualized theoretical development, while the triple representation, for well-chosen axes, pro-

vides the strongest approach to computation. Some mechanical concepts are next listed in both forms.

Momentum of a particle:

$$m\mathbf{V} = m(dx_1/dt, dx_2/dt, dx_3/dt)$$

Impulse exerted by a force:

$$\int_{t_0}^{t_1} \mathbf{F} dt = \left(\int_{t_0}^{t_1} f_1 dt, \int_{t_0}^{t_1} f_2 dt, \int_{t_0}^{t_1} f_3 dt \right)$$

Work done by a force:

$$\int_{\mathbf{R}'}^{\mathbf{R}''} \mathbf{F} \cdot d\mathbf{R} = \int_{x_1'}^{x_1''} f_1 dx_1 + \int_{x_2'}^{x_2''} f_2 dx_2$$

$$+ \int_{x_3'}^{x_3''} f_3 dx_3$$

The integrands of the preceding equation must, of course, assume the values dictated by the path along which the force is allowed to act. For rotation about an axis, angular momentum is given by $I\omega$, I being the moment of inertia. In more general situations, the equivalent notion of moment of momentum is appropriate: $\mathbf{H} = \int \mathbf{R} \textbf{ X } \mathbf{V} dm$. The details are not discussed here, but, corresponding to $\sum \mathbf{F} = (d/dt)(m\mathbf{V})$ we may write equations of the form

$$\sum \mathbf{R} \textbf{ X } \mathbf{F} = \frac{d}{dt} \mathbf{H}$$

In rotation about a fixed axis, the second equation takes the familiar form

$$\sum \mathbf{M} = \frac{d}{dt} (I\omega) = I\boldsymbol{\alpha}$$

where each $\mathbf{M}$ is a moment about the axis, interpreted as a vector along it.

Vector Fields and Their Uses A scalar field (scalar point function) assigns to each point (and hence to each position vector) in a suitable domain a particular number. For example, to each point, $\mathbf{R}$, in a room is assigned a number called temperature, $\theta(\mathbf{R})$, another number called density, $\rho(\mathbf{R})$, another number called height above sea level, $h(\mathbf{R})$. Similarly, to each point in a room may be assigned a vector called gravitational field intensity, $\mathbf{G}(\mathbf{R})$, another vector called velocity (e.g., of air currents), $\mathbf{V}(\mathbf{R})$, another vector called magnetic flux density, $\mathbf{B}(\mathbf{R})$. These exemplify vector fields. When such scalar or vector fields have derivatives, important new fields may be derived. The pressure function in an ideal fluid is a scalar field $p(\mathbf{R})$. A related vector field is the pressure gradient, $\text{grad } p(\mathbf{R})$. The *pressure gradient* is a function assigning to each point the direction and magnitude of the maximum directional derivative of p. This new

vector function is often written ∇p. Pressure gradient is intimately related to buoyant force: the net buoyant force per volume at $\mathbf{R}$ equals $-\nabla p(\mathbf{R})$. Thus an equation for hydrostatic equilibrium is

$$\rho(\mathbf{R})\mathbf{G}(\mathbf{R}) = \nabla p(\mathbf{R})$$

In terms of ordinary coordinates, the vector ∇p may be represented as triple:

$$\nabla p = (\partial p/\partial x_1, \partial p/\partial x_2, \partial p/\partial x_3)$$

Many other examples of gradient fields occur in physics. For instance, if a field intensity is conservative, it equals minus the gradient of a suitable potential function.

One simple vector field assigns to each position vector $\mathbf{R}$ the corresponding velocity vector, $\mathbf{V}(\mathbf{R})$. For a rigid body rotating about a fixed axis, taking the origin on the axis, a formula for the velocity field is

$$\mathbf{V}(\mathbf{R}) = \boldsymbol{\omega} \times \mathbf{R}$$

where $\boldsymbol{\omega}$ is the instantaneous angular velocity. For the most general motion of a rigid body the formula is almost as simple: for any fixed point $\mathbf{R}'$ of the body,

$$\mathbf{V}(\mathbf{R}) = \mathbf{V}(\mathbf{R}') + \boldsymbol{\omega} \times (\mathbf{R} - \mathbf{R}')$$

For details see reference 5.

The velocity pattern for a fluid will usually be more complicated than the one just considered. Compressions or expansions might occur. This sort of tendency may, at each point, be evaluated by the net outward flux per volume, called the *divergence* of the velocity field, written div $\mathbf{V}(\mathbf{R})$. Since this flux is measured in terms of volume rather than number of particles (as on p. 985), $\rho(\mathbf{R})$ is 1, and we have

$$\text{div } \mathbf{V}(\mathbf{R}) = \lim_{\Delta v \to 0} \frac{1}{\Delta v} \int_{\Delta a} \mathbf{V} \cdot d\mathbf{A}$$

Δa is the area of the solid element of volume Δv for which the net efflux per volume is expressed. Each such solid element contains the point with position vector $\mathbf{R}$. Divergence yields a scalar field for a given vector field. Using cartesian coordinate triples

$$\text{div }(v_1, v_2, v_3) = \partial v_1/\partial x_1 + \partial v_2/\partial x_2 + \partial v_3/\partial x_3$$

Since the net efflux per volume of mass is merely the rate of decrease of density, one can write at once the *equation of continuity* of hydromechanics

$$\text{div }(\rho \mathbf{V}) = -\partial \rho/\partial t$$

The concept of divergence has particular use in the theory of electromagnetism. For free space,

$$\text{div } \mathbf{B} = 0$$

$$\text{div } \mathbf{E} = 4\pi\rho$$

where $\mathbf{B}$ is the magnetic flux density and $\mathbf{E}$ the electric field intensity. This time ρ stands for electric charge density.

For a rigid body, the rotational aspect of a velocity field has been characterized by the vector $\boldsymbol{\omega}$. For a more general differentiable velocity field, one considers a derived vector function proportional to the local angular velocity vector. Only a formal cartesian expression for this new field, curl $\mathbf{V}$, is given here. For more general treatments not depending on particular coordinates, see reference 13.

$$\text{Curl }(v_1, v_2, v_3) = (\partial v_3/\partial x_2 - \partial v_2/\partial x_3,$$
$$\partial v_1/\partial x_3 - \partial v_3/\partial x_1,$$
$$\partial v_2/\partial x_1 - \partial v_1/\partial x_2)$$

The concept of curl plays a vital role in many parts of physics. A field intensity is conservative if and only if its curl vanishes. The interrelationships between electrical and magnetic fields are most concisely expressed in terms of curl (see Maxwell's equations in most books on electromagnetism).

The formal expressions for gradient, divergence, and curl suggest regarding

$$\nabla = \mathbf{i}_1 \, \partial/\partial x_1 + \mathbf{i}_2 \, \partial/\partial x_2 + \mathbf{i}_3 \, \partial/\partial x_3$$

as a vector operator. Here we have used $\mathbf{i}_1, \mathbf{i}_2, \mathbf{i}_3$ as unit vectors parallel to coordinate axes, i.e., as abbreviations for the triples $(1, 0, 0), (0, 1, 0)$, and $(0, 0, 1)$. With this convention we may write:

$$\text{grad } \rho = \nabla \rho$$

$$\text{div } \mathbf{V} = \nabla \cdot \mathbf{V}$$

$$\text{curl } \mathbf{V} = \nabla \times \mathbf{V}$$

For more information about formal uses of ∇ see Appendix 3 of reference 5 or 16.

Our defining equation for divergence is a local version of the following symbolic summary of the divergence theorem of Gauss:

$$\int_a \mathbf{V} \cdot d\mathbf{A} = \int_b \nabla \cdot \mathbf{V} \, dv$$

This theorem relates flux, associated with a continuously differentiable vector field $\mathbf{V}(\mathbf{R})$, through an oriented boundary surface a, to an integral over a suitable region b. The Gauss theorem is indispensable in electromagnetism, elasticity, hydrodynamics, magnetofluids, and potential theory. (See articles on ELECTROMAGNETIC THEORY and ELASTICITY as well as references 1, 4, 8, 12, and 15). A similar proposition relates a line integral around the boundary of an oriented surface to the surface integral of the normal component of the curl:

$$\oint \mathbf{V} \cdot d\mathbf{R} = \int_a \nabla \times \mathbf{V} \cdot d\mathbf{A}.$$

This important result, a form of Stokes' theorem, is applicable to computations of potential energy and of circulation in a flow. This theorem, properly interpreted in an elementary setting, is the fundamental theorem of calculus. It also plays an important role in the theory of differential forms (see references 2, 7, 9, and 14).

Extensions of Elementary Vector Physics In preceding sections, we considered several vector functions of position. The function $V(R) = \omega \times R$ is a *linear* function, and hence can be represented in matrix notation. Equations for changes of coordinates can be expressed as translations combined with linear transformations (usually orthogonal). Linear transformations also occur in expressions for strain in the theory of elasticity. Further details on linear transformations and vector physics[1,5,10,12] and treatments [1,2,7,9,13,17,] of vectors in a more advanced mathematical setting can be found in the literature.

In this article we have considered mainly three-dimensional vector spaces. For the use of four-dimensions in special relativity,[10,12] for vector treatments of variational mechanics,[6,10] and for higher dimensional vectors used in phase spaces,[5] and even for the use of vector ideas in thermodynamic theory,[11] see the references listed below. Note that references 3 and 12 emphasize the role of vector spaces in several branches of physical mathematics, and that reference 14 includes articles on several aspects of more sophisticated applicable mathematics.

DAN E. CHRISTIE

References

The subject of vector physics is so inclusive that a suitable reference list would be very long, including books on classical mechanics, vector and tensor analysis, linear algebra, etc. Longer bibliographies will be found in references 3, 5, and 12 below. Here we list only new or particularly pertinent sources.

1. Aris, R., "Vectors, Tensors, and the Basic Equations of Fluid Mechanics," Englewood Cliffs, N.J., Prentice-Hall, 1962.
2. Buck, R. C., "Advanced Calculus," Second edition, New York, McGraw-Hill Book Co., 1965.
3. Byron, F. W., Jr., and Fuller, R. W., "Mathematics of Classical and Quantum Physics," Vol. One, Reading, Mass., Addison-Wesley Publishing Co., 1969.
4. Cabannes, H., "Theoretical Magnetofluiddynamics," New York, Academic Press, 1970.
5. Christie, D. E., "Vector Mechanics," Second edition, New York, McGraw-Hill Book Co., 1964.
6. Coe, C. J., "Theoretical Mechanics. A Vectorial Treatment," New York, The Macmillan Co., 1938.
7. Edwards, H. M., "Advanced Calculus," Boston, Houghton-Mifflin Co., 1969.
8. Eskinazi, S., "Vector Mechanics of Fluids and Magnetofluids," New York, Academic Press, 1967.
9. Flanders, H., "Differential Forms with Applications to the Physical Sciences," New York, Academic Press, 1963.
10. Goldstein, H., "Classical Mechanics," Reading, Mass., Addison-Wesley, 1950.
11. Kestin, J., Chapter 10 of "A Course in Thermodynamics," Waltham, Mass., Blaisdell Publishing Co., 1966.
12. Kyrala, A., "Theoretical Physics: Applications of Vectors, Matrices, Tensors, and Quaternions," Philadelphia, W. B. Saunders Co., 1967.
13. Nickerson, H. K., Spencer, D. C., and Steenrod, N. E., "Advanced Calculus" (paperbound), New York, Van Nostrand Reinhold, 1959.
14. Roubine, E., ed., "Mathematics Applied to Physics," New York, Springer-Verlag, 1970. See especially article by G. A. Deschamps on applications of exterior differential forms.
15. Schwartz, M., Green, S., and Rutledge, W. A., "Vector Analysis with Applications to Geometry and Physics," New York, Harper and Row, 1960.
16. Spiegel, M. R., "Theory and Problems of Vector Analysis," Schaum, 1959.
17. Wrede, R. C., "Vector and Tensor Analysis," New York, John Wiley & Sons, 1963.

Cross-references: ELASTICITY, ELECTROMAGNETIC THEORY, FIELD THEORY, FLUID DYNAMICS, GYROSCOPE, MECHANICS, RELATIVITY, ROTATION–CIRCULAR MOTION, STATICS, TENSORS.

VELOCITY OF LIGHT

Every elementary electric charge occupies a small volume. The charge is surrounded by a radially directed electric field, the strength of which decreases by the square of distance. By any motion with a velocity $v > 0$ of the charge relative to some fixed point, the distance and/or direction is changed and, thereby, the (vector) value of the field strength at the point. Here the field change occurs a while after the moment of charge motion. Otherwise expressed, the field change propagates with a finite velocity, usually labeled c. Moreover, during the short time for the action from a *certain part* of the charge volume to pass the rest of it, the volume moves a small distance proportional to v/c. This very small displacement creates the magnetic field always associated with an electric field change. In fact, magnetism is due to a (usually very small) part of the electric field.

Any change in the electromagnetic field propagates with the very high velocity of $c = 3 \times 10^{10}$ cm/sec, called the velocity of light. For, if the charge motion happens to be an oscillation of frequency ν between 4×10^{14} and 8×10^{14} cps, we note the corresponding field variations as visible light. According to definition it is

$$c = \nu \cdot \lambda \tag{1}$$

where λ is the wavelength in vacuum. The movements of the elementary charges are

mostly oscillatory. By means of the field, after the delay due to c, they act on surrounding charges, and in that way all events in the atomistic world depend on the value of c. Therefore, the knowledge of c has turned out to be of extreme importance to our modern civilization.

The wave velocity according to Eq. (1) has a constant value, independent of all movements and, strictly speaking, independent of the medium where the propagation takes place. In a transparent body, in the intermediate space the action among the elementary charges of the atoms disperses with the velocity c. By inertia, the oscillating of the charges due to the active field is somewhat delayed as compared to the field. Now, the oscillating charge itself is a radiating source and its own delayed field interferes with the original one, creating a sum-wave, the velocity v of which is $v < c$. Exceptionally, in cases of resonance and absorption $v > c$. Our observation of light propagation in a substantial body relates to that slower interference wave. For the body, e.g., the medium of atmospheric air, we obtain corresponding to Eq. (1):

$$v = v \cdot \lambda_a \qquad (2)$$

From plain optical geometry we know that the refractive index of a medium is

$$n = \frac{c}{v} = \frac{\lambda}{\lambda_a} \qquad (3)$$

The technique for determining the wavelengths of light has progressed very far, and one can easily obtain an accurate value of n. For visible light, n depends on the wavelength used according to

$$n = A + \frac{B}{\lambda^2} + \frac{C}{\lambda^4} \qquad (4)$$

where A, B and C are positive constants. Close to resonance, the formula is not valid.

Direct determinations of the velocity of light, usually performed in air, are all based on the measurement of the time for a light pulse to cover a known distance. Such a pulse means an increase, followed by a decrease, of the amplitude of the light vibrations. What we observe is energy exchange associated with the amplitude changes, and as a result, we obtain the propagation velocity of the light energy. A change of amplitude is, however, equivalent to an interference among a series of adjacent wavelengths, since that change is created by just such an interference. The light pulse, therefore, consists of a whole group of adjacent wavelengths, interfering with each other. Interference is a sum-product. If the participating waves have different velocities, one will find by simple addition of two sine oscillations, that the group formed has a velocity different from those of the waves creating the group. On the surface

of a calm sea, we observe a group of waves moving forward. The waves are created at the back of the group, travel through it, and disappear at the front. The difference between wave and group velocity is directly proportional to the wavelength and to the dependence of the wave velocity on the wavelength. Thus, calling the group velocity u, we obtain the difference:

$$v - u = \lambda_a \cdot \frac{dv}{d\lambda_a} \qquad (5)$$

Analogously to Eq. (3), we introduce a "group index"

$$n_g = \frac{c}{u} \qquad (6)$$

If, as in the case of air, $dv/d\lambda_a$ is a small quantity, we get, after some recalculation,

$$n_g = n - \lambda \cdot \frac{dn}{d\lambda} \qquad (7)$$

From Eq. (4) it is evident that $dn/d\lambda$ is a negative quantity, i.e., $n_g > n$. In vacuum, all velocities are equal: $u = v = c$.

The group velocity refers to the energy transport. Thus, in a medium there are the original waves of vacuum velocity c. By interference with waves from local charge oscillators, they create a wave system characteristic of the medium being considered and with the velocity $v < c$. By external energy action, that system is divided into an increasing number of adjacent waves, again interfering, of "second order," thereby forming groups of velocity $u < v$ (if normally $dn/d\lambda < 0$). Application of Eq. (7) to Eq. (4) yields:

$$n_g = A + \frac{3B}{\lambda^2} + \frac{5C}{\lambda^4} \qquad (8)$$

In the case of visible light or $\lambda = 0.4 - 0.8\mu$ ($\mu = 0.001$ mm) and in dry air of $0°C$, 760 mm Hg, $A = 1.000287619$, $B = 16.204 \times 10^{-7}$, $C = 0.1391 \times 10^{-7}$ (based on values derived by Edlén). Inserting n_{0g} corresponding to the λ used, we get

$$n_g = 1 + \frac{n_{0g} - 1}{1 + \alpha t} \cdot \frac{p}{760} - 0.55 \times 10^{-7} \cdot \frac{e}{1 + \alpha t}$$

$$(9)$$

where t is expressed in degrees Celsius, p in millimeters Hg, e in millimeters Hg of humidity, and $\alpha = 1/273$. For visible light, the error of Eq. (9) is less than 5×10^{-8}.

There is an experimental check of Eq. (8) for glass and calcite. Their refraction is 1000 times that of air. In calcite the group velocity ellipsoid was situated inside the ordinary one (Bergstrand, 1954). A more accurate control is proposed by Danielmeyer and Weber (Danielmeyer, 1971).

For micro- and radar waves with $\lambda > 700\mu$ the influence of λ in Eq. (8) is insignificant. Increasing influence of humidity, however, makes

$$n = 1 + \left[\frac{103.64}{T}(p - e) + \right.$$
$$\left. + \frac{86.26}{T}\left(1 + \frac{5748}{T}\right)e\right] \times 10^{-6} \quad (10)$$

where $T = t + 273.16$. By using 103.64 in place of 103.49, as recommended by the International Association of Geodesy, the influence of a CO_2-term is partly compensated for. The uncertainty of Eq. (10) is about 5×10^{-7}.

There are a variety of methods for the determination of c. Among the direct ones, is the measurement of the travel time for a light pulse to cover a known distance. Usually there is a continuous series of pulses; i.e., the intensity is varied with a definite and known frequency. At every moment, there is a definite state of phase of the variation period. After reflection, the light returns, and one makes a phase comparison between emitted and received intensity. Thus, the intensity variation is used as a clock for the measurement of the running time. If the phase comparison is based on having the maximum of emitted light intensity coincide with the maximum of received intensity, the running time evidently is an even multiple of the period (=time) of a complete intensity variation cycle. Usually only one definite multiple number yields reasonable values, and there is no need for a special determination of the multiple.

The indirect methods are of much more varied character.

Determination of c Galileo was the first to try to show a finite light velocity. In his direct method, he used lanterns which could be screened off rapidly. The time elapsed on a distance of a few kilometers was, of course, too small to be observed visually.

In August 1676 at Paris, the Danish astronomer Ole Römer determined the revolution period of a satellite of Jupiter by its eclipse times into the planet's shadow. He used the result, 42 hours, to calculate the point of time for an eclipse occurring in November. It really occurred 10 minutes later. Römer explained this by the longer time for the light to reach the earth, now at a considerably greater distance from Jupiter. From the dimensions of the earth's orbit Römer defined c to be

$$c = 214\ 300\ \text{km/sec}$$

A modern value according to the same method is $299\ 840 \pm 60$ km/sec.

In 1725 the Englishman Bradley discovered astronomic aberration. Due to the velocity v of the earth in her orbit, the apparent direction to the stars normal to v is changed by v/c. Bradley could detect and measure the angle v/c because of its alternate sign for opposite parts of the earth orbit. Knowing v Bradley computed

$$c = 295\ 000\ \text{km/sec}$$

A modern value is $299\ 857 \pm 120$ km/sec.

In 1849 the Frenchman Fizeau took the next step. By projection of the image of a point source on the edge of a rapidly revolving cogged wheel, he got the required light pulse series. A blink or pulse passing through a cog interspace traveled the distance of 8633 meters to a reflector and back again along the optically identical path. Once more, now in the opposite direction, the pulse reached the cogged edge. For a suitable rotational speed the next cog interspace had now moved into position to let through the pulse; a case of "coincident maxs" (maxima). The time was computed from the revolution speed and the number of cogs. Fizeau's value was:

$$c = 315\ 300 \pm 500\ \text{km/sec}$$

In 1850, after an idea of Arago, using a point light source, Fizeau's compatriot Foucault directed a beam of constant intensity to a rapidly revolving plane mirror. During the time for the light to cover the distance to a second fixed mirror and back the revolving mirror had turned through a small angle, and the image of the light source was slightly displaced from its position when the mirror was stationary. Foucault's value was:

$$c = 298\ 000 \pm 500\ \text{km/sec}$$

In 1856 the German scientists Kohlrausch and Weber achieved a very important indirect determination. The magnetic field strength depends on v/c, the charge velocity v creating the magnetic field. Therefore, based on the same unit of force, the ratio between the unit of charge in electric and in magnetic measuring systems becomes c. Kohlrausch and Weber measured a charge (1) by its attraction to a second equal charge and (2) by the current produced at the passage of the charge through a galvanometer which showed a deflection due to the magnetic force. From $(1)/(2) = c$, they got:

$$c = 310\ 800\ \text{km/sec}$$

Rosa and Dorsey in 1906 measuring a capacity obtained $299\ 784 \pm 30$ km/sec.

In 1891 the Frenchman Blondlot transmitted Hertz waves along two straight and parallel wires, a Lecher guide system. After reflection, the waves created a standing wave system. Observing the nodal points Blondlot determined the wavelength. The frequency was known, and using Eq. (1) he obtained:

$$295\ 000 < c < 305\ 000\ \text{km/sec}$$

At this time, however, one was very uncertain as to the ratio between the velocities in vacuum and along the wires. Gutton solved this problem

in 1911 by aid of the Kerr cell, making possible light variations of a frequency equal to that applied to the Lecher system. In a Kerr cell, the light passes between two condenser plates, lowered into nitrobenzene. Due to the directive action of the electric field between the plates on the oblong dipole molecules, the fluid acquires optical double-refracting properties. As soon as the field ceases, the molecules recover their random directions through the influence of their thermal movements. Placing the cell between an optic polarizer and a normally oriented analyzer, the light intensity leaving the combination, within certain limits, is directly proportional to the voltage applied to the condenser. The voltage may be that from a high-frequency radio transmitter.

Later on, Gutton's compatriot Mercier derived a theoretical formula for the ratio between light velocity and the velocities of guided waves. Using a valve oscillator for the high-frequency voltage on a Lecher system and applying his formula to the result, he obtained, in 1921,

$$c = 299\ 782 \pm 30 \text{ km/sec}$$

In the 1870's, Newcomb had introduced a revolving, reflecting multi-surface prism in place of Foucault's mirror. Michelson improved the system further, first in 1879 and finally at Mt. Wilson in 1926, his most accurate measurement. During the time required for the light to cover the distance of 35 km and back, the prism turned the next of its 12 surfaces in place for reflection. Only for exactly correct rotational speed was the position of the image of the suddenly illuminated distant reflector in the field of sight independent of the direction of rotation. The comparison of phase may be said, here too, to have occurred at "coincident maxs," and the high accuracy was due to the great displacement of the image for a turn of the revolving prism. Michelson's value was

$$c = 299\ 796 \pm 4 \text{ km/sec}$$

He overlooked a group correction of +2 km/sec. (Michelson, 1927)

Michelson, Pease and Pearson planned a determination in vacuum. It was completed by Pease and Pearson after Michelson's death in 1931. By multiple reflection in a 1-mile evacuated pipe, the light path was 10 miles. Due to the pipe, the geometry of the measuring device was considerably less symmetrical than in the case of the Mt. Wilson determination. The experiment was much talked about and the result was considered of high quality (Michelson, 1935),

$$c = 299\ 774 \pm 11 \text{ km/sec}$$

In 1928 the German scientists Karolus and Mittelstaedt performed the first direct determination using a Kerr cell. Their result was

$$c = 299\ 778 \pm 20 \text{ km/sec}$$

Here too, the group correction seems to have been overlooked.

Now Michelson's 1926 result was regarded as doubtful, and in 1940 Anderson, an American, tried to arrive at a decision. He used a Kerr cell. For phase comparison a photomultiplier received light from two nearby mirrors, the second of them at a somewhat greater distance in order to obtain intensity maxima from the one mirror coincident with minima from the second. The alternating photo-current then was equal to zero. Thereupon, the second mirror was moved away some 170 meters, and the distance was adjusted anew to yield a photo-current equal to zero. After the known mirror displacement, the light's travel time had increased an even multiple of the intensity period, known from the frequency. Anderson's value:

$$c = 299\ 776 \pm 14 \text{ km/sec}$$

Thereby the Michelson 1926 value was ruled out. Anderson carefully considered the group correction. Possibly, Anderson on occasions of his apparatus yielding values very different from the evacuated pipe result, might have felt particularly called upon to search for error sources and in that way unconsciously influenced the result. Or it might have been pure chance. In any case, his value superseded the pipe result (Anderson, 1941).

Anderson's value was used for radar systems. Thereby a microwave transmitter emits short pulses (10^{-6} second) which after distant reflection and return are received again. On the screen of a cathode ray tube the rapid sweep of the ray is marked by emitted and received pulses. The difference of mark positions and the sweep speed yields the pulse travel time. By knowing c the distance is obtained. "Oboe" (0.1-meter wave) and "Shoran" (1-meter) applied to known distances gave low values. Was the c-value used too low?

In 1947 Jones and Conford used Oboe in a manner opposite to its usual operation for the determination of c over known distances and got

$$c = 299\ 782 \pm 25 \text{ km/sec}$$

In the case of Shoran the main pulse-giving radar station is in an aircraft traversing the known straight distance between two points. In order to get strong echoes, there are radar slave stations at the points. Immediately after receiving the pulses, the slave stations reemit them on a slightly different wavelength. By that the main station receiver is not disturbed by its own transmitter. The distances to the two slave stations are continuously registered, and the shortest distance and also that used are obtained at the moment of transversing. A typical distance is 300 km. By careful treatment of Shoran results, Aslakson in 1949 obtained a velocity value

$$c = 299\ 792.3 \pm 2.3 \text{ km/sec}$$

In 1951 he used "Hiran," by which errors from varying signal strengths are avoided, and obtained

$$c = 299\ 794.2 \pm 1\ \text{km/sec}$$

(Aslakson, 1951).

Meanwhile Essen attacked the problem in a quite new manner by his indirect determination using a cavity resonator. Microwave guides may be circular tubes of sufficient diameter to let the waves through. If such a tube, whose length is an even multiple of half the wavelength, is closed by plane reflecting covers, the oscillating energy supplied remains in the cavity as a standing wave. This state only occurs in case of an exact, definite resonance frequency. In practice, there are several adjacent resonance frequencies depending on remaining oscillation states, e.g., including different multiples over a diameter or over several symmetrically oriented diameters. Sarbacher and Edson have derived the exact mathematical expression for all these resonance frequencies as functions of the tube length, tube diameter and the inside wave velocity. Essen and Gordon-Smith very carefully measured length, diameter and frequency of the evacuated cavity used. By calculations, they found the vacuum value c. Their result, in 1947, was:

$$c = 299\ 792.2 \pm 4.5\ \text{km/sec}$$

In 1949 Essen repeated the determination using a cavity whose length could be varied by an inserted movable plunger. By the dependence of the results on the cavity length, systematic errors could be rejected. The final value was

$$c = 299\ 792.5 \pm 1\ \text{km/sec}$$

Applying current practices, the error limits of 1 km/sec may be reduced perhaps by half (Essen, 1956).

At this time, Bergstrand performed direct experiments using visible light. The alternating voltage, supplied by a 10-M/Hz radio transmitter, coincidently fed a Kerr cell and a photo tube. In place of "coincident maxs" the phase comparison was carried out in moments of light pulses reaching half of maximum intensity. Then the photocurrent was strongly dependent on the distance to the reflector. By low-frequency phase shift of the emitted light intensity modulation (interchange of maximum and minimum), there were periodically two photocurrents, and by exactly chosen distance, they balanced each other to 0-current on the control instrument. In this way, by known displacement of the reflector through several successive such 0-points, the wavelength of intensity variation, i.e., the group length L_g, could be determined. The group velocity was obtained from $u = vL_g$, reduced to c by Eqs. (6) and (9). Besides some preliminary results from 1947–48, the 1950 value was:

$$c = 299\ 793.1 \pm 0.3\ \text{km/sec}$$

(Bergstrand, 1957).

Under the name of "Geodimeter," Bergstrand's instrument is used all over the world for measuring distances with high accuracy, c being considered as known. The error in 30 km need not exceed 5 cm. When the geodimeter was used to check the rocket-camera positions around Cape Kennedy, the accuracy turned out to be still better.

Using the geodimeter on known distances, of course, one can obtain c. The experience from recent, improved models now shows that the just related value of 1950 is slightly too high. In 1953 Mackenzie on the Ridge Way and Caithness base lines obtained

$$c = 299\ 792.3 \pm 0.5\ \text{km/sec}$$

Kolibayev performed measurements on many different base lines in the USSR during the years 1958 to 1963, and obtained the value

$$c = 299\ 792.6 \pm 0.1\ \text{km/sec}$$

Likewise, with a geodimeter, Grosse in Germany reported a result in 1967

$$c = 299\ 792.5 \pm 0.1\ \text{km/sec}$$

For the most recent geodimeters, the AGA Ltd. has applied a modulation system more suited for digital display. Also, by introducing a laser as the light source, full daylight measurements are possible.

In several countries nowadays, different forms of electro-optic distance-measuring instruments are manufactured. Intended for the same purpose are instruments using microwave (1 to 10 cm) radiation sources, such as Wadley's Tellurometer of 1957. By this method, a moving wave system is created between two equal instruments, one on each end of the distance, and having slightly different measuring frequencies (10.000 and 10.001 M/Hz). The phase comparison is done by the low-beat frequency of 1000 Hz.

Due to the marked influence of air humidity (Eq. 10) and occasionally occurring side reflections from ground-bound objects, the accuracy of these instruments is somewhat reduced. The results respecting c agree with those of the geodimeter.

One of the most accurate c determinations was that by Froome. In 1950 he started preliminary measurements and in 1958 he used a klystron transmitter delivering harmonics of 0.4 cm wavelength. By guiding pipes the microwave emission was divided into two equal parts. The two pipes terminated in transmitting horns supplied with lenses to form the front surface of the emitted wave as plane as possible. The pipes were bent 180° each in order to get the horns directed opposite to each other. The distance between the horns was 6 to 14 meters.

Between the horns there was created a standing wave system, where the nodal points were observed by aid of a movable receiving detector. The displacement of the detector was measured interferometrically. In this way the microwave length was determined with great accuracy. By carrying through the determination for different horn distances, systematic errors were rejected. These errors may depend on disturbing reflections or on the wave fronts not being sufficiently plane or of known shape. The frequency was controlled by aid of an atomic clock. The result of 1958 was

$$c = 299\ 792.5 \pm 0.1\ \text{km/sec}$$

In 1967 Simkin, Lukin, Sikora, and Strelenski used a system very similar to that of Froome. The result was

$$c = 299\ 792.56 \pm 0.11\ \text{km/sec,}$$

strongly supporting the Froome value and in excellent accordance with the latest geodimeter results (Simkin, 1967).

A further step towards shorter waves was made by V. Daneu et al. using a laser for the far infrared at $\lambda = 0.1$ mm. In a Michelson vacuum interferometer of 4 m path difference, the laser wave is compared to visible light of accurately known wavelength. The laser frequency is directly determined by comparison with high harmonics of a quartz oscillator. The preliminary results are in concordance with the present accepted value of c (V. Daneu, 1969).

A proposal by Mockler and Brittin is very interesting in two respects:

(1) The use of gamma rays.
(2) Light travels only once over the distance (as Roemer!).

First I refer to the article in this book on the MÖSSBAUER EFFECT. The vertical gable surface A of a quartz rod is directed towards the 3 m distant gable B of an identical rod. Both rods are vibrating longitudinally by stimulation from a common quartz-controlled 10^{10}-Hz oscillator. On A is a film of ^{57}Co, including ^{57}Fe decaying to ground state and thereby emitting gamma rays, marked by the Doppler-variation due to the vibrational movements of A. B is covered with ^{57}Fe, absorbing the emission by excitation from the ground state. Due to the very narrow common bandwidth of emission and absorption, 4 MHz of 4×10^{18} Hz, one will observe absorption at B only when its vibratory movement is in phase with the Doppler variation of the radiation hitting the surface. By then, there is an even number of "Doppler waves" over the known distance from A to B, yielding the "wave length." Again we use Eq. (1) to obtain c. Important for a good result is a strong quartz vibration (Mockler, 1961).

There is an indirect method which does not give such high accuracy: The exactly known frequency of an atomic clock is the ground rotational molecular frequency with quantum number $=1$ of some diatomic gas. From the quantum spectral formula of the rotational line series, one obtains the frequency at high quantum numbers of visible or infrared light, where the wavelength is known with great accuracy. The connection between wavelength and frequency yields c, and in 1955 Rank, Bennet and Bennet obtained the value $299\ 791.9 \pm 2.2$ km/sec.

Finally, E. Richard Cohen quotes a numerical value based on what he considers to be the most accurate and consistent measurements available as of June 1972. The velocity of light was determined by measuring the wavelength and frequency of a methane-stabilized helium-neon laser and taking the product of these two quantities. He quotes a value of $299\ 792.46$ km·sec^{-1} See CONSTANTS, FUNDAMENTAL.

ERIK BERGSTRAND

References

Brillouin, Léon, "Wave Propagation and Group Velocity," New York, Academic Press, 1960.

Michelson, A., *Astrophys. J.*, **65** (1927).

Michelson, A., *Astrophys. J.*, **82** (1935).

Anderson, W. C., *J. Opt. Soc. Am*, **31** (1941).

Essen, L., *Proc. Roy. Soc. London Ser. A*, **204** (1950).

Froome, K. D., *Proc. Roy. Soc. London Ser. A*, **109** (1958).

Aslakson, C. I., *Trans. Am. Geophys. Union*, **32** (1951).

Dorsey, *Trans. Am. Phil. Soc.*, **34**, Pt. 1 (1944).

Bergstrand, E., in Flügge, S., Ed., "Encyclopedia of Physics," Vol. 24, Berlin, Springer, 1957.

Bergstrand, E., *K. Sv. Vet. Akad: Arkiv för Fysik*, **8** (45), Stockholm (1954).

Simkin, G. S., Lukin, I. V., Sikora, S. V., and Strelenskii, V. E., 1967, *Izmeritel. Tekhn.*, **8**, 92 (1967). (Translation: *Meas. Tech.*, 1967, 1018).

Danielmeyer, H. G., and Weber, H. P., *Phys. Rev. A*, **3** (5), 1708 (May 1971).

Daneu, V., Hocker, L. O., Javan, A., Ramachandra Rao, D., and Szoke, A., *Phys. Letters*, **29a** (6), 2 (June 1969).

Mockler, R. C., Brittin, W. E., Nat. Bur. Stand., Rpt. Nr. 6762, Boulder, Colorado, 1961.

Froome, K. D., and Essen, L., "The Velocity of Light and Radio Waves," London and New York, Academic Press, 1969.

Cross-references: ATOMIC CLOCKS; CONSTANTS, FUNDAMENTAL; ELECTROMAGNETIC THEORY; INTERFERENCE AND INTERFEROMETRY; KERR EFFECTS; MÖSSBAUER EFFECT; OPTICS, GEOMETRICAL; PROPAGATION OF ELECTROMAGNETIC WAVES; RADAR; WAVEGUIDES; WAVE MOTION.

VIBRATION

In physics, the term "vibration" is used for any sustained motion, characteristic of a finite system, in which each particle or element of the system moves to-and-fro about an equilibrium position. In the simplest situation, such a motion

possesses a unique "periodic time." The inverse of this quantity, the "frequency," is the number of complete to-and-fro excursions per unit time.

It might appear that reference to a finite system in the above definition is gratuitous: infinite systems are mere figments of the theorist's imagination; only finite systems have real existence. Nevertheless, the emphasis is intentional. As will appear, the natural frequencies of vibrating systems depend, in general, on the size (spatial extent) of such systems.

In order to introduce the subject, the motion of a simple pendulum will first be considered—though, strictly, this motion does not fulfil the conditions that have been specified for vibrations: the natural frequency is not characteristic of the pendulum alone, it depends also on the acceleration due to gravity at the place where the pendulum is used. It is usual to speak, therefore, of the oscillations of a pendulum, rather than of its vibrations.

An ideal simple pendulum consists of a very small massive bob (of mass m) attached to one end of a perfectly flexible massless string (of length ℓ), the other end of the string being fixed to a rigid support. In equilibrium, the pendulum hangs vertically; when the bob is displaced sideways and let go, the pendulum oscillates in a vertical plane. In such motion, the string, being massless and under tension, remains straight, and the whole system may be regarded as rigid. An ideal simple pendulum, then, is effectively a rigid body of moment of inertia $m\ell^2$ about its axis of oscillation, and, the moment of the weight of the bob about this axis being $mg\ell \sin \theta$, when the angular displacement is θ, the equation of motion is

$$m\ell^2 \ddot{\theta} = -mg\ell \sin \theta$$

Here g is the acceleration due to gravity. For small displacements, therefore,

$$\ddot{\theta} = -(g/\ell)\theta \qquad (1)$$

and, under this limitation

$$\theta = \alpha \cos \left(2\pi \frac{t}{\tau} + \delta\right) \qquad (2)$$

α and δ being arbitrary constants, and τ, the periodic time, being given by

$$\tau = 2\pi(\ell/g)^{1/2} \qquad (3)$$

Equations (2) and (3) provide the general solution of Eq. (1). On examination, they will be seen to represent an oscillation in angle, between limits $-\alpha \leqslant \theta \leqslant \alpha$, of periodic time τ which is independent of α. The constant δ specifies the displacement at the instant arbitrarily chosen as the zero of time: it is referred to as the "phase angle" of the motion related to this choice of time zero. The constant α is referred to as the (angular) amplitude of the oscillation. The fact that the periodic time (or frequency), in pendulum motion, is independent

of amplitude (for small amplitudes) was first discovered empirically by Galileo, in 1581. A similar result is true for any motion (in angle, or any other coordinate) in which the acceleration towards the equilibrium position is proportional to the displacement, as required by Eq. (1). Motion having this character is "simple harmonic motion."

Pendulum motion has been considered in some detail because, historically, it was the first example of simple harmonic motion to be understood. For present purposes, however, more direct relevance might be seen in the motion of a load suspended by a helical spring. If such a load is displaced vertically, it executes simple harmonic motion about its position of equilibrium. The extra upwards force acting on the load (by Hooke's law) being proportional to the extra extension of the spring, the acceleration of the load towards equilibrium is proportional to the displacement, as is required. But it is not easy, in practice, to approximate to the ideal of a massless spring supporting a massive load, and a theoretical account of the oscillations of a loaded spring which does not take account of the mass of the spring is oversimplified.

Simple harmonic motion is referred to as "isochronous" because, in a given case, the periodic time is the same whatever the amplitude. If the vibratory motion of an extended system were not similarly isochronous, there would be little point in claiming, as has already been done, that such motion, at its simplest, may be characterised by a periodic time which is unique. But the fact is that we have ample experience of real physical systems whose vibrations are of this character: it is natural to conclude, therefore, that the motion of each particle or element of a system so vibrating is simple harmonic motion. That is the reason why simple harmonic motion has been considered in its own right, as a preliminary to the discussion of vibratory motion.

In vibratory motion, the restoring forces responsible for the individual motions of the constituent elements of a vibrating system may arise from tensions externally applied to the system (as with stretched strings and membranes), from elastic stresses developed internally as the system is deformed (as with rods vibrating longitudinally, transversely or torsionally; with air columns in organ pipes; with thin plates of regular shape), or occasionally in other ways (surface tension forces, for example are involved in the pulsation vibrations of thin films of liquid).

The simplest system of the first type is the stretched string. Imagine a uniform string, of length ℓ and total mass $m\ell$, stretched under tension T between rigid supports. Let rectangular axes OX, OY be taken, along and at right angles to the length of the string in its undisturbed state, and let us consider possible transverse vibrations of the string in the XY plane. Suppose that all displacements (y) are very small compared with ℓ, so that any over-all increase in the

length of the string is negligible, and the tension may be regarded as constant throughout. Under these conditions, imagine that the string is in steady vibration, and at an arbitrary instant, let the transverse displacement vary along the length of the string as represented by the expression $y_0 = f(x)$. The instantaneous value of the curvature of the "displacement profile" of the string, at x, being given by $f''(x)$, the instantaneous magnitude of the force per unit length of the string about x is $Tf''(x)$. Under these imposed conditions, this force is essentially at right angles to OX and in the direction of y increasing—and, as a result, the acceleration of the element of the string around x is $(T/m)f''(x)$, instantaneously. Only if this acceleration is proportional to the instantaneous displacement at x, and if the proportionality constant is independent of x, will each element of the string execute simple harmonic motion of the same period—and only then will the postulated vibration of the string as a whole be well-defined. For such sustained motion, therefore, the necessary condition is

$$(T/m)f''(x) = -\mu f(x) \qquad (4)$$

where μ is a constant, independent of x. When μ has been evaluated, ν, the frequency of the vibration, will likewise be known, for, in this case [compare Eqs. (1) and (3)]

$$\nu = \mu^{1/2}/2\pi \qquad (5)$$

Now, the general solution of Eq. (4) is

$$f(x) = A_0 \sin\left\{\left(\frac{\mu m}{T}\right)^{1/2} x + \epsilon\right\}$$

but, because the string is fixed at its two ends, so that $f(0) = f(\ell) = 0$,

$$\epsilon = 0$$

and

$$\left(\frac{\mu m}{T}\right)^{1/2} \ell = n\pi$$

n being a positive integer. For ν, therefore, we have [see Eq. (5)]

$$\nu = \frac{n}{2\ell}\left(\frac{T}{m}\right)^{1/2}$$

and, for $f(x)$,

$$f(x) = A_0 \sin\frac{n\pi x}{\ell}$$

Again, since each element of the string executes simple harmonic motion of frequency ν, we have the following general expression for the displacement (y) of any element of string, given as a function of x, and the time t, namely

$$y = A_0 \sin\frac{n\pi x}{\ell} \cos\frac{n\pi}{\ell}\left(\frac{T}{m}\right)^{1/2} t \qquad (6)$$

Taking account of all possible values of n, Eq. (6) represents the whole series of simple modes in which the stretched string may vibrate. Generally, these modes are referred to as the "normal modes" of the system. Because the frequencies of these normal mode vibrations are the successive integral multiples of a basic frequency, $(1/2\ell)(T/m)^{1/2}$, they are said to form a "harmonic series," and the vibrations themselves are often described as the "first harmonic," "second harmonic," and so on. Alternatively, the first harmonic may be referred to as the "fundamental mode," the second harmonic as the "first overtone," and similarly throughout the series. It will be seen, from Eq. (6), that in the fundamental mode, the only points in the string which remain permanently at rest are the ends of the string; in the nth normal mode, in general, there are $(n-1)$ other points of permanent rest ("nodes") equally spaced between the two ends. Mid-way between the nodes are the points of greatest amplitude of motion ("antinodes").

By restricting consideration to the case in which the shape of the displacement profile of the string is the same at all instants throughout the vibration (being represented by $y_0 = f(x)$, above), we made certain that only normal mode vibrations should emerge from our analysis. But more complex sustained motion is possible in which the shape of the displacement profile continuously changes. To sustained motion of this general type, no single periodic time may be assigned. On the other hand it may be shown that every such motion may be regarded as resulting from the superposition of normal mode vibrations, the amplitudes and phases of the various modes being uniquely determinable in terms of the details of the actual motion as observed over a sufficient interval of time. From this point of view, the potentialities of the system for sustained motion are completely given in Eq. (6) describing the normal modes.

With essentially linear systems, such as strings and rods and organ pipes, when the conditions at the two ends of the system are the same (as they are with the stretched string), and there is no internal constraint, the normal modes in general constitute a harmonic series; when the end conditions are different (as in a pipe which is closed at one end and open at the other) in general the even-numbered harmonics are not represented. In all cases, however, the theorem concerning the decomposition of the most complex sustained motion in terms of the normal modes applies.

As an example of elastic vibrations, we consider, briefly, the transverse vibrations of a thin, uniform rod, which is clamped at one end. For a displacement profile of arbitrary shape, the elastic forces brought into play across any section of the rod are proportional to the displacement of the rod at that section, and the unbalanced restoring force acting on a small finite element of the rod is similarly proportional to its displacement. But the proportionality constant

relating restoring force per unit length to displacement will, in general, vary along the rod. Only for displacement profiles of certain shapes will this constant be the same over-all. These are the shapes of displacement profile corresponding to the normal mode vibrations, and it is the object of theory to identify them and to deduce the corresponding frequencies. Even an approximate theory is complicated; all that can be done here is merely to quote the ratios of the frequencies of the first three normal mode vibrations, namely 1:6.27:17.55. Very clearly, the normal modes in this case do not constitute a harmonic series: in musical parlance, the first overtone is some $2\frac{1}{2}$ octaves higher than the fundamental.

Throughout the above discussions, actual physical situations have been consistently idealized, in that it has been assumed, implicitly, that all periodic motion is sustained indefinitely. In fact, all such motion, unless energy is continually supplied from outside, gradually loses amplitude and dies away. This process is referred to as "damping," and the dissipation of energy which is its essential feature is generally, in mechanical systems, attributable to friction. Detailed consideration of damping is, however, beyond the scope of this article.

N. FEATHER

References

Feather, N., "An Introduction to the Physics of Vibrations and Waves," Edinburgh, Edinburgh University Press, 1961.

French, A. P., "Vibrations and Waves," New York, W. W. Norton & Co. Inc., 1971.

Rayleigh (Lord), "Theory of Sound," Second edition, London, The Macmillan & Co., Ltd., 1894.

Cross-references: DYNAMICS, MUSIC, WAVE MOTION.

VISCOELASTICITY

Viscoelasticity is a material property possessed by solids and liquids which, when deformed, exhibit both viscous and elastic behavior through simultaneous dissipation and storage of mechanical energy. The *material constants* linking stress and strain in the theory of elasticity become *time-dependent material functions* in the constitutive equations of viscoelastic theory. At sufficiently small (theoretically infinitesimal) strains the behavior of viscoelastic materials is well described by the *linear theory of viscoelasticity* epitomized by the celebrated *Boltzmann superposition principle*. Expressed in its simplest form

$$\sigma(t) = \int_0^t Q(t-u)\epsilon(u)\,du$$

$$\epsilon(t) = \int_0^t U(t-u)\sigma(u)\,du$$

it states that the stress (or strain) at time t under an arbitrary strain (or stress) history is a linear superposition of all strains (or stresses) applied at previous times u multiplied by the values of a weighting function $Q(t)$ [or $U(t)$] corresponding to the time intervals $t - u$ which have elapsed since imposition of the respective strains (or stresses).

Put another way (see *operator equation* below) the Boltzmann superposition principle expresses the fact that the material behavior can be described by linear differential equations with constant coefficients and time as variable.

Considerable simplification of the viscoelastic relations is achieved by mapping them from the real t axis into the complex s plane through the Laplace transformation. The resulting transforms in s may be manipulated algebraically and then inverted to regain the time-dependent form. Thus the above convolution integrals become

$$\sigma(s) = Q(s)\epsilon(s) \qquad \epsilon(s) = U(s)\sigma(s)$$

and $Q(t)$ and $U(t)$ can be seen to be the material functions representing the response to a unit impulse of strain or stress. The unit step response functions, the material functions under constant strain ϵ_0 and constant stress σ_0, are the *relaxation modulus* and *creep compliance*, obtained as

$$G(t) = \sigma(t)/\epsilon_0 = \mathcal{L}^{-1}\,Q(s)/s$$

$$J(t) = \epsilon(t)/\sigma_0 = \mathcal{L}^{-1}\,U(s)/s$$

where $\mathcal{L}^{-1}$ denotes inversion of the transform. For sinusoidal steady state strain $\epsilon(\omega)$ and stress $\sigma(\omega)$, there result the *complex modulus* and *complex compliance*

$$G^*(\omega) = \sigma(\omega)/\epsilon(\omega) = [Q(s)]_{s=i\omega}$$

$$J^*(\omega) = \epsilon(\omega)/\sigma(\omega) = [U(s)]_{s=i\omega}$$

whose real and imaginary parts are the *storage modulus* $G'(\omega)$, *storage compliance* $J'(\omega)$, *loss modulus* $G''(\omega)$, and *loss compliance* $J''(\omega)$. Their ratio is the loss tangent

$$\tan\delta\,(\omega) = G''(\omega)/G'(\omega) = J''(\omega)/J'(\omega)$$

Any of the above functions (or any other that may be derived, e.g., for constant rate of strain), if known over a sufficiently extended time scale (or, equivalently, over a sufficient range of frequencies), provides complete information on the viscoelastic properties of a homogeneous isotropic material. As formulated above, the equations refer to deformation in simple shear. When dealing with combined stresses, as in viscoelastic stress analysis, the tensorial character of stress and strain must, of course, be taken into account. The equations for other types of deformation, e.g., dilatation or uniaxal extension, are analogous to those for shear. The relations between the frequency-dependent viscoelastic functions in shear, extension, and dilatation are the same as those between the elastic constants, while for the time-dependent functions these

relations are valid between the s-multiplied Laplace transforms. Thus the relaxation modulus in extension $E(t)$ is related to $G(t)$ through the *time-dependent Poisson's ratio* $v(t)$ by

$$E(s) = 2G(s) \, [1 + sv(s)]$$

and for $v(t) = 1/2$, $E(t) = 3G(t)$. Data obtained in shear and extension on incompressible bodies are thus readily combined. Moreover, if a viscoelastic function can be formulated analytically, it can be converted into any of the others, allowing combination of measurements made under different stress or strain histories. Use is made of this to extend the experimentally accessible time scale. Thus at short times, dynamic (frequency-dependent) measurements are more convenient than transient (time-dependent) measurements, and *vice versa* for long times.

Another important extension of the time scale is available through *time-temperature superposition*. An increase in temperature generally shortens the time necessary for the molecular rearrangement processes responsible for viscoelastic behavior. If all such processes are affected by temperature in the same way, the material is *thermorheologically simple*, and a change in temperature simply shifts the viscoelastic functions along the logarithmic time or frequency axis. For polymers (the typical viscoelastic materials) above the *glass transition temperature* (at which main chain motion effectively ceases), the shift factor a_T is given by an equation of the form (WLF equation)

$$\ln a_T = - \frac{c_1(T - T_0)}{c_2 + T - T_0}$$

where T_0 is a suitably chosen reference temperature, and c_1 and c_2 are constants. Measurements made at different temperatures can thus be combined to yield a single *master curve*.

Measurements made under different stress or strain histories are often combined for experimental reasons and the linear theory of viscoelasticity furnishes a number of methods to this end. Interconversion of the viscoelastic functions is faciliated by the introduction of *spectral distribution functions*. The spectral functions may be derived conveniently by rewriting the Boltzmann superposition principle, given above as an integral operator equation, in the form of the *differential operator equation*:

$$[\sum p_m D^m] \, \sigma(t) = \sum [q_n D^n] \, \epsilon(t)$$

where $D^r = d^r/dt^r$. The Laplace transformation leads to

$$Q(s) = 1/U(s) = \sum q_n s^n / \sum p_m s^m$$

a definition of $Q(s)$ and $U(s)$ which is readily linked with the useful representation of viscoelastic behavior by *models* consisting of series-parallel combinations of springs (elastic or storage elements) and dashpots (viscous or dissipative elements). A parallel combination (Voigt model) is characterized by a *retardance* $U(s) = 1/(G + \eta s) = J/(1 + \lambda s)$, where $\lambda = \eta/G$ is the *retardation time*, η signifies viscosity, and $J = 1/G$. A series combination (Maxwell model) is characterized by a *relaxance* $Q(s) = 1/(J + 1/\eta s) = G\tau s/(1 + \tau s)$ where $\tau = \eta/G$ is the *relaxation time*.

Through the *combination rules*: "relaxances add in parallel, retardances add in series," $Q(s)$ and $U(s)$ are readily derived from a given more complex model as illustrated below.

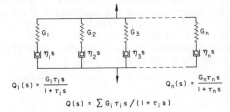

$$U_i(s) = \frac{J_i}{1 + \lambda_i s} \qquad U_n(s) = \frac{J_n}{1 + \lambda_n s}$$

$$U(s) = J + \sum J_i/(1 + \lambda_i s) + 1/\eta s$$

GENERALIZED VOIGT MODEL

$$Q_i(s) = \frac{G_i \tau_i s}{1 + \tau_i s} \qquad Q_n(s) = \frac{G_n \tau_n s}{1 + \tau_n s}$$

$$Q(s) = \sum G_i \tau_i s/(1 + \tau_i s)$$

GENERALIZED MAXWELL MODEL

FIG. 1

These models are *conjugate*, i.e., with suitable choices for the parameters, they describe the same viscoelastic material. Representation of viscoelastic behavior by a (small) finite number of elements is often inadequate. Molecular theories of polymer behavior lead to models with an infinite number of parameters, characterized by a *discrete distribution* (or *line spectrum*) *of relaxation or retardation times*. These distributions are normally so closely spaced that they cannot be resolved experimentally. One can therefore define *continuous distribution functions*

$$Q(s) = \int_0^\infty G(\tau) \frac{\tau s \, d\tau}{1 + \tau s} = \int_{-\infty}^\infty H(\tau) \frac{\tau s \, d \ln \tau}{1 + \tau s}$$

$$U(s) = J + \int_0^\infty J(\lambda) \frac{d\lambda}{1 + \lambda s} + 1/\eta s =$$

$$J + \int_{-\infty}^\infty L(\lambda) \frac{d \ln \lambda}{1 + \lambda s} + 1/\eta s$$

where $G(\tau)$ and $J(\lambda)$ are distributions of relaxation and retardation times (more properly: modulus and compliance densities on time)

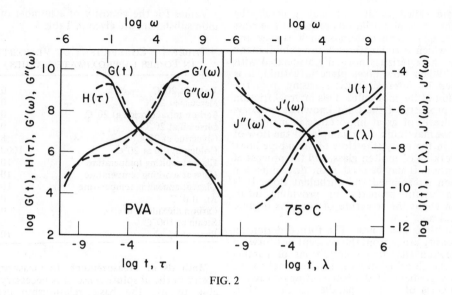

FIG. 2

respectively, and $H(\tau) = \tau G(\tau)$ and $L(\lambda) = \lambda J(\lambda)$ are their counterparts on the more convenient logarithmic time scale. The spectral functions may be derived from experimentally determined curves of the viscoelastic functions through any of several approximation methods.

The various viscoelastic functions are illustrated above on the example of an uncross-linked amorphous polyvinyl acetate with a molecular weight of about 300 000. Data obtained in extension and shear at different temperatures were combined and interconverted. The functions are grouped to display their qualitative symmetries.

Singling out the relaxation modulus for a broad interpretation of the viscoelastic behavior of an uncross-linked polymer, one sees that at short times (in the *glassy region*), the modulus approaches an asymptotic value, the *glass modulus*. It then drops through the glass-to-rubber transition region and levels out somewhat in the *plateau region* reflecting the effect of molecular entanglements. At still longer times, it decays to zero through the *terminal region*. For cross-linked networks this region is absent (if there is no chemical degradation). In this case, the flow term $1/\eta s$ is missing from $U(s)$ above; an additive constant, the *equilibrium modulus* G_e, characterizing the (level) *rubbery region*, appears in $Q(s)$.

Current efforts in the field of viscoelasticity are directed chiefly towards the development of nonlinear (large deformation) theory, theories of multiphase materials, anisotropic and inhomogeneous (semicrystalline and filled) systems, the solution of viscoelastic boundary problems (viscoelastic stress analysis), and the explanation of viscoelastic behavior on the molecular level (molecular theories).

N. W. TSCHOEGL

References

Alfrey, T., and Gurnee, E. F., "Dynamics of Visco-elastic Behavior," in Eirich, F. R., Ed., "Rheology," Vol. 1, New York, Academic Press, 1956.

Bueche, F., "Physical Properties of Polymers," New York, Interscience Publishers, 1962.

Christensen, R. M., "Theory of Viscoelasticity—An Introduction," New York, Academic Press, 1971.

Ferry, J. D., "Viscoelastic Properties of Polymers," New York, John Wiley & Sons, 1961.

Leaderman, H., "Viscoelasticity Phenomena in Amorphous High Polymeric Systems," in Eirich, F. R., Ed., "Rheology," Vol. 2, New York, Academic Press, 1958.

Nielsen, L. E., "Mechanical Properties of Polymers," New York, Van Nostrand Reinhold, 1962.

Staverman, A. J., and Schwarzl, F., "Linear Deformation Behavior of High Polymers," in Stuart, H. A., Ed., "Die Physik der Hochpolymeren," Vol. 4, Berlin, Springer, 1956.

Tobolsky, A. V., "Properties and Structure of Polymers," New York, John Wiley & Sons 1960.

Cross-references: ELASTICITY, MECHANICAL PROPERTIES OF SOLIDS, POLYMER PHYSICS, RHEOLOGY, VISCOSITY.

VISCOSITY

Materials in general show two broad kinds of behavior with regard to their reaction when subject to an applied force. In one type, they deform until a position of equilibrium is reached, when no further change of shape takes place. Many solids show this kind of behavior. Alternatively, there is no permanent resistance to change of shape, and continuous deformation takes place for as long as the force is applied. The material is said to flow. Substances possessing this prop-

erty are called fluids and may generally be thought of as either liquids or gases. The class also includes some materials, such as glass and pitch, which at room temperature exhibit many of the characteristics normally associated with solids. When flow takes place in a fluid, it is opposed by internal friction arising from the cohesion of the molecules. This internal friction is the property of the fluid known as *viscosity*. It is clearly of great importance in many contexts; we may think, for example, of the flow of blood in the body, the flow of oil in pipe lines, the working of molten glass, and the process of lubrication. It may be used in the discrimination between streamlined and turbulent flow. It is also a useful property in providing information about the structure of complex organic molecules.

Definitions and Units The formal definition of viscosity arises from the concept put forward by Newton that under conditions of parallel flow, the shearing stress is proportional to the velocity gradient. If the force acting on each of two planes of area A parallel to each other, moving parallel to each other with a relative velocity V, and separated by a perpendicular distance X, be denoted by F, the shearing stress is F/A and the velocity gradient, which will be linear for a true liquid, is V/X.

Thus

$$\frac{F}{A} = \eta \cdot \frac{V}{X}$$

The constant η is known as the viscosity coefficient, dynamic viscosity, or viscosity of the liquid. The unit, expressed in dyne second per square centimeter, is known as the "poise," after Poiseuille who worked on viscosity in the early part of the nineteenth century. For practical purposes it is often more convenient to use a smaller unit, known as the centipoise, equal to a hundredth of a *poise*. It is useful to note that water at room temperature has a viscosity of approximately 1 centipoise. In many applications of viscometry, it is useful to note another quantity, called the kinematic viscosity, which is obtained by dividing the dynamic viscosity by the density. It is frequently denoted by the Greek letter ν, and the unit in which it is expressed is the "stokes," after Sir George Stokes, another pioneer worker in viscometry. In practical viscometry, viscosity is sometimes expressed in seconds; this is a measure of the time for a prescribed quantity of liquid to flow through a tube or aperture of defined dimensions.

In considering many problems of fluid motion, an important non-dimensional quantity is $\nu d/\nu$, where v is the velocity of the fluid, ν its kinematic viscosity, and d a linear dimension, such as the diameter of a tube. This quantity is known as Reynolds' number; when it is less than about 1000, flow is generally streamlined, whereas at values over 1000 it is turbulent.

Values for the viscosity of a number of common substances are given in Table 1.

TABLE 1. COEFFICIENT OF VISCOSITY IN POISES (APPROXIMATE VALUES)

Water at 20°C	0.010
Mercury at 20°C	0.015
Carbon tetrachloride at 20°C	0.009
Olive oil at 20°C	0.84
Glycerine at 20°C	8.3
Golden Syrup at 20°C	1000
Glass at melting temperature	10^3
Glass at working temperature	10^7
Glass at annealing temperature	10^{13}
Air at 0°C	0.00017
Carbon dioxide at 0°C	0.00014
Steam at 100°C	0.00013
Pitch at 15°C	10^{10}

Methods of Measurement In measuring viscosity in the absolute sense, it is necessary to be able to use the basic relationship between shearing stress and velocity gradient in order to derive a relationship between the measurable quantities involved in flow in an apparatus of a particular shape. For example, it can be shown that the volume Q of a liquid of viscosity η flowing per unit time through a tube of length l and internal radius a, when the pressure difference between the ends is P, is given by

$$Q = \frac{\pi P a^4}{8 l \eta}$$

Capillary viscometers enable all the variables in this equation to be measured and the viscosity to be determined.

Similarly, a viscometer can be constructed in which one cylinder rotates inside another with the liquid under test in the annular space between the two. Measurement of the angular velocity and the applied torque, together with a knowledge of the dimensions of the apparatus, enables the viscosity to be calculated.

Another method involves the measurement of the rate of fall of a sphere in a column of liquid. If the liquid has viscosity η and density ρ, and the sphere has radius r and density σ, then the velocity of fall is

$$v = \frac{2gr^2(\sigma - \rho)}{9\eta}$$

a relationship commonly known as Stokes' law.

There are also a number of empirical methods that can be used to obtain comparative values, the instruments being calibrated by using liquids of known viscosity.

Variation with Temperature The viscosity of liquids decreases rapidly with increasing temperature. For example, the viscosity of molten glass may be halved by raising the temperature 30°C.

On the other hand, the viscosity of gases increases with temperature. This feature is of practical importance in two senses. In all methods of measurement strict temperature control is necessary, and when results are quoted, it is essential to state the temperature to which they refer.

The variation of viscosity with temperature is of great significance in the problem of lubrication, where oils may have to operate over widely different conditions. So-called viscostatic oils have a low temperature coefficient and can thus be used over a wide temperature range. As an indication of this property, the oil industry uses an empirical number known as the "viscosity index"; the higher the viscosity index, the less is the variation of viscosity with temperature.

Molecular Weight Determinations The viscosity of organic materials in solution was suggested by Staudinger as a useful index of their molecular structure, since the flow properties would be influenced by the size and shape of the molecules. For example, some high polymers give appreciable increases of viscosity even at low concentrations on account of the effect of randomly coiled long-chain molecules. Generally speaking, the higher the molecular weight, the greater is the increase in viscosity for a given weight in the solution. The values of molecular weight obtained by this method are not absolute, but they depend on the establishment of empirical relations by measurements on substances of known molecular weight in a given series (see MOLECULAR WEIGHT).

Non-Newtonian Systems A large number of industrially important materials do not obey the simple Newtonian relationship between shearing stress and shearing rate. In some cases the viscosity varies with the shearing rate, and in others, it varies with time when the shearing rate is constant. An important group of such materials is known as thixotropic substances—they become thinner when stirred. Paint, suspensions of clay in water, and many other substances behave in this way, and the property has considerable industrial significance. In the case of paint, for example, the low viscosity when brushed in a thin film makes for easy application, whereas the high viscosity under low shearing stresses enables the film to be retained on vertical surfaces. Some substances thicken up on stirring, and there are a number of other classes of behavior (e.g. VISCOELASTICITY) that constitute departure from Newtonian laws. The study of such anomalous systems is an important branch of modern RHEOLOGY.

A. DINSDALE

References

Newman, F. H., and Searle, V. H. L., "The General Properties of Matter," London, Ed. Arnold, 1962.

Dinsdale, A., and Moore, F., "Viscosity and Its Measurement," New York, Van Nostrand Reinhold, 1963.

Perry, J. H., "Chemical Engineers Handbook," 4th Ed., New York, McGraw-Hill Book Co., 1963.

Flory, P. J., "Principles of Polymer Chemistry," New York, Cornell University Press, 1963.

Scott-Blair, G. W., "A Survey of General and Applied Rheology," London, Pitman, 1949.

Eirich, F. R., Ed., "Rheology, Theory and Applications," Three volumes, New York, Academic Press, 1958.

Cross-references: FLUID DYNAMICS, MOLECULAR WEIGHT, RHEOLOGY, VISCOELASTICITY.

VISION AND THE EYE

The meaningful experience of vision requires light, the eye, and a conscious observer (animal or human) having an intact *visual system*. In its gross aspects, the visual system includes the eyes, the *extraocular muscles* which control eye position in the *bony orbit* (eye socket), the optic and other nerves that connect the eyes to the brain, and those several areas of the brain that are in neural communication with the eyes. This summary will stress the informational aspects of human vision; it should be realized however that no visual system could function without its *protective mechanisms* (tears and eyelids, especially) or if its normal metabolism (mediated through the vascular supply of eye and brain) were seriously interfered with.

The visual system is particularly well adapted for the rapid and precise extraction of spatial information from a more-or-less remote external world; it does this by analyzing, in ways that are as yet imperfectly understood, the continuously changing patterns of radiant flux impinging upon the surfaces of the eyes. Much of this light is reflected from objects which must be discriminated, recognized, attended to, and/or avoided in the environment; this ability transcends enormous variations in intensity, quality, and geometry of illumination as well as vantage point of the observer. A block diagram of the visual system is given in Fig. 1.

Although image formation in the eye is importantly involved, the analogy between eye and photographic camera has been badly overworked and tends to create the erroneous impression that little else is needed to explain how we see. Image formation is greatly complicated by the movement of the eyes within the head, and of both eyes and head relative to the external sea of radiant energy. Such visual input is ordinarily sampled by discrete momentary pauses of the eyes called *fixations*, interrupted by very rapid ballistic motions known as *saccades* which bring the eyes from one fixation position to the next. Smooth movements of the eyes can occur when an object having a predictable motion is available to be followed. A large body of evidence suggests that the visual input is processed by the brain in "time frames"

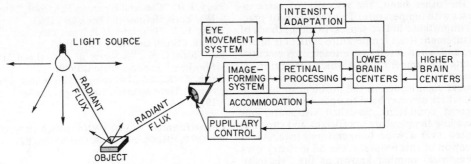

FIG. 1. Block diagram of the functional components of the visual system.

of about 100 msec, although the peripheral parts of the visual system operate with much shorter time constants than this.

Each eye controls many important functions within one mobile housing: it is a device to form an image upon a vast array of light sensitive *photoreceptors*, but it also contains systems to dissect, encode, and transmit information derived therefrom. A cross section of the human eye is shown in Fig. 2. The primary refracting surface is the *cornea*, a complex yet transparent structure which admits light through the anterior part of the outer surface of the eye. The *iris* contains muscles which alter the size of the entrance port of the eye, the *pupil*. The *crystalline lens* has a variable shape, under the indirect control of the *ciliary* muscle. Since it has a refractive index higher than the surrounding media, it gives the eye a variable focal length, allowing *accommodation* to objects at varying distances from the eye. The iris muscles and the ciliary muscle, known collectively as the *intra-*

ocular muscles of the eye, are controlled by impulses having their origins in separate but interacting centers in the brain stem. These brain centers also receive nerve impulses from the eye. These loops, and those involving the extraocular musculature and thus eye position, have some of the properties of nonlinear servosystems, and have been actively investigated as such.

Much of the remainder of the eye is filled with fluids and materials under pressure, which help the eye maintain its shape. The *aqueous humor*—thin, watery, and continuously being replaced—fills the *anterior* chamber between cornea and lens. The *vitreous humor*—thinly jellylike and of very low metabolism—fills the majority of the eye's volume. The image produced through these structures is formed upon the *retina* at the back of the eye. The retinal image is very small, because the eye itself is small and has a short posterior focal length of about 19 to 23 mm, depending upon accom-

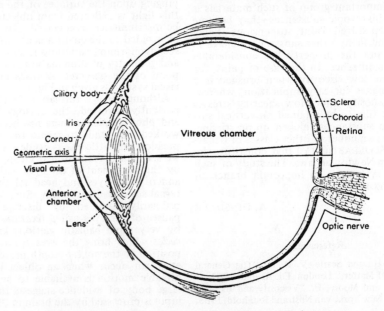

FIG. 2. Horizontal cross section of the right eye of the human.

modative state. The retinal image has a point-spread function on the order of two to three minutes of arc, corresponding to about 10μ on the retina for ideal conditions. These conditions include a 2 to 3 mm pupil, monochromatic light, optimal accommodation and a normal, young, and healthy eye. This quality approaches, but is somewhat worse, than that produced by diffraction-limited imagery in an ideal optical system. The retinal image is always in motion: even during the best efforts at steady fixation, there exists an irreducible tremor of the eye whose high-frequency components are in the 20 to 30 seconds-of-arc range, with larger drifting and saccadic movements up to 5 minutes of arc. It is possible to eliminate this residual motion by various optical techniques; such stabilization usually results in a total loss of vision, providing an elegant demonstration that the visual system responds primarily to *changes* in light patterns, rather than to steady states. Electrophysiological evidence from animals amply confirms this.

The *retina* is a thin structure of extreme complexity. It is considered embryologically to be a displaced part of the brain, and it is of clinical importance as the only part of the central nervous system that can be directly observed in the intact living subject. The receptors, the *rods* and *cones*, line the back surface of the retina, in immediate contact with dark layers (including the pigment epithelium and choroid) which help to nourish the receptors and to prevent multiple reflection of light. There are about 125 000 000 receptors in each human eye, of which only about 5 per cent are cones. The cones are however of an importance disproportionate to their relative number: in particular there is a small central bouquet of about 2000 of them, located in a rod-free depression of the retina known as the *fovea centralis* where they are packed together into a hexagonal array having a density of about $150\ 000/\text{mm}^2$; these are capable of dissecting the finest details of the optimal retinal image. This process is aided by the lateral displacement of other retinal structures through which light must pass to reach the cone receptors. Moreover, this is the area of the retina where images have the highest attention value and which "projects" to a disproportionately huge area of the visual brain; the extraocular muscles move the eye more or less automatically, in the act of fixation, to put objects of interest into this region where their details can be most critically appreciated, while the accommodative mechanism alters the shape of the lens to produce the sharpest possible image in this region. The cones, including those in the fovea, function only at high luminance levels (approximately, above .01 candela/m^2), below which they are functionally blind and the rods take over. Thus the retina contains two systems intermixed: (a) the cone system (photopic), good for high-acuity vision, which also mediates all color vision; (b) the achromatic rod system, which

has relatively poor spatial resolving power, but very high sensitivity.

The rods and cones are synaptically connected to the *bipolar cells*, which in turn relate to the *ganglion cells*, whose axons constitute the optic nerve fibers. There are also rich horizontal connections among the receptors, among the bipolar cells, and among the ganglion cells. In addition, there is a high degree of convergence: the 125 000 000 receptors ultimately feed into only 1 000 000 nerve fibers of the flexible optic nerve, which therefore constitutes the principal "bottleneck" of information flow in the visual system. The convergence ratio for the fovea is about 1:1, helping to preserve the high-detail vision of this region, while in the peripheral retina this ratio is many thousands to one, leading to high sensitivity at the sacrifice of resolving power.

The pathways from retina to brain are by no means independent, including those emerging from the central fovea. The horizontal interconnections are utilized to allow inhibitory processes to sharpen the "neural image" by a process of border enhancement, but much more complicated preprocessing of information occurs also. It is abundantly clear that the brain does not receive a replica of what is on the retina, although a spatial isomorphism between retina and brain does exist; rather, the messages sent to the brain tend to carry information that is already processed in complex ways to make efficient use of the limited communications pathways between eye and brain in an adaptively significant manner.

Because the two eyes are located in slightly different places in space, a disparity of the two retinal images results. Rather than to produce a blurred or confused picture, this *retinal disparity* results in the appearance of *stereoscopic depth*. Such depth judgments are remarkably precise, consistent with the findings that all but the smallest eye movements and accommodative adjustments are highly correlated between the two eyes, and that neural units in the visual brain are precisely connected, by way of intermediate synapses, to optically corresponding areas.

The normal eye exhibits a large amount of chromatic aberration which is not normally noticeable. There are at least two reasons for this: (a) the cone receptors exhibit a directional sensitivity which reduces the visual effectiveness of light entering the marginal zones of the pupil; (b) the visual system has a remarkable capacity to adapt to systematic distortions of almost any kind which do not carry useful information from the external world. For example, observers learn with practice to compensate for the effects of gross visual displacement caused by prisms placed before the eyes, and are no longer able to see the chromatic fringes produced by such prisms. Removal of the prisms produces reappearance of chromatic fringes and an apparent displacement in the opposite direction. The explanation of such ef-

fects is not simple: in this example, the adaptation to displacement is probably kinesthetic rather than visual, but the adaptation to fringes is almost certainly confined to the visual system. Related to this are many entoptic phenomena that are seldom preceived: (a) the shadows of the retinal blood vessels, which are in front of the receptors; (b) the blind spot in the visual field, caused by the receptor-free optic disc, large enough to contain 200 images of the moon; (c) "floaters," usually shadows of debris in the vitreous humor, clearly visible if attended to against bright, uniform surfaces such as the sky; (d) fleeting specks of light probably caused by the movements of corpuscles within the retinal blood vessels; (e) Maxwell's spot, probably corresponding to the region of the macular pigment, and many others.

The initial nonoptical event in the visual process is the absorption of single light quanta by single molecules of visual photopigment, of which millions are located in each rod or cone. Under ideal conditions, as few as a half-dozen of these elemental events within fairly broad bounds of time and area, are sufficient to lead to a visual sensation. The visual photopigment contained in the rods is *rhodopsin*, having a peak sensitivity at about 505 nm. It has been much studied and is found in most animals including man. Absorption of light by rhodopsin probably produces graded potentials at the receptors that trigger all-or-none nerve impulses by the time the ganglion cells are activated, if not before. The exact mechanisms whereby light absorption gives rise to receptor potentials (and these to nerve impulses), although under active investigation, cannot be said yet to be satisfactorily understood.

Color vision depends upon the existence of three classes of visual photopigment, all different from rhodopsin, housed in different proportions in different classes of cone receptors. When two fields of light that are physically different look exactly alike in color (*metameric* matches), it is probable that the rate at which light is being absorbed in the three classes of cone photopigment is the same from both fields, although this is not yet definitely established. The perception of color clearly involves the higher levels of the visual system as well.

Another important property of the eye is its adaptation to intensity by means of which the eye changes its gain and other characteristics, enabling it to respond discriminatively over a stimulus intensity range of about ten billion to one. At one time, it was felt that the bleaching of photopigments was primarily involved in this process; recent evidence indicates that this plays only a minor role and the true mechanisms are numerous and include changes in the organizational properties of retinal networks.

ROBERT M. BOYNTON

References

Brindley, G. S., "Physiology of the Retina and the Visual Pathway," Baltimore, Williams and Wilkins Co., Second Edition, 1970.

Davson, H., Ed., "The Eye," New York, Academic Press, 1962, 4 vols.

Graham, C. H., "Vision and Visual Perception," New York, John Wiley & Sons, 1965.

Helmholtz, H. von, "Physiological Optics," translated by J. P. C. Southall, Optical Society of America, 1924, New York, Dover Publications, Inc., 1962.

LeGrand, Y., "Light, Colour, and Vision," translated by R. W. G. Hunt, J. W. T. Walsh and F. R. W. Hunt, Second edition, London, Chapman and Hall, Ltd., 1968.

Piéron, H., "The Sensations," translated by M. H. Pirenne and B. C. Abbott, London, F. Müller, 1952.

Pirenne, M. H., "Vision and the Eye," London, Chapman & Hall, 1948.

Polyak, M., "The Vertebrate Visual System," Chicago, University of Chicago Press, 1957.

Smelser, G. K., Ed., "The Structure of the Eye," New York, Academic Press, 1961.

Weale, R. A., "The Eye and Its Function," London, Hatton Press Ltd., 1960.

Wolff, E., "The Anatomy of the Eye and Orbit," Philadelphia, Blakiston Co., 1948.

Cross-references: COLOR; LENS; LIGHT; LUMINANCE; OPTICS, GEOMETRICAL; OPTICS, PHYSICAL; PHOTON; REFLECTION; REFRACTION.

VITREOUS STATE

The vitreous state, or the glassy state, is a special metastable condition in which a substance can exist. A material in the vitreous state may be termed a noncrystalline solid or a rigid liquid. The attainment of the vitreous state is illustrated by the volume-temperature relationship of an ideal system in Fig. 1. When a liquid is cooled slowly, crystallization will usually occur when the temperature reaches the melting point T_m as described by the path a-b. In the case of a complex liquid, crystallization will similarly commence when the temperature reaches the liquidus. Crystallization is generally considered to take place by a two-step mechanism, namely, nucleation and then crystal growth. In the absence of crystallization, a liquid can be supercooled below T_m, and the cooling path is now described by a-c. Since the fluidity of a liquid generally exhibits an exponential dependence on temperature, progressive undercooling along a-c will be accompanied by a rapid increase of viscosity. If crystallization has still not occurred when point d is reached, the viscosity of the liquid will have reached 10^{13} poises. (By comparison, the viscosity of glycerol at room temperature is only 10 poises.) For a particular cooling rate, say 5 deg/min, the cooling curve will now follow d-e. At any temperature below that corresponding to the point d, the material is said to be in the vitreous state. It now has the rigidity of the corresponding crystalline solid, but its structure is still devoid of long-range order similar to that of the parent liquid. A substance in the vitreous state is called a glass.

At the point d, the viscosity of the supercooled liquid is 10^{13} poises. At such high viscos-

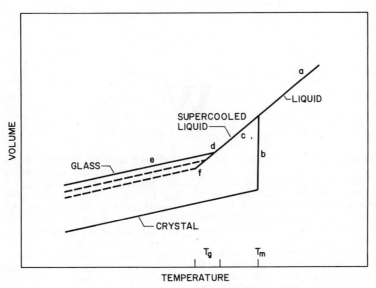

FIG. 1. Volume-temperature relationship of an ideal glass-forming system.

ity, molecular motions are retarded since the relaxation times are of the order of minutes and hours. The time taken for experimental measurements may now be actually less than the time needed to attain internal equilibrium. Thus for a particular cooling rate, an inflection will occur at d. For a slower cooling rate, d-e will be displaced to the first dashed line below it. For an even slower cooling rate, the inflection will occur at point f; the cooling curve will now be described by the lowest dashed curve. Similar behavior is shown by the heat content-temperature relationship of the system. The inflection points d and f, and hence the specific volume of a glass at the lower temperatures, are dependent on the cooling rate. The temperature region over which this inflection occurs is termed the glass-transition temperature T_g. Although the supercooled liquid at above T_g is metastable with respect to the crystalline phase, it is in internal thermodynamic equilibrium. A glass, however, is generally considered not to be in internal thermodynamic equilibrium.[1]

Many substances are easily rendered into the vitreous state by supercooling the melt. These include organic liquids such as toluene and the alcohols, polymeric materials, fused salts of the system $Ca(NO_3)_2$—KNO_3 and many silicates, borates, phosphates and their mixtures.[2] In general the ease of glass formation via the liquid is dependent on the crystallization kinetic constants as well as the cooling rate. Although the crystallization kinetic constants of metallic systems, for instance, are not favorable for glass formation, the vitreous state is attainable by very rapid cooling. The condensation of vapor at low temperatures can also yield noncrystalline solid phases. Little is known about the relationship between such phases and the more common glassy phase obtained from the cooling of the melt. Present theoretical interests are centered on the nature of the glass transition at T_g. Two important questions are: (a) Is the glass-transition region an iso-free volume state for all substances? (b) Is there a theoretical lower temperature limit to T_g? No unambiguous answers to these questions are presently available.

JOHN D. MACKENZIE

References

Kauzmann, W., "The Nature of the Glassy State and the Behavior of Liquids at Low Temperatures," *Chem. Rev.* **43**, 219 (1948).

Mackenzie, J. D., "Modern Aspects of the Vitreous State," Vol. 1, London, Butterworths, 1960.

Cross-references: CONDENSATION, CRYSTALLIZATION, CRYSTALLOGRAPHY.

W

WAVE MECHANICS

Introduction It has been known since the early part of the present century that systems of atomic dimensions do not obey the laws of classical mechanics, as formulated by Newton. A new mechanics has had to be constructed, and this is called *quantum mechanics*.

There were initially two apparently different formulations of quantum mechanics, one called MATRIX MECHANICS and the other *wave mechanics*. It was ultimately shown that the two formulations are completely equivalent and complicated quantum mechanical problems are nowadays usually solved by a combination of both. However, there are still many applications of quantum mechanics which can be treated by purely wave mechanical methods, and as these generally make a more direct appeal to physical intuition, it is perhaps worth while to give an account of wave mechanics quite separate from matrix mechanics.*

Waves and Particles The work of Planck, in 1900, on thermal radiation, and of Einstein, in 1905, on the photoelectric effect, suggested that light must, for some purposes, be regarded as consisting of particles, called *light quanta* or *photons*. The energy of a photon is given by

$$E = h\nu \qquad (1)$$

and its momentum by

$$p = h/\lambda \qquad (2)$$

where ν is the frequency and λ the wavelength of the light, and h is Planck's constant, which has the value 6.624×10^{-27} erg sec. On the other hand, diffraction phenomena, for example, can only be explained on the assumption that light consists of waves, so that neither the corpuscular nor the wave theory is completely satisfactory. In fact, it must simply be accepted that light can behave *either* as particles *or* as waves. The nature of a given experiment will emphasize one aspect or the other, and the relations between the two aspects are given by Eq. (1) and (2).

In 1924, de Broglie went further and suggested

*According to Dirac (1964), the validity of wave mechanics does not extend to quantum field theory, but it remains perfectly adequate in the domain of atomic and molecular physics.

that *any* moving particle, with mass m and speed v, will in some experiments display wavelike properties, the wavelength being given by Eq. (2), with $p = mv$. This purely theoretical suggestion received experimental confirmation in 1927, when Davisson and Germer observed the diffraction of a beam of electrons by a crystal of nickel, and similar results have since been obtained with beams of other kinds of particles, including atoms and molecules.

De Broglie's theory was the beginning of wave mechanics, but its further development was due to Schrödinger, who showed, in 1926, how the theory could be used to account for the existence of stationary states of atoms.

In 1911, Rutherford had proposed that an atom consists of a small nucleus surrounded by a planetary system of electrons. The electrons are continually accelerated; hence, according to classical electromagnetic theory, there should be a continual emission of radiation, accompanied by a diminution in the size of the electronic orbits and consequent increase in frequency. The existence of line spectra, that is, the emission of radiation in a discrete series of frequencies, and indeed the stability of matter itself, proves that this is not the case, and in 1913 Bohr suggested that an atom can exist in any one of a set of so-called *stationary states*, each with a definite energy, and with a finite energy difference between one and the next. Radiation is emitted only when an atom passes from a stationary state with energy E_1 to a state of lower energy E_2, and the frequency ν of the radiation is given by

$$h\nu = E_1 - E_2 \qquad (3)$$

Bohr attempted to graft this idea on to the classical picture of electrons describing planetary orbits about the nucleus by postulating that only certain orbits were permissible. This theory successfully explained the line spectrum of hydrogen and had several other partial successes, but it was soon superseded by the more revolutionary but also more versatile quantum mechanics.

The Schrödinger Equation According to de Broglie's theory a freely moving particle should be represented by a wave of the form

$$\Psi(x,t) = A \exp\left[2\pi i\left(\frac{x}{\lambda} - \nu t\right)\right]$$

where A is a constant. Using Eq. (1) and (2), this becomes

$$\Psi(x,t) = A \exp [i(px - Et)/\hbar]$$

$$= \psi(x) \exp (- iEt/\hbar) \qquad (4)$$

where $\hbar = h/2\pi$ and

$$\psi(x) = A \exp (ipx/\hbar) \qquad (5)$$

is the time-independent part of the wave (we shall deal with the time-dependent factor later). Differentiation shows that

$$\frac{d^2 \psi}{dx^2} = - \frac{p^2}{\hbar^2} \psi \qquad (6)$$

However, the energy of the particle is

$$E = \frac{p^2}{2m} + V$$

the first term on the right-hand side being the kinetic energy and the second term the potential energy, which is constant if the particle is moving under no forces. Equation (6) thus becomes

$$\frac{d^2 \psi}{dx^2} + \frac{2m}{\hbar^2}(E - V)\psi = 0 \qquad (7)$$

Although this equation has been plausibly derived only for a free particle, Schrödinger assumed that it also applies to a particle moving under a force, so that the potential energy V is a function of x. It is known as the *Schrödinger equation* or the *wave equation* for a particle moving in one dimension, and the function $\psi(x)$ is called the *wave function*. We will consider the interpretation of ψ below, but meanwhile let us note that ψ is to be *single-valued*, *continuous*, *smooth* [except at infinities of $V(x)$] and *finite everywhere*. Also, although $\psi = 0$ is always a solution of Eq. (7), it is not permitted as a wave function.

Particle in a One-dimensional Box That the Schrödinger equation does lead to discrete energy values, at least when classical mechanics would predict a limited range of motion or a *bound* particle, can easily be seen by considering a particle moving in one dimension between infinite potential barriers—this is known as a one-dimensional box.

Suppose that the potential energy is zero from $x = 0$ to $x = L$, and infinite everywhere else. In the region of zero potential energy, Eq. (7) becomes

$$\frac{d^2 \psi}{dx^2} + \frac{2mE}{\hbar^2} \psi = 0 \qquad (8)$$

with the general solution

$$\psi = A \cos \sqrt{\frac{2mE}{\hbar^2}} x + B \sin \sqrt{\frac{2mE}{\hbar^2}} x \qquad (9)$$

The condition of finiteness on ψ (which we will not consider in detail) demands that it vanish in the region of infinite potential energy and because of the condition of continuity, we must then have $\psi(0) = \psi(L) = 0$. The only solutions in the region of zero potential energy satisfying these boundary conditions are of the form

$$\psi_n = B_n \sin \frac{n\pi x}{L}, \qquad n = 1, 2, 3, \cdots$$

$$(10)$$

corresponding to the energy values E_n given by

$$\sqrt{\frac{2mE_n}{\hbar^2}} = \frac{n\pi}{L}$$

or

$$E_n = \frac{n^2 \pi^2 \hbar^2}{2mL^2} \qquad (11)$$

($n = 0$ gives $\psi \equiv 0$, which is not allowed).

The energy E can thus have any one of an infinite set of discrete values, corresponding to the integral values of n, but no other value. These values are called the *eigenvalues* of the Schrödinger equation or *energy levels* of the system, and the corresponding wave functions are called the *eigenfunctions* of the equation and represent the stationary states of the system.

Operators The Hamiltonian $H(x,p)$ of the one-dimensional system we have been considering is simply the energy expressed in terms of the momentum p and coordinate x, and the *equation of energy* is

$$H(x,p) \equiv \frac{p^2}{2m} + V(x) = E \qquad (12)$$

If we formally convert this into an *operator* equation by letting

$$p = \frac{\hbar}{i} \frac{d}{dx} \qquad (13)$$

(the coordinate x becomes the operator "multiply by x", but this is trivial), and allow both sides to operate on a function $\psi(x)$, we obtain

$$- \frac{\hbar^2}{2m} \frac{d^2 \psi}{dx^2} + V\psi = E\psi \qquad (14)$$

which, when rearranged, is seen to be the Schrödinger equation [Eq. (7)].

The representation of dynamical variables by operators is fundamental to quantum mechanics, but the choice of operators made above is not unique. It may be confirmed by differentiation that

$$\frac{\hbar}{i} \frac{d}{dx} (x\psi) - x \frac{\hbar}{i} \frac{d\psi}{dx} = \frac{\hbar}{i} \psi$$

and using Eq. (13), this gives the operator equation

$$px - xp = \frac{\hbar}{i} \qquad (15)$$

The operator on the left is called the *commutator* of p and x, and is generally written $[p, x]$. Equation (15) is the basic equation of matrix mechanics and existed before Schrödinger's equation, p and x then being represented by MATRICES. This shows in an elementary way the close connection between wave mechanics and matrix mechanics.

Particles in Three Dimensions Equation (13) gives the clue to the extension of Schrödinger's equation to systems of one or more particles moving in three dimensions. We first write down the Hamiltonian of the system and transform each Cartesian component of momentum into a differential operator like Eq. (13) with respect to its corresponding (canonically conjugate) coordinate. For example, for a single particle moving in three dimensions, the Hamiltonian is

$$H(x, y, z, p_x, p_y, p_z) = \frac{1}{2m}(p_x{}^2 + p_y{}^2 + p_z{}^2)$$
$$+ V(x, y, z)$$

where p_x, p_y, p_z are the Cartesian components of the momentum, and the equation of energy is

$$H(x, y, z, p_x, p_y, p_z) = E \qquad (16)$$

If we transform the latter into an operator equation by writing

$$p_x = \frac{\hbar}{i}\frac{\partial}{\partial x}, \quad p_y = \frac{\hbar}{i}\frac{\partial}{\partial y}, \quad p_z = \frac{\hbar}{i}\frac{\partial}{\partial z}$$
$$(17)$$

(partial derivatives are now required as several variables are present), and operate upon a function $\psi(x, y, z)$, we obtain the equation

$$-\frac{\hbar^2}{2m}\left(\frac{\partial^2\psi}{\partial x^2} + \frac{\partial^2\psi}{\partial y^2} + \frac{\partial^2\psi}{\partial z^2}\right)$$
$$+ V(x, y, z)\psi = E\psi \qquad (18)$$

which is the Schrödinger equation of the system. The essential correctness of this equation has been amply demonstrated by many successful applications (this is, of course, the *only* justification of any of the postulates of quantum mechanics). In particular, in the case of the hydrogen atom, where there is a single electron moving under the Coulomb attraction of a single proton (which may as a good approximation be considered to be at rest), the equation can be solved analytically, and the energy levels so found, together with the Bohr frequency rule [Eq. (3)], correctly give the line spectrum of hydrogen.

The extension to many particles is straightforward; in the Hamiltonian of the system, the substitutions of Eq. (17) are made for the momentum components of each particle of the system, and the equation of energy is thus transformed into the Schrödinger equation. Again the equation has had many successful applications, an early one being the calculation of the energy of the normal helium atom by Hylleraas in 1930, which the earlier Bohr theory failed to do. Unfortunately, owing to the interaction of the electrons, the equation cannot be solved analytically for many-electron systems and resort must be made to approximate methods of solution which have become extremely complicated in recent years [see e.g., Raimes (1972)].

Intrepretation of the Wave Function Let us consider the Schrödinger equation for a single particle moving in three dimensions. This is a linear equation, so that if ψ is a solution, so also is $C\psi$, where C is any constant. This means that (in most cases) we can choose ψ so that

$$\int_{-\infty}^{\infty}\int_{-\infty}^{\infty}\int_{-\infty}^{\infty} |\psi(x, y, z)|^2\, dx\, dy\, dz = 1$$
$$(19)$$

The function ψ is generally complex and $|\psi|$ is its *modulus* ($|\psi|^2 = \psi^*\psi$, where ψ^* is the complex conjugate of ψ). If it satisfies Eq. (19), the function ψ is said to be *normalized*.

The interpretation of ψ demands that it be normalized. If this is not possible, owing to the divergence of the integral in Eq. (19), as is the case with a free particle, then normalization has to be affected artificially by enclosing the system in a large box.

It was proposed by Born, in 1926, that if the particle is in a stationary state, with normalized wave function ψ, then $|\psi|^2$ may be interpreted as a *probability density*, such that

$$|\psi(x, y, z)|^2\, dx\, dy\, dz$$

is the *probability* of finding the particle in the small volume element $dx\, dy\, dz$ at the point (x, y, z).

It is clear from this why normalization is necessary—Eq. (19) expresses the fact that the probability of finding the particle *somewhere* is unity.

An important extension of this interpretation, which we will not justify in detail, relates to the *average* or *expectation value* $\langle f \rangle$ of a dynamical variable f (such as momentum) for a system in a state ψ, i.e., the average of a large number of measurements of f made on a system in this state. It is found that

$$\langle f \rangle = \int_{-\infty}^{\infty}\int_{-\infty}^{\infty}\int_{-\infty}^{\infty} \psi^* f_{\text{op}}\psi\, dx\, dy\, dz$$
$$(20)$$

where f_{op} is the quantum mechanical operator representing f. Here we have restricted ourselves to a single-particle system, but the same applies to systems of any number of particles, so long as the integral is a multiple integral taken throughout the full range of all the variables appearing in ψ.

The interpretation of ψ, or rather of $|\psi|^2$ (ψ itself has no physical significance), which we have presented above, gives rise to a fundamental and important difference between classical mechanics and quantum mechanics. According to the latter, there is a finite probability of finding a particle in regions of space where its presence would be forbidden by classical mechanics—regions where its kinetic energy would be negative.

Let us take as an example the linear harmonic oscillator. Suppose a particle of mass m is moving along the x axis under the action of a force $-kx$ (k is positive) directed towards the origin. Classically, the particle executes simple harmonic motion with frequency $\omega/2\pi$, where $\omega = \sqrt{k/m}$. It is easy to see that the potential energy is $V(x) = \frac{1}{2}m\omega^2 x^2$, if the zero of potential energy is taken to be at $x = 0$, so that the Schrödinger equation [Eq. (7)] becomes

$$\frac{d^2\psi}{dx^2} + \frac{2m}{\hbar^2}\left(E - \frac{1}{2}m\omega^2 x^2\right)\psi = 0 \quad (21)$$

It may be verified by substitution that the function

$$\psi_0 = \exp\left(-m\omega x^2/2\hbar\right) \quad (22)$$

satisfies this equation, provided E has the value

$$E_0 = \frac{1}{2}\hbar\omega \quad (23)$$

This is, in fact, the *ground state* of the oscillator, that is to say, E_0 is the lowest energy level.

Now according to classical mechanics, the particle, having energy E_0, would be confined to a region of the x axis whose limits are given by setting $V(x) = E_0$, that is, $x = \pm\sqrt{\hbar/m\omega}$. However, ψ_0 tends to zero asymptotically as x tends to $\pm\infty$, so that, according to the interpretation of $|\psi|^2$, there is a finite probability of finding the particle at very large distances from the origin. This is known as the *tunnel effect* and has an important application in the theory of radioactive decay.

The foregoing example demonstrates another point in which quantum mechanics differs from classical mechanics. According to the latter, the oscillator could have zero energy (when the particle is at rest at the origin), but this is not permitted in quantum mechanics—the *lowest* energy the oscillator can have is $\frac{1}{2}\hbar\omega$, which is called its *zero-point energy*.

Time-Dependence So far we have only considered the stationary states of a system and, furthermore, only of a *conservative* system, i.e., one whose energy is constant. However, if a system is subject to a disturbance which varies with time, for example, due to the passage of a charged particle or a light wave through it, there is a probability that the system will in a certain time make a transition from its initial stationary state to some other stationary state. In order to calculate such *transition probabilities*, it is necessary to consider explicitly the time dependence of wave functions, which we have so far neglected, and this entails the use of a modified Schrödinger equation.

Differentiation of the function $\Psi(x, t)$, Eq. (4) gives

$$E\Psi = i\hbar\frac{\partial\Psi}{\partial t} \quad (24)$$

which suggests that the energy E should in general be represented by the operator

$$E = i\hbar\frac{\partial}{\partial t} \quad (25)$$

If we convert the equation of energy [Eq. (12)] for a one-dimensional system into an operator, using Eqs. (13) and (25), and if we allow both sides to operate upon a function $\Psi(x, t)$, we obtain

$$-\frac{\hbar^2}{2m}\frac{\partial^2\Psi}{\partial x^2} + V\Psi = i\hbar\frac{\partial\Psi}{\partial t} \quad (26)$$

[the derivative in Eq. (13) has been replaced by a partial derivative as we now have two variables, x and t]. This is known as the *time-dependent Schrödinger equation*; it applies even when the potential energy function V depends explicitly upon the time. If more than one dimension or several particles are involved, it is only necessary to use the appropriate quantum mechanical Hamiltonian operator on the left-hand side. It should be emphasized that this equation has *not* been rigorously derived, but only plausibly suggested. No such derivation exists, either for Eq. (26) or for Eq. (7)—their justification lies entirely in their successful application.

If we are, in fact, dealing with a conservative system, so that V does not depend explicitly upon t, it is easy to verify by substitution (and indeed this is obvious from the way in which the equation was derived) that Eq. (26) has solutions of the form

$$\Psi(x, t) = \psi(x)\exp\left(-iEt/\hbar\right) \quad (27)$$

where $\psi(x)$ is an eigenfunction of Eq. (7) and E is its corresponding eigenvalue. The function $\psi(x)$ is the time-independent wave function of a stationary state, and $\Psi(x, t)$ is the time-dependent wave function. Since it is not ψ but $|\psi|^2$ which has physical significance, and Eq. (27) shows that $|\Psi|^2 = |\psi|^2$, it is clear that so long as we are dealing with the stationary states of a conservative system, the time dependence of the wave function is of no importance.

Conclusion The foregoing account has been confined to the elementary ideas of wave mechanics, due to de Broglie and Schrödinger. No mention has been made, for example, of the relativistic wave equation, due to Dirac, or of the important concept of electron spin. Further information on wave mechanics, its applications, and its relationship with the rest of quantum mechanics can be obtained from the article on MATRIX MECHANICS in this book and from a vast number of books of which those listed in the references are a very small sample.

S. RAIMES

References

Born, M., "Atomic Physics," Eighth edition, London, Blackie and Son Limited, 1969.
Dirac, P. A. M., *Nature*, **203**, 115 (1964).
Merzbacher, E., "Quantum Mechanics," Second edition, New York, John Wiley & Sons, 1970.
Mott, N. F., and Sneddon, I. N., "Wave Mechanics and Its Applications," London, Oxford University Press, 1948; reprinted, New York, Dover, 1963.
Raimes, S., "The Wave Mechanics of Electrons in Metals," Amsterdam, North-Holland Pub. Co., 1961.
Raimes, S., "Many-Electron Theory," Amsterdam, North-Holland Pub. Co., 1972.

Cross-references: MATHEMATICAL PRINCIPLES OF QUANTUM MECHANICS, MATRICES, MATRIX MECHANICS, PHOTOELECTRICITY, PHOTON, PHYSICAL CHEMISTRY, QUANTUM THEORY, SCHRÖDINGER EQUATION.

WAVE MOTION

Wave motion can be said to be the most common and the most important type of motion that we know. It is through wave motion that sounds come to our ears, light to our eyes, electromagnetic waves to our radios and television sets, and tidal waves and earthquakes to our cities. Wave motion can be defined as that mechanism by which energy is transported from a source to a distant receiver without the transfer of matter between the two points.

Waves can be classified according to the manner of their production, namely, a vibrating material object or, in the case of electromagnetic waves, sources such as electrical oscillations in an aerial. The wind blowing across water causes surface waves; a piezoelectric quartz crystal vibrating under an applied electric field generates underwater wave motion. Or, waves could be classified according to the medium in which they travel. The most useful classification, however, involves the direction of motion of the particles of a medium (or of an electric or magnetic field in the case of electromagnetic waves) relative to the direction in which the energy of the wave is itself propagated. Such a classification is useful because

wave motions falling into the same class according to the selected criterion will have other similar properties.

Wave motion can be most easily understood if one considers first, as an example, wave motion in a horizontal, stretched string and then, by analogy, other types of wave motion. If one end of such a string is moved up and down, a rhythmic disturbance travels along the string. Each particle of the string moves up and down, while, at the same time, the wave motion moves along the length of the string. It is the state of the particles that advances, the medium as a whole returning to its initial condition after the disturbance has passed. Such a wave motion, one in which the vibratory motion of the medium is at right angles, or essentially at right angles, to the direction of propagation, is called transverse. Surface waves on liquids are transverse; so also are electromagnetic waves (x-rays, visible light, radio waves, and so forth), but here, since electromagnetic waves can travel in a vacuum, we must think of the electric and magnetic fields associated with such waves as changing in intensity in a direction at right angles to the direction of propagation.

Another type of wave motion, one termed longitudinal or compressional, can occur only in material media and has the particles of the medium moving forward and backward along the direction of propagation of the wave. Compressional waves are exemplified by sound waves in air, in which a volume in the path of the wave is alternately compressed and rarefied. These variations in pressure are very small. Even for the loudest sounds that an ear can tolerate, the pressure variations are of the order of 280 dyne/cm^2 (above and below atmospheric pressure of about 1 000 000 dyne/cm^2).

Yet another type of wave motion is the torsional wave, which can take place only in solids. Less frequently seen, this type can be demonstrated by a long helical spring supported on a flat surface. As one end of the spring is given a quick, momentary twist about the axis of the spring, a pulse travels down the spring.

Whatever the type of wave, certain useful definitions can be set forth and general statements made. Phase describes the relative position and direction of movement of a particle in its periodic motion as it participates in wave motion, or the relative intensity at a point of the electric field accompanying electromagnetic waves. Frequency is the number of complete vibrations performed per unit of time by a particle (or field) through which a wave passes. Period is the time required for one complete vibration of a particle participating in wave motion. Wavelength is the distance between any two points that are in phase on successive waves or pulses. The velocity of a wave is the product of the frequency and the wavelength. All waves except electromagnetic waves require a medium for their propagation.

Wave motions may vary in the energy they

transport per unit of time. This property depends on the amplitude. The amplitude of a wave in a string, to take again an example, is the maximum displacement experienced by the particles of the string as they move from their equilibrium positions. The intensity of the wave is the power (energy per second) passing through a square centimeter perpendicular to the wave front, and it is related to the square of the amplitude. In the case of sound, intensity is related to loudness.

Two or more waves crossing one another's paths will not cause any change in the direction, frequency, or intensity of any of them. The displacement effects of two or more waves of the same kind passing through a medium are additive at any point; and at any moment, the displacement at a point is the vector sum of the separate displacements caused by the separate waves. Two transverse wave motions passing at right angles through a point in a medium cause a particle at that point to perform a path called a Lissajous figure, whose form depends upon the amplitudes and frequencies of the two waves and upon their phase relationship.

Standing (stationary) waves are produced by combining two similar wave trains moving in opposite directions. Not themselves waves, they are patterns of vibration that simulate waves standing still. An example is exhibited by a string one end of which is fastened rigidly and the other vibrated transversely at a constant frequency. Waves traveling down the string from the source meet waves reflected from the fixed end. If the tension in the string is adjusted properly, the string can be made to display nodes, points where the string does not move transversely because at those points the two waves cancel the effects of one another. Between the regularly spaced nodes are found the antinodes or loops where the two waves reinforce one another.

Wave motion also experiences the phenomena of absorption, reflection, refraction, interference, diffraction, beats, resonance, and polarization. However, longitudinal waves do not exhibit the property of polarization.

Complex waves can be analyzed into sets of simple waves according to the principles of Fourier analysis, where by "simple waves" are meant waves whose variations of displacement with time can be represented by sine curves.

Compressional waves require about 5 seconds to travel a mile in air, 1 second to travel a mile in water, and 1/3 second to travel a mile in iron. Though varying in speed from material to material, low-frequency compressional waves travel with the same speed in a particular medium, i.e., they do not exhibit dispersion. Small variations in speed sometimes found at high frequencies are due to relaxation phenomena.

Compressional waves in a fluid have a speed v that depends only on the density ρ and the adiabatic bulk modulus β of the medium according to the relation

$$v = \sqrt{\frac{\beta}{\rho}}$$

In solids, the speed of compressional waves is given by the relation

$$v = \sqrt{\frac{Y}{\rho}}$$

where Y is Young's Modulus. Thus it may be seen that a study of the propagation of waves in a medium gives important information about the medium.

Transverse waves on the surfaces of liquids do not travel with a fixed speed dependent only on the properties of the liquid. Their speed depends upon their wavelength and amplitude, the depth of the liquid, and whether the surface is confined, as in a canal. Surface tension waves on the surface of water have wavelengths less than 1.7 cm, while gravity waves on the surface of water have wavelengths greater than 1.7 cm. Ripples on water often move only 30 cm/sec. They have higher velocity as their wavelength becomes smaller. In contrast, for example, ocean waves measuring 244 m (800 feet) from crest to crest have been found to travel 20 m/sec (45 mph).

Transverse waves in strings (or wires) travel with a speed that depends only on the tension in the string T and the mass per unit length of the string m, according to the formula

$$v = \sqrt{T/m}$$

Electromagnetic waves of all frequencies travel with the same speed in a vacuum (2.9979×10^{10} cm/sec). In a particular medium, however, different frequencies (colors in the case of visible light) travel with different speeds. The speeds at particular frequencies also vary with the media.

The observed wavelength of a wave motion, whether it be longitudinal or transverse, depends on whether the source and the receiver are moving relative to one another, a phenomenon known as the Doppler effect. In the case of electromagnetic waves, the Doppler effect depends only on the relative velocity; in the case of a compressional wave, as for instance, sound, the magnitude of the effect depends not only on the relative velocity of the source and receiver but upon which is in motion with respect to the transmitting medium. In both cases the wavelength of the wave is increased if the source and receiver move away from one another and decreased if they move toward one another.

In some uses of wave motion, care must be taken to differentiate between "phase" and "group" velocity. The group velocity of a wave is the velocity usually observed, and the energy in a wave is transmitted with the group velocity. For example, measurements of the

speed of light wherein the time for "chopped" pulses to travel a known distance is determined, result in values of the group velocity. On the other hand, again for example, if one carefully observes the expanding group of ripples when a stone is dropped into water, the group travels with one velocity, the group velocity, while a particular wave crest will advance through the group to the outer leading edge and exhibit the phase velocity. The difference in the two velocities depends on the wavelength in the material medium and on the dispersion, i.e., on the change in phase velocity with wavelength. In a vacuum—interstellar space for instance—the two velocities are the same for light, whatever the color.

ROBERT T. LAGEMANN

References

Alanso, M., and Finn, E. J., "Fundamental University Physics," Vol. II, "Fields and Waves," Reading, Mass., Addison-Wesley Press, 1967.

Towne, D. H., "Wave Phenomena," Reading, Mass., Addison-Wesley Press, 1967.

Strong, J., "Concepts of Classical Optics," San Francisco, W. H. Freeman and Co., 1957.

Cross-references: ACOUSTICS, DOPPLER EFFECT, DYNAMICS, ELECTROMAGNETIC THEORY, HEARING, INTERFERENCE AND INTERFEROMETRY, LIGHT, MICROWAVE TRANSMISSION, MUSICAL SOUND, REFLECTION, REFRACTION, RESONANCE, SEISMOLOGY, SONAR, ULTRASONICS.

WAVEGUIDES

Fundamental Principles A waveguide is a hollow pipe used as a transmission line. Its cross section is usually rectangular, square, or round, but irregular shapes are sometimes used for special applications. The electromagnetic wave in the waveguide can have an infinite variety of patterns, called modes, and, in general, these modes are of two kinds. In one set of modes, the electric vector is always transverse to the direction of propagation; in the other set, the magnetic vector is always transverse to this direction. The former are called TE or *transverse electric* modes, the latter are TM or *transverse magnetic*. Two subscripts are used to designate a particular mode. The first subscript (in either kind of mode) designates the number of half-wave variations of the electric field across the wide dimension of the waveguide, and the second designates the number of half-wave variations of the electric field across the narrower dimension. Thus, a $TE_{2,1}$ mode would designate a field pattern in which the electric field is always transverse to the propagation direction and in which the electric field has two half-wave variations across the wide dimension and one across the narrow.

For each mode of operation there is a cutoff wavelength, determined by the size and shape of the waveguide. For the $TE_{1,0}$ mode in a rectangular waveguide, the cutoff wavelength is twice the wide dimension. This means that when the signal wavelength is less than cutoff, the energy will propagate in the waveguide; but, when it is greater, the energy is attenuated exponentially. In the latter case, the frequency is too low to propagate through the waveguide and is said to be "below cutoff." Cutoff for other modes in rectangular guides is higher than for the $TE_{1,0}$. Consequently, for any frequency it is possible to choose dimensions so that only the $TE_{1,0}$ mode is above cutoff, and all other modes will be rapidly attenuated. The $TE_{1,0}$ mode is called the *dominant mode* and is the one most commonly used.

The attenuation through a waveguide is a function of the material of which it is fabricated. With suitable materials, the waveguide will have less attenuation at a particular frequency than a coaxial line of the same size. The losses in the waveguide are copper losses in the walls, and consequently the walls should be made of a highly conducting material. At microwave frequencies the skin depth is only a few thousandths of an inch. Therefore, it is common practice to make the waveguide out of an inexpensive material such as brass, or a lightweight material, such as aluminum, and then to plate it with silver or copper for good conductivity. For prevention of oxidation, the conducting layer may be plated with a thin coating of rhodium. However, since rhodium has a higher resistivity than silver, this coating must be thinner than the skin depth of rhodium so that the current flows mainly in the silver layer.

Brass is the most common metal for waveguides because it is easily machined and easily soldered. For airborne applications where weight is a consideration, aluminum or magnesium is preferred. At very high frequencies, above 40 GHz silver is frequently used, since the amount of metal used is small and costs less than the cost of a brass guide, silver plated.

Besides the simpler construction and lower loss, waveguides have higher power carrying capacity than coaxial cables. The waveguide is a completely shielded transmission line and may be bent and twisted with no radiation loss. However, whenever the waveguide is made to change direction, care must be taken to keep the cross section uniform or there will be a reflection from the discontinuity.

All discontinuities in waveguides are equivalent to lumped-circuit elements in conventional transmission lines. A screw inserted in the broad wall or a dent in this wall is a shunt capacity. A post across the waveguide is a shunt inductance. An iris across the waveguide with its edges parallel to the voltage vector is a shunt inductance. If its edges are parallel to the magnetic vector, the iris is a shunt capacity. A change in dimensions of the waveguide is a change

in characteristic impedance, and a quarter-wave length of guide with new dimensions is thus a quarter-wave transformer. All of these elements are used to match out the effects of more complicated mismatches.

In matching impedances or making quarter-wave transformers, the wavelength used is not the wavelength in free space, for the wave travels in the waveguide at a velocity apparently greater than that of light. Actually, this is the *phase velocity* of the wave and is the apparent speed of an unmodulated wave. The signal or modulation on the wave travels at a speed less than that of light called the *group velocity*. The product of the group velocity and the phase velocity is equal to the square of the speed of light. The phase velocity divided by the frequency is equal to the quantity called the *guide wavelength*, which is used for all matching calculations.

Waveguide Components Two pieces of waveguide or two waveguide components may be joined together by means of flanges soldered on the ends of the guides. Flanges are of two types: (1) *cover* flanges, which are flat plane surfaces, and (2) choke flanges, which have a quarter-wave deep groove cut in them. This groove is also a quarter-wave from the waveguide wall. The choke presents a short-circuit impedance between the two pieces of guide even if they are separated slightly or misaligned. It is thus possible to have a microwave coupling which is a short at radio frequency and an open circuit at direct current. By using a quarter-wave transformer, the reverse is also possible.

A choke joint is also used in a rotary or motional joint, where it is desired to move one waveguide with respect to another and at the same time to maintain electrical continuity. This goal is accomplished by physically separating the two pieces and using the choke to present an electrical short circuit at the microwave frequency.

In the rotary joint and in other microwave circuits, it is necessary to change from one form of waveguide to another or from waveguide to coaxial line. The problem in designing such adapters is basically one of matching impedances over a required frequency range. Coaxial line-to-waveguide adapters have been built with a voltage standing-wave ratio (VSWR) of 1.10 or better over a 30 per cent frequency band. Adapters from the dominant mode ($TE_{1,0}$) in rectangular guide to the dominant mode ($TE_{1,1}$) in round guide have been built with a VSWR of 1.05 over the same frequency range. In both cases the rectangular guide may be either perpendicular to, or in line with, the other transmission line.

The VSWR is measured by means of a *slotted* line. This is a section of waveguide, identical to that being tested, with a thin slot in the center of one broad wall, parallel to the direction of propagation. A probe is lightly coupled through the slot, and as it is moved along the slot, volt-age maxima may be determined. This information can be used to calculate the impedance of the piece being tested.

In making the impedance measurements, the piece being tested must be properly terminated. That is, in order to measure only the discontinuity at the face of the slotted line, there must be no other discontinuities reflecting energy back to this point. The termination or *matched load* is usually a piece of waveguide containing an absorbent material which has been tapered to a point in the direction from which the energy is coming. Absorbent materials frequently used are resistance cards, carbon, plastics loaded with metal particles, sand, and wood. For very accurate measurements, the load material may be slid along the guide to determine whether it is properly matched. If a load is perfect there will be no voltage variations observed at the slotted line probe as the load is moved in the guide.

A tee is a component consisting of a straight piece of waveguide with another piece fastened to it at right angles. The junction is open so that energy fed into any arm sees two possible paths at the junction. When the auxiliary arm is fastened to the broad wall of the main waveguide, the voltage or E vector in the side arm is perpendicular to the E vector in the main guide. Such a tee is called an *E-plane tee*. When properly matched, energy fed into the E-arm will divide equally in the other two arms but 180° out of phase. This tee is also called a *series junction tee*. When the auxiliary arm is fastened to the narrow wall of the main waveguide, the magnetic or H vector in the side arm is perpendicular to the H vector in the main guide. This is an *H-plane tee* or *shunt junction tee*. When properly matched, energy fed into the H-arm will divide equally and in phase in the other two arms.

When the component has both an E-arm and and an H-arm at the same point in the main line, it is called a *hybrid tee*. (The two main line terminals are now called side arms.) When properly matched, the tee has special properties and is called a *magic tee*. In this tee, energy fed into the E-arm or the H-arm divides equally in the other two arms and there is no coupling between the E- and H-arms. Energy fed into one side arm divides equally between the E and H arms, and there is no coupling to the other side arm.

When energy is fed into both side arms, the algebraic sum of the signal intensities appears at the H-arm, and the difference appears at the E-arm.

When two waveguides are joined together by two or more coupling paths, it is possible to choose dimensions such that energy in the first guide will be coupled a predetermined amount to the second and will travel in only one direction in the second guide. Then the output at one terminal in the second guide will be a measure of the power flowing in one direction only in the first guide. This component is called a *directional coupler*.

A piece of waveguide with two large discontinuities will have strong reflections between them. If the two discontinuities are spaced a multiple of half wavelengths apart, the reflections will reinforce each other and the section will be *resonant*. A resonant section or cavity is analogous to a fixed tuned circuit at lower frequencies. If the spacing of the discontinuities is adjustable, it is a variable tuned circuit. Since the frequency or resonance depends on the spacing, resonant cavities are used as wavemeters. The storage factor Q of the cavity depends upon the conductivity of the walls, the shape, the magnitude of the discontinuities, and the lightness of coupling. With silver plated walls and short-circuits, Q's above 5000 have been obtained.

Attenuators and phase shifters are made by moving a piece of material into the waveguide so that it couples with the electric field. The motion can be calibrated and related to the amount of attenuation or phase shift. If the material is lossy, the component is an attenuator. If the material has low loss, but a dielectric constant more than unity, the velocity of propagation through it will be different from that in the empty guide, and phase shift results.

GERSHON J. WHEELER

References

Adam, Stephen F., "Microwave Theory and Applications," Englewood Cliffs, N.J., Prentice-Hall, 1969.
Wheeler, Gershon J., "Introduction to Microwaves," Englewood Cliffs, N.J. Prentice-Hall, 1963.

Cross-references: CAPACITANCE, DIELECTRIC THEORY, INDUCTANCE, MICROWAVE TRANSMISSION, PROPAGATION OF ELECTROMAGNETIC WAVES.

WEAK INTERACTIONS

The weak interactions present a fascinating aspect of the problem of elementary particles. They appear at first to be totally unrelated to the other interactions that we know, nonetheless there have been discovered striking regularities among them, which can only be described in terms of symmetries that were originally ascribed to strong interactions alone. We present here a brief history of the subject, which has been marked by many surprises.

To avoid the difficulties found in understanding processes of β-decay (see RADIOACTIVITY), in 1931 Pauli suggested that the emission of a β-particle from a nucleus is always accompanied by that of a spin-$\frac{1}{2}$ neutral particle of small mass, which takes account of energy and angular momentum conservation in β-decay. Calorimetric measurements of the average energy release in a β-decay transition agree quite well with the value calculated from direct measurement of the β-decay spectrum, indicating that the hypothetical particles, which were called neutrinos, must interact extremely weakly with matter, since they escape from the apparatus without giving up any measurable energy. A quantitative theory of β-decay, incorporating the NEUTRINO hypothesis, was formulated in 1934 by Fermi, who wrote down the simplest relativistic expressions that would describe the basic β-transition: the transformation of a neutron into a proton accompanied by the creation of an electron and a neutrino. This theory has been strikingly successful in describing all aspects of β-decay—with one qualification to be described later—and is the one employed to this day. It could be anticipated from the weakness of the neutrino's interaction with matter that the coupling constant characteristic of β-decay would be small; it is in fact extremely small.[*] Adopting a simile of Lord Rutherford, one may say that from the point of view of the nucleus, β-decay practically never happens! To judge the scale, we note that lifetimes for β-decay are commonly several minutes whereas γ-transitions of similar energy occur in nanoseconds or less.

The success of Fermi's theory in accounting for the shapes of β-spectra and the dependence of the lifetimes on the available energy release could be regarded as indirect evidence for the existence of the neutrino; there were also other indications such as the occurrence of the predicted nuclear recoil after processes of orbital electron capture, a phenomenon predicted by the theory. Nonetheless, there was considerable satisfaction when the existence of the neutrino was directly demonstrated by Cowan and Reines in 1955 (for Reines' discussion see NEUTRINO). They used the intense neutrino flux arising from free neutron decays near a reactor to induce inverse β-decay, i.e., the conversion of a proton into a neutron with the emission of a positron, at roughly the expected rate. A similar experiment by Davis gave a negative result. In Davis' case, however, the reaction sought was the inverse of a β^+-decay transition although the neutrinos available to him were the same as those used by Cowan and Reines, i.e., neutrinos arising from the β^--decay of neutrons. The nonoccurrence of the Davis reactions demonstrates that the neutrinos emitted in β^--decays must be physically distinct from the neutrinos associated with β^+-decay. This conclusion is supported by the absence of neutrinoless double β-decay, a process in which the neutrino from the β-decay of one nucleon could be reabsorbed within the same nucleus to induce the β-transition of a second nucleon. Davis subsequently enlarged his apparatus [using 610 tons of dry-cleaning fluid $(C_2 Cl_4)$!] to obtain the extreme sensitivity at which he should expect to see reactions induced by neutrinos emitted together with B$^+$-particles in fusion reactions in the interior

---

[*]An average β-decay neutrino must pass through a thickness of matter of the order of 10^{20} g/cm^2 before suffering an interaction.

of the sun. At latest report,[4] the low rate of events which he finds is about an order of magnitude below that expected from current solar-model calculations. Whether this reflects our ignorance of the solar interior or a failure in our understanding of weak interactions is not certain at the moment.

Universal Fermi Interaction The μ-mesons, or muons (see ELEMENTARY PARTICLES), which were originally identified with Yukawa's mesons, were found to interact only very weakly with matter. In fact, it was noted that their absorption could be regarded as a process exactly like electron capture, i.e., by an interaction just like that of β-decay, with even the same coupling constant! The decay of a muon into an electron and two neutral particles, presumably neutrinos, was also accounted for by assuming a Fermi coupling of these four particles, again with a coupling constant of the same magnitude. This led to the hypothesis of a Universal Fermi interaction between fermions, and after the discovery of "strange" particles (see STRONG INTERACTIONS), the natural extension of this hypothesis to include hyperons led to a qualitative understanding of all strange-particle decays. The relatively meager data available on hyperon β-decays is accounted for quite adequately by the Fermi theory provided one uses coupling constants somewhat smaller than for nuclear β-decay. To explain this in terms of a Universal Fermi interaction one must modify the definition of universality, in a way suggested by Cabibbo.

The Universal Fermi Interaction does not, however, act between any set of four fermions. Interactions involving an electron or a muon always include a neutrino; furthermore, simple selection rules are found to operate for the weak interactions of strongly interacting particles. On the other hand, detailed experiments have revealed that the form of the Fermi Interaction is that of a current-current coupling, just as the electromagnetic interaction of two systems may be regarded as the interaction between their currents. It has therefore been suggested that the Fermi interaction may arise as a result of the interaction between currents which generate a vector field similar to the electromagnetic field which mediates the weak interaction. To account for the short range of the Fermi interaction, the quanta of this W-field must be very massive, which may account for the fact that these W-particles have not been seen so far. The selection rules for weak interactions could be understood by assigning suitable properties to this field. Whether or not such a field exists, the selection rules obeyed by weak interactions show that the participating currents have rather simple properties. Gell-Mann's suggestion that these currents form a certain algebra automatically incorporates these selection rules and also leads to a mathematically precise definition of universality. It has also led to the remarkable Adler-Weisberger relation between the β-decay constants.

Fermi's theory predicts that the cross section for neutrino interactions increases quadratically with neutrino energy. For the reaction $\nu + n \rightarrow \binom{e^-}{\mu^-} + p$, this growth is not expected to continue after the neutrino wavelength becomes smaller than nucleon dimensions, but the cross section at the corresponding energy, about 1 GeV, is already sufficient for experiments using the high-energy neutrino beams from the decays of fast π- and K-mesons produced by high-energy accelerators. One of the first results of such experiments has been to demonstrate the striking fact that the neutrino associated with muon capture, which is the one predominantly produced in meson decays, is unable to produce electrons, proving that it is physically distinct from the neutrino of β-decay. The *total* neutrino cross section continues to increase as E_ν^2 to the highest neutrino energies E_ν that have been studied thus far, supporting the idea of point-like constituents (partons) in the nucleon, which has been suggested to explain the "point-like" cross sections found in the inelastic scattering of high-energy electrons. It will be very interesting to see whether this feature persists at the higher energies which have become available at the 500 GeV accelerator at the National Accelerator Laboratory. In any case high-energy neutrino experiments can give us much more information about the structure of weak interactions than the limited number of decay processes which are available for study, and one of the main uses of the 500 GeV accelerator will be to study high-energy neutrino reactions. The greater energies available may also allow W-particles to reveal themselves.

The similarity of form of the weak and electromagnetic interactions may be a hint that the two are related. The principal difficulty with this notion was that while the carrier of electromagnetic interactions, the photon, has zero mass, the postulated W-meson must be very massive. Recently, it was realized that this extreme difference of masses can be understood in a unified gauge theory of weak and electromagnetic interactions if one is dealing with a situation of spontaneous symmetry-violation, through a mechanism discovered by Higgs. This scheme also possesses the advantage that calculations of higher-order effects of weak interactions, which previously yielded meaningless infinities, can be made finite in the same sense as in quantum electrodynamics. While a detailed theory which accounts for all the known features of weak interactions is yet to be formulated, many theorists believe that it will have to be constructed along these lines. The predicted mass of the W-meson is in the range of 40–50 GeV in these theories.

An aspect of weak interactions which we have not mentioned thus far is that they possess fewer space-time symmetries than the strong

interactions. Until Lee and Yang pointed out the possibility in 1956, it was not suspected that any interaction could distinguish between left-handed and right-handed coordinate systems.

It was then found that weak interactions discriminate between them very strongly; in the case of β-decay processes, this preference of a certain handedness could be attributed to the previously unknown fact that neutrinos are handed objects, a concept which can be given a relativistically invariant meaning only for massless particles. For other weak processes, the failure of reflection invariance remains totally unexplained. An answer to the question of how one system could be preferred over the other was offered by Landau's principle of symmetry under combined inversion. According to this principle the apparent spatial asymmetry in a given experiment is predicted to be exactly the mirror image of that to be expected in an experiment performed with the corresponding antiparticles; this prediction has been verified in several experiments and for several years all observations were in agreement with this hypothesis, until the discovery of $K_L \rightarrow 2\pi$ decays proved that combined inversion could not be an exact symmetry. A consequence of the CPT theorem (see ANTIPARTICLES) is that, if CP-invariance fails, T-invariance must also fail; this prediction appears to have been confirmed.[5] Many speculations have been advanced regarding the nature of the CP-noninvariant interaction.[6] Although it is not yet conclusively established, a strong possibility is that CP-noninvariance is confined to interactions much weaker than the usual weak interactions, which have observable consequences only in neutral kaon decays, which are the only phenomena where CP-noninvariance has been conclusively established. If that is the case, it may be a long time before weak interactions are fully understood.

P. KABIR

References

1. Fermi, E., "Elementary Particles," New Haven, Conn., Yale University Press, 1951.
2. Feynman, R. P., "The Theory of Fundamental Processes," New York, Benjamin, 1961.
3. Marshak, R. E., Riazuddin, and Ryan, C. P., "The Theory of Weak Interactions in Particle Physics," New York, Wiley-Interscience, 1969.
4. Davis, R., Rogers, L. C., and Radeka, V., *Bull. Am. Phys. Soc.*, **16**, 631 (1971).
5. Kabir, P. K., *Phys. Rev.*, **D2**, 540 (1970).
6. Kabir, P. K., "The CP Puzzle," London, Academic Press, 1968.

Cross-references: ANTIPARTICLES, CONSERVATION LAWS AND SYMMETRY, ELECTRON, NEUTRINO, NEUTRON, PROTON, RADIOACTIVITY, STRONG INTERACTIONS.

WORK, POWER, AND ENERGY

In the strict physical sense, work is performed only when a force is exerted on a body while the body moves at the same time in such a way that the force has a component in the direction of motion. In the simplest case where a constant force is applied in the same direction as the motion, it may be stated that work equals force multiplied by distance, or

$$W = Fs.$$

An example could be the raising of mass m from elevation h_1 to elevation h_2 in a constant gravitational field where the acceleration of gravity is g. The work performed would be

$$W = mg(h_2 - h_1).$$

To generalize for more complex situations, the amount of work done during motion from point "a" to point "b" can be expressed by:

$$W = \int_a^b F \cos \theta \, ds$$

where F is the total force exerted and θ is the angle between the direction of F and the direction of the elemental displacement ds. In the cgs system the unit of work is the dyne-centimeter or erg, in the mks system the newton-meter or joule, and in the English system the unit of work is the foot-pound.

In rotational motion, the definition just given can be exactly applied, but it is often convenient to express the force as a torque and the motion as an angular displacement. The work done will be:

$$W = \int_a^b \tau \cos \theta \, d\omega$$

where in this case θ is always the angle between the torque τ expressed as a vector quantity and the elemental angular motion $d\omega$, also expressed as a vector. The units of work performed in angular motion will, of course, be the same as in the case of linear motion. Notice that the definition of work involves no time element.

Power is defined as the rate at which work is performed. The average power accomplished by an agent during a given period of time is equal to the total work performed by the agent during the period, divided by the length of the time interval. The instantaneous power can be expressed simply as

$$P = \frac{dW}{dt}.$$

In the cgs system, power has the units of ergs per second; in the mks system, units of joules per second (or watts), and in the English system,

units of foot-pounds per second. A common engineering unit is the horsepower, defined as 550 foot-pounds per second, or 33 000 foot-pounds per minute.

Energy may be defined as the capacity for performing work. This definition may be better understood when stated as: the energy is that which diminishes when work is done by an amount equal to the work so done. The units of energy are identical with the units of work, previously given.

Energy can exist in a variety of forms, some more recognizable as being capable of performing work than others. Forms in which the energy is not dependent upon mechanical motion are generally referred to as forms of potential energy. The most common example in this category is gravitational potential energy. A body near the earth's surface undergoes a change in potential energy when it is changed in elevation, the amount being equal to the product of the weight of the body and the change in elevation.

Potential energy may also be stored in an elastic body such as a spring or a container of compressed gas. It may exist in the form of chemical potential energy, as measured by the amount of energy made available when given substances react chemically. Potential energy also exists in the nucleii of atoms and can be released by certain nuclear rearrangements.

Kinetic energy is the energy associated with mechanical motion of bodies. It is quantitatively equal to $\frac{1}{2}mv^2$ where m is the mass of a body moving with velocity v. In the case of rotational motion, the kinetic energy is more easily calculated using the expression $\frac{1}{2}I\omega^2$, where I is the moment of inertia of the body about its axis of rotation and ω is the angular velocity. Kinetic energy, like all forms of energy, is a scalar quantity. In a system made up of an assembly of particles, such as a given volume of gas, the total kinetic energy is equal to the sum of the kinetic energies of all the molecules contained in the volume. Calculation of the energy of such systems is very successfully treated theoretically on the basis of statistical averages.

Within a given system, energy may be transformed back and forth from one form to another, without changing the total energy in the system. A simple example is the pendulum, in which the energy is periodically converted from gravitational potential energy to kinetic energy and then back to gravitational potential energy. A similar situation, but on a submicroscopic scale, occurs in solid materials where the atoms are vibrating under the effect of interatomic rather than gravitational forces. As the temperature of a solid increases, the energy associated with the vibration of the atoms increases.

The example just given illustrates how, on a macroscopic scale, heat can be considered a form of energy. Regardless of the material involved, any amount of heat absorbed or re-leased may be quantitatively expressed as an amount of energy. A gram-calorie of heat is equivalent to 4.19 joules, and in the English system a British thermal unit (Btu) is equivalent to 778 foot-pounds.

Potential energy is also present in electric and magnetic fields. The energy available in a region of electric field is equal to $E^2/8\pi$ per unit volume, where E is the electric field strength. Within a given volume, the total energy represented by the electric field is the integral of $E^2/8\pi$ over the volume. Similarly, the energy represented by a magnetic field may be independently calculated by integrating $H^2/8\pi$ over any given volume, where H represents the magnetic field strength. In the case of an electrically charged capacitor, the total energy in the electric field, and hence in the capacitor, can be shown to be $\frac{1}{2}CV^2$. Here C is the capacitance and V the electric potential to which the capacitor is charged. Similarly the total energy in the magnetic field associated with an inductor carrying an electric current is $\frac{1}{2}LI^2$, where L is the inductance and I the current.

Electromagnetic radiation is a combination of rapidly alternating electric and magnetic fields. Energy is associated with these fields and is exchanged between the electric and magnetic forms. This energy in a quantum of electromagnetic radiation, such as light or gamma radiation, can be represented in different ways, but is commonly expressed as $E = h\nu$. Here h is Planck's Constant and ν is the frequency of the radiation.

For particulate radiation or any very rapidly moving mass, the expression previously given for the kinetic energy, $\frac{1}{2}mv^2$, is not accurate when the velocity approaches that of the velocity of light. The theory of relativity requires a correction be made, and the exact kinetic energy, T, may be calculated in terms of mass, m_0, of the body measured when at rest, and the speed of light in vacuum, c, as follows:

$$T = m_0 c^2 \left[\left(1 - \frac{v^2}{c^2}\right)^{-1/2} - 1\right]$$

Notice that this formula may also be written:

$$T = (m - m_0)c^2$$

where m is the variable quantity $m_0 \left(1 - \dfrac{v^2}{c^2}\right)^{-1/2}$.

This quantity represents the mass of the body, reducing to m_0 when v is zero, and approaching infinity as v approaches the speed of light.

This example illustrates another result of the theory of relativity, namely, the equivalence of mass and energy. Rewriting the last equation,

$$m = m_0 + \frac{T}{c^2}$$

The mass is seen to increase linearly with the

kinetic energy of the body, the proportionality factor being c^2. Indeed, even the rest mass, m_0, represents an amount of energy equal to $m_0 c^2$. The total energy of a body of mass, m, can be generally given as:

$$E = mc^2 \text{ or } E = m_0 c^2 + T$$

In dealing with radiation, whether particulate or electromagnetic, it is customary to express energy in terms of electron volts. An electron volt is equal to the amount of work done when an electron moves through an electric field produced by a potential difference of one volt. One electron volt is equivalent to 1.60×10^{-12} erg. When charged particles such as electrons or protons are given kinetic energy by an accelerator, their kinetic energy is stated in terms of electron volts (eV) or million electron volts (MeV). In addition, any such particle will have a rest mass which can also be specified as an energy. For an electron,

$$m_0 = 9.11 \times 10^{-28} \text{ gram}$$

which is equivalent to 8.18×10^{-7} erg or 0.515 MeV.

A basic principle of physics is known as conservation of energy. This principle requires that within any closed system, the total energy must remain a constant. Energy can be changed from one form to another; but the total, so long as no energy is added to or lost from the system, must be constant. In the case of the swinging pendulum, decreases in kinetic energy reappear as increases in potential energy and vice versa. Eventually, of course, the pendulum will stop due to the effect of frictional forces. At that time, all of the kinetic and gravitational potential energy will have been converted to heat.

In another example involving a radioactive atom, the total energy represented by the atom and the emitted radiation must be constant. If a gamma ray is emitted, the rest mass of the atom will be decreased by an amount equivalent to the sum of the energy of the gamma ray and the recoil kinetic energy of the atom, which will be very small. If a beta ray is emitted, the rest mass of the atom will be decreased by an amount equivalent to the sum of the rest mass of the emitted electron, the kinetic energy of the electron, and the recoil kinetic energy of the atom.

WILLIAM E. PARKINS

Cross-references: CONSERVATION LAWS AND SYMMETRY, DYNAMICS, MECHANICS, RELATIVITY, ROTATION–CIRCULAR MOTION, STATICS.

X

X-RAY DIFFRACTION

X-rays are electromagnetic radiations, and, like visible light, they can be diffracted (see OPTICS, PHYSICAL and DIFFRACTION). If a diffraction grating is used, the situation is as shown in Fig. 1. The points, B, B′, B″, ··· along OX represent the lines of the grating seen end-on, and ABC, A′B′C′, ··· are typical incident and scattered rays of a parallel incident beam. If D′ is the foot of the perpendicular dropped from B on to A′B′ and D is the foot of the perpendicular from B′ to BC, the extra distance traveled by the ray A′B′C′ is clearly D′B′−DB. This path difference can be expressed in terms of the grating space a, the angle of incidence ϕ_1, and the angle of scattering ϕ_2. From the triangle BB′D′, D′B′ = $a \cos \phi_1$, and from the triangle BB′D, DB = $-a \cos \phi_2$. If there is to be appreciable intensity diffracted in the direction BC, the path difference must be an integral multiple of the wavelength λ, say $h\lambda$. Then

$$h\lambda = a(\cos \phi_1 + \cos \phi_2) \qquad (1)$$

In order to obtain any appreciable scattering of x-rays from a grating it is necessary in practice to use very small angles of incidence, so that total external reflexion occurs. (The refractive index of matter for x-rays is very slightly less than unity, so that under suitable conditions they exhibit total external reflexion, whereas light exhibits total internal reflexion.) The points B, B′, ··· thus correspond to the centers of the smooth reflecting portions of the grating. From measurements of the angles of incidence and diffraction under such conditions, the absolute values of the x-ray wavelengths have been derived.

A geometrical representation of Eq. (1) is helpful in extending the theory of diffraction by a grating (an object with a one-dimensional variation of scattering power) to diffraction by a crystal (an object with a three-dimensional variation of scattering power). Equation (1) can be rewritten:

$$\frac{\cos \phi_1}{\lambda} + \frac{\cos \phi_2}{\lambda} = \frac{h}{a} \qquad (2)$$

In Fig. 2, OP is a line of length $1/\lambda$ drawn parallel to BA, so that the angle XOP = ϕ_1, and PQ is a line of the same length drawn parallel to BC, so that it makes an angle ϕ_2 with OX. The projection of OP on OX, OP′, is clearly of length $\cos \phi_1/\lambda$, and the projection of PQ, P′Q′, is of length $\cos \phi_2/\lambda$. If Eq. (2) is satisfied, the length of OQ′ = OP′ + P′Q′ must be h/a. Clearly, fixing h is not sufficient to fix the angles ϕ_1 and ϕ_2. If we imagine that the lines XO, OP and PQ are jointed together at O and P, and Q is free to slide up and down the line GQ′H within wide limits without affecting the equality of Eq. (2), and so giving considerable freedom to the directions of incident and diffracted rays having a constant path difference $h\lambda$. Different values of h lead to different lines GH, G′H′, ··· spaced at integral multiples of the distance $1/a$ along OX. All possible mutual relationships between the incident and strongly diffracted rays are represented

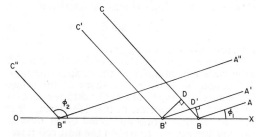

FIG. 1. Diffraction by a linear grating or line of scattering centres.

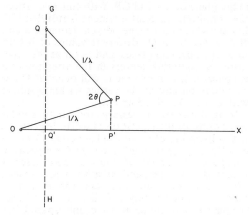

FIG. 2. Geometrical representation of the condition for strong reflection.

by those portions of the set of parallel lines of spacing $1/a$ that lie within a circle with radius $2/\lambda$ and center O.

The exterior angle between AB and BC is generally denoted by 2θ. From Fig. 1 it is clear that

$$2\theta = \phi_2 - \phi_1 \qquad (3)$$

and from Fig. 2

$$OQ = OP \sin \theta + PQ \sin \theta$$

$$= (2 \sin \theta)/\lambda \qquad (4)$$

With a little reinterpretation, Figs. 1 and 2 can be used to derive the condition for strong diffraction by a crystal. A crystal is a three-dimensionally periodic object, with a certain arrangement of atoms repeating indefinitely at intervals of a in one direction, b in another, and c in a third. The intervals a, b, c are not generally equal to each other, nor necessarily at right angles to each other. They define a parallelepiped called the *unit cell* of the crystal. For determining the geometrical conditions for the existence of a strong diffracted beam, the manner in which the atoms are arranged in the cell is not important, and for the moment we may think of them as forming a single scattering center at the corner of the cell. In Fig. 1, the points B, B', $\cdots$ now represent a row of scattering centers parallel to a, and ABC, A'B'C', $\cdots$ represent a sequence of incident and diffracted rays. The difference is that for a ruled grating one can expect constructive interference between the various scattered rays only if OX, AB, BC, A'B', B'C', $\cdots$ are coplanar, whereas an arrangement of atoms can scatter out of the plane of OX and AB, and hence BC need not lie in this plane. The condition for reinforcement, however, remains

$$D'B' - DB = h\lambda \qquad (5)$$

and its geometrical representation in Fig. 2 is changed only in that Q does not necessarily lie in the plane of OX and OP. With this relaxation, the condition for reinforcement is fulfilled if Q lies anywhere on a plane perpendicular to a and distant h/a from O. Different values of h lead to a set of parallel planes, and as far as the repetition of scattering centers in the direction of a is concerned, reinforcement will occur if Q lies anywhere on any of the planes within a sphere with center O and radius $2/\lambda$.

It is, however, necessary to satisfy similar conditions for the repetition of scattering centers in the directions of b and c. These conditions are exactly analogous: reinforcement for repetition along b will occur only if Q lies in one of a set of planes that are perpendicular to b and spaced $1/b$ apart, and reinforcement for repetition along c will occur only if Q lies in one of a set of planes perpendicular to c and spaced $1/c$ apart. There can be a strong beam diffracted by the crystal only if Q satisfies these three condi-

tions simultaneously. Two sets of planes intersect in a set of parallel lines, and the third set of planes will intersect these lines in a lattice of points. This is called the lattice reciprocal to the crystal lattice, or the reciprocal lattice for short. A strong diffracted beam can occur, then, only if Q coincides with one of the points of the reciprocal lattice, and only those points within a sphere of radius $2/\lambda$ are possible, since the maximum length of OQ is $2/\lambda$. This sphere is called the *limiting sphere*.

The repeat distances in the reciprocal lattice are usually called a^*, b^*, c^*. They have the same general directions as a, b, c, but are actually parallel to them only in those crystal systems that have their axes at right angles. There are a number of "reciprocal" relations between the two sets of axes, some obvious from the way in which the reciprocal lattice has been constructed, others obtainable only by analysis. For further details the article on CRYSTALLOGRAPHY should be consulted.

For a given wavelength λ, a given direction of incidence PO, and a fixed position of the crystal, the loci of possible positions of Q is a sphere with center P and radius $1/\lambda$. This sphere is called the *sphere of reflexion*, since strong diffraction can take place only if one of the points of the reciprocal lattice lies in or passes through its surface. With all parameters fixed, this is an unlikely coincidence, and in the practical study of x-ray diffraction, provision must be made for variation of either λ (the Laue method), or the orientation of the crystal (most types of single-crystal and crystal-powder cameras and diffractometers), or the direction of the incident x-rays (some special-purpose techniques). Space does not permit discussion of the practical details.

In the preceding treatment diffraction has been considered from the viewpoint of adding contributions scattered by centers arranged in a regular lattice. It can also be considered as reflexion from sets of parallel planes of atoms, the rays reflected by successive planes in a set being added. It can be shown that the connection between the two views is that (1) the line OQ joining the origin of the reciprocal lattice to the point hkl is perpendicular to the corresponding set of reflecting planes, and (2) its length is the reciprocal of their spacing d. From the second viewpoint, then, Eq. (4) may be rewritten

$$\lambda = 2d \sin \theta \qquad (6)$$

a relation known as *Bragg's law*.

The arrangement of atoms within the unit cell influences the intensity of the various orders of diffraction hkl, just as the shape of the ruling influences the intensities of the different orders produced by an optical diffraction grating. It is easy to see that x-rays diffracted by an atom at the position xa, yb, zc within the unit cell travel a shorter distance than those diffracted at the hypothetical scattering center at the origin, and

that the corresponding phase difference is $2\pi(hx + ky + lz)$. If the cell contains n atoms whose scattering factors (the ratio of the actual scattered amplitude to the amplitude scattered by a free electron under the same conditions) are $f_1, f_2, \cdots, f_n$, the total amplitude scattered by the cell will thus have an in-phase component of

$$A = f_1 \cos 2\pi(hx_1 + ky_1 + lz_1) + \cdots$$
$$+ f_n \cos 2\pi(hx_n + ky_n + lz_n) \quad (7)$$

and an in-quadrature component of

$$B = f_1 \sin 2\pi(hx_1 + ky_1 + lz_1) + \cdots$$
$$+ f_n \sin 2\pi(hx_n + ky_n + lz_n) \quad (8)$$

the scattering by an atom at the origin of the cell being taken as the reference phase. The total intensity of scattering is thus proportional to

$$F^2 = A^2 + B^2 \quad (9)$$

The quantity F is called the *structure factor*; it is sometimes convenient to regard it as a complex quantity $F = A + iB$. It can vary in magnitude from zero to $f_1 + f_2 + \cdots + f_n$, with a root-mean-square value of $\sqrt{(f_1{}^2 + \cdots + f_n{}^2)}$. The total intensity of the order hkl is proportional to NF^2, where N is the number of unit cells in the crystal. The scatter of the actual values of the intensity above and below the mean value depends on the symmetry of the atomic arrangement. Although the relationship is statistical, a study of the scatter can often provide evidence about the *point group* of the crystal when other methods are not available. From Eq. (7) through (9) it is clear that for any hkl the actual intensity of diffraction depends on the atomic positions $x_1 y_1 z_1 \cdots x_n y_n z_n$. Measurement of the intensities of a sufficient number of diffraction maxima thus makes it possible to infer the atomic positions. Unfortunately there is no single direct procedure that can be guaranteed to lead from the intensities to the atomic coordinates, but there are many that are successful in appropriate cases.

The maximum intensity of diffraction occurs when the point Q, defined above, coincides with one of the points hkl of the reciprocal lattice. As the point Q moves away from its ideal position, the intensity of diffraction does not drop instantaneously to zero, but falls off gradually in a manner depending on the size and perfection of the crystal. The study of the manner in which the falling off occurs is a fascinating exercise both experimentally and theoretically, but space permits only the quotation of a few qualitative results. The main varieties of imperfection considered are (1) the crystal is too small to give sharp diffraction maxima, (2) there are "mistakes" in the arrangement of atoms in the sequence of unit cells, and (3) the crystal is twisted, bent, or affected by dislocations. In case (1) the regions round each reciprocal-lattice point are identical except for variations in F, and extend in any direction to a distance that is roughly the reciprocal of the thickness of the crystal in the corresponding direction. In case (2) the size and shape of the regions may vary in a complex manner with hkl, but they show no general increase in size with increasing distance from the origin of reciprocal space. In case (3) the size of the regions shows a general increase in direct proportion to their distance from the origin of reciprocal space, as well as varying with hkl.

The intensity of many diffraction maxima may be recorded simultaneously on a photographic film with a suitable emulsion, and later measured with a densitometer, or individual diffraction maxima may be investigated one by one with a counter diffractometer. In spite of the complexity of the mechanism the latter is becoming the preferred method; various methods of automation, including on-line computer control, have removed the tedium associated with early diffractometric measurements. For determination of the atomic arrangement only the total ("integrated") intensity of each maximum is required, but for investigations of crystal imperfection much more detailed information about the variation of intensity with position in reciprocal space is needed. Often the material exhibiting imperfections is not available in crystals large enough to be examined individually, and the specimen has to take the form of an aggregate of many small crystallites in a more or less random orientation. In such cases measurement of the three-dimensional variation of intensity in reciprocal space is not possible, but by the use of a powder diffractometer the one-dimensional variation of intensity with Bragg angle [θ in Eq. (6) above] can be measured with considerable precision, and there is an extensive theory for the interpretation of such "line profiles."

A. J. C. WILSON

References

Azároff, L. V., ed., "X-ray Diffraction," New York, McGraw-Hill, 1974.

Guinier, A., "X-ray Diffraction in Crystals, Imperfect Crystals, and Amorphous Bodies," San Francisco, Freeman, 1963.

Hosemann, R., and Bagchi, S. N., "Direct Analysis of Diffraction by Matter," Amsterdam, North Holland, 1962.

James, R. W., "The Optical Principles of the Diffraction of X-rays," London, Bell, 1948.

Wilson, A. J. C., "Elements of X-ray Crystallography," Reading, Mass., Addison-Wesley, 1970.

Wilson, A. J. C., "Mathematical Theory of X-ray Powder Diffractometry," Eindhoven, Philips Technical Library, 1963.

Zachariasen, W. H., "Theory of X-ray Diffraction in Crystals," New York, John Wiley & Sons, 1945.

Cross-references: CRYSTALLOGRAPHY; DIFFRAC-
TION BY MATTER AND DIFFRACTION GRAT-
INGS; ELECTRON DIFFRACTION; NEUTRON DIF-
FRACTION; OPTICS, PHYSICAL; PARACRYSTALS.

X-RAYS

The portion of the electromagnetic spectrum
known as x-rays has been recognized for over
three quarters of a century and yet the radiation
in this area continues to find new applications
in many fields of science and technology. It
seems unlikely that Wilhelm Conrad Roentgen
could possibly have foreseen the impact that
these rays would have when he discovered them
in 1895 at the University of Wurzburg. For
seventeen years the exact nature of x-rays was
obscure. They certainly deserved their designation of x (for unknown) rays. In 1912, M. von
Laue and his associates showed that x-rays could
be diffracted from crystals which simulated
three-dimensional gratings. This historic experiment not only proved the wave-like nature of
x-rays, but also showed the regular three-dimensional arrangement of atoms in a crystal lattice.
Two new fields of science were thus launched,
namely, x-ray spectroscopy and x-ray crystallography. The crystal spectrometer was developed
by W. L. Bragg and then he, H. G. J. Moseley,
M. Siegbahn, and others began the laborious
task of cataloging lists of characteristic x-ray
wavelengths. It was Moseley who recognized the
simplicity and periodicity of the K series, for
instance, whose main four lines varied step by
step in going from one element to the next in
the periodic table. The power of the technique
is illustrated by the fact that spectral gaps were
noted which indicated that certain elements
were missing from the then known elemental
scheme. In each case the missing elements were
found and their x-ray spectra fell into the predicted places.

X-rays may be produced by a variety of
methods, but the general method employed by
Roentgen, that is using electrons, continues to
be the most popular. Roentgen operated his
discharge tube at high voltage and with the gas
pressure sufficient to allow the cathode rays
(electrons) to travel through the tube and collide
with the walls to produce x-rays. Now, most
x-ray tubes use a hot filament with electrons
produced by the Edison effect. The fast-moving
electrons convert their energy to an x-ray photon
according to the law,

$$h\nu = E_1 - E_2$$

where E_1 and E_2 are the initial and final energies
of the electron, h is Planck's constant and ν is
the frequency of the x-ray photon created. The
radiation thus produced consists of a continuum
of radiations, corresponding to the many possible energy losses that the electrons can undergo
on striking the target of the x-ray tube. Such

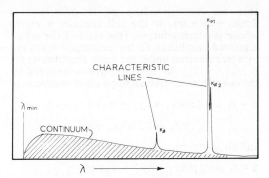

FIG. 1. A typical x-ray continuum and line spectrum.

a continuum is represented in Fig. 1. When the
electron loses all of its energy in a single collision, then $E_2 = 0$ and the x-ray photon of the
highest energy is produced. This energy corresponds to the shortest possible wavelength or
λ_{min}. Upon introduction of appropriate constants, λ_{min} in angstroms may be approximated
by

$$\lambda_{min} = \frac{12400}{E\,(\text{volts})}$$

where E is the x-ray tube voltage. Therefore, if
an x-ray tube is operated at 40 kV, then the
shortest possible wavelength λ_{min} will be about
0.3 Å. The peak of the "white" or continuous
radiation will be about 3/2 times λ_{min}.

Superimposed on the continuum is a simple
line and band spectrum characteristic of each
element such as that shown in Fig. 1. These
spectral features are produced by an ejection of
an electron in an inner energy level followed by
the filling of this vacancy by an electron from a
higher energy state. The energy of the x-ray
quantum is the difference between the energies
of the two levels involved. The x-ray series are
named according to the final energy state involved in the transition with the familiar nota-
tions K, L, M, N, etc., as devised by Barkla in
1905 to emphasize the analogy with optical
spectral series. It is not easy to place exact
limits on the position of x-rays in the electromagnetic spectrum since they overlap with γ-rays
on the short-wavelength end and with vacuum
ultraviolet radiation on the long-wavelength end.
Generally, however, they are classified as ultra-
hard (< 0.1 Å), hard ($0.1–1.0$ Å), soft ($1–10$ Å)
and ultrasoft (> 10 Å).

As the wavelength of x-rays is increased (or
as they become "softer"), they are as a rule
more easily absorbed by all materials. The decrease in intensity of a beam of x-rays passing
through matter follows the law,

$$I = I_0\, e^{-\mu x}$$

where I_0 is the incident intensity, I the reduced

intensity after a thickness x (cm) of homogeneous matter has been traversed, and μ the linear absorption or attenuation coefficient for the material traversed.

In addition to this general attenuation in matter, there occur sharp absorption discontinuities in the x-ray spectrum corresponding to the energy necessary to just eject an electron from a given level. The discontinuity or edge is designated as K, L_I, L_{II}, L_{III}, etc., which indicates where the initial vacancy has occurred. The emission lines of a given element fall at longer wavelengths compared to the corresponding absorption edge. The absorption edge position and the fine structure on the edge depend strongly on the state of chemical combination of the emitting element, and the detailed study of edge structure provides a powerful tool for the determination of chemical bonding.

The major uses of x-rays are in the areas of x-ray emission, x-ray diffraction, and x-ray absorption (to include interaction, such as ionization, with matter). X-ray emission analysis is a precision technique for elemental analysis which uses a high-intensity beam of x-rays from a primary source to excite characteristic x-rays in a sample. These x-rays are dispersed by a crystal spectrometer and detected by a scintillation or proportional detector which measures the angle at which the x-rays are diffracted by the analyzing crystal. The familiar Bragg equation

$$n\lambda = 2d \sin \theta$$

is used to deduce the wavelength λ of the secondary x-rays from the sample. θ is the angle that the x-ray beam makes with the crystal and is measured by the spectrometer, d is the lattice or interplanar spacing of the single-crystal analyzer, and n is the order of diffraction. This technique, commonly called x-ray fluorescence, is generally applicable to qualitative and quantitative analysis of all elements higher than atomic number 11 in the periodic table. With special instrumentation, the technique can be extended to low atomic number elements such as carbon and oxygen. An extraordinary development in x-ray emission analysis has occurred with the development of the electron microbeam probe which collimates a beam of electrons to produce characteristic x-rays from a total sample volume of about one cubic micrometer. In addition to elemental analysis, the method provides a map of elemental distribution on a highly magnified image of the specimen. Scanning spectrometers and nondispersive Si (Li) detectors on scanning electron microscopes allow elemental distribution mapping in addition to the extremely high resolution scanning pictures which are obtained from low-energy secondary electron emission from the sample surface. An important new development in x-ray emission spectroscopy is the use of the fine features on x-ray lines and bands to deduce chemical bonding and the effects of chemical combination. Another significant use of monochromatic characteristic x-rays is to produce photoelectrons in the newly emerging technique known as ESCA (electron spectroscopy for chemical analysis), pioneered by Kai Siegbahn at Uppsala.

X-ray diffraction is a widely used technique for characterization of solid crystalline materials and takes the form of single-crystal analysis, powder diffraction analysis, and texture or topographical analysis. The same Bragg law mentioned earlier for x-ray emission analysis also applies to diffraction analysis, since it is a diffraction technique which is used to analyze or disperse the x-rays in the x-ray emission scheme. In x-ray diffraction, however, the wavelength λ is known, the angle θ (or 2θ) is measured, and the d spacing is calculated. Each crystalline material produces a diffraction pattern unlike any other material and this pattern identifies each material unambiguously. An extensive file of diffraction patterns is provided by the American Society for Testing and Materials, which allows quick identification of crystalline materials. The reader is referred to the articles in this volume on X-RAY DIFFRACTION and DIFFRACTION BY MATTER AND DIFFRACTION GRATINGS for further details and the theory of diffraction phenomena, and to CRYSTALLOGRAPHY for applications to single-crystal analysis.

Perhaps the most familiar of the uses of x-rays concerns the absorption (attenuation) and interaction with matter of an x-ray beam since these phenomena provide the basis for radiography and uses in medical technology. Radiography is the registration on film or a fluorescent screen (fluoroscopy) of the differential absorption of a beam passing through a heterogeneous sample. This technique is used in medical diagnosis and to determine the soundness and perfection of manufactured products such as castings and forgings. An important development has been in cineradiography where extremely high fluxes of x-rays are pulsed to give sequential radiographs of transient phenomena lasting 10^{-9} sec or less. Microradiographic techniques are used to obtain magnifications of 100X to 200X of radiographs resulting from passage of monochromatic x-rays through a sample which is in direct contact with the recording film. Magnification is then realized by photographic enlargement. An improvement over contact microradiography is point projection radiography where a fine point source of x-rays registers the sharp absorption discontinuities from a sample which is placed at varying distances from the film to achieve different sharp magnifications of the image. A further use of the absorption phenomenon is in absorptiometry, where measurement is made of the attenuation of a beam passing through a sample to determine, for instance, density, porosity, and coating thickness. Chemical analysis is also achieved by measuring characteristic absorption edges with a

crystal spectrometer. Fine structure on these edges may also be used in certain cases to deduce bonding and chemical combination.

The areas of radiation chemistry, physics, biology, genetics, therapy, and protection all depend on the effects and changes produced when x-ray quanta are absorbed in matter. X-rays are, of course, ionizing radiations, and induce chemical reactions by formation of intermediate species, free radicals, and ions. These reactions may be used profitably for dosimetry, to produce mutations, and to irradiate selectively cancerous tissue, among many of the possible uses.

Because of space limitations, this review only sketchily refers to some of the numerous uses of x-rays. For further information it is suggested that the reader refer to the excellent books listed under references.

WILLIAM L. BAUN

References

Compton, A. H., and Allison, S. K., "X-Rays in Theory and Experiment," Second Edition, New York, Van Nostrand Reinhold, 1935.

Azaroff, Leonid, "X-Ray Diffraction" (Vol. I) and "X-Ray Spectroscopy" (Vol. II), New York, McGraw-Hill Book Co., Inc., 1974.

Kaelble, E. F., "Handbook of X-Rays," New York, McGraw-Hill Book Co., Inc., 1974.

Clark, G. L, "The Encyclopedia of X-Rays and Gamma Rays," New York, Van Nostrand Reinhold, 1963.

Flügge, S., "Encyclopedia of Physics, X-Rays," Vol. XXX, Berlin, Springer-Verlag, 1957.

Clark, G. L., "Applied X-Rays," 4th Edition, New York, McGraw-Hill Book Co., Inc., 1955.

Cross-references: ATOMIC SPECTRA, BREMS-STRAHLUNG, COMPTON EFFECT, CRYSTALLOG-RAPHY, DIFFRACTION BY MATTER AND DIFFRACTION GRATINGS, ELECTRON, X-RAY DIFFRACTION.

Z

ZEEMAN AND STARK EFFECTS*

In 1896 Zeeman observed that the yellow lines of a sodium flame were considerably broadened when it was placed in a strong magnetic field. Using his classical electron theory of matter and radiation, Lorentz showed that the light should be circularly polarized when viewed along the field (σ-components), and linearly polarized along (π-components) and perpendicular to the field direction (σ-components), when viewed transversely to the magnetic field. These theoretical conclusions of Lorentz were verified by Zeeman by using a quarter-wave plate and a Nicol prism to analyze the polarization of the radiation from the broadened lines of the sodium flame in the magnetic field.

Classically, a magnetic field exerts a force $-e/c[\mathbf{v} \times \mathbf{H}]$ on an electron moving with a velocity. $\mathbf{v}$. For an electron moving in a circular orbit, a field H_z normal to the plane of the orbit does not affect motion in the z direction. During the creation of the magnetic field, however, an electric field is generated as follows from Faraday's law of induction and Lenz's law, and this speeds up or slows down the electron in its orbit. The resulting Coriolis force is exactly balanced by the above radial force due to the magnetic field and the orbit retains the same diameter. If the magnetic field is directed upwards, then electrons moving in a counterclockwise direction are speeded up, while those moving in a clockwise direction are slowed down giving orbital frequency changes

$$\Delta \nu = \pm \, eH/4\pi m_e c = \pm \, 1.4H \times 10^6 \, \text{Hz} \quad (1)$$

(e is the electronic charge in electrostatic units, H is the magnetic field in oersteds, m_e is the mass of the electron, and c is the velocity of light).

Expressed in wave numbers

$$\Delta \bar{\nu} = eH/4\pi m_e c^2 = 4.6688 \times 10^{-5} \, H \, \text{cm}^{-1} \quad (2)$$

which is called a Lorentz unit.

Alternatively, the action of a magnetic field on an electron in orbital motion may be regarded as a precession of the orbit about the direction of the magnetic field, the size and inclination of the orbit, together with the velocity of the

*Sponsored by Lockheed Independent Research Program.

electron in its orbit, remaining the same. However, the resultant velocity of the electron is changed by this precession as before since we may now regard the orbit as rotating in its own plane. This is called the Larmor precession of the orbit in a magnetic field and is an important concept in the development of quantum-mechanical interpretations of the Zeeman effect. The frequency of precession is again given by Eq. (1).

The main results of this classical theory of the Zeeman effect follow by regarding the linear oscillator as a quasi-elastically bound electron. Thus the equation of motion in the magnetic field becomes

$$\frac{d^2 \mathbf{r}}{dt^2} + \omega_0^2 \mathbf{r} = -\frac{e}{m_e c} \left(\frac{d\mathbf{r}}{dt} \times \mathbf{H} \right) , \quad (3)$$

where ω_0 is the frequency in radians/sec of the bound electron in zero magnetic field, and $\mathbf{r}$ is the position vector of the electron. Equation (3) may be solved in a Cartesian (x,y,z) set of coordinates, such that the z axis is along the magnetic field, by assuming a solution of the form

$$x = x_0 e^{i\omega t} ; y = y_0 e^{i\omega t}, \quad (4)$$

motion in the z direction being unaffected by the field H_z. It is found that

$$\omega = \omega_0 \pm \Delta\omega \quad (5)$$

where $\Delta\omega = eH_z/2 \, m_e c$, which agrees with the frequency in Eq. (1), and also that

$$x_0/y_0 = \pm \, i,$$

so that the amplitudes of vibration along the x and y axes are equal and in phase quadrature. The linear oscillator in a magnetic field thus consists of a linearly polarized oscillation of constant frequency ω_0 along the field or z direction, and two oppositely circularly polarized oscillations of frequency $\omega_0 + \Delta\omega$ in the x-y plane. These results agree with observations along and perpendicular to the field direction allowing for the transverse nature of light sources.

Figure 1 shows the normal Zeeman effect, or Lorentz triplet, obtained with this theory. Such triplets were soon observed in cadmium and zinc by Preston, and provided clear indication

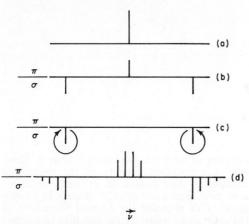

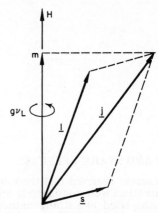

FIG. 1. Zeeman effect on spectral line: (a) No magnetic field—unshifted line. (b) Normal Zeeman effect. Transverse magnetic field, π and σ components of normal Lorentz triplet. (c) Normal Zeeman effect viewed along magnetic field. Circularly polarized σ components. (d) Anomalous Zeeman effect of the transition $^2D_{5/2} - {}^2P_{3/2}$.

FIG. 2. Vector model of angular momenta $\mathbf{l}$, $\mathbf{s}$, $\mathbf{j}$, and projection m of $\mathbf{j}$ along H for a single valence electron. Classical precession of $\mathbf{j}$ around H.

that the emission of light by atoms involved the motion of negatively charged electrons. Most Zeeman patterns are anomalous, however, and show more than three components (see Fig. 1). Such complex patterns require a quantum mechanical interpretation, including the concept of electron spin. They depend only on the angular momentum quantum numbers of the terms in the spectral series (Preston's rule), and all known patterns are rational multiples of the normal triplet separation (Runge's rule).

According to quantum theory, the angular momentum, $P_l = lh/2\pi$, of the electron is quantized and is represented by a vector $\mathbf{l}$ normal to the orbit. The magnetic moment of the electron is then $\mu_l = - le/2m_ec$. Magnetic field effects are then equivalent to a precession of $\mathbf{l}$ around $\mathbf{H}$ at the Larmor frequency $\nu_L = eH/4\pi m_ec$. Only discrete angles between $\mathbf{l}$ and $\mathbf{H}$ are allowed given by the projection m of $\mathbf{l}$ on $\mathbf{H}$, where m takes values $-l$ to $+l$. The energy splitting of the l term is thus $mheH/4\pi m_ec$, and the selection rules $\Delta m = 0, \pm 1$ apply for allowed transitions between different l terms. Corresponding frequency shifts are 0 and $\pm eH/4\pi m_ec$, which again gives the normal Zeeman effect. Landé used such vector models and introduced empirically the g_l factor for each l term, with energy separations $\Delta E_l = mhg_leH/4\pi m_ec$. He was able to deduce the appropriate g_l factors and explain the Zeeman patterns to a remarkable degree.

The spin of the electron, postulated by Uhlenbeck and Goudsmit, allowed a more satisfactory deduction of these g factors. To account for the doublet fine structure in the alkali metals, e.g., the D-lines of sodium, a spin s of $(1/2)(h/2\pi)$, and a magnetic moment $\mu_s = - s\,2e/2m_ec$, were ascribed to the electron as inherent properties,

and a total angular momentum quantum number $j = l + s$ for a single valence electron. The resulting vector model of the atom is shown in Fig. 2. The magnetic interaction between the angular and spin momenta of the electron results in a coupling between $\mathbf{l}$ and $\mathbf{s}$ which then precess rapidly about their resultant $\mathbf{j}$. In weak magnetic fields, $\mathbf{j}$ precesses slowly about H_z at Larmor frequency times the g factor. From this vector model, we obtain

$$g = 1 + \frac{j(j + 1) + s(s + 1) - l(l + 1)}{2j(j + 1)}$$

where, in accordance with observation and the more accurate quantum mechanical deduction, j^2, l^2, and s^2 are replaced by $j(j + 1)$, $l(l + 1)$, and $s(s + 1)$ respectively.

The magnetic quantum number m takes values $-j$ through $+j$; transitions $\Delta m = 0$ correspond to π components, $\Delta m = \pm 1$ to σ components. Selection rules $\Delta j = 0, + 1$ ($j = 0$ to $j = 0$ excluded) are also effective. For the transition $^2S_{1/2} \to {}^2P_{3/2}$, or the D_2-line of sodium, $l = 0, s = 1/2, j = 1/2$, $g = 2$; and $l = 1, s = 1/2, j = 3/2, g = 4/3$ for the lower and upper levels respectively. In terms of the normal Zeeman separation, namely, $eH/4\pi m_ec$, the mg values for the upper and lower levels are

$$m \quad\quad = \quad -3/2 \quad -1/2 \quad 1/2 \quad 3/2$$
$$mg_{\text{upper}} = \quad -2 \quad\quad -2/3 \quad 2/3 \quad 2$$
$$mg_{\text{lower}} = \quad\quad\quad\quad -1 \quad\quad 1$$

where the arrows indicate possible transitions $\Delta m = 0, + 1$, and give the positions of all Zeeman lines as differences between the mg terms of the two levels. These differences are $\pm 5/3$, ± 1, $\pm(1/3)$ and give a Zeeman pattern of 6 lines for the D_2-line of sodium (π transitions are in parentheses). Figure 3 shows the splitting and the intensities of the various transitions which de-

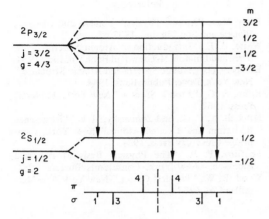

FIG. 3. Transitions involved in the anomalous Zeeman effect of the 5890A D_2-line of sodium ($^2S_{1/2}-$ $^2P_{3/2}$). Intensities of the π and σ components also shown.

pend on the quantum numbers j and m. Anomalous Zeeman effects for other transitions and atoms are dealt with similarly. For atoms with more than one valence electron, appropriate coupling schemes between the angular and spin momenta of the electrons, such as Russell-Saunders L-S coupling, must be used in an analogous way.

For very strong magnetic fields, the precession frequency of j around H becomes comparable with that of l and s around j, or with the fine structure separation. This is the Paschen-Back effect region, where the fine structure coupling breaks down; l and s then precess independently around H, and the normal Zeeman pattern is observed. Paschen-Back effects have been observed in lighter elements such as Li, where the doublet separation of the ^2P levels is only 0.34 cm^{-1} as compared with 17.2 cm^{-1} for the D-lines of sodium. Since 10 000 oersteds corresponds to a Larmor splitting of 0.47 cm^{-1}, very high magnetic fields are necessary with heavier atoms. In the intermediate region of magnetic fields, more elaborate quantum mechanical methods are necessary; however, a magnetic field is only strong or weak in a relative sense as compared with other internal fields in the atom. Hyperfine structure of spectral lines involves the nuclear spin I, and a magnetic field which is weak for fine structure may be quite strong for hyperfine structure. Here the quantum number $F = I + J$ is used to determine the magnetic splitting. In optical spectra, such weak-field magnetic splittings are rarely observed because the hyperfine structure splitting is comparable with the Doppler width of the line or the instrumental resolution. Hyperfine splittings of the ground state are used in atomic beam resonance techniques to determine I, and also in atomic beam frequency standards. At higher values of magnetic field, the coupling between I and J breaks down and I and J precess independently

around H giving the Back-Goudsmit effect in hyperfine structure.

Zeeman spectra of many atoms have been observed with magnetic fields of 20 000 to 40 000 oersteds and diffraction gratings capable of resolving 1/10 of a Lorentz unit. Completely resolved spectra give the g factors and the j values of both levels involved in the transition, and the Zeeman effect has played a dominant role in the elucidation of atomic spectra.

In 1913 Stark demonstrated that every spectral line of the Balmer series of hydrogen was split into a number of components when the emitting atoms, obtained from the positive rays in a hydrogen discharge were subjected to electric fields of 100 000 volts/cm. Lo Surdo obtained similar results using the large potential gradient in the dark space of a glow discharge. This symmetrical splitting of the hydrogen lines is due to a linear Stark effect, with a shift of the atomic levels in wave numbers given by

$$T = AF + am_l m_s$$

Here $A = 6\cdot45 \times 10^{-5} n(n_2 - n_1)$; F is the electric field in volts per centimeter; a is a constant; m_l and m_s are the projections of orbital and spin angular momentum on the field direction (cf. the magnetic quantum number m); n is the principal quantum number, and n_1, n_2 are other quantum numbers deduced from the Bohr quantum theory which successfully explained the effect. Certain components of the Stark pattern occur only in transverse observation and are polarized with the electric vector parallel to the field (π components). Others are polarized perpendicular to the field (σ components). For observations along the field, only the σ components appear, and these are unpolarized.

Such a linear Stark effect occurs only in hydrogen, or hydrogen-like atoms, and is due to the close proximity of levels with the same n but different angular momenta l. The quantum number m_j is analogous to the magnetic quantum number m, but with the important difference that values $\pm m_j$ now give identical splittings of energy levels. This occurs since the energy depends only on the orientation of the orbit to the electric field and not on the sense of precession as in a magnetic field. The unpolarized nature of the σ components when observed along the electric field is also due to this independence of energy on the sign of m_j.

For fields greater than 100 000 volts/cm hydrogen exhibits a quadratic Stark effect, with a shift of all spectral lines towards the red or violet. A similar quadratic Stark effect is observed in all other atoms, where the fields are now weak compared with the separation of states of different parity, or l values. For the sodium D-lines, transitions $3s^2S_{1/2} - 3p^2P_{1/2},\ _{3/2}$, the states arising from different electron orbits, or l values, with the same quantum number n are widely separated. These were studied by Ladenburg at fields of 160 000 volts/cm, when only a quadratic Stark effect was observed. The various

components of the D-lines, which split into levels with $m_j = \pm 1/2$, and $m_j = \pm 1/2, \pm 3/2$ respectively, were shifted towards the red by a fraction of an angstrom unit. Similar results were obtained for other alkali metals. The effect increases rapidly with the total quantum number n and may be observed in absorption as well as emission. Forbidden transitions, violating the selection rule $\Delta l = \pm 1$, also occur due to a mixing of the energy levels in strong electric fields. These have been observed, particularly in helium by Foster who used electric fields up to 85 000 volts/cm.

The Stark effect is closely connected with the polarizability of the otherwise neutral atom. The various orientations of the angular momentum l then correspond to states of slightly different energies and produce the observed quadratic Stark effect. Because of its complex nature, the Stark effect, in comparison with the Zeeman effect, has not played a dominant role in the analysis of complex spectra or of atomic structure.

W. CULSHAW

References

Born, Max, "Atomic Physics," London and Glasgow, Blackie and Son Limited, 1937.

White, H. E., "Introduction to Atomic Spectra," New York and London, McGraw-Hill Book Co. Inc., 1934.

Herzberg, G., "Atomic Spectra and Atomic Structure," New York, Dover Publications, 1944.

Kuhn, H. G., "Atomic Spectra," New York, Academic Press, 1962.

Mitchell, A. C. G., and Zemansky, M. W., "Resonance Radiation and Excited Atoms," New York, Cambridge University Press, 1934.

Feofilov, P. P., "The Physical Basis of Polarized Emission," New York, Consultants Bureau, 1961.

Wood, R. W., "Physical Optics," New York, The Macmillan Co., 1934.

Cross-references: ATOMIC SPECTRA, ELECTROMAGNETIC THEORY, POLARIZED LIGHT, QUANTUM ELECTRODYNAMICS, QUANTUM THEORY, SPECTROSCOPY.

INDEX

Bold face numbers designate more important passages and small capital letters are used for titles of articles in the book.

Abacus, 156
Abbe, Ernst, **276, 638**
Abbe expression, **284**
Abelson, P. H., 960
ABERRATION (theory), **1, 495,** 571
  astigmatic, 495
  eye, 1001
  holography, 430
Aberration, spherical, 495, 650
Abbot, C. G., 854
Abrikosov, A. A., 905
Absolute ampere, 254
Absolute reaction rate theory, **225**
Absolute space, 559, 807
Absolute temperature function, 942
Absolute temperature scale, 122
Absolute time, 559
Absorbance, 4
Absorptance, **4,** 418, 772
Absorptiometry, 1021
Absorption (see ADSORPTION), **21**
  general, **4**
  optical, **4**
  selective, **4**
Absorption bands, **4**
Absorption coefficient, **3,** 770
  atomic, **6**
  mass, **6**
Absorption edge, **1021**
Absorption index, 4
Absorption of light, 321, 704
ABSORPTION SPECTRA, **3,** 881
Absorption spectrophotometry, **6**
Absorptive power, **4**
Absorptivity, 418
ac theory, 599
Accelerated system, 951
Acceleration, 237, 357, 534, **557,** 984
  centrifugal, 559
  centripetal, 821, 985
  Coriolis, 173
  radial, 821
  true, 173
Accelerator, 608
  Cockcroft-Walton, **7**
  electrostatic, **7**
ACCELERATOR, LINEAR, **7,** 10
Accelerator, medical application, **17**
ACCELERATOR, PARTICLE, **9**
Accelerator, shielding of, 620
Accelerator, tandem, **15**
ACCELERATOR, VAN DE GRAAFF, **13**
Accelerometer, 439
Acceptor, 840
Acceptor impurity, 842
Accommodation (eye), 1000
Achromatic lens, **573**
Ace (quark), **756**

Acoustic attenuation, **971**
Acoustic energy, 873
Acoustic excitation, 123
Acoustic horn, 970
Acoustic lens, 970
Acoustic phonon, **837-838**
Acoustic properties, 407
Acoustic velocity, 971
Acoustic wave, 874
Acoustical branch, 681
Acoustical engineering, 614
ACOUSTICAL NOISE, **613**
ACOUSTICS, **17,** 262, 712
ACOUSTICS, ARCHITECTURAL, 18, **50**
Acoustics, geometrical, **18**
Acoustics, microwave, 263
ACOUSTICS, PHYSICAL, **17, 705**
Acoustics, psychological, **18**
Acoustics, physiological, **18**
Actin, 99
Actinide contraction, 788
Actinide series, **960**
Action-at-a-distance, 755
Activation analysis, 607
Activation energy, 128, 402
Activator, 510, 511
Activity, induced, 608
Adair, R. K., 467
Adams, J. C., 425
Adaptation, chromatic, **145**
Adaptive control, 198
Adenosine diphosphate, 703
Adenosine triphosphate, 703
Adhesion, 376
Adiabatic, 941
Adiabatic compressibility, 150
Adiabatic cooling, 135
Adiabatic process, **121**
Adjoint, 544
Adler, S. L., 197
Adler-Weisberger sum rule, **197**
Adler's neutrino sum rule, 197
Adsorbate, 20
Adsorbent, 20
ADSORPTION AND ABSORPTION, **20**
AERODYNAMICS, **21,** 366
Aeronomy, 390
Aerostatics, 21, **23**
Aerophysics, 22
Aether, **568**
Aftershock, 828
Air pollution, 567
Air quality, 567
Air-breathing engine, **363**
Airglow, 88, 454, 459
Air-core transformer, 953
Airy disc, 276
Aizu, Kêitsiro, **337**

Alfvén,Hannes, 736
Alfvén speed, 522
Alchemy, 131
Algebra of tensors, 934
Algebra, von Neumann, **37**
Algorithm, 155
Alice mirror, 378
Allen, Douglas L., **982**
Alley, Charles L., **581**
Alloying method, 843
Alloys, **562**
Alpha particle, 79, 633, **782**
Alpha ray, **617**
ALTERNATING CURRENT, **23**, 242, 852, 925
Ambipolar diffusion, **252**
Ambler, E., **674**
Americium, **961**
Amme, Robert C., **458**
Ammeter, 256
Amorphous matter, 217
Amorphous polymer, 727
Amorphous semiconductor, 836
Ampere, 253
    absolute, 254
Ampère, André, 259
Ampère's law, 269
Amplification factor, **294**
Amplification, maser, **531**
Amplifier, class A, AB, B, C, **296**
    maser, 530
    parametric, 336
    sound, 814
    traveling-wave, 263
Amplitude, 601, 993, **1009**
Amplitude modulation, 580
Analog computer, 155
Analog state, **466**
Analogy, 938
Analysis, activation, 607
Analysis, dimensional, **227**
Analytical chemistry, 132
Analytical geometry, 347
Analyzer, 686
Anatomy of the ear, **407**
Anaximenes of Miletus, 311, 424
Anderson, C. D., 32, **727**
Anderson, David L., **274**
Anderson, Ernest R., **875**
Anderson, J. S., **224**
Andrews, C. L., **236**
Angle of contact, 914
Angström, K. J., 853
Angstrom (unit), (footnote) 661
Angular acceleration, 985
Angular aperture, **638**
Angular impulse, 432
Angular magnification, 637
Angular momentum, **42, 64,** 106–107, 314, 431, 542,
    670, **821,**985
    of electron, 1024
    specific, **64**
Angular velocity, **821,** 985
    of earth, 477
Animal electricity, 98
Anion, 164, **265, 456**
Anisotropy, 339
    magnetic, **31**
    magnetocrystalline, 519
Annihilation, 604
    pair, **32**
Anomalous dispersion, 720
Anomalous scattering, neutron, 611

Anomalous skin effect, 853
Anomalous Zeeman effect, 1025
Anode, 92, **265, 456**
Anode electrode, **296**
Anode fall, 252
Anomaly, Lambda, 415
Anschutz-Kampfe, Hermann, 398
Antarctica, 454
ANTENNA, **27,** 579, 761
    rhombic, **28**
    Yagi, **28**
Anterior chamber, 1000
Antiferromagnet, 888
Antiferromagnetic resonance, 32
Antiferromagnetic rotation, **329**
ANTIFERROMAGNETISM, **30,** 519, 612
Antimatter, 169
Antineutrino, **604,** 674, 783
Antinode, 1009
Antiparticle, 308, 349
ANTIPARTICLES, theory, **32**
Antiphoton, **699**
Antireflection coating, 798, **948**
Anti-Stokes' emission, 509
Anti-Stokes' line, 785
Antisymmetric tensor, 934
Anvil, tapered, 731
Aperture, angular, **638**
    numerical, 573, **638**
    relative, 495, **638**
Aperture stop, 495
Aphelion, **475**
Aphochromatic lens, 573
Apostilb, 507
Appleton-Hartree equation, 735
Applied physics, 550
Approximation, 938
Aqueous humor, 1000
Aquinas, Thomas, 424
Arago, Francois, **989**
Arc, **252,** 498
    auroral, 88
    mercury, 972
Ardenne, M. von, 281
Archimedes, 23, **207,** 895
Archimedes' principle, 23, **207,** 371
ARCHITECTURAL ACOUSTICS, 18, **50**
Archytas of Taras (or Tarentum), 895
Argus experiment, **764**
Aristarchos of Samos, 424
Aristotle, 424
Arm, lever, 559
Armature, 242
    disc, 599
    drum, 599
    ring, 599
Armstrong, H. L., **891**
Arrhenius, Svante, 99, 264, 588, 708
Arrhenius relation, 226
Arrow (vector), 984
Artificial radioactivity, **618**
Artificial transmutation, **469**
Ashby, W. R., 198, 329
Asperity, 374
Aspheric surface, lens, 494
Assembly, 944
Associated liquid, 506
Astatic magnetometer, 524
Astigmatic aberration, 495
Astigmatism, 496, 650
Astrochemistry, 71
Aston, Francis William, 535, **567,** 633

ASTRODYNAMICS, **55**
ASTROMETRY, **60**
ASTRONAUTICS, PHYSICS OF, **63**
Astronomic aberration, 989
Astronomy (see ASTROMETRY and
    ASTROPHYSICS), **60**, 237
Astronomy, geodetic, 388
ASTRONOMY, RADIO, **777**
ASTROPHYSICS, **68**, 711
Asymmetric scattering, 722
Atkinson, L., 599
Atmosphere, 565
  circulation of, 174
  earth, **875**
  ionization of, 458
  particle precipitation into, 88
ATMOSPHERES, PLANETARY, 586, **713**
Atmospheric refraction, 387
Atmospheric window, 444
Atom, 79, 479, 589, 633, 739
  displaced, **460**
  hydrogen, 739
  magnetic, 611
  structure, **79**
ATOMIC AND MOLECULAR BEAMS, **72**
Atomic beam, **72**, 76
Atomic bomb, **352**
  UV from, 972
Atomic building block model, 163
ATOMIC CLOCK, **75**, 170, 643, 950
ATOMIC ENERGY, **76**
Atomic Energy Commission, 352
Atomic gyroscope, 643
Atomic masses, scale of, 582
Atomic number, 80, 467
  table, **468**
ATOMIC PHYSICS, **79**
Atomic power, 77
ATOMIC SPECTRA, **81**, 583, 883
Atomic structure, 675
  periodicity of, 676
Atomic weight, 587, 589
  table, **468**
Attenuation, acoustic, 874, **971**
Attraction, long-range, 451
Auditorium, acoustics of, **54**
Auditory pathway, 407, 409
Auger, Pierre, **85–86**, 687
AUGER EFFECT, **85**, 470, 687
Auger spectra, 86
Auger yield, 86, 470
Auricle, 407
Aurora, **88**, 389, 454, 459, 763, 876
AURORA AND AIRGLOW, **88**
Aurora borealis, 523
Auroral arc, 88
Auroral electrojet, 89
Auroral zone, 89
Austin, 825
Automatic volume controls, 329
Automation, 329
Avalanche multiplication, 794
Avalanche transistor, 744
Averbach, B. L., 661
AVF cyclotron, **11**
Avogadro, Amedeo, **131**, 582, 589
Avogadro constant, 587
Avogadro's hypothesis, 131, 589
Avogadro's number, 110, **582**
Avogadro's principle, **582**
Axial vector, 934
Axis, optical, 494

Axon, 409
Azbel and Kaner apparatus, 204
Azimuthal quantum number, 82
Azimuthally varying-field synchrotron, 925

Babbage, Charles, 156
Back, E., 290
Background radiation, isotropic, 397
Backscattered electrons, 825
Bacon, G. E., **612**
Bacon, Roger, 424, 571
Bacteriochlorophyll, 703
Bailly, Jean-Sylvain, 463
Balescu, Radu C., **899**
Ballistic pendulum, 91
Ballistic trajectory, **55**
BALLISTICS, **91**, 173
Balmer, J. J., 81
Balmer series, 81, 1025
Band, William, 161, **540**
Band degeneracy, 839
Band spectrum, **583**
Band structure, 203, 400, 872
Bander, Myron, **807**
Bandwidth, 658
Barbrow, L. E., **696**
Bardeen, J., **836**, 906, **954**
Bare charge, 750
Bare mass, 750
BARITT diode, **833**
Barium titanate, 969
Barkhausen effect, 519
Barkla, Charles Glover, **1020**
Barn (unit), **185**, 471
Barrel distortion, 650
Barrier, potential, 827
Barrier-layer cell, 688
Bartlett, Neil, 132, **593**
Barycentric coordinate system, 141
Baryon, 32, 305, 757
Baryon conservation, 168
Base vector, 541
Bastnasite, 788
Batholinus, Erasmus, **655**
BATTERIES, **92**
Battery storage, 92
Baun, William L., **1022**
Bay, Z., 777
Bayard-Alpert gauge, 980
Bayesian, 902
Beam, atomic, **72**
  extraordinary, 655
  molecular, **72**
  ordinary, 655
Beam attenuation, synchrotron, **926**
Beam-power tube, **295**
Beams, J. W., **125**
Beccari, E., 538
Beck, Clifford K., **630**
Becker, Joseph J., **520**
Becquerel, Antoine Henri, 131, 764, **782**
Beer, Albert C., **403**
Beer, August, (footnote), **3**
Beer's law, (footnote), **3**
behavior, elastic, **553–554**
Behavior, plastic, 553–554
bel, **602**
Bell, D. A., **199**
Bell, S. J., 779
Bellman, R., 538
BELT, RADIATION, **763**
Bénard cell, 524

Bennett, H. L., 798
Bennett, W. R., 489
Benumof, Reuben, **26**
Beran, Mark J., 138, **140**
Beranek, Leo L., **55**
Bergstrand, Erik, 988, 991, **992**
Berkelium, **962**
Berman, Arthur I., **68**
Bernal, J. D., 661
Bernoulli, Daniel, 22, **227**, 479
Bernouli formula, **368**
Bernoulli's equation, 22, **227**
Besançon, Robert M., **713**, **933**
Beta decay, 304, **604**, 674, 1012
  inverse, 604
Beta emission, 471
Beta radiation, **782**
Beta ray, **617**
BETATRON, 10, **95**
Bethe, Hans, 632, **749**, 750, (scattering) 826
Beyer, George L., **592**
Bias, forward, 230
Bias, reverse, 230
Big-bang, 72
Billing, P. J., **439**
Bimetallic strip, 933
Binary stars, 63
Binary system, 778
Binder, Raymond C., **371**
Binding energy, 631, 633
  defects, 493
Binding forces, 971
Biochemistry, 132, 538
Biomathematics, 537
Biomedical engineering, 560
BIONICS, **96**
BIOPHYSICS, **98**, 536, 560, 712
BIOPHYSICS, MATHEMATICAL, 99, **536**
Bipolar cell (vision), 1001
Bipolar transistor, 829
Bipropellant rocket, 359
Birefringence, **686**, 723, **800**
Birss, R. R., 527
Bivariant system, 679
Black hole, 72, **395**
Black light, 974
Blackbody, **4**, 69, 418, 699, **772**
Blackbody radiation, **772**
  universal, 176
Blankenbecler, R., 143
Blackman, 205
Blasius of Parma, 895
Blewett, John P., **9**
Blewett, M. Hildred, **13**
Block, F., **887**
Block polymer, 726
Blocking oscillator, 742
Bloembergen, N., 224, **499**
Blum, Harold, 464
Boast, Warren B., **731**
Bode, H. W., 198
Bode plot, **846**
Bogoliubov, N. N., 482
Bohm, H. V., **334**
Bohr, Niels, 80, 132, 233, 314, 330, **351**, 530, 634,
     708, 739, 772, 826, 1004
Bohr magneton, 233, **288**, 515, 518
Bohr's model, **708**
Bohr-Sommerfeld quantization condition, 205
Bohr-Sommerfeld theory, 82
Boldwood, 467
Bolometer, 776

Boltzmann, Ludwig, **100–102**, 122, 320, 464, 480,
     481, **772**
Boltzmann constant, 101, 772
BOLTZMANN DISTRIBUTION LAW, **100**
Boltzmann equation, 481, **620**
Boltzmann H-theorem, **320**, 481
Boltzmann hypothesis, 320
Boltzmann superposition principle, 995
Bomb, atomic, 352
Bomb, hydrogen, 78, 352
Bomb, nuclear, 764
BOND, CHEMICAL, **102**, 587, **592**
  coordinate-covalent, **592**
  delta, 103
  double, 592
  electron-pair, 102
  electrovalent, **592**
  electrostatic, 102
  hydrogen, 102, **104**, 593
  metallic, 102
  pi, 103
  semipolar, 592
  sigma, 103
  triple, **592**
Bond dipole moment, **104**
Bond angle, 593
Bond dissociation energy, 103
Bond energy, 103
Bond length, 593
Bond moment, 232
Bondi, H., 178, 397
Bonding, 586
Bonding, chemical, 677
Bonding, ionic, 102
Boole, George, 484
Boolian algebra, 157
Born, Max, 107, 274, 482, 594, 1006
Born-Oppenheimer approximation, 594
Bose, Satyendra Nath, 104, (statistics) 331
Bose-Einstein statistics, 331
BOSE-EINSTEIN STATISTICS AND BOSONS, **104**
Boson, **32**, **105**, 331, 898
Bottle, magnetic, 78
Bouguer, Pierre, **3**, **854**
Bouguer and Lambert, law of, **3**
Bouguer's law, irradiance, **854**
Bound particle, 824
Boundary, grain, 842
Boundary impedance, 706
Boundary layer, 22
Boundary value problem, 212, 214
Boyle, Robert, 131, 311, 462, 479
Boynton, Robert M., **999**
Braddick, H. J. J., **553**
Bradley, C. S., 599
Bradley, James, **989**
Bradley, John N., **848**
Bragg, W. L., **1020**
Bragg's law, **6**, 1018
Bragg reflection, 223
Brahe, Tycho, **475**
Branching ratio, 470
Brandstatter, J. J., **739**
Brans, C. H., 394
Brattain, W. H., **836**, **954**
Bravais lattice, 195
Brazing, 562
Breeder reactor, 353, 619, **627–628**
Bremsstrahlung, 154, 377, 608, 719
BREMSSTRAHLUNG AND PHOTON BEAMS, **105**
Breneman, John W., 851
Brett, J., 599

Brewster, David, 655
Brewster's angle, **722**
Brewster's law, **655**
Bridge, impedance, 255
Bridge, Kelvin, 255
Bridge, Tacoma Narrows, 817
Bridge, Wheatstone, 255
Bridgman, P. W., (crystal growth) 193, **731**
Bridgman technique, **193**
Briggs, G. E., **660**
Brightness, 145, 693
Brightness temperature, **744**
Brillouin, Louis Marcel, **500, 670**
Brillouin function, **670**
Brillouin zone, 333
British thermal unit, 411
Brodsky, Stanley J., **751**
Broers, A. N., 283
Broglie, Louis de (see de Broglie)
Bromwich integral, 485
Brown, F. C., **725**
Brown, Robert, **110**
BROWNIAN MOTION, **110,** 124, 464
Brüche, E., 276
Brueckner, K. A., 529, 632
Brueckner theory of nuclei, 529
Brush, Stephen G., **464, 483**
BUBBLE CHAMBER, **878, 880**
Bubble domain, 336
Buchdahl, H. A., **944**
Bucket-brigade device, 832
Buckingham, E. (theorem) 228
Buckingham's PI theorem 228
Bueche, F., 726
Bulk modulus, 554
Bulk photovoltaic effect, 844
Bunches (electrons), 297
Bunsen, Robert Wilhelm, 118
Bunsen ice calorimeter, 118
Buoyancy, **207**
Buoyant force, 986
Burbidge, B. R., 779
Burbury, S. H., 464
Burgers vector, 492
Burgh, Donald A., **575**
Burke, B. F., 778
Burkhard, Donald G., **578**
Burst, underground, 327
Burton, W. K., 163
Bush, Vannevar, 157
Butsch, Leonard M., Jr., 98
Byer, Robert L., **479**

Cabibbo, 1003
Cabibbo angle, 196
Cabibbo-Radicati sum rule, 197
Cabrera, N., 163
Caianiello, E. R., **350**
Calcite, 722, 497
CALCULUS OF PHYSICS, **112**
Calculus of tensors, **935**
Californium, **963**
Callen, Earl, **528**
Caloric, 410
Calorie, 411, 1015
Calorimeter, **116** , 118
  bomb, 118
  solution, 118
CALORIMETRY, **115**
  low-temperature, 117
Calutron, **469**
Camera, 639, 688

Camera objective, 496
Campbell, N. R., 825
Candela, 507, 693
Cannizzaro, Stanislao, **589**
Canonical distribution, 898
Canonical ensemble, 320
Canonical partition function, 383
Canut, M., 223
CAPACITANCE, 24, **118,** 209, 253
  nonlinear, 120
Capacitor, **118,** 135
  ceramic, 119
  relaxation in, 811
Capacity, heat, 410
Capillarity, **914**
Carbon, compounds of, 131
Carbon, radioactive, 626
Carbon cycle, solar, **859**
Cardinal point, 494
Cardiovascular system, 537
Carlisle, Anthony, 264
Carnot, Sadi, 120–122
CARNOT CYCLES AND CARNOT ENGINES, **120**
Carnot engine, 931
Carnot refrigerator, 122
Carrier, charged, 835
  excess, 684
  free, 684
  minority, **229**
  majority, **229**
Carrier density, 838
Carrier rotation, **328**
Carrier separation, 609
Carrier wave, **580**
Carver, Thomas R., **643**
Cascade process, 501
Casey, E. J., **100**
Casimir invariant, **40**
Casimir operator, **40**
Casting, 562
Catalyst, **129**
  chemical, 628
Cathode, 92, 250, **265, 291, 456**
Cathode fall, 252
Cathode ray, 272
Cathode-ray oscilloscope, **656**
Cathode-ray tube, **285,** 657, 970
Cathodoluminescence, 508
Cation, 164, **265, 456**
Cauchy, A. L., 4
Cauchy formula, 800
Causality, principle of, 755
Cavendish, Henry, 423
CAVITATION, **123,** 705
CCD, 832
Celestial mechanics, 68
Cell, Bénard, 524
  concentration, 92
  convective, 524
  fuel, 95
  galvanic, **92**
  Kerr, 479
  lattice, 661
  Leclanché, 92
  mercury-cadmium, 95
  primary, **94**
  radioisotope, 245
  secondary, **94**
  solar, 245
  solarblind, **688**
  standard, **94, 254**
  thermionic, 245

Cell, (*Continued*)
unit, **194,** 590, 1018
voltaic, **92**
Weston, 95
Celsius, Anders, **931**
Celsius scale, **931**
CENTER, COLOR, **147**
Center, recombination, **685**
Center of gravity, 896
Center of mass, 896
Centigrade scale, **931**
Centrifugal acceleration, 559
Centrifugal force, 123, **822**
CENTRIFUGE, **123,** 469
gas, 125
Centripetal acceleration, 821, 985
Centripetal force, **822**
Centroid, 896
Čerenkov, P. A., **126-127**
Čerenkov counters, 127
ČERENKOV RADIATION, **126**
Cerium earth, 788
Chadwick, Sir James, **605, 630**
Chain reaction, **352, 626, 635**
Chako, Nicholas, 3
Chamber, ionization, 615
proportional, 879
Chancourtois, 675
Chandrasekhar, B. S., **908**
Change of pressure (thermometry), 933
Channeltron, 827
Chapman, Sydney, 480, **481**
Characteristic x-rays, 316
Charge, bare, 750
electric, 118, 422, 729
electronic, 171
neutralization of, 894
photo-liberated, 704
space, **293**
Charge carrier, 400, 401
Charge conjugation, **169,** 672
Charge conservation, 168
Charge dissipation, 894
Charge exchange, 377, 457
Charge independence, 465
Charge migration, 704
Charge parity, 672
Charge recombination, 704
Charge-separation, **704**
Charge-transfer device, **830, 832**
Charged carrier, 835
Charged particle, 768
Charles, Jacques, 382
Chelate, 510
CHEMICAL BOND, **102**
Chemical catalyst, 628
CHEMICAL ELEMENT, **310,** 675
Chemical energy, from sun, 865
Chemical equivalent weight, **265**
Chemical industry, **131**
CHEMICAL KINETICS, **128**
CHEMICAL PHYSICS, **130**
Chemical potential, 319, 943
Chemical reaction, 128
Chemiluminescence, 508
Chemisorption, 20, **21**
CHEMISTRY, 129, 130, **131**
analytical, 132
inorganic, 132
organic, 132
CHEMISTRY, PHYSICAL, **708**
CHEMISTRY, RADIATION, **764**
Chew, G. F., 143

Chirality, 169
Chlorophyll, 683, 702
Chloroplast, **702**
Choke joint (wave guide), 1011
Choppin, 963
Chorlton, Frank, **215**
Christie, Dan E., **987**
Christoffel, Elwin, **934**
Christofilos, 925
Chromatic aberration, 495
Chromatic adaptation, **145**
Chromatography, 711
Chromosphere, **868**
Cilliary muscle, 1000
Cineradiography, 1021
Circuit, 133
nonlinear, 134
series, **24**
Circuit analysis, 133
CIRCUITRY, **133**
Circular motion, **820**
Circularly polarized light, 721
Cladding, **629**
Clapeyron, B. P. E., 122
Clapeyron relation, 319
Clathrate, 592-593
Claude, Georges, 503
Claude process, **501**
Clausius, Rudolph, **122,** 232, **317,** (formula) 325, 463, 480
Clausius and Mosotti equation, 720
Clausius-Clapeyron equation, **981**
Clausius-Mosotti formula, 325
Clebsch-Gordon coefficient, 196
Cleaners, ultrasonic, 123
Clipping amplifier, 742
Clock, **950**
Clock, atomic, 75, 170
Clockwork universe, 462
Close, K. J., **980**
Closed shell, **633**
Cloud, cumulus, 137
Cloud, microphysics of, **136**
Cloud chamber, 615, 727
CLOUD PHYSICS, **135,** 567
Cloud seeding, **136, 567**
Cluster expansion, 898
Cluster integral, 383
Clutter, radar, 762
Coactivator, 511
Coating, antireflection, 948
Coaxial cable, 1010
Coaxitron, 297
Coblentz, W. W., 586
Cochin, Ira, 399
Cochlea, 408
Cochlear duct, 408
Cockcroft, J. D., 7, **636**
Cockcroft-Walton accelerator, 7
Cockcroft-Walton generator, 10
Cockcroft-Walton deuteron accelerator, 608
Coefficient of expansion, 322
Coercive force, 3, **39,** 519
Cohen, E. Richard, **173,** 992
Cohen, V. W., 606
COHERENCE, 127, **137**
quantum aspects, **139**
range of, 906
Coherence function, mutual, **138**
Coherence length, 905
Coherent radiation, **530**
Coil, inductance, 437
primary, **951**
secondary, **981**

Cold trap, 978
Cole, E. A. B., **844**
Cole, Kenneth, 538
Cole and Cole, method of, 210
Cole and Davidson equation, 210
Coleberd, B. Thompson, **717**
Coleman lantern, 774
Collective model, **632**
Collective motion, 529
Collective motion theory, **529**
Collector, 954
Collector, concentrating, 863
Colligative property, 589, 590
Collins, S. C., 503
Collapse, gravitational, **394**
Colliding-beam device, **13**
Colliding-beam experiment, 749
Collision, 957
Collision, heavy-particle, 457
Collision of molecules, 481
COLLISION OF PARTICLES, **140**
Collision, probability of, 957
Collision time, 203
COLOR, **144**, 497
Color center, 493
COLOR CENTERS, **147**
Color match, **144**
Color perception, **145**
Color photography, **691**
Color reversal, 691
Color scale, **146**
Color television tube, **286**
Color temperature, 773
Color theory, **147**
Color vision, 1002
Colorant, 145
Columbus principle, 44
Column, positive, 252
Coma (aberration), 495
Combustion, heat of, 118
Comet Kohoutek, 778
Communication, 198, 407, 929
  acoustic, 874
  sonar, 874
Commutation, 541
Commutation (of translations), **34**
Commutation rule, 542
Commutator, 242, 599, 600, (operator) 1006
  quantum mechanical, **542**
Comparator, current, **258**
Comparator technique, 609
Compatible observables, 46
Compatibility equation, 241
Compensation point, 335
Complete primitive, 212
Complex, molecular, 593
Complex impedance, 26
Complex spectra, 83
Complex-number method (circuits), **26**
Compound, 311
  ionic, **588**
  molecular, **592-593**
  noble gas, 132
  rare gas, 593
COMPRESSIBILITY, GAS, **149**, 385
Compressibility, isothermal, 151
Compressibility factor, 150
Compression factor, 385
Compressional wave, **1008**
Compton, Arthur Holly, 108, **151**, 404, 687, 699
Compton, W. Dale, **149**
Compton collision, 618
COMPTON EFFECT, **151**, 421, 687, 699
  inverse, 108

Compton scattering, 769
Compton wavelength, **152**
COMPUTERS, **155**, 330
Computer hardware, **158**
Concentrating collector, 863
Concentration cell, 92
Concepts, 936
Condensation, 136
CONDENSATION, 136, **161**, 947
Condenser, 209
Condenser lens, 278, 496, 574
Conduction, electrical, **164**
  electronic, 400, 837
  heat, 116, **228**
  thermal, **415**
Conduction band, 684, 966
Conduction of electricity, 717
Conductivity, 733
CONDUCTIVITY, ELECTRICAL, **164**, 684
Conductivity, equivalent, 456
Conductivity mobility, 402
Conductivity tensor, 401
Conductor, electrolyte, 264
Cone, retinal, 147, 1001
Configuration integral, 383
Congruent melting point, 680
Conjugation, 305
  charge, **169**
  CP, 699
Conjugation theorem, **48**
Conjugation-invariant, **32**
Connes, J., 586
Connes, P., 586
Conrady formula, 799
Conservation law of momentum, 431
Conservation laws, **304, 166**, 539
CONSERVATION LAWS AND SYMMETRY, **166**
Conservation of energy, **559, 1016**
Conservation of momentum, **559**
Constant, dielectric, **209**
  multiplication, 353
  screening, **708**
Constant energy surface, 203
CONSTANTS, FUNDAMENTAL, **170**
Constants, numerical values, **171-172**
Constant-gradient synchrotron, 925
Constitutive coordinate, **943**
Constitutive parameters, **733**
Consolute point, 680
Contact, angle, of, 914
Contact electrification, **892**
Continuity equation, **706**
Continuity equation, fluids, 22
Continuous-thrust trajectory, 68
Continuum dynamics, 366
Continuum of radiation, 1020
Contravariance, 935
Contravariance vector, 544
Control, 197, 329
  adaptive, 198
  automatic volume, 329
Control grid, **295**
Control rod, 353
Control system, 198
Controlled rectifier, 743, 792
Convection, 116, 415, **416**
Convective cell, 524
Conversion, internal, 470
Conversion factors, energy units, **173**
Conversion, temperature scales, **931**
Converter, pentagrid, 295
Convolution integral, 663
Convolution theorem, 485
Cook, C. Sharp, **327**

Cooke, Sir William F., 599
Cooling, adiabatic, 135
Cooper, L. N., 906
Cooper pair, 906
Cooperative order, 222
Coordinate, momentum, 331
Coordinate system, 167, 671
  barycentric, 141
Coordinate-covalent bond, **592**
Coordination number, 505
Coparity, 36
Cope, Freeman, 537
Copernicus, Nicholas, 424, **571**
Copolymer, 726
Copper oxide cell, 688
Corbin, John C., Jr., **853**
Corbino, O. M., 403
Corbino effect, 403
Corbino magnetoresistance, 403
Core of earth, 828
Coriolis, G. G., **173**
Coriolis acceleration, 559
Coriolis component, 238
CORIOLIS EFFECT, **173**
Coriolis force, 822
Cornea, 1000
Corngold, N. R., 606
Corona, 423, **868**
Correlation function, 181, 500
Correlation length, 181
Corrosion, 564
Corrosion fatigue, 564
COSMIC RAY, 71, **175**, 763
COSMOLOGY, **177**, 397
Cosmology, steady-state, 178
Coster, D. (Coster-Kronig effect), 87
Coster-Kronig effect, 87
Coster-Kronig transitions, 470
Cotton, H., **652**
Cotton-Mouton effect, 233
Cottony, H. V., **30**
Couette flow, 367
Coulomb, Charles Augustin de (law), **259**
Coulomb displacement energy, 466
Coulomb equivalent, **265**
Coulomb force, **350**
Coulomb interaction, 343
Coulomb repulsion, 342
Coulomb's law, **259**
Counter, Čerenkov, 127
  Geiger-Müller, 616
  proportional, 615
Couper, Archibald, 131
Couple, **895**
Coupled system, 817
Coupling constant, **32**
Courant, E. D., **925**
Covalent bond, 102
Covalent compound, 587
Covariance, **755**, 935
Covariant observable, 36
Covariant vector, 544
Cowan, C. L., **1012**
CP conjugation, 699
C𝒫T theorem, 35
Crab Nebula, 741
Crampton, P., 751
Crane, H. R., 750
Crawford, Franzo H., **412**
Cream separator, 124
Creation, pair, **32**
Creep, 564
Creep compliance, 995
Crewe, A. V., 283

Critical field, 904
CRITICAL MASS, 77, **179**, 352
CRITICAL PHENOMENA, **180**, 898
Critical point, 181, 680, 890
Critical pressure, 890
Critical size, **179**
Critical temperature, 150, **180**, 501, 890, 981
Critical temperature (superconductivity), 904
Criticality factor, 353
Cros, Charles, 813
Cross product, vector, 400
Cross section, 606, 621, 1013
  fission, 353
  isotopic, 608
  macroscopic, 957
  scattering, 140
CROSS SECTION AND STOPPING POWER, **185**
Cross section (for ionization), 457
Cross-linking, 556
Cross-relaxation, 532
Crowdion-interstitial, 493
Cryogenic pumping, 979
CRYOGENICS, **186**
Cryohydric point, 680
Cryoscopic method (molecular weight), 590
Cryotron, 188
Crystal, **188**, **193**, 493, 661, 1018
  dendritic, 191
  liquid, 661
  molecular, 321
  spherulitic, 191
Crystal lattice, **194**
Crystal momentum, 203
Crystal structure, 869
CRYSTAL STRUCTURE ANALYSIS, **188**
Crystal system, **194**, **195**
Crystalline lens, 1000
Crystalline state, 661
Crystallization, **191**, 1002
CRYSTALLOGRAPHY, **193**
Crystallometry, 194
Culshaw, W., **1026**
Cumulus convection, 137
Cumulus clouds, 137
Cummingham, R. G., **895**
Curie, P., 187, 325, 337, **518**, **670**
Curie constant, **670**
Curie law, 187, 518
Curie temperature, 325, **335**, **337**, **518**, 969
Curie (unit), (footnote) **469**, **784**
Curie-Joliot, I., **469**, 618, 782
Curie-Weiss law, 325, 518, **670**
Curium, **962**
Curl (vectors), 986
Current, alternating, **23**, 242, 852
Current, dark, 553
Current, electric, 133, 253, **259**, **260**, 435
Current, magnetic, 433
CURRENT ALGEBRA, **196**
Current comparator, **258**
Current density, 730
Current electricity, **260**
Current-current coupling, 1013
Curtiss, L. F., **607**
Curvature, field, 495
CYBERNETICS, **197**, 329
Cycle, Carnot, **120**
  Rankine, 245
CYCLOTRON, **11**, **199**
  sector focused, 201
Cyclotron frequency, 203
Cyclotron orbit, 203
Cyclotron radius, 276
CYCLOTRON RESONANCE, 201, **203**, **334**

Cylindrical lens, 689
Czerlinsky, Ernst R., **527**
Czochralski method, **193**, 843

DCF hypothesis, 183
D.C.X. mirror, 378
D region, 458
d'Alembert, Jean le Rond, 319
d'Alembert principle, 319
Dallas, A. E., 85
Dalton, John, **588**
Dalton's law, 981
Damping (vibrations), 995
Danielli, J. F., 538
Danielmeyer, H. G., 988
Danziger, L., 538
Dark current, 553
Dark ground illumination, 639
Dark noise (photomultipliers), 698
Dark space, Faraday, 252
Dashpot (relaxation), 811
Data, nuclear, 621
Data analysis, 930
Data link, **929**
Data transmission system, **929**
Dauvillier, A., 972
Davis, R., 1012
Davis, R. H., **740**
Davisson, Clinton Joseph, 217, 274, 709, 1004
Davy, Sir Humphry, 264
Davydov splitting, 321
Day, Jack E., **658**
Dayglow, 89
de Broglie, Louis Victor, 132, 273, **421**, 699, **752**, 1004
de Broglie equation, 699
de Broglie hypothesis, 283–284, **824**
de Broglie wavelength, 276, 708
de Sitter, Willem, 178
De Wames, R. E., **888**
Dean, L. Wallace, III, **707**
Debrunner, P., **598**
Debye, Peter, 165, 186, 217, 414, 661, 718, 719
Debye equation, 209–210
Debye phonon spectrum, 165
Debye shielding distance, 718
Debye temperature, 165, 414
Debye theory, **264**
Debye theory, specific heat, 681
Debye-Hückel radius, 457
Debye-Hückel theory, **264**
Debye-Rayleigh scattering, 500
Decay, particle, 305
  radioactive, 78
Decay rate, radioactivity, **784**
Decay scheme, radioactivity, **783–784**
Decibel (unit), **18**, **602**, **874**
Decomposition, thermal, 128
Defares, J., 538
Dee, **200**
Defect, Frenkel, 842
DEFECTS, LATTICE, **491**
  point, **493**
  Schottky, 842
  surface, 842
Deflection, electrostatic, **285**
  magnetic, **285**
Deformation, **240**
  plastic, 842
Deformation of matter, 818
Deformation of solid, **553**
Degeneracy, 82
Degenerate state, 101
Degree of freedom, 101, 413, **679**, 755, 901

de Haas, W. J., 187, **205**
DE HAAS-VAN ALPHEN EFFECT, 187, **205**, **334**
Delay line, 263
Delayed neutron, 355, 631, **635**
Delta, Kronecker, 935
Delta function, **372**, **539**
Delta-ray, 765, **768**, 880
Delvaille, John P., **177**
Demagnetization, adiabatic, 186
Dember voltage, 685
Democritus of Abdera, 424, 479
Dempster, A. J., **469**
Denisyuk, Y. N., 426
Density, 367
  flux, 517
DENSITY AND SPECIFIC GRAVITY, **207**
Density function, 505
Density matrices, 38
Density operator, 897
Deposition electrification, 892
Deposition charging, **893**
Deposition methods, 946
Depth of field, **639**
Depth of focus, 573, **639**
Depth recording, 970
Derivative, **113**
Derived unit, **918**
Descartes, René, **347**, 462
Deshpande, N. G., **197**
Desroziers, 599
Destriau, G. (effect), 267
Destriau effect, 267
Destructive interference, 447
Detection of ultraviolet, 973
Detector, infrared, 445, 776
  quantum, **776**
  radiation, 615
  scintillation, 615, **616**
Deuterium, 78, 376, 739
Deuteron, 739
Deutsch, M., 153
Developer, photographic, 689
Deviation, standard, 900
DEVICE, SEMICONDUCTOR, **829**
  thermonuclear, **352**
Dewar, Sir James, 502
Dexter, David L., **873**
DEW radar line, 580
Diagonal matrix, 543
Diagram, Hertzsprung-Russell, **70**
Diagram, phase, 504
Diamagnetic material, 518
DIAMAGNETIC RESONANCE, **203**
DIAMAGNETISM, **208**
Diameter, stellar, 448
Diamond lattice, 493
Diaphram, photographic, 688
Diathermic, 941
Diatomic molecule, 583
Dichroic polarizer, 722
Dicke, R. H., 178, 393–394, 558, 778
Didymium filter, 6
Diebold, Edward J., **794**
Dielectric, **119**, 126, **209**
Dielectric constant, 720
Dielectric loss, **720**
DIELECTRIC THEORY, **209**
Dienes, G. J., **462**
Differential equation, partial, 486
DIFFERENTIAL EQUATIONS IN PHYSICS, **211**
Differential pulley, 849
Diffraction, **188**, 653, **1017**
DIFFRACTION, ELECTRON, **274**, 837, 1004
DIFFRACTION, NEUTRON, **609**

DIFFRACTION, X-RAY, 194, 610, **1017**
  molecular weight determination, **590**
DIFFRACTION BY MATTER AND DIFFRACTION
  GRATINGS, 215
Diffraction grating, **215**
Diffractometer, 1019
Diffuse series, 82
Diffused junction, 955
Diffusion, 129
  ambipolar, **252**
  self, 225
  surface, 911
  thermal, 480
Diffusion coefficient, **224**, 226
Diffusion drag force, 537
DIFFUSION IN LIQUIDS, **223**
Diffusion in plasmas, 379
DIFFUSION IN SOLIDS, **225**
Diffusion pump, 978
Diffusion rate (measurement of), 781
Diffusion theory, 623
Diffusivity, thermal, 228, 416
Digital computer, 155
Digital voltmeter, **257**
Di-interstitial, 493
Dilatation, 240
Dilution refrigerator, 803
Dimensional analysis, **227**
Dimensionality, of tensors, 934
DIMENSIONS, **227**
Dimensions, molecular, 587
Dimer, 588
Dinsdale, A., **999**
Diode, **291**, **293**
  Gunn, 231
  hot carrier, 231
  IMPATT, 231
  injection, 231
  junction, **229**
  light-emitting, 231, **834**
  rectifier, **230**, 791
  Schottky, 231
DIODE (SEMICONDUCTOR), **229**
Diode, tunnel, 744
Diode, Zener, 231
Diopter, **651**
Dipole, electric, 209
  magnetic, 516
  oscillating, **271**
Dipole interaction, 578
Dipole moment, 209, 479, 575, 517, **719**
DIPOLE MOMENT (ELECTRICAL AND
  MAGNETIC), **232**
Dipole moment, magnetic, 233
Dirac, P. A. M., 32, 152, 178, 273–274, **330**, 539,
  727, **747**, 772
Dirac delta function, 372
Dirac equation, 349
Dirac statistics, **330**
Dirac theory, 152
Direct current, generation, 242
Direct listening system, 874
Direct reaction, 626
Directional coupler, 1011
Directivity index, sound, **51**
Disc, Airy, 276
Disc armature, 599
Discharge, electrical, **249**
  glow, **252**
Discrete ordinate, **622**
Disintegration, 608
Disintegration, spontaneous, 782
Dislocation, 163, 226, 347, **491**, 971
  edge, 842
  screw, **191–192**

Dislocation lines, 562
Dispersion, **653**, 799
Dispersion, optical, **572**
Dispersion curve, normal, **4**
Dispersion energy, 383
Dispersion potential, 451
Dispersion relation, 735
Dispersion theory, 143
Displacement (vector geometry), 984
Displacement energy, Coulomb, 466
Displacement field, 735
Displacement law, **772**
Display panel, 268
Dissipation factor, 119, 209
Dissociation, heat of, 586
Dissociative recombination, 459
Distance, 421
Distillation tower, 982
Distortion, barrel, 650
  lens, 495
  pincushion, 650
Distribution function, **897**
Distribution law, Wien, **772**
Di-vacancy, 493
Divergence, 986
Divider, voltage, **254**
DNA, 100
Dollond, John, 571
Domain, 337, **338**, 518
Domain rotation, 527
Donor, 840
Donor impurity, 842
Doping, **229**
Doppler, Christian, **234**
DOPPLER EFFECT, **234**, 397, 595, 761, 1009
Doppler shift, 75, 774
Doremus, R. H., **193**
Dosimetry, 405, 561, **766**
Double bond, 592
Double refraction, **655**, **800**
Doublet structure, 82
Downey, Glenn L., **239**
Drag, 22, **358**
Drain (transistor), 955
Dresselhaus, G., **204**
Dresselhaus, Mildred S., **842**
Drickamer, H. G., **733**
Drift, ether, 568
Drift tube, 7
Drift velocity, 837
Drude, Paul Karl Ludwig, 564, 797, 837, 939
Drum armature, 599
Duality, waves and particles, **152**
Ductile-brittle transition, 564
Dulong, Pierre Louis, 414
Dumbell model, 584
Dumas, Jean (method), 589
Dürer, Albrecht, 194
Dushman, S., **293**, 939
Dwarf, white, 70, 859
Dwight, C. Harrison, **6**, **656**
Dwight, H. B., 852
Dyadic, **240**, 934
  strain, **240**
  stress, **240**
Dye, 145
Dye, luminescence of, 509
Dye coupling process, 691
Dye laser, 490
Dyke, W. P., 344
Dynamic multiplier, 697
Dynamic plate resistance, **294**
Dynamical state, 593
DYNAMICS, **236**, 985

Dynamics, continuum, 366
Dynamics, field, 366
Dynamitron, 10
Dyne-centimeter, 1014
Dynode, **696**
Dyson, F., 750

e by m experiment, **272**
E region, 458
Ear, **407**
  anatomy of, **407**
  physiology of, **407**
Ear drum, 408
Earth, 714
  atmosphere of, **875**
  core of, 828
  mantle of, 828
  rotation of, 950
Earth inductor, 526
Earth storm, 453
Earthquake, **828**
EARTHS, RARE, 788
Ebulliometric technique, 589
Eccentricity, orbit, **58**
Echo-ranging system, 874
Eckert, E. R. G., **420**
Eckert, J. P., 157
Eddington, Sir Arthur Stanley, 178, 463
Eddy currents, 208
Edge dislocation, 842
Edge focusing, 201
Edge-defined film-fed growth, **193**
Edelson, D., **720**
Edison, Thomas Alva, 939
Edison effect, **939**, 1020
Edlefsen, N. E., 200
EDVAC, 157
Edwards, J. D. (gas density balance), 207
Edwards gas density balance, **207**
Effective current, **24**
Effective field method, **529**
Effective interaction, 529
Effective mass, 203, 206, 401, 529, 837
Effective voltage, **24**
Effector, 97
Efficiency, **851**
  electrochemical, 93
  engine, 363
  luminous, 506
  thruster, 244
  transformer, 952
Eickmeyer, R., 599
Eigenfunction, 594
Eigenstate, **541**, 700
Eigenvalue, 82, 466, **541**, 547, 700, 756, 824, 1005
Eikonal equation, 737
Eikonal matrix, 737
Einstein, Albert, 104, **110**, 132, 178, 234, 331, **393**,
    414, 500, 530, 534, 686, 699, 772, **807**, 1004
Einstein field equations, 809
Einstein photoelectric equation, **686**
Einstein tensor, 810
Einstein theory of gravitation, **393**
Einstein theory of relativity, **807**
Einstein (unit), 582, 682
Einstein universe, 178
Einsteinium, **963**
Eisele, John A., **936**
Eisner, Leonard, 777
Elastic behavior, **553-554**
Elastic limit, 554
Elastic rebound theory, 828
Elastic wave, 680
Elasticoviscous behavior, 819

ELASTICITY, **240**, 560, 819, 995
  modulus of, **554**
Electret, 263
Electric charge, 422
Electric current, **259, 160**
Electric dipole, 209
Electric field, 209, **260, 270**, 422, 734
Electric field intensity, 432, 729
Electric flux, **260**
Electric generator, 434
Electric mode, **1010**
Electric conduction, **164**
Electrical conductivity, 835
ELECTRICAL DISCHARGES IN GASES, **249**
Electrical instruments, **255**
ELECTRICAL MEASUREMENTS, **253**
Electrical oscillation, 1008
Electrical resistance, 904
ELECTRICITY, **259**, 712
Electricity, current, **260**
ELECTRICITY, STATIC, **891**
Electrification, 891
Electric potential difference, **260**
Electric power, 243
ELECTRIC POWER GENERATION, **242**
ELECTRIC PROPULSION, **243**
Electric quadrupole moments, 631
Electric rocket, 243-244, 245
ELECTROACOUSTICS, 18, **262**
Electrochemical efficiency, 93
Electrochemical equivalent, **265**
Electrochemical equivalent weight, **456**
Electrochemiluminescence, 268
ELECTROCHEMISTRY, **264**, 456
Electrode, **265**, 422
Electrode, hydrogen, **265**
Electrodynamic instrument, **256-257**
Electrodynamics, 349
ELECTRODYNAMICS, QUANTUM, 309, **747**
Electrofax, **691**
Electrojet, auroral, 89
ELECTROLUMINESCENCE, **267**, 508
Electrolysis, **264**, 455
Electrolyte, 264, 455-456
Electrolytic conductor, 264
Electrolytic oxidation, **265**
Electrolytic reduction, **265**
Electromagnetic field, **349**, 599, 987
Electromagnetic induction, 259, 433
Electromagnetic induction, Faraday's law of, 269
Electromagnetic interaction, 32, 305, 747
Electromagnetic radiation, 881
Electromagnetic shielding, 551
ELECTROMAGNETIC THEORY, **268**, 512, 773
Electromagnetic wave, 261
ELECTROMAGNETIC WAVES, PROPAGATION OF,
    733
Electromotive force, 133, 259, 265, 951
Electromotive force, induced, **261**, 432
ELECTRON, 151, 164, 203, 249, 260, **272**, 303,
    355, 615, 618, 633, 644, 686, 747, 763, 765,
    902
  angular momentum, **288**
  Auger, 86
  backscattered, 825
  charge on, **273**
  creation of, 1012
  emission of, 284
  free, 229
  in metals, 971
  kinetic energy, 284
  positive, **274**
  radius of, 274
  sources, **284**

ELECTRON (*Continued*)
  trapped, 733
  wavelength of, 284
Electron avalanche, 878
Electron beam, 277
Electron capture, 470, 685, **783**
Electron collision, **250**
ELECTRON DIFFRACTION, **274**, 1004
Electron diffraction, low-energy, **275**
Electron emission, **292**, 940
Electron gas, 342, 529
Electron hopping, 725
Electron lens, **284**
Electron microbeam probe, 1021
ELECTRON MICROSCOPE, **275**
  electrostatic, 280
  emission, 280
  scanning, **281**
ELECTRON OPTICS, **283**
Electron orbital motion, 518
Electron paramagnetic resonance, 290
Electron plasma frequency, 719
Electron spectrometer, 303
Electron spectroscopy for chemical analysis, 1021
ELECTRON SPIN, 80, **288**, 336, 515, 518
Electron spin resonance, 290, 316, **516**, 711, 813,
    818, 886
Electron synchrotron, 928
ELECTRON TUBES, **290**
Electron tunneling, 967
Electron volt, (footnote) **10**, **1016**
Electron-hole pair, 321, 871
Electronic charge, 171
Electronic conduction, **937**
Electronic detector, 880
Electronic instrument, 256
Electronic states, 320
Electronic structure of solids, 870
Electronic transition (high pressure), 732
ELECTRONICS, **302**
Electronics, film, **948**
Electron-pair bond, 102
Electro-optic effect, linear, 478
Electro-optic effect, quadratic, **478**
Electro-osmosis, 660
Electrophotography, **691**
Electrostatic accelerator, 7
Electrostatic bond, 102
Electrostatic deflection, **285**
Electrostatic electron microscope, 280
Electrostatic lens, **278**, **284**
Electrostatic shielding, 551
Electrostatic thruster, 246
Electrostatics, **259**
Electrothermal thruster, 246
Electrovalent bond, **592**
Element, atomic number, (table) **468**
  chemical, 675
  distribution of, **312**
  mononuclidic, 467
  origins of, **312**
  superheavy, **965**
  transitional, 676
  transuranic, 469
ELEMENTS, CHEMICAL, **310**
ELEMENTS, TRANSURANIUM, **959**
Elementary oscillator, 772
ELEMENTARY PARTICLES, 168, 196, **303**,
    (table) 306
e-leptic charge, 32
Ellipsometry, 796
Elliptical polarization, 721
Elmergreen, G., 538

Elster, Julius, 686, 939
Embedding (see imbedding)
emf (equation), **432**
Emission, electron, **292**, 940
Emission, radio (from galaxy), 777
EMISSION, SECONDARY, **825**
  spontaneous, 530
  stimulated, **488**, **530**
  Stokes', 509
  thermionic, **938**
Emission electron microscope, 280
Emission of electrons, 284
Emissivity, spectral, **745**
Emittance, 772, 773
  spectral, 444
Emitter, 954
Empedocles, 311
Empirical temperature, 941
Emrich, Raymond J., **369**
End group, 592
Endocrine system, 538
Endoergic reaction, **625**
Energy, 166, 421, **558**, 595, **1015**
  activation, 128
  ATOMIC, **76**
  binding, defects, 493
  bond, 103
  bound, 824
  conservation of, **559**
  dissipation of, 463
  electrical, 253
  electrical, from the sun, 864
  exchange, 338
  equation of, 1005
  fission, 354
  formation, 493
  free, 319, **910**
  Gibbs, 384
  heat, 412
  Helmholtz, 384
  internal, 384
  kinetic, particle, 824
  lattice, 102
  magnetic, 514
  migration, 493
  nuclear, **76**, 354
  of neutron, 605
  of particles, 1005
  of photon, 699
  orbital, **55**, 65
  potential, 167, 318, 729
  rotational, 385, **559**
  solar, **860**
  thermal, 771
  vibrational, 385
  vis viva, **56**
Energy band, 795, 838
Energy band extrema, 204
Energy change, 116
Energy conversion, 861
Energy density, 753
Energy equation, 22
Energy function, 386
Energy gap, 838, 967
ENERGY LEVEL, 203, 205, **314**, 795, 824, 838,
    1005
  molecular, 316
  nuclear, 618
  in crystals, 316
Energy sources, 243, 625
ENERGY SOURCES, SOLAR, **858**, 860
Energy state, 489
Energy storage, 729

Energy units, conversion factors, **173**
Energy-momentum, 42
Engine, air-breathing, 363
    Carnot, **120**
    nuclear, 364
    piston, 364
    rocket, **358**
Engineering, 712
Engineering, biomedical, 560
ENIAC, 157
Ensemble, **897**
    canonical, 320
    representative, 944
Enskog, David, 480, **481**
Enthalpy, 116, 384, **943**
    free, 319
Entrance pupil, 638
ENTROPY, 116, 117, 122, 198, **317**, 319, 384,386,
    463,464,482
    metrical, 942
Enzyme, **129**
Eötvös, R. von, 393, 558
Epitaxial growth, 837
Epitaxy, 946
Equalization (in recording), 814
Equation, differential, **211**, 486
    linear, 212
    wave, 1005
Equation of continuity (hydrodynamics), 986
Equation of energy, 1005
Equation of state, 22, 941
EQUILIBRIUM, **318**, 553, 896, 941
    statistical, **319**
    thermodynamic, 415
Equilibrium equation, **241**
Equilibrium position, 553
Equilibrium theory, 481, **710**
Equipartition theorem, 480
Equivalence, principle of, **392**, 809
Equivalence-value, 463
Equivalent, coulomb, **265**
Equivalent, electrochemical, **265**
Equivalent conductivity, 456
Equivalent weight, **591**
    chemical, **265**
    electrochemical, **456**
Erg, 1014
Error, 901
    random, 550
    standard, 900
    systematic, 550
Error function, 901
Erway, Duane D., **866**
Erythema, 974
ESCA, 1021
Escape criterion, **56**
Essen, L., 991
Eskola, K., 964, 965
Eskola, P., 964, 965
Estimator, 900
Eta particle, 305
Ether, luminiferous, 570
Ether drift, 449, 568
Ettingshausen, A. von, 403
Ettingshausen effect, 403, 804
Eucken, 385
Euclides, 424
Euler, Leonard, 537
Eutectic, 680
Evacuation, **976**
Evanescent wave, 656
Evans, Howard T., Jr., **190**, **195**
EVAPORATION, 891, **981–982**

Evaporator, 982
Evaporograph, 776
Evolution, stellar, **70**
Evolutionary model, 397
Ewen, H. I., **779**
Excess carrier, 684
Exchange, charge, 377, 457
    spin, 642
Exchange anisotropy, 519
Exchange energy, 338, **634**
Exchange force, 518
Exchange Hamiltonian, 887
Exchange integral, **338**
Exchange interaction, 31, **337**
Excitance, 443
Excitation, acoustic, 123
    multilevel, 531
Excited atom, 765
EXCITON, 148, **320**, 529, 793
    triplet, 321
Exclusion principle, Pauli, **289**, 330, 451, 675
Exit pupil, **637**
Exner, F. M., 110
Exoergic reaction, **625**
Exosphere, 390
Expansion, 413
EXPANSION, THERMAL, **322**
Expansion (thermometry), 933
Expectation value, 549, 1006
Expected flux, 957
Expected value theory, 957
Experiment, scientific, **550**
Experimental physics, 713, 937
Experiments, fluctuations in, 552
    thermal effects on, 551
Explorer I, 763
Explorer satellite, 777
Extensive properties, 385
Exterior ballistics, 91
Extinction coefficient, **795**
Extraordinary beam, 655
Extreme ultraviolet, 85, 971
EYE, **999**
Eyepiece, 496, **573**, **637**
Eyring, Henry, 162, **711**, 720

F region, 458
Fabry, Charles, 450
Fabry-Perot interferometer, 449
Face-centered cubic lattice, 493
Factor, amplification, **294**
    criticality, 353
    dissipation, 119
    loss, 119
    power, 119
Fadeev, L. D., **143**
Fahrenheit scale, 931
Fall, cathode, 252
FALLOUT, **327**
Fano profile, 85
Faraday, Michael, 259, 264, **265**, 272, 328, 433, 456,
    539, 599
Faraday dark space, 252
FARADAY EFFECT, **328**, 735
Faraday law of induction, 208, 269
Faraday (unit), 265, **456**, 582
Farley, F. J. M., 751
Far ultraviolet, 85, 688, 971
Fast neutron, 607, 619, 634
F-center, **147**, 493, 733
F'-center, **148**
F_A-center, 149
Feather, N., **995**

Feedback, 198, 329, 552, **844**
  negative, 329
Fermat's principle, **737**
Fermi, Enrico, 77, 205, 330, **331, 332, 351, 604, 618,** 1012
Fermi energy, 332
Fermi function, **631**
Fermi level, **331**, 332, 966
Fermi particle, 289
Fermi sea, 741
FERMI SURFACE, 204, **205, 331**
Fermi (unit), **624**
Fermi-Dirac distribution, 104
FERMI-DIRAC STATISTICS AND FERMIONS, **330**
Fermion, 32, 105, **330**, 898
Fermium, **963**
Fermi-Thomas approximation, 529
Ferraris, G., 599
FERRIMAGNETISM, **335**, 519, 612
Ferrite, 335, 437, 612, 953,
Ferroelasticity, **336**
Ferroelectric crystal, 969
FERROELECTRICITY, **336**
Ferroelectrics, **336**
Ferroicity, **336**
Ferromagnet, 887
Ferromagnetic insulator, 328
Ferromagnetic material, 518, 611
Ferromagnetic rotation, 329
FERROMAGNETISM, 233, **337**, 518
Feshbach, H., 143
Feynman, Richard P., **196, 339,** 350, 529, 604, **724,** 747, **748,** 804
FEYNMAN DIAGRAM, **339,** 529, 748
Feynman propagator, 748
FFAG, 96
Fibril, 667
Fick, Adolf, 98, **223, 225**
Fick's laws, **223, 225**
"fictitious" force, 173
Field, G., 396
Field, depth of, **639**
  displacement, 735
  electric, 209, **260**, 270, 422
  electromagnetic, **349**, 599
  gravitational, **392**
FIELD, MAGNETIC, 261, 270, **512,** 517
Field, mathematics of, **348**
  radiation, **349**
  scalar, **985**
  self-consistent, 594
  superstrong, 757
  uniform, 119
  vector, **985**
Field curvature, 495
Field dynamics, 366
FIELD EMISSION, **343**, 940, 996
Field emission source, 535
Field intensity, 729
Field intensity, electric, 423, 432
Field ion microscope, **346**
Field of view, 495, **639**
Field stop, 639
Field strength, 27
FIELD THEORY, 143, **347,** 529
Field theory, mean, **181**
Field theory, quantum, 310
Field-effect device, 949
Field-effect transistor, 955
Filament, **291**
  film, magnetic, 520
  photographic, **689**
FILM, THIN, 275, 449, **946**
Film electronics, **948**

Filter, infrared, 444
  optical, **5**
Fine structure, 83, 289, 315, 585, 640
Fine structure of alpha rays, 618
First law, thermodynamics, **941**
Fischer, A. G., 268
FISSION, **76, 179,** 327, **351,** 471, 625, 634
Fission cross section, 353
Fission fragment, 356
Fission isomer, 356
Fission product, 327, 355, 615, 627
Fissionability parameter, 353
FitzGerald, G. F., **570**
Fixation, **999**
Fixed-field alternating-gradient, 96
  synchrotron, 925
Fixing solution, 689
Fizeau, Armand Hypolyte Louis, **989**
Flare star, 778
Flash photolysis, 683
Flat-plate collector, 860
Flerov, G. N., 965
Flight, interplanetary, **59**
Flight, lunar, **59**
FLIGHT PROPULSION FUNDAMENTALS, **357**
Flow, Couette, **367**
Flow, supersonic, 368
Flow of matter, 818
Fluctuations in experiments, 552
FLUID DYNAMICS, **366**
FLUID STATICS, **369**
Fluids, 998
  kinetic theory, 479
Fluorescence, **489**
  delayed, 321
  resonance, **595**
  x-ray, 1021
Fluorescence yield, 86, 470
Fluorescent light, 498, **974**
Fluorite lens, **573**
Fluoroscopy, 1021
Flutter, 23, 814
Flux, 437, 984
  electric, **260**
  luminous, 506
  magnetic, 433, 513, 951
  radiant, 418
Flux density, 517
Flux density, magnetic, **261,** 433
Flux-gate magnetometer, 526
Fluxmeter, 526
Flywheel, 398
FM transmission, **581**
f-number, 495
Focal length, 495
Focal point, 495, 651
Focus, depth of, 573, **639**
Fog limit, 162
Foley, P. J., **507**
Foley, H. M., 750
Folk equation, 594
Footlambert (unit), 507, 694
Foot-pound, 1014
Forbush decrease, 176
Force, 238, 259, 431, 534, **557,** 895, 1014
  balanced, 819
  centrifugal, 123, **822**
  centripetal, **822**
  components of, 984
  Coriolis, **173,** 822
  Coulomb, **350**
  electromotive, 259, 265
  exchange, 518
  "fictitious", 173

FORCE, INDUCED ELECTROMOTIVE, **432**
FORCE, INTERMOLECULAR, 382, **451**
  long range nuclear, **634**
  magnetic, 514
  ponderomotive, 521
  short range nuclear, **634**
  van der Waals, **451**
Force constant, **104**, 586
Force potential, 506
Forging, 562
Form factor, 500
Formation energy, 493
Forward bias, 230
Foucault, Leon, 398, 989
Four-dimensional coordinate system, 167
Fourier, Jean Baptiste Joseph, **371**, 415, **602**
FOURIER ANALYSIS, **371**
Fourier equation, 415
Fourier integral, 134, **372**
Fourier series, **371**
Fourier-Bessel transform, 373
Four-vectors, 539
Fovea centralis, 1001
Fowler, Alfred (theory), 687
Fowler, R. H., **319**, 343
Fowler equation, 687
Fowler-Nordheim theory, 344
Fowles, Grant R., 824
Frame of reference, inertial, 173
Frank, F. C., 163, **191**
Frank, J., 538
Frank, O., 537
Frank and Tamm theory, 127
Franklin, Benjamin, 259, 423
Franklin, K. L., 778
Fraser, J. S., 356
Fraunhofer, Joseph von, **3**, 215, 853
Fraunhofer line, 774, **818**
Fraunhofer pattern, 217
Frautschi, S. C., 143
Free carrier, 684
Free electron model, 332
Free energy, 319, **910**, 943
Free enthalpy, 319
Free particle, 824
Free radical, **765**
Freedom, degree of, 413, **679**
Freezing point, 589
Frenkel, J., **321**
Frenkel defect, 842
Frequency, 421, 497, 601, 993, 1008
  electrical, 242
  plasma, 328
Frequency modulation, **581**
Fresnel, J., 215, **448**
Fresnel coefficient, 947
Freundlich, Martin M., 283
Fricke, H., 561
FRICTION, **374**, 558
Frictional electrification, 893
Friedel's law, 188
Friedrich, W., 217, **610**
Fringe, interference, 138, 448
Frisch, Otto, **351**
Fritsche, 599
Fröhlich, H., 724, 906
Froissart, M., 47
Front, shock, 368
Froome, K. D., 991
Fuchtbauer, C., 825
Fuel, 243
Fuel cell, 95
Fugacity, 385

Function, **112**
  correlation, 181
  generalized homogeneous, 183
  Gibbs, 319
  partition, 101
  periodic, 113
  potential, 452
  response, 180
  step, 658
  wave, 1005
Function space, 539
Functional simulation, 97
FUNDAMENTAL CONSTANTS, **170**
Fundamental physics, 550
Fundamental quantity, 227
Fundamental series, 82
Furth, Harold P., **515**
FUSION, 77, **376**, 625
Fusion curve, 680
Fusion reactor, **377**, 620

Gabor, Dennis, **426**
Galaxy, 71, 175, **177**, 395, 779
Galilean transformation equations, 808
Galilei, Galileo, 347, 392, **425**, **557**, 571, 989
Gallium arsenide, 954
Gal-Or, B., 464
Galvani, Luigi, 98, **264**
Galvanic cell, **92**
Galvanometer, **255**
Gamma absorption, **595**
Gamma emission, **595**
Gamma radiation, 404, 470, 627, **783**
Gamma ray, **176**, 355, 606–607, 615, 617, 619
  prompt, 607
  stellar sources, 69
Gamma transition, **595**
Gamow, George, **312**, 397
Ganglion cell, 1001
Gans, 500
Gantmakher, V. F., effect, **334**
Gas, 589, 661, 889
  density of, **207**
  ideal, 382, 385, **413**
  kinetic theory, 479
  liquefaction of, **501**
  noble, 132
  perfect, **382**
  properties of, 480
  rare, compounds of, 593
GAS: THERMODYNAMIC PROPERTIES, **384**
Gas centrifuge, 125
Gas density balance, Edwards, **207**
Gas dynamics, 21–22
Gas equation, **382**
Gas hydrate, 593
GAS LAWS, **382**
gas multiplication, 616
Gas pressure, **976**
Gauge, vacuum, **979**
Gauge invariance, 168
Gauss, Karl Friedrich, **260**, 539, 558, 934, 986
Gauss magnetometer, 526
Gauss theorem, **260**, **986**
Gaussian error curve, 223
Gaussian error function, 901
Gaussian system, 400
Gaussian unit (footnote), 400
Gaussmeter, 526
Gay-Lussac, Joseph, 382, 480
Gay-Lussac law, 150
Gear, **850**
Gear train, **850**
Geballe, T. H., **118**
Gehlen, W., 538

Geiger, Hans Wilhelm, **79**, 615
Geiger counter, 763, 973
Geiger-Müller counter, 615, 616
Geitel, Hans Friedrich, 686, 939
Gell-Mann, M., 143, **196**, 529, 604, **756, 757**, 1013
Gell-Mann-Nishijima relation, **45**
Generator, electric, 434
General relativity, **807**
Generalized homogeneous functions, 183
Generator, **242**
  magnetohydrodynamic (MHD), **243, 245–246**
Geochronology, 389
Geodesic, 809
GEODESY, **387, 389**
Geodimeter, **991**
Geodetic astronomy, 388
Geoid, 387
Geomagnetic disturbance, 88, 459
Geomagnetism, 389, 454
GEOMETRICAL OPTICS, 497, **643**
Geophysical prospecting, 391
GEOPHYSICS, **388**, 712
George, Barry A., **288**
Geothermal power, 243
Gerlach, Walther, 73, **289**
Germanium, 229, 954
Germer, L. H., 217, **274**, 709, 1004
Getter, 291
Getter-ion pump, 978
GHF, 183
Ghiorso, A., 961, 962, 963, 964, 965
Giant, red, 859
Giant planets, **716**
Giant star, 70
Giauque, William Francis, 186
Gibbs, J. Willard, **318**, 319, 384, 480, 539, 679, 709, 897
Gibbs energy, 384
Gibbs function, 319, 582, **943**
Gibbs phase rule, **943**
Gilbert, William, 259
Ginzburg, V. L., **905–906**
Ginzburg-Landau parameter, 906
Giordano, Anthony B., **580**
Glass, 504
Glass modulus, 997
Glass transition range, 556
Glass transition temperature, 726, 1003
Glassy state, **1002**
Glow, negative, 252
Glow discharge, **252**
Glow tube, 291
Goddard, Robert Hutchings, 247
Golay cell, 776
Gold, T. M. N., 178
Goldberg, Joshua N., **398**
Goldberger, M. L., 143
Goldberger-Treiman relation, 196
Goldhammer, Paul, **632**
Goldman, D. E., 538
Goldstein, Eugen, 939
Goldstone antenna, 580
Goniometer, 194
Good, R. H., Jr., **702**
Goodenough, John B., **209**
Goodman, Charles D., **180, 467**
Goodman, Clark, 186
Goodman, Joseph W., **374**
Gorter, C. J., 186
Goudsmit, Samuel A., **80**, 273, 288, 314, **1024**
Gouy, M., 110
G-parity, 308
Gradient, 985
  temperature, 415

Grain boundary, 842
Gram equivalent weight, **591**
Gram molecular weight, **582**, 587
Gram-calorie, 1015
Gramme, Z. T., 599
Grand partition function, 383
Grand potential, 383
Grashof number, **417**
Grating, 1017
Grating, diffraction, **215**
Gravimetry, **388**
GRAVITATION, 387, **391**
  Einstein's theory, **393**
  law of, **558**
  quantum theory of, 396
Gravitational collapse, 72, **394**
Gravitational field, **392**
Gravitational force, 534
Gravitational interaction, **32**
Gravitational mass, **558**
Gravitational potential, 392
Gravitational wave, **395**
Gravity, specific, **208**
Gray, J. A., 151
Gray body, **773**
Gray-body radiator, 444
Gregg, Donald C., **133**
Gregg, S. J., **21**
Greek absorption band, 148
Greek geometry, 347
Green, George, **729**
Green, H. S., 482
Green, M. S., 899
Green's functions, **340**
Grid, 291
Grid, control, **295**
Grid, screen, **294**
Grid, suppressor, **295**
Grid glow tube, 291
Griffiths, J., 888
Grimaldi, Francesco M., 215, 448
Groseclose, B. Clark, 729
Ground wave, 579
Group, Poincaré, **34**
Group theory, 348
Group velocity, **17**, 754, 988, 1009, 1011
Grubbé, 404
Grüneisen, E., 165, 324
Grüneisen relation, 324
Grüneisen-Bloch relation, 165
Guggenheim, E. A., **102**
GUIDANCE, INERTIAL, **439**
Guinn, Vincent P., **609**
Gun, electron, 278
Gun diode, 231
Gwinn, Cecil W., 98
Gyro frequency, **736**
Gyrocompass, 398
Gyromagnetic ratio, **288**, 750–751
Gyromagnetic splitting factor, 336
GYROSCOPE, **398**, **440**
Gyro-stabilized platform, 439

H center, 149, 493
Hadron, **32**, 196, 308, **757**
Hadronic interaction, **32**
Hagstrum, H. D., 827
Hahn, O., **351**
Hahnium, 965
Halban, H. von, 217
Haldane, J. B. S., 536
Half-life, (footnote) **469**, 595, **785**

Half thickness, 771
Halides, silver, 688
Hall, E. H., **400**
Hall device, 402, 526
Hall effect, 844
HALL EFFECT AND RELATED PHENOMENA, **400**
Hall field, 400, 403
Hall generator, **400, 842**
Hall mobility, **842**
Hallwachs, Wilhelm, 686
Hamer, Walter J., 267
Hamilton, Sir William Rowan, 1, 558, **738**
Hamiltonian, 167, **541**, 575, 700, 1005
Hamilton's equations, 738
Hankel transform, 487
Hanle effect, 85
Hanson, A. O., **155**
Harasima, Akira, **915**
Harder, D. S., 329
Hardware, computer, **158**
Harmonic motion, **993**
Harmonic series, **994**
Harris, 965
Harris, Forest K., **258**
Harrison, Roland H., 386
Hart, R. W., **500**
Harteck, P., **717**
Hartkemeier, Harry Pelle, 92
Hartmann formula, 800
Hartmann number, 521
Hartree, D. R. (equation), 594
Hartree-Fock equation, 594
Hartree-Fock theory, 529
Harvey, B. G., 963
Hasiguti, Ryukiti R., 494
Hauy, René Just, **194**, 661
Hawking, S., 395
Haynes, Sherwood K., **88**
Haystack facility, 580
Hayward, Raymond W., **674, 675**
Heading, John, **546**
HEALTH PHYSICS, **403**, 561
HEARING, **407**
Hearon, J. Z., 538
HEAT, 115, **410**, 712
Heat, mechanical equivalent of, **559**
HEAT CAPACITY, 116, 385, 386, 410, **412**
   electronic, 414
Heat conduction, **228**
Heat conductivity, 681
Heat death, 463, 482
Heat engine, 122
Heat equation, 349
Heat of combustion, 118
Heat of dissociation, 586
Heat of vaporization, **981**
HEAT TRANSFER, **415**
Heat treatment, 563
Heating, radiant, 445
Heat pump, 801
Heat reservoir, 121
Heaviside, Oliver, 484, 539
Heeschen, D. S., 779
Heidt, Lawrence J., **683**
Heisenberg, Werner, 140, **465**, 542, **634**, 672, 747, 772
Heisenberg relation, 672
Heisenberg representation, 542
Heisenberg S-matrix, 142
HEISENBERG UNCERTAINTY PRINCIPLE, **420, 540**, 897
Heitler, W., 102, 451
Helicity, **35**

Helicon wave, 844
Helium, 504, **908, 909**
Helium, liquid, 186
Helium, superfluid, 187
Helmholtz, H. L. F. von, 122, 384, 412, 560, 601, **602**
Helmholtz energy, 384
Helmholtz function, 383, **943**
Henry, J., 599
Henry (unit), 436
Heraclitus, 311
Herapath, John, 480
Hering theory, 147
Hermans, J. J., 661
Hermitian adjoint, 547
Hermitian conjugate, 701
Hermitian matrix, 544
Hermitian operator, **37**, 421
Herriott, D. R., 489
Herschel, William, 853
Hertz, Heinrich, 259, 270, 272, 686, **761**
Hertz potential, 270
Hertzsprung-Russell diagram, **70**
Hess, Victor, **175**
Hess, Wilmot N., **764**
Hetényi, M., **686**
Heterojunction, 835
Hewish, Antony, **742**, 778, 779
Higgs, 1013
High pressure phase transitions, 732
High voltage generation, **14**
HIGH VOLTAGE RESEARCH, **422**
Hilbert, David, 539, 542
Hilbert space, **542**
Hilbert transform, 487
Hill, A. V., 99, 100
Hill, H., 394
Hill, T. L., 161
Hiran (light velocity), 991
Hiss, from magnetosphere, 89
HISTORY OF PHYSICS, **423**
Hittorf, Johann Wilhelm, **264**, 939
Hodgkin, A. L., 538
Hogerton, John F., 78
Hohlraum, 771
Hohmann ellipse, 67
Hohmann transfer, **58**
Hole, 871
   black, 72, **395**
Hollerith, Herman, 157
Hollerith machine, 157
Holland, M. G., **682**
Hologram, **426**
HOLOGRAPHY, **426**, 688, 690
Holt, Charles A., **435**
Homopolar bond, 592
Hooke, Robert, 241, 554, 571, 722
Hooke's law, 241, 554
Hopkins, Robert E., **497**
Hoppes, D. D., **674**
Horizontal control, 387
Horn, acoustic, 970
Horn antenna, 28
Horn equation, 706
Horsepower, **1015**
Hosemann, Rolf, **223**, 669
Hot carrier diode, 231
Houston, W. V., **81**
Howard, W. E., 779
Hoyle and Narliker theory, 179
H-sheet, 722,
H-theorem, Boltzmann, **320**, 481
Hubble, Edwin Powell, 72, 177, 178, 397
Hubble's constant, 177

Hubble's law, 72
Hückel, E., **264**, 457
Hudson, R. P., **674**
Hue, 145
Hughes, V., 751
Hujer, Karel, **425**
Hull, McAllister H., Jr., **115**
Hulst, H. C. van de, 779
Hume-Rothery, W., 564
Humidity, relative, **890**
Humphreys, Curtis J., **586**
Hund, F., rule, 31, 338, 518
Hunt, F. V., **123**
Hutchison, T. S., **971**
Huxley, A. F., 538
Huygens, Christian, 215, 448, **652**, 655, **722**, 799
Huygens' hypothesis, 448
Huygens' principle, **652**, 706
Hybrid computer, 155–156,
Hydrate, gas, 593
Hydrodynamics, 22, 366, 521
Hydrogen, twenty-one cm line of, 779
Hydrogen atom, 739
Hydrogen bomb, 78, **352**
Hydrogen bond, 102, **104**, 593
Hydrogen electrode, **265**
Hydrology, **390**
Hydrophone, 875
Hydrostatic equilibrium, 986
Hylleraas, E. A., 1006
Hyper Raman effect, 787
Hypercharge, 39, 308
Hyperfine splitting, 739
Hyperfine structure, **84**, 315, 640, **1025**
Hyperon, 169, 305
Hyperpolarizabilities, 788
Hypothesis, statistical, 900
Hypothesis, universality, **183**
Hysteresis, 335, **339**

Ice point, **931**
Iconoscope, 827
Ideal gas, 120, **382**, **385**, **413**
IGFET, **831**
Ignitron, 291, **301**, 743, 793
Illumination in microscopes, 639
Illuminator, microscope, 574
Illuminometer, **693**
Imbedding, **623**
Imbibition, **660**
Image, 495
Image, holograph, 428
Imagery, optical, 426
Image formation, **645**, 999
Image intensifier, 303
Image intensifying tube, 827
Image orthicon, 827
Impact ionization, **825**
IMPATT diode, 231, **832**
Impedance, 25, 133, **436**
	boundary, 706
	complex, 26
	transfer, 134
Impedance bridge, 255
Impedance matching, 262
Imperfection, lattice, **491**
Impulse, **431**, 985
IMPULSE AND MOMENTUM, **431**
Impulse, specific, 67, 244, **358**
Impurity, 869
	acceptor, 842
	donor, 842
	interstitial, 842
	substitutional, 842

Impurity diffusion, 225
Impurity ion, 493
Incandescent light, 498
Inclined plane, **850**
Independent particle model, 740
Index of refraction, 4, 448, 500, 643, 735, 795, **799**
Indices, Miller, 195
Induced electrification, 892
Induced radioactivity, **618**
INDUCTANCE, 24, 253, **435**
Inductance coil, 437
INDUCED ELECTROMOTIVE FORCE, 24, **261**, **432**
Induction, electromagnetic, 259, 433
	electromagnetic, Faraday law, 269
	magnetic, 512, 513, 517
INDUCTION HEATING, **438**, 852
Inductor, 135, 437
Industrial telemetering, 929
Industry, chemical, **131**
Inertia, **534**, **557**
Inertia, moment of, 821
Inertial frame, 755, 809
Inertial frame of reference, 173
Inertial group, 755
INERTIAL GUIDANCE, **439**
Inertial mass, **558**
Inertial navigation, **399**
Inertial observer, 950
Information, 198, 329
Information handling, 197
Information theory, 930
Information transfer, 97
Infrared false color photography, 691
INFRARED RADIATION, **443**, 773
Infrared spectroscopy, 445
Infrasonic region, 18
Ingalls, R., 598
INHOMOGENEOUS SEMICONDUCTORS, **842**
Initial value problem, 212
Injection diode, 231
Injection laser, **267**
Inner product, 983
Inorganic chemistry, 132
Instrument, electrical, **255**
	electrodynamic, 256–257
	electronic, 256
INSTRUMENT, OPTICAL, **637**
Instrument, thermocouple, 256
INSTRUMENTS, NUCLEAR, **614**
Insulated gate field effect device, 949
Insulator, 166, 684, 870
	conductivity of, **165**
	ferromagnetic, 328
	thermal, 415
Integral, **114**, 484
	convolution, 663
	Fourier, **372**
Integral transform, 213
Integrating sphere, 694
Integration, **114**
Intensifier, image, 303
Intensity, luminous, 693
	radiant, 506
	sound, **601**, 705
	wave, **1009**
Intensity level, sonar, **874**
Intensity scale (earthquake), 828
Intensive properties, 385
Interaction, electromagnetic, **32**, **196**, 305
	fundamental, 166
	gravitational, **32**
	hadronic, **32**
	particle, **339**
	phonon, 681

INTERACTION, STRONG, **196**, 305, **902**
INTERACTION, WEAK, **32**, **196**, 305, **1012**
Interaction potential, 324
Interatomic distance, 586
Interfacial angles, 194
Interface device, **830**
Interference, **653**, 686
Interference, constructive, 653
   destructive, 447, 653
   theory, **447**
INTERFERENCE AND INTERFEROMETRY, **446**
Interference fringe, 138, 569
Interference microscopy, 639
Interferometer, **449**, 992
   Fabry-Perot, 450
   Michelson, 449
   radio, **778**
Interferometry, **446**
Interferometry, holographic, 428
   radio, **778**
Interior ballistics, 91
INTERMOLECULAR FORCE, 382, **451**, 914
Intermolecular potential, 383, 452
Internal conversion, **470**
Internal energy, 384
Internal energy function, 942
Internal reflection, 644, **796**
Internal reflection spectroscopy, **655**
INTERNATIONAL GEOPHYSICAL YEAR AND
     INTERNATIONAL YEARS OF THE QUIET
     SUN, **453**
International System, **253**
International Union of Pure and Applied Physics, **915**
International Years of the Quiet Sun, **453**
Interplanetary flight, **59**
Interplanetary mission, 244
Interplanetary space, 876
Interstellar material, **70**
Interstitial, 347, **491**, **493**
Interstitial impurity, 842
Intuition, 937
Invariance, 141, 169, 305, 671
Invariance, gauge, 168
Invariant, Casimir, **40**
Invariant, system, 679
Invariant imbedding, 959
Invariant system, **167**
Inverse Raman effect, 787
Inversion, space, 671
Inversion integral, 485
Inverter transformer, 952
Involution, 34
Ion, 200, 264, 455, 458, 535
   metastable, 536
   positive, **81**, 765
Ion implantation, 843
Ion rocket, **247**
Ion source, synchrotron, **925**
Ion thruster, 247
Ion-acoustical wave, 458
Ionic bonding, 102
Ionic compound, **588**
Ionic yield, 766
IONIZATION, **250**, 264, 316, **455**, 605, 618, 717,
   765, 768
Ionization by electron impact, 457
Ionization chamber, 615, 973
Ionization energy, thermal, 685
Ionization in spark chamber, 878
Ionizing radiation, 404, 764, **767**
Ionophone, 262
IONOSPHERE, 88, 390, 455, **458**
Ionospheric current, 89
Iris (eye), 1000

Irradiance, solar, **853**, (table) **856**
Irradiance standard, 775
Irradiation, 608
IRRADIATION, DISPLACED ATOMS, **460**
Irradiation, ultraviolet, 974
Irreducible representation, **41**
IRREVERSIBILITY, **462**, 481, 899
Isentropic energy change, 318
Ising model, **182**
Islands of isomerism, 631
Isobaric spin, **465**
Isochromatic, 686
Isochronous motion, 993
Isoclinic, 686
Iso-electronic sequence, 81
Isolator, 135
Isomer, 131
Isomer, nuclear, 783
Isomer shift, **598**
Isomeric transition, 470, 607
Isomerism, 131
Isomerism, islands of, 631
Isopiestic method, 589
ISOSPIN, **465**
Isospin conservation, 168
Isospin group, 309
Isotherm, 121
Isothermal compressibility, 149
Isothermal process, 121
ISOTOPE, 311, **467**
   identification of, 586
   transuranic, 472
Isotope effect, 315
Isotope shift, **84**, 739
Isotopes, separation of, **469**
Isotopic cross section, 608
Isotopic neutron sources, 608
Isotopic power, 78
Isotopic spin, 168, **465**
Isotopic weight, 633
Isotropic background radiation, 72, 397
Isotropy, cosmic rays, 175
Isotropy of space, 167
IUPAP, **915**
Ives, H. E., 236

Jacobi, C. G. J., 558
Jacobi identity, 984
Jacquard, Joseph Marie, 156
Jacquez, J. A., 538
Jakobi, Wm. W., 95
James, 961, 962
Jammer, Max, 896
Jansky, K. G., 777
Javan, A., 489
Jeans, Sir James Hopwood, 424, 463, 772
Jeffries, Z., 633
Jelley, J. V., **127**
Jet power, 244
Jet stream, 567
Jodrell Bank, 778
Joenk, R. J., **339**
Johannson, H., 276
Johnsen, Russell H., **313**
Johnson, Francis S., 878
Johnson, J. B., **940**
Joining, 562
Joliot, Frederick, **618**, 782
Jones, H., 564
Jordan, 178
Jordan, P., 747
Jordanus de Nemore (Nemorarius), 895
Josephs, Jess J., **603**
Josephson, B. D. (junction), 254, 749, **907**

Josephson effect, 749, 907, 967
Josephson equation, **907**
Josephson junction, 254, 778, **907**
Joule, James Prescott, 122, 186, 412, **559**
Joule heat, **164, 945**
Joule (unit), **559**, 1014
Joule-Thomson coefficient, 385
Joule-Thomson cooling, 502
Joule-Thomson expansion, **186**
Judd, Deane B., **147**
Junction, Josephson, 254, 778, **907**
Junction, manufacture of, **843**
Junction, p-n, **229**
Junction, p-n, photovoltaic effect, **704**
Junction, properties of, **843**
Junction diode, **229**, 267
Junction field-effect transistor, **829**
Junction transistor, 829, **954**
Jupiter, 716, 764

Kabir, P., **1014**
Kalaba, R., 538
Kamerlingh Onnes, Heike, **186-187**, 502
Kaon, 305
Kapitza, Peter, 503
Kaplow, F., 661
Karle, I. L., 190
Karle, J., 190
Kastler, A., **640**
Kaula, William A., **388**
Kayser (unit), 443
Kekulé, Friedrich, 131
Kelvin, Lord (see William Thomson)
Kelvin bridge, 255
Kelvin scale, 931
Kennedy, J. W., 961
Kennelly, A. E., 852
Kenney, Robert W., **110**
Kepler, Johannes, 58, **64-65,** 391, 472
Kepler's equation, **58**
Kepler's law of areas, 515
Kepler's laws, **64-65,** 391
KEPLER'S LAWS OF PLANETARY MOTION, **475**
Kernel technique, 623
Kerr, John, 478
Kerr cell, 479, **990**
KERR EFFECTS, **478**
Kerr shutter, 490
Kerst, D. W., **96,** 925
Kieffer, William F., **582**
Kilocalorie, 411, **559**
Kinematics, 152, **236, 237**
Kinetic energy, 558, 824, **1015**
KINETIC THEORY, **479**
Kinetics, **236**
KINETICS, CHEMICAL, **128**
King, Allen L., 537, 804
King, G. W., **595**
Kingslake, R., **801**
Kingston, R. H., **491**
Kirchhoff, G. R., 3, 25, 215, **418,** 599, 771
Kirchhoff's formula, 706
Kirchhoff's integral (diffraction), **2**
Kirchhoff's law, **4, 25, 418,** 771
Kirkendall effect, 226
Kirkwood, J. G., 482
Kitagaki, T., 925
Kitt Peak, 778
Klauder, J., 139
Klein and Nishina equation, **152**
Klein-Gordon equation, 349
Kleppner, D., 751
Kline, O., 152

Klystron, **297**
Knipping, P., 217, **610**
Knock-on, 460
Knoll, M., 276, 281
Kohrausch, Hans, 99
Kohlrausch, 989
Kohoutek, comet, 778
Kosevich, A. M., 206
Kossel, W., 102, 163, 592
Kostitzin, 536
Kostkowski, H. J., **745**
Kozyrev, N. A., 714
Kremers, Howard E., 790
Krishnan, K. S., **785**
Kronecker delta, 935
Kroon, Reinout P., **228**
Kubo, R., 899
Kubo formulas, 899
Kuhn, H. G., 85
Kuiper, G. P., 717
Kumar, Kailash, **530**
Kunzler, J. E., **118**
Kuper, C. G., **725**
Kurşunoğlu, Behram, **756**
Kurti, K., 186
Kurti and Simon, method of, 186, 187
Kusch, P., 73, 289, 750

Lagemann, Robert T., **1010**
Lagrange, Joseph Louis, 484
Lagrange equations, **558**
Laing, Ronald A., **671**
Lamb, W. E., **73,** 749
Lamb shift, 83, **749**
Lamb wave, 969
Lambda anomaly, 415
Lambert, Heinrich Johann, 3, 507, 704, **797**
Lambert's law, 694, **704, 774, 797**
Lambert (unit), 694
LAMPF, 11
Land, E. H., **690**
Lamp, fluorescent, **974**
Landahl, H. D., 537
Landau, L. D., 205, **208,** 671, (polarization) 724, 905-906
Landau damping, 719
Landau level, 206, 208
Landé, Alfred, 670, **1024**
Landé factor, 515, 670
Landsberg, H. E., **391**
Lane, C. T., **910**
Langenberg, D. N., 749, 907
Langevin, Paul, 233
Langevin function, 518, **670**
Langley, S. P., 854
Langmuir, Irving, 719
Langmuir oscillation, 719
Lanthanide, **788**
Lanthanide contraction, 788
Lanthanon, **788**
Laplace, Pierre Simon de, 349, 425, 462, **484,** 539, 730
Laplace equation, 270, 349, 486, 730
LAPLACE TRANSFORM, 213-214, **484**
Laplacian, 730
Laporte, 674
Larmor, Sir Joseph, 208, 328, 515, **1023**
Larmor frequency, 328, 515, **736,** 1024
Larmor precession, 1023
Larmor theorem, 208
Larsh, 964
LASER, **488,** 498, 722
dye, 490

gas, **489**, 787
injection, **267**
junction, **490**
liquid, **490**
ruby, 510
semiconductor, **490**
Latent heat, **982**
Latent image, 689
Latimer, R. M., 964
Lattice, crystal, **194**
   point, 217
   reciprocal, **195**, 935
   relaxation of, 872
Lattice cell, 661
   reciprocal, 217
LATTICE DEFECTS, **491**
Lattice distortion, 798
Lattice energy, 102
Lattice heat capacity, 414
Lattice imperfection, 347, **491**
Lattice polarization, 724
Lattice vibration, 595, 837, **872**
Laue, M. von, 189, 194, 217, **218**, 610, 661, **1020**
Lauritsen, C. C., 343
Laval, **218**
Lavite, 135
Lavoisier, Antoine Laurent, 131, 311
Law of gravitation, **558**
Law of reflection, 643
Lawden, D. F., **543**
Lawrence, E. O., 200, 925
Lawrencium, **964**
Laws, F. A., 852
Laws, conservation, **304**
LAWS, GAS, **382**
Laws of motion, Newton's, **238**
Layer, boundary, 22
Le Chatelier, Henry Louis (principle), 319
Le Fèvre, R. J. W., **234**
Leaning Tower of Pisa, 392
Least squares, 171
Leclanché cell, 92
LED (diode), 231
Leduc, Anatole (Righi-Leduc effect), 403
Lee, Reuben, **953**
Lee, T.-D., **169**, 674, 724, **1014**
Lee-Yang theory, 188
LEED, 275
Leeuwenhoek, Anton van, **571**
Left-handedness, 674
Leibniz, Gottfried Wilhelm, 156, 462, 484
Leith, E. N., 426
Lemaître, Georges Edouard, Abbé, 178
Lenard, Philipp, 686, 825
Length, correlation, 181
   unit of, 170
Lennard-Jones potential, 384, 451
LENS, **494**, 571, 649
   achromatic, **573**
   acoustic, 970
   aphochromatic, **573**
   condenser, 278, 496, 574
   Einzel, **278**
   electron, 284
   electrostatic, **278, 284**
   fluorite, **573**
   magnetic, **276, 277, 285**
   objective, 278, 571, **637**
   power of, **651**
   projector, 279
   spectacle, **494**
   thick, 651
   unipotential, **278**

Lens testing, 496
Lensless photography, 688
Lenz, Heinrich, 208, 599
Lenz's law, 208, 436
Leonardo da Vinci, 424, 895
Lepton, **32,** 305
Lepton conservation, 168
LEVELS, ENERGY, 205, **314**
Level crossing, 643
Lever, **849**
Lever arm, 559
Leverrier, Urbain, 425
Levi-Civita, Tullio, 934
Levi-Civita symbol, 935
Levine, Joseph, **137**
Lewis, G. N., 102, 592, 711
Libby, W. F., 177
Libron, 787
Lie algebra, 543
Lifshitz, I. M., 206
Lift, **358**
LIGHT, **497,** 692, 712
   absorption of, 321, 704
   black, 974
   circularly polarized, 721
   fluorescent, 498
   incandescent, 498
   nature of, **498,** 568
   POLARIZED, 685, **721**
   propagation of, **497**
   sources of, 498
   VELOCITY OF, 170, 171, **987**
   wave theory of, **448**
Light emission, **508**
Light propagation, law of, 808
LIGHT SCATTERING, **499,** 590, 725, 785
Light-emitting diode, 231, **834**
Lighthouse effect, 741
Lightness, 145
Lightning, 422
Lilienfeld, J. E., 343
Limit, elastic, 554
   proportional, 554
Limit of resolution, **638**
Limiter, 336
Limiting sphere, 1018
Linac, **7,** 10
Linde, Carl von (process), 501–502
Linden, Bernard R., **699**
Lindsay, Robert, 818
Line, delay, 263
Line defect, 491, 869
Line profile, 1019
Line spectra, 1004
LINEAR ACCELERATOR, **7,** 10
Linear electro-optic effect, 478
Linear energy transfer, 765, 769
Linear equation, 212, 544
Linear harmonic oscillator, 548, 1007
Linear impulse, 431
Linear momentum, 431
Linear operator, 542
Lines of force, 261
Linked molecules, 691
Liouville equation, 897
Lippincott, Ellis R., **886**
Lippman, B., 140, **142**
LIQUEFACTION OF GASES, **501**
Liquid, 123, **223,** 589, 661, 889
   associated, 506
   density of, **207**
   quantum, **504**
   structure of, **505**

Liquid crystal, 661
Liquid drop model, 351, **353**, 634
Liquid propellant, 359
LIQUID STATE, **504**
Liquidus, **680**
Lissajous figure, 1009
Littauer, R. M., **744**
Livingston, M. Stanley, 200, 925
Llewellyn, F. B., **135**
Lloyd, Humphrey, 448
Local vertical system, **441**
Loeb, A. L., **422**
Loferski, Joseph, **705**
Lofgren, Edward J., **202**
Log-periodic antenna, **30**
London, F., 102, 188, 451, 905
Longitudinal magnetoresistance, 403
Longitudinal wave, 969, **1008**
Long-range attraction, **451**
Loop (wave), 1009
Lorenz, 232
Lorenz-Lorentz formula, 232
Lorentz, Hendrik Antoon, 79, 232, 269, 349, 564, 570, 733, 797, **1023**
Lorentz equations, **808**
Lorentz force, 199–200, 205, 400
Lorentz force equation, 269
Lorentz invariance, 141, 809
Lorentz theory, 734
Lorentz transformation, 349, 671
Lorentz trapping, 378
Lorentz triplet, 84, 1023
Lorentz unit, 1023
Los Alamos proton linac, 11
Loschmidt, Josef, 480
Loss compliance, 996
Loss factor, 119
Loss tangent, 209
Lossev, 267
Lotka, Alfred J., 536
Loudness, **19, 601**
Low, F., **724**
Low-energy electron diffraction, **275**
Low-temperature calorimetry, 117
Lu, E. Y. C., 48
Lubricant, **375**
Lüders band, 556
Lufburrow, Robert A., **122**
Lukens, H. R., Jr., **781**
Lumen, 507, **693**
LUMINANCE, 145, **506**, 507, 693, 694
LUMINESCENCE, 148, 489, **508**
Luminiferous ether, 570
Luminosity, 178
Luminosity, intrinsic, 178
Luminosity, star, **69**
Luminosity of sun, 867
Luminous efficiency, 506, 693
Luminous flux, 506, 693
Luminous intensity, 507, 693
Luminous reflectance, 693
Luminous transmittance, 693
Lunar flight, **59**
Lunar mission, 244
Lunar occultations, 779
Luxon, 309
Lykoudis, Paul S., **524**
Lyman, Theodore, 81, 972
Lyman alpha, 81
Lyman series, 81
Lyon, David N., **503**

M center, 198, 493
Mac Rae, Alfred U., **275**

Mach, Ernst, **179**, 228, **534**, 540, 558
Mach number, 228, 848
Mach principle, **179**
MACHINE, SIMPLE, **849**
Machurek, Joseph E., **636**
Mackenzie, John D., **1003**
Macroscopic cross section, 957
Macroscopic theory, 936
Maddida, 157.
Magic number, **631**
Magnet, permanent, 298, 520
Magnet, superconducting, **188**
Magnetic anisotropy, **31**
Magnetic bottle, 78
Magnetic bubble, 336
Magnetic deflection, **285**
Magnetic dipole, 516
Magnetic dipole moment, 233
Magnetic energy, 514
MAGNETIC FIELD, 261, 270, 400, **512**, 517, 524, 730, 1023
Magnetic field strength, 271
Magnetic film, 520, **949**
Magnetic flux, 433, 513, 951
Magnetic flux density, **261**, 433
Magnetic force, 514
Magnetic induction, 512, 513, 517
Magnetic induction field, 734
Magnetic lens, **276, 285**, 927
Magnetic material, 513
Magnetic mirror, **378**
Magnetic moment, 513, 517, 524, 525, 577
Magnetic moment (electron), 750
Magnetic moment (neutron), 606
Magnetic moment, nuclear, 516
Magnetic permeability, 513, 522
Magnetic pole, 389, 517
Magnetic potential, 730
Magnetic pressure, 522, 523
Magnetic pumping, 378
MAGNETIC RESONANCE, 73, 316, **515**, 818
Magnetic resonance, nuclear, 224
Magnetic Reynolds number, **522**
Magnetic semiconductor, 836
Magnetic shielding, 517, 551
Magnetic storm, **89, 389**, 764
Magnetic susceptibility, **670**
Magnetic well, 379
MAGNETISM, 259, 512, **517**, 712, 871
Magnetization, 337, 513, 517, 524, 904
  remanent, 339
  reversal, 949
Magnetoacoustic effect, **334**
Magnetocrystalline anisotropy, 519
Magneto-fluid dynamics, 366
MAGNETO-FLUID-MECHANICS, **521**, 717
Magneto-gas-dynamics, **521**
Magnetohydrodynamic generator, 243, 245–246
Magneto-hydrodynamic power, 522
Magnetohydrodynamics, 400, **521**, 718, 736
Magneto-hydro-mechanics, **521**
Magnetometer, nuclear precession, 526
  pendulum, 525
  vibrating coil, 525
  vibrating reed, 525
  vibrating sample, 525
MAGNETOMETRY, **524**
Magneton, Bohr, 233, 288, 515
  nuclear, 516
Magneto-optic effect, 336
Magnetopause, **763**
Magneto-plasma dynamics, **521**
Magnetoresistance, **334, 843**

Magnetoresistance, longitudinal, 403
  transverse, 403
Magnetosphere, **763, 876**
Magnetostatic theory, 270
MAGNETOSTRICTION, **527**
Magnetothermoelectric refrigerator, 804
Magnetron, **298, 579**
Magnification, 573
  angular, **637**
Magnifying power, **637**
Magnon, **787, 887**
  localized, 888
Maienschein, Fred C., **624**
Maiman, T. H., **489**
Main sequence dwarf, 860
Main sequence star, 858
Majority carrier, **229**
Malus, Étienne Louis, **655**
Malus' law, **722**
Manometer, 589
Mantle (of earth), 828
Mantle, Welsbach, 774
MANY-BODY PROBLEM, **528**
Map, Patterson, **190**
  vector, 190
Maran, Stephen P., 779, **780**
Mariner space craft, 764
Mars, 476, 716
Marsden, E., 79
Marshak, R. E., 196, 604
Martin, John W., **565**
Martinville, Léon Scott de, 813
Marton, L., **688**
Marx method, 422
MASER, 488, **530**
Maser materials, **531**
Maser oscillators, **533**
Mason, Robert M., **936**
Mass, 63, 166, 239, 534, **557**
  bare, 750
  CRITICAL, 77, **179**
  effective, 203, 400, 837
  gravitational, 809
  inertial, 809
  reduced, 708
  relativistic, 431
  specific, propulsion system, **244**
  star, 69
Mass action, law of, 319
Mass and energy equivalence, 807
MASS AND INERTIA, **534**
Mass defect, 633
Mass discrepancy, 72
Mass number, 633
Mass of sun, 867
Mass spectrograph, **469**
MASS SPECTROMETRY, **535**
Mass stopping power, 769
Massless particle, 699
Material, diamagnetic, 518
  ferromagnetic, 518
  paramagnetic, 517
Mathematical biology, 536
MATHEMATICAL BIOPHYSICS, 99, **536**
MATHEMATICAL PHYSICS, **539**
MATHEMATICAL PRINCIPLES OF QUANTUM
    MECHANICS, **540**
Mathematical symbols, **924**
MATRICES, **543**
Matrices, density, 38
Matrix, **543**, 547, 935
MATRIX MECHANICS, **546**, 1004
Matter, 131, 889
Matthews, P. T., **904**

Matthiessen's rule, 165, **948**
Mattuck, R. D., **343**
Mauchly, J. W., 157
Mauro, A., **538**
Maximal set, 541
Maxwell, James Clerk, **102**, 133, 211, 259, 320, 464,
    480, 599, 652, 700, 709, 722, 733, 752, 807
Maxwell distribution, 481, 606
Maxwell distribution law, **102**
Maxwell electromagnetic theory, 761
Maxwell equations, 512, 700, 752
Maxwell stress, 521
Maxwell theory, 733
Maxwell-Boltzmann distribution, 104
Maxwell-Faraday law, 433
Maxwell-Wagner effect, 211
Mayer, J. E., 383, **506**, 538, 898
McCready, L. L., 777
McCusker, C. B. A., **760**
M-center, **148**, 493
McFee, R. H., **446**
McGrath, J. W., **131**
McIntyre, D. F., **568**
McKenzie, A. E. E., **640**
McKenzie, N. C., **640**
McLeod gauge, **979**
McMillan, E. M., 201, 925, 960, 961
Meaden, G. T., **166**
Mean field theory, **181**
Mean free path, 480
Mean value, **709**
Measurement at a distance, **929**
MEASUREMENTS, ELECTRICAL, **253**
MEASUREMENTS, PRINCIPLES OF, **550**
Mechanical advantage, **849**
Mechanical behavior of crystals, 493
Mechanical energy, dissipation of, 462
Mechanical energy from sun, 865
Mechanical equivalent of heat, **559**
Mechanical oscillator, 815
MECHANICAL PROPERTIES OF SOLIDS, **553**
Mechanics, 240, 557, 712, 936
  celestial, 68
  MATRIX, **546**, 1004
  quantum, 1004
  STATISTICAL, 311, 383, 413, **896**
  WAVE, **1004**
MEDICAL PHYSICS, **560**
Meitner, Lise, 208, **351**
Meissner effect, 208, 904
Mel, Howard C., **771**
Mel (unit), 601
Mellin transform, 487
Meltzer, Carl H., **301**
Melvin, M. A., **50**
Membrane, biological, 538
  permeable, 660
  semipermeable, 589
  structure of, 538
  transport phenomena in, 538
Memory storage, 97
Mendeleev, Dmitri, 675
Mendelevium, **963**
Mercury, 714
Mercury arc, 972
Mercury cadmium cell, 95
Mercury vapor rectifier, **299**
Meson, 32, 176, **305**, 604, 634, 757
Meson factory, **9**
Mesopause, 567
Mesoscale, 566
Mesosphere, 390, 567
Metabolite, 538

Metal, **562,** 870
 conductivity of, **165**
 shaping of, **562**
Metal-insulator-semiconductor structure, 831
Metallic bond, 102
METALLURGY, **562**
Metallurgy, powder, 562
Metal-oxide-semiconductor transistor, 955
METEOROLOGY, 174, 390, 454, **565**
Meter, speed measuring, 761
Method of invariance, 959
Method of singular eigenfunctions, 959
Metric tensor, 935
Metrical entropy, 942
Metzger, F., 153
Meyer, Lothar, 675
Meyer, Victor, 589
Meyerhofer, Dietrich, **968**
Mica, 723
Michell, 259
Michelson, Albert A., 138, 448, 449, 568, 653, 990
Michelson interferometer, 449, 568
MICHELSON-MORLEY EXPERIMENT, **568**
Michelson-Morley interferometer, **568–569**
Microbeam probe, 1021
Micron (unit), (footnote) 661
Microphone, 262
Microradiographic technique, 1021
Microscale, 566
MICROSCOPE, **571,** 637
MICROSCOPE, ELECTRON, **275**
 field emission, **345**
 field ion, **346**
 mirror, **281**
 phase contrast, **574**
 polarizing, 575
 stereoscopic, 575
 objective, 496
Microscopic theory, 937
Microseism, 829
Microstate, 944
Microtron, **11**
Microwave, velocity of, 989
Microwave acoustics, 263
Microwave background radiation, 780
Microwave device, **832**
MICROWAVE SPECTROSCOPY, **575,** 885
MICROWAVE TRANSMISSION, **579**
Microwave tube, 296
Micro-wire grid, 722
Middle ultraviolet, 971
Midnight vector, 476
Migration energy, 493
Miles, John L., **188**
Milky Way, 71, 237
Miller indices, 195
Millikan, Robert Andrews, 79, 171, **273,** 343, 972
Millikan's oil drop experiment, **273**
Mills Cross, 778
Milton, J. C. D., 356
Minkowski space, 539
Minority carrier, **229**
Mirror, Alice, 378
 concave, 647
 convex, 647
 D.C.X., 378
 magnetic, **378**
 parabolic, 648
 Phoenix, 378
 spherical, 647
Mirror microscope, **281**
Mirror nuclei, 465
MIS structure, **831**
Missiles, 91

Mission, interplanetary, 244
Mission, lunar, 244
Mitchell, D. P., 217
Mixed characteristic, 1
Mobile, Primum, 424
Mobility, 402, **837**
Mobility, Hall, **842**
Mobility of charge carriers, **164**
Mobility of defects, 461
Mode, normal, 994
Mode locking, **491**
Model, nuclear, **631**
Moderator, 179, 608, **629**
Modern physics, 712
MODULATION, **580,** 642, 930
 amplitude, **580**
 frequency, **581**
 phase, 581
Modulus, bulk, 554
 rigidity, 554
Modulus of elasticity, **554**
Moeckel, W. E., **248**
Mohler, Orren C., **868**
Mohole, 390
Mohorovičić, A. (discontinuity), **390**
Molar, **917**
Molar concentration, 588
Molar polarization, 719
Molar quantity, 582
Molar solution, 582
Molar susceptibility, 233
Mole, 587
MOLE CONCEPT, **582**
Molecular beam, **72,** 75
Molecular complex, 593
Molecular compound, 592–593
Molecular density, 976
Molecular dimension, 587
Molecular energy levels, 316
Molecular orbital, 103, 594
Molecular spectra, 583, **585**
MOLECULAR SPECTROSCOPY, 316, **583,** 884
Molecular structure, **592**
Molecular theory of states, 891
MOLECULAR WEIGHT, 125, **587,** 725, 999
 distribution of, **588**
molecule, 102, 382, 590, **592,** 891
 electronic states of, 594
 linked, 691
 nonpolar, **232**
 POLAR, 232, 452, **719**
 rotating, 575
MOLECULES AND MOLECULAR STRUCTURE,
 592
Moment, **895**
 dipole, 232, 575, **719**
 electric quadrupole, 631
 magnetic, 571
 magnetic (neutron), 606
Moment of force, 432, **559**
Moment of inertia, 821
Moment of momentum, 985
Momentum, 166, 357, 421, **431,** 540, **558,** 595, 985
 angular, 166–167, 542, 670, 821, 985
 conservation of, 431, 559
 moment of, 985
 photon, 699
 rotational, **821**
Momentum coordinates, 331
Momentum density, 753
Momentum space, **331**
Monazite, 788
Monochromatic radiation, 530
Monomer, 588

Mononuclidic element, 467
Monopole (sound), 707
Monte Carlo method, **622,** 959
Montgomery, D. J., **895**
Moon, 475, 877
  motion of, 477
Morgan, K. Z., 405, 406
Morgan, R., 961
Morley, Edward W., 449, **568**
Morphology (of crystals), **194**
Morse potential, 452
MOS device, 955
Moseley, G. J., **1020**
Mössbauer, Rudolph L., **595**
MÖSSBAUER EFFECT, 393, **595**
Mosotti, 720
Mossotti formula, 325
Mossotti (polarization), 232
Mossotti-Clausius-Debye equation, 232
Motion, circular, **820**
  laws of, 534
  planetary, 475
  rotary, **820**
  simple harmonic, 584
Motor, alternating, 599
  compound, 599
  induction, 599
  polyphase, 599
  series wound, 599
  shunt, 599
  synchronous, **600**
MOTORS, ELECTRIC, **599**
Mott, N. F., 165, 564
Mott transition, 165
Motz, J. W., 154
Mu-leptic charge, 32
Müller, E. W., 283, 344, **347**
Müller, W., 615
Mullin, Albert A., **330**
Multilevel excitation, 531
Multiplet, 309
Multiplexing, 930
Multiplication constant, 353
Multipole, 379, 674
Multipole radiation, 673
Multivibrator, 742
Mu-meson, 176
Muon, 168, 305, 619, 747
Music, **601**
MUSICAL SOUND, **601**
Mutual coherence function, **138**
Mutual inductance, **435**
Myers, Raymond R., **820**
Myosin, 99

Nadeau, Gérard, **242**
Nachtrieb, Norman H., **225**
Nahordnung, 222
Natural frequency, 815
Natural philosopher, 557
Navier-Stokes equation, 416, **707**
Navigation, inertial, **399**
Near ultraviolet, 971
Nebula, 70
Néel, Louis, 335
Néel temperature, **31,** 519
Ne'eman, 196
Negative feedback, 329
Negative glow, 252
Negative lens, 494
Negative temperature, 531
Negatron, 783
Neptune, 717
Neptunium, **960**

Nernst, Hermann W., 403
Nernst effect, 403
Nernst glower, 775
Nerve excitation, 538
Nerve fiber, 538
Network, 133, 134
Neuberger, Jacob, **325**
Neumann, J. von, 539, 897
Neumann equation, 435
Neutral equivalent, 591
Neutralization of charge, 894
Neutrino, 176, 304, 355, **604,** 783, 860, 1012
Neutrino astronomy, 619
Neutron, 76, **179,** 351, 465, 470, 604, **605,** 607, 615,
      625, 627, 633, 756, 763, 782
  anomalous scattering, 611
  delayed, 355, **635**
  fast, 607, 619, 634
  prompt, **635**
  sources of, **606**
  structure of, **607**
  thermal, 607, **770**
NEUTRON ACTIVATION ANALYSIS, **607**
Neutron capture, 313, 631
NEUTRON DIFFRACTION, **610**
Neutron diffusion theory, 959
Neutron emission, delayed, 631
Neutron flux, 608
Neutron interaction, **606**
Neutron scattering, 224
Neutron sources, 608, 627
Neutron star, 70, **395, 740, 741**
Neutron transport, 957
Newlands, J. A. R., 675
Newton, Sir Isaac, 3, 22, 63, **238,** 347, 391, **425, 448,**
      475, 534, 539, **557,** 807, 809
Newton's equation (heat flow), 416
Newton's experiment (dispersion), 654
Newton's law of cooling, 117
Newton's laws of motion, 65, **238, 534, 557**
Newton's rings, 449
Newton's second law, 985
Newton's second law, fluids, 22
Newton (unit), **557**
Newton-meter (unit), 1014
Newtonian world machine, 462
Newtonian time, 950
Neyman-Pearson theory, 900
Nicholson, William, 264
Nicolas, Cardinal, 424
Nielsen, Lawrence E., **727**
Nightglow, 89
Nijboer, B. R. A., **1**
Nimbus satellite, 776
Nishina, Y., 152
Nit (unit), 507
Nobelium, **964**
Noble gas, 132
Noble gas compound, 132
Nodal point, 495
Node, 1009
Nodes, laser, 489
Noise, 19, 53, 762
NOISE, ACOUSTICAL, **613**
Noise (fluctuations in experimental data), 552
Noise, maser, 530
Noise, pink, 601
Noise, shot, 552
Noise, white, 601
Nomenclature, **915**
Nonadditivity effects, 451
Non-Euclidian geometry, 539
Nonlinear circuit, 134
Nonlinear optics, 499

Non-Newtonian systems, **999**
Nordheim, L. W., 343
Norm, **541**
Normal dispersion curve, **4**
Normal mode, 680
Normal mode (vibration), 994
Normal mode analysis, 529
Normal stress, 553
Normalization (wave function), 1006
Nova, 778
Noys (unit), 19
Nuclear bomb, 764
Nuclear data, 621
Nuclear decay, 727
Nuclear energy, **76**
Nuclear fission, **351**
Nuclear force, **630, 634,** 756
Nuclear fuel production, 627
Nuclear fusion, **636**
NUCLEAR INSTRUMENTS, **614**
Nuclear isomer, 783
Nuclear magnetic moment, 516
Nuclear magnetic resonance, 316, 516, 711, 818, 886
Nuclear magneton, 516
Nuclear model, **631**
Nuclear polarization, 674
Nuclear power, 352
Nuclear precession magnetometer, 526
NUCLEAR RADIATION, **617**
Nuclear radiation detection, **614**
NUCLEAR RADIATION SHIELDING, **619**
NUCLEAR REACTIONS, 466, 607, **624**
Nuclear reactions (notation for), 917
NUCLEAR REACTOR, 77, 352, 608, 619, **626**
Nuclear science, 633
Nuclear shell model, 466
NUCLEAR STRUCTURE, **630**
Nuclear turboelectric system, 245
Nuclear weapon, 327, **352,** 620
Nucleation, **161, 162, 191,** 947
Nucleogenesis, 70
Nucleon, **168, 465, 630,** 631, **739,** 902
NUCLEONICS, **633**
Nucleon-nucleon interaction, 631
Nucleus, 80, 304, 376, 605, 633, 782
    mirror, 465
    residual, 626
    stability of, **782**
Nuclide, 76, 607
Number, atomic, 80, (table) **468**
Number, coordination, 505
Number, magic, **631**
Number, quantum, 289
Number, laws, 168
Numerical aperture, **573, 638**
Nurmia, 964, 965
Nusselt number, **417**

Oberman, Carl, **719**
Oberth, H., 247
Objective, camera, 496
    microscope, 496
    telescope, 496
Objective lens, 278, 571, **637**
Oboe (distance measurement), 990
Obry, 398
Observable, 46, **540,** 672
    conjugation-invariant, 41
    conjugation-reversing, 41
    superselection, 35
Occultation, lunar, 779
Oceanography, 174, **390**
Oersted, Hans Christian, 259

Ohm, Georg Simon, **164,** 259, 599
Ohm (unit), 253
OH, 18-cm line of, 779
Ohm's law, 24, **164**
Oil drop experiment, **273**
Oil immersion objective, 638
Olbers, H. W. M., 178
Olive, D. I., 48
Oliver, Jack, **829**
Olson, Harry F., **614**
Olson, John M., **703**
One-dimensional box, 1005
O'Neil, Stephen J., 846
Onnes, Heike Kamerlingh (see Kamerlingh Onnes, Heike)
Onsager, Lars, 205, 720
Onsager equation, 209
Operational methods, 484
Operational telemetry, 929
Operator, 46, 484, 701, 1005
    Casimer, 40
    Hermitian, 37, 421
    Linear, 542
    quantum-mechanical, 465
    symmetry, 33
    total, 466
    Unitary, 38
Oponent-colors theory (of vision), 147
Oppenheimer, J. Robert, 352
Optical activity, 655
Optical axis, 494
Optical branch, 681
Optical electronic device, 446
Optical imagery, 426
OPTICAL INSTRUMENTS, **637**
Optical path, 653
Optical phonon, 681, 724, **837–838**
Optical properties of solids, 322
OPTICAL PUMPING, 531, **640**
Optical pyrometer, 933
OPTICAL PYROMETRY, **744**
Optical rotation, 328
Opticks, 462
OPTICS, ELECTRON, **283**
OPTICS, GEOMETRICAL, 497, **643**
Optics, nonlinear, 499
OPTICS, PHYSICAL, 497, **652**
Optics, physiological, 497
Optics, thin-film, **947**
Optoelectronic device, **834**
Orbit, 475
    anomalous effects, 65
    cotangential, **56**
    transfer, **67**
Orbital electron, 675
Orbital energy, **55**
Orbital moment, 233
Orbital motion, 203
Orbitals, mixing of, 732
Order parameter, 906
Ordinary beam, 655
Ordinary differential equation, 211, **212**
Oresme, 424
Organic chemistry, 129, 132
Organizations, physics, **713**
Oriented polymer, 727
Orthicon, image, 827
Ortho-positronium, 728
Oscillating dipole, **271**
Oscillation, 816, 993
    electrical, 1008
    electron, 205
Oscillator, elementary, 772
    linear harmonic, 548, 1007

maser, **533**
mechanical, 815
OSCILLOSCOPE, 286, **656**
Osgood, T. H., 972
Osmometry, 590
OSMOSIS, **658**
Osmotic pressure, 588, 589, 590, 708, 725
Ossicle, 408
Ostwald, Wilhelm (dilution law), 708
Outer product, 983
Overman, Ralph T., **785**
Overtone, 994
Oxidation, 456, 564
    electrolytic, 265
Oxidation state, 960
Ozone layer, 390

Pacinotti, Antonio, 599
Packing fraction, **633**
Page, Thornton, **72**
Pair, electron-hole, 321, 684
    electron-positron, 176, 727
Pair annihilation, 32
Pair creation, **32**
Pair density function, 505
Pair production, 153, 727, **769**
Palomar telescope, 639
PARACRYSTAL, **661**
Paracrystalline distortion, 220
Paradox, recurrence, 482
    reversibility, 482
Paraelectric phase, 337
Parallelogram law, 982
Parallax panoramogram, 689
Paramagnetic material, 517, 611
Paramagnetic rotation, **329**
Paramagnetic salts, 186
PARAMAGNETISM, 233, **669**
Parameters, constitutive, **733**
Parametric amplifier, 336
Para-positronium, 728
Paraxial rays, 494
PARITY, **43, 169,** 305, **671**
    charge, 672
    intrinsic, 44, 672
    time, 672
Parker, W. H., 749
Parkins, William E., 317, **1016**
Parrent, G., Jr., 138
Parsec (footnote), 177
Parseval's theorem, 372
Partial conservation of axial current hypothesis, 196
Partial differential equation, 211, 213, 486
Partial pressure, 890
Partial summation, 340
Particle, 36, **303,** 528
    bound, 824
    charged, 768
    ELEMENTARY, **196, 303,** (table) 306
    free, 824
    strange, **305**
    strongly interacting (table), **307**
Particle accelerator, **9**
Particle statistics, 32
Particle conjugation, 34
Particle decay, 305
Particle ray, 617
Particle transport, 957
Partition function, 101, 898, 944
Partition function, replacement, 162
Parton, 1014
Parvin, Richard H., **60, 442**
Pascal, Blaisé, 156, 233
Pascal's law, **369**

Pascal (unit), **976**
Paschen, F., 81, 290
Paschen series, 81
Paschen-Back effect, 290, 1025
Paschen's law, **251**
Patch board, 155
Pathway, auditory, 407
Patlack, C., 538
Pattern, Fraunhofer, 217
Patterson, A. L., **190**
Patterson function, **190**
Patterson map, **190**
Pauli, Wolfgang, 273, 289, **314, 604,** 633, 671, 675,
    739, 747, 1012
Pauli exclusion principle, 83, 104, **289,** 330, 331, 451,
    633, 675
Pauli matrix, 543
Pauling, Linus, 720
Pawsey, J. L., 777
Payne-Scott, R., 777
PCAC, 196
Peak, Snoek, 971
Pearson, F., 990
Pease, Francis Gladheim, 990
Peierls, R., 205
Peierls potential, **492**
Pekar, S. I., **724**
Peltier, J. C. A., **945**
Peltier effect, 803, **945**
Peltier heat transport, 844
Pelzer, H., 724
Pendulum, **993,** 1015
    ballistic, 91
Pendulum magnetometer, 525
Penning cold-cathode gauge, 980
Penning discharge, 642
Penrose, R., 395
Pentagrid converter, 295
Pentode, 291, **295**
Perception, color, **145**
    pitch, 407
Perfect gas, **382**
Periapsis distance, 56
Perihelion, **475**
Period, **1008**
    synodic, **59**
PERIODIC LAW AND PERIODIC TABLE, **675**
Periodic table, 678
Periodic time, 993
Periscope, 496
Peritectic, 680
Permalloy film, 949
Permanent magnet, **520**
Permeability, **261,** 437, 733
Permeability, magnetic, 513, 522
Permittivity, **209,** 733
Perot, A. (Fabry-Perot interferometer), 450
Perpetual motion, 464
Perrin, Jean, **110,** 272
Perturbation, orbital, **58**
Peter, Martin, **76**
Peters, Robert W., **409**
Petit, A. T., 414
Phase, 504, 679, **1008**
Phase contrast illumination, 639
Phase contrast microscope, **574**
Phase diagram, 504, 562, **890**
Phase equilibrium constant, 982
Phase modulation, 581
Phase plane, 101
PHASE RULE, **679,** 943
Phase shift (light), 570
Phase stability, 201
Phase stability principle, **8**

Phase transition, **180**
Phase transitions, high pressure, 732
Phase velocity, **17**, 754, 1010, 1011
Phasotron, 201
PHENOMENA, CRITICAL, **180**
Phillips, Norman E., 415
Philosopher, natural, 557
Phoenix mirror, 378
Phoenix two, 380
Phon, **19, 602,** 613
Phonautograph, 813
Phonograph, **813**
PHONON, **165,** 529, 612, **680,** 787, 872, 906, 971
  acoustic, **837–838**
  optical, 681, 724, **837–838**
  scattering by, 837
Phonon interactions, 681
Phosphor, 510, 511
Phosphorescence, **508**
Phosphorescence (relaxation), 811
Photoabsorption, 456
Photocathode, **696,** 973
Photocell, 687
PHOTOCHEMISTRY, **682**
PHOTOCONDUCTIVITY, **684**
PHOTOELASTICITY, 655, **685**
Photoelectric effect, 153, 686, 699, 769
Photoelectric pyrometer, **745**
PHOTOELECTRICITY, **686**
Photoelectron, 86, **687**
Photographic film, **689**
Photographic image, 688
PHOTOGRAPHY, 426, **688**
  scanning, 692
Photoionization, 456, 459, **704**
Photoluminescence, 508
Photolysis, flash, 683
Photometer, **693**
Photometric units (table), **695**
PHOTOMETRY, **692**
PHOTOMULTIPLIER, 303, 687, **696,** 827, 973
Photon, 151, 303, 304, 305, 418, 625, **699,** 721, 747,
  752, 1004
  high-energy, **176**
  polarized, **108**
  x-ray, **1020**
Photon (unit), 682
Photon beam, **105**
Photon gas, 105
Photon propulsion, 366
Photonuclear reaction, 687
Photopeak, 609
Photopigment, 14, 1002
Photoreceptor, 1000
Photosphere, **867**
PHOTOSYNTHESIS, 682, **702,** 866
Photosynthetic bacteria, 702
Photosynthetic unit, 703
Photovoltaic cell, 860
PHOTOVOLTAIC EFFECT, 685, 688, **704**
Photovoltaic effect, bulk, 844
Photovoltaic effect, solar cell, 864
Photoemission, 696
Photoemitter, 687
PHYSICAL ACOUSTICS, **705**
PHYSICAL CHEMISTRY, 130, 132, **708,** 712
PHYSICAL OPTICS, 497, **652**
Physical quantity, 915
PHYSICS, 130, **711**
Physics, applied, 550
PHYSICS, CHEMICAL, **130**
Physics, fundamental, 550
Physics, future trends, **713**
PHYSICS, HISTORY OF, **423**

Physics, Newtonian, 425
PHYSICS, SOLID STATE, **869**
PHYSICS, THEORETICAL, **936**
Physics organizations, **713**
Physiological optics, 497
Physiology of the ear, **407**
Phytotoxicant, 974
Pi meson, 176, 740, 756
PI theorem, 228
Picht-Luneburg integral, **2**
Pickoff, 728
Pickup reaction, 626
Pictet, Raoul, 186
Pierce, P. H., 852
Piezoelectric crystal, 969
Piezoelectricity, 262
Piezomagnetism, 262
Piezoresistance, 262
Pigment, 145, 703
Pike, Julian M., **175**
Pile (nuclear reactor), **627,** 635
Pinajian, J. J., **472**
Pinch, theta, 377
Pinch, Z, 377
Pinch effect, **253, 523**
Pincushion distortion, 650
Pines, D., 724
Pink noise, 601
Pinning (of dislocations), 971
Pion, 305, 619, 756, 902
Pippard, A. B., 333–334, 905
Pisa, Leaning Tower of, 392
Piston engine, 364
Pitch, 601
Pitch perception, 407
Pitot tube, 369
Pixii, H., 599
Placzek, G., 786
Planar transistor, 955
Plancherel's theorem, 373
Planck, Max, 69, 132, **314,** 418, 464, **699,** 752, 772,
  1004
Planck constant, **699,** 1004
Planck distribution law, 105
Planck equation, 418, 699
Plane, inclined, **850**
Plane, principal, 651
Plane defect, 491
Plane wave, 707
Plane wave field, 735
Planet, 475, **713,** 877
Planet, giant, **716**
PLANETARY ATMOSPHERES, **713**
Planetary motion, 475
Planetary system (nuclear), 529
PLASMA, **376,** 458, **717,** 898
Plasma, diffusion in, 379
Plasma frequency, 328, **735**
Plasma heating, 377
Plasma number, 718
Plasma propulsion, 524
Plasma thruster, 246
Plasma waves, **736**
Plastic behavior, 493, 553–554
Plastic deformation, 842
Plastic flow, 562
Plate, vacuum tube, **296**
Plate, current, 294
Plate tectonics, 828
Platform, gyro-stabilized, 439
Plato, 424
Plücker, Julius, **272**
Pluto, 476, 717
Plutonium, 76, **961**

p-n diode, 267
p-n junction, **229, 829**
Pneumatic detector, 776
Pockels effect, 478
Poincaré, Jules Henri, 482, 539, **570,** 723
Poincaré group, **34**
Poincaré sphere, 723
Poincaré symmetries, 168
Poincaré's theorem, 482, **528**
Point, critical, 181, 890
Point, focal, 651
Point, yield, 555
Point characteristic, 1
Point defect, 491, **493,** 869
Point group, 195
Point lattice, 217
Point-contact transistor, **954**
Poise (unit), 998
Poiseuille, Jean Louis Marie, 99, 560, 998
Poiseuille flow, 368
Poisoning, reactor, **629**
Poisson, Siméon D., 241, **729,** 730
Poisson bracket, 897
Poisson equation, 269, 730
Poisson ratio, 554
Polacolor, **691**
Polar Cap Absorption, 459
POLAR MOLECULES, 452, **719**
Polarimeter, 655
Polariton, 787
Polarizability, 232, 479
Polarization, 126, 328, 1023
   dielectric, **209**
   interfacial, 211
   light, 654
   molar, 719
   nuclear, 674
   radio wave, **28**
   rotation of plane of, 328
Polarization in cells, **93**
polarization vector, 734
POLARIZED LIGHT, 685, **721**
Polarizer, dichroic, **722**
Polarizing microscope, 575
Polaroid camera, **690**
Polaroid photography, 688
POLARON, 204, 529, **723**
Pole, magnetic, 389, **517**
Pole, Regge, **804**
Pole, unit, 517
Pollution, 243, 327
   air, 567
   thermal, 776
Polydisperse system, 591
Polymer, 556, 588
POLYMER PHYSICS, **725**
Polyphase motor, 599
Pomeranchuck trajectory, **806**
Pomerantz, Martin A., **455**
Pompage optique, **640**
Ponderomotive force, 521
Population inversion, 531, 643
Portis, A. M., 329
Position vector, 237, 984
Positive column, 252
Positive electron, **274**
Positive ion, **81**
Positive ion sheath, 299
Positive lens, 494
Positive ray, 535
POSITRON, **274,** 304, 604, 618, **727**
Positron (creation of), 1012
Positron annihilation, **334**
Positron emission, 607, 783

Positronium, **728**
Post-uranic element, 611
POTENTIAL, **729**
   chemical, 319, 943
   gravitational, 392
   Hertz, 270
   interaction, 324
   intermolecular, 383, 453
   ionization, 456
   magnetic, 730
   Peierls, **492**
   shell model, 631
   vector, 270, 512
Potential barrier, 827, 963
Potential difference, electric, 250, **260**
Potential energy, 167, 319, **1015**
Potential equation, 349
Potential function, 452
Potential in solids, **872**
Potential scattering, **140, 141**
Potentiometer, 255
Pouillet, 853
Pound, G. M., **163**
Pound, R. V., 224, **596**
Powder metallurgy, 562
Powder model, 631
Powell, C. F., 162
Power, **1014**
   alternating current (ac), **26**
   atomic, 77
   average, **25**
   electric, **242, 243,** 253
   geothermal, 243
   isotopic, 78
   magnetohydrodynamic, 522
   magnifying, **637**
   nuclear, 352
   resolving, **638**
   solar, 858
   transmission of, 952
   ultrasonic, 970
Power conversion, 599
Power dissipation, 948–949
Power factor, 119, 436
Power generation, 242
Power sources, 243
Powers, P. N., 217
Poynting, John Henry (vector), 271
Prandtl number, **417**
Prebuncher, 8
Precession, 985
Preiswerk, P., 217
Present, R. D., 384, **453**
Pressure, 369, 384, 479
   atmospheric, **369**
   change of (thermometry), 933
   critical, 890
   imbibitional, **660**
   low, **976**
   osmotic, 708
   partial, 890
   vapor, 589, **981**
PRESSURE, VERY HIGH, **731**
Pressure gradient, 983
Pressure head, 370
Preston's rule, 1023, 1024
Prévost, Pierre (principle), **418**
Priestley, Joseph, 259
Price, William J., **617**
Primary cell, **94**
Primary coil, **951**
Primary quantity, 227
Primary radiation, **175**
Primum mobile, 424

Princeton Heavy Ion Synchrotron, 926
Principal plane, 651
Principal point, 495
Principal quantum number, 82
Principia, **557**
Principle, Columbus, 44
Principle of Carathéodory, 942
Principle of equivalence, **392**
PRINCIPLE(S) OF MEASUREMENT, **550**
Principle of uncertainty, 755
Prins, I. A., 217
Prism, 646, 654
Probability, 331, 900
Probability density, 1006
Probability density function, 505
Probability distribution, **900**
Probability of collision, 957
Probability-in-phase, 944
Probe, electron microbeam, 1021
Process, adiabatic, **121**
  isothermal, 121
  thermodynamic, 120
Programming, 158
Projectiles, 91, **173**
Projector lens, 279
Prompt gamma ray, 607
Prompt neutron, 635
Propagation equation (elasticity), **242**
PROPAGATION OF ELECTROMAGNETIC WAVES,
  733
Propagation vector, 887
Propagator, **340**
Propellant, 243, **357**
Propellant, liquid, 359
Propellant, performance of (table), 361
Propellant, solid, 360
Property, extensive, 385
  intensive, 385
Properties of solids, **553**
Proportional chamber, 879
Proportional counter, 615
Proportional limit, 554
Propulsion, **357**
PROPULSION, ELECTRIC, **243**
  photon, **366**
  plasma, 524
Propulsion-system specific mass, **244**
Prospecting, geophysical, **391**
Protection, radiological, 406
Proto-Cleo, 380
PROTON, 175, 465, 615, 633, **739,** 756, 763, 782
Proton conduction, 164
Proton precession, 254
Protonosphere, 458
Proton-proton chain, **858**
Ptolemy, 424
Ptolemaic system, 347
Puchstein, A. F., **601**
Pulley, 849
Pulley, differential, 849
PULSARS, 70, 395, 580, **740,** 779
PULSE GENERATION, 657, **742**
Pulse radiolysis, 765
Pulse transformer, 953
Pulsed field method, 206
Pump, vacuum, **976**
PUMPING, OPTICAL, 531, **640**
Pupil, exit, **637**
Pupil (eye), 1000
Purcell, E. M., 224, 779
Pure state, 540
Pycnometer, 207
Pyroelectric crystal, 776

PYROMETRY, OPTICAL, **744**
Pythagoras, 324

Q-factor, 436
Quadratic electro-optic effect, **478**
Quadratic Stark effect, 531
Quadrupole, nuclear electric, 577
Quadrupole splitting (nuclear), 598
Quality, sound, **601**
Quanta, (see quantum)
Quantity, fundamental, 227
  physical, 227
  primary, 227
Quantization, second, 348
Quantum, 468, 498, **1004**
Quantum detector, 776
QUANTUM ELECTRODYNAMICS, 309, 728, **747**
Quantum field theory, 143, 310, **349**
Quantum hypothesis, 772
Quantum level, 675
Quantum liquid, **504**
Quantum mechanics, 80, 349, 420, 546, 936, 1004
QUANTUM MECHANICS, MATHEMATICAL PRIN-
  CIPLES OF, **540**
Quantum-mechanical operator, 465
Quantum number, 289, **314, 675**
Quantum statistics, 104
QUANTUM THEORY, 152, **751**
  general relativistic, 46
Quantum yield, 683
QUARK, 309, **756,** 904
Quasar, 72, 780
Quasi-electron, 342
Quasi-free electron model, 332
Quasi-particle, 529, 873
Quasi-stellar object, 397
Quiet D region, 459
QSO, 397
Q-switch, 490

Rabi, I. I., **73,** 289
Rabinowicz, Ernest, **376**
Rad (unit), 561, **766**
RADAR, **761,** 990
Radar astronomy, 777
Radar equation, 761
Radar wave, velocity of, 989
Radial acceleration, 821
Radial density function, 500
Radial distribution function, 151, 384
Radian, 112, 918
Radiance, 506
  spectral, **744**
Radiant heating, 445
Radiant intensity, 506
Radiation, 116, 415
  blackbody, universal, 176
  ČERENKOV, **126**
  coherent, 530
  cosmic, **175**
  IONIZING, BASIC INTERACTIONS, **767**
  isotropic background, 72
  microwave background, 780
  monochromatic, 530
  NUCLEAR, **617**
  primary, **175**
  secondary, **176**
  THERMAL, **418,** 731, **771**
  ULTRAVIOLET, **971**
RADIATION BELTS, **763**

RADIATION CHEMISTRY, **764**
Radiation damage, 406
radiation detector, 615
Radiation detector, semiconductor, **617**
Radiation field, 349
Radiation intensity, 27
Radiation pattern, 27, **28**
Radiation protection, 404
Radiation shielding, 619
Radiative recombination, 267, 459
Radiative transfer, 957
Radiator, dipole, **28**
  monopole, **28**
Radio, 761
RADIO ASTRONOMY, 236, **777**
Radio aurora, 89
Radio frequency size effect, **334**
Radio waves, 458
Radioactive carbon, 626
Radioactive decay, 78
RADIOACTIVE TRACERS, **780**
RADIOACTIVITY, **782**
  artificial, **618**
  induced, **618**
Radiofrequency spectra, 84
Radiography, **1021**
Radioisotope, 467, 469, 780
  artificial, 727
Radioisotope cell, 245
Radioisotope production, 627
Radiological protection, 406
Radiolysis, pulse, 765
Radiometric units (table), 695
Radionuclide, 470, 607
Radiosonde, 565
Radius, cyclotron, 276
Radius of sun, 867
Radium, 404
Raether criterion, 879
Raimes, S., **1008**
Rain, **136**
Rajaraman, R., **535**
Rall, W., 538
Raman, Sir Chandrasekhara, 500, **785**
RAMAN EFFECT AND RAMAN SPECTROSCOPY,
  785
Raman spectroscopy, 882
Ramjet, 364
Ramsey, N., 606, 751
Random error, 550
Random variable, 900
Range, alpha particle, 618
  beta ray, 618
Range of coherence, 906
Ranger spacecraft, 865
Rank, of tensors, 934
Rankine cycle, 245
Rankine scale, 931
Raoult, François Marie, **588**
Raoult's law, 981
Raphael, 424
RARE EARTHS, **788**
Rare gas compound, 593
Rashevsky, N., 99, **536**, 538
Ratio, gyromagnetic, **288**
Ratio, Poisson, 554
Rauch, Lawrence L., **930**
Ray, cathode, 272
  COSMIC, **175**
  gamma, 619
  paraxial, 494
  positive, 535
Rayleigh, Lord (John William Strutt), **500**, 772

Rayleigh (unit), **89**
Rayleigh formula, 500
Rayleigh number, **417**, 524
Rayleigh wave, 969
Rayleigh-Debye scattering, 500
Rayleigh-Gans scattering, 500
Rayleigh-Jeans divergence, 310
Rayleigh-Jeans equation, **772**
R-center, **148**
Reactance, 25
Reaction, bimolecular, 129
  chain, 352, **635**
  chemical, 128
  direct, 626
  endoergic, **625**
  exoergic, **625**
  heat of, 116
  NUCLEAR, **624**
  photonuclear, 687
  pickup, 626
  stripping, 626
  transfer, 626
  unimolecular, 128
Reaction amplitude, 310
Reaction rate, 128, **710**
Reaction rate theory, absolute, **225**
Reactor, breeder, 353, **627–628**
  fusion, 377
  NUCLEAR, 77, 352, **626**, 635
  types of, **628**
Reactor control, **629**, 635
Reactor core, 628
Réaumur scale, 931
Rebka, G. A., **596**
Receptor, 97
Reciprocal lattice, **195**, 935, 1018
Reciprocal lattice cell, 217
Reciprocity theorem, **270**
Recoil energy, 595
Recombination, 684
  dissociative, 459
  radiative, 267, 459
Recombination center, **685**
Recording system, **814**
RECTIFIER, **791**
  diode, **230**
  half-wave, 231
  mercury vapor, **299**
  semiconductor, **829**
Rectifier tube, 291
Recurrence paradox, 482
Recursion formula, 947
Red giant, 859
Red shift, 72, 177, **236**, 393
Redhead gauge, 980
Reduced mass, 708
Reducing power, 266
Reduction, 456
  electrolytic, 265
Reeves, Hubert, **860**
Rees, M., 396
Reference wave, holography, 428
Reflectance, 694, **795**
  luminous, 693
Reflectance factor, 694
REFLECTION, **794**, 969
  Bragg, 223
  internal, **796**
Reflection coefficient, **796**
Reflection of ultraviolet, 973
Reflectivity, 419, **796**
Reflector, microwave, 580
  steerable, 778

REFRACTION, 494, 799, 969
  double, **655**
  law of, 643
Refractive index, 448, 478, 591, 643, 720, 735, **799**, 941
Refractometer, 448, 640
REFRIGERATION, **801**
Refrigerator, Carnot, 122
  helium dilution, 117
  magnetothermoelectric, 804
  thermoelectric, 804
  thermomagnetic, 804
Regge, T., **804**
Regge cuts, 807
Regge family, 309
REGGE POLES AND REGGE THEORY, **804**
Regge theory, **804**
Regge trajectory, 805
Reichenbach, H., 482
Reiner, Marcus, 818
Reines, Frederick, 605, **1012**
Relative aperture, 495, **638**
Relative humidity, **890**
RELATIVITY, 178, 349, 534, 539, 559, **807**, 950
  general, 807
  special, 807
Relaxance, 996
RELAXATION, **810**
  lattice, 872
Relaxation in shock waves, 848
Relaxation modulus, 995
Relaxation time, 971
Relaxation time, spin-lattice, 224
Remanence, 339, 519
Remanent magnetization, 339
Remote cutoff tube, 295
Renaissance, 424
Renormalization, 350
Rep (particle theory), **41**
Repeater satellite, 580
Replacement partition function, 162
Representation space, 541
Representative ensemble, 944
Reproducing system, 814
REPRODUCTION OF SOUND, **813**
Repulsion, short-range, **451**
Residual nucleus, 626
Residue function, 805
Rescigno, A., 538
Resistance, electrical, 164, 253, 254, 904
Resistance thermometer, 933
Resistivity, 844
  specific electrical, 164
Resistor, 135, 254, 948
Resolution, electron optics, 284
Resolution, limit of, **638**
Resolving power, 572–573, **638**
RESONANCE, 25, 606, 804, **815**
  antiferromagnetic, **32**
RESONANCE, CYCLOTRON, 201, **203**
RESONANCE, DIAMAGNETIC, **203**
Resonance, electron paramagnetic, 290
Resonance, electron spin, 290, 316
RESONANCE, MAGNETIC, 316, **515**
Resonance, nuclear magnetic, 316
Resonance, particle (table), **307**
Resonance equation, 212
Resonance fluorescence, 508, **595**
Resonance scattering, 610
Resonant cavity, 1012
Resonant mode, 872
Response function, 180
Rest mass, 1016

Retardance, 996
Retarded potential, 730
Retarder, 722, 723
Retina, 147, 1000, **1001**
Retinal cone, 147
Retinal rod, 147
Reversal, time, **169**
Reverse bias, 230
Reversible process, 120, 481
Reversible transition, 941
Reversibility paradox, 482
Revolving mirror method, 989
Reynolds, J. A., 381
Reynolds, O., 368
Reynolds number, 123, 228, 368, **417**, 998
Reynolds number, magnetic, **522**
RHEOLOGY, **818**
Rheometer, 819
Rhodopsin, 147, 1002
Rhombic antenna, **28**
Ricci, Gregorio, 934
Rich, A., 750
Richards, James A., Jr., **111**, **331**
Richardson, O. W., 293, 939
Richardson equation, **939**
Richardson-Dushman equation, **293**
Rice, F. O., 716
Richter scale, 828
Riemann, Georg F. B., 934
Riemannian tensors, 539
Righi-Leduc effect, 403
Right-hand rule, 432–433
Rigidity modulus, 554
Rindler, W., **810**
Ring armature, 599
Rinne, F., 661
Rise time, 742
Ritter, Johann Wilhelm, 972
Robertson, B. L., 243
Robins, Benjamin, 91
Robiscoe, R. T., 750
Robson, J. H., **605**
Rocket, bipropellant, 359
Rocket, electric, 243–244, 245
Rocket, ion, **247**
Rocket engine, **358**
Rocket propulsion, 66
Rod, retinal, 147, 1001
Roentgen, Wilhelm Konrad, 764, **1020**
Roentgen (unit), 561
Romain, Jacques E., **951**
Römer, Ole, 989
Root locus plot, 846
Root-mean-square value, 24
Roozeboom, H. W. B., 679
Rosa, Edward Bennett, 989
Rosenblum, S., 618
Rossby, C.-G. (waves), 566
Roston, S., 537
Rotary motion, **820**
Rotary oil-sealed pump, 976
Rotating molecule, 575
Rotation, 173, **238**
Rotation, antiferromagnetic, **329**
Rotation, ferromagnetic, **329**
Rotation, carrier, **328**
ROTATION-CIRCULAR MOTION, **820**
Rotation, optical, 328
Rotation, paramagnetic, **329**
Rotational energy, 385, **559**
Rotational kinetic energy, molecular, 576
Rotational equation, 545
Rotational momentum, **821**

Rotational state, 316
Rothman, Milton A., **170**
Rotor, **242, 600**
Rotor, squirrel-cage, 599
Round, 267
Rouse, Arthur G., 726, **823**
Rusk, Rogers D., **619**
Rumble, 814
Rumford, Count, 412
Runge's rule, 1024
Rupp, A. F., **472**
Rushbrooke, G. S., 183
Rushbrooke inequality, 183
Ruska, E., 276
Russ, S., 404
Rutherford, Sir Ernest, **79**, 478, 616, **624**, 633, 739,
    1004, 1012
Rutherfordium, **964**
Ryle, M., 778
Ryschkewitsch, G. E., **104**

Saccade, **999**
Saddington, K., **224**
Sadler, C. A., 85
Saint Augustine, 424
Salpeter, E., 750
Samarium-cobalt alloy, 790
sample space, 900
sampling theorem, 330
Sanderson, R. T., **679**
Sargent, W. L. W., **179**
Satellite, **478,** 717, 763
    Jovian, 778
Satellite magnetometer, 526
Satellite temperature control, **774–775**
Saturation, 145
Saturn, 716
Sayre, D., 190
Scalar concept, **982**
Scalar field, **985**
Scalar function, 729
Scalar product (inner product), 541, **983**
Scalar-tensor theory of gravitation, 394
Scala tympani, 408
Scale of atomic masses, 582
Scale symmetry, 169
Scaling hypothesis, **182**
Scanning array (ultrasonic), 970
Scanning electron microscope, **281,** 1021
Scanning photography, 692
Scattering, **140,** 401, 957
Scattering, asymmetric, 722
Scattering, charge-carrier, 402
Scattering, light, **499,** 590, 725
Scattering, potential, 140, **141**
Scattering, Rayleigh-Debye, 500
Scattering, Rayleigh-Gans, 500
Scattering amplitude, 804
Scattering length, **610**
Scattering matrix element, 310
Scattering power, **610**
Scattering theory, **142**
SCF hypothesis, 183
Schawlow, A. L., **488**
Schiff, Leonard, **549**
Schilling effusion method, 207
Schlicke, H. M., **120**
Schottky, Walter, 414, **830,** 939, 940
Schottky defect, 842
Schottky diode, 231
Schrieffer, J. R., 906
Schrödinger, Erwin, 82, 234, 709, 772, **824,** 1004

SCHRÖDINGER EQUATION, 141, 332, 541,
    (variation) 547, 753, **824**
Schrödinger representation, **542**
Schumann, Victor, 972
Schumann region, **972**
Schwarzschild, 810
Schwarzschild radius, **392**
Schwarzschild solution, 395
Schwarzschild theory, 1
Schwinger, J., 140, 142, 747, 750
Sciama, D., 396
Scientific experiment, **550**
Scintillation counter, 609, 699
Scintillation detector, 615, **616**
Screen grid, **294**
Screening constant, **708**
Screw, **850**
Screw dislocation, **191–192,** 492
Seaborg, Glenn T., 961, 962, 963, 964, **965**
Sears, G. W., 192
Second law, thermodynamics, **942**
Second quantization, 348
Second (unit), **170**
SECONDARY EMISSION, **825**
Secondary cell, **94**
Secondary coil, **951**
Secondary radiation, **176**
Secondary-electron emission, 696
Sector focused cyclotron, **11**
Sedimentation, 123, 591
Seebeck, T. J., **945**
Seebeck coefficient, 945
Seebeck effect, **945**
Seeber, L. A., 661
Seeding, cloud, **136,** 567
Segré, G., 338
Seidel theory, 1
Seidman, Arthur H., **231**
Seismic wave, **828**
Seismograph, 829
SEISMOLOGY, **390, 828**
Selection rule, 168, 314
Self-capacitance, 437
Self-consistent approximation, 718
Self-consistent field, 529
Self-diffusion, 225
Self-mass, 749
Self-inductance, **435**
Sellmeier, W., 4
Sellmeier equation, **5**
Sellmeier formula, 800
SEM, 281
SEMICONDUCTOR, 166, 493, **835,** 870
    amorphous, 836
    conductivity of, **165**
    cyclotron resonance in, 204
    degenerate, 841
    INHOMOGENEOUS, **842**
    magnetic, 836
    thin-film, 949
    radiation induced defects in, 461
SEMICONDUCTOR DEVICES, **829**
Semiconductor laser, **834**
Semiconductor detector, 609
Semiconductor radiation detector, **617**
Semiconductor rectifier, **793**
Semimetal, 204
Semipolar bond, 592
Sengers, J. M. H. Levelt, **151**
Sensor, 97
Separated-function, alternating-gradient synchrotron,
    925
Separated-function synchrotron, 927

Separation of variables, 213
Separator, cream, 124
Serber, R., 750
Series, Fourier, **371**
Serson, 398
SERT, 248
SERVOMECHANISM, **844**
Set, maximal, 541
Sewell, G. L., 725
Shain, C. A., 778
Shaknov, I., 153
Shankland, R. S., **571**
Shannon, C. E., 198, 317, 539
Shapiro, I. I., 394
Sharkey, A. G., Jr., **536**
Sharp series, 82
Shaw, E. A. G., **263**
Shear strain, 240
Shear wave, 707, 969
Shearing stress, 553, 998
Sheath, positive ion, 299
Sheehan, William F., **129**
Sheet resistance, 948
Shell, closed, **633**
Shell, electrons, **314**
Shell, valence, 592
Shell model, 529, **631**
Shell model, nuclear, 466
Sheppard, C. W., 538
Shielding, electromagnetic, 551
    electrostatic, 551
    magnetic, 517, 551
    NUCLEAR RADIATION, **619**
    transport methods, 623
Shielding of military system, 620
Shielding of space vehicles, **620**
Shielding theory, 620
Shift, Lamb, 83
Shift, red, 177, **236**
Ship stabilizer, 398
Shire, E. S., **261**
Shock front, 368
Shock tube, 848
SHOCK WAVE, 123, **847**
Shockley, W., **836**
Shoran (distance measurement), 990
Short-range repulsion, **451**
Shot noise, 552, (photomultipliers) 698
Shower, cosmic ray, **176**
Shugart, Howard A., **75**
Shurcliff, William A., **723**
Shutt, R. P., **881**
Shutter, photographic, 688
Shyn, T. W., 750
SI unit, **253, 918**
Side band, 581
Side conditions, 33
Side frequency, 580
Sidran, Miriam, **692**
Siegbahn, Kai, 1021
Siegbahn, M., **1020**
Siemens, W. von, 599
Signature trajectory, 805
Sikkeland, T., 964
Silicon, 229, 954
Silicon solar cell, **705**
Silsbee rule, **905**
Silver halides, 688
Simon, F., 186
Simple harmonic motion, 584, **993**
SIMPLE MACHINES, **849**
Simultaneity, 808
Sine galvanometer, 526
Singlet, 83

Singular eigenfunctions, method of, 959
Size, critical, **179**
Skaggs, Lester S., 561
Skin depth, 204
SKIN EFFECT, **851**
Skin effect, anomalous, **334**
Skolnik, Merrill I., **762**
Sky wave, 579
Slepian, J., 827
Sliding, 375
Slifkin, Lawrence, **227**
S-matrix, **33, 39,** 47
S-matrix theory, 34, **143**
Smekal, A., 785
Smidt, J., **813**
Smith, Howard M., **430**
Smith, James T., **517**
Smith, M. G., **488**
Smith theory, 1
Smog, Los Angeles type, 974
Smoluchowski, R., 500
Smyth, Charles P., **211,** 720
Snap diode, 744
Snell, Willebrord, 494, **497,** (law) 795, 799
Snell's law, 494, **497, 795,** 969
Snoek, J. L., **335**
Snoek peak, 971
Snow blindness, 974
Snyder, 925
Socrates, 424
Software, computer, 159
Soddy, Frederick, **467**
Solar battery, 688
Solar blind cell, **688**
Solar blind surface, 973
Solar cell, 245, **705,** 860, 864
SOLAR CONSTANT AND SOLAR SPECTRUM, **853**
Solar cycle, 454
SOLAR ENERGY SOURCES, **858**
SOLAR ENERGY UTILIZATION, **860**
Solar flare, 176, 459, **868**
Solar furnace, 775
Solar irradiance, **853,** (table) **856**
Solar outburst, 454
Solar photovoltaic converter, 688
SOLAR PHYSICS, **866**
Solar power, 858
Solar spectrum, **853, 857**
Solar ultraviolet, 974
Solar wind, 523, 763
Solenoidal coil, 437
Solid, **872, 890**
    deformation of, **553**
    density of, **207**
    electronic structure of, 870
    MECHANICAL PROPERTIES OF, **553**
    optical properties of, 322
    properties of, **553**
Solid propellant, 360
SOLID-STATE PHYSICS, 712, **869**
SOLID-STATE THEORY, **872**
Solidus, **680**
    use of, **916**
Solvated electron, **765**
Solvation, **765**
Sommerfeld, Arnold, 314, 414, 564, 772
SONAR, 263, **873**
Sone, **19, 613**
Soo, S. L., **320**
Soroka, W. W., **19**
Sorption pump, 978
Sound, 409
SOUND, MUSICAL, **601**
SOUND, REPRODUCTION OF, **813**

Sound analyzer, 613
Sound intensity level, **51**
Sound level meter, **613**
Sound power level, **51**
Sound pressure level, **51, 613**
Sound velocity, 969
Sound wave, 682, **705**
Source (transistor), 955
Space, 755, **875**
    absolute, 559, 807
    interplanetary, **876**
    momentum, **331**
Space charge, 284, **293**, 940
Space charge, spark chamber, 878
Space flight, **63**
Space inversion, 671, 672
Space isotropy, 167
SPACE PHYSICS, **875**
Space vehicles, shielding of, **620**
Space wave, 579
Space-time, 33, 808
Space-time correlation function, 224
SPARK AND BUBBLE CHAMBERS, 878
Spark breakdown, **250**
Spark breakdown time lag, **251**
Spatial symmetry, **169**
Special relativity, 546, **807**
Special unitary group, **308**, 309
Specific (use of word in physics), **917**
Specific electrical resistivity, 164
Specific fuel consumption, **358**
Specific gravity, 207, **208**
Specific heat, 116, 180, 323, 410, 681
Specific impulse, 67, 244, **358**
Specific mass, propulsion system, **244**
Spectacle lens, 494
Spectra (see spectrum)
Spectral distribution function, 996
Spectral emissivity, **745**
Spectral emittance, 444
Spectral radiance, 744
Spectral width, 420
Spectrograph, mass, **469**
Spectrometer, 640
    electron, 303
    MASS, **535**
Spectrophotometer, 640
Spectrophotometry, 450
    absorption, **6**
Spectroscopic analysis, 974
Spectroscopic splitting factor, 328
Spectrum, 497
    ATOMIC, 81, 883
    ABSORPTION, 3
    molecular, 585
    SOLAR, 236, **857**
    x-ray, **1020**
SPECTROSCOPY, 132, 498, 871, **881**
    beta-ray, 883
    infrared, 445
    internal reflection, **655**
    MICROWAVE, **575**
    MOLECULAR, 316, **583**
    RAMAN, **785**
Speed measuring meter, 761
Sperry, Elmer, 398
Sphere of reflection, 1018
Spherical aberration, 495, 650
Spherical surface, lens, 494
Spherical-drop model, 161
Spherulitic crystal, 191
Spin, 82, 543, 985
    ELECTRON, **288**, 515
    isobaric, **465**

isotopic, 168, 465
    nucleus, 515
    photon, 721
Spin exchange, 642
Spin moment, 233
Spin polarization, 643
SPIN WAVES (MAGNONS), 338, 787, **887**
Spin-lattice, 224
Spin-lattice relaxation, 812
Spin-lattice relaxation time, 516
Spin-orbit coupling, 83
Spin-spin interaction, 516
Spin-statistics theorem, **48**
Spinks, J. W. T., **767**
Spinor, 543
Spinor analysis, 539
Split-interstitial, 493
Splitting, Davydov, 321
Splitting factor, gyromagnetic, 336
    spectroscopic, 328
Sporadic E, 458
Spontaneous disintegration, **782**
Spontaneous emission, 530
Sprackling, M. T., **556**
Spread F, 458
Sputnik, 478
Square wave, 23
Squid, 907
Squirrel-cage rotor, 599
S-representation, 541
Stabilizer, ship, 398
Stacking fault, 493, 562
Stage theories, 147
Standard cell, **94**, 254
Standard deviation, **900**
Standing wave, 992, 1009
Stanley, H. Eugene, **185**
Stanley, W. M., 661
Stanton number, 417
Stapes, 408
Star, **177**
    binary, 63
    diameter of, 448
    diameter, angular, **139**
    faint, 62
    giant, 70
    main-sequence, 858
    neutron, 70, **395**
Star catalog, 60
Starfish explosion, 764
Stark, Johannes, 575, 825, **1025**
Stark effect, 84, 315–316, 375, 377, **1025**
State, degenerate, 101
    quadratic, 531
    pure, 540
    stationary, 1004
State equation, 382
STATES OF MATTER, 680, **889**
STATIC ELECTRICITY, **891**
Static multiplier, 697
STATICS, **895**
STATICS, FLUID, **369**
Stationary state, 1004
Statistical equilibrium, **319**
STATISTICAL MECHANICS, 331, 383, 413, 709,
    896
Statistical thermodynamics, 944
STATISTICS, **899**
Stator, **242**, 600
Steady-state cosmology, 178
Steady-state theory, 397
Steam-turbine, 242
Stearns, Robert L., **105**
Steerable reflector, 778

Stefan, Joseph, **772**
Stefan constant, 69
Stefan-Boltzmann constant, 419
Stefan-Boltzmann equation, 857
Stefan-Boltzmann law, **772**
Stellar diameter, 448
Stellar distance, **62**
Stellar evolution, **70**
Stellarator, **379**
Step function, **658**
Stephens, William E., **290**
Stephenson, R. J., **560**
Steradian, **918**
Stereoisomerism, 585
Stereophony, 814
Stereoscopic depth (vision), 1001
Stereoscopic microscope, 575
Sterilization of food, 628
Stern, Otto, **73**, **289**
Stern-Gerlach experiment, 73, **289**
Sternglass, E. J., 826, **827**
Stevenson, J. S., 538
Stevin (Stevinus), Simon, 895
Steward, G. C., 2
Stilb, 507
Stilwell, A. R., 236
Stimulated emission, 488, **530**
Stimulated Raman scattering, 787
Stoichiometry, 582
Stokes, George Gabriel, 972, 998
Stokes' emission, 509
Stokes' law, 368, 998
Stokes line, **785**
Stokes' theorem, 387
Stokes shift, 148
Stokes (unit), 998
Stokes-Navier equation, 416
Stoney, G. Johnstone, 132
Stopping distance, 558
Stopping number, 769
Stopping power, **185**, 769
Storage battery, 92
Storage compliance, 995
Storage modulus, 995
Storage tube, 827
Storage-ring device, **13**
Storm, earth, 453
  geomagnetic, 389
  magnetic, **89**
Strain, 492, **553**, 560, 995
  shear, 240
Strain components, 820
Strain dyadic, **240**
Strain energy, 492
Strand, K. Aa., **63**
Strange particle, **305**
Strangeness, **169**, 757
Stranski, I. N., 163
Strapdown system, 442
Strassmann, F., **351**
Stratopause, 567
Stratosphere, 390, 567
Stratospheric fallout, **327**
Streater, R. F., 48
Street, Kenneth, Jr., 963
Stress, 492, **553**, 560, 995
  internal, 241
  normal, 553
  shearing, 553, 998
  state of, 820
  ultimate, 556
  yield, 555
Stress corrosion, 564
Stress distribution, 685

Stress dyadic, **240**
Stress tensor, 545
Stress vs strain, 555
Stretching correction, 576
String, vibratory, 1008
Stripper, 9
Stripping reaction, 626
STRONG INTERACTIONS, 305, **902**
Structure, atomic, 675
  crystal, 188, **189**
  liquid, **505**
  molecular, **592**
  NUCLEAR, **630**
Structure factor, **1019**
Structure of membranes, 538
Student's distribution, 901
Stuhlinger, E., 248
SU(1), **43**
SU(2), 45, **308**
SU(3), 34, **45**, 196, 309
SU(6), 309
Subshell, **314**
Sublimation, 136, 890
Sublimation curve, 680
Subjectivist, 902
Substitutional impurity, 842
Suchy, K., 736
Sudarshan, E. C. G., 196, 310, 604
Sum rule, Adler's neutrino, 197
Sum rule, Adler-Weisberger, **197**
Sum rule, Cabibbo-Radicati, 197
Summation, partial, 340
Sun, 453
  composition of, 867
  luminosity of, 867
  mass of, 867
  radius of, 867
  velocity of, **62**
Suna, A., **322**
Sunburn, 974
Sunspot, 454, 522–523, **867**
Superactinide series, **965**
SUPERCONDUCTIVITY, **187**, 529, **904**, 909, 948,
  967, 971
Superconductor, diamagnetism in, **208**
Supercooling, 136
Supercooling, constitutional, 843
Superelastic collision, 457
Superexchange, 31, 519
Superheavy element, **965**
SUPERFLUIDITY, **187**, 505, 529, 907, **908**
Supermicroscope, **276**
Supermultiplet, 309
Supernova, 70, 395, 741
Superparamagnetism, 520
Superposition, 368
Superposition principle, 995
Supersaturation ratio, **162**
Superselection observable, **35**
Supersonic flow, 368
Superstrong field, 757
Superstructure (in polymers), **667**
Supressor grid, **295**
SURFACE, FERMI, **205**, **331**
Surface, of liquid, 891
Surface area, 914
Surface defect, 842, 869
Surface diffusion, 910
SURFACE PHYSICS, **910**
Surface recombination, 685
Surface state, 842
SURFACE TENSION, 869, 891, 910, **914**
Susceptibility, 180, 187, **205**, **208**, 517, 518
  diamagnetic, 233

magnetic, **670**
molar, 233
nuclear, 671
Süsskind, Charles, **303**
Sutton, G. P., **366**
Sutton, Richard M., **478**
Svedberg, The (in full, Theodore), 124
Svedberg (unit), 124
Swift, J. D., **253**
Symbols, mathematical, **924**
Symbols, table of, **919–924**
SYMBOLS, UNITS, AND NOMENCLATURE, **915**
Symmetrization, 541
Symmetry, 33, **166,** 304, 308, 539, 937
  crystal, **194**
  scale, 169
  spatial, **169**
Symmetry in particle theory, 38
Symmetry point group, 593
Symmetry violation, 1013
Synchrocyclotron, **11, 201**
SYNCHROTRON, **12, 925**
  AG, **12**
  electron, **12**
  focusing of, **927**
  proton, **12**
Synodic periods, **59**
Synoptic scale, 566
System, crystal, **195**
System invariant, 679
Systematic error, 550
Système International, **253**
Sze, S. M., **835**
Szillard, L., 635

Table, periodic, **675–679**
Tachyon, 309
Tacoma Narrows Bridge, 817
Tamm, I., 913
Tamm state, 913
Tandem accelerator, **15**
Tardyon, 309
Target detection, 762
Taylor, D. N., 749
Taylor, J. R., 47
TE mode, **1010**
Teaney, Dale T., **32**
Tectonics, plate, 828
Tee (waveguide), 1011
Telegdi, V., 751
Telemetering, **929**
TELEMETRY, **929**
  operational, 929
  test, 929
Telescope, **637**
  radio, 777
Telescope objective, 496
Television tube, color, **286**
Tellurometer, 991
Telstar, 580
Temperature, 384, 410
  brightness, **744**
  color, **773**
  critical, **180, **890
  Curie, **518**
  low, **186**
TEMPERATURE AND THERMOMETRY, **930**
Temperature scales, **930**
Temperature measurement, 945
Tensile strength, ultimate, 556
Tensor, **240,** 544, **933,** (type style for) 915
  antisymmetric, 934
  calculus of, 935

conductivity, 400
metric, 935
Tensor analysis, **933**
TENSORS AND TENSOR ANALYSIS, **933**
Teorell, Torston, 538
Tepley, Norman, **334**
Terbium earth, 788
Terminal ballistics, 91
Terminology, 915
Terrell, James, **356**
Tesla, N., 599
Test telemetry, 929
Testing, ultrasonic, **970**
Tetrahedral press, 731
Tetrode, 291, **294**
TF hypothesis, 183
Thales of Miletus, 311, 424
Thekaekara, Matthew P., 450, **857**
THEORETICAL PHYSICS, 713, **936**
  color, **147**
  ELECTROMAGNETIC, **268**
  FIELD, **347**
  microscopic, 936, 937
  QUANTUM, **751**
Theory of vision, 147
Thermal decomposition, 128
Thermal diffusion, 480
Thermal diffusivity, 228
Thermal effects on experiments, 551
Thermal emission, 443
Thermal energy, **771, **861
THERMAL EXPANSION, **322**
Thermal ionization energy, 685
Thermal neutron, 607
Thermal pollution, 776
THERMAL RADIATION, 751, **771**
Thermal reactor, water boiler, 353
Thermal spike, 460
Thermal vibration, 971
Thermal wave, 707
Thermionic cell, 245
Thermionic emission, **938**
Thermionic tube, **291**
THERMIONICS, **938**
Thermocouple, 776, 973
Thermocouple instrument, **256**
Thermodynamic potential, 943
Thermodynamic process, 120
Thermodynamic properties, 385
Thermodynamic relationships, **323**
Thermodynamic scale, 931
Thermodynamic state, 120
Thermodynamic system, **941**
THERMODYNAMICS, 318, 319, 413, 679, 711, **941**
  first law of, 121, **941**
  second law of, 122 , **942**
  third law of,**942**
Thermoelectric effect, 933
Thermoelectric refrigerator, 803, 804
THERMOELECTRICITY, **944**
Thermography, 776
Thermomagnetic emf, 402
Thermomagnetic refrigerator, 804
Thermometer, 410, **933**
THERMOMETRY, **930**,933
Thermonuclear device, **352,**636
Thermonuclear reaction, **77–78**
Thermopile, 776, 945
Thermo-plastic, 556
Thermostat, 330, 933
Thermostatics, 318
Theta pinch, 377, 972
Thick lens, 651
THIN FILM, 275, 449, **946**

Thin-film optics, **947**
Thin-film semiconductor, 949
Third law, thermodynamics, **942**
Thirring, W., 143
Thixotropic substance, 999
Thomas, C. X., 156
Thomas, L. H., 201
Thomas-Reiche-Kuhn sum rule, 196
Thompson, Benjamin (see Rumford, Count)
Thompson, Stanley G., 962, 963
Thomson, E., 599
Thomson, G. P., **274**, 709
Thomson, Sir J. J., 79, 151, 259, **272**, 535, 686,
    825, 939
Thomson, William (Lord Kelvin), **122,** 462, 464, 481,
    852, **945**
Thomson cross section, 153
Thomson effect, **945**
Thomson heat, 945
Thoriated tungsten, 939
Thorsen, A. C., **206**
Thought experiment, 937
Three degree radiation, 780
Thrust, 22, 244, 357
Thruster, 243, **246**
Thun, Rudolph, **949**
Thyratron, 291, 300, 743, 792
Tie-line, 680
Timbre, **602**
TIME, 421, **949**
Time, absolute, 559
Time base generator, 657
Time dilatation, 236
Time inversion, 36
Time interval, 420
Time lag, spark breakdown, **251**
Time parity, 672
Time reversal, **169,** 672
Time-dependent Schrödinger equation, 1007
Time's arrow, 463
Titan, 717
TM mode, **1010**
Todd, Paul W., **770**
Tokamak, **379**
Toroidal coil, 437
Toroidal confinement, **379**
Torpedo, 398
Torque, 239, 432, **559, 895,** 1014
Torr (unit), **976**
Torsion balance method, 206
Torsional wave, **1008**
Total reflection, 644
Tousey, Richard, 975
Townes, C. H., **488, 530**
Townsend coefficient, 879
Toy top, 378
Trace quantities (actinides), 960
TRACER, RADIOACTIVE, **626, 780**
Track core, **768**
Trajectory, continuous-thrust, 68
Transactinide element, 960
Transconductance, **294**
Transducer, **262, 969**
Transduction, **262,** 407
TRANSFER, HEAT, **415**
Transfer, Hohmann, **58**
Transfer function, 845
Transfer impedance, 134
Transfer orbit, **67**
Transfer reaction, 626
Transferred electron device, **833**
Transform, Fourier-Bessel, 373
Transform, integral, 213
TRANSFORM, LAPLACE, **484**

Transformation, Lorentz, 671
Transformation matrix, 548
TRANSFORMER, 95, **951**
    air-core, 953
    instrument, 257
Transformer action, 438
Transformer emf, 433
Transition, 541, 941
    ductile-brittle, 564
    gamma, **595**
    isomeric, 607
    Mott, 165
    phase, **180**
    vibrational, 584
Transition probability, 1007
Transition state, 128
Transitional element, 676
TRANSISTOR, 829, 836, **954**
    junction, **954**
    planar, 955
Transition, rotational, 584
Transmission, electrical, 929
TRANSMISSION, MICROWAVE, **579**
Transmission line, 1010
Transmission loss, sound, 51
Transmission of power, 952
Transmission of ultraviolet, 972
Transmittance, **694**
Transmittance factor, 694
Transmitting tube, **295**
Transmutation, artificial, **469**
Transport coefficient, 899
Transport properties, 204
Transport theory, 481
TRANSPORT THEORY, (radiative transfer), **957**
Transpose (matrices), 543
TRANSURANIUM ELEMENTS, 469, **959**
Transverse magnetic mode, **1010**
Transverse magnetoresistance, 403
Transverse wave, **1008**
Trapp, Walter , (footnote) 661
Traveling-wave amplifier, 263
Traveling-wave maser, **532**
Traveling wave tube, **298**
Tremolo, 601
Triboelectric series, 892
Tribus, M., **318**
Trigonometric function, **112,** (symbols for) 924
Tri-interstitial, 493
Triode, 291, **293**
Triple (vectors), **984**
Triple bond, 592
Triple point, 504, 890
Triplet, 83
Triplet exciton, 321
Tristimulus value, **144**
Tritium, 78, 376, 636, 739
Tritium target, 608
Triton, 739
Tri-vacancy, 493
Tropopause, 390, 567
Troposphere, 390, 567
Tropospheric fallout, **327**
Troup, G. J., **533**
Trouton's rule, 506
Trump, John G., **17, 423**
Tschoegl, N. W., **997**
Tsuya, 527
Tube, beam-power, **295**
    cathode ray, **285**
    ELECTRON, **290**
    image-intensifying, 827
    microwave, **296**
    rectifier, 291

shock, **848**
television, **286**
thermionic, **291**
transmitting, **290**
traveling wave, **298**
vacuum, **290**
Tuning fork, 602
Tunnel, wind, **23**
Tunnel diode, 744
Tunnel effect, 1007
TUNNELING, 782, **965**
  nuclear, **967**
Turbojet, 364
Turbomolecular pump, 979
Turbulence, 368
Turing, Allan, 157
Turnover frequency, 814
Twilight glow, 89
Tyndall, John, 499
Tyndall scattering, 499
Type-observable, **33**

Ubaldi, Guido, 895
Uehling, E. A., 750
Uhlenbeck, George Eugene, **80,** 273, **288, 314,**
  482, **1024**
Ultimate stress, 556
Ultimate tensile strength, 556
Ultracentrifuge, **124,** 591
Ultrafiber, 665
Ultrasonic cleaners, 123
Ultrasonic power, 970
Ultrasonic region, 18
Ultrasonic testing, **970**
ULTRASONICS, **969**
Ultrastability, 329
Ultraviolet, solar, 974
Ultraviolet catastrophe, 752
Ultraviolet irradiation, 974
Ultraviolet light, 682
Ultraviolet microscope, 638
ULTRAVIOLET RADIATION, **971**
Uncertainty limitation, 552
Uncertainty principle, 420, **540,** 755, 937
Unijunction transistor, 743
Unipotential lens, **278**
Unit, **915**
  fundamental, **170**
  magnetic, 514
  photometric (table), 695
  radiometric (table), 695
  SI, **253, 918**
Unit cell, **194,** 590, 1018
Unit pole, 517
Univariant system, 679
Universal Fermi interaction, **1013**
Universality hypothesis, **183**
Universe, **177**
  expanding, 236
Univibrator, 742
Unwin, R. S., **90**
Upatnieks, J., 426
Uranium, 76
Uranus, 717
Urbach law, 322
Ure, Roland W., Jr., **946**
Urey, H. C., 714, 716
Ursell, H. D., 383, **898**
Ussing, H. H., 538

VA theory, **196**
Vacancy (lattice), 347, 491, 493
Vacuum, 369

Vacuum gauge, **979**
Vacuum pump, **976**
Vacuum system, 279
VACUUM TECHNIQUES, **976**
Vacuum tube, **290**
Vaks-Larkin model, 184
Valdes, L. B., **956**
Valence band, 684
Valence repulsion energy, 383
Valence shell, 592
Valency, **592**
Van Allen, James Alfred, 176, **763**
Van Allen radiation belt, 176
van Alphen, P. M., 187, **205**
Van de Graaff, Robert Jemison, **13**
VAN DE GRAAFF ACCELERATOR, **13,** 608
Van de Graaff generator, 10
van de Hulst, H. C., **779**
Van der Pol, Balth, 134
van der Waals, Johannes Diderik, **382,** 383
van der Waals equation, **382**
van der Waals force, **451**
van Helmont, Jan Baptista, 311
Van Hove, L., 224, 804
Van Hove singularity, 872
van Niel equation, **702**
van't Hoff, Jacobus Henricus, **588, 659,** 708
van't Hoff's equation, **659**
VanZandt, T. E., **459**
Vapor deposition, 837
Vapor ejector pump, 978
Vapor pressure, 589, 890
VAPOR PRESSURE AND EVAPORATION, **981**
Vapor pump, 976
Vapor-absorption refrigerator, 802
Vapor-compression refrigerator, 801
Vaporization curve, 680
Vaporous, 680
Varacter, 231
Variable-mu tube, 295
Variables, separation of, 213
Variation of parameters, 212
Variational emf, 433
Varignon's theorem, **896**
Vaucanson, Jacques de, 156
V_k-center, 149
Vector, 544, 982, (type style for) 983
  axial, 934
  base, 541
  contravariant, 544
  covariant, 544
  position, 237
  Poynting, 271
Vector algebra, **983**
Vector cross product, 400
Vector diagram (circuits), **25**
Vector field, 985
Vector map, **190**
Vector potential, 270, 512
Vector product (outer product), **983**
VECTOR PHYSICS, **982**
Vector space, 983
Vector sum, 983
Veksler, V., 201, 925
Velocity, 237, 431
  angular, 173, **821,** 985
  drift, 837
  molecular, 480
  radial, 174
  tangential, **173**
VELOCITY OF LIGHT, **987**
Velocity reversal, 672
Venera seven, 714
Venturi, 368

Venus, 714, 764
  spectrum of, 586
Verneuil method, **193**
Vertical control, 387
Vertical deflection channel, 657
Vibrating coil magnetometer, 525
Vibrating reed magnetometer, 525
Vibrating sample magnetometer, 525
Vibrating string, 993, 1008
VIBRATION, 601, **992**
  attenuation of, 551
  lattice, 595
Vibrational energy, 385, 584
Vibrational spectra, 583
Vibrational state, 316
Vibrational transition, 489
Vibrational wavefunction, 594
Vibrato, 601
Vibron, **787**
Vieille, Paul Marie Eugène, 848
Vignetting, 639
Villard, 617
Villchur, Edgar, **815**
Virial coefficient, 944
Virial equation, 383
Virial equation of state, **382**, 898
Virtual work, 896
Vis viva energy, **56**
Viscoelastic behavior, 819
VISCOELASTICITY, **995**
Viscometer, 998
VISCOSITY, 725, 726, 819, **997**
Viscous behavior, 995
Vision, 506
  anomalous trichromatic, 144
  dichromatic, 144
  monochromatic, 144
  opponent-colors theory, 147
  stage theories of, 147
  theory of, 147
VISION AND THE EYE, **999**
Vitreous humor, 1000
VITREOUS STATE, **1002**
Vlasov approximation, **718**
Volume, 384
Volcanology, **390**
Volmer, M., 161
Volt, **254**
Volta, Alessandro, **264**
Voltage, 253, 254
Voltage divider, **254**
Voltage drop, **432**
Voltage standing-wave ratio, 1011
Voltaic cell, **92**
Volterra, Vito, 536
Volterra equation, 485
Voltmeter, **256**
Voltmeter, digital, **257**
von Alteneck, 599
von Aulock, W. H., **336**
von Guericke, Otto, 14
von Helmholtz, H. L. F., 98, 560
von Neumann, J., **157, 897**
von Neumann algebra, **37**
VSWR, 1011

Wade, C. M., 779
Wagner, K. W., 211
Wahl, A. C., 961
Walker, William W., **729**
Waller, I., 218
Walter, W. G., 199
Walton, E. T. S., 7, **636**

Walton, J. R., 964
Wang, 451
Wangsness, Roald K., **938**
Wannier-Mott model, 321
Warning devices (radar), 761
Water boiler thermal reactor, 353
Waterston, J. J., 480
Watson, Kenneth M., **143**
Watt, 1014
Watthourmeter, **258**
Wave, 234, **1008**
  acoustic, 874
  compressional, **1008**
  electromagnetic, 261, **733**
  gravitational, **395**
  ground, 579
  intensity of, **1009**
  longitudinal, **1008**
  reference, holography, 428
  plasma, **736**
  progressive, 447
  seismic, **828**
  SHOCK, **847**
  sound, **705**
  sky, 579
  space, 579
  torsional, **1008**
  transverse, **1008**
  ultrasonic, 969
Wave equation, 349, 753, 1005
Wave function, **542, 576, 754**, 1005
WAVE MECHANICS, 546, 634, **1004**
WAVE MOTION, **1008**
Wave number, 443, 584
Wave packet, 754, **755**
Wave velocity, 988, 1008
WAVEGUIDES, 579, **1010**
  linac, 11
Wavelength, 421, 497, **1008**
  de Broglie, 276
Wavelength of particle, 824
Wavemeter, 1012
WEAK INTERACTION, 32, 305, 604, **1012**
Weapon, nuclear, 327, 352, 620
Wear, 376
Weather, 174
Weather forecasting, **566**
Weather modification, **136**
Weaver, Elbert C., **208**
Webb, M. B., **913**
Weber, H. P., 988
Weber, J., 395
Weber, Wilhelm, 989
Weeks, W. L., **272**
Wehnelt, A., 939
Weight, 63, 392, **534, 557**
  atomic (table), **468**
  gram equivalent, **591**
  gram molecular, **582**
  MOLECULAR, 125, **587**, 725
Weightlessness, **63, 392**
Wein constant, 857
Weinberg, S., 197
Weiss, Pierre, 518, **670**
Weiss law, 325, 337
Welding, 562
Welsbach mantle, 774
Welsby, V. G., **438**
Welsh, H. L., **788**
Wendelstein II, 380
Wentzel, Kremers, Brillouin approximation, 966
Wert, Charles A., **871**
Wesley, J. C., 750
Weston cell, 95

Westphal balance, 207
Whatley, Linda S., **886**
Wheatstone, C., 599
Wheatstone bridge, 255
Wheeler, Gershon J., **1012**
Wheeler, J. A., **351**
Whiskers, 192
Whistler, 736, 764
White, Milton G., 925, **928**
White dwarf, 70, 395, 859
White light, 497
White noise, 601
Whitehead, A. N., 540
Wien, Wilhelm, 535, **772**
Wien's law, 418, 857
Wiener, Norbert, **198, 329,** 539
Wightman, A. S., **48**
Wigner, Eugene P., 143, 465, 539, 747
Wigner-Kadison theory, 38–39
Wigner-Seitz cell model, 529
Wilkinson, D. T., 750
Williams, Ferd, **511**
Williams, B. F., 826
Wills, John H., **680**
Wilson, A. J. C., **1019**
Wilson, C. T. R., 162
Wind, 174–175
Wind tunnel, **23**
Window, atmospheric, 444
Wing, G. Milton, **959**
Wisnosky, Dennis E., **161**
W-meson, 1013
Wolf, E., 138
Wolf, Frank L., **902**
Wolfe, Hugh C., **925**
Wolfram, T., **888**
Wollan, E. O., 405
Wollaston, William Hyde, **3,** 853
Womersley, J., 537
Wood, Elizabeth A., 911
Wood, R. W., 343, 785
Woods, Joseph F., **685**
Woods, R. J., **767**
Work, **558, 1014**
    electrical, 260
WORK, POWER, AND ENERGY, **1014**
work function, 284, 292, **686, 939**
Worm, 851
Worm wheel, 851
Wow, 814
Wrench, 896
Wright, Sewall, 536
Wu, C. S., **674**

Xerography, **691**
Xi hyperon, 305
X-RAY, 188, 404, **1020**
    characteristic, 316
    stellar sources of, 69
X-ray absorption spectra, **6**
X-RAY DIFFRACTION, 188, 194, 610, **1017**
    molecular weight determination by, 590
X-ray fluorescence, 881, 1021
X-ray in medicine, 560
X-ray scattering, 151
X-ray spectra, 85

Yagi antenna, 28
Yang, C. N., **169, 674, 1014**
Yarwood, J., **980**
Yeh, Hsuan, **432**
Yerkes telescope, 639
Yield, Auger, 470
Yield, fluorescence, 470
Yield point, 555
Yield stress, 555
Young, Thomas, 98, **137, 447, 653,** 722, 813
Young's experiment, 137, **447**
Young's modulus, **241,** 554
Young-Helmholtz theory, 147
Yttrium, 788
Yttrium earth, 788
Yukawa, Hideki, **350, 634,** 740, 756

Z pinch, 377
Zarem, A. M., **866**
Zeeman, Pieter, 79, 272, 273, 290, 1023
ZEEMAN AND STARK EFFECTS, **1022**
Zeeman effect, 84, 290, 315–316
Zeeman splitting (nuclear), 598
Zener diode, 231
Zener tunneling, 967
Zernike, F., **1,** 217, **574,** 661
Zernike polynomial, 2
Zernike-Nijboer expansion, 1
Zero-point energy, 1007
Zeroth law, **941**
Zeta pinch, 972
Zienau, S., 724
Zimm theory, 726
Zinn, W. H., 635
Zucker, A., **626**
Zweig, G., **756, 757**
Zworykin, V. K., 280